Great Britain & Ireland 2008

Contents

Sommaire
Sommario
Inhaltsverzeichnis

INTRODUCTION

→ INTRODUCTION

→ INTRODUZIONE

→ EINLEITUNG

How to use this guide

TOURIST INFORMATION

Distances from the main towns, tourist offices, local tourist attractions, means of transport, golf courses and leisure activities...

HOTELS

From 🏨🏨🏨🏨🏨 to 🏨, 🏠: categories of comfort.
In red 🏨🏨🏨🏨🏨 ... 🏨, 🏠: the most pleasant.

RESTAURANTS AND PUBS

From XXXXX to X, 🍺: categories of comfort.
In red XXXXX... X, 🍺: the most pleasant.

STARS

✿✿✿ Worth a special journey.
✿✿ Worth a detour.
✿ A very good restaurant.

GOOD FOOD AND ACCOMMODATION AT MODERATE PRICES

Bib Gourmand
Bib Hotel

CAMBRIDGE – Cambs – 504 U27 – pop. 117 717 – Great B
London 55 – Coventry 88 – Ipswich 54 – Leiceste
Nottingham 88 – Oxford 100
Cambridge Airport : ☎ (01223) 373737, E: 2 m o
The Old Library, Wheeleer St, ☎ (01223) 45758
Cambridgeshire Moat House Hotel, Bar Hill, ☎
Town : St John's College AC Y – King's A
Fitzwilliam Museumy Z M1 – Trinity College
College AC Z
Audley End, S: 13m by A1309 – Imperi
on M11

Hotel Gloria
Whitehouse lane, Huntington Rd, CB3 OLX,
– ☎ (01223) 277985 – help@hotelgloria.co.
Rest The Melrose – Menu £16 (lunch) – C
52 rm – †£136 ††£168/255 – £7.50
♦ Built as a private house in 1852, now
contemporary rooms include state of
garden and terrace.

Alexander House (Johns)
Midsummer Common, CB4 1HA – ☎
– resa@alexanderhouse.co.uk – Fa
– closed 2 weeks Christmas, 2 wee
Rest – Menu (dinner only and lu
Spec. Salad of smoked eel, pig'
nuts and pistachios and aspara
des bois and mint.
♦ A river Cam idyll. Chic con
terrace with blissful views c

The Roasted Pepper
35 Chesterton Rd,CB4 3AX
– Fax (01223) 351873 – cl
Rest (booking essential)
♦ Personally run Victor
Italian dishes with mil

at Histon North : 3 m on B1

Blue House Far
44 High St, CB3 7H
– Fax (01223) 2621
22 rm – †£38
♦ Red-brick 18C
house overlook
bread and pre

ENGLAND

NTERBURY – K
ndon

OTHER MICHELIN PUBLICATIONS

References for the Michelin map and Green Guide which cover the area.

LOCATING THE TOWN

Locate the town on the map at the end of the guide (map number and coordinates).

QUIET HOTELS

Quiet hotel.
Very quiet hotel.

DESCRIPTION OF THE ESTABLISHMENT

Atmosphere, style, character and specialities.

LOCATING THE ESTABLISHMENT

Located on the town plan (coordinates and letters giving the location).

FACILITIES AND SERVICES

PRICES

A 3
orwich 61 –
X
m@cambridge.gov.uk
) 249988 X
ge Z – The Backs YZ –
ne's Yardx Y **M2** – Queen's
Museumx, Duxford, S: 9m
Z **d**
st: 1,5 m by A1307
(01223) 277986
20/35.50
dern and stylish public areas. The
cilities. Sleek restaurant overlooks
Y **a**
69 245
369246
1 week spring, Sunday and Monday
-Saturday) £30/50
nd apple purée. Braised turbot with pea-
elloni of apricot, Strawberry sorbet, fraises
dining room with smart first floor bar and
er.
Y **c**
) 351872 – seancarter@roastedpepper.co.uk
nas-New Year and Sunday
ly) Menu £25
ouse with smartly clad tables. Classic French and
ences, served at reasonable prices.
ambridge
rest
3) 262164 – reservations@bluehousefarm.uk.co
2 weeks Christmas-New Year
ouse on a working farm... with beautiful blue windows;
Sunny garden room for breakfast, including home-made
aculate rooms.
A **12**
29 – pop. 47 123 (inc. Frimley) – Great Britain
on 76 – Dover 15 – Maidstone 28 – Margate 17
st: 0,75m off Portsmouth Rd (A325) – (0870) 400 8245
.co.uk – Fax (0870) 4008246
...to the bedrooms; some
...d modern. 19C

Commitments

"This volume was created at the turn of the century and will last at least as long".

This foreword to the very first edition of the MICHELIN Guide, written in 1900, has become famous over the years and the Guide has lived up to the prediction. It is read across the world and the key to its popularity is the consistency of its commitment to its readers, which is based on the following promises.

The Michelin Guide's commitments :

Anonymous inspections: our inspectors make regular and anonymous visits to hotels and restaurants to gauge the quality of products and services offered to an ordinary customer. They settle their own bill and may then introduce themselves and ask for more information about the establishment. Our readers' comments are also a valuable source of information, which we can then follow up with another visit of our own.

Independence: Our choice of establishments is a completely independent one, made for the benefit of our readers alone. The decisions to be taken are discussed around the table by the inspectors and the editor. The most important awards are decided at a European level. Inclusion in the Guide is completely free of charge.

Selection and choice: The Guide offers a selection of the best hotels and restaurants in every category of comfort and price. This is only possible because all the inspectors rigorously apply the same methods.

Annual updates: All the practical information, the classifications and awards are revised and updated every single year to give the most reliable information possible.

Consistency: The criteria for the classifications are the same in every country covered by the Michelin Guide.

... and our aim: to do everything possible to make travel, holidays and eating out a pleasure, as part of Michelin's ongoing commitment to improving travel and mobility.

Dear reader

Dear reader,

We are delighted to introduce the 35th edition of The Michelin Guide Great Britain & Ireland.

This selection of the best hotels and restaurants in every price category is chosen by a team of full-time inspectors with a professional background in the industry. They cover every corner of the country, visiting new establishments and testing the quality and consistency of the hotels and restaurants already listed in the Guide.

Every year we pick out the best restaurants by awarding them from ✿ to ✿✿✿. Stars are awarded for cuisine of the highest standards and reflect the quality of the ingredients, the skill in their preparation, the combination of flavours, the levels of creativity and value for money, and the ability to combine all these qualities not just once, but time and time again.
This year again, a number of restaurants have been newly awarded stars for the quality of their cuisine. ´**N**´ highlights the new promotions for this new 2008 edition, announcing their arrival with one, two or three stars.

In addition, we have continued to pick out a selection of « *Rising Stars* ». These establishments, listed in red, are the best in their present category. They have the potential to rise further, and already have an element of superior quality; as soon as they produce this quality consistently, and in all aspects of their cuisine, they will be hot tips for a higher award. We've highlighted these promising restaurants so you can try them for yourselves; we think they offer a foretaste of the gastronomy of the future.
We're very interested to hear what you think of our selection, particularly the " *Rising Stars* ", so please continue to send us your comments. Your opinions and suggestions help to shape your Guide, and help us to keep improving it, year after year. Thank you for your support. We hope you enjoy travelling with the Michelin Guide 2008.

Consult the Michelin Guide at **www.ViaMichelin.com**
and write to us at:
themichelinguide-gbirl@uk.michelin.com

Classification & awards

CATEGORIES OF COMFORT

The Michelin Guide selection lists the best hotels and restaurants in each category of comfort and price. The establishments we choose are classified according to their levels of comfort and, within each category, are listed in order of preference.

🏨🏨🏨🏨🏨	✕✕✕✕✕	Luxury in the traditional style
🏨🏨🏨🏨	✕✕✕✕	Top class comfort
🏨🏨🏨	✕✕✕	Very comfortable
🏨🏨	✕✕	Comfortable
🏨	✕	Quite comfortable
	🍺	Traditional pubs serving good food
⌂		Other recommended accommodation (Guesthouses, farmhouses and private homes)
without rest.		This hotel has no restaurant
with rm		This restaurant also offers accommodation

THE AWARDS

To help you make the best choice, some exceptional establishments have been given an award in this year's Guide. They are marked ✿ or ☺ and **Rest.**

THE BEST CUISINE

Michelin stars are awarded to establishments serving cuisine, of whatever style, which is of the highest quality. The cuisine is judged on the quality of ingredients, the skill in their preparation, the combination of flavours, the levels of creativity, the value for money and the consistency of culinary standards.

✿✿✿ **Exceptional cuisine, worth a special journey**
One always eats extremely well here, sometimes superbly.

✿✿ **Excellent cooking, worth a detour**

✿ **Very good cooking in its category**

GOOD FOOD AND ACCOMMODATION AT MODERATE PRICES

☺ **Bib Gourmand**
Establishment offering good quality cuisine for under £28 or €40 in the Republic of Ireland (price of a 3 course meal not including drinks).

☺ **Bib Hotel**
Establishment offering good levels of comfort and service, with most rooms priced at under £75 or under €105 in the Republic of Ireland (price of a room for 2 people, including breakfast).

PLEASANT HOTELS AND RESTAURANTS

Symbols shown in red indicate particularly pleasant or restful establishments: the character of the building, its décor, the setting, the welcome and services offered may all contribute to this special appeal.

⌂, 🏠 to 🏠🏠🏠🏠 **Pleasant hotels**

🍺, X to XXXXX **Pleasant restaurants**

OTHER SPECIAL FEATURES

As well as the categories and awards given to the establishment, Michelin inspectors also make special note of other criteria which can be important when choosing an establishment.

LOCATION

If you are looking for a particularly restful establishment, or one with a special view, look out for the following symbols:

- **Quiet hotel**
- **Very quiet hotel**
- < **Interesting view**
- < **Exceptional view**

WINE LIST

If you are looking for an establishment with a particularly interesting wine list, look out for the following symbol:

Particularly interesting wine list
This symbol might cover the list presented by a sommelier in a luxury restaurant or that of a simple pub or restaurant where the owner has a passion for wine. The two lists will offer something exceptional but very different, so beware of comparing them by each other's standards.

SMOKING

In Great Britain and the Republic of Ireland the law prohibits smoking in all pubs, restaurants and hotel public areas.

Facilities & services

- **30 rm** Number of rooms
- Lift (elevator)
- Air conditioning (in all or part of the establishment)
- Fast Internet access in bedrooms
- Wi-fi Internet access in bedrooms
- Establishment at least partly accessible to those of restricted mobility
- Special facilities for children
- Meals served in garden or on terrace
- An extensive facility for relaxation and well-being
- Sauna – Exercise room
- Swimming pool: outdoor or indoor
- Garden – Park
- Tennis court – Golf course and number of holes
- Landing stage
- Fishing available to hotel guests. A charge may be made
- Equipped conference room
- Private dining rooms
- Hotel garage (additional charge in most cases)
- Car park for customers only
- No dogs allowed (in all or part of the establishment)
- Nearest Underground station (in London)
- *May-October* Dates when open, as indicated by the hotelier

Prices

Prices quoted in this Guide were supplied in autumn 2007 and apply to low and high seasons. They are subject to alteration if goods and service costs are revised. By supplying the information, hotels and restaurants have undertaken to maintain these rates for our readers.
In some towns, when commercial, cultural or sporting events are taking place the hotel rates are likely to be considerably higher.
Prices are given in £ sterling, except for the Republic of Ireland where euro are quoted.
All accommodation prices include both service and V.A.T. All restaurant prices include V.A.T. Service is also included when an **s** appears after the prices.
Where no **s** is shown, prices may be subject to the addition of a variable service charge which is usually between 10 % - 15 %.
(V.A.T. does not apply in the Channel Islands).
Out of season, certain establishments offer special rates. Ask when booking.

RESERVATION AND DEPOSITS

Some hotels will require a deposit which confirms the commitment of both the customer and the hotelier. Ask the hotelier to provide you with all the terms and conditions applicable to your reservation in their written confirmation.

CREDIT CARDS

	Credit cards accepted by the establishment:
AE ⓓ MC VISA	American Express – Diners Club – MasterCard – Visa

ROOMS

rm 🚹 50.00/90.00	Lowest price 50.00 and highest price 90.00 for a comfortable single room
rm 🚹🚹 70.00/120.00	Lowest price 70.00 and highest price 120.00 for a double or twin room for 2 people
rm ☕ 55.00/85.00	Full cooked breakfast (whether taken or not) is included in the price of the room
☕ 6.00	Price of breakfast

SHORT BREAKS

Many hotels offer a special rate for a stay of two or more nights which comprises dinner, room and breakfast usually for a minimum of two people. Please enquire at hotel for rates.

RESTAURANT

Set meals: lowest price £13.00, highest price £28.00, usually for a 3 course meal. The lowest priced set menu is often only available at lunchtimes.
A la carte meals: the prices represent the range of charges from a simple to an elaborate 3 course meal.

s	Service included
🎭	Restaurants offering lower priced pre and/or post theatre menus

⌂: Dinner in this category of establishment will generally be offered from a fixed price menu of limited choice, served at a set time to residents only. Lunch is rarely offered. Many will not be licensed to sell alcohol.

Towns

GENERAL INFORMATION

✉ *York*	Postal address
501 M27, ⑩	Michelin map and co-ordinates or fold
Great Britain	See the Michelin Green Guide Great Britain
pop. 1057	Population Source: 2001 Census (Key Statistics for Urban Areas) Crown copyright 2004
BX **a**	Letters giving the location of a place on a town plan
18	Golf course and number of holes (handicap sometimes required, telephone reservation strongly advised)
✳ ⋞	Panoramic view, viewpoint
	Airport
	Shipping line (passengers & cars)
	Passenger transport only
i	Tourist Information Centre

STANDARD TIME

In winter, standard time throughout the British Isles is Greenwich Mean Time (GMT). In summer, British clocks are advanced by one hour to give British Summer Time (BST). The actual dates are announced annually but always occur over weekends in March and October.

TOURIST INFORMATION

STAR-RATING

★★★	Highly recommended
★★	Recommended
★	Interesting
AC	Admission charge

LOCATION

	Sights in town
	On the outskirts
	In the surrounding area
N, S, E, W	The sight lies North, South, East or West of the town
A 22	Take road A 22, indicated by the same symbol on the Guide map
2m.	Distance in miles (In the Republic of Ireland kilometres are quoted).

Town plans

a ● a Hotels – restaurants

SIGHTS

Place of interest
Interesting place of worship

ROADS

M 1 Motorway
4 4 Numbered junctions: complete, limited
Dual carriageway with motorway characteristics
Main traffic artery
A 2 Primary route (GB) and National route (IRL)
One-way street – Unsuitable for traffic or street subject to restrictions
Pedestrian street – Tramway
Piccadilly Shopping street – Car park – Park and Ride
Gateway – Street passing under arch – Tunnel
15'5 Low headroom (16'6" max.) on major through routes
Station and railway
Funicular – Cable-car
B Lever bridge – Car ferry

VARIOUS SIGNS

Tourist Information Centre
Church/Place of worship - Mosque – Synagogue
Communications tower or mast – Ruins
Garden, park, wood – Cemetery
Stadium - Racecourse - Golf course
Golf course (with restrictions for visitors) – Skating rink
Outdoor or indoor swimming pool
View – Panorama
Monument – Fountain – Hospital – Covered market
Pleasure boat harbour – Lighthouse
Airport – Underground station – Coach station
Ferry services: passengers and cars
Main post office
Public buildings located by letter:
C H J - County Council Offices – Town Hall – Law Courts
M T U - Museum – Theatre – University, College
POL. - Police (in large towns police headquarters)

LONDON

BRENT WEMBLEY Borough – Area
Borough boundary
Congestion Zone – Charge applies Monday-Friday 07.00-18.00
Nearest Underground station to the hotel or restaurant

Mode d'emploi

INFORMATIONS TOURISTIQUES

Distances depuis les villes principales, offices de tourisme, sites touristiques locaux, moyens de transports, golfs et loisirs...

L'HÉBERGEMENT

De 🏠🏠🏠🏠🏠 à 🏠, ⌂ : catégories de confort.
En rouge 🏠🏠🏠🏠🏠 ... 🏠, ⌂ : les plus agréables.

LES RESTAURANTS ET LES PUBS

De XXXXX à X, 🍺 : catégories de confort.

En rouge XXXXX ... X, 🍺 : les plus agréables.

LES TABLES ÉTOILÉES

✿✿✿ Vaut le voyage.
✿✿ Mérite un détour.
✿ Très bonne cuisine.

LES MEILLEURES ADRESSES À PETITS PRIX

Bib Gourmand.
Bib Hôtel.

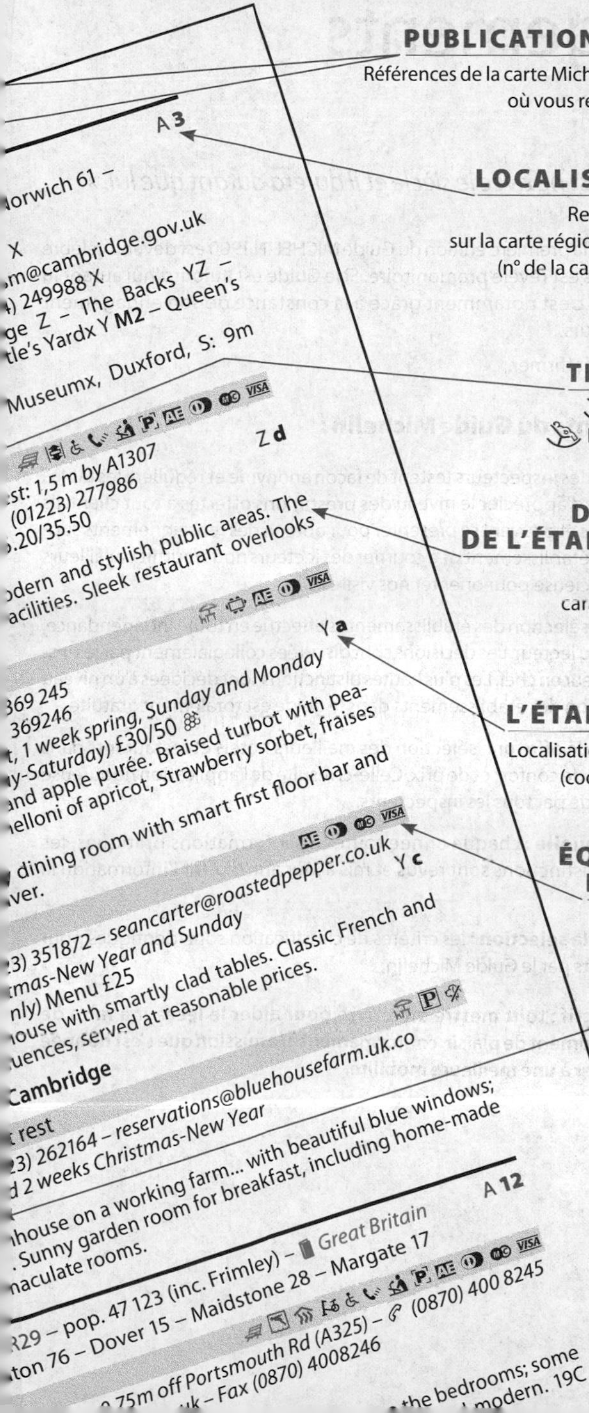

AUTRES PUBLICATIONS MICHELIN

Références de la carte Michelin et du Guide Vert où vous retrouverez la localité.

LOCALISER LA VILLE

Repérage de la localité sur la carte régionale en fin de guide (n° de la carte et coordonnées).

LES HÔTELS TRANQUILLES

Hôtel tranquille.
Hôtel très tranquille.

DESCRIPTION DE L'ÉTABLISSEMENT

Atmosphère, style, caractère et spécialités.

LOCALISER L'ÉTABLISSEMENT

Localisation sur le plan de ville (coordonnées et indice).

ÉQUIPEMENTS ET SERVICES

PRIX

Engagements

« Ce guide est né avec le siècle et il durera autant que lui. »

Cet avant-propos de la première édition du Guide MICHELIN 1900 est devenu célèbre au fil des années et s'est révélé prémonitoire. Si le Guide est aujourd'hui autant lu à travers le monde, c'est notamment grâce à la constance de son engagement vis-à-vis de ses lecteurs.

Nous voulons ici le réaffirmer.

Les engagements du Guide Michelin :

La visite anonyme : les inspecteurs testent de façon anonyme et régulière les tables et les chambres afin d'apprécier le niveau des prestations offertes à tout client. Ils paient leurs additions et peuvent se présenter pour obtenir des renseignements supplémentaires sur les établissements. Le courrier des lecteurs nous fournit par ailleurs une information précieuse pour orienter nos visites.

L'indépendance: la sélection des établissements s'effectue en toute indépendance, dans le seul intérêt du lecteur. Les décisions sont discutées collégialement par les inspecteurs et le rédacteur en chef. Les plus hautes distinctions sont décidées à un niveau européen. L'inscription des établissements dans le guide est totalement gratuite.

La sélection: le Guide offre une sélection des meilleurs hôtels et restaurants dans toutes les catégories de confort et de prix. Celle-ci résulte de l'application rigoureuse d'une même méthode par tous les inspecteurs.

La mise à jour annuelle : chaque année toutes les informations pratiques, les classements et les distinctions sont revus et mis à jour afin d'offrir l'information la plus fiable.

L'homogénéité de la sélection : les critères de classification sont identiques pour tous les pays couverts par le Guide Michelin.

… et un seul objectif : tout mettre en œuvre pour aider le lecteur à faire de chaque sortie un moment de plaisir, conformément à la mission que s'est donnée Michelin : contribuer à une meilleure mobilité.

Édito

Cher lecteur,

Nous avons le plaisir de vous proposer notre 35e édition du Guide Michelin Great Britain & Ireland. Cette sélection des meilleurs hôtels et restaurants dans chaque catégorie de prix est effectuée par une équipe d'inspecteurs professionnels, de formation hôtelière. Tous les ans, ils sillonnent le pays pour visiter de nouveaux établissements et vérifier le niveau des prestations de ceux déjà cités dans le Guide.

Au sein de la sélection, nous reconnaissons également chaque année les meilleures tables en leur décernant de ✿ a ✿✿✿. Les étoiles distinguent les établissements qui proposent la meilleure qualité de cuisine, dans tous les styles, en tenant compte des choix de produits, de la créativité, de la maîtrise des cuissons et des saveurs, du rapport qualité/prix ainsi que de la régularité.

Cette année encore, de nombreuses tables ont été remarquées pour l'évolution de leur cuisine. Un « **N** » accompagne les nouveaux promus de ce millésime 2008, annonçant leur arrivée parmi les établissements ayant une, deux ou trois étoiles.

De plus, nous souhaitons indiquer les établissements « *espoirs* » pour la catégorie supérieure. Ces établissements, mentionnés en rouge dans notre liste, sont les meilleurs de leur catégorie. Ils pourront accéder à la distinction supérieure dès lors que la régularité de leurs prestations, dans le temps et sur l'ensemble de la carte, aura progressé. Par cette mention spéciale, nous entendons vous faire connaître les tables qui constituent à nos yeux, les espoirs de la gastronomie de demain.

Votre avis nous intéresse, en particulier sur ces « espoirs » ; n'hésitez pas à nous écrire. Votre participation est importante pour orienter nos visites et améliorer sans cesse votre Guide. Merci encore de votre fidélité. Nous vous souhaitons de bons voyages avec le Guide Michelin 2008.

Consultez le Guide Michelin sur **www.ViaMichelin.com**
Et écrivez-nous à : **themichelinguide-gbirl@uk.michelin.com**

Classement & distinctions

LES CATÉGORIES DE CONFORT

Le Guide Michelin retient dans sa sélection les meilleures adresses dans chaque catégorie de confort et de prix. Les établissements sélectionnés sont classés selon leur confort et cités par ordre de préférence dans chaque catégorie.

🏨🏨🏨🏨🏨	XXXXX	Grand luxe et tradition
🏨🏨🏨🏨	XXXX	Grand confort
🏨🏨🏨	XXX	Très confortable
🏨🏨	XX	De bon confort
🏨	X	Assez confortable
	🍺	Pub traditionnel servant des repas
⌂		Autres formes d'hébergement conseillées (b&b, logis à la ferme et cottages)
without rest.		L'hôtel n'a pas de restaurant
with rm		Le restaurant possède des chambres

LES DISTINCTIONS

Pour vous aider à faire le meilleur choix, certaines adresses particulièrement remarquables ont reçu une distinction : étoiles ou Bib Gourmand. Elles sont repérables dans la marge par ✿ ou ☺ et dans le texte par **Rest.**

LES ÉTOILES : LES MEILLEURES TABLES

Les étoiles distinguent les établissements, tous les styles de cuisine confondus, qui proposent la meilleure qualité de cuisine. Les critères retenus sont : le choix des produits, la créativité, la maîtrise des cuissons et des saveurs, le rapport qualité/prix ainsi que la régularité.

✿✿✿ **Cuisine remarquable, cette table vaut le voyage**
On y mange toujours très bien, parfois merveilleusement.

✿✿ **Cuisine excellente, cette table mérite un détour**

✿ **Une très bonne cuisine dans sa catégorie**

LES BIB : LES MEILLEURES ADRESSES À PETIT PRIX

☺ **Bib Gourmand**
Établissement proposant une cuisine de qualité à moins de £28 ou €40 en République d'Irlande (repas composé de 3 plats, hors boisson).

Bib Hôtel
Établissement offrant une prestation de qualité avec une majorité des chambres à moins de £75 ou moins de €105 en République d'Irlande (prix d'une chambre double, petit-déjeuner compris).

LES ADRESSES LES PLUS AGRÉABLES

Le rouge signale les établissements particulièrement agréables. Cela peut tenir au caractère de l'édifice, à l'originalité du décor, au site, à l'accueil ou aux services proposés.

⌂, 🏠 to 🏨 **Hôtels agréables**

🍺, X to XXXXX **Restaurants agréables**

LES MENTIONS PARTICULIÈRES

En dehors des distinctions décernées aux établissements, les inspecteurs Michelin apprécient d'autres critères souvent importants dans le choix d'un établissement.

SITUATION

Vous cherchez un établissement tranquille ou offrant une vue attractive ?
Suivez les symboles suivants :

- **Hôtel tranquille**
- **Hôtel très tranquille**
- **Vue intéressante**
- **Vue exceptionnelle**

CARTE DES VINS

Vous cherchez un restaurant dont la carte des vins offre un choix particulièrement intéressant ? Suivez le symbole suivant :

Carte des vins particulièrement attractive
Toutefois, ne comparez pas la carte présentée par le sommelier d'un grand restaurant avec celle d'un pub ou d'un restaurant beaucoup plus simple. Les deux cartes vous offriront de l'exceptionnel, mais de niveau très différent.

FUMEUR

En Grande Bretagne et République d'Irlande il est formellement interdit de fumer dans les pubs, restaurants et hotels.

Équipements & services

30 rm	Nombre de chambres
	Ascenseur
	Air conditionné (dans tout ou partie de l'établissement)
	Connexion Internet à haut débit dans la chambre
	Connection Internet « Wireless Lan » dans la chambre
	Établissement en partie accessible aux personnes à mobilité réduite.
	Équipements d'acceuil pour les enfants
	Repas servi au jardin ou en terrasse
Spa	Bel espace de bien-être et de relaxation
	Sauna - Salle de remise en forme
	Piscine : de plein air ou couverte
	Jardin – Parc
18	Court de tennis, golf et nombre de trous
	Ponton d'amarrage
	Pêche ouverte aux clients de l'hôtel (éventuellement payant)
	Salles de conférences
	Salon privé
	Garage dans l'hôtel (généralement payant)
P	Parking réservé à la clientèle
	Accès interdit au chiens (dans tout ou partie de l'établissement)
	Station de métro à proximité (Londres)
May-October	Période d'ouverture (ou fermeture), communiquée par l'hôtelier

Prix

Les prix indiqués dans ce guide ont été établis à l'automne 2007 et s'appliquent en basse et haute saisons. Ils sont susceptibles de modifications, notamment en cas de variation des prix des biens et des services. Les hôteliers et restaurateurs se sont engagés, sous leur propre responsabilité, à appliquer ces prix aux clients. Dans certaines villes, à l'occasion de manifestations commerciales ou touristiques, les prix demandés par les hôteliers risquent d'être considérablement majorés. Les prix sont indiqués en livres sterling sauf en République d'Irlande où ils sont donnés en euros. Les tarifs de l'hébergement comprennent le service et la T.V.A. La T.V.A. est également incluse dans les prix des repas. Toutefois, le service est uniquement compris dans les repas si la mention « **s** » apparaît après le prix. Dans le cas contraire, une charge supplémentaire variant de 10 à 15% du montant de l'addition est demandée. (La T.V.A. n'est pas appliquée dans les Channel Islands). Hors saison, certains établissements proposent des conditions avantageuses, renseignez-vous dès votre réservation.

LES ARRHES

Certains hôteliers demandent le versement d'arrhes. Il s'agit d'un dépôt-garantie qui engage l'hôtelier comme le client. Bien demander à l'hôtelier de vous fournir dans sa lettre d'accord toutes les précisions utiles sur la réservation et les conditions de séjour.

CARTES DE PAIEMENT

	Carte de paiement acceptées :
AE ⊕ MC VISA	American Express – Diners Club – Mastercard – Visa.

CHAMBRES

rm 🚹 50.00/90.00	Prix minimum/maximum pour une chambre confortable d'une personne
rm 🚹🚹 70.00/120.00	Prix minimum/maximum pour une chambre de deux personnes
rm ☕ 55.00/85.00	Prix de la chambre petit-déjeuner compris
☕ 6.00	Prix du petit-déjeuner si non inclus

SHORT BREAKS

Certains hôtels proposent des conditions avantageuses pour un séjour de deux ou trois nuits. Ce forfait, calculé par personne pour 2 personnes au minimum, comprend le dîner, la chambre et le petit-déjeuner. Se renseigner auprès de l'hôtelier.

RESTAURANT

Menu à prix fixe : minimum £13, maximum £28 comprenant généralement 3 plats. Le prix minimum correspond souvent à celui d'un déjeuner.

Repas à la carte : le 1er prix correspond à un repas simple comprenant une entrée, un plat du jour et un dessert. Le 2e prix concerne un repas plus complet (avec spécialité) comprenant un hors d'œuvre, un plat principal, fromage ou dessert

s	Service compris
🎭	Restaurants proposant des menus à prix attractifs servis avant ou après le théâtre

⌂ : Dans les établissements de cette catégorie, le dîner est servi à heure fixe exclusivement aux personnes résidentes. Le menu à prix unique offre un choix limité de plats. Le déjeuner est rarement proposé. Beaucoup de ces établissements ne sont pas autorisés à vendre des boissons alcoolisées.

Villes

GÉNÉRALITÉS

✉ *York*	Numéro de code postal et nom du bureau distributeur du courrier
501 M27, ⑩	Numéro des cartes Michelin et carroyage ou numéro du pli
Great Britain	Voir le Guide Vert Michelin Grande-Bretagne
pop. 1057	Population (d'après le recensement de 2001)
BX **a**	Lettre repérant un emplacement sur le plan
18	Golf et nombre de trous (handicap parfois demandé, réservation par téléphone vivement recommandée)
✳ ⋞	Panorama, point de vue
	Aéroport
	Transports maritimes
	Transports maritimes (pour passagers seulement)
i	Information touristique

HEURE LÉGALE

Les visiteurs devront tenir compte de l'heure officielle en Grande-Bretagne : une heure de retard sur l'heure française.

INFORMATIONS TOURISTIQUES

INTÉRÊT TOURISTIQUE

★★★	Vaut le voyage
★★	Mérite un détour
★	Intéressant
AC	Entrée payante

SITUATION

	Dans la ville
	Aux environs de la ville
	Excursions dans la région
N, S, E, W	La curiosité est située : au Nord, au Sud, à l'Est, à l'Ouest
A 22	On s'y rend par la route A 22, repérée par le même signe que sur le plan du Guide
2 m.	Distance en miles (calculée en kilomètre pour la République d'Irlande)

@● a Hôtels – Restaurants

CURIOSITÉS

Bâtiment intéressant
Édifice religieux intéressant

VOIRIE

M 1 Autoroute
4 4 Numéro d'échangeur : complet, partiel
Route à chaussée séparées de type autoroutier
Grande voie de circulation
A 2 Itinéraire principal (GB) - Route nationale (IRL)
Sens unique – Rue impraticable, réglementée
Rue piétonne – Tramway
Piccadilly P R Rue commerçante – Parking – Parking Relais
Porte – Passage sous voûte – Tunnel
15'5 Passage bas (inférieur à 16'6") sur les grandes voies de circulation
Gare et voie ferrée
Funiculaire – Téléphérique, télécabine
B Pont mobile – Bac pour autos

SIGNES DIVERS

Information touristique
Église/édifice religieux – Mosquée – Synagogue
Tour ou pylône de télécommunication – Ruines
Jardin, parc, bois – Cimetière
Stade – Hippodrome – Golf
Golf (réservé) – Patinoire
Piscine de plein air, couverte
Vue – Panorama
Monument – Fontaine – Hôpital – Marché couvert
Port de plaisance – Phare
Aéroport – Station de métro – Gare routière
Transport par bateau :
– passagers et voitures
Bureau principal
Bâtiment public repéré par une lettre :
C H - Bureau de l'Administration du comté – Hôtel de ville
J Palais de justice
M T U - Musée - Théâtre - Université, grande école
POL. - Police (Commissariat central)

LONDRES

BRENT WEMBLEY Nom d'arrondissement (borough) - de quartier (area)
Limite de « borough »
Zone à péage du centre-ville lundi-vendredi 7h-18h
Station de métro à proximité de l'hôtel ou du restaurant

Come leggere la guida

INFORMAZIONI TURISTICHE

Distanza dalle città di riferimento, uffici turismo, siti turistici locali, mezzi di trasporto, golfs e tempo libero...

L'ALLOGGIO

Da 🏨 a 🏨, ⌂:
categorie di confort.
In rosso 🏨 ... 🏨, ⌂:
I più ameni.

I RISTORANTI E I PUBS

Da XXXXX a X, 🍺:
categorie di confort.
In rosso XXXXX ... X, 🍺: i più ameni.

LE TAVOLE STELLATE

✿✿✿ Vale il viaggio.
✿✿ Merita una deviazione.
✿ Ottima cucina.

I MIGLIORI ESERCIZI A PREZZI CONTENUTI

Bib Gourmand.
Bib Hotel.

CAMBRIDGE – Cambs – **504** U27 – pop. 117 717 – Great B
London 55 – Coventry 88 – Ipswich 54 – Leicest
Nottingham 88 – Oxford 100
Cambridge Airport : ℘ (01223) 373737, E: 2 m o
The Old Library, Wheeleer St, ℘ (01223) 45758
Cambridgeshire Moat House Hotel, Bar Hill, ℘
Town : St John's College AC Y – King's A
Fitzwilliam Museumy Z **M1** – Trinity College
College AC **Z**
Audley End, S: 13m by A1309 – Imper
on M11

Hotel Gloria
Whitehouse lane, Huntington Rd, CB3 OLX,
– ℘ (01223) 277985 – help@hotelgloria.co
Rest The Melrose – Menu £16 (lunch) –
52 rm – £136 £168/255 – £7.50
• Built as a private house in 1852, now
contemporary rooms include state of
garden and terrace.

Alexander House (Johns)
Midsummer Common, CB4 1HA – ℘
– resa@alexanderhouse.co.uk – Fa
– closed 2 weeks Christmas, 2 wee
Rest – Menu (dinner only and lu
Spec. Salad of smoked eel, pig'
nuts and pistachios and aspara
des bois and mint.
• A river Cam idyll. Chic con
terrace with blissful views c

The Roasted Pepper
35 Chesterton Rd,CB4 3AX
– Fax (01223) 351873 – clo
Rest *(booking essential)*
• Personally run Victori
Italian dishes with mild

at Histon North : 3 m on B1

Blue House Farm
44 High St, CB3 7HV
– Fax (01223) 2621
22 rm – £38
• Red-brick 18C
house overlook
bread and pres

ERBURY – Ke

ENGLAND

ALTRE PUBBLICAZIONI MICHELIN

Riferimento alla carta Michelin ed alla Guida Verde in cui figura la località..

LOCALIZZARE LA CITTÀ

Posizione della località sulla carta regionale alla fine della guida (n° della carta e coordinate).

GLI ALBERGHI TRANQUILLI

Albergo tranquillo.
Albergo molto tranquillo.

DESCRIZIONE DELL'ESERCIZIO

Atmosfera, stile, carattere e spécialità.

LOCALIZZARE L'ESERCIZIO

Localizzazione sulla pianta di città (coordinate ed indice).

INSTALLAZIONI E SERVIZI

PREZZI

Principi

« Quest'opera nasce col secolo e durerà quanto esso. »

La prefazione della prima Edizione della Guida MICHELIN 1900, divenuta famosa nel corso degli anni, si è rivelata profetica. Se la Guida viene oggi consultata in tutto il mondo è grazie al suo costante impegno nei confronti dei lettori.

Desideriamo qui ribadirlo.

I principi della Guida Michelin:

La visita anonima: per poter apprezzare il livello delle prestazioni offerte ad ogni cliente, gli ispettori verificano regolarmente ristoranti ed alberghi mantenendo l'anonimato. Questi pagano il conto e possono presentarsi per ottenere ulteriori informazioni sugli esercizi. La posta dei lettori fornisce peraltro preziosi suggerimenti che permettono di orientare le nostre visite.

L'indipendenza: la selezione degli esercizi viene effettuata in totale indipendenza, nel solo interesse del lettore. Gli ispettori e il caporedattore discutono collegialmente le scelte. Le massime decisioni vengono prese a livello europeo. La segnalazione degli esercizi all'interno della Guida è interamente gratuita.

La selezione: la Guida offre una selezione dei migliori alberghi e ristoranti per ogni categoria di confort e di prezzo. Tale selezione è il frutto di uno stesso metodo, applicato con rigorosità da tutti gli ispettori.

L'aggiornamento annuale: ogni anno viene riveduto e aggiornato l'insieme dei consigli pratici, delle classifiche e della simbologia al fine di garantire le informazioni più attendibili.

L'omogeneità della selezione: i criteri di valutazione sono gli stessi per tutti i paesi presi in considerazione dalla Guida Michelin.

… e un unico obiettivo: prodigarsi per aiutare il lettore a fare di ogni spostamento e di ogni uscita un momento di piacere, conformemente alla missione che la Michelin si è prefissata: contribuire ad una miglior mobilità.

Editoriale

Caro lettore,

Abbiamo il piacere di presentarle la nostra 35a edizione della Guida Michelin Gran Bretagna & Irlanda.
Questa selezione, che comprende i migliori alberghi e ristoranti per ogni categoria di prezzo, viene effettuata da un'équipe di ispettori professionisti di formazione alberghiera. Ogni anno, percorrono l'intero paese per visitare nuovi esercizi e verificare il livello delle prestazioni di quelli già inseriti nella Guida.

All'interno della selezione, vengono inoltre assegnate ogni anno da ✿ a ✿✿✿ alle migliori tavole. Le stelle contraddistinguono gli esercizi che propongono la miglior cucina, in tutti gli stili, tenendo conto della scelta dei prodotti, della creatività, dell'abilità nel raggiungimento della giusta cottura e nell'abbinamento dei sapori, del rapporto qualità/prezzo, nonché della costanza.

Anche quest'anno diversi ristoranti hanno ricevuto la stella per la qualità della loro cucina. Una « **N** » evidenzia le nuove promozioni per questa edizione del 2008 annuniciandone il loro inserimento con una, due o tre stelle.

Abbiano inoltre continuato a selezionare le « *promesse* » per la categoria superiore. Questi esercizi, evidenziati in rosso nella nostra lista, sono i migliori della loro categoria e potranno accedere alla categoria superiore non appena le loro prestazioni avranno raggiunto un livello costante nel tempo, e nelle proposte della carta. Con questa segnalazione speciale, è nostra intenzione farvi conoscere le tavole che costituiscono, dal nostro punto di vista, le principali promesse della gastronomia di domani.

Il vostro parere ci interessa, specialmente riguardo a queste « *promesse* ». Non esitate quindi a scriverci, la vostra partecipazione è importante per orientare le nostre visite e migliorare costantemente la vostra Guida. Grazie ancora per la vostra fedeltà e vi auguriamo buon viaggio con la Guida Michelin 2008.

Consultate la Guida Michelin su
www.ViaMichelin.com
e scriveteci a:
themichelinguide-gbirl@uk.michelin.com

Categorie & simboli distintivi

LE CATEGORIE DI CONFORT

Nella selezione della Guida Michelin vengono segnalati i migliori indirizzi per ogni categoria di confort e di prezzo.Gli esercizi selezionati sono classificati in base al confort che offrono e vengono citati in ordine di preferenza per ogni categoria.

🏨🏨🏨🏨🏨	XXXXX	Gran lusso e tradizione
🏨🏨🏨🏨	XXXX	Gran confort
🏨🏨🏨	XXX	Molto confortevole
🏨🏨	XX	Di buon confort
🏨	X	Abbastanza confortevole
	🍺	Pub tradizionali con cucina
⌂		Pensione, fattorie, case private (forme alternative di ospitalità)
without rest.		L'albergo non ha ristorante
with rm		Il ristorante dispone di camere

I SIMBOLI DISTINTIVI

Per aiutarvi ad effettuare la scelta migliore, segnaliamo gli esercizi che si distinguono in modo particolare. Questi ristoranti sono evidenziati nel testo con ✿ o ☺ e **Rest.**

LE MIGLIORI TAVOLE

Le stelle distinguono gli esercizi che propongono la miglior qualità in campo gastronomico, indipendentemente dagli stili di cucina. I criteri presi in considerazione sono: la scelta dei prodotti, l'abilità nel raggiungimento della giusta cottura e nell'abbinamento dei sapori, il rapporto qualità/prezzo nonché la costanza.

✿✿✿ **Una delle migliori cucine, questa tavola vale il viaggio**
Vi si mangia sempre molto bene, a volte meravigliosamente.

✿✿ **Cucina eccellente, questa tavola merita una deviazione**

✿ **Un'ottima cucina nella sua categoria**

I MIGLIORI ESERCIZI A PREZZI CONTENUTI

☺ **Bib Gourmand**
Esercizio che offre una cucina di qualità a meno di £28 (€40 per l'Irlanda). Prezzo di un pasto, bevanda esclusa.

☺ **Bib Hotel**
Esercizio che offre un soggiorno di qualità a meno di £75 (€105 per l'Irlanda) per la maggior parte delle camere. Prezzi per 2 persone, prima colazione esclusa.

GLI ESERCIZI AMENI

Il rosso indica gli esercizi particolarmente ameni. Questo per le caratteristiche dell'edificio, le decorazioni non comuni, la sua posizione ed il servizio offerto.

⌂, ⌂ to ⌂⌂⌂	**Alberghi ameni**
X, X to XXXXX	**Ristoranti ameni**

LE SEGNALAZIONI PARTICOLARI

Oltre alle distinzioni conferite agli esercizi, gli ispettori Michelin apprezzano altri criteri spesso importanti nella scelta di un esercizio.

POSIZIONE

Cercate un esercizio tranquillo o che offre una vista piacevole ? Seguite i simboli seguenti:

Albergo tranquillo

Albergo molto tranquillo

Vista interessante

Vista eccezionale

CARTA DEI VINI

Cercate un ristorante la cui carta dei vini offre una scelta particolarmente interessante ? Seguite il simbolo seguente:

Carta dei vini particolarmente interessante

Attenzione a non confrontare la carta presentata da un sommelier in un grande ristorante con quella di un pub o di un ristorante più semplice. Le due carte vi offriranno degli ottimi vini di diverso livello.

FUMARE

In Gran Bretagna & Irlanda la legge vieta il fumo in tutti pub, Ristoranti e le zone comuni degli alberghi.

Installazioni & servizi

30 rm	Numero di camere
	Ascensore
A/C	Aria condizionata (in tutto o in parte dell'esercizio)
	Connessione Internet ad alta velocità in camera
	Connessione Internet « Wireless Lan » in camera
	Esercizio accessibile in parte alle persone con difficoltà motorie
	Attrezzatura per accoglienza e ricreazione dei bambini
	Pasti serviti in giardino o in terrazza
Spa	Centro attrezzato per il benessere ed il relax
	Sauna - Palestra
	Piscina: all'aperto, coperta
	Giardino – Parco
18	Campo di tennis – Golf e numero di buche
	Pontile d'ormeggio
	Pesca aperta ai clienti dell'albergo (eventualmente a pagamento)
	Sale per conferenze
	Saloni particolari
	Garage nell'albergo (generalmente a pagamento)
P	Parcheggio riservato alla clientela
	Accesso vietato ai cani (in tutto o in parte dell'esercizio)
	Stazione della metropolitana più vicina (a Londra)
May-October	Periodo di apertura, comunicato dall'albergatore

Prezzi

I prezzi riportati nella guida ci sono stati forniti nell'autunno del 2007 e si applicano alla bassa e all'alta stagione. Potranno subire delle variazioni in relazione ai cambiamenti dei prezzi di beni e servizi. Gli albergatori e i ristoratori si sono impegnati, sotto la propria responsabilità, a praticare questi prezzi ai clienti. In occasione di alcune manifestazioni commerciali o turistiche i prezzi richiesti dagli albergatori potrebbero subire un sensibile aumento nelle località interessate e nei loro dintorni. I prezzi sono indicati in lire sterline (1 £ = 100 pence) ad eccezione per la Repubblica d'Irlanda dove sono indicati in euro. Tutte le tariffe per il soggiorno includono sia servizio che I.V.A. Tutti i prezzi dei ristoranti includono l'I.V.A., il servizio è incluso quando dopo il prezzo appare « **s** ». Quando non compare « **s** », il prezzo può essere soggetto ad un aumento per il servizio solitamente compreso tra il 10 % e il 15 %. In bassa stagione, alcuni esercizi applicano condizioni più vantaggiose, informatevi al momento della prenotazione. Entrate nell'albergo o nel ristorante con la guida in mano, dismostrando in tal modo la fiducia in chi vi ha indirizzato.

LA CAPARRA

Alcuni albergatori chiedono il versamento di una caparra. Si tratta di un deposito-garanzia che impegna sia l'albergatore che il cliente. Vi consigliamo di farvi precisare le norme riguardanti la reciproca garanzia di tale caparra.

CARTE DI CREDITO

	Carte di credito accettate:
AE ⓓ MC VISA	American Express – Diners Club – MasterCard – Visa

CAMERE

rm 🚹 50.00/90.00	Prezzo minimo e massimo per una camera singola di buon confort
rm 🚹🚹 70.00/120.00	Prezzo minimo e massimo per una camera doppia per due persone
rm ☕ 55.00/85.00	Prezzo della camera compresa la prima colazione
☕ 6.00	Prezzo della prima colazione

SHORT BREAKS

Alcuni alberghi propongono delle condizioni particolarmente vantaggiose o short break per un soggiorno minimo di due notti. Questo prezzo, calcolato per persona e per un minimo di due persone, comprende: camera, cena e prima colazione. Informarsi presso l'albergatore.

RISTORANTE

Menu a prezzo fisso: prezzo minimo £13 e massimo £28 comprendente generalmente 3 piatti. Il menu a prezzo minimo è spesso disponibile solo a pranzo.

Pasto alla carta: il primo prezzo corrisponde ad un pasto semplice comprendente: primo, piatto del giorno e dessert. Il secondo prezzo corrisponde ad un pasto più completo (con specialità) comprendente: due piatti e dessert.

s	Servizio compresso
🎭	Ristoranti che offrono menu a prezzi ridotti prima e/o dopo gli spettacoli teatrali

⌂ : Negli alberghi di questa categoria, la cena viene servita, ad un'ora stabilita, esclusivamente a chi vi allogia. Il menu, a prezzo fisso, offre una scelta limitata di piatti. Raramente viene servito anche il pranzo. Molti di questi esercizi non hanno l'autorizzazione a vendere alcolici.

Città

GENERALITÀ

✉ *York*	Codice di avviamento postale
501 M27, ⑩	Numero della carta Michelin e del riquadro
Great Britain	Vedere la Guida Verde Michelin Gran Bretagna
pop. 1057	Popolazione residente
BX **a**	Lettere indicanti l'ubicazione sulla pianta
18	Golf e numero di buche (handicap generalmente richiesto, prenotazione telefonica vivamente consigliata)
	Panorama, vista
	Aeroporto
	Trasporti marittimi
	Trasporti marittimi (solo passeggeri)
i	Ufficio informazioni turistiche

ORA LEGALE

I visitatori dovranno tenere in considerazione l'ora ufficiale nelle Isole Britanniche: un'ora di ritardo sull'ora italiana.

INFORMAZIONI TURISTICHE

INTERESSE TURISTICO

★★★	Vale il viaggio
★★	Merita una deviazione
★	Interessante
AC	Entrata a pagamento

UBICAZIONE

	Nella città
	Nei dintorni della città
	Nella regione
N, S, E, W	Il luogo si trova a Nord, a Sud, a Est, a Ovest della località
A 22	Ci si va per la strada A 22 indicata con lo stesso segno sulla pianta
2 m.	Distanza in miglia (solo per la Gran Bretagna)

Piante

a ● a Alberghi – Ristoranti

CURIOSITÀ

Edificio interessante
Costruzione religiosa interessante

VIABILITÀ

M 1 Autostrada
4 4 numero dello svincolo: completo, parziale
Strada a carreggiate separate
Grande via di circolazione
A 2 Itinerario principale: Primary route (GB) o National route (IRL)
Senso unico – Via impraticabile, a circolazione regolamentata
Via pedonale – Tranvia
Piccadilly P R Via commerciale – Parcheggio – Parcheggio Ristoro
Porta – Sottopassaggio – Galleria
15'5 Sottopassaggio (altezza inferiore a 15'5) sulle grandi vie di circolazione
Stazione e ferrovia
Funicolare – Funivia, cabinovia
B Ponte mobile – Traghetto per auto

SIMBOLI VARI

Ufficio informazioni turistiche
Chiesa – Moschea – Sinagoga
Torre o pilone per telecomunicazioni – Ruderi
Giardino, parco, bosco – Cimitero
Stadio – Ippodromo – Golf
Golf riservato – Pattinaggio
Piscina: all'aperto, coperta
Vista – Panorama
Monumento – Fontana – Ospedale – Mercato coperto
Porto turistico – Faro
Aeroporto – Stazione della metropolitana – Autostazione
Trasporto con traghetto: passeggeri ed autovetture
Ufficio postale centrale
Edificio pubblico indicato con lettera:
C H J Sede dell'Amministrazione di Contea – Municipio – Palazzo di Giustizia
M T U Museo – Teatro – Università, Scuola superiore
POL. Polizia (Questura, nelle grandi città)

LONDRA

BRENT WEMBLEY Distretto amministrativo (Borough) – Quartiere (Area)
Limite del Borough
Area con circolazione a pagamento Lunedì-Venerdì 07.00-18.00
Stazione della metropolitana più vicina all'albergo o al ristorante

Hinweise zur Benutzung

TOURISTISCHE INFORMATIONEN

Entfernungen zu größeren Städten, Informationsstellen, Sehenswürdigkeiten, Verkehrsmittel, Golfplätze und lokale Veranstaltungen...

DIE UNTERBRINGUNG

Von bis , : Komfortkategorien.
In rot ... , : Besonders angenehme Häuser.

DIE RESTAURANTS UND DIE PUBS

Von bis , : Komfortkategorien.
In rot ... , : Besonders angenehme Häuser.

DIE STERNE-RESTAURANTS

Eine Reise wert.
Verdient einen Umweg.
Eine sehr gute Küche.

DIE BESTEN PREISWERTEN ADRESSEN

Bib Gourmand.
Bib Hotel.

CAMBRIDGE – Cambs – 504 U27 – pop. 117 717 – Great B
London 55 – Coventry 88 – Ipswich 54 – Leicest
Nottingham 88 – Oxford 100
Cambridge Airport : (01223) 373737, E: 2 m c
The Old Library, Wheeleer St, (01223) 45758
Cambridgeshire Moat House Hotel, Bar Hill,
Town : St John's College AC Y – King's A
Fitzwilliam Museumy Z M1 – Trinity College
College AC Z
Audley End, S: 13m by A1309 – Imper
on M11

Hotel Gloria
Whitehouse lane, Huntington Rd, CB3 OLX,
– (01223) 277985 – help@hotelgloria.co
Rest The Melrose – Menu £16 (lunch) –
52 rm – £136 £168/255 – £7.50
• Built as a private house in 1852, now
contemporary rooms include state of
garden and terrace.

Alexander House (Johns)
Midsummer Common, CB4 1HA –
– resa@alexanderhouse.co.uk – Fa
– closed 2 weeks Christmas, 2 wee
Rest – Menu (dinner only and lu
Spec. Salad of smoked eel, pig'
nuts and pistachios and aspara
des bois and mint.
• A river Cam idyll. Chic con
terrace with blissful views

ENGLAND

The Roasted Pepper
35 Chesterton Rd, CB4 3AX
– Fax (01223) 351873 – cl
Rest (booking essential
• Personally run Victor
Italian dishes with mild

at Histon North : 3 m on B1

Blue House Far
44 High St, CB3 7H
– Fax (01223) 2621
22 rm – £38
• Red-brick 18C
house overlook
bread and pres

ERBURY – Ke

ANDERE MICHELIN-PUBLIKATIONEN

Angabe der Michelin-Karte und des Grünen Michelin-Reiseführers, wo der Ort zu finden ist.

LAGE DER STADT

Markierung des Ortes auf der Regionalkarte am Ende des Buchs (Nr. der Karte und Koordinaten).

RUHIGE HOTELS

Ruhiges Hotel.
Sehr ruhiges Hotel.

BESCHREIBUNG DES HAUSES

Atmosphäre, Stil, Charakter und Spezialitäten.

LAGE DES HAUSES

Markierung auf dem Stadtplan (Planquadrat und Koordinate).

EINRICHTUNG UND SERVICE

PREISE

Grundsätze

„Dieses Werk hat zugleich mit dem Jahrhundert das Licht der Welt erblickt, und es wird ihm ein ebenso langes Leben beschieden sein."

Das Vorwort der ersten Ausgabe des MICHELIN-Führers von 1900 wurde im Laufe der Jahre berühmt und hat sich inzwischen durch den Erfolg dieses Ratgebers bestätigt. Der MICHELIN-Führer wird heute auf der ganzen Welt gelesen. Den Erfolg verdankt er seiner konstanten Qualität, die einzig den Lesern verpflichtet ist und auf festen Grundsätzen beruht.

Die Grundsätze des Michelin-Führers:

Anonymer Besuch: Die Inspektoren testen regelmäßig und anonym die Restaurants und Hotels, um deren Leistungsniveau zu beurteilen. Sie bezahlen alle in Anspruch genommenen Leistungen und geben sich nur zu erkennen, um ergänzende Auskünfte zu den Häusern zu erhalten. Für die Reiseplanung der Inspektoren sind die Briefe der Leser im Übrigen eine wertvolle Hilfe.

Unabhängigkeit: Die Auswahl der Häuser erfolgt völlig unabhängig und ist einzig am Nutzen für den Leser orientiert. Die Entscheidungen werden von den Inspektoren und dem Chefredakteur gemeinsam getroffen. Über die höchsten Auszeichnungen wird sogar auf europäischer Ebene entschieden. Die Empfehlung der Häuser im Michelin-Führer ist völlig kostenlos.

Objektivität der Auswahl: Der Michelin-Führer bietet eine Auswahl der besten Hotels und Restaurants in allen Komfort- und Preiskategorien. Diese Auswahl erfolgt unter strikter Anwendung eines an objektiven Maßstäben ausgerichteten Bewertungssystems durch alle Inspektoren.

Einheitlichkeit der Auswahl: Die Klassifizierungskriterien sind für alle vom Michelin-Führer abgedeckten Länder identisch.

Jährliche Aktualisierung: Jedes Jahr werden alle praktischen Hinweise, Klassifizierungen und Auszeichnungen überprüft und aktualisiert, um ein Höchstmaß an Zuverlässigkeit zu gewährleisten.

... und sein einziges Ziel – dem Leser bestmöglich behilflich zu sein, damit jede Reise und jeder Restaurantbesuch zu einem Vergnügen werden, entsprechend der Aufgabe, die sich Michelin gesetzt hat: die Mobilität in den Vordergrund zu stellen.

Lieber Leser

Lieber Leser,

Wir freuen uns, Ihnen die 35. Ausgabe des Michelin-Führers Great Britain & Ireland vorstellen zu dürfen. Diese Auswahl der besten Hotels und Restaurants in allen Preiskategorien wird von einem Team von Inspektoren mit Ausbildung in der Hotellerie erstellt. Sie bereisen das ganze Jahr hindurch das Land. Ihre Aufgabe ist es, die Qualität und Leistung der bereits empfohlenen und der neu hinzu kommenden Hotels und Restaurants kritisch zu prüfen. In unserer Auswahl weisen wir jedes Jahr auf die besten Restaurants hin, die wir mit ✿ bis ✿✿✿ kennzeichnen. Die Sterne zeichnen die Häuser mit der besten Küche aus, wobei untersc-hiedliche Küchenstilrichtungen vertreten sind. Als Kriterien dienen die Wahl der Produkte, die fachgerechte Zubereitung, der Geschmack der Gerichte, die Kreativität und das Preis-Leistungs-Verhältnis, sowie die Beständigkeit der Küchenleistung. Auch in diesem Jahr werden einige Restaurants erstmals für die Qualität ihrer Küche ausgezeichnet. Um diese neuen Ein-, Zwei- oder Drei-Sterne-Häuser zu präsentieren, haben wir sie in der Sterneliste mit einem "**N**" gekennzeichnet.

Außerdem haben wir wieder eine Auswahl an *"Hoffnungsträger"* für die nächsthöheren Kategorien getroffen. Diese Häuser, die in der Liste in Rot aufgeführt sind, sind die besten ihrer Kategorie und könnten in Zukunft aufsteigen, wenn sich die Qualität ihrer Leistungen dauerhaft und auf die gesamte Karte bezogen bestätigt hat. Mit dieser besonderen Kennzeichnung möchten wir Ihnen die Restaurants aufzeigen, die in unseren Augen die Hoffnung für die Gastronomie von morgen sind. Ihre Meinung interessiert uns! Bitte teilen Sie uns diese mit, insbesondere hinsichtlich dieser *"Hoffnungsträger"*. Ihre Mitarbeit ist für die Planung unserer Besuche und für die ständige Verbesserung des Michelin-Führers von großer Bedeutung.

Wir danken Ihnen für Ihre Treue und wünschen Ihnen angenehme Reisen mit dem Michelin-Führer 2008.

Den Michelin-Führer finden Sie auch im Internet unter
www.ViaMichelin.com
oder schreiben Sie uns eine E-Mail:
themichelinguide-gbirl@uk.michelin.com

Kategorien & Auszeichnungen

KOMFORTKATEGORIEN

Der Michelin-Führer bietet in seiner Auswahl die besten Adressen jeder Komfort- und Preiskategorie. Die ausgewählten Häuser sind nach dem gebotenen Komfort geordnet; die Reihenfolge innerhalb jeder Kategorie drückt eine weitere Rangordnung aus.

🏨🏨🏨🏨🏨	XXXXX	Großer Luxus und Tradition
🏨🏨🏨🏨	XXXX	Großer Komfort
🏨🏨🏨	XXX	Sehr komfortabel
🏨🏨	XX	Mit gutem Komfort
🏨	X	Mit Standard-Komfort
	🍺	Traditionelle Pubs, die Speisen anbieten
🏠		Andere empfohlene Übernachtungsmöglichkeiten (Gästehäuser, Bauernhäuser und private Übernachtungsmöglichkeiten)
without rest.		Hotel ohne Restaurant
with rm		Restaurant vermietet auch Zimmer

AUSZEICHNUNGEN

Um ihnen behilflich zu sein, die bestmögliche Wahl zu treffen, haben einige besonders bemerkenswerte Adressen dieses Jahr eine Auszeichnung erhalten. Die Sterne bzw. „Bib Gourmand" sind durch das entsprechende Symbol ✿ bzw. ☺ und **Rest** gekennzeichnet.

DIE BESTEN RESTAURANTS

Die Häuser, die eine überdurchschnittlich gute Küche bieten, wobei alle Stilrichtungen vertreten sind, wurden mit einem Stern ausgezeichnet. Die Kriterien sind: die Wahl der Produkte, die Kreativität, die fachgerechte Zubereitung und der Geschmack, sowie das Preis-Leistungs-Verhältnis und die immer gleich bleibende Qualität.

✿✿✿ **Eine der besten Küchen: eine Reise wert**
Man isst hier immer sehr gut, öfters auch exzellent.

✿✿ **Eine hervorragende Küche: verdient einen Umweg**

✿ **Ein sehr gutes Restaurant in seiner Kategorie**

DIE BESTEN PREISWERTEN HÄUSER

☺ **Bib Gourmand**
Häuser, die eine gute Küche für weniger als £28 (GB) bzw. €40 (IRE) bieten (Preis für eine dreigängige Mahlzeit ohne Getränke).

🛏 **Bib Hotel**
Häuser, die eine Mehrzahl ihrer komfortablen Zimmer für weniger als £75 (GB) bzw. €105 (IRE) anbieten (Preis für 2 Personen inkl. Frühstück).

DIE ANGENEHMSTEN ADRESSEN

Die rote Kennzeichnung weist auf besonders angenehme Häuser hin. Dies kann sich auf den besonderen Charakter des Gebäudes, die nicht alltägliche Einrichtung, die Lage, den Empfang oder den gebotenen Service beziehen.

⌂, 🏠 to 🏠🏠🏠🏠 **Angenehme Hotels**

🍺, X to XXXXX **Angenehme Restaurants**

BESONDERE ANGABEN

Neben den Auszeichnungen, die den Häusern verliehen werden, legen die Michelin-Inspektoren auch Wert auf andere Kriterien, die bei der Wahl einer Adresse oft von Bedeutung sind.

LAGE

Wenn Sie eine ruhige Adresse oder ein Haus mit einer schönen Aussicht suchen, achten Sie auf diese Symbole:

- Ruhiges Hotel
- Sehr ruhiges Hotel
- Interessante Sicht
- Besonders schöne Aussicht

WEINKARTE

Wenn Sie ein Restaurant mit einer besonders interessanten Weinauswahl suchen, achten Sie auf dieses Symbol:

Weinkarte mit besonders attraktivem Angebot

Aber vergleichen Sie bitte nicht die Weinkarte, die Ihnen vom Sommelier eines großen Hauses präsentiert wird, mit der Auswahl eines Gasthauses, dessen Besitzer die Weine der Region mit Sorgfalt zusammenstellt.

RAUCHEND

In GroBritannien und der Republik Irland ist Rauchen per Gesetz verboten: In allen Pubs, Restaurants und in den offentlichen Bereichen der Hotels.

Einrichtung & Service

30 rm	Anzahl der Zimmer
	Fahrstuhl
A/C	Klimaanlage (im ganzen Haus bzw. in den Zimmern oder im Restaurant)
	High-Speed Internetzugang in den Zimmern möglich
	Internetzugang mit W-Lan in den Zimmern möglich
	Für Körperbehinderte leicht zugängliches Haus
	Spezielle Angebote für Kinder
	Terrasse mit Speisenservice
Spa	Wellnessbereich
	Sauna - Fitnessraum
	Freibad oder Hallenbad
	Liegewiese, Garten – Park
18	Tennisplatz – Golfplatz und Lochzahl
	Bootssteg
	Angelmöglichkeit für Hotelgäste, evtl. gegen Gebühr
	Konferenzraum
	Veranstaltungsraum
	Hotelgarage (wird gewöhnlich berechnet)
P	Parkplatz reserviert für Gäste
	Hunde sind unerwünscht (im ganzen Haus bzw. in den Zimmern oder im Restaurant)
	Nächstgelegene U-Bahnstation (in London)
May-October	Öffnungszeit, vom Hotelier mitgeteilt

Preise

Die in diesem Führer genannten Preise wurden uns im Herbst 2007. Der erste Preis ist der Mindestpreis in der Nebensaison, der zweite Preis der Höchstpreis in der Hauptsaison. Sie können sich mit den Preisen von Waren und Dienstleistungen ändern. Die Häuser haben sich verpflichtet, die von den Hoteliers selbst angegebenen Preise den Kunden zu berechnen. Anlässlich größerer Veranstaltungen, Messen und Ausstellungen werden von den Hotels in manchen Städten und deren Umgebung erhöhte Preise verlangt. Die Preise sind in Pfund Sterling angegeben (1 £ = 100 pence) mit Ausnahme der Republik Irland, wo sie in Euro angegeben sind. Alle Übernachtungspreise enthalten Bedienung und MWSt. Die Restaurantpreise enthalten die MWSt., Bedienung ist enthalten, wenn ein **s** nach dem Preis steht. Wo kein **s** angegeben ist, können unterschiedliche Zuschläge erhoben wer-den, normalerweise zwischen 10%-15% (keine MWSt. auf den Kanalinseln). Erkundigen Sie sich bei den Hoteliers nach eventuellen Sonderbedingungen.

RESERVIERUNG UND ANZAHLUNG

Einige Hoteliers verlangen zur Bestätigung der Reservierung eine Anzahlung. Dies ist als Garantie sowohl für den Hotelier als auch für den Gast anzusehen. Bitten Sie den Hotelier, dass er Ihnen in seinem Bestätigungsschreiben alle seine Bedingungen mitteilt.

KREDITKARTEN

	Akzeptierte Kreditkarten:
AE ⓓ MC VISA	American Express – Diners Club – Mastercard – Visa

ZIMMER

rm 🚹 50.00/90.00	Mindestpreis 50.00 und Höchstpreis 90.00 für ein Einzelzimmer
rm 🚹🚹 70.00/120.00	Mindestpreis 70.00 und Höchstpreis 120.00 für ein Doppelzimmer
rm ☕ 55.00/85.00	Zimmerpreis inkl. Frühstück (selbst wenn dieses nicht eingenommen wird)
☕ 6.00	Preis des Frühstücks

SHORT BREAKS

Einige Hotels bieten Vorzugskonditionen für einen Mindestaufenthalt von zwei Nächten oder mehr (Short break). Der Preis ist pro Person kalkuliert, bei einer Mindestbeteiligung von zwei Personen und schließt das Zimmer, Abendessen und Frühstück ein. Bitte fragen Sie im Hotel nach dieser Rate.

RESTAURANT

Menupreise: mindestens £13.00, höchstens £28.00 für eine dreigängige Mahlzeit. Das Menu mit dem niedrigen Preis ist oft nur mittags erhältlich.

Mahlzeiten "à la carte": Die Preise entsprechen einer dreigängigen Mahlzeit.

s	Bedienung inkl.
🎭	Restaurants mit preiswerten Menus vor oder nach dem Theaterbesuch

⌂ : In dieser Hotelkategorie wird ein Abendessen normalerweise nur zu bestimmten Zeiten für Hotelgäste angeboten. Es besteht aus einem Menu mit begrenzter Auswahl zu festgesetztem Preis. Mittagessen wird selten angeboten. Viele dieser Hotels sind nicht berechtigt, alkoholische Getränke auszuschenken.

Städte

ALLGEMEINES

✉ *York*	Postadresse
501 M27, ⑩	Nummer der Michelin-Karte mit Koordinaten
Great Britain	Siehe Grünen Michelin-Reiseführer Großbritannien
pop. 1057	Einwohnerzahl
BX **a**	Markierung auf dem Stadtplan
18	Golfplatz mit Lochzahl (Handicap manchmal erforderlich, telefonische Reservierung empfehlenswert)
☼ <	Rundblick, Aussichtspunkt
✈	Flughafen
	Autofähre
	Personenfähre
i	Informationsstelle

UHRZEIT

In Großbritannien ist eine Zeitverschiebung zu beachten und die Uhr gegen-über der deutschen Zeit um 1 Stunde zurückzustellen.

SEHENSWÜRDIGKEITEN

BEWERTUNG

★★★	Eine Reise wert
★★	Verdient einen Umweg
★	Sehenswert
AC	Eintrittspreis

LAGE

	In der Stadt
	In der Umgebung der Stadt
▶	Ausflugsziele
N, S, E, W	Im Norden, Süden, Osten, Westen der Stadt
A 22	Zu erreichen über die Straße A 22
2 m.	Entfernung in Meilen (in der Republik Irland in Kilometern)

Stadtpläne

a ● a Hotels – Restaurants

SEHENSWÜRDIGKEITEN

Sehenswertes Gebäude
Sehenswerte Kirche

STRASSEN

M 1 Autobahn
4 4 Nummern der Anschlussstellen: Autobahnein - und/oder - ausfahrt
Schnellstraße
Hauptverkehrsstraße
A 2 Fernverkehrsstraße (Primary route: GB – National route: IRL))
Einbahnstraße – Gesperrte Straße, mit Verkehrsbeschränkungen
Fußgängerzone – Straßenbahn
Piccadilly P R Einkaufsstraße – Parkplatz, Parkhaus – Park-and-Ride-Plätze
Tor – Passage – Tunnel
15'5 Unterführung (Höhe bis 16'6") auf Hauptverkehrsstraßen
Bahnhof und Bahnlinie
Standseilbahn – Cable Car
B Bewegliche Brücke – Autofähre

SONSTIGE ZEICHEN

Informationsstelle
Kirche/Gebetshaus – Moschee – Synagoge
Funk-, Fernsehturm – Ruine
Garten, Park, Wäldchen – Friedhof
Stadion – Pferderennbahn – Golfplatz
Golfplatz (Zutritt bedingt erlaubt) – Eisbahn
Freibad – Hallenbad
Aussicht – Rundblick
Denkmal – Brunnen – Krankenhaus – Markthalle
Jachthafen – Leuchtturm
Flughafen – U-Bahnstation – Autobusbahnhof
Schiffsverbindungen: Autofähre – Personenfähre
Hauptpostamt
Öffentliches Gebäude, durch einen Buchstaben gekennzeichnet:
C H J – Sitz der Grafschaftsverwaltung – Rathaus-Gerichtsgebäude
M T U – Museum – Theater – Universität, Hochschule
POL. – Polizei (in größeren Städten Polizeipräsidium)

LONDON

BRENT WEMBLEY – Name des Stadtteils (borough) – Name des Viertels (area)
– Grenze des «borough»
– Gebührenpflichtiger Innenstadtbereich (Mo-Fr 7-18 Uhr)
⊖ – Dem Hotel oder Restaurant nächstgelegene U-Bahnstation

Awards 2008

Distinctions 2008
Le distinzioni 2008
Auszeichnungen 2008

Starred establishments 2008

The colour corresponds to the establishment with the most stars in this location.

London	This location has at least one 3 star restaurant	✻✻✻
Dublin	This location has at least one 2 star restaurant	✻✻
Belfast	This location has at least one 1 star restaurant	✻

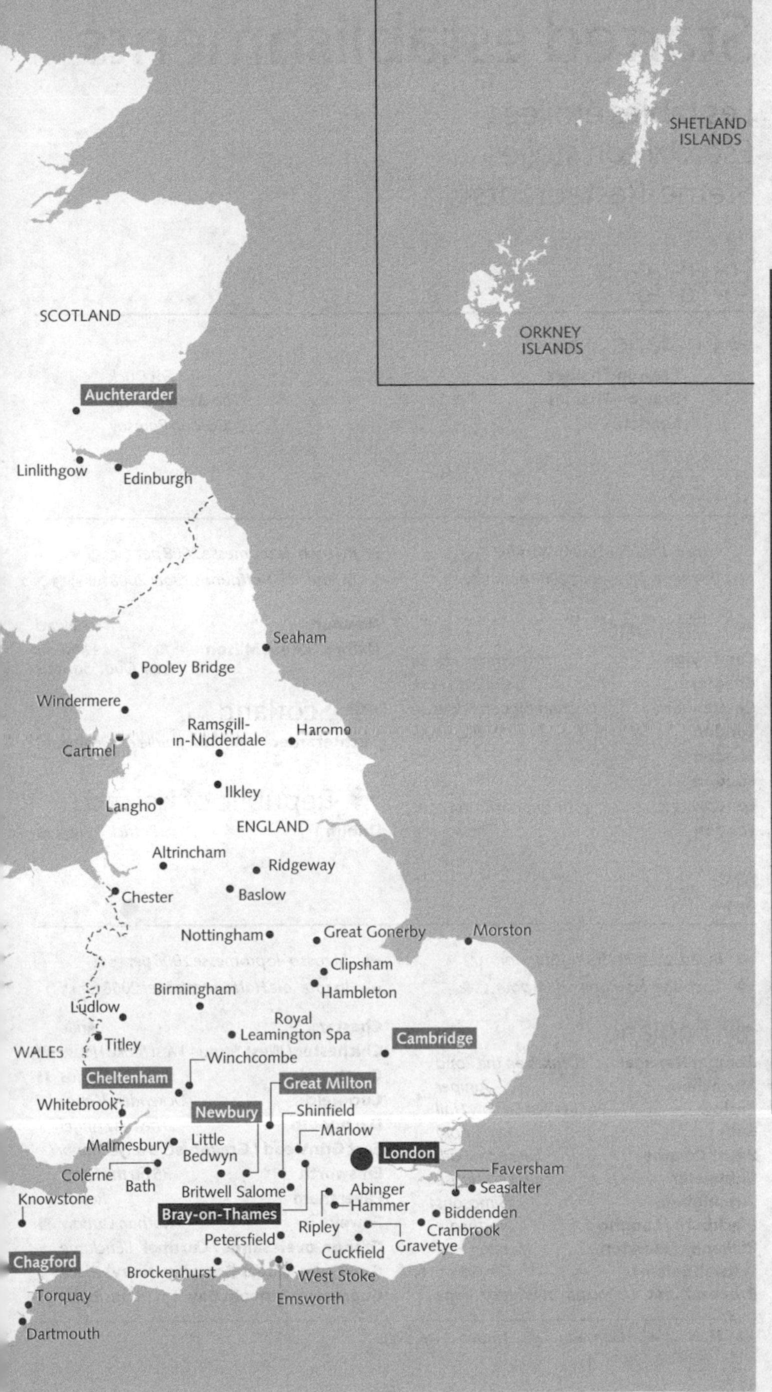
SHETLAND ISLANDS
ORKNEY ISLANDS
SCOTLAND
Auchterarder
Linlithgow
Edinburgh
Seaham
Pooley Bridge
Windermere
Ramsgill-in-Nidderdale
Harome
Cartmel
Ilkley
Langho
ENGLAND
Altrincham
Ridgeway
Chester
Baslow
Nottingham
Great Gonerby
Morston
Clipsham
Hambleton
Birmingham
Ludlow
Royal Leamington Spa
Cambridge
Titley
WALES
Winchcombe
Cheltenham
Great Milton
Whitebrook
Newbury
Shinfield
Marlow
Malmesbury
Little Bedwyn
London
Colerne
Bath
Faversham
Seasalter
Britwell Salome
Abinger Hammer
Knowstone
Bray-on-Thames
Biddenden
Ripley
Cranbrook
Petersfield
Gravetye
Cuckfield
Chagford
Brockenhurst
West Stoke
Torquay
Emsworth
Dartmouth

Starred establishments

Les tables étoilées
Esercizi con stelle
Sterne-Restaurants

✿✿✿

➜ England

Bray-on-Thames	*Fat Duck*
Bray-on-Thames	*The Waterside Inn*
London	*Gordon Ramsay*

✿✿

➜ *In red* *the 2008 Rising Stars for* ✿✿✿
➜ *En rouge* *les espoirs 2008 pour* ✿✿✿
➜ *In rosso* *le promesse 2008 per* ✿✿✿
➜ *In rote* *die Hoffnungsträger 2008 fur* ✿✿✿

➜ England

Cambridge	*Midsummer House*
Chagford	*Gidleigh Park*
Cheltenham	*Le Champignon Sauvage*
London	*Le Gavroche*
London	*Pied à Terre*
London	*Pétrus*
London	*The Capital Restaurant*
London	*The Square*
Newbury	*Vineyard*
Oxford / Great Milton	*Le Manoir aux Quat' Saisons*

➜ Scotland

Auchterarder	*Andrew Fairlie at Gleneagles*

➜ Republic of Ireland

Dublin	*Patrick Guilbaud*

✿

➜ *In red* *the 2008 Rising Stars for* ✿✿
➜ *En rouge* *les espoirs 2008 pour* ✿✿
➜ *In rosso* *le promesse 2008 per* ✿✿
➜ *In rote* *die Hoffnungsträger 2008 fur* ✿✿

➜ England

Abinger Hammer	*Drakes on the Pond*	
Altrincham	*Juniper*	
Baslow	*Fischer's at Baslow Hall*	
Bath	*Bath Priory*	
Bath / Colerne	*Lucknam Park*	
Biddenden	*The West House*	
Birmingham	*Simpsons*	
Blackburn / Langho	*Northcote*	
Blakeney / Morston	*Morston Hall*	
Britwell Salome	*The Goose*	**N**
Brockenhurst	*Le Poussin at Whitley Ridge*	
Chester	*Arkle*	
Chichester / West Stoke	*West Stoke House*	**N**
Cranbrook	*Apicius*	**N**
Cuckfield	*Ockenden Manor*	
Dartmouth	*The New Angel*	
East Grinstead / Gravetye	*Gravetye Manor*	
Emsworth	*36 on the Quay*	
Faversham	*Read's*	
Fowey	*Nathan Outlaw*	**N**
Grange-over-Sands / Cartmel	*L'Enclume*	
Grantham / Great Gonerby	*Harry's Place*	
Guernsey / Fermain Bay	*Christophe*	

➜ **N** *New* ➜ *Nouveau* ➜ *Nuovo* ➜ *Neu*

Helmsley / Harome	*The Star Inn*	
Ilkley	*Box Tree*	
Jersey / La Pulente	*Atlantic*	
Jersey / St Helier	*Bohemia*	
Kington / Titley	*The Stagg Inn*	
London	*1 Lombard Street (Restaurant)*	
London	*Amaya*	
London	*Arbutus*	
London	*Assaggi*	
London	*Aubergine*	
London	*Benares*	
London	*Chez Bruce*	
London	*Club Gascon*	
London	*Foliage*	
London	*Gordon Ramsay at Claridge's*	
London	*Hakkasan*	
London	*Hibiscus*	**N**
London	*L'Atelier de Joël Robuchon*	
London	*L'Escargot*	
London	*La Noisette*	
London	*La Trompette*	**N**
London	*Locanda Locatelli*	
London	*Maze*	
London	*Mirabelle*	
London	*Nahm*	
London	*Nobu*	
London	*Nobu Berkeley St*	
London	*Quilon*	**N**
London	*Rasoi*	
London	*Rhodes Twenty Four*	
London	*Rhodes W1 Restaurant*	**N**
London	*Richard Corrigan at Lindsay House*	
London	*River Café*	
London	*Roussillon*	
London	*Sketch (The Lecture Room and Library)*	
London	*Tamarind*	
London	*The Glasshouse*	
London	*The Greenhouse*	
London	*The Ledbury*	
London	*Tom Aikens*	
London	*Umu*	
London	*Wild Honey*	**N**
London	*Yauatcha*	
London	*Zafferano*	
Ludlow	*Mr Underhill's at Dinham Weir*	
Malmesbury	*Whatley Manor*	
Marlborough / Little Bedwyn	*The Harrow at Little Bedwyn*	
Marlow	*The Hand and Flowers*	
Nottingham	*Restaurant Sat Bains*	
Oakham / Hambleton	*Hambleton Hall*	
Pateley Bridge / Ramsgill-in-Nidderdale	*The Yorke Arms*	
Penzance	*The Abbey*	
Petersfield	*JSW*	
Reading / Shinfield	*L'Ortolan*	
Ripley	*Drake's*	
Royal Leamington Spa	*Mallory Court*	
Scilly Isles / St Martin's	*Tean*	**N**
Seaham	*Seaham Hall*	
Sheffield / Ridgeway	*Old Vicarage*	
South Molton / Knowstone	*The Masons Arms Inn*	
Stamford / Clipsham	*The Olive Branch and Beech House*	
Torquay	*The Room in the Elephant*	
Ullswater / Pooley Bridge	*Sharrow Bay Country House*	
Whitstable / Seasalter	*The Sportsman*	**N**
Winchcombe	*5 North St*	
Windermere	*Holbeck Ghyll*	

→ Scotland

Achiltibuie	*Summer Isles*	
Ballachulish	*Ballachulish House*	**N**
Ballantrae	*Glenapp Castle*	
Dalry	*Braidwoods*	
Edinburgh	*Martin Wishart*	
Edinburgh	*Number One*	
Edinburgh	*The Kitchin*	
Fort William	*Inverlochy Castle*	
Linlithgow	*Champany Inn*	**N**
Portpatrick	*Knockinaam Lodge*	

→ Wales

Monmouth / Whitebrook	*The Crown at Whitebrook*
Pwllheli	*Plas Bodegroes*

→ Northern Ireland

Belfast	*Deanes*

→ Republic of Ireland

Dublin	*Chapter One*	
Dublin	*L'Ecrivain*	
Dublin	*Thornton's*	
Dublin / Ranelagh	*Mint*	**N**
Malahide	*Bon Appétit*	**N**

THE RISING STARS FOR ✿

Les espoirs pour ✿

Le promesse per ✿

Die Hoffnungsträger fur ✿

Bath / Combe Hay	*The Wheatsheaf*
Honiton / Gittisham	*Combe House*
London	*Galvin at Windows*
Murcott	*The Nut Tree*
Welwyn Garden City	*Auberge du Lac*

The 2008 Bib Gourmands

• Places with at least one Bib Gourmand establishment.

SHETLAND ISLANDS
ORKNEY ISLANDS
SCOTLAND
Ardeonaig
Crieff
trathyre
North Queensferry
Edinburgh
Sorn
Newcastle upon Tyne
Tynemouth
Durham
Hutton Magna
Ferrensby
Masham
Boroughbridge
Hetton
Sutton-on-the-Forest
Preston
Thornton
Ribchester
Leeds
York
South Dalton
Southport
Sowerby Bridge
Bury
Oldham
Sheffield
Manchester
Alderley Edge
Didsbury
Birchover
Ringstead
Burnham Market
Stathern
ENGLAND
Itteringham
Stamford
Kenilworth
Norwich
WALES
Birmingham
Royal Leamington Spa
Stanton
Stoke Holy Cross
Stratford-upon-Avon
Cambridge
Little Wilbraham
Saxmundham
Ullingswick
Stow-on-the-Wold
Aldeburgh
Paxford
Chipping Norton
Orford
Ross-on-Wye
Sudbury
Mistley
bergavenny
Leafield
Haddenham
Hemel Hempstead
Tetbury
St Albans
Newport
Stanton-St John
London
Toot Baldon
Wells
Radnage
West Malling
Hurley
Lower Hardres
South Cadbury
Bray-on-Thames
Speldhurst
Reigate
Westfield
Rockbeare
Hastings and St Leonards
Hove
Brighton
Rushlake Green
Danehill

Bib Gourmand

Good food at moderate prices
Repas soignés à prix modérés
Pasti accurati a prezzi contenuti
Sorgfältig zubereitete, preiswerte Mahlzeiten

➜ England

Aldeburgh	*The Lighthouse*	
Alderley Edge	*The Wizard*	
Beverley / South Dalton	*The Pipe and Glass Inn*	**N**
Birmingham	*Pascal's*	**N**
Blackpool / Thornton	*Twelve*	
Boroughbridge	*thediningroom*	
Bray-on-Thames	*The Hinds Head*	
Bray-on-Thames	*The Royal Oak*	**N**
Brighton	*Terre à Terre*	
Brighton	*The Real Eating Company*	
Brighton / Hove	*The Ginger Pig*	**N**
Burnham Market	*The Hoste Arms*	
Bury	*The Waggon*	
Cambridge	*22 Chesterton Road*	
Cambridge / Little Wilbraham	*The Hole in the Wall*	
Canterbury / Lower Hardres	*The Granville*	
Castle Cary / South Cadbury	*The Camelot*	
Chipping Campden / Paxford	*Churchill Arms*	
Chipping Norton	*The Masons Arms*	**N**
Danehill	*Coach and Horses*	
Durham	*Bistro 21*	
Exeter / Rockbeare	*Jack in the Green Inn*	
Guernsey / St Saviour	*The Pavilion*	
Haddenham	*The Green Dragon*	
Hastings and St. Leonards	*St Clements*	**N**
Hemel Hempstead	*Restaurant 65*	**N**
Hunstanton / Ringstead	*The Gin Trap Inn*	**N**
Hurley	*Black Boys Inn*	
Hutton Magna	*The Oak Tree Inn*	
Itteringham	*The Walpole Arms*	
Jersey / Gorey	*Village Bistro*	
Jersey / Green Island	*Green Island*	
Kenilworth	*Simply Simpsons*	
Knaresborough / Ferrensby	*The General Tarleton Inn*	
Leeds	*Anthony's at Flannels*	
Leeds	*Brasserie Forty Four*	
London	*Agni*	
London	*Al Duca*	
London	*Benja*	**N**
London	*Brasserie Roux*	
London	*Brula Bistrot*	
London	*Cafe Spice Namaste*	
London	*Chapter Two*	
London	*Comptoir Gascon*	
London	*Galvin*	**N**
London	*Great Queen Street*	**N**
London	*Kastoori*	**N**
London	*L'Accento*	
London (Barnes)	*Ma Cuisine*	**N**
London (Kew)	*Ma Cuisine*	
London (Twickenham)	*Ma Cuisine*	
London	*Malabar*	
London	*Metrogusto*	
London	*Salt Yard*	
London	*Tangawizi*	
London	*The Anchor and Hope*	
London	*The Brown Dog*	**N**
London	*The Butcher and Grill*	
London	*The Havelock Tavern*	
London	*The Narrow*	**N**
London	*Trenta*	**N**
London	*Upstairs*	**N**
London	*Via Condotti*	
Manchester	*Palmiro*	
Manchester / Didsbury	*Café Jemandl*	
Masham	*Vennell's*	
Matlock / Birchover	*The Druid Inn*	**N**
Melton Mowbray / Stathern	*Red Lion Inn*	
Millbrook / Freathy	*The View*	**N**
Mistley	*The Mistley Thorn*	
Newcastle upon Tyne	*Amer's*	

➜ **N** *New* ➜ *Nouveau* ➜ *Nuovo* ➜ *Neu*

Norwich	*1 Up at the Mad Moose Arms*
Norwich / Stoke Holy Cross	*Wildebeest Arms*
Oldham	*The White Hart Inn*
Orford	*The Trinity*
Oxford / Stanton-St John	*The Talkhouse* **N**
Oxford / Toot Baldon	*The Mole Inn*
Padstow	*Rick Stein's Café*
Preston	*Inside Out*
Preston	*Winckley Square Chop House*
Reigate	*The Westerly* **N**
Ribchester	*The White Bull* **N**
Ross-on-Wye	*The Lough Pool at Sellack*
Royal Leamington Spa	*Oscar's* **N**
Royal Tunbridge Wells / Speldhurst	*George and Dragon*
Rushlake Green	*Stone House*
Saint Albans	*Sukiyaki*
Saxmundham	*The Bell*
Sheffield	*Artisan*
Skipton / Hetton	*The Angel Inn*
Southport	*Warehouse Brasserie*
Sowerby Bridge	*The Millbank*
Stamford	*Jim's Yard*
Stanton	*The Leaping Hare* **N**
Stokenchurch / Radnage	*The Three Horseshoes Inn* **N**
Stow-on-the-Wold	*The Old Butchers*
Stratford-upon-Avon	*Malbec* **N**
Sudbury	*Hitchcock's* **N**
Summercourt	*Viners*
Sutton-on-the-Forest	*Rose and Crown*
Tetbury	*The Gumstool Inn*
Tynemouth	*Sidney's*
Ullingswick	*Three Crowns Inn*
Wells	*The Old Spot*
Westfield	*The Wild Mushroom*
West Malling	*The Swan*
Witney / Leafield	*The Navy Oak*
York	*J. Baker's*

➜ Scotland

Crieff	*The Bank*
Edinburgh	*Atrium*
Edinburgh	*Duck's at Le Marche Noir* **N**
Killin / Ardeonaig	*The Restaurant* **N**
Kintyre / Kilberry	*The Kilberry Inn*
North Queensferry	*The Wee Restaurant* **N**
Sorn	*The Sorn Inn*
Strathyre	*Creagan House*

➜ Wales

Abergavenny	*The Hardwick*
Newport (S.Wales)	*The Chandlery*

➜ Northern Ireland

Belfast	*Cayenne*
Holywood	*Fontana*
Warrenpoint	*Restaurant 23* **N**

➜ Republic of Ireland

Baltimore	*Customs House*
Cashel	*Cafe Hans*
Clonegall	*Sha Roe Bistro* **N**
Dingle	*The Chart House*
Dublin	*Bang Café*
Dublin	*La Maison des Gourmets*
Dublin	*The Winding Stair* **N**
Duncannon	*Aldridge Lodge*
Durrus	*Good Things Cafe*
Kenmare	*The Lime Tree*
Kilbrittain	*Casino House*
Kinsale	*Fishy Fishy Cafe*

Bib Hotel

Good accommodation at moderate prices
Bonnes nuits à petits prix
Buona sistemazione a prezzo contenuto
Hier übernachten Sie gut und preiswert

➜ England

Alderney / St Anne *Maison Bourgage*
Armscote *Willow Corner*
Askrigg *The Apothecary's House*
Barnard Castle *Greta House*
Battle *Fox Hole Farm*
Belford *Market Cross*
Biddenden *Barclay Farmhouse*
Bishop's Stortford / Stansted Mountfitchet *Chimneys*
Bledlow *The Old Station* **N**
Bodmin *Bokiddick Farm*
Bovey Tracey *Brookfield House*
Bury St Edmunds / Beyton *Manorhouse*
Cheddleton *Choir Cottage*
Churchill *The Forge* **N**
Corbridge *Town Barns*
Devizes / Potterne *Blounts Court Farm*
Eastbourne *Brayscroft*
East Mersea *Mersea Vineyard*
Ely / Little Thetford *Springfields*
Enstone *Swan Lodge* **N**
Harrogate / Kettlesing *Knabbs Ash*
Hartland *Golden Park*
Hastings and St. Leonards *Tower House 1066*
Henfield / Wineham *Frylands*
Hexham *West Close House*
Holbeach *Pipwell Manor* **N**
Hope *Underleigh House* **N**
Hungerford *Fishers Farm*
Iron Bridge *Bridge House*
Longtown *Bessiestown Farm*
Morpeth / Longhorsley *Thistleyhaugh Farm*
Nantwich *The Limes*
North Bovey *The Gate House*
Norwich *Beaufort Lodge*
Oxhill *Oxbourne House*
Penrith / Newbiggin *The Old School*
Pickering *Bramwood*
Ripon *Sharow Cross House*
Ripon / Aldfield *Bay Tree Farm*
Rochdale *Hindle Pastures*
Ross-on-Wye / Kerne Bridge *Lumleys*
Rothbury *Farm Cottage*
Rothbury *Thropton Demesne Farmhouse*
St Just *Boscean Country*
Saxmundham *The Bell*
Southend-on-Sea *Beaches* **N**
South Molton *Kerscott Farm*
Stow-on-the-Wold *Number Nine*
Taunton / West Bagborough *Tilbury Farm*
Telford / Bratton *Dovecote Grange*
Torquay *Colindale*
Upton-upon-Severn / Hanley Swan *Yew Tree House*
Wallingford *North Moreton House*
Wareham *Gold Court House*
Warwick *Park Cottage* **N**
Wells / Easton *Beaconsfield Farm*
Whitby / Briggswath *The Lawns*
Winchelsea *Strand House*
Windermere *Newstead* **N**
Woodstock *The Laurels*

➜ Scotland

Aberdeen *Penny Meadow*
Anstruther *The Spindrift*
Auchencairn *Balcary Mews*
Aviemore *The Old Minister's Guest House*
Ayr *Coila* **N**
Ayr *No.26 The Crescent*
Ballater *Moorside House*
Banchory *The Old West Manse*
Blairgowrie *Gilmore House*

➜ **N** *New* ➜ *Nouveau* ➜ *Nuovo* ➜ *Neu*

Brora	*Glenaveron*
Carnoustie	*The Old Manor*
Crieff	*Merlindale*
Dunkeld	*Letter Farm*
Duror	*Bealach House*
Edinburgh	*The Beverley*
Forres / Dyke	*The Old Kirk*
Killin	*Breadalbane House*
Kingussie	*Hermitage*
Linlithgow	*Arden House*
Lochearnhead	*Mansewood Country House*
Nairn	*Bracadale House*
North Berwick	*Beach Lodge*
Oban	*The Barriemore*
Perth	*Taythorpe*
Skye (Isle of) / Broadford	*Tigh an Dochais*
Strathpeffer	*Craigvar*
Thornhill	*Gillbank House*
Ullapool	*Point Cottage*

➜ Wales

Betws Garmon	*Betws Inn*
Betws-y-Coed	*Bryn Bella*
Brecon	*Canal Bank*
Dolgellau	*Tyddyn Mawr*
Llandrindod Wells / Crossgates	*Guidfa House*
Llangrannog	*The Grange*
Llanuwchllyn	*Eifionydd*
Ruthin	*Firgrove*
St Clears	*Coedllys Country House*

➜ Northern Ireland

Bangor	*Cairn Bay Lodge*
Bangor	*Hebron House*
Belfast	*Ravenhill House*
Crumlin	*Caldhame Lodge*
Downpatrick	*Pheasants' Hill Farm*
Dundrum	*The Carriage House*

➜ Republic of Ireland

Ballynamult	*Sliabh gCua Farmhouse* **N**
Ballyvaughan	*Drumcreehy House*
Carlingford	*Beaufort House*
Carlow	*Barrowville Town House*
Cashel	*Aulber House*
Castlegregory	*The Shores Country House*
Donegal	*Ardeevin*
Dundalk	*Rosemount* **N**
Dungarvan	*An Bohreen*
Killarney	*Kingfisher Lodge*
Listowel	*Allo's*
New Ross	*Riversdale House*
Oughterard	*Railway Lodge* **N**
Oughterard	*Waterfall Lodge*
Skull/Schull	*Corthna Lodge*
Toormore	*Fortview House*
Tramore	*Glenorney*

Particularly pleasant hotels

Hôtels agréables
Alberghi ameni
Angenehme Hotels

➜ England

London	*Claridge's*
London	*Dorchester*
London	*Mandarin Oriental Hyde Park*
London	*The Berkeley*
London	*The Ritz*
New Milton	*Chewton Glen*
Taplow	*Cliveden*

➜ Republic of Ireland

Straffan	*The K Club*

➜ England

Aylesbury	*Hartwell House*
Bath	*The Royal Crescent*
Bath / Colerne	*Lucknam Park*
Ipswich / Hintlesham	*Hintlesham Hall*
Jersey / St Saviour	*Longueville Manor*
London	*One Aldwych*
London	*The Goring*
London	*The Soho*
Malmesbury	*Whatley Manor*
Newbury	*Vineyard*
Oxford / Great Milton	*Le Manoir aux Quat' Saisons*

➜ Scotland

Ballantrae	*Glenapp Castle*
Bishopton	*Mar Hall*
Dunkeld	*Kinnaird*
Eriska	*Isle of Eriska*
Fort William	*Inverlochy Castle*

➜ Republic of Ireland

Dublin	*The Merrion*
Kenmare	*Park*
Kenmare	*Sheen Falls Lodge*
Killarney	*Killarney Park*

➜ England

Amberley	*Amberley Castle*
Bath	*Bath Priory*
Bolton Abbey	*The Devonshire Arms Country House*
Bourton-on-the-Water / Lower Slaughter	*Lower Slaughter Manor*
Broadway / Buckland	*Buckland Manor*
Castle Combe	*Manor House H. and Golf Club*
Chagford	*Gidleigh Park*
Dedham	*Maison Talbooth*
East Grinstead / Gravetye	*Gravetye Manor*
Evershot	*Summer Lodge*
Gillingham	*Stock Hill Country House*

Jersey / La Pulente	*Atlantic*
Littlehampton	*Bailiffscourt and Spa*
London	*Blakes*
London	*Capital*
London	*Charlotte Street*
London	*Covent Garden*
London	*Draycott*
London	*Stafford*
London	*The Halkin*
London	*The Milestone*
London	*The Pelham*
Oakham / Hambleton	*Hambleton Hall*
Reading	*The Forbury*
Royal Leamington Spa	*Mallory Court*
Scilly Isles / St Martin's	*St Martin's on the Isle*
Scilly Isles / Tresco	*The Island*
Seaham	*Seaham Hall*
Tetbury	*Calcot Manor*
Ullswater / Pooley Bridge	*Sharrow Bay Country House*
Windermere / Bowness-on-Windermere	*Gilpin Lodge*
York	*Middlethorpe Hall*

➜ Scotland

Blairgowrie	*Kinloch House*
Edinburgh	*Prestonfield*
Edinburgh	*The Howard*
Peebles	*Cringletie House*
Torridon	*The Torridon*

➜ Wales

Llandudno	*Bodysgallen Hall*
Llangammarch Wells	*Lake Country House and Spa*

➜ Northern Ireland

Belfast	*The Merchant*

➜ Republic of Ireland

Dublin	*Dylan*
Galway	*The G*
Mallow	*Longueville House*

➜ England

Ambleside	*The Samling*
Bath	*Queensberry*
Bigbury-on-Sea	*Burgh Island*
Blakeney / Morston	*Morston Hall*
Brampton	*Farlam Hall*
Burnham Market	*The Hoste Arms*
Cheltenham	*On the Park*
Cirencester / Barnsley	*Barnsley House*
Cuckfield	*Ockenden Manor*
Frome	*Babington House*
Helmsley	*Feversham Arms*
Hereford	*Castle House*
Horley	*Langshott Manor*
Jersey / St Helier	*Eulah Country House*
King's Lynn / Grimston	*Congham Hall*
Kingsbridge / Goveton	*Buckland-Tout-Saints*
Lewdown	*Lewtrenchard Manor*
London	*Knightsbridge*
London	*Number Sixteen*
Milford-on-Sea	*Westover Hall*
Orford	*The Crown and Castle*
Purton	*Pear Tree at Purton*
Rushlake Green	*Stone House*
Saint Mawes	*Tresanton*
Tavistock / Milton Abbot	*Hotel Endsleigh*
Torquay / Maidencombe	*Orestone Manor*
Wareham	*Priory*
Wellington	*Bindon Country House*
Wight (Isle of)	*The George*
Windermere	*Holbeck Ghyll*
Woodstock	*Feathers*

➜ Scotland

Achiltibuie	*Summer Isles*
Arran (Isle of)	*Kilmichael Country House*
Gullane	*Greywalls*
Port Appin	*Airds*
Portpatrick	*Knockinaam Lodge*

➜ Wales

Llandudno	*Osborne House*
Machynlleth	*Ynyshir Hall*
Swansea / Llanrhidian	*Fairyhill*
Talsarnau	*Maes-y-Neuadd*

➜ Republic of Ireland

Arthurstown	*Dunbrody Country House*
Ballingarry	*Mustard Seed at Echo Lodge*
Castlebaldwin	*Cromleach Lodge*
Craughwell	*St Clerans*
Glin	*Glin Castle*
Kinsale	*Perryville House*

England

Ashwater	*Blagdon Manor*
Bourton-on-the-Water	*The Dial House*
Dartmouth / Kingswear	*Nonsuch House*
Dorchester	*Birkin House*
Dulverton	*Ashwick House*
Helmsley / Harome	*Cross House Lodge at The Star Inn*
Keswick / Portinscale	*Swinside Lodge*
Leominster / Pudleston	*Ford Abbey*
Lynton	*Hewitt's - Villa Spaldi*
North Walsham	*Beechwood*
Porlock	*Oaks*
Portscatho	*Driftwood*
Saint Ives	*Blue Hayes*
Salisbury / Teffont Magna	*Howard's House*
Staverton	*Kingston House*

Scotland

Annbank	*Enterkine*
Ballater	*Balgonie Country House*
Kelso / Ednam	*Edenwater House*
Killin / Ardeonaig	*Ardeonaig*
Maybole	*Ladyburn*
Muir of Ord	*Dower House*
Nairn	*Boath House*
Tain / Hilton of Cadboll	*Glenmorangie House*

Wales

Betws-y-Coed	*Tan-y-Foel Country House*
Conwy / Llansanffraid Glan Conwy	*Old Rectory Country House*

Republic of Ireland

Bagenalstown	*Kilgraney Country House*
Dingle	*Emlagh Country House*
Lahinch	*Moy House*

England

Ash	*Great Weddington*
Askrigg	*Helm*
Bath	*Haydon House*
Billingshurst	*Old Wharf*
Blackpool	*Number One*
Budleigh Salterton	*Downderry House*
Calne	*Chilvester Hill House*
Chipping Campden / Broad Campden	*Malt House*
Clun	*Birches Mill*
Crackington Haven	*Manor Farm*
Cranbrook	*Cloth Hall Oast*
East Hoathly	*Old Whyly*
Grange-over-Sands / Cartmel	*Hill Farm*
Hawkshead / Far Sawrey	*West Vale*
Helmsley / Byland Abbey	*Oldstead Grange*
Honiton / Payhembury	*Cokesputt House*
Iron Bridge	*Severn Lodge*
Ivychurch	*Olde Moat House*
Kendal	*Beech House*
Lavenham	*Lavenham Priory*
Ledbury / Kynaston	*Hall End*
Lizard	*Landewednack House*
Ludlow	*Bromley Court*
Malpas / Tilston	*Tilston Lodge*
Man (Isle of) / Port St Mary	*Aaron House*
Marazion / Perranuthnoe	*Ednovean Farm*
North Bovey	*The Gate House*
Petworth	*Old Railway Station*
Pickering	*17 Burgate*
Pickering / Levisham	*The Moorlands Country House*
Ripon	*Sharow Cross House*
Saint Austell / Tregrehan	*Anchorage House*
Saint Blazey	*Nanscawen Manor House*
Shrewsbury	*Pinewood House*
Stow-on-the-Wold / Lower Swell	*Rectory Farmhouse*
Stratford-upon-Avon / Pillerton Priors	*Fulready Manor*
Tavistock / Chillaton	*Tor Cottage*
Tavistock / Quither	*Quither Mill*
Teignmouth	*Thomas Luny House*
Thursford Green	*Holly Lodge*
Wareham	*Gold Court House*
Wold Newton	*Wold Cottage*
York	*Alexander House*

Scotland

Ballantrae	*Cosses Country House*
Bute (Isle of) / Ascog	*Balmory Hall*
Connel	*Ards House*
Edinburgh	*Davenport House*

Fort William	*Crolinnhe*
Fort William	*The Grange*
Fortrose	*Water's Edge*
Islay (Isle of) / Ballygrant	*Kilmeny*
Linlithgow	*Arden House*
Mull (Isle of) / Gruline	*Gruline Home Farm*
Mull (Isle of) / Tobermory	*Ptarmigan House*
Skirling	*Skirling House*
Strathpeffer	*Craigvar*

➜ Wales

Betws-y-Coed / Penmachno	*Penmachno Hall*
Colwyn Bay	*Rathlin Country House*
Dolfor	*Old Vicarage*
Menai Bridge	*Neuadd Lwyd*
Pwllheli / Boduan	*The Old Rectory*

➜ Northern ireland

Dungannon	*Grange Lodge*
Holywood	*Beech Hill*

➜ Republic of ireland

Castlegregory	*The Shores Country House*
Castlelyons	*Ballyvolane House*
Cong	*Ballywarren House*
Fethard	*Mobarnane House*
Galway	*Killeen House*
Kanturk	*Glenlohane*
Kenmare	*Sallyport House*
Kilkenny	*Blanchville House*
Portlaoise	*Ivyleigh House*

Particularly pleasant restaurants

Restaurants agréables
Ristoranti ameni
Angenehme Restaurants

XXXXX

➜ England

London	*The Ritz Restaurant*

XXXX

➜ England

Bray-on-Thames	*The Waterside Inn*
London	*Pétrus*
Taplow	*Waldo's*
Winteringham	*Winteringham Fields*

➜ Republic of ireland

Dublin	*Patrick Guilbaud*

XXX

➜ England

Birmingham	*Simpsons*
Brockenhurst	*Le Poussin at Whitley Ridge*
Cambridge	*Midsummer House*
Dedham	*Le Talbooth*
Emsworth	*36 on the Quay*
Grange-over-Sands / Cartmel	*L'Enclume*
London	*Bibendum*
London	*Oxo Tower*
London	*Scott's*
London	*The Capital Restaurant*
London	*The Wolseley*
Newcastle upon Tyne	*Fisherman's Lodge*
Skipton / Hetton	*Angel Inn and Barn Lodgings*
Tavistock / Sulworthy	*The Horn of Plenty*
Welwyn Garden City	*Auberge du Lac*

➜ Wales

Llandrillo	*Tyddyn Llan*

➜ Republic of ireland

Newcastle	*The Mill*

XX

➜ England

Derby / Darley Abbey	*Darleys*
Goring	*Leatherne Bottel*
Grantham / Great Gonerby	*Harry's Place*
Grantham / Hough-on-the-Hill	*The Brownlow Arms*
Jersey / Gorey	*Suma's*
Kirkby Lonsdale / Cowan Bridge	*Hipping Hall*
London	*J. Sheekey*
London	*Le Caprice*
London	*Mon Plaisir*
London	*Rules*

Ludlow	*Mr Underhill's at Dinham Weir*
Malmesbury	*Le Mazot*
Nayland	*The White Hart Inn*
Padstow	*The Seafood*
Pateley Bridge / Ramsgill-in-Nidderdale	*The Yorke Arms*
Yeovil / Barwick	*Little Barwick House*

➜ Scotland

Kingussie	*The Cross at Kingussie*
Lochinver	*The Albannach*
Isle of Skye / Dunvegan	*The Three Chimneys and The House Over-By*

➜ Wales

Builth Wells	*The Drawing Room*
Pwllheli	*Plas Bodegroes*

➜ Republic of Ireland

Clogheen	*Old Convent*
Dunfanaghy	*The Mill*
Kenmare	*The Lime Tree*
Kilbrittain	*Casino House*
Newcastle	*Cafe La Serre*

➜ England

Bray-on-Thames / Bray Marina	*Riverside Brasserie*
Burnham Market	*The Hoste Arms*
High Ongar	*The Wheatsheaf*
London	*L'Atelier de Joël Robuchon*
London	*Oxo Tower Brasserie*
London	*Petersham Nurseries Café*
Mousehole	*Cornish Range*
Stanton	*The Leaping Hare*
Studland	*Shell Bay*

➜ Wales

Aberaeron	*Harbourmaster*

➜ Republic of Ireland

Dingle	*The Chart House*

➜ England

Ambleside	*Drunken Duck Inn*
Barnard Castle / Romaldkirk	*Rose and Crown*
Bath / Combe Hay	*The Wheatsheaf*
Biggleswade / Old Warden	*Hare and Hounds*
Bildeston	*The Bildeston Crown*
Broadhembury	*The Drewe Arms*
Chichester / East Lavant	*The Royal Oak Inn*
Cirencester / Sapperton	*The Bell*
Corscombe	*The Fox Inn*
Evershot	*Acorn Inn*
Helmsley / Harome	*The Star Inn*
Ilmington	*The Howard Arms*
Kendal / Crosthwaite	*The Punch Bowl Inn*
Keyston	*The Pheasant*
Lydford	*The Dartmoor Inn*
Melksham / Whitley	*The Pear Tree Inn*
Milton Keynes / Newton Longville	*The Crooked Billet*
Shefford	*The Black Horse*
Skipton / Hetton	*The Angel Inn*
South Molton / Knowstone	*The Masons Arms Inn*
Stamford / Clipsham	*The Olive Branch and Beech House*
Stockbridge / Longstock	*The Peat Spade Inn*
Stokenchurch / Radnage	*The Three Horseshoes Inn*
Stow-on-the-Wold / Lower Oddington	*The Fox Inn*
Summercourt	*Viners*
Sutton-on-the-Forest	*Rose and Crown*
Tarr Steps	*Tarr Farm Inn*
Taunton / Triscombe	*The Blue Ball Inn*
Winchester	*The Wykeham Arms*
Woburn	*The Birch*

➜ Wales

Brecon	*The Felin Fach Griffin*
Caersws / Pontdolgoch	*The Talkhouse*
Newport / Tredunnock	*The Newbridge*
Skenfrith	*The Bell at Skenfrith*

Further information

Pour en savoir plus
Per saperne di piú
Gut zu wissen

Beer

Beer is one of the oldest and most popular alcoholic drinks in the world. Traditional draught beer is made by grinding malted barley, heating it with water and adding hops which add the familiar aroma and bitterness. Beers in Britain can be divided into 2 principal types: Ales and Lagers which differ principally in their respective warm and cool fermentations. In terms of sales the split between the two is approximately equal. Beer can also be divided into keg or cask.

Kàg beer – is filtered, pasteurised and chilled and then packed into pressurised containers from which it gets its name.

Cask beer – or `Real Ale' as it is often referred to, is not filtered, pasteurised or chilled and is served from casks using simple pumps. It is considered by some to be a more characterful, flavoursome and natural beer.

There are several different beer styles in Britain and Ireland:

Bitter – whilst it is the most popular traditional beer in England and Wales it is now outsold by lager. Although no precise definition exists it is usually paler and dryer than Mild with a high hop content and slightly bitter taste.

Mild – is largely found in Wales, the West Midlands and the North West of England. The name refers to the hop character as it is gentle, sweetish and full flavoured beer. It is generally lower in alcohol and sometimes darker in colour, caused by the addition of caramel or by using dark malt.

Stout – the great dry stouts are brewed in Ireland and are instantly recognisable by their black colour and creamy head. They have a pronounced roast flavour with plenty of hop bitterness.

In Scotland the beers produced are full bodied and malty and are often known simply as Light, Heavy, or Export which refers to the body and strength of the beer.

Although Ireland is most famous for its stouts, it also makes a range of beers which have variously been described as malty, buttery, rounded and fruity with a reddish tinge.

Whisky

The term whisky is derived from the Scottish Gaelic *uisage beatha* and the Irish Gaelic *uisce beathadh*, both meaning "water of life". When spelt without an e it usually refers to Scotch Whisky which can only be produced in Scotland by the distillation of malted and unmalted barley, maize, rye, and mixtures of two or more of these. Often simply referred to as Scotch it can be divided into 2 basic types: malt whisky and grain whisky.

Malt whisky – is made only from malted barley which is traditionally dried over peat fires. The malt is then milled and mixed with hot water before mashing turns the starches into sugars and the resulting liquid, called wort, is filtered out. Yeast is added and fermentation takes place followed by two distilling processes using a pot still. The whisky is matured in oak, ideally sherry casks, for at least three years which affects both its colour and flavour. All malts have a more distinctive smell and intense flavour than grain whiskies and each distillery will produce a completely individual whisky of great complexity. A single malt is the product of an individual distillery. There are approximately 100 malt whisky distilleries in Scotland.

Grain whisky – is made from a mixture of any malted or unmalted cereal such as maize or wheat and is distilled in the Coffey, or patent still, by a continuous process. Very little grain whisky is ever drunk unblended.

Blended whisky – is a mix of more than one malt whisky or a mix of malt and grain whiskies to produce a soft, smooth and consistent drink. There are over 2,000 such blends which form the vast majority of Scottish whisky production.

Irish Whiskey – differs from Scotch whisky both in its spelling and method of production.
It is traditionally made from cereals, distilled three times and matured for at least 7 years. The different brands are as individual as straight malt and considered by some to be gentler in character.

La bière

La bière est l'une des plus anciennes et populaires boissons alcoolisées dans le monde. Pour produire la bière pression traditionnelle, on écrase l'orge maltée que l'on chauffe ensuite avec de l'eau à laquelle on ajoute le houblon. C'est ce qui lui donne son arôme et son goût amer bien connus. Deux types de bières sont principalement vendues en Grande-Bretagne : les Ales fermentées à chaud et les Lagers fermentées à froid. Elles se divisent en « keg beer » et en « cask beer ».

Bière en keg : elle est filtrée, pasteurisée et refroidie, puis versée dans des tonnelets pressurisés appelés kegs.

Bière en cask ou « Real Ale » : elle n'est ni filtrée, ni pasteurisée, ni refroidie mais tirée directement du tonneau à l'aide d'une simple pompe. Selon certains, cette bière, de qualité bien distincte, a plus de saveur et est plus naturelle.

Types de bières vendues au Royaume-Uni et en Irlande :

Bitter – C'est la bière traditionnelle la plus populaire en Angleterre et au pays de Galles mais ses ventes diminuent au profit des lagers. La Bitter est généralement plus pâle et son goût plus sec que la Mild. Son contenu en houblon est élevé et elle a un goût légèrement amer.

La Mild se consomme surtout au pays de Galles, dans le Midlands de l'Ouest et dans le Nord-Ouest de l'Angleterre. On l'appelle ainsi en raison de son goût moelleux légèrement douceâtre conféré par le houblon. Cette bière, généralement moins alcoolisée, est plus foncée par le caramel qui lui est ajouté ou par l'utilisation de malt plus brun.

Stout – les grandes marques de bières brunes sont brassées en Irlande et sont reconnaissables par leur couleur noire rehaussée de mousse crémeuse. Elles ont un goût prononcé de houblon grillé et une saveur amère.

Celles produites en Écosse sont maltées ; elles ont du corps et se dénomment le plus souvent Light, Heavy ou Export en référence au corps et à leur teneur en alcool.

Whisky

Le mot whisky est un dérivé du gaélique écossais *uisage beatha* et du gaélique irlandais *uisce beathadh* signifiant tous deux « eau de vie ». Quand il est écrit sans e, il se réfère au whisky écossais qui ne peut être produit qu'en Écosse par la distillation de céréales maltées ou non comme l'orge, le maïs, le seigle ou d'un mélange de deux ou plus de ces céréales. Souvent appelé tout simplement Scotch il se réfère à deux types de whiskies : whisky pur malt ou whisky de grain.

Le whisky pur malt est fait seulement à partir d'orge maltée qui est traditionnellement séchée au-dessus de feux de tourbe. Le malt est moulu et mélangé avec de l'eau chaude, puis le brassage transforme l'amidon en sucre ; le moût est ensuite filtré. On y ajoute de la levure et après la fermentation on fait distiller deux fois dans un alambic. Le whisky est alors vieilli pendant au moins trois ans dans des fûts de chêne, ayant contenu de préférence du sherry, ce qui transforme son goût et sa couleur. Tous les whiskies pur malt ont un arôme particulier et une saveur plus intense que les whiskies de grain et chaque distillerie produit son propre whisky avec des qualités bien distinctes. Il y a environ une centaine de distilleries de whiskies pur malt en Écosse.

Le whisky de grain est fait d'un mélange de céréales, maltées ou non, comme le maïs ou le froment et est distillé dans un alambic de type Coffey suivant un procédé continu. Très peu de whiskies de grain sont consommés à l'état pur. On procède à des mélanges pour la consommation.

Blended whisky est le mélange d'un ou de plusieurs whiskies pur malt et de whiskies de grain afin de produire un alcool léger, moelleux et de qualité. Il existe plus de 2 000 marques de blended whiskies qui forment la majeure partie de la production écossaise.

Le whisky irlandais, différent du whisky écossais par sa fabrication, est traditionnellement produit à partir de céréales ; il est ensuite distillé trois fois et vieilli pendant au moins sept ans. Certains le trouvent plus moelleux.

La Birra

La birra è una delle bevande alcoliche più antiche e popolari. La tradizionale birra alla spina si ottiene macinando l'orzo, riscaldandolo con l'acqua e aggiungendo il luppolo, che le conferiscono l'aroma e il tipico sapore amaro.

Le birre britanniche si dividono in due tipi principali: **Ales e Lagers**, che differiscono essenzialmente per la fermentazione, rispettivamente calda e fredda. In termini di vendita, i due tipi approssimativamente si equivalgono. La birra può anche dividersi in keg (lett, barilotto), e cask (lett botte).

La keg beer è filtrata, pastorizzata e raffreddata, e poi messa in contenitori pressurizzati, da cui deriva il nome.

La cask beer, o **Real Ale**, come viene comunemente indicata, non è filtrata, pastorizzata o raffeddata, ed è servita dalle botti, usando semplici pompe. Alcuni la considerano una birra più ricca di carattere e di gusto e più naturale.

In Gran Bretagna e Irlanda, le birre si caratterizzano anche in base a « stili » diversi.

Le bitter costituisce la birra tradizionalmente più popolare in Inghilterra e nel Galles, ma è ora « superata » dalla lager. Non esiste definizione specifica per la birra bitter, ma si può dire che si tratta in genere di una birra più pallida e secca della mild, dall'alto contenuto di luppolo e dal gusto leggermente amaro.

La mild è diffusa in Galles, West Midlands e Inghilterra nord-occidentale. Il nome richiama il carattere del luppolo, essendo delicata, dolce e dal gusto pieno. Contiene solitamente una limitata quantità di alcol ed è talvolta scura per l'aggiunta di caramello e per l'impiego di malto scuro.

La secche stouts vengono prodotte in Irlanda e sono immediatamente riconoscibili dal colore nero e dalla schiuma cremosa. Hanno una decisa fragranza di tostatura e un gusto amaro di luppolo.

Whisky

Il termine whisky deriva dal gealico scozzese *uisage beatha* e dal gaelico irlandese *uisce beathadh*, che significano « acqua di vita ». Se scritto senza la e, indica di solito lo Scotch Whisky, che può essere unicamente prodotto in Scozia dalla distillazione di malto e orzo, granturco e segale, e dall'unione di due o più di questi ingredienti. Spesso chiamato semplicemente Scoveri, si divide in due tipi: malt whisky e grain whisky.

Il malt whisky viene prodotto unicamente con malto, tradizionalmente seccato su fuochi alimentati con torba. Il malto viene poi macinato e gli viene aggiunta acqua bollente prima che l'impasto muti gli amidi in zuccheri e il liquido che ne deriva, chiamato wort (mosto di malto), venga filtrato. Si amalgama poi il lievito e avviene la fermentazione, seguita da due processi di distillazione nell'alambicco. Il whisky è lasciato invecchiare in legno di quercia, idealmente in botti di sherry, per almeno tre anni, perchè acquisti colore e sapore. Ogni tipo di malt whisky ha un profumo più distintivo e un gusto più intenso del grain whisky. Ogni distilleria produce un whisky dal carattere individuale, che richiede un processo di grande complessità. Un solo malt whisky è il prodotto di una specifica distilleria. In Scozia, esistono circa 100 distillerie di malt whisky.

Il grain whisky è il risultato della fusione di qualsiasi cereale con o senza malto, come il granturco o il frumento, es viene distillato nel Coffey, o alambicco brevettato, grazie ad un processo continuo. È molto scarsa la quantità di grain whisky che si beve puro.

Il blended whisky nasce dalla fusione di più di un malt whisky, o da quella di *malt* e grain whiskies. Il risultato è una bevanda dal gusto delicato, dolce e pieno. Esistono più di 2000 whisky di questo tipo, che costituiscono la parte più consistente della produzione scozzese.

Bier

Bier ist eines der ältesten und beliebtesten alkoholischen Getränke der Welt. Das traditionelle Fassbier wird aus gemahlener und gemalzter Gerste hergestellt, die in Wasser erhitzt wird. Durch Beigabe von Hopfen werden das bekannte Aroma und der typische bittere Geschmack erzeugt.

Die Biersorten in Großbritannien unterteilen sich in zwei Hauptgruppen: Ales und Lagers, wobei die Art der Gärung – im einen Fall warm, im anderen kalt – ausschlaggebend für das Endresultat ist. Beide Sorten haben hierzulande einen ungefähr gleichen Marktanteil. Da sich die meisten Brauvorgänge anfangs gleichen, entscheiden erst die Endphasen des Brauens, welche der verschiedenen Biersorten entsteht.

Darüber hinaus kann das englische Bier auch nach der Art seiner Abfüllung in Keg- bzw. Cask-Bier unterschieden werden:

Keg beer wird gefiltert, pasteurisiert, abgekühlt und anschließend in luftdichte, unter Druck gesetzte Metallbehälter gefüllt, von denen das Bier auch seinen Namen erhält.

Cask beer, gewöhnlich Real Ale genannt, wird weder gefiltert, noch pasteurisiert oder gekühlt, sondern mit einfachen (zumeist Hand-) Pumpen vom Faß gezapft.

Es gibt folgende Biersorten in Großbritannien und Irland: Bitter ist das meistbekannte traditionelle Bier in England und Wales. Eine genaue Definition, was ein Bitter ausmacht, sucht man vergeblich; es ist gewöhnlich heller und trockener als das Mild, hat einen hohen Hopfenanteil und einen leicht bitteren Geschmack. In den letzten Jahren hat das – meist importierte oder in Lizenz gebraute – Lager ihm jedoch den Rang abgelaufen.

Mild ist übergwiegend in Wales, in den westlichen Midlands und Nordwestengland zu finden. Der Name bezieht sich auf den Hopfenanteil, der es zu einem milden, etwas süßlichen und vollmundigen Bier macht. Es hat einen geringeren Alkoholgehalt und besitzt wegen der Zugabe von Karamel oder dunklem Malz bisweilen eine dunklere Farbe.

Stouts von hervorragendem trockenem Geschmack werden in Irland gebraut und sind unmittelbar an ihrer schwarzen Farbe und der cremigen Blume erkennbar. Sie haben einen ausgesprochen starken Geschmack nach bitterem Hopfen.

In Schottland hergestellte Biere sind alkoholstark und malzig; sie sind oft einfach bekannt als: Light, Heavy oder Export – Bezeichnungen, die auf Körper und Stärke des Bieres hinweisen.

Whisky

Die Bezeichnung Whisky entstammt dem Gälischen, wo im Schottischen der Ausdruck *uisage beatha*, im Irischen des Ausdruck *uisce beathadh* jeweils « Wasser des Lebens » bedeuten. Wird Whisky ohne ein e am Ende geschrieben, ist Scotch Whisky gemeint, der nur in Schottland aus gemalzter und ungemalzter Gerste, Mais, Roggen oder aus Mischungen zweier oder mehrerer dieser Zutaten gebrannt werden darf. Oft auch nur als Scotch bezeichnet, kann dieser in zwei Grundarten unterschieden werden: malt whisky und grain whisky.

Malt (Malz) whisky wird nur aus gemalzter Gerste hergestellt, die traditionell über Torffeuern getrocknet wird. Danach wird das Malz gemahlen und mit heißem Wasser vermischt, wonach in der Maische die Stärke in Zucker umgewandelt wird. Die dadurch entstandene Flüssigkeit, « wort » genannt, wird gefiltert und mit Hefe versetzt, was den Gärungsprozess einleitet. Anschließend folgen zwei Destillierungen im herkömmlichen Topf über offenem Feuer. Der Whisky reift danach mindestens drei Jahre lang in Eichenholz, idealerweise in Sherry-Fässern, was sich sowohl auf Farbe wie auf Geschmack des Whiskys auswirkt. Alle malts haben einen ausgeprägteren Geruch und intensiveren Geschmack als die grain-Whiskies; und jede Destillerie erzeugt einen völlig eigenen Whisky mit individueller Geschmacksnote und großer Komplexität. Ein sogenannter single malt enstammt aus einer einzigen Destillerie. Es gibt ungefähr 100 Malt Whisky-Destillerien in Schottland.

Grain (Korn) whisky wird aus Mischungen von gemalzten und ungemalzten Getreidesorten, wie Mais oder Weizen, hergestellt und wird in einem kontinuierlichen Prozeß in dem sogenannten « Coffey » destilliert. Nur sehr wenige Kornwhisky-Sorten sind nicht das Ergebnis von blending, dem Abstimmen des Geschmacks durch Mischung.

Blended whisky wird aus mehr als einer Sorte Malt Whisky oder aus Malt und Grain Whiskies gemischt, um ein weiches, geschmacklich harmonisches Getränk von beständiger Güte zu garantieren. Die über 2000 im Handel zu findenden blends stellen den Großteil der schottischen Whiskyerzeugung dar.

Irish Whiskey unterscheidet sich vom Scotch Whisky sowohl in der Schreibweise wie auch dem Herstellungsverfahren. Er wird traditionell aus Getreide hergestellt, wird dreifach destilliert und reift mindestens sieben Jahre lang. Die verschiedenen Sorten sind so individuell ausgeprägt wie reine Malt Whiskies und werden oft als weicher und gefälliger empfunden.

C. Labonne/MICHELIN

Great
Britain

C. Labonne/MICHELIN

Towns
from A to Z

Villes
de A à Z

Città
de A a Z

Städte
von A bis Z

England
Channel Islands
Isle of Man

ABBERLEY – Worcs. – 503 M 27 – pop. 654 – ✉ Worcester 18 **B2**

London 137 m – Birmingham 27 m – Worcester 13 m

The Elms

West : 2 m. on A 443 ✉ WR6 6AT – ☎ (01299) 896 666 – info@theelmshotel.co.uk – Fax (01299) 896 804

23 rm – †£ 155/255 ††£ 170/270 – **Rest** – Menu £ 18/40

◆ Impressive Queen Anne mansion in well-kept grounds, with countryside views from most bedrooms. Stylishly refurbished interior with antique furniture and a contemporary style. Restaurant serving classically based dishes with modern touches.

ABBOT'S SALFORD – Warks. – 503 O 27 – see Evesham (Worcs.)

ABBOTSBURY – Dorset – 503 M 32 – pop. 422 3 **B3**

London 146 m – Bournemouth 44 m – Exeter 50 m – Weymouth 10 m

Town★★ - Chesil Beach★★ - Swannery★ **AC** – Sub-Tropical Gardens★ **AC**

St Catherine's Chapel★, ½ m. uphill (30 mn rtn on foot). Maiden Castle★★ (≤ ★) NE : 7½ m

Abbey House without rest

Church St ✉ DT3 4JJ – ☎ (01305) 871 330 – Fax (01305) 871 088

5 rm – †£ 65/80 ††£ 75/80

◆ Historic stone house, part 15C abbey infirmary. Garden holds a unique Benedictine water mill. Breakfast room with low beamed ceiling and fireplace. Cosy bedrooms.

ENGLAND

ABINGDON – Oxon. – 503 Q 28 – pop. 36 010 *Great Britain* 10 **B2**

London 64 m – Oxford 6 m – Reading 25 m

from Abingdon Bridge to Oxford (Salter Bros. Ltd) 2 daily (summer only)

Abbey Close ☎ (01235) 522711, abingdontic@btconnect.com

Drayton Park Drayton Steventon Rd, ☎ (01235) 550 607 .

Town★ – County Hall★

Upper Reaches

Thames St ✉ OX14 3JA – ☎ (01235) 522 536 – info@upperreaches-abingdon.co.uk – Fax (01235) 555 182

31 rm – †£ 130/140 ††£ 150/230 – **Rest** – (Closed Sunday dinner) Menu £ 22 – Carte £ 30/36

◆ Former corn mill on island on River Thames accessed via small bridge. Period buildings, traditional décor. Bedrooms in modern block are the most spacious and have river views. Open plan restaurant houses revolving mill wheel and millrace.

ABINGER HAMMER – Surrey – 504 S 30 7 **C2**

London 35 m – Brighton 40 m – Dover 91 m – Portsmouth 50 m – Reading 33 m

Drakes on the Pond (John Morris)

Dorking Rd, on A 25 ✉ RH5 6SA – ☎ (01306) 731 174 – Fax (01306) 731 174 – closed 2 weeks late August, 1 week Christmas, Saturday lunch, Sunday and Monday

Rest – Menu £ 24 (lunch) – Carte £ 41/50

Spec. Foie gras, spiced pineapple chutney and brioché. Slow cooked pork, black pudding, fondant potato, pancetta sauce. Lemon posset, lemon meringue ice cream, stem ginger biscotti.

◆ Friendly neighbourhood restaurant in long, simply furnished room; a former cowshed! Selection of simply-presented, classical dishes. Appealing, confident and flavourful cooking.

ACTON BURNELL – Shrops. – 503 L 26 – see Shrewsbury

ACTON GREEN – Worcs. – 503 M 27 – see Great Malvern

omdesign

IN HOC SIGNO VINCES

RAMOS PINTO

PORTO 10 ANOS

TAWNY ENVELHECIDO EM CASCO

QUINTA DE ERVAMOIRA

Innovation has good prospects whenever it is cleaner, safer and more efficient.

The MICHELIN Energy green tyre lasts 25% longer*.
It also provides fuel savings of 2 to 3%
while reducing CO_2 emissions.

* on average compared to competing tyres in the same category.

ADDINGHAM – W. Yorks. – 502 O 22 – pop. 3 215 *Great Britain* 22 B2

London 225 m – Bradford 16 m – Ilkley 4 m
Bolton PrioryAC, N : 3.5 m. on B 6160

The Fleece

152-154 Main St ✉ LS29 0LY – ☎ (01943) 830491 – thefleece@mac.com
Rest – Carte £ 15/22
◆ Personally run pub on village main street. Open fires, solid stone floor, rustic walls filled with country prints. Wide ranging menu with good use of seasonal ingredients.

ALBRIGHTON – Shrops. – 502 L 25 – see Shrewsbury

ALDEBURGH – Suffolk – 504 Y 27 – pop. 2 654 15 D3

London 97 m – Ipswich 24 m – Norwich 41 m
152 High St ☎ (01728) 453637, atic@suffolkcoastal.gov.uk
Thorpeness Golf Hotel Thorpeness, ☎ (01728) 452 176 .

Wentworth

Wentworth Rd ✉ IP15 5BD – ☎ (01728) 452 312
– stay@wentworth-aldeburgh.co.uk – Fax (01728) 454 343
35 rm – †£ 79/139 ††£ 145/185 – **Rest** – Menu £ 20 (dinner) – Carte £ 19/24
◆ Carefully furnished, traditional seaside hotel; coast view bedrooms are equipped with binoculars and all have a copy of "Orlando the Marmalade Cat", a story set in the area. Formal dining room offers mix of brasserie and classic dishes.

The Lighthouse

77 High St ✉ IP15 5AU – ☎ (01728) 453 377 – sarafox@diron.co.uk
– Fax (01728) 454 38 31
Rest – (booking essential) Carte £ 18/28
◆ Busy, unpretentious bistro boasts a wealth of Suffolk produce from local meats to Aldeburgh cod and potted shrimps. Good choice of wines; amiable service.

152

152 High St ✉ IP15 5AX – ☎ (01728) 454 594 – info@152aldeburgh.co.uk
– Fax (01728) 454 618
Rest – Menu £ 19 – Carte approx. £ 28
◆ Choose between the bright, informal restaurant or the courtyard terrace on summer days to enjoy the keenly priced menu that features a wide variety of local produce.

Regatta

171-173 High St ✉ IP15 5AN – ☎ (01728) 452 011 – Fax (01728) 453 324
– Closed 24-26 December, 31 December and 1 January
Rest – Seafood Carte £ 18/28
◆ Maritime murals on the walls and cheerful décor make this fish-inspired eatery a good catch. Local seafood's a speciality: it's good quality and prepared in a sure-footed way.

at Friston Northwest : 4 m. by A 1094 on B 1121 – ✉ Aldeburgh

The Old School without rest

✉ IP17 1NP – ☎ (01728) 688 173 – fristonoldschool@btinternet.com
3 rm – †£ 60 ††£ 65
◆ Redbrick former school house in pleasant garden. Good breakfast served family style in spacious room. Comfortable modern rooms with good amenities in the house or annexe.

Your opinions are important to us:
please write and let us know about your discoveries and experiences – good and bad!

ENGLAND

ALDERLEY EDGE – Ches. – 502 N 24 – pop. 5 280 20 B3

London 187 m – Chester 34 m – Manchester 14 m – Stoke-on-Trent 25 m
Wilmslow MobberleyGreat Warford, ✆ (01565) 872 148 .

Alderley Edge

Macclesfield Rd ✉ SK9 7BJ – ✆ (01625) 583 033 – sales@alderleyedgehotel.com – Fax (01625) 586 343
50 rm – †£ 70/130 ††£ 175/220, ☕ £ 12.50 – 1 suite
Rest *The Alderley* – see restaurant listing
◆ A substantial late Victorian house with an easy-going style. Relaxing lounges furnished with cushion-clad easy chairs. Well-furnished, comfortable bedrooms, some with views.

The Alderley – at Alderley Edge H.

Macclesfield Rd ✉ SK9 7BJ – ✆ (01625) 583 033 – sales@alderleyedgehotel.com – Fax (01625) 586 343
Rest – (Closed Sunday Dinner) Menu £ 19 (lunch) – Carte £ 37/43
◆ Conservatory dining room; comfortably spaced tables. The cuisine, served by dinner-suited staff, is modern British. Particularly proud of 500 wine list and 100 Champagnes.

London Road Restaurant and Wine Bar

46 London Rd ✉ SK9 7DZ – ✆ (01625) 584 163
Rest – Carte £ 23/53
◆ Sleek, modern brasserie with bar, basement, private dining room and terrace. Large menus offer modern European dishes with Northern influences; cooking is clean and unfussy.

ENGLAND

The Wizard

Macclesfield Rd, Southeast : 1 ¼ m. on B 5087 ✉ SK10 4UB – ✆ (01625) 584 000 – Fax (01625) 585 105 – Closed Christmas-New Year, Sunday dinner and Monday
Rest – Menu £ 10/15 – Carte £ 22/37
◆ Located in a National Trust area, this 200-year old pub restaurant serves up-to-date dishes at reasonable prices. Sticky puddings of chocolate, toffee or caramel feature.

ALDERNEY – C.I. – 503 Q 33 – see Channel Islands

ALDFIELD – N. Yorks. – 502 P 21 – see Ripon

ALDFORD – Ches. – 502 L 24 20 A3

London 189 m – Chester 6 m – Liverpool 25 m

The Grosvenor Arms

Chester Rd ✉ CH3 6HJ – ✆ (01244) 620 228 – grosvenor-arms@brunningandprice.co.uk – Fax (01224) 620 247 – closed dinner 25-26 December and 1 January
Rest – Carte £ 16/32
◆ Vast 19C red brick inn in pretty village; rustic décor, stone/tiled floors and open fires. Menu offers large selection of modern, seasonal dishes. Spacious rear garden.

ALDRIDGE – W. Mids. – 502 O 26 – pop. 15 659 – ✉ Walsall 19 C2

London 130 m – Birmingham 12 m – Derby 32 m – Leicester 40 m – Stoke-on-Trent 38 m

Plan : see Birmingham p. 5

Fairlawns

rm, rest,

178 Little Aston Rd, East : 1 m. on A 454 ✉ WS9 0NU – ✆ (01922) 455 122 – welcome@fairlawns.co.uk – Fax (01922) 743 148 – restricted opening 24 December-2 January CT **n**
54 rm ☕ – †£ 80/165 ††£ 115/195 – 6 suites – **Rest** – (closed lunch Saturday and Bank Holidays) Menu £ 19/35
◆ Privately owned hotel with well-equipped leisure facility. A choice range of rooms from budget to superior, all comfy and spacious, some with good views over open countryside. Restaurant gains from its rural ambience.

ALFRISTON – E. Sussex – **504** U 31 – **pop. 1 721** – ✉ **Polegate** 8 **A3**

London 66 m – Eastbourne 9 m – Lewes 10 m – Newhaven 8 m

Star Inn

High St ✉ BN26 5TA – ✆ (01323) 870495 – bookings@star-inn-alfriston.com – Fax (01323) 870922

37 rm – †£ 49/74 ††£ 98/108 – **Rest** – (bar lunch Monday-Saturday) Menu £ 29

◆ 14C coaching inn with original half-timbered façade where smugglers once met. Décor includes flagstone floor and beamed ceilings; bar serves real ale. Well-kept bedrooms. Atmospheric Tudor style restaurant.

The George Inn with rm

High St ✉ BN26 5SY – ✆ (01323) 870319 – info@thegeorge-alfriston.com – Closed 25-26 December

6 rm – †£ 60 ††£ 130 – **Rest** – Carte £ 20/26

◆ Revered 15C timbered pub with dried hops, open fire, original floor boards. Popular with walkers. Local suppliers provide backbone to eclectic menus. Carefully restored rooms.

ALNWICK – Northd. – **501** O 17 – **pop. 7 767** *Great Britain* 24 **B2**

London 320 m – Edinburgh 86 m – Newcastle upon Tyne 34 m

2 The Shambles ✆ (01665) 510665, alnwicktic@alnwick.gov.uk

Swansfield Park, ✆ (01665) 602632 .

Town ★ - Castle★★ **AC**

Dunstanburgh Castle★ **AC**, NE : 8 m. by B 1340 and Dunstan rd (last 2 ½ m. on foot)

Aln House without rest

South Rd, Southeast : ¾ m. by B 6346 on Newcastle rd ✉ NE66 2NZ – ✆ (01665) 602265 – enquiries@alnhouse.co.uk

6 rm – †£ 35/40 ††£ 45/65

◆ Semi detached Edwardian house with mature front and rear gardens, an easy walk from castle. Homely lounge enhanced by personal touches. Individually appointed rooms.

Charlton House without rest

2 Aydon Gdns, South Rd, Southeast : ½ m. on B 6346 ✉ NE66 2NT – ✆ (01665) 605185 – March-October

5 rm – †£ 30/70 ††£ 60/70

◆ Victorian terraced house, the first to be lit by hydro-electricity. Breakfast in colourful front room where local produce is proudly served. Bright and breezy bedrooms.

at North Charlton North : 6 ¾ m. by A 1 – ✉ Alnwick

North Charlton Farm without rest

✉ NE67 5HP – ✆ (01665) 579443 – stay@northcharltonfarm.co.uk – Fax (01665) 579407 – April-October

3 rm – †£ 40 ††£ 70

◆ Attractive house on working farm with agricultural museum. Offers traditional accommodation. Each bedroom is individually decorated and has countryside views.

at Newton on the Moor South : 5 ½ m. by A 1 – ✉ Alnwick

The Cook and Barker Inn with rm

✉ NE65 9JY – ✆ (01665) 575234 – Fax (01665) 575234

18 rm – †£ 47 ††£ 75 – **Rest** – Menu £ 10/25 – Carte £ 30/40

◆ Characterful stone inn with rustic rooms and snugs furnished in period style. Eclectic menus offer classic pub food as well as more adventurous dishes. Smart, modern bedrooms.

ENGLAND

ALSTON – Cumbria – 501 M 19 – pop. 2 218 21 B2

London 309 m – Carlisle 28 m – Newcastle upon Tyne 45 m
The Alstonmorry Information Centre, Town Hall ✆ (01434) 382244
Alston Moor The Hermitage, ✆ (01434) 381 675 .

Lovelady Shield Country House

Nenthead Rd, East : 2½ m. on A 689 ✉ CA9 3LF – ✆ (01434) 381 203 – enquiries@lovelady.co.uk – Fax (01434) 381 515 – Weekends only in January

12 rm (dinner included) – £ 125 £ 250 – **Rest** – (dinner only and Sunday lunch) (booking essential for non-residents) Menu £ 40

◆ Victorian country house in beautiful countryside location with peaceful garden and view to River Nent. Traditional bar and cosy lounge with open fire. Refurbished bedrooms. Ambitious menus served in dining room.

ALTON – Hants. – 504 R 30 – pop. 16 005 6 B2

London 53 m – Reading 24 m – Southampton 29 m – Winchester 18 m
7 Cross and Pillory Lane ✆ (01420) 88448, altoninfo@btconnect.com
Old Odiham Rd, ✆ (01420) 82 042 .

Alton Grange

London Rd, Northeast : 1 m. on A 3004 ✉ GU34 4EG – ✆ (01420) 86 565 – info@altongrange.co.uk – Fax (01420) 541 346 – closed 24-30 December and 1 January

34 rm – £ 80/110 £ 100/110

Rest *Truffles* – Menu £ 33

◆ Hotel set in well-kept, oriental inspired gardens. The bar serves bistro-style snacks. Bedrooms are individually decorated, particularly junior suites and Saxon room. Dining room boasts myriad of Tiffany lamps and fusion cuisine.

ENGLAND

ALTRINCHAM – Gtr Manchester – 502 N 23 – pop. 40 695 20 B3

London 191 m – Chester 30 m – Liverpool 30 m – Manchester 8 m
20 Stamford New Rd ✆ (0161) 912 5931, tourist.information@trafford.gov.uk
Altrincham Municipal Timperley Stockport Rd, ✆ (0161) 928 0761 ;
Dunham Forest Oldfield Lane, ✆ (0161) 928 2605 ;
Ringway Hale Barns Hale Mount, ✆ (0161) 980 2630 .

Juniper (Paul Kitching)

21 The Downs ✉ WA14 2QD – ✆ (0161) 929 4008 – reservations@juniper-restaurant.co.uk – Fax (0161) 929 4009 – restricted opening Christmas and closed 1 week February, 2 weeks August, Sunday, Monday and lunch Tuesday-Thursday

Rest – (Tuesday dinner set menu only) Menu £ 22/48

Spec. Celeriac, vanilla purée, lemon pancake, chicken, morels and pistachio. Best end of lamb, kidney and neck, banana and aubergine confit, garlic pancake, apricot and broccoli purée. Glazed lemon curd tart.

◆ Simple appearance; pre-prandials in basement bar/lounge. Recently refurbished restaurant serves original dishes created from highly innovative alchemy of ingredients.

Dilli

60 Stamford New Rd ✉ WA14 1EE – ✆ (0161) 929 7484 – info@dilli.co.uk – Fax (0161) 929 1213 – closed 25 December and lunch 1 January

Rest – Indian Menu £ 15 – Carte £ 17/32

◆ Intriguing interior: the décor is a mix of Indian wooden fretwork and minimalism. Totally authentic Indian dishes use quality ingredients. Lunches are particularly good value.

at Little Bollington Southwest : 3 ¼ m. on A 56 – ✉ Altrincham

Ash Farm

Park Lane ✉ WA14 4TJ – ✆ (0161) 929 9290 – enquiries@ashfarm.co.uk – Fax (0161) 928 5002

4 rm – £ 57 £ 84 – **Rest** – Carte £ 13/22

◆ Attractive, creeper-clad 18C former farmhouse in quiet location, a short walk from Dunham Deer Park. Pretty stone-flagged breakfast room; cosy, individually styled bedrooms. Home-cooked dinners proudly served.

ALVELEY – Shrops. – 502 M 26 – see Bridgnorth

ALVESTON – Warks. – see Stratford-upon-Avon

ALWESTON – Dorset – 503 M 31 – see Sherborne

AMBERLEY – W. Sussex – 504 S 31 – pop. 525 – ✉ Arundel 7 C2

Great Britain

London 56 m – Brighton 24 m – Portsmouth 31 m

Bignor Roman Villa (mosaics★) AC, NW : 3½ m. by B 2139 via Bury

Amberley Castle

Southwest : ½ m. on B 2139 ✉ BN18 9LT – ☎ (01798) 831 992 – info@amberleycastle.co.uk – Fax (01798) 831 998

13 rm – †£ 155/175 ††£ 155/175, ☐ £16.50 – 6 suites

Rest *Queen's Room* – (booking essential) Menu £ 25/50

◆ Enchanting 12C castle with serene gardens, majestic battlements, intimate sitting rooms and sumptuous, characterful bedrooms with luxurious jacuzzi bathrooms. Formal dining, with professional, attentive service. Barrel-vaulted ceiling and mural.

AMBLESIDE – Cumbria – 502 L 20 – pop. 3 064 *Great Britain* 21 A2

London 278 m – Carlisle 47 m – Kendal 14 m

Central Buildings, Market Cross ☎ (015394) 32582 AZ, amblesidetic@southlakeland.gov.ukMain Car Park, Waterhead ☎ (015394) 32729 (summer only) BY

Lake Windermere★★ – Dove Cottage, Grasmere★ AC AY A – Brockhole National Park Centre★ AC, SE : 3 m. by A 591 AZ. Wrynose Pass★★, W : 7½ m. by A 593 AY – Hard Knott Pass★★, W : 10 m. by A 593 AY

Plan on next page

The Samling

< Lake Windermere and mountains,

Ambleside Rd, South : 1½ m. on A 591 ✉ LA23 1LR – ☎ (015394) 31 922 – info@thesamling.com – Fax (015394) 30 400

9 rm (dinner included) ☐ – †£ 200 ††£ 525 – 2 suites – **Rest** – (booking essential for non-residents) Menu £ 40/55 **s** – Carte £ 55/68

◆ Traditional manor house appearance belies boutique interior; stylish lounge and highly individual bedrooms; two with stunning lake views. Marvellous garden with croquet lawn. Traditional linen-laid dining room; cooking has a classic base and an inventive edge.

The Waterhead

Lake Rd ✉ LA22 0ER – ☎ (015394) 32 566 – waterhead@elhmail.co.uk – Fax (015394) 31 255 BY **x**

41 rm ☐ – †£ 69/123 ††£ 176/196

Rest *The Bay* – (light lunch Monday-Saturday) Carte £ 21/32 **s**

◆ Traditional lakeside house boasting modern interior. Bright, contemporary bedrooms and stylish en suites with heated floors; Luxury rooms have the best lake views. European menu served under purple-hued lighting in The Bay restaurant.

Rothay Manor

rm,

Rothay Bridge, South : ½ m. on A 593 ✉ LA22 0EH – ☎ (015394) 33 605 – hotel@rothaymanor.co.uk – Fax (015394) 33 607 – closed 3-25 January BY **r**

16 rm ☐ – †£ 115/120 ††£ 150/185 – 3 suites – **Rest** – Menu £ 19/36 – Carte lunch £ 16/20

◆ Elegant Regency house boasting modern, stylish interior. Contemporary drawing room decorated in warm tones. Finely-kept bedrooms; 'Superior' rooms at the front have balconies. Mixture of modern and classic dishes with a distinct French flavour served in formal dining room.

AMBLESIDE

GRASMERE

ENGLAND

BUILT UP AREA
KESWICK A 591
GRASMERE
TOWN END
RYDAL
Rydal Mount
CHAPEL STILE
ELTERWATER
Loughrigg Tarn
AMBLESIDE
SKELWITH BRIDGE
CLAPPERSGATE
WATERHEAD
CONISTON A 593
WINDERMERE A 591

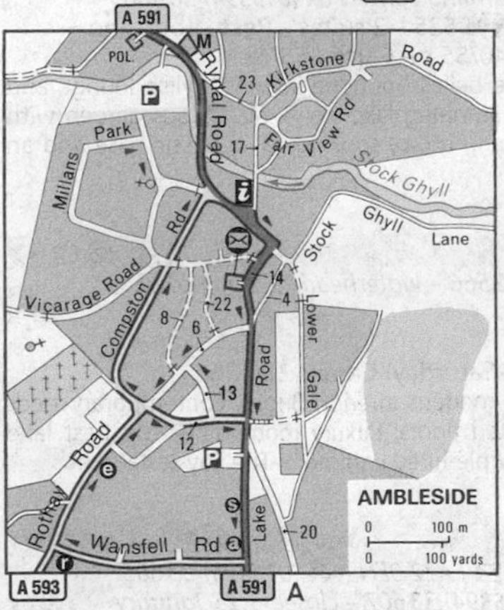

AMBLESIDE
Rydal Road
Kirkstone Road
Fair View Rd
Stock Ghyll Lane
Vicarage Road
Compston Road
Lake Road
Rothay Road
Wansfell Rd

GRASMERE
College St.
Red Bank Road
Stock Lane

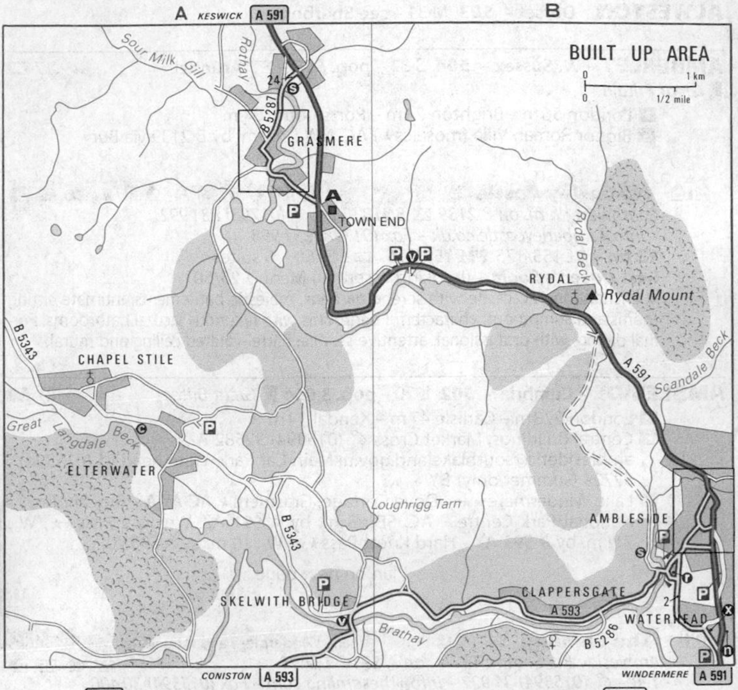

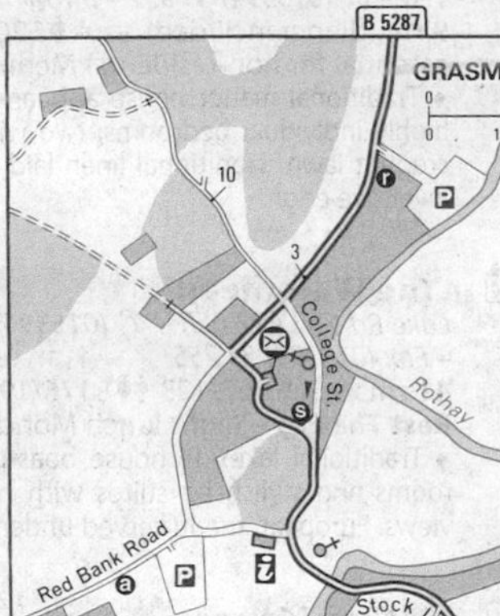

Look out for red symbols, indicating particularly pleasant establishments.

Lake House without rest
Waterhead Bay ✉ LA22 0HD – ✆ (015394) 32 360 – info@lakehousehotel.co.uk – Fax (015394) 31 474 BY **n**
12 rm – †£ 91/112 ††£ 130/160
◆ Traditional house of lakeland stone with relaxed, comfortable feel and pleasant gardens. Light, modern bedrooms, some with lake views. Extensive buffet or cooked breakfast.

Brathay Lodge without rest
Rothay Rd ✉ LA22 0EE – ✆ (01539) 432 000 – info@brathay-lodge.com AZ **e**
21 rm – †£ 48/80 ††£ 60/86
◆ Stylish accommodation in the heart of Ambleside. Unfussy, bright and warm décor. Continental breakfast only. All bedrooms have spa baths and some boast four posters.

Lakes Lodge without rest
Lake Rd ✉ LA22 0DB – ✆ (015394) 33 240 – info@lakeslodge.co.uk – Fax (015394) 33 240 – Closed 16-26 December AZ **s**
12 rm – †£ 49/99 ††£ 79/110
◆ Imposing traditional stone house with relaxed, laid back feel. Contemporary bedrooms in white; 10 has the best view. Continental breakfast plus homemade pastries and muffins.

Elder Grove without rest
Lake Rd ✉ LA22 0DB – ✆ (015394) 32 504 – info@eldergrove.co.uk – Fax (015394) 32 251 – Closed 24-27 December and 2 weeks January AZ **a**
10 rm – †£ 27/78 ††£ 56/84
◆ Ivy-clad stone house with cosy lounge bar full of firemen's memorabilia and bright, traditionally-furnished bedrooms. Locally sourced produce served in neat breakfast room.

Red Bank without rest
Wansfell Rd ✉ LA22 0EG – ✆ (015394) 34 637 – info@redbank.co.uk – Closed 24-26 December AZ **r**
3 rm – †£ 60/78 ††£ 84
◆ Edwardian house, a minute's walk from town. Cosy central lounge and pleasant breakfast room overlooking garden. Immaculate, tastefully furnished rooms; room 2 is most popular.

Riverside without rest
Under Loughrigg ✉ LA22 9LJ – ✆ (015394) 32 395 – info@riverside-ambleside.co.uk – Fax (015394) 32 240 – closed 18 December-26 January BY **s**
6 rm – †£ 78/82 ††£ 96/100
◆ Stone house beside river with delightful sun deck and garden. Light, airy breakfast room. Individually-styled bedrooms, immaculately kept; room 2 has four poster and spa bath.

The Log House with rm
Lake Rd ✉ LA22 0DN – ✆ (015394) 31 077 – nicola@loghouse.co.uk – closed 7 January-7 February, 24-25 December, Monday and Tuesday in winter BY **v**
3 rm – †£ 60/80 ††£ 80 – **Rest** – (booking essential in winter) Menu £ 15 (lunch) – Carte £ 26/32
◆ Imported from Norway by artist Alfred Heaton Cooper to use as a studio, this is now a characterful restaurant, with a flower-filled terrace and a modern, international menu. Comfortable bedrooms.

Drunken Duck Inn with rm
Barngates, Southwest : 3 m. by A 593 and B 5286 on Tarn Hows rd ✉ LA22 0NG – ✆ (01539) 436 347 – info@drunkenduckinn.co.uk – Fax (01539) 436 781 – closed 25 December
16 rm – †£ 130 ††£ 235 – **Rest** – (booking essential) Carte £ 30/60
◆ Busy 16C pub with on-site brewery; cross the road and admire the view from the benches. Eat in the cosy, firelit bar or at linen-laid tables in one of the beamed dining rooms. Individually decorated bedrooms, with complimentary cream tea on arrival.

ENGLAND

at Skelwith Bridge **West : 2½ m. on A 593 – ✉ Ambleside**

Skelwith Bridge — rm, rest, P, VISA

✉ *LA22 9NJ – ☎ (015394) 32 115 – info@skelwithbridgehotel.co.uk*
– Fax (015394) 34 254 AY **v**
28 rm – ♦£ 45/96 ♦♦£ 80/142
Rest ***The Bridge*** – (dinner only) Menu £ 28 **s**

◆ 17C Lakeland inn at entrance to the stunningly picturesque Langdale Valley. Traditional, simple bedrooms; panelled, clubby bar; busy Talbot Bar for walkers. Popular restaurant has large windows overlooking fells.

at Little Langdale **West : 5 m. by A 593 – ✉ Langdale**

Three Shires Inn — P, VISA

Little Langdale ✉ LA22 9NZ – ☎ (015394) 37 215 – info@threeshiresinn.co.uk
– Fax (015394) 37 127 – Restricted opening December-January AY **c**
10 rm – ♦£ 60/75 ♦♦£ 80/106 – **Rest** – (bar lunch) Carte £ 19/27 **s**

◆ Traditional family-owned lakeland inn in prime walking country. Homely front lounge and busy back bar. Neat, floral bedrooms; those at front have countryside views. Homemade fare served in cloth-clad dining room. Plenty of whiskies and wines.

ENGLAND

AMERSHAM (Old Town) – Bucks. – 504 S 29 – pop. 21 470 11 D2

London 29 m – Aylesbury 16 m – Oxford 33 m
Little Chalfont Lodge Lane, ☎ (01494) 764 877 .

Artichoke — VISA

9 Market Sq. ✉ HP7 0DF – ☎ (01494) 726 611
– info@theartichokerestaurant.co.uk – closed 2 weeks August, 1 week spring, 1 week Christmas, Sunday and Monday
Rest – Menu £ 23/38 – Carte £ 38/42

◆ 16C brick house with smart façade; an artichoke etched on its window. Narrow room with stylish, modern look but retaining period detail. Accomplished, well-presented cooking.

Gilbey's — AC, VISA, AE

1 Market Sq. ✉ HP7 0DF – ☎ (01494) 727 242 – oldamersham@gilbeygroup.com
– Fax (01494) 431 243 – closed 24-26 December and 1 January
Rest – (booking essential) Carte £ 26/31

◆ Part of a former 17C school, this busy neighbourhood restaurant is cosy and informal with modern artwork on walls. Eclectic range of British cooking with global influences.

AMESBURY – Wilts. – 503 O 30 – pop. 8 312 4 D2

London 87 m – Bristol 52 m – Southampton 32 m – Taunton 66 m
Amesbury Libary, Smithfield St ☎ (01980) 622833, amesburytic@salisbury.gov.uk
Stonehenge★★★ **AC**, W : 2 m. by A 303. Wilton Village★ (Wilton House★★ **AC**, Wilton Carpet Factory★ **AC**), SW : 13 m. by A 303, B 3083 and A 36

Mandalay without rest — P, VISA, AE

15 Stonehenge Rd, via Church St ✉ SP4 7BA – ☎ (01980) 623 733
– Fax (01980) 626 642
5 rm – ♦£ 45/55 ♦♦£ 65/70

◆ Only two minutes' drive from Stonehenge, this brick-built house boasts a bygone style and pleasant garden. Varied breakfasts. Individual rooms, named after famous authors.

AMPLEFORTH – N. Yorks. – 502 Q 21 – see Helmsley

APPLEBY-IN-WESTMORLAND – Cumbria – 502 M 20 – pop. 2 570 21 B2

London 285 m – Carlisle 33 m – Kendal 24 m – Middlesbrough 58 m
Moot Hall, Boroughgate ✆ (017683) 51177, tic@applebytown.org.uk
Appleby Brackenber Moor, ✆ (017683) 51 432 .

Appleby Manor Country House

Roman Rd, East : 1 m. by B 6542 and Station Rd
✉ CA16 6JB – ✆ (017683) 51 571 – reception@applebymanor.co.uk
– Fax (017683) 52 888 – closed 24-26 December
31 rm – £ 90/95 £ 140/180 – **Rest** – Carte £ 25/34 s
◆ Wooded grounds and good views of Appleby Castle at this elevated 19C pink sandstone country manor. Traditional bedrooms in extension; those in main house are more contemporary. Conservatory restaurant serves classic menu.

Tufton Arms

Market Sq ✉ CA16 6XA – ✆ (017683) 51 593 – info@tuftonarmshotel.co.uk
– Fax (017683) 52 761 – closed 25-26 December
20 rm – £ 70/84 £ 155 – 2 suites – **Rest** – Carte £ 19/27
◆ 16C former coaching inn in traditional market town boasts new contemporary interior; chic, comfortable bedrooms in bold colours. Fishing, shooting and stalking can be arranged. Easy-going menu served in modern dining room.

APPLEDORE – Devon – 503 H 30 – pop. 2 114 2 C1

London 228 m – Barnstaple 12 m – Exeter 46 m – Plymouth 61 m
– Taunton 63 m
Town★

West Farm without rest

Irsha St, West : ¼ m. ✉ EX39 1RY – ✆ (01237) 425 269
– westfarm@appledore-devon.co.uk – closed Christmas and New Year
3 rm – £ 60 £ 97
◆ 17C house, boasting particularly pleasant garden at the back, in a charming little coastal village. Delightfully appointed sitting room. Bedrooms feel comfortable and homely.

APPLETREEWICK – N. Yorks. – 502 O 21 22 B2

London 236 m – Harrogate 25 m – Skipton 11 m

Knowles Lodge without rest

South : 1 m. on Bolton Abbey rd ✉ BD23 6DQ – ✆ (01756) 720 228
– pam@knowleslodge.com – Fax (01756) 720 381
3 rm – £ 50 £ 80
◆ Unusual Canadian ranch-house style guesthouse, clad in timber and sited in quiet dales location. Large sitting room with fine outlook. Cosy bedrooms have garden views.

ARDENS GRAFTON – Warks. – see Stratford-upon-Avon

ARLINGHAM – Glos. – 503 M 28 – pop. 377 – ✉ Gloucester 4 C1

London 120 m – Birmingham 69 m – Bristol 34 m – Gloucester 16 m

The Old Passage Inn with rm

Passage Rd, West : ¾ m ✉ GL2 7JR – ✆ (01452) 740 547
– oldpassage@ukonline.co.uk – Fax (01452) 741 871 – Closed 24-30 December, Sunday dinner and Monday
3 rm – £ 65 £ 110 – **Rest** – Seafood Carte £ 23/33
◆ Former inn with simple style and bright ambience, attractively set on banks of Severn. Friendly, relaxed dining. Seafood based menu. Modern, funky bedrooms in a vivid palette.

ENGLAND

ARMSCOTE – Warks. – 504 P 27 19 C3

London 91 m – Birmingham 36 m – Oxford 38 m

Willow Corner without rest

✉ *CV37 8DE – ☎ (01608) 682 391 – trishandalan@willowcorner.co.uk – closed two weeks Christmas-New Year*

3 rm – †£ 50 ††£ 74

◆ Lovely thatched property in quaint village with stable door, mullioned windows and low ceilings. Pretty bedrooms with thoughtful extras; homemade biscuits and tea on arrival.

The Fox & Goose Inn with rm

Front St ✉ CV37 8DD – ☎ (01608) 682 293 – email@foxandgoose.co.uk – Fax (01608) 682 293

4 rm – †£ 49/70 ††£ 120 – **Rest** – Menu £ 10/15 – Carte £ 24/35

◆ Creeper-clad red brick inn with modern interior; bright open-plan bar and dining room. Mix of fairly-priced pub and restaurant dishes. Bright, buzzy service. Bedrooms named after Cluedo characters.

ARNCLIFFE – N. Yorks. – 502 N 21 – pop. 79 – ✉ Skipton 22 A2

London 232 m – Kendal 41 m – Leeds 41 m – Preston 50 m – York 52 m

Amerdale House with rm

✉ *BD23 5QE – ☎ (01756) 770 250 – info@amerdalehouse.co.uk – closed January and February*

10 rm (dinner included) – †£ 125 ††£ 200 – **Rest** – (dinner only) (booking essential) Carte £ 24/32 **s**

◆ Rurally located 17C house. The classical menu changes weekly and the seasonal ingredients come from within 5 miles, with eggs from the chickens and fruit from the garden. Comfortable bedrooms, immaculately kept.

ENGLAND

ARUNDEL – W. Sussex – 504 S 31 – pop. 3 297 *Great Britain* 7 C2

London 58 – Brighton 21 – Southampton 41 – Worthing 9

61 High St ☎ (01903) 882268, tourism@arun.gov.uk

Castle★★ AC

The Town House with rm

65 High St – ☎ (01903) 883 847 – info@thetownhouse.co.uk – closed 2 weeks January, 2 weeks October, 25-26 December

4 rm – †£ 75 ††£ 120 – **Rest** – (closed Sunday and Monday) Menu £ 16/28

◆ Grade II listed house at top of town. Beautiful Renaissance ceiling with gilded walnut panels. Cooking is rich, classic, unfussy and skilled, and uses local, seasonal produce. Simple, traditional bedrooms. Best are at front facing castle.

at Burpham Northeast : 3 m. by A 27 – ✉ Arundel

Burpham Country House

✉ *BN18 9RJ – ☎ (01903) 882 160 – info@burphamcountryhouse.com – Fax (01903) 884 627 – closed Christmas Day*

10 rm – †£ 45/80 ††£ 120/140 – **Rest** – (Wednesday to Saturday only) Menu £ 25

◆ Reputedly a hunting lodge for the Duke of Norfolk, this quiet hotel constitutes the ideal "stress remedy break". Calm, pastel coloured bedrooms overlook exquisite gardens.

George and Dragon

Main St ✉ BN18 9RR – ☎ (01903) 883 131 – Fax (01903) 883 341 – Closed 25 December and Sunday dinner

Rest – Carte £ 22/32

◆ Pleasant, characterful pub in pretty village. Bar and more formal restaurant both serve robust British menus, prepared with care and attention, employing seasonal produce.

at Walberton **West : 3 m. by A 27 off B 2132 – ✉ Arundel**

Hilton Avisford Park (heated)
Yapton Lane, on B 2132 ✉ BN18 0LS – ☎ (01243) 558 300 – general.manager@hilton.com – Fax (01243) 552 485 rm,
134 rm – †£ 69/189 ††£ 74/199 – 5 suites – **Rest** – ☎ (01243) 551 215 (bar lunch Monday-Saturday) Menu £ 26 – Carte £ 26/41
◆ Former school and one-time home of Baronet Montagu, Nelson's admiral; retains a stately air with grand façade and 62-acre grounds. Generous drapes and furnishings in rooms. Dining room features honours board listing prefects of yesteryear.

ASCOT – **Windsor & Maidenhead** – **504** R 29 – **pop. 17 509** 11 **D3**
London 36 m – Reading 15 m
Mill Ride Ascot, ☎ (01344) 886 777.

Berystede rm,
Bagshot Rd, Sunninghill, South : 1½ m. on A 330 ✉ SL5 9JH – ☎ (0870) 400 81 11 – general.berystede@macdonald-hotels.co.uk – Fax (01344) 873 061
119 rm – †£ 99/215 ††£ 99/215 – 7 suites
Rest *Hyperion* – (closed Saturday lunch) Menu £ 20/30
◆ Turreted red brick Victorian house in mature gardens, boasts classically-styled lounge, panelled bar with terrace and variously-sized bedrooms, with warm, contemporary feel. Formal dining at Hyperion, with classic menus and countryside outlook.

XX **Ascot Oriental**
East : 2¼ m. on A 329 ✉ SL5 0PU – ☎ (01344) 621 877 – info@ascotoriental.com – Fax (01344) 621 885 – closed 25-26 December
Rest – Chinese Menu £ 25/26 – Carte £ 26/40
◆ Stylish modern restaurant with a vibrantly hued interior. Private dining in attractive conservatory. An interesting menu of Chinese dishes prepared with originality and verve.

at Sunninghill **South : 1½ m. by A 329 on B 3020 – ✉ Ascot**

XX **Jade Fountain**
38 High St ✉ SL5 9NE – ☎ (01344) 627 070 – jadefountain328@aol.com – Fax (01344) 627 070
Rest – Chinese Menu £ 21/27 – Carte £ 23/28
◆ Chinese restaurant specialising in sizzling dishes from Szechuan and Beijing - Peking duck, spring rolls and noodles amongst them. Also some Thai specialities.

ASENBY – **N. Yorks.** – **see Thirsk**

ASH – **Kent** – **504** X 30 9 **D2**
London 70 m – Canterbury 9 m – Dover 15 m

Great Weddington
Northeast : ½ m. by A 257 on Weddington rd ✉ CT3 2AR – ☎ (01304) 813 407 – traveltale@aol.com – Fax (01304) 812 531 – Closed 21 December-2 January
4 rm – †£ 70/78 ††£ 102/108 – **Rest** – (by arrangement, communal dining) Menu £ 32
◆ Charming Regency country house, ideally located for Canterbury and Dover. Well appointed drawing room and terrace. Thoughtfully furnished, carefully co-ordinated rooms. Communal dining room; owner an avid cook.

The ✿ award is the crème de la crème.
This is awarded to restaurants
which are really worth travelling miles for!

ENGLAND

ASHBOURNE – Derbs. – **502** O 24 – pop. 5 020 *Great Britain* 16 **A2**

London 146 m – Birmingham 47 m – Manchester 48 m – Nottingham 33 m – Sheffield 44 m

13 Market Pl ✆ (01335) 343666, ashbourneinfo@derbyshiredales.gov.uk

Dovedale★★ (Ilam Rock★) NW : 6 m. by A 515

Callow Hall

Mappleton Rd, West : ¾ m. by Union St (off Market Pl) ✉ DE6 2AA – ✆ (01335) 300 900 – reservations@callowhall.co.uk – Fax (01335) 300 512 – closed 25-26 December and 1 week Februrary

15 rm – †£ 105/140 ††£ 150/195 – 1 suite – **Rest** – (dinner only and Sunday lunch) Menu £ 27 (lunch) – Carte dinner £ 33/39

◆ Victorian country house in 42 acres. Cosy period bar lounge. Spacious bedrooms in main house have views of parkland; those in former servants' wing recently refurbished. Modern European menu; home-smoked salmon.

the dining room

33 St Johns St ✉ DE6 1GP – ✆ (01335) 300 666 – closed 26 December-9 January, 1 week March, 1 week September, Sunday and Monday

Rest – Menu £ 22/36

◆ Modern, stylish décor blends agreeably with period features including exposed beams and cast iron range. Well sourced, seasonal ingredients inform intricate modern dishes.

at Marston Montgomery South : 7 ½ m. by A 515 – ✉ Ashbourne

The Crown Inn with rm

Riggs Lane ✉ DE6 2FF – ✆ (01889) 590 541 – info@thecrowninn-derbyshire.co.uk – Fax (01889) 591 576 – Closed 25 December, 1 January and Sunday dinner,

7 rm – †£ 50 ††£ 75 – **Rest** – Menu £ 15 – Carte £ 20/30

◆ Creeper-clad pub with small terrace. Intimate beamed bar boasts leather sofas and an open fire. Simple lunch menu morphs into more lengthy and adventurous evening carte. Simply furnished bedrooms.

ENGLAND

ASHBURTON – Devon – **503** I 32 – pop. 3 309 2 **C2**

London 220 m – Exeter 20 m – Plymouth 25 m

Dartmoor National Park★★

Holne Chase

West : 3 m. on Two Bridges rd ✉ TQ13 7NS – ✆ (01364) 631 471 – info@holne-chase.co.uk – Fax (01364) 631 453

8 rm – †£ 90 ††£ 180 – 9 suites – **Rest** – (light lunch Monday) Menu £ 20/36 **s**

◆ Former hunting lodge to Buckfast Abbey, with country house ambience, in 70 acres of Dartmoor woodland. This is walking country - dogs welcome. Rooms in main house or stables. Country style dining room utilising local produce.

Agaric with rm

30 and 36 North St ✉ TQ13 7QD – ✆ (01364) 654 478 – eat@agaricrestaurant.co.uk – closed last 2 weeks August, 2 weeks Christmas, Sunday, Monday and Tuesday

5 rm – †£ 50/60 ††£ 120 – **Rest** – (booking essential) Carte £ 28/36

◆ 200 year-old house, selling home-made jams, fudge and olives. Relaxed neighbourhood restaurant using a blend of cooking styles. Very stylish, individually themed bedrooms.

ASHFORD – Kent – **504** W 30 9 **C2**

London 56 m – Canterbury 14 m – Dover 24 m – Hastings 30 m – Maidstone 19 m

Access Channel Tunnel : Eurostar information and reservations ✆ (08705) 186186

18 The Churchyard ✆ (01233) 629165, tourism@ashford.gov.uk

Eastwell Manor (heated)

Eastwell Park, Boughton Lees, North : 3 m. by A 28 on A 251 ✉ TN25 4HR – ✆ (01233) 213 000 – enquiries@eastwellmanor.co.uk – Fax (01233) 635 530

20 rm – †£ 160/235 ††£ 190/265 – 42 suites

Rest *Manor* – Menu £ 18/38 – Carte £ 42/83

Rest *Brasserie* – Menu £ 15 (lunch) – Carte £ 26/38

◆ Mansion house in formal gardens, replete with interesting detail including carved panelled rooms and stone fireplaces. Smart individual bedrooms. Manor offers seasonal menus. Swish brasserie in luxury spa with marbled entrance hall.

Ashford International rm,

Simone Weil Ave, North : 1½ m. by A 20 ✉ TN24 8UX – ✆ (01233) 219 988 – ashford@qhotels.co.uk – Fax (01233) 647 743

179 rm – †£ 109 ††£ 119

Rest *Zest* – Carte £ 23/39

◆ Enormous corporate oriented hotel with large central atrium containing shops and coffee bars to relax in. Modern, comfortable bedrooms. Alhambra noted for range of modern dishes.

ASHFORD-IN-THE-WATER – Derbs. – 502 – see Bakewell

ASHINGTON – W. Sussex – 504 S 31 – pop. 2 351 – ✉ Pulborough 7 D2

London 50 m – Brighton 20 m – Worthing 9 m

Mill House

Mill Lane ✉ RH20 3BZ – ✆ (01903) 892 426 – info@millhousesussex.co.uk – Fax (01903) 893 846 – Closed 1 week August, 4 days Easter and 25 December

9 rm – †£ 59 ††£ 92/125 – **Rest** – Menu £ 16/26

◆ Once the home of the owners of Ashington Water and Wind Mills, this 17C cottage with conservatory, inglenook fireplace and pastel painted rooms makes a quiet retreat. Restaurant with tranquil blue décor and watercolours on the walls.

ASHURST – W. Sussex – 504 T 31 – see Steyning

ASHWATER – Devon 2 C2

London 218 m – Bude 16 m – Virginstow 3 m

Blagdon Manor

Beaworthy, Northwest : 2 m. by Holsworthy rd on Blagdon rd ✉ EX21 5DF – ✆ (01409) 211 224 – stay@blagdon.com – Fax (01409) 211 634 – closed 2 weeks January, 2 weeks October

7 rm – †£ 85 ††£ 130 – **Rest** – (closed lunch Monday and Tuesday) (booking essential) (residents only Monday and Sunday dinner) Menu £ 20/35

◆ Proudly run former farmhouse in peaceful, rural location. Modern country house bedrooms, spotlessly kept, named after surrounding villages. Library, lounges and flag-floored bar. Classically-based cooking with a modern touch, served in dining room with conservatory extension.

ASKRIGG – N. Yorks. – 502 N 21 – pop. 1 002 – ✉ Leyburn 22 A1

London 251 m – Kendal 32 m – Leeds 70 m – Newcastle upon Tyne 70 m – York 63 m

Helm without rest Wensleydale,

Helm, West : 1½ m., turning right at Helm rd after 1 m. ✉ DL8 3JF – ✆ (01969) 650 443 – holiday@helmyorkshire.com – Fax (01969) 650 443 – closed mid November-2 January

3 rm – †£ 63 ††£ 90

◆ A steep lane winds up to this 17C stone farmhouse still in possession of an underground dairy with cheese press used in making Wensleydale cheese. Compact, homely bedrooms.

ENGLAND

The Apothecary's House without rest

Market Pl ✉ DL8 3HT – ☏ (01969) 650626 – bookings@apothecaryhouse.co.uk – closed 24-26 December, 31 December and 1 January

3 rm ☕ – 🕴£40 👥£70

◆ Built in 1756 by the local apothecary in centre of village; overlooks church. Combined lounge and breakfast room has fresh, modern feel. Rear bedroom boasts exposed timbers.

The Kings Arms

Market Place – ☏ (01969) 650817 – thekingsarms@yahoo.co.uk – Fax (01969) 650856 – closed one week early January

Rest – Carte £21/30 **s**

◆ Characterful pub built in mid-18C by racehorse owner; what is now the bar area was once the tack room. Huge open fire, beamed ceilings and games room. Rustic, hearty cooking.

ASTON CANTLOW – Warks. – 503 O 27 *Great Britain* 19 C3

London 106 m – Birmingham 20 m – Stratford-upon-Avon 5 m

Mary Arden's House★ AC, SE : 2 m. by Wilmcote Lane and Aston Cantlow Rd

The King's Head

21 Bearley Rd ✉ B95 6HY – ☏ (01789) 488242 – info@thekh.co.uk – Fax (01789) 488137 – Closed 25 December

Rest – Menu £15 – Carte £20/25

◆ Pretty 15C pub in idyllic village. Chic, French farmhouse style restaurant. Heavily beamed lounge bar with large stone fireplaces. Regularly held duck suppers.

ASTON CLINTON – Bucks. – 504 R 28 – pop. 3 467 – ✉ Aylesbury 11 C2

London 42 m – Aylesbury 4 m – Oxford 26 m

West Lodge

45 London Rd ✉ HP22 5HL – ☏ (01296) 630362 – jibwl@westlodge.co.uk – Fax (01296) 630151

10 rm ☕ – 🕴£60/70 👥£85 – **Rest** – (closed Sunday) (dinner only) (residents only) Menu £23

◆ 19C former hunting lodge for Rothschild estate with walled Victorian garden. Bedrooms in converted outbuilding are largest/quietest. Balloon theme throughout adds interest. Conservatory dining room serving residents only.

ASTON TIRROLD – Oxon. 10 B3

London 58 m – Reading 16 m – Streatley 4 m

The Sweet Olive at The Chequers Inn

Baker St ✉ OX11 9DD – ☏ (01235) 851272 – Closed February

Rest – (closed Wednesday and Sunday dinner in winter) (booking essential) Carte £21/31

◆ Busy, friendly 18C dining pub in the centre of the village serving rustic, French-influenced cooking. Good value blackboard menu. Cosy bar with open fire, popular with locals.

The red symbol?
This denotes the very essence of peace – only the sound of birdsong first thing in the morning ...

AUSTWICK – N. Yorks. – 502 M 21 – pop. 467 – ✉ Lancaster (Lancs.) 22 A2

London 259 m – Kendal 28 m – Lancaster 20 m – Leeds 46 m

Austwick Traddock

✉ LA2 8BY – ✆ (015242) 51 224 – info@austwicktraddock.co.uk – Fax (015242) 51 796

10 rm – †£ 100/120 ††£ 170/190 – **Rest** – (dinner only and Saturday and Sunday lunch) (booking essential for non-residents) Carte £ 20/44

◆ A Georgian country house decorated with both English and Asian antiques. Bedrooms are individually styled to a high standard and overlook the secluded gardens. Dining room split into two rooms and lit by candlelight.

Wood View without rest

The Green ✉ LA2 8BB – ✆ (015242) 51 190 – woodview@austwick.org – Fax (015242) 51 190

5 rm – †£ 40 ††£ 74

◆ In a charming spot on the village green, the cottage dates back to 17C with many of the original features still in place including exposed rafters in several bedrooms.

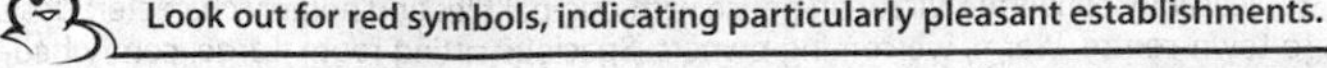

Look out for red symbols, indicating particularly pleasant establishments.

ENGLAND

AVONWICK – Devon 2 C2

London 202 m – Plymouth 17 m – Totnes 8 m

The Turtley Corn Mill

Northwest : 1 m. on Plymouth rd ✉ TQ10 9ES – ✆ (01364) 646 100 – mill@avonwick.net – Fax (01364) 646 101 – Closed 25 December

Rest – Carte £ 22/30

◆ Refurbished 18C mill in six acres, with original beams and pillars in situ. A clean, light and airy feel helps enhance the enjoyment of dishes ranging from classics to modern.

The Avon Inn

✉ TQ10 9NB – ✆ (01364) 73 475 – rosec@beeb.net – closed Monday lunch and Sunday dinner

Rest – Carte £ 14/28

◆ Homely pub with an interior of beams and hop bines. French owner/chef serves accomplished dishes with classic Gallic base and plenty of local seafood and fish.

AXBRIDGE – Somerset – 503 L 30 – pop. 2 025 3 B2

London 142 m – Bristol 17 m – Taunton 27 m – Weston-Super-Mare 11 m

The Parsonage without rest

Parsonage Lane, Cheddar Rd, East : ¾ m. on A 371 ✉ BS26 2DN – ✆ (01934) 733 078 – Fax (01934) 733 078

3 rm – †£ 47 ††£ 57

◆ Former Victorian parsonage nestling in the southern slopes of the Mendip Hills overlooking the Somerset Levels. The comfortable bedrooms are tastefully furnished.

AXFORD – Wilts – pop. 1 717 – ✉ Marlborough 4 D2

London 74 m – Marlborough 3 m – Swindon 15 m

The Red Lion Inn

✉ SN8 2HA – ✆ (01672) 520 271 – info@redlionaxford.com – Closed 25 December, dinner 26 December and 1 January

Rest – Carte £ 24/29

◆ 17C brick-and-flint inn with warm, welcoming feel. Lovely lounge bar with roaring fire. Traditional cooking served in neatly-kept dining room and conservatory.

AXMINSTER – Devon – **503** L 31 – **pop. 4 952** 2 **D2**

London 156 m – Exeter 27 m – Lyme Regis 5 m – Taunton 22 m – Yeovil 24 m

The Old Courthouse, Church St ✆ (01297) 34386, axminster@btopenworld.com

Lyme Regis★ - The Cobb★, SE : 5½ m. by A 35 and A 3070

Fairwater Head Country House

Axe Vale,

Hawkchurch, Northeast : 5¼ m. by B 3261 and A 35 off B 3165 VISA

✉ EX13 5TX – ✆ (01297) 678 349 – info@fairwaterheadhotel.co.uk – Fax (01297) 678 459 – Closed January

18 rm (dinner included) – £ 80/95 £ 140/210 – **Rest** – (Closed Monday-Tuesday) Menu £ 18/29 **s**

◆ Edwardian hotel in flower-filled gardens. Tea and fresh cakes served in the afternoon. Many rooms have Axe Valley views. Attractive outlook over garden and countryside accompanies diners enjoying locally sourced cooking.

Kerrington House without rest

VISA

Musbury Rd, Southwest : ½ m. ✉ EX13 5JR – ✆ (01297) 35 333 – enquiries@kerringtonhouse.com

6 rm – £ 75 £ 110

◆ Pleasantly converted Victorian house with original tiles and homely character; close to town centre. Warm, welcoming owners. Spacious sitting room. Large, comfy bedrooms.

ENGLAND

AYCLIFFE – Darlington – see Darlington

AYLESBURY – Bucks. – **504** R 28 – **pop. 69 021** *Great Britain* 11 **C2**

London 46 m – Birmingham 72 m – Northampton 37 m – Oxford 22 m

8 Bourbon St ✆ (01296) 330559, tic@aylesburyvaledc.gov.uk

Weston Turville New Rd, ✆ (01296) 424 084 ;

Bierton Hulcott Lane, ✆ (01296) 393 644.

Waddesdon Manor★★, NW : 5½ m. by A 41 – Chiltern Hills★

Hartwell House

Oxford Rd, Southwest : 2 m. on A 418 ✉ HP17 8NL – ✆ (01296) 747 444 – info@hartwell-house.com – Fax (01296) 747 450 VISA AE

38 rm – £ 220 £ 290, £6.50 – 10 suites

Rest *The Soane* – Menu £ 20/38 **s** – Carte £ 44/51 **s**

◆ Stunning stately home in beautiful grounds; elegant rooms, portraits and antique furniture. Magnificent Gothic staircase leading to luxurious bedrooms, some with four posters. Neo-classical dining room serves elaborate cooking.

AYLESFORD – Kent – **504** V 30 8 **B1**

London 37 m – Maidstone 3 m – Rochester 8 m

Hengist

A/C VISA AE

7-9 High St ✉ ME20 7AX – ✆ (01622) 719 273 – restaurant@thehengist.co.uk – Fax (01622) 715 077 – closed Sunday dinner and Monday

Rest – Menu £ 13 (lunch) – Carte £ 28/37

◆ Converted 16C town house, elegantly appointed throughout, with bonus of exposed rafters and smart private dining room upstairs. Accomplished modern cooking with seasonal base.

AYSGARTH – N. Yorks. – **502** O 21 22 **A1**

London 249 m – Ripon 28 m – York 56 m

George and Dragon Inn with rm

VISA

✉ DL8 3AD – ✆ (01969) 663 358 – info@georgeanddragonaysgarth.co.uk – Fax (01969) 663 773 – Closed 2 weeks January

7 rm – £ 40 £ 99 – **Rest** – Menu £ 14/17 – Carte £ 20/35

◆ Traditional pub near Aysgarth falls. Smart terrace with thatched umbrellas. Local ales dominate welcoming bar. Wide range of fresh fare: local produce to fore. Comfy rooms.

BABCARY – Somerset – 403 M 30 4 C2

London 128 m – Glastonbury 12 m – Yeovil 12 m

The Red Lion Inn

✉ TA11 7ED – ✆ (01458) 223 230 – Fax (01458) 224 510 – Closed 25 December and Sunday dinner

Rest – Carte £ 19/26

◆ Attractive thatched pub in cosy village. Tasteful interior that's full of squashy sofas and dining pub style. Accomplished menus, modern in substance, suit the surroundings.

BAGSHOT – Surrey – 504 R 29 – pop. 5 247 7 C1

London 37 m – Reading 17 m – Southampton 49 m

Windlesham Grove End, ✆ (01276) 452 220 .

Pennyhill Park

(heated) rm,

London Rd, Southwest : 1 m. on A 30 ✉ GU19 5EU – ✆ (01276) 471 774 – enquiries@pennyhillpark.co.uk – Fax (01276) 473 217

113 rm – †£ 250 ††£ 250, ☐ £20 – 10 suites

Rest *Michael Wignall at The Latymer* – see restaurant listing

Rest *Brasserie and Oyster bar* – (buffet lunch) Menu £ 30 (lunch) – Carte £ 33/49

◆ Sympathetically extended ivy-clad 19C manor house in wooded parkland. Intimate lounges. Outstanding spa. Rooms with fine antique furniture share a relaxing period elegance. Marble and stained glass enhanced restaurant overlooks garden.

Michael Wignall at The Latymer – at Pennyhill Park H.

AC

London Rd, Southwest : 1 m. on A 30 ✉ GU19 5EU – ✆ (01276) 471 774 – pennyhillpark@msn.com – Fax (01276) 473 217 – Closed 26-30 December, 1-15 January, Monday and lunch Saturday

Rest – (booking essential) Menu £ 32/60

◆ Fine dining at this recently refurbished restaurant, courtesy of the eponymous new chef. Get closer to the action with a seat at the chef's table. Elaborate, original cooking.

BAKEWELL – Derbs. – 502 O 24 – pop. 3 676 *Great Britain* 16 A1

London 160 m – Derby 26 m – Manchester 37 m – Nottingham 33 m – Sheffield 17 m

Old Market Hall, Bridge St ✆ (01629) 816558), bakewell@peakdistrict-mpa.gov.uk

Chatsworth★★★ (Park and Garden★★★) **AC**, NE : 2½ m. by A 619 – Haddon Hall★★ **AC**, SE : 2 m. by A 6

at Ashford-in-the-Water Northwest : 1 ¾ m. by A 6 and A 6020 – ✉ Bakewell

Riverside House

Fennel St ✉ DE45 1QF – ✆ (01629) 814 275 – riversidehouse@enta.net – Fax (01629) 812 873

14 rm (dinner included) ☐ – †£ 140/165 ††£ 230/295

Rest *The Riverside Room* – see restaurant listing

◆ Delightful former shooting lodge by River Wye. Comfortable, tastefully decorated rooms boast period features. Ground floor bedrooms in newer wing open onto garden.

The Riverside Room – at Riverside House

Fennel St ✉ DE45 1QF – ✆ (01629) 814 275 – Fax (01629) 812 873

Rest – Menu £ 19/45

◆ Popular restaurant serving classic French cooking; comprises Regency Room, Garden Room, Range Room and Conservatory.

BALSALL COMMON – W. Mids. – see Coventry

ENGLAND

BAMBURGH – Northd. – 501 O 17 Great Britain 24 B1

London 337 m – Edinburgh 77 m – Newcastle upon Tyne 51 m
Castle★ AC

Lord Crewe Arms

Front Street ✉ NE69 7BL – ☎ (01668) 214243 – lordcrewebamburgh@tiscali.co.uk – Fax (01668) 214273 – Closed January

18 rm – ♦£ 52/78 ♦♦£ 98 – **Rest** – (bar lunch) Carte £ 17/31

◆ In the shadow of the Norman castle, a neat and traditional market town hotel, still in private hands. Smartly fitted bedrooms; spacious, comfy lounge. Characterful beamed bar. Alluring timber and stone retaurant.

at Waren Mill West : 2 ¾ m. on B 1342 – ✉ Belford

Waren House

✉ *NE70 7EE – ☎ (01668) 214581 – enquiries@warenhousehotel.co.uk – Fax (01668) 214484*

11 rm – ♦£ 85/110 ♦♦£ 130/165 – 2 suites – **Rest** – (dinner only) Menu £ 28

◆ A Georgian country house in attractive grounds and formal gardens, with views to Lindisfarne. Individually decorated bedrooms with themes ranging from Oriental to Edwardian. Classical dining room overlooking gardens.

Good food and accommodation at moderate prices?
Look for the Bib symbols:
red Bib Gourmand for food, blue Bib Hotel for hotels

ENGLAND

BAMPTON – Devon – 503 J 31 – pop. 1 617 2 D1

London 189 m – Exeter 18 m – Minehead 21 m – Taunton 15 m

Bark House

Oukfordbridge, West : 3 m. by B 3227 on A 396 ✉ EX16 9HZ – ☎ (01398) 351236 – bark.house.hotel@btinternet.com

5 rm – ♦£ 50/55 ♦♦£ 95/119 – **Rest** – (dinner only) (booking essential for non-residents) (set menu only) Menu £ 30

◆ Neat, personally run stone cottages which once stored wood from Exmoor forest. Bright bedrooms of different sizes are decorated in pretty floral fabrics. Terraced rear garden. Home-cooking proudly served in neat dining room.

BANBURY – Oxon. – 503 P 27 – pop. 43 867 Great Britain 10 B1

London 76 m – Birmingham 40 m – Coventry 25 m – Oxford 23 m
Spiceball Park Rd ☎ (01295) 259855
Cherwell Edge Chacombe, ☎ (01295) 711591 .
Upton House★ AC, NW : 7 m. by A 422

Mercure Whately Hall

Horsefair, by Banbury Cross ✉ OX16 0AN – ☎ (01295) 253261 – h6633-gm@accor.com – Fax (01295) 271736

64 rm – ♦£ 135 ♦♦£ 135/175, £13.95 – 5 suites – **Rest** – ☎ (0870) 400 81 04 – Menu £ 20 (dinner) – Carte £ 23/34

◆ Imposing 17C hotel known for its secret passages, hidden staircases and resident ghost, Father Bernard. Panelled bar and lounge; well-appointed bedrooms - some in extension. Breakfast room overlooks rear garden. Smaller side room offers formal dining.

Banbury House

rm,  rest,

Oxford Rd ✉ OX16 9AH – ☎ (01295) 259361 – sales@banburyhouse.co.uk – Fax (01295) 270954 – closed 24 December-2 January

64 rm – ♦£ 123/150 ♦♦£ 150, £15 – **Rest** – (bar lunch) Menu £ 24

◆ Georgian property combining the traditional with the more modern. Well-maintained bedrooms in contemporary styles. Uptons restaurant offering contemporary British menu. Bar 29 popular for lunchtime snacks.

at Milton South : 5 ½ m. by A 4260 – ✉ Banbury

The Black Boy Inn

✉ *OX15 4HH – ✆ (01295) 722 111 – info@blackboyinn.com*

Rest – Menu £ 20 – Carte £ 22/29

◆ Popular dining destination. Enthusiastic, confident kitchen sources local produce, serving modern menu with French edge. Keen service. Candles and fresh flowers decorate.

at Wigginton Southwest : 7 m. by A 361 – ✉ Banbury

Pretty Bush Barn without rest

✉ *OX15 4LD – ✆ (01608) 738 262 – trev@prettybushbarn.wanadoo.co.uk – Fax (01608) 738 263 – closed 12 December-20 January*

3 rm – †£ 40 ††£ 65

◆ Barn conversion dating from 1827 situated in middle of village. Good value bed rooms with up-to-date furnishings; rustic breakfast room with communal table.

at North Newington West : 2 ¼ m. by B 4035 – ✉ Banbury

The Mill House without rest

✉ *OX15 6AA – ✆ (01295) 730 212 – lamadonett@aol.com – Fax (01295) 730 363 – closed Christmas and New Year*

7 rm ☕ – †£ 69 ††£ 109

◆ Keenly run 17C manor house and converted cottages set in tranquil location, with lawned garden to front and 15C mill and stream behind. Comfy bedrooms include one four poster.

at Sibford Gower West : 8 m. by B 4035 – ✉ Banbury

The Wykham Arms

Temple Mill Road ✉ OX15 5RX – ✆ (01295) 788 808 – info@wykhamarms.co.uk – Fax (01295) 788 806 – Closed Sunday dinner and 1 January

Rest – (closed Sunday dinner and Monday) Carte £ 15/30

◆ Thatched 17C inn in picturesque village. Modernised interior retains rural character with exposed beams, flag floors and glass-covered well. Local suppliers listed on board.

at Hanwell Northwest : 3 ½ m. by A 422 and B 4100 – ✉ Oxon

Moon and Sixpence

Main St ✉ OX17 1HW – ✆ (01295) 730 544 – moonand.sixpence@virgin.net – Closed 26 December, lunch Sunday and Monday

Rest – Menu £ 8 – Carte £ 8/30

◆ Traditional thatched pub with beamed ceilings, wood panelled walls, sofa in snug and shotguns as door handles. Pub favourites mix with more modern dishes on good value menu.

BANSTEAD 7 D1

London 27 m – Reading 79 m – Portsmouth 115 m – Luton 103 m

Post

28 High St ✉ SM7 2LQ – ✆ (01737) 373 839 – info@postrestaurant.co.uk – Closed 26 December

Rest – Carte £ 21/30

Rest *Brasserie* – Carte £ 17/30

◆ Restaurant, brasserie and deli in former post office, owned by celebrity chef Tony Tobin; a piece of London brought to the suburbs. Informal dining upstairs in restaurant. Vast choice on menu in airy brasserie.

BAR HILL – Cambs. – **504** U 27 – see Cambridge

If breakfast is included the ☕ symbol appears after the number of rooms.

ENGLAND

BARNARD CASTLE – Durham – 502 O 20 – pop. 6 714 Great Britain 24 A3

London 258 m – Carlisle 63 m – Leeds 68 m – Middlesbrough 31 m – Newcastle upon Tyne 39 m
Woodleigh, Flatts Rd (01833) 630272
Harmire Rd, (01833) 638 355 .
Bowes Museum★ AC
Raby Castle★ AC, NE : 6½ m. by A 688

Greta House without rest
89 Galgate ✉ DL12 8ES – (01833) 631 193 – kathchesman@btinternet.com – Fax (01833) 631 193
3 rm – £ 50 £ 70
♦ Part of a Victorian terrace with leafy garden. Bedrooms are spacious and individually decorated. Evening snacks may be taken in your room; plenty of books to browse through.

Demesnes Mill without rest
Southeast : ½ m. by The Bank and Gray Lane, through the playing field ✉ DL12 8PE – (01833) 637 929 – themillbarnardcastle@btopenworld.com – March-October
3 rm – £ 40 £ 55/75
♦ Set just out of town centre, a sensitively restored 15C mill abounding in period character. Large rooms, including one with an open fire. Conservatory with views of the Tees.

Homelands without rest
85 Galgate ✉ DL12 8ES – (01833) 638 757 – enquiries@homelandsguesthouse.co.uk – closed 23 December-2 January
5 rm – £ 35/60 £ 60/67
♦ Immaculately maintained 19C terraced house on main road. Cosy lounge and compact but pleasantly furnished, well-priced rooms, some overlooking the long mature rear garden.

at Greta Bridge Southeast : 4½ m. off A 66 – ✉ Barnard Castle

Morritt Arms
✉ DL12 9SE – (01833) 627 232 – relax@themorritt.co.uk – Fax (01833) 627 392
27 rm – £ 85/160 £ 160
Rest *The Morritt* – Carte £ 20/38
Rest *Bistro/Bar* – Carte £ 20/38
♦ 19C coaching inn where Charles Dickens stayed in 1839. The Dickens bar has murals by John Gilroy, historian of the Guinness firm. All rooms individually designed. The Morritt is oak panelled restaurant. Informal warmth at Bistro/Bar.

at Romaldkirk Northwest : 6 m. by A 67 on B 6277 – ✉ Barnard Castle 24 A3

Rose and Crown with rm
✉ DL12 9EB – (01833) 650 213 – hotel@rose-and-crown.co.uk – Fax (01833) 650 828 – Closed 24-26 December
12 rm – £ 80 £ 215
Rest – Menu £ 17/28 – Carte £ 15/28
Rest *The Restaurant* – (dinner only and Sunday lunch) Menu £ 26
♦ Ivy-clad former 18C coaching inn overlooking village green. Characterful, snug bar with open fires. Comfortable bedrooms. Rustic restaurant and polite organised service.

BARNARD GATE – Oxon. – 503 P 28 – see Witney

BARNSLEY – Glos. – 503 O 28 – see Cirencester

Good food without spending a fortune?
Look out for the Bib Gourmand

BARNSLEY – S. Yorks. – **502** P 23 – **pop. 71 599** 22 **B3**

London 177 m – Leeds 21 m – Manchester 36 m – Sheffield 15 m
46 Eldon St ✆ (01226) 206757
Staincross Wakefield Rd, ✆ (01226) 382 856 ;
Silkstone Elmhirst Lane, Field Head, ✆ (01226) 790 328 ;
Wombwell Hillies Wombwell Wentworth View, ✆ (01226) 754 433 .

Tankersley Manor
rm, rest,

Church Lane, South : 6 ¼ m. on A 61 ✉ S75 3DQ
– ✆ (01226) 744 700 – adminbm@marstonhotels.com – Fax (01226) 74 242
98 rm – ♦£ 139 ♦♦£ 177 – 2 suites
Rest – (closed Saturday lunch) Menu £ 20 – Carte £ 30/41
♦ Part 17C house, sympathetically enlarged to cater for corporate functions and weddings. Low-beamed lounge and bar with Regency-style furniture. Rooms have useful mod cons. Formal or informal option: characterful pub or stone-walled dining room.

Your opinions are important to us:
please write and let us know about your discoveries and experiences – good and bad!

BARNSTAPLE – Devon – **503** H 30 – **pop. 30 765** 2 **C1**

London 222 m – Exeter 40 m – Taunton 51 m
36 Boutport St ✆ (01271) 375000
Chulmleigh Leigh Rd, ✆ (01769) 580 519.
Town★ - Long Bridge★
Arlington Court★★ (Carriage Collection★) AC, NE : 6 m. by A 39

Imperial
rest,

Taw Vale Parade ✉ EX32 8NB – ✆ (01271) 345 861 – info@brend-imperial.co.uk – Fax (01271) 324 448
63 rm – ♦£ 90/190 ♦♦£ 100/190, £ 13
Rest – Menu £ 15/35 – Carte £ 44/50
♦ Attractive riverside hotel dating from the turn of 20C. Convivial bar and smart accommodation: deluxe front bedrooms have balconies overlooking the Taw. Grand, bay-windowed dining room.

at Bishop's Tawton South : 2 ¾ m. by A 39 on A 377 – ✉ Barnstaple

Halmpstone Manor without rest

Southeast : 3 m. by Chittlehampton rd ✉ EX32 0EA – ✆ (01271) 830 321 – charles@halmpstonemanor.co.uk – Fax (01271) 830 826 – closed Christmas and New Year
4 rm – ♦£ 70 ♦♦£ 140
♦ A 400 year old manor set in charming Devon countryside. Log fires, deep sofas, sherry decanters, four poster and brass coronet beds; peace and relaxation assured.

BARNT GREEN – Birmingham 19 **C2**

London 114 m – Birmingham 11 m – Bromsgrove 9 m

The Barnt Green Inn

22 Kendal End Rd, on B 4120 ✉ B45 8PZ – ✆ (0121) 445 4949 – Fax (0121) 447 9912
Rest – Carte £ 16/32
♦ Huge mock Tudor establishment in the Birmingham hinterland. Smoochy lounge area and bar; separate restaurant with an informal air: modern international menus predominate.

ENGLAND

BARROWDEN – Rutland 17 C2

London 94 m – Peterborough 17 m – Stamford 8 m

Exeter Arms with rm

28 Main St ✉ LE15 8EQ – ☎ (01572) 747 247 – info@exeterarms.com – Fax (01572) 747 247 – Closed Sunday dinner and Monday lunch

3 rm – ♦£ 38 ♦♦£ 75 – **Rest** – Carte £ 21/29

◆ Stone-built, family owned 17C inn overlooking green and duck pond. Ales from pub's own micro brewery. Accomplished cuisine proffers modernity with Asian undercurrent.

BARSTON – W. Mids. – 504 O 26 19 C2

London 110 m – Birmingham 17 m – Coventry 11 m

The Malt Shovel

Barston Lane, West : 3/4 m ✉ B92 0JP – ☎ (01675) 443 223 – Fax (01675) 443 223 – Closed 25 December

Rest – (closed Sunday dinner) (lunch bookings not accepted) Menu £ 25 – Carte £ 18/31

◆ Modern dining pub, an oasis in a rustic hideaway, with large garden and patio. Good sized menus: noteworthy seafood specials. Busy at lunchtimes - you can't book so go early!

ENGLAND

BARTON-ON-SEA – Hants. – 503 P 31 6 A3

London 108 m – Bournemouth 11 m – Southampton 24 m – Winchester 35 m

Pebble Beach with rm

Marine Drive ✉ BH25 7DZ – ☎ (01425) 627 777 – email@pebblebeach-uk.com – Fax (01425) 610 689

3 rm – ♦£ 60 ♦♦£ 80, £ 5 – **Rest** – Seafood Carte £ 27/46

◆ Cliff-top position: striking terrace views over Solent and The Needles. Bright, modish interior with large windows. Wide range of choice on modern menus. Well-equipped rooms.

BARWICK – Somerset – 503 M 31 – see Yeovil

BASILDON – Essex – 504 V 29 – pop. 102 913 13 C3

London 30 m – Chelmsford 17 m – Southend-on-Sea 13 m

18 Sparrow's Hearne Clayhill Lane, ☎ (01268) 533 297 ;

9 Langdon Hills Bulphan Lower Dunton Rd, ☎ (01268) 548 444 .

at Wickford North : 5 1/4 m. by A 132 – ✉ Basildon

Chichester rm, rest,

Old London Rd, Rawreth, East : 2 3/4 m. by A 129 ✉ SS11 8UE – ☎ (01268) 560 555 – reception@chichester-hotel.com – Fax (01268) 560 580

35 rm – ♦£ 64 ♦♦£ 70, £ 8.95 – **Rest** – (dinner only and Sunday lunch) Carte £ 17/24 **s**

◆ Traditional, family-run hotel surrounded by farmland. Open lounge and immaculately-kept bedrooms set around central courtyard. Simply furnished restaurant serves tried-and-tested dishes.

Good food without spending a fortune?
Look out for the Bib Gourmand

BASINGSTOKE – Hants. – 503 Q 30 – pop. 90 171 6 B1

London 55 m – Reading 17 m – Southampton 31 m – Winchester 18 m

Willis Museum, Old Town Hall, Market Pl ✆ (01256) 817618

Test Valley Overton Micheldever Rd, ✆ (01256) 771 737 ;

Weybrook Park Basingstoke Rooksdown Lane, ✆ (01256) 320 347 .

Apollo

rest, VISA

Aldermaston Roundabout, North : 1 m. on A 340 ✉ RG24 9NU – ✆ (01256) 796 700 – enquiries@apollohotels.com – Fax (01256) 796 794 Z **a**

122 rm – ♦£ 165 ♦♦£ 180/200, ☐ £15.50 – 3 suites

Rest *Vespers* – (Closed Sunday) (dinner only) Carte £ 28/34 **s**

Rest *Brasserie* – (buffet) Carte £ 19/31 **s**

◆ Smart, modern hotel aimed at business clients; well situated on Basingstoke ring road. Extensive conference and leisure facilities. Modern, well equipped rooms. Vespers is an intimate fine dining room. Large, modern Brasserie with centre servery.

BASINGSTOKE

Aldermaston Rd	Z	2
Beaconsfield Rd	Y	3
Buckland Ave	Z	5
Chequers Rd	Y	6
Churchill Way	Z	9
Churchill Way East	Z	10
Church St	Y	7
Council Rd	Y	12
Cross St	Y	13
Fairfields Rd	Y	14
Festival Place Shopping Centre	Y	
Houndmills Rd	Z	17
London St	Y	19
New Rd	Y	20
Reading Rd	Z	22
Southern Ringway	Z	23
Upper Church St	Y	24
Victoria St	Y	25
Winchester St	Y	27
Wote St	Y	28

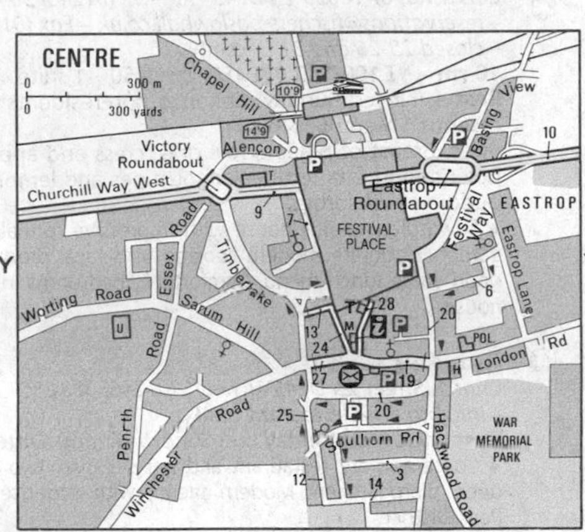

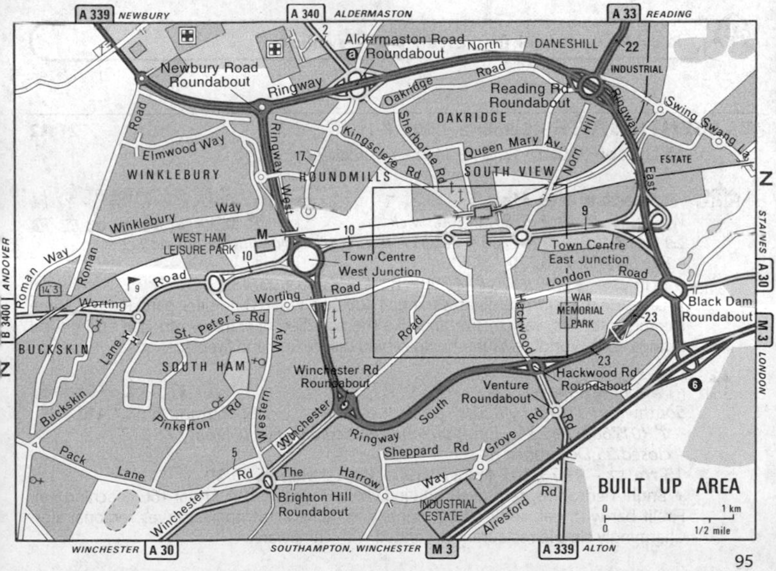

A 339 NEWBURY A 340 ALDERMASTON A 33 READING

Aldermaston Road Roundabout
Newbury Road Roundabout
Reading Rd Roundabout
OAKRIDGE
WINKLEBURY
HOUNDMILLS
SOUTH VIEW
DANESHILL
INDUSTRIAL ESTATE
WEST HAM LEISURE PARK
Town Centre West Junction
Town Centre East Junction
Black Dam Roundabout
BUCKSKIN
SOUTH HAM
Winchester Rd Roundabout
Venture Roundabout
Hackwood Rd Roundabout
Brighton Hill Roundabout
INDUSTRIAL ESTATE
BUILT UP AREA
1 km
1/2 mile

WINCHESTER A 30 SOUTHAMPTON, WINCHESTER M 3 A 339 ALTON B 3400 ANDOVER A 30 STAINES M 3 LONDON

BASLOW – Derbs. – 502 P 24 – ✉ Bakewell ▮ *Great Britain* 16 A1

London 161 m – Derby 27 m – Manchester 35 m – Sheffield 13 m
Chatsworth★★★ (Park and Garden★★★) AC

The Cavendish
< Chatsworth Park,

Church Lane, on A 619 ✉ DE45 1SP – ✆ (01246) 582 311 – info@cavendish-hotel.net – Fax (01246) 582 312 – Closed 25 December

VISA MC AE

23 rm – †£ 122 ††£ 177, ☐ £15.95 – 1 suite
Rest *The Gallery* – Menu £ 39
Rest *Garden Room* – Carte £ 25/32

◆ Well established, elegant hotel; handsomely decorated, with antiques, oil paintings and log fires. Individually furnished, country house style bedrooms. Classical cooking served in The Gallery, with table in kitchen for watching chefs. Conservatory Garden Room with views of Chatsworth Estate.

Fischer's at Baslow Hall with rm
P VISA MC AE

Calver Rd, on A 623 ✉ DE45 1RR – ✆ (01246) 583 259 – reservations@fischers-baslowhall.co.uk – Fax (01246) 583 818 – closed 25-26 and 31 December

10 rm – †£ 100/140 ††£ 180, ☐ £9.50 – 1 suite
Rest – (closed Sunday dinner to non-residents and Monday lunch) (booking essential) Menu £ 35/65

Spec. Breast of pigeon, foie gras, cress and apple salad. Pan-fried red mullet, polenta and feta terrine, langoustines and lemon oil. Mocha parfait, chocolate pudding and sorbet.

◆ Edwardian manor house with impressive formal gardens and walled vegetable garden. Elaborate modern cooking uses local produce. Adventurous à la carte and good value lunch menu. Comfortable bedrooms in main house and newer garden house.

ENGLAND

Rowley's
P VISA MC AE

Church Street ✉ DE45 1RY – ✆ (01246) 583 880 – info@towleysrestaurant.co.uk

Rest – (closed Monday and Sunday dinner) Carte £ 21/37

◆ Contemporary restaurant and bar set over two floors; downstairs with view of open plan kitchen. Modern menu, with produce sourced from in and around Peak District.

Red = Pleasant. Look for the red ✗ and ⌂ symbols.

BASSENTHWAITE – Cumbria – 501 K 19 21 A2

London 300 m – Carlisle 24 m – Keswick 7 m

Armathwaite Hall
< Bassenthwaite Lake,

West : 1½ m. on B 5291, ✉ Keswick ✉ CA12 4RE – ✆ (017687) 76551 – reservations@armathwaite-hall.com – Fax (017687) 76220

P VISA MC AE

42 rm ☐ – †£ 140/170 ††£ 300 – **Rest** – Menu £ 23/43

◆ Lakeside mansion dominates tranquil 400-acre woods and deer park. Rooms, some in rebuilt stables, vary in size and, like the panelled hall, marry modern and period fittings. 'Old-World' restaurant with carved oak ceiling and fireplace.

The Pheasant
P VISA MC

Southwest : 3¼ m. by B 5291 on Wythop Mill rd, ✉ Cockermouth ✉ CA13 9YE – ✆ (017687) 76234 – info@the-pheasant.co.uk – Fax (017687) 76002 – closed 25 December

15 rm ☐ – †£ 75/105 ††£ 170/190 – **Rest** – Menu £ 26/30

◆ Bright bedrooms, sensitively and individually updated, in a rural 16C coaching inn. Firelit bar with oak settles, local prints and game fish trophies serves regional ales. Charmingly simple restaurant decorated with chinaware.

BATCOMBE - Somerset - 503 M 30 - ✉ Shepton Mallet 4 C2

London 130 m - Bournemouth 50 m - Bristol 24 m - Salisbury 40 m - Taunton 40 m

The Three Horseshoes Inn with rm

✉ *BA4 6HE - ✆ (01749) 850359 - Fax (01749) 850615 - Closed Sunday dinner and Monday*

3 rm - †£50 ††£75 - **Rest** - Carte £25/35

◆ Characterful, low beamed pub with rustic bar, intimate snug and more formal restaurant. Chickens roam in neat garden and local, organic produce features highly on menu. Neat, simply decorated bedrooms.

ENGLAND

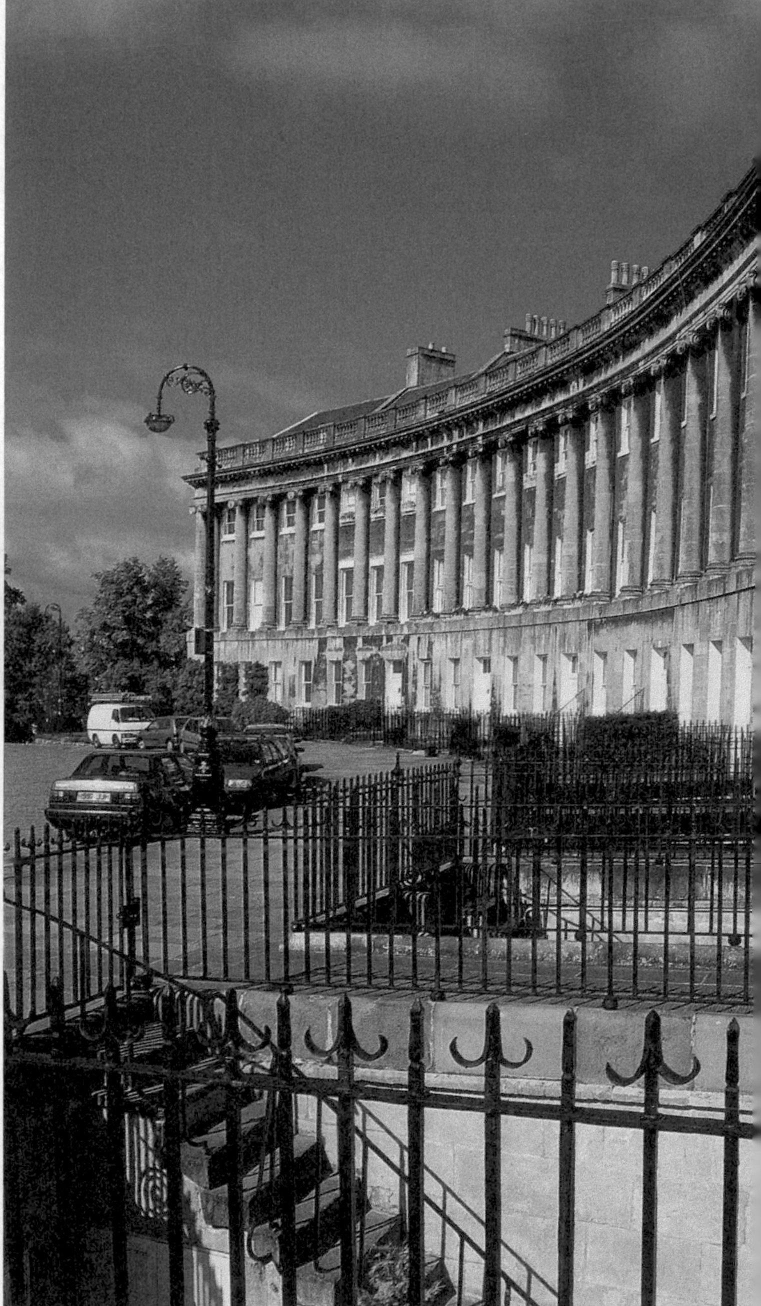

H. Champollion/MICHELIN

BATH

County: Bath & North East Somerset
Michelin REGIONAL map: n° **503** M 29
London 119 m – Bristol 13 m – Southampton 63 m – Taunton 49 m

Population: 90 144
Great Britain

4 **C2**

PRACTICAL INFORMATION

Tourist Information

Abbey Chambers, Abbey Church Yard ✆ (0906) 711 2000, tourism@bathnes.gov.uk

Golf Courses

27 Tracy Park Wick Bath Rd, ✆ (0771) 737 2251 ;
18 Lansdown, ✆ (01225) 422 138 ;
9 Entry Hill, ✆ (01225) 834 248.

ENGLAND

SIGHTS

IN TOWN

City★★★ - Royal Crescent★★★ AV (No.1 Royal Crescent★★ **AC** AV **A**) – The Circus★★★ AV – Museum of Costume★★★ **AC** AV **M7** – Roman Baths★★ **AC** BX **D** – Holburne Museum and Crafts Study Centre★★ **AC** Y **M5** – Pump Room★ BX **B** - Assembly Rooms★ AV – Bath Abbey★ BX – Pulteney Bridge★ BV – Bath Industrial Heritage Centre★ **AC** AV **M1** – Lansdown Crescent★★ (Somerset Place★) Y – Camden Crescent★ Y – Beckford Tower and Museum **AC** (prospect★) Y **M6** – Museum of East Asian Art★ AV **M9** – Orange Grove★ BX

ON THE OUTSKIRTS

Claverton (American Museum★★ **AC**, Claverton Pumping Station★ **AC**) E: 3 m. by A 36 Y

IN THE SURROUNDING AREA

Corsham Court★★ **AC**, NE: 8 ½ m. by A 4 – Dyrham Park★ **AC**, N: 6 ½ m. by A 4 and A 46

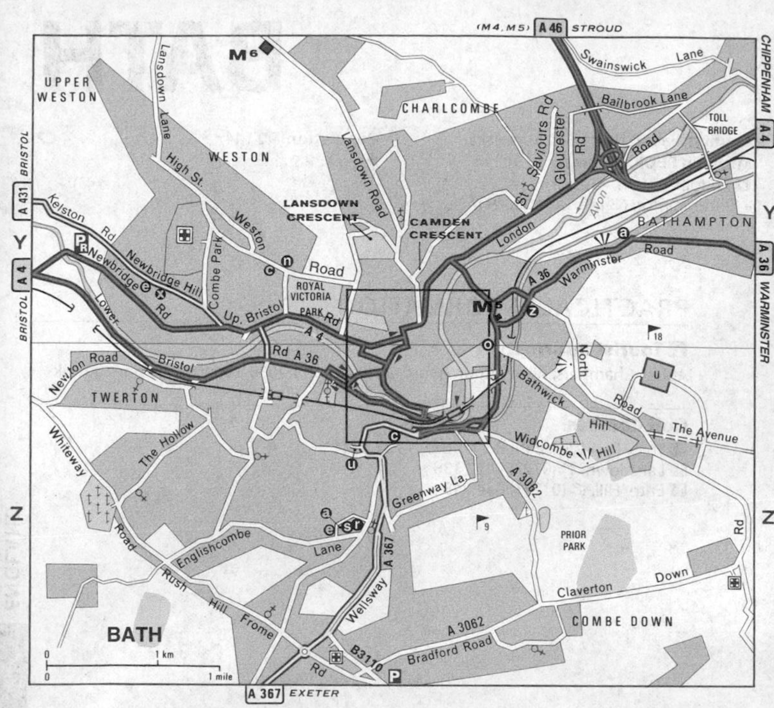

The Royal Crescent

16 Royal Crescent ✉ *BA1 2LS – ☎ (01225) 823 333*
– info@royalcrescent.co.uk – Fax (01225) 339 401
VISA MC AE
AV **a**
35 rm – £ 225/227 £ 225/245 – 10 suites
Rest *The Dower House* – see restaurant listing
◆ Meticulously restored historic town house in sweeping Georgian crescent. Classically styled bedrooms and drawing rooms; period furniture. Stylish spa. Professional service.

Bath Spa

rm, rest,

Sydney Rd ✉ *BA2 6JF – ☎ (0870) 400 82 22*
– sales.bathspa@macdonald-hotels.co.uk – Fax (01225) 444 006
VISA MC AE
Y **z**
118 rm – £ 284 £ 298, £ 6 – 11 suites
Rest *Vellore* – (dinner only and Sunday lunch) Menu £ 38 – Carte £ 43/50
Rest *Alfresco* – Mediterranean (closed Sunday lunch) Carte £ 24/34
◆ Impressive 19C mansion in mature gardens; refurbished, with new wing of rooms. Period lounges and contemporary bedrooms in bold colours with full butler service. Superb spa. Vellore is smart with intimate lounge and terrace. Alfresco more informal, with Mediterranean menus.

Bath Priory

(heated) rm,

Weston Rd ✉ *BA1 2XT – ☎ (01225) 331 922*
– mail@thebathpriory.co.uk – Fax (01225) 448 276 – Closed 3 January-11 February
VISA MC AE
Y **c**
27 rm – £ 200 £ 245/360 – **Rest** – Menu £ 25/55
Spec. Veal sweetbread, kohlrabi two ways. Skate with charcuterie, potato and caraway. Apple and pear with anise, pear sorbet.
◆ Extended Georgian property with mature gardens. Comfortable, stylish drawing rooms in rich reds and golds. Classic bedrooms with contemporary touches. Two dining rooms; the smaller more romantic, the larger more modern. Accomplished modern cooking with some unusual combinations. Attentive service.

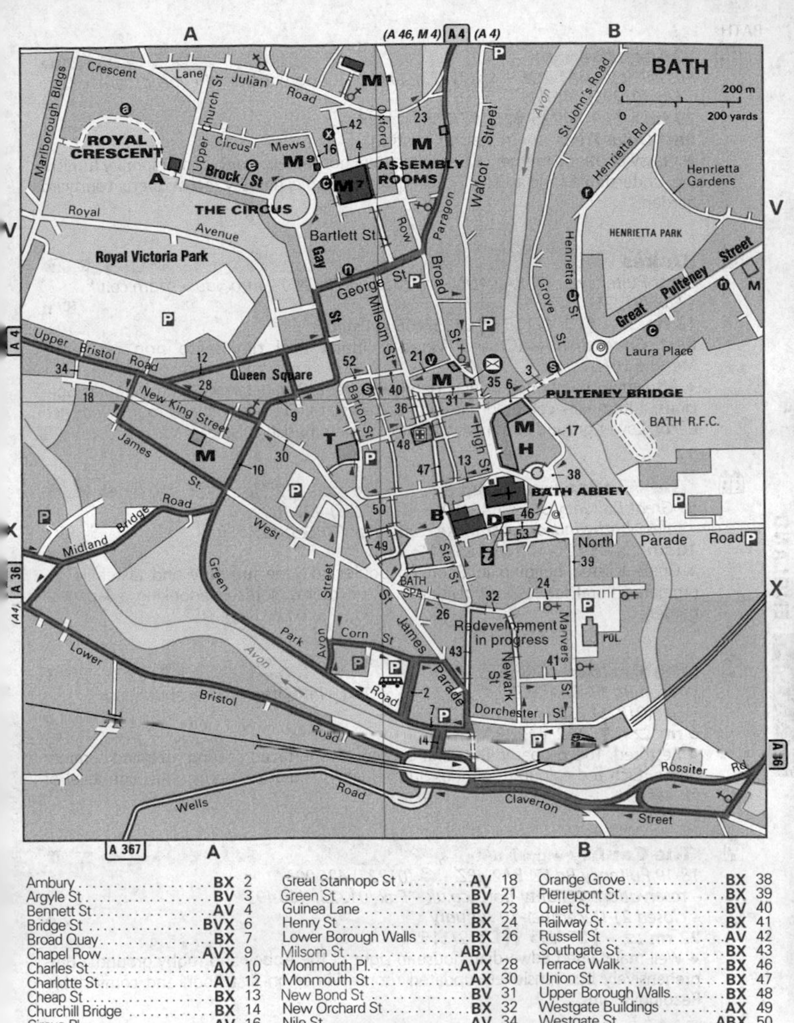

Ambury	BX	2	Great Stanhope St	AV	18	Orange Grove	BX	38
Argyle St	BV	3	Green St	BV	21	Pierrepont St	BX	39
Bennett St	AV	4	Guinea Lane	BV	23	Quiet St	BV	40
Bridge St	BVX	6	Henry St	BX	24	Railway St	BX	41
Broad Quay	BX	7	Lower Borough Walls	BX	26	Russell St	AV	42
Chapel Row	AVX	9	Milsom St	ABV		Southgate St	BX	43
Charles St	AX	10	Monmouth Pl.	AVX	28	Terrace Walk	BX	46
Charlotte St	AV	12	Monmouth St	AX	30	Union St	BX	47
Cheap St	BX	13	New Bond St	BV	31	Upper Borough Walls	BX	48
Churchill Bridge	BX	14	New Orchard St	BX	32	Westgate Buildings	AX	49
Circus Pl.	AV	16	Nile St	AV	34	Westgate St	ABX	50
Gay St	AV		Northgate St	BVX	35	Wood St	AV	52
Grand Parade	BX	17	Old Bond St	BX	36	York St	BX	53

Homewood Park (heated)

Abbey Lane, Hinton Charterhouse, Southeast : 6½ m. on A 36 ✉ BA2 7TB – ✆ (01225) 723731 – info@homewoodpark.co.uk – Fax (01225) 723820

19 rm – 🚹£ 145 🚹🚹£ 185 – **Rest** – Menu £ 18/44

◆ Well-proportioned bedrooms, with views of the idyllic wooded gardens and croquet lawn, and cosy country house drawing rooms retain strong elements of the Georgian interior. Ask for dining room window table when garden is in full bloom.

Queensberry

Russell St ✉ BA1 2QF – ✆ (01225) 447 928 – reservations@thequeensberry.co.uk – Fax (01225) 446 065 AV **x**

29 rm – 🚹£ 105/235 🚹🚹£ 105/235, ☕ £14

Rest *Olive Tree* – see restaurant listing

◆ Classy boutique merger of Georgian town house décor with contemporary furnishing, understated style and well-chosen detail. Ample, unfussy rooms; pretty courtyard garden.

Dukes

Great Pulteney St ✉ BA2 4DN – ✆ (01225) 787 960 – info@dukesbath.co.uk – Fax (01225) 787 961 BV **n**

13 rm ☕ – 🚹£ 100/115 🚹🚹£ 135/165 – 4 suites

Rest *Cavendish* – (Closed Monday lunch and dinner to non residents) Menu £ 16/40

◆ Attractive townhouse in fine Georgian street. Paved terrace with parasols. Spacious, autumnally coloured bar with leather sofas. Classically styled rooms with rich décor. Lower ground floor restaurant for modern British cuisine.

The Windsor without rest

69 Great Pulteney St ✉ BA2 4DL – ✆ (01225) 422 100 – sales@bathwindsorguesthouse.com – Fax (01225) 422 550 BV **c**

10 rm ☕ – 🚹£ 70/100 🚹🚹£ 85/215

◆ Grade I listed building in Georgian boulevard. Fine furniture and tastefully coordinated floral fabrics in individually styled rooms, some overlooking a Japanese garden.

The Residence without rest

Weston Rd ✉ BA1 2XZ – ✆ (01225) 750 180 – info@theresidencebath.com – Fax (01225) 750 181 Y **n**

6 rm ☕ – 🚹£ 162 🚹🚹£ 300

◆ Restored, 18C property. Beautiful garden with terraced seating area and summer house. Rich red-coloured lounges. Individually decorated rooms with high level of facilities.

The County without rest

18-19 Pulteney Rd ✉ BA2 4EZ – ✆ (01225) 425 003 – reservations@county-hotel.co.uk – Fax (01225) 466 493 – closed 21 December-10 January Z **o**

22 rm ☕ – 🚹£ 75/95 🚹🚹£ 112/115

◆ Well-maintained Edwardian house in sight of the Abbey and rugby ground. Comprehensively but sensitively updated rooms, larger on first floor, and comfortable Reading Room.

The Ayrlington without rest

24-25 Pulteney Rd ✉ BA2 4EZ – ✆ (01225) 425 495 – mail@ayrlington.com – Fax (01225) 469 029 – closed 23 December-2 January Z **o**

14 rm ☕ – 🚹£ 80/125 🚹🚹£ 100/175

◆ An interesting blend of Georgian styling and Asian artefacts develops through twelve spacious, subtly themed rooms. Charming cherry tree garden overlooks croquet club.

Paradise House without rest

86-88 Holloway ✉ BA2 4PX – ✆ (01225) 317 723 – info@paradise-house.co.uk – Fax (01225) 482 005 – closed 24-25 December Z **c**

11 rm ☕ – 🚹£ 65/115 🚹🚹£ 75/165

◆ Elegant yet homely hotel on Beechen Cliff. Most rear-facing rooms have exceptional city views; all reflect 18C origins in their décor and boast Jacuzzis. Beautiful gardens.

ENGLAND

Oldfields without rest
102 Wells Rd ✉ BA2 3AL – ☎ (01225) 317 984 – info@oldfields.co.uk – Fax (01225) 444 471 – Closed 3 days Christmas Z **u**
16 rm ☕ – †£ 49/115 ††£ 165
◆ Spaciously elegant Victorian house with comfy, well-furnished drawing room, breakfast room boasting 'Bath rooftops' view and bedrooms that exude a high standard of comfort.

Apsley House without rest
141 Newbridge Hill ✉ BA1 3PT – ☎ (01225) 336 966 – info@apsley-house.co.uk – Fax (01225) 425 462 – closed 24-26 December Y **x**
11 rm ☕ – †£ 70/85 ††£ 100/150
◆ Built for the Duke of Wellington and staffed with the unobtrusive calm of an English private house. Spacious individual rooms; two open on to a peaceful, mature rear garden.

Kennard without rest
11 Henrietta St ✉ BA2 6LL – ☎ (01225) 310 472 – reception@kennard.co.uk – Fax (01225) 460 054 – closed Christmas and New Year BV **u**
12 rm ☕ – †£ 58/89 ††£ 98/130
◆ Classic Georgian town house with tranquil garden and charming breakfast room. Bedrooms vary in style; some classic, some contemporary.

Cheriton House without rest
9 Upper Oldfield Park ✉ BA2 3JX – ☎ (01225) 429 862 – info@cheritonhouse.co.uk – Fax (01225) 428 403 Z **u**
12 rm ☕ – †£ 63/90 ††£ 85/115
◆ Comfortable, sizeable rooms and lounge, refurbished in keeping with the house's 19C origins, with some fine tiled fireplaces. Conservatory breakfast room. Charming hosts.

Dorian House without rest
1 Upper Oldfield Park ✉ BA2 3JX – ☎ (01225) 426 336 – info@dorianhouse.co.uk – Fax (01225) 444 699 Z **u**
11 rm ☕ – †£ 55/95 ††£ 90/180
◆ Charming 19C house preserves original tiling and stained glass; attic rooms are refreshingly modern, others Victorian. Breakfast to recordings of owner's cello performances.

Bloomfield House without rest
146 Bloomfield Rd ✉ BA2 2AS – ☎ (01225) 420 105 – info@ecobloomfield.com Z **r**
6 rm ☕ – †£ 65 ††£ 100/140
◆ Bath's first eco-hotel is in this Grade II listed Georgian building. Breakfast produce is organic, fair trade or, whenever possible, locally sourced. Tastefully elegant rooms.

Tasburgh House without rest
Warminster Rd, East : 1 m. on A 36 ✉ BA2 6SH – ☎ (01225) 425 096 – hotel@bathtasburgh.co.uk – Fax (01225) 463 842 – closed 23 December-15 January Y **a**
12 rm – †£ 65/90 ††£ 95/130, ☕ £ 7.50
◆ Personally run by charming owner. Rear bedrooms, decorated with original artwork and named after British authors, overlook Avon Valley. Walk along the canal into Bath.

Villa Magdala without rest
Henrietta Rd ✉ BA2 6LX – ☎ (01225) 466 329 – office@villamagdala.co.uk – Fax (01225) 483 207 – closed 25-26 December and 1 January BV **r**
18 rm – †£ 85/110 ††£ 130
◆ Named after Napier's 1868 victory. Well-equipped rooms, floral furnishings; carefully preserved ornate balustrade and showpiece bedroom with four-poster and chaise longue.

ENGLAND

Harington's

8-10 Queen St ✉ BA1 1HE – ✆ (01225) 461 728 – post@haringtonshotel.co.uk – Fax (01225) 444 804 AV **s**

13 rm – ♦£ 80/98 ♦♦£ 108/150 – **Rest** – Carte £ 22/30

♦ 18C houses on a cobbled street in the heart of the city and perfectly located for the shops. Simply styled but diligently maintained accommodation on offer. Bar in hot ochre and yellow adjoins restaurant.

Haydon House without rest

9 Bloomfield Park, off Bloomfield Rd ✉ BA2 2BY – ✆ (01225) 444 919 – stay@haydonhouse.co.uk Z **a**

5 rm – ♦£ 60/95 ♦♦£ 80/145

♦ Pristine bedrooms and lounge in calm pastels, full of the charming, thoughtful details of a family home. Leafy bowers and trellises. Friendly hosts serve delicious breakfasts.

The Town House without rest

7 Bennett St ✉ BA1 2QJ – ✆ (01225) 422 505 – stay@thetownhousebath.co.uk – Fax (01225) 422 505 – closed January-February AV **c**

3 rm – ♦£ 84 ♦♦£ 95

♦ Welcoming 18C house in excellent location, designed by John Wood and rebuilt after war damage. Spacious bedrooms with South African wildlife décor. Communal breakfast.

Lavender House

17 Bloomfield Park, (off Bloomfield Rd) ✉ BA2 2BY – ✆ (01225) 314 500 – lavenderhouse@btinternet.com – Fax (01225) 448 564 Z **s**

5 rm – ♦£ 55/65 ♦♦£ 80/120 – **Rest** – (by arrangementr) Menu £ 20

♦ Edwardian house run with confidence and brio. Comfortable, smartly refurbished rooms in rose, blue, gold, terracotta and lavender. Guesthouse cats patrol a pleasant garden.

Meadowland without rest

36 Bloomfield Park, off Bloomfield Rd ✉ BA2 2BX – ✆ (01225) 311 079 – stay@meadowlandbath.co.uk – Closed 24 December-2 January Z **e**

4 rm – ♦£ 60/65 ♦♦£ 95/110

♦ Small suburban guesthouse with a welcoming ambience; comfortably furnished and immaculately maintained accommodation. A neat breakfast room gives onto a lawned garden.

Brocks without rest

32 Brock St ✉ BA1 2LN – ✆ (01225) 338 374 – brocks@brocksguesthouse.co.uk – Closed Christmas and New Year AV **e**

6 rm – ♦£ 65/70 ♦♦£ 79/87

♦ Between the Circus and the Royal Crescent, a 1765 terraced house, welcoming and well run, offering homely, comfortable en suite rooms. Well-priced for its excellent location.

Athole without rest

33 Upper Oldfield Park ✉ BA2 3JX – ✆ (01225) 320 000 – info@atholehouse.co.uk – Fax (01225) 320 009 Z **i**

4 rm – ♦£ 55 ♦♦£ 66/85

♦ Spacious, bay windowed Victorian guesthouse with large garden, away from city centre. Bright breakfast room; conservatory lounge. Light, airy, contemporary bedrooms.

Cranleigh without rest

159 Newbridge Hill ✉ BA1 3PX – ✆ (01225) 310 197 – cranleigh@btinternet.com – Fax (01225) 423 143 – closed 25-26 December Y **e**

9 rm – ♦£ 50/65 ♦♦£ 60/95

♦ Airy, high-ceilinged bedrooms, the largest ideal for families, with brightly patterned fabrics. Pleasant south-facing garden. Smoked salmon and eggs a breakfast speciality.

The Dower House – at The Royal Crescent H.
16 Royal Crescent ✉ BA1 2LS – ✆ (01225) 823 333
– info@royalcrescent.co.uk AV **a**
Rest – Menu £ 25/60
◆ Impressive restaurant with striking green and brown décor and seaweed art feature. Intimate feel. Attentive service. Flavourful, well-presented, classically-based cooking.

Olive Tree – at Queensberry H.
Russell St ✉ BA1 2QF – ✆ (01225) 447 928 – reservations@thequeensberry.co.uk
– Fax (01225) 446 065 – closed Monday lunch AV **x**
Rest – Menu £ 18 – Carte £ 31/43
◆ Up-to-date restaurant with a classy, stylish and contemporary ambience. Modern artworks adorn the split-level basement. Modern British cooking. Helpful staff.

Hole in the Wall
16 George St ✉ BA1 2EH – ✆ (01225) 425 242 – info@theholeinthewall.co.uk
– Closed 25-26 December and Sunday lunch AV **n**
Rest – Menu £ 14 (lunch) – Carte £ 11/20
◆ Once a starting point of British culinary renaissance; former coal hole mixes white-washed walls, antique chairs and a relaxed mood. Slightly eclectic cuisine.

No.5
5 Argyle St ✉ BA2 4BA – ✆ (01225) 444 499 – Fax (01225) 444 499
– Closed 24-26 December and 1 January BV **s**
Rest – Carte £ 26/31
◆ Unfussy bistro with a distinctly buzzy feel. Personally run by cheery French owner. Fish night on Wednesday a speciality. Menus offer ample variety; some are good value, too.

Fishworks
6 Green St ✉ BA1 2JY – ✆ (01225) 448 707 – bath@fishworks.co.uk
– Closed 25-26 December and 1 January BV **a**
Rest – Seafood (booking essential) Carte £ 25/49
◆ Behind a quality fish shop, whose produce appears on menus. Bustling ambience. Extensive, daily changing blackboard specials; the cooking is straightforward and unfussy.

at Box Northeast : 4 ¾ m. on A 4 - Y – ✉ Bath

The Northey
Bath Road ✉ SN13 8AE – ✆ (01225) 742 333 – office@ohhcompany.co.uk
– Closed 25-26 December
Rest – Carte £ 21/29
◆ Spacious roadside pub with pleasant rear terrace. Modern interior dominated by chunky wooden tables and rattan chairs. Serious modern cooking lays claim to restaurant style.

at Colerne Northeast : 6 ½ m. by A 4 - Y - Batheaston rd and Bannerdown Rd – ✉ Chippenham

Lucknam Park
North : ½ m. on Marshfield rd ✉ SN14 8AZ
– ✆ (01225) 742 777 – reservations@lucknampark.co.uk
– Fax (01225) 743 536
37 rm – †£ 255 ††£ 415, ☕ £ 18.50 – 4 suites – **Rest** – (booking essential)
Menu £ 25/60 **s**
Spec. Mackerel, spiced lentils, marinaded beetroot and horseradish. Roast pigeon, cabbage and chicory tart, sloe gin and chocolate sauce. Passion fruit tart, yoghurt sorbet.
◆ Impressive Palladian mansion in 500 acres. Equestrian centre. Spacious, stylish rooms for drinks and afternoon tea. Modern facilities in bedrooms. New spa opening 2008. Formal restaurant offers accomplished, classic British cooking and professional service.

ENGLAND

at Combe Hay Southwest : 5 m. by A 367 – ✉ Bath

The Wheatsheaf with rm
✉ BA2 7EF – ☎ (01225) 833 504 – info@wheatsheafcombehay.com – Fax (01225) 836 123 – Closed 25 December, Sunday dinner and Monday
3 rm – †£ 95 ††£ 120 – **Rest** – Carte £ 22/45
◆ Part 17C inn on side of hill with well kept gardens and stylish terrace. Fireside sofas, stark modern dining rooms, informal atmosphere and appealing, flavoursome cooking. Three smart bedrooms.

BATTLE – E. Sussex – 504 V 31 – pop. 5 190 *Great Britain* 8 B3

London 55 m – Brighton 34 m – Folkestone 43 m – Maidstone 30 m
High St ☎ (01424) 773721, battletic@rother.gov.uk
Town★ – Abbey and Site of the Battle of Hastings★ AC

PowderMills
Powdermill Lane, South : 1½ m. by A 2100 on Catsfield rd ✉ TN33 0SP – ☎ (01424) 775 511 – powdc@aol.com – Fax (01424) 774 540
40 rm – †£ 105 ††£ 195
Rest *Orangery* – Menu £ 20/35
◆ Part Georgian gunpowder mill in 150 acres of woods and lakes. Individually decorated rooms - more sizable in annex and with better views - combine antiques and modern pieces. Dining room terrace overlooks pool.

Fox Hole Farm without rest
Kane Hythe Rd, Northwest : 2½ m. by A 2100 and A 271 on B 2096 (Netherfield rd) ✉ TN33 9QU – ☎ (01424) 772 053 – foxholefarm@kanehythe.orangehome.co.uk – Fax (01424) 772 053 – Closed last 3 weeks January and Christmas
3 rm – †£ 42/49 ††£ 65/69
◆ Peaceful 18C woodcutters cottage by 1000 acres of protected forest. Simple pine furnished bedrooms with sea-grass matting. Timbered lounge centred around a log stove.

BAUGHURST – Hants. 6 B1

London 61 m – Camberley 28 m – Farnborough 27 m

The Wellington Arms
Baughurst Rd, Southwest : ¾ m. ✉ RG26 5LP – ☎ (0118) 982 0110 – info@thewellingtonarms.com – Closed Sunday dinner, Monday and Tuesday lunch
Rest – (booking essential) Menu £ 15/18 – Carte £ 22/33
◆ 16C former hunting lodge: characterful interior includes books, ornaments and original terracotta tiles. Worldwide influences smoothly underpin modern British cooking.

BAWBURGH – Norfolk – 504 X 26 – see Norwich

BEACONSFIELD – Bucks. – 504 S 29 – pop. 12 292 11 D3

London 26 m – Aylesbury 19 m – Oxford 32 m
Beaconsfield Seer Green, ☎ (01494) 676 545 .

at Wooburn Common Southwest : 3 ½ m. by A 40 – ✉ Beaconsfield

Chequers Inn
Kiln Lane, Southwest : 1 m. on Bourne End rd ✉ HP10 0JQ – ☎ (01628) 529 575 – info@chequers-inn.com – Fax (01628) 850 125
17 rm – †£ 83 ††£ 108 – **Rest** – (Closed dinner 25 December and 1 January) Menu £ 20 – Carte £ 27/41
◆ Attractive red brick 17C inn with cosy beamed bar and spacious, stylish lounge. Good-sized bedrooms; one with four poster. Formal restaurant serves modern English dishes.

BEADNELL – Northd. – 501 P 17 24 B1

London 341 m – Edinburgh 81 m – Newcastle upon Tyne 47 m

Beach Court without rest — Beadnell Bay, P VISA

Harbour Rd ✉ NE67 5BJ – ✆ (01665) 720225 – info@beachcourt.com – Fax (01665) 721499 – closed Christmas-New Year

3 rm – ♦£75 ♦♦£99/139, £5.95

◆ Turreted house enjoys fine views of Beadnell Bay. Simple, traditional en suite rooms; leafy little conservatory. Hospitable owners with a real enthusiasm for entertaining.

BEAMHURST – Staffs. – see Uttoxeter

BEAMINSTER – Dorset – 503 L 31 – pop. 2 791 3 B3

London 154 m – Exeter 45 m – Taunton 30 m – Weymouth 29 m

Chedington Court South Perrott, ✆ (01935) 891413.

Bridge House — P VISA AE

3 Prout Bridge ✉ DT8 3AY – ✆ (01308) 862200 – enquiries@bridge-house.co.uk – Fax (01308) 863700

14 rm – ♦£ 82/106 ♦♦£ 170/180 – **Rest** – (closed Monday-Tuesday November-April) (residents only Sunday and Monday dinner) Menu £14/32 – Carte £32/42

◆ Priest's house reputed to date back to the 1200s. Large bedrooms, in the new block, with cheerful floral fabrics. Firelit lounge, charming walled garden, informal, rural feel. Oak beamed restaurant with conservatory.

BEARSTED – Kent – 504 V 30 – see Maidstone

BEAULIEU – Hants. – 503 P 31 – ✉ Brockenhurst *Great Britain* 6 B2

London 102 m – Bournemouth 24 m – Southampton 13 m – Winchester 23 m

Town★★ - National Motor Museum★★ **AC**

Buckler's Hard★ (Maritime Museum★ **AC**) SE : 2 m

Montagu Arms — P VISA AE

Palace Lane ✉ SO42 7ZL – ✆ (01590) 612324 – reservations@montaguarmshotel.co.uk – Fax (01590) 612188

18 rm – ♦£135 ♦♦£190 – 4 suites

Rest *Terrace* – Menu £22/45

Rest *Monty's Brasserie* – Carte £20/30

◆ Ivy-covered 18C inn. Bedrooms, in various shapes and sizes, can't quite match the warmth of the inviting panelled lounge with log fires, but are tidy with useful mod cons. A pretty garden adjoins panelled Terrace. Monty's is bright, warm brasserie.

at Bucklers Hard South : 2½ m. – ✉ Brockenhurst

Master Builder's House — P VISA AE

✉ SO42 7XB – ✆ (01590) 616253 – res@themasterbuilders.co.uk – Fax (01590) 616297

23 rm – ♦£99/140 ♦♦£189/254 – 2 suites

Rest *Riverview* – Menu £20/30 – Carte £29/36

◆ In 18C village, once home to the master shipwright. Lounge boasts inglenook, restored with easy country house style. Rooms in the old house have naval prints and sea chests. Riverview is smartly set by Beaulieu River.

BEAUMONT – C.I. – see Channel Islands

A good night's sleep without spending a fortune?
Look for a Bib Hotel

ENGLAND

BEDFORD

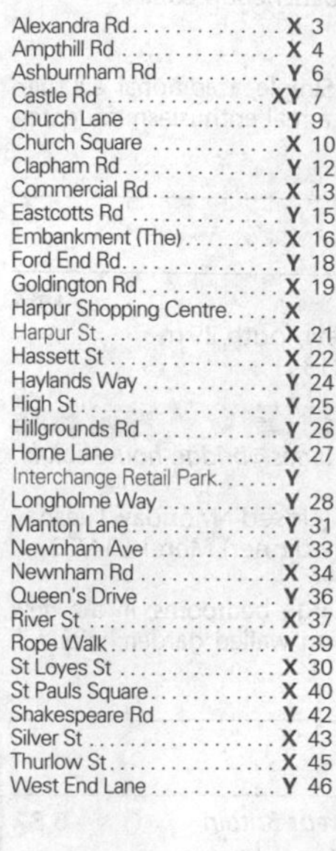

Alexandra Rd . . . . X 3
Ampthill Rd . . . . X 4
Ashburnham Rd . . . . Y 6
Castle Rd . . . . XY 7
Church Lane . . . . Y 9
Church Square . . . . X 10
Clapham Rd . . . . Y 12
Commercial Rd . . . . X 13
Eastcotts Rd . . . . Y 15
Embankment (The) . . . . X 16
Ford End Rd. . . . . Y 18
Goldington Rd . . . . X 19
Harpur Shopping Centre. X
Harpur St . . . . X 21
Hassett St . . . . X 22
Haylands Way . . . . Y 24
High St . . . . Y 25
Hillgrounds Rd . . . . Y 26
Horne Lane . . . . X 27
Interchange Retail Park. . . . . . Y
Longholme Way . . . . Y 28
Manton Lane . . . . Y 31
Newnham Ave . . . . Y 33
Newnham Rd . . . . X 34
Queen's Drive . . . . Y 36
River St . . . . X 37
Rope Walk . . . . Y 39
St Loyes St . . . . X 30
St Pauls Square . . . . X 40
Shakespeare Rd . . . . Y 42
Silver St . . . . X 43
Thurlow St . . . . X 45
West End Lane . . . . Y 46

A 6
Tavistock St
Union St.
Foster Hill Rd
De Parys Av.
Kimbolton Rd
A 428
Bromham Rd
Greyfriars
Dame Alice St.
St Peters St.
ST PETERS
High St.
Mill Street
HARPUR SHOPPING CENTRE
POL
Midland Rd
ST PAUL'S
Prebend St.
Great Ouse
River
ST MARYS
St. Marys St.
Cardington Rd
Street
Kingsway
St. John's St.
ST JOHN'S
Rope Walk
Cauldwell St.
ST-JOHNS
(A 428) (A 6)
X
200 m
200 yards

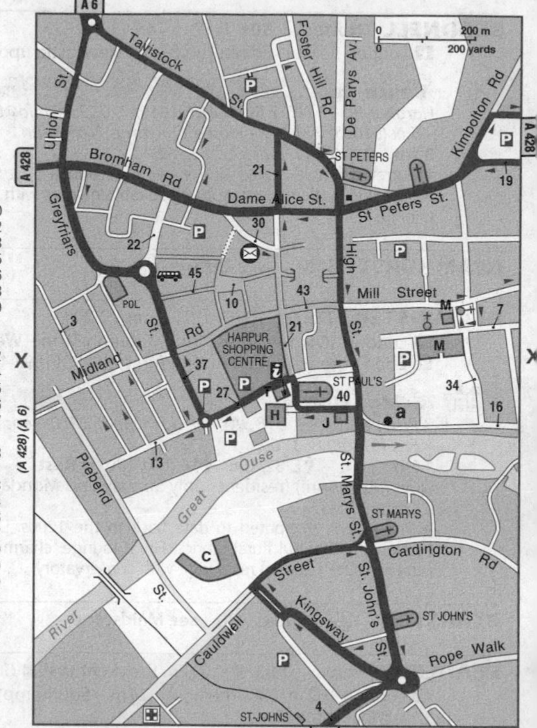

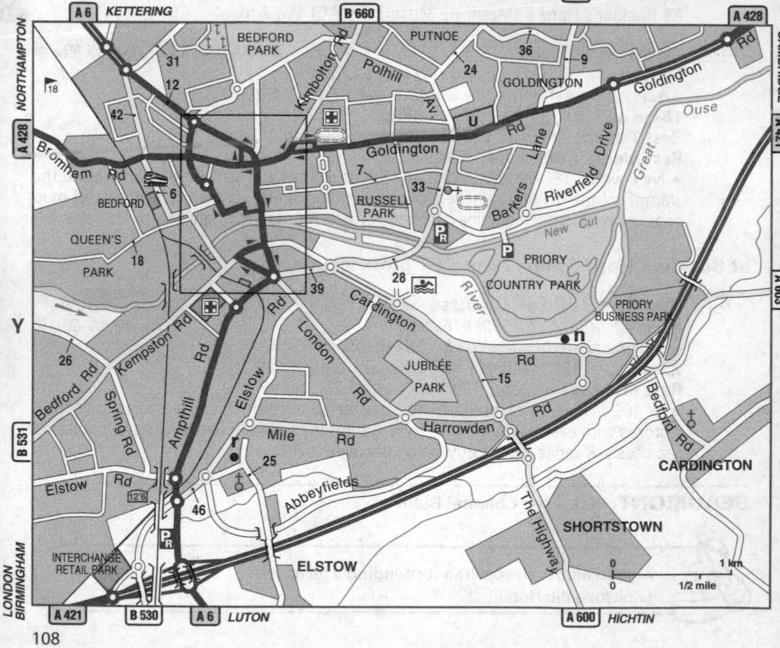

A 6 KETTERING
B 660
A 428
NORTHAMPTON
BEDFORD PARK
PUTNOE
Kimbolton Rd
Polhill Av.
GOLDINGTON
Goldington Rd
Bromham Rd
BEDFORD
RUSSELL PARK
Barkers Lane
Riverfield Drive
Great Ouse
New Cut
QUEEN'S PARK
PRIORY COUNTRY PARK
River
PRIORY BUSINESS PARK
Cardington Rd
London Rd
Kempston Rd
Ampthill Rd
Elstow Rd
JUBILEE PARK
Bedford Rd
Spring Rd
Mile Rd
Harrowden Rd
Bedford Rd
CARDINGTON
Elstow Rd
Abbeyfields
The Highway
SHORTSTOWN
INTERCHANGE RETAIL PARK
ELSTOW
LONDON BIRMINGHAM
A 421
B 530
A 6 LUTON
A 600 HICHTIN
B 531
A 421
A 603
Y
1 km
1/2 mile

BEDFORD – Beds. – 504 S 27 – pop. 82 488 12 A1

London 59 m – Cambridge 31 m – Colchester 70 m – Leicester 51 m – Lincoln 95 m – Luton 20 m – Oxford 52 m – Southend-on-Sea 85 m

The Old Town Hall, St Paul's Sq (01234) 215226, tourisminfo@bedford.gov.uk

Bedfordshire Biddenham Bromham Rd, (01234) 261 669;

Mowsbury Kimbolton Rd, (01234) 771 041.

Plan opposite

The Barns

rm, P VISA AE

Cardington Rd, East : 2 m. on A 603 MK44 3SA – (0870) 609 61 08 – reservations.barns@foliohotels.com – Fax (01234) 273 102 Y **n**

49 rm – £ 99 £ 99/140, £10.50 – **Rest** – (Closed Saturday lunch) Menu £ 19 (lunch) – Carte £ 22/33

◆ Hotel set in three acres of gardens with spacious bedrooms and a delightful 13C tithe barn conversion; now a function room. Semi-split level dining room with views of the Great Ouse. Fish-based menu.

Bedford Swan

AC rest, P VISA AE

The Embankment MK40 1RW – (01234) 346 565 – info@bedfordswanhotel.co.uk – Fax (01234) 212 009 X **a**

113 rm – £ 60/99 £ 60/119, £11.95 – **Rest** – Menu £ 17/23 – Carte £ 17/35 **s**

◆ Impressive Georgian house built in 1794 for the 5th Duke of Bedford. Bedrooms split between main house and more modern in adjacent block. Beautiful Roman style indoor pool. Long, narrow dining room and pleasant terrace.

at Elstow South : 2 m. by A 6 – Bedford

XX

St Helena

P VISA AE

High St MK42 9XP – (01234) 344 848 – closed Christmas-New Year, Saturday lunch, Sunday and Monday Y **r**

Rest – Menu £ 27/35

◆ Delightful 16C house in mature gardens with intimate, personally-furnished bar, homely dining room and conservatory extension. Seasonally based menus and appetising specials.

at Houghton Conquest South : 6½ m. by A 6 - Y – Bedford

Knife and Cleaver

AC P VISA AE

The Grove MK45 3LA – (01234) 740 387 – info@knifeandcleaver.com – Fax (01234) 740 900 – Closed 27-30 December

9 rm – £ 59 £ 84 – **Rest** – Menu £ 17/24 – Carte £ 21/37

◆ Personally-run by long-established owners. Snug bar with Jacobean panelling and a relaxing feel; homely bedrooms in converted stables. Spacious conservatory overlooking garden. Seasonal, daily-changing menus with the emphasis on fresh fish.

BEELEY – Derbyshire – pop. 165 16 B1

London 160 m – Derby 26 m – Matlock 5 m

The Devonshire Arms with rm

P VISA AE

Devonshire Square DE4 2NR – (01629) 733 259 – enquiries@devonshirebeeley.co.uk – Fax (01629) 733 259

4 rm – £ 145 £ 165 – **Rest** – Carte £ 18/28

◆ Low ceilings, oak beams and inglenook fireplace, plus a brightly furnished modern extension. Dishes' seasonal ingredients come from the Chatsworth Estate. Stylish bedrooms.

We try to be as accurate as possible when giving room rates. But prices are susceptible to change, so please check rates when booking.

ENGLAND

BEESTON – Notts. – 502 Q 25 – see Nottingham

BELCHFORD – Lincs. – 502 T 24 – ✉ Horncastle 17 C1

London 169 m – Horncastle 5 m – Lincoln 28 m

The Blue Bell Inn

1 Main Rd ✉ LN9 6LQ – ✆ (01507) 533 602 – Closed 2nd and 3rd weeks January, 25 December, Sunday dinner and Monday

Rest – Carte £ 15/30

◆ A popular stop off for walkers on the Viking Way. Cosy and beamed, with cosy armchairs and a large blue bell hanging outside. Numerous blackboard menus hang above fire.

BELFORD – Northd. – 501 O 17 24 A1

London 335 m – Edinburgh 71 m – Newcastle upon Tyne 49 m

Belford South Rd, ✆ (01668) 213 323 .

Market Cross without rest

1 Church St ✉ NE70 7LS – ✆ (01668) 213 013 – details@marketcross.net

4 rm – †£ 40/70 ††£ 70/80

◆ 200 year-old stone house in rural town centre. Warmly decorated lounge, homely touches in tasteful bedrooms. Wide, locally inspired breakfast choice in cosy pine surroundings.

ENGLAND

BELPER – Derbs. – 502 P 24 – pop. 21 938 16 B2

London 141 m – Birmingham 59 m – Leicester 40 m – Manchester 55 m – Nottingham 17 m

Shottle Hall

White Lane, West : 4 m. by A 517 and B 5023 on Shottle rd ✉ DE56 2EB – ✆ (01773) 550 577 – relax@shottlehall.co.uk

8 rm – †£ 95/145 ††£ 210 – **Rest** – (closed Sunday dinner) Menu £ 20 (lunch) – Carte dinner £ 29/37

◆ Attractive country house offering high levels of comfort. Light, airy lounge; library and bar. Bedrooms are individually styled; some traditional, others more contemporary. The Orangery restaurant serves traditional as well as more adventurous dishes. Celestial décor.

at Shottle Northwest : 4 m. by A 517 – ✉ Belper

Dannah Farm

Bowmans Lane, North : ¼ m. by Alport rd ✉ DE56 2DR – ✆ (01773) 550 273 – reservations@dannah.co.uk – Fax (01773) 550 590 – closed 25-26 December

4 rm – †£ 75/85 ††£ 130/180 – 4 suites – **Rest** – (dinner only (booking essential) (set menu only) Menu £ 25

◆ Family-run converted farmhouse - part of a working farm. Spacious, contemporary bedrooms are diverse in style; the two level Studio suite includes hot tub and spiral staircase. Traditional, rustic restaurant.

BELTON – Leics. – see Loughborough

Undecided between two equivalent establishments?
Within each category, establishments are classified
in our order of preference.

BEPTON – W. Sussex – see Midhurst

BERKHAMSTED – Herts. – **504** S 28 – **pop. 18 800** *Great Britain* 12 **A2**

London 34 m – Aylesbury 14 m – St Albans 11 m

Whipsnade Wild Animal Park★ **AC**, N : 9½ m. on A 4251, B 4506 and B 4540

XX **The Pink Orchid**

333-337 High St ✉ HP4 1AL – ✆ (01442) 878 799 – closed 25-26 December and Monday

Rest – Thai Menu £ 10/30 – Carte £ 18/26 **s**

◆ Spacious restaurant on busy high street. Warm welcome and very professional service. Authentic Thai food on extensive menu, supplemented by daily specials.

X **Eatfish**

163-165 The High St ✉ HP4 3HB – ✆ (01442) 879 988 – info@eatfish.co.uk – Fax (01442) 879 977 – closed 25-26 December

Rest – Seafood Menu £ 10 (lunch) – Carte £ 26/68

◆ Well-run seafood restaurant with characterful, rustic feel; photos of Scottish produce and its suppliers on walls. Flexible menu, with large/smaller portions. Summer terrace.

Red = Pleasant. Look for the red X and symbols.

ENGLAND

BERWICK-UPON-TWEED – Northd. – **501** O 16 – **pop. 12 870** 24 **A1**

Great Britain

London 349 m – Edinburgh 57 m – Newcastle upon Tyne 63 m

106 Marygate ✆ (01289) 330733, tourism@berwick-upon-tweed.gov.uk

Goswick, ✆ (01289) 387 256 ;

Magdalene Fields, ✆ (01289) 306 130 .

Town★★ - Walls★

Foulden★, NW : 5 m. – Paxton House (Chippendale furniture★) **AC**, W : 5 m. by A 6105, A 1 and B 6461. St Abb's Head★★ (≤ ★), NW : 12 m. by A 1, A 1107 and B 6438 - SW : Tweed Valley★★ – Eyemouth Museum★ **AC**, N : 7½ m. by A 1 and A 1107 – Holy Island★ (Priory ruins★ **AC**, Lindisfarne Castle★ **AC**), SE : 9 m. by A 1167 and A 1 – Manderston★ (stables★), W : 13 m. by A 6105 - Ladykirk (Kirk o'Steil★), SW : 8½ m. by A 698 and B 6470

Sallyport

1 Sallyport, off Bridge St ✉ TD15 1EZ – ✆ (01289) 308 827 – info@sallyport.co.uk

6 rm – †£ 95/150 ††£ 95/150

Rest – (communal dining) Menu £ 24/35

◆ 17C Grade II listed house on cobbled alley. The bedrooms are a strong point: they boast a boutique style, with a high standard of facilities, and lots of homely extra touches. Characterful farmhouse kitchen style dining room.

West Coates

30 Castle Terrace, North : ¾ m. by Castlegate on Kelso rd ✉ TD15 1NZ – ✆ (01289) 309 666 – karenbrownwestcoates@yahoo.com – Fax (01289) 309 666 – closed Christmas-New Year

3 rm – †£ 60/70 ††£ 100

Rest – (dinner only) (by arrangement, communal dining) Menu £ 35

◆ Step off the train and you're practically at the front door of this personally run 19C house set in mature garden and grounds. Welcoming lounge; annex boasts pool and hot tub. Communal dining table; fine border ingredients are sourced.

BEVERLEY – East Riding – **502** S 22 – **pop. 29 110** – 23 **D2**
✉ **Kingston-upon-Hull** *Great Britain*

London 188 m – Kingston-upon-Hull 8 m – Leeds 52 m – York 29 m
34 Butcher Row ✆ (01482) 867430, beverley.tic@eastriding.gov.uk
The Westwood, ✆ (01482) 868 757 .
Town★ - Minster★★ – St Mary's Church★

at Tickton **Northeast : 3½ m. by A 1035** – ✉ **Kingston-upon-Hull**

Tickton Grange

Tickton, Northeast : 3¾ m. on A 1035 ✉ HU17 9SH – ✆ (01964) 543 666 – info@ticktongrange.co.uk – Fax (01964) 542 556
17 rm – †£ 90 ††£ 120
Rest *Squires Dining Room* – Menu £ 21/39 – Carte approx. £ 38
◆ Carefully renovated bedrooms blend Georgian and contemporary architecture, antique and period-inspired furniture. Richly swagged fabrics and open fires in an inviting lounge. Dine in the Georgian style; large bay windows look out onto the lawn.

at South Dalton **Northwest : 5 m. by A 164 and B 1248** – ✉ **Beverley**

The Pipe and Glass Inn

West End ✉ HU17 7PN – ✆ (01430) 810 246 – email@pipeandglass.co.uk – Fax (01430) 810 246 – Closed 2 weeks January
Rest – (closed Sunday dinner and Monday) Carte £ 21/28
◆ Resurrected 18C inn benefitting from injection of money, time and effort. Snug bar, stylish sitting area, and restaurant serving tasty, seasonal food with East Riding accent.

ENGLAND

The sun's out – let's eat alfresco!
Look for a terrace:

BEYTON – Suffolk – **504** W 27 – **see Bury St Edmunds**

BIBURY – Glos. – **503** O 28 – ✉ **Cirencester** *Great Britain* 4 **D1**

London 86 m – Gloucester 26 m – Oxford 30 m
Village★

The Swan

✉ GL7 5NW – ✆ (01285) 740 695 – info@swanhotel.co.uk – Fax (01285) 740 473
18 rm – †£ 180 ††£ 265 – 3 suites
Rest *Gallery* – (closed 25 and 31 December to non residents) (dinner only) Menu £ 18/30
Rest *Café Swan* – Menu £ 18/30
◆ Ivy-clad 17C coaching inn with private gardens; idyllic location by a trout stream. Comfortable rooms in pretty country style, some with canopied beds. Gallery is formally stylish and spacious. Café Swan is a brasserie with stone-flagged courtyard.

Cotteswold House without rest

Arlington, on B 4425 ✉ GL7 5ND – ✆ (01285) 740 609 – enquiries@cotteswoldhouse.org.uk – Fax (01285) 740 609
3 rm – †£ 48 ††£ 68
◆ Set in a manicured garden outside the picturesque village. Simple, spotless and modestly priced bedrooms, comprehensively remodelled behind a Victorian façade. Non smoking.

BIDDENDEN – Kent – 504 V 30 – pop. 2 205 Great Britain 9 C2

London 52 m – Ashford 13 m – Maidstone 16 m

Bodiam Castle★★, S : 10 m. by A 262, A 229 and B 2244 – Sissinghurst Garden★, W : 3 m. by A 262 – Battle Abbey★, S : 20 m. by A 262, A 229, A 21 and A 2100

Barclay Farmhouse without rest

Woolpack Corner, South : ½ m. by A 262 on Benenden rd ✉ TN27 8BQ – ✆ (01580) 292 626 – info@barclayfarmhouse.co.uk – Fax (01580) 292 288

3 rm – †£ 60 ††£ 75

◆ Set in an acre of pleasant garden: well-priced, very comfortable accommodation with fine French oak flooring and furniture. Inventive breakfasts in granary or barn conversion.

Bishopsdale Oast

South : 3 m. by A 262 and Benenden rd on Tenterden rd ✉ TN27 8DR – ✆ (01580) 291 027 – drysdale@bishopsdaleoast.co.uk – closed Christmas

5 rm – †£ 57 ††£ 83 – **Rest** – (by arrangement, communal dining) Menu £ 29

◆ Extended oast house in four acres of mature grounds with wild flower garden. Comfy lounge with log fire; plenty of trinkets and books in bright, clean, good sized rooms. Family size dining table; interesting meals employ home-grown, organic produce.

The West House (Graham Garrett)

28 High St ✉ TN27 8AH – ✆ (01580) 291 341 – thewesthouse@btconnect.com – Fax (01580) 291 341 – closed Christmas-New Year, 2 weeks in summer, Saturday lunch, Sunday dinner and Monday

Rest – Menu £ 24/30

Spec. Poached egg, oxtail sauce and truffle. Grilled John Dory, fennel salad, sauce Maltaise. Rhubarb and vanilla panna cotta, ginger madeleine.

◆ Pretty part 16C former weavers' cottages in picturesque village. Charming beamed interior with inglenook and modern artwork. Concise seasonal menu; assured, precise cooking.

The Three Chimneys

Hareplain Road, West : 1 ½ m. off A 262 ✉ TN27 8LW – ✆ (01580) 291 472 – Closed 25 and 31 December

Rest – (booking essential) Carte £ 22/33

◆ 15C pub with coir mat, yellow walls, dried hops, characterful original beams. Smart rear restaurant facing garden. Tasty, regularly changing menus: home-made puds of renown.

Your opinions are important to us:
please write and let us know about your discoveries and experiences – good and bad!

BIDEFORD – Devon – 503 H 30 – pop. 16 262 2 C1

London 231 m – Exeter 43 m – Plymouth 58 m – Taunton 60 m

to Lundy Island (Lundy Co. Ltd) (1 h 45 mn)

Victoria Park, The Quay ✆ (01237) 477676, bidefordtic@torridge.gov.uk

Royal North Devon Westward Ho Golf Links Rd, ✆ (01237) 473 824 ;

Torrington Weare Trees, ✆ (01805) 622 229 .

Bridge★★ – Burton Art Gallery★ **AC**

Appledore★, N : 2 m. Clovelly★★, W : 11 m. by A 39 and B 3237 – Lundy Island★★, NW : by ferry - Rosemoor★ – Great Torrington (Dartington Crystal★ **AC**) SE : 7 ½ m. by A 386

ENGLAND

Yeoldon House

Durrant Lane, Northam, North : 1½ m. by B 3235 off A 386 ✉ EX39 2RL – ✆ (01237) 474400 – yeoldonhouse@aol.com – Fax (01237) 476618 – closed Christmas

10 rm – †£ 70/75 ††£ 125

Rest – (closed Sunday) (dinner only) (booking essential for non-residents) Menu £ 30 **s**

◆ Privately run 19C house with lovely gardens overlooking the Torridge. Comfortable lounge bar with books, dried flowers and curios. Period-style rooms, some with balconies. Smart restaurant overlooking river.

Memories

8 Fore St, Northam, North : 2 m. by B 3235 off A 386 ✉ EX39 1AW – ✆ (01237) 473419 – Fax (01237) 473419 – closed 1 week September, 24-26 December and Sunday-Tuesday

Rest – (dinner only) Menu £ 20 – Carte £ 20/27

◆ Simple, blue and white painted restaurant with vibrant local ambience. Enthusiastic owners serve well-prepared, traditional menus at a reasonable price.

at Instow North : 3 m. by A 386 on B 3233 – ✉ Bideford

ENGLAND

Commodore

Appledore and Torridge estuary,

Marine Parade ✉ EX39 4JN – ✆ (01271) 860347 – admin@commodore-instow.co.uk – Fax (01271) 861233

25 rm (dinner included) – †£ 76/96 ††£ 153/180

Rest – (bar lunch Monday-Saturday) Menu £ 28

◆ Extended former gentleman's residence, family run in a friendly spirit for over 30 years. Trim, comfy accommodation: front-facing balcony rooms overlook the estuary. Immaculate, classically styled dining room.

Decks

Appledore and Torridge estuary,

Marine Parade ✉ EX39 4JJ – ✆ (01271) 860671 – decks@instow.net – Fax (01271) 860820 – closed 1 week October, 1 week December, 25 December and Sunday-Monday

Rest – Menu £ 25 (dinner) – Carte £ 18/29

◆ Sit on the outside deck and watch the sun go down over Appledore. Enjoy accomplished modern dishes while contemplating the wacky murals. Superb views from all vantage points.

BIGBURY – Devon – 503 I 33 — 2 C3

London 195 m – Exeter 41 m – Plymouth 22 m

Kingsbridge★, E : 13 m. by B 3392 and A 379

The Oyster Shack

Milburn Orchard Farm, Stakes Hill, East : 1 m. on Easton rd ✉ TQ7 4BE – ✆ (01548) 810876 – bigbury@oystershack.co.uk

Rest – Seafood (booking essential) Carte £ 23/32

◆ Eccentric venue, half a lovely covered terrace, decorated with fishing nets. Seafood, particularly local oyster dishes; classic and modern dishes using the freshest produce.

The ✿ award is the crème de la crème. This is awarded to restaurants which are really worth travelling miles for!

BIGBURY-ON-SEA – Devon – 503 I 33 – ✉ Kingsbridge 2 C3

London 196 m – Exeter 42 m – Plymouth 23 m

Burgh Island – Bigbury Bay,

South : ½ m. by sea tractor ✉ TQ7 4BG – ✆ (01548) 810 514 – reception@burghisland.com – Fax (01548) 810 243

13 rm – ♦£ 285 ♦♦£ 355 – 11 suites – ♦♦£ 355/550

Rest – (booking essential for non-residents) Menu £ 38/55

◆ Unique Grade II listed 1930s country house in private island setting: stylishly romantic Art Deco interior. Charmingly individual rooms with views: some have fantastic style. Ballroom dining: dress in black tie. Owners pride themselves on accomplished cooking.

Henley – Bigbury Bay and Bolt Tail,

Folly Hill ✉ TQ7 4AR – ✆ (01548) 810 240 – thehenleyhotel@btconnect.com – Fax (01548) 810 240 – March-October

6 rm – ♦£ 60/65 ♦♦£ 100/124

Rest – (dinner only) (booking essential for non-residents) Menu £ 30 s

◆ Personally run cottage of 16C origin. Stunning views of the bay and Bolt Tail from modern conservatory with deep wicker chairs and pleasant, individual rooms in pastel tones. Homely dining room with magnificent sea views.

ENGLAND

BIGGLESWADE – Beds. – 504 T 27 – pop. 15 383 12 B1

London 46 m – Bedford 12 m – Luton 24 m

at Old Warden West : 3 ½ m. by A 6001 off B 658 – ✉ Biggleswade 12 A1

Hare & Hounds

The Village ✉ SG18 9HQ – ✆ (01767) 627 225 – thehareandhounds@hotmail.co.uk – Fax (01767) 627 588 – Closed 2 weeks in January and 25 December

Rest – (closed Sunday dinner and Monday except Bank Holiday) Carte £ 22/30

◆ Picture postcard village pub with mature gardens, warm atmosphere and immense charm and style. Locally sourced ingredients. Regularly changing British menu. Attentive service.

BILBROUGH – N. Yorks. – 502 Q 22 23 C2

The Three Hares Country Inn

Main St ✉ YO23 3PH – ✆ (01937) 832 128 – info@thethreehares.co.uk – Fax (01937) 834 626 – Closed Monday

Rest – Carte £ 21/30

◆ Immaculately extended inn with 18C origins. There are four different rooms in which to dine: menus, featuring much that is local, mix Yorkshire staples and modish invention.

The red symbol?
This denotes the very essence of peace
– only the sound of birdsong first thing in the morning …

BILDESTON – Suffolk – **504** W 27 15 **C3**

London 85 m – Bury St Edmunds 18 m – Ipswich 15 m

The Bildeston Crown with rm

104 High Street ✉ *IP7 7EB* – ☎ *(01449) 740 510 – info@thebildestoncrown.co.uk – Fax (01449) 741 843*

10 rm – †£ 70 ††£ 170 – **Rest** – Menu £ 20 – Carte £ 22/37

◆ Stylishly modernised pub with 15C roots, typified by beamed bar and inglenook. Dining room merges period and modern decor. Elaborate or classic dishes. Delightful bedrooms.

BILLESLEY – Warks. – see Stratford-upon-Avon

BILLINGSHURST – W. Sussex – **504** S 30 – **pop. 5 465** 7 **C2**

London 44 m – Brighton 24 m – Guildford 25 m – Portsmouth 40 m

Old Wharf without rest

Wharf Farm, Newbridge, Wisborough Green, West : 1 ¾ m. on A 272 ✉ *RH14 OJG* – ☎ *(01403) 784 096 – david.mitchell@farming.co.uk – Fax (01403) 784 096 – closed 2 weeks Christmas-New Year*

3 rm – †£ 70 ††£ 100

◆ Charming touches to former 19C canalside warehouse: antiques, dried flowers and brimming bookshelves. Breakfast in farmhouse kitchen; cosy country house rooms overlook water.

ENGLAND

BILSBORROW – Lancs. – see Garstang

BINGHAM – Notts. – **502** R 25 – **pop. 8 658** 16 **B2**

London 125 m – Leicester 26 m – Lincoln 28 m – Nottingham 11 m – Sheffield 35 m

Yeung Sing

Market St ✉ *NG13 8AB* – ☎ *(01949) 831 222 – info@yeungsing.com – Fax (01949) 838 833 – closed 25-26 December*

Rest – Chinese (closed lunch Monday-Wednesday) Menu £ 17 (dinner) – Carte £ 21/25

◆ Long-standing, family-owned restaurant with lounge and bar, serving authentic Cantonese and regional Chinese cuisine. Deep red décor, carved wood and huge 3D dragons on walls.

BINGLEY – W. Yorks. – **502** O 22 – **pop. 19 884** – ✉ **Bradford** 22 **B2**

London 204 m – Bradford 6 m – Leeds 15 m – Skipton 13 m

St Ives Est., ☎ (01274) 562 436 .

Five Rise Locks

Beck Lane, via Park Rd ✉ *BD16 4DD* – ☎ *(01274) 565 296 – info@five-rise-locks.co.uk – Fax (01274) 568 828*

9 rm – †£ 50/60 ††£ 75 – **Rest** – (dinner only and Sunday lunch) (residents only Sunday and Monday) Carte £ 17/25

◆ Neat mid-Victorian house named after the locks on the nearby Leeds-Liverpool canal. Cheerful, modern, individuallly styled rooms, some with views of the distant dales. Well-kept dining room employs local produce on menus.

BINLEY – W. Mids. – see Coventry

BIRCHOVER – Derbs. – see Matlock

BIRKENHEAD – Mersey. – **502** K 23 – **pop. 83 729** 20 **A3**

London 222 m – Liverpool 2 m
Access Mersey Tunnels (toll)
to Liverpool and Wallasey (Mersey Ferries) frequent services daily
Woodside Ferry Booking Hall ✆ (0151) 647 6780, touristinfo@wirral.gov.uk
Arrowe Park Woodchurch, ✆ (0151) 677 1527 ;
Prenton Golf Links Rd, ✆ (0151) 609 3426 .

Plan : see Liverpool p. 3

River Hill

Talbot Rd, Oxton, Southwest : 2 ¼ m. by A 552 on B 5151 ✉ CH43 2HJ – ✆ (0151) 653 3773 – reception@theriverhill.co.uk – Fax (0151) 653 7162
15 rm – †£ 70/75 ††£ 90, £8.95 – **Rest** – (dinner only and Sunday lunch) Menu £ 16/19 – Carte £ 20/39
◆ Imposing redbrick Victorian house with purpose-built extension. Sizeable lounge and bar. Spacious, characterful rooms with chintz décor and fabrics. Carefully tended garden adjoins restaurant.

Fraiche

11 Rose Mount, Oxton, Southwest : 2 ¼ m. by A 552 and B 5151 ✉ CH43 5SG – ✆ (0151) 652 2914 – contact@restaurantfraiche.com – Closed 2 weeks August, 1 week January, 25 December, Sunday and Monday
Rest – (booking essential) Menu £ 22/38
◆ Smart, intimate restaurant enhanced by modern artwork and coloured glassware. Innovative flavour combinations and eye-catching presentation. Attentive, well-paced service.

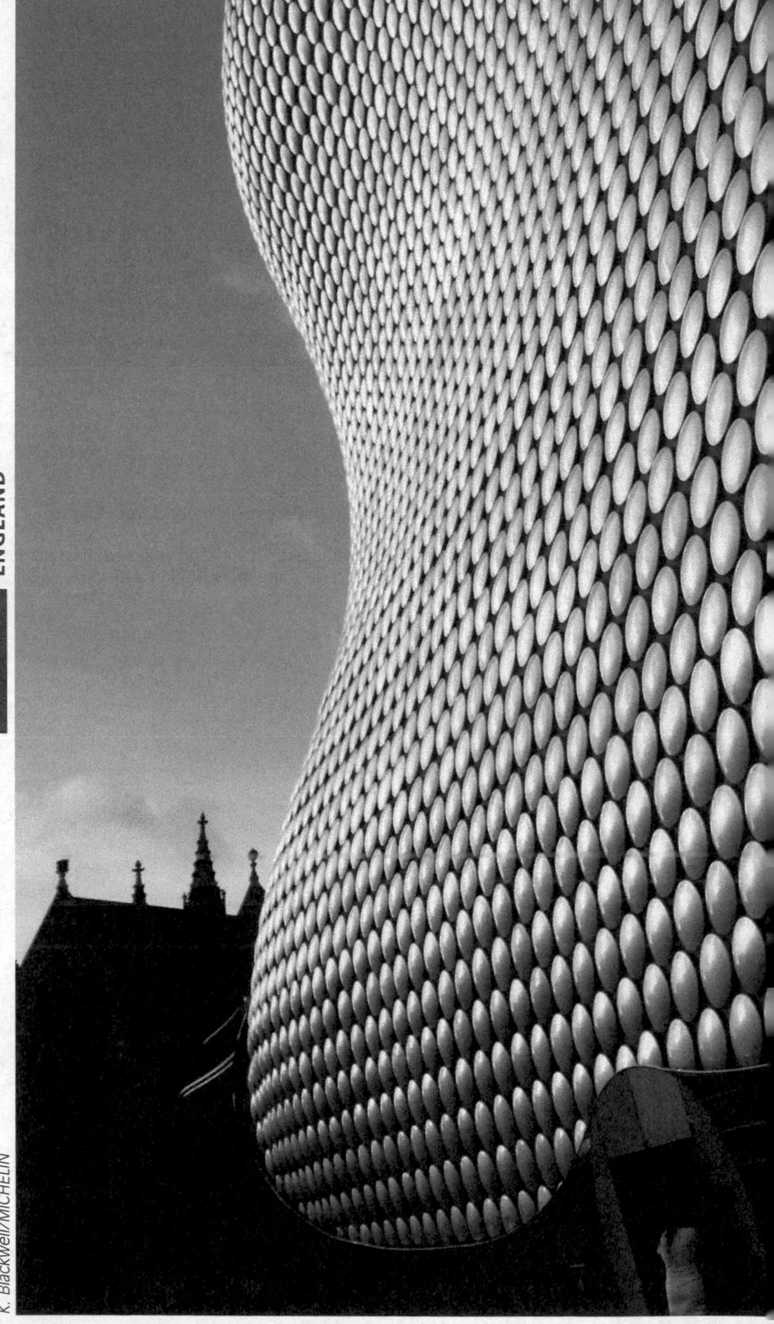

K. Blackwell/MICHELIN

BIRMINGHAM

County: W. Mids.
Michelin REGIONAL map: n° 503 O 26
London 122 m – Bristol 91 m – Liverpool 103 m – Manchester 86 m – Nottingham 50 m

Population: 970 892
Great Britain

19 **C2**

PRACTICAL INFORMATION

Tourist Information

The Rotunda, 150 New St ℘ (0870) 225 0127, (0121) 616 1038

Tourism Centre, National Exhibition Centre ℘ (0121) 202 5099

Airport

Birmingham International Airport: ℘ (08707) 335511, E: 6 ½ m. by A 45 DU

Golf Courses

18 Edgbaston Church Rd, ℘ (0121) 454 1736 ;

18 Hilltop Handsworth Park Lane, ℘ (0121) 554 4463 ;

18 Hatchford Brook Sheldon Coventry Rd, ℘ (0121) 743 9821 ;

18 Brandhall Warley Heron Rd, Oldbury, ℘ (0121) 552 2195 ;

9 Harborne Church Farm Harborne Vicarage Rd, ℘ (0121) 427 1204.

SIGHTS

IN TOWN

City★ – Museum and Art Gallery★★ LY **M2** – Barber Institute of Fine Arts★★ (at Birmingham University) EX **U** – Cathedral of St Philip (stained glass portrayals★) LMY – Millennium Point FV

ON THE OUTSKIRTS

Aston Hall★★ FV **M**

IN THE SURROUNDING AREA

Black Country Museum★ , Dudley, NW: 10 m. by A 456 and A 4123 AU – Bournville★ , SW: 4 m. on A 38 and A 441

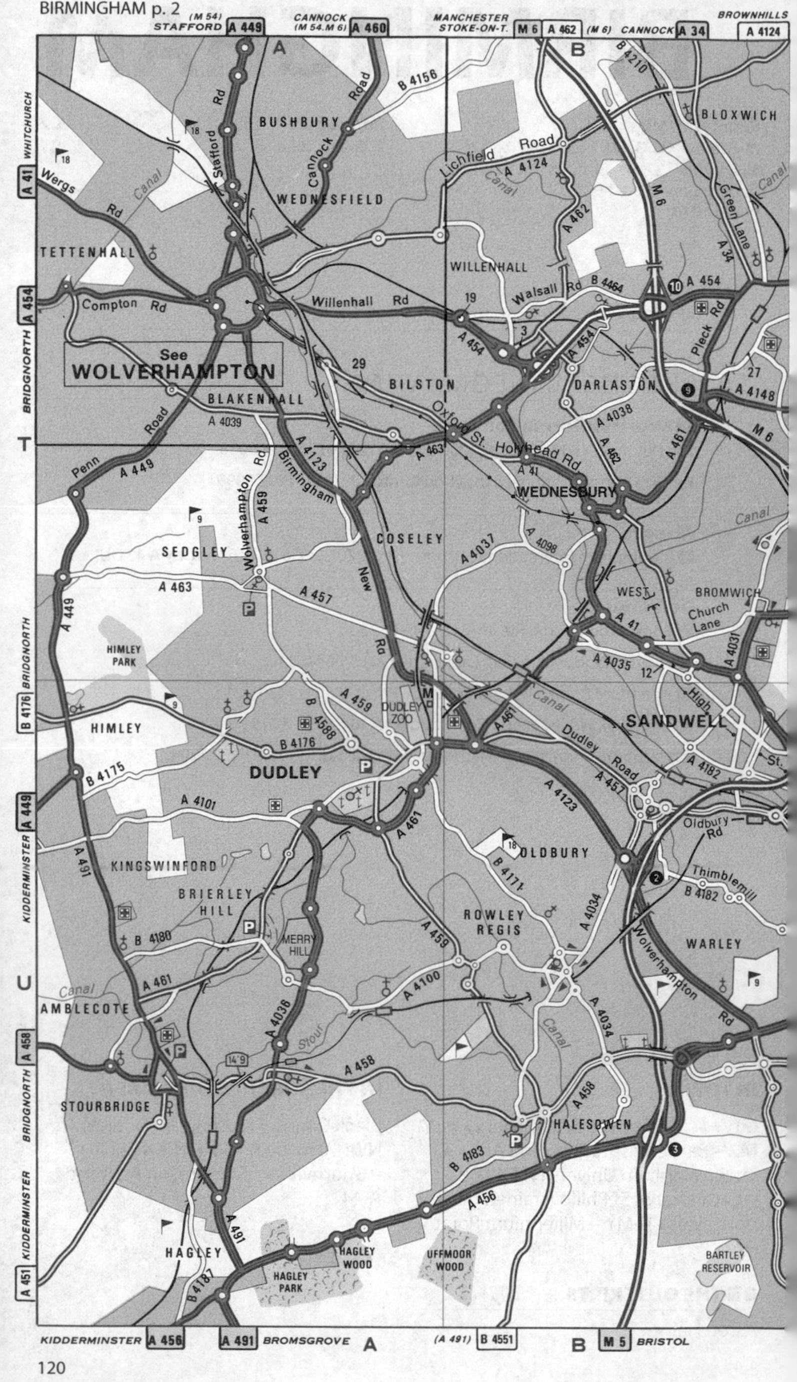
(M 54) STAFFORD A 449
CANNOCK (M 54.M 6) A 460
MANCHESTER STOKE-ON-T. M 6 A 462 (M 6) CANNOCK A 34
BROWNHILLS A 4124
WHITCHURCH A 41
BRIDGNORTH A 454
BRIDGNORTH B 4176
KIDDERMINSTER A 449
BRIDGNORTH A 458
KIDDERMINSTER A 451
KIDDERMINSTER A 456
A 491 BROMSGROVE
(A 491) B 4551
M 5 BRISTOL
BUSHBURY
WEDNESFIELD
BLOXWICH
TETTENHALL
WILLENHALL
See WOLVERHAMPTON
BLAKENHALL
BILSTON
DARLASTON
WEDNESBURY
SEDGLEY
COSELEY
WEST BROMWICH
HIMLEY PARK
HIMLEY
DUDLEY
DUDLEY ZOO
SANDWELL
KINGSWINFORD
BRIERLEY HILL
MERRY HILL
OLDBURY
ROWLEY REGIS
WARLEY
AMBLECOTE
STOURBRIDGE
HALESOWEN
HAGLEY
HAGLEY WOOD
HAGLEY PARK
UFFMOOR WOOD
BARTLEY RESERVOIR
Wergs Rd
Compton Rd
Stafford Rd
Cannock Road
Lichfield Road
Willenhall Rd
Walsall Rd
Green Lane
Pleck Rd
Penn Road
Wolverhampton Rd
Birmingham New Rd
Oxford St.
Holyhead Rd
Church Lane
High St.
Dudley Road
Oldbury Rd
Thimblemill
Wolverhampton Rd
Canal
Stour
A
B
T
U

BIRMINGHAM AND WOLVERHAMPTON

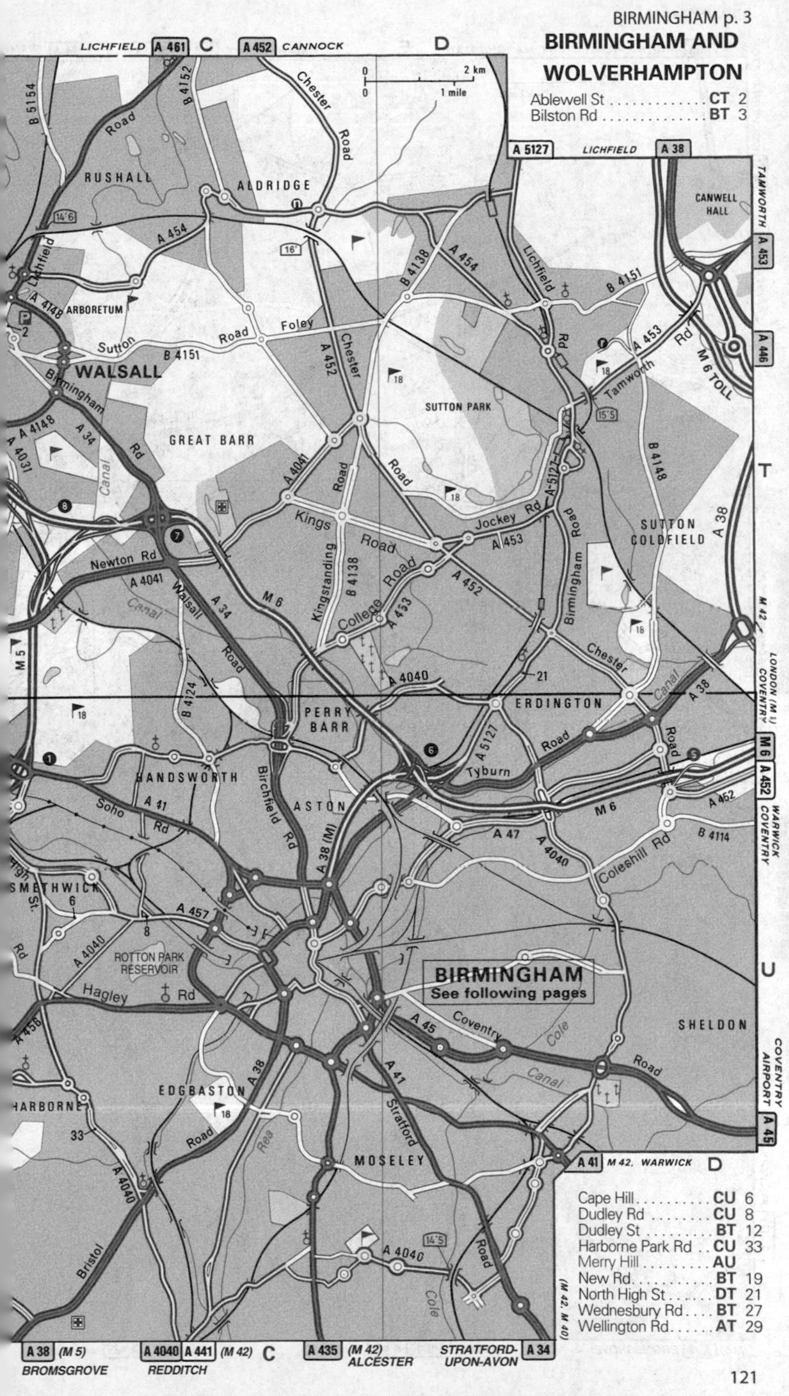

M 5 (M6), STOKE-ON-TRENT, MANCHESTER
CANNOCK. (M6) A 34 A 453
M 6 TRENT
A 41 WOLVERHAMPTON
M 5 BRISTOL
A 456 (M5). KIDDERMINSTER
A 4123 WOLVERHAMPTON
(M 5) A 38 BROMSGROVE
REDDITCH A4040 A 441 REDDITCH
A 435 ALCESTER
HANDSWORTH
PERRY BARR
ASTON
SMETHWICK
HARBORNE
EDGBASTON
MOSELEY
KING'S HEATH
Hockley Circus
ROTTON PARK RESERVOIR
MILLENNIUM POINT

G
A 5127 LICHFIELD
CANNOCK A 452
H
A 38
A 4040
ERDINGTON
GRAVELLY HILL JUNCTION
Wood End Rd
Hill
Bromford Lane
B 4148 Tyburn Rd
Chester Rd
Kingsbury Road
Canal
Gravelly
Tyburn
A 47
Newport Rd
CASTLE BROMWICH
B 4118
LONDON (M 1) COVENTRY
M 6
A 452
NUENATON
Road
M 6
Bromford Road
Rd
Bradford Rd
Aston Church Rd
Heath
Coleshill
Bromford Lane
Washwood
Highfield Rd
Road
Cole
V
Alum Rock Rd
31
SALTLEY
Rock Rd
Stechford
La.
Bowyer Rd
Alum
Station Rd
Road
Bordesley Green Rd
Bordesley
Green
Green
Cattell Rd
Bordesley
Sheldon Heath Road
Church
YARDLEY
Stoney La
Small Heath
Coventry
Rd
Rd
A 45
Highway
Road
Church
Coventry
SHELDON
Church Road
Golden Hillock
Rd
X
Stoney Lane
Warwick
Road
A 4040 Stockfield Rd
Yardley
Wagon Lane
Sheaf La.
Rd
A 45
COVENTRY AIRPORT
Stratford
A 34
Road
25
87
Hob's Moat Rd
Yardley Rd
Shaftmoor Lane
Hollies
Olton Boulevard East
Richmond Road
College Rd
Cole
Wood
H
A 41 M 42, WARWICK
Rd
Fox
Road
Lane
Robin Hood
Highfield
Road
Shirley
74
Lane
Road
G
STRATFORD-UPON-AVON A 34

BIRMINGHAM

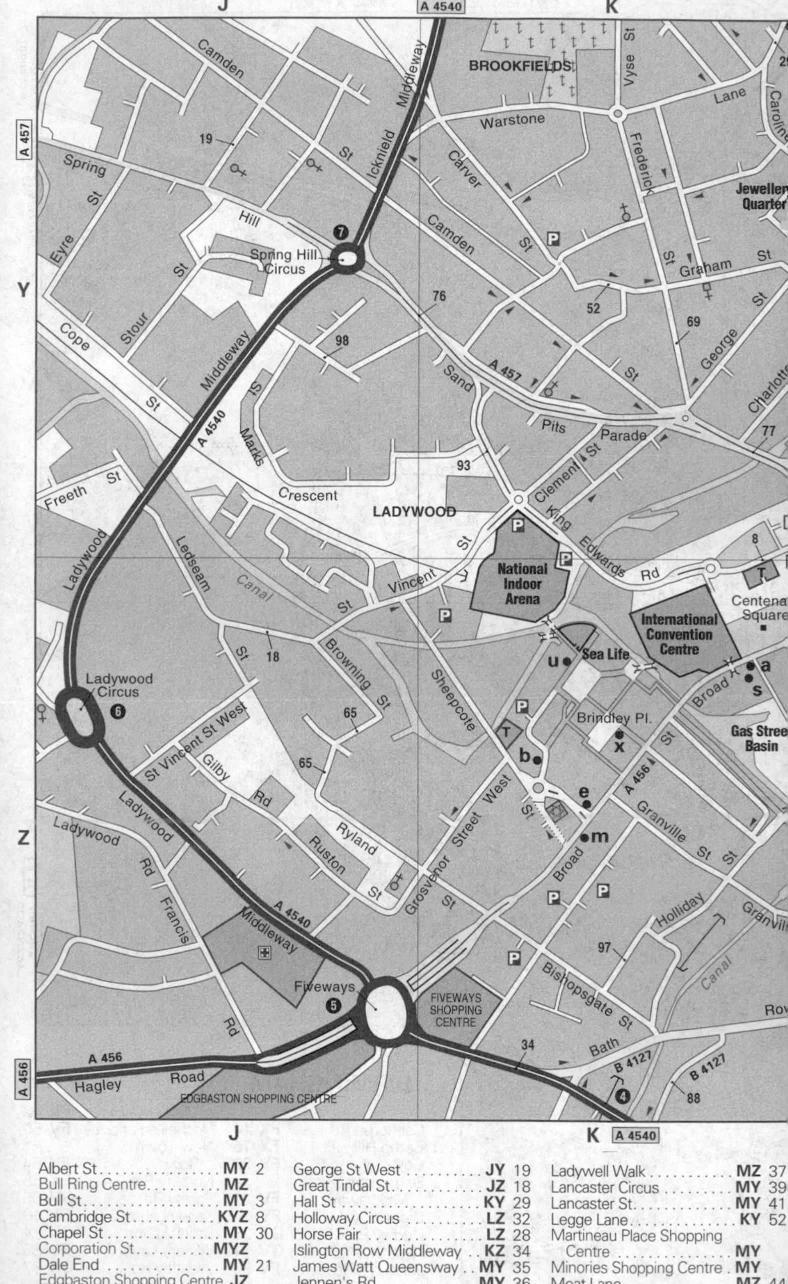
J
K
A 4540
Y
Z
A 457
A 456
BROOKFIELDS
Vyse St
Camden
Middleway
Icknield
St
Warstone
Lane
Caroline
19
Spring
St
Carver
Frederick
Jewellery Quarter
Hill
Camden
St
Eyre
Spring Hill Circus
St
Graham
St
76
52
69
George
St
Stour
98
Cope
St
Middleway
Sand
A 457
St
St
Marks
A 4540
Pits
Parade
Charlotte
77
93
Freeth
St
Crescent
Clement St
LADYWOOD
King Edwards Rd
8
Ladywood
LedsEam
Canal
St
Vincent
National Indoor Arena
Centenary Square
International Convention Centre
St
18
Browning St
Sheepcote
Sea Life
Ladywood Circus
St Vincent St West
65
Brindley Pl.
Broad St
Gas Street Basin
65
Gilby
Rd
Ryland
Ruston
St
Grosvenor Street West
St
A 456
Granville St
St
Ladywood
Ladywood
Rd
Francis
Broad
A 4540
Middleway
Holliday
Granville
97
Bishopsgate St
Canal
Fiveways
FIVEWAYS SHOPPING CENTRE
Rd
34
Bath
B 4127
B 4127
88
A 456
Hagley
Road
EDGBASTON SHOPPING CENTRE
J
K
A 4540

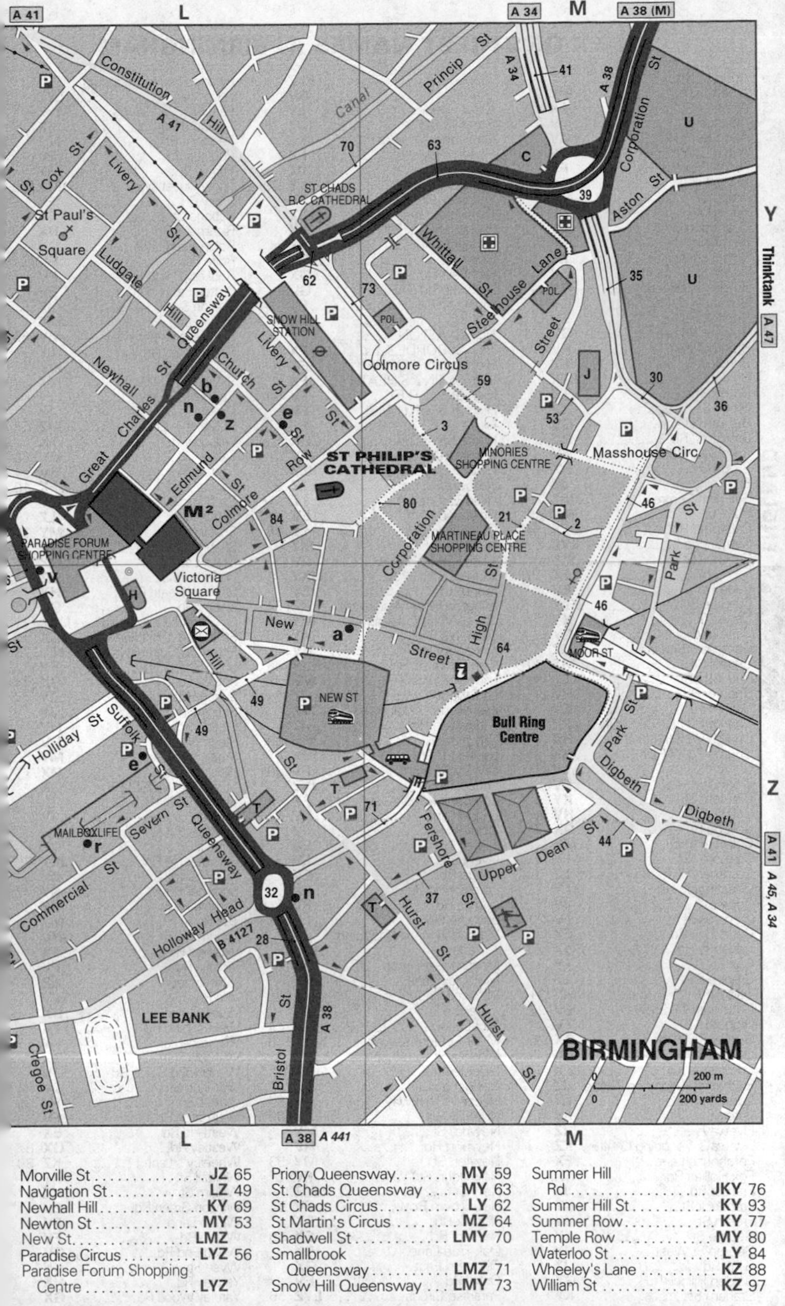
A 41
L
A 34
M
A 38 (M)
Constitution
Hill
A 41
Princip
St
Canal
St Paul's
Square
Cox
St
Livery
St
Ludgate
Hill
ST CHADS
R.C. CATHEDRAL
SNOW HILL
STATION
Colmore Circus
Whittall
St
Steelhouse
Lane
Corporation
St
Aston
St
Queensway
Church
Newhall
Great
Charles
St
Edmund
Colmore
Row
ST PHILIP'S
CATHEDRAL
MINORIES
SHOPPING CENTRE
Masshouse Circ.
MARTINEAU PLACE
SHOPPING CENTRE
PARADISE FORUM
SHOPPING CENTRE
Victoria
Square
New
Street
High
MOOR ST
NEW ST
Bull Ring
Centre
Holliday
Suffolk
Digbeth
MAILBOXLIFE
Severn
Commercial
Holloway
Head
B 4127
Fershore
Upper
Dean
Hurst
LEE BANK
Cregoe
Bristol
A 38
BIRMINGHAM
200 m
200 yards
Thinktank
A 47
A 41
A 45, A 34
Y
Z
A 38
A 441

INDEX OF STREET NAMES IN BIRMINGHAM

ENGLAND

Hyatt Regency

2 Bridge St ✉ B1 2JZ – ✆ (0121) 643 1234 – birmingham@hyattintl.com – Fax (0121) 616 2323 – closed 25-30 September KZ **a**

315 rm – ♦£ 199 ♦♦£ 199, ☕ £15.25 – 4 suites

Rest *Aria* – Menu £ 14/17 – Carte £ 25/41

♦ Striking mirrored exterior. Glass enclosed lifts offer panoramic views. Sizeable rooms with floor to ceiling windows. Covered link with International Convention Centre. Contemporary style restaurant in central atrium; modish cooking.

Radisson SAS

12 Holloway Circus ✉ B1 1BT – ✆ (0121) 654 6000 – info.birmingham@radissonsas.com – Fax (0161) 654 6001 LZ **n**

204 rm – ♦£ 135/205 ♦♦£ 135/205, ☕ £14.95 – 7 suites

Rest *Filini* – (Closed Saturday lunch and Sunday) Carte £ 20/48

♦ Occupies 18 uber-modern floors of a city centre skyscraper. Well-equipped business facilities; ultra stylish bedrooms in three distinctly slinky themes. Modern bar leads to airy, easy-going Italian restaurant, Filini.

Malmaison

Mailbox, 1 Wharfside St ✉ B1 1RD – ✆ (0121) 246 5000 – Fax (0121) 246 5002 LZ **e**

184 rm – ♦£ 150 ♦♦£ 150, ☕ £13.95 – 5 suites

Rest *Brasserie* – Menu £ 16 – Carte approx. £ 26

♦ Stylish, modern boutique hotel, forms centrepiece of Mailbox development. Stylish bar. Spacious contemporary bedrooms with every modern facility; superb petit spa. Brasserie serving contemporary French influenced cooking at reasonable prices.

ENGLAND

Hotel Du Vin

25 Church St ✉ B3 2NR – ✆ (0121) 200 0600 – info.birmingham@hotelduvin.com – Fax (0121) 236 0889 LY **e**

66 rm – ♦£ 150/185 ♦♦£ 150/185, ☕ £13.50

Rest *Bistro* – Menu £ 18 (lunch) – Carte £ 25/33

♦ Former 19C eye hospital in heart of shopping centre; has relaxed, individual, boutique style. Low lighting in rooms of muted tones: Egyptian cotton and superb bathrooms. Champagne in "bubble lounge"; Parisian style brasserie.

The Burlington

Burlington Arcade, 126 New St ✉ B2 4JQ – ✆ (0121) 643 9191 – general.burlington@macdonald-hotels.co.uk – Fax (0121) 628 5005 – Closed 25-26 December LZ **a**

110 rm ☕ – ♦£ 175 ♦♦£ 195 – 2 suites

Rest *Berlioz* – (dinner only) Menu £ 29 – Carte £ 30/43

♦ Approached by a period arcade. Restored Victorian former railway hotel retains much of its original charm. Period décor to bedrooms yet with fax, modem and voice mail. Elegant dining room: ornate ceiling, chandeliers and vast mirrors.

Copthorne

Paradise Circus ✉ B3 3HJ – ✆ (0121) 200 2727 – reservations.birmingham@mill-cop.com – Fax (0121) 200 1197 LZ **v**

209 rm – ♦£ 165 ♦♦£ 165, ☕ £15.75 – 3 suites

Rest *Turners Grill* – (closed Saturday lunch and Sunday) Menu £ 14 (lunch) – Carte £ 23/29

♦ Overlooking Centenary Square. Corporate hotel with extensive leisure club and cardiovascular gym. Cricket themed bar. Connoisseur rooms offer additional comforts. Flambé dishes offered in intimate Turner's Grill.

City Inn
1 Brunswick Sq, Brindley Pl ✉ B1 2HW – ☎ (0121) 643 1003 – birmingham.reservations@cityinn.com – Fax (0121) 643 1005 KZ **b**
238 rm – †£ 89/195 ††£ 99/205
Rest *City Café* – Menu £ 13/17 – Carte £ 17/35
◆ In heart of vibrant Brindley Place; the spacious atrium with bright rugs and blond wood sets the tone for equally stylish rooms. Corporate friendly with many meeting rooms. Eat in restaurant, terrace or bar.

TOTEL without rest
19 Portland Rd, Edgbaston ✉ B16 9HN – ☎ (0121) 454 5282 – info@toteluk.com – Fax (0121) 456 4668 EX **c**
1 rm – 9 suites – ††£ 75/105
◆ 19C house converted into comfortable, spacious fully-serviced apartments, individually styled with modern facilities. Friendly service. Continental breakfast served in room.

Novotel
70 Broad St ✉ B1 2HT – ☎ (0121) 643 2000 – h1077@accor.com – Fax (0121) 643 9786 KZ **e**
148 rm – †£ 155/175 ††£ 165/185 – **Rest** – Menu £ 20 **s** – Carte £ 21/28 **s**
◆ Well located for the increasingly popular Brindleyplace development. Underground parking. Modern, well-kept, branded bedrooms suitable for families. Modern, open-plan restaurant.

ENGLAND

Simpsons (Andreas Antona) with rm
20 Highfield Rd, Edgbaston ✉ B15 3DU – ☎ (0121) 454 3434 – info@simpsonsrestaurant.co.uk – Fax (0121) 454 3399 – closed 24-27 December and 31 December-1 January EX **e**
4 rm – †£ 110 ††£ 160/225 – **Rest** – (closed Sunday dinner) Menu £ 20/65 – Carte £ 42/49
Spec. Quail, pear purée with vanilla, compote of onions and port syrup. Beef fillet, potato and pancetta terrine and Madeira sauce. Poached peach, pistachio ice cream, meringue and lemon verbena sauce.
◆ Impressive Georgian mansion with blend of contemporary furnishings and period touches. L-shaped dining room set around terrace. Classically based menus with a personal twist. Large, individually themed bedrooms.

Pascal's
1 Montague Rd ✉ B16 9HN – ☎ (0121) 455 0999 – info@pascalsrestaurant.co.uk – Fax (0121) 455 0999 – closed 1 week Easter, last 2 weeks July, 1 week Christmas, Saturday lunch, Sunday and Monday EX **c**
Rest – Menu £ 19/26 – Carte approx. £ 29
◆ Two main rooms; a darker inner hall and lighter, more airy conservatory with views of the small rear garden. Classical, carefully priced cooking with strong French overtones.

Purnell's
55 Cornwall St ✉ B3 2DH – ☎ (0121) 212 9799 – closed 1 week Easter, last week July, 1st week August, 1 week Christmas, Saturday lunch, Sunday and Monday LY **b**
Rest – Menu £ 26/54
◆ Red brick Victorian building in heart of city, boasting large arched floor to ceiling windows and central bar. Well-priced, modern and innovative food uses quality ingredients.

Opus
54 Cornwall St ✉ B3 2DE – ☎ (0121) 200 2323 – restaurant@opusrestaurant.co.uk – Fax (0121) 200 2090 – closed 25 December-4 January, Saturday lunch, Sunday and Bank Holidays LY **z**
Rest – Menu £ 18 – Carte £ 28/39
◆ Restaurant of floor-to-ceiling glass in evolving area of city. Seafood and shellfish bar for diners on the move. Assured cooking underpins modern menus with traditional base.

XX **Lasan** VISA MC AE

3-4 Dakota Buildings, James St ✉ B3 1SD – ✆ (0121) 212 3664 – info@lasan.co.uk – Fax (0121) 212 3665 – closed 25-26 December KY **a**

Rest – Indian Carte £ 28/36

◆ Jewellery quarter restaurant of sophistication and style; good quality ingredients allow the clarity of the spices to shine through in this well-run Indian establishment.

XX **Bank** A/C VISA MC AE

4 Brindleyplace ✉ B1 2JB – ✆ (0121) 633 4466 – birmres@bankrestaurants.com – Fax (0121) 633 4465 – closed 26 December and 1 January KZ **u**

Rest – Menu £ 15 – Carte £ 31/37

◆ Capacious, modern and busy bar-restaurant where chefs can be watched through a glass wall preparing the tasty modern dishes. Pleasant terrace area.

XX **Metro Bar and Grill** A/C VISA MC AE

73 Cornwall St ✉ B3 2DF – ✆ (0121) 200 1911 – Fax (0121) 200 1611 – closed 25 December-2 January, Sunday and Bank Holidays LY **n**

Rest – (booking essential) Carte £ 21/29

◆ Gleaming chrome and mirrors in a bright, contemporary basement restaurant. Modern cooking with rotisserie specialities. Spacious, ever-lively bar serves lighter meals.

XX **Shimla Pinks** A/C VISA MC AE

214 Broad St ✉ B15 1AY – ✆ (0121) 633 0366 – info@shimlapinks.com – Fax (0121) 643 3325 KZ **m**

Rest – Indian Menu £ 25 – Carte £ 21/32

◆ A vast establishment In a street full of restaurants. Buzzy ambience prevails: open-plan kitchen adds to atmosphere. Authentic, modern Indian cuisine; impressive set menus.

XX **Zinc Bar and Grill** A/C VISA MC AE

Regency Wharf, Broad St ✉ B1 2DS – ✆ (0121) 200 0620 – zinc.birmingham@irpic.co.uk – Fax (0121) 200 0630 – closed 24-26 December, 1 January, Sunday and Monday KZ **s**

Rest – Menu £ 13 – Carte £ 23/30

◆ Purpose-built restaurant in lively pub and club area of city. Spiral staircase leads to dining area, including terrace overlooking canal. Modern, classically toned, dishes.

X **Brasserie Blanc** A/C VISA MC AE

9 Brindleyplace ✉ B1 2HS – ✆ (0121) 633 7333 – birmingham@brasserieblanc.com – Fax (0121) 633 7444 – closed 25 December KZ **x**

Rest – Menu £ 14 (lunch) – Carte £ 22/29

◆ Outside, a central square and offices. Within, an atmospheric brasserie in relaxed, contemporary environment serving predominantly French classics. Special menu for children.

X **Lazeez Signature** A/C VISA MC AE

116 Wharfside St, The Mailbox ✉ B1 1RF – ✆ (0121) 643 7979 – Fax (0121) 643 4546 LZ **r**

Rest – Indian Menu £ 20 – Carte £ 20/40

◆ Located in fashionable Mailbox. Large, open plan establishment, kitchen included. Polite, friendly service. Authentic accurate Indian cooking with quality ingredients.

at Hall Green Southeast : 5 ¾ m. by A 41 on A 34 – ✉ Birmingham

XX **Liaison** VISA MC

1558 Stratford Rd ✉ B28 9HA – ✆ (0121) 733 7336 – Fax (0121) 733 1677 – Closed first week January, first week September, Saturday lunch, Sunday and Monday GX **i**

Rest – Menu £ 17/18 – Carte approx. £ 30

◆ Pleasant restaurant with understated décor in residential location. Linen table cloths and friendly service. Classically based modern eclectic cooking.

ENGLAND

at Birmingham Airport Southeast : 9 m. by A 45 - DU – ✉ Birmingham

Novotel Birmingham Airport

Terminal 1 ✉ B26 3QL – ✆ (0121) 782 7000 – h1158@accor.com – Fax (0121) 782 0445

195 rm – †£ 135 ††£ 135, ☕ £13.95 – **Rest** – (bar lunch Saturday, Sunday and Bank Holidays) Menu £ 18 (lunch) **s** – Carte £ 20/34 **s**

◆ Opposite main terminal building: modern hotel benefits from sound proofed doors and double glazing. Mini bars and power showers provided in spacious rooms with sofa beds. Open-plan garden brasserie.

at National Exhibition Centre Southeast : 9½ m. on A 45 - DU – ✉ Birmingham

Crowne Plaza

Pendigo Way ✉ B40 1PS – ✆ (0870) 400 9160 – necroomsales@ihg.com – Fax (0121) 781 4321

242 rm – †£ 99/259 ††£ 119/279, ☕ £15.95 – **Rest** – (closed Saturday lunch) Carte £ 28/38

◆ Modern hotel adjacent to NEC. Small terrace area overlooks lake. Extensive conference facilities. State-of-the-art bedrooms with a host of extras. Basement dining room: food with a Yorkshire twist.

ENGLAND

Good food and accommodation at moderate prices?
Look for the Bib symbols:
red Bib Gourmand for food, blue Bib Hotel for hotels

BIRMINGHAM AIRPORT – W. Mids. – 503 O 26 – see Birmingham

BISHOP'S STORTFORD – Herts. – 504 U 28 – pop. 35 325 12 B2

Great Britain

London 34 m – Cambridge 27 m – Chelmsford 19 m – Colchester 33 m

Stansted Airport : ✆ (0870) 0000303, NE : 3½ m

The Old Monastery, Windhill ✆ (0871) 7162529, tic@bishopsstortford.org

Audley End★★ **AC**, N : 11 m. by B 1383

The Cottage without rest

71 Birchanger Lane, Northeast : 2¼ m. by B 1383 on Birchanger rd ✉ CM23 5QA – ✆ (01279) 812 349 – bookings@thecottagebirchanger.co.uk – Fax (01279) 815 045 – closed Christmas and New Year

14 rm ☕ – †£ 50/60 ††£ 75/80

◆ Rurally-set part 17/18C cottages - yet close to airport. Cosy reception rooms with oak panelling and exposed beams. Conservatory style breakfast room and homely bedrooms.

The Lemon Tree

14-16 Water Lane ✉ CM23 2LB – ✆ (01279) 757 788 – mail@lemontree.co.uk – Fax (01279) 757 766 – Closed 25-26 December, 1 January, Sunday dinner and Monday Y **s**

Rest – Carte £ 20/30

◆ Cosy, vibrant restaurant in centre of town. Light and airy dining rooms, open bar; spacious private dining room on first floor. Wide-ranging menu, locally sourced ingredients.

Host

4 The Corn Exchange, Market Sq ✉ CM23 3UU – ✆ (01279) 657 000 – Fax (01279) 655 566 – Closed 25 December

Rest – Menu £ 15 (lunch) – Carte £ 15/30

◆ Grade I listed building with unique roof terrace. Main restaurant has industrial feel, with modern bar and open kitchen. Oft-changing menu incorporates global influences.

at Stansted Mountfitchet **Northeast : 3 ½ m. by B 1383 on B 1051 – ✉ Bishop's Stortford**

Chimneys without rest
44 Lower St, on B 1351 ✉ CM24 8LR – ✆ (01279) 813 388 – info@chimneysguesthouse.co.uk – Fax (01376) 310 169
4 rm – £ 50/58 £ 75
◆ Charming 17C house with friendly hosts, beamed ceilings, snug breakfast room and homely lounge. Comfy bedrooms - single has largest bathroom. Usefully located for airport.

at Hatfield Heath **Southeast : 6 m. on A 1060 – ✉ Bishop's Stortford**

Down Hall Country House
rest,
South : 1 ½ m. by Matching Lane ✉ CM22 7AS – ✆ (01279) 731 441 – reservations@downhall.co.uk – Fax (01279) 730 416
99 rm – £ 79/114 £ 99/124, £ 15.95
Rest *Ibbetsons* – (dinner only Thursday-Saturday) (booking essential for non-residents) Carte £ 31/44
Rest *The Grill Room* – (closed Saturday lunch) (dinner only Thursday-Saturday) Carte £ 25/39
◆ Ornate 19C Italianate mansion house in delightful grounds. Period style bedrooms; the most characterful in the old part of the house. Fine dining in traditional Ibbetsons restaurant. The contemporary Grill Room is less formal.

BISHOP'S TAWTON – Devon – **503** H 30 – **see Barnstaple**

BLACKAWTON – **see DARTMOUTH**

BLACKBURN – Blackburn – **502** M 22 – **pop. 105 085** 20 **B2**

London 228 m – Leeds 47 m – Liverpool 39 m – Manchester 24 m – Preston 11 m
15-17 Railway Rd ✆ (01254) 53277, askus@blackburn.gov.uk
18 Pleasington, ✆ (01254) 202 177;
18 Wilpshire 72 Whalley Rd, ✆ (01254) 248 260;
9 Great Harwood Harwood Bar, ✆ (01254) 884 391.

at Langho **North : 4 ½ m. on A 666 – ✉ Whalley**

The Avenue
A/C rest, P VISA AE
Brockhall Village, Old Lango, North : 1 ¼ m. by A 666 and A 59 on Northcote rd ✉ BB6 8AY – ✆ (01254) 244 811 – bookingenquiries@theavenuehotel.co.uk – Fax (01254) 244 812 – Closed 24-25 December
19 rm – £ 55/65 £ 60/70 – 2 suites – **Rest** – (Closed Sunday) (bar lunch) Carte £ 15/20
◆ Modern hotel located within a new village near old Langho, and ideal for football fans as it overlooks Blackburn Rovers' training ground. Stylish, contemporary bedrooms. Modern, informal café/bar style restaurant.

Northcote (Nigel Haworth) with rm
rm, P VISA AE
Northcote Rd, North : ½ m. on A 59 at junction with A 666 ✉ BB6 8BE – ✆ (01254) 240 555 – sales@northcotemanor.com – Fax (01254) 246 568 – closed 25 December and 1 January
14 rm – £ 195 £ 225 – **Rest** – Menu £ 24 – Carte £ 39/52
Spec. Black pudding and buttered pink trout with mustard and nettle sauce. Lamb in puff pastry, pear purée, caramelised shallot. Apple crumble soufflé, Lancashire cheese ice cream.
◆ Red brick Victorian house with welcoming fire-lit lounges. Passionate kitchen serves modern dishes with emphasis on Lancashire produce. Window tables most popular. Bedrooms have country house style with a contemporary edge.

ENGLAND

at Mellor **Northwest : 3 ¼ m. by A 677 – ✉ Blackburn**

Stanley House

Southwest : ¾ m. by A 677 and Further Lane ✉ BB2 7NP – ✆ (01254) 769 200 – info@stanleyhouse.co.uk – Fax (01254) 769 206
12 rm ☕ – **†£ 165 ††£ 190**
Rest *Cassis* – see restaurant listing
◆ 17C manor with superb rural views. Relaxing, tastefully toned bar. Strong emphasis on conference facilities. Elegantly proportioned rooms defined by wonderfully rich colours.

Millstone

Church Lane ✉ BB2 7JR – ✆ (01254) 813 333 – info@millstonehotel.co.uk – Fax (01254) 812 628
22 rm ☕ – **†£ 109/125 ††£ 155 – 1 suite**
Rest – (bar lunch) Menu £ 30 (dinner) **s** – Carte £ 30 **s**
◆ Attractive little sandstone former coaching inn in quiet village. Lounge bar with log fire and comfy sofas. Cosy bedrooms: matching floral patterns, botanical prints. Elegant wood panelled dining room warmed by fire.

Cassis – at Stanley House

Southwest : ¾ m. by A 677 and Further Lane ✉ BB2 7NP – ✆ (01254) 769 220 – Fax (01254) 769 206 – closed lunch Monday, Tuesday and Saturday
Rest – Menu £ 20 (lunch) – Carte £ 35/45
◆ Independent from main hotel. Name derives from rich blackcurrant theme throughout! Vast raised mezzanine for apéritifs. Weekly evolving menus with vibrant Lancashire accent.

ENGLAND

at Mellor Brook **Northwest : 3 ½ m. by A 677 and branch rd – ✉ Blackburn**

Feilden's Arms with rm

Whalley Rd ✉ BB2 7PR – ✆ (01254) 769 010 – Closed Sunday dinner
4 rm – †£ 45 ††£ 55 – Rest – Carte £ 14/22
◆ Spacious bar, comfy lounge and conservatory-style dining room. Vibrant use of regional ingredients to produce unfussy British pub favourites. Bright modern bedrooms.

Do not confuse X with ✿!
X defines comfort, while stars are awarded for the best cuisine, across all categories of comfort.

BLACKMORE – Essex 13 C2

London 26 m – Brentwood 7 m – Chelmsford 8 m

The Leather Bottle

The Green ✉ CM4 0RL – ✆ (01277) 823 538 – leatherbottle@tiscali.co.uk
Rest – (closed Sunday dinner) Menu £ 10 – Carte £ 19/30
◆ Pub dating from 1750s, overlooking village green. Cosy, flagstoned bar; dining area and airy conservatory. All-encompassing seasonal menu includes European and Asian flavours.

BLACKPOOL – Blackpool – 502 K 22 – pop. 142 283 *Great Britain* 20 A2

London 246 m – Leeds 88 m – Liverpool 56 m – Manchester 51 m – Middlesbrough 123 m
Blackpool Airport : ✆ (0871) 8556868, S : 3 m. by A 584
1 Clifton St ✆ (01253) 478222
Blackpool Park North Park Drive, ✆ (01253) 397 916 ;
Poulton-le-Fylde Breck Rd, Myrtle Farm, ✆ (01253) 892 444 .
Tower★ AC AY A

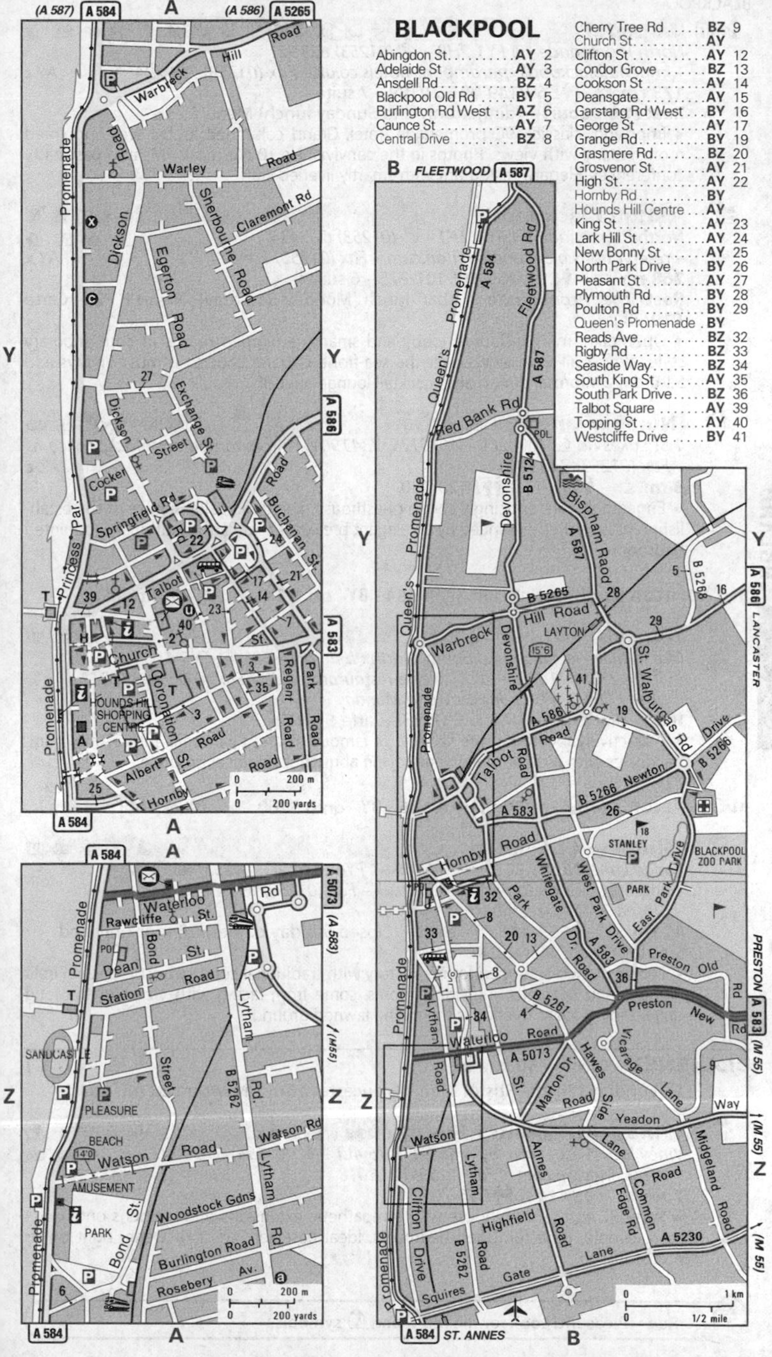
(A 587)
A 584
A
(A 586)
A 5265
Warbreck
Hill
Road
Promenade
Road
Warley
Road
Dickson
Sherbourne Road
Claremont Rd
Egerton
Road
Y
27
Dickson
Exchange St.
Street
A 586
Cocker
Springfield Rd
Rd
22
Buchanan St.
Road
24
Princess Par.
Talbot
17
14
21
39
12
23
40
2
7
St.
A 583
Church
Coronation
3
35
Regent Road
Park Road
HOUNDS HILL SHOPPING CENTRE
Promenade
Albert
St
Road
Road
25
Hornby
A 584
0 200 m
0 200 yards
A 5073
(A 583)
Waterloo
Rd
Rawcliffe
St.
Bond
St.
Dean
Road
Station
Lytham
Street
B 5262
Rd.
SANDCASTLE
PLEASURE
BEACH
Watson
Road
Watson Rd
Lytham
AMUSEMENT
PARK
Woodstock Gdns
Rd
Bond
St.
Burlington Road
Av.
Rosebery
6
0 200 m
0 200 yards
(M 55)
Z
B
FLEETWOOD
A 587
Promenade
A 584
Fleetwood Rd
Queen's
A 587
Red Bank Rd
POL
Devonshire
B 5124
Bispham Raod
A 587
5
B 5268
16
A 586
LANCASTER
B 5265
28
Hill Road
29
LAYTON
Warbreck
Devonshire
St. Walburgas Rd
41
A 586
19
Road
Drive
B 5266
Talbot
Road
B 5266 Newton
A 583
26
18
STANLEY
BLACKPOOL ZOO PARK
Road
Hornby
Park
Whitegate
West Park Drive
PARK
East Park Drive
32
8
33
20
13
Dr. Road
A 583
Preston Old
Rd
PRESTON
A 583
(M 55)
8
36
Preston
New
Rd
B 5261
4
34
Waterloo
Road
A 5073
Hawes
Vicarage
Lane
9
Road
St.
Marton Dr.
Road
Side
Yeadon
Way
Watson
Lane
Annes
Lytham
Road
Common
Edge Rd
Midgeland
Road
N
Highfield
Road
A 5230
Clifton
Drive
B 5262
Road
Lane
Gate
Squires
0 1 km
0 1/2 mile
A 584
ST. ANNES

BLACKPOOL

Imperial

North Promenade ✉ *FY1 2HB* – ☎ *(01253) 623 971*
– imperialblackpool@paramount-hotels.co.uk – Fax (01253) 751 784 AY **c**
173 rm – £ 69/149 £ 69/189 – 7 suites
Rest *Palm Court* – (dinner only and Sunday lunch) Menu £ 23 **s**
◆ Imposing, classic 19C promenade hotel. Grand columned lobby, well-appointed rooms, many with views. Photos in the convivial No.10 bar recall PMs and past party conferences. Elegant restaurant with smartly liveried staff.

Hilton Blackpool

rm, rest,
North Promenade ✉ *FY1 2JQ* – ☎ *(01253) 623 434*
– reservations.blackpool@hilton.com – Fax (01253) 294 371 AY **x**
268 rm – £ 91/265 £ 101/275 – 6 suites
Rest *The Promenade* – (bar lunch Monday-Saturday) Menu £ 22 – Carte £ 19/28
◆ Open-plan, marble-floored lobby and smartly equipped rooms in contemporary style, almost all with views over the sea-front. Cabaret shows on most Fridays and Saturdays. Informal dining after cocktail lounge aperitifs.

Number One without rest

1 St Lukes Rd ✉ *FY4 2EL* – ☎ *(01253) 343 901 – info@numberoneblackpool.com*
– Fax (01253) 343 901 AZ **a**
3 rm – £ 75/100 £ 125/130
◆ Engagingly run, enticingly stylish guesthouse. The good value nature of the establishment is further enhanced by an elegant breakfast room and luxuriously appointed bedrooms.

ENGLAND

at Thornton Northeast : 5 ½ m. by A 584 - BY - on B 5412 – ✉ Blackpool

Twelve

Marsh Mill, Fleetwood Rd South, North : ½ m. on A 585 ✉ *FY5 4JZ*
– ☎ (01253) 821 212 – info@twelve-restaurant.co.uk – Fax (01253) 821 212
– closed first 2 weeks January and Monday
Rest – (light lunch) Menu £ 19/26 – Carte £ 29/42
◆ Attractively located in the shadow of famous restored windmill. Interesting, original dishes with a modern flair, employing abundance of local produce.

at Singleton Northeast : 7 m. by A 586 - BY - on B 5260 – ✉ Blackpool

Singleton Lodge

Lodge Lane, North : ¼ m. on B 5260 ✉ *FY6 8LT* – ☎ *(01253) 883 854*
– enquiries@singletonlodgehotel.co.uk – Fax (01253) 894 432
– Closed 25-31 December
12 rm – £ 55 £ 75 – **Rest** – (Closed Sunday dinner) (dinner only and Sunday lunch) Menu £ 17
◆ Family owned Georgian former rectory with traditional country house décor. Firelit lounges and spacious, individual rooms, some front-facing with views of the long drive. Dining room overlooks the rolling lawned grounds.

BLAKENEY – Glos. – 503 M 28 4 C1

London 134 m – Bristol 31 m – Gloucester 16 m – Newport 31 m

Viney Hill Country Guesthouse without rest

Viney Hill, West : ¾ m. by A 48 ✉ *GL15 4LT* – ☎ *(01594) 516 000*
– info@vineyhill.com – Fax (01594) 516 018
7 rm – £ 44/50 £ 66/70
◆ Part 18C former farmhouse with sympathetic extensions and gardens on a quiet road. Simple, pine furnished bedrooms. Ideal base for Forest of Dean, right on its doorstep.

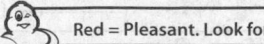

Red = Pleasant. Look for the red and symbols.

BLAKENEY – Norfolk – 504 X 25 – ✉ Holt 15 C1

London 127 m – King's Lynn 37 m – Norwich 28 m

Blakeney

The Quay ✉ NR25 7NE – ✆ (01263) 740 797 – reception@blakeney-hotel.co.uk – Fax (01263) 740 795

64 rm (dinner included) – £ 85/140 £ 170/200 – **Rest** – (light lunch Monday-Saturday) Menu £ 28 – Carte £ 28/42

◆ Traditional hotel on the quayside with views of estuary and a big sky! Sun lounge a delightful spot for the vista. Bedrooms vary in size and décor, some with private patio. Armchair dining with estuary views.

White Horse with rm

4 High St ✉ NR25 7AL – ✆ (01263) 740 574 – info@blakeneywhitehorse.co.uk – Fax (01263) 741 303 – Closed 25 December

9 rm – £ 70 £ 150 – **Rest** – Menu £ 26 – Carte £ 18/30

◆ Part 17C brick-and-flint coaching inn near the harbour. Friendly, real ale bar and rustic restaurant in the old stables offering seafood specials. Cosy rooms.

at Cley next the Sea East : 1 ½ m. on A 149 – ✉ Holt

Cley Windmill

The Quay ✉ NR25 7RP – ✆ (01263) 740 209 – Fax (01263) 740 209

9 rm – £ 46/138 – **Rest** – (by arrangement, communal dining) Menu £ 23 (dinner)

◆ Restored 18C redbrick windmill in salt marshes with a viewing gallery: a bird-watcher's paradise. Neatly kept rooms, full of character, in the mill, stable and boatshed. Flagstoned dining room; communal table.

The George with rm

High St ✉ NR25 7RN – ✆ (01263) 740 652 – thegeorge@cleynextthesea.com – Fax (01263) 741 275 – Closed 25 December

12 rm – £ 65/80 £ 130 – 1 suite – **Rest** – Carte £ 22/30

◆ Imposing, stalwart Victorian/Edwardian pub. Warmly hued bar and restaurant. Rustic British cuisine to fore; lots of local seafood. Book top floor bedrooms for best views.

at Morston West : 1 ½ m. on A 149 – ✉ Holt

Morston Hall (Galton Blackiston)

The Street ✉ NR25 7AA – ✆ (01263) 741 041 – reception@morstonhall.com – Fax (01263) 740 419 – closed January

13 rm (dinner included) – £ 180/200 £ 290/310

Rest – (dinner only and Sunday lunch) (booking essential) (set menu only) Menu £ 48

Spec. Soup of beets with walnut foam. Fillet of cod, garlic mashed potato, sorrel beurre blanc. Millefeuille of English fruits, vanilla ice cream.

◆ Attractive, ivy covered country house in quiet village, very personally run by husband and wife team. Traditional rooms. Accomplished menu offers balanced, seasonal dishes made from fine, locally sourced ingredients. Beautiful new conservatoty.

BLANDFORD FORUM – Dorset – 503 N 31 – pop. 9 854 4 C3

London 124 m – Bournemouth 17 m – Dorchester 17 m – Salisbury 24 m

1 Greyhound Yard ✆ (01258) 454770

Ashley Wood Wimbourne Rd, ✆ (01258) 452 253.

Town★

Kingston Lacy★★ AC, SE : 5 ½ m. by B 3082 – Royal Signals Museum★, NE : 2 m. by B 3082. Milton Abbas★, SW : 8 m. by A 354 – Sturminster Newton★, NW : 8 m. by A 357

ENGLAND

at Chettle **Northeast : 7 ¼ m. by A 354 – ✉ Blandford Forum**

XX **Castleman** with rm

✉ *DT11 8DB – ✆ (01258) 830096 – enquiry@castlemanhotel.co.uk – Fax (01258) 830051 – closed February and 25-26 and 31 December*
8 rm – †£50 ††£80/90
Rest – (dinner only and Sunday lunch) Menu £21 (lunch) – Carte £20/25
◆ Attractive part 16C dower house with Victorian extensions. Ingredients sourced from small local producers: game from their own estate. Classic cooking with a French base. Spacious, traditionally-styled bedrooms.

at Farnham **Northeast : 7 ½ m. by A 354 – ✉ Blandford Forum**

The Museum Inn with rm

✉ *DT11 8DE – ✆ (01725) 516261 – enquiries@museuminn.co.uk – Fax (01725) 516988 – Closed 25 December, dinner 31 December and 1 January*
8 rm – †£85 ††£150
Rest – (bookings not accepted) Carte £28/31
◆ Part thatched 17C inn offering locally produced and carefully prepared modern British cooking. Dine in the bar or more formal Shed restaurant. Comfortable bedrooms.

ENGLAND

BLEDINGTON – Oxon. – 503 P 28 – see Stow-on-the-Wold

BLEDLOW – Bucks – pop. 2 249 – ✉ Princes Risborough 11 C2

London 43 m – High Wycombe 9 m – Oxford 21 m

The Old Station without rest

Sandpit Lane ✉ HP27 9QQ – ✆ (01844) 345086 – ianmackinson@hotmail.com – Fax (01844) 274732
4 rm – †£49/59 ††£69
◆ A station until 1994 - the owner's relations used to be station masters. Now a comfortable guest house, the breakfast room was once the station waiting room. Homely bedrooms.

BLOCKLEY – Glos. – 503 O 27 – ✉ Moreton-in-Marsh 4 D1

London 91 m – Birmingham 39 m – Oxford 34 m

Lower Brook House

Lower St ✉ GL56 9DS – ✆ (01386) 700286 – info@lowerbrookhouse.com – Fax (01386) 701400 – closed Christmas
6 rm – †£80/95 ††£175
Rest – (closed Sunday) (dinner only) (booking essential for non-residents) Menu £25
◆ Personally run, adjoining 17C Cotswold stone cottages with huge inglenooks, beams and flagged floors. Characterful and stylish from every aspect. Individually appointed rooms. Imaginative evening menus of local Cotswold produce.

BLUNDELLSANDS – Mersey. – 502 L 23 – see Liverpool

We try to be as accurate as possible when giving room rates. But prices are susceptible to change, so please check rates when booking.

BLUNSDON – Wilts. – 503 O 29 – see Swindon

BLYTH – Notts. – 502 Q 23 – ✉ Worksop 16 B1

London 166 m – Doncaster 13 m – Lincoln 30 m – Nottingham 32 m – Sheffield 20 m

Charnwood

Sheffield Rd, West : ¾ m. on A 634 ✉ S81 8HF – ☎ (01909) 591 610 – charnwood@bestwestern.co.uk – Fax (01909) 591 427

45 rm – ♦£ 60/95 ♦♦£ 85/110 – **Rest** – (bar meal Sunday dinner) Menu £ 17 (lunch) – Carte £ 25/35

◆ Well suited to the business traveller, this hotel offers consistently well-kept bedrooms. Its most recent additions are spacious, stylish, well-equipped and overlook the garden. A lounge bar offers informal dining; the large restaurant is smart with up-to-date décor.

BODIAM – E. Sussex – 504 V 30 *Great Britain* 8 B2

London 58 m – Cranbrook 7 m – Hastings 13 m

Castle★★

Battle Abbey★, S : 10 m. by B 2244, B 2089, A 21 and minor rd – Rye★★, SW : 13 m. by A 268

The Curlew

Junction Rd, Northwest : 1½ m. at junction with B 2244 ✉ TN32 5UY – ☎ (01580) 861 394 – enquiries@thecurlewatbodiam.co.uk

Rest – (closed Sunday and Monday dinner) Menu £ 20 – Carte £ 25/33

◆ Grade II listed inn dating from 17C with traditional beamed interior, homely main bar and two spacious, elegantly dressed dining rooms. Formal service and a wide-ranging menu.

Undecided between two equivalent establishments? Within each category, establishments are classified in our order of preference.

BODMIN – Cornwall – 503 F 32 – pop. 12 778 1 B2

London 270 m – Newquay 18 m – Plymouth 32 m – Truro 23 m

Shire Hall, Mount Folly Sq ☎ (01208) 76616

St Petroc Church★

Bodmin Moor★★ - Lanhydrock★★, S : 3 m. by B 3269 – Blisland★ (Church★), N : 5½ m. by A 30 and minor roads – Pencarrow★, NW : 4 m. by A 389 and minor roads – Cardinham (Church★), NE : 4 m. by A 30 and minor rd – St Mabyn (Church★), N : 5½ m. by A 389, B 3266 and minor rd. St Tudy★, N : 7 m. by A 389, B 3266 and minor rd

Trehellas House

(heated)

Washaway, Northwest: 3 m. on A 389 ✉ PL30 3AD – ☎ (01208) 72 700 – trehellashouse@btconnect.com – Fax (01208) 73 336

11 rm – ♦£ 60/68 ♦♦£ 130 – **Rest** – Carte £ 24/40 **s**

◆ Relaxed, personally run country house with a cottage facade. Owners' original Cornish art on show in listed room. Cosy lounges with flag floors. Airy, pastel painted bedrooms. Characterful restaurant; owners take pride in local, fresh, seasonal produce.

Bokiddick Farm without rest

Lanivet, South : 5 m. by A 30 following signs for Lanhydrock and Bokiddick ✉ PL30 5HP – ☎ (01208) 831 481 – gillhugo@bokiddickfarm.co.uk – Fax (01208) 831 481 – closed Christmas and New Year

5 rm – ♦£ 45/50 ♦♦£ 75

◆ Sizeable house on dairy farm: do take a quick tour. Warm welcome assured. Neat, well priced rooms with added amenities in old house; smart stable conversion for more rooms.

ENGLAND

at Helland Northeast : 4½ m. by A 389 off B 3266 – ✉ Bodmin

Tredethy House
Helland Bridge ✉ PL30 4QS – ✆ (01208) 841 262 – info@tredethyhouse.co.uk – Fax (01208) 841 707
11 rm – †£ 105 ††£ 125/175 – **Rest** – (residents only by arrangement) Menu £ 25/30
◆ Victorian house overlooking the Camel Valley. Books and family photos of former resident, Prince Chula of Thailand, in the reading room. Spacious, well-appointed bedrooms. Homecooking in period style dining room.

BODSHAM – Kent 9 **C2**
London 65 m – Ashford 10 m – Canterbury 10 m

Froggies at the Timber Batts
School Lane ✉ TN25 5JQ – ✆ (01223) 750 237 – post@thetimberbatts.co.uk – Fax (01223) 750 176 – Closed 25-26 December and 1 January
Rest – French (closed Monday and Tuesday after Bank Holidays) Menu £ 26 – Carte £ 24/36
◆ Creeper-clad, 15C pub with welcoming Gallic owner. Large dining area has menus in French: staff readily translate. Fine local produce in unfussy, French country style dishes.

ENGLAND

BOLNHURST – Beds 12 **A1**
London 64 m – Bedford 8 m – St Neots 7 m

The Plough at Bolnhurst
Kimbolton Rd, South : ½ m. on B 660 ✉ MK44 2EX – ✆ 01234 376 274 – theplough@bolnhurst.com – Closed 2 weeks January
Rest – (closed Sunday dinner and Monday) Menu £ 16 – Carte £ 25/37
◆ Restored, whitewashed pub with spacious, rustic interior, smart terrace and pleasant gardens. Assured service from smartly dressed staff. Wide-ranging, seasonal menu.

BOLTON ABBEY – N. Yorks. – **502** O 22 – ✉ **Skipton** *Great Britain* 22 **B2**
London 216 m – Harrogate 18 m – Leeds 23 m – Skipton 6 m
Bolton Priory★ **AC**

The Devonshire Arms Country House
✉ BD23 6AJ – ✆ (01756) 718 111 – res@devonshirehotels.co.uk – Fax (01756) 710 564
38 rm – †£ 175 ††£ 220/365 – 2 suites
Rest ***The Burlington*** – (closed Monday) (dinner only and Sunday lunch) Menu £ 33/58
◆ Extended part 17C coaching inn owned by Duke and Duchess of Devonshire: elegant country house rooms with art and antiques. Close to spectacular ruins of 12C Bolton Priory. Refined dining with views of Italian Garden.

BOLTON-BY-BOWLAND – Lancs. – **502** M/N 22 *Great Britain* 20 **B2**
London 246 m – Blackburn 17 m – Skipton 15 m
Skipton - Castle★, E : 12 m. by A 59 – Bolton Priory★, E : 17 m. by A 59

Middle Flass Lodge
Settle Rd, North : 2½ m. by Clitheroe rd on Settle rd ✉ BB7 4NY – ✆ (01200) 447 259 – middleflasslodge@btconnect.com – Fax (01200) 447 300
7 rm – †£ 38/48 ††£ 60/70 – **Rest** – (by arrangement) Carte £ 23/30
◆ Friendly, welcoming owners in a delightfully located barn conversion. Plenty of beams add to rustic effect. Pleasantly decorated, comfy rooms with countryside outlook. Blackboard's eclectic menu boasts local, seasonal backbone.

BOROUGHBRIDGE – N. Yorks. – 502 P 21 – pop. 3 311 22 B2

London 215 m – Leeds 19 m – Middlesbrough 36 m – York 16 m
Fishergate (0871) 7161924 (summer only)

thediningroom

20 St James's Sq YO51 9AR – (01423) 326 426 – chris@thediningroom.wanadoo.co.uk – Fax (01423) 326 426 – closed 26 December, 1 January, Sunday dinner and Monday

Rest – (dinner only and Sunday lunch) (booking essential) Menu £ 26 – Carte approx. £ 25

◆ Characterful cottage with beamed dining room. Vivid fireside sofas and Impressionist oils, as modern as the well-prepared dishes: duck on rocket and pesto features.

BORROWDALE – Cumbria – 502 K 20 – see Keswick

BOSCASTLE – Cornwall – 503 F 31 1 B2

London 260 m – Bude 14 m – Exeter 59 m – Plymouth 43 m
Village ★
Poundstock Church ★ – Tintagel Old Post Office ★

The Bottreaux

South : ¾ m. by B 3263 on B 3266 PL35 0BG – (01840) 250 231 – info@boscastlecornwall.co.uk – Fax (01840) 250 170

8 rm – £ 70/85 £ 85/100 – **Rest** – (closed Sunday-Monday) (lunch from June to September) (booking essential in winter) Menu £ 10/28 – Carte approx. £ 28

◆ On a hill outside the village, a privately owned, well-run hotel. The rooms, some with king-size beds, and the public areas have a sleek, stylish ambience. Dining room offers well-sourced, local, modern dishes.

Trerosewill Farm without rest

Paradise, South : 1 m. off B 3263 PL35 0BL – (01840) 250 545 – cheryl@trerosewill.co.uk – Fax (01840) 250 727 – closed mid December-mid January

9 rm – £ 38/75 £ 62/90

◆ Modern house on 50-acre working farm: fine views of the coast and good clifftop walks. Lovely conservatory breakfast room. Bedrooms in matching patterns, some with Jacuzzis.

Old Rectory without rest

St Juliot, Northeast : 2 1/2 m. by B 3263 PL35 0BT – (01840) 250 225 – sally@stjuliot.com – Fax (01840) 250 225 – February-October

4 rm – £ 54/58 £ 78/86

◆ Communal breakfast room, with views of Victorian walled garden, from whence much of the produce comes. Characterful bedrooms; one in converted stables. Thomas Hardy stayed here.

BOSHAM – W. Sussex – 504 R 31 – see Chichester

BOSTON SPA – W. Yorks. – 502 P 22 – pop. 5 952 22 B2

London 127 m – Harrogate 12 m – Leeds 12 m – York 16 m

Four Gables without rest

Oaks Lane, West : ¼ m. by A 659 LS23 6DS – (01937) 845 592 – info@fourgables.co.uk – Fax (01937) 849 031 – closed Christmas and January

4 rm – £ 56 £ 77

◆ Down a quiet private road, a 1900 house, after Lutyens: period fireplaces, stripped oak and terracotta tile floors. Traditional, individually decorated rooms. Croquet lawn.

Look out for red symbols, indicating particularly pleasant establishments.

BOUGHTON MONCHELSEA Kent – Kent – pop. 2 863 8 B2

London 46 m – Southend-on-Sea 60 m – Basildon 48 m – Maidstone 4 m

The Mulberry Tree

Hermitage Lane, South : 1 1/2 m. by Park Lane and East Hall Hill ✉ ME17 4DA – ✆ (01622) 749 082 – info@themulberrytreekent.co.uk – Fax (01622) 741 058

Rest – (closed Sunday dinner and Monday) Carte £ 23/28

◆ Remotely situated, stylishly decorated, family-owned restaurant with enclosed garden. Daily-changing menus offer modern, tasty dishes, homemade using the best local produce.

BOULEY BAY – C.I. – 503 L 33 – see Channel Islands

BOURNEMOUTH – Bournemouth – 503 – pop. 167 527 4 D3

London 114 m – Bristol 76 m – Southampton 34 m
Bournemouth (Hurn) Airport : ✆ (01202) 364000, N : 5 m. by Hurn - DV
Westover Rd ✆ (0845) 0511700
Queens Park Queens Park West Drive, ✆ (01202) 302 611 ;
Bournemouth and Meyrick Park Central Drive, ✆ (01202) 786 000.
Compton Acres★★ (English Garden ≤ ★★★) **AC** AX – Russell-Cotes Art Gallery and Museum★★ **AC** DZ **M1** - Shelley Rooms **AC** EX **M2**
Poole★, W : 4 m. by A 338 – Brownsea Island★ (Baden-Powell Stone ≤ ★★) **AC**, by boat from Sandbanks BX or Poole Quay – Christchurch★ (Priory Church★) E : 4½ m. on A 35. Corfe Castle★, SW : 18 m. by A 35 and A 351 – Lulworth Cove★ (Blue Pool★) W : 8 m. of Corfe Castle by B 3070 – Swanage★, E : 5 m. of Corfe Castle by A 351

Plans on following pages

Bournemouth Highcliff Marriott

(heated) rm,

St Michael's Rd, West Cliff ✉ BH2 5DU – ✆ (0870) 400 72 11 – reservations.bournemouth@marriotthotels.co.uk – Fax (0870) 400 73 11 CZ **z**

158 rm – †£ 150 ††£ 160 – 2 suites – **Rest** – (carvery lunch) Menu £ 19/25 – Carte £ 25/36

◆ Imposing white clifftop landmark, linked by funicular to the beach. Elegant drawing rooms; bedrooms, in the grand tradition, and leisure centre are comprehensively equipped. Secure a bay view table in elegant formal restaurant.

Royal Bath

Bath Rd ✉ BH1 2EW – ✆ (01202) 555 555 – royal.bath@devere-hotels.com – Fax (01202) 554 158 DZ **a**

133 rm – †£ 90/200 ††£ 150/210 – 7 suites

Rest *Oscars* – see restaurant listing

Rest – (dinner only) Carte £ 27/43

◆ Classic Victorian hotel in secluded gardens retains the conscientious service of another age. Tastefully co-ordinated, generously appointed rooms, some with sea views. Tall windows flood elegant restaurant with natural light.

Norfolk Royale

rm, rest,

Richmond Hill ✉ BH2 6EN – ✆ (01202) 551 521 – sales@englishrosehotels.co.uk – Fax (01202) 294 031 CY **u**

91 rm – †£ 129/159 ††£ 179 – 4 suites

Rest *Echoes* – Menu £ 15/28 **s** – Carte £ 33/37 **s**

◆ Edwardian hotel, once the summer retreat of the Duke of Norfolk. Bold, modern colours brighten the neat bedrooms; the lobby, with its deep sofas, has a more clubby feel. Spacious candlelit conservatory dining room.

Chine (heated)

Boscombe Spa Rd ✉ BH5 1AX – ✆ (01202) 396 234
– reservations@chinehotel.co.uk – Fax (01202) 391 737 DX **e**
88 rm – £ 45/85 £ 150/170 – **Rest** – (closed Saturday lunch) (buffet lunch) Menu £ 26
◆ Extended former spa takes its name from its location, perched on a ridge over Poole Bay. Modern rooms vary in shape and size; conference suites extend over several floors. Restaurant with sweeping views over the treetops.

Miramar rm,

19 Grove Rd, East Overcliff ✉ BH1 3AL – ✆ (01202) 556 581
– sales@miramar-bournemouth.com – Fax (01202) 291 242 DZ **u**
43 rm – £ 47/100 £ 94/150 – **Rest** – (closed Saturday lunch) Menu £ 15/27
◆ Along the handsome lines of a grand Edwardian villa. Large, well cared for rooms, a few with curved balconies, in floral patterns. Library and a sun terrace facing the sea. Traditional menu.

Collingwood

11 Priory Rd ✉ BH2 5DF – ✆ (01202) 557 575 – info@hotel-collingwood.co.uk
– Fax (01202) 293 219 CZ **n**
53 rm – £ 55/105 £ 110/150 – **Rest** – (bar lunch Monday-Saturday) Menu £ 21
◆ A smoothly run hotel, its modern accommodation comfortably decorated in warm pastel shades. Bar terrace and reverently hushed snooker room. Effusively decorative dining room.

The Orchid without rest

34 Gervis Rd ✉ BH1 3DH – ✆ (01202) 551 600
– reservations@orchid-hotel.co.uk – Fax (01202) 553 737
– Closed 24 December-2 January DY **a**
34 rm – £ 50/75 £ 100/130
◆ As you might expect, images of the orchid abound in this personally run hotel with lovely rear courtyard. Modern, minimalist style prevails. Comfy rooms with designer touches.

Oscars – at Royal Bath H.

Bath Rd ✉ BH1 2EW – ✆ (01202) 555 555 – royal.bath@devere-hotels.com
– Fax (01202) 554 158 DZ **a**
Rest – Carte £ 28/43
◆ Pristine settings and discreet, impeccable service distinguish this elegant restaurant, serving modern British dishes, many infused with flavours of French country cooking.

Noble House

3-5 Lansdowne Rd ✉ BH1 1RZ – ✆ (01202) 291 277 – Fax (01202) 291 312
– Closed Sunday DEY **i**
Rest – Chinese Menu £ 6/17 – Carte £ 12/29
◆ A hospitable family team are behind a comprehensive menu of authentic Chinese cuisine, carefully prepared from fresh ingredients. Smoothly run; handy town centre location.

West Beach

Pier Approach ✉ BH2 5AA – ✆ (01202) 587 785
– Closed 25 December DZ **c**
Rest – Seafood (booking essential at lunch) Carte £ 31/41
◆ Seafood restaurant on the beach, with folding glass doors and a decked terrace. Busy - particularly at lunch. Fish and shellfish caught locally; some in front of restaurant.

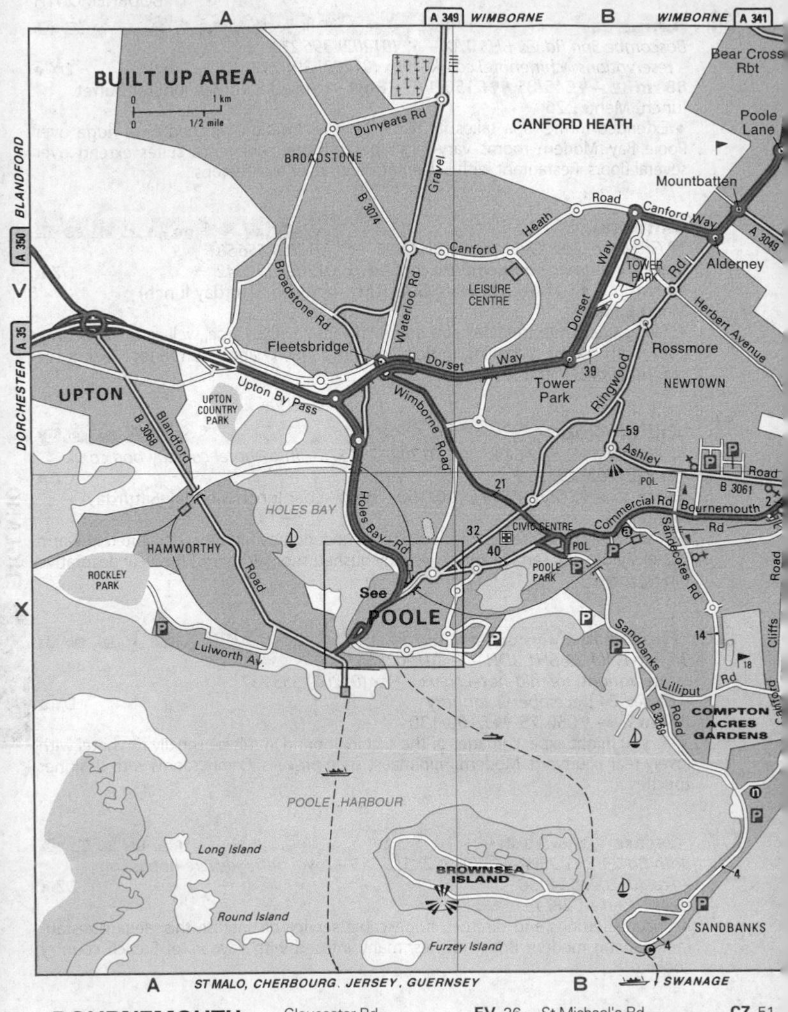

BOURNEMOUTH AND POOLE

Archway Rd . . . . BX 2
Banks Rd . . . . BX 4
Boscombe Overcliff Rd . . . . EX 6
Boscombe Spa Rd . . . . DX 7
Branksome Wood Rd . . . . . CY 9
Chessel Ave . . . . EX 10
Clarendon Rd . . . . CX 12
Commercial Rd . . . . CY 13
Compton Ave . . . . BX 14
Cranleigh Rd . . . . EV 16
Durley Rd . . . . CZ 17
Ensbury Park Rd . . . . CV 19
Exeter Rd . . . . CDZ 20
Fernside Rd . . . . ABX 21
Fir Vale Rd . . . . DY 23
Gervis Pl . . . . DY 24
Gloucester Rd . . . . EV 26
Hampshire Centre . . . . DV
Hinton Rd . . . . DZ 27
Lansdowne Rd . . . . DY 30
Lansdowne (The) . . . . DY 28
Leven Ave . . . . CX 31
Longfleet Rd . . . . BX 32
Madeira Rd . . . . DY 34
Manor Rd . . . . EY 35
Meyrick Rd . . . . EYZ 36
Old Christchurch Rd . . . . . . DY
Old Wareham Rd . . . . BV 39
Parkstone Rd . . . . BX 40
Pinecliff Rd . . . . CX 42
Post Office Rd . . . . CY 43
Priory Rd . . . . CZ 45
Queen's Rd . . . . CX 46
Richmond Hill . . . . CY 47
Richmond Park Rd . . . . DV 48
Russell Cotes Rd . . . . DZ 49
St Michael's Rd . . . . CZ 51
St Paul's Rd . . . . EY 52
St Peter's Rd . . . . DY 53
St Stephen's Rd . . . . CY 55
St Swithuns Rd South . . . . . EY 56
Seabourne Rd . . . . EV 57
Seamoor Rd . . . . CX 58
Sea View Rd . . . . BV 59
Southbourne Grove . . . . EX 61
Southbourne Overcliff Drive . . . . EX 62
Sovereign Shopping Centre . EX
Square (The) . . . . CY 63
Suffolk Rd . . . . CY 64
Surrey Rd . . . . CX 66
Triangle (The) . . . . CY 67
Upper Hinton Rd . . . . DZ 68
Wessex Way . . . . CX 70
Western Rd . . . . CX 73
Westover Rd . . . . DZ 75
West Cliff Promenade . . . . . CZ 71

A 348 SOUTHAMPTON
A 347 FERNDOWN INTERNATIONAL AIRPORT
INTERNATIONAL AIRPORT
A 338
SOUTHAMPTON SALISBURY
BEAR CROSS
KINSON
Northbourne
Redhill
A 3060
Blackwater Junction
Broadway Lane
CASTLE POINT
Woodbury
MOORDOWN
REDHILL PARK
Cooper Dean
CHARMINSTER
WINTON
QUEEN'S PARK
Springbourne
KING'S PARK
A 35 LYNDHURST
WEST SOUTHBOURNE
MEYRICK PARK
SOVEREIGN SHOPPING CENTRE
BOURNEMOUTH
BOSCOMBE
WESTBOURNE
POOLE BAY
Wimborne Road
Castle Lane
Wessex Way
Christchurch Rd
University
Boundary
Talbot
A 347
A 338
BOURNEMOUTH WEST
UPPER CENTRAL GARDENS
LOWER CENTRAL GARDENS
RICHMOND HILL
ST PAULS
INTERNATIONAL CENTRE
WATERFRONT COMPLEX
Undercliff Drive
West Undercliff Promenade
400 m
400 yards
C
D
E
V
X
Y
Z

BOURTON-ON-THE-HILL – Glos. – see Moreton-in-Marsh

BOURTON-ON-THE-WATER – Glos. – 503 O 28 – pop. 3 093 4 D1

Great Britain

London 91 m – Birmingham 47 m – Gloucester 24 m – Oxford 36 m

Town★

Northleach (Church of SS. Peter and Paul★, Wool Merchants' Brasses★), SW : 5 m. by A 429

The Dial House

The Chestnuts, High St ✉ GL54 2AN – ✆ (01451) 822 244 – info@dialhousehotel.com – Fax (01451) 810 126

13 rm – ♦£ 55/110 ♦♦£ 190 – **Rest** – (booking essential for non-residents) Menu £ 15 (lunch) – Carte £ 25/35

◆ House of Cotswold stone - the oldest in the village - with lovely lawned gardens, refurbished bar and drawing room and contemporary, eye-catching bedrooms. Rustic, bistro-style dining rooms. Unfussy, well-cooked food makes good use of local ingredients.

Coombe House without rest

Rissington Rd ✉ GL54 2DT – ✆ (01451) 821 966 – info@coombehouse.net – Fax (01451) 810 477 – restricted opening in winter

6 rm – ♦£ 50/60 ♦♦£ 70/80

◆ Creeper-clad 1920s house on the quiet outskirts of the village, near the local bird sanctuary. Homely lounge and spotless, comfortable, cottage style bedrooms in soft chintz.

ENGLAND

Alderley without rest

Rissington Rd ✉ GL54 2DX – ✆ (01451) 822 788 – alderleyguesthouse@hotmail.com – Fax (01451) 822 788

3 rm – ♦£ 45/50 ♦♦£ 55/70

◆ Short walk from town centre on main road. Combined lounge and eating room; terrace for summer breakfasts; good quality local produce used. Bright, homely, floral bedrooms.

Manor Close without rest

High St ✉ GL54 2AP – ✆ (01451) 820 339 – manorclose@aol.com – closed 25 December

3 rm – ♦£ 50 ♦♦£ 65

◆ Superb central but quiet location. Lounge and breakfast room in Cotswold stone house; comfortable floral rooms in purpose-built garden annexe, one on ground floor.

at Lower Slaughter Northwest : 1 ¾ m. by A 429 – ✉ Cheltenham

Lower Slaughter Manor

✉ GL54 2HP – ✆ (01451) 820 456 – info@lowerslaughter.co.uk – Fax (01451) 822 150

19 rm – ♦£ 170 ♦♦£ 315 – **Rest** – Menu £ 25 (lunch) – Carte dinner £ 45/53

◆ Beautiful listed part 17C manor in warm Cotswold stone. A wealth of objets d'art, fine oils and sense of enveloping period comfort extends from firelit hall to airy bedrooms. Ornate dining room with lithographs and Wedgewood.

Washbourne Court

✉ GL54 2HS – ✆ (01451) 822 143 – info@washbournecourt.co.uk – Fax (01451) 821 045

20 rm – ♦£ 130/150 ♦♦£ 160/200 – 10 suites – **Rest** – (bar lunch Monday-Saturday) Menu £ 40 **s** – Carte £ 32/44 **s**

◆ Extended part 1800s manor house by the Eyre. Spacious rooms in floral fabrics at their traditional best in the old building. Flag-floored, timbered bar with terrace. Restaurant offers views of tree-lined lawns.

at Upper Slaughter Northwest : 2 ½ m. by A 429 – ✉ Bourton-on-the-Water

Lords of the Manor
✉ *GL54 2JD – ☎ (01451) 820 243 – enquiries@lordsofthemanor.com – Fax (01451) 820 696*
26 rm – ♦£ 160/240 ♦♦£ 200/240 – 1 suite – **Rest** – (light lunch) Carte £ 49/59
◆ Attractive 17C former rectory set in pretty Cotswold village. Neat gardens; smart leather furnished lounge and bar; traditionally styled bedrooms with good facilities. Formal dining room. Classically based cooking with a modern twist.

BOVEY TRACEY – Devon – 503 I 32 – ✉ Newton Abbot 2 C2

London 214 m – Exeter 14 m – Plymouth 32 m
Newton Abbot, ☎ (01626) 52 460 .
St Peter, St Paul and St Thomas of Canterbury Church★
Dartmoor National Park★★

Edgemoor
Haytor Rd, West : 1 m. on B 3387 ✉ TQ13 9LE – ☎ (01626) 832 466 – reservations@edgemoor.co.uk – Fax (01626) 834 760 – closed 27 December-10 January
16 rm – ♦£ 95/120 ♦♦£ 140 – **Rest** – (bar lunch) Menu £ 35
◆ Country style, creeper-clad former school house. Lofty beamed, firelit lounge has deep chintz armchairs. Smart rooms - in main house or ex-schoolrooms - in floral prints. Elegantly proportioned dining room.

Brookfield House without rest 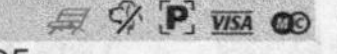
Challabrook Lane, Southwest : ¾ m. by Brimley rd ✉ TQ13 9DF – ☎ (01626) 836 181 – enquiries@brookfield-house.com – closed December-January
3 rm – ♦£ 48/54 ♦♦£ 66/78
◆ Well-kept early Edwardian house in two acres of attractive gardens surrounded by Dartmoor. The three large bedrooms have expansive windows and are immaculately appointed.

at Haytor Vale West : 3 ½ m. by B 3387 – ✉ Newton Abbot

The Rock Inn with rm
✉ *TQ13 9XP – ☎ (01364) 661 305 – cg@rock-inn.co.uk – Fax (01364) 661 242 – Closed 25-26 December*
9 rm – ♦£ 66 ♦♦£ 107 – **Rest** – Menu £ 20 – Carte £ 19/30
◆ Attractive 18C former coaching inn. Rustic charm aplenty with log fires, beams and sloping floors. Simple bar menu; more elaborate restaurant menu. Bedrooms named after Grand National winners.

BOWNESS-ON-WINDERMERE – Cumbria – 502 L 20 – see Windermere

BOX – Bath & North East Somerset – 503 N 29 – see Bath

BRADFORD – W. Yorks. – 502 O 22 – pop. 293 717 *Great Britain* 22 B2

London 212 m – Leeds 9 m – Manchester 39 m – Middlesbrough 75 m – Sheffield 45 m
Leeds and Bradford Airport : ☎ (0113) 250 9696, NE : 6 m. by A 658 BX
City Hall ☎ (01274) 753678
West Bowling Rooley Lane, Newall Hall, ☎ (01274) 728 036 ;
Woodhall Hills Pudsley Woodhall Rd, Calverley, ☎ (0113) 256 4771 ;
Bradford Moor Pollard Lane Scarr Hill, ☎ (01274) 771 716 ;
East Brierley South View Rd, ☎ (01274) 681 023 ;
Queensbury Brighouse Rd, ☎ (01274) 882 155.
City★ – National Media Museum★ AZ M

Plan of Enlarged Area : see Leeds

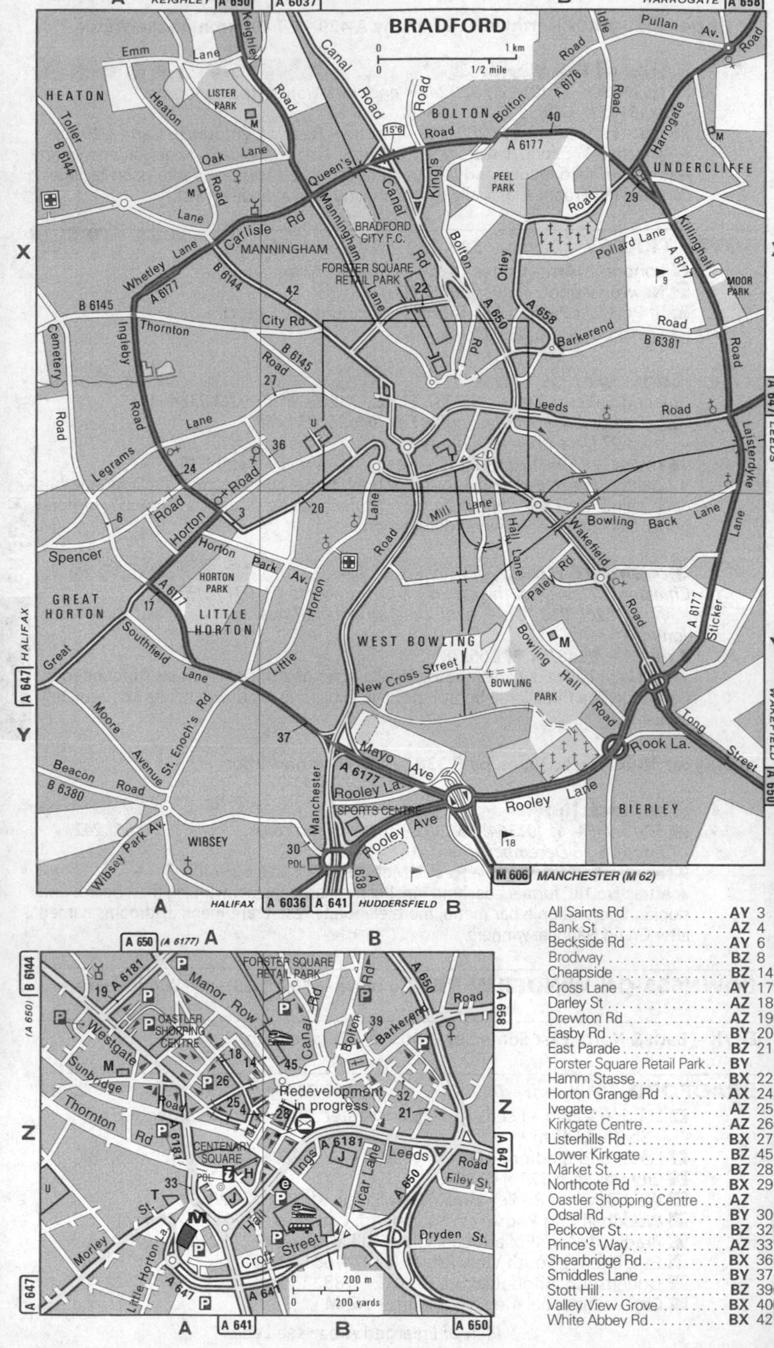

All Saints Rd	AY	3
Bank St	AZ	4
Beckside Rd	AY	6
Brodway	BZ	8
Cheapside	BZ	14
Cross Lane	AY	17
Darley St	AZ	18
Drewton Rd	AZ	19
Easby Rd	BY	20
East Parade	BZ	21
Forster Square Retail Park	BY	
Hamm Stasse	BX	22
Horton Grange Rd	AX	24
Ivegate	AZ	25
Kirkgate Centre	AZ	26
Listerhills Rd	BX	27
Lower Kirkgate	BZ	45
Market St.	BZ	28
Northcote Rd	BX	29
Oastler Shopping Centre	AZ	
Odsal Rd	BY	30
Peckover St	BZ	32
Prince's Way	AZ	33
Shearbridge Rd	BX	36
Smiddles Lane	BY	37
Stott Hill	BZ	39
Valley View Grove	BX	40
White Abbey Rd	BX	42

Hilton Bradford rm, rest,
Hall Ings ✉ *BD1 5SH – ☎ (01274) 734 734 – Fax (01274) 306 146* BZ **e**
116 rm – †£ 71/101 ††£ 121/141, ☕ £15.95 – 4 suites
Rest *City 3* – Menu £ 20 (dinner) – Carte £ 24/37
◆ City centre hotel, convenient for rail travellers. Don't be put off by dated 60s exterior. Neatly equipped modern accommodation; smart and comfortable cocktail lounge. Easy informality is the by-word in restaurant.

at Gomersal Southeast : 7 m. by A 650 on A 651 – ✉ Bradford

Gomersal Park rm, rest,
Moor Lane, Northeast : 1 ½ m. by A 651 off A 652 ✉ *BD19 4LJ – ☎ (01274) 869 386 – reservations@gomersalparkhotel.com – Fax (01274) 861 042* BU **u**
100 rm ☕ – †£ 105 ††£ 105/240
Rest *Brasserie 101* – (closed Saturday lunch) Carte £ 21/28.50 **s**
◆ Well-equipped corporate hotel on greenfield site; comprehensive conference facilities. Modern bedrooms: the executive style provides more comfort. Well-stocked, comfortable bar is ideal stopping point before dining.

BRADFORD-ON-AVON – Wilts. – 503 N 29 – pop. 9 072 4 C2

London 118 m – Bristol 24 m – Salisbury 35 m – Swindon 33 m
34 Silver St ☎ (01225) 865797
Town★★ - Saxon Church of St Lawrence★★ - Tithe Barn★ – Bridge★
Great Chalfield Manor★ (All Saints★) **AC**, NE : 3 m. by B 3109 – Westwood Manor★ **AC**, S : 1 ½ m. by B 3109 – Top Rank Tory (≤ ★). Bath★★★, NW : 7 ½ m. by A 363 and A 4 – Corsham Court★★ **AC**, NE : 6 ½ m. by B 3109 and A 4

Woolley Grange (heated)
Woolley Green, Northeast : ¾ m. by B 3107 on Woolley St ✉ *BA15 1TX – ☎ (01225) 864 705 – info@woolleygrangehotel.co.uk – Fax (01225) 864 059*
19 rm ☕ – †£ 100/170 ††£ 200/280 – 7 suites – **Rest** – Menu £ 36 (dinner) – Carte lunch £ 18/28
◆ Modern art, period furniture: innumerable charming details spread through the rooms of a beautiful Jacobean manor. This is an hotel very much geared to families. Classic British cooking in restaurant, conservatory or terrace.

Widbrook Grange rm,
Trowbridge Rd, Widbrook, Southeast : 1 m. on A 363 ✉ *BA15 1UH – ☎ (01225) 864 750 – stay@widbrookgrange.com – Fax (01225) 862 890 – Closed 24-30 December*
20 rm ☕ – †£ 95 ††£ 120
Rest *The Medlar Tree* – (Closed Sunday) Menu £ 15 (lunch) – Carte £ 23/31
◆ Georgian house and outbuildings, once the centre of an 11-acre model farm; cosy bedrooms, subtly reflecting the past, overlook peaceful fields and a pleasant mature garden. Pre-prandial relaxation in comfy drawing rooms.

Swan
1 Church St ✉ *BA15 1LN – ☎ (01225) 868 686 – theswan-hotel@btconnect.com*
12 rm ☕ – †£ 85/95 ††£ 140 – **Rest** – Menu £ 16 (lunch) – Carte £ 20/26
◆ Smart former 16C coaching inn refurbished in modern browns and creams, with rear dining terrace. Stylish bedrooms have contemporary touches and up-to-date facilities. Large, wood furnished dining room.

Bradford Old Windmill
4 Masons Lane, on A 363 ✉ *BA15 1QN – ☎ (01225) 866 842 – Fax (01225) 866 648 – March-October*
3 rm ☕ – †£ 59/99 ††£ 89/109 – **Rest** – Turkish (by arrangement, communal dining) Menu £ 25
◆ 1807 windmill in redressed local stone; Gothic windows and restored bridge. Rooms and circular lounge, stacked with books and curios, share a homely, unaffected quirkiness. Flavourful vegetarian menus.

ENGLAND

The Beeches Farmhouse without rest
Holt Rd, East : 1 ¼ m. on B 3107 ✉ BA15 1TS – ✆ (01225) 865 170 – beeches-farmhouse@netgates.co.uk – Fax (01225) 865 170
4 rm – ♦£ 50/85 ♦♦£ 80/90
◆ 18C farmhouse where sheep and ducks roam. Charming main bedroom boasts Victorian bath; log stove heats a cosy lounge. Pine furnished bedrooms in converted outbuildings.

at Holt East : 2 m. on B 3107 – ✉ Bradford-on-Avon

The Tollgate Inn with rm
Ham Green ✉ BA14 6PX – ✆ (01225) 782 326 – alison@tollgateholt.co.uk – Fax (01225) 782 805 – Closed 25-26 December, 1 January, Sunday dinner and Monday
4 rm – ♦£ 50 ♦♦£ 95 – **Rest** – (booking essential) Menu £ 14 – Carte £ 24/35
◆ Friendly, log-fired pub built of Bath stone. Twin dining areas with simple wooden tables and chairs. Interesting à la carte menu serves food with international elements.

Red = Pleasant. Look for the red and symbols.

BRAITHWAITE – Cumbria – **502** K 20 – see Keswick

BRAMFIELD – Suffolk – **504** Y 27 – **pop. 1 778** – ✉ Ipswich 15 **D2**
London 215 m – Ipswich 27 m – Norwich 28 m

Queen's Head
The Street ✉ IP19 9HT – ✆ (01986) 784 214 – qhbfield@aol.com – Closed 26 December
Rest – Carte £ 16/25
◆ Roadside pub in heart of village. Characterful beamed interior with flagstone floors and small conservatory. Eclectic menu uses locally sourced food and organic farm produce.

BRAMHOPE – W. Yorks. – **502** P 22 – see Leeds

BRAMPTON – Cumbria – **501** L 19 – **pop. 3 965** *Great Britain* 21 **B1**
London 317 m – Carlisle 9 m – Newcastle upon Tyne 49 m
Moot Hall, Market Pl ✆ (016977) 3433
Talkin Tarn, ✆ (016977) 2255 ; Huntingdon, ✆ (01480) 434 700 .
Hadrian's Wall★★, NW : by A 6077

at Gilsland Northeast : 9 m. by A 6071 and A 69 on B 6318 – ✉ Brampton

Farlam Hall
Southeast : 2 ¾ m. on A 689 ✉ CA8 2NG – ✆ (016977) 46 234 – Fax (016977) 46 683 – closed 24-30 December
12 rm (dinner included) – ♦£ 150/175 ♦♦£ 330 – **Rest** – (dinner only) (booking essential for non-residents) Menu £ 39
◆ Long-standing, family-owned Victorian country house. Comfortable guest areas overlook ornamental gardens and lake. Traditional bedrooms in bold florals. Resident llamas. Fine, formal dining in sumptuous dining room. Attentive, pristine service.

The Hill on the Wall without rest — Hadrian's wall and Irthing valley,
West : ½ m. on Kirkcambeck rd ✉ CA8 7DA – ✆ (016977) 47 214 – info@hadrians-wallbedandbreakfast.com – Fax (016977) 47 214 – closed December-January
3 rm – ♦£ 40/50 ♦♦£ 68
◆ Spacious 16C guest house in fabulous elevated location overlooking the Irthing Valley, with terrific views from the garden and the lounge. Comfortable bedrooms.

ENGLAND

at Castle Carrock South : 4 m. on B 6413 – ✉ **Brampton**

The Weary at Castle Carrock with rm
✉ *CA8 9LU – ☎ (01228) 670 230 – relax@theweary.com – Fax (01228) 670 089 – Closed 25-26 December, 1 January*
5 rm – †£79/85 ††£145 – **Rest** – (Monday dinner residents only) Carte £15/35
◆ Conservatory, terrace and relaxed candlelit bar. Seasonal food with international flavours. Friendly service. Striking, contemporary bedrooms equipped with latest technology.

BRANCASTER STAITHE – Norfolk 15 **C1**

The White Horse with rm ≤ Brancaster marshes and Scolt Head Island,
✉ *PE31 8BY – ☎ (01485) 210 262 – reception@whitehorsebrancaster.co.uk – Fax (01485) 210 930*
15 rm – †£75/89 ††£136/178 – **Rest** – (booking essential) Carte £21/30
◆ Elevated position affords beautiful coastal views from rear conservatory and terrace, while landscaped front terrace boasts parasols, heaters and lights. Local seafood menu. Up-to-date, comfortable bedrooms.

BRANDESBURTON – East Riding – **502** T 22 – **pop. 1 835** – ✉ **Great Driffield** 23 **D2**
London 197 m – Kingston-upon-Hull 16 m – York 37 m

Burton Lodge
Southwest : ½ m. on Leven rd ✉ YO25 8RU – ☎ (01964) 542 847 – enquiries@burton-lodge.co.uk – Fax (01964) 544 771 – closed 25-26 December
9 rm – †£40/42 ††£62 – **Rest** – (dinner only) (residents only) Menu £18
◆ Personally run, extended 1930s house. Neat, modern bedrooms in soft pastels, some overlooking the golf course - perfect for an early round. A short drive to Beverley Minster. Neat dining room overlooks grounds.

BRANDS HATCH – Kent – **504** U 29 – ✉ **Dartford** 8 **B1**
London 22 m – Maidstone 18 m
Corinthian Dartford Fawkham, Gay Dawn Farm, ☎ (01474) 707 144 .

at Fawkham Green East : 1 ½ m. by A 20 – ✉ **Ash Green**

Brands Hatch Place rm, rest,
✉ *DA3 8NQ – ☎ (01474) 875 000 – brandshatchplace@handpicked.co.uk – Fax (01474) 879 652*
38 rm – †£99/140 ††£120/255 – **Rest** – (closed Saturday lunch) Carte £28/39 **s**
◆ Sensitively extended Georgian house in 12 acres offering smart bedrooms, some in the annexe, with hi-tech facilities. Also, a range of conference and entertainment packages. Smart, contemporary restaurant.

BRANSCOMBE – Devon – **503** K 31 – ✉ **Seaton** 2 **D2**
London 167 m – Exeter 20 m – Lyme Regis 11 m
Village★
Seaton (≤ ★★), NW : 3 m – Colyton★

Masons Arms
✉ *EX12 3DJ – ☎ (01297) 680 300 – reception@masonsarms.co.uk – Fax (01297) 680 500*
22 rm – †£85 ††£165 – **Rest** – (bar lunch) Menu £28 – Carte £16/26
◆ Family run 14C inn; cosy, unspoilt bar with slate floors and ships' timbers, popular with locals. Bedrooms in the inn have more character; those in the annex are much larger. Dine in the populous bar with its dressed stone interior and huge open fire.

BRANSFORD – Worcs. – see Worcester

ENGLAND

BRANSTON – Lincs. – **502** S 24 – see Lincoln

BRATTON – Wrekin – see Telford

BRAY MARINA – Windsor & Maidenhead – see Bray-on-Thames

BRAYE – C.I. – **503** Q 33 – see Channel Islands

BRAY-ON-THAMES – Windsor & Maidenhead – **504** R 29 – ✉ Maidenhead 11 **C3**

London 34 m – Reading 13 m

Plan : see Maidenhead

XXXX ✿✿✿ **The Waterside Inn** (Alain Roux) with rm ≤ Thames-side setting,
Ferry Rd ✉ SL6 2AT – ✆ (01628) 620691 – reservations@waterside-inn.co.uk – Fax (01628) 784710 – closed 26 December-1 February and 26-27 March X **s**
8 rm – †£ 180/280 ††£ 180/280 – 3 suites – **Rest** – French (closed Tuesday except dinner June-August and Monday) (booking essential) Menu £ 46/91 – Carte £ 79/123
Spec. Tronçonnettes de homard poêlées minute au Porto blanc. Filets de lapereau grillés aux marrons glacés. Péché Gourmand selon "Alain" et "Michel".
◆ Ever delightful Thames idyll: sip an aperitif on the terrace overlooking the river. Exquisite French cuisine and exemplary service. Luxurious bedrooms are spacious and classically chic.

XXX ✿✿✿ **Fat Duck** (Heston Blumenthal)
High St ✉ SL6 2AQ – ✆ (01628) 580333 – Fax (01628) 776188 – closed 2 weeks Christmas, Sunday dinner and Monday X **e**
Rest – (booking essential) Menu £ 80/115
Spec. Roast scallop tartare, white chocolate and caviar. Pot roast pork loin, gratin of truffled macaroni. Nitro scrambled egg and bacon ice cream, parsnip cereal.
◆ Low-beamed, converted pub where history and science combine in an exciting, innovative alchemy of contrasting flavours and textures. Colourful artwork, stylish milieu; attentive, formal service.

The Hinds Head
High St ✉ SL6 2AD – ✆ (01628) 626151 – info@thehindshead.co.uk – Fax (01628) 623394 – Closed 25-26 December and Sunday dinner X **e**
Rest – (booking essential) Carte £ 24/35
◆ Characterful 17C village pub; inside a wealth of panelling and charm. Enjoy a sip of mead or a glass of perry with tasty and heart-warming classic British cooking.

The Royal Oak
Paley Street, Southwest : 3½ m. by A 308, A 330 on B 3024 ✉ SL6 3JN – ✆ (01628) 620541 – Closed 27 December-2 January and Sunday dinner
Rest – Carte £ 20/30
◆ Characterful roadside pub with beamed ceilings, comfy leather sofas and pretty patio. Seasonally-changing menus offer satisfying homemade food. Relaxed, friendly atmosphere.

at Bray Marina Southeast : 2 m. by B 3208, A 308 - X - on Monkey Island Lane – ✉ Bray-on-Thames

X **Riverside Brasserie**
(follow road through the marina) ✉ SL6 2EB – ✆ (01628) 780553 – April-September
Rest – (booking essential) Carte £ 28/36
◆ Marina boathouse, idylically set on the banks of the Thames. Very simply appointed interior and decked terrace. Inventive cooking in informal, busy and buzzy surroundings.

ENGLAND

BREEDON ON THE HILL – Leics. – see Castle Donington

BRENTWOOD – Essex – 504 V 29 – pop. 47 593 13 C2

London 22 m – Chelmsford 11 m – Southend-on-Sea 21 m
Pepperell House, 44 High St ✆ (01277) 200300
Bentley G. & C.C. Ongar Rd, ✆ (01277) 373 179 ;
Warley Park Little Warley Magpie Lane, ✆ (01277) 224 891 .

Marygreen Manor

London Rd, Southwest : 1 ¼ m. on A 1023 ✉ CM14 4NR – ✆ (01277) 225 252 – info@marygreenmanor.co.uk – Fax (01277) 262 809

55 rm – £ 135 £ 150, £ 15 – 1 suite

Rest *Tudors* – see restaurant listing

◆ Charming Tudor building with wood panelled rooms and open fires. Bedrooms split between main house and courtyard - some named after Henry VIII's wives. Professionally run.

Tudors – at Marygreen Manor

London Rd, Southwest : 1 ¼ m. on A 1023 ✉ CM14 4NR – ✆ (01277) 225 252 – info@marygreenmanor.co.uk – Fax (01277) 262 809 – Closed Sunday dinner

Rest – Menu £ 21/43

◆ Spacious Tudor-style dining room with stained glass, wood beams and tapestries. Well-spaced, dressed tables and formal service. Appealing, modern food with a seasonal base.

at Great Warley Southwest : 2 m. on B 186 – ✉ Brentwood

The Headley

The Common, Northeast : ½ m. off B 186 ✉ CM13 3HS – ✆ (01277) 216 104 – reservations@theheadley.co.uk

Rest – Carte £ 20/35

◆ Spacious pub over two floors, with comfy leather furniture and open fires. Confident cooking comes out in classic French/British dishes made from local, seasonal ingredients.

BRIDGNORTH – Shrops. – 502 M 26 – pop. 11 891 *Great Britain* 18 B2

London 146 m – Birmingham 26 m – Shrewsbury 20 m – Worcester 29 m
The Library, Listley St ✆ (01746) 763257
Stanley Lane, ✆ (01746) 763 315 .
Ironbridge Gorge Museum★★ AC (The Iron Bridge★★ - Coalport China Museum★★ - Blists Hill Open Air Museum★★ - Museum of the Gorge and Visitor Centre★) NW : 8 m. by B 4373

at Worfield Northeast : 4 m. by A 454 – ✉ Bridgnorth

The Old Vicarage

✉ WV15 5JZ – ✆ (01746) 716 497 – admin@the-old-vicarage.demon.co.uk – Fax (01746) 716 552 – Closed 24-26 December

13 rm – £ 90/110 £ 140/175 – 1 suite

Rest – (Closed dinner 24-26 December) (dinner only and Sunday lunch) (booking essential) Menu £ 40 – Carte £ 22/35

◆ Antiques, rare prints and rustic pottery: a personally run Edwardian parsonage in a rural setting with thoughtfully appointed bedrooms, some in the coach house. Delightful orangery dining room overlooking garden; modern British cooking.

at Alveley Southeast : 7 m. by A 442 – ✉ Bridgnorth

Mill

Birdsgreen, Northeast : ¾ m. ✉ WV15 6HL – ✆ (01746) 780 437 – info@themill-hotel.co.uk – Fax (01746) 780 850

41 rm – £ 90/125 £ 180, £ 15

Rest *Waterside* – Menu £ 15/22 – Carte £ 27/43

◆ Hugely extended water mill. Below traditionally styled rooms in flowery patterns, ducks paddle around the pond and fountain. Popular wedding venue. Capacious restaurant, busy at weekends, overlooks garden and duck pond.

BRIDGWATER – Somerset – 503 L 30 – pop. 35 563 3 B2

London 160 m – Bristol 39 m – Taunton 11 m
King Sq ✆ (0871) 7162724
Enmore Park Enmore, ✆ (01278) 671 103 .
Town★ - Castle Street★ – St Mary's★ – Admiral Blake Museum★ AC
Westonzoyland (St Mary's Church★★) SE : 4 m. by A 372 – North Petherton (Church Tower★★) S : 3 ½ m. by A 38. Stogursey Priory Church★★, NW : 14 m. by A 39

at Woolavington Northeast : 5 m. by A 39 on B 3141 – ✉ Bridgwater

Chestnut House Village H.
Hectors Stones Lower Road ✉ TA7 8EF – ✆ (01278) 683 658 – paul@chestnuthousehotel.com – Fax (01278) 684 333 – closed Christmas-New Year
7 rm – †£ 70 ††£ 90 – **Rest** – (dinner only) (residents only) Menu £ 22 **s**
◆ Converted farmhouse, spotless and personally run, the exposed stone and beams in the homely lounge testify to its 16C origins. Rooms are neat, comfortable; and all en suite. Dining room with comfy wicker chairs and garden views.

at Cannington Northwest : 3 ½ m. by A 39 – ✉ Bridgwater

Blackmore Farm without rest
Southwest : 1 ½ m. by A 39 on Bradley Green rd ✉ TA5 2NE – ✆ (01278) 653 442 – dyerfarm@aol.com – Fax (01278) 653 427
6 rm – †£ 45/55 ††£ 70/85
◆ Part 15C manor, now a working dairy farm, with great hall and chapel, set against a backdrop of the Quantocks. Huge, well-priced bedrooms brimming with character.

ENGLAND

Look out for red symbols, indicating particularly pleasant establishments.

BRIDPORT – Dorset – 503 L 31 – pop. 12 977 3 B3

London 150 m – Exeter 38 m – Taunton 33 m – Weymouth 19 m
47 South St ✆ (01308) 424901
Bridport and West Dorset West Bay East Cliff, ✆ (01308) 422 597 .
Mapperton Gardens★, N : 4 m. by A 3066 and minor rd. Lyme Regis★ - The Cobb★, W : 11 m. by A 35 and A 3052

Roundham House without rest
Roundham Gdns, West Bay Rd, South : 1 m. by B 3157 ✉ DT6 4BD – ✆ (01308) 422 753 – cyprencom@compuserve.com – Fax (01308) 421 500 – March-October
8 rm – †£ 49/85 ††£ 85/95
◆ Elegant 1903 house with trim, spacious bedrooms, their broad windows overlooking woods, fields and a lawned garden. Coffee in the smart lounge with its marble fireplace.

Britmead House without rest
West Bay Rd, South : 1 m. on B 3157 ✉ DT6 4EG – ✆ (01308) 422 941 – britmead@talk21.com – Fax (01308) 422 516 – Closed 24 December-1 January
8 rm – †£ 40/50 ††£ 60/74
◆ On the road to West Bay and the Dorset Coast Path, a neat, redbrick Edwardian house with well-proportioned rooms and a comfortable lounge leading out to the garden.

Riverside
West Bay, South : 1 ¾ m. by B 3157 ✉ DT6 4EZ – ✆ (01308) 422 011 – Fax (01308) 458 808 – Closed Sunday dinner and Monday except Bank Holidays
Rest – Seafood (restricted opening February-March and October-November) (booking essential) Carte £ 28/44
◆ Follow the footbridge across the river to this popular seafood café overlooking the harbour, renowned for its extensive choice of specials and its friendly service.

Chez Cuddy

47 East St ✉ DT6 3JX – ✆ (01308) 458 770 – badrtmam@aol.com – closed 24-27 December and Sunday

Rest – (lunch only) Carte £ 15/24

◆ Inviting, personably run, centrally located, café style eatery, Simple décor enhanced by vivid artwork. Interesting seasonal menus: accomplished execution of modern dishes.

The Bull with rm

34 East St ✉ DT6 3LF – ✆ (01308) 422 878 – info@thebullhotel.co.uk – Fax (01308) 426 872

13 rm – †£ 50 ††£ 180 – **Rest** – Carte £ 16/28

◆ Grade II listed, 16C coaching inn with striking blue façade and trendy, stylish interior. Regularly-changing menu sourced from local produce. Confident, unfussy cooking.

at Shipton Gorge Southeast : 3 m. by A 35 – ✉ Bridport

Innsacre Farmhouse

Shipton Lane, North : 1 m. ✉ DT6 4LJ – ✆ (01308) 456 137 – innsacre.farmhouse@btinternet.com – Closed 2 weeks Christmas and New Year

4 rm – †£ 80/110 ††£ 80/110 – **Rest** – (by arrangement) Menu £ 23

◆ 17C farmhouse in acres of lawns and orchards. Simple comfortable lounge centred on old fireplace. Sizeable rooms in bold colours. Intimate dining room using carefully sourced ingredients.

**Your opinions are important to us:
please write and let us know about your discoveries and experiences – good and bad!**

ENGLAND

BRIGGSWATH – N. Yorks. – 502 S 20 – see Whitby

BRIGHOUSE – W. Yorks. – 502 O 22 – pop. 32 360 — 22 B2

London 213 m – Bradford 12 m – Burnley 28 m – Leeds 15 m – Manchester 35 m – Sheffield 39 m

Crow Nest Park Hove Edge Coach Rd, ✆ (01484) 401 121 .

Brook's

6 Bradford Rd ✉ HD6 1RW – ✆ (01484) 715 284 – info@brooks-restaurant.co.uk – Fax (01484) 712 641 – Closed 10 days January, last week July, first week August and Sunday

Rest – (dinner only) Menu £ 27

◆ Eclectic art collection fills the walls of this informal restaurant and wine bar with its vaguely Edwardian upstairs lounge. Robust, tasty cooking with 'Spam' on the menu!

BRIGHSTONE – Isle of Wight – 504 P 32 – see Wight (Isle of)

BRIGHTON AND HOVE – Brighton and Hove – 504 T 31 – pop. 206 628 Great Britain — 8 A3

London 53 m – Portsmouth 48 m – Southampton 61 m

Shoreham Airport : ✆ (01273) 296900, W : 8 m. by A 27 AV

10 Bartholomew Sq ✆ (0906) 711 2255

East Brighton Roedean Rd, ✆ (01273) 604 838 ;

The Dyke Dyke Rd, Devil's Dyke, ✆ (01273) 857 296 ;

Hollingbury Park Ditchling Rd, ✆ (01273) 552 010 ;

Waterhall Waterhall Rd, ✆ (01273) 508 658 .

Town★★ - Royal Pavilion★★★ **AC** CZ – Seafront★★ – The Lanes★ BCZ – St Bartholomew's★ **AC** CX **B**

Devil's Dyke (≤ ★) NW : 5 m. by Dyke Rd (B 2121) BY

BRIGHTON AND HOVE

Street	Grid	No.
Adelaide Crescent	AY	2
Brunswick Pl.	AY	3
Brunswick Square	AYZ	4
Carlton Terrace	AV	5
Chatham Pl.	BX	6
Churchill Square Shopping Centre	BYZ	
Denmark Rd	BY	7
Eastern Rd	CV	9
East St.	CZ	8
George St	AV	10
Gladstone Terrace	CX	12
Gloucester Pl.	CY	13
Gloucester Rd	CY	14
Goldsmid Rd	BX	15
Grand Junction Rd	CZ	16
Hollingbury Park Ave	BV	17
Hollingdean Rd.	CV	18
Hove St.	AV	19
London Rd	CX	
Marlborough Pl.	CY	21
Montpelier Pl.	BY	22
North St.	CZ	
Old Steine	CZ	23
Pavillon Parade	CZ	26
Richmond Pl.	CY	27
Richmond Terrace	CX	28
St George's Pl.	CY	30
St Peter's Pl.	CX	31
Terminus Rd	BCX	32
Upper Lewes Rd	CX	33
Warren Rd	CV	37
Waterloo Pl.	CX	39
Wellington Rd.	AV	40
Western Rd.	ABY	
York Pl.	CY	42

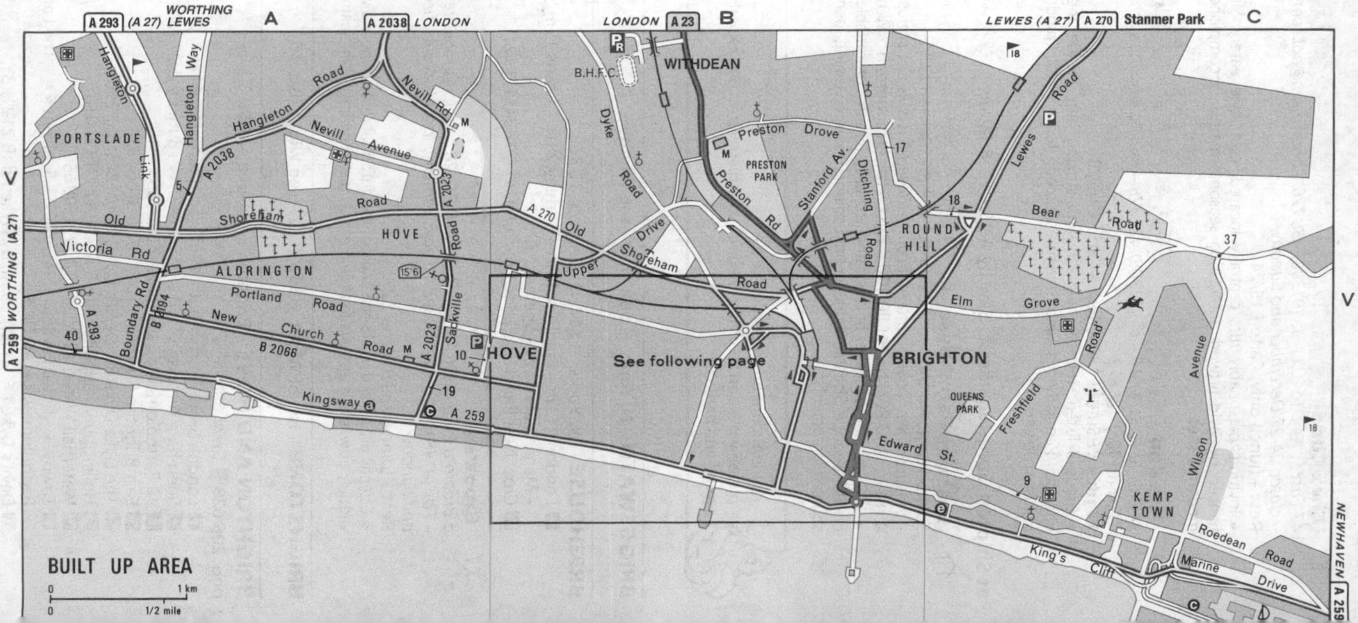

A 293 (A 27) WORTHING LEWES
A 2038 LONDON
LONDON A 23
LEWES (A 27) A 270 Stanmer Park
A 259 WORTHING (A27)
NEWHAVEN A 259

PORTSLADE
WITHDEAN
PRESTON PARK
ROUND HILL
HOVE
ALDRINGTON
BRIGHTON
QUEENS PARK
KEMP TOWN
B.H.F.C.

See following page

BUILT UP AREA

0 — 1 km
0 — 1/2 mile

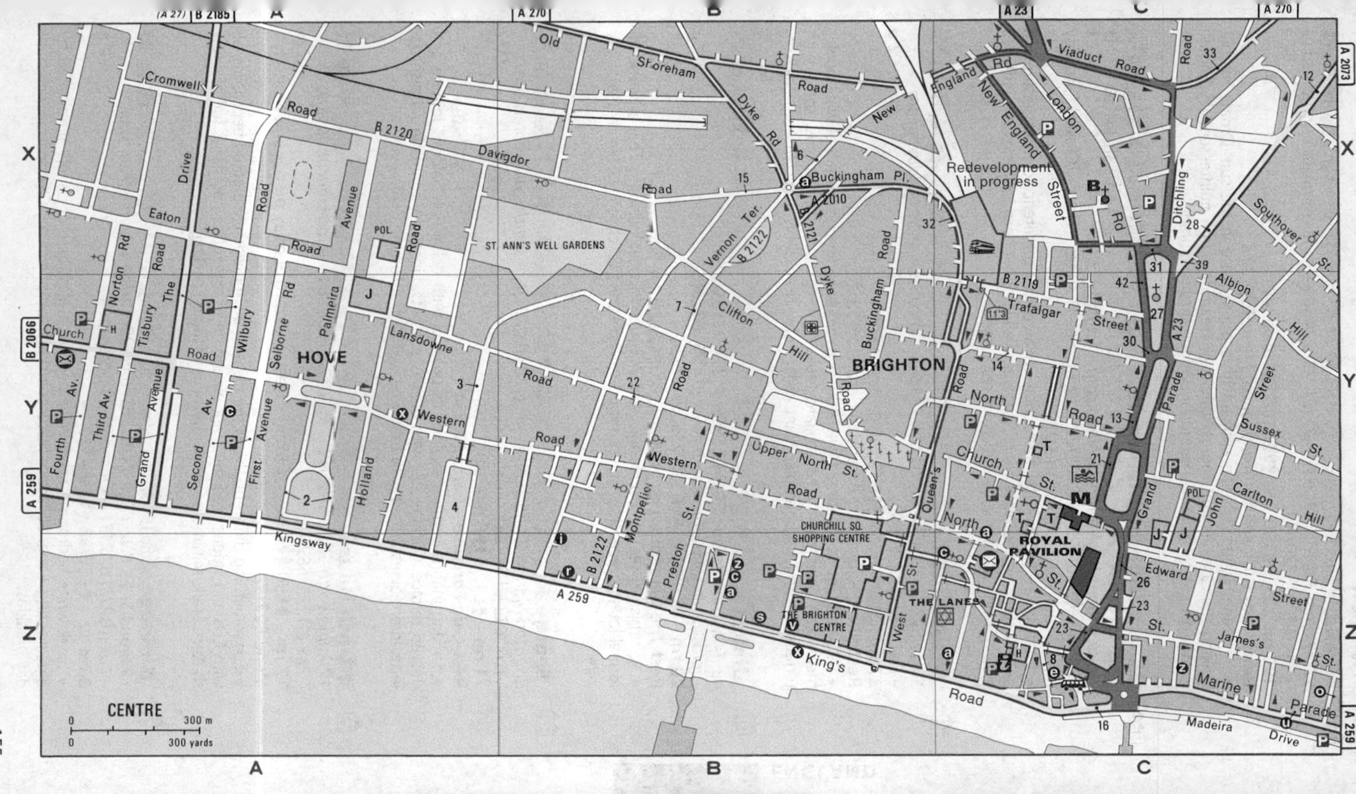

BRIGHTON
HOVE
ROYAL PAVILION
THE LANES
CHURCHILL SQ. SHOPPING CENTRE
THE BRIGHTON CENTRE
ST. ANN'S WELL GARDENS
Redevelopment in progress
CENTRE
300 m
300 yards
A 2073
A 259
A 270
A 23
A 27
B 2185
B 2066
A 2010
B 2121
B 2122
B 2119
B 2120
Viaduct Road
London Rd
New England Street
England Rd
Ditchling
Southover St.
Albion Hill
Sussex Street
Carlton Hill
John
Grand Parade
Edward Street
St. James's St.
Marine Parade
Madeira Drive
Trafalgar Street
North Road
Church St.
North St.
Queen's Road
West St.
King's Road
Buckingham Road
Buckingham Pl.
Dyke Road
Dyke Rd
New Road
Old Shoreham Road
Clifton Hill
Vernon Ter.
Upper North St.
Western Road
Montpelier Road
Preston St.
Davigdor Road
Lansdowne Road
Holland Road
Palmeira Avenue
Selborne Rd
Wilbury Road
First Avenue
Second Av.
The Drive
Grand Avenue
Tisbury Road
Norton Rd
Third Av.
Fourth Av.
Church Road
Eaton Road
Cromwell Road
Kingsway

Grand
97-99 Kings Rd BN1 2FW – (01273) 224 300 – general@grandbrighton.co.uk – Fax (01273) 720 613 BZ **v**
196 rm – £ 100/260 £ 110/270 – 4 suites
Rest *Kings* – (Closed Saturday lunch) Menu £ 20/32 **s**
♦ Imposing, white Victorian edifice with a prime place in the sun. Ornate marble, striking staircase, elegant rooms, indulgent cream teas in a quintessentially English lounge. Discreet, traditional grandeur distinguishes restaurant.

Hilton Brighton Metropole rm, rest,
Kings Rd BN1 2FU – (01273) 775 432 – reservations.brightonmet@hilton.com – Fax (01273) 207 764 BZ **s**
327 rm – £ 60/225 £ 105/225, £15.50 – 7 suites – **Rest** – (Closed Saturday lunch) (buffet lunch) Menu £ 23
♦ Impressive late 19C hotel, thoroughly updated: vast conference centres; leisure and beauty suites in the west wing. Spacious, well-kept, modern rooms, some with sea views. Strong traditionality underpins restaurant.

Hotel du Vin
Ship St BN1 1AD – (01273) 718 588 – info.brighton@hotelduvin.com – Fax (01273) 718 599 CZ **a**
37 rm – £ 150/160 £ 325/410, £13.50
Rest *Bistro* – (booking essential) Carte £ 28/38
♦ 19C part Gothic building. Style is the keyword here: lounge bar full of wine books; mezzanine cigar gallery has billiard table. Striking, minimalist rooms, some with terraces. Bistro with bohemian slant: cellar stocks predictably huge wine selection.

ENGLAND

drakes
43-44 Marine Parade BN2 1PE – (01273) 696 934 – info@drakesofbrighton.com – Fax (01273) 684 805 CZ **u**
20 rm – £ 95/145 £ 120/255, £12.50
Rest *The Gingerman at drakes* – see restaurant listing
♦ Refurbished seaside hotel, now with Asian ambience, including Thai artwork. Informal lounge/reception. Stylish rooms with plasma TVs: choose between sea or city views.

Seattle rm, rest,
Brighton Marina BN2 5WA – (01273) 679 799 – seattle@aliashotels.com – Fax (01273) 679 899 CV **c**
71 rm – £ 125 £ 180, £13.50
Rest *Café Paradiso* – Carte £ 21/34
♦ Striking marina setting: exploits its position with delightful "Saloon" lounge and decked terrace. Cocktail bar with Beatles portraits. Light, airy rooms in modish palette. Informal restaurant with totally relaxed feel; absorbing marina views.

Blanch House
17 Atlingworth St BN2 1PL – (01273) 603 504 – info@blanchhouse.co.uk – Fax (01273) 689 813 CZ **o**
12 rm – £ 90 £ 190, £5.50 – **Rest** – (Closed Sunday dinner and Monday) Menu £ 22/32
♦ For something different, this is the place to be. Individually themed bedrooms, all with CDs and videos. Red roses are pinned up in one room; another is full of snow shakers. Stark, minimalist restaurant beyond famed cocktail bar.

Nineteen without rest
19 Broad St BN2 1TJ – (01273) 675 529 – info@hotelnineteen.co.uk – Fax (01273) 675 531 – Closed 24-26 December CZ **z**
8 rm – £ 56/98 £ 90/130
♦ Sleek white bedrooms, some have beds with glass base of panels illuminated by blue lighting. Other attractive features include complimentary Champagne with Sunday breakfast.

Hotel Una without rest

55-56 Regency Square ✉ BN2 2FF – ✆ (01273) 820 464 – reservation@hotel-una.co.uk – Fax (01273) 724 895 BZ **a**

22 rm – †£ 65/160 ††£ 170/270

◆ Comfortable, modern, slightly quirky hotel with alphabetical bedrooms named after rivers around the world. Aragon and Belise are most spacious and come with sauna and jacuzzi.

Adelaide without rest

51 Regency Sq ✉ BN1 2FF – ✆ (01273) 205 286 – info@adelaidehotel.co.uk – Fax (01273) 220 904 – Closed 20-27 December BZ **z**

12 rm – †£ 39/75 ††£ 75/95

◆ Listed Regency town house run by friendly owners. Pretty, period-inspired rooms in floral patterns, some with coronet draped bed heads, and a spacious bow fronted lounge.

Brighton Pavilions without rest

7 Charlotte St ✉ BN2 1AG – ✆ (01273) 621 750 – brightonpavilions@tiscali.co.uk – Fax (01273) 622 477 CV **e**

10 rm – †£ 45/70 ††£ 90/104

◆ Terraced house yards from seafront with something a little different - bedrooms all have individual themes: for example, Titanic Room has clock set at time it hit iceberg!

Brighton House without rest

52 Regency Sq ✉ BN1 2FF – ✆ (01273) 323 282 – info@brighton-house.co.uk – Fax (01273) 773 307 BZ **c**

16 rm – †£ 45/85 ††£ 85/125

◆ Beautiful Regency house on four floors in charming square. Clean, classic décor throughout. Rooms benefit from period detail such as high ceilings and plenty of space.

The Gingerman at drakes

44 Marine Parade ✉ BN2 1PE – ✆ (01273) 696 934 – info@gingermanrestaurants.com – Fax (01273) 684 805 – closed 25 December CZ **u**

Rest – Menu £ 18/32

◆ Set in hotel basement, this cool, contemporary eatery conveys a soft, moody atmosphere. The menus present a good balanced choice of modern British dishes with Gallic twists.

The Gingerman

21A Norfolk Sq ✉ BN1 2PD – ✆ (01273) 326 688 – info@gingermanrestaurants.com – Fax (01273) 326 688 – Closed 1 week Christmas-New Year and Monday BZ **i**

Rest – (booking essential) Menu £ 17/27

◆ Tucked away off the promenade; French and Mediterranean flavours to the fore in a confident, affordable, modern repertoire: genuine neighbourhood feel.

Sevendials

1 Buckingham Pl ✉ BN1 3TD – ✆ (01273) 885 555 – sam@sevendialsrestaurant.co.uk – Fax (0870) 912 74 08 – closed 25-26 December BX **a**

Rest – Carte £ 22/38

◆ Former bank on street corner: the vault now acts as function room. Light, airy feel with high ceiling. Modern menus with local ingredients admirably to fore. Good value lunch.

Terre à Terre

71 East St ✉ BN1 1HQ – ✆ (01273) 729 051 – mail@terreaterre.co.uk – Fax (01273) 327 561 – Closed 24-26 December and Monday CZ **e**

Rest – Vegetarian Menu £ 30 (dinner) – Carte £ 21/35

◆ Hearty helpings of bold, original vegetarian cuisine lyrically evoked on an eclectic menu. Despite its popularity, still friendly, hip and suitably down-to-earth.

ENGLAND

Havana

32 Duke St ✉ BN1 1AG – ✆ (01273) 773 388 – Fax (01273) 748 923 – Closed dinner 25-26 December CZ **c**

Rest – Menu £ 20/35 – Carte £ 17/51

◆ 1790s theatre, now a busy, spacious, two-tiered restaurant, its pediments and balustrades combined with mock-colonial styling. International dishes and exotic combinations.

The Real Eating Company

86-87 Western Rd ✉ BN3 1JB – ✆ (01273) 221 444 – hove@real-eating.co.uk – Fax (01273) 221 442 – closed Christmas, 1 January, Sunday and Monday dinner AY **x**

Rest – (booking essential at dinner) Carte £ 20/29

◆ Unique food store, bursting with speciality foods and 'food to go'. Ground floor dining area exudes buzzy ambience: superb in-house cooking using produce sold in the shop.

Due South

139 King's Rd Arches ✉ BN1 2FN – ✆ (01273) 821 218 – info@duesouth.co.uk BZ **x**

Rest – Carte £ 23/33

◆ Beside the beach, with lovely arch interior: best tables upstairs facing half-moon window overlooking sea. Organic prominence in modern menus using distinctly local produce.

ENGLAND

at Hove

The Claremont without rest

Second Ave ✉ BN3 2LL – ✆ (01273) 735 161 – info@theclaremont.eu – Fax (01273) 736 836 AY **c**

11 rm – †£ 80/90 ††£ 185

◆ Personally run Victorian town house with a neat garden; its tall windows and high ceilings lend a sense of space to the spotlessly kept, traditionally decorated bedrooms.

The Ginger Pig

3 Hove Street ✉ BN3 2TR – ✆ (01273) 736 123 AV **c**

Rest – (bookings not accepted) Carte £ 18/25

◆ Striking pub just off seafront. Contemporary interior with sofas and bold artwork. Spacious dining area and terrace. Keen service. Appealing menu; flavourful, filling food.

BRIGSTEER – Cumbria – see Kendal

BRIMFIELD – Herefordshire – **503** L 27 – see Ludlow

BRIMSCOMBE – Glos. – **503** N 28 – see Stroud

Y. Duhamel/MICHELIN

BRISTOL

County: Bristol
Michelin REGIONAL map: n° 503 M 29
London 121 m – Birmingham 91 m

Population: 420 556
Great Britain

4 **C2**

Access Severn Bridge (toll)

PRACTICAL INFORMATION

Tourist Information

Explore at Bristol, Anchor Rd, Harbourside ✆ (0906) 711 2191, bristol@tourism.bristol.gov.uk

Airport

Bristol Airport: ✆ (0871) 334444, SW: 7 m. by A 38 AX

Bridge

Severn Bridge (toll)

Golf Courses

Mangotsfield Carsons Rd, ✆ (0117) 956 5501 ;

Clifton Beggar Bush Lane, Failand, ✆ (01275) 393 117 ;

Knowle, Fairway Brislington West Town Lane, ✆ (0117) 977 0660 ;

Long Ashton Clarken Coombe, ✆ (01275) 392 229 ;

Stockwood Vale Keynsham Stockwood Lane, ✆ (0117) 986 6505.

ENGLAND

SIGHTS

IN TOWN

City★★ – St Mary Redcliffe★★ DZ - At-Bristol★★ CZ - Brandon Hill★★ AX - Georgian House★★ AX **K** – Harbourside Industrial Museum★★ CZ **M3** - SS Great Britain and Maritime Heritage Centre★ **AC** AX **S2** – The Old City★ CYZ : Theatre Royal★★ CZ **T** - Merchant Seamen's Almshouses★ CZ **Q** – St Stephen's City★ CY **S1** - St John the Baptist★ CY – College Green★ CYZ (Bristol Cathedral★, Lord Mayor's Chapel★) – City Museum and Art Gallery★ AX **M1**

ON THE OUTSKIRTS

Clifton★★ AX (Suspension Bridge★★ (toll), RC Cathedral of St Peter and St Paul★★ **F1**, Bristol Zoological Gardens★★ **AC**, Village★) – Blaise Hamlet★★ - Blaise Castle House Museum★, NW: 5 m. by A 4018 and B 4057 AV

IN THE SURROUNDING AREA

Bath★★★, SE: 13 m. by A 4 BX – Chew Magna★ (Stanton Drew Stone Circles★ **AC**) S: 8 m. by A 37 - BX - and B 3130 – Clevedon★ (Clevedon Court★ **AC**, ⋞ ★) W: 11 ½ m. by A 370, B 3128 - AX - and B 3130

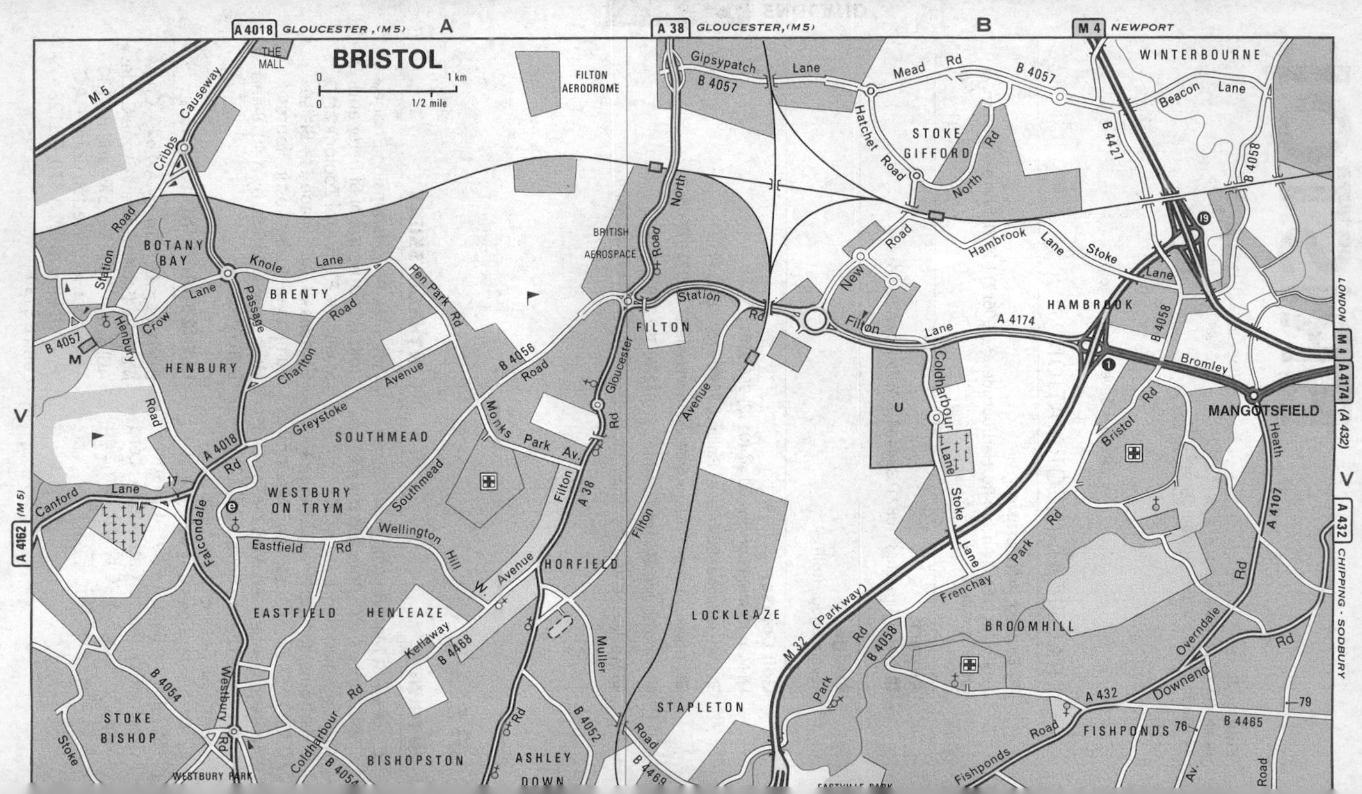
BRISTOL
0 1 km
0 1/2 mile
A 4018 GLOUCESTER ,(M5)
A
A 38 GLOUCESTER,(M5)
B
M 4 NEWPORT
LONDON M 4 A 4174 (A 432)
A 432 CHIPPING - SODBURY
A 4162 (M 5)
THE MALL
M 5
FILTON AERODROME
BRITISH AEROSPACE
WINTERBOURNE
STOKE GIFFORD
HAMBROOK
MANGOTSFIELD
BOTANY BAY
BRENTY
HENBURY
SOUTHMEAD
WESTBURY ON TRYM
FILTON
HORFIELD
LOCKLEAZE
STAPLETON
BROOMHILL
FISHPONDS
EASTFIELD
HENLEAZE
STOKE BISHOP
BISHOPSTON
ASHLEY DOWN
WESTBURY PARK
Cribbs Causeway
Station Road
Knole Lane
Passage
Crow Lane
Henbury Road
B 4057
Charlton Road
Pen Park Rd
Greystoke Avenue
B 4056 Road
Monks Park Av.
A 4018 Rd
Canford Lane
Falcondale
Eastfield Rd
Wellington Hill
W. Avenue
Southmead
Filton A 38
Gloucester Rd
North Road
Station Rd
Filton Avenue
Gipsypatch Lane
B 4057
Mead Rd
Hatchet Road
North Rd
B 4427
Beacon Lane
B 4058
Hambrook Lane
Stoke Lane
New Road
Filton Lane
A 4174
Coldharbour Lane
Stoke Lane
Bromley
Bristol Rd
Heath
A 4107
Frenchay Park Rd
M 32 (Park way)
B 4058 Rd
Park
Overndale Rd
Downend Rd
A 432
B 4465
Fishponds Road
Av.
Road
Kellaway B 4468
Coldharbour Rd
B 4054
Westbury Rd
Stoke
Muller Rd
B 4052
Road B 4469
Rd
U
M
17
76
79

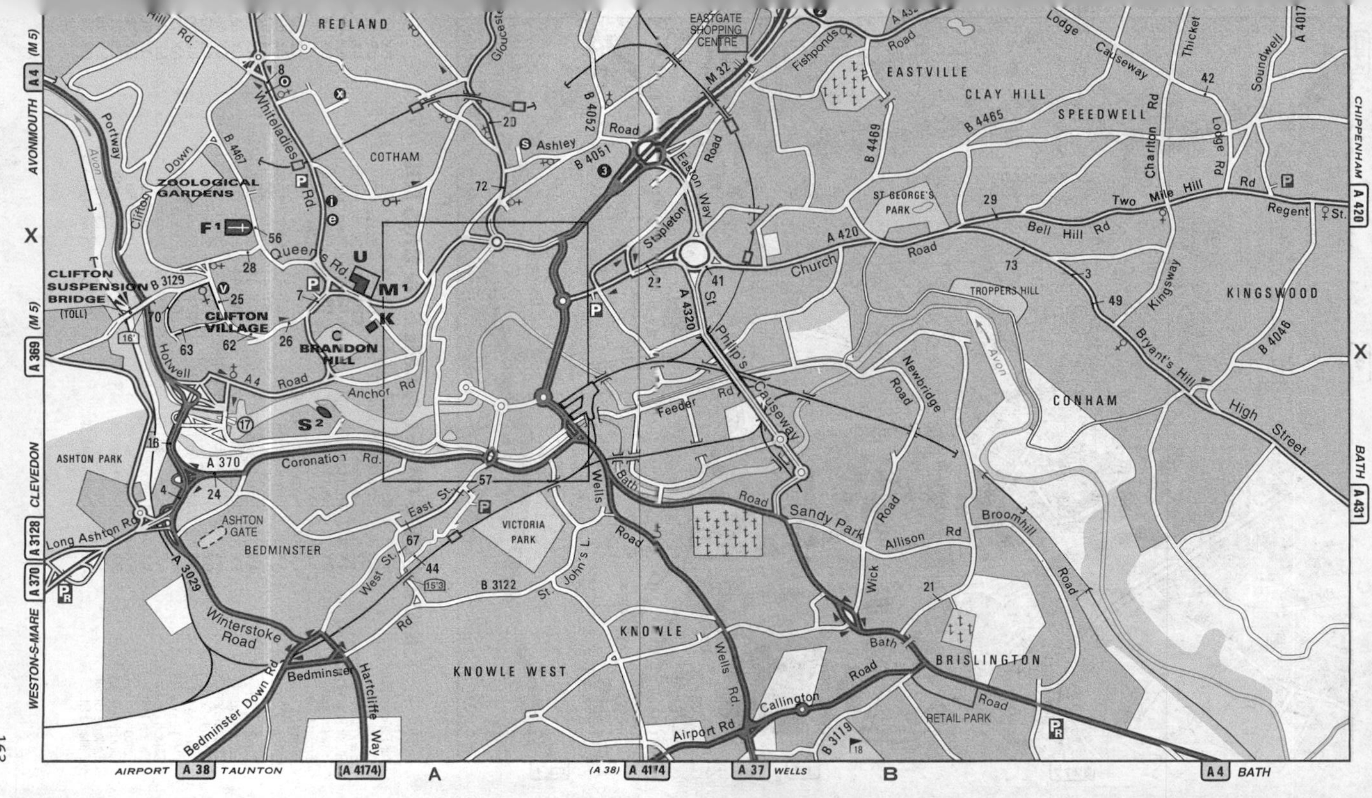

REDLAND
EASTGATE SHOPPING CENTRE
EASTVILLE
CLAY HILL
SPEEDWELL
COTHAM
ZOOLOGICAL GARDENS
CLIFTON SUSPENSION BRIDGE (TOLL)
CLIFTON VILLAGE
BRANDON HILL
ST GEORGE'S PARK
TROPPERS HILL
KINGSWOOD
CONHAM
ASHTON PARK
ASHTON GATE
BEDMINSTER
VICTORIA PARK
KNOWLE
KNOWLE WEST
BRISLINGTON
RETAIL PARK
Avon
Portway
Clifton Down
Whiteladies Rd.
Queen's Rd.
B 4467
B 3129
Hotwell Road
A 4
Anchor Rd
Coronation Rd.
A 370
A 3029
Long Ashton Rd
Winterstoke Road
Bedminster Down Rd
Bedminster
Hartcliffe Way
East St.
West St.
B 3122
St. John's L.
Wells Road
Wells Rd.
Airport Rd
Callington Road
B 3119
Bath Road
Wick Road
Sandy Park Road
Allison Rd
Broomhill Road
Newbridge Road
Feeder Rd
St Philip's Causeway
A 4320
Stapleton Road
Easton Way
Church Road
A 420
Bell Hill Rd
Two Mile Hill Rd
Regent St.
Kingsway
Bryant's Hill
High Street
B 4046
Charlton Rd
Lodge Rd
Lodge Causeway
Thicket
Soundwell
A 4017
Fishponds Road
B 4469
B 4465
M 32
B 4052
B 4051
Ashley
Gloucester
AVONMOUTH A 4 (M 5)
A 369 (M 5)
CLEVEDON A 3128
WESTON-S-MARE A 370
CHIPPENHAM A 420
BATH A 431
AIRPORT A 38 TAUNTON
(A 4174)
(A 38) A 4174
A 37 WELLS
A 4 BATH
A
B
X

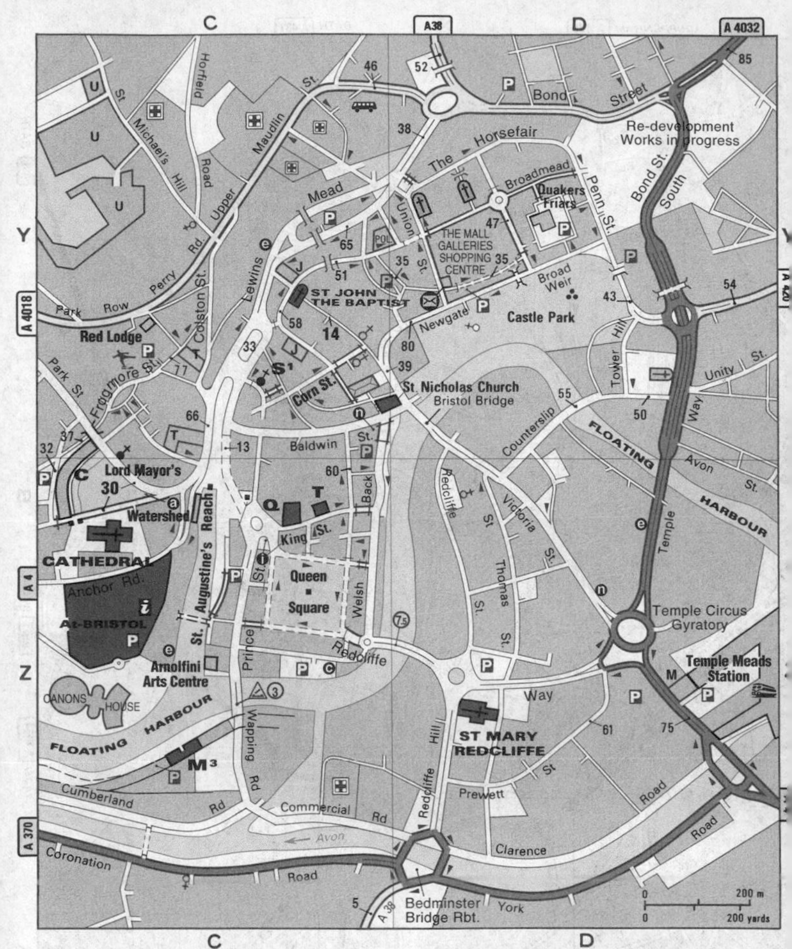

INDEX OF STREET NAMES IN BRISTOL

Bristol Marriott Royal

College Green ✉ *BS1 5TA* – ✆ *(0117) 925 51 00*
– Fax (0117) 251 515 CZ **a**
230 rm – ††£ 159/169, ☕ £ 16.95 – 12 suites
Rest *Terrace* – (bar lunch) Carte approx. £ 38 **s**
◆ Striking Victorian building next to the cathedral and facing College Green. Bedrooms, classic and individual, combine period styling and an array of modern facilities. Classic style at Terrace: wide variety of dishes to suit all tastes.

Hotel du Vin

The Sugar House, Lewins Mead ✉ *BS1 2NU* – ✆ *(0117) 925 5577*
– info.bristol@hotelduvin.com – Fax (0117) 925 1199 CY **e**
40 rm – †£ 140/170 ††£ 140/170, ☕ £ 13.50
Rest *Bistro* – see restaurant listing
◆ A massive chimney towers over the 18C sugar refinery; stylish loft rooms in minimalist tones: dark leather and wood, low-slung beds, Egyptian linen and subtle wine curios.

Mercure Brigstow Bristol

5-7 Welsh Back ✉ *BS1 4SP* – ✆ *(0117) 929 1030*
– H6548@accor.com – Fax (0117) 929 2030 CY **n**
115 rm ☕ – †£ 187 ††£ 199 – 1 suite
Rest *Ellipse* – Carte £ 24/34
◆ Smart city centre hotel with charming riverside position. Stylish public areas typified by lounges and mezzanine. 21C rooms, full of curves, bright colours and plasma TVs. Modern brasserie and bar overlooking river.

City Inn

Temple Way ✉ *BS1 6BF* – ✆ *(0117) 925 1001 – bristol.reservations@cityinn.com*
– Fax (0117) 910 2727 – closed 24-27December DZ **e**
167 rm – †£ 175 ††£ 175, ☕ £ 12.50
Rest *City Café* – Menu £ 15/17 **s** – Carte £ 19/33 **s**
◆ An affordable, central hotel. Airy, well-insulated rooms in intelligent contemporary designs and usefully supplied with mod cons. Sharp brasserie; terrace overlooks Temple Gardens.

Novotel

Victoria St ✉ *BS1 6HY* – ✆ *(0117) 976 9988 – h5622@accor.com*
– Fax (0117) 925 5040 DZ **n**
130 rm – †£ 139 ††£ 139, ☕ £ 12 – 1 suite – **Rest** – (meals in bar Saturday-Sunday) Carte £ 21/33
◆ Purpose-built hotel in heart of business district, close to Temple Meads station. Ample conference facilities. Bedrooms are spacious and up-to-date. Open-plan lounge bar and restaurant catering for many tastes.

Bordeaux Quay (The Restaurant)

First Floor, V-Shed, Canons Way ✉ *BS1 5UH* – ✆ *(0117) 943 1200*
– info@bordeaux-quay.co.uk – Fax (0117) 906 5567 – Closed 25 December and Sunday CZ **e**
Rest – Menu £ 24 (lunch) – Carte dinner £ 25/37
◆ Former dockside warehouse for Bordeaux wine, now a deli and vast restaurant with concrete ceiling, good quayside views and frequently changing menus with strong ethical base.

Bell's Diner

1 York Rd, Montpelier ✉ *BS6 5QB* – ✆ *(0117) 924 0357 – info@bellsdiner.co.uk*
– Fax (0117) 924 4280 – Closed 24-30 December, Saturday and Monday lunch and Sunday AX **s**
Rest – Menu £ 45 – Carte £ 26/33
◆ Two-roomed restaurant; rear more modern; front more characterful. Small lounge. Innovative menus with clever combinations of taste, flavours and texture. Precise cooking.

ENGLAND

XX **Bistro** – at Hotel du Vin

The Sugar House, Narrow Lewins Mead ✉ BS1 2NU – ☎ (0117) 925 5577 – Fax (0117) 925 1199 CY **e**

Rest – (booking essential) Menu £ 18 (lunch) – Carte £ 27/34

◆ A stylish candlelit milieu artfully created; flavourful, well-judged menu of classics, alongside plethora of wine memorabilia and very good wine list: a bon viveur's treat.

XX **Deason's**

43 Whiteladies Rd ✉ BS8 2LS – ☎ (0117) 973 6230 – enquiries@deasons.co.uk – Fax (0117) 923 7394 – Closed 25-26 December, Sunday dinner and Monday AX **e**

Rest – Carte £ 20/37

◆ Modern art hangs stylishly from the walls of this period terraced property. Seasonally influenced menus offer a bold mix of modern, classic and traditional dishes.

XX **Casamia**

38 High St, Westbury-on-Trym, Northwest : 2 m. by A 4018 ✉ BS9 3DZ – ☎ (0117) 959 2884 – Fax (0117) 959 3658 – Closed 25 -31 December, first week January, first week September, Sunday and Bank Holidays AV **e**

Rest – Italian Carte £ 24/43

◆ Seek and find this neighbourhood restaurant hidden in a pleasant village suburb. Sip an aperitif in cosy bar and select from a wide-ranging menu with strong Italian roots.

ENGLAND

X **Riverstation**

The Grove, Harbourside ✉ BS1 4RB – ☎ (0117) 914 4434 – relax@riverstation.co.uk – Fax (0117) 934 9990 – Closed 24-26 December and 1 January CZ **c**

Rest – Menu £ 15 – Carte £ 28/34

◆ Striking first floor restaurant, and ground floor café, with great views of harbour activity. Open plan with lots of glass. Full-flavoured mains; good value lunches, too.

X **Quartier Vert**

85 Whiteladies Rd, Clifton ✉ BS8 2NT – ☎ (0117) 973 4482 – info@quartiervert.co.uk – Fax (0117) 904 8617 – Closed Christmas and Sunday dinner in winter AX **i**

Rest – Menu £ 15 (lunch) – Carte £ 26/38

◆ Modern, bustling eatery at forefront of city's organic movement. Med influenced daily changing menus, tapas bar, coffees on terrace. Good organic ingredients always to fore.

X **Culinaria**

1 Chandos Rd, Redland ✉ BS6 6PG – ☎ (0117) 973 7999 – closed 2 weeks Summer, Christmas, Easter, Sunday-Wednesday AX **x**

Rest – (dinner only and lunch Friday and Saturday) Carte £ 24/30

◆ Combined deli and eatery; the personally run diner is informal with lots of light and space. Sound cooking behind a collection of Mediterranean, English and French dishes.

X **Fishworks**

128 Whiteladies Rd, Clifton ✉ BS8 2RS – ☎ (0117) 974 4433 – bristol@fishworks.co.uk – Fax (0117) 974 4933 – Closed 25-26 December, 1 January and Monday AX **o**

Rest – Seafood (booking essential) Carte £ 25/49

◆ Bustling seafood restaurant in a fishmongers: choose your ingredients from the fish counter. Menus created from whatever arrives fresh on the day. Vibrant blackboard choice.

Queen Square Dining Room and Bar

63 Queen Square ✉ BS1 4JZ – ☎ (0117) 929 0700 – info@queen-square.com – Closed 25-30 December, 1-6 January and Monday AV **v**

Rest – Menu £ 16 – Carte £ 20/28

◆ Contemporary, open plan pub with leather sofas and lively atmosphere. More formal restaurant serving precisely cooked modern dishes made with local produce. Polite service.

The Albion Public House and Dining Rooms
Boyces Avenue, Clifton Village ✉ *BS8 4AA – ✆ (0117) 973 3522 – info@thealbionclifton.co.uk – Fax (0117) 973 9768 – Closed 25-26 December, 1 January, Sunday dinner and Monday* AX **v**
Rest – (booking essential) Carte £ 24/34
◆ Grade II listed 17C inn hidden away in Clifton. Loads of character: settles, beams and roaring fire lend a suitably rustic feel for the enjoyment of tasty West Country fare.

at Patchway North : 6½ m. on A 38 - BV – ✉ Bristol

Aztec rm,
Aztec West Business Park, North : 1 m. by A 38 ✉ *BS32 4TS – ✆ (01454) 201 090 – aztec@shirehotels.com – Fax (01454) 201 593 – Closed 22-28 December*
125 rm – £ 179 £ 229/269 – 3 suites
Rest *Quarterjacks* – (Closed lunch Saturday and Sunday) Carte £ 27/35
◆ Reclaimed beams and Cotswold stone add warmth to a smartly run group hotel. State of art gym facilities. Large, well-appointed rooms; some, with patios, overlook small lake. Restaurant has sheltered terrace for alfresco dinners.

at Hunstrete Southeast : 10 m. by A 4 and A 37 - BX - off A 368 – ✉ Bristol

Hunstrete House (heated)
✉ *BS39 4NS – ✆ (01761) 490 490 – reception@hunstretehouse.co.uk – Fax (01761) 490 732*
22 rm – £ 115/135 £ 225 – 3 suites – **Rest** – Menu £ 20/48
◆ Fine late 17C manor and deer park near the Mendips. Drawing room, library and bedrooms with antiques, period style furniture and the idiosyncratic charm of a family seat. Restaurant, overlooking courtyard, uses produce from its walled kitchen garden.

at Chew Magna South : 8¼ m. by A 37 - BX - on B 3130 – ✉ Bristol

Bear & Swan
South Parade ✉ *BS40 8SL – ✆ (01275) 331 100 – enquiries@bearandswan.co.uk – Fax (01275) 331 204 – Closed Monday*
Rest – (Closed Sunday dinner) Menu £ 9 – Carte £ 25/30
◆ Food is very much the emphasis of this 19C stone pub. At a pleasant dining area of reclaimed floorboards and antique tables and chairs, you can enjoy modern eclectic dishes.

at Stanton Wick South : 9 m. by A 37 - BX - and A 368 on Stanton Wick rd – ✉ Bristol

Carpenters Arms with rm
✉ *BS39 4BX – ✆ (01761) 490 202 – carpenters@buccaneer.co.uk – Fax (01761) 490 763 – Closed dinner 25-26 December*
12 rm – £ 67 £ 95 – **Rest** – Carte £ 20/29
◆ A row of converted miners' cottages in a rural village: cosy, firelit real ale bar with exposed stone walls and good-sized, pine furnished rooms in subtle floral patterns. Popular beamed "parlour" for meals.

BRITWELL SALOME – Oxon. 11 **C2**

London 75 m – Oxford 21 m – Reading 19 m

The Goose
✉ *OX49 5LG – ✆ (01491) 612 304 – thegooseatbritwellsalome@fsmail.net – Fax (01491) 613 945 – Closed dinner Sunday and Monday*
Rest – Menu £ 15 (lunch) – Carte £ 31/43
Spec. Pig's trotter, smoked ham hock, tomato salad, caper and raisin purée. Roast lamb rump, seared liver, minted spring vegetables. Savarin of strawberries, natural yoghurt cream and mint syrup.
◆ Elegant yet snug, its cosy bar lit by tea lamps and an intimate main dining room. Assured and knowledgeable modern cooking makes good use of well-sourced local ingredients. Friendly service.

BROAD CAMPDEN – Glos. – see Chipping Campden

BROAD OAK – E. Sussex 9 D1

London 62 m – Hastings 8 m – Rye 7 m

Fairacres without rest

Udimore Rd, on B 2089 ✉ TN31 6DG – ✆ (01424) 883 236 – john-shelagh@fairacres.fsworld.co.uk – Fax (01424) 883 236 – closed Christmas

3 rm – †£ 40/60 ††£ 90

◆ Listed 17C cottage in picture-postcard pink. Big breakfasts under low beams. Individual rooms: one overlooks superb magnolia tree in garden. All have many thoughtful extras.

BROADHEMBURY – Devon – 503 K 31 – ✉ Honiton 2 D2

London 191 m – Exeter 17 m – Honiton 5 m – Taunton 23 m

The Drewe Arms

✉ EX14 3NF – ✆ (01404) 841 267 – Closed 25 December

Rest – Seafood (closed Sunday dinner) (booking essential) Carte £ 20/50

◆ At heart of a historic cob and thatch village; snug bar, rustic dining areas and marine theme. Prime local fish, simply prepared with quality ingredients. Relaxed atmosphere.

ENGLAND

The red symbol?
This denotes the very essence of peace
– only the sound of birdsong first thing in the morning …

BROADSTAIRS – Kent – 504 Y 29 9 D1

London 77 m – Canterbury 18 m – Ramsgate 2 m

The Victoria without rest

23 Victoria Parade ✉ CT10 1QL – ✆ (01843) 871 010 – mullin@thevictoriabroadstairs.co.uk – Fax (01843) 860 888 – Closed 25-26 December

9 rm – †£ 35/60 ††£ 129

◆ Large 19C house with views to Viking Bay, harbour and gardens. Proud use of Kentish produce at breakfast. Spotless rooms: The Balcony, in prime position, overlooks the front.

BROADWAY – Worcs. – 503 O 27 – pop. 2 496 *Great Britain* 19 C3

London 93 m – Birmingham 36 m – Cheltenham 15 m – Oxford 38 m – Worcester 22 m

1 Cotswold Court ✆ (01386) 852937

Town★

Country Park (Broadway Tower ✵ ★★★), SE : 2 m. by A 44 – Snowshill Manor★ (Terrace Garden★) AC, S : 2½ m

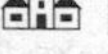

The Lygon Arms AC rest,

High St ✉ WR12 7DU – ✆ (01386) 852 255 – info@thelygonarms.co.uk – Fax (01386) 854 470

75 rm – †£ 101/241 ††£ 113/253 – 6 suites

Rest *Goblets* – see restaurant listing

Rest *The Great Hall* – (dinner only and Sunday lunch) Menu £ 39 (dinner) – Carte £ 40/70

◆ Superbly enticing, quintessentially English coaching inn with many 16C architectural details in its panelled, beamed interiors and rooms Charles I and Cromwell once stayed in. Refined dining and baronial splendours: heraldic friezes and minstrels' gallery.

Dormy House
Willersey Hill, East : 3 ¼ m. by A 44 and Broadway Golf Club rd ✉ WR12 7LF – ✆ (01386) 852 711 – reservations@dormyhouse.co.uk – Fax (01386) 858 636 – closed 25-26 December
42 rm – †£ 150/200 ††£ 200 – 3 suites
Rest *The Dining Room* – (dinner only and Sunday lunch) Menu £ 27/37 – Carte £ 27/47
Rest *Barn Owl* – Carte £ 20/28
◆ Creeper-clad 17C farmhouse and outbuildings. Sizeable rooms and comfortable lounge: open fires, wing armchairs and a warm country house palette. Dine in cosy, rustic rooms or conservatory. Barn Owl is an A-framed hall with flagged floors.

The Broadway
The Green ✉ WR12 7AA – ✆ (01386) 852 401 – info@broadwayhotel.info – Fax (01386) 853 879
19 rm – †£ 70/140 ††£ 70/200
Rest *The Courtyard* – Menu £ 16/26
◆ A 16C inn on the green, built as an abbot's retreat; sympathetically updated rooms in a pretty mix of rural patterns with an atmospheric, horse racing themed, timbered bar. Half-timbered restaurant with leaded windows.

The Olive Branch without rest
78 High St ✉ WR12 7AJ – ✆ (01386) 853 440 – davidpam@theolivebranch-broadway.com – Fax (01386) 859 070
8 rm – †£ 45/65 ††£ 75/85
◆ A 1590s former staging post on the high street run by a friendly husband and wife team. Flagged floors, sandstone walls and compact bedrooms with a few charming touches.

ENGLAND

Windrush House without rest
Station Rd ✉ WR12 7DE – ✆ (01386) 853 577 – evan@broadway-windrush.co.uk – Fax (01386) 852 850
5 rm – †£ 70/80 ††£ 80/90
◆ Personally run guesthouse and landscaped garden with an updated Edwardian elegance and subtle period style. Tastefully individual rooms; pleasant views to front and rear.

Whiteacres without rest
Station Rd ✉ WR12 7DE – ✆ (01386) 852 320 – whiteacres@btinternet.com
5 rm – †£ 60 ††£ 70/75
◆ Spacious accommodation - homely, pleasantly updated and modestly priced - in a personally owned Victorian house, a short walk from the village centre.

Russell's with rm
20 High St ✉ WR12 7DT – ✆ (01386) 853 555 – info@russellsofbroadway.com – Fax (01386) 853 964
7 rm – †£ 90/125 ††£ 245 – **Rest** – (closed Sunday dinner and Bank Holiday Monday dinner) Menu £ 17/23 – Carte £ 31/44
◆ Behind the splendid Cotswold stone façade lies a stylish modern restaurant with terrace front and rear. Seasonally influenced, regularly changing menus. Smart, comfy bedrooms.

Goblets
High St ✉ WR12 7DU – ✆ (01386) 854 418 – Fax (01386) 858 611
Rest – (booking essential) Carte £ 25/30
◆ Characterfully firelit in rustic dark oak. Modern dining room at front more atmospheric than one to rear. Menus of light, tasty, seasonal dishes offered.

at Buckland Southwest : 2 ¼ m. by B 4632 – ✉ **Broadway**

Buckland Manor

✉ *WR12 7LY – ✆ (01386) 852 626 – info@bucklandmanor.co.uk*
– Fax (01386) 853 557
14 rm – †£ 260 ††£ 470 – **Rest** – (booking essential for non-residents)
Menu £ 26 (lunch) – Carte £ 41/58
◆ Secluded part 13C country house with beautiful gardens. Individually furnished bedrooms boast high degree of luxury. Fine service throughout as old-world serenity prevails. Restaurant boasts elegant crystal, fine china and smooth service.

BROCKDISH – Norfolk – **504** X 26 – see Diss

BROCKENHURST – Hants. – **503** P 31 – **pop. 2 865** *Great Britain* 6 **A2**

London 99 m – Bournemouth 17 m – Southampton 14 m – Winchester 27 m
Brockenhurst Manor Sway Rd, ✆ (01590) 623 332 .
New Forest★★ (Rhinefield Ornamental Drive★★, Bolderwood Ornamental Drive★★)

Rhinefield House

Rhinefield Rd, Northwest : 3 m. ✉ *SO42 7QB*
– ✆ (01590) 622 922 – rhinefieldhouse@handpicked.co.uk
– Fax (01590) 622 800
50 rm – †£ 175/240 ††£ 185/250
Rest *Armada* – Menu £ 20/38 – Carte approx. £ 38
◆ A long ornamental pond reflects this imposing 19C New Forest mansion, surveying parterres and a yew maze. Panelled drawing room. Handsomely appointed bedrooms in 21C wing. Dining room in gleaming oak with forest views.

Careys Manor

Lyndhurst Rd, on A 337 ✉ *SO42 7RH – ✆ (01590) 623 551*
– stay@careysmanor.com – Fax (01590) 622 799
78 rm – †£ 145/150 ††£ 198 – 1 suite
Rest – (dinner only) Menu £ 34 – Carte approx. £ 50
Rest *Blaireau's* – French – ✆ (01590) 623 032 – Carte £ 22/32
Rest *The Zen Garden* – Thai (closed dinner Sunday and Monday)
Carte £ 24/41
◆ Smartly run, substantial 19C house near main road, with modern additions and superb new spa. Some bedrooms have balcony overlooking gardens; manor house rooms are the best. Fine dining in smart restaurant. Blaireau's is informal bistro with hints of French styling. Authentic Thai cuisine in The Zen Garden.

New Park Manor (heated)

Lyndhurst Rd, North : 1½ m. on A 337 ✉ *SO42 7QH*
– ✆ (01590) 623 467 – info@newparkmanorhotel.co.uk
– Fax (01590) 622 268
24 rm – †£ 153/188 ††£ 205/275
Rest *Stag* – Menu £ 42 (dinner) – Carte £ 35/42
◆ Extended, elegantly proportioned hunting lodge with equestrian centre for guided forest treks. Rooms, some in former servants' quarters, have four posters and parkland views. Candlelit fine dining.

Cloud

Meerut Rd ✉ *SO42 7TD – ✆ (01590) 622 165*
– enquiries@cloudhotel.co.uk – Fax (01590) 622 818
– Closed 2 weeks December-January
17 rm – †£ 72/150 ††£ 145/166 – **Rest** – Menu £ 15/33 **s**
◆ Well-kept, comfortable and personally owned, with something of a country cottage character. Simple, pine furnished accommodation; views over the wooded countryside. Intimate little restaurant with pleasant covered terrace.

ENGLAND

The Cottage without rest
Sway Rd ✉ S042 7SH – ✆ (01590) 622 296 – chris@cottagehotel.org – Fax (01590) 623 014 – closed Christmas
12 rm – ♦£ 50/80 ♦♦£ 50/140
◆ 300-year old former forester's cottage in the heart of the village: family run and faultlessly kept. Low oak beamed ceiling, cosy snug bar and large, neatly appointed rooms.

Le Poussin at Whitley Ridge (Alex Aitken) with rm
Beaulieu Rd, East : 1 m. on B 3055 ✉ SO42 7QL – ✆ (01590) 622 354 – info@whitleyridge.co.uk – Fax (01590) 622 856
17 rm – ♦£ 190/230 ♦♦£ 190/310 – 1 suite
Rest – Menu £ 20/45
Spec. Poached breast of quail, confit leg salad, Scotch egg with truffle. Roast turbot with shellfish broth. Passion fruit soufflé with passion fruit sauce, sorbet and curd.
◆ Attractive, wisteria-clad Georgian house located in 14 acres of mature gardens in the New Forest. Stylish, individually decorated bedrooms. Attractive dining room overlooking front lawn; well-dressed tables and formal service. Extensive use of local/wild ingredients and touches of individuality in the cooking.

Simply Poussin
The Courtyard, rear of 49-51 Brookley Rd ✉ SO42 7FZ – ✆ (01590) 623 063 – simply@lepoussin.co.uk – Fax (01590) 623 144 – closed Sunday-Monday
Rest – (booking essential) Menu £ 16 (lunch) – Carte approx. £ 21
◆ Intimate little mews restaurant, tucked away off the village centre, with well-spaced, subtly spotlit tables. Capable, flavourful modern British menu; unobtrusive service.

Thatched Cottage with rm
16 Brookley Rd ✉ SO42 7RR – ✆ (01590) 623 090 – sales@thatchedcottage.co.uk – Fax (01590) 623 479
5 rm – ♦£ 70/90 ♦♦£ 140/170 – **Rest** – (closed Monday and Tuesday) (booking essential) Menu £ 15 (lunch) – Carte approx. £ 50
◆ 17C farmhouse and one-off rooms with a touch of eccentricity to their blend of curios, pictures and bright flowers. Open kitchen; elaborate, locally sourced menu.

at Sway Southwest : 3 m. by B 3055 – ✉ Lymington

The Nurse's Cottage with rm
Station Rd ✉ SO41 6BA – ✆ (01590) 683 402 – nurses.cottage@lineone.net – Fax (01590) 683 402 – closed 3 weeks February-March and 3 weeks November
5 rm – ♦£ 85/105 ♦♦£ 160/180 – **Rest** – (dinner only) (booking essential) Menu £ 24
◆ Personally run, welcoming conservatory restaurant with an intimate charm. Traditional menus make good use of Hampshire's larder. Pristine, comfy rooms with pretty details.

BROCKTON – Shrops. – see Much Wenlock

BROCKWORTH – Glos. – **504** N 28 – see Cheltenham

BROME – Suffolk – **504** X 26 – see Diss (Norfolk)

ENGLAND

Good food and accommodation at moderate prices?
Look for the Bib symbols:
red Bib Gourmand for food, blue Bib Hotel for hotels

BROMFIELD – Shrops. – 503 L 26 – see Ludlow

BROMSGROVE – Worcs. – 503 N 26 – pop. 29 237 19 C2

London 117 m – Birmingham 14 m – Bristol 71 m – Worcester 13 m
Bromsgrove Museum, 26 Birmingham Rd ☎ (01527) 831809

Bromsgrove Country House without rest
249 Worcester Rd, Stoke Heath, Southwest : 2 m. on B 4091 ✉ B61 7JA – ☎ (01527) 835 522 – Closed 2 weeks Christmas-New Year
8 rm – †£ 55 ††£ 66
◆ Personally run, redbrick Victorian house, on a main road, converted but with original tiling and other period features intact. Sizeable rooms are homely and well kept.

BROOK – Hants. – 503 P 31 – ✉ Lyndhurst 6 A2

London 92 m – Bournemouth 24 m – Southampton 14 m

Bell Inn
✉ SO43 7HE – ☎ (023) 8081 2214 – bell@bramshaw.co.uk – Fax (023) 8081 3958
25 rm (dinner included) – †£ 105/130 ††£ 210 – **Rest** – (bar lunch Monday-Saturday) Menu £ 30 – Carte £ 18/29
◆ Family owned for over 200 years, an extended inn with golf course and clubhouse. Cosy, clubby bar with an open fire and tasty light menu; neat, modern, pine fitted rooms.

BROUGHTON – Cambs. – see Huntingdon

BROUGHTON – Lancs. – 502 L 22 – see Preston

BROXTON – Ches. – 502 L 24 20 A3

London 197 m – Birmingham 68 m – Chester 12 m – Manchester 44 m – Stoke-on-Trent 29 m

De Vere Carden Park rm, rest,
West : 1½ m. on A 534 ✉ CH3 9DQ – ☎ (01829) 731 000 – reservations.carden@devere-hotels.co.uk – Fax (01829) 731 032
189 rm – †£ 90/190 ††£ 100/200 – 7 suites
Rest ***Redmonds Restaurant*** – (dinner only) Carte £ 28/32
Rest ***The Brasserie*** – Carte £ 17/28
◆ Very well equipped and up-to-date leisure hotel with extensive grounds in a rural location. Golf breaks a speciality. Main house or courtyard rooms are equally comfortable. Formal Redmonds Restaurant with Carden estate wines. Smart Brasserie.

XX **Cock O Barton**
Barton Rd, Barton, West : 2 m. on a 534 ✉ SY14 7HU – ☎ (01829) 782 277 – info@thecockobarton.co.uk – Fax (01829) 782 888 – closed 25 December, 2 January and Sunday dinner
Rest – Menu £ 13 – Carte £ 28/47
◆ Stylishly furnished restaurant; delightful dining room featuring antler chandeliers. Local, traceable ingredients and regional meats and cheeses. Sharing plates a speciality.

BRUNDALL – Norfolk – 504 Y 26 15 D2

London 118 m – Great Yarmouth 15 m – Norwich 8 m

XX **The Lavender House**
39 The Street ✉ NR13 5AA – ☎ (01603) 712 215 – closed 23 - 31 December, Sunday and Monday
Rest – (dinner only) (booking essential) Menu £ 38 s
◆ Locally renowned restaurant with pleasant lounge for pre-prandials. Intimate, beamed dining room. Proudly local menus with the suppliers listed; ingredients are in season.

ENGLAND

BRUNTINGTHORPE – Leics. *Great Britain* 16 **B3**

London 96 m – Leicester 10 m – Market Harborough 15 m

Leicester - Museum and Art Gallery★, Guildhall★ and St Mary de Castro Church★, N : 11 m. by minor rd and A 5199

Joiners Arms

Church Walk ✉ LE17 5QH – ✆ (0116) 247 8258 – stephenjoiners@btconnect.com – Closed 25-26 December

Rest – (closed Sunday dinner and Monday) (booking essential) Menu £ 13 – Carte £ 20/26

◆ A charming 18C with small front terrace, large main bar and chatty service. Hearty, classical dishes are homemade using locally sourced ingredients.

BRUSHFORD – Somerset – 503 J 30 – see Dulverton

BRUTON – Somerset – 503 M 30 – pop. 2 982 4 **C2**

London 118 m – Bristol 27 m – Bournemouth 44 m – Salisbury 35 m – Taunton 36 m

Stourhead★★★ AC, W : 8 m. by B 3081

Bruton House with rm

2-4 High St ✉ BA10 0AA – ✆ (01749) 813 395 – info@brutonhouse.co.uk – closed 2 weeks January, 2 weeks August, Sunday and Monday

2 rm – †£ 45 ††£ 70, ☕ £ 7.50 – **Rest** – Menu £ 39 (dinner) **s** – Carte £ 20/39 **s**

◆ Comfy lounge for canapés and drinks. Intimate dining room with dark beams and contemporary artwork. Classic British dishes with modern touches, cooked using local produce. Simple bedrooms – rear one is quieter.

Truffles

95 High St ✉ BA10 0AR – ✆ (01749) 812 255 – deborah@trufflesbruton.co.uk – closed Sunday Evening and Monday

Rest – (dinner only and Sunday lunch) Menu £ 20/30

◆ Cottagey façade; intimate and cosy two-level interior. Personally run, the husband and wife team take pride in a small, well prepared menu rich in market fresh local produce.

Do not confuse ✗ with ✿!
✗ defines comfort, while stars are awarded for the best cuisine, across all categories of comfort.

BRYHER – Cornwall – 503 ?30 – see Scilly (Isles of)

BUCKDEN – Cambs. – 504 T 27 – pop. 2 385 – ✉ Huntingdon 14 **A2**

London 65 m – Bedford 15 m – Cambridge 20 m – Northampton 31 m

The George

High St ✉ PE19 5XA – ✆ (01480) 812 300 – manager@thegeorgebuckden.com – Fax (01480) 813 920

12 rm – †£ 80/100 ††£ 130

Rest *Brasserie* – see restaurant listing

◆ Delightfully restored former 19C coaching inn with stylish, contemporary look, typified by leather tub chairs and sofas. Smart bedrooms are all named after famous Georges.

Lion

High St ✉ PE19 5XA – ✆ (01480) 810 313 – reception@thelionbuckden.co.uk – Fax (01480) 811 070 – closed 1 January

15 rm ☕ – †£ 65/74 ††£ 80/90 – **Rest** – Carte £ 19/32

◆ Charming 15C inn with panelled bar, period fireplace and beautifully ornate ceiling. Individually decorated bedrooms, some with four posters. Resident ghost: the Lady in Grey. Dining room with stained glass windows.

ENGLAND

Brasserie – at The George H.

High St ✉ PE19 5XA – ☎ (01480) 812 300 – manager@thegeorgebuckden.com – Fax (01480) 813 920

Rest – Carte £ 24/36

◆ Spacious, modern brasserie serving a range from traditional English game to Mediterranean and Moroccan influenced dishes. French windows lead to courtyard, creating airy feel.

BUCKHORN WESTON – Dorset 4 C3

The Stapleton Arms with rm

Church Hill ✉ SP8 5HS – ☎ (01963) 370 396 – relax@thestapletonarms.com – Fax (01963) 370 396

4 rm – †£ 72/96 ††£ 120 – **Rest** – Carte £ 19/26

◆ Smart, stylish pub with flag-floored bar and more formal dining room. Menu offers wide range; from traditional pub dishes to those with Mediterranean touches. Comfortable bedrooms, some with under-floor heating.

BUCKINGHAM – Bucks. – 503 Q 27 *Great Britain* 11 C1

London 64 m – Birmingham 61 m – Northampton 20 m – Oxford 25 m

Silverstone Stowe Silverstone Rd, ☎ (01280) 850 005 ;

Tingewick Rd, ☎ (01280) 815 566 .

Stowe Gardens★★, NW : 3 m. by minor rd. Claydon House★ AC, S : 8 m. by A 413

Villiers rest,

3 Castle St ✉ MK18 1BS – ☎ (01280) 822 444 – villiers@oxfordshire-hotels.co.uk – Fax (01280) 822 113

43 rm – †£ 70/150 ††£ 85/160 – 3 suites

Rest *Villiers* – Carte £ 30/36

◆ 17C former coaching inn at centre of town opposite old town hall. Attractive cobbled courtyard for al fresco dining. Traditionally furnished lounge and bedrooms. Modern restaurant serves inspired dishes with Mediterranean influences.

BUCKLAND – Glos. – 503 O 27 – see Broadway (Worcs.)

BUCKLAND – Oxon. – 503 P 28 – ✉ Faringdon 10 A2

London 78 m – Oxford 16 m – Swindon 15 m

The Lamb at Buckland

Lamb Lane ✉ SN7 8QN – ☎ (01367) 870 484 – enquiries@thelambatbuckland.co.uk – Fax (01367) 870 675 – Closed 24 December-8 January, Sunday dinner and Monday

Rest – Carte £ 17/36

◆ Family-owned 17C pub decorated with ovine-inspired curios. Rear garden and sunken terrace. Heavily beamed restaurant; tasty traditional British cooking on blackboard menu.

BUCKLAND MARSH – Oxon. – pop. 2 243 10 A2

London 76 m – Faringdon 4 m – Oxford 15 m

The Trout at Tadpole Bridge with rm

✉ SN7 8RF – ☎ (01367) 870 382 – info@troutinn.co.uk – Fax (01367) 870 912 – Closed 25 and 31 December and 1 January

6 rm – †£ 80 ††£ 110 – **Rest** – (closed Sunday dinner) Carte £ 23/32

◆ Pretty stone pub with gardens leading to River Thames. Own moorings. Open plan bar with log burners. Quality cooking using local produce. Comfortable, well-furnished bedrooms.

BUCKLERS HARD – Hants. – 503 P 31 – see Beaulieu

BUDE – Cornwall – 503 G 31 – pop. 8 071 1 B2

London 252 m – Exeter 51 m – Plymouth 50 m – Truro 53 m
Bude Visitor Centre, The Crescent (01208) 76616
Burn View, (01288) 352 006 .
The Breakwater★★ – Compass Point (< ★)
Poughill★ (church★★), N : 2½ m. - E : Tamar River★★ – Kilkhampton (Church★), NE : 5½ m. by A 39 – Stratton (Church★), E : 1½ m. – Launcells (Church★), E : 3 m. by A 3072 – Marhamchurch (St Morwenne's Church★), SE : 2½ m. by A 39 – Poundstock★ (< ★★, church★, guildhouse★), S : 4½ m. by A 39. Morwenstow (cliffs★★, church★), N : 8½ m. by A 39 and minor roads - Jacobstow (Church★), S : 7 m. by A 39

Falcon

Breakwater Rd EX23 8SD – (01288) 352 005 – reception@falconhotel.com – Fax (01288) 356 359 – closed 25 December
29 rm – £ 60/75 £ 120/125 – **Rest** – Carte £ 19/28 **s**
◆ An imposing, personally run hotel with the proudly traditional character of a bygone age. Contemporary and classic blend in bedrooms. Separate private garden. Formal dining.

Hartland

(heated)

Hartland Terrace EX23 8JY – (01288) 355 661 – hartlandhotel@aol.com – Fax (01288) 355 664 – Closed January-February
28 rm – £ 59/72 £ 100/110 – **Rest** – (bar lunch) Menu £ 24/26
◆ Sizeable seaside hotel, family owned and run for over 30 years. Individually appointed rooms mix modern or period furniture with African, Egyptian and nautical themes. Dine by the dance floor on red leather banquettes.

Bude Haven

Flexbury Ave EX23 8NS – (01288) 352 305 – enquiries@budehavenhotel.com – Fax (01288) 352 662
10 rm – £ 38/58 £ 75/85 – **Rest** – (closed Sunday and Wednesday) (dinner only) (booking essential for non-residents) Carte £ 15/22
◆ Large, privately owned Edwardian house on the quiet outskirts of the town. Comfortable lounge, traditionally styled rooms with hot-tubs; affordable and well kept. Dining room with jazz piano on a Saturday night.

ENGLAND

BUDLEIGH SALTERTON – Devon – 503 K 32 – pop. 4 801 2 D2

London 182 m – Exeter 16 m – Plymouth 55 m
Fore St (01395) 445275
East Devon North View Rd, (01395) 443 370 .
East Budleigh (Church★), N : 2½ m. by A 376 – Bicton★ (Gardens★) AC, N : 3 m. by A 376

Downderry House without rest

10 Exmouth Rd, Northwest : 1 m. on B 3178 EX9 6AQ – (01395) 442 663 – info@downderryhouse.co.uk
5 rm – £ 70/80 £ 85/95
◆ Comfortable guest house where charming owners extend warm welcome. Breakfast room overlooks lawned garden. Modern, individually decorated bedrooms named after local villages.

The Long Range

5 Vales Rd, by Raleigh Rd EX9 6HS – (01395) 443 321 – info@thelongrangehotel.co.uk – Fax (01395) 442 132
7 rm – £ 45/70 £ 84/100 – **Rest** – (closed Sunday, Monday and Thursday) (dinner only) Menu £ 27 – Carte £ 22/27
◆ Homely and unassuming guesthouse, personally run in quiet residential street. Sun lounge with bright aspect, overlooking broad lawn and neat borders. Simple, unfussy rooms. Tasty, locally sourced dishes in a comfy dining room.

BUDOCK WATER – Cornwall – see Falmouth

BUNBURY – Ches. – 502 M 24 – see Tarporley

BUNGAY – Suffolk – **504** Y 26 – **pop. 4 895** *Great Britain* 15 **D2**

London 108 m – Beccles 6 m – Ipswich 38 m

Norwich★★ - Cathedral★★, Castle Museum★, Market Place★, NW : 15 m. by B 1332 and A 146

at Earsham Southwest : 3 m. by A 144 and A 143 – ✉ Bungay

Earsham Park Farm without rest

Old Railway Rd, on A 143 ✉ NR35 2AQ – ✆ (01986) 892 180 – bobbie@earsham-parkfarm.co.uk – Fax (01986) 894 796

3 rm – £ 45/65 £ 70/90

◆ Isolated red-brick Victorian farmhouse, surrounded by working farm. Admire the view while enjoying local produce for breakfast. Well appointed rooms with rural names.

BURCOMBE – Wilts. – see Salisbury

BURFORD – Oxon. – **503** P 28 10 **A2**

London 76 m – Birmingham 55 m – Gloucester 32 m – Oxford 20 m

The Brewery, Sheep St ✆ (01993) 823558

✆ (01993) 822 583 .

Bay Tree

12-14 Sheep St ✉ OX18 4LW – ✆ (01993) 822 791 – info@baytreehotel.info – Fax (01993) 823 008

21 rm – £ 119/129 £ 240/250 – **Rest** – Menu £ 16/28 – Carte £ 24/27

◆ Characterful, creeper-clad 16C house with coaching inn style, antique furnishings and original features. Two front lounges with vast stone fireplaces. Comfortable bedrooms. Light, airy restaurant overlooking beautiful landscaped garden.

Burford House without rest

99 High St ✉ OX18 4QA – ✆ (01993) 823 151 – stay@burfordhouse.co.uk – Fax (01993) 823 240

8 rm – £ 95/130 £ 130/170

◆ 17C town house. Welcoming lounge with honesty bar. Individually decorated bedrooms with contemporary touches are named after local villages – four poster Southrop is the best.

The Lamb Inn

Sheep St ✉ OX18 4LR – ✆ (01993) 823 155 – info@lambinn-burford.co.uk – Fax (01993) 822 228

17 rm – £ 145 £ 165 – **Rest** – (bar lunch Monday-Saturday) Menu £ 33 – Carte £ 20/33

◆ Attractive 14C Cotswold stone inn with deep sofas, open fires and uneven flag floors. Cosy bedrooms named after flowers. Restaurant has glass skylight and dressed tables.

The Carpenter's Arms

Fulbrook Hill, Northeast : ½ m. on A 361 ✉ OX18 4BH – ✆ (01993) 823 275 – Closed Sunday dinner, Monday

Rest – Menu £ 13 – Carte £ 22/30

◆ Characterful pub with flagged floors, beamed ceilings, wood burners and a selection of contemporary art. Simple, carefully-presented cooking and bright, friendly service.

at Swinbrook East : 2 ¾ m. by A 40 – ✉ Burford

The Swan Inn

✉ OX18 4DY – ✆ (01993) 823 339 – swanninnswinbrook@btconnect.com – Closed 25 December

Rest – Carte £ 20/30

◆ Wisteria-clad dining pub owned by the Dowager Duchess of Devonshire. Modernised and spacious yet cosy, with huge glass wall in green oak conservatory. Locally sourced food.

BURGHCLERE – Hants. – 503 Q 29 6 B1

London 67 m – Newbury 4 m – Reading 30 m

Carnarvon Arms with rm

Winchester Rd, Whitway, South : 1½ m. by Highclare rd on Whitway rd
RG20 9LE – (01635) 278 222 – carnarvon@merchant-inns.com
– Fax (01635) 278 444

23 rm – £ 80 £ 90 – **Rest** – Menu £ 10/15 – Carte £ 20/32

◆ Spacious modern dining pub serving up-to-date British cooking. Comfy sofas in bar; more formal dining area in converted barn with hieroglyphics on the walls. Contemporary bedrooms.

BURLEYDAM – Ches. – see Whitchurch (Shrops.)

BURLEY-IN-WHARFEDALE – W. Yorks. – 502 O 22 – pop. 1 387 22 B2

London 216 m – Leeds 13 m – York 33 m

Main Street

78 Main St LS29 7BT – (01943) 864 602 – info@mainstreetrestaurant.co.uk
– closed Sunday dinner and Monday

Rest – Menu £ 19 (dinner) – Carte £ 22/32

◆ Modern, refurbished restaurant over three rooms. Quality seasonal ingredients used to create flavourful, traditional dishes. Themed evenings are popular. Enthusiastic team.

BURLTON – Shrops. – Shrewsbury 18 B1

London 235 m – Shrewsbury 10 m – Wrexham 20 m

The Burlton Inn with rm

SY4 5TB – (01939) 270 284 – robertlesterrc@yahoo.co.uk
– Closed 25 December and 1 January

6 rm – £ 60 £ 90 – **Rest** – (restricted lunch Monday) Carte £ 18/30

◆ Bustling, family run pub with a characterful, wood furnished interior. Extensive menus of traditional fare. Bedrooms in contemporary style. Four Poster bed available.

BURNHAM MARKET – Norfolk – 504 W 25 *Great Britain* 15 C1

London 128 m – Cambridge 71 m – Norwich 36 m

Lambourne Dropmore Rd, (01628) 666 755 .

Holkham Hall★★ **AC**, E : 3 m. by B 1155

The Hoste Arms

The Green PE31 8HD – (01328) 738 777 – reception@hostearms.co.uk
– Fax (01328) 730 103

35 rm – £ 90/268 £ 193/273 – 1 suite

Rest *The Restaurant* – see restaurant listing

◆ Renowned and restored 17C inn in this pretty village. Intriguing wing in Zulu style. Individually designed rooms provide a high level of comfort. Informal ambience.

The Hoste Arms – at The Hoste Arms

The Green PE31 8HD – (01328) 738 777 – reception@hostearms.co.uk
– Fax (01328) 730 103

Rest – (booking essential) Carte £ 23/44

◆ North Sea fish features in an Anglo-European and oriental fusion menu. Delightful terrace with Moroccan theme for summer dining. Invariably friendly staff.

Fishes with rm

Market Pl PE31 8HE – (01328) 738 588 – info@fishesrestaurant.co.uk
– Fax (01328) 730 534 – Closed 1 week January, 25-26 December, Sunday dinner and Monday except Bank Holidays

2 rm – £ 80 £ 160 – **Rest** – Seafood Menu £ 22/38

◆ Attractive restaurant with simple bistro feel and local artwork in centre of popular North Norfolk town. Locally caught seafood dishes are well prepared and tasty. Two elegant new bedrooms overlook the village green.

at Burnham Thorpe Southeast : 1 ¼ m. by B 1355 – ✉ Burnham Market

The Lord Nelson

Walsingham Rd ✉ PE31 8HL – ✆ (01328) 738 241
– enquiries@nelsonslocal.co.uk – Fax (01328) 738 241 – Closed Sunday dinner and Monday, except Bank Holidays, school holidays and half term holidays
Rest – Menu £ 20 – Carte £ 21/29
◆ Cosy, characterful pub in small village - Nelson was indeed born here: much memorabilia to remind you. Flagged floors, beams and a tiny bar. Good value, tasty dishes.

BURNHAM THORPE – Norfolk – 504 W 25 – see Burnham Market

BURNLEY – Lancas. – 502 N 22 – pop. 73 021 — 20 B2

London 236 m – Bradford 32 m – Leeds 37 m – Liverpool 55 m – Manchester 25 m – Middlesbrough 104 m – Preston 22 m – Sheffield 68 m
Bus Station, Croft St ✆ (01282) 664421
Towneley Todmorden Rd, Towneley Park, ✆ (01282) 451 636 ;
Glen View, ✆ (01282) 451 281 .

Oaks

Colne Rd, Reedley, Northeast : 2½ m. on A 56 ✉ BB10 2LF – ✆ (01282) 414 141
– oaks@lavenderhotels.co.uk – Fax (01282) 433 401
51 rm – †£ 104 ††£ 110
Rest *Quills* – (dinner only) Carte £ 20/30
Rest *Archives Brasserie* – (lunch only, buffet only) Menu £ 20
◆ Extended 19C house with accent on business traveller. Clubby lounge with leather sofas and mahogany staircase dappled in colour from superb stained glass window. Comfy rooms. Quills boasts views over neat lawns. Archives Brasserie in brick vaulted cellars.

Rosehill House

Rosehill Ave, Manchester Rd, South : 1 ¼ m. by A 56 ✉ BB11 2PW
– ✆ (01282) 453 931 – rhhotel@provider.co.uk – Fax (01282) 455 628
31 rm – †£ 60/75 ††£ 75 – 2 suites
Rest *Dugdales* – Carte £ 15/28
◆ Turreted 19C house in wooded grounds; residentially set. Airy lounge with long leather Chesterfields. Carefully repaired ornate ceilings a particular feature of various rooms. Imposing, elegantly panelled Dugdales evokes period charm.

We try to be as accurate as possible when giving room rates. But prices are susceptible to change, so please check rates when booking.

BURNSALL – N. Yorks. – 502 O 21 – ✉ Skipton — 22 A2

London 223 m – Bradford 26 m – Leeds 29 m

The Red Lion

✉ BD23 6BU – ✆ (01756) 720 204 – redlion@daelnet.co.uk – Fax (01756) 720 292
14 rm – †£ 60/65 ††£ 120/150 – 3 suites
Rest *The Restaurant* – see restaurant listing
◆ Part 16C inn on the River Wharfe, ideal for walks, fishing and shooting. Cosy bedrooms, some in adjacent cottage: all have 19C brass beds or overlook the village green.

Devonshire Fell

✉ BD23 6BT – ✆ (01756) 729 000 – andrew.forbes@devonshirefell.co.uk
– Fax (01756) 729 009
10 rm – †£ 75 ††£ 155/195 – 2 suites – **Rest** – Carte £ 25/30
◆ Once a club for 19C mill owners; strikingly updated by Lady Hartington with vivid colours and Hockney prints. Wide-ranging modern menu. Stylish rooms with Dales views.

ENGLAND

The Red Lion – at The Red Lion H.
✉ BD23 6BU – ✆ (01756) 720204 – redlion@daelnet.co.uk – Fax (01756) 720292
Rest – (bar lunch Monday-Saturday) Carte £ 25/40
◆ Dales meat, game and local cheeses in robust, seasonal menu. Eat in the firelit, oak-panelled bar or the dining room with mullioned windows facing the green. Keen staff.

BURPHAM – W. Sussex – 504 S 30 – see Arundel

BURRINGTON – Devon – 503 I 31 2 C1

London 260 m – Barnstaple 14 m – Exeter 28 m – Taunton 50 m

Northcote Manor
Northwest : 2 m. on A 377 ✉ EX37 9LZ – ✆ (01769) 560501 – rest@northcotemanor.co.uk – Fax (01769) 560770
10 rm – †£ 100/135 ††£ 155/315 – 1 suite – **Rest** – (booking essential) (lunch by arrangement) Menu £ 15/38 **s**
◆ Creeper-clad hall above River Tew dating from 1716. Fine fabrics and antiques in elegant, individually styled rooms; attention to well-judged detail lends air of idyllic calm. Country house restaurant features eye-catching murals.

BURTON-UPON-TRENT – Staffs. – 502 O 25 – pop. 43 784 19 C1

London 128 m – Birmingham 29 m – Leicester 27 m – Nottingham 27 m – Stafford 27 m
Coors Visitor Centre, Horninglow St ✆ (01283) 508111
Branston G. & C.C. Burton Rd, ✆ (01283) 528320 ;
Craythorne Stretton Craythorne Rd, ✆ (01283) 564329 .

at Stretton North : 3 ¼ m. by A 5121 (A 38 Derby) – ✉ Burton-upon-Trent

Dovecliff Hall rest,
Dovecliff Rd ✉ DE13 0DJ – ✆ (01283) 531818 – enquiries@dovecliffhallhotel.co.uk – Fax (01283) 516546
14 rm – †£ 70/95 ††£ 180 – **Rest** – (closed Sunday dinner) Menu £ 18 (lunch) – Carte £ 30/41
◆ Imposing, listed 1790s house with lovely gardens and spacious rooms, nestling in an elevated position above the Trent. Airy bedrooms, most boasting garden vistas. Formal dining rooms in restaurant and delightful orangery.

BURY – Gtr Manchester – 502 N 23 – pop. 60 718 20 B2

London 211 m – Leeds 45 m – Liverpool 35 m – Manchester 9 m
The Met Art Centre, Market St ✆ (0161) 253 5111
Greenmount, ✆ (01204) 883712 .

The Waggon
131 Bury and Rochdale Old Rd, Birtle, East : 2 m. on B 6222 ✉ BL9 6UE – ✆ (01706) 622955 – closed 2 weeks August, 1 week January, Saturday lunch, Monday and Tuesday
Rest – Menu £ 16 – Carte £ 19/28
◆ Unprepossessing façade hides a pleasantly decorated eatery with good value, no-nonsense cooking featuring a decidedly strong Lancashire base and the famous Bury Black Pudding.

BURY ST EDMUNDS – Suffolk – 504 W 27 – pop. 36 218 15 C2

Great Britain

London 79 m – Cambridge 27 m – Ipswich 26 m – Norwich 41 m
6 Angel Hill ✆ (01284) 764667
Suffolk G. & C.C. The Street, St John's Hill Plantation, ✆ (01284) 706777 .
Town★ - Abbey and Cathedral★
Ickworth House★ AC, SW : 3 m. by A 143

ENGLAND

Angel rm, rm, VISA AE

3 Angel Hill ✉ IP33 1LT – ☎ (01284) 714 000 – reservations@theangel.co.uk – Fax (01284) 714 001

74 rm – †£ 85/127 ††£ 137 – 2 suites

Rest *The Eatery* – Carte £ 24/35

◆ 15C inn near the Abbey Gardens with a fine Georgian façade. Rooms offer a bright, modern take on classic style: a few, named after famous visitors, have four poster beds. The Eatery is in atmospheric 12C cellars.

Priory rm, VISA AE

Tollgate, North : 1 ¾ m. on A 1101 ✉ IP32 6EH – ☎ (01284) 766 181 – reservations@prioryhotel.co.uk – Fax (01284) 767 604 – Closed 27-29 December

39 rm – †£ 88/129 ††£ 143

Rest *The Garden* – (Closed Saturday lunch) Carte £ 18/24

◆ 13C former Franciscan Priory with a listed Georgian façade. Traditionally styled in the main house with some usefully appointed modern rooms in the later Garden wings. Conservatory restaurant overlooks neatly manicured garden.

Ounce House without rest VISA AE

Northgate St ✉ IP33 1HP – ☎ (01284) 761 779 – enquiries@ouncehouse.co.uk – Fax (01284) 768 315

5 rm – †£ 75/85 ††£ 110/120

◆ 1870s redbrick town house; very well furnished with Victorian elegance. Spacious, individually styled bedrooms; well-chosen antiques contribute to a characterful interior.

ENGLAND

Maison Bleue VISA

30-31 Churchgate St ✉ IP33 1RG – ☎ (01284) 760 623 – info@maisonbleue.co.uk – Fax (01284) 761 611 – closed January, 2 weeks summer, Sunday and Monday

Rest – Seafood Menu £ 17/26 – Carte £ 21/43

◆ 17C house with attractive façade and window boxes. Timbered interior with maritime memorabilia. A number of different rooms to eat in; predominantly seafood menu.

at Ixworth Northeast : 7 m. by A 143 – ✉ Bury St Edmunds

Theobalds VISA

68 High St ✉ IP31 2HJ – ☎ (01359) 231 707 – Fax (01359) 231 707 – closed 10 days spring, Sunday dinner and Monday

Rest – (dinner only and lunch Sunday, Wednesday and Friday) Menu £ 27 (lunch) – Carte £ 31/36

◆ Beamed part 16C cottage with a cosy firelit lounge. Friendly service and well-judged seasonal menus combine heartwarming favourites and contemporary dishes.

at Rougham Green East : 4 m. by A 14 – ✉ Bury St Edmunds

Ravenwood Hall (heated) VISA AE

✉ IP30 9JA – ☎ (01359) 270 345 – enquiries@ravenwood.co.uk – Fax (01359) 270 788

14 rm – †£ 99 ††£ 200 – **Rest** – Menu £ 35 – Carte £ 24/37

◆ Tudor dower house set in seven acres of calm lawns and woods. Welcoming lounge and individually designed bedrooms, more compact in the mews, are furnished with antiques. Restaurant with old wooden beams and inglenook fireplace.

at Beyton East : 6 m. by A 14 – ✉ Bury St Edmunds

Manorhouse without rest

The Green ✉ IP30 9AF – ☎ (01359) 270 960 – manorhouse@beyton.com – closed Christmas

4 rm – †£ 47/55 ††£ 65/70

◆ Part 15C Suffolk longhouse in idyllic spot overlooking village green. Two rooms are in converted barn; all have a rustic feel to them. Breakfast of eggs from owner's hens.

at Horringer Southwest : 3 m. on A 143 – ✉ **Bury St Edmunds**

The Ickworth ← (heated) VISA AE
✉ *IP29 5QE* – ☎ *(01284) 735 350*
– *info@ickworthhotel.com – Fax (01284) 736 300*
29 rm (dinner included) – †£ 200 ††£ 310/440 – 10 suites
Rest *Fredericks* – (dinner only) Menu £ 38
◆ Ickworth House's east wing mixes modern and country house styles. Three airy drawing rooms; conservatory breakfasts. Comfy rooms with views. A favourite with young families. Fredericks overlooks gardens.

The Beehive P VISA
The Street ✉ *IP29 5SN* – ☎ *(01284) 735 260 – Fax (01284) 735 532*
– *Closed 25-26 December*
Rest – (closed Sunday dinner) Carte £ 19/27
◆ Rustic, low-ceilinged, brick-and-flint pub near Ickworth House. Tasty daily specials like scallops in garlic butter affably served at pine tables or on a sheltered terrace.

Undecided between two equivalent establishments? Within each category, establishments are classified in our order of preference.

BUSHEY – Herts. – **504** S 29 12 **A2**
London 18 m – Luton 21 m – Watford 3 m
18 Bushey Hall Bushey Hall Drive, ☎ (01923) 222 253 ;
9 Bushey G. & C.C. High St, ☎ (020) 8950 2283 .

Plan : see Greater London (North-West) 1

XX **st James** A/C VISA AE
30 High St ✉ *WD23 3HL* – ☎ *(020) 8950 2480 – Fax (020) 8950 4107*
– *closed 25 December and Sunday* BT **c**
Rest – Carte £ 26/34
◆ Long-standing, likeable restaurant with wood floored front room and bar, plus rear room for large parties. Appealing British menu shows real understanding of what guests want.

BUTTERMERE – Cumbria – **502** K 20 – ✉ **Cockermouth** 21 **A2**
London 306 m – Carlisle 35 m – Kendal 43 m

Bridge ← P VISA
✉ *CA13 9UZ* – ☎ *(017687) 70 252 – enquiries@bridge-hotel.com*
– *Fax (017687) 70 215*
21 rm (dinner included) – †£ 70/120 ††£ 170/190 – **Rest** – (bar lunch Monday-Saturday) (booking essential) Menu £ 30
◆ Well-established family-owned hotel in superb spot, surrounded by Buttermere fells. Charming sitting room, stylish bedrooms; some with four posters. Local real ales a feature. Warm yellow dining room in oldest part of the house. Classic fine dining.

Wood House ← Crummock Water and Melbreak, P
Northwest : ½ m. on B 5289 ✉ *CA13 9XA* – ☎ *(017687) 70 208*
– *woodhouse.guest@virgin.net – Fax (017687) 70 241 – April - October*
3 rm – †£ 60 ††£ 90 – **Rest** – (by arrangement, communal dining) Menu £ 29
◆ 16C guest house with wonderfully serene lakeside setting and stunning views. Well-appointed lounge; antique furnished bedrooms. Meals cooked on the Aga using fresh seasonal, local ingredients and served family-style around an antique table.

ENGLAND

BUXTON – Derbs. – 502 O 24 – pop. 20 836 16 A1

London 172 m – Derby 38 m – Manchester 25 m – Stoke-on-Trent 24 m
The Crescent ✆ (01298) 25106
Buxton and High Peak Townend, ✆ (01298) 26 263 .

Lee Wood

The Park, on A 5004 ✉ SK17 6TQ – ✆ (01298) 23 002
– reservations@leewoodhotel.co.uk – Fax (01298) 23 228
40 rm – £ 68/88 £ 100/145
Rest *Elements* – Menu £ 28 (dinner) – Carte £ 24/37
◆ Family-owned hotel - a popular wedding venue - with contemporary, leather-furnished bar. Bedrooms come in standard or executive grades - the front ones are the best. Large conservatory restaurant serves classical dishes.

Buxton's Victorian without rest

3A Broad Walk ✉ SK17 6JE – ✆ (01298) 78 759 – buxtonvictoria@btconnect.com
– Fax (01298) 74 732 – closed Christmas-New Year
7 rm – £ 54/74 £ 90/100
◆ Charming Victorian house built in 1860 for the Duke of Devonshire. Cosy lounge and breakfast room with views over boating lake and bandstand. Bedrooms boast period furniture.

Grendon without rest

Bishops Lane ✉ SK17 6UN – ✆ (01298) 78 831
– grendonguesthouse@hotmail.com – Fax (01298) 79 257 – closed January - mid February
5 rm – £ 38/65 £ 80/90
◆ Cosy Edwardian house on edge of town, built for a wealthy mill owner in the 1900s, with period features and pleasant gardens. Comfortable, traditionally furnished bedrooms.

ENGLAND

BYFORD – Herefordshire – 503 L 27 – see Hereford

BYLAND ABBEY – N. Yorks. – 502 Q 21 – see Helmsley

CADNAM – Hants. – 503 P 31 – pop. 1 875 6 A2

London 91 m – Salisbury 16 m – Southampton 8 m – Winchester 19 m

Walnut Cottage without rest

Old Romsey Rd, off A 3090 ✉ SO40 2NP – ✆ (023) 8081 2275
– closed 25-26 December
3 rm – £ 40 £ 55
◆ A pretty white Victorian forester's cottage with views over the garden and good for forays into the New Forest. Charming, simply furnished bedrooms.

CALLINGTON – Cornwall – 503 H 32 2 C2

London 237 m – Exeter 53 m – Plymouth 15 m – Truro 46 m

Langmans

3 Church St ✉ PL17 7RE – ✆ (01579) 384 933 – dine@langmansrestaurant.co.uk
– closed Sunday-Wednesday
Rest – (dinner only) (booking essential) (set tasting menu only) Menu £ 33
◆ Truly individual establishment: seven course tasting menus change monthly, employing skilful cooking with finesse; ingredients from small local suppliers. Booking essential.

Your opinions are important to us:
please write and let us know about your discoveries and experiences – good and bad!

CALNE - Wilts. - 503 O 29 - pop. 13 789 4 C2

London 91 m - Bristol 33 m - Southampton 63 m - Swindon 17 m
Bowood House★ AC, (Library ≤ ★) SW : 2 m. by A 4 - Avebury★★ (The Stones★, Church★) E : 6 m. by A 4

Chilvester Hill House

West : ¾ m. by A 4 on Bremhill rd ✉ SN11 OLP - ✆ (01249) 813 981 - gill.dilley@talk21.com - Fax (01249) 814 217
3 rm - £ 60/70 £ 90/100 - **Rest** - (by arrangement, communal dining) Menu £ 20/25
◆ 19C Bath stone house with lots of William Morris wallpapering, Persian carpeted drawing room, and spacious bedrooms. Charming mature owners are its very heart and soul. Simple homecooking.

CAMBER - E. Sussex - 504 W 31 - see Rye

CAMBERLEY - Surrey - 504 R 29 - pop. 47 123 7 C1

London 40 m - Reading 13 m - Southampton 48 m
Camberley Heath Golf Drive, ✆ (01276) 23 258 .

Frimley Hall H & Spa

Lime Ave via Conifer Drive, East : ¾ m. off Portsmouth Rd (A 325) ✉ GU15 2BG - ✆ (0870) 400 8224 - sales.frimleyhall@macdonald-hotels.co.uk - Fax (01276) 691 253
98 rm - £ 99/225 £ 99/275
Rest *Linden* - (closed Saturday lunch) Menu £ 19/30 **s** - Carte £ 30/41 **s**
◆ Ivy-clad Victorian manor. A carved wooden staircase leads to the bedrooms; some are traditional with inlaid mahogany furniture, others are bright and modern. 19C restaurant with contemporary furnishings.

ENGLAND

We try to be as accurate as possible when giving room rates. But prices are susceptible to change, so please check rates when booking.

CAMBOURNE - Cambs. - see Cambridge

CAMBRIDGE - Cambs. - 504 U 27 - pop. 117 717 *Great Britain* 14 B3

London 55 m - Coventry 88 m - Ipswich 54 m - Kingston-upon-Hull 137 m - Leicester 74 m - Norwich 61 m - Nottingham 88 m - Oxford 100 m
Cambridge Airport : ✆ (01223) 373765, E : 2 m. on A 1303 X
The Old Library, Wheeler St ✆ (0871) 2268006, tourism@cambridge.gov.uk
Cambridge Menzies Hotel Bar Hill, ✆ (01954) 249 988.
Town★★★ - St John's College★★★ **AC** Y - King's College★★ (King's College Chapel★★★) Z The Backs★★ YZ - Fitzwilliam Museum★★ Z **M1** - Trinity College★★ Y - Clare College★ Z **B** - Kettle's Yard★ Y **M2** - Queen's College★ **AC** Z
Audley End★★, S : 13 m. on Trumpington Rd, A 1309, A 1301 and B 1383 - Imperial War Museum★, Duxford, S : 9 m. on M 11

Plan on next page

Hotel Felix

Whitehouse Lane, Huntingdon Rd, Northwest : 1½ m. by A 1307 ✉ CB3 0LX - ✆ (01223) 277 977 - help@hotelfelix.co.uk - Fax (01223) 277 973
52 rm - £ 145 £ 225, £7.50
Rest *Graffiti* - Menu £ 17 (lunch) - Carte dinner £ 28/37
◆ Privately owned Victorian mansion set in 3 acres of gardens with contemporary interior. Majority of bedrooms in extension; spacious and luxurious. Modern artwork decorates. Graffiti restaurant overlooks terrace and gardens.

CAMBRIDGE

Street	Grid	No.
Bridge St	Y	2
Coldham's Lane	X	5
Corn Exchange St	Z	6
Downing St	Z	7
Free School Lane	Z	12
Grafton Centre	Y	
Hobson St	Y	14
King's Parade	Z	15
Lion Yard Centre	Z	
Madingley Rd	X	16
Magdalene St	Y	17
Market Hill	YZ	18
Market St	Y	19
Milton Rd	Y	20
Newmarket Rd	Y	21
Northampton St	Y	22
Parker St	Z	23
Peas Hill	Z	25
Pembroke St	Z	26
Petty Cury	Z	27
Rose Crescent	Y	28
St Andrew's St	Z	30
St John's St	Y	31
Short St	Y	32
Sidney St	Y	34
Trinity St	Y	36
Trumpington Rd	Z	37
Wheeler St	Z	39

COLLEGES

College	Grid	Key
Christ's	Y	A
Churchill	X	B
Clare	Z	B
Clare Hall	X	N
Corpus Christi	Z	G[1]
Darwin	Z	D
Downing	Z	E[1]
Emmanuel	Z	F
Fitzwilliam	X	G
Gonville and Caius	Y	G[2]
Hugues Hall	Z	K
Jesus	Y	K
King's	Z	
Lucy Cavendish	Y	O[1]
Magdalene	Y	N
Newnham	X	E[2]
New Hall	X	D
Pembroke	Z	N
Peterhouse	Z	O[2]
Queen's	Z	
Robinson	X	K
St Catharine's	Z	R
St Edmund's House	Y	U
St John's	Y	
Selwyn	X	F
Sidney Sussex	Y	P
Trinity	Y	
Trinity Hall	Y	V
Wolfson	X	U

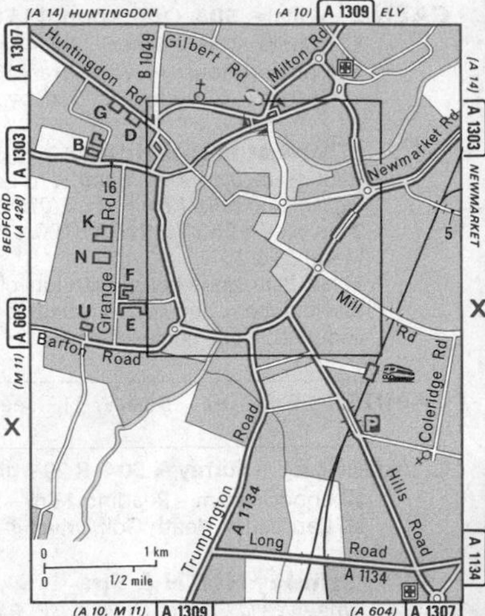

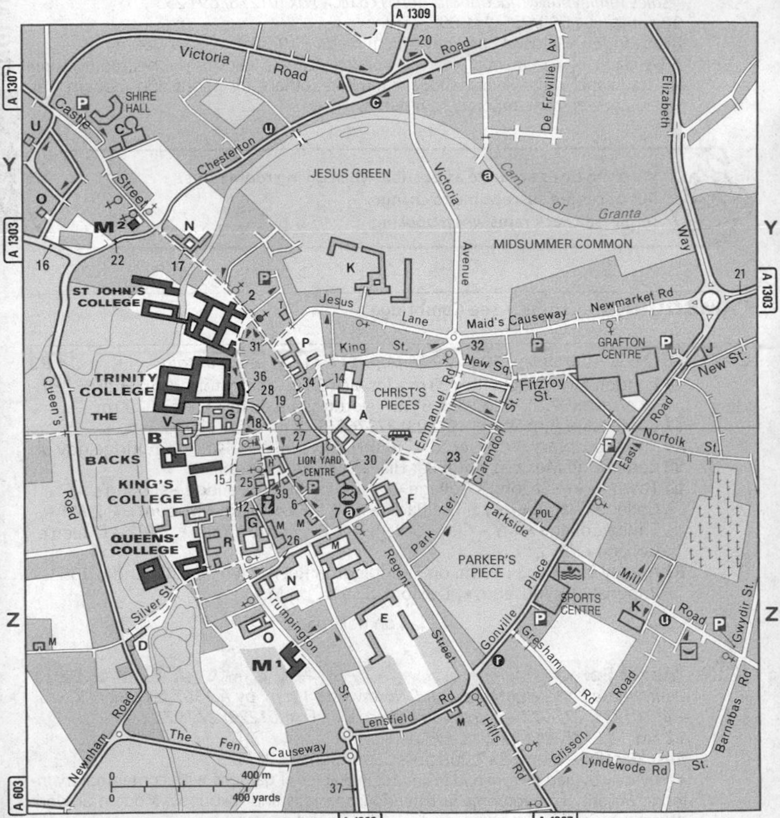

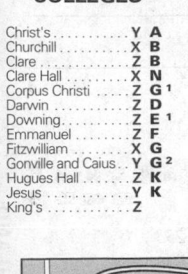

Crowne Plaza
Downing St ✉ CB2 3DT – ✆ (0870) 400 91 80
– reservations-cambridgecp@ihg.com – Fax (01223) 464 440 Z **a**
198 rm – ♦£ 90/295 ♦♦£ 90/295 – **Rest** – (Closed lunch Saturday and Sunday) Carte £ 18/28
◆ Modern, centrally-located hotel with vast atrium. Contemporary bar and bedrooms, with ample facilities for those on business, including a large selection of meeting rooms. A la carte restaurant.

University Arms
Regent St ✉ CB2 1AD – ✆ (01223) 273 000 – dua.sales@devere-hotels.com
– Fax (01223) 273 037 Z **e**
119 rm – ♦£ 200/215 ♦♦£ 220 – 1 suite
Rest ***Restaurant 17*** – (dinner only and Sunday lunch) Carte £ 26/35
◆ Charming Victorian hotel overlooking Parker's Piece. Dramatic atrium. Bedrooms are a mix of older period rooms and more modern; some with balconies and views over the green. Stylish, contemporary restaurant.

Gonville
Gonville Pl ✉ CB1 1LY – ✆ (01223) 366 611 – info@gonvillehotel.co.uk
– Fax (01223) 315 470 Z **r**
73 rm – ♦£ 79/150 ♦♦£ 99/170, £ 12 – **Rest** – (bar lunch) Carte £ 17/25
◆ Popular family-owned, personally-run hotel with spacious, traditional interior. Newer bedrooms at rear of hotel. International menu served in the relaxed Atrium. Formal main dining room used only at weekends.

Midsummer House (Daniel Clifford)
Midsummer Common ✉ CB4 1HA – ✆ (01223) 369 299
– reservations@midsummerhouse.co.uk – Fax (01223) 302 672
– Closed 22 December-10 January, 1 week Easter, 2 weeks August, Sunday, Monday and Tuesday lunch Y **a**
Rest – (dinner only and lunch Friday-Saturday) Menu £ 55/75
Spec. Caramelised sweetbreads, turnip, pistachio, tongue and maple jelly. Poached and grilled pigeon, cherries, spinach and Valrhona sauce. Liquorice parfait, gingerbread, pear and cassis.
◆ Idyllic location beside the River Cam, with conservatory dining. Mediterranean menus offer inventive, precise and detailed cooking. Smooth, formal service.

22 Chesterton Road
22 Chesterton Rd ✉ CB4 3AX – ✆ (01223) 351 880
– davidcarter@restaurant22.co.uk – Fax (01223) 323 814
– closed 1 week Christmas-New Year, Sunday and Monday Y **c**
Rest – (dinner only) (booking essential) Menu £ 27
◆ Converted Victorian house with distinctive dining room decorated in rich colours. Monthly-changing classical menu; tasty, good value French-influenced dishes. Formal service.

Bruno's Brasserie
52 Mill Rd ✉ CB1 2AS – ✆ (01223) 312 702 – bruno5@btconnect.com
– Closed 23 December-6 January, Sunday, Monday lunch and Bank Holidays Z **u**
Rest – Menu £ 15 (lunch) – Carte £ 20/32
◆ Personally and passionately run restaurant with delightful enclosed rear courtyard. Seasonal cooking has strong Mediterranean base, with plenty of fish. Bubbly service.

at Histon North : 3 m. on B 1049 - X – ✉ Cambridge

Phoenix
20 The Green ✉ CB4 9JA – ✆ (01223) 233 766 – closed 24-27 December
Rest – Chinese Menu £ 18/22 – Carte £ 45/102
◆ Popular Chinese restaurant in former pub on village green. Comfortable, homely inner. Polite, smartly attired staff. Vast menu with plenty of Peking and Szechuan favourites.

ENGLAND

at Horningsea **Northeast : 4 m. by A 1303 - X - and B 1047 on Horningsea rd – ✉ Cambridge**

Crown and Punchbowl with rm

High St ✉ CB25 9JG – ✆ (01223) 860 643 – info@the crownandpunchbowl.co.uk – Fax (01223) 441 814 – closed 26-28 December

5 rm – ♦£ 70 ♦♦£ 90 – **Rest** – (closed Sunday dinner) Carte £ 13/35

◆ Pub noteable for its lack of a bar. Snug, charming and rustic, with open fires and low beamed ceilings. Two main dining areas serving appealing seasonal and local food. Modern, spacious and relaxing bedrooms.

at Little Wilbraham **East : 7 ¼ m. by A 1303 - X – ✉ Cambridge**

The Hole in the Wall

2 High St ✉ CB21 5JY – ✆ (01223) 812 282 – Closed 2 weeks in January and 25 December

Rest – (closed Sunday dinner and Monday except Bank Holiday Monday dinner) Carte £ 20/26

◆ An experienced team run this pretty, remotely set 15C inn, heated by open fires. Seasonal, traceable ingredients are used in classical ways to produce robust British dishes.

ENGLAND

at Little Shelford **South : 5 ½ m. by A 1309 - X - off A 10 – ✉ Cambridge**

Sycamore House

1 Church St ✉ CB22 5HG – ✆ (01223) 843 396 – closed Christmas-New Year and Sunday-Tuesday

Rest – (dinner only) (booking essential) Menu £ 25

◆ Converted 16C cottage in a sleepy hamlet. Long narrow dining room with thick walls, low ceiling and open fire. Frequently-changing, seasonal menu with hearty base.

at Madingley **West : 4 ½ m. by A 1303 - X – ✉ Cambridge**

The Three Horseshoes

High St ✉ CB4 8SA – ✆ (01954) 210 221 – Fax (01954) 212 043 – closed 1-2 January

Rest – Menu £ 16 – Carte £ 16/35

◆ Thatched inn with snug, fire-warmed bar and dressed tables in more formal dining room. Seasonal, Italian food made with best local produce. Professional, unobtrusive service.

at Hardwick **West : 5 m. by A 1303 - X – ✉ Cambridge**

Wallis Farmhouse without rest

98 Main St ✉ CB23 7QU – ✆ (01954) 210 347 – enquiries@wallisfarmhouse.co.uk – Fax (01954) 210 988

4 rm – ♦£ 50/55 ♦♦£ 68/75

◆ Remotely set Georgian house in picturesque village. Immaculately kept bedrooms in a converted barn across courtyard. Breakfast served in main house. Spacious rear garden.

at Cambourne **West : 7 m. by A 428 - X – ✉ Cambridge**

The Cambridge Belfry

rest,

Back Lane ✉ CB23 6BW – ✆ (01954) 714 600 – cambridgebelfry@qhotels.co.uk – Fax (01954) 714 998

110 rm – ♦£ 80/140 ♦♦£ 90/150 – 10 suites

Rest *Bridge* – (bar lunch Sunday) Carte £ 24/30

◆ Brick-built hotel in centre of new town. Large, well-equipped gym and spa facilities; several conference rooms. Refurbished, high quality bedrooms. Formal dining in the spacious Bridge.

at Bar Hill Northwest : 5½ m. by A 1307 - X - off A 14 – ✉ Cambridge

Menzies Cambridge
Bar Hill ✉ CB23 8EU – ☎ (0871) 472 00 02
– lisa.porter@menzieshotels.co.uk – Fax (01954) 780 010
136 rm – †£ 89/125 ††£ 89/145, ☕ £14.95 – **Rest** – (dinner only) Menu £ 23
– Carte £ 23/32
◆ Well-located, tastefully refurbished hotel with high quality bedrooms; ideal for tourists as well as the business traveller. Up-to-the-minute conference rooms; golf course and spa. Family-friendly dining in Brasserie restaurant.

CANNINGTON – Somerset – **503** K 30 – see Bridgwater

CANTERBURY – Kent – **504** X 30 – **pop. 43 552** *Great Britain* 9 **D2**
London 59 m – Brighton 76 m – Dover 15 m – Maidstone 28 m
– Margate 17 m
12-13 Sun St, Buttermarket ☎ (01227) 378100,
canterburyinformation@canterbury.gov.uk
City★★★ - Cathedral★★★ Y - St Augustine's Abbey★★ **AC** YZ **K** – King's School★ Y – Mercery Lane★ Y **12** - Christ Church Gate★ Y **D** – Museum of Canterbury★ **AC** Y **M1** – St Martin's Church★ Y **N** – West Gate Towers★ **AC** Y **R**

Plan on next page

Abode Canterbury
High St ✉ CT1 2RX – ☎ (01227) 766 266
– reservationscanterbury@abodehotels.co.uk – Fax (01227) 784 874 Y **a**
71 rm – †£ 130 ††£ 180, ☕ £13
Rest Michael Caines – see restaurant listing
Rest *The Old Brewery Tavern* – Carte £ 18/32
◆ Centrally located, this smart hotel has undergone a vast top-to-toe transformation. A distinctive modern feel pertains, typified by sleek, airy bedrooms. Appealingly eclectic menu in The Old Brewery Tavern.

Ebury
65-67 New Dover Rd ✉ CT1 3DX – ☎ (01227) 768 433
– info@ebury-hotel.co.uk – Fax (01227) 459 187
– closed 21 December-14 January Z **r**
15 rm ☕ – †£ 75/105 ††£ 95/115 – **Rest** – (closed Sunday) (dinner only)
Menu £ 22 **s**
◆ 1850s redbrick hotel where drinks are served in a lounge holding a collection of Bulls Eye clocks. Bedrooms are all spacious and comfortable. Restaurant ambience reflects age of hotel.

Magnolia House without rest
36 St Dunstan's Terrace ✉ CT2 8AX – ☎ (01227) 765 121
– info@magnoliahousecanterbury.co.uk – Fax (01227) 765 121
– Closed 1 week Christmas Y **s**
6 rm ☕ – †£ 55/75 ††£ 110/135
◆ Gracious Georgian house with calm, sunny interior and plush bedrooms including four-poster suite. Breakfast room offers good choice, and boasts charming garden outlook.

Michael Caines – at Abode Canterbury
High St ✉ CT1 2RX – ☎ (01227) 826 684
– Fax (01227) 784 874 Y **a**
Rest – (Closed Sunday dinner) Menu £ 18/25 – Carte £ 36/43
◆ Enjoy a glass of Champagne in smart bar before repairing to the upmarket restaurant to enjoy modern British cooking utilising a variety of styles and classical techniques.

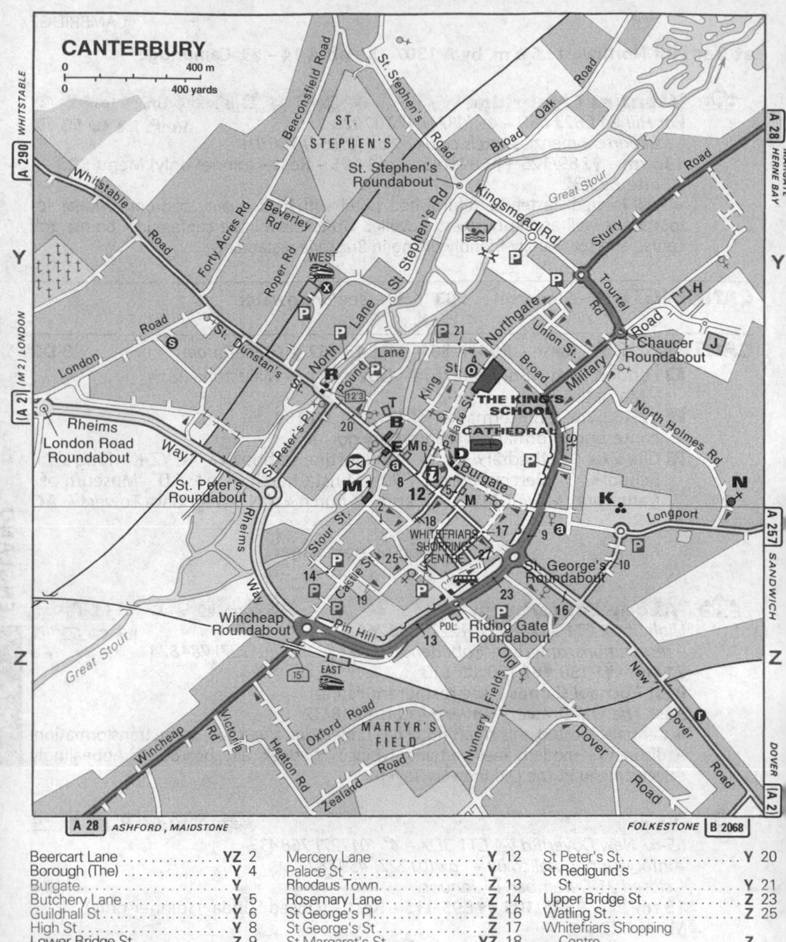

The Goods Shed

Station Rd West, St Dunstans ✉ CT2 8AN – ✆ (01227) 459 153 – Closed Sunday dinner and Monday Y **x**

Rest – Carte £ 22/31

◆ Once derelict railway shed, now a farmers' market that's open all day. Its eating area offers superbly fresh produce with no frills and real flavours very much to the fore.

Augustines

1-2 Longport ✉ CT1 1PE – ✆ (01227) 453 063 – info@augustinesrestaurant.co.uk – Fax (01227) 453 063 – closed 24 December-10 January, Easter, Sunday dinner and Monday Z **a**

Rest – Menu £ 17 (lunch) – Carte £ 29/36

◆ Handsome Georgian house - former home to retired nuns - with cosy, high-ceilinged dining room. Seasonal, local food.

at Lower Hardres South : 3 m. on B 2068 - Z - ✉ **Canterbury**

The Granville
Street End ✉ CT4 7AL – ✆ (01227) 700 402 – Fax (01227) 700 925
– Closed 25 December, Sunday dinner and Monday
Rest – Carte £ 21/32
◆ A close relative to The Sportsman in Whitstable. Relax in leather sofas, then enjoy quality ingredients on a well-priced, very interesting modern menu featuring superb fish.

CARBIS BAY – Cornwall – **503** D 33 – see St Ives

CARLISLE – Cumbria – **501** L 19 – **pop. 71 773** *Great Britain* 21 **B1**

London 317 m – Blackpool 95 m – Edinburgh 101 m – Glasgow 100 m – Leeds 124 m – Liverpool 127 m – Manchester 122 m – Newcastle upon Tyne 59 m

Carlisle Airport ✆ (01228) 573641, NW : 5 ½ m. by A 7 - BY - and B 6264

Carlisle Visitor Centre, Old Town Hall, Green Market ✆ (01228) 625600

Aglionby, ✆ (01228) 513 029 ;

Stony Holme St Aidan's Rd, ✆ (01228) 625 511 ;

Dalston Hall Dalston, ✆ (01228) 710 165 .

Town★ - Cathedral★ (Painted Ceiling★) AY **E** – Tithe Barn★ BY **A**

Hadrian's Wall★★, N : by A 7 AY

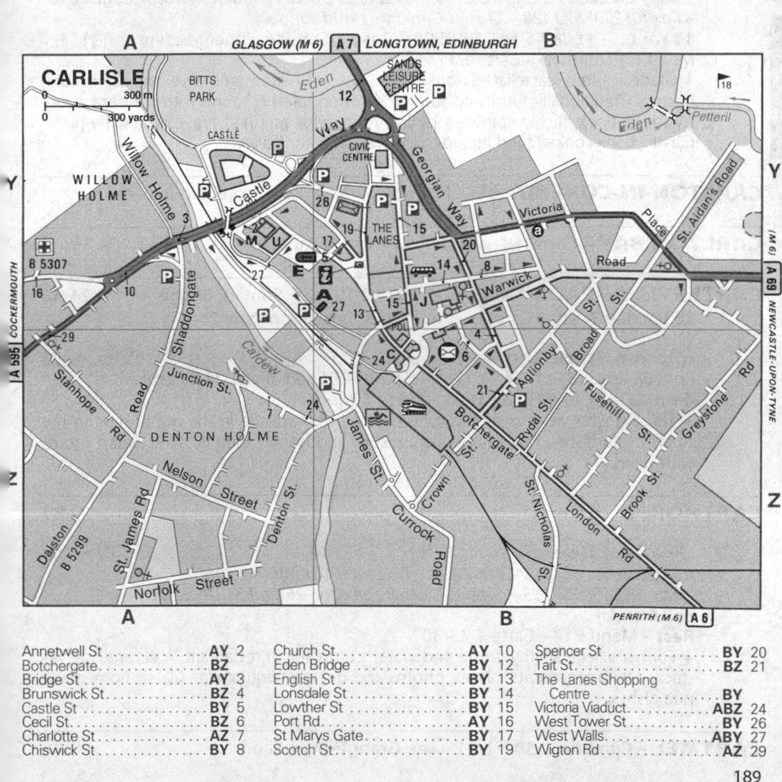

Annetwell St . . . . . AY 2	Church St. . . . . AY 10	Spencer St . . . . . BY 20
Botchergate. . . . . BZ	Eden Bridge . . . . . BY 12	Tait St. . . . . BZ 21
Bridge St . . . . . AY 3	English St . . . . . BY 13	The Lanes Shopping Centre . . . . . BY
Brunswick St. . . . . BZ 4	Lonsdale St . . . . . BY 14	Victoria Viaduct. . . . . ABZ 24
Castle St . . . . . BY 5	Lowther St . . . . . BY 15	West Tower St . . . . . BY 26
Cecil St. . . . . BZ 6	Port Rd. . . . . AY 16	West Walls. . . . . ABY 27
Charlotte St . . . . . AZ 7	St Marys Gate. . . . . BY 17	Wigton Rd. . . . . AZ 29
Chiswick St . . . . . BY 8	Scotch St . . . . . BY 19	

Cumbria Park rest,

32 Scotland Rd, North : 1 m. on A 7 ✉ CA3 9DG – ☎ (01228) 522 887 – cumbriaparkhotel@wightcablenorth.net – Fax (01228) 514 796 – closed 25-26 December

47 rm – £78 £150 – **Rest** – (bar lunch) Carte £15/28 **s**

◆ Traditional hotel with well kept bedrooms; some with jacuzzi baths. Corridor walls filled with postcards and posters from owner's travels. Bottle green restaurant with Roman theme serves classic menu. Bar meals among the fishtanks in lounge/bar.

Number Thirty One

31 Howard Place ✉ CA1 1HR – ☎ (01228) 597 080 – pruirving@aol.com – Fax (01228) 597 080 BY **a**

3 rm – £65 £90/100 – **Rest** – (dinner only) (by arrangement) Menu £20 **s**

◆ Well-appointed Victorian townhouse with sumptuous lounge and immaculately-kept bedrooms. Richly decorated dining room with window onto plant-filled terrace.

Gallo Rosso

Parkhouse Rd, Kingstown, Northwest : 2 ¾ m. by A 7 ✉ CA6 4BY – ☎ (01228) 526 037 – Fax (01228) 550 074 – Closed January and Tuesday

Rest – Italian Carte £15/29

◆ Busy Italian restaurant with cosy lounge, linen-laid tables and a large open kitchen so you can watch chef at work. Good value cooking including freshly baked bread.

ENGLAND

at High Crosby Northeast : 5 m. by A 7 - BY - off A 689 – ✉ Carlisle

Crosby Lodge Country House

Crosby-on-Eden ✉ CA6 4QZ – ☎ (01228) 573 618 – enquiries@crosbylodge.co.uk – Fax (01228) 573 428 – Closed Christmas-mid January

11 rm – £88/95 £160/200 – **Rest** – (Sunday dinner residents only) Menu £40 (dinner) – Carte £17/40

◆ Grade II listed, castellated house built in 1802. Warm ambience and welcoming hostess. Traditionally furnished lounge. Comfortable bedrooms with pleasant countryside outlook. Richly coloured dining room with polished brass around fireplace. Classic, homecooked food includes renowned sweet trolley.

CARLTON-IN-COVERDALE – N. Yorks. – 502 O 21 – see Middleham

CARLYON BAY – Cornwall – 503 F 33 – see St Austell

CARTERWAY HEADS – Northd. – 501 O 19 – ✉ Shotley Bridge 24 A2

London 272 m – Carlisle 59 m – Newcastle upon Tyne 21 m

Manor House Inn with rm

on A 68 ✉ DH8 9LX – ☎ (01207) 255 268 – Closed dinner 25 December

4 rm – £45 £75 – **Rest** – Carte £20/30

◆ 18C inn with views over the moors; whet your whistle in the bar or dine in the smartly refurbished restaurant. Tasty dishes and home-made desserts. Smart rooms with views.

CARTHORPE – N. Yorks 22 B1

Fox and Hounds

✉ DL8 2LG – ☎ (01845) 567 433 – helenst36@btinternet.com – Fax (01845) 567 155 – Closed 1 week January, 25 and 31 December and Monday

Rest – Menu £17 – Carte £23/30

◆ Former village smithy; forge and water pump still in restaurant. Walls and shelves stacked with ornaments, plates, photos and old farm equipment. Classic homemade pub dishes.

CARTMEL – Cumbria – 502 L 21 – see Grange-over-Sands

CASTLE CARROCK – Cumbria – 502 L 19 – see Brampton

CASTLE CARY – Somerset – 503 M 30 – pop. 3 056 4 C2

London 127 m – Bristol 28 m – Wells 13 m

Clanville Manor without rest (heated)

West : 2 m. by B 3152 and A 371 on B 3153 ✉ BA7 7PJ – ✆ (01963) 350 124 – info@clanvillemanor.co.uk – Fax (01963) 350 719 – Closed Christmas and New Year

4 rm – †£ 30/60 ††£ 65/75

◆ Comely 18C house full of period style and charm. Heirlooms and antiques abound. Breakfasts served from the Aga. Walled garden boasts heated pool. Individualistic rooms.

at South Cadbury South : 4½ m. by B 3152 off A 359 – ✉ Castle Cary

Lower Camelot without rest

Church Rd ✉ BA22 7HA – ✆ (01963) 440 581 – info@southcadbury.co.uk – Closed January-March and 24-26 December

4 rm – †£ 40/45 ††£ 70

◆ Owners go out of their way to make your stay pleasurable in guesthouse named after King Arthur's castle. Lovely garden; good breakfasts in the conservatory. Smart rooms.

The Camelot

Chapel Rd ✉ BA22 7EX – ✆ (01963) 440 448 – enquiries@thecamelot.co.uk

Rest – Carte £ 23/36

◆ Creeper-clad inn with stylish local artwork on the walls and a light, airy feel. Hearty and traditional British dishes are precisely cooked, using locally sourced produce.

at Lovington West : 4 m. by B 3152 and A 371 on B 3153 – ✉ Castle Cary

The Pilgrims at Lovington

✉ BA7 7PT – ✆ (01963) 240 597 – Closed October

Rest – (closed Monday, Tuesday and dinner Sunday) Carte £ 15/33

◆ Unprepossessing façade disguises lovely olive green rustic interior with water-colours and beams. Interesting, hearty menus include meat, ice cream and beer from the village!

The ✿ award is the crème de la crème.
This is awarded to restaurants
which are really worth travelling miles for!

CASTLE COMBE – Wilts. – 503 N 29 – ✉ Chippenham 4 C2

London 110 m – Bristol 23 m – Chippenham 6 m

Village★★

Manor House H. and Golf Club

✉ SN14 7HR – ✆ (01249) 782 206 – enquiries@manor-housecc.co.uk – Fax (01249) 783 100

44 rm – †£ 150/180 ††£ 230/800 – 4 suites

Rest *The Bybrook* – Menu £ 28/53 **s** – Carte £ 53/70 **s**

◆ Particularly peaceful manor in a sweeping green with trout in the river. Fine fabrics and oak panelling exude history. Luxurious bedrooms in mews cottages or main house. Smart restaurant: English country style menus.

Castle Inn

✉ SN14 7HN – ✆ (01249) 783 030 – enquiries@castle-inn.info – Fax (01249) 782 315 – closed 25 December

11 rm – †£ 75/140 ††£ 150/180 – **Rest** – Carte £ 18/31

◆ A hostelry dating back to the 12C in the middle of a delightful and historic village. Much character, from the wooden beams in the bedrooms to the rustic bar. Large glass ceiling creates light-flooded dining room.

ENGLAND

at Nettleton Shrub West : 2 m. by B 4039 on Nettleton rd (Fosse Way) – ✉ Chippenham

Fosse Farmhouse
✉ SN14 7NJ – ✆ (01249) 782 286 – caroncooper@compuserve.com – Fax (01249) 783 066 – Closed 4 January-4 February
3 rm – †£ 65/75 ††£ 125/135 – **Rest** – (by arrangement) Menu £ 28
◆ 18C Cotswold Stone farmhouse personally run by enthusiastic owner. Cream teas served in the garden in summer. Welcoming bedrooms with French artefacts and Gallic style.

CASTLE DONINGTON – Leics. – **502** P 25 – **pop. 5 977** – ✉ **Derby** 16 **B2**

London 123 m – Birmingham 38 m – Leicester 23 m – Nottingham 13 m
Nottingham East Midlands Airport : ✆ (0871) 919 9000, S : by B 6540 and A 453

Priest House on the River
Kings Mills, West : 1 ¾ m. by Park Lane ✉ DE74 2RR – ✆ (01332) 810 649 – enquiries.priesthouse@handpicked.co.uk – Fax (01332) 811 141
39 rm – †£ 70/140 ††£ 120/200 – 3 suites
Rest *Restaurant* – Menu £ 22/30 **s** – Carte £ 31/50 **s**
Rest *Brasserie* – Carte £ 20/32 **s**
◆ Stylish, contemporary hotel in tranquil riverside setting. Comfortable bedrooms - some with views of the river - decorated in neutral shades, with giant plasma screen TVs. Intimate restaurant serves bold, modern cooking. Terrace bistro has bar as well as tables laid with starched linen.

ENGLAND

at Breedon on the Hill Southwest : 4 m. by Breedon rd off A 453 – ✉ Castle Donington

The Three Horseshoes Inn
Main St ✉ DE73 8AN – ✆ (01332) 695 129 – ian@thehorseshoes.com – Closed 25-26 December, 1 January and Sunday dinner
Rest – Carte £ 26/33
◆ Former farrier's, sympathetically refurbished, with great attention to detail and an intimate Red Room. Bold, honest cooking with international touches and classic puddings.

CATEL – C.I. – **503** P 33 – **see Channel Islands**

CAUNTON – Notts. – **502** R 24 – **see Newark-on-Trent**

CAVENDISH – Suffolk – **504** V 27 14 **B3**

London 70 m – Cambridge 30 m – Colchester 20 m

Embleton House without rest (heated)
Melford Rd ✉ CO10 8AA – ✆ (01787) 280 447 – silverned@aol.com – Fax (01787) 282 396 – Closed New Year
5 rm – †£ 40/50 ††£ 60/75
◆ Spacious, comfy Edwardian house in attractive, mature gardens. Breakfast with extensive menu served at large communal table. Well-kept rooms. Holistic therapies available.

CHADDESLEY CORBETT – Worcs. – **503** N 26 – **see Kidderminster**

If breakfast is included the symbol appears after the number of rooms.

CHADWICK END – W. Mids. – 503 O 26 19 C2

London 106 m – Birmingham 13 m – Leicester 40 m – Stratford-upon-Avon 16 m

The Orange Tree
Warwick Road, on A 4141 ✉ B93 0BN – ✆ (01564) 785 364 – Fax (01564) 782 988 – Closed 25 December and Sunday dinner
Rest – (booking essential) Carte £ 18/35
◆ Modern roadside dining pub with attractive exterior and stylish interior. The menu of modish classics is good value and has an appealing, flexible range.

CHAGFORD – Devon – 503 I 31 2 C2

London 218 m – Exeter 17 m – Plymouth 27 m
Dartmoor National Park★★

Gidleigh Park (Michael Caines) ← Teign Valley, woodland and Meldon Hill,
Northwest : 2 m.
by Gidleigh Rd ✉ TQ13 8HH – ✆ (01647) 432 367 – gidleighpark@gidleigh.co.uk – Fax (01647) 432 574
23 rm (dinner included) – †£ 360 ††£ 620 – 1 suite – **Rest** – (booking essential) Menu £ 35/85
Spec. Tuna and scallop tartare, caviar, beetroot, soy and honey. Roast duck, cabbage and bacon, honey jus. Banana parfait, lime sorbet and chocolate.
◆ Smart, stylish and beautifully situated in 45 Dartmoor acres; sumptuous rooms the epitome of style, with fine English fabrics and antiques; those to front have best views. Classically based cooking, prepared with skill and flair, proudly showcases local produce. Excellent choice of wines.

at Easton Northeast : 1 ½ m. on A 382 – ✉ Chagford

Easton Court without rest
Easton Cross ✉ TQ13 8JL – ✆ (01647) 433 469 – stay@easton.co.uk – Fax (01647) 433 654
5 rm – †£ 49/51 ††£ 72/75
◆ Well appointed accommodation and a high ceilinged lounge overlooking the immaculate gardens. Home made marmalade a speciality. Friendly atmosphere.

at Sandypark Northeast : 2 ¼ m. on A 382 – ✉ Chagford

Mill End
on A 382 ✉ TQ13 8JN – ✆ (01647) 432 282 – info@millendhotel.com – Fax (01647) 433 106
14 rm – †£ 90/150 ††£ 150/210 – **Rest** – (light lunch Monday-Saturday) Menu £ 38
◆ Country house with mill wheel; river Teign runs through garden. Framed pictures, curios grace interiors. Upstairs bedrooms have views; those downstairs have private patios. Pretty restaurant, bright and comfortable.

Parford Well without rest
on Drewsteignton rd ✉ TQ13 8JW – ✆ (01647) 433 353 – tim@parfordwell.co.uk – Closed Christmas and New Year
3 rm – †£ 45/50 ††£ 85
◆ Tastefully maintained with superbly tended gardens. Elegant sitting room has plenty of books and French windows to garden. Two breakfast rooms. Homely, immaculate rooms.

The Sandy Park Inn with rm
✉ TQ13 8JW – ✆ (01647) 433 267 – enquiries@sandyparkinn.co.uk
5 rm – †£ 60 ††£ 98 – **Rest** – Carte £ 20/26
◆ Small but characterful 17C thatched inn with flagged floors, heavy beams and open fires. Delightful hillside garden. Modern, sophisticated cooking. Cosy bedrooms have flat screen TVs.

ENGLAND

ALDERNEY – C.I. – 503 M 32 – pop. 2 294 5 B1

Aurigny Air Services ☎ (0871) 871 0717
States Office, Queen Elizabeth II St ☎ (01481) 822994
Braye Bay★ – Mannez Garenne (≤ ★ from Quesnard Lighthouse) – Telegraph Bay★ – Vallee des Trois Vaux★ – Clonque Bay★

Braye – C.I. 5 B1

Braye Beach ≤ rest, VISA MC AE

GY9 3XT – ☎ (01481) 824 300 – reception@brayebeach.com – Fax (01481) 824 301
27 rm – †£ 120/160 ††£ 160/180 – **Rest** – Carte £ 22/30 s
◆ Smart, contemporary hotel set on edge of beach. Vaulted basement houses a series of lounges, dining room and a 19-seat cinema. Modern European cooking with a subtle seafood slant.

First and Last ≤ harbour, VISA MC AE

GY9 3TH – ☎ (01481) 823 162 – Easter-October
Rest – Seafood (Closed Monday) (dinner only) Carte £ 22/33
◆ Positioned by the harbour with scenic views. Simple pine furniture, blue gingham tablecloths. Nautical theme prevails. Keen use of island produce with seafood base.

St Anne – C.I. 5 B1

Farm Court without rest VISA MC

Le Petit Val GY9 3UX – ☎ (01481) 822 075 – relax@farmcourt-alderney.co.uk – Fax (01481) 822 075 – closed 1 week Christmas
11 rm – †£ 39/60 ††£ 78/98
◆ Converted stone farm buildings around cobbled courtyard and garden. Sitting room and breakfast room. Spacious well-appointed bedrooms with contemporary and antique furniture.

Maison Bourgage without rest VISA MC

2 Le Bourgage GY9 3TL – ☎ (01481) 824 097 – info@maisonbourgage.com – closed December
4 rm – †£ 44/64 ††£ 60/76
◆ Part Georgian house on quiet, cobbled, town centre street. Neat, enclosed decked patio and garden face south. Leather furnished lounge and breakfast room. Bright, airy rooms.

GUERNSEY – C.I. – 503 L 32 – pop. 58 867 5 A2

Service Air ☎ (01481) 237766, Aurigny Air ☎ (0871) 871 0717
from St Peter Port to France (St Malo) and Jersey (St Helier) (Condor Ferries Ltd) – from St Peter Port to Jersey (St Helier) and Weymouth (Condor Ferries Ltd)
from St Peter Port to France (St Malo) and Jersey (St Helier) (Condor Ferries Ltd) 2 weekly – from St Peter Port to France (Dielette) (Manche Iles Express) (summer only) (60 mn) – from St Peter Port to Herm (Herm Seaway) (25 mn) – from St Peter Port to Sark (Isle of Sark Shipping Co. Ltd) (45 mn) – from St Peter Port to Jersey (St Helier) (HD Ferries) (1hr) – from St Peter Port to Jersey (St Helier) (Condor Ferries Ltd) daily
P.O. Box 23, North Esplanade ☎ (01481) 723552 Passenger Terminal, New Jetty ☎ (01481) 715885
Island★ - Pezeries Point★★ – Icart Point★★ – Côbo Bay★★ - St Martin's Point★★ – St Apolline's Chapel★ – Vale Castle★ – Fort Doyle★ – La Gran'mere du Chimquiere★ – Rocquaine Bay★ – Jerbourg Point★

The red symbol?
This denotes the very essence of peace
– only the sound of birdsong first thing in the morning …

Catel/Castel – C.I. 5 A2

Hougue du Pommier (heated)

Hougue du Pommier Rd ✉ GY5 7FQ – ☎ (01481) 256531
– hotel@houguedupommier.guernsey.net – Fax (01481) 256260
41 rm – †£53/80 ††£85/125
Rest *Tudor Bar* – Carte £16/26
Rest *The Restaurant* – (dinner only and Sunday lunch) Carte £21/38
♦ A personally run 18C farmhouse with later extensions. Lovely outdoor pool and decking area. Occasional medieval banquets. Comfortable bedrooms, warmly decorated. Tudor Bar for unique Feu du Bois cooking over open flame. Restaurant with beams and oak panelling.

Cobo Bay rest,

Cobo Coast Rd ✉ GY5 7HB – ☎ (01481) 257102
– reservations@cobobayhotel.com – Fax (01481) 254542 – Closed January
36 rm – †£49/99 ††£75/125 – **Rest** – (dinner only and Sunday lunch) Menu £23
♦ Modern hotel on peaceful, sandy Cobo Bay; an ideal location for families. The rooms are pleasant with bright décor and some have the delightful addition of seaview balconies. Romantic dining with views of sunsets.

Harton Lodge

Rue de Galaad ✉ GY5 7FJ – ☎ (01481) 256341 – Fax (01481) 255716
20 rm – †£40/70 ††£80/100 – **Rest** – (bar lunch) Menu £20 **s** – Carte £19/30
♦ Sunny yellow painted house with a neat and tidy appeal; close to beach. Two bars, one with a pool table. Decking to rear with small pool and sauna. Bright bedrooms. Linen-laid dining room: conservatory extension boasts comfy leather sofas.

Fermain Bay – C.I. 5 A2

Fermain Valley rm, rest,

Fermain Lane ✉ GY1 1ZZ – ☎ (01481) 235666
– info@fermainvalley.com – Fax (01481) 235413
45 rm – †£170 ††£230
Rest *Restaurant* – (dinner only and Sunday lunch) Menu £25 (dinner) **s** – Carte £25/31 **s**
Rest *Brasserie* – Menu £25 (dinner) **s** – Carte £23/27 **s**
♦ Fine sea views through the trees. Smart contemporary country house theme prevails: sleek lounges, decked terrace, library, and fresh, carefully appointed rooms with balconies. Fine dining in comfortable Restaurant. Fresh fish and simple grills at the Brasserie.

Christophe (Christophe Vincent)

Fort Rd ✉ GY1 1ZP – ☎ (01481) 230725 – christophe@fermainvalley.com
– Fax (01481) 230726 – Closed Sunday dinner and Monday
Rest – Menu £19 (lunch) – Carte £29/46
Spec. Crab, pea purée, poached yolk and verbena oil. Turbot, crushed new potatoes, girolle butter sauce. Peach tarte Tatin, amaretto soufflé, pistachio dantelle.
♦ Contemporary and seriously stylish restaurant with superb sea views, serving good value, boldly flavoured, seasonal dishes using quality French produce. Personable service.

Forest – C.I. – pop. 1 386 5 A2

Maison Bel Air without rest

Le Chene ✉ GY8 0AL – ☎ (01481) 238503 – juliette@maisonbelair.com
– Fax (01481) 239403 – Closed December
6 rm – †£25/42 ††£46/64
♦ Welcoming peach and white guesthouse, near airport; overlooking Petit Bot Valley with shady, peaceful, south facing garden. Smart breakfast room. Comfortable bedrooms.

ENGLAND

Kings Mills – C.I. 5 A2

Fleur du Jardin with rm (heated) P VISA AE
Castel ✉ GY5 7JT – ✆ (01481) 257 996 – info@fleurdujardin.com – Fax (01481) 256 834 – closed dinner 25-26 December
17 rm – ♦£ 50/70 ♦♦£ 125 – **Rest** – (bar lunch) Menu £ 13 – Carte £ 25/30
◆ Daily menus of local seafood give this granite 15C inn a standing of quiet renown. Cosy interior: rough hewn walls, alcoves, stone fireplace. Cottagey, traditional rooms.

St Martin – C.I. – pop. 6 082 5 A2

St Peter Port 2 m

Bon Port ← Moulin Huet Bay and Jerbourg Point, P VISA
Moulin Huet Bay ✉ GY4 6EW – ✆ (01481) 239 249 – mail@bonport.com – Fax (01481) 239 596 – Closed January-February
21 rm – ♦£ 65/115 ♦♦£ 95/195 – 1 suite – **Rest** – (bar lunch Monday-Saturday) Menu £ 26 (dinner) – Carte £ 22/41
◆ Perched on the top of the cliff, with a commanding view of the bay, this hotel is very keenly and personally run. Rooms vary in size and style and some have balconies. Large two tier dining room with bay views.

Jerbourg ← sea and neighbouring Channel Islands, A/C rest, P VISA
Jerbourg Point ✉ GY4 6BJ – ✆ (01481) 238 826 – stay@hoteljerbourg.com – Fax (01481) 238 238 – March-October
29 rm – ♦£ 42/107 ♦♦£ 82/117 – **Rest** – Menu £ 20 (dinner) – Carte £ 15/34
◆ In a prime position for walks to sandy bays. Popular terrace for afternoon teas. Equipped with solar heated outdoor pool and garden patio. Most rooms have pleasant sea views. Finely presented, fish based cuisine.

La Barbarie (heated) P VISA
Saints Bay ✉ GY4 6ES – ✆ (01481) 235 217 – reservations@labarbariehotel.com – Fax (01481) 235 208 – March-October
21 rm – ♦£ 53/72 ♦♦£ 66/104 – 1 suite – **Rest** – (residents only bar lunch) Menu £ 20 – Carte £ 19/29
◆ Stone-built former farmhouse with a welcoming, cottagey style. Characterful bar; well-kept pool and terrace. Eclectic range of rooms, including 10 larger annexed apartments. Mediterranean buzz from the restaurant.

Saints Bay (heated) P VISA AE
Icart ✉ GY4 6JG – ✆ (01481) 238 888 – info@saintsbayhotel.com – Fax (01481) 235 558
35 rm – ♦£ 38/83 ♦♦£ 55/117 – **Rest** – (bar lunch Monday-Saturday) Menu £ 19 – Carte £ 19/28
◆ Located on Icart Point, overlooking Fisherman's Harbour, the southern tip of the island, perfect for cliff top walks. Multilingual staff; neat bedrooms with all amenities. Broad choice of menus.

La Michele (heated) P VISA AE
Les Hubits ✉ GY4 6NB – ✆ (01481) 238 065 – info@lamichelehotel.com – Fax (01481) 239 492 – mid March-10 October
16 rm – ♦£ 42/58 ♦♦£ 84/116 – **Rest** – (dinner only) (residents only) Menu £ 16
◆ Painted and canopied façade with conservatory lounge and secluded garden. Lovely seating area around the pool. Fermain bay is nearby; pleasant, unfussy bedrooms.

Sunnydene Country (heated) P VISA AE
Rue des Marettes ✉ GY4 6JH – ✆ (01481) 236 870 – info@sunnydenecountryhotel.com – Fax (01481) 237 468 – 4 April-October
20 rm – ♦£ 35/60 ♦♦£ 60/80 – **Rest** – (dinner only) Menu £ 17 – Carte £ 14/21
◆ Neat and tidy hotel with pitch and putt to rear of garden! Comfortable, homely lounge; linen-laid dining room. Pretty pool and terrace area. Rooms in house or garden.

ENGLAND

The Auberge ⩤ Sea and neighbouring Channel Islands,

Jerbourg Rd ✉ GY4 6BH – ✆ (01481) 238485
– theauberge@cwgsy.net – Fax (01481) 710936
– Closed 25-26 December and 1 January

Rest – (booking essential) Carte £20/32

◆ A splendid spot to sample contemporary brasserie-style dishes. Modern informal style, attractive terrace and excellent views of sea and islands.

St Peter Port – C.I. – pop. 16 648 5 **A2**

Rohais St Pierre Park, ✆ (01481) 727039.

Town★★ - St Peter's Church★ Z – Hauteville House★ **AC** Z – Castle Cornet★ (⩤ ★) **AC** Z

Saumarez Park★ (Guernsey Folk Museum★), W : 2 m. by road to Catel Z – Little Chapel★, SW : 2 ¼ m. by Mount Durand road Z

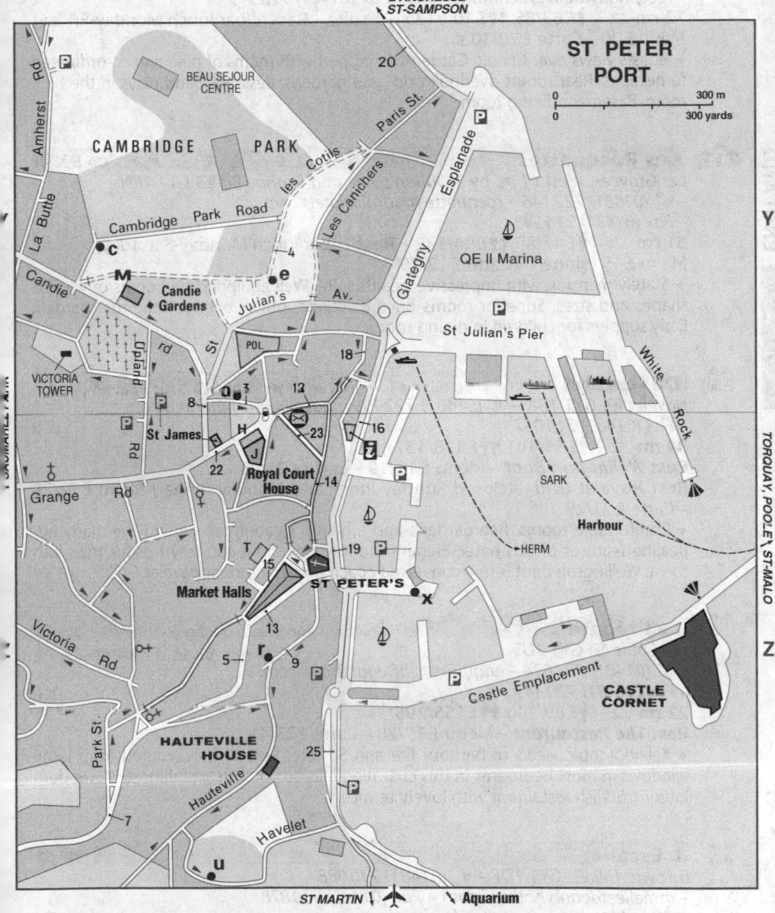

Ann's Place . . . Y 3	Forest Lane . . . Y 12	Quay (The) . . . Z 19
Beauregard Lane . . . Y 4	Fountain Street . . . Z 13	St-George's Esplanade . . . Y 20
Bordage . . . Z 5	High Street . . . Z 14	St-James Street . . . Z 22
Charroterie . . . Z 7	Market Street . . . Z 15	Smith Street . . . Z 23
College Street . . . YZ 8	North Esplanade . . . YZ 16	South Esplanade . . . Z 25
Cornet Street . . . Z 9	Pollet . . . Y 18	

Old Government House H. & Spa (heated)
St Ann's Pl ✉ GY1 2NU rm,
– ✆ (01481) 724 921 – ogh@theoghhotel.com – Fax (01481) 724 429 Y **a**
63 rm – ♦£ 125/160 ♦♦£ 205/300
Rest *Governors* – (Closed Monday and lunch Saturday-Sunday) (booking essential) Menu £ 22 (lunch) – Carte £ 27/36
Rest *The Brasserie* – Menu £ 16/22 – Carte £ 23/45
◆ Refurbished hotel in 18C house, built for island governors. State-of-art leisure facilities. Conservatory is popular for tea. Comfortable rooms, some boasting harbour views. Impressively spacious Governors. Informal Mediterranean favourites at the Brasserie.

Duke of Richmond (heated)
Cambridge Park ✉ GY1 1UY – ✆ (01481) 726 221
– reception@dukeofrichmond.com – Fax (01481) 728 945 Y **c**
72 rm – ♦£ 63/85 ♦♦£ 105/135 – 1 suite – **Rest** – (bar lunch Monday-Friday) Menu £ 20 – Carte £ 20/30 **s**
◆ Boasts views over Candie Gardens. Equipped with rooms of pine and co-ordinated furnishings. Rear rooms overlook pool and gardens. Resident band plays in the ballroom. Basement dining room.

Les Rocquettes
Les Gravees, West : 1 m. by St Julian's Ave and Grange Rd ✉ GY1 1RN
– ✆ (01481) 722 146 – rocquettes@sarniahotels.com
– Fax (01481) 714 543
51 rm – ♦£ 47/85 ♦♦£ 94/132 – **Rest** – (bar lunch Monday-Saturday) Menu £ 15 (dinner) – Carte £ 12/25
◆ Stately mansion with impressive health suite. Well-equipped bedrooms of various shapes and sizes. Superior rooms have balconies; others overlook the rear garden. Early suppers for children in dining room.

ENGLAND

De Havelet rest,
Havelet ✉ GY1 1BA – ✆ (01481) 722 199 – havelet@sarniahotels.com
– Fax (01481) 714 057 Z **u**
34 rm – ♦£ 51/101 ♦♦£ 118/137
Rest *Wellington Boot* – Menu £ 12/19 – Carte £ 21/28
Rest *Havelet Grill* – (closed Sunday lunch and Monday dinner) Menu £ 12/20 – Carte £ 21/28
◆ Comfortable rooms, fine gardens and a hilltop location are among the many appealing features of this hotel. Elegant indoor pool and a courtesy bus for trips into town. Wellington Boot is in a converted coach house. Informal Havelet Grill.

La Frégate ≤ town harbour and neighbouring Channel Islands,
Les Cotils ✉ GY1 1UT rest,
– ✆ (01481) 724 624 – enquiries@lafregatehotel.com
– Fax (01481) 720 443 Y **e**
22 rm – ♦£ 89/140 ♦♦£ 155/195
Rest *The Restaurant* – Menu £ 19/28 – Carte £ 23/41
◆ Kaleidoscopic views of harbour life and St Peter Port to be savoured from large windows in most bedrooms in this charming hillside hotel. Peaceful location; modern interior. Stylish restaurant with lovely terrace.

L'Escalier
6 Tower Hill ✉ GY1 1DF – ✆ (01481) 710 088
– armelleetdean@hotmail.com – Fax (01481) 710 878
– Closed Monday and Saturday lunch Z **r**
Rest – Menu £ 16/30 – Carte £ 24/40
◆ Tucked away in the old quarter of town, a personally run restaurant with a sheltered terrace and attentive service. Complex dishes use both local and French produce.

Saltwater
Albert Pier ✉ *GY1 1AD – ✆ (01481) 720 823 – info@saltwater.gg – Fax (01481) 772 702 – Closed 2 weeks Christmas-New Year, Saturday lunch and Sunday* Z x
Rest – Seafood Menu £ 15 – Carte approx. £ 40
◆ Warmly run restaurant in impressive location at end of historic pier overlooking harbour near large marina. Modern feel. Extensive menus have a solid seafood slant.

The Absolute End
Longstore, North : ¾ m. by St George's Esplanade ✉ *GY1 2BG – ✆ (01481) 723 822 – theabsoluteend@cwgsy.net – Fax (01481) 729 129 – closed 26 December-25 January and Sunday*
Rest – Seafood Carte £ 20/40
◆ Distinctive whitewashed house just out of town. Inspired freshly cooked seafood dishes, prepared with flair, served by friendly staff. Lovely enclosed decked terrace to rear.

St Saviour – C.I. – pop. 2 419 5 **A2**

St Peter Port 4 m

Atlantique (heated) rest,
Perelle Bay ✉ *GY7 9NA – ✆ (01481) 264 056 – enquiries@perellebay.com – Fax (01481) 263 800 – April-October*
22 rm – £ 30/100 £ 50/140 – 1 suite
Rest *Atlantique* – (dinner only and Sunday lunch) Menu £ 25
◆ Traditionally styled hotel in a delightful spot on Perelle Bay, only a few metres from the sea: fine views from front-facing rooms. Charmingly formal Atlantique.

The Pavilion
Le Gron ✉ *GY7 9RN – ✆ (01481) 264 165 – lecknleck@cwgsy.net – Fax (01481) 267 396 – Closed Christmas-mid January, 1 week November and Monday in winter*
Rest – (lunch only and dinner Friday and Saturday in summer) Carte £ 18/25
◆ Located in grounds of jewellers Bruce Russell and Son. Pleasant interior of exposed stone and beams. Excellent value, well executed dishes using good quality local produce.

Vazon Bay – C.I. – ✉ Catel 5 **A2**

La Grande Mare (heated)
Vazon Coast Rd ✉ *GY5 7LL – ✆ (01481) 256 576 – hotellagrandemare@cwgsy.net – Fax (01481) 256 532*
12 rm – £ 93 £ 166 – 12 suites – £ 218/250 – **Rest** – Menu £ 15/20 **s** – Carte £ 24/33 **s**
◆ Resort complex with large bedrooms of magnolia and pine furnishings; some have balconies, some well-equipped small kitchens. Family friendly, with indoor/outdoor activities. Formal dining room overlooks golf course.

HERM – C.I. – 503 M 33 – pop. 97

to Guernsey (St Peter Port) (Herm Seaway) (20 mn)
Le Grand Monceau ★

White House Belle Greve Bay and Guernsey, (heated)
✉ *GY1 3HR – ✆ (01481) 722 159 – hotel@herm-island.com – Fax (01481) 710 066 – 20 March-6 October*
40 rm – £ 80/116 £ 184/200
Rest *Conservatory* – (booking essential) Menu £ 25 (dinner) – Carte lunch £ 19/26
Rest *Ship Inn* – Carte approx. £ 19
◆ Hotel with real country house feel: offset by verdant hills, the beach extends to the door. Guernsey and Jethou can be viewed from the hushed lounge. Attractive rooms. Formal Conservatory with seafood emphasis. Relaxed Ship Inn.

ENGLAND

JERSEY – C.I. – 503 L 33 – pop. 87 500 5 B2

States of Jersey Airport : ☎ (01534) 492000

from St Helier to France (St Malo) and Guernsey (St Peter Port) (Condor Ferries Ltd) – from St Helier to Sark (Condor Ferries Ltd) (50 mn) – from St Helier to Guernsey (St Peter Port) and Weymouth (Condor Ferries Ltd)

from St Helier to France (St Malo) (Condor Ferries Ltd) (summer only) – from St Helier to France (St Malo) (Condor Ferries Ltd) 3 weekly - from Gorey to France (Carteret) (Manche Iles Express) (summer only) (60mn) – from St Helier to Guernsey (St Peter Port) (Condor Ferries Ltd) (50 mn) – from St Helier to Guernsey (St Peter Port) (Condor Ferries Ltd) daily

Liberation Sq, St Helier ☎ (01534) 500777

Island★★ - Jersey Zoo★★ **AC** – Jersey Museum★ - Eric Young Orchid Foundation★ – St Catherine's Bay★ (≤ ★★) – Grosnez Point★ - Devil's Hole★ – St Matthews Church, Millbrook (glasswork★) – La Hougue Bie★ (Neolithic tomb★ **AC**) - Waterworks Valley - Hamptonne Country Life Museum★ – St Catherine's Bay★ (≤ ★★) – Noirmont Point★

Beaumont – C.I. 5 B2

Bistro Soleil
≤ St Aubins Bay, P VISA AE

La Route de la Haule ✉ JE3 7BA – ☎ (01534) 720 249 – bistrosoleil@aboutjersey.net – Fax (01534) 625 621 – Closed 25-26 December, Sunday dinner, Monday and Bank Holidays

Rest – Menu £ 15/25 – Carte £ 25/32

◆ Series of connected rooms with superb views over St Aubins Bay. Minimalist style: just a couple of modern pictures. Freshly prepared, bold menus with Mediterranean accent.

ENGLAND

Bouley Bay – C.I. 5 B2

St Helier 6 m

The Water's Edge
≤ Bouley Bay, (heated) P VISA AE

✉ JE3 5AS – ☎ (01534) 862 777 – mail@watersedgehotel.co.je – early April-mid October

47 rm – ♦£ 43/69 ♦♦£ 110/162 – 3 suites

Rest *Waterside* – (dinner only) Menu £ 25 **s** – Carte £ 32/38 **s**

Rest *Black Dog Bar* – (Closed Christmas and New Year and Monday in Winter) Carte £ 16/21 **s**

◆ Refurbished, revitalised hotel of long standing that boasts breathtaking bay views. Secluded garden with well-manicured lawns. Comfortable, well-appointed accommodation. Formal Waterside for tables-with-a-view. Black Dog Bar with quarterdeck al fresco area.

Gorey – C.I. – ✉ St Martin 5 B2

St Helier 4 m

Mont Orgueil Castle★ (≤ ★★) **AC** – Jersey Pottery★

Old Court House
(heated) P VISA

Gorey Village ✉ JE3 9FS – ☎ (01534) 854 444 – ochhotel@itl.net – Fax (01534) 853 587 – mid April-mid October

58 rm – ♦£ 48/98 ♦♦£ 95/131

Rest – (residents only bar lunch) Menu £ 22

◆ A popular, spacious hotel opposite three miles of sandy beach of the Royal Bay of Grouville. Large balconies in the second and third floor bedrooms. Pleasant gardens. Part 15C dining room: low beamed ceilings, exposed granite walls.

Moorings
AC rest, VISA AE

Gorey Pier ✉ JE3 6EW – ☎ (01534) 853 633 – reservations@themooringshotel.com – Fax (01534) 857 618

15 rm – ♦£ 50/90 ♦♦£ 100/130

Rest – Menu £ 17/20 – Carte £ 30/57

◆ Located at the base of Gorey Castle, overlooking the waterfront, once the heart of the oyster fishing industry. Well-priced; the first floor bedrooms have terraces. Pleasant decked area at front of restaurant.

Suma's ← Gorey harbour and castle,

Gorey Hill ✉ JE3 6ET – ✆ (01534) 853 291 – Fax (01534) 851 913 – Closed 23 December- 22 January

Rest – (booking essential) Menu £ 18 (lunch) – Carte £ 30/46 **s**

◆ Cheerful and contemporary; fine terrace views of Gorey Castle and harbour. Dishes are carefully prepared and innovatively presented; pleasant service enhances the enjoyment.

Village Bistro

Gorey Village ✉ JE3 9EP – ✆ (01534) 853 429 – thevillagebistro@yahoo.co.uk – Closed Sunday dinner and Monday

Rest – Menu £ 15 (lunch) – Carte £ 22/29

◆ Local produce sourced daily from small suppliers. Unpretentious feel; interesting choices to be made, particularly of seafood dishes.

Green Island – C.I. 5 B2

Green Island

St Clement ✉ JE2 6LS – ✆ (01534) 857 787 – greenislandrestaurant@jerseymail.co.uk – closed 22 December-3 February, Sunday dinner and Monday

Rest – Seafood (booking essential) Carte £ 26/35

◆ Lovely location on the beach; coir carpeted, nautically fitted restaurant with wide ranging, daily changing menu at affordable prices. Welcoming, casual atmosphere.

Grouville – C.I. 5 B2

St Helier 3 m

Cafe Poste

La Rue de la ville ES Renauds ✉ JE3 9FY – ✆ (01534) 859 696 – Closed 2 weeks February, 2 weeks November, Monday and Tuesday

Rest – (booking essential) Menu £ 15 (lunch) – Carte £ 26/33

◆ Former post office and general store with hidden decked area for outdoor dining. Very much a neighbourhood favourite. Strong use of island produce on eclectic, modish menus.

La Haule – C.I. – ✉ St Brelade 5 B2

La Place (heated)

Route du Coin, by B 25 on B 43 ✉ JE3 8BT – ✆ (01534) 744 261 – reservations@hotellaplacejersey.com – Fax (01534) 745 164

42 rm – †£ 124 ††£ 198/256

Rest *The Retreat* – (dinner only and Sunday lunch) Menu £ 23 – Carte £ 22/30

◆ Built round the remains of a 17C farmhouse; peaceful gardens and pool. Suited to both holiday makers and business clientele; spacious rooms, includes executive study rooms. Medieval inspired restaurant and adjoining conservatory.

La Haule Manor without rest ← St Aubin's Fort and Bay,

St Aubin's Bay ✉ JE3 8BS – ✆ (01534) 746 013 – lahaulemanor@jerseymail.co.uk – Fax (01534) 745 501

10 rm – †£ 37/52 ††£ 74/104

◆ Attractive, extended Georgian house with fine coastal outlook. Period style sitting room; stylish breakfast room; large basement bar. Airy, well-kept bedrooms with good view.

Au Caprice

Route de la Haule, on A 1 ✉ JE3 8BA – ✆ (01534) 722 083 – aucaprice@jerseymail.co.uk – Fax (01534) 280 058 – 15 March-October

12 rm – †£ 30/55 ††£ 44/66 – **Rest** – (by arrangement) Menu £ 12

◆ Clean-lined white guesthouse with French windows; light and airy, providing homely good value rooms: two of them share large balcony at the front. Close to large sandy beach. Each morning, guests told dining room menu.

La Pulente – C.I. – ✉ St Brelade 5 B2

St Helier 7 m

Les Mielles G. & C.C. St Ouens Bay, ✆ (01534) 482 787 .

Atlantic (heated)

Le Mont de la Pulente, on B 35 ✉ JE3 8HE – ✆ (01534) 744 101 – info@theatlantichotel.com – Fax (01534) 744 102 – Closed 2 January-1 February

49 rm – £ 130/190 £ 165/285 – 1 suite

Rest *Ocean* – (booking essential) Menu £ 20/55

Spec. Pan-fried foie gras, macadamia nut crust, mango tart and sorbet. Thyme roast cod and sea bass, crushed peas, scallop tortellini and marjoram. Chocolate crisp, crème de menthe soufflé.

◆ Striking hotel with contemporary style overlooking La Pulente Bay. Bedrooms are spacious; Garden suites have own terrace; others have balconies. Elegant restaurant serving precise, unfussy cooking; chef an ambassador of Jersey's fine larder. High calibre service.

La Rocque – C.I. 5 B2

St Helier 8 m

Borsalino Rocque

✉ JE3 9FF – ✆ (01534) 852 111 – reservations@borsalinorocque.com – Fax (01534) 856 404 – Closed Tuesday

Rest – Seafood Menu £ 11/22 – Carte £ 22/32

◆ Well-spaced tables in large conservatory and dining room filled with curios. A long-established family business, popular with island residents. Wide choice in menus.

ENGLAND

Rozel Bay – C.I. – ✉ St Martin 5 B2

St Helier 6 m

Chateau La Chaire

Rozel Valley ✉ JE3 6AJ – ✆ (01534) 863 354 – res@chateau-la-chaire.co.uk – Fax (01534) 865 137

12 rm – £ 80/115 £ 170/245 – 2 suites – **Rest** – Menu £ 15/33 – Carte £ 34/43

◆ Imposing chateau dated 1843, rich in paintings and antiques: individually decorated bedrooms overlook the quiet wooded grounds. Ornate sitting room. Conservatory dining room; terrace popular in summer.

St Aubin – C.I. – ✉ St Brelade 5 B2

St Helier 4 m

Somerville St Aubin's Bay, (heated) rest,

Mont du Boulevard, South : ¾ m. via harbour ✉ JE3 8AD – ✆ (01534) 741 226 – somerville@dolanhotels.com – Fax (01534) 746 621

55 rm – £ 65/135 £ 86/210 – 1 suite

Rest *Tides* – Menu £ 13/25 – Carte £ 27/36 **s**

◆ Delightful views of the harbour, bay and village. Courtesy bus runs from hotel into town. Evening entertainment laid on. Cheerful rooms, some in superior style. Cloth clad, classic dining room.

Panorama without rest St Aubin's Fort and Bay,

La Rue du Crocquet ✉ JE3 8BZ – ✆ (01534) 742 429 – info@panoramajersey.com – Fax (01534) 745 940 – March-October

14 rm – £ 40/91 £ 100/124

◆ Personally run hotel with conservatory, garden and bay views. Also boasts a teapot collection. The superior style bedrooms are very pleasant. All rooms boast good amenities.

Sabots d'or
High St ✉ JE3 8BZ – ✆ (01534) 743 732 – mail@sabotsdor.com – Fax (01534) 490 142 – Closed Christmas and New Year
12 rm – †£ 26/38 ††£ 52/66 – **Rest** – (dinner only) Menu £ 14
◆ Traditional floral furnishings in homely and cosy bedrooms. Well located for shops, watersports; its cobbled high street position not far from picturesque harbour. Home-made desserts a dining room highlight.

Porthole Cottage without rest
La Rue au Moestre (Market Hill) ✉ JE3 8AE – ✆ (01534) 745 007 – portcott@itl.net – Fax (01534) 490 336 – mid March-10 October
11 rm – †£ 25/59 ††£ 49/79
◆ Brick and stone guesthouse overlooking St Aubins harbour; shrub-filled, elevated rear garden. Nautically inspired breakfast room with beams and galley window. Cottagey rooms.

Salty Dog Bar and Bistro
Le Boulevard ✉ JE3 8AB – ✆ (01534) 742 760 – info@saltydogbistro.com – Fax (01534) 742 932 – Closed 2 weeks from 24 December
Rest – Asian influences (Closed lunch Monday-Thursday except in Summer) Menu £ 19 (lunch) – Carte £ 25/39
◆ Wood panelled walls and church pews create rustic feel in quirky, informal restaurant in St. Aubin's harbour. Menus blend local produce with New World and Asian influences.

ENGLAND

Old Court House Inn with rm
St Aubin's Harbour ✉ JE3 8AB – ✆ (01534) 746 433 – info@oldcourthousejersey.com – Fax (01534) 745 103 – Closed 25 December
9 rm – †£ 40/60 ††£ 120 – **Rest** – Menu £ 13/23 – Carte £ 30/50
◆ Atmospheric quayside inn, once a courthouse and merchant's house, dating from 15C. Bar featured in Bergerac TV series. Cosmopolitan menu with seafood emphasis. Neat bedrooms.

St Brelade's Bay – C.I. – pop. 9 560 – ✉ St Brelade 5 B2

St Helier 6 m
Fishermen's Chapel (frescoes★)

L'Horizon St Brelade's Bay, rm, rest,
✉ JE3 8EF – ✆ (01534) 743 101 – lhorizon@handpicked.co.uk – Fax (01534) 746 269 – Closed 2 weeks Christmas and New Year
99 rm – †£ 125/175 ††£ 330/370 – 7 suites
Rest *The Grill* – see restaurant listing
Rest *Brasserie* – (Closed Sunday) Carte £ 21/31
◆ Period hotel right on the beach and consequently popular for its stunning views from the terrace and some of its tastefully decorated front bedrooms. Serene indoor pool. Informal brasserie adjacent to the sea.

St Brelade's Bay St Brelade's Bay, (heated)
La Route de la Baie ✉ JE3 8EF – ✆ (01534) 746 141 – info@stbreladesbayhotel.com – Fax (01534) 747 278 – 4 April-3 November
88 rm – †£ 83/192 ††£ 130/284 – 3 suites – **Rest** – Menu £ 15/30 – Carte £ 24/37
◆ Traditional seafront hotel with mouth-watering views of bay and resplendent gardens with pool. Rattan furnished sitting room and spacious bedrooms. Friendly and family run. Front, sea-facing restaurant.

Golden Sands

La Route de la Baie ✉ JE3 8EF – ✆ (01534) 741 241 – goldensands@dolanhotels.com – Fax (01534) 499 366 – April-October
62 rm – †£ 46/130 ††£ 72/182 – **Rest** – (bar lunch) Menu £ 23 (dinner) **s** – Carte £ 17/29 **s**
◆ With adjacent sweep of a sandy bay and many of the bedrooms south-facing with balconies, this hotel is a popular spot. Within easy reach of the airport and St Helier. Seasonal menus.

The Grill – at L'Horizon H.

< St Brelade's Bay,
✉ *JE3 8EF – ✆ (01534) 490 082 – lhorizon@handpicked.co.uk – Fax (01534) 746 269 – Closed Sunday and Monday*
Rest – (dinner only) Menu £ 43
◆ Intimately styled grill room with tasteful cream and brown banquettes and framed photos of film stars. Seafood stars but faces competition from a strong suit of meat dishes.

St Helier – C.I. – pop. 27 523 — 5 B2

Jersey Museum★ **AC** Z - Elizabeth Castle (< ★) **AC** Z – Fort Regent (< ★ AC) Z
St Peter's Valley - German Underground Hospital★ **AC**, NW : 4 m. by A 1, A 11 St Peter's Valley rd and C 112

Plan opposite

Royal Yacht

rm,
Weighbridge ✉ JE2 3NF – ✆ (01534) 720 511 – reception@theroyalyacht.com – Fax (01534) 767 729 Z **b**
108 rm – †£ 105 ††£ 150/230 – 2 suites
Rest *Sirocco* – (Closed Sunday dinner) Menu £ 20/26 – Carte £ 45/65
Rest *Cafe Zephyr* – (Closed 25 December) Carte £ 18/36
Rest *The Grill* – (Closed 25 December and Sunday) Carte £ 25/34
◆ Striking hotel with contemporary interior and stunning spa. The most spacious bedrooms look towards harbour; the quietest over inner courtyard. Two stunning suites with hot tubs. Lively brasserie with pavement terrace. More formal dining in Sirocco restaurant. The Grill retains traditional feel.

Radisson SAS Waterfront

< harbour, rm,
Rue de l'Etau ✉ JE2 4HE – ✆ (01534) 769 744 – info@jersey.radissonsas.com Z **c**
181 rm – †£ 120 ††£ 120 – 14 suites – **Rest** – Carte £ 24/45
◆ Fantastic location overlooking the harbour. Very spacious bedrooms, light and contemporary in style; most of them with views. Vast fish tank in reception. Waterfront terrace. Contemporary brasserie style restaurant.

The Club Hotel & Spa

rm,
Green St ✉ JE2 4UH – ✆ (01534) 876 500 – reservations@theclubjersey.com – Fax (01534) 720 371 – Closed 24-27 December Z **e**
42 rm – †£ 195 ††£ 195, £ 12 – 4 suites
Rest *Bohemia* – see restaurant listing
Rest – (Saturday brunch) Carte £ 24/37
◆ Above the Bohemia restaurant, a town house hotel of contemporary luxury with particularly pleasant roof terrace; the cosy bedrooms are fitted with many stylish mod cons. Small New York café style restaurant.

Hotel de France

St Saviours Rd ✉ JE1 7XP – ✆ (01534) 614 000 – general@defrance.co.uk – Fax (01534) 614 999 – Closed 20 December-7 January Y **b**
277 rm – †£ 110 ††£ 190 – 8 suites
Rest *Gallery* – (Closed Sunday) (dinner only) Carte £ 28/35
Rest *Café Aroma* – ✆ (01534) 614 176 – Carte £ 21/28
◆ A well-located grand hotel with sweeping balustraded staircase leading to neatly furnished rooms. Cinema on complex and extensive range of business facilities. Gallery restaurant boasts intimate, fine dining experience. Informal Cafe Aroma.

ENGLAND

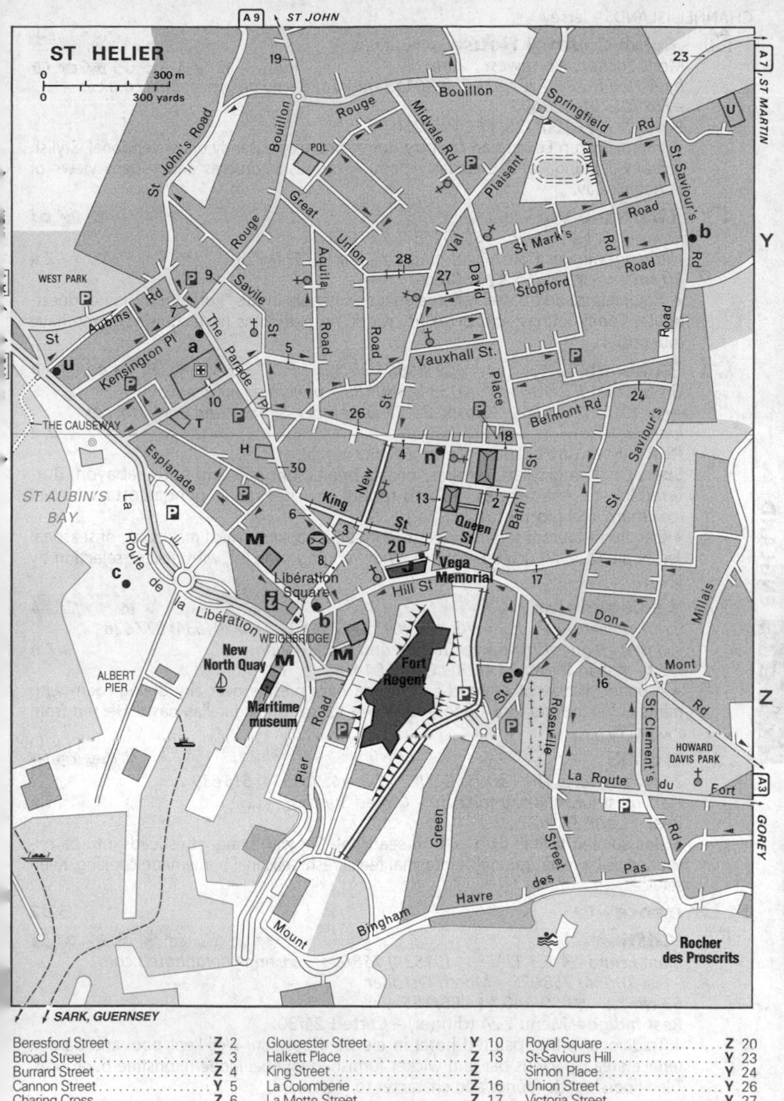

Beresford Street	Z 2	Gloucester Street	Y 10	Royal Square	Z 20
Broad Street	Z 3	Halkett Place	Z 13	St-Saviours Hill	Y 23
Burrard Street	Z 4	King Street	Z	Simon Place	Y 24
Cannon Street	Y 5	La Colomberie	Z 16	Union Street	Y 26
Charing Cross	Z 6	La Motte Street	Z 17	Victoria Street	Y 27
Cheapside	Y 7	Minden Place	Z 18	Windsor Road	Y 28
Conway Street	Z 8	Queen Street	Z	York Street	Y 30
Elizabeth Place	Y 9	Queen's Road	Y 19		

Grand

The Esplanade ✉ *JE4 8WD – ✆ (01534) 722301*
– grand.jersey@devere-hotels.com – Fax (01534) 737815 Y **u**

117 rm – £ 129/205 £ 182/300 – 5 suites

Rest *The Regency* – Esplanade (Closed Saturday lunch) Menu £ 26 (dinner) **s** – Carte £ 29/45 **s**

◆ Impressive Victorian hotel with pitched white façade overlooking St Aubins Bay. Elegant wing armchairs in smart lounge. Strong leisure facilities and comfortable bedrooms. Smart dining room.

Eulah Country House without rest — St Aubin's Bay, (heated)
Mont Cochon, Northwest : 2 m. by A 1 on B 27 ✉ JE2 3JA – ✆ (01534) 626 626 – eulah@jerseymail.co.uk – Fax (01534) 626 600
9 rm – ♦£ 100/125 ♦♦£ 190/230
◆ Informally run Edwardian country house proves pleasantly unconventional. Stylish combined lounge and breakfast room, luxurious bedrooms and superb views of St Aubin's Bay.

La Bonne Vie without rest
Roseville St ✉ JE2 4PL – ✆ (01534) 735 955 – labonneviequesthouse@yahoo.com – Fax (01534) 733 357 Z **a**
10 rm – ♦£ 25/65 ♦♦£ 50/65
◆ Floral fabrics and pastel colours enliven interiors in this "home from home" guest-house. Comfy lounge and breakfast room. All bedrooms have showers; some have four posters.

Bohemia – at The Club Hotel & Spa
Green St ✉ JE2 4UH – ✆ (01534) 880 588 – bohemia@huggler.com – Fax (01534) 875 054 – Closed 24-27 December, Sunday and Bank Holiday lunches Z **e**
Rest – (Saturday brunch) Menu £ 20/49
Spec. Duck egg salad, girolles, broad beans, gnocchi and herb sabayon. Buttered lobster, macaroni, crab and fennel ceviche. Vanilla panna cotta, caramel ice cream and ginger bread.
◆ Elegant restaurant serving precise, confident cooking which makes use of seasonal Jersey produce. Meticulous service. Wide-ranging wine list, with decent selection by the glass.

La Capannina
65-67 Halkett Pl ✉ JE2 4WG – ✆ (01534) 734 602 – Fax (01534) 877 628 – closed 10 days Christmas, Sunday and Bank Holidays Z **n**
Rest – Italian Menu £ 14/23 – Carte £ 14/48
◆ A buffet display of seafood and Parma ham preside over airy dining room with prints of Venice and Pisa. Choose between Jersey fish and Italian pasta. Dessert from the trolley.

Ad-Lib
2 Edward Place, The Parade ✉ JE2 3QP – ✆ (01534) 615 639 – adlibrestaurant@hotmail.com – Closed Sunday Y **a**
Rest – Carte £ 19/27
◆ Unassuming former pub just off sea front. Bar with banquettes leads into barrel-vaulted cellar restaurant with informal feel. Fresh, seasonal homemade cooking. Keen service.

St Lawrence – C.I. 5 B2

Cristina (heated)
Mont Felard ✉ JE3 1JA – ✆ (01534) 758 024 – cristina@dolanhotels.com – Fax (01534) 758 028 – March-October
63 rm – ♦£ 59/140 ♦♦£ 85/155
Rest *Indigo* – Menu £ 24 (dinner) – Carte £ 24/30
◆ Traditional, white painted hotel in elevated position. Well-kept pool and garden terrace area. Spacious bar and wicker furnished lounge. Modern, pristine bedrooms. Tiled floors, suede fabrics add character to restaurant.

St Peter – C.I. – pop. 4 228 5 B2

St Helier 5 m
Living Legend★

Greenhill's Country H. (heated) rest,
Mont de l'Ecole, Coin Varin, on C 112 ✉ JE3 7EL – ✆ (01534) 481 042 – greenhills@messages.co.uk – Fax (01534) 485 322 – 7 February-20 December
30 rm – ♦£ 53/106 ♦♦£ 115/162 – 1 suite – **Rest** – Menu £ 14/27 – Carte £ 27/40
◆ Very popular with regular guests, this part 17C stone farmhouse is a fine place to settle down in, with flower-filled gardens, country style rooms and wood panelled lounge. Restaurant with plush pink predominating.

ENGLAND

St Saviour – C.I. – pop. 12 680 5 **B2**

St Helier 1 m

Longueville Manor (heated)

Longueville Rd, on A 3 JE2 7WF – (01534) 725 501
– longuevillemanor@relaischateaux.com – Fax (01534) 731 613
28 rm – £ 300 £ 420 – 2 suites – **Rest** – Menu £ 20/55
◆ Exemplary part 14C manor for a special stay; every detail from furnishings to service is considered. Sumptuous rooms, delightful garden, poolside terrace. Panelled restaurant and terrace room overlooking garden; locally-inspired classics with modern twists.

SARK – C.I. – **503** L 33 – **pop. 550** 5 **B2**

to Jersey (St Helier) (Condor Ferries Ltd) (50 mn)
to Guernsey (St Peter Port) (Isle of Sark Shipping Co. Ltd) (summer only) (45 mn)
Harbour Hill (01481) 832345
Island★★ - La Coupée★★★ – Port du Moulin★★ - Creux Harbour★ – La Seigneurie★ **AC** – Pilcher Monument★ – Hog's Back★

Aval du Creux (heated)

Harbour Hill GY9 0SB – (01481) 832 036 – reservations@avalducreux.co.uk
– Fax (01481) 832 368 – mid April-mid October
20 rm – £ 72/83 £ 103/127
Rest *The Restaurant* – Menu £ 24 – Carte £ 21/34
◆ Secluded stone built hotel - the closest to the harbour - with 21C extensions. South facing mature gardens. Comfortable modern bedrooms. Dining room and terrace overlook garden and pool.

Stocks Island

GY9 0SD – (01481) 832 001 – enquiries@stockshotel.com
– Fax (01481) 832 130 – April-September
18 rm (dinner included) – £ 75/115 £ 150/190 – **Rest** – (bar lunch) Menu £ 20/29 **s** – Carte £ 20/34 **s**
◆ A mellow granite former farmhouse built in 1741, family owned and very personally run. Quiet location facing wooded valley. Well-kept bedrooms and period beamed bar. Organic produce to fore in charming restaurant.

Petit Champ < coast, Herm, Jetou and Guernsey, (heated)

GY9 0SF – (01481) 832 046
– info@hotelpetitchamp.co.uk – Fax (01481) 832 469 – 22 April-October
10 rm – £ 64/74 £ 124/143 – **Rest** – Menu £ 22 (dinner) – Carte £ 15/29
◆ Ideal for views of neighbouring islands, with three sun lounges to enjoy them from; neat, trim rooms. Quarry, from which hotel's stone comes, is site of solar heated pool. Dining room features Sark specialities.

La Sablonnerie with rm

Little Sark GY9 0SD – (01481) 832 061 – lasablonnerie@cwgsy.net
– Fax (01481) 832 408 – Easter-mid October
21 rm (dinner included) – £ 60/67 £ 135/169 – 1 suite
Rest – Menu £ 26/29 – Carte £ 22/30
◆ Immaculately whitewashed 16C former farmhouse: a long low building. Diners greeted from jetty by Victorian horse and carriage. Home-produced ingredients to fore. Smart rooms.

Good food and accommodation at moderate prices?
Look for the Bib symbols:
red Bib Gourmand for food, blue Bib Hotel for hotels

CHANNEL TUNNEL – Kent – 504 X 30 – see Folkestone

CHAPEL-EN-LE-FRITH – Derbs – 504 O24 16 A1

London 175 m – Sheffield 27 m – Manchester 21 m – Stoke-on-Trent 34 m

High Croft without rest

Manchester Rd, West : 3/4 m. on B 5470 ✉ SK23 9UH – ✆ (01298) 814 843 – elaine@highcroft-guesthouse.co.uk

4 rm – †£ 50/55 ††£ 90/95

◆ Edwardian house with period features and lovely mature garden. Comfortable bedrooms overlook surrounding hills and valleys; Atholl suite - a four poster with tub - is best.

CHAPELTOWN – N. Yorks. – 502 P 23 – see Sheffield

CHARD – Somerset – 503 L 31 – pop. 12 008 3 B3

London 157 m – Exeter 32 m – Lyme Regis 12 m – Taunton 18 m – Yeovil 17 m

15 High St ✆ (01460) 67463

Bellplot House

High St ✉ TA20 1QB – ✆ (01460) 62 600 – info@bellplothouse.co.uk – Fax (01460) 62 600

7 rm – †£ 80/90 ††£ 90, £ 10 – **Rest** – (closed Sunday) (dinner only) Carte £ 24/31

◆ Impressive mid-Georgian house named after shape of original plot of land. Lounge with plush sofas and fitted bar. Bedrooms stylishly modern with bright yellow décor. Locally renowned restaurant where local, seasonal produce is very much centre stage.

ENGLAND

CHARLESTOWN – Cornwall – 503 F 32 – see St Austell

CHARLTON – W. Sussex – 504 R 31 – see Chichester

CHARLTON – Wilts. – 503 N 29 – see Malmesbury

CHARLWOOD – Surrey – 504 T 30 – ✉ Horley 7 D2

London 30 m – Brighton 29 m – Royal Tunbridge Wells 28 m

Stanhill Court

Stan Hill, Northwest : 1 m. by Norwood Hill Rd ✉ RH6 0EP – ✆ (01293) 862 166 – enquiries@stanhillcourthotel.co.uk – Fax (01293) 862 773

34 rm – †£ 110 ††£ 125/165 – **Rest** – (booking essential for non-residents) Menu £ 19/26 – Carte £ 31/45

◆ Attractive Victorian country house in 30 acres of parkland. Striking panelled baronial hall with stained glass. Huge conservatory. Bedrooms retain some original features. Pleasant dining room in classic style.

CHARMOUTH – Dorset – 503 L 31 – ✉ Bridport 3 B3

London 157 m – Dorchester 22 m – Exeter 31 m – Taunton 27 m

White House

2 Hillside, The Street ✉ DT6 6PJ – ✆ (01297) 560 411 – restricted opening in winter

6 rm – ††£ 110/180 – **Rest** – (dinner only) Menu £ 33

◆ Gleaming white Regency hotel a stone's throw from magnificent coastal scenery; popular with fossil hunters. Tasteful rooms, with pretty furnishings and a bold palette. Garden herbs and fruit used in home-cooked meals.

CHARTHAM HATCH – Kent – 504 X 30 – see Canterbury

CHEADLE – Ches. – 502 N 23 20 B3

London 200 m – Manchester 7 m – Stoke-on-Trent 33 m

Village H. & Leisure Club rm, rest,

Cheadle Rd, South : ¾ m. by A 5149 ✉ SK8 1HW
– ✆ (0161) 428 0404 – village.cheadle@village-hotels.com
– Fax (0161) 428 1191

117 rm – †£ 65/125 ††£ 65/125 – **Rest** – Carte £ 12/26

◆ Corporate hotel in leafy suburb, convenient for Manchester airport and offering range of rooms; the executive rooms are larger with extra touches. Excellent leisure club. Bustling restaurant with cosmopolitan offerings.

CHEDDLETON – Staffs. – 502 N 24 – pop. 2 719 – ✉ Leek 19 C1

London 125 m – Birmingham 48 m – Derby 33 m – Manchester 42 m – Stoke-on-Trent 11 m

Choir Cottage without rest

Ostlers Lane, via Hollow Lane (opposite Red Lion on A 520) ✉ ST13 7HS
– ✆ (01538) 360 561 – enquiries@choircottage.co.uk

3 rm – †£ 49/59 ††£ 70/80

◆ Personally run 17C stone cottage, formerly church owned, and let to the poor, rent used to buy choir gowns. Individually furnished bedrooms with four-posters.

CHELMSFORD – Essex – 504 V 28 – pop. 99 962 13 C2

London 33 m – Cambridge 46 m – Ipswich 40 m – Southend-on-Sea 19 m
Unit 3, Dukes Way, Duke St ✆ (01245) 283400, tic@cheltenham.gov.uk

Barda

30-32 Broomfield Rd ✉ CM1 1SW – ✆ (01245) 357 799 – Fax (01245) 350 333
– Closed 25-26 December, Saturday lunch, Sunday dinner and Monday

Rest – Menu £ 17 – Carte £ 22/36

◆ Modern restaurant with spacious interior, decked terrace, banquette seating and contemporary art on walls. Precise, modern menu offers seasonal dishes with a French flavour.

The Alma

37 Arbour Lane, Northeast : 1 m. by B 1137 (Springfield Rd) ✉ CM1 7RG
– ✆ (01245) 256 783 – info@thealma.biz – Fax (01245) 256 793
– Closed 25-26 December

Rest – Menu £ 8/10 – Carte £ 18/25

◆ Welcoming, yellow-painted characterful restaurant with spacious front bar and more formal rear dining room. Modern European cooking, with classic pub dishes served in bar.

at Great Baddow Southeast : 3 m. by A 1114 – ✉ Chelmsford

Pontlands Park (heated)

West Hanningfield Rd ✉ CM2 8HR – ✆ (01245) 476 444
– sales@pontlandsparkhotel.co.uk – Fax (01245) 478 393
– Closed 24-30 December

31 rm – †£ 115 ††£ 155/170, £ 12 – 4 suites – **Rest** – (Closed Saturday lunch) Carte £ 31/36

◆ Charming, extended Victorian house with comfortable, individually-furnished bedrooms, well run leisure facilities and popular meeting rooms. Formal linen-clad dining room.

CHELTENHAM – Glos. – 503 N 28 – pop. 98 875 *Great Britain* 4 C1

London 99 m – Birmingham 48 m – Bristol 40 m – Gloucester 9 m – Oxford 43 m
77 Promenade ✆ (01242) 226554
Cleeve Hill, ✆ (01242) 672 025 ;
Cotswold Hills Ullenwood, ✆ (01242) 515 264.
Town★
Sudeley Castle★ (Paintings★) AC, NE : 7 m. by B 4632 A

ENGLAND

CHELTENHAM

Street	Grid	No.
Berkeley St	CYZ	4
Clarence St	CY	6
Crescent Terrace	BY	7
Deep St.	AX	9
Dunalley St	CY	10
Henrietta St.	CY	13
High St	BCY	
High St PRESTBURY	AX	14
Keynsham Rd	CZ	15
Knapp Rd.	BY	16
Montpellier Ave.	BZ	17
Montpellier Walk	BZ	18
North St.	CY	20
Norwood Rd	BZ	21
Oriel Rd	CZ	22
Pittville St	CY	26
Portland St.	CY	27
Promenade (The)	BZCY	28
Regent Arcade Shopping Centre	CY	
Regent St	CY	29
Rodney Rd.	CY	30
Royal Well Rd	BCY	32
St James St.	CY	33
St Johns Ave.	CY	34
St Margaret's Rd	CY	35
Sandford Mill Rd	CZ	36
Sandford Terrace	CZ	37
Winchcombe St.	CY	38

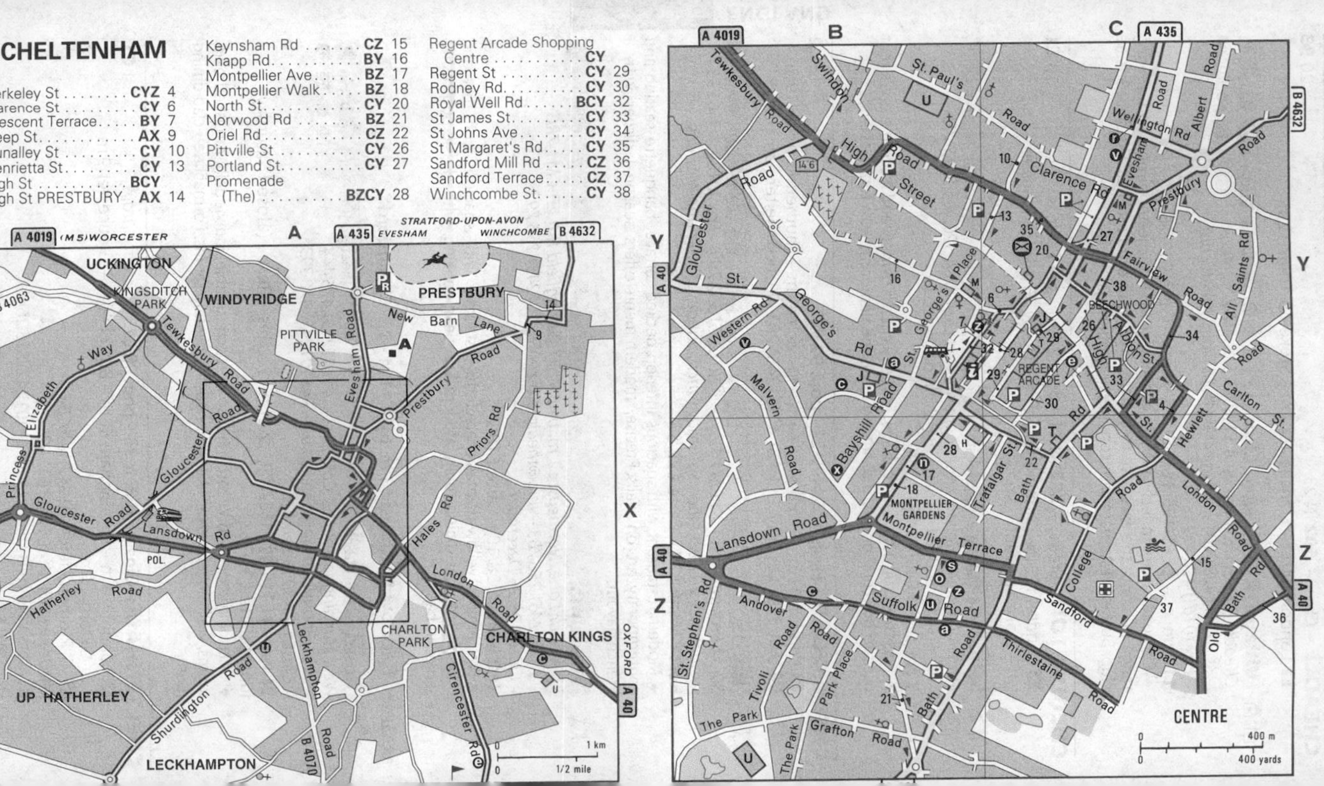

Hotel du Vin

Parabola Rd ✉ GL50 3AQ – ✆ (01242) 588 450 – info.cheltenham@hotelduvin.com – Fax (01242) 588 455 BY **c**

48 rm – †£ 135 ††£ 185, ☕ £ 13.50 – 1 suite

Rest *Bistro* – Menu £ 19 (lunch) – Carte £ 30/35

◆ Stylish Regency house in smart area: lounge features chandelier made from wine glasses; bedrooms named after wines boast contemporary furnishings and wine-themed artwork. Bistro restaurant with paved terrace offers classic menus with French influences.

The Queen's

Promenade ✉ GL50 1NN – ✆ (01242) 514 754 – h3632@accor.com – Fax (01242) 224 145 BZ **n**

79 rm ☕ – †£ 120/170 ††£ 130/170

Rest *Napier* – Menu £ 25/35 – Carte £ 22/35

◆ A white columned neo-classical building with views over Imperial Square and the Ladies College. Grand reception and wood panelled bar. Individually styled bedrooms. Restaurant named after the famous British general.

On the Park

38 Evesham Rd ✉ GL52 2AH – ✆ (01242) 518 898 – stay@hotelonthepark.com – Fax (01242) 511 526 CY **r**

12 rm – †£ 93/107 ††£ 130/190, ☕ £ 11.95

Rest *Parkers* – see restaurant listing

◆ Regency town house of distinction. Bedrooms are named after dukes and dignitaries; individually decorated with paintings, antiques, mirrors and lamps. Stately library.

ENGLAND

Kandinsky

Bayshill Rd ✉ GL50 3AS – ✆ (01242) 527 788 – kandinsky@aliashotels.com – Fax (01242) 226 412 BZ **x**

47 rm – †£ 100/140 ††£ 130/140 – 1 suite

Rest *Café Paradiso* – Menu £ 15 – Carte £ 19/28

◆ Bohemian set-up with distressed furniture in minimalist bedrooms; each contains a different Kandinsky print. Sparkle in 1950s style basement club; live jazz some nights. Restaurant boasts long, open-plan kitchen with wood fired pizza oven.

The George

St George's Rd ✉ GL50 3DZ – ✆ (01242) 235 751 – hotel@stayatthegeorge.co.uk – Fax (01242) 224 359 – Closed 25-27 December BY **a**

38 rm ☕ – †£ 92/102 ††£ 127

Rest *Monty's* – Carte £ 23/37

◆ In a good central location amongst other Regency town houses. Bright, modern, well-equipped bedrooms; larger variety boasts extra facilities. Two rooms called 'Monty's' serve brasserie style food and seafood respectively.

Beaumont House without rest

56 Shurdington Rd ✉ GL53 0JE – ✆ (01242) 223 311 – reservations@bhhotel.co.uk – Fax (01242) 520 044 AX **u**

16 rm ☕ – †£ 62/69 ††£ 164/218

◆ Keenly run Georgian house with comfy drawing room and bar; breakfast room overlooks lawned garden. Refurbished bedrooms are stylish and contemporary with excellent bathrooms.

Lypiatt House without rest

Lypiatt Rd ✉ GL50 2QW – ✆ (01242) 224 994 – stay@lypiatt.co.uk – Fax (01242) 224 996 – Closed Christmas BZ **c**

10 rm ☕ – †£ 70 ††£ 110

◆ A privately owned, serene Victorian house with friendly service. Rooms on top floor with dormer roof tend to be smaller than those on the ground floor. Soft, pale colours.

Butlers without rest

Western Rd ✉ GL50 3RN – ✆ (01242) 570 771 – info@butlers-hotel.co.uk – Fax (01242) 528 724 BY **v**

9 rm – †£ 50/65 ††£ 75/95

◆ Personally managed hotel where bedrooms constitute a peaceful haven with stylish drapes and canopies. Rooms named after famous butlers; some overlook wooded garden to rear.

Charlton Kings

London Rd, Charlton Kings ✉ GL52 6UU – ✆ (01242) 231 061 – enquiries@charltonkingshotel.co.uk – Fax (01242) 241 900 AX **c**

14 rm – †£ 65/75 ††£ 125 – **Rest** – (bar lunch Monday-Saturday) Carte £ 21/26

◆ A clean-lined, white purpose-built hotel with unfussy pastel interiors. Pristine, plainly painted bedrooms with light wood furniture. The rural setting bestows tranquillity. Dining room enhanced by a simple, modern design.

Georgian House without rest

77 Montpellier Terrace ✉ GL50 1XA – ✆ (01242) 515 577 – penny@georgianhouse.net – Fax (01242) 545 929 – Closed Christmas and New Year BZ **s**

3 rm – †£ 58 ††£ 95

◆ Smart, terraced Georgian house, hospitably run, in sought-after Montpelier area. Good-sized bedrooms decorated in authentic period style. Comfy, elegant communal rooms.

Hannaford's without rest

20 Evesham Rd ✉ GL52 2AB – ✆ (01242) 515 181 – sue@hannafords.icom43.net – Fax (01242) 580 102 CY **v**

10 rm – †£ 45 ††£ 80

◆ Attractive, family run Georgian terraced townhouse near the centre. Hearty breakfast selection; cosy bar overlooks snug flagstoned terraced area. Ask for a coach-house room.

Le Champignon Sauvage (David Everitt-Matthias)

24-28 Suffolk Rd ✉ GL50 2AQ – ✆ (01242) 573 449 – mail@lechampignonsauvage.com – Fax (01242) 254 365 – Closed Easter, 3 weeks June, 10 days Christmas and New Year, Sunday and Monday and Tuesday after Bank Holidays. BZ **a**

Rest – Menu £ 28/48

Spec. Seared scallops with artichokes and liquorice root. Lamb, pea purée, wilted lettuce, braised onions with eucalyptus. Bitter chocolate and olive tart, fennel ice cream.

◆ Professionally run restaurant stylishly decorated in blue and cream, with modern art on walls. Confident, accomplished cooking uses excellent produce; some original touches.

Lumière

Clarence Parade ✉ GL50 3PA – ✆ (01242) 222 200 – dinner@lumiere.cc – Closed first 2 weeks January, 2 weeks late summer, dinner 25 December, Sunday and Monday BCY **z**

Rest – (dinner only) Menu £ 38

◆ Personally run, intimate glass fronted restaurant decked out in chic browns and leather. Original colourful artwork. Skilfully concocted cooking covering a modern range.

Parkers – at On the Park H.

38 Evesham Rd ✉ GL52 2AH – ✆ (01242) 518 898 – stay@hotelonthepark.com – Fax (01242) 511 526 – Closed Monday lunch CY **r**

Rest – Menu £ 15 (lunch) – Carte dinner £ 26/35

◆ A carefully decorated restaurant with mirrors, high ceilings, hand painted cornices and murals. Modern British cooking with classical undertones and a good range of wine.

ENGLAND

XX **The Daffodil** AC VISA MC AE

18-20 Suffolk Parade ✉ GL50 2AE – ✆ (01242) 700055 – eat@thedaffodil.com – Fax (01242) 700088 – Closed 25 December, Sunday and Bank Holidays BZ **u**

Rest – Menu £ 15 (lunch) – Carte £ 23/35

◆ Move from the art of film to the art of food in this 1920s converted cinema. The open-plan kitchen occupies the original screen area. Modern cooking with generous puddings.

X **Brosh** VISA MC

8 Suffolk Parade, Montpellier ✉ GL50 2AB – ✆ (01242) 227277 – info@broshrestaurant.co.uk – Fax (01242) 227277 – Closed 2 weeks January and Sunday-Tuesday BZ **o**

Rest – Mediterranean (dinner only) Carte £ 21/33

◆ Cosy restaurant with atmospheric Moroccan-styled interior: evening candles and dimmed lights make for a great atmosphere. Specialist 'east' Mediterranean cooking with mezze.

X **Vanilla** VISA MC

9-10 Cambray Pl ✉ GL50 1JS – ✆ (01242) 228228 – info@vanillainc.co.uk – Fax (01242) 228228 – Closed 24-26 December, 1 January, Sunday and Bank Holidays CY **e**

Rest – Carte £ 15/29

◆ Centrally located, in Regency house basement; discreet, soft spot lighting, wooden floors, scoopback chairs. Staff serve light, modern dishes garnished with home-made sauces.

X **Brasserie Blanc** AC VISA MC AE

Promenade ✉ GL50 1NN – ✆ (01242) 266800 – cheltenham@lbrasserieblanc.com – Fax (01242) 266801 BZ **n**

Rest – Carte £ 20/28

◆ Spacious, invariably busy brasserie from Raymond Blanc stable. Gallic mainstays on the menu are enhanced by wine suggestions. The large bar is a high volume, buzzy area.

The Beehive VISA MC AE

1-3 Montpellier Villas ✉ GL50 2XE – ✆ (01242) 702270 – beehive@slak.co.uk – Fax (01242) 269330 – Closed 25 December and Sunday dinner BZ **z**

Rest – Menu £ 15 – Carte £ 20/28

◆ Georgian corner pub with original green and frosted glass façade. Based in charming Montpellier area. Genuine, unaffected ambienece. Good, honest cooking in restaurant style.

at Cleeve Hill Northeast : 4 m. on B 4632 - AX – ✉ Cheltenham

Cleeve Hill without rest P VISA MC AE

✉ GL52 3PR – ✆ (01242) 672052 – info@cleevehill hotel.co.uk – Fax (01242) 679969

10 rm – †£ 45/65 ††£ 75/105

◆ Edwardian house in elevated spot; most bedrooms have views across Cleeve Common and the Malvern Hills. Breakfast room is in the conservatory; admire the landscape over coffee.

XX **Hacketts** with rm P VISA MC

✉ GL52 3PR – ✆ (01242) 672017 – paul.hackett@btconnect.com – Closed first 3 weeks January and last week October

4 rm – †£ 65 ††£ 90 – **Rest** – (Closed Tuesday lunch, Sunday dinner and Monday) Menu £ 16/25 – Carte £ 30/41

◆ Pleasant, personally run restaurant up a hill with views to distant Malverns. Classically styled lounges; modern British cooking with good value choice. Well-appointed rooms.

ENGLAND

at Shurdington Southwest : 3 ¾ m. on A 46 - AX – ✉ Cheltenham

The Greenway

✉ *GL51 4UG* – ✆ *(01242) 862 352 – info@thegreenway.co.uk – Fax (01242) 862 780*

20 rm – ♦£ 95/130 ♦♦£ 145/160 – 1 suite – **Rest** – Menu £ 23 (lunch) – Carte dinner £ 23/47

◆ Ivy-clad Elizabethan manor house set in large grounds and peaceful lawned gardens. Spacious, classically styled lounges and drawing rooms. Bedrooms have country house feel. Garden and lily pond on view from formal restaurant.

at Brockworth Southwest : 5 ½ m. on A 46 - AX – ✉ Cheltenham

Cheltenham Chase rm, rest,

Shurdington Rd, on A 46 ✉ *GL3 4PB – ✆ (01452) 519 988 – cheltenham@qhotels.co.uk – Fax (01452) 519 977*

120 rm – ♦£ 119/129 ♦♦£ 129/139 – 2 suites – **Rest** – (bar lunch) Carte £ 31/37

◆ A modern corporate hotel located in landscaped grounds on the edge of the Cotswolds. Good leisure and conference facilities, relaxing bar and lounge and spacious bedrooms. Contemporary restaurant.

at Witcombe Southwest : 6 m. by A 46 - AX - and Bentham rd – ✉ Cheltenham

Crickley Court without rest

Dog Lane ✉ *GL3 4UF – ✆ (01452) 863 634 – lispilgrimmorris@yahoo.co.uk – Fax (01452) 863 634*

3 rm – ♦£ 35 ♦♦£ 70

◆ Old inn dating from 16C. Lounge provided with an array of books. Family style breakfast. Outdoor pool. Spacious, bright and clean rooms with modern amenities.

ENGLAND

CHENIES – Bucks. – 504 S 28 – ✉ Rickmansworth (Herts.) 11 **D2**

London 30 m – Aylesbury 18 m – Watford 7 m

Bedford Arms rm,

✉ *WD3 6EQ – ✆ (01923) 283 301 – contact@bedfordarms.co.uk – Fax (01923) 284 825*

18 rm – ♦£ 90/110 ♦♦£ 120/130 – **Rest** – Carte £ 21/33

◆ A homely hotel, pub-like in character. Well proportioned rooms, some with views of a pretty garden. Country house style bars and a meeting room for business guests. Oak panelled dining room; adjacent cocktail bar.

CHESTER – Ches. – 502 L 24 – pop. 80 121 *Great Britain* 20 **A3**

London 207 m – Birkenhead 7 m – Birmingham 91 m – Liverpool 21 m – Manchester 40 m – Preston 52 m – Sheffield 76 m – Stoke-on-Trent 38 m

Chester Visitor and Craft Centre, Vicars Lane ✆ (01244) 402111.

Upton-by-Chester Upton Lane, ✆ (01244) 381 183 ;

Curzon Park, ✆ (01244) 675 130 .

City★★ - The Rows★★ B – Cathedral★ B – City Walls★ B

Chester Zoo★ AC, N : 3 m. by A 5116

Plan opposite

The Chester Grosvenor and Spa

Eastgate ✉ *CH1 1LT – ✆ (01244) 324 024 – reservations@chestergrosvenor.com – Fax (01244) 313 246 – Closed 25-26 December* B **a**

76 rm – ♦£ 195 ♦♦£ 285, £ 19 – 4 suites

Rest Arkle and **La Brasserie** – see restaurant listing

◆ 19C coaching inn in heart of city. Lavishly furnished with antiques and oil paintings. Superb spa facilities. Luxuriously appointed, individually styled bedrooms.

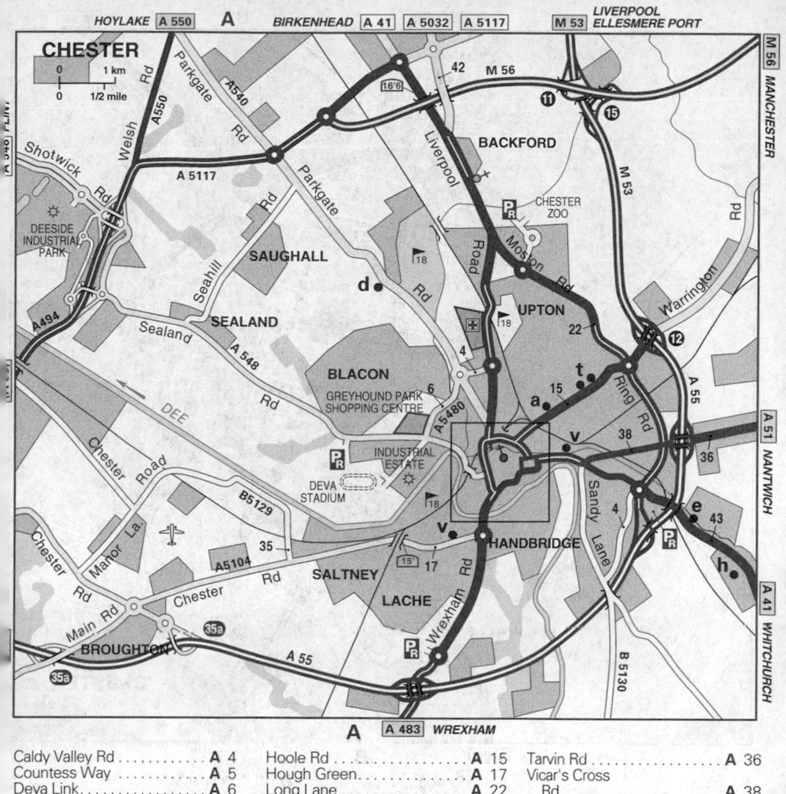

Caldy Valley Rd . . . . **A** 4
Countess Way . . . . **A** 5
Deva Link. . . . . **A** 6
Greyhound Park
Shopping Centre . . . . **A**
Hoole Rd . . . . **A** 15
Hough Green. . . . . **A** 17
Long Lane . . . . **A** 22
Saltney Ferry
Rd. **A** 35
Tarvin Rd . . . . **A** 36
Vicar's Cross
Rd. . . . . **A** 38
Whitby Lane . . . . **A** 42
Whitchurch Rd . . . . **A** 43

Crabwall Manor

rest,

Parkgate Rd, Mollington, Northwest : 2 ¼ m. on A 540 ✉ *CH1 6NE*
– ✆ (01244) 851 666 – crabwall@brook-hotels co.uk
– Fax (01244) 851 400 **A d**
43 rm – £ 85/170 £ 180/400 – 5 suites
Rest *Conservatory* – (light lunch) Menu £ 28 **s**
◆ 17C manor with castellated façade and mature grounds heavily extended into an individually furnished and comfortable business and leisure hotel. Amply proportioned bedrooms. Fine dining at classic conservatory restaurant.

Green Bough

60 Hoole Rd, on A 56 ✉ *CH2 3NL – ✆ (01244) 326 241*
– luxury@greenbough.co.uk – Fax (01244) 326 265
– Closed 24 December-2 January **A t**
13 rm – £ 115/125 £ 195/245 – 2 suites
Rest *Olive Tree* – Menu £ 20/45 **s**
◆ Personally run and very comfortable, boasting high quality decor; owner pays notable attention to detail. Individually styled, generously sized rooms with wrought iron beds. Dine formally in attractive surroundings.

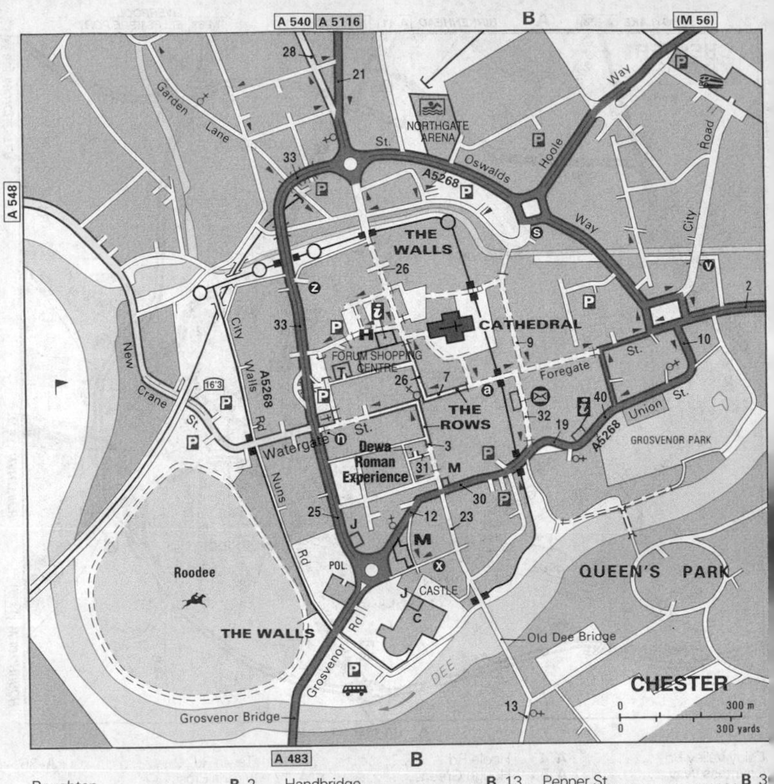

Alton Lodge

78 Hoole Rd ✉ CH2 3NT – ✆ (01244) 310213 – reception@altonlodge.co.uk – Fax (01244) 319206 – Closed Christmas and New Year A **t**

18 rm – 🚹£49/80 🚹🚹£80/100 – **Rest** – (dinner only) (residents only) Carte £11/20 **s**

◆ A family run, good value hotel. Pine furnished breakfast room, bar and lounge. Compact, annexed rooms provide a comfy night's accommodation after enjoying the city's sights.

Mitchell's of Chester without rest

28 Hough Green, Southwest : 1 m. by A 483 on A 5104 ✉ CH4 8JQ – ✆ (01244) 679004 – mitoches@dialstart.net – Fax (01244) 659567 – Closed 21-30 December A **v**

7 rm – 🚹£40/70 🚹🚹£69/75

◆ Large Victorian house, attractively restored and privately run. Homely breakfast room with large central table; lounge with views to garden. Individually decorated bedrooms.

The Limes without rest
12 Hoole Rd ✉ CH2 3NJ – ✆ (01244) 328 239 – bookings@limes-chester.co.uk – Fax (01244) 322 874 A **a**
9 rm – £35/65 £55/65
◆ Personally run guesthouse in a redbrick Victorian property. Good value accommodation in well-maintained and furnished bedrooms, with convenient access to city centre.

Chester Town House without rest
23 King St ✉ CH1 2AH – ✆ (01244) 350 021 – davidbellis@chestertownhouse.co.uk – closed 25 December B **z**
5 rm – £45 £60/70
◆ 17C redbrick house on a quiet, cobbled, lamplit street in a conservation area. Bedrooms have matching furnishings. Sunny breakfast room and period lounge.

Arkle – at The Chester Grosvenor and Spa
Eastgate ✉ CH1 1LT – ✆ (01244) 324 024 – Fax (01244) 313 246 – Closed 25-26 December, Sunday and Monday B **a**
Rest – (dinner only and lunch in December) Menu £55
Spec. Lobster, oxtail and five spice bouillon lobster dumplings. Duck with peppercorn crust, ravioli, sweet beetroot and sour cream. White chocolate and passion fruit soufflé.
◆ Formally run restaurant featuring framed painting of the eponymous racehorse. Highly polished tables and fine tableware. Skilful kitchen produces interesting, original dishes.

La Brasserie – at The Chester Grosvenor and Spa
Eastgate ✉ CH1 1LT – ✆ (01244) 324 024 – Fax (01244) 313 246 – Closed 25-26 December B **a**
Rest – Carte £28/45
◆ Burnished interior, Parisian-style eatery with mirrors and glass frontage. Eclectic menu with classic French and Italian staples of pasta and meat dishes. Weekend live music.

Upstairs at the Grill
70 Watergate St ✉ CH1 2LA – ✆ (01244) 344 883 – katie.hearse@upstairsatthegrill.co.uk – Fax (01244) 329 720 – Closed Sunday lunch and Monday B **n**
Rest – Beef specialities (dinner only) Carte £21/34
◆ Door bell entry to 19C building; sumptuous first floor bar has leather sofas and roulette table. Cow theme predominates. Prime quality Welsh steaks chargrilled to perfection.

Locus
111 Boughton ✉ CH3 5BH – ✆ (01244) 311 112 – Fax (01244) 344 860 – Closed Christmas and New year, 2 weeks January and Monday A **v**
Rest – (dinner only) Carte £24/31
◆ Unprepossessing exterior, but this small restaurant has a stylish, modern interior with atmospheric low lighting. Varied, interesting menus using well-sourced ingredients.

Brasserie 10-16
Brookdale Pl ✉ CH1 3DY – ✆ (01244) 322 288 – info@brasserie1016.com – Fax (01244) 322 325 – Closed Christmas and New Year B **s**
Rest – Carte £20/31
◆ Contemporary brasserie on two levels. Open plan kitchen on ground floor. Large modern British menu with Mediterranean touches, including plenty for the more adventurous.

Old Harkers Arms
1 Russell St ✉ CH3 5AL – ✆ (01244) 344 525 – harkers.arms@brunningandprice.co.uk – Fax (01244) 344 814 – Closed 25-26 December B **v**
Rest – Carte £19/25
◆ Converted canalside warehouse with rustically-styled décor, serving an appealing range of English dishes. Spacious bar, buzzing, informal atmosphere and friendly staff.

ENGLAND

at Little Barrow Northeast : 6½ m. by A 56 (Warrington Rd) - A - on B 5132 – ✉ Chester

The Foxcote
Station Lane ✉ CH3 7JN – ✆ (01244) 301 343 – Fax (01244) 303 287 – Closed Sunday dinner
Rest – Seafood Menu £ 10/15 – Carte £ 15/25
◆ Off the beaten track; traditional inn now given over to dining tables. Vast number of blackboard specials, mostly seafood dishes utilising broad range of fresh ingredients.

at Rowton Southeast : 3 m. on A 41 – ✉ Chester

Rowton Hall H. & Spa rest, VISA AE
Whitchurch Rd ✉ CH3 6AD – ✆ (01244) 335 262 – reception@rowtonhallhotelandspa.co.uk – Fax (01244) 335 464 A **h**
36 rm – †£ 145 ††£ 155, ☕ £12.50 – 2 suites
Rest *Langdale* – Menu £ 17/27 – Carte £ 27/40
◆ Gracious 18C sandstone hotel with many original features: hand-carved staircase, Robert Adam fireplace, range of bedrooms. Business facilities offered. Country house style. Colonial style restaurant with wooden blinds and rattan furniture.

ENGLAND

at Pulford Southwest : 5 m. by A 483 - A - and B 5445 – ✉ Chester

The Grosvenor Pulford rm, VISA AE
Wrexham Rd, on B 5445 ✉ CH4 9DG – ✆ (01244) 570 560 – reservations@grosvenorpulfordhotel.co.uk – Fax (01244) 570 809
73 rm ☕ – †£ 95 ††£ 150
Rest *Ciro's* – Carte £ 20/27
◆ Family owned hotel 10 minutes' drive from city. Popular business and wedding venue. Pleasant gardens; spacious gym and pool. Diverse range of individualistic rooms.

CHESTER-LE-STREET – Durham – 501 24 B2

London 275 m – Durham 7 m – Newcastle upon Tyne 8 m
Lumley Park, ✆ (0191) 388 3218;
Roseberry Grange Grange Villa, ✆ (0191) 370 0660.

Lumley Castle VISA AE
East : 1 m. on B 1284 ✉ DH3 4NX – ✆ (0191) 389 1111 – reservations@lumleycastle.com – Fax (0191) 389 1881 – Closed 24-26 December and 1-2 January
73 rm ☕ – †£ 99 ††£ 299 – 1 suite
Rest *Black Knight* – (Closed Saturday lunch) Menu £ 20/33 – Carte dinner £ 38/53
◆ Norman castle, without additions, underscoring its uniqueness. Rich, gothic interiors of carved wood, chandeliers, statues, tapestries, rugs. Rooms imbued with atmosphere. Restaurant offers classical dishes with an original twist.

CHETTLE – Dorset – see Blandford Forum

CHEW MAGNA – Somerset – 503 M 29 – see Bristol

CHICHESTER – W. Sussex – 504 R 31 – pop. 27 477 *Great Britain* 7 C2

London 69 m – Brighton 31 m – Portsmouth 18 m – Southampton 30 m
29a South St ✆ (01243) 775888
Goodwood Kennel Hill, ✆ (01243) 755 135 ;
Chichester Golf Centre Hunston Village, ✆ (01243) 533 833 .
City★★ – Cathedral★★ BZ **A** – St Mary's Hospital★ BY **D** – Pallant House★ **AC** BZ **M**
Fishbourne Roman Palace★★ (mosaics★) **AC** AZ **R.** Weald and Downland Open Air Museum★★ **AC**, N : 6 m. by A 286 AY

CHICHESTER

Street	Grid	No.
Birdham Rd	AZ	2
Bognor Rd	AZ	3
Chapel St	BY	6
Chartres (Av. de)	BZ	7
Chichester Arundel Rd	AY	8
East Pallant	BZ	9
East St	BZ	
Florence Rd	AZ	10
Hornet (The)	BZ	12
Kingsham Rd	BZ	13
Lavant Rd	AY	14
Little London	BY	15
Market Rd	BZ	16
Northgate	BY	17
North Pallant	BZ	19
North St	BYZ	
Oaklands Way	BY	18
St Jame's	AZ	21
St John's St	BZ	23
St Martin's Square	BY	24
St Pancras	BY	25
St Paul's Rd	BY	27
Sherborne Rd	AZ	28
Southgate	BZ	29
South Pallant	BZ	31
South St	BZ	
Spitalfield Lane	BY	32
Stockbridge Rd	AZ	33
Tower St	BY	35
Via Ravenna	AZ	37
Westhampnett Rd	AYZ	38
West Pallant	BZ	39

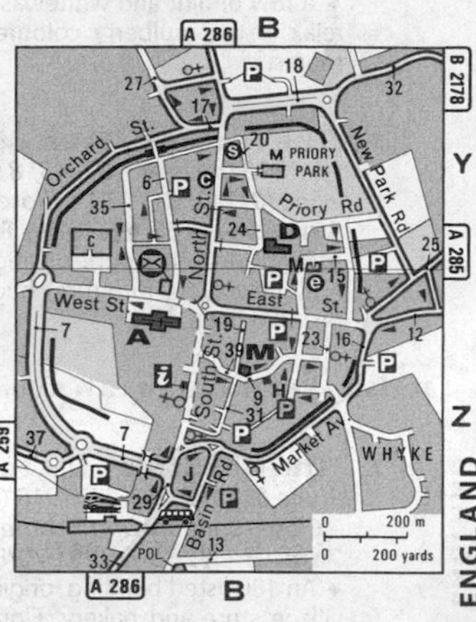

Crouchers Country H.

Birdham Rd, Apuldram, Southwest : 2½ m. on A 286 ✉ PO20 7EH – ✆ (01243) 784995 – info@crouchersbottom.com – Fax (01243) 539797

18 rm – †£ 65/95 ††£ 120/140 – **Rest** – Menu £ 20/24 – Carte £ 27/35

◆ 1900s farmhouse surrounded by fields. Bedrooms are in a separate coach house, some on ground floor; furnished with matching floral fabrics. Admire waterfowl in nearby pond. Bright, modern dining room.

XX **Comme ça**

67 Broyle Rd, on A 286 ✉ PO19 6BD – ✆ (01243) 788724 – comme.ca@commeca.co.uk – Fax (01243) 530052 – Closed Christmas-7 January, Monday, Tuesday lunch and Sunday dinner AY **c**

Rest – French Menu £ 23 (lunch) – Carte dinner approx. £ 30

◆ Strong French cooking ministered by Normand chef; generous à la carte, set menus and French family lunch on Sundays. Festoons of hops on exposed beams complete the décor.

XX **The Dining Room at Purchases**

31 North St ✉ PO19 1LY – ✆ (01243) 537352 – info@thediningroom.biz – Fax (01243) 780773 – Closed dinner 24-26 December, 1 and 2 January, Sunday and Bank Holiday Mondays BY **c**

Rest – Carte £ 27/34

◆ Charming Georgian house owned by country's oldest wine merchant; garden terrace, new wine bar, deep red hued restaurant serving shellfish and game menus. Great wine selection.

at East Lavant **North : 2½ m. off A 286 - AY – ✉ Chichester** 7 **C2**

The Royal Oak Inn with rm

Pook Lane ✉ PO18 0AX – ✆ (01243) 527434 – ro@thesussexpub.co.uk – Closed 25 December and 1 January

5 rm – †£ 65 ††£ 120 – **Rest** – Carte £ 20/30

◆ Utterly charming village pub with summer terraces. Modern rustic feel enhanced by leather sofas. All-encompassing restaurant: very well executed cooking. Comfy, modern rooms.

at Charlton **North : 6 ¼ m. by A 286 - AY – ✉ Chichester**

Woodstock House without rest

✉ *PO18 0HU – ✆ (01243) 811 666 – info@woodstockhousehotel.co.uk – Fax (01243) 811 666*

13 rm – †£ 60/80 ††£ 90/116

◆ A row of flint and whitewashed cottages close to Goodwood Racecourse. Indoors, relax in the mulberry coloured, cottage style lounge or the floral furnished bedrooms.

The Fox Goes Free with rm

✉ *PO18 0HU – ✆ (01243) 811 461 – thefoxgoesfree-always@virgin.net – Fax (01243) 811 712 – Closed 25 December*

5 rm – †£ 55 ††£ 140 – **Rest** – Carte £ 20/28

◆ Flint and brick pub, oozing 14C charm, balanced by appealing, modern tones. Antique church furniture, huge fire, cosy snug; hearty, fresh cooking. Welcoming beamed bedrooms.

at Halnaker **Northeast : 3 ¼ m. on A 285 - BY – ✉ Chichester**

ENGLAND

The Old Store without rest

Stane St, on A 285 ✉ PO18 0QL – ✆ (01243) 531 977 – theoldstore4@aol.com – Closed January and February

7 rm – †£ 35/60 ††£ 70/80

◆ An 18C listed building, originally belonging to the Goodwood Estate and used as a village store and bakery. Floral bedrooms. Well placed for Goodwood events and Chichester.

at Tangmere **East : 2 m. by A 27 - AY – ✉ Chichester**

Cassons

Arundel Rd, Northwest : ¼ m. off A 27 (westbound) ✉ PO18 0DU – ✆ (01243) 773 294 – cassonsresto@aol.com – Closed 25-26 December, 2 weeks January, Sunday dinner, Monday and Tuesday lunch

Rest – Menu £ 18 – Carte £ 31/48

◆ Eponymous owners run a homely and appealing neighbourhood restaurant where theme evenings (eg, India, New Zealand) gel with the locally renowned classical, seasonal cooking.

at Bosham **West : 4 m. by A 259 - AZ – ✉ Chichester**

Millstream rm, rest,

Bosham Lane ✉ PO18 8HL – ✆ (01243) 573 234 – info@millstream-hotel.co.uk – Fax (01243) 573 459

32 rm – †£ 82/112 ††£ 142/162 – 3 suites – **Rest** – Menu £ 33 (dinner) – Carte lunch £ 21/31

◆ Pretty hotel with garden that backs onto stream bobbing with ducks. Cosy bedrooms, individually co-ordinated fabric furnishings, sandwash fitted furniture and large windows. Seasonal, daily changing menus.

Charters without rest

Bosham Lane ✉ PO18 8HG – ✆ (01243) 572 644 – louise@chartersbandb.co.uk – Fax (01243) 572 644 – Closed 2 weeks Christmas and New Year

5 rm – †£ 55/60 ††£ 100/110

◆ Luxurious appointments knit seamlessly with a contemporaray design, as defined by freshly painted walls, teak and leather furnishings, and smart, swish rooms. Aga breakfasts.

at West Stoke **Northwest : 2 ¾ m. by B 2178 - AY - off B 2146 – ✉ Chichester**

XX **West Stoke House** with rm
Downs Rd ✉ PO18 9BN – ✆ (01243) 575 226 – info@weststokehouse.co.uk – Fax (01243) 574 655 – Closed 25-26 December
7 rm – †£ 95 ††£ 175 – **Rest** – (Closed Monday, Tuesday and Sunday dinner) (booking essential) Menu £ 23/40 **s**
Spec. Roast breast of pigeon, cep gnocchi, carrot purée and bacon foam. Roast loin of lamb, braised shoulder pie and kidney tart. Chocolate moelleux, cherry and chocolate terrine, white chocolate ice cream.
◆ Charmingly peaceful part 17C manor, set in very pleasant gardens. Reception with log burner seamlessly blends subtle elegance to modern art; strikingly understated rooms. Ambitious, skilled kitchen; local produce and seasonality to the fore. Personable service.

at Funtington **Northwest : 4 ¾ m. by B 2178 - AY - on B 2146 – ✉ Chichester**

XX **Hallidays**
Watery Lane ✉ PO18 9LF – ✆ (01243) 575 331 – Closed 2 weeks March, 1 week August, Monday, Tuesday, Saturday lunch and Sunday dinner
Rest – Menu £ 20/33 – Carte lunch £ 28/36
◆ A row of part 13C thatched cottages; confident and keen chef delivers a lively medley of frequently changing set menus and à la carte. Modern meals sit alongside classics.

CHIDDINGFOLD – Surrey – 504 S 30 — 7 C2

London 47 m – Guildford 10 m – Haslemere 5 m

The Swan Inn with rm
Petworth Rd ✉ GU8 4TY – ✆ (01428) 682 073 – enquiries@theswaninn.biz – Fax (01428) 683 259
11 rm – †£ 70/120 ††£ 95 – **Rest** – Carte £ 19/34
◆ Located on the main road of a leafy, red-brick village; refurbishment has created a pub with a neo-rustic atmosphere. Elaborate menus. Smart, contemporary bedrooms.

CHIEVELEY – Berks. – 503 Q 29 — 10 B3

London 60 m – Newbury 5 m – Swindon 25 m

XX **The Crab at Chieveley** with rm
Wantage Rd, West : 2 ½ m. by School Rd on B 4494 ✉ RG20 8UE – ✆ (01635) 247 550 – info@crabatchieveley.com – Fax (01635) 248 440
15 rm – †£ 80/120 ††£ 210 – **Rest** – Seafood Menu £ 15/30 – Carte £ 25/40
◆ Thatched former inn, a lively venue, on a country road with wheat fields. Choice of bistro or restaurant for seafood menu. Highly original bedrooms themed as famous hotels.

CHILLATON – Devon – 503 H 32 – see Tavistock

CHINNOR – Oxon. – 504 R 28 – pop. 5 407 *Great Britain* — 11 C2

London 45 m – Oxford 19 m
Ridgeway Path ★★

at Sprigg's Alley **Southeast : 2 ½ m. by Bledlow Ridge rd – ✉ Chinnor**

XX **Sir Charles Napier**
✉ OX39 4BX – ✆ (01494) 483 011 – info@sircharlesnapier.co.uk – Fax (01494) 485 311 – Closed 25-26 December, Sunday dinner and Monday
Rest – Menu £ 16/17 – Carte £ 31/40
◆ Early 18C inn serving modern British food with French influences. Quarry-tiled bar with sofas; beamed dining rooms; beautiful rear garden and vine-covered terrace. Sculptures.

ENGLAND

at Kingston Blount Southwest : 1 ¾ m. on B 4009 – ✉ Chinnor

Lakeside Town Farm without rest
Brook St, (off Sydenham rd) ✉ OX39 4RZ – ☎ (01844) 352 152
– townfarmcottage@oxfree.com – Fax (01844) 352 152
– Closed Christmas
3 rm – †£ 55 ††£ 80
◆ Modern building, on a working farm, in a sympathetic style that engenders a traditional, old-fashioned ambience. Charming, Victorian-style bedrooms. Attractive gardens.

CHIPPENHAM – Wilts. – **503** N 29 – **pop. 33 189** 4 **C2**

London 106 m – Bristol 27 m – Southampton 64 m – Swindon 21 m
Yelde Hall, Market Place ☎ (01249) 665970
Monkton Park (Par Three), ☎ (01249) 653 928 .
Yelde Hall ★
Corsham Court ★★ **AC**, SW : 4 m. by A 4 – Sheldon Manor ★ **AC**, W : 1 ½ m. by A 420 – Biddestone ★, W : 3 ½ m. – Bowood House ★ **AC** (Library ≤ ★) SE : 5 m. by A 4 and A 342. Castle Combe ★★, NW : 6 m. by A 420 and B 4039

at Stanton Saint Quintin North : 5 m. by A 429 – ✉ Chippenham

Stanton Manor
✉ SN14 6DQ – ☎ (0870) 890 28 80 – reception@stantonmanor.co.uk
– Fax (0870) 890 28 81 – Closed 26-29 December
23 rm – †£ 115 ††£ 220 – **Rest** – Menu £ 20/29
◆ Extended 19C manor in formal gardens; popular commercial/wedding venue. There's some noise from adjacent M4, but this is more than made up for by appealing range of bedrooms. Elegant restaurant uses produce from the garden.

ENGLAND

CHIPPING – Lancs. – **502** M 22 – ✉ Preston 20 **B2**

London 233 m – Lancaster 30 m – Leeds 54 m – Manchester 40 m – Preston 12 m

Gibbon Bridge
East : 1 m. on Clitheroe rd ✉ PR3 2TQ – ☎ (01995) 61 456
– reception@gibbon-bridge.co.uk – Fax (01995) 61 277
– Closed 1-12 January
11 rm – †£ 85/100 ††£ 130/250 – 18 suites – **Rest** – Menu £ 18 (lunch) – Carte dinner £ 28/34
◆ Converted stone farm buildings set in the heart of the Trough of Bowland. Bedrooms, all of which are very comfy and individual, include split-level suites with four-posters. Own bakery produce in restaurant, which overlooks delightful gardens.

CHIPPING CAMPDEN – Glos. – **503** O 27 – **pop. 1 943** *Great Britain* 4 **D1**

London 93 m – Cheltenham 21 m – Oxford 37 m – Stratford-upon-Avon 12 m
Old Police Station ☎ (01386) 841206
Town ★
Hidcote Manor Garden ★★ **AC**, NE : 2 ½ m

Cotswold House
The Square ✉ GL55 6AN – ☎ (01386) 840 330 – reception@cotswoldhouse.com
– Fax (01386) 840 310
27 rm – †£ 150/265 ††£ 295/395 – 2 suites
Rest *Hicks'* – see restaurant listing
Rest *Juliana's* – (dinner only and Sunday lunch) Menu £ 50
◆ Enviably stylish Regency town house with graceful spiral staircase winding upwards to luxurious rooms, some very modern, boasting every mod con imaginable. Impressive service. Formal though stylish Juliana's for accomplished cooking with an original style.

Noel Arms
High St ✉ GL55 6AT – ✆ (01386) 840 317 – reception@noelarmshotel.com – Fax (01386) 841 136
26 rm – †£ 90/120 ††£ 130/220 – **Rest** – Menu £ 15 – Carte £ 25/45
♦ A 14C former coaching inn; lounge and reception decked in civil war armoury and antique furniture. This extends to some heritage style rooms, one has 14C ornate four-poster. Colourful, intimate dining room with menu of Asian dishes.

The Kings with rm
The Square ✉ GL55 6AW – ✆ (01386) 840 256 – info@kingscampden.co.uk – Fax (01386) 841 598 – Closed 25-26 December
12 rm – †£ 73/85 ††£ 165 – **Rest** – Carte £ 20/35
♦ Attractive red brick house in centre of town; modernised but retaining period character. Intimate dining room serves well-presented, quality cooking. Garden and rear terrace. Stylish bedrooms on upper two floors.

Hicks' – at Cotswold House
The Square ✉ GL55 6AN – ✆ (01386) 840 330 – Fax (01386) 840 310
Rest – (booking essential) Menu £ 20/22 – Carte £ 23/32
♦ Named after local benefactor. Booking advised; open all day serving locals and residents with modern varied menu. Morning coffees, afternoon teas, home-made cake available.

Eight Bells Inn with rm
Church St ✉ GL55 6JG – ✆ (01386) 840 371 – neilhargreaves@bellinn.fsnet.co.uk – Fax (01386) 841 669 – Closed 25 December
7 rm – †£ 55 ††£ 95 – **Rest** – Carte £ 20/30
♦ A 14C stone inn, once used by stonemasons working on adjacent church; still exudes history in wood and stone interior. Traditional robust menu: blackboard specials.

ENGLAND

at Mickleton North : 3 ¼ m. by B 4035 and B 4081 on B 4632 – ✉ Chipping Campden

Three Ways House rest,
✉ GL55 6SB – ✆ (01386) 438 429 – reception@puddingclub.com – Fax (01386) 438 118
48 rm – †£ 95/105 ††£ 210 – **Rest** – (dinner only Sunday lunch) Menu £ 33
♦ Built in 1870; renowned as home of the "Pudding Club". Two types of room, in original house and modern block, all very comfy and modern. Bar with antique tiled floor. Arcaded dining room; Pudding Club meets here to vote after tastings.

Nineveh Farm without rest
West : ½ m. on B 4081 ✉ GL55 6PS – ✆ (01386) 438 923 – ninevehfarm@hotmail.com
5 rm – †£ 65 ††£ 75
♦ Georgian farmhouse in pleasant garden. Warm welcome; local information in resident's lounge. Comfortable rooms with view in house or with French windows in garden house.

Myrtle House without rest
✉ GL55 6SA – ✆ (01386) 430 032 – louanne@myrtlehouse.co.uk
5 rm – †£ 45 ††£ 65/80
♦ Part Georgian house with large lawned garden. Bedrooms named and styled after flowers and plants, those on top floor most characterful.

at Paxford Southeast : 3 m. by B 4035 – ✉ Chipping Campden

Churchill Arms with rm
✉ GL55 6XH – ✆ (01386) 594 000 – mail@thechurchillarms.com – Fax (01386) 594 005
4 rm – †£ 40 ††£ 70 – **Rest** – (bookings not accepted) Carte £ 17/30
♦ Popular Cotswold stone and brick pub; mellow interior. Good value menus chalked on blackboard. Organic local produce used. Comfortable bedrooms.

at Broad Campden **South : 1 ¼ m. by B 4081 – ✉ Chipping Campden** 4 **D1**

Malt House without rest
✉ GL55 6UU – ✆ (01386) 840 295 – info@malt-house.co.uk – Fax (01386) 841 334 – Closed 1 week Christmas
7 rm – £ 90 ££ 145
◆ For a rare experience of the countryside idyll, this 16C malting house is a must. Cut flowers from the gardens on view in bedrooms decked out in fabrics to delight the eye.

CHIPPING NORTON – Oxon. – **503** P 28 – **pop. 5 688** 10 **A1**

London 77 m – Oxford 22 m – Stow-on-the-Wold 9 m

The Masons Arms
Banbury Rd, Swerford, Northeast : 5 m. on A 361 ✉ OX7 4AP – ✆ (01608) 683 212 – themasonschef@hotmail.com – Fax (01608) 683 105 – Closed 25-26 December
Rest – Menu £ 11/16 – Carte £ 20/27
◆ Light and airy rural pub. Experienced chef-owner, friendly atmosphere. Precise, well-presented and flavourful dishes on blackboard menus. Neat gardens with picnic benches.

CHISELDON – Wilts. – **503** O 29 – see Swindon

CHORLEY – Lancs. – **502** M 23 – **pop. 33 536** 20 **A2**

London 222 m – Blackpool 30 m – Liverpool 33 m – Manchester 26 m
Duxbury Park Duxbury Hall Rd, ✆ (01257) 265 380 ;
Shaw Hill Hotel G. & C.C. Whittle-le-Woods Preston Rd, ✆ (01257) 269 221 .

at Whittle-le-Woods **North : 2 m. on A 6 – ✉ Chorley**

Vardon
Preston Rd ✉ PR6 7PP – ✆ (01257) 269 221 – info@shaw-hill.co.uk – Fax (01257) 261 223
30 rm – £ 85 ££ 130
Rest *Vardon* – (Closed Saturday lunch) Menu £ 15/22 **s** – Carte £ 28/34 **s**
◆ Dignified Georgian hotel presides over 18 hole golf course. Golfing memorabilia adorns smart interiors. Variety of rooms, tastefully wallpapered; some overlook course. Classic dining room with golfing views.

Parkville Country House
174 Preston Rd ✉ PR6 7HE – ✆ (01257) 261 881 – Fax (01257) 273 171
5 rm – £ 50/70 ££ 60/70, £5
Rest *Truffles* – (closed Monday) Menu £ 18 – Carte £ 18/31
◆ A large converted house with conservatory extension not far from Shaw Hill Golf Club. Tidy bedrooms, all similarly furnished, some with jacuzzis. Well tended lawned gardens. Conservatory restauarant with gourmet club.

CHORLTON-CUM-HARDY – Gtr Manchester – **502** N 23 – see Manchester

---

CHRISTCHURCH – Dorset – **503** O 31 – **pop. 40 208** 4 **D3**

London 111 m – Bournemouth 6 m – Salisbury 26 m – Southampton 24 m – Winchester 39 m
23 High St ✆ (01202) 471780
Highcliffe Castle Highcliffe-on-Sea 107 Lymington Rd, ✆ (01425) 272 953 ;
Riverside Ave, ✆ (01202) 436 436 .
Town★ - Priory★
Hengistbury Head★ (≤ ★★) SW : 4 ½ m. by A 35 and B 3059

ENGLAND

Captains Club
Wick Ferry, Wick Lane ✉ BH23 1HU – ✆ (01202) 475 111 – enquiries@captainsclubhotel.com – Fax (01202) 490 111
17 rm – 🛉£ 125/185 🛉🛉£ 145/269, ☕ £15 – 12 suites
Rest *Tides* – Carte £ 26/35
◆ Stylish hotel on banks of River Stour, with light, contemporary décor and a nautical edge. Large rooms with river views and modern amenities. Spa with hydrotherapy pool. Tides restaurant has river-facing terrace and offers tempting, modern European menus.

Druid House without rest
26 Sopers Lane ✉ BH23 1JE – ✆ (01202) 485 615 – reservations@druid-house.co.uk – Fax (01202) 473 484
9 rm ☕ – 🛉£ 35/76 🛉🛉£ 70/86
◆ 1930s house that appeals with bright, fresh ambience: cottagey breakfast room, light and airy conservatory sitting room, smart bar. Spacious bedrooms, two with balconies.

Splinters
12 Church St ✉ BH23 1BW – ✆ (01202) 483 454 – eating@splinters.uk.com – Fax (01202) 480 180 – Closed 1-10 January, Sunday and Monday
Rest – Menu £ 14/26 – Carte £ 37/43
◆ Brasserie-like exterior; two dining areas inside: one has intimate pine booths; upstairs more formal with high-backed chairs. French-influenced cuisine.

Fishworks
10 Church St ✉ BH23 1BW – ✆ (01202) 487 000 – christchurch@fishworks.co.uk – Fax (01202) 487 001 – Closed 25-26 December, 1 January and Monday
Rest – Seafood (booking essential) Carte £ 25/49
◆ An informal eatery which has its own well-stocked fish counter: choose your selection with the aid of helpful chefs. Tasty, prime quality produce.

at Mudeford Southeast : 2 m. – ✉ Christchurch

Waterford Lodge
87 Bure Lane, Friars Cliff ✉ BH23 4DN – ✆ (01425) 282 100 – waterford@bestwestern.co.uk – Fax (01425) 279 130
18 rm ☕ – 🛉£ 54/79 🛉🛉£ 108/138 – **Rest** – Menu £ 10/28 **s**
◆ Family run hotel. Take a sea stroll with the dog, as they are welcome, or enjoy free swimming at local leisure centre. Rooms overlook rooftops and countryside on top floor. Hand-made truffles round off tasty meals.

CHRISTMAS COMMON – Oxon. 11 C2

London 41 m – Oxford 18 m – Reading 13 m

The Fox and Hounds
✉ OX49 5HL – ✆ (01491) 612 599 – kiran.daniels@btconnect.com – Closed Sunday
Rest – Menu £ 10/15 – Carte £ 23/38
◆ Pretty 17C pub popular with ramblers has cosy, warm feel. Dine in modern barn conversion featuring open kitchen. Passionate chef cooks with fresh, seasonal ingredients.

CHURCH ENSTONE – Oxon. – ✉ Chipping Norton 10 B1

London 72 m – Banbury 13 m – Oxford 38 m

The Crown Inn
Mill Lane ✉ OX7 4NN – ✆ (01608) 677 262 – Fax (01608) 677 394 – Closed 25-26 December, 1 January, Sunday dinner and Monday lunch
Rest – Carte £ 17/25
◆ Pretty, well-run inn with homely feel and good mix of drinkers and diners. Light and airy conservatory. Display of handcrafted walking sticks in hall. Unfussy, honest cooking.

ENGLAND

CHURCH STRETTON – Shrops. – 502 L 26 – pop. 3 941 18 B2

Great Britain

London 166 m – Birmingham 46 m – Hereford 39 m – Shrewsbury 14 m
Trevor Hill, ✆ (01694) 722 281 .
Wenlock Edge★, E : by B 4371

Jinlye without rest

Castle Hill, All Stretton, North : 2¼ m. by B 4370 turning left beside telephone box in All Stretton ✉ SY6 6JP – ✆ (01694) 723 243 – info@jinlye.co.uk – Fax (01694) 723 243

6 rm – £64 £88

◆ Enjoy wonderful views of Long Mynd from this characterful crofter's cottage high in the hills, run by charming owner and daughter. Grandiose breakfast room. 19C conservatory.

The Studio

59 High St ✉ SY6 6BY – ✆ (01694) 722672 – info@thestudiorestaurant.net – Closed Christmas and New Year, 3 weeks January, 1 week Spring, 1 week Autumn, Sunday and Monday

Rest – (dinner only) Carte £ 26/32

◆ Personally run former art studio; walls enhanced by local artwork. Pleasant rear terrace for sunny lunches. Tried-and-tested dishes: much care taken over local produce.

ENGLAND

CHURCHILL – Oxon. – 503 P 28 – ✉ Chipping Norton 10 A1

London 79 m – Birmingham 46 m – Cheltenham 29 m – Oxford 23 m – Swindon 31 m

The Forge without rest

✉ OX7 6NJ – ✆ (01608) 658 173 – rushbrooke@madasafish.com

5 rm – £52/57 £66/81

◆ Former village smithy, now an immaculately-kept guest house, with comfy lounge and breakfast room. Front bedrooms are more luxurious; some with four posters and jacuzzi baths.

The Chequers

Church Rd ✉ OX7 6NJ – ✆ (01608) 659393 – Closed 25 December

Rest – Menu £ 20/26 – Carte £ 19/23

◆ Popular, open plan pub built of Cotswold stone, with high-ceilings, inglenook fireplace and warm, welcoming atmosphere. Traditional dishes made with local ingredients.

CIRENCESTER – Glos. – 503 O 28 – pop. 15 861 *Great Britain* 4 D1

London 97 m – Bristol 37 m – Gloucester 19 m – Oxford 37 m
Corn Hall, Market Pl ✆ (01285) 654180
Bagendon Cheltenham Rd, ✆ (01285) 652465 .
Town★ – Church of St John the Baptist★ – Corinium Museum★ (Mosaic pavements★) AC
Fairford : Church of St Mary★ (stained glass windows★★) E : 7 m. by A 417

No 12 without rest

12 Park St ✉ GL7 2BW – ✆ (01285) 640 232 – no12cirencester@ukgateway.net

4 rm – £65 £85/100

◆ 16C property with Georgian façade, hidden away in the old alleyways. Delightful rear walled garden. Excellent organic breakfast. Stylish rooms charmingly blend old and new.

The Old Brewhouse without rest

7 London Rd ✉ GL7 2PU – ✆ (01285) 656 099 – info@theoldbrewhouse.com – Fax (01285) 656 099 – Closed 1 week Christmas

7 rm – £50/55 £60/70

◆ Former 17C brewhouse with a cosy, cottagey ambience. Exposed stone in two breakfast rooms. Cast iron bedsteads adorn some of the rooms, all of which boast period character.

at North Cerney North : 4 m. on A 435 – ✉ Cirencester

The Bathurst Arms with rm
✉ GL7 7BZ – ✆ (01285) 831 281 – james@bathurstarms.com
6 rm – †£ 55 ††£ 85 – **Rest** – Carte £ 20/28
◆ Characterful pink pub cloaked in a coat of ivy with River Churn running alongside. 17C beamed bar; dining area in former stables. No wine list - pick a bottle of the shelves. Comfortable bedrooms, one with a four poster.

at Barnsley Northeast : 4 m. by A 429 on B 4425 – ✉ Cirencester

Barnsley House
✉ GL7 5EE – ✆ (01285) 740 000 – info@barnsleyhouse.com
– Fax (01285) 740 925
11 rm – †£ 290 ††£ 405, ☕ £ 12.50 – 7 suites – **Rest** – (booking essential for non-residents at dinner) Menu £ 26/40
◆ Impressive 17C Cotswold manor house. Contemporary interior, with hi tech bedrooms; largest and most modern in annexed courtyard. Well kept gardens, hydrotherapy pool, cinema. Dining room has pleasant outlook. Modern, interesting menus.

Village Pub with rm
✉ GL7 5EE – ✆ (01285) 740 421 – info@thevillagepub.co.uk
– Fax (01285) 740 925
7 rm ☕ – †£ 75 ††£ 150 – **Rest** – Carte £ 20/29
◆ 17C pub: flagstone and oak floors, exposed timbers, open fireplaces. Home-made bread, local drinks, organic ingredients allied to modern English cooking. Rustic bedrooms.

at Ewen Southwest : 3 ¼ m. by A 429 – ✉ Cirencester

The Wild Duck Inn with rm
Drake's Island ✉ GL7 6BY – ✆ (01285) 770 310 – wduckinn@aol.com
– Fax (01285) 770 924 – closed dinner 25 December
12 rm ☕ – †£ 70 ††£ 120 – **Rest** – Carte £ 20/35
◆ Part 16C former mill with characterful, rustic interior where dried hops hang from low beams. Intimate atmosphere. Distinctive deep red dining room hung with portraits. Modernised bedrooms with four posters.

at Sapperton West : 5 m. by A 419 – ✉ Cirencester 4 **C1**

The Bell
✉ GL7 6LE – ✆ (01285) 760 298 – thebell@sapperton66.freeserve.co.uk
– Fax (01285) 760 761 – Closed 25 December
Rest – Carte £ 21/32
◆ Charming, personally run pub made up of three cottages. Log fires and beams inside and a terrace outside. Mix of English and European cooking; superb wine list.

Do not confuse X with ✿!
X defines comfort, while stars are awarded for the best cuisine, across all categories of comfort.

CLANFIELD – **Oxon.** – **503** P 28 – **pop. 1 709** 10 **A2**
London 75 m – Oxford 24 m – Swindon 16 m

Plough at Clanfield
Bourton Rd, on A 4095 ✉ OX18 2RB – ✆ (01367) 810 222
– info@theploughclanfield.co.uk – Fax (01367) 810 596
12 rm ☕ – †£ 75 ††£ 125 – **Rest** – Carte £ 17/36
◆ Restored Elizabethan manor (1560), sitting in pretty gardens. Serene lounge with original fireplace; choice of rooms with character in main house and larger, newer rooms. Intimate restaurant.

ENGLAND

CLARE – Suffolk – 504 V 27 – pop. 1 975 – ✉ Sudbury 14 B3

London 67 m – Bury St Edmunds 16 m – Cambridge 27 m – Colchester 24 m – Ipswich 32 m

Ship Stores without rest

22 Callis St ✉ CO10 8PX – ☎ (01787) 277 834 – shipclare@aol.com – Fax (01787) 277 183

7 rm – †£ 35/60 ††£ 60/65

◆ Three converted cottages which once sheltered sheep farmers and now double as the village shop. Simple, pine furnished rooms, four in the adjacent annex.

CLAVERING – Essex – 504 U 28 – pop. 1 663 – ✉ Saffron Walden 12 B2

London 44 m – Cambridge 25 m – Colchester 44 m – Luton 29 m

The Cricketers with rm

✉ CB11 4QT – ☎ (01799) 550 442 – cricketers@lineone.net – Fax (01799) 550 882 – Closed 25-26 December

14 rm – †£ 75 ††£ 110 – **Rest** – Menu £ 27 – Carte £ 21/27

◆ 16C pub where Jamie Oliver first learned to chop an onion - still run by his parents. Traditional feel; low beamed ceilings. Choice of cottagey or more modern bedrooms. Homemade dishes made from locally sourced produce. Refreshing mix of the classic and the more modern, with an Italian slant.

CLAYTON WEST – W. Yorks. – 502 P 23 – pop. 7 932 – ✉ Huddersfield 22 B3

London 190 m – Leeds 19 m – Manchester 35 m – Sheffield 24 m

Bagden Hall rm, rest,

Wakefield Rd, Scissett, Southwest : 1 m. on A 636 ✉ HD8 9LE – ☎ (01484) 865 330 – info.bagdenhall@classiclodges.co.uk – Fax (01484) 861 001

36 rm – †£ 70/95 ††£ 130

Rest *Glendale* – Carte £ 26/38

Rest *Pippins* – Carte £ 25/32

◆ 19C house in Georgian style with extensive, mature gardens, lake, 16C boathouse and golf course. Suites and bedrooms in country house style. Bar with conservatory extension. Formal dining in Glendale. Pippins brasserie named after racehorse buried in grounds!

CLAYTON-LE-WOODS – Lancs. – 502 M 24 – pop. 14 173 – ✉ Chorley 20 A2

London 220 m – Liverpool 34 m – Manchester 26 m – Preston 5 m

The Pines

570 Preston Rd, on A 6 at junction with B 5256 ✉ PR6 7ED – ☎ (01772) 338 551 – mail@thepineshotel.co.uk – Fax (01772) 629 002

34 rm – †£ 75 ††£ 85/125 – 2 suites

Rest *Haworths Bistro* – Menu £ 15 (lunch) – Carte £ 15/24

◆ Prospering on a heady round of weddings and cabarets, this redbrick Victorian hotel boasts two fashionable lounges and a smart set of bedrooms, all individually decorated. Restaurant with unique stained glass roof and modern, assured cooking.

CLEARWELL – Glos. – see Coleford

CLEETHORPES – N.E. Lincs. – 502 U 23 – pop. 31 853 23 D3

London 171 m – Lincoln 38 m – Sheffield 77 m

Humberside Airport : ☎ (01652) 688456, W : 16 m. by A 46 and A 18 Y

42-43 Alexandra Rd ☎ (01472) 323111

Riverside Bar and Restaurant

2 Alexandra Rd ✉ DN35 8LQ – ☎ (01472) 600 515 – info@theriversidebarandrestaurant.com – Fax (01472) 290 270 – Closed 25-26 December, Monday lunch and Sunday

Rest – Menu £ 16 (lunch) – Carte dinner £ 24/33

◆ Actually looking out to sea, this 19C terraced property has a modern interior with a ground floor bar and smart restaurant upstairs where modern classics take centre stage.

ENGLAND

CLEEVE HILL – Glos. – 503 N 28 – see Cheltenham

CLENT – Worcs. – 504 N 26 *Great Britain* 19 C2

London 127 m – Birmingham 12 m – Hagley 2 m

Black Country Museum★, N : 7 m. by A 491 and A 4036 – Birmingham★ - Museum and Art Gallery★★, Aston Hall★★, NE : 10 m. by A 491 and A 456

Bell & Cross

Holy Cross, West : ½ m. off A 491 (northbound carriageway) (Bromsgrove rd)
DY9 9QL – (01562) 730 319
– Closed dinner 25-26, 31 December and 1 January
Rest – Carte £ 15/25

◆ Early 19C village pub with gardens and dining terrace. Traditional public bar and five intimate dining rooms. Friendly service; blackboard specials and seasonal produce.

CLEY NEXT THE SEA – Norfolk – 504 X 25 – see Blakeney

CLIMPING – W. Sussex – 504 S 31 – see Littlehampton

CLIPSHAM – Rutland – see Stamford

CLITHEROE – Lancs. – 502 M 22 – pop. 14 697 20 B2

London 64 m – Blackpool 35 m – Manchester 31 m

12-14 Market Pl (01200) 425566

Whalley Rd, (01200) 422 618 .

Brooklyn without rest

32 Pimlico Rd BB7 2AH – (01200) 428 268
4 rm – £ 32 £ 60

◆ Stone 19C house, two minutes' walk from town, with floral furnished rooms, quieter at the rear. Homely lounge to relax in after a day's exploration of the Trough of Bowland.

CLOVELLY – Devon – 503 G 31 – pop. 439 – Bideford 1 B1

London 241 m – Barnstaple 18 m – Exeter 52 m – Penzance 92 m

Village★★

SW : Tamar River★★. Hartland : Hartland Church★ - Hartland Quay★ (viewpoint★★) - Hartland Point ≤ ★★★, W : 6½ m. by B 3237 and B 3248 – Morwenstow (Church★, cliffs★★), SW : 11½ m. by A 39

Red Lion

The Quay EX39 5TF – (01237) 431 237 – redlion@clovelly.co.uk
– Fax (01237) 431 044
11 rm – £ 59/79 £ 117/127 **Rest** – (bar lunch) Carte £ 14/37

◆ Cosy little hotel/inn on the quayside; a superb location. All rooms enjoy sea and harbour views and are dressed in soft, understated colours, providing a smart resting place. Simple dining room looks out to harbour.

CLOWS TOP – Worcs. – pop. 1 164 18 B2

London 141 m – Bewdley 6 m – Stourport-on-Seven 10 m

The Colliers Arms

Tenbury Road, East : ½ m. on A 456 DY14 9HA – (01299) 832 242
– thecolliersarms@aol.com – Closed Sunday dinner,27-29 December
Rest – Carte £ 20/27

◆ Snug, traditional bar; open main bar with log fire and fishy wallpaper; airy rear dining room with views of garden. Hearty British classics - all fresh, seasonal and homemade.

ENGLAND

CLUN – Shrops. – 503 K 26 — 18 A2

London 173 m – Church Stretton 16 m – Ludlow 16 m

Birches Mill without rest 

Northwest : 3 m. by A 488, Bicton rd, Mainstone rd and Burlow rd ✉ SY7 8NL – ✆ (01588) 640 409 – gill@birchesmill.fsnet.co.uk – Fax (01588) 640 409 – April-October

3 rm – †£ 66/70 ††£ 76/84

◆ High quality comforts in remote former corn mill: interior has characterful 17C/18C structures. Flagged lounge with lovely inglenook. Simple but tastefully decorated rooms.

COBALT BUSINESS PARK – Tyne and Wear – see Newcastle upon Tyne

COBHAM – Surrey – 504 S 30 – pop. 16 360 — 7 D1

London 24 m – Guildford 10 m

Plan : see Greater London (South-West) 5

at Stoke D'Abernon Southeast : 1½ m. on A 245 – ✉ Cobham

Woodlands Park

Woodlands Lane, on A 245 ✉ KT11 3QB – ✆ (01372) 843 933 – woodlandspark@handpicked.co.uk – Fax (01372) 842 704

57 rm – †£ 200 ††£ 220

Rest *Oak Room* – (Closed Sunday dinner and Monday) (dinner only and Sunday lunch) Menu £ 39

Rest *Brasserie* – Carte £ 18/30

◆ Designed in 1885 for son of founder of Bryant and May match company; one of first houses with electricity. Frequented by Prince of Wales and Lillie Langtry. Modish rooms. Appealingly welcoming Oak Room restaurant; also brasserie.

COCKERMOUTH – Cumbria – 501 J 20 – pop. 7 446 — 21 A2

London 306 m – Carlisle 25 m – Keswick 13 m

Town Hall, Market St ✆ (01900) 822634

Embleton, ✆ (017687) 76 223 .

Trout

Crown St ✉ CA13 0EJ – ✆ (01900) 823 591 – enquiries@trouthotel.co.uk – Fax (01900) 827 514

47 rm – †£ 60/109 ††£ 115/145

Rest *The Restaurant* – Carte £ 30/42

Rest *The Terrace* – Carte £ 19/26

◆ Well run, extended hotel on banks of River Derwent. Refurbished, contemporary lounges and classically styled bedrooms; some in main house have original beams. The linen-laid Restaurant offers a daily set menu. The Terrace Bar and Bistro offers informal and al fresco dining, with a modern, international choice.

at Lorton Southeast : 4¼ m. by B 5292 – ✉ Cockermouth

Winder Hall Country House

on B 5289 ✉ CA13 9UP – ✆ (01900) 85 107 – nick@winderhall.co.uk – Fax (01900) 85 479 – closed 23 December-7 February

7 rm – †£ 61/66 ††£ 81/92 – **Rest** – (dinner only) (booking essential for non-residents) Menu £ 37 **s** – Carte approx. £ 32

◆ Part-Jacobean manor house with mullioned windows and tranquil garden.Comfortable lounge and high quality bedrooms retain rich history of house and include two four posters. Oak panelled dining room overlooks garden. Local produce well-used in homemade dishes. Relaxed, friendly service.

New House Farm

South : 1¼ m. on B 5289 ✉ CA13 9UU – ✆ (01900) 85 404 – hazel@newhouse-farm.co.uk – Fax (01900) 85 478

5 rm – †£ 75/95 ††£ 150 – **Rest** – (residents only) Menu £ 24

◆ Very well appointed, richly decorated guest house. Hot tub in garden, sumptuous bedrooms; one with double jacuzzi, two with four posters. Fine furnishings, roll top baths. Aga-cooked breakfasts and evenings meals.

The Old Vicarage
Church Lane, North : ¼ m. on Lorton Church rd ✉ CA13 9UN – ✆ (01900) 85 656 – enquiries@oldvicarage.co.uk
8 rm – †£ 43/55 ††£ 100/110 – **Rest** – (by arrangement) Menu £ 27
◆ Well kept Victorian house in beautiful countryside spot. Comfortable lounge. Hospitable owners. Sympathetically modernised bedrooms; four-postered Room 1 is the best. Cosy dining room; homecooked meals made with local produce.

COCKLEFORD – Glos. – ✉ Cheltenham 4 C1

London 95 m – Bristol 48 m – Cheltenham 7 m

The Green Dragon Inn with rm
✉ GL53 9NW – ✆ (01242) 870 271 – green-dragon@buccaneer.co.uk – Fax (01242) 870 171 – Closed dinner 25-26 December and 1 January
9 rm – †£ 65 ††£ 85 – **Rest** – (booking essential) Carte £ 22/28
◆ 17C country inn of old Cotswold stone with beams, log fire and large outside terrace. Tasty meals employing good use of local ingredients. Smart rooms.

CODFORD ST MARY – Wilts. – 504 N 30 *Great Britain* 4 C2

London 101 m – Bristol 38 m – Warminster 8 m
Stonehenge★★★ **AC**, E : 10½ m. by A 36 and A 303

The George with rm
High St ✉ BA12 0NG – ✆ (01985) 850 270 – Closed Tuesday and Sunday dinner in winter
3 rm – †£ 45 ††£ 70 – **Rest** – Carte £ 18/35
◆ Whitewashed 18C pub/hotel in pretty village. Large bar with real ales, mix and match furniture. Concise menu, accomplished dishes using fresh produce. Simply appointed rooms.

COGGESHALL – Essex – 504 W 28 – pop. 3 919 – ✉ Colchester 13 C2

London 49 m – Braintree 6 m – Chelmsford 16 m – Colchester 9 m

White Hart
Market End ✉ CO6 1NH – ✆ (01376) 561 654 – whitehart.coggeshall@greeneking.co.uk – Fax (01376) 561 789
18 rm – †£ 75/85 ††£ 95 – **Rest** – (in bar Sunday dinner) Menu £ 20/25 – Carte £ 21/30
◆ Part 15C guildhall in centre of this historic market town, boasting solid stone floor and walls and warmed by open fires. Characterful bedrooms with exposed timbers. Formal rear dining room serves cooking with an Italian emphasis.

Baumanns Brasserie
4-6 Stoneham St ✉ CO6 1TT – ✆ (01376) 561 453 – food@baumanns.brasserie.co.uk – Fax (01376) 563 762 – Closed first 2 weeks January, Monday and Tuesday
Rest – Menu £ 16/22 – Carte £ 27/35
◆ Characterful 16C building, its walls packed with pictures and prints. Tasty cooking, made using local produce, brings out classic flavour combinations. Speedy service.

at Pattiswick Northwest : 3 m. by A 120 (Braintree Rd) – ✉ Coggeshall

The Compasses at Pattiswick
Compasses Rd ✉ CM77 8BG – ✆ (01376) 561 322 – info@thecompassesatpattiswick.co.uk – Fax (01376) 564 343 – Closed Sunday dinner
Rest – Carte £ 17/25
◆ Modern interior with rustic bar, cosy leather sofas and open fire. Appealing, seasonally-changing menus include hearty favourites. Extensive gardens; pleasant outdoor terrace.

ENGLAND

COLCHESTER – Essex – **504** W 28 – **pop. 104 390** *Great Britain* 13 **D2**

London 52 m – Cambridge 48 m – Ipswich 18 m – Luton 76 m – Southend-on-Sea 41 m

Visitor Information Centre, 1 Queen St ✆ (01206) 282920

Birch Grove Layer Rd, ✆ (01206) 734 276 .

Castle and Museum★ **AC** BZ

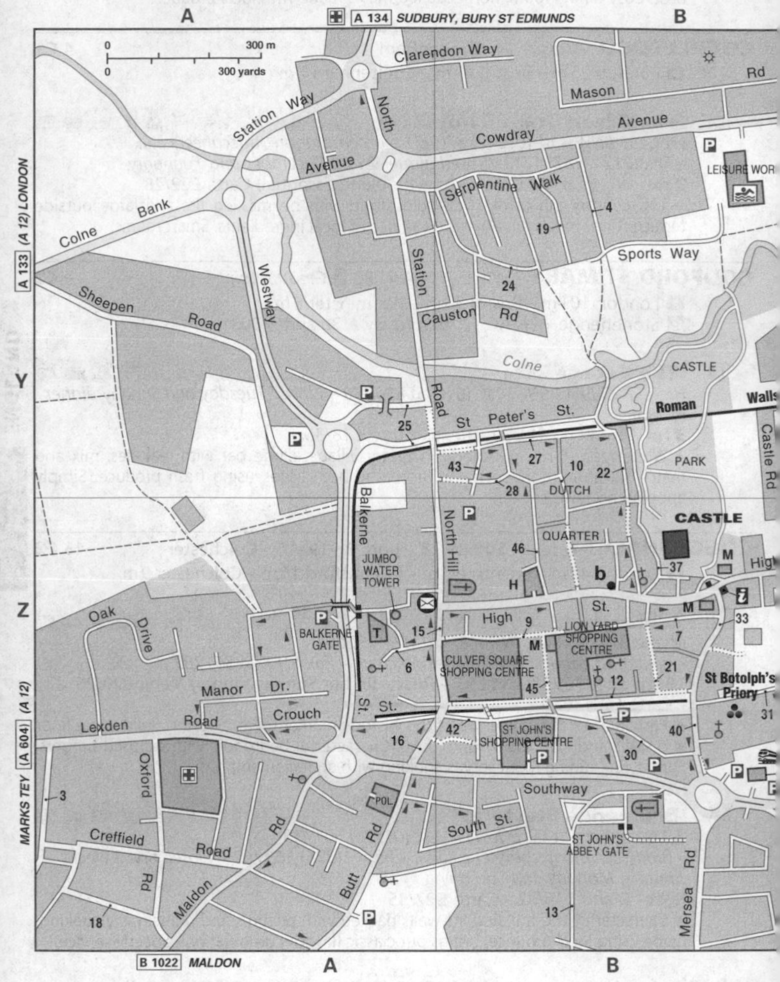

Rose and Crown

rm,

East St, Eastgates ✉ CO1 2TZ – ✆ (01206) 866 677 – info@rose-and-crown.com – Fax (01206) 866 616 CZ **d**

39 rm – †£ 89/109 ††£ 99/109, ☕ £10.95 – **Rest** – Carte £ 16/21

♦ Part 15C black and white inn boasting original stained glass and exposed beams. Characterful four posters in the main house; larger rooms in lodge better suit business needs. Formal dining room with open feel. Wide-ranging menu features fusion cooking with a strong Indian base.

Red House without rest

29 Wimpole Rd ✉ CO1 2DL – ✆ (01206) 509 005
– theredhousecolchester@hotmail.com – Fax (01206) 509 005 CZ **a**

3 rm – ♦£40 ♦♦£65

◆ Red-brick Victorian house away from main centre. Original fittings include stained glass and ornate plasterwork on ceiling in sitting room. Ample bedrooms; personal touches.

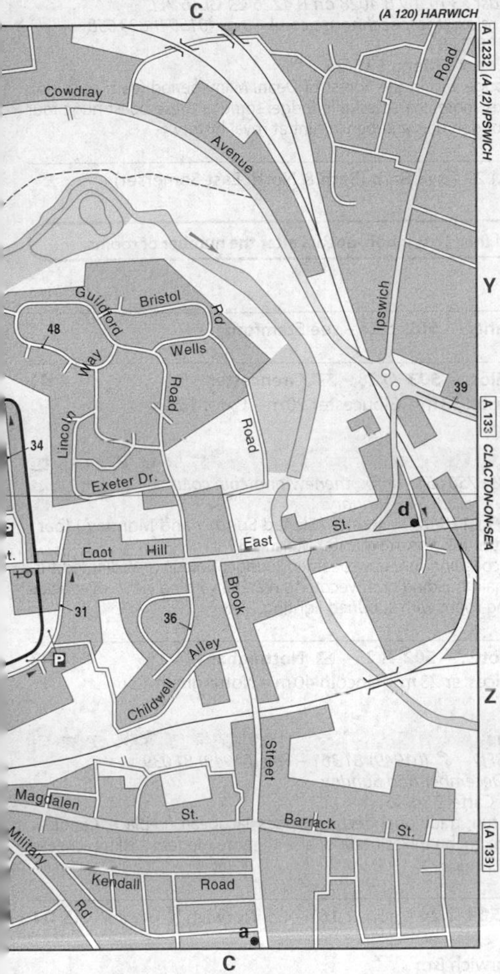

COLCHESTER

We try to be as accurate as possible when giving room rates.
But prices are susceptible to change,
so please check rates when booking.

COLEFORD – Glos. – **503** M 28 – **pop. 10 145** *Great Britain* 4 **C1**

London 143 m – Bristol 28 m – Gloucester 19 m – Newport 29 m
High St ✆ (01594) 812388
Forest of Dean Lords Hills, ✆ (01594) 832 583 ;
Forest Hills Mile End Rd, ✆ (01594) 810 620 .
W : Wye Valley★

Speech House — rm, rest, VISA AE

Forest of Dean, Northeast : 3 m. by B 4028 on B 4226 ✉ GL16 7EL – ✆ (01594) 822 607 – relax@thespeechhouse.co.uk – Fax (01594) 823 658

37 rm – £ 65 £ 98/125

Rest ***The Verderer's Court*** – Menu £ 15/25

◆ Charles II's hunting lodge within the Forest of Dean. Many period features in situ. Modern rooms in annexe; more characterful in lodge: some of these boast huge four posters. Dining room wooden dais and bench hint at royal history.

COLERNE – Wilts. – **503** M 29 – **see Bath (Bath & North East Somerset)**

If breakfast is included the symbol appears after the number of rooms.

COLLYWESTON – Northants. – **502** S 26 – **see Stamford**

COLN ST ALDWYNS – Glos. – **503** O 28 – ✉ **Cirencester** 4 **D1**

London 101 m – Bristol 53 m – Gloucester 20 m – Oxford 28 m – Swindon 15 m

New Inn At Coln — VISA AE

✉ GL7 5AN – ✆ (01285) 750 651 – info@thenewinnatcoln.co.uk – Fax (01285) 750 657 – Closed 7-22 January

13 rm – £ 85/99 £ 120/180 – **Rest** – (Closed Sunday and Monday) (bar lunch) (booking essential for non-residents) Menu £ 38

◆ Pretty 16C Cotswold coaching inn. Low-beamed lounge. Colour co-ordinated furnishings. Bedrooms in main building or dovecote to rear. Rewarding views over fields or village. Intimate dining room with subdued lighting.

COLSTON BASSETT – Notts. – **502** R 25 – ✉ **Nottingham** 16 **B2**

London 129 m – Leicester 23 m – Lincoln 40 m – Nottingham 15 m – Sheffield 51 m

The Martins Arms — VISA AE

School Lane ✉ NG12 3FD – ✆ (01949) 81 361 – Fax (01949) 81 039 – Closed dinner 25-26 December and Sunday

Rest – Menu £ 17/23 – Carte £ 30/45

◆ Welcoming and well run; traditional décor includes Jacobean fireplace. Candlelit snug, formal dining room; menu mixes traditional with more modern - Stilton cheese features.

COLTISHALL – Norfolk – **504** Y 25 – **pop. 2 161** – ✉ **Norwich** *Great Britain* 15 **D1**

London 133 m – Norwich 8 m
Norfolk Broads★

Norfolk Mead — VISA AE

✉ NR12 7DN – ✆ (01603) 737 531 – info@norfolkmead.co.uk – Fax (01603) 737 521

14 rm – £ 85 £ 180 – **Rest** – (dinner only and Sunday lunch) Carte £ 27/33

◆ Restful 18C manor; gardens lead down to river Bure; also has a fishing lake. Rooms are individually colour themed: blue, terracotta. Room 7 has jacuzzi and lovely views. Candlelit restaurant overlooking the grounds.

ENGLAND

King's Head
26 Wroxham Rd, on B 1354 ✉ NR12 7EA – ✆ (01603) 737426 – Fax (01603) 266113 – Closed dinner 25-26 December and 1 January
Rest – Menu £10 (lunch) – Carte £19/32
◆ Fishing curios hang from the roof of this unassuming pub by the Bure. Modern menu served in the firelit bar or more formal dining room. Good choice blackboard menus.

COLTON – N. Yorks. – see Tadcaster

COLWALL – Herefordshire – see Great Malvern

COLYFORD – Devon – **503** K 31 – ✉ **Colyton** *Great Britain* 2 **D2**
London 168 m – Exeter 21 m – Taunton 30 m – Torquay 46 m – Yeovil 32 m
Colyton★ (Church★), N : 1 m. on B 3161 – Axmouth (≤ ★), S : 1 m. by A 3052 and B 3172

Swallows Eaves
✉ EX24 6QJ – ✆ (01297) 553184 – swallows-eaves@hotmail.com – Fax (01297) 553574 – March-October
8 rm – †£59/65 ††£98/110 – **Rest** – (dinner only) (residents only) Menu £28
◆ Pristine 1920s house with bright, spright rooms, some with views over the Axe Valley. Personally run by friendly, experienced couple. Listen out for birdsong on the marshes. Cooking for residents by the owner.

Red = Pleasant. Look for the red ✗ and symbols.

COMBE HAY – Bath & North East Somerset – see Bath

COMPTON ABBAS – Dorset – see Shaftesbury

CONEYTHORPE – North Yorkshire – **502** P 21 – see Knaresborough

CONGLETON – Ches. – **502** N 24 – **pop. 25 400** *Great Britain* 20 **B3**
London 183 m – Liverpool 50 m – Manchester 25 m – Sheffield 46 m – Stoke-on-Trent 13 m
Town Hall, High St ✆ (01260) 271095
Biddulph Rd, ✆ (01260) 273540.
Little Moreton Hall★★ **AC**, SW : 3 m. by A 34

Sandhole Farm without rest
Hulme Walfield, North : 2 ¼ m. on A 34 ✉ CW12 2JH – ✆ (01260) 224419 – veronica@sandholefarm.co.uk – Fax (01260) 224766
15 rm – †£60/65 ††£70/75
◆ Former farm with its stable block converted into comfy, well-equipped bedrooms with a rustic feel. Breakfast taken in the farmhouse's conservatory overlooking the countryside.

Pecks
Newcastle Rd, Moreton, South : 2 ¾ m. on A 34 ✉ CW12 4SB – ✆ (01260) 275161 – info@pecksrest.co.uk – Fax (01260) 299640 – Closed 25 December-2 January, Sunday dinner and Monday
Rest – Menu £16 (lunch) – Carte £21/27
◆ Airy, modish restaurant with jaunty yellow décor: well regarded locally. 5 or 7 course dinners served sharp at 8pm. Dishes are an interesting mix of modern and traditional.

ENGLAND

L'Endroit

70-72 Lawton St ✉ CW12 1RS – ✆ (01260) 299548 – Fax (01260) 299548 – Closed 2 weeks February, 1 week late June, 1 week late September, Saturday lunch, Sunday lunch May-September, Sunday dinner and Monday
Rest – French Carte £ 20/34
◆ Relaxing eatery, away from town centre, boasting the tangible feel of a bistro: vivid walls with foodie prints, chunky wood tables. Tasty French dishes with seasonal specials.

CONGRESBURY – North East Somerset – 503 L 29 3 B2

London 234 m – Bristol 21 m – Cardiff 90 m – Swansea 153 m

Cadbury House H. & Spa

Frost Hill, North : 1/2m. on B3133 ✉ BS49 5AD – ✆ (01934) 834343 – info@cadburyhouse.com – Fax (01934) 834390
72 rm – †£ 125/160 ††£ 125/350, ☕ £12.50
Rest *The Restaurant* – (dinner only) Menu £ 28 – Carte £ 28/39 **s**
Rest *The Lounge* – Carte £ 13/24 **s**
◆ 18C country house and 5 storey extension, plus impressive leisure club. Modern, stylish bedrooms with smart bathrooms; Executive rooms are larger with good northerly views. Large restaurant offers seasonal à la carte. The Lounge offers popular all day dining menu and has pleasant balcony terrace.

CONISTON – Cumbria – 502 K 20 – pop. 1 304 *Great Britain* 21 A2

London 285 m – Carlisle 55 m – Kendal 22 m – Lancaster 42 m
Ruskin Ave ✆ (015394) 41533, conistontic@lake-district.gov.uk
Coniston Water★ – Brantwood★ **AC**, SE : 2 m. on east side of Coniston Water. Hard Knott Pass★★, Wrynose Pass★★, NW : 10 m. by A 593 and minor road

Coniston Lodge without rest

Station Rd ✉ LA21 8HH – ✆ (015394) 41201 – info@coniston-lodge.com – Fax (015394) 41201
6 rm ☕ – †£ 69 ††£ 105
◆ Personally run hotel; Donald Campbell's Bluebird memorabilia adorns lounge. Home-made jams for sale - and for breakfast. Rooms named after tarns; some overlook garden.

at Torver Southwest : 2 ¼ m. on A 593 – ✉ Coniston

Old Rectory

Northeast : ¼ m. by A 593 ✉ LA21 8AX – ✆ (015394) 41353 – enquiries@theoldrectoryhotel.com
9 rm ☕ – †£ 48 ††£ 78 – **Rest** – (dinner only) (residents only) Menu £ 24 **s**
◆ Beneath the Coniston Old Man, close to Coniston Water stands this country house built in 1868 for the Rev Thomas Ellwood. Snug bedrooms afford panoramic views of landscape. Fine meadow vistas from conservatory style dining room.

CONSTABLE BURTON – N. Yorks. – 502 O 21 – see Leyburn

CONSTANTINE BAY – Cornwall – 503 E 32 – see Padstow

COOKHAM – Windsor & Maidenhead – 504 R 29 – pop. 5 304 – ✉ Maidenhead *Great Britain* 11 C3

London 32 m – High Wycombe 7 m – Oxford 31 m – Reading 16 m
to Marlow, Maidenhead and Windsor (Salter Bros. Ltd) (summer only)
Stanley Spencer Gallery★ **AC**

Manzano's

19-21 Station Hill Parade ✉ SL6 9BR – ✆ (01628) 525775 – closed Saturday lunch, Sunday and Bank Holidays
Rest – Spanish Menu £ 18/20 – Carte £ 27/36
◆ Popular, personally run neighbourhood restaurant on a busy parade. Warm, homely feel pervades. Frequently changing seasonal Spanish influenced menus with a classical base.

ENGLAND

The Ferry
Sutton Rd ✉ SL6 9SN – ☎ (01628) 525 123
Rest – Menu £ 25 – Carte £ 21/30
◆ Part 14C riverside inn with its own landing stage. Delightful decked dining terrace. Inside, characterful beams and sofas mix the modern and the rustic. Eclectic pub dishes.

COOKHAM DEAN – Windsor & Maidenhead *Great Britain* 11 C3

London 32 m – High Wycombe 7 m – Oxford 31 m – Reading 16 m
Windsor Castle★★★, Eton★★ and Windsor★, S : 5 m. by B 4447, A 4 (westbound) and A 308

The Inn on the Green with rm
The Old Cricket Common ✉ SL6 9NZ – ☎ (01628) 482 638 – reception@theinnonthegreen.com – Fax (01628) 487 474 – Closed first week January, Sunday dinner and Monday
9 rm – £ 100 ££ 120/150 – **Rest** – (booking essential) Carte £ 28/46
◆ Part timbered inn with delightful patio terrace. Rustic bar; two dining rooms and conservatory: modern British cooking. Individually furnished rooms in the inn or annex.

Look out for red symbols, indicating particularly pleasant establishments.

COPTHORNE – W. Sussex – 504 T 30 – see Crawley

CORBRIDGE – Northd. – 501 N 19 – pop. 2 800 *Great Britain* 24 A2

London 300 m – Hexham 3 m – Newcastle upon Tyne 18 m
Hill St ☎ (01434) 632815 (Easter-October)
Hadrian's Wall★★, N : 3 m. by A 68 – Corstopitum★ AC, NW : ½ m

Town Barns without rest
by Middle St and Hexham rd ✉ NE45 5HP – ☎ (01434) 633 345 – March-September
3 rm – £ 50 ££ 62
◆ Modern cottage-style house on edge of town enjoys views of the Tyne Valley. Spacious, comfortable guests' sitting room and well-furnished bedrooms.

Riggsacre without rest
Appletree Lane, by B 6321 (Aydon rd) ✉ NE45 5DN – ☎ (01434) 632 617 – atclive@supernet.com – closed Christmas and New Year
3 rm – £ 46/50 ££ 76/80
◆ Charming owners run an immaculate, well-priced guesthouse in a peaceful area. Mature gardens; communal breakfast room. Thoughtful extras enhance delightful, good sized rooms.

The Angel of Corbridge with rm
Main St ✉ NE45 5LA – ☎ (01434) 632 119 – Fax (01434) 633 796 – Closed Sunday dinner
5 rm – £ 60 ££ 85 – **Rest** – Carte £ 16/35
◆ 18C cream-washed village centre coaching inn. Wood-panelled lounge with leather Chesterfield. Tasty, Northumbrian dishes in bar or restaurant. Smart rooms with quality decor.

at Great Whittington North : 5 ½ m. by A 68 off B 6318 – ✉ Corbridge

Queens Head Inn
✉ NE19 2HP – ☎ (01434) 672 267 – Fax (01434) 672 267 – Closed 25 December
Rest – (closed Sunday dinner and Monday) Carte £ 17/30
◆ 17C coaching inn in sleepy village serving classic, regionally-influenced cooking. Characterful, timbered bar, open fire and stone walls. Friendly staff, informal atmosphere.

CORFE CASTLE – Dorset – 503 N 32 – ✉ Wareham 4 C3

London 129 m – Bournemouth 18 m – Weymouth 23 m
Castle★ (≤ ★★) AC

Mortons House

45 East St ✉ BH20 5EE – ☎ (01929) 480 988 – stay@mortonshouse.co.uk – Fax (01929) 480 820

18 rm – £ 75/154 £ 154/174 – 3 suites – **Rest** – Carte £ 25/50

◆ Elizabethan manor built in the shape of an "E" in Queen's honour. Wood panelled drawing room; range of bedrooms, some themed: the Victoria room has original Victorian bath. Colourful dining room with views over courtyard.

CORNHILL-ON-TWEED – Northd. – 501 N 17 *Scotland* 24 A1

London 345 m – Edinburgh 49 m – Newcastle upon Tyne 59 m
Ladykirk (Kirk o'Steil★), NE : 6 m. by A 698 and B 6470

Tillmouth Park

Northeast : 2½ m. on A 698 ✉ TD12 4UU – ☎ (01890) 882 255 – reception@tillmouthpark.f9.co.uk – Fax (01890) 882 540 – (closed for refurbishment until mid July)

14 rm – £ 55/95 £ 95/130

Rest – Menu £ 9/33 – Carte £ 27/43

Rest *The Library* – (bar lunch Monday-Saturday) Menu £ 9/33 – Carte £ 27/43

◆ In an area renowned for its fishing, a 19C country house in mature grounds and woodland. Inside one finds stained glass windows, grand staircases and antique furniture. Light meals in bistro. Large, panelled Library restaurant has good views of grounds.

Coach House

Crookham, East : 4 m. on A 697 ✉ TD12 4TD – ☎ (01890) 820 293 – stay@coachhousecrookham.com – Fax (01890) 820 284 – closed Christmas and New Year

10 rm – £ 39/49 £ 96 – **Rest** – (dinner only) (booking essential for non-residents) Menu £ 20

◆ Converted from a collection of farm buildings, including a 1680s dower house, and set around a courtyard. Recently modernised, comfortable rooms with character.

CORSCOMBE – Dorset – 503 L 31 – ✉ Dorchester 3 B3

London 153 m – Exeter 47 m – Taunton 30 m – Weymouth 24 m

The Fox Inn with rm

Northeast : ¾ m. on Halstock rd ✉ DT2 0NS – ☎ (01935) 891 330 – Fax (01935) 891 330 – closed 25 December

4 rm – £ 55 £ 100 – **Rest** – Carte £ 20/27

◆ Popular thatched inn with quaint interior: gingham tablecloths, beamed ceiling and conservatory. Light, modern cooking with fine fish dishes. Country style bedrooms.

CORSE LAWN – Worcs. – see Tewkesbury (Glos.)

CORSHAM – Wilts. – 504 N 29 – pop. 11 318 4 C2

London 107 m – Bristol 22 m – Chippenham 5 m

Heatherly Cottage without rest

Ladbrook Lane, Gastard, Southeast : 1¼ m. by B 3353 ✉ SN13 9PE – ☎ (01249) 701 402 – pandj@heatherly.plus.com – Fax (01249) 701 412 – March-October

3 rm – £ 64 £ 68/70

◆ Part 17C stone cottage set down a quiet country road close to small village. Three very good value rooms: spacious, individually furnished and with good facilities.

CORTON DENHAM – Somerset – see Sherborne

COSHAM – Portsmouth – 503 Q 31 – see Portsmouth and Southsea

COTEBROOK – Ches. – see Tarporley

COTTERED – Herts – 504 T 28 – pop. 1 788 12 B2

London 46 m – Luton 24 m – Cambridge 29 m – Watford 43 m

The Bull of Cottered

SG9 9QP – (01763) 281 243 – cordell39@btinternet.com

Rest – Carte £ 17/31

◆ Traditional, homely pub with flower baskets, polished horse brasses and log fires - a popular stop off point on way to Stansted Airport. Traditional menu offers eclectic mix.

COTTINGHAM – Kingston-upon-Hull – 502 S 22 – see Kingston-upon-Hull

COVENTRY – W. Mids. – 503 P 26 – pop. 303 475 *Great Britain* 19 D2

London 100 m – Birmingham 18 m – Bristol 96 m – Leicester 24 m – Nottingham 52 m

4 Priory Row (024) 7622 7264

Windmill Village Allesley Birmingham Rd, (024) 7640 4041 ;

Sphinx Sphinx Drive, (024) 7645 1361 .

City★ - Cathedral★★★ **AC** AV – Old Cathedral★ AV **B** – Museum of British Road Transport★ **AC** AV **M2**

Plan on next page

Brooklands Grange

Holyhead Rd, Northwest : 2½ m. on A 4114 CV5 8HX – (024) 7660 1601 – info@brooklands-grange.co.uk – Fax (024) 7660 1277 – Closed 26 December-3 January AY **e**

31 rm – £ 75/95 £ 95/120 – **Rest** – Menu £ 26 – Carte £ 28/39

◆ Part 16C yeoman's farmhouse with comfy, snug bar and neatly kept rooms furnished in dainty prints. Attentive service. On main route into city with good motorway connections. Victorian restaurant and conservatory.

at Shilton Northeast : 6 ¾ m. by A 4600 - BX - on B 4065 – Coventry

Barnacle Hall without rest

Shilton Lane, West : 1 m. by B 4029 following signs for garden centre CV7 9LH – (024) 7661 2629 – rose@barnaclehall.co.uk – Fax (024) 7661 2629 – closed 24 December-2 January

3 rm – £ 32/42 £ 70

◆ Interesting part 16C farmhouse in rural location. Westerly facing 18C stone façade; remainder 16/17C. Beamed rooms have countryside outlook and farmhouse style furnishings.

at Binley East : 3 ½ m. on A 428 - BY – Coventry

Coombe Abbey

Brinklow Rd, East : 2 m. following signs for Coombe Abbey Country Park (A 427) CV3 2AB – (024) 7645 0450 – reservations@combeabbey.com – Fax (024) 7663 5101 – Closed 25-26 December and 1 January

82 rm – £ 165/185 £ 215, £ 14.50 – 1 suite

Rest *Cloisters* – Menu £ 24/30 – Carte dinner £ 27/52

◆ A most individually styled 12C former Cistercian abbey in Capability Brown gardens. Strong medieval feel predominates: the staff are costumed, and the bedrooms are striking. Dining room boasts ornate ceiling and unusual raised, canopied tables.

COVENTRY

Street	Grid	No.
Bayley Lane	AV	3
Bishop St.	AV	5
Broadgate	AV	6
Burges (The)	AV	7
Central Six Retail Park Shopping	AV	
Corporation St.	AV	
Earl St	AV	10
Fairfax St.	AV	12
Far Gosford St.	AV	13
Gallagher Retail Park	BX	
Gosford St.	AV	15
Greyfriars Lane	AV	16
Hales St.	AV	17
Hearsall Lane	AY	21
High St	AV	22
Ironmonger Rd	AV	23
Jordan Well	AV	26
Leicester Row	AV	29
Light Lane	AV	30
Little Park St	AV	31
Precincts Shopping	AV	
Primrose Hill St	AV	34
Queen Victoria Rd	AV	35
St Johns (Ringway)	AV	38
St Nicholas (Ringway)	AV	39
Swanswell (Ringway)	AV	40
Trinity St	AV	41
Upper Well St	AV	43
Vecqueray St.	AV	45
Victoria St	AV	46
Warwick Rd.	AV	49
White Friars (Ringway)	AV	54
White St	AV	51
Windsor St	AV	52

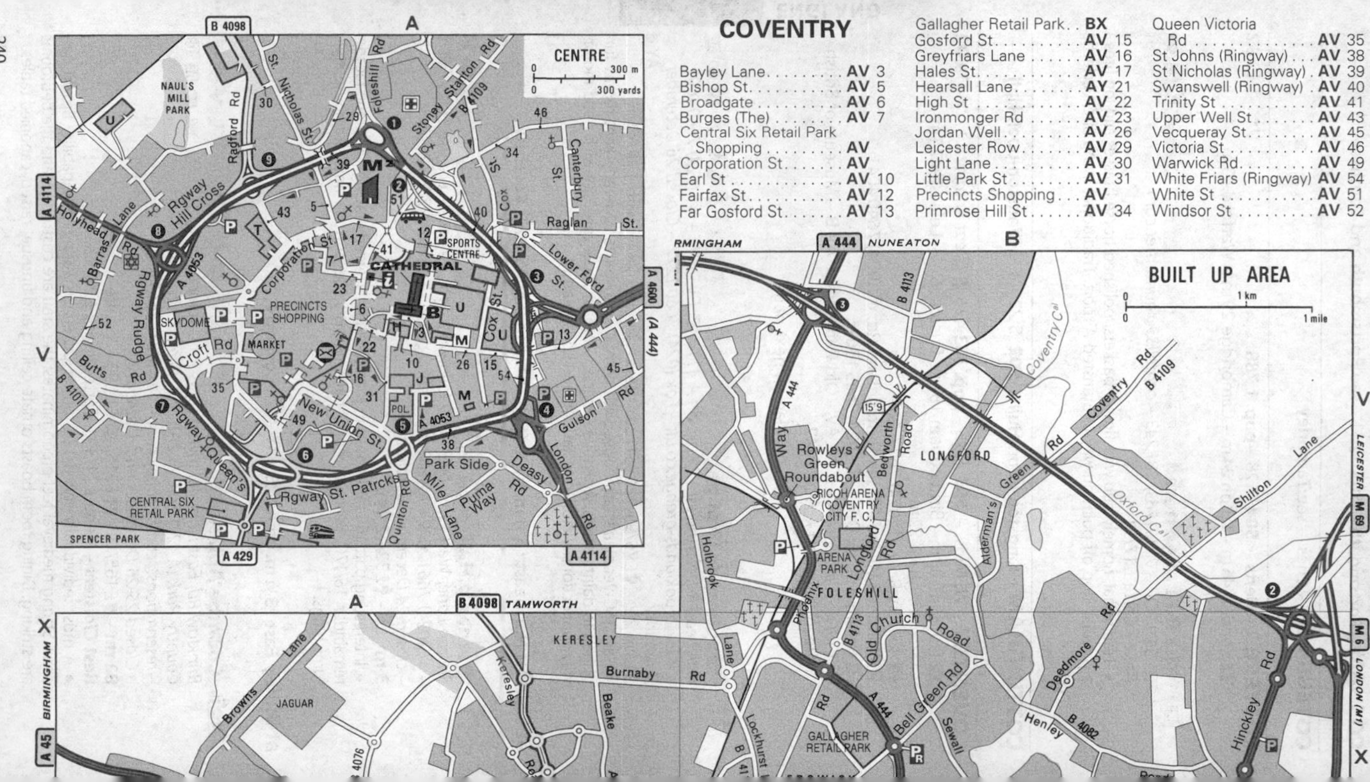

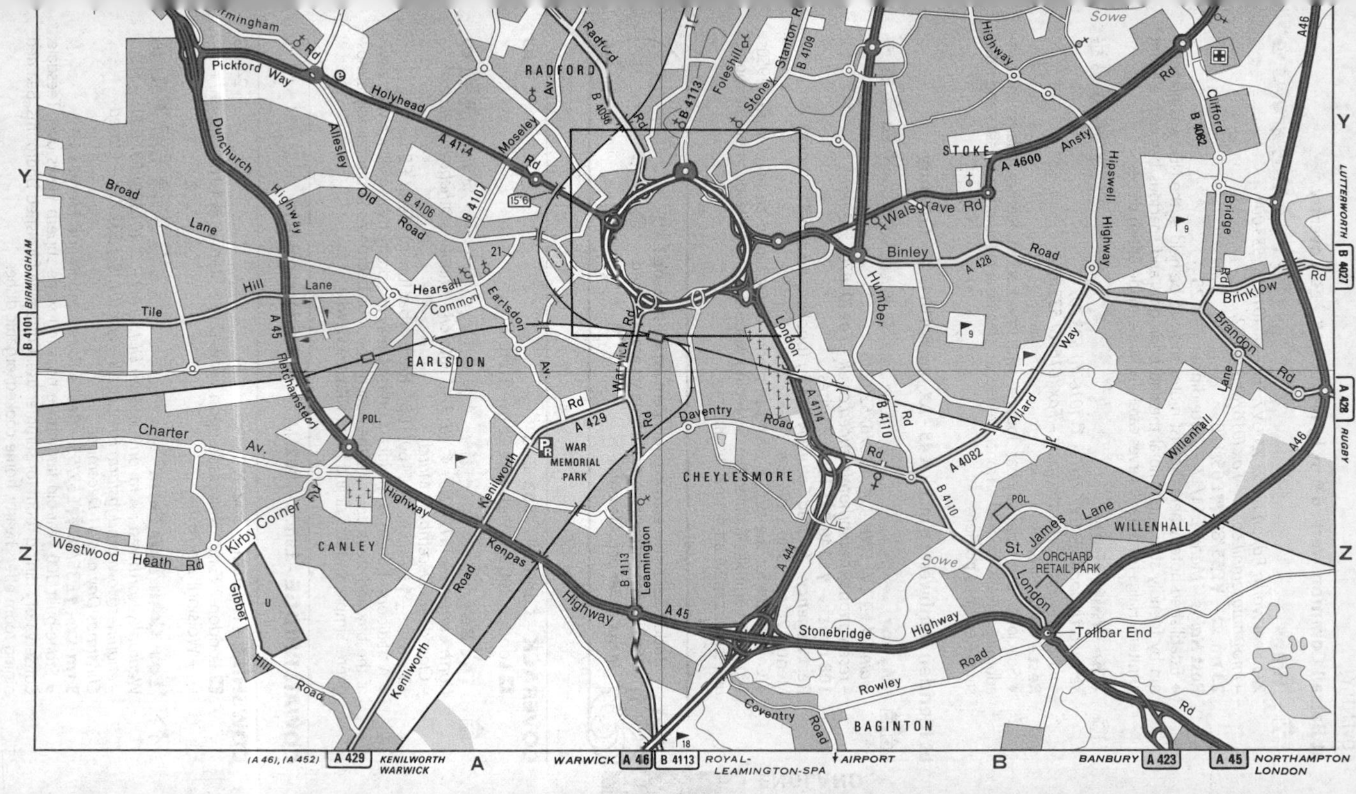

Y
B 4101
BIRMINGHAM
Birmingham Rd
Pickford Way
Holyhead
A 4114
Moseley
Rd
RADFORD
Av.
Radford Rd
B 4098
B 4113
Foleshill
Stoney
Stanton R
B 4109
Dunchurch
Highway
Allesley
Old
Road
B 4106
B 4107
Broad
Lane
Hill
Lane
Tile
Hearsall
Common
Earlsdon
Av.
A 45
Fletchamstead
EARLSDON
Warwick
Rd
A 429
WAR MEMORIAL PARK
Kenilworth
Road
Kenpas
Highway
Charter
Av.
POL.
Kirby Corner
Rd
CANLEY
Westwood
Heath
Gibbet
Hill
Road
Daventry
Road
CHEYLESMORE
Leamington
B 4113
A 45
A 444
London
A 4114
Walsgrave Rd
Binley
Road
A 428
Humber
Rd
B 4110
STOKE
A 4600
Ansty
Hipswell
Highway
Allard
Way
A 4082
Brinklow
Brandon
Willenhall
Lane
Clifford
Bridge
B 4082
A46
POL.
St. James
Lane
WILLENHALL
ORCHARD RETAIL PARK
Sowe
Stonebridge
Highway
Rowley
Coventry
BAGINTON
Tollbar End
LUTTERWORTH
B 4027
A 428
RUGBY
Z
(A 46), (A 452)
A 429
KENILWORTH
WARWICK
A
WARWICK
A 46
B 4113
ROYAL-
LEAMINGTON-SPA
AIRPORT
B
BANBURY
A 423
A 45
NORTHAMPTON
LONDON

at Balsall Common West : 6 ¾ m. by B 4101 - AY – ✉ Coventry

Haigs
273 Kenilworth Rd, on A 452 ✉ CV7 7EL – ☎ (01676) 533 004
– info@haigsemail.co.uk – Fax (01676) 535 132
23 rm – †£ 55/88 ††£ 65/120
Rest *Haigs* – Menu £ 11/17 – Carte dinner £ 18/25
◆ Established hotel where the first motor show to be held at the NEC was planned; run by friendly staff. Light floral themed bedrooms and spacious bar with elegant furniture. Haigs restaurant serves carefully home-made British dishes.

The White Horse
Kenilworth Road ✉ CV7 7DT – ☎ (01676) 533 207
– info@thewhitehorseatbc.co.uk – Fax (01676) 532 827
Rest – Carte £ 16/28
◆ Spacious, contemporary bar lounge with low backed leather chairs and art-adorned walls. Decked front terrace. Universal menu offers classics and rotisserie. Generous portions.

at Meriden Northwest : 6 m. by A 45 - AX - on B 4104 – ✉ Coventry

Manor
rest,
Main Rd ✉ CV7 7NH – ☎ (01676) 522 735
– reservations@manorhotelmeriden.co.uk – Fax (01676) 522 186
108 rm – †£ 140 ††£ 150 – 2 suites
Rest *Regency* – (closed Saturday lunch) (booking essential at lunch)
Menu £ 28 **s** – Carte £ 25/36 **s**
◆ Convenient for the NEC, a Georgian manor converted to an hotel in the 1950s. Triumph motorbike themed bar. Sweeping wooden staircase leads to sizable rooms, quieter at rear. Smart, formal restaurant.

ENGLAND

Undecided between two equivalent establishments?
Within each category, establishments are classified
in our order of preference.

COVERACK – Cornwall – 503 E 33 1 A3
London 300 m – Penzance 25 m – Truro 27 m

The Bay
North Corner ✉ TR12 6TF – ☎ (01326) 280 464 – enquiries@thebayhotel.co.uk
– Closed Mid December - March
13 rm – †£ 79/111 ††£ 160/180 – **Rest** – (bar lunch) Menu £ 25
◆ A traditional hotel run by a local Cornish family in a pretty fishing village with views of the bay and steps down to the beach. Spacious bedrooms and a homely atmosphere. Simple, spotless dining room with sea views.

COWAN BRIDGE – Lancs. – 502 M 21 – see Kirkby Lonsdale

COWSHILL – Durham – 502 N 19 24 A3
London 295 m – Newcastle upon Tyne 42 m – Stanhope 10 m
– Wolsingham 16 m

Low Cornriggs Farm
Weardale, Northwest : ¾ m. on A 689 ✉ DL13 1AQ – ☎ (01388) 537 600
– enquiries@lowcornriggsfarm.fsnet.co.uk – Fax (01388) 537 777 – Closed Christmas Day and 31 December
3 rm – †£ 35/38 ††£ 52/55 – **Rest** – (by arrangement) Menu £ 17
◆ Stone-built 300 year-old farmhouse boasting some superb views over Teesdale. Conservatory dining room for summer use. Cosy, pine-furnished bedrooms. Beamed dining room offers hearty, home-cooked, organic dishes.

CRACKINGTON HAVEN – Cornwall – 503 G 31 – ✉ Bude 1 B2

London 262 m – Bude 11 m – Plymouth 44 m – Truro 42 m
Poundstock★ (≤ ★★, church★, guildhouse★), NE : 5½ m. by A 39 – Jacobstow (Church★), E : 3½ m

Manor Farm without rest
Southeast : 1 ¼ m. by Boscastle rd taking left turn onto Church Park Rd after 1.1 m. then taking first right onto unmarked lane ✉ EX23 0JW – ☎ (01840) 230 304 – closed 25 December
3 rm – †£ 50 ††£ 80
◆ Appears in the Domesday Book and belonged to William the Conqueror's half brother. A lovely manor in beautifully manicured grounds. Affable owner and comfortable rooms.

CRANBROOK – Kent – 504 V 30 – pop. 4 225 *Great Britain* 8 B2

London 53 m – Hastings 19 m – Maidstone 15 m
Vestry Hall, Stone St ☎ (01580) 712538 (summer only)
Sissinghurst Castle★ AC, NE : 2½ m. by A 229 and A 262

George
Stone St ✉ TN17 3HE – ☎ (01580) 713 348 – reservations@thegeorgehotelkent.co.uk – Fax (01580) 715 532 – Closed 25-26 December
12 rm – †£ 70/80 ††£ 90/145 – **Rest** – Carte £ 22/30
◆ Part 14C former coaching inn blends period features with the more modern. Individually-styled bedrooms. Modern British menu served in Brasserie or more formal restaurant.

Cloth Hall Oast (heated)
Coursehorn Lane, East : 1 m. by Tenterden rd ✉ TN17 3NR – ☎ (01580) 712 220 – clothhalloast@aol.com – Fax (01580) 712 220 – closed Christmas
3 rm – †£ 60/95 ††£ 120/130 – **Rest** – (by arrangement, communal dining) Menu £ 26
◆ Run by former owner of Old Cloth Hall, with well-tended garden, rhododendrons lining the drive. Peaceful spot. Charming sitting room. Immaculate bedrooms exude personal style.

Apicius (Tim Johnson)
23 Stone St ✉ TN17 3HE – ☎ (01580) 714 666 – Closed 2 weeks Christmas-New Year, 2 weeks August, Sunday dinner, Monday, Tuesday and Saturday lunch
Rest – Menu £ 24/30
Spec. Roast scallop and bacon brochette, vanilla linguini. Pan-fried sea bass, leeks, cep and fennel sauce. Pear flan, crushed macaroons, crème Anglaise
◆ Named after Roman author of world's first cookbook. Cosy interior mixes original features with modern style. Passionate, well balanced, precise cooking uses local ingredients.

at Sissinghurst Northeast : 1 ¾ m. by B 2189 on A 262 – ✉ Cranbrook

Rankins
The Street, on A 262 ✉ TN17 2JH – ☎ (01580) 713 964 – rankins@btconnect.com – Closed Sunday dinner, Monday, Tuesday and Bank Holidays
Rest – (dinner only and Sunday lunch) (booking essential) Menu £ 27/33
◆ A friendly, well-established, family run bistro-style restaurant, not far from Sissinghurst Castle. The set menu has an international focus.

CRANTOCK – Cornwall – 503 E 32 – see Newquay

Your opinions are important to us:
please write and let us know about your discoveries and experiences – good and bad!

ENGLAND

CRAWLEY - W. Sussex - **504** T 30 - pop. 100 547 **7 D2**

London 33 m - Brighton 21 m - Lewes 23 m - Royal Tunbridge Wells 23 m
County Mall Shopping Centre ✆ (01293) 846968, vip@countymall.co.uk
Cottesmore Pease Pottage Buchan Hill, ✆ (01293) 528 256 ; Tilgate Forest Tilgate Titmus Drive, ✆ (01293) 530 103 ; Gatwick Manor Lowfield Heath London Rd, ✆ (01293) 538 587 ; Pease Pottage Horsham Rd, ✆ (01293) 521 706 .

Plan of enlarged Area : see Gatwick Z

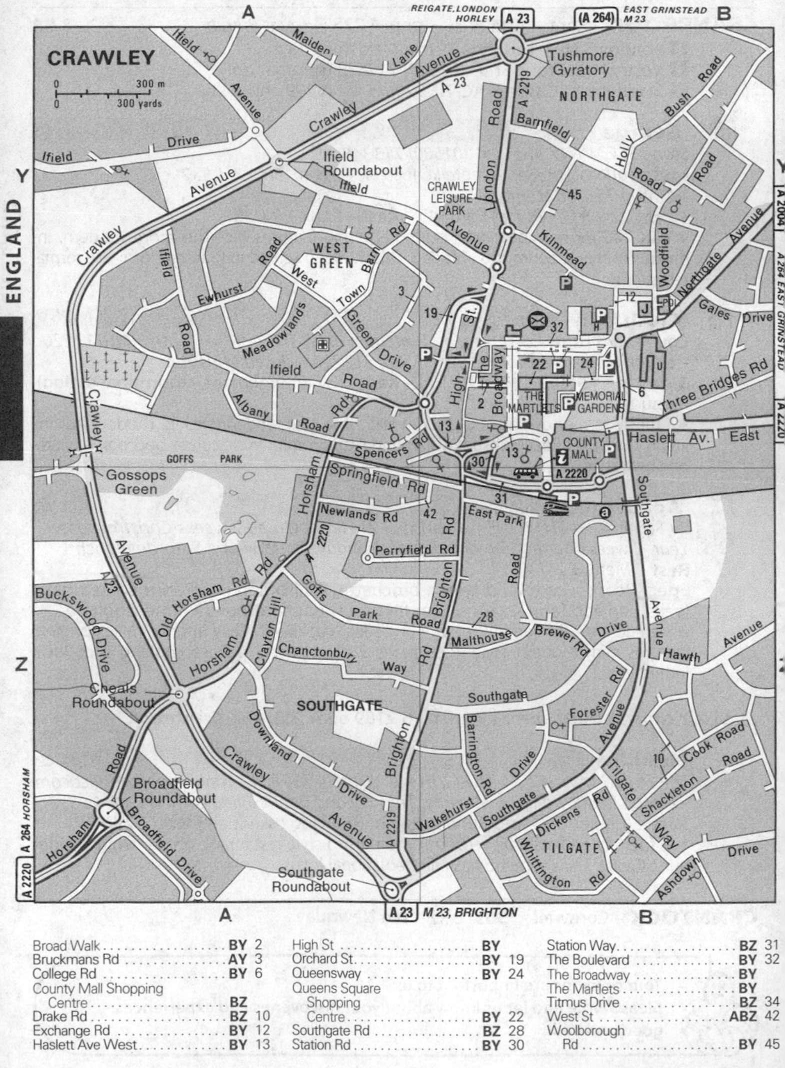

Arora International rm,

Southgate Ave, Southgate ✉ RH10 6LW – ✆ (01293) 530 000 – gatwickreservations@arorainternational.com – Fax (01293) 517 715 BZ **a**

431 rm – †£ 118/165 ††£ 118/165, ☕ £ 11.95 – 1 suite

Rest *mono brasserie* – Menu £ 17 (lunch) – Carte £ 20/31

◆ Futuristically designed, business oriented hotel with airport rail access. Calming water features and striking open-plan atrium. Impressive leisure facilities and bedrooms. Easy-going brasserie offers tried-and-tested menus.

CRAYKE – **N. Yorks.** – **see Easingwold**

CRAY'S POND – **Oxon.** – **see Goring**

CREWE – **Ches.** – **502** M 24 – **pop. 67 683** 20 **B3**

London 174 m – Chester 24 m – Liverpool 49 m – Manchester 36 m – Stoke-on-Trent 15 m

Queen's Park Queen's Park Drive, ✆ (01270) 662 378 ;

Haslington Fields Rd, ✆ (01270) 584 227 .

Crewe Hall rm,

Weston Road, Southeast : 1 ¾ m. on A 5020 ✉ CW1 6UZ – ✆ (01270) 253 333 – crewehall@qhotels.co.uk – Fax (01270) 253 322

60 rm ☕ – †£ 89/159 ††£ 99/169 – 5 suites

Rest *Ilrá Brasserie* – ✆ (01270) 259 319 (closed Sunday lunch) Menu £ 17 (lunch) **s** – Carte £ 25/36 **s**

◆ Impressive 17C mansion with formal gardens. Victorian décor featuring alabaster, marble and stained glass. Rooms offer luxurious comfort. Popular modern menu in the chic Brasserie.

The ✿ award is the crème de la crème.
This is awarded to restaurants
which are really worth travelling miles for!

CROFT-ON-TEES – **Durham** – **502** P 20 – **see Darlington**

CROMER – **Norfolk** – **504** X 25 – **pop. 8 836** 15 **D1**

London 132 m – Norwich 23 m

Prince of Wales Rd ✆ (01263) 512497

Royal Cromer Overstrand Rd, ✆ (01263) 512 884 .

at Overstrand Southeast : 2 ½ m. by B 1159 – ✉ Cromer

Sea Marge

16 High St ✉ NR27 0AB – ✆ (01263) 579579 – info@mackenziehotels.com – Fax (01263) 579 524

25 rm ☕ – †£ 87 ††£ 134 – **Rest** – (bar lunch) Carte £ 20/31

◆ Mock Elizabethan house built in 1908; gardens lead down to beach. Interiors feature Delft tiles alongside panelled bar, minstrel gallery. Most bedrooms have sea views. Restaurant offers views from a large leaded window.

at Northrepps Southeast : 3 m. by A 149 and Northrepps rd – ✉ Cromer

Shrublands Farm without rest

✉ NR27 0AA – ✆ (01263) 579 297 – youngman@farming.co.uk – Fax (01263) 579 297

3 rm ☕ – †£ 40 ††£ 64

◆ Whitewashed part 18C arable farm in wooded gardens. Conservatory, lounge, neat rooms with cut flowers and garden views. Guests are encouraged to explore the farm.

ENGLAND

CROSTHWAITE – Cumbria – 502 L 21 – see Kendal

CROYDE – Devon – 503 H 30 – ✉ Braunton 2 C1

London 232 m – Barnstaple 10 m – Exeter 50 m – Taunton 61 m

Whiteleaf

Hobbs Hill ✉ EX33 1PN – ☎ (01271) 890 266 – closed 24-27 December
5 rm – †£ 50/60 ††£ 70/90 – **Rest** – (by arrangement) Carte £ 22/30

◆ Homely guesthouse close to North Devon and Somerset coastal path; views of Baggy Point, Lundy Island. Co-ordinated accommodation with mini-bars: choose the four-poster room. Restaurant looks out onto garden.

CRUDWELL – Wilts. – 503 N 29 – see Malmesbury

CUCKFIELD – W. Sussex – 504 T 30 – pop. 2 879 7 D2

London 40 m – Brighton 15 m

Ockenden Manor

Ockenden Lane ✉ RH17 5LD – ☎ (01444) 416 111
– reservations@ockenden-manor.com – Fax (01444) 415 549
19 rm – †£ 110/120 ††£ 360 – 3 suites – **Rest** – (booking essential at lunch) Menu £ 26 (lunch) – Carte £ 49/68

Spec. Roast wood pigeon, apple beignets, foie gras and confit beetroot. Saddle of lamb, sweetbreads, asparagus, tomato confit and fondue. Chocolate délice, strawberry sorbet.

◆ Secluded part 16C manor; heritage is on display in antique furnished bedrooms, many named after previous owners. Ideal for golfers, historians and the romantic. Wood panelled dining room offers some of Sussex's finest cooking.

ENGLAND

CUDDINGTON – Bucks. – 503 M 24 *Great Britain* 11 C2

London 48 m – Aylesbury 6 m – Oxford 17 m

Waddesdon Manor★★ AC, NE : 6 m. via Cuddington Hill, Cannon's Hill, Waddesdon Hill and A 41

The Crown

Aylesbury Rd ✉ HP18 0BB – ☎ (01844) 292 222
– david@thecrowncuddington.co.uk – Closed 25 December and Sunday dinner
Rest – Menu £ 17 – Carte £ 22/28

◆ Thatched 16C pub with traditional décor, low beamed ceilings and huge inglenooks featuring beehive chimneys. Tasty, modern dishes made with an eclectic range of ingredients.

CULLINGWORTH – W. Yorks. – 502 O 22 – see Haworth

CUTNALL GREEN – Worcs. – 503 N 27 – see Droitwich Spa

DALTON – N. Yorks. – 502 O 20 – see Richmond

DALTON-IN-FURNESS – Cumbria – 502 K 21 – pop. 8 057 21 A3

London 283 m – Barrow-in-Furness 3 m – Kendal 30 m – Lancaster 41 m

The Dunnerholme Askham-in-Furness Duddon Rd, ☎ (01229) 462 675 .

Clarence House Country

Skelgate, North : ½ m. on Askam rd ✉ LA15 8BQ – ☎ (01229) 462 508
– clarencehsehotel@aol.com – Fax (01229) 467 177 – closed 25-26 December
18 rm – †£ 82 ††£ 110/130
Rest *The Orangery* – Menu £ 16 (lunch) – Carte £ 28/40

◆ Welcoming hotel with spacious, comfortable bedrooms in a distinctive 19C building. Features a conservatory sitting room and fine period tiling in the entrance hall. Dine in a most attractive conservatory overlooking gardens.

Park Cottage without rest

Park, North : 2 m. by Askam rd off Romney Park Rd turning left after 1 m. onto unmarked rd ✉ LA15 8JZ – ✆ (01229) 462 850 – joan@parkcottagedalton.co.uk – closed January-12 February

3 rm – †£ 40/45 ††£ 60/64

◆ Quaint little 18C house hidden away in four wooded acres. Cosy, comfortable bedrooms overlook garden and lake - as does the bird watching room. Rooms 1 and 3 are the largest.

DANEHILL – E. Sussex Great Britain 8 A2

London 53 m – Brighton 21 m – East Grinstead 7 m

Sheffield Park Garden★, S : 3 m. on A 275

Coach & Horses 

School Lane, Northeast : ¾ m. on Chelwood Common rd ✉ RH17 7JF – ✆ (01825) 740 369 – coachandhorses@danehill.biz – Fax (01825) 740 369 – Closed 25- 26 December, 1 January and Sunday dinner

Rest – Carte £ 20/26

◆ An atmospheric 'locals' bar leads to two separate dining areas: one is a converted beamed stable. Modern menus have a distinctly French base and fine dining style.

The red symbol?
This denotes the very essence of peace
– only the sound of birdsong first thing in the morning …

ENGLAND

DARESBURY – Warrington – 502 M 23 – see Warrington

DARLEY – N. Yorks 22 B2

London 217 m – Harrogate 8 m – Ripon 16 m

Cold Cotes 

Cold Cotes Rd, Felliscliffe, South : 2 m. by Kettlesing rd, going straight over crossroads and on Harrogate rd ✉ HG3 2LW – ✆ (01423) 770 937 – info@coldcotes.com – Fax (01423) 779 284 – restricted opening in January

5 rm – †£ 70 ††£ 80/90 – **Rest** – (by arrangement) Menu £ 20 **s**

◆ Victorian farmhouse in five acres of lovely gardens. Cosy lounge with open fire. Communal breakfasts overlooking grounds. Extra touches adorn the pleasant, well-priced rooms. Victorian farmhouse in five acres of lovely gardens. Cosy lounge with open fire. Communal breakfasts overlooking grounds. Extra touches adorn the pleasant, well-priced rooms.

DARLEY ABBEY – Derbs. – 502 P 25 – see Derby

DARLINGTON – Darlington – 502 P 20 – pop. 86 082 22 B1

London 251 m – Leeds 61 m – Middlesbrough 14 m – Newcastle upon Tyne 35 m

Teesside Airport : ✆ (01325) 332811, E : 6 m. by A 67

13 Horsemarket ✆ (01325) 388666

Blackwell Grange Briar Close, ✆ (01325) 464 458 ;

Stressholme Snipe Lane, ✆ (01325) 461 002.

at Aycliffe North : 5½ m. on A 167 – ✉ Darlington

The County

13 The Green ✉ DL5 6LX – ✆ (01325) 312 273 – Closed 25-26 December

Rest – (closed Sunday) (booking essential) Menu £ 18 – Carte £ 26/32

◆ A village pub, overlooking the green, with minimalist décor and a busy atmosphere. Tasty, balanced modern dishes. Seasonally inspired menus of modern British cooking.

at Croft-on-Tees South : 3 ½ m. on A 167 – ✉ Darlington

Clow Beck House
Monk End Farm, West : ¾ m. by A 167 off Barton rd ✉ DL2 2SW – ✆ (01325) 721 075 – heather@clowbeckhouse.co.uk – Fax (01325) 720 419 – closed 24 December-2 January
13 rm – ♦£ 80 ♦♦£ 130 –
Rest – (dinner only) (residents only) Carte £ 25/38 **s**
◆ Collection of stone houses styled on an old farm building. The residence has a friendly, homely atmosphere. Spacious rooms with individual character. Tasty, home-cooked meals.

at Headlam Northwest : 8 m. by A 67 – ✉ Gainford

Headlam Hall
✉ DL2 3HA – ✆ (01325) 730 238 – admin@headlamhall.co.uk – Fax (01325) 730 790 – closed 25-26 December
40 rm – ♦£ 85 ♦♦£ 135 – 1 suite –
Rest – Menu £ 14 (lunch) – Carte £ 24/35 **s**
◆ Part Georgian, part Jacobean manor house in delightful, secluded countryside with charming walled gardens. Period interior furnishings and antiques. Good leisure facilities. Country house restaurant in four distinctively decorated rooms.

ENGLAND

at Redworth Northwest : 7 m. by A 68 on A 6072 – ✉ Bishop Auckland

Redworth Hall
✉ DL5 6NL – ✆ (01388) 770 600 – redworthhall@paramount-hotels.co.uk – Fax (01388) 770 654
135 rm – ♦£ 69/150 ♦♦£ 69/250, £ 13.95 – 4 suites
Rest ***The Restaurant*** – Menu £ 25 – Carte £ 18/46 **s**
◆ 17C manor house of Elizabethan origins with a tranquil ambience. Original features include a period banqueting hall. Comfortable, modern bedrooms. Good leisure. Conservatory restaurant has light, open atmosphere.

Look out for red symbols, indicating particularly pleasant establishments.

DARTFORD – Kent – 504 U 29 – pop. 56 818 8 B1

London 20 m – Hastings 51 m – Maidstone 22 m
Access Dartford Tunnel and Bridge (toll)

at Wilmington Southwest : 1 ½ m. A 225 on B 258 – ✉ Dartford

Rowhill Grange
Southwest : 2 m. on Hextable rd (B 258) ✉ DA2 7QH – ✆ (01322) 615 136 – admin@rowhillgrange.com – Fax (01322) 615 137
37 rm – ♦£ 175/260 ♦♦£ 200/370 – 1 suite
Rest ***Truffles*** – (Closed Saturday lunch) Menu £ 20/35 – Carte £ 35/46
Rest ***Brasserie*** – Carte £ 22/28
◆ Extended 19C thatched house set in pretty, nine-acre gardens. Bold-coloured rooms with teak beds, eight in the converted clockhouse. Smart, up-to-date leisure club. Kentish ingredients to fore in modern Truffles. Flag-floored Brasserie next to Leisure.

DARTMOUTH – Devon – 503 J 32 – pop. 5 512 2 C3

London 236 m – Exeter 36 m – Plymouth 35 m
The Engine House, Mayor's Ave ✆ (01803) 834224, enquire@dartmouth-tourism.org.uk
Town★★ (≤ ★) - Old Town - Butterwalk★ - Dartmouth Castle (≤ ★★★) AC
Start Point (≤ ★), S : 13 m. (including 1 m. on foot)

Dart Marina Dart Marina, rm, rest,
Sandquay ✉ TQ6 9PH – ✆ (01803) 832580
– reservations@dartmarina.com – Fax (01803) 835040
47 rm – £110/146 £200/245 – 2 suites
Rest *River Restaurant* – (dinner only) Menu £29
Rest *Wildfire* – Carte £26/37
◆ Lovely location with excellent views over the Dart Marina. The hotel has smart, comfy bedrooms, many with balconies. Welcoming, bright, modern public areas. Stylish River Restaurant; terrace overlooks river. Modern, informal Wildfire offers eclectic menus.

Royal Castle
11 The Quay ✉ TQ6 9PS – ✆ (01803) 833033 – enquiry@royalcastle.co.uk
– Fax (01803) 835445
25 rm – £90/95 £175/220 – **Rest** – Carte £24/35 **s**
◆ Harbour views and 18C origins enhance this smart hotel with its cosy bar and open log fires. Each of the comfortable rooms is individually styled, some boast four-poster beds. Harbour-facing restaurant particularly proud of sourcing fresh fish.

Brown's Hotel
27-29 Victoria Rd ✉ TQ6 9RT – ✆ (01803) 832572
– enquiries@brownshoteldartmouth.co.uk
– Closed January and 23-28 December
10 rm – £65/85 £175 – **Rest** – Tapas (dinner only Thursday-Saturday) Carte £17/33
◆ Georgian charm, in a personally run hotel, close to the harbour, with a chic modern townhouse style. Bedrooms are individually appointed with clean modern lines. Informal tapas-style dining; great original art.

New Angel Rooms
51 Victoria Rd ✉ TQ6 9RT – ✆ (01803) 839425
– reservations@thenewangel.co.uk – Fax (01803) 839567 – Closed January
6 rm – £120/135 £140/165
Rest *The New Angel* – see restaurant listing
◆ Townhouse tucked away from quayside towards rear of town. Good quality breakfasts amongst oak wood and rattan. Stylish guests' lounge; rooms a mix of modish and antique.

Broome Court without rest
Broomhill, West : 2 m. by A 3122 and Venn Lane ✉ TQ6 0LD
– ✆ (01803) 834275 – boughtontml@aol.com
– Fax (01803) 833260
3 rm – £55/65 £100/150
◆ Pretty house in a stunning, secluded location. Two sitting rooms: one for winter, one for summer. Breakfast "en famille" in huge kitchen, complete with Aga. Cottagey bedrooms.

The New Angel (John Burton-Race) Dart Estuary,
2 South Embankment ✉ TQ6 9BH – ✆ (01803) 839425
– reservations@thenewangel.co.uk – Fax (01803) 839567 – Closed January, dinner 25-26 December, Sunday dinner and Monday except Bank Holidays
Rest – (booking essential) Menu £30 (lunch) – Carte £35/46
Spec. Tortellini of crab with a mussel butter sauce. Best end of lamb, herb crust, glazed shallot and tomato juice. Nougat glacé with passion fruit granita and red fruit.
◆ Busy, modern restaurant with open kitchen; first floor is quieter, with the best views over the Dart Estuary. Classically-based cooking concentrates on quality local produce.

at Kingswear East : via lower ferry – ✉ Dartmouth

Nonsuch House Dartmouth Castle and Warfleet,
Church Hill, from lower ferry take first right onto Church Hill before Steam Packet Inn ✉ TQ6 0BX – ✆ (01803) 752829 – enquiries@nonsuch-house.co.uk
– Fax (01803) 752357
4 rm – £75/110 £100/135 – **Rest** – (closed Tuesday, Wednesday and Saturday) (dinner only) (residents only, set menu only, unlicensed) Menu £30 **s**
◆ Charming, personably run Edwardian house stunningly sited above the river town. Smart conservatory terrace and large, well appointed bedrooms. Good, homely breakfasts.

ENGLAND

at Strete Southwest : 4 m. on A 379 – ✉ Dartmouth

The Kings Arms

Dartmouth Rd ✉ TQ6 0RW – ✆ (01803) 770 377 – closed Sunday dinner and Monday November-Easter

Rest – Seafood Carte £ 23/33

◆ Mid-18C pub with rear terrace that looks to sea. Smart restaurant is where serious, accomplished cooking takes place: local, seasonal produce well utilised on modern menus.

at Blackawton West : 6 m. by B 3122

Woodside Cottage without rest

Northeast : ½ m. on Dartmouth rd ✉ TQ9 7BL – ✆ (01803) 898 164 – Fax (0870) 686 417

3 rm – †£ 45 ††£ 75/85

◆ Pleasant former farmhouse/cottage in pretty rural setting. Attractive landscaped gardens lead into well-furnished sitting room and conservatory. Simple, bright and airy rooms.

ENGLAND

The Normandy Arms

Chapel St ✉ TQ9 7BN – ✆ (01803) 712 884 – peter.alford@btconnect.com – Fax (01830) 712 374 – closed 1 week January, 1 week September, 25 December and Monday

Rest – (closed Sunday dinner November - May) (dinner only lunch Friday-Sunday) Carte £ 25/33

◆ Refurbished village pub, popular with locals and simple in style with comfy leather seats and two distinct dining areas. Straightforward cooking, homemade using local produce.

DARWEN – Blackburn – 502 M 22 — 20 B2

London 222 m – Blackburn 5 m – Blackpool 34 m – Leeds 59 m – Liverpool 43 m – Manchester 24 m

Winter Hill, ✆ (01254) 701 287 .

Astley Bank

Bolton Rd, South : ¾ m. on A 666 ✉ BB3 2QB – ✆ (01254) 777 700 – sales@astleybank.co.uk – Fax (01254) 777 707 – Closed 25-27 December and 1 January

37 rm – †£ 84/94 ††£ 94/134 –

Rest – Menu £ 18/25 – Carte £ 23/35

◆ Part Georgian, part Victorian privately owned hotel in elevated position above town. Varied rooms overlook the pleasant gardens. Well-equipped conference rooms. Conservatory dining is elegantly semi-split.

DATCHWORTH – Herts. – 504 T 28 — 12 B2

London 31 m – Luton 15 m – Stevenage 6 m

Coltsfoot Country Retreat

Coltsfoot Lane, Bulls Green, South : ¾ m. by Bramfield Rd ✉ SG3 6SB – ✆ (01438) 212 800 – info@coltsfoot.com – Fax (01438) 212 840 – closed 25, 26 and 31 December

15 rm – †£ 115 ††£ 160 –

Rest – (closed Sunday) (dinner only) (booking essential) Carte £ 29/37

◆ Stylish hotel, once a working farm, in 40 rural acres. Lounge bar with log-burning stove. Highly individual rooms around courtyard have vaulted ceilings and rich furnishings. Main barn houses restaurant: concise modern menus employ good seasonal produce.

The Tilbury

Watton Rd ✉ SG3 6TB – ✆ (01438) 815 550 – info@thetilbury.co.uk – Fax (01438) 718 340 – closed Monday

Rest – Menu £ 11 (lunch) – Carte £ 21/32

◆ Red brick pub with flower baskets, terrace, garden and fresh, contemporary interior. Modern European menu offers honest, locally sourced food. Cookery school spans the globe.

DAVENTRY – Northants. – 504 Q 27 – pop. 21 731 16 B3

London 79 m – Coventry 23 m – Leicester 31 m – Northampton 13 m – Oxford 46 m

Moot Hall, Market Sq ✆ (01327) 300277

Norton Rd, ✆ (01327) 702 829 ;

Hellidon Lakes H. & C.C. Hellidon, ✆ (01327) 62 550 ;

Staverton Park Staverton, ✆ (01327) 302 000.

Fawsley Hall

Fawsley, South : 6½ m. by A 45 off A 361 ✉ NN11 3BA – ✆ (01327) 892 000 – reservations@fawsleyhall.com – Fax (01327) 892 001

47 rm – †£ 159/169 ††£ 289/319, ☕ £ 8 – 5 suites

Rest *The Knightley* – (booking essential at lunch Monday-Saturday) Menu £ 38 (dinner) – Carte £ 33/46

◆ Magnificent Tudor manor house with Georgian and Victorian additions in a secluded rural location. Open fires, a great hall and impressive period interiors throughout. Interesting, Italian influenced dishes, in three-roomed restaurant.

The Daventry

Sedgemoor Way, off Ashby Rd, North : 2 m. on A 361 ✉ NN11 0SG – ✆ (01327) 307 000 – daventry@paramount-hotels.co.uk – Fax (01327) 706 313

155 rm – †£ 55 ††£ 110, ☕ £ 12.95 – **Rest** – (bar lunch) Menu £ 19 – Carte £ 25/41

◆ A large and spacious modern hotel with comprehensive conference facilities and a well equipped leisure centre. Contemporary, comfy rooms, some with "study areas". Restaurant has pleasant views over Drayton Water.

at Staverton Southwest : 2¾ m. by A 45 off A 425 – ✉ Daventry

Colledges House

Oakham Lane, off Glebe Lane ✉ NN11 6JQ – ✆ (01327) 702 737 – lizjarrett@colledgeshouse.co.uk – Closed 25 December

4 rm ☕ – †£ 65 ††£ 102 – **Rest** – (by arrangement, communal dining) Menu £ 31

◆ Part 17C house in a quiet village. Full of charm with antiques, curios, portraits and an inglenook fireplace. Homely rooms are in the main house and an adjacent cottage. Evening meals served at elegant oak table.

DAWLISH – Devon – 503 J 32 2 D2

London 184 m – Exeter 13 m – Teignmouth 3 m

Lammas Park House

3 Priory Rd, via High St and Strand Hill ✉ EX7 9JF – ✆ (01626) 888 064 – lammaspark@hotmail.com – Fax (01626) 888 064

3 rm ☕ – †£ 60 ††£ 90 – **Rest** – (by arrangement, communal dining) Menu £ 17

◆ Lovely early 19C townhouse boasting a superb secluded rear terrace garden and handsome period details in situ. Clean, uncluttered rooms. Sit and admire views from observatory. Dinners served in communal style; owners are experiened restaurateurs.

Do not confuse X with ✿!
X defines comfort, while stars are awarded for the best cuisine, across all categories of comfort.

ENGLAND

DEAL – Kent – 504 Y 30 – pop. 29 248 — 9 D2

London 78 m – Canterbury 19 m – Dover 8 m – Margate 16 m
129 High St ☎ (01304) 369576
Walmer & Kingsdown Kingsdown The Leas, ☎ (01304) 373 256 .

Dunkerley's

19 Beach St ✉ CT14 7AH – ☎ (01304) 375 016 – ddunkerley@btconnect.com – Fax (01304) 380 187
16 rm – †£ 70 ††£ 100/130
Rest *Restaurant* – see restaurant listing
◆ The hotel faces the beach and the Channel. Bedrooms are comfortably furnished and the principal rooms have jacuzzis. Comfortable bar offers a lighter menu than the restaurant.

Sutherland House

186 London Rd ✉ CT14 9PT – ☎ (01304) 362 853 – info@sutherlandhouse.fsnet.co.uk – Fax (01304) 381 146
4 rm – †£ 57 ††£ 69 – **Rest** – (by arrangement) Menu £ 24
◆ An Edwardian house with garden in a quiet residential area. Stylish, welcoming bedrooms are individually decorated. Friendly, relaxed atmosphere. Refined dining room with homely ambience.

Restaurant – at Dunkerley's H.

19 Beach St ✉ CT14 7AH – ☎ (01304) 375 016 – Fax (01304) 380 187 – closed Monday lunch
Rest – Menu £ 15/27
◆ With views of the Channel, the restaurant is best known for preparing locally caught seafood, although non-seafood options are also available. Wide ranging wine list.

ENGLAND

DEDDINGTON – Oxon. – 503 Q 28 – pop. 1 595 — 10 B1

London 72 m – Birmingham 46 m – Coventry 33 m – Oxford 18 m

Deddington Arms

rest,

Horsefair ✉ OX15 0SH – ☎ (01869) 338 364 – deddarms@oxfordshire-hotels.co.uk – Fax (01869) 337 010
27 rm – †£ 90 ††£ 110/130 – **Rest** – Carte £ 28/32
◆ Traditional coaching inn with a smart, modish ambience, on the market place. Spacious modern bedrooms in rear extension. Stylish rooms, two four-postered, in the main house. The restaurant is decorated in a warm and contemporary style.

Otters

Market Place ✉ OX15 0SA – ☎ (01869) 338 813 – ottersrestaurant@hotmail.co.uk – Fax (01295) 273 205 – closed 2 weeks in summer, 1 week Christmas, Monday and Sunday dinner
Rest – Menu £ 10 (lunch) – Carte £ 19/27
◆ Cosy restaurant set over two floors; low ceilinged and heavily beamed, but with a light airy feel. Traditional menu; well presented dishes.

DEDHAM – Essex – 504 W 28 – ✉ Colchester *Great Britain* — 13 D2

London 63 m – Chelmsford 30 m – Colchester 8 m – Ipswich 12 m
Stour Valley★ – Flatford Mill★, E : 6 m. by B 1029, A 12 and B 1070

Maison Talbooth

Stratford Rd, West : ½ m. ✉ CO7 6HN – ☎ (01206) 322 367 – maison@milsomhotels.com – Fax (01206) 322 752 – Closed for refurbishment until 1 April
13 rm – †£ 175 ††£ 350
Rest *Le Talbooth* – see restaurant listing
◆ Quiet, Victorian country house with intimate atmosphere, lawned gardens and views over river valley. Some rooms are smart and contemporary, others more traditional in style.

Milsoms
rm, rest, VISA AE

Stratford Rd, West : ¾ m. ✉ CO7 6HW – ✆ (01206) 322 795 – milsoms@milsomhotels.co.uk – Fax (01206) 323 689

15 rm – £ 85 £ 145 – **Rest** – (bookings not accepted) Carte £ 20/29

◆ Modern hotel overlooking Constable's Dedham Vale with attractive garden and stylish lounge. Bright, airy and welcoming rooms feature unfussy décor and modern colours. Likeably modish, wood-floored bistro.

Le Talbooth
VISA AE

Gun Hill, West : 1 m. ✉ CO7 6HP – ✆ (01206) 323 150 – talbooth@milsomhotels.com – Fax (01206) 322 309 – Closed Sunday dinner October-May

Rest – Menu £ 28 (lunch) – Carte £ 36/47

◆ Part Tudor house in attractive riverside setting. Exposed beams and real fires contribute to the traditional atmosphere matched by a traditional menu. Well chosen wine list.

Fountain House & Dedham Hall with rm
VISA

Brook St ✉ CO7 6AD – ✆ (01206) 323 027 – sarton@dedhamhall.demon.co.uk – Fax (01206) 323 293 – Closed Christmas-New Year

5 rm – £ 55 £ 95 – **Rest** – (Closed Sunday-Monday) (dinner only) (booking essential) Menu £ 30

◆ In a quiet, country house dating back to 15C with traditional, uncluttered ambience. Weekly changing traditionally based set menu. Comfortable rooms also available.

The Sun Inn with rm
VISA

High St ✉ CO7 6DF – ✆ (01206) 323 351 – info@thesuninndedham.com – Closed 25-27 December and Sunday dinner

5 rm – £ 60/105 £ 130 – **Rest** – Menu £ 16/18 – Carte £ 15/25

◆ Modernised 15C coaching inn in heart of village. Welcoming sunny yellow façade; spacious interior. Interesting, original Mediterranean style menus. Boutique bedrooms.

We try to be as accurate as possible when giving room rates. But prices are susceptible to change, so please check rates when booking.

DENBY DALE – W. Yorks. – 502 P 23 — 22 B3

London 192 m – Leeds 22 m – Manchester 37 m

Aagrah
VISA AE

250 Wakefield Rd, Northeast : ¾ m. on A 636 ✉ HD8 8SU – ✆ (01484) 866 266 – info@aagrah.com – closed 25 December

Rest – Indian (dinner only) (booking essential) Carte £ 12/20 **s**

◆ The Eastern influenced interior décor reflects the authentic feel of the good quality Indian-Kashmiri dishes on offer. A busy, bustling atmosphere prevails.

DENHAM – Bucks. – 504 S 29 – pop. 2 269 *Great Britain* — 11 D3

London 20 m – Buckingham 42 m – Oxford 41 m

Windsor Castle★★★, Eton★★ and Windsor★, S : 10 m. by A 412

The Swan Inn
VISA AE

Village Rd ✉ UB9 5BH – ✆ (01895) 832 085 – info@swaninndenham.co.uk – Fax (01895) 835 516 – Closed 25-26 December

Rest – (booking essential) Carte £ 19/29

◆ Ivy-covered inn; part bar, part restaurant leading through to pleasant terrace and spacious garden. Good modern dishes with blackboard specials changing daily.

ENGLAND

DENMEAD – Hants. – 503 Q 31 – pop. 5 788 6 B2

London 70 m – Portsmouth 11 m – Southampton 27 m

Barnard's

Hambledon Rd ✉ PO7 6NU – ☎ (023) 9225 7788 – mail@barnardsrestaurant.co.uk – Fax (023) 9225 7788 – closed 1 week January, 1 week July, 1 January, 25-26 December Saturday lunch, Sunday and Monday

Rest – (light lunch) Carte £ 22/35

◆ Friendly village centre shop conversion; bright and airy with a small bar area. Classic and modern dishes: ricotta and basil gnocchi, chorizo salad or pork in mustard sauce.

Undecided between two equivalent establishments? Within each category, establishments are classified in our order of preference.

DERBY – Derby – 502 P 25 – pop. 229 407 *Great Britain* 16 B2

London 132 m – Birmingham 40 m – Coventry 49 m – Leicester 29 m – Manchester 62 m – Nottingham 16 m – Sheffield 47 m – Stoke-on-Trent 35 m

Nottingham East Midlands Airport, Castle Donington : ☎ (0871) 919 9000, SE : 12 m. by A 6 X

Assembly Rooms, Market Pl ☎ (01332) 255802

Sinfin Wilmore Rd, ☎ (01332) 766 323 ;

Mickleover Uttoxeter Rd, ☎ (01332) 516 011 ;

Kedleston Park Quardon Kedlston, ☎ (01332) 840 035 ;

Marriott Breadsall Priory H. & C.C. Morley Moor Rd, ☎ (01332) 836 106 ;

Allestree Park Allestree Allestree Hall, ☎ (01332) 550 616 .

City★ – Museum and Art Gallery★ (Collection of Derby Porcelain★) YZ **M1** – Royal Crown Derby Museum★ **AC** Z **M2**

Kedleston Hall★★ **AC**, NW : 4½ m. by Kedleston Rd X

Plan opposite

Midland

Midland Rd ✉ DE1 2SQ – ☎ (01332) 345 894 – sales@midland-derby.co.uk – Fax (01332) 293 522 – closed 22-28 December, 1 January Z i

94 rm – †£ 106/114 ††£ 114, ☕ £14.50 – 1 suite – **Rest** – (closed Saturday lunch) Menu £ 23

◆ A pleasant, early-Victorian railway hotel with good sized modern rooms and traditionally decorated public areas. Wide array of conference rooms. Pretty dining room in the Victorian style of the hotel.

at Darley Abbey North : 2½ m. off A 6 - X – ✉ Derby

Darleys

Darley Abbey Mill ✉ DE22 1DZ – ☎ (01332) 364 987 – info@darleys.com – Fax (01332) 364 987 – closed 25 December-9 January, Sunday dinner and Bank Holidays

Rest – Menu £ 17 (lunch) – Carte (dinner) £ 30/34

◆ A converted cotton mill in an attractive riverside setting. The interior is modern, stylish and comfortable. High quality British cuisine of satisfying, classical character.

at Weston Underwood Northwest : 5½ m. by A 52 - X - and Kedleston Rd – ✉ Derby

Park View Farm without rest

✉ DE6 4PA – ☎ (01335) 360 352 – enquiries@parkviewfarm.co.uk – Fax (01335) 360 352 – closed Christmas

3 rm ☕ – †£ 60 ††£ 80

◆ Friendly couple run this elegant house on a working farm, in sight of Kedleston Hall. Antique-filled lounge with oils and a Victorian fireplace. Simple rooms in stripped pine.

ENGLAND

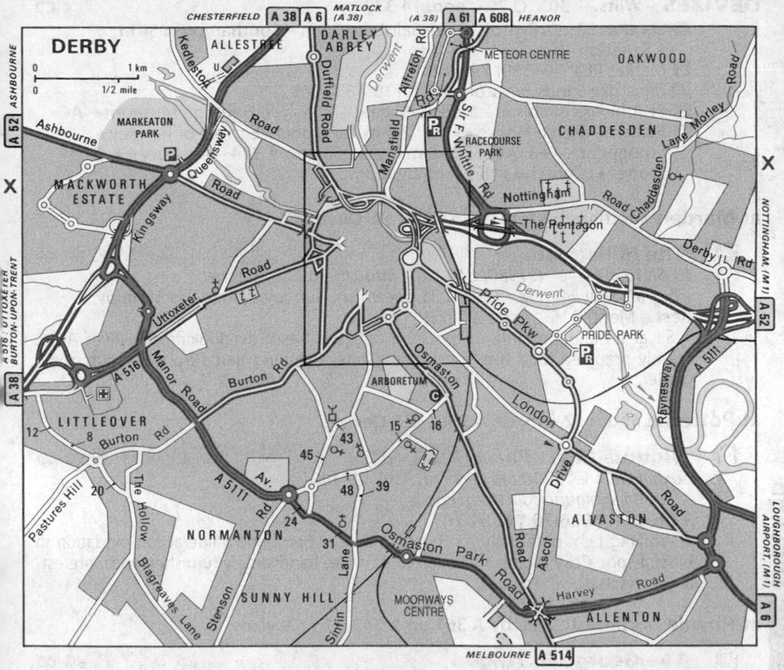

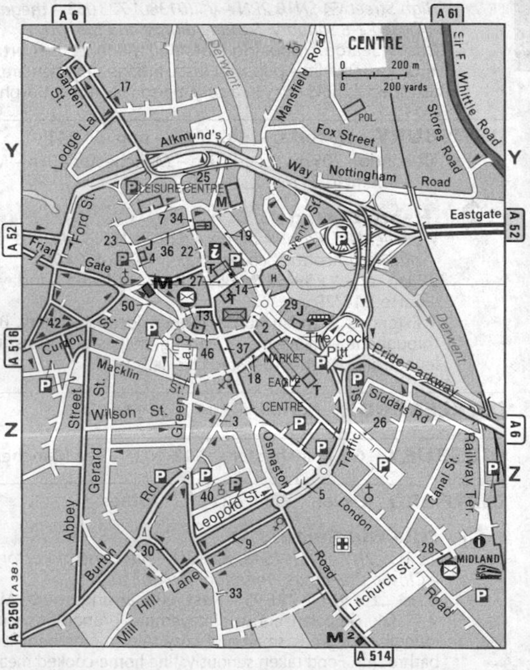

DERBY

CENTRE

DEVIZES – Wilts. – 503 O 29 – pop. 14 379 4 C2

London 98 m – Bristol 38 m – Salisbury 25 m – Southampton 50 m – Swindon 19 m

Market Pl ✆ (01380) 729408

Erlestoke Sands Erlestoke, ✆ (01380) 831 069 .

St John's Church★★ – Market Place★ – Wiltshire Heritage Museum★ AC

Potterne (Porch House★★) S : 2½ m. by A 360 – E : Vale of Pewsey★. Stonehenge★★★ AC, SE : 16 m. by A 360 and A 344 – Avebury★★ (The Stones★, Church★) NE : 7 m. by A 361

at Marden Southeast : 6½ m. by A 342 – ✉ Devizes

The Millstream

✉ SN10 3RH – ✆ (01380) 848 308 – info@the-millstream.net – Fax (01380) 848 337 – Closed 25 December, Sunday dinner and Monday

Rest – Menu £ 15 – Carte £ 25/36

◆ Sit at an antique table in the snug or eat al fresco overlooking the River Avon. Freshly prepared food uses local ingredients, including herbs from the pub's own garden.

at Potterne South : 2¼ m. on A 360 – ✉ Devizes

Blounts Court Farm without rest

Coxhill Lane ✉ SN10 5PH – ✆ (01380) 727 180 – caroline@blountscourtfarm.co.uk

3 rm – 🛉£ 36/70 🛉🛉£ 64/70

◆ Working farm personally run by charming owner: good value accommodation in blissful spot. Cosy rooms in converted barn are handsomely furnished with interesting artefacts.

at Rowde Northwest : 2 m. by A 361 on A 342 – ✉ Devizes

The George & Dragon

High Street ✉ SN10 2PN – ✆ (01380) 723 053 – thegandd@tiscali.co.uk – Closed 1-8 January, Sunday dinner and Monday

Rest – Seafood (booking essential) Menu £ 16 – Carte £ 28/35

◆ Characterful little pub with rustic fittings and open fire. Robust modern classics and fish specials hold sway in a cosy, personally run atmosphere. Real ale.

DEWSBURY – W. Yorks. – 502 P 22 – pop. 54 341 22 B3

London 205 m – Leeds 9 m – Manchester 40 m – Middlesbrough 76 m – Sheffield 31 m

Heath Cottage AC rest,

Wakefield Rd, East : ¾ m. on A 638 ✉ WF15 6PD – ✆ (01924) 465 399 – info@heathcottage.co.uk – Fax (01924) 459 405

28 rm – 🛉£ 39/50 🛉🛉£ 50 – **Rest** – (Closed Sunday dinner) Menu £ 13 – Carte £ 16/28 **s**

◆ Extended Victorian house; former doctors' surgery. Bright décor and furnishings throughout with rooms of varying shapes and sizes. Cocktail bar in comfortable lounge area. Tried-and-tested cuisine.

DICKLEBURGH – Norfolk – 504 X 26 – see Diss

DIDSBURY – Gtr Manchester – 502 N 23 – see Manchester

DIPTFORD – Devon – 503 I 32 – ✉ Totnes 2 C2

The Old Rectory

✉ TQ9 7NY – ✆ (01548) 821 575 – hitchins@oldrectorydiptford.co.uk – Closed Christmas, minimum 2 night stay

4 rm – 🛉£ 58 🛉🛉£ 95 – **Rest** – (by arrangement) Menu £ 27

◆ Classic Georgian house of cavernous proportions with a three-acre garden. The lounge, though, is small and cosy. Airy rooms benefit from rural views; luxurious bathrooms. Food taken seriously: fine home-cooked meals served with pride.

ENGLAND

DISS – Norfolk – 504 X 26 – pop. 7 444 — 15 C2

London 98 m – Ipswich 25 m – Norwich 21 m – Thetford 17 m
Meres Mouth, Mere St (01379) 650523

at Dickleburgh Northeast : 4 ½ m. by A 1066 off A 140 – ✉ Diss

Dickleburgh Hall Country House without rest
Semere Green Lane, North : 1 m. ✉ IP21 4NT – (01379) 741 259 – johntaylor05@btinternet.com – 2 March-October
3 rm – £ 45 £ 70/80
◆ 16C house still in private hands. Trim rooms in traditional patterns, beamed lounge with an inglenook fireplace; snooker room and golf course.

at Brockdish East : 7 m. by A 1066, A 140 and A 143 – ✉ Diss

Grove Thorpe without rest
Grove Rd, North : ¾ m. ✉ IP21 4JR – (01379) 668 305 – grovethorpe@btinternet.com – March-October
3 rm – £ 55 £ 82
◆ Pretty 17C bailiff's house in peaceful pastureland with fishing; very welcoming owners. Cosy ambience. Characterful interior with oak beams, inglenook and antique furniture.

at Brome Southeast : 2 ¾ m. by A 1066 on B 1077 – ✉ Eye

The Cornwallis
✉ IP23 8AJ – (01379) 870 326 – reservations.cornwallis@ohiml.com – Fax (01379) 870 051
16 rm – £ 90 £ 120/175 – **Rest** – (Closed Sunday-Monday) (booking essential) Carte £ 20/31
◆ Part 16C dower house with quiet topiary gardens. Spacious, individually decorated timbered rooms with antique furniture. 60ft well in very characterful bar dating from 1561. Dining room with delightful conservatory lounge overlooking gardens.

Your opinions are important to us: please write and let us know about your discoveries and experiences – good and bad!

DITCHEAT – Somerset — 4 C2

London 124 m – Bath 29 m

The Manor House Inn with rm
✉ BA4 6RB – (01749) 860 276 – info@manorhouseinn.co.uk – Closed 25 December
3 rm – £ 50 £ 90 – **Rest** – (closed Sunday dinner) Menu £ 17 – Carte £ 16/29
◆ Watch the horses on their way to the gallops from this characterful 17C pub. Drink at flag-floored or sports bars. Dishes are satisfyingly rustic. Pleasant rooms in annex.

DOGMERSFIELD – Hants. — 7 C1

London 44 m – Farnham 6 m – Fleet 2 m

Four Seasons
Dogmersfield Park, Chalky Lane ✉ RG27 8TD – (01252) 853 000 – Fax (01252) 853 010
111 rm – £ 285/325 £ 285/325, £ 24 – 22 suites
Rest *Seasons* – Carte £ 34/45
◆ Part Georgian splendour in extensive woodlands; many original features in situ. Superb spa facilities: vast selection of leisure pursuits. Luxurious, highly equipped bedrooms. Restaurant has thoroughly modish, relaxing feel.

ENGLAND

DONCASTER – S. Yorks. – **502** Q 23 – **pop. 67 977** 23 **C3**

▶ London 173 m – Kingston-upon-Hull 46 m – Leeds 30 m – Nottingham 46 m – Sheffield 19 m
✈ Robin Hood Airport : ☎ (08708) 332210, SE : 7m off A638
ℹ 38-40 High St ☎ (01302) 734309
18 Doncaster Town Moor Belle Vue Bawtry Rd, ☎ (01302) 533 778 ;
18 Crookhill Park Conisborough, ☎ (01709) 862 979 ;
18 Wheatley Amthorpe Rd, ☎ (01302) 831 655 ;
9 Owston Park Owston Owston Hall, ☎ (01302) 330 821.

DONCASTER

Albion Pl. . . . . **C** 3
Apley Rd . . . . **C** 5
Balby Rd . . . . **C** 8
Broxholme Lane . . . . **C**
Carr House Rd. . . . . **C**
Chequer Ave . . . . **C** 12
Chequer Rd . . . . **C**
Christ Church Rd. . . . . **C**
Church Way. . . . . **C**
Cleveland St . . . . **C**
Colonnades Shopping Centre . . . . **C**
Cunningham Rd . . . . **C** 17
East Laith Gate . . . . **C** 24
Frenchgate Shopping Centre . . . . **C**
Grey Friars Rd . . . . **C**
Hall Gate . . . . **C**
Highfield Rd. . . . . **C**
High St. . . . . **C** 36
Milton Walk . . . . **C** 40
Nether Hall Rd. . . . . **C** 43
North Bridge Rd . . . . **C** 44
Queen's Rd . . . . **C** 46
St George's Bridge . . . . **C**
St Jame's Bridge. . . . . **C** 48
St Jame's St . . . . **C**
Silver St . . . . **C**
South Parade. . . . . **C**
Thorne Rd . . . . **C**
Trafford Way . . . . **C**
Waterdale . . . . **C**
Waterdale Shopping Centre **C**
White Rose Way. . . . . **C** 70
Wood St. . . . . **C**

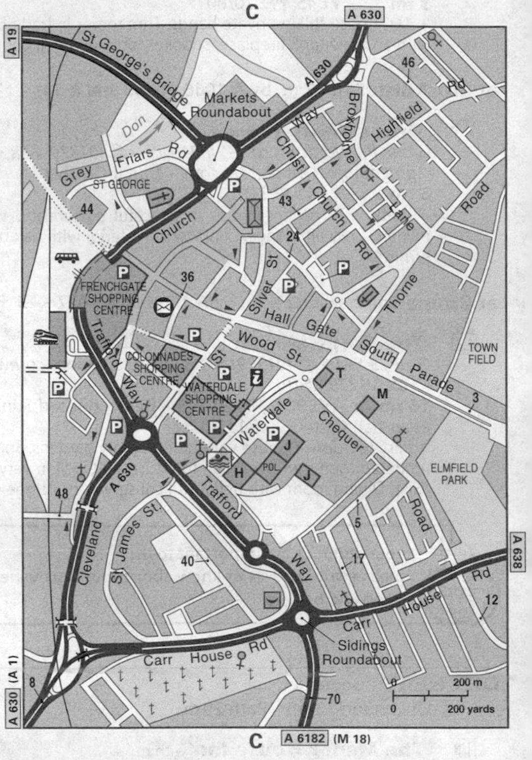

Mount Pleasant &, rm, AC rest, P VISA MC AE

Great North Rd, Southeast : 6 m. on A 638 ⊠ DN11 0HW – ☎ (01302) 868 696 – reception@mountpleasant.co.uk – Fax (01302) 865 130 – Closed 25 December
54 rm – †£ 79 ††£ 99 – 2 suites
Rest *Garden* – Menu £ 16 (lunch) – Carte dinner £ 29/39
◆ Stone-built farmhouse with sympathetic extension. Traditionally styled throughout: wood panelled lounges and a small bar. Well-kept bedrooms, including one with a five-poster! Restaurant with garden views.

Aagrah AC P VISA MC AE

Great North Rd, Woodlands, Northwest : 4 m. on A 638 ⊠ DN6 7RA – ☎ (01302) 728 888 A r
Rest – Indian (dinner only and Sunday lunch) (booking essential) Menu £ 16 – Carte £ 10/14
◆ The Eastern influenced interior décor reflects the authentic feel of the good quality Indian-Kashmiri dishes. Busy, bustling atmosphere.

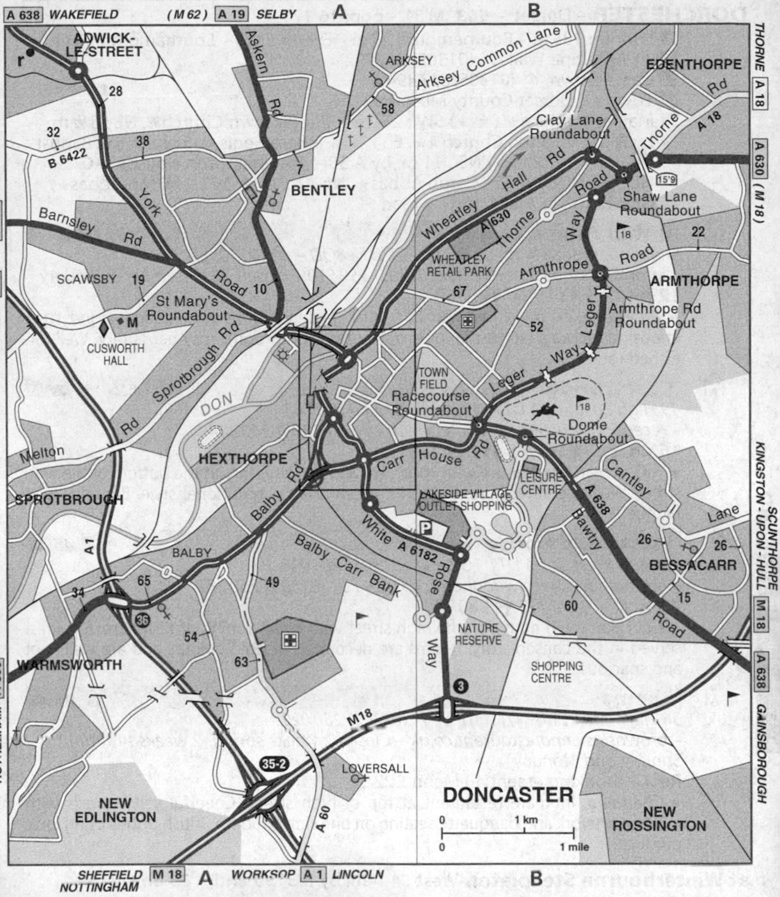

A 638 WAKEFIELD
(M 62) A 19 SELBY
A
B
THORNE A 18
A 630 (M 18)
KINGSTON-UPON-HULL M 18
SCUNTHORPE
A 638 GAINSBOROUGH
BARNSLEY A 635
LEEDS A 1
ROTHERHAM A 630
SHEFFIELD M 18
NOTTINGHAM
WORKSOP A 1 LINCOLN
ADWICK-LE-STREET
ARKSEY
Arksey Common Lane
EDENTHORPE
Askern Rd
58
28
32
B 6422
38
7
BENTLEY
Clay Lane Roundabout
Thorne Rd
A 18
Shaw Lane Roundabout
York
Barnsley Rd
Wheatley Hall Rd
A 630
Thorne Road
Way
22
WHEATLEY RETAIL PARK
Armthrope Road
ARMTHORPE
SCAWSBY
19
10
Road
St Mary's Roundabout
67
Armthrope Rd Roundabout
Leger Way
52
CUSWORTH HALL
M
Sprotbrough Rd
TOWN FIELD
Racecourse Roundabout
DON
Dome Roundabout
Melton Rd
HEXTHORPE
Carr House Rd
Cantley Lane
LEISURE CENTRE
A 638
Bawtry Road
SPROTBROUGH
LAKESIDE VILLAGE OUTLET SHOPPING
Balby Rd
White Rose Way
A 6182
P
26
BESSACARR
A1
BALBY
Balby Carr Bank
49
15
34
65
60
36
54
NATURE RESERVE
63
WARMSWORTH
SHOPPING CENTRE
3
M18
35-2
LOVERSALL
NEW EDLINGTON
A 60
DONCASTER
0 1 km
0 1 mile
NEW ROSSINGTON

Arksey Lane	A	7	High Rd	A	34	Tickhill Rd	A	63
Bentley Rd	A	10	Jossey Lane	A	38	Warmsworth Rd	A	65
Church Lane	B	15	Sandford Rd	A	49	Wentworth Rd	B	67
Cusworth Lane	A	19	Sandringham Rd	B	52	Wheatley Retail Park Shopping Centre	B	
Doncaster Rd	B	22	Springwell Lane	A	54	Yorkshire Outlet Shopping Centre	B	
Goodison Boulevard	B	26	Sprotbrough Rd	A	56			
Great North Rd	A	28	Station Rd	A	58			
Green Lane	A	32	Stoops Lane	B	60			

DONHEAD ST ANDREW – Wilts. – **503** N 30 – see Shaftesbury (Dorset)

The ✿ award is the crème de la crème. This is awarded to restaurants which are really worth travelling miles for!

DORCHESTER – Dorset – **503** M 31 – **pop. 16 171** 4 **C3**

London 135 m – Bournemouth 27 m – Exeter 53 m – Southampton 53 m
11 Antelope Walk ✆ (01305) 267992
Came Down, ✆ (01305) 813494.
Town★ - Dorset County Museum★ **AC**
Maiden Castle★★ (≤ ★) SW : 2½ m. – Puddletown Church★, NE : 5½ m. by A 35. Moreton Church★★, E : 7½ m. – Bere Regis★ (St John the Baptist Church★ - Roof★★) NE : 11 m. by A 35 – Athelhampton House★ **AC**, NE : 6½ m. by A 35 - Cerne Abbas★, N : 7 m. by A 352 – Milton Abbas★, NE : 12 m. on A 354 and by-road

Birkin House without rest
Stinsford, East : 1¼ m. by B 3150 ✉ DT2 8QD – ✆ (01305) 260262 – info@birkinhouse.com – Fax (01305) 259510 – closed 22 December-5 January
12 rm – £55/60 £160
◆ Greystone Victorian mansion in formal gardens. Brims with antiques and style. Imposing hallway; elegant lounge; opulent drawing room; cosy bar/library. Well furnished rooms.

Casterbridge without rest
49 High East St ✉ DT1 1HU – ✆ (01305) 264043 – reception@casterbridgehotel.co.uk – Fax (01305) 260884
15 rm – £60/85 £99/135
◆ A Georgian town house with courtyard and conservatory at the bottom of the high street. Well decorated throughout in a comfortable, traditional style. Bar and quiet lounge.

Westwood House without rest
29 High West St ✉ DT1 1UP – ✆ (01305) 268018 – reservations@westwoodhouse.co.uk – Fax (01305) 250282
7 rm – £45/55 £80/85
◆ Georgian town house on the high street with a welcoming atmosphere. Breakfast served in the conservatory. Rooms are decorated in bold colours and are well kept and spacious.

Sienna
36 High West St ✉ DT1 1UP – ✆ (01305) 250022 – browns@siennarestaurant.co.uk – Closed 2 weeks spring, 2 weeks Autumn, Sunday and Monday
Rest – (booking essential) Menu £22/36
◆ Charming, intimate restaurant at top of high street. Cheerful yellow walls with modern artwork and banquette seating on one side. Modern British dishes using local produce.

at Winterbourne Steepleton West : 4¾ m. by B 3150 and A 35 on B 3159 – ✉ Dorchester

Old Rectory without rest
✉ DT2 9LG – ✆ (01305) 889468 – caroline@theoldrectorybandb.co.uk – closed Christmas and New Year
4 rm – £60 £100
◆ Built in 1850 and having a characterful exterior. Situated in the middle of a charming village. Well kept, good sized rooms overlook the pleasant garden.

DORCHESTER-ON-THAMES – Oxon. – **503** Q 29 – **pop. 2 256** 10 **B2**

Great Britain

London 51 m – Abingdon 6 m – Oxford 8 m – Reading 17 m
Town★
Ridgeway Path★★

White Hart rm,
26 High St ✉ OX10 7HN – ✆ (01865) 340074 – whitehart@oxfordshire-hotels.co.uk – Fax (01865) 341082
26 rm – £85/95 £105/115 – 2 suites – **Rest** – Menu £14 – Carte £25/36
◆ 17C coaching inn with charm and character. The comfortable bar has large leather armchairs. Well-kept pretty bedrooms with smart bathrooms. Striking beamed dining room.

DORKING – Surrey – 504 T 30 – pop. 16 071 7 D2

London 26 m – Brighton 39 m – Guildford 12 m – Worthing 33 m
Betchworth Park Reigate Rd, ✆ (01306) 882 052 .

Burford Bridge (heated)
Box Hill, North : 1½ m. on A 24 ✉ RH5 6BX – ✆ (01306) 884 561 – h6635@accor.com – Fax (01306) 880 386
57 rm – †£ 135/185 ††£ 145/195 – **Rest** – Menu £ 30
◆ Wordsworth and Sheridan frequented this part 16C hotel. Well run, high quality feel throughout. Antique paintings in public areas, embossed wallpaper in bedrooms. The dining room has a smart, well kept air.

DORRIDGE – W. Mids. – 503 O 26 – ✉ Birmingham 19 C2

London 109 m – Birmingham 11 m – Warwick 11 m

The Forest with rm rest,
25 Station Approach ✉ B93 8JA – ✆ (01564) 772 120 – info@forest-hotel.com – Fax (01564) 732 680 – closed 25 December
12 rm – †£ 93/130 ††£ 110/140 – **Rest** – (closed Sunday dinner) Carte £ 17/30
◆ Attractive red-brick and timber former pub with a busy ambience. Food is its backbone: modern classics served in stylish bar and restaurant. Cool, modern bedrooms.

DOUGLAS – Isle of Man – 502 G 21 – see Man (Isle of)

DOVER – Kent – 504 Y 30 – pop. 34 087 *Great Britain* 9 D2

London 76 m – Brighton 84 m
to France (Calais) (P & O Stena Line) frequent services daily (1 h 15 mn) – to France (Calais) (SeaFrance S.A.) frequent services daily (1 h 30 mn) – to France (Boulogne) (SpeedFerries) 3-5 daily (50 mn)
The Old Town Gaol, Biggin ✆ (01304) 205108, tic@doveruk.com
Castle★★ **AC** Y
White Cliffs, Langdon Cliffs, NE : 1 m. on A 2 Z and A 258

Plan on next page

East Lee without rest
108 Maison Dieu Rd ✉ CT16 1RT – ✆ (01304) 210 176 – elgh@eclipse.co.uk – Fax (01304) 206 705 – closed Christmas and New Year Y **o**
4 rm – †£ 38/45 ††£ 55/60
◆ Tile hung, mid-terraced Victorian residence. Thoughtfully restored with attractive breakfast room and antique pine furnished bedrooms. A totally non-smoking establishment.

Number One without rest
1 Castle St ✉ CT16 1QH – ✆ (01304) 202 007 – res@number1guesthouse.co.uk – Fax (01304) 214 078 – Closed 24-26 December Y **c**
4 rm – †£ 35/45 ††£ 50/60
◆ Peach painted Georgian townhouse with traditional guesthouse appeal. Breakfast offered in bedrooms: these are compact, and cosy with a cottagey feel.

at St Margaret's at Cliffe Northeast : 4 m. by A 258 - Z – ✉ **Dover**

Wallett's Court
West Cliffe, Northwest : ¾ m. on Dover rd ✉ CT15 6EW – ✆ (01304) 852 424 – Fax (01304) 853 430 – closed 24 and 25 December
17 rm – †£ 109 ††£ 129/169
Rest *The Restaurant* – see restaurant listing
◆ With origins dating back to the Doomsday Book, a wealth of Jacobean features remain in this relaxed country house. Most characterful rooms in main house; luxurious spa rooms.

ENGLAND

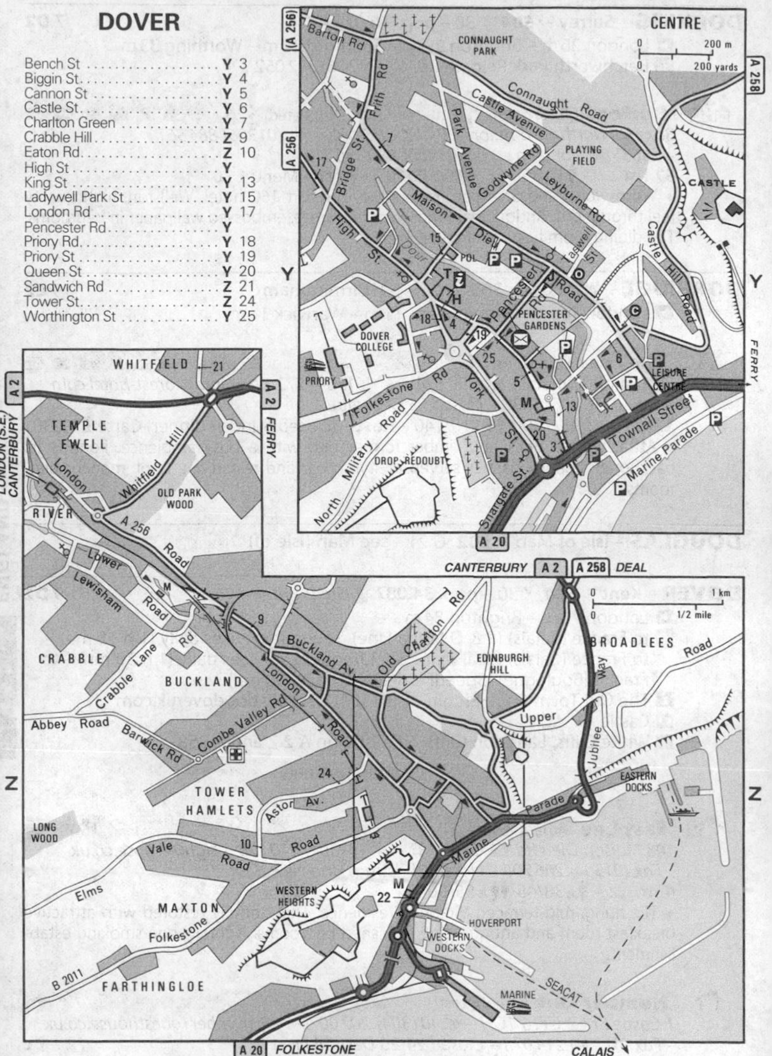

XX **The Restaurant** – at Wallett's Court H.

West Cliffe, Northwest : 3/4 m. on Dover rd ✉ CT15 6EW – ✆ (01304) 852 424 – Fax (01304) 853 430 – closed 24-26 December and lunch Monday and Saturday

Rest – Menu £ 23/40

◆ Local produce dominates the imaginative, monthly changing, seasonal menu. Dine by candlelight in the beamed restaurant after drinks are taken by the open fire.

DOWNHOLME – N. Yorks. – **502** O 20 – see Richmond

DOWNTON – Hants. – **503** P 31 – see Lymington

DRIFT – Cornwall – see Penzance

DROITWICH SPA – Worcs. – 503 N 27 – pop. 22 585 19 C3

London 129 m – Birmingham 20 m – Bristol 66 m – Worcester 6 m
St Richard's House, Victoria Sq ✆ (01905) 774312
Droitwich G. & C.C. Ford Lane, ✆ (01905) 774344 .

at Cutnall Green North : 3 m. on A 442 – ✉ Droitwich Spa

The Chequers
Kidderminster Rd ✉ WR9 0PJ – ✆ (01299) 851 292 – Fax (01299) 851 744 – Closed 25 December, 1 January and dinner 26 December
Rest – Carte £ 18/25
♦ Half-timbered roadside pub, comprising main bar with beams and fire or cosy garden room. Impressively wide range of highly interesting dishes, firmly traditional or modern.

at Hadley Heath Southwest : 4 m. by Ombersley Way, A 4133 and Ladywood rd – ✉ Droitwich Spa

Old Farmhouse without rest
✉ WR9 0AR – ✆ (01905) 620837 – judylambe@theoldfarmhouse.uk.com – Fax (01905) 621 722 – closed Christmas-New Year
5 rm – 🚹£ 40 🚹🚹£ 70
♦ Converted farmhouse in quiet and rural location. Spacious comfortable rooms, three in the main house and two, more private and perhaps suited to families, in the annex.

ENGLAND

The red symbol?
This denotes the very essence of peace
– only the sound of birdsong first thing in the morning …

DULVERTON – Somerset – 503 J 30 3 A2

London 198 m – Barnstaple 27 m – Exeter 26 m – Minehead 18 m – Taunton 27 m
Village ★
Exmoor National Park ★★ - Tarr Steps ★★, NW : 6 m. by B 3223

Ashwick House
Northwest : 4¼ m. by B 3223 turning left after second cattle grid ✉ TA22 9QD – ✆ (01398) 323 868 – reservations@ashwickhouse.com – Fax (01398) 323 868
6 rm – 🚹£ 70 🚹🚹£ 150 – **Rest** – (booking essential for non-residents) (lunch by arrangement) Menu £ 25/31
♦ Delightful, peaceful and secluded Edwardian country house in extensive gardens with pheasants and rabbits. Smartly appointed, airy rooms with thoughtful touches. Classic cuisine with strong local flavour in elegant dining room.

at Brushford South : 1 ¾ m. on B 3222 – ✉ Dulverton

Three Acres Country House without rest
✉ TA22 9AR – ✆ (01398) 323 730 – enquiries@threeacrescountryhouse.co.uk
6 rm – 🚹£ 55 🚹🚹£ 110

♦ Keenly run 20C guesthouse that's more impressive in than out: super-comfy bedrooms are the strong point. There's an airy lounge, cosy bar and breakfasts are locally sourced.

DUNSLEY – N. Yorks. – see Whitby

see Whitby

DUNSTER – Somerset – 503 J 30 3 A2

London 185 m – Minehead 3 m – Taunton 23 m

Town★★ - Castle★★ AC (upper rooms ≤ ★) - Water Mill★ AC - St George's Church★ - Dovecote★

Exmoor House without rest

12 West St ✉ TA24 6SN – ☎ (01643) 821 268 – stay@exmoorhousedunster.co.uk – Fax (01643) 821 268 – early March-early November

6 rm – ♦£ 35/40 ♦♦£ 65

◆ Georgian terraced house with pink exterior, enhanced by colourful window boxes. Spacious, comfy lounge and welcoming breakfast room. Chintz rooms with pleasing extra touches.

No 7 West Street

7 West St ✉ TA24 6SN – ☎ (01643) 821 064 – info@no7weststreet.co.uk – Closed 22-29 December

3 rm – ♦£ 55 ♦♦£ 75/80 – **Rest** – (by arrangement) Menu £ 33

◆ Passionately run 17C guest house in village centre, with bedrooms decorated in classic English style and beamed ceilings throughout. Open plan lounge; open fire, comfy sofas. Local Exmoor produce used in French-influenced cooking, including 7 course tasting menu.

Your opinions are important to us:
please write and let us know about your discoveries and experiences – good and bad!

ENGLAND

DURHAM – Durham – 501 P 19 – pop. 42 939 Great Britain 24 B3

London 267 m – Leeds 77 m – Middlesbrough 23 m – Newcastle upon Tyne 20 m – Sunderland 12 m

2 Millennium Pl ☎ (0191) 384 3720

Mount Oswald South Rd, ☎ (0191) 386 7527 .

City★★★ - Cathedral★★★ (Nave★★★, Chapel of the Nine Altars★★★, Sanctuary Knocker★) B – Oriental Museum★★ AC (at Durham University by A 167) B – City and Riverside (Prebends' Bridge ≤ ★★★ A, Framwellgate Bridge ≤ ★★ B) – Monastic Buildings (Cathedral Treasury★, Central Tower≤ ★) B – Castle★ (Norman chapel★) AC B

Hartlepool Historic Quay★, SE : 14 m. by A 181, A 19 and A 179

Plan opposite

Durham Marriott H. Royal County

Old Elvet ✉ DH1 3JN – ☎ (0191) 386 6821 – mhrsvudm.frontdesk@marriott.com – Fax (0191) 386 0704 B a

147 rm – ♦£ 130/195 ♦♦£ 130/195, £ 14.95 – 3 suites

Rest *County* – (dinner only and Sunday lunch) Carte £ 25/44

Rest *Cruz* – Menu £ 13 (lunch) **s** – Carte dinner £ 19/29 **s**

◆ Scene of miners' rallies in the 1950s and 60s. The quality of accommodation at this town centre hotel is of a comfortable, refined, modern standard. Good leisure facilities. County has elegant décor and linen settings. Bright, relaxed Cruz brasserie.

Farnley Tower

The Avenue ✉ DH1 4DX – ☎ (0191) 375 0011 – enquiries@farnley-tower.co.uk – Fax (0191) 383 9694 A c

15 rm – ♦£ 55/70 ♦♦£ 90

Rest *Gourmet Spot* – Menu £ 15/25 – Carte £ 25/39 **s**

◆ Spacious Victorian house in quiet residential area close to city centre. Modern, airy, well-equipped bedrooms with a good degree of comfort. Gourmet Spot, stylish and slick in black granite and leather, specialises in molecular gastronomy.

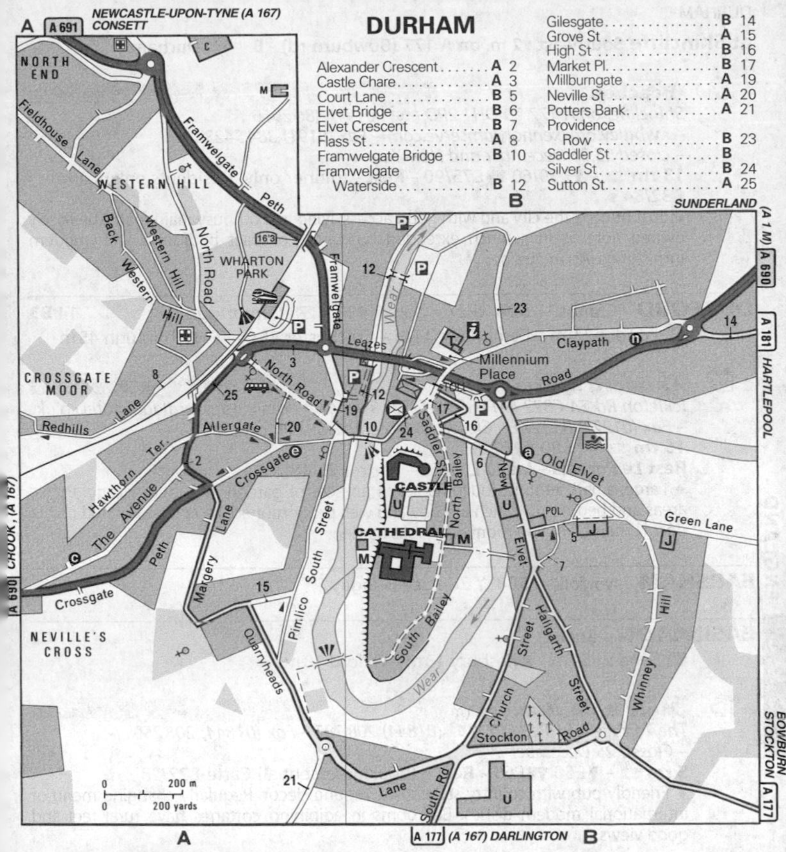

Cathedral View Town House without rest

212 Lower Gilesgate ✉ DH1 1QN – ℘ (0191) 386 9566 – cathedralview@hotmail.com B **n**

6 rm – ♦£ 60/80 ♦♦£ 80/90

◆ Alluring Georgian townhouse with terraced garden in older part of the city near the centre. Attractive breakfast room with good views. Spacious, individually named rooms.

Castle View without rest

4 Crossgate ✉ DH1 4PS – ℘ (0191) 386 8852 – castle-view@hotmail.com – closed Christmas and New Year A **e**

6 rm – ♦£ 50/75 ♦♦£ 75/80

◆ Attractive Georgian townhouse off steep cobbled hill, reputedly once the vicarage to adjacent church. Breakfast on terrace in summer. Individually furnished bedrooms.

Bistro 21

Aykley Heads House, Aykley Heads, Northwest : 1½ m. by A 691 and B 6532 ✉ DH1 5TS – ℘ (0191) 384 4354 – Fax (0191) 384 1149 – closed Sunday and Bank Holidays

Rest – Menu £ 17 – Carte £ 22/40

◆ Part 17C villa with an interior modelled on a simple, Mediterranean style. Good modern British food, with some rustic tone, served in a beamed room or an enclosed courtyard.

at Shincliffe Southeast : 2 m. on A 177 (Bowburn rd) - B – ✉ Durham

Bracken

Shincliffe, on A 177 ✉ DH1 2PD – ✆ (0191) 386 2966 – r.whitley.brackenhol@amserve.com – Fax (0191) 384 5423 – closed 25,26 December and New Year

13 rm – £ 50/60 £ 75/90 – **Rest** – (dinner only) (residents only) Carte £ 32/34 **s**

◆ Just outside the city and with good access, lying just off busy main road. The family owned hotel is in a much extended building. Compact bedrooms with modern furnishings. Asian cuisine.

DUXFORD – Cambs. – 504 U 27 – pop. 1 836 – ✉ Cambridge 14 **B3**

London 50 m – Cambridge 11 m – Colchester 45 m – Peterborough 45 m

Duxford Lodge

Ickleton Rd ✉ CB22 4RT – ✆ (01223) 836 444 – admin@duxfordlodgehotel.co.uk – Fax (01223) 832 271 – Closed 26 December-2 January

15 rm – £ 89 £ 129

Rest *Le Paradis* – Menu £ 17/28 – Carte £ 29/48

◆ Large, smart, redbrick building set in an acre of garden in a quiet village. Public areas and bedrooms, which are tidy and well proportioned, have co-ordinated chintz décor. Themed dining room overlooks garden.

EARSHAM – Norfolk – 504 Y 26 – see Bungay

EASINGTON – Bucks. 11 **C2**

London 54 m – Aylesbury 13 m – Oxford 18 m

Mole & Chicken with rm

The Terrace ✉ HP18 9EY – ✆ (01844) 208 387 – Fax (01844) 208 250 – Closed 25 December

5 rm – £ 50 £ 65 – **Rest** – (booking essential) Carte £ 22/28

◆ Friendly pub with country style character and décor. Regularly changing menu of international modern dishes. Bedrooms in adjoining cottages have rural feel and good views.

EASINGWOLD – N. Yorks. – 502 Q 21 – pop. 3 975 – ✉ York 23 **C2**

London 217 m – Leeds 38 m – Middlesbrough 37 m – York 14 m

Chapel St ✆ (0871) 7161924

Stillington Rd, ✆ (01347) 821 486 .

Old Vicarage without rest

Market Pl ✉ YO61 3AL – ✆ (01347) 821 015 – kirman@oldvic-easingwold.freeserve.co.uk – Fax (01347) 823 465 – restricted opening January and December

4 rm – £ 65 £ 90

◆ Spacious, part Georgian country house with walled rose garden and adjacent croquet lawn. Immaculately kept throughout with fine period antiques in the elegant sitting room.

at Crayke East : 2 m. on Helmsley Rd – ✉ York

The Durham Ox with rm

Westway ✉ YO61 4TE – ✆ (01347) 821 506 – enquiries@thedurhamox.com – Fax (01347) 823 326 – Closed 25 December

4 rm – £ 60 £ 100 – **Rest** – (booking essential) Carte £ 18/30

◆ Open fires, finest English oak bar panelling and exposed beams create a great country pub atmosphere. Hearty dishes from local ingredients. Well-kept rooms.

ENGLAND

EAST ALLINGTON - Devon 2 C3

Fortescue Arms with rm

TQ9 7RA – (01548) 521 215 – info@fortescuearms.co.uk

3 rm – £ 40 £ 60 – **Rest** – (closed Monday lunch) Carte £ 17/33

♦ Ivy-clad pub with decked terrace, set in rural village. Beamed bar serves rustic pub dishes and warm organic bread, while focus is on more refined dishes in smart dining room. Simple bedrooms.

EASTBOURNE - E. Sussex - 504 U 31 - pop. 106 562 Great Britain 8 B3

London 68 m – Brighton 25 m – Dover 61 m – Maidstone 49 m

Cornfield Rd (01323) 411400, tic@eastbourne.gov.uk

Royal Eastbourne Paradise Drive, (01323) 729 738 ;

Eastbourne Downs East Dean Rd, (01323) 720 827 ;

Eastbourne Golfing Park Lottbridge Drove, (01323) 520 400.

Seafront★

Beachy Head★★★, SW : 3 m. by B 2103 Z

Plan on next page

Grand (heated) rm, rest,

King Edward's Parade BN21 4EQ – (01323) 412 345 – reservations@grandeastbourne.co.uk – Fax (01323) 412 233 Z **x**

131 rm – £ 150/480 £ 180/510 – 21 suites

Rest *Mirabelle* – see restaurant listing

Rest *Garden Restaurant* – Menu £ 19/35 **s** – Carte £ 38/57 **s**

♦ Huge, pillared lobby with ornate plasterwork sets the tone of this opulently refurbished, Victorian hotel in prime seafront location. High levels of comfort throughout. Garden Restaurant exudes a light, comfy atmosphere.

ENGLAND

Lansdowne rm,

King Edward's Parade BN21 4EE – (01323) 725 174 – reception@lansdowne-hotel.co.uk – Fax (01323) 739 721 – closed 2-13 January Z **z**

102 rm – £ 53/148 £ 133/173 – **Rest** – (bar lunch Monday to Saturday) Menu £ 23 (dinner) – Carte £ 23/27

♦ Traditional seaside hotel in the same family since 1912. Bedrooms are a mix of décor, either traditional or modern, some with sea views. Dining room has classic feel.

Cherry Tree without rest

15 Silverdale Rd BN20 7AJ – (01323) 722 406 – lynda@cherrytree-eastbourne.co.uk Z **u**

9 rm – £ 45/75 £ 90/110

♦ Comfy guesthouse in semi-detached redbrick building, in quiet residential area near the seafront. Interior of traditional standard and spotlessly kept. A non smoking house.

Brayscroft

13 South Cliff Ave BN20 7AH – (01323) 647 005 – brayscroft@hotmail.com – Closed 25 December Z **n**

6 rm – £ 36/46 £ 72 – **Rest** – (by arrangement) Menu £ 14

♦ Immaculately kept with individual style, antiques, original local art and comfy furnishings throughout. Well run by charming owners. Dining room overlooks a smart terrace.

Mirabelle – at Grand H.

King Edward's Parade BN21 4EQ – (01323) 435 066 – reservations@grandeastbourne.co.uk – Fax (01323) 412 233 – closed Sunday and Monday Z **x**

Rest – (booking essential) Menu £ 21/37 **s** – Carte dinner £ 46/60 **s**

♦ Elegant, comfortable restaurant with a seasonally changing menu of original dishes. A bar lounge in the basement and wine list of impressive names.

EASTBOURNE

Arndale Centre V
Ashford Rd . . . . V 2
Bedfordwell Rd . . . . V 3
Church St . . . . Z 4
Cornfield Rd . . . . V 5
Devonshire Pl. . . . . X 6
Gildredge Rd . . . . V 7
Grove Rd V
Hailsham Rd . . . . Y 8
High St . . . . Z 9
Lewes Rd . . . . Y 13
Lismore Rd . . . . V 14
North St . . . . V 15
Polegate By-Pass . . . . Y 18
St Anthony's Ave. . . . . Y 21
Seaside Rd V
South St V
Station Rd . . . . Y 24
Susan's Rd . . . . V 25
Terminus Rd V
The Goffs . . . . Z 26
Trinity Trees . . . . V 27
Upperton Rd . . . . V, Z 28

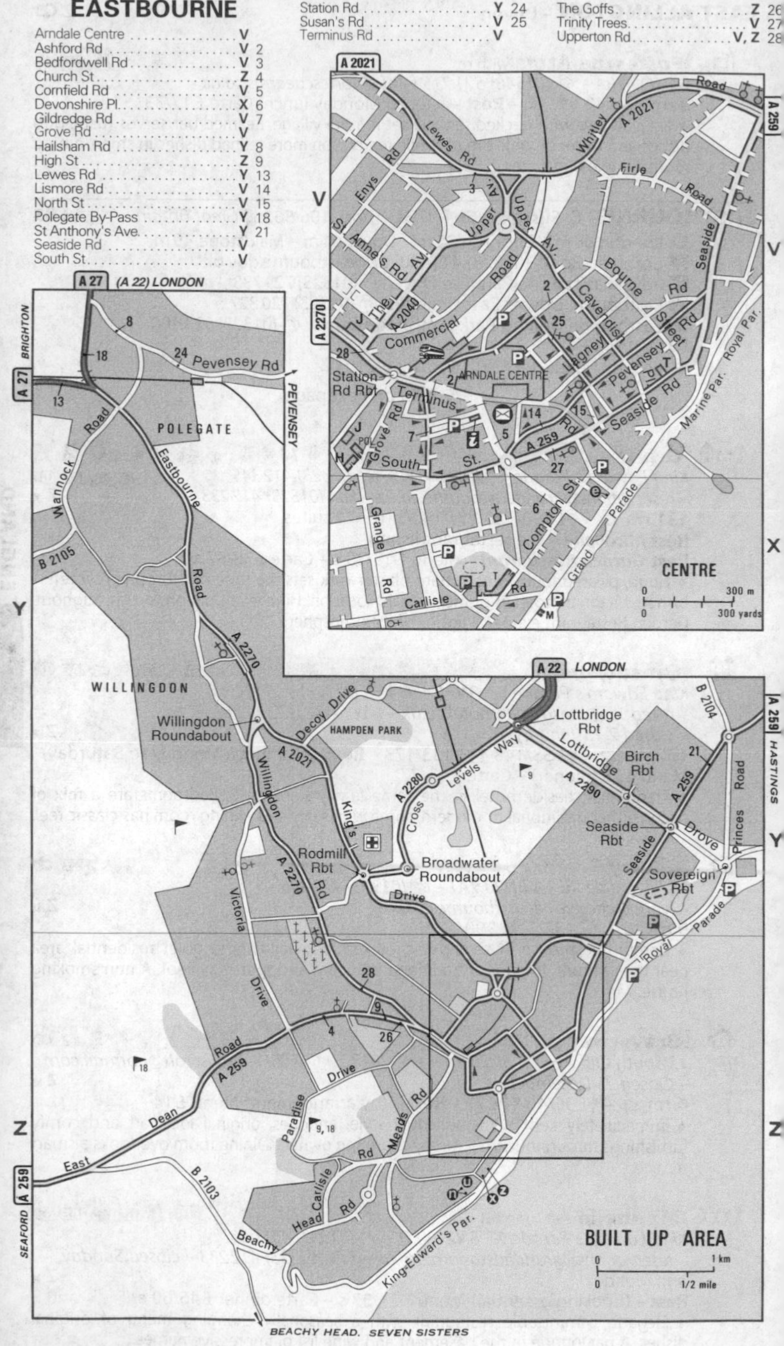

at Jevington Northwest : 6 m. by A 259 - Z - on Jevington Rd – ✉ Polegate

Hungry Monk

The Street ✉ BN26 5QF – ✆ (01323) 482 178 – Fax (01323) 483 989 – Closed 24-25 December, Bank Holiday Monday and lunch Monday to Saturday

Rest – (dinner only and Sunday lunch) (booking essential) Menu £ 30/34

◆ Part 17C Elizabethan cottages with garden. Welcoming, relaxed atmosphere; antique chairs and log fires add to the charm. Menu offers good and hearty, traditional fare.

at Wilmington Northwest : 6½ m. by A 22 on A 27 - Y – ✉ Eastbourne

Crossways

Lewes Rd ✉ BN26 5SG – ✆ (01323) 482 455 – stay@crosswayshotel.co.uk – Fax (01323) 487 811 – closed 23 December-23 January

7 rm – †£ 70/105 ††£ 125 – **Rest** – (closed Sunday-Monday) (dinner only) Menu £ 36

◆ Pretty, detached country house with well tended garden. Linen covered tables in cosy dining room. Cuisine acknowledges the classics with locally sourced, seasonal dishes.

Good food and accommodation at moderate prices?
Look for the Bib symbols:
red Bib Gourmand for food, blue Bib Hotel for hotels

ENGLAND

EAST CHILTINGTON – E. Sussex – see Lewes

EAST DEREHAM – Norfolk – **504** W 25 – pop. 17 779 — 15 **C1**

London 109 m – Cambridge 57 m – King's Lynn 27 m – Norwich 16 m

at Wendling West : 5½ m. by A 47

Greenbanks Country H. with rm

Swaffham Rd ✉ NR19 2AB – ✆ (01362) 687 742 – jenny@greenbanks.co.uk – closed 1 week Christmas

9 rm – †£ 65/75 ††£ 80/120 – **Rest** – (booking essential at lunch) Carte £ 21/29 **s**

◆ Friendly, informal restaurant and pine fitted rooms share a simple cottage style. Traditional cooking is fresh and locally sourced - special diets can be catered for.

EASTGATE – Durham – **502** N 19 — 24 **A3**

London 288 m – Bishop Auckland 20 m – Newcastle upon Tyne 35 m – Stanhope 3 m

Horsley Hall

Southeast : 1 m. by A 689 ✉ DL13 2LJ – ✆ (01388) 517 239 – hotel@horsleyhall.co.uk – Fax (01388) 517 608 – Closd 22 December-5 January

7 rm – †£ 75/85 ††£ 110/135 – **Rest** – (closed Sunday dinner to non-residents) (booking essential for non-residents) (lunch by arrangement) Menu £ 19/23 **s**

◆ Ivy-clad 17C former shooting lodge, built for Bishop of Durham, in exquisitely tranquil setting. Country house style lounge. Spacious bedrooms with telling extra touches. Baronial style dining room with ornate ceiling: homecooked local produce.

EAST GRINSTEAD – W. Sussex – 504 T 30 – pop. 26 222 7 D2

London 48 m – Brighton 30 m – Eastbourne 32 m – Lewes 21 m – Maidstone 37 m

Copthorne Borers Arm Rd, (01342) 712 508 .

at Gravetye Southwest : 4½ m. by B 2110 taking second turn left towards West Hoathly – ✉ East Grinstead

Gravetye Manor (Mark Raffan)

Vowels Lane ✉ RH19 4LJ – (01342) 810 567 – info@gravetyemanor.co.uk – Fax (01342) 810 080

18 rm – †£ 110/340 ††£ 170/340, £ 20 – **Rest** – (closed dinner 25 December to non-residents) (booking essential) Menu £ 23/35 – Carte £ 23/49 **s**

Spec. Essence of tomato, asparagus tips, quail egg and basil. Roast turbot, shallots, girolles and béarnaise. Dark chocolate marquise with coffee mascarpone cream.

◆ Beautiful 16C manor house featuring polished oak, fine English fabrics, antiques and charming log fires. Beautiful grounds house gazebo for al fresco dining. Luxurious bedrooms, some with fine views. Classic cooking; seasonal menus; professional service.

EAST HOATHLY – E. Sussex – 504 U 31 8 B3

London 60 m – Brighton 16 m – Eastbourne 13 m – Hastings 25 m – Maidstone 32 m

Old Whyly (heated)

London Rd, West : ½ m., turning right after post box on right, taking centre gravel drive after approx. 400 metres ✉ BN8 6EL – (01825) 840 216 – stay@oldwhyly.co.uk – Fax (01825) 840 738

3 rm – ††£ 90/130 – **Rest** – (by arrangement, communal dining) Menu £ 30

◆ Charming, secluded Georgian manor house decorated with antiques, oils and watercolours. Airy bedrooms individually styled. Delightful owner. Warm, informal dining room.

EAST LAVANT – W. Sussex – see Chichester

EAST MERSEA – Essex 13 D2

London 72 m – Colchester 13 m – Ipswich 29 m

Mersea Vineyard without rest

Rewsalls Lane ✉ CO5 8SX – (01206) 385 900 – roger.barber@merseawine.com – Fax (01206) 383 600 – Closed Christmas, New Year and Easter

3 rm – †£ 55/70 ††£ 70

◆ Serious working vineyard producing about 15,000 bottles a year. Sunny courtyard; family style breakfast room. Well priced. Carefully co-ordinated rooms have vineyard views.

EASTON – Devon – 503 I 31 – see Chagford

EASTON – Hants. – see Winchester

EASTON – Somerset – see Wells

EAST WITTON – N. Yorks. – 502 O 21 – ✉ Leyburn 22 B1

London 238 m – Leeds 45 m – Middlesbrough 30 m – York 39 m

The Blue Lion with rm

✉ *DL8 4SN – ✆ (01969) 624 273 – bluelion@breathe.net – Fax (01969) 624 189*
15 rm – £ 58 £ 110 – **Rest** – (closed 25 December and Sunday lunch) (booking essential) Carte £ 11/39
◆ Characterful, rustic feel throughout: flagstone floors, log fires, antiques and curios. Good value, traditional bar food. Extensive wine list and hand-pumped ales. Cosy rooms.

ECCLESTON – Lancs. – 502 L 23 – pop. 4 708 20 A2

London 219 m – Birmingham 103 m – Liverpool 29 m – Preston 11 m

Parr Hall Farm without rest

Parr Lane ✉ PR7 5SL – ✆ (01257) 451 917 – enquiries@parrhallfarm.com – Fax (01257) 453 749
12 rm – £ 35/45 £ 60/100
◆ Part 18C former farmhouse with neat lawned gardens in small, pleasant town. Warmly decorated breakfast room with pine dressers. Cosy bedrooms with flowery fabrics.

Do not confuse X with ✿!
X defines comfort, while stars are awarded for the best cuisine, across all categories of comfort.

EDENBRIDGE – Kent – 504 U 30 – pop. 7 196 *Great Britain* 8 A2

London 35 m – Brighton 36 m – Maidstone 29 m
Edenbridge G & C.C. Crouch House Rd, ✆ (01732) 867 381 .
Hever Castle★ **AC**, E : 2½ m. – Chartwell★ **AC**, N : 3 m. by B 2026

Haxted Mill

Haxted Rd, West : 2¼ m. on Haxted Rd ✉ TN8 6PU – ✆ (01732) 862 914 – david@haxtedmill.co.uk – closed 23 December-15 January, Sunday dinner and Monday
Rest – Menu £ 23/28 – Carte £ 29/39
◆ Converted 17C clapboard stables located next to the watermill with large terrace overlooking the river Eden. Seasonally changing menu with emphasis on seafood in the summer.

EGHAM – Surrey – 504 S 29 – pop. 27 666 7 C1

London 29 m – Reading 21 m

Great Fosters (heated)

Stroude Rd, South : 1¼ m. by B 388 ✉ TW20 9UR – ✆ (01784) 433 822 – enquiries@greatfosters.co.uk – Fax (01784) 472 455
41 rm – £ 120/165 £ 165, £ 16 – 3 suites – **Rest** – (closed Saturday lunch) Menu £ 24/36 – Carte £ 39/46
◆ Elizabethan mansion with magnificent gardens. Delightfully original interior has tapestries, oak panelling and antiques. Bedooms in the main house especially notable. Two historic dining rooms: one an ancient tithe barn, the other in 16C French style.

Monsoon

20 High St ✉ TW20 9DT – ✆ (01784) 432 141 – Fax (01784) 432 194 – closed 25-26 December
Rest – Indian Carte £ 12/20
◆ Smart, stylish restaurant that prides itself on immaculate upkeep and personable service. Contemporary artwork enlivens the walls. Freshly cooked, authentic Indian dishes.

ELLAND – W. Yorks. – 502 O 22 – pop. 14 554 – ✉ Halifax 22 B3

London 204 m – Bradford 12 m – Burnley 29 m – Leeds 17 m – Manchester 30 m

Hullen Edge Hammerstones Leach Lane, ✆ (01422) 372 505 .

La Cachette

31 Huddersfield Rd ✉ HX5 9AW – ✆ (01422) 378 833 – Fax (01422) 327 567 – closed last 2 weeks August, 26 December-4 January, Sunday and Bank Holiday Mondays

Rest – Menu £ 18 (dinner) – Carte £ 19/31 **s**

◆ A busy, bustling brasserie-style restaurant with sprinkling of French panache. Menu of eclectically blended interpretations served in the dining room or well-stocked wine bar.

ELLESMERE PORT – Mersey. – 502 L 24 – pop. 66 265 20 A3

London 211 m – Birkenhead 9 m – Chester 9 m – Liverpool 12 m – Manchester 44 m

Holiday Inn Ellesmere Port Cheshire Oaks

Centre Island, Waterways, Lower Mersey St, Northeast : 1½ m. by A 5032 (M 53 junction 9) ✉ CH65 2AL – ✆ (0151) 356 8111 – sales@hiellesmereport.com – Fax (0151) 356 8444

83 rm – †£ 79/87 ††£ 79/87

Rest ***The Locks*** – Carte £ 17/30 **s**

◆ Purpose-built hotel on marina beside boat museum. Uniform styling in carefully designed, modern rooms, all with waterway views. Convenient for land and air transport links. Bustling, split-level restaurant.

ELSLACK – North Yorkshire – see SKIPTON

ELSTED – W. Sussex – 504 R 31 – see Midhurst

ELSTOW – Beds. – 504 S 27 – see Bedford

ELTON – Cambs. – 504 S 26 14 A2

The Crown Inn

8 Duck St ✉ PE8 6RQ – ✆ (01832) 280 232 – marcus@marcuslamb4.wanadoo.co.uk – Closed 2 weeks January, 25 December, Monday and Sunday dinner

Rest – Carte £ 13/25

◆ Thatched inn in picture postcard village. Open main bar, large dining room and spacious rear conservatory. Daily-changing menu has traditional base. Lighter lunchtime snacks.

ELY – Cambs. – 504 U 26 – pop. 13 954 *Great Britain* 14 B2

London 74 m – Cambridge 16 m – Norwich 60 m

Oliver Cromwell's House, 29 St Mary's St ✆ (01353) 662062

107 Cambridge Rd, ✆ (01353) 662 751 .

Cathedral★★ AC

Wicken Fen★, SE : 9 m. by A 10 and A 1123

The Boathouse

5-5A Annesdale ✉ CB7 4BN – ✆ (01353) 664 388 – boathouse@cambscuisine.com – Fax (01353) 666 688

Rest – (booking essential) Carte £ 20/28

◆ A riverside setting makes for a charming ambience: bag a terrace table if you can. Airy, dark wood interior where worldwide menus benefit from numerous creative touches.

ENGLAND

at Little Thetford South : 2 ¾ m. off A 10 – ✉ Ely

Springfields without rest

Ely Road, North : ½ m. on A 10 ✉ CB6 3HJ – ℘ (01353) 663 637 – springfields@talk21.com – Fax (01353) 663 130 – closed December

3 rm ☕ – †£ 50 ††£ 70

◆ Spotlessly kept guesthouse and gardens. Breakfast served at communal table. Chintz bedrooms with bric-a-brac and extras such as perfume, fresh flowers and sweets.

at Sutton Gault West : 8 m. by A 142 off B 1381 – ✉ Ely

The Anchor Inn with rm

✉ CB6 2BD – ℘ (01353) 778 537 – anchorinn@popmail.bta.com – Fax (01353) 776 180 – closed 26 December

4 rm ☕ – †£ 60/95 ††£ 155 – **Rest** – Menu £ 11 – Carte £ 15/30

◆ Part 17C inn on the western edge of the Isle of Ely, enhanced by open fires. Balanced à la carte menu of traditional British food from the blackboard. Comfortable bedrooms.

If breakfast is included the ☕ symbol appears after the number of rooms.

EMSWORTH – Hants. – 504 R 31 – pop. 18 139 6 B2

London 75 m – Brighton 37 m – Portsmouth 10 m – Southampton 22 m

36 on the Quay (Ramon Farthing) with rm

47 South St, The Quay ✉ PO10 7EG – ℘ (01243) 375592 – Fax (01243) 375593 – closed 3 weeks January, 1 week May and 1 week October

4 rm – †£ 70 ††£ 95 – 1 suite – **Rest** – (closed Sunday-Monday) (booking essential) Menu £ 25/46

Spec. Seared scallops, Serrano ham and pea shoot salad, passion fruit dressing. Veal fillet, sweetbreads,Lyonnaise potato and artichoke sauce. Iced peanut parfait, butterscotch doughnuts, coffee foam.

◆ A delightful quayside restaurant with smart, slinky cream and brown interior and comfortable, contemporary bedrooms; Vanilla is the most luxurious, with the best view. Well presented, flavourful international dishes. Informal, friendly service.

Spencers

36 North St ✉ PO10 7DG – ℘ (01243) 372744 – Fax (01243) 372744 – closed 25-26 December, Sunday and Bank Holidays

Rest – Menu £ 14 (lunch) – Carte £ 22/28

◆ Ground floor brasserie-style with central bar and wood flooring, first floor more formal with brightly coloured dining-booths. Good variety of modern English dishes.

Fat Olives

30 South St ✉ PO10 7EH – ℘ (01243) 377914 – info@fatolives.co.uk – closed 2 weeks June-July 2 weeks Christmas, Sunday and Monday

Rest – (booking essential) Menu £ 19 (lunch) – Carte £ 26/38

◆ Small terraced house with a welcoming ambience. Simply decorated with wood floor and rough plaster walls. Tasty modern British menu and, yes, fat olives are available!

ENSTONE – Oxon. – 503 P 28 – ✉ Chipping Norton 10 B1

London 73 m – Birmingham 48 m – Gloucester 32 m – Oxford 18 m

Swan Lodge without rest

on A 44 ✉ OX7 4NE – ℘ (01608) 678 736 – Fax (01608) 678 736 – Closed 1 week Christmas

3 rm ☕ – †£ 50/60 ††£ 70/80

◆ 18C former coaching inn ideally situated for the Cotswolds. Well kept and furnished with antiques and log fires. Sizeable, comfy, mahogany furnished bedrooms.

ENGLAND

EPSOM – Surrey – **504** T 30 – **pop. 64 493** 7 **D1**

London 17 m – Guildford 16 m
Longdown Lane South Epsom Downs, ✆ (01372) 721 666 ;
Horton Park C.C. Hook Rd, ✆ (020) 8393 8400.

Chalk Lane

Chalk Lane, Southwest : ½ m. by A 24 and Woodcote Rd ✉ KT18 7BB – ✆ (01372) 721 179 – smcgregor@chalklanehotel.com – Fax (01372) 727 878
22 rm – †£ 95/150 ††£ 130/180 – **Rest** – Menu £ 15/39
◆ At the foot of the Epsom Downs and near to the racecourse. Quality furnishings throughout; the neatly kept bedrooms are most comfortable. Smart, modern dining room.

Le Raj

211 Fir Tree Rd, Epsom Downs, Southeast : 2 ¼ m. by B 289 and B 284 on B 291 ✉ KT17 3LB – ✆ (01737) 371 371 – bookings@lerajrestaurant.co.uk – Fax (01737) 211 903 – closed 25 December
Rest – Bangladeshi Menu £ 20 (lunch) – Carte £ 25/41
◆ Original, interesting menu makes good use of fresh ingredients and brings a modern style to traditional Bangladeshi cuisine. Smart, vibrant, contemporary interior décor.

ERMINGTON – Devon 2 **C2**

London 216 m – Plymouth 11 m – Salcombe 15 m

Plantation House with rm

Totnes Rd, Southwest : ½ m. on A 3121 ✉ PL21 9NS – ✆ (01548) 831 100 – info@plantationhousehotel.co.uk
8 rm – †£ 55/79 ††£ 120/130 – **Rest** – (closed Sunday and Monday to non-residents) (dinner only) (booking essential for non-residents) Menu £ 30/45
◆ Appealing, converted Georgian rectory with smart gardens and terraced seating area. Personally run. Sound cooking of locally sourced ingredients. Individually styled bedrooms.

ERPINGHAM – Norfolk – **504** X 25 15 **D1**

London 123 m – Cromer 8 m – King's Lynn 46 m – Norwich 16 m

The Saracen's Head with rm

Wolterton, West : 1 ½ m. on Itteringham rd ✉ NR11 7LX – ✆ (01263) 768 909 – saracenshead@wolterton.freeserve.co.uk – Fax (01263) 768 993 – Closed 25 December and dinner 26 December
6 rm – †£ 50 ††£ 90 – **Rest** – (booking essential) Menu £ 8 – Carte £ 22/27
◆ Personally run 19C coaching inn with courtyard and walled garden. Log fires, stone floors and bright en suite rooms. Blackboard menu of unpretentious, country dishes.

ESCRICK – N. Yorks. – **502** Q 22 – **see York**

ESHER – Surrey – **504** S 29 – **pop. 50 344** 7 **D1**

London 20 m – Portsmouth 58 m
Thames Ditton & Esher Portsmouth Rd, ✆ (020) 8398 1551 ;
Moore Place Portsmouth Rd, ✆ (01372) 463 533 ;
Sandown Park More Lane, ✆ (01372) 468 093.

Plan : see Greater London (South-West) 5

George

104 High St ✉ KT10 9QJ – ✆ (01372) 471 500 – reservations@george-esher.com – Fax (01372) 469 217 – closed 25-26 December, 1 January, Sunday dinner and lunch Saturday and Monday
Rest – Menu £ 25/43
◆ Elegant and understated restaurant with added refinement of airy cocktail bar. Immaculately laid tables lend a formal air to modern dishes that change with the seasons.

ENGLAND

XX **Good Earth**

14-18 High St ✉ KT10 9RT – ✆ (01372) 462 489 – Fax (01372) 460 668 – Closed 23-30 December BZ **e**

Rest – Chinese Menu £ 29/36 – Carte £ 30/60

◆ A large Chinese restaurant with a smart, smooth style in décor and service. Well presented menu with much choice including vegetarian sections.

ESHOTT – **Northd.** – **see Morpeth**

EVERSHOT – Dorset – 503 M 31 – ✉ Dorchester 4 C3

London 149 m – Bournemouth 39 m – Dorchester 12 m – Salisbury 53 m – Taunton 30 m – Yeovil 10 m

Summer Lodge

9 Fore St ✉ DT2 0JR – ✆ (01935) 482 000 – summer@relaischateaux.com – Fax (01935) 482 040

20 rm – †£ 195/515 ††£ 225/500 – 4 suites – **Rest** – Menu £ 25 – Carte dinner £ 41/53

◆ Part Georgian dower house in quiet village, in the best tradition of stylish, English country hotels. Boasts a range of sleek, smart, up-to-date bedrooms. Elegant dining room overlooking walled garden and terrace.

Acorn Inn with rm

28 Fore St ✉ DT2 0JW – ✆ (01935) 83 228 – stay@acorn-inn.co.uk – Fax (01935) 83 707

10 rm – †£ 155 ††£ 170 – **Rest** – Carte £ 24/34

◆ 16C inn in idyllically archetypal English setting. Characterful main bar with open fire and beamed ceiling. Hearty British cooking with modern touches. Smart, cottagey rooms.

We try to be as accurate as possible when giving room rates. But prices are susceptible to change, so please check rates when booking.

EVESHAM – Worcs. – 503 O 27 – pop. 22 179 19 C3

London 99 m – Birmingham 30 m – Cheltenham 16 m – Coventry 32 m

The Almonry, Abbey Gate ✆ (01386) 446944

Wood Norton Hall

Northwest : 2¼ m. on A 4538 ✉ WR11 4WN – ✆ (01386) 425 780 – info@wnhall.co.uk – Fax (01386) 425 781

44 rm – †£ 95/125 ††£ 150/160 – 1 suite

Rest *Le Duc's* (booking essential) Carte £ 33/40

◆ Superbly wood-panelled 19C Vale of Evesham country house. Built by a French duke, and once a BBC training centre. Antiques, original fittings and a library. Large, airy rooms. Formal elements define restaurant.

Evesham

Coopers Lane, off Waterside ✉ WR11 1DA – ✆ (01386) 765 566 – reception@eveshamhotel.com – Fax (01386) 765 443 – closed 25-26 December

40 rm – †£ 78/92 ††£ 130/175

Rest *Cedar* – Carte £ 22/28 **s**

◆ Idiosyncratic family run hotel in a quiet location. Guest families well catered for, with jolly japes at every turn. Individual rooms with cottage décor and eclectic themes. Unconventional menus in keeping with hotel style.

EWEN – **Glos.** – **503** O 28 – **see Cirencester**

ENGLAND

EXETER – Devon – 503 J 31 – pop. 106 772 2 D2

London 201 m – Bournemouth 83 m – Bristol 83 m – Plymouth 46 m – Southampton 110 m

Exeter Airport : ✆ (01392) 367433, E : 5 m. by A 30 V

Princesshay Shopping Centre ✆ (01392) 665700

Downes Crediton Hookway, ✆ (01363) 773 025 .

City★★ - Cathedral★★ Z – Royal Albert Memorial Museum★ Y

Killerton★★ **AC**, NE : 7 m. by B 3181 V – Ottery St Mary★ (St Mary's★) E : 12 m. by B 3183 - Y - A 30 and B 3174 – Crediton (Holy Cross Church★), NW : 9 m. by A 377

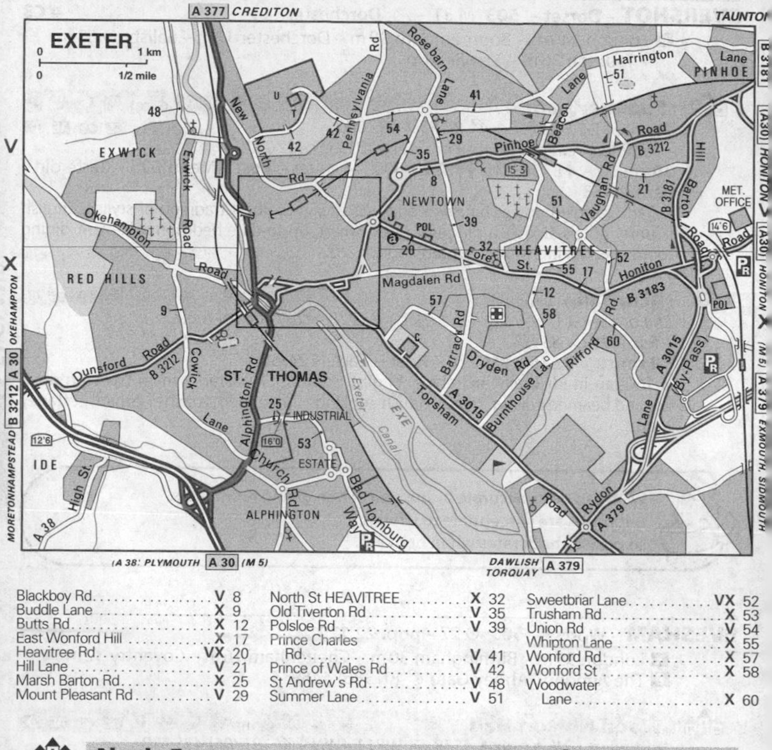

Blackboy Rd . . . . . V 8
Buddle Lane . . . . . X 9
Butts Rd . . . . . X 12
East Wonford Hill . . . . . X 17
Heavitree Rd . . . . . VX 20
Hill Lane . . . . . V 21
Marsh Barton Rd . . . . . X 25
Mount Pleasant Rd . . . . . V 29
North St HEAVITREE . . . . . X 32
Old Tiverton Rd . . . . . V 35
Polsloe Rd . . . . . V 39
Prince Charles Rd . . . . . V 41
Prince of Wales Rd . . . . . V 42
St Andrew's Rd . . . . . V 48
Summer Lane . . . . . V 51
Sweetbriar Lane . . . . . VX 52
Trusham Rd . . . . . X 53
Union Rd . . . . . V 54
Whipton Lane . . . . . X 55
Wonford Rd . . . . . X 57
Wonford St . . . . . X 58
Woodwater Lane . . . . . X 60

Abode Exeter

rest, VISA AE

The Royal Clarence, Cathedral Yard ✉ *EX1 1HD* – ✆ *(01392) 319955 – info@abodehotels.co.uk – Fax (01392) 439423* Y **z**

52 rm – †£ 125/145 ††£ 260, ☕ £ 14.50 – 1 suite

Rest *Michael Caines* – see restaurant listing

◆ Georgian-style frontage; located on the doorstep of the cathedral. Boutique style hotel with a very modern, stylish interior. Understated bedrooms feature good mod cons.

Barcelona

VISA AE

Magdalen St ✉ *EX2 4HY* – ✆ *(01392) 281 000 – barcelona@aliashotels.com – Fax (01392) 281 001* Z **s**

46 rm – †£ 109/139 ††£ 129/149, ☕ £ 11.95

Rest *Café Paradiso* – Menu £ 15 (lunch) – Carte £ 24/33

◆ Trendy hotel located in Victorian former infirmary. Informal atmosphere. Two fashionable lounges with contemporary furniture. Autumnal coloured rooms with modern facilities. Informality marks dining room style and menus.

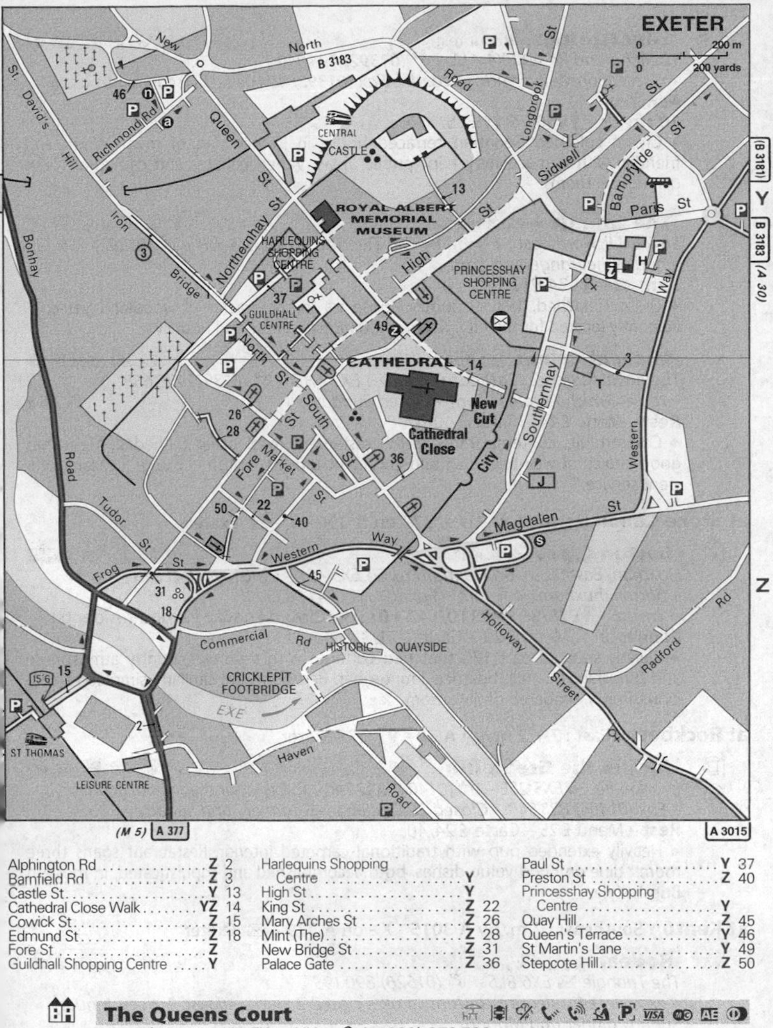

EXETER

Street	Grid	No.
Alphington Rd	Z	2
Barnfield Rd	Z	3
Castle St	Y	13
Cathedral Close Walk	YZ	14
Cowick St	Z	15
Edmund St	Z	18
Fore St	Z	
Guildhall Shopping Centre	Y	
Harlequins Shopping Centre	Y	
High St	Y	
King St	Z	22
Mary Arches St	Z	26
Mint (The)	Z	28
New Bridge St	Z	31
Palace Gate	Z	36
Paul St	Y	37
Preston St	Z	40
Princesshay Shopping Centre	Y	
Quay Hill	Z	45
Queen's Terrace	Y	46
St Martin's Lane	Y	49
Stepcote Hill	Z	50

The Queens Court

Bystock Terrace ✉ EX4 4HY – ✆ (01392) 272 709 – enquiries@queenscourt-hotel.co.uk – Fax (01392) 491 390 – Closed 25-26 December Y **n**

18 rm ☕ – †£85 ††£109

Rest *Olive Tree* – Mediterranean (dinner only) Carte £22/30

◆ A town house hotel located close to Central train station. Bright public areas decorated in a clean, modern style. Well-equipped, tidily furnished and co-ordinated bedrooms. Brightly painted, clean-lined restaurant.

The Edwardian without rest

30-32 Heavitree Rd ✉ EX1 2LQ – ✆ (01392) 276 102 – michael@edwardianexeter.co.uk V **a**

13 rm ☕ – †£55 ††£80

◆ Personally run hotel with a welcoming ambience. Edwardian themed lounge. Rooms vary between the modern and the traditional and some have four-poster beds.

Silversprings without rest
12 Richmond Rd ✉ EX4 4JA – ✆ (01392) 494 040 – reservations@silversprings.co.uk – Fax (01392) 494 040 – Closed Christmas to New Year Y **a**
10 rm – †£ 50/75 ††£ 85/120
◆ Cream coloured Georgian terraced house in Roman part of town. Warm and friendly, with immaculately kept public areas. Varied palettes and cathedral views distinguish rooms.

The Grange without rest (heated)
Stoke Hill, Northeast : 1 ¾ m. by Old Tiverton Rd ✉ EX4 7JH – ✆ (01392) 259 723 – dudleythegrange@aol.com
3 rm – †£ 34 ††£ 54
◆ Quiet, detached, 1930s country house set in three acres of woodland yet conveniently located for the city. Accommodation is simple and homely.

Michael Caines – at Abode Exeter
The Royal Clarence, Cathedral Yard ✉ EX1 1HD – ✆ (01392) 223 638 – tables@michaelcaines.com – closed Sunday Y **z**
Rest – Menu £ 14 – Carte £ 40/47
◆ Comfortable, contemporarily stylish restaurant overlooking Cathedral. Menu has good choice of well-balanced and confident modern British cooking. Pleasant, efficient service.

at Stoke Canon North : 5 m. by A 377 on A 396 - V – ✉ Exeter

Barton Cross
Huxham, East : ½ m. on Huxham rd ✉ EX5 4EJ – ✆ (01392) 841 245 – bartonxhuxham@aol.com – Fax (01392) 841 942
9 rm – †£ 78/86 ††£ 110/140 – **Rest** – (Closed Sunday for non-residents) (dinner only) Menu £ 29 – Carte £ 21/32
◆ Quietly situated part 17C thatched cottages with a simple, country atmosphere and furnishings. Small, beamed lounge bar. Bedrooms are similarly simple yet spacious. Pretty, timbered dining room.

at Rockbeare East : 7 1/2 m. by A 30 - V – ✉ Exeter

Jack in the Green Inn
London Rd ✉ EX5 2EE – ✆ (01404) 822 240 – info@jackinthegreen.uk.com – Fax (01404) 823 540 – Closed 25 December-6 January and Sunday
Rest – Menu £ 25 – Carte £ 24/40
◆ Heavily extended pub with traditional carpeted interior. Restaurant spans three rooms: dine on good value dishes, both accomplished and sophisticated, in modern British style.

at Kenton Southeast : 7 m. by A 3015 - X - on A 379 – ✉ Exeter

Rodean
The Triangle ✉ EX6 8LS – ✆ (01626) 890 195 – excellence@rodeanrestaurant.co.uk – closed 2 weeks August, 1 week January, Sunday dinner and Monday
Rest – (dinner only and Sunday lunch) Carte £ 26/35
◆ Family run early 20C butchers shop in pretty spot. Bar area for pre-prandials. Restaurant in two rooms with beams and local photos. Menus employ good use of local ingredients.

EXFORD – Somerset – **503** J 30 3 **A2**

London 193 m – Exeter 41 m – Minehead 14 m – Taunton 33 m
Church★
Exmoor National Park★★

The Crown
✉ TA24 7PP – ✆ (01643) 831 554 – info@crownhotelexmoor.co.uk – Fax (01643) 831 665
17 rm – †£ 68/101 ††£ 105/135 – **Rest** – (bar lunch) Menu £ 19/33
◆ Pretty 17C coaching inn with a delightful rear water garden. Open fires and country prints. Comfy, individualistic rooms, some retaining period features.

EXMOUTH – Devon – 503 J 32 – pop. 32 972 2 D2

London 210 m – Exeter 11 m
Alexandra Terr ☎ (01395) 222299
A la Ronde★ AC, N : 2 m. by B 3180

The Barn without rest ← Exmouth Bay, (heated) P
Foxholes Hill, East : 1 m. via Esplanade and Queens Drive VISA
✉ EX8 2DF – ☎ (01395) 224411 – info@barnhotel.co.uk – Fax (01395) 225445 – closed 23 December-10 January
11 rm – £38/63 £76/96
◆ Grade II listed Arts and Crafts house in a peacefully elevated position offering sea views from many bedrooms. Personal and friendly service.

EXTON – Devon 2 D2

London 176 m – Exmouth 4 m – Topsham 3 m

The Puffing Billy AC P VISA
Station Rd ✉ EX3 0PR – ☎ (01392) 877888 – Closed 25 December to early January
Rest – Carte £19/29
◆ Modernised pub with barn-like extension. Relaxed ambience: comfy leather seating in lounge bar. Menus designed to please all, from informal favourites to fine dining.

FADMOOR – N. Yorks. – see Kirkbymoorside

FAIRFORD – Glos. – 503 O 28 – pop. 2 960 *Great Britain* 4 D1

London 88 m – Cirencester 9 m – Oxford 29 m
Church of St Mary★ (Stained glass windows★★)
Cirencester★ - Church of St John the Baptist★ - Corinium Museum★ (Mosaic Pavements★), W : 9 m. on A 429, A 435, Spitalgate Lane and Dollar St – Swindon - Great Railway Museum★ **AC** - Railway Village Museum★ **AC**, S : 17 m. on A 419, A 4312, A 4259 and B 4289

XXX **Allium** VISA
1 London St, Market Pl ✉ GL7 4AH – ☎ (01285) 712200 – restaurant@allium.uk.net – Fax (01285) 712658 – closed 2 weeks January, Christmas; Monday, Tuesday and Sunday dinner
Rest – Menu £14/35
◆ Pair of Cotswold stone cottages on a main road. Squashy sofas in lounge and bar. Food's a serious matter here: modern dishes are prepared with skill and care. Personally run.

Good food without spending a fortune?
Look out for the Bib Gourmand

FALMOUTH – Cornwall – 503 E 33 – pop. 21 635 1 A3

London 308 m – Penzance 26 m – Plymouth 65 m – Truro 11 m
28 Killigrew St ☎ (01326) 312300
18 Swanpool Rd, ☎ (01326) 311262 ;
9 Budock Vean Hotel Mawnan Smith, ☎ (01326) 252102 .
Town★ – Pendennis Castle★ (← ★★) **AC** B
Glendurgan Garden★★ **AC** - Trebah Garden★, SW : 4½ m. by Swanpool Rd A – Mawnan Parish Church★ (← ★★) S : 4 m. by Swanpool Rd A – Cruise along Helford River★. Trelissick★★ (← ★★) NW : 13 m. by A 39 and B 3289 A – Carn Brea (← ★★) NW : 10 m. by A 393 A – Gweek (Setting★, Seal Sanctuary★) SW : 8 m. by A 39 and Treverva rd – Wendron (Poldark Mine★) **AC**, SW : 12½ m. by A 39 - A - and A 394

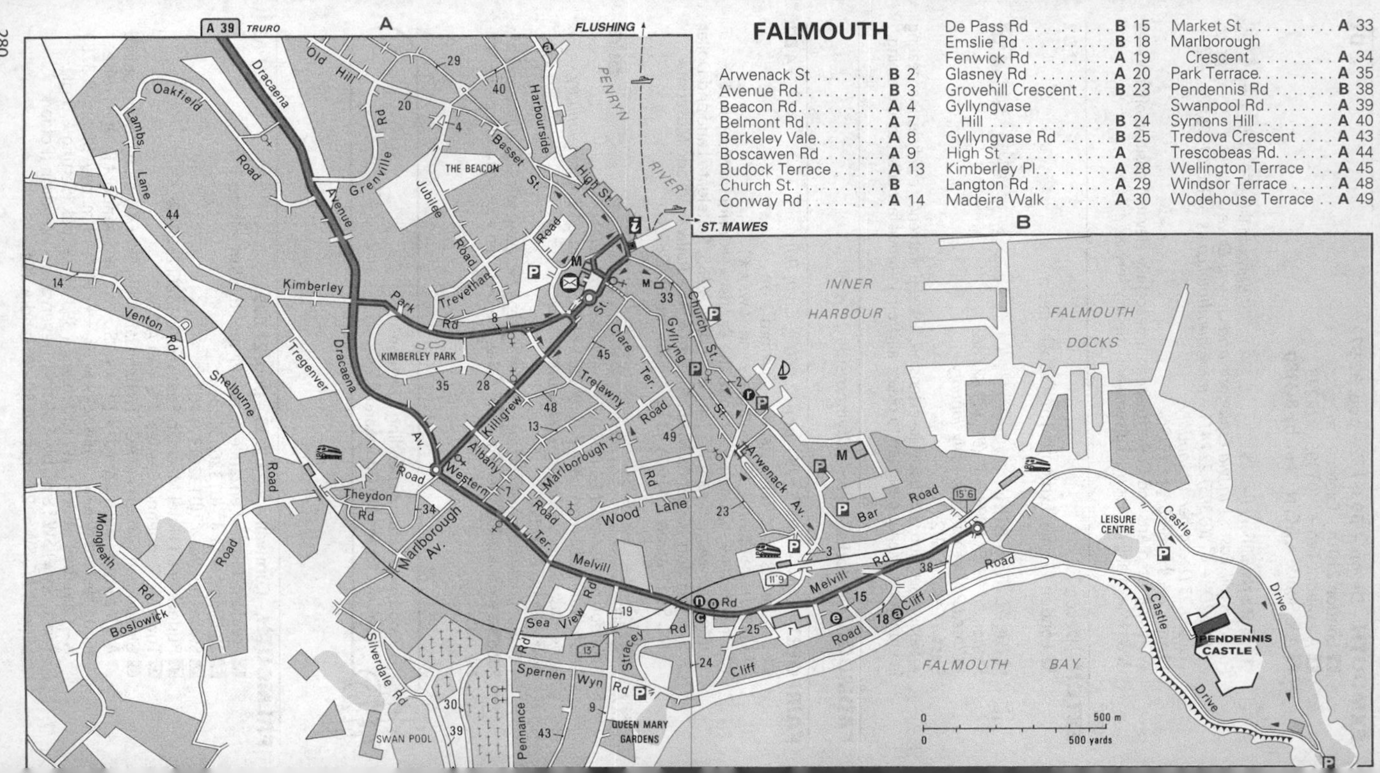
FALMOUTH
Arwenack St . . . . B 2
Avenue Rd. . . . . B 3
Beacon Rd. . . . . A 4
Belmont Rd . . . . A 7
Berkeley Vale. . . . . A 8
Boscawen Rd . . . . A 9
Budock Terrace . . . . . . A 13
Church St. . . . . B
Conway Rd . . . . A 14
De Pass Rd . . . . B 15
Emslie Rd . . . . B 18
Fenwick Rd . . . . A 19
Glasney Rd . . . . A 20
Grovehill Crescent . . . . B 23
Gyllyngvase Hill . . . . . . B 24
Gyllyngvase Rd . . . . . . B 25
High St . . . . A
Kimberley Pl. . . . . A 28
Langton Rd . . . . A 29
Madeira Walk . . . . A 30
Market St . . . . A 33
Marlborough Crescent . . . A 34
Park Terrace. . . . . A 35
Pendennis Rd . . . . B 38
Swanpool Rd. . . . . A 39
Symons Hill . . . . A 40
Tredova Crescent . . . . . A 43
Trescobeas Rd. . . . . A 44
Wellington Terrace . . . . A 45
Windsor Terrace . . . . . . A 48
Wodehouse Terrace . . . . A 49
A 39 TRURO
A
B
FLUSHING
ST. MAWES
PENRYN RIVER
INNER HARBOUR
FALMOUTH DOCKS
FALMOUTH BAY
PENDENNIS CASTLE
LEISURE CENTRE
THE BEACON
KIMBERLEY PARK
QUEEN MARY GARDENS
SWAN POOL
Dracaena Avenue
Old Hill
Harbourside
Basset St.
Grenville Rd
Jubilee Road
Trevethan Rd
Kimberley Park Rd
Oakfield Road
Lambs Lane
Venton Rd
Shelburne Road
Tregenver
Dracaena Av.
Killigrew St.
Clare Ter.
Trelawny Road
Marlborough Rd
Albany Road
Western Ter.
Wood Lane
Church St.
Gyllyng St.
Arwenack Av.
Bar Road
Melvill Rd
Cliff Road
Castle Drive
Theydon Rd
Marlborough Av.
Mongleath Rd
Boslowick Road
Silverdale Rd
Sea View Rd
Stracey Rd
Spernen Wyn Rd
Pennance
500 m
500 yards

Greenbank
harbour,

Harbourside ✉ TR11 2SR – ✆ (01326) 312 440 – reception@greenbank-hotel.co.uk – Fax (01326) 211 362 A **a**

57 rm ☕ – 🚹£ 70/80 🚹🚹£ 175/215 – 1 suite

Rest *Harbourside* – (bar lunch Monday-Saturday) – Carte approx. £ 33

◆ Flagstones and sweeping staircase greet your arrival in this ex-17C coaching inn, just as they once did for Florence Nightingale and Kenneth Grahame. Rooms with harbour views. Fine vista of bay from modern restaurant.

Royal Duchy

Cliff Rd ✉ TR11 4NX – ✆ (01326) 313 042 – info@royalduchy.com – Fax (01326) 319 420 B **a**

42 rm ☕ – 🚹£ 83/95 🚹🚹£ 118/130 – 1 suite

Rest *Restaurant* – Menu £ 35 **s**

◆ Located on clifftop next to beach with stunning views of Pendennis Castle on headland beyond. Indoor swimming pool and leisure area. Comfortable bedrooms, many with sea views. Restaurant has good choice menus promoting local, seasonal dishes.

Dolvean without rest

50 Melvill Rd ✉ TR11 4DQ – ✆ (01326) 313 658 – reservations@dolvean.co.uk – Fax (01326) 313 995 – closed Christmas and New Year B **n**

10 rm ☕ – 🚹£ 35/60 🚹🚹£ 90

◆ Smart cream property with local books and guides in parlour: exceptionally good detail wherever you look. Elegant, neatly laid breakfast room. Bright, well-kept bedrooms.

Prospect House without rest

1 Church Rd, Penryn, Northwest : 2 m. by A 39 on B 3292 ✉ TR10 8DA – ✆ (01326) 373 198 – stay@prospecthouse.co.uk

4 rm ☕ – 🚹£ 28 🚹🚹£ 38/65

◆ Large Georgian guesthouse on Penryn river, set within walled garden, run by welcoming owner. Super breakfasts with local produce in abundance. Individually styled rooms.

Rosemullion without rest

Gyllyngvase Hill ✉ TR11 4DF – ✆ (01326) 314 690 – gail@rosemullionhotel.demon.co.uk – Fax (01326) 210 098 – Closed Christmas B **c**

3 rm ☕ – 🚹£ 35/45 🚹🚹£ 64/70

◆ Spacious, whitewashed Tudor guesthouse. Wood panelled breakfast room and well-kept chintz lounge. Comfortable rooms. Personally run by pleasant owner.

Melvill House without rest

52 Melvill Rd ✉ TR11 4DQ – ✆ (01326) 316 645 – melvillhouse@btconnect.com – Fax (01326) 211 608 B **o**

6 rm ☕ – 🚹£ 30/40 🚹🚹£ 54/60

◆ Elegant Victorian house in pink, 200 yards from sandy beach. Guest lounge at the front; newspapers provided at breakfast. Well-kept, simple rooms.

Chelsea House without rest

2 Emslie Rd ✉ TR11 4BG – ✆ (01326) 212 230 – info@chelseahousehotel.com B **e**

8 rm ☕ – 🚹£ 37/45 🚹🚹£ 46/86

◆ Large Victorian house in quiet residential area with partial sea-view at front. Neat breakfast room; well-appointed bedrooms, two with their own balconies.

The Three Mackerel

Swanpool Beach, South : ¾ m. off Pennance Rd ✉ TR11 5BG – ✆ (01326) 311 886 – Fax (01326) 316 014 A **n**

Rest – Carte £ 17/44

◆ Casually informal beachside restaurant with white clapperboard façade. Super terrace or light interior. Seasonal, local ingredients provide the core of modern menus.

Bistro de la Mer

28 Arwenack St – ✆ (01326) 316 509 – bistrodelamer@aol.com – closed 2 weeks November, 25-26 December, 1 January and Sunday B **r**

Rest – (closed Monday dinner November - March) Menu £ 16 (lunch) – Carte £ 25/35

◆ Modest bistro with a subtle Mediterranean feel, set over two floors and decorated in sunny seaside colours of yellow and blue. Extensive seafood-oriented menu; honest cooking.

at Mylor Bridge North : 4½ m. by A 39 - A - and B 3292 on Mylor rd – ✉ Falmouth

Pandora Inn

Restronguet Creek, Northeast : 1 m. by Passage Hill off Restronguet Hill ✉ TR11 5ST – ✆ (01326) 372 678 – Fax (01326) 378 958 – Closed Sunday and 25 December

Rest – Carte £ 19/27

◆ A very characterful thatched inn of 13C origins in stunning location next to harbour. Flagstone flooring, low ceilings, exposed beams. Dining room has more formal style.

at Mawnan Smith Southwest : 5 m. by Trescobeas Rd - A – ✉ Falmouth

ENGLAND

Meudon

East : ½ m. by Carwinion Rd ✉ TR11 5HT – ✆ (01326) 250 541 – wecare@meudon.co.uk – Fax (01326) 250 543 – closed January

27 rm (dinner included) – †£ 70/125 ††£ 150/250 – 2 suites –

Rest – Menu £ 17/33 – Carte £ 22/46

◆ Landscaped sub-tropical gardens are the abiding allure of this elegant hotel. Antiques, oil paintings, log fires and fresh flowers abound. Comfy rooms, many with views. Conservatory restaurant highlighted by fruiting vine.

Trelawne

Maenporth, East : ¾ m. by Carwinion Rd ✉ TR11 5HS – ✆ (01326) 250 226 – info@trelawnehotel.co.uk – Fax (01326) 250 909 – March-October

14 rm – †£ 55/75 ††£ 90/160

Rest *The Hutches* – (bar lunch) Menu £ 25 – Carte £ 24/30

◆ Purpose-built hotel with neat gardens in two acres of grounds. Good views across bay. Traditionally charming open lounge and very well-kept, individually furnished rooms. Smartly dressed dining room with fine bay views.

at Budock Water West : 2¼ m. by Trescobeas Rd - A – ✉ Falmouth

Crill Manor

South : ¾ m. ✉ TR11 5BL – ✆ (01326) 211 880 – info@crillmanor.com – Fax (01326) 211 229 – Closed November and January

14 rm (dinner included) – †£ 49/94 ††£ 98/138 – **Rest** – (dinner only) Menu £ 25

◆ Small country house hotel in secluded location near Helford river. Spacious, well-furnished lounge. Individually styled, smartly appointed bedrooms. Smart dining room for meals featuring Cornish produce.

Undecided between two equivalent establishments? Within each category, establishments are classified in our order of preference.

FAR SAWREY – Cumbria – 502 L 20 – see Hawkshead

FAREHAM – Hants. – 503 Q 31 – pop. 56 160 *Great Britain* 6 B2

London 77 m – Portsmouth 9 m – Southampton 13 m – Winchester 19 m
Westbury Manor, 84 West St ✆ (01329) 221342
Portchester castle★ AC, SE : 2½ m. by A 27

Lysses House

51 High St ✉ PO16 7BQ – ✆ (01329) 822622 – lysses@lysses.co.uk – Fax (01329) 822762 – Closed 24 December-2 January
21 rm – †£ 83/98 ††£ 105
Rest ***The Richmond*** – (Closed Saturday lunch, Sunday lunch and Bank Holidays) Menu £ 14/20 **s** – Carte £ 22/29 **s**
◆ Former private residence built in the Georgian era. Elegant and stylish, in the heart of town. Quiet rear garden. Bright, smart bedrooms, practically appointed. Busy dining room caters for breakfasts to four course dinners.

Springfield without rest

67 The Avenue, West : 1 m. on A 27 ✉ PO14 1PE – ✆ (01329) 828325
6 rm – †£ 45 ††£ 55
◆ Sizeable redbrick guesthouse, both comfortable and well-equipped - quieter rear bedrooms face a pleasant garden. The friendly owner cooks a hearty full breakfast at weekends.

Lauro's brasserie

8 High St ✉ PO16 7AN – ✆ (01329) 234179 – lauros@ntlworld.com – Fax (01329) 822776 – closed Monday and Sunday lunch
Rest – Menu £ 12/22 – Carte £ 26/34
◆ Picture-window façade; long narrow interior with red hued walls and open-plan kitchen. The unpretentious cooking has influences ranging from the Mediterranean to Japan.

FARNHAM – Dorset – 503 N 31 – see Blandford Forum

FARNHAM – Surrey – 504 R 30 – pop. 36 298 7 C2

London 45 m – Reading 22 m – Southampton 39 m – Winchester 28 m
Council Offices, South St ✆ (01252) 715109
Farnham Park (Par Three), ✆ (01252) 715216 .

Bishop's Table

27 West St ✉ GU9 7DR – ✆ (01252) 710222 – welcome@bishopstable.com – Fax (01252) 733494
17 rm – †£ 97 ††£ 107/120, £ 12.50 – **Rest** – Carte £ 24/31
◆ Stylish Georgian hotel once owned by the Marquis of Lothian and a former training school for clergy. Take a drink in secluded walled garden. Individually decorated rooms. Original dishes in pastel pink restaurant.

FARNHAM ROYAL – Bucks. – 503 S 29 11 D3

London 27 m – Burnham 2 m – Windsor 5 m

The King of Prussia

Blackpond Lane, Northwest : ¾ m. by A 355 off Cherry Tree Rd ✉ SL2 3EG – ✆ (01753) 643006 – gm@tkop.co.uk – Closed Sunday dinner and 1 January
Rest – Menu £ 10 – Carte £ 20/31
◆ Beamed barn conversion, formal conservatory and stylish bar, with rear garden and children's play area. Menus contain classic English pub dishes; all homemade, even the bread.

ENGLAND

FARNINGHAM – Kent – 504 U 29 8 B1

London 22 m – Dartford 7 m – Maidstone 20 m

Beesfield Farm without rest

Beesfield Lane, off A 225 ✉ DA4 0LA – ✆ (01322) 863 900 – kim.vingoe@btinternet.com – Fax (01322) 863 900 – closed 14 December-14 January

3 rm – £ 65/70 ££ 80/90

◆ Peaceful valley setting, with attractive garden. Exudes character: oldest part is 400 year-old Kentish longhouse. Comfy sitting room; bedrooms boast beams and garden outlook.

FAVERSHAM – Kent – 504 W 30 – pop. 18 222 9 C1

London 52 m – Dover 26 m – Maidstone 21 m – Margate 25 m

Fleur de Lis Heritage Centre, 13 Preston St ✆ (01795) 534542

Read's (David Pitchford) with rm

Macknade Manor, Canterbury Rd, East : 1 m. on A 2 ✉ ME13 8XE – ✆ (01795) 535 344 – enquiries@reads.com – Fax (01795) 591 200 – Closed 25-26 December, 1 January, Sunday and Monday

6 rm – £ 125/195 ££ 155/195 – **Rest** – Menu £ 24/52

Spec. Cheddar cheese and smoked haddock soufflé. Roast lamb cutlet, rolled breast, Shepherd's pie, celeriac fondant and spinach. Valrhona chocolate and caramel tart, salted almond ice cream.

◆ Georgian house with immaculate grounds and kitchen garden. Relax in bar before indulging in classic dishes making best use of delicious local produce. Very comfortable rooms.

ENGLAND

Your opinions are important to us: please write and let us know about your discoveries and experiences – good and bad!

FAWKHAM GREEN – Kent – 504 U 29 – see Brands Hatch

FENCE – Blackburn – see Padiham

FERMAIN BAY – C.I. – 503 L 33 – see Channel Islands

FERRENSBY – N. Yorks. – see Knaresborough

FINDON – W. Sussex – 504 S 31 – pop. 1 720 – ✉ Worthing 7 C2

London 49 m – Brighton 13 m – Southampton 50 m – Worthing 4 m

Findon Manor

High St, off A 24 ✉ BN14 0TA – ✆ (01903) 872 733 – hotel@findonmanor.com – Fax (01903) 877 473 – Closed Christmas-New Year

11 rm – £ 80 ££ 154 – **Rest** – (bar lunch Monday-Saturday) Menu £ 29 (dinner) **s** – Carte £ 17/30 **s**

◆ Flint-built former rectory dating from the 16C. Characterful lounge with heavy drapes, real fire and flagstones. Spacious, country house bedrooms. Elegant restaurant opening onto secluded gardens.

FLAUNDEN – Herts – pop. 5 468 12 **A2**

London 35 m – Reading 43 m – Luton 23 m – Milton Keynes 42 m

The Bricklayers Arms

Hogpits Bottom ✉ HP3 0PH – ☎ (01442) 833 322 – goodfood@bricklayersarms.com – Fax (01442) 834 841

Rest – Carte £ 25/35

◆ Charming 18C pub with slate roof, wooden beams and low ceilings. Spacious main bar, with country-style prints and exposed brick walls. Emphasis on French classics.

FLETCHING – E. Sussex – 504 U 30/31 8 **A2**

London 45 m – Brighton 20 m – Eastbourne 24 m – Maidstone 20 m

The Griffin Inn with rm

✉ TN22 3SS – ☎ (01825) 722 890 – info@thegriffininn.co.uk – Fax (01825) 722 810 – Closed 25 December

13 rm – †£ 70 ††£ 130 – **Rest** – (meals in bar Sunday dinner) Menu £ 30 – Carte £ 20/35

◆ 16C coaching inn; rustic ambience with real fire, stone floor. Generous, traditional cooking. Beamed rooms with four-poster beds, rushmat flooring, hand-painted wall murals.

The ✿ award is the crème de la crème.
This is awarded to restaurants
which are really worth travelling miles for!

FLITWICK – Beds. – 504 S 27 – pop. 12 700 12 **A1**

London 45 m – Bedford 13 m – Luton 12 m – Northampton 28 m

Flitwick Manor

Church Rd, off Dunstable Rd ✉ MK45 1AE – ☎ (0871) 472 4016 – flitwick@menzies-hotels.co.uk – Fax (01525) 718 753

18 rm – †£ 125/175 ††£ 145/195, £ 19 – **Rest** – Menu £ 25/60 – Carte £ 29/50

◆ Georgian manor house set in 27 acres. Elegant lounge. Individually decorated rooms: those on ground floor have garden seating areas, others overlook 300-year old cedar tree. Formal restaurant in Georgian house style.

FOLKESTONE – Kent – 504 X 30 – pop. 45 273 *Great Britain* 9 **D2**

London 76 m – Brighton 76 m – Dover 8 m – Maidstone 33 m

Access Channel Tunnel : Eurotunnel information and reservations ☎ (08705) 353535

Harbour St ☎ (01303) 258594, tourism@folkestone.org.uk

The Leas★ (≤ ★) Z

Plan on next page

Clifton

The Leas ✉ CT20 2EB – ☎ (01303) 851 231 – reservations@thecliftonhotel.com – Fax (01303) 223 949 Z **r**

80 rm – †£ 60/70 ††£ 90/100, £ 10.50 – **Rest** – (Closed lunch Monday-Thursday) Menu £ 14/20 **s** – Carte £ 26/37 **s**

◆ Seafront hotel with gardens and views over Channel. Traditional style; bar has sun terrace and flower-boxes. Comfortable bedrooms. Traditionally appointed restaurant.

The Relish without rest

4 Augusta Gardens ✉ CT20 2RR – ☎ (01303) 850 952 – Fax (01303) 850 958 – Closed 22 December-2 January, minimum 2 night stay at weekends Z **n**

10 rm – †£ 65 ††£ 80/140

◆ Large Regency townhouse overlooking private parkland. Stylish black canopy to entrance; modish furnishings. Handy food and drink area at foot of stairs. Light, airy rooms.

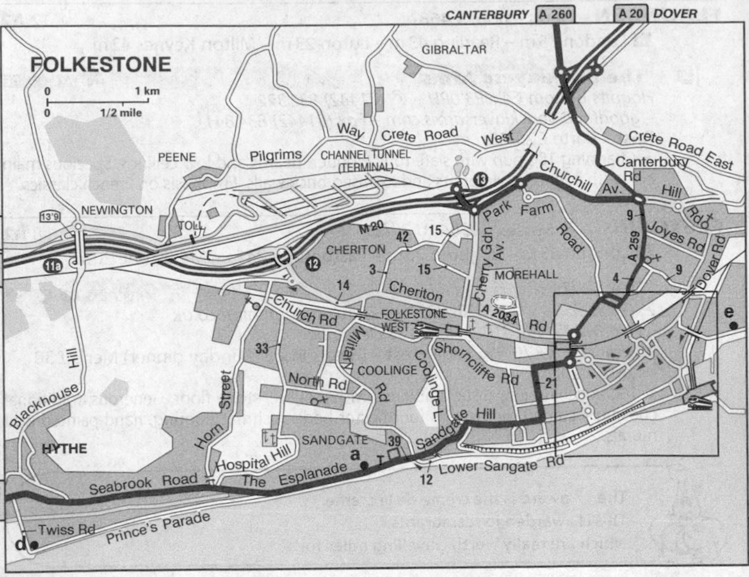

FOLKESTONE

Street	Grid	No.
Ashley Ave	X	3
Black Bull Rd	X, Y	4
Bouverie Pl.	Z	6
Bradstone Rd	Y	8
Canterbury Rd	X	9
Castle Rd	X	12
Cheriton High St	X	14
Cheriton Pl.	Z	13
Cherry Garden Lane	X	15
Clifton Crescent	Z	16
Clifton Rd	Z	17
Durlocks (The)	Y	20
Earl's Ave	X	21
Grace Hill	Y	22
Guildhall St	YZ	23
Harbour App. Rd	Z	25
Harbour St	Z	24
Langhorne Gardens	Z	27
Manor Rd	Z	28
Marine Terrace	Z	29
Middelburg Sq.	Z	30
North St.	Y	32
Old High St	YZ	
Pond Hill Rd	X	33
Radnor Bridge Rd	Y	34
Remembrance (Rd of)	Z	35
Rendezvous St	Y	37
Ryland Pl.	Y	38
Sandgate High St	X	39
Sandgate Rd	Z	
Shorncliffe Rd	Y	41
Tilekiln Lane	X	42
Tontine St	Y	
Trinity Gardens	Z	43
Victoria Grove	Y	45
West Terrace	Z	47

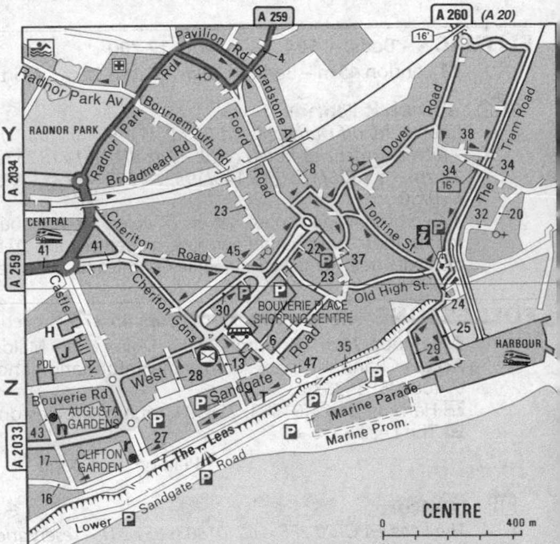

at Sandgate West : 1 ¾ m. on A 259 – ✉ Folkestone

Sandgate

8-9 Wellington Terrace ✉ CT20 3DY – ✆ (01303) 220 444
– info@sandgatehotel.com – Fax (01303) 220 496 X **a**

15 rm – †£ 50/55 ††£ 75/95

Rest *Restaurant* – Carte approx. £ 20

◆ 19C seafront hotel with smart beige and brown façade. Relaxed, modern boutique style public areas. Bedrooms have a crisp, simple freshness; some boast seaviews and balconies. Distinctively modern restaurant; very pleasant terrace.

FORD – Bucks. Great Britain 11 **C2**

London 43 m – Aylesbury 5 m – Oxford 20 m

Waddesdon Manor★★ **AC, NW : 7 m. on A 418, Cuddington Rd, Aylesbury Rd and Cannon's Hill**

The Dinton Hermit with rm

Water Lane ✉ HP17 8XH – ✆ (01296) 747 473 – dintonhermit@btconnect.com – Fax (01296) 748 819 – Closed 25-31 December

13 rm – †£ 80 ††£ 125 – **Rest** – (closed Sunday dinner) Carte £ 23/33

◆ Charming 17C inn in pretty village; landscaped gardens, roaring fires and beams. Freshly prepared menus using local produce. Mix of rooms in main house, extension and barn.

FORDINGBRIDGE – Hants. – **503** O 31 – **pop. 5 755** 6 **A2**

London 101 m – Bournemouth 17 m – Salisbury 11 m – Southampton 22 m – Winchester 30 m

Kings Yard, Salisbury St ✆ (01425) 654560 (summer only)

The Hour Glass with rm

Salisbury Rd, North : 1 m. on A 338 ✉ SP6 1LX – ✆ (01425) 652 348 – hglassrestaurant@aol.com – Fax (01425) 656 002 – Closed 25-26 December and 1 January

3 rm – †£ 65 ††£ 75 – **Rest** – (Closed Sunday dinner and Monday) Carte £ 25/39

◆ Thatched cottage restaurant on main Salisbury road. Exposed black beams create a cosy ambience. Eclectic modern menu with a traditional base; carefully sourced local produce. Stylish, contemporary bedrooms.

at Stuckton Southeast : 1 m. by B 3078 – ✉ Fordingbridge

Three Lions with rm

Stuckton Rd, Stuckton ✉ SP6 2HF – ✆ (01425) 652 489 – Fax (01425) 656 144 – Closed last 2 weeks January and first week February

4 rm – †£ 59/85 ††£ 95 – **Rest** – (Closed Sunday dinner and Monday) Menu £ 16 (lunch) – Carte £ 24/32

◆ Personally run former farmhouse. Impressive blackboard menu includes local produce like wild New Forest mushrooms or venison. Bright, cosy rooms with thoughtful extras.

FOREST – C.I. – **503** P 33 – **see Channel Islands**

FOREST GREEN – Surrey – **pop. 1 843** – ✉ **Dorking** 7 **D2**

London 34 m – Guildford 13 m – Horsham 10 m

Parrot Inn

✉ *RH5 5RZ – ✆ (01306) 621 339 – drinks@the parrot.co.uk*

Rest – Carte £ 18/25

◆ Overlooks the green in a picturesque village. Low-beamed bar with inglenook; formally-laid restaurant. Concise, seasonal menu. Wholesome, robust dishes in sizeable portions.

FOREST ROW – E. Sussex – **504** U 30 – **pop. 3 623** 8 **A2**

London 35 m – Brighton 26 m – Eastbourne 30 m – Maidstone 32 m

Royal Ashdown Forest Forest Row, Chapel Lane, ✆ (01342) 822 018 .

at Wych Cross South : 2½ m. on A 22 – ✉ Forest Row

Ashdown Park

East : ¾ m. on Hartfield rd ✉ RH18 5JR – ✆ (01342) 824 988 – reservations@ashdownpark.com – Fax (01342) 826 206

100 rm – †£ 150 ††£ 180 – 6 suites

Rest ***Anderida*** – Menu £ 24/35 **s** – Carte dinner only £ 48/54

◆ Part 19C manor in landscaped woodland with antiques, real fires. Former convent. Extensive leisure facilities. Immaculate rooms in two wings boast writing desks, armchairs. Ornate ceiling dominates formal restaurant.

ENGLAND

FORTON – Lancs. – 502 M 25 – ✉ Lancaster ▮ *Great Britain* 18 **B1**

▶ London 236 m – Blackpool 18 m – Manchester 45 m
Lancaster - Castle★, N : 5½ m. by A 6

The Bay Horse Inn with rm

Bay Horse Lane, North : 1¼ m. by A 6 on Quernmore rd ✉ LA2 0HR – ☎ (01524) 791 204 – bayhorseinfo@aol.com – Fax (01524) 791 204 – Closed 25-26 December, 1 January, Monday and Tuesday,
3 rm – †£ 75 ††£ 95 – **Rest** – Menu £ 16 – Carte £ 18/35
◆ Rurally set inn dating from 18C with open fires, exposed beams and enthusiastic owners. Good selection of real ales. Tasty, well-prepared, home-made dishes.

FOWEY – Cornwall – 503 G 32 – pop. 2 064 1 **B2**

▶ London 277 m – Newquay 24 m – Plymouth 34 m – Truro 22 m
ℹ 4 Custom Hill House ☎ (01726) 833616, info@fowey.co.uk
Town★★
Gribbin Head (≤ ★★) 6 m. rtn on foot – Bodinnick (≤ ★★) - Lanteglos Church★, E : 5 m. by ferry – Polruan (≤ ★★) SE : 6 m. by ferry – Polkerris★, W : 2 m. by A 3082

Fowey Hall

Hanson Drive, West : ½ m. off A 3082 ✉ PL23 1ET – ☎ (01726) 833 866 – info@fallhallhotel.co.uk – Fax (01726) 834 100
24 rm – †£ 165 ††£ 180/255 – 12 suites – **Rest** – (light lunch Monday-Saturday) Menu £ 35 – Carte approx. £ 20 **s**
◆ Imposing 19C country house within walled garden. Two spacious lounges with real fires, wicker furnished garden room. Smart, plush rooms. Special facilities for children. Impressive oak-panelled restaurant.

Marina Villa

≤ Fowey river and harbour,

17 The Esplanade ✉ PL23 1HY – ☎ (01726) 833 315 – enquiries@themarinahotel.co.uk – Fax (01726) 832 779
17 rm – †£ 85/150 ††£ 154/248 – 1 suite
Rest *Nathan Outlaw* – see restaurant listing
◆ Small house in tiny street with splendid views of river and quay. Attractive interior with well-kept lounge, and rooms of varying size with a contemporary, individual feel.

Old Quay House

28 Fore St ✉ PL23 1AQ – ☎ (01726) 833 302 – info@theoldquayhouse.com – Fax (01726) 833 668
11 rm – †£ 100/130 ††£ 160/220 – **Rest** – (Closed lunch midweek in low season) Menu £ 35 (dinner) – Carte £ 28/35
◆ Former Victorian seamen's mission idyllically set on the waterfront. Stylish, contemporary lounge. Rear terrace overlooks the river. Smart, individually decorated bedrooms. Spacious restaurant with wicker and wood furniture, serving modern British dishes.

Nathan Outlaw – at Marina Villa H.

≤ Fowey River and harbour,

17 The Esplanade ✉ PL23 1HY – ☎ (01726) 833 315 – Fax (01726) 832 779 – closed 6 January-14 February and Monday
Rest – (dinner only) Carte £ 38/49
Spec. Lobster risotto, orange and basil. Roast Veal, cauliflower, sage and onion. Peach tarte Tatin, raspberry sorbet.
◆ Restaurant with feel of ship's cabin. Understated menu descriptions belie inherent understanding of first class ingredients. Accomplished cooking; perfectly balanced dishes.

at Golant North : 3 m. by B 3269 – ✉ Fowey

Cormorant

≤ River Fowey,

✉ PL23 1LL – ☎ (01726) 833 426 – relax@cormoranthotel.co.uk – Fax (01726) 833 219
14 rm – †£ 70/160 ††£ 90/190 – **Rest** – (dinner only) Menu £ 34 (dinner) – Carte £ 20/42
◆ Stunningly located with wonderful views. All bedrooms have river vista, flatscreen TVs, fridges and large beds; several also have balconies. Comfortable lounge with fireplace. Pretty dining room with balcony terrace. Appealing menus.

ENGLAND

L'infini pluriel

Route du Fort-de-Brégançon - 83250 La Londe-les-Maures - Tél. 33 (0)4 94 01 53 53
Fax 33 (0)4 94 01 53 54 - domaines-ott.com - ott.particuliers@domaines-ott.com

ViaMichelin

Click...make your choice,
Click...place your booking!

HOTEL BOOKING AT

www.ViaMichelin.com

Plan your route on-line with ViaMichelin to make the most of all your trips. You can compare routes, select your stops at recommended restaurants and learn more about any not-to-be-missed tourist sites along your route. And...for peace of mind, you can check real-time availability in 60,000 hotels across Europe (independents and chains). Simply specify your preferences (parking, restaurant, etc) and place your booking on-line.

- *No booking fee*
- *No cancellation fee*
- *No credit card fee*
- *Best available prices*
- *The option to filter and select hotels from The Michelin Guide*

MICHELIN
A better way forward

FRAMLINGHAM – Suffolk – **504** Y 27 – **pop. 2 839** – ✉ **Woodbridge** 15 **D3**

London 92 m – Ipswich 19 m – Norwich 42 m

Off the Square

3 Church St ✉ IP13 9BE – ✆ (01728) 621 232 – greatfood@otsframltd.co.uk – closed Sunday dinner and Monday

Rest – Menu £ 15/20 – Carte £ 20/29

◆ Modern, keenly run, brasserie style restaurant with spacious, open plan interior and buzzy, informal atmosphere. Good value, neat cooking with a touch of the Mediterranean.

at Badingham Northeast : 3 ¼ m. by B 1120 on A 1120 – ✉ **Woodbridge**

Colston Hall without rest

Badingham, North : 4 ¼ m. by B 1120 off A 1120 ✉ IP13 8LB – ✆ (01728) 638 375 – lizjohn@colstonhall.com – Fax (01728) 638 084

6 rm – †£ 50 ††£ 100

◆ Part Elizabethan farmhouse in rural location with lakes and garden. Comfy rooms - three of which are in stables - with character: plenty of timbers and small sitting areas.

Red = Pleasant. Look for the red and symbols.

FRAMPTON MANSELL – Glos. *Great Britain* 4 **C1**

London 106 m – Bristol 34 m – Gloucester 17 m

Cirencester★ - Corinium Museum★, E : 7 m. by A 419

The White Horse

Cirencester Rd, on A 419 ✉ GL6 8HZ – ✆ (01285) 760 960 – emmawhitehorse@aol.com – Closed first week January, 24-26 December and Sunday dinner

Rest – Menu £ 17 – Carte £ 24/30

◆ Stone-built public house on main road. Cosy small bar and attractive dining room. Friendly service. Daily menu of classic and modern British dishes with original touches.

FREATHY – Cornwall – see Millbrook

FRESHWATER BAY – I.O.W. – **503** – see Wight (Isle of)

FRESSINGFIELD – Suffolk – **504** X 26 15 **D2**

London 104 m – Ipswich 34 m – Lowestoft 27 m

The Fox & Goose Inn

Church Rd ✉ IP21 5PB – ✆ (01379) 586 247 – Fax (01379) 586 106 – Closed 2nd and 3rd weeks January, 27-30 December and Monday

Rest – (booking essential) Menu £ 14/17 – Carte £ 20/30

◆ Spacious black and white inn with leaded panes. Beams and wooden floor in dining room. Extensive menu of traditional dishes with modern influence; some use of local produce.

FRILSHAM – Newbury – see Yattendon

FRISTON – Suffolk – see Aldeburgh

FRITHSDEN – Herts. – see Hemel Hempstead

ENGLAND

FRITTON – Norfolk 15 D2

London 133 m – Great Yarmouth 8 m – Norwich 19 m

Fritton House

Church Lane NR31 9HA – (01493) 484 008
– frittonhouse@somerleyton.co.uk
7 rm – £ 100/130 £ 140/170 – 1 suite – **Rest** – Carte £ 25/32
◆ Successful meeting point of 15C charm and contemporary boutique style. Elegant drawing room with sumptuous sofas and fresh flowers. No expense spared in sleek bedrooms. Dine on intriguing 21C dishes in relaxed, raftered surroundings.

FRODSHAM – Ches. – 502 L 24 20 A3

London 198 m – Liverpool 20 m – Runcorn 5 m

Netherton Hall

Chester Road, Southwest : ¾ m. on A 56 WA6 6UL – (01928) 732 342
– Fax (01928) 739 140 – closed 25-26 December and 1 January
Rest – Carte £ 19/30
◆ Converted Georgian farmhouse with spacious gardens. Homely interior: walls lined with books and curios. Four separate dining areas serving freshly prepared, eclectic menus.

FROGGATT EDGE – Derbs. – 502 P 24 16 A1

London 167 m – Bakewell 6 m – Sheffield 11 m

The Chequers Inn with rm

Froggatt Edge, on A 625 S32 3ZJ – (01433) 630 231
– info@chequers-froggatt.com – Fax (01433) 631 072 – Closed 25 December
5 rm – £ 70 £ 90 – **Rest** – Carte £ 21/28
◆ Refurbished 16C Grade II listed building, retaining many period features. Wide-ranging, modern menus enhanced by accomplished cooking. Pleasant, cosy bedrooms.

FROME – Somerset – 503 M/N 30 4 C2

London 118 m – Bristol 24 m – Southampton 52 m – Swindon 44 m

Babington House

(heated)
Babington, Northwest : 6½ m. by A 362
on Vobster rd BA11 3RW – (01373) 812 266
– enquiries@babingtonhouse.co.uk – Fax (01373) 812 112
23 rm – £ 355 £ 355/440, £12.50 – 5 suites
Rest *The Log Room* – (residents and members only) Carte approx. £ 28
◆ Country house with vivid difference: Georgian exterior; cool, trendy interior. Laid-back dining, health club, even a cinema: modern minimalism prevails. Trendy 21C rooms.

The Settle

16 Cheap St, off Market Pl BA11 1BN – (01373) 465 975
– Fax (01373) 465 975 – closed 2 weeks Christmas-New Year, 2 weeks August, Sunday-Wednesday and Bank Holidays
Rest – (dinner only) Menu £ 26
◆ First-floor restaurant above tea shop in town centre. Vivid red and blue linen colour scheme adds panache to compact dining area. Well-prepared dishes using local produce.

FRYERNING – Essex 13 C2

London 33 m – Brentwood 6 m – Chelmsford 7 m

The Woolpack

Mill Green Rd CM4 0MS – (01277) 352 189
– info@thewoolpack-fryerning.co.uk – Fax (01277) 356 802
– closed 26 December-7 January, Monday, Sunday dinner and Tuesday lunch
Rest – Menu £ 18 (lunch) – Carte £ 24/36
◆ 19C inn located in a delightful rural village. Neighbourhood feel prevails with distinctive modish interior full of stylish charm. Accomplished cooking in the modern vein.

FUNTINGTON – W. Sussex – 504 R 31 – see Chichester

FYFIELD – Oxon – pop. 540 – ✉ Abingdon 10 B2

London 70 m – Abingdon 6 m – Oxford 9 m

The White Hart

Main Road ✉ OX13 5LW – ✆ (01865) 390 585 – info@whitehart-fyfield.com – Closed Sunday lunch

Rest – Menu £ 17 – Carte £ 22/35

◆ 15C former chantry house complete with minstrels' gallery and cellar room. Globally influenced menu; fresh, flavoursome food. Uplit terrace and large garden.

GALMPTON – Devon – 503 J 32 – ✉ Brixham 2 C2

London 229 m – Plymouth 32 m – Torquay 6 m

Maypool Park

Maypool, South : 1 m. ✉ TQ5 0BJ – ✆ (01803) 842 442 – tilleyandco@tiscali.co.uk

3 rm – £ 60 £ 100 – **Rest** – (by arrangement) Menu £ 25 **s**

◆ Guesthouse of converted 19C cottages in heart of estate bought by Agatha Christie in 1938. Secluded, 300 feet above the Dart. Terrace with good views. Country style bedrooms. Traditional cooking.

Look out for red symbols, indicating particularly pleasant establishments.

GARFORTH – W. Yorks. – 502 P 22 – see Leeds

GARSTANG – Lancs. – 502 L 22 – pop. 6 293 20 A2

London 233 m – Blackpool 13 m – Manchester 41 m

Discovery Centre, Council Offices, High St ✆ (01995) 602125

Garstang Country H. and Golf Club

Bowgreave, South : 1 ¼ m. on B 6430 ✉ PR3 1YE – ✆ (01995) 600 100 – reception@ghgc.co.uk – Fax (01995) 600 950

32 rm – £ 65/75 £ 75/85 – **Rest** – (bar lunch Monday-Saturday) Menu £ 17 – Carte £ 17/24

◆ Stone-built hotel, privately owned. Rooms overlook golf course and driving range. Golfing breaks throughout year. Uniformly sized rooms with colourful fabrics and drapes. Restaurant with course outlook.

at Bilsborrow South : 3 ¾ m. by B 6430 on A 6 – ✉ Preston

Olde Duncombe House without rest

Garstang Rd ✉ PR3 0RE – ✆ (01995) 640 336 – oldedunc@aol.com – Fax (01995) 640 336

9 rm – £ 45 £ 59

◆ Whitewashed, stonebuilt guesthouse, formerly three cottages dating back 400 years. Simple rooms with free-standing pine furniture. Rear rooms overlook the canal.

GATESHEAD – Tyne and Wear – 501 P 19 – pop. 78 403 *Great Britain* 24 B2

London 282 m – Durham 16 m – Middlesbrough 38 m – Newcastle upon Tyne 1 m – Sunderland 11 m

Access Tyne Tunnel (toll)

Central Library, Prince Consort Rd ✆ (0191) 433 8420 BX - Metrocentre, Portcullis, 7 The Arcade ✆ (0191) 478 4222 AX

Ravensworth Wrekenton Moss Heaps, ✆ (0191) 487 6014 ;

Heworth Gingling Gate, ✆ (0191) 469 9832 .

Beamish : North of England Open Air Museum★★ AC, SW : 6 m. by A 692 and A 6076 BX

Plan : see Newcastle upon Tyne

ENGLAND

Hilton Newcastle Gateshead
Bottle Bank ✉ NE8 2AR – ☎ (0191) 490 9700 – Fax (0191) 490 9800 CZ **e**
251 rm – ♦£ 108/188 ♦♦£ 118/198, ☕ £17.95 – 3 suites
Rest *Windows on the Tyne* – (closed lunch Saturday and Sunday) Menu £ 27
♦ Modern hotel on steep riverbank, with fine views across the Tyne. Well-equipped leisure centre. Extensive conference facilities. Stylish, modern rooms, many with river vistas. Informal, modern restaurant overlooks the bridges.

McCoys at the Baltic City skyline,
6th Floor, Baltic Centre, South Shore Rd ✉ NE8 3BA – ☎ (0191) 440 4949 – reservations@mccoysbaltic.com – Fax (0191) 440 4950 – Closed 25 December, 1 January and Sunday dinner BX **c**
Rest – (booking essential) Menu £ 20 (lunch) – Carte £ 20/42
♦ Restaurant atop the Baltic Arts Centre; glass walls give fine city views. Stylish modern décor; original cooking to match the inventive art on show elsewhere in the building.

at Low Fell South : 2 m. on A 167 - BX – ✉ Gateshead

Eslington Villa
8 Station Rd, West : ¾ m. by Belle Vue Bank, turning left at T junction, right at roundabout then taking first turn right ✉ NE9 6DR – ☎ (0191) 487 6017 – home@eslingtonvilla.co.uk – Fax (0191) 420 0667 – closed Bank Holidays
18 rm ☕ – ♦£ 75/80 ♦♦£ 95/100
Rest *The Restaurant* – see restaurant listing
♦ Well-run, stylish, privately owned hotel 10 minutes' drive from city centre. Nicely furnished lounge bar leads from smart reception. Attractively styled, modern bedrooms.

The Restaurant – at Eslington Villa
8 Station Rd, West : ¾ by Belle Vue Bank, turning left at T junction, right at roundabout then taking first turn right ✉ NE9 6DR – ☎ (0191) 487 6017 – home@eslingtonvilla.co.uk – Fax (0191) 420 0667 – closed Bank Holidays, Saturday lunch and Sunday dinner
Rest – Menu £ 16/20 – Carte £ 23/37
♦ Two separate dining areas, one of which is a conservatory. Both are classically decorated and serve good range of traditionally based dishes with modern twists.

at Whickham West : 4 m. by A 184, A 1, A 692 on B 6317 – ✉ Gateshead

Gibside rm, rest,
Front St ✉ NE16 4JG – ☎ (0191) 488 9292 – reception@gibside-hotel.co.uk – Fax (0191) 488 8000 AX **s**
45 rm – ♦£ 75 ♦♦£ 85/95, ☕ £8.95 – **Rest** – (bar lunch Monday-Saturday) Carte £ 25/36 **s**
♦ Purpose-built hotel in small town near Gateshead with views over Tyne Valley. Set on hill, so its up to date facilities are on different levels. Cosy, unfussy rooms. Newly refurbished modern restaurant.

GATWICK AIRPORT – W. Sussex – 504 T 30 – ✉ Crawley 7 D2

London 29 m – Brighton 28 m
Gatwick Airport : ☎ (0870) 0002468

Plan opposite

Hilton London Gatwick Airport rm,
South Terminal ✉ RH6 0LL – ☎ (01293) 518 080 – londongatwick@hilton.com – Fax (01293) 528 980 Y **u**
823 rm – ♦£ 195/285 ♦♦£ 195/285, ☕ £18.50 – **Rest** – Menu £ 18 – Carte £ 35/40
♦ Large, well-established hotel, popular with business travellers. Two ground floor bars, lounge and leisure facilities. Older rooms co-ordinated, newer in minimalist style. Restaurant enlivened by floral profusions.

ENGLAND

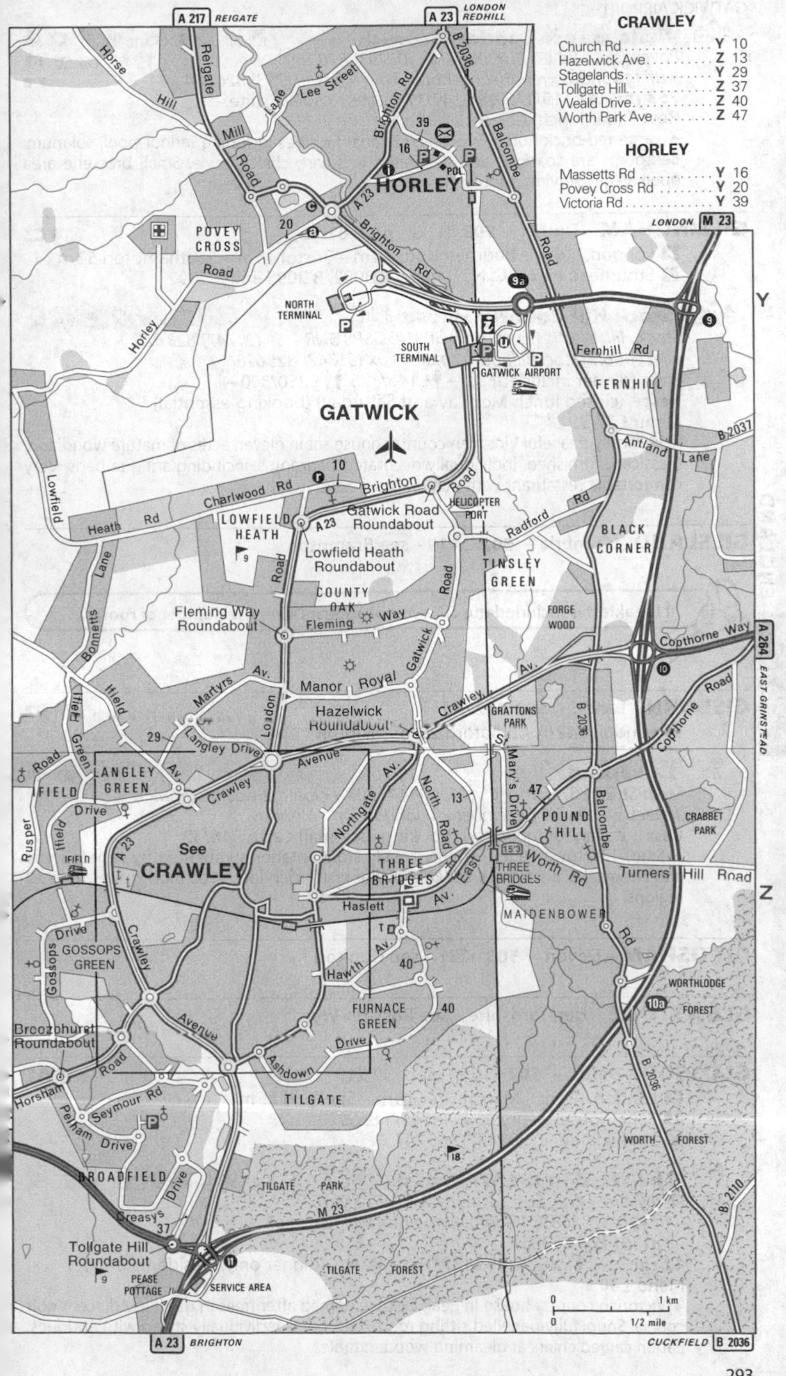
CRAWLEY
Church Rd . . . . Y 10
Hazelwick Ave. . . . . Z 13
Stagelands . . . . Y 29
Tollgate Hill. . . . . Z 37
Weald Drive. . . . . Z 40
Worth Park Ave. . . . . Z 47
HORLEY
Massetts Rd . . . . Y 16
Povey Cross Rd . . . . Y 20
Victoria Rd . . . . Y 39
A 217 REIGATE
A 23 LONDON REDHILL
LONDON M 23
A 264 EAST GRINSTEAD
A 23 BRIGHTON
CUCKFIELD B 2036
HORLEY
POVEY CROSS
NORTH TERMINAL
SOUTH TERMINAL
GATWICK AIRPORT
GATWICK
FERNHILL
LOWFIELD HEATH
Gatwick Road Roundabout
Lowfield Heath Roundabout
HELICOPTER PORT
BLACK CORNER
TINSLEY GREEN
COUNTY OAK
Fleming Way Roundabout
FORGE WOOD
Hazelwick Roundabout
GRATTONS PARK
LANGLEY GREEN
IFIELD
POUND HILL
CRABBET PARK
See CRAWLEY
THREE BRIDGES
MAIDENBOWER
GOSSOPS GREEN
FURNACE GREEN
WORTHLODGE FOREST
Broadfield Roundabout
TILGATE
BROADFIELD
WORTH FOREST
TILGATE PARK
Tollgate Hill Roundabout
PEASE POTTAGE
SERVICE AREA
TILGATE FOREST
Y
Z
0 1 km
0 1/2 mile

Renaissance London Gatwick
Povey Cross Rd ✉ RH6 0BE – ✆ (01293) 820 169 – rhi.lgwbr.dos@renaissancehotels.com – Fax (01293) 826 934 Y a
253 rm – †£ 119/145 ††£ 149/175, ☕ £16.50 – 1 suite –
Rest – (bar lunch) Carte £ 21/38 **s**
◆ Large red-brick hotel. Good recreational facilities including indoor pool, solarium. Bedrooms are spacious and decorated in smart, chintzy style. Small brasserie area open all day serving popular meals.

GILLINGHAM – Dorset – **503** N 30 – pop. 8 630 — 4 C3

London 116 m – Bournemouth 34 m – Bristol 46 m – Southampton 52 m
Stourhead★★★ **AC**, N : 9 m. by B 3092, B 3095 and B 3092

Stock Hill Country House
Stock Hill, West : 1½ m. on B 3081 ✉ SP8 5NR – ✆ (01747) 823 626 – reception@stockhillhouse.co.uk – Fax (01747) 825 628
8 rm (dinner included) ☕ – †£ 145/175 ††£ 250/300 –
Rest – (closed lunch Monday and Saturday) (booking essential)
Menu £ 27/39
◆ Idyllically peaceful Victorian country house set in eleven acres of mature woodland. Classically furnished. Individually decorated bedrooms, including antique beds. Very comfortable restaurant with rich drapes, attentive service.

ENGLAND

GILSLAND – Cumbria – **502** M 19 – see Brampton

If breakfast is included the ☕ symbol appears after the number of rooms.

GISBURN – Lancs. – **502** N 22 — 20 B2

London 242 m – Bradford 28 m – Skipton 12 m

La Locanda
Main St ✉ BB7 4HH – ✆ (01200) 445 303 – closed 2 weeks summer, 1 week winter, 26 December - 1 January and Monday
Rest – Italian (dinner only) (booking essential) Carte £ 16/32
◆ Snug 17C town centre osteria. Lovely stone interior augmented by superb joists and beams. Italian 'nonna' cooking of the first order: lots of comfort dishes from all regions.

GITTISHAM – Devon – **503** K 31 – see Honiton

GLEWSTONE – Herefordshire – see Ross-on-Wye

GLOSSOP – Derbs. – **502** O 23 – pop. 32 219 — 16 A1

London 194 m – Manchester 18 m – Sheffield 25 m
Bank House, Henry St ✆ (01457) 855920
Sheffield Rd, ✆ (01457) 865 247 .

The Wind in the Willows
Derbyshire Level, East : 1 m. by A 57 ✉ SK13 7PT – ✆ (01457) 868 001 – info@windinthewillows.co.uk – Fax (01457) 853 354
12 rm ☕ – †£ 88/98 ††£ 130/155 – **Rest** – (dinner only) (residents only)
Menu £ 30 **s**
◆ Victorian country house in Peak District, named after trees in garden. Adjacent golf course. Snug, fully-panelled sitting room. Bedrooms individually styled with antiques. Eat on carved chairs at gleaming wooden tables.

GOATHLAND – N. Yorks. – **502** R 20 – ✉ **Whitby** 23 **C1**

London 248 m – Middlesbrough 36 m – York 38 m

Heatherdene

The Common ✉ YO22 5AN – ☎ (01947) 896 334 – info@heatherdenehotel.com – Fax (01947) 896 334 – Closed January and 1 week Christmas-New Year

7 rm – †£ 40/65 ††£ 95 – **Rest** – (dinner only) (booking essential for non residents) Menu £ 20

◆ Country house hotel in converted vicarage with good village views. Sitting room has contemporary styling, which is reflected to slightly lesser degree in the bedrooms. Hearty, home-cooked meals in modern dining room.

GOLCAR – W. Yorks. – see Huddersfield

GOMERSAL – W. Yorks. – **502** O 22 – see Bradford

GOODNESTONE – Kent – see Wingham

The red symbol?
This denotes the very essence of peace
– only the sound of birdsong first thing in the morning …

GOREY – C.I. – **503** P 33 – see Channel Islands

GORING – Oxon. – **503** Q 29 – **pop. 3 934** *Great Britain* 10 **B3**

London 56 m – Oxford 16 m – Reading 12 m

Ridgeway Path★★

Leatherne Bottel

The Bridleway, North : 1½ m. by B 4009 ✉ RG8 0HS – ☎ (01491) 872 667 – leathernebottel@aol.com – Fax (01491) 875 308 – closed Sunday dinner and Monday

Rest – (booking essential) Carte £ 35/41

◆ Charming Thames-side restaurant; idyllic views of Berkshire Downs. Neat, linen-clad round tables, sparkling windows, travel photos on walls. Imaginative international menu.

at Cray's Pond East : 2 m. on B 4526 – ✉ **Goring**

The White Lion

Goring Rd, Goring Heath ✉ RG8 7SH – ☎ (01491) 680 471 – reservations@whitelioncrayspond.com – Fax (01491) 684 254 – Closed 25-26 December, Sunday dinner and Monday

Rest – Carte £ 24/33

◆ Part 18C pub sporting 21C appearance. Front terrace for summer dining. Stylish interior: mix of old beams, low ceilings and soft lights. Eclectic dishes and British staples.

GOSFORTH – Tyne and Wear – **501** P 18 – see Newcastle upon Tyne

GOUDHURST – Kent – **504** V 30 8 **B2**

London 50 m – Hastings 25 m – Maidstone 17 m

West Winchet without rest

Winchet Hill, North : 2½ m. on B 2079 ✉ TN17 1JX – ☎ (01580) 212 024 – annieparker@jpa-ltd.co.uk – Fax (01580) 212 250 – closed 26-30 December

3 rm – †£ 50/55 ††£ 75

◆ Victorian house with large, attractive rear garden. Breakfast taken in vast and attractively decorated drawing room. Traditional bedrooms offer country style décor.

GRAMPOUND – Cornwall – 503 F 33 – ✉ Truro 1 B2

London 287 m – Newquay 16 m – Plymouth 44 m – Truro 8 m
Trewithen★★★ AC, W : 2 m. by A 390 – Probus★ (tower★, Country Demonstration Garden★ AC) W : 2½ m. by A 390

Creed House without rest

Creed, South : 1 m. by Creed rd turning left just past the church ✉ TR2 4SL – ☎ (01872) 530 372 – Closed Christmas

3 rm – †£ 60 ††£ 90

◆ Smart Georgian rectory with restful gardens featured in several Cornish gardening books. Well-appointed sitting room. Fine art in breakfast room. Country house bedrooms.

GRANGE-OVER-SANDS – Cumbria – 502 L 21 – pop. 4 835 21 A3

Great Britain

London 268 m – Kendal 13 m – Lancaster 24 m
Victoria Hall, Main St ☎ (015395) 34026
Meathop Rd, ☎ (015395) 33 180 .
Cartmel Priory★, NW : 3 m

Netherwood Morecambe Bay, rm, rest,

Lindale Rd ✉ LA11 6ET – ☎ (015395) 32 552 – enquiries@netherwood-hotel.co.uk – Fax (015395) 34 121

32 rm – †£ 75 ††£ 200 – **Rest** – Menu £ 15/32 **s** – Carte £ 26/34 **s**

◆ Unusual, castellated late 18C hotel offering fine view of Morecambe Bay. Atmospheric wood-panelled lounges, each boasting open log fire. Comfy rooms with good mod cons. Dine formally and enjoy superb bay vistas.

Clare House

Park Rd ✉ LA11 7HQ – ☎ (015395) 33 026 – info@clarehousehotel.co.uk – Fax (015395) 34 310 – mid March-October

18 rm (dinner included) – †£ 76/133 ††£ 152 – **Rest** – (dinner only) (booking essential for non-residents) Menu £ 28

◆ Longstanding family run hotel, its lovely lawned garden looking over Morecambe Bay. Two smartly furnished lounges. Traditionally styled rooms, most with bay views. Two pleasant dining rooms; daily changing five-course menus show care and interest.

at Cartmel Northwest : 3 m – ✉ Grange-over-Sands

Aynsome Manor

North : ¾ m. by Cartmel Priory rd on Wood Broughton rd ✉ LA11 6HH – ☎ (015395) 36 653 – info@aynsomemanorhotel.co.uk – Fax (015395) 36 016 – Closed 25-26 December and 2-28 January

12 rm (dinner included) – †£ 90/95 ††£ 140/168 – **Rest** – (Closed Sunday dinner to non-residents) (dinner only and Sunday lunch) Menu £ 24

◆ Country house, personally run by two generations of the same family. Open fired snug bar and lounge with fine clocks. Sitting room has Priory view. Airy, traditional rooms. Dine on candle-lit, polished wood tables with silver.

Hill Farm without rest

Northwest : 1½ m. bearing to right of village shop in Market Square then left onto Cul-de-Sac rd after the racecourse ✉ LA11 7SS – ☎ (015395) 36 477 – Fax (015395) 36 477 – February-October

3 rm – †£ 40/45 ††£ 80/100

◆ Superb hospitality a feature of this 16C farmhouse with cottagey interior and lovely gardens: a peaceful setting. Individual colour schemes enhance the pretty bedrooms.

L'Enclume (Simon Rogan) with rm

Cavendish St ✉ LA11 6PZ – ☎ (015395) 36 362 – info@lenclume.co.uk – Fax (015395) 38 907

10 rm – †£ 68/128 ††£ 158 – **Rest** – (closed Monday and lunch Tuesday-Wednesday) (booking essential) Menu £ 25/70

Spec. Chicken croquettes, granola, sweet potato and yoghurt. Bream fillet, bacon polenta, calamari jelly. Chocolate cake, apricot, hyssop and passion fruit.

◆ Converted smithy in quaint village with contemporary look. Intriguingly innovative menus include the 9 course 'Introduction' and 14 course 'Tour' menu. Great cheese selection. Cosy, individually decorated bedrooms.

GRANTHAM – Lincs. – 502 S 25 – pop. 34 592 Great Britain 17 C2

London 113 m – Leicester 31 m – Lincoln 29 m – Nottingham 24 m
The Guildhall Centre, St Peter's Hill (01476) 406166
Belton Park Londonthorpe Rd, Belton Lane, (01476) 567 399 ;
Belton Woods H., (01476) 593 200 .
St Wulfram's Church★
Belton House★ **AC**, N : 2½ m. by A 607. Belvoir Castle★★ **AC**, W : 6 m. by A 607

Belton Woods rm,
Belton, North : 2 m. on A 607 NG32 2LN
– (01476) 593 200 – belton.woods@devere-hotels.com
– Fax (01476) 574 547
132 rm – £ 159 £ 169/249 – 4 suites
Rest *Stantons Brasserie* – (dinner only) Menu £ 38
◆ Set in acres of countryside, this modern hotel offers impressive leisure facilities, including three golf courses. Range of conference suites. Spacious bedrooms. Light, modern décor in Stantons Brasserie.

at Hough-on-the-Hill North : 6¾ m. by A 607 – Grantham

XX **The Brownlow Arms** with rm rest,
High Rd NG32 2AZ – (01400) 250 234 – armsinn@yahoo.co.uk
– closed 3 weeks January, 1 week September and 25-27 December
4 rm – £ 65 £ 96 – **Rest** – (closed Sunday and dinner Monday) (dinner only and Sunday lunch) Carte £ 25/35
◆ Attractive part 17/19C inn in heart of rural Lincolnshire. Wood-panelled bar with deep armchairs. Formal dining: well executed modern British dishes. Very tasteful rooms.

at Great Gonerby Northwest : 2 m. on B 1174 – Grantham

XX **Harry's Place** (Harry Hallam)
17 High St NG31 8JS – (01476) 561 780
– closed Christmas-New Year, Sunday, Monday and Bank Holidays
Rest – (booking essential) Carte £ 48/61
Spec. Sautéed foie gras in black pepper sherry jelly. Loin of roe deer with a Madeira, white wine and herb sauce. Apricot soufflé.
◆ Discreet listed Georgian building with cerise interior. Just three tables, bedecked with lilies and candles. Charming and attentive service. Robust, exquisite modern cooking.

at Woolsthorpe-by-Belvoir West : 7½ m. by A 607 – Grantham

The Chequers with rm
Main Street NG32 1LU – (01476) 870 701 – justinnabar@yahoo.co.uk
– Closed dinner 25-26 December, 1 January
4 rm – £ 49 £ 59 – **Rest** – (closed Sunday dinner in winter) Menu £ 15 – Carte £ 22/32
◆ Attractive pub, orginally built as 17C farmhouse. Various nooks, crannies, exposed bricks and beams. Traditional English cuisine with emphasis on game. Simple, clean rooms.

at Harlaxton Southwest : 2½ m. on A 607 – Grantham

The Gregory
The Drift NG32 1AD – (01476) 577 076
Rest – Carte £ 20/34 **s**
◆ Ivy-clad roadside inn with modernised open plan interior, glass topped well, small rear terrace and shop selling homemade fare. Informal dining.

Luxury pad or humble abode?
and denote categories of comfort.

ENGLAND

GRASMERE – Cumbria – 502 K 20 – ✉ Ambleside ▮ *Great Britain* 21 A2

London 282 m – Carlisle 43 m – Kendal 18 m
Redbank Rd ✆ (015394) 35245 (summer only) BZ
Dove Cottage★ AC AY A
Lake Windermere★★, SE : by A 591 AZ

Plans : see Ambleside

Gold Rill
rest,

Red Bank Rd ✉ LA22 9PU – ✆ (015394) 35 486 – reception@gold-rill.com – Fax (015394) 85 486 – Closed 2 weeks January and 2 weeks December BZ **a**
31 rm – †£ 58/136 ††£ 116/146 – 1 suite – **Rest** – (bar lunch) Carte £ 19/29
◆ Liberally proportioned, privately owned hotel in quiet part of town. Good views, open fires, slate based walls, traditional décor. Large bar with fine ales. Homely bedrooms. Quiet rear dining room overlooking lake.

Moss Grove Organic without rest

✉ LA22 9SW – ✆ (015394) 35 251 – enquiries@mossgrove.com – Fax (015394) 35 306 – closed 24-25 December BZ **s**
11 rm – †£ 115/185 ††£ 125/195
◆ Uniquely organic hotel whose bedrooms offer top comforts; all have spa baths, some have four posters or balconies with rocking chairs. Mediterranean buffet in breakfast room.

Grasmere

Broadgate ✉ LA22 9TA – ✆ (015394) 35 277 – enquiries@grasmerehotel.co.uk – Fax (015394) 35 277 – closed 2 January-1 February BZ **r**
13 rm (dinner included) – †£ 60/113 ††£ 130/150 – 1 suite – **Rest** – (dinner only) (booking essential for non-residents) Menu £ 30
◆ Small Victorian country house with pleasant acre of garden through which River Rothay flows. Snug, open-fired bar with good malt whisky selection. Individually styled rooms. Pleasant pine roofed rear dining room.

Lake View Country House without rest

Lake View Drive ✉ LA22 9TD – ✆ (015394) 35 384 – info@lake-view.grasmere.com BZ
4 rm – †£ 60/70 ††£ 94/99
◆ Country house whose large garden boasts views of lake and a badger sett. Comfy bedrooms, two with spa baths. Breakfast includes homemade yoghurt, compotes and fruit platters.

Riversdale

White Bridge, North : 1/2 m. on B 5287 ✉ LA22 9RH – ✆ (015394) 35 619 – info@riversdalegrasmere.co.uk AY **s**
3 rm – †£ 50/65 ††£ 72/88 – **Rest** – (by arrangement) Menu £ 21 **s**
◆ Immaculately kept lakeland guest house run by friendly couple who offer tea and cake on arrival and on the patio in good weather. Comfy bedrooms offer every conceivable extra. Homecooked meals served in neat dining room; wide choice available on breakfast menu.

GRASSENDALE – Mersey. – 502 L 23 – see Liverpool

GRASSINGTON – N. Yorks. – 502 O 21 – ✉ Skipton 22 A2

London 240 m – Bradford 30 m – Burnley 28 m – Leeds 37 m
National Park Centre, Colvend, Hebden Rd ✆ (01756) 751690

Ashfield House

Summers Fold, off Main St ✉ BD23 5AE – ✆ (01756) 752 584 – sales@ashfieldhouse.co.uk
8 rm – †£ 65/120 ††£ 88/147 – **Rest** – (closed Sunday) (dinner only) (booking essential for non-residents) Menu £ 30
◆ Sturdy 17C small stone hotel with beams and flagged floors: oozes period charm. Individually decorated, cottagey bedrooms with occasional exposed timber. Delightful garden. Tasty, locally-inspired dishes.

Grassington Lodge without rest

8 Wood Lane ✉ BD23 5LU – ☎ (01756) 752518 – relax@grassingtonlodge.co.uk – Fax (01756) 752518

10 rm – 🚹£65/80 🚹🚹£80/85

◆ Modern guesthouse at gateway to Yorkshire Dales. Built over 100 years ago as home of village doctor. Gallery of local photos on display around the house. Stylish, smart rooms.

GRAVESEND – Kent – 504 V 29 – pop. 53 045 — 8 B1

London 25 m – Dover 54 m – Maidstone 16 m – Margate 53 m

18a St George's Sq ☎ (01474) 337600

Manor — rest, VISA AE

Hever Court Rd, Singlewell, Southeast : 2½ m. by A 227 off A 2 (eastbound carriageway) ✉ DA12 5UQ – ☎ (01474) 353100 – manor@bestwestern.co.uk – Fax (01474) 354978 – Closed 24-27 December

59 rm – 🚹£75/89 🚹🚹£82/150 – **Rest** – (closed Sunday) Carte £21/32

◆ Privately owned hotel close to A2 motorway. Useful for visitors to Bluewater shopping complex. Bar, small health club. Comfortable bedrooms with limed oak style furniture. Cosy, wood floored restaurant.

GRAVETYE – W. Sussex – see East Grinstead

GREAT BADDOW – Essex – 504 V 28 – see Chelmsford

GREAT BIRCHAM – Norfolk – 502 V 25 — 15 C1

London 115 m – Hunstanton 10 m – King's Lynn 15 m

King's Head — rest, VISA

✉ PE31 6RJ – ☎ (01485) 578265 – welcome@the-kings-head-bircham.co.uk – Fax (01485) 578635

12 rm – 🚹£75/125 🚹🚹£150/225 – **Rest** – Carte £30/37

◆ Sign saying '1860' denotes age of property. Smart interior: relaxed bar and stylish residents lounge with big leather chairs. Well-equipped rooms in striking, earthy tones. Modern menus in a contemporary restaurant boasting sheltered courtyard terrace.

GREAT BROUGHTON – N. Yorks. – 502 Q 20 – ✉ Middlesbrough — 23 C1

London 241 m – Leeds 61 m – Middlesbrough 10 m – Newcastle upon Tyne 51 m – York 54 m

Wainstones — rm, VISA AE

31 High St ✉ TS9 7EW – ☎ (01642) 712268 – reception@wainstoneshotel.co.uk – Fax (01642) 711560

24 rm – 🚹£88/99 🚹🚹£120 – **Rest** – (Closed Sunday dinner) (dinner only) Menu £23/28

◆ Converted 17C farmhouse named after local outcrop of rocks. A good base for exploring North Yorkshire Moors. Large, atmospheric bar and sitting room. Good-sized bedrooms. Unfussy dining room.

GREAT DUNMOW – Essex – 504 V 28 – pop. 5 943 — 13 C2

London 42 m – Cambridge 27 m – Chelmsford 13 m – Colchester 24 m

XXX **The Starr** with rm — VISA AE

Market Place ✉ CM6 1AX – ☎ (01371) 874321 – starrestaurant@btinternet.com – Fax (01371) 876337 – closed 27 December-5 January

8 rm – 🚹£80/95 🚹🚹£120/145 – **Rest** – (closed Sunday dinner) Menu £35/45

◆ Former 15C pub with rustic bar and fire. Characterful restaurant has exposed beams and conservatory. Strong, interesting cooking, traditionally inspired. Smart bedrooms.

ENGLAND

Dish
15 High St ✉ CM6 1AB – ✆ (01371) 859 922 – Fax (01371) 859 888 – closed 25-28 December, 1 January and Sunday dinner
Rest – Menu £ 15 (lunch) – Carte dinner £ 25/31
◆ Modern family-run restaurant in 14C monastic reading room. Stylish interior with vibrant artwork and open plan kitchen. Contemporary menu with subtle Mediterranean feel.

GREAT GONERBY – Lincs. – 502 S 25 – see Grantham

GREAT HENNY – Essex – pop. 126 13 C2

London 64 m – Braintree 14 m – Sudbury 4 m

Henny Swan
Henny St ✉ CO10 7LS – ✆ (01787) 269 238 – harry@hennyswan.com – Closed Sunday dinner
Rest – Carte £ 18/25
◆ Spacious pub set over two floors boasts comfy leather furniture and open fires. Oft-changing menus; confident, flavoursome cooking uses locally produced, seasonal ingredients.

GREAT MALVERN – Worcs. – 503 N 27 – pop. 35 588 18 B3

London 127 m – Birmingham 34 m – Cardiff 66 m – Gloucester 24 m
21 Church St ✆ (01684) 892289 B

Plan opposite

ENGLAND

Bredon House without rest Severn Valley,
34 Worcester Rd ✉ WR14 4AA – ✆ (01684) 566 990 – enquiries@bredonhouse.co.uk – Fax (01684) 577 530 B a
10 rm – †£ 45/70 ††£ 90/110
◆ Elegant, Grade II listed Regency house with spectacular views. Personable owners make breakfast a special event. Most of the individually styled rooms enjoy the fine vista.

Cowleigh Park Farm without rest
Cowleigh Rd, Northwest : 1½ m. by B 4232 on B 4219 ✉ WR13 5HJ – ✆ (01684) 566 750 – cowleighpark@ukonline.co.uk – closed 24-26 December A r
4 rm – †£ 45 ††£ 70/75
◆ Part 17C farmhouse nestling in rustic position by gurgling stream. Vast inglenook fireplace complements comfy, adjacent sitting room. Cosy, snug bedrooms with exposed beams.

at Guarlford East : 2 1/2 m. on B 4211

Plough and Harrow
Rhydd Rd, East 3/4 m. on B 4211 ✉ WR13 6NY – ✆ (01684) 310 453 – info@theploughandharrow.co.uk – closed 2 weeks November, 1 week March, 25 December, Sunday dinner, Monday and bank holidays
Rest – Carte £ 17/32
◆ Modernised country pub with low-beamed bar and open fire; more formal dining room and large lawned garden. Unfussy cooking uses good quality produce, some from kitchen garden.

at Malvern Wells South : 2 m. on A 449 – ✉ Malvern

Cottage in the Wood Severn and Evesham Vales,
Holywell Rd ✉ WR14 4LG – ✆ (01684) 575 859 rest,
– reception@cottageinthewood.co.uk – Fax (01684) 560 662 A z
31 rm – †£ 79 ††£ 179 – **Rest** – Carte £ 23/37 s
◆ Early Victorian house, family owned and run, with superb view over surrounding vales. Very comfortable sitting room and bar. Individually furnished rooms in traditional style. Lovely restaurant with Oriental silk prints and Vale views.

GREAT MALVERN

Street	Grid	No.
Albert Rd South	B	3
Blackmore Park Rd	A	5
Church St.	B	
Clerkenwell Crescent	B	6
Cockshot Rd	B	8
Court Rd	B	12
Croft Bank	A	13
Happy Valley off St Ann's Rd	B	15
Imperial Rd	B	16
Jubilee Drive	A	17
Lygon Bank	B	18
Madresfield Rd	B	20
Moorlands Rd	B	22
North Malvern Rd	B	23
Orchard Rd	B	24
Richmond Rd	B	25
Townsend Way	A	26
Upper Welland Rd	A	27
Walwyn Rd	A	29
Wells Rd	A, B	30
Zetland Rd	B	31

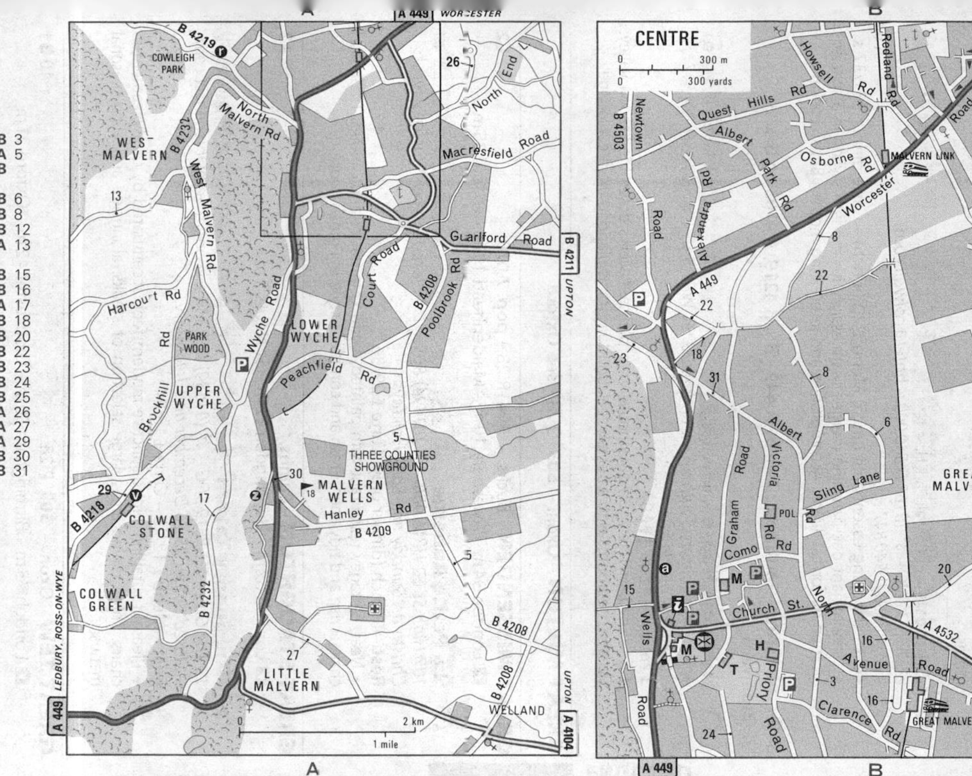

at Colwall **Southwest : 3 m. on B 4218 – ✉ Great Malvern**

Colwall Park
✉ *WR13 6QG – ☎ (01684) 540 000 – hotel@colwall.com – Fax (01684) 540 847* A **v**
20 rm – £ 80/90 £ 120 – 2 suites
Rest *Seasons* – see restaurant listing
◆ Built in 1903, this personally run hotel has a distinct Edwardian feel. Play croquet in the garden or wander into the nearby Malvern Hills. Individually decorated bedrooms.

Seasons – at Colwall Park H.
✉ *WR13 6QG – ☎ (01684) 540 000 – hotel@colwall.com – Fax (01684) 540 847* A **v**
Rest – (booking essential at lunch) Menu £ 20 (lunch) – Carte dinner £ 31/37 **s**
◆ Predominant oak panelling merges seamlessly with modern styling in a spacious location for formal dining. Accomplished and interesting modern British cooking.

at Acton Green **Northwest : 7 m. by A 449 - B -, B 4219, A 4103 on B 4220 – ✉ Bromyard**

Hidelow House without rest
Acton Beauchamp, South : ¾ m. on B 4220 ✉ WR6 5AH – ☎ (01886) 884 547 – Fax (01886) 884 658
3 rm – £ 45 £ 94
◆ Secluded, privately run guesthouse with pleasant views down the Leadon Valley. Sizeable bedrooms with a homely feel. Boudoir grand piano in the firelit lounge.

ENGLAND

GREAT MILTON – Oxon. – 503 Q 28 – see Oxford

GREAT MISSENDEN – Bucks. – 504 R 28 – pop. 7 070 11 C2

London 34 m – Aylesbury 10 m – Maidenhead 19 m – Oxford 35 m

La Petite Auberge
107 High St ✉ HP16 0BB – ☎ (01494) 865 370 – closed 2 weeks Easter, 2 weeks Christmas, Sunday and Bank Holidays
Rest – French (dinner only) Carte £ 29/36
◆ Neat, cottagey restaurant with painted wood chip paper and candles. Traditional chairs, crisp and tidy linen. Fresh and confident style of French cooking.

GREAT STAUGHTON – Cambs. 14 A2

London 62 m – Huntingdon 12 m – St Neots 5 m

The Snooty Tavern
12 The Green ✉ PE19 5DG – ☎ (01480) 860 336 – snootytavern@btconnect.com – Closed dinner 25-26 December and 1 January
Rest – Menu £ 12/15 – Carte £ 16/24
◆ Pleasant rural inn with distinctive modern feel, accentuated by comfy leather tub chairs. Three dining areas: large selection of steaks, alongside appealing seasonal menus.

GREAT TEW – Oxon. – 503 P 28 10 B1

London 75 m – Birmingham 50 m – Gloucester 42 m – Oxford 21 m

Falkland Arms with rm
✉ *OX7 4DB – ☎ (01608) 683 653 – sjcourage@btconnect.com – Fax (01608) 683 656*
5 rm – £ 110 £ 115 – **Rest** – (closed Sunday dinner) (booking essential) (bookings not accepted at lunch) Carte £ 15/30
◆ 17C inn on the green in picturesque village. Flag floors, exposed beams, inglenook fireplace guarantee warm ambience. Traditional, rustic food. Compact, cosy bedrooms.

GREAT WARLEY – Essex – see Brentwood

GREAT WHITTINGTON – Northd. – 501 O 18 – see Corbridge

GREAT WOLFORD – Warks. – 503 P 27 19 C3

London 84 m – Birmingham 37 m – Cheltenham 26 m

The Fox & Hounds Inn with rm

✉ CV36 5NQ – ✆ (01608) 674220 – *info@thefoxandhoundsinn.com*
– Closed 2 weeks January, Sunday dinner and Monday
3 rm – †£60 ††£90 – **Rest** – Carte £18/35

◆ 16C inn occupying central position in pleasant village. Endearing interior, featuring exposed beams, hop bines and log fire. Hearty, wholesome blackboard menus. Keen service. Cosy, well-kept bedrooms.

GREAT YARMOUTH – Norfolk – 504 Z 26 – pop. 58 032 15 D2

Great Britain

London 126 m – Cambridge 81 m – Ipswich 53 m – Norwich 20 m
25 Marine Parade ✆ (01493) 842195
Gorleston Warren Rd, ✆ (01493) 661 911 ;
Beach House Caister-on-Sea, ✆ (01493) 728 699.
Norfolk Broads★

Imperial

rest, VISA AE

North Drive ✉ *NR30 1EQ* – ✆ *(01493) 842 000* – *reception@imperialhotel.co.uk*
– Fax (01493) 852 229
39 rm – †£84 ††£100
Rest *Rambouillet* – (closed Sunday dinner) (dinner only and Sunday lunch)
Carte £20/33 **s**

◆ Turn of 20C classic promenade hotel, still privately owned. Imposing exterior with large public areas. Pleasant bedrooms in light fabrics include four wine-themed rooms. French feel pervades basement restaurant.

Seafood

A/C VISA AE

85 North Quay ✉ *NR30 1JF* – ✆ *(01493) 856 009*
– seafood01@btconnect.com – Fax (01493) 332 256
– closed 22 December-7 January, 11-26 May, Saturday lunch, Sunday and Bank Holidays
Rest – Seafood Carte £21/48

◆ Run by a husband and wife team, a long-standing neighbourhood restaurant. Lobster tank, fish display, fresh, generous seafood, attentive service and home-made chocolates!

GREEN ISLAND – C.I. – see Channel Islands

GRETA BRIDGE – Durham – 502 O 20 – see Barnard Castle

GRIMSTON – Norfolk – 504 V 25 – see King's Lynn

GRINSHILL – Shrops. – 503 L 25 – see Shrewsbury

The ✿ award is the crème de la crème. This is awarded to restaurants which are really worth travelling miles for!

ENGLAND

GROUVILLE – C.I. – **503** M 33 – see Channel Islands

GUERNSEY – C.I. – **503** OP 33 – see Channel Islands

GUILDFORD – **Surrey** – **504** S 30 – **pop. 69 400** *Great Britain* 7 **C1**

London 33 m – Brighton 43 m – Reading 27 m – Southampton 49 m

14 Tunsgate ✆ (01483) 444333 Y

Clandon Park★★, E : 3 m. by A 246 Z – Hatchlands Park★, E : 6 m. by A 246 Z. Painshill★★, Cobham, NE : 10 m – Polesden Lacey★, E : 13 m. by A 246 Z and minor rd

GUILDFORD

Bedford Rd	Y	2
Bridge St	Y	3
Castle St	Y	5
Chertsey St	Y	6
Commercial Rd	Y	8
Eastgate Gardens	Y	9
Friary Bridge	Y	12
Friary Centre	Y	
High St	Y	
Ladymead	Z	13
Leapale Lane	Y	15
Leapale Rd	Y	16
Leas Rd	Y	17
Market St	Y	18
Mary Rd	Y	19
Midleton Rd	Z	20
Millbrook	Y	21
New Inn Lane	Z	22
North St	Y	
One Tree Hill Rd	Z	24
Onslow St	Y	25
Park St	Y	27
Quarry St	Y	28
Stoughton Rd	Z	30
Trood's Lane	Z	31
Tunsgate	Y	33
Tunsgate Shopping Centre	Y	
Warwick's Bench	Y	34
Woodbridge Rd	Z	37

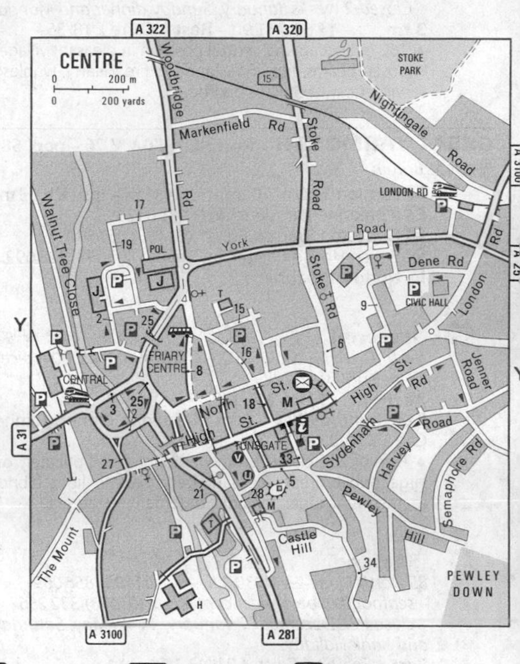

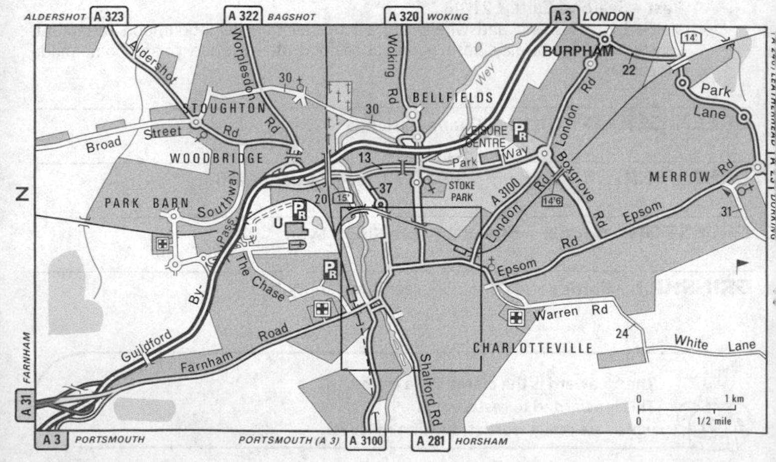

XX **Café de Paris**

35 Castle St ✉ GU1 3UQ – ✆ (01483) 534 896 – Fax (01483) 300 411 – Closed Sunday and Bank Holidays (except Good Friday) Y **u**

Rest – French (booking essential) Carte £ 23/37

◆ French-style backstreet eatery. Take your pick of brasserie in front or restaurant at back. Prix fixe or à la carte dishes with traditional twist and seasonal changes.

X **Zinfandel**

4-5 Chapel St ✉ GU1 3UH – ✆ (01483) 455 155 – mail@zinfandel.org.uk – Closed 25-26 December, 1 January, dinner Sunday and Monday Y **v**

Rest – Carte £ 18/30

◆ Welcoming, modern and irresistibly laid back; Napa Valley cuisine mixes grills, Pacific Rim salads, full-flavoured, wood-fired pizzas and picket-fence classics like pecan pie.

at Shere East : 6 ¾ m. by A 246 off A 25 - Z - ✉ Guildford

XX **Kinghams**

Gomshall Lane ✉ GU5 9HE – ✆ (01483) 202 168 – paul@kinghams-restaurant.co.uk – Closed 25 December-6 January, Sunday dinner and Monday

Rest – (booking essential) Menu £ 16.50 – Carte £ 26/37

◆ Popular restaurant in 17C cottage in appealing village. Daily blackboard and fish specials are particularly good value. Adventurous modern menus with bold combinations.

ENGLAND

GUISBOROUGH – Redcar and Cleveland – 502 Q 20 24 B3

London 265 m – Middlesbrough 9 m – Newcastle upon Tyne 50 m – Whitby 22 m

Gisborough Hall rm,

Whitby Lane, East : 1 m. on Whitby rd ✉ TS14 6PT – ✆ (0870) 400 8191 – Fax (01287) 610 844

70 rm – †£ 60 ††£ 140, ☕ £ 14.95 – 1 suite

Rest *Tocketts* – Menu £ 30/45

◆ Imposing, ivy-clad 19C country house with modern wing. Very comfy drawing room; main hall has minstrel gallery; cosy library bar. Rooms more individually styled in main house. Restaurant, set in billiard room, infused with classical style.

GUITING POWER – Glos. – 503 O 28 – ✉ Cheltenham 4 D1

London 95 m – Birmingham 47 m – Gloucester 30 m – Oxford 39 m

Guiting Guest House

Post Office Lane ✉ GL54 5TZ – ✆ (01451) 850 470 – info@guitingguesthouse.com

6 rm ☕ – †£ 43/48 ††£ 85 – **Rest** – (by arrangement) Menu £ 30

◆ 16C stone-built former Cotswold farmhouse in centre of charming village. Cosy lounge, wood floors and original open fire. Two particularly comfortable converted cottage rooms. Intimate, low-beamed 'hop-strung' dining-room.

GUNNERSIDE – N. Yorks. – 502 N 20 – ✉ Darlington 22 A1

London 268 m – Newcastle upon Tyne 60 m – Richmond 17 m

Oxnop Hall without rest

Low Oxnop, West : 1 ½ m. on B 6270 ✉ DL11 6JJ – ✆ (01748) 886 253 – Fax (01748) 886 253 – March-October

5 rm ☕ – †£ 47 ††£ 64/74

◆ Pleasant stone-built 17C farmhouse and working sheep farm in agreeable hillside position. Cosy little lounge. Bedrooms feature beams, mullion windows and rural views.

GUNWALLOE – Cornwall – 503 E 33 – see Helston

HACKNESS – N. Yorks. – 502 S 21 – see Scarborough

HADDENHAM – Bucks. – 504 R 28 – pop. 4 720 11 C2

London 54 m – Aylesbury 8 m – Oxford 21 m

The Green Dragon

8 Churchway ✉ HP17 8AA – ✆ (01844) 291 403 – sue@eatatthedragon.co.uk – Fax (01844) 299 532 – Closed 25 December and Sunday dinner

Rest – (booking essential) Carte £ 24/32

◆ Warmly decorated, modern-style pub-restaurant with a friendly atmosphere and pleasant service. Very good value, from simple pub food to more elaborate restaurant-style dishes.

HADLEIGH – Suffolk – 504 W 27 – pop. 7 124 15 C3

London 72 m – Cambridge 49 m – Colchester 17 m – Ipswich 10 m

Hadleigh Library, 29 High St ✆ (01473) 823778

Edge Hall without rest

2 High St ✉ IP7 5AP – ✆ (01473) 822 458 – r.rolfe@edgehall.co.uk

10 rm – †£ 60/65 ††£ 85/120

◆ One of the oldest houses in the town (1590), with a Georgian façade. Spacious, comfy bedrooms are traditionally furnished, as are the communal areas. Very well-kept gardens.

ENGLAND

HADLEY HEATH – Worcs. – see Droitwich Spa

HAILSHAM – E. Sussex – 504 U 31 – pop. 19 177 8 B3

London 57 m – Brighton 23 m – Eastbourne 7 m – Hastings 20 m

Wellshurst G. & C.C. Hellingly North St, ✆ (01435) 813 636 .

at Magham Down Northeast : 2 m. by A 295 on A 271 – ✉ Hailsham

Olde Forge

✉ BN27 1PN – ✆ (01323) 842 893 – theoldeforgehotel@tesco.net – Fax (01323) 842 893

7 rm – †£ 48 ††£ 75 – **Rest** – (dinner only) Menu £ 25

◆ Privately owned timbered house with cottage feel, charmingly run by helpful, friendly owners. Rooms are individually furnished in elegant pine; one boasts a four-poster bed. Beamed restaurant with carefully compiled menu.

HALAM – Notts. *Great Britain* 16 B1

London 134 m – Derby 8 m – Nottingham 8 m

Southwell Minster★★ AC, E : 2 m. on Mansfield Rd, Halam Hill, Market Pl and A 612

Waggon and Horses

The Turnpike, Mansfield Rd ✉ NG22 8AE – ✆ (01636) 813 109 – info@thewaggonathalam.co.uk – Fax (01636) 816 228 – Closed Sunday dinner, 25-26 December and 1 January

Rest – Menu £ 15 – Carte £ 20/30

◆ Cosy, low-beamed pub with well-stocked bar and cricket themed curios. Owners are members of 'Campaign For Real Food' and menus have emphasis on fresh, local, seasonal produce.

Good food and accommodation at moderate prices?
Look for the Bib symbols:
red Bib Gourmand for food, blue Bib Hotel for hotels

HALFORD – Warks – **503** P 27 – pop. 301 19 **C3**

London 94 m – Oxford 43 m – Stratford-upon-Avon 8 m

Old Manor House

Queens St CV36 5BT – (01789) 740 264 – info@oldmanor-halford.fsnet.co.uk – Fax (01789) 740 609 – closed Christmas and New Year

3 rm – £ 50/60 £ 90/110 – **Rest** – (by arrangement, communal dining) Menu £ 18

◆ Characterful house in quiet residential area, well located for Stratford and the Cotswolds. Spacious garden next to River Stour. Well appointed drawing room and atmospheric bedrooms with rich fabrics. Family style dining; fine tableware; good use of local produce.

HALFWAY BRIDGE – W. Sussex – **504** R 31 – **see Petworth**

HALIFAX – W. Yorks. – **502** O 22 – pop. 83 570 22 **B2**

London 205 m – Bradford 8 m – Burnley 21 m – Leeds 15 m – Manchester 28 m

Piece Hall (01422) 368725

Halifax Bradley Hall Holywell Green, (01422) 374 108 ;

Halifax West End Highroad Well Paddock Lane, (01422) 341 878 ;

Ryburn Sowerby Bridge Norland, (01422) 831 355 ;

Lightcliffe Knowle Top Rd, (01422) 202 459 ;

Ogden Union Lane, (01422) 244 171 .

Holdsworth House

rm,

Holmfield, North : 3 m. by A 629 and Shay Lane HX2 9TG – (01422) 240 024 – info@holdsworthhouse.co.uk – Fax (01422) 245 174 – closed 24 December-3 January

36 rm – £ 105/125 £ 150 – 4 suites – **Rest** – (closed Saturday lunch and Sunday) Carte £ 25/42

◆ Characterful and extended part 17C manor house in a quiet location. Comfortable, traditionally decorated rooms with wood furniture. Country house-style throughout. Three-roomed, wood-panelled restaurant overlooks garden.

Design House

Dean Clough (Gate 5) HX3 5AX – (01422) 383 242 – enquiries@designhouserestaurant.co.uk – Fax (01422) 322 732 – Closed 26 December-9 January, Saturday lunch and Sunday

Rest – Menu £ 14/18 – Carte £ 24/34

◆ Located within converted mill on outskirts of town, an impressively stylish and modern restaurant with Philippe Starck furniture. Varied menu of contemporary British cooking.

Shibden Mill Inn with rm

Shibden Mill Fold, Northeast : 2 ¼ m. by A 58 and Kell Lane (turning left at Stump Cross public house) on Blake Hill Rd HX3 7UL – (01422) 365 840 – glenpearson@shibdenmillinn.com – Fax (01422) 362 971 – Closed 25-26 December, 1 January and Sunday dinner

11 rm – £ 75 £ 90 – **Rest** – Carte £ 18/29

◆ Part 17C inn hidden away in wooded Shibden Valley. Beamed areas and open fires; first floor restaurant. Classic or modern English dishes. Comfy rooms in converted barn.

at Shelf Northeast : 3 m. on A 6036 – Halifax

Bentley's

12 Wadehouse Rd HX3 7PB – (01274) 690 992 – bentleys@btinternet.com – Fax (01274) 690 011 – Closed 25-26 December, 1 January, Sunday, Monday and Saturday lunch

Rest – Menu £ 11 – Carte £ 30/33

◆ Converted terraced house with characterful interior, highlighted by rustic brickwork. Appealing, wide-ranging blackboard menu serving hearty food with a Yorkshire base.

ENGLAND

HALL GREEN – W. Mids. – 502 O 26 – see Birmingham

HALLAND – E. Sussex – 504 U 31 – ✉ Lewes 8 **A3**

London 59 m – Brighton 17 m – Eastbourne 15 m – Maidstone 35 m

 **Shortgate Manor Farm** without rest

Southwest : 1 m. on B 2192 ✉ BN8 6PJ – ✆ (01825) 840 320 – david@shortgate.co.uk – Fax (01825) 840 320

3 rm – £ 50/75 £ 85

◆ Extended 18C shepherd's cottage with extensive, pretty gardens. Neat and spacious bedrooms. Communal rooms decorated with home-grown dried flowers.

HALNAKER – W. Sussex – see Chichester

HALTWHISTLE – Northd. – 501 M 19 – pop. 3 811 *Great Britain* 24 **A2**

London 335 m – Carlisle 22 m – Newcastle upon Tyne 37 m

Railway Station, Station Rd ✆ (01434) 322002

Wallend Farm Greenhead, ✆ (01697) 747 367

Hadrian's Wall★★, N : 4½ m. by A 6079 – Housesteads★★ **AC**, NE : 6 m. by B 6318 – Roman Army Museum★ **AC**, NW : 5 m. by A 69 and B 6318 – Vindolanda (Museum★) **AC**, NE : 5 m. by A 69 – Steel Rig (< ★) NE : 5½ m. by B 6318

ENGLAND

 **Centre of Britain**

Main St ✉ NE49 0BH – ✆ (01434) 322 422 – enquiries@centre-of-britain.org.uk – Fax (01434) 322 655 – closed 24-26 December

12 rm – £ 44/75 £ 110/176 – **Rest** – (dinner only) Menu £ 22 – Carte £ 16/25 **s**

◆ Attractive hotel on busy main street. Oldest part, a pele tower, dates from 15C. Comfortable modern décor, including bedrooms, incorporates original architectural features. Glass-roofed restaurant with light, airy feel.

Ashcroft without rest

Lantys Lonnen ✉ NE49 0DA – ✆ (01434) 320 213 – ashcroft.1@btconnect.com – Fax (01434) 321 641 – closed 25 December

7 rm – £ 35/55 £ 80/90

◆ Imposing Victorian house, formerly a vicarage, with beautifully kept gardens. Family run and attractively furnished throughout creating a welcoming atmosphere. Large bedrooms.

HAMBLE-LE-RICE – Southampton – 503 Q 31 – see Southampton

HAMBLETON – Rutland – see Oakham

HANLEY SWAN – Worcs. – 503 N 27 – see Upton-upon-Severn

HANWELL – Oxon. – see Banbury

Do not confuse X with ✿!
X defines comfort, while stars are awarded for the best cuisine, across all categories of comfort.

HARDWICK – Cambs. – see Cambridge

HARLAXTON – Lincs. – **502** S 25 – see Grantham

HAROME – N. Yorks. – see Helmsley

HARPENDEN – Herts. – **504** S 28 – **pop. 28 452** 12 **A2**

London 32 m – Luton 6 m
Harpenden Common East Common, (01582) 711 320 ;
Hammonds End, (01582) 712 580 .

XX **The Bean Tree**

20A Leyton Rd ✉ AL5 2HU – (01582) 460 901 – enquiries@thebeantree.com – Fax (01582) 460 826 – closed Saturday lunch, Sunday dinner and Monday

Rest – Menu £ 22 – Carte £ 26/47

◆ Converted red-brick cottage with bean tree and smart terrace. Intimate, softly lit restaurant with sage green palette. Carefully sought ingredients; precise modern cooking.

The White Horse

Hatching Green, Southwest : 1 m. by A 1081 on B 487 ✉ AL5 2JW – (01582) 469 290 – info@atouchofnovelli.com – Closed 24-25 December and Sunday dinner

Rest – (booking essential) Menu £ 22 – Carte £ 29/36

◆ Stylish and informal 17C pub, part-owned by Jean-Christophe Novelli, with a hearty classical French menu. Open log fire warms the small bar; semi-open kitchen in dining room.

The Three Horseshoes

136 East Common, Southeast : 1 ¾ m. by A 1081 and Cross Lane, turning right at crossroads ✉ AL5 1AW – (01582) 713 953 – threehorseshoes@spiceinns.co.uk – Closed Sunday dinner

Rest – Carte £ 27/33

◆ Peaceful rural location, open fire and low ceiling. Small interior, so not the place for claustrophobes. An eclectic mix of European dishes, seasoned by the pub's herb garden.

The Fox

469 Luton Rd, Kinsbourne Green, Northwest : 2 m. on A 1081 ✉ AL5 3QE – (01582) 713 817

Rest – Carte £ 25/30

◆ Busy pub with cosy beamed interior and decked terrace. Spacious sitting room boasts open fire and comfy leather sofas. Menu includes sharing plates and rotisserie sections.

HARROGATE – N. Yorks. – **502** P 22 – **pop. 85 128** *Great Britain* 22 **B2**

London 211 m – Bradford 18 m – Leeds 15 m – Newcastle upon Tyne 76 m – York 22 m
Royal Baths, Crescent Rd (01423) 537300, tic@harrogate.gov.uk
Forest Lane Head, (01423) 863 158 ;
Pannal Follifoot Rd, (01423) 872 628 ;
Oakdale, (01423) 567 162 ;
Crimple Valley Hookstone Wood Rd, (01423) 883 485.
Town★
Fountains Abbey★★★ **AC** :- Studley Royal **AC** (< ★ from Anne Boleyn's Seat) - Fountains Hall (Fa½ade★), N : 13 m. by A 61 and B 6265 AY – Harewood House★★ (The Gallery★) **AC**, S : 7½ m. by A 61 BZ

Plan on next page

ENGLAND

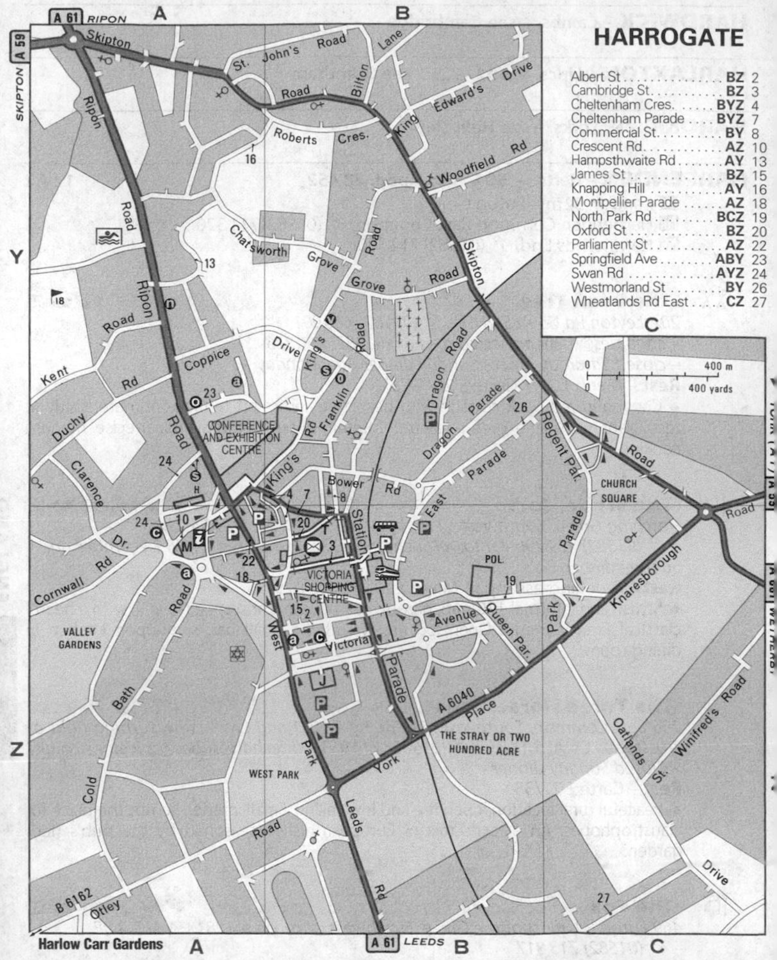

Rudding Park

Rudding Park, Follifoot, Southeast : 3 ¾ m. by A 661
✉ HG3 1JH – ✆ (01423) 871 350 – sales@ruddingpark.com
– Fax (01423) 872 286
46 rm – †£ 155 ††£ 185 – 3 suites
Rest *The Clocktower* – Carte £ 25/45 **s**

◆ Grade I listed Georgian house in rural location with modern extension. Comfortable, elegant style throughout. Rooms are simple and classical with modern, colourful fabrics. Smart, contemporary brasserie with oak floors.

rm, rest, VISA AE

Hotel du Vin

Prospect Pl ✉ HG1 1LB – ✆ (01423) 856 800 – info.harrogate@hotelduvin.com
– Fax (01423) 856 801 BZ **a**
43 rm – †£ 125/170 ††£ 125/170, £13.50
Rest *Bistro* – Menu £ 18 (lunch) – Carte £ 26/37

◆ Terrace of Georgian houses overlooking pleasant green. Individually appointed bedrooms with wine-theme decor and modern facilities. Buzzy, modern, stylish French bistro and private dining rooms. Good menu of Gallic influenced dishes.

VISA AE

Grants rest,
Swan Rd ✉ HG1 2SS – ✆ (01423) 560 666
– enquiries@grantshotel-harrogate.com – Fax (01423) 502 550 AY **s**
41 rm – £70/130 £110/165 – 1 suite
Rest *Chimney Pots Bistro* – Menu £12/20 – Carte £17/28
◆ Victorian terraced house in a residential area. Comfortable, traditionally decorated public areas. Bedrooms in varying styles, sizes and shapes. Close to conference centre. Brightly painted, basement bistro restaurant.

The Balmoral rest,
Franklin Mount ✉ HG1 5EJ – ✆ (01423) 508 208 – info@balmoralhotel.co.uk
– Fax (01423) 530 652 BY **v**
20 rm – £85/110 £110/130, £10 – 3 suites
Rest *Villu Toots* – (dinner only) Carte £25/33
◆ Privately run, Gothic-style, Victorian property; charm accentuated by antique furnishings and individually decorated rooms. Bar with Harry Houdini memorabilia. Bustling informality in restaurant, where modern minimalism prevails.

Alexa House without rest
26 Ripon Rd ✉ HG1 2JJ – ✆ (01423) 501 988 – enquires@alexa-house.co.uk
– Fax (01423) 504 086 – Closed 1-16 August and 22-26 December AY **n**
13 rm – £50/70 £80/85
◆ Georgian house built in 1830 for Baron-de-Ferrier: contemporary interior touches provide a seamless contrast. Bedrooms in two buildings: more characterful in main house.

Alexandra Court without rest
8 Alexandra Rd ✉ HG1 5JS – ✆ (01423) 502 764 – office@alexandracourt.co.uk
– Fax (01423) 850 383 BY **o**
13 rm – £52/68 £78
◆ Detached, family owned Victorian house, retaining original features, in quiet residential area. Bedrooms and communal areas have a simple elegance in décor and ambience.

Brookfield House without rest
5 Alexandra Rd ✉ HG1 5JS – ✆ (01423) 506 646
– office@brookfieldhousehotel.co.uk – closed Christmas and New Year BY **s**
6 rm – £68/75 £75/85
◆ Family owned Victorian property in a quiet, residential location close to the town centre. Homely feel in communal areas and comfortable bedrooms with a mix of styles.

Acacia without rest
3 Springfield Ave ✉ HG1 2HR – ✆ (01423) 560 752 – dee@acaciaharrogate.co.uk
– Closed Christmas to New Year and restricted opening November-March, minimum stay 2 nights AY **o**
4 rm – £55/80 £75/85
◆ Centrally located Victorian solid stone guesthouse, within a few minutes' walk of the shops; very personably run. Immaculately kept throughout. Attractive, pine-clad bedrooms.

Ashwood House without rest
7 Spring Grove ✉ HG1 2HS – ✆ (01423) 560 081 – ashwoodhouse@aol.com
– Fax (01423) 527 928 – Closed 20 December- 2 January AY **a**
5 rm – £35/65 £65/70
◆ An Edwardian house minutes from the International Conference Centre. Simply decorated, pine furnished rooms and communal areas have a homely ambience.

Quantro
3 Royal Par ✉ HG1 2SZ – ✆ (01423) 503 034 – info@quantro.co.uk
– Fax (01423) 503 034 – closed 25-26 December, 1 January and Sunday AZ **a**
Rest – Menu £14 – Carte £22/27
◆ Modern art murals and mirrors adorn this smart restaurant. Comfy banquettes and black tables. Good value mix of interesting dishes with Mediterranean underpinnings.

ENGLAND

Orchid

28 Swan Rd ✉ HG1 2SE – ✆ (01423) 560 425 – info@orchidrestaurant.co.uk – Fax (01423) 530 967 – Closed Saturday lunch AZ **c**

Rest – South East Asian Carte £ 23/38

◆ Unfussy, uncluttered restaurant with Asian styling. Polite, friendly service adds to the enjoyment of richly authentic dishes from a wide range of south-east Asian countries.

Sasso

8-10 Princes Sq ✉ HG1 1LX – ✆ (01423) 508 838 – Fax (01423) 508 838 – closed Sunday, Monday lunch and Bank Holidays BZ **c**

Rest – Italian Carte £ 24/32

◆ In the basement of a 19C property. Antiques, ceramics and modern art embellish the interior. The menu offers a good choice of authentic Italian dishes with modern influences.

at Kettlesing West : 6½ m. by A 59 - AY – ✉ Harrogate

Knabbs Ash without rest

Skipton Rd, on A 59 ✉ HG3 2LT – ✆ (01423) 771 040 – sheila@knabbsash.co.uk – closed 25-26 December

3 rm – †£ 50/70 ††£ 70/75

◆ Stone built cottage with spacious gardens and grounds. Cosy lounge; pine furnished breakfast room. Homely and simple, largely floral interior; rooms individually decorated.

ENGLAND

HARTINGTON – Derbs. – 502 O 24 – ✉ Buxton 16 **A1**

London 168 m – Derby 36 m – Manchester 40 m – Sheffield 34 m – Stoke-on-Trent 22 m

Biggin Hall

Biggin, Southeast : 2 m. by B 5054 ✉ SK17 0DH – ✆ (01298) 84 451 – enquiries@bigginhall.co.uk – Fax (01298) 84 681

20 rm – †£ 50/84 ††£ 120/130 – **Rest** – (dinner only) (booking essential) Menu £ 19 **s**

◆ Charming house with much rustic personality and individuality. Stone floored lounges and open fires. Antique furnished bedrooms vary in size and shape. Elegant dining room with low beams.

HARTLAND – Devon – 503 G 31 1 **B1**

London 221 m – Bude 15 m – Clovelly 4 m

Golden Park without rest

Southwest : 5 m. following signs for Elmscott and Bude ✉ EX39 6EP – ✆ (01237) 441 254 – lynda@goldenpark.co.uk – closed 25 December

3 rm – †£ 60/65 ††£ 70/85

◆ Walk to the North Devon coast from this delightfully set part 17C farmhouse. Style and character prevail, particularly in guests' lounge and beamed, smartly decorated rooms.

We try to be as accurate as possible when giving room rates. But prices are susceptible to change, so please check rates when booking.

HARWELL – Oxon. – 503 Q 29 – pop. 2 015 10 B3

London 64 m – Oxford 16 m – Reading 18 m – Swindon 22 m

Kingswell rm, VISA AE

Reading Rd, East : ¾ m. on A 417 ✉ OX11 0LZ – ✆ (01235) 833 043 – kingswell@breathemail.net – Fax (01235) 833 193 – closed 24-30 December

20 rm – £ 102/105 £ 118/125 – **Rest** – Carte £ 20/43 **s**

◆ Large redbrick hotel located on the south Oxfordshire Downs. Convenient for Didcot rail and Oxford. Spacious, uniform, traditional bedrooms and pubby public areas. Classic menus served in traditional dining room.

HARWICH and DOVERCOURT – Essex – 504 X 28 – pop. 20 130 13 D2

London 78 m – Chelmsford 41 m – Colchester 20 m – Ipswich 23 m

to Denmark (Esbjerg) (DFDS Seaways A/S) 3-4 weekly (20 h) – to The Netherlands (Hook of Holland) (Stena Line) 2 daily (3 h 30 mn)

Iconfield Park, Parkeston ✆ (01255) 506139

Parkeston Station Rd, ✆ (01255) 503 616 .

Pier at Harwich VISA AE

The Quay ✉ CO12 3HH – ✆ (01255) 241 212 – pier@milsomhotels.com – Fax (01255) 551 922

14 rm – £ 73/85 £ 98/173

Rest *Harbourside* – Seafood Menu £ 18 (lunch) – Carte £ 27/42

Rest *Ha'Penny* – Carte £ 21/25

◆ Bright Victorian building located on the quayside giving many bedrooms views of the area's busy sea lanes. Décor is comfortably stylish and contemporary with a nautical theme. Seafood restaurant with North Sea outlook. Informal bistro.

HASTINGS and ST LEONARDS – E. Sussex – 504 V 31 – pop. 85 828 8 B3

London 65 m – Brighton 37 m – Folkestone 37 m – Maidstone 34 m

Town Hall, Queen's Sq, Priory Meadow ✆ (01424) 781111, hic-info@hastings.gov.uk -The Stade, Old Town Hall ✆ (01424) 781111

Beauport Park St Leonards-on-Sea Battle Rd, ✆ (01424) 854 243 .

Plan on next page

Tower House 1066 VISA

26-28 Tower Road West ✉ TN38 0RG – ✆ (01424) 427 217 – reservations@towerhousehotel.com – Fax (01424) 430 165 AY **c**

10 rm – £ 45/60 £ 65/105 – **Rest** – (Closed Thursday to Sunday) (dinner only) (residents only, set menu only) Menu £ 19

◆ Friendly and well run, a redbrick Victorian house in a residential area. Comfortably furnished with individually decorated bedrooms and a conservatory bar lounge area.

Parkside House without rest VISA AE

59 Lower Park Rd ✉ TN34 2LD – ✆ (01424) 433 096 – bkentparksidehouse@aol.com – Fax (01424) 421 431 BY **e**

5 rm – £ 30/45 £ 65/70

◆ Detached Victorian house in quiet area of town overlooking a park. Traditionally decorated; the spacious bedrooms are smart and well kept.

Zanzibar without rest VISA

9 Eversfield Place ✉ TN34 6BY – ✆ (01424) 460 109 – info@zanzibarhotel.co.uk AZ **c**

8 rm – £ 99/105 £ 140/160

◆ Contemporary guest house with slightly unusual design. Bedrooms are named after countries and continents; South America is largest, with feature whirlpool bath and seaview.

ENGLAND

HASTINGS ST. LEONARDS

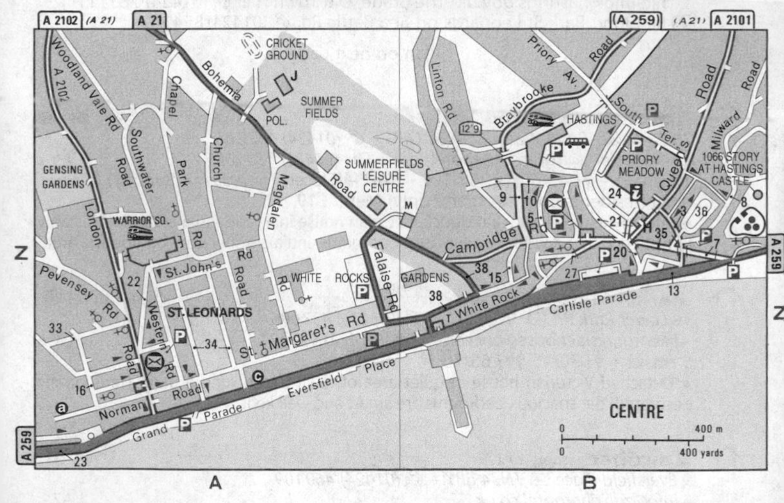

If breakfast is included the ☕ symbol appears after the number of rooms.

St Clements

3 Mercatoria, St Leonards on Sea ✉ TN38 0EB – ✆ (01424) 200 355 – closed Sunday dinner and Monday AZ **a**

Rest – Menu £ 13 (weekdays)/18 **s** – Carte approx. £ 29 **s**

◆ Charming, contemporary restaurant minutes from the sea. Classically based, seasonal menus showcase local produce, with seafood fresh off the boats. Relaxed, intimate mood.

HATCH BEAUCHAMP – Somerset – 503 K 30 – see Taunton

HATFIELD HEATH – Essex – 504 U 28 – see Bishop's Stortford (Herts.)

HATFIELD PEVEREL – Essex – 504 V 28 – pop. 3 258 *Great Britain* 13 C2

London 39 m – Chelmsford 8 m – Maldon 12 m

Colchester - Castle and Museum★, E : 13 m. by A 12

Blue Strawberry Bistrot

The Street ✉ CM3 2DW – ✆ (01245) 381 333 – Fax (01245) 340 498 – closed Saturday lunch and Sunday dinner

Rest – Menu £ 14 (weekdays)/20 – Carte £ 19/36

◆ Make your reservation by first name only in this characterful converted pub with inglenook and Victorian style. Rear dining terrace. Classic British cooking off large menus.

HATHERSAGE – Derbs. – 502 P 24 – pop. 1 582 – ✉ Sheffield (S. Yorks.) 16 A1

London 177 m – Derby 39 m – Manchester 34 m – Sheffield 11 m – Stoke-on-Trent 44 m

Sickleholme Bamford, ✆ (01433) 651 306 .

The George

✉ S32 1BB – ✆ (01433) 650 436 – info@george-hotel.net – Fax (01433) 650 099

22 rm – †£ 88/97 ††£ 165

Rest ***George's*** – Carte £ 28/35 **s**

◆ Built in 14C as an inn to serve the packhorse route. Sympathetically restored in rustic style, with oak beams and stone walls. Bedrooms have a bright, more modern feel. Rustically decorated, vibrant-hued dining room.

The Walnut Club

The Square, Main Rd ✉ S32 1BB – ✆ (01433) 651 155 – nick@thewalnutclub.com – closed Sunday dinner and Monday October-April

Rest – Menu £ 20 (lunch) – Carte £ 20/37

◆ Contemporary style restaurant found deep in Derbyshire walking country, serving generously portioned organic dishes. All day dining. Varied menus. Live jazz at weekends.

HAWES – N. Yorks. – 502 N 21 22 A1

London 253 m – Kendal 27 m – Leeds 72 m – Newcastle upon Tyne 76 m – York 65 m

Dales Countryside Museum, Station Yard ✆ (01969) 666210

Simonstone Hall

Simonstone, North : 1½ m. on Muker rd ✉ DL8 3LY – ✆ (01969) 667 255 – email@simonstonehall.demon.co.uk – Fax (01969) 667 741

18 rm – †£ 75/90 ††£ 170/190 – 1 suite – **Rest** – (bar lunch) Menu £ 30 (dinner) – Carte £ 15/30

◆ Part 18C country house, with historic feel, amidst lovely countryside. Individually furnished bedrooms, many of which enjoy pleasant views from the front of the building. Dining room or tavern eating options.

ENGLAND

Stone House
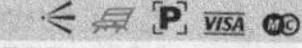

Sedbusk, North : 1 m. by Muker rd ✉ DL8 3PT – ✆ (01969) 667571 – daleshotel@aol.com – Fax (01969) 667720 – closed January and mid week in December

23 rm – †£46/65 ††£131 – **Rest** – (dinner only) Menu £30

◆ Built in 1908 as a family home. Interior decorated in traditional style; public areas include billiard room and oak panelled lounge. Some rooms with private conservatories. Dining room has exposed beams and wooden tables.

Rookhurst Country House

Gayle, South : ½ m. by Gayle rd ✉ DL8 3RT – ✆ (01969) 667454 – enquiries@rookhurst.co.uk

5 rm – †£55/100 ††£110/130 – **Rest** – (dinner only) (booking essential) (residents only) Menu £25 **s**

◆ Spacious yet cosy country house with a very comfortable, smart, traditional atmosphere that's friendly and informal. Convenient for the Pennine Way. Uncluttered bedrooms.

Cockett's

Market Pl ✉ DL8 3RD – ✆ (01969) 667312 – enquiries@cocketts.co.uk – Fax (01969) 667162 – closed 25-26 December and January

8 rm – †£45/50 ††£64/79 – **Rest** – (closed Tuesday) (dinner only) Menu £20 – Carte £20/28

◆ Grade II listed building with a historic inscribed door lintel - reputedly the most photographed doorway in the country. Cosy, traditional atmosphere throughout. Dining room with enticing, age-old ambience.

ENGLAND

Bulls Head without rest

Market Pl ✉ DL8 3RD – ✆ (01969) 667437 – rob@bullsheadhotel.co.uk – Fax (01969) 667048

6 rm – †£40 ††£65

◆ Substantial, listed 19C house, in former incarnations a bank and a pub. Lounge with original range and crackling fire. Pleasant rooms; two are vaulted and in the cellars.

East House without rest

Gayle, South : ½ m. by Gayle rd on Bainbridge rd ✉ DL8 3RZ – ✆ (01969) 667405 – lornaward@lineone.net – Closed January and February

3 rm – †£27/30 ††£54/60

◆ Attractive, very tidily run stone house dating from early 1800s in peaceful hamlet: lovely views over Wensleydale. Combined breakfast and lounge area. Pleasant bedrooms.

HAWKSHEAD – Cumbria – 502 L 20 – pop. 570 – ✉ Ambleside   21 A2

Great Britain

- London 283 m – Carlisle 52 m – Kendal 19 m
- Main Car Park ✆ (015394) 36525 (summer only)
- Village★
- Lake Windermere★★ – Coniston Water★ (Brantwood★, on east side), SW : by B 5285

at Near Sawrey Southeast : 2 m. on B 5285 – ✉ Ambleside

Ees Wyke Country House

Esthwaite Water and Grizedale Forest,

✉ LA22 0JZ – ✆ (015394) 36393 – mail@eeswyke.co.uk – restricted opening in winter

8 rm (dinner included) – †£82/111 ††£164/190 – **Rest** – (dinner only) (booking essential) Menu £33

◆ Panoramic views of Esthwaite Water and Grizedale Forest from this large, impressive Georgian house. Good sized bedrooms with distinctive, homely charm. Dining room's large windows afford lovely views.

at Far Sawrey **Southeast : 2 ½ m. on B 5285 – ✉ Ambleside**

West Vale

✉ *LA22 0LQ – ✆ (015394) 42 817 – enquiries@westvalecountryhouse.co.uk – Fax (015394) 45 302 – Closed 25-26 December*

7 rm – †£ 70/80 ††£ 118/160 – **Rest** – (by arrangement) Menu £ 36

◆ Victorian house on edge of hamlet with attractive country views. A warm welcome to an interior with open-fired, stone-floored sitting room and snug bedrooms. Meals locally sourced, proudly home cooked.

HAWNBY – N. Yorks. – **502** Q 21 – ✉ **Helmsley** 23 **C1**

London 245 m – Middlesbrough 27 m – Newcastle upon Tyne 69 m – York 30 m

Hawnby

✉ *YO62 5QS – ✆ (01439) 798 202 – info@hawnbyhotel.co.uk – Fax (01439) 798 344*

9 rm – †£ 69 ††£ 89 – **Rest** – (Closed Monday lunch) Carte £ 17/30

◆ Personally run small hotel in a very rural location with commanding views of nearby countryside - ideal for walking in the Dales. Snug bedrooms with a cottage feel. Tried-and-tested menus.

at Laskill **Northeast : 2 ¼ m. by Osmotherley rd – ✉ Hawnby**

Laskill Grange without rest

Easterside ✉ YO62 5NB – ✆ (01439) 798 268 – suesmith@laskillfarm.fsnet.co.uk

3 rm – †£ 28/80 ††£ 77/100

◆ A working farm with four cottagey bedrooms set in two converted Victorian stable blocks, surrounded by 1000 acres of rolling farmland. Breakfast served in sunny conservatory.

Red = Pleasant. Look for the red and symbols.

HAWORTH – W. Yorks. – **502** O 22 – **pop. 6 078** – ✉ **Keighley** 22 **A2**

Great Britain

London 213 m – Burnley 22 m – Leeds 22 m – Manchester 34 m

2-4 West Lane ✆ (01535) 642329, haworth@ytbtic.co.uk

Bront£ Parsonage Museum **AC**

Ashmount without rest

Mytholmes Lane ✉ BD22 8EZ – ✆ (01535) 645 726 – info@ashmounthaworth.co.uk – Fax (01535) 645 726

11 rm – †£ 40/90 ††£ 70/140

◆ Built in 1870 by the physician to the Brontë sisters, this refurbished house has extremely comfortable bedrooms with period furniture and state-of-the-art bathrooms.

Hill Top Farmhouse Haworth Moor,

Haworth Moor, West : 1 m. by Colne rd and Penistone Hill rd on Brontë Waterfall rd ✉ BD22 0EL – ✆ (01535) 643 524

3 rm – †£ 40 ††£ 62 – **Rest** – (by arrangement) Menu £ 20

◆ Attractive 17C farmhouse wonderfully set on the moors, close to Brontë Parsonage Museum. Welcoming fires, wood carved furniture. Cosy rooms with fresh flowers and fine views. Good home cooking is assured.

Rosebud Cottage

1 Belle Isle Rd ✉ BD22 8QQ – ✆ (01535) 640 321 – info@rosebudcottage.co.uk – closed 25-26 December

5 rm – †£ 33/45 ††£ 65/75 – **Rest** – (by arrangement) Menu £ 16

◆ Compact, cosy sandstone end-of-terrace cottage built in 1752, next to station on preserved railway line. The homely bedrooms are all very different with individual themes. Pine-furnished dining room overlooks conservatory; home-cooked dishes.

ENGLAND

Aitches

11 West Lane ✉ BD22 8DU – ✆ (01535) 642 501 – aitches@talk21.com – Closed 24-27 December
4 rm – £35/40 £60/70 – **Rest** – (by arrangement) Menu £19
◆ Imposing Victorian house in centre of historic town: two minutes' walk from Brontë parsonage, and adjacent to famous cobbled streets. Distinctive homely feel; comfy rooms.

Weaver's with rm — rest,

15 West Lane ✉ BD22 8DU – ✆ (01535) 643 822 – weaversinhaworth@aol.com – Fax (01535) 644 832 – Closed 25 December-4 January
3 rm – £55/70 £90 – **Rest** – (Closed lunch Saturday and Tuesday, Sunday dinner and Monday) Menu £16 (lunch) – Carte £20/31
◆ Former weavers cottages with an informal atmosphere and some charm. Characterful cluttered lounge with ornaments and artefacts. Homely cooking, surroundings and bedrooms.

at Cullingworth Southeast : 3 m. by B 6144 – ✉ Haworth

The Manor without rest

Sutton Drive ✉ BD13 5BQ – ✆ (01535) 274 374 – info@cullingworthmanor.co.uk – Fax (01535) 274 374
3 rm – £55 £75
◆ Modernised former manor house with formal gardens and spacious, tastefully converted bedrooms. Breakfast room/lounge with leather sofas and French windows onto decking.

ENGLAND

HAYDON BRIDGE – Northd. – 501 N 19 – see Hexham

HAYLING ISLAND – Hants. – 504 R 31 – pop. 14 842 6 B3

London 77 m – Brighton 45 m – Southampton 28 m
Beachlands, Seafront ✆ (023) 9246 7111 (summer only)
Links Lane, ✆ (023) 9246 4446 .

Cockle Warren Cottage without rest — (heated)

36 Seafront ✉ PO11 9HL – ✆ (023) 9246 4961 – cockle-warren@amserve.com – Fax (023) 9243 3518
6 rm – £50/65 £65/90
◆ A pleasant cottage just across the road from the beach. Conservatory breakfast room overlooks pool. Comfortable, well-kept bedrooms. Families particularly welcome.

HAYTOR VALE – Devon – see Bovey Tracey

HAYWARDS HEATH – W. Sussex – 504 T 31 – pop. 29 110 7 D2

Great Britain

London 41 m – Brighton 16 m
Paxhill Park Lindfield East Mascalls Lane, ✆ (01444) 484467.
Sheffield Park Garden★, E : 5 m. on A 272 and A 275

Jeremy's at Borde Hill

Borde Hill Gdns, North : 1 ¾ m. by B 2028 on Balcombe Rd ✉ RH16 1XP – ✆ (01444) 441 102 – reservations@jeremysrestaurant.com – Fax (01494) 441 355 – closed 1-11 January, Sunday dinner and Monday - except Bank Holidays
Rest – Carte £23/37
◆ Converted 19C stables with delightful views to Victorian walled garden. Contemporary interior with modern art. Confident, vibrant cooking in a light Mediterranean style.

HEACHAM – Norfolk – 504 V 25 14 B1

London 116 m – Hunstanton 2 m – King's Lynn 15 m

The Grove without rest
17 Collins Lane ✉ PE31 7DZ – ☎ (01485) 570513 – tm.shannon@tiscali.co.uk
3 rm – †£45 ††£60/66
◆ Victorian house set on high street continuation. Cosy, book-strewn guest lounge. Full cooked breakfasts with fruit plates. Two rooms homely and spotless; secluded stable room.

HEADLAM – Durham – 502 O 20 – see Darlington

HEATHROW AIRPORT – Middx. – 504 S 29 – see Hillingdon (Greater London)

HEDDON ON THE WALL – Northd. 24 A2

London 288 m – Blaydon 7 m – Newcastle upon Tyne 8 m

Close House
Southwest : 2¼ m. by B 6528 ✉ NE15 0HT – ☎ (01661) 852255 – events@closehouse.co.uk – Fax (01661) 853322 – Closed 1-16 January
7 rm – †£123/195 ††£170/195 – **Rest** – (Closed Sunday dinner) Menu £20 (lunch) – Carte dinner £32/42
◆ Wedding oriented Georgian manor house in 300 acres of grounds in Hadrian's Wall country. Marble-floored reception leads to comfy lounge and bar. Stylish Regency rooms. Dining room in warm burgundy serves modern menus.

HELLAND – Cornwall – see Bodmin

HELMSLEY – N. Yorks. – 502 Q 21 – pop. 1 559 *Great Britain* 23 C1

London 239 m – Leeds 51 m – Middlesbrough 28 m – York 24 m
The Old Town Hall, Market Pl ☎ (01439) 770173
Ampleforth College Castle Drive, Gilling East, ☎ (01439) 788212 .
Rievaulx Abbey★★ AC, NW : 2½ m. by B 1257

The Black Swan
Market Pl ✉ YO62 5BJ – ☎ (01439) 770466 – enquiries@blackswan-helmsley.co.uk – Fax (01439) 770174
45 rm – †£84/174 ††£110/200
Rest *The Rutland Room* – Menu £30 – Carte £30/41
◆ Part 16C coaching inn in a historic market town; indeed it overlooks the market. Charming rustic interior with exposed beams. Many bedrooms with period fittings and features. Formal dining in classically furnished restaurant.

Feversham Arms (heated)
on B 1257 ✉ YO62 5AG – ☎ (01439) 770766 – info@fevershamarmshotel.com – Fax (01439) 770346
27 rm – †£160 ††£235
Rest *Conservatory* – Menu £33 – Carte £22/44
◆ A former coaching inn; its stone façade conceals surprisingly modern rooms of a quiet restful nature: walls, floors in muted colours, spot lighting, quality fabrics. Range of dining locations, including around the pool.

No.54
54 Bondgate ✉ YO62 5EZ – ☎ (01439) 771533 – lizzie@no54.co.uk – Fax (01439) 771533
4 rm – †£35/45 ††£80 – **Rest** – (by arrangement, communal dining) Menu £20/35
◆ Victorian terraced cottage, formerly the village vet's. Charming owner. Bedrooms are strong point: set around flagged courtyard, they're airy, bright and very well-equipped. Dine round antique communal table in homely lounge.

ENGLAND

Carlton Lodge without rest

Bondgate ✉ YO62 5EY – ✆ (01439) 770 557 – b+b@carlton-lodge.com – Fax (01439) 770 623

8 rm – †£40/45 ††£75/95

◆ Late 19C house set just out of town. Homely and traditional air to the décor in the communal areas and the bedrooms, some of which have period features. Cosy breakfast room.

at Nawton East : 3 ¼ m. on A 170 – ✉ York

Plumpton Court without rest

High St ✉ YO62 7TT – ✆ (01439) 771 223 – mail@plumptoncourt.com – January and December

9 rm – †£40 ††£63

◆ The emphasis here is on homeliness; this is well provided by cottage-style traditional décor, open fires and a friendly welcome. Top floor bedrooms have modern style.

at Harome Southeast : 2 ¾ m. by A 170 – ✉ York

The Pheasant

✉ YO62 5JG – ✆ (01439) 771 241 – reservations@thepheasanthotel.com – Fax (01439) 771 744 – closed late December -early March

12 rm – †£82/88 ††£164/180 – 2 suites – **Rest** – (bar lunch) Menu £25

◆ Family run and hidden away in picturesque hamlet with a duck pond and mill stream close by. Open fires and beams in traditionally styled building with modern furniture. Conservatory dining room.

ENGLAND

Cross House Lodge at The Star Inn

✉ YO62 5JE – ✆ (01439) 770 397 – Fax (01439) 771 833 – closed 25 December, and 1 week January

11 rm – †£140/150 ††£230

Rest ***The Star Inn*** – see restaurant listing

Rest ***The Piggery*** – (booking essential) (residents only, set menu only) Menu £45

◆ Converted farm building set opposite pub in pretty village. Open-plan, split-level lounge. Ultra-stylish, super-smart rooms in either main building, annex or local cottages.

The Star Inn (Andrew Pern)

High St ✉ YO62 5JE – ✆ (01439) 770 397 – starinn@btopenworld.com – Fax (01439) 771 833 – Closed 25 December, Sunday dinner, Monday, and Bank Holidays

Rest – (booking essential) Carte £25/35 **s**

Spec. Soused halibut, potato salad and dill vodka. Wild rabbit pie with chanterelles and truffles. Harrogate sponge fingers, elderflower jelly, lemon balm custard.

◆ Beautiful 14C thatched inn boasting snug, rustic inner with wood beams and open fire. Appealing, seasonal cooking celebrates the pub's Yorkshire roots. Efficient service.

at Ampleforth Southwest : 4 ½ m. by A 170 off B 1257 – ✉ Helmsley

Shallowdale House — Gilling Gap,

West : ½ m. ✉ YO62 4DY – ✆ (01439) 788 325 – stay@shallowdalehouse.co.uk – Fax (01439) 788 885 – closed Christmas - New Year

3 rm – †£70/80 ††£88/108 – **Rest** – (by arrangement) Menu £33

◆ Modern guesthouse with spectacular views of the Howardian Hills; an area of outstanding beauty. Spacious rooms with large picture windows for the scenery. Warm and relaxed. Owners proud of their home-cooked menus.

at Byland Abbey Southwest : 6 ½ m. by A 170 – ✉ Helmsley

Oldstead Grange without rest

Oldstead, Northwest : 1 ¼ m. on Oldstead rd ✉ YO61 4BJ – ✆ (01347) 868 634 – oldsteadgrange@yorkshireuk.com – closed Christmas

3 rm – †£60/90 ††£72/92

◆ Comfort is paramount in this part 17C farmhouse on working farm. Cosy, warm lounge with real fire. Hand-made oak furniture adorns bedrooms which benefit from rural outlook.

The Abbey Inn with rm

✉ *YO61 4BD – ✆ (01347) 868 204 – abbeyinn@english-heritage.org.uk – Fax (01347) 868678 – Closed 25-26 December, 1 January, Sunday dinner and Monday lunch*

3 rm – †£ 155 ††£ 155 – **Rest** – (booking essential) Carte £ 21/28

◆ Characterful part 17C ivy-clad inn uniquely positioned overlooking Byland Abbey ruins. Tasty mix of modern and traditional food and very smart, stylish bedrooms.

at Scawton West 8½ m. by A 170 – ✉ Helmsley

The Hare Inn

✉ *YO7 2HG – ✆ (01845) 597 769 – geoff@brucearms.com – Closed Sunday dinner and Monday*

Rest – Carte £ 20/30

◆ Smart yellow façade. Delightful bar with open fired stove. Spacious main dining room. Satisfying, seasonal cooking with a classical base, freshly prepared with local ingredients.

HELSTON – Cornwall – 503 E 33 – pop. 10 578 — 1 A3

London 306 m – Falmouth 13 m – Penzance 14 m – Truro 17 m

The Flora Day Furry Dance★★

Lizard Peninsula★ - Gunwalloe Fishing Cove★, S : 4 m. by A 3083 and minor rd - Culdrose (Flambards Village Theme Park★), SE : 1 m. - Wendron (Poldark Mine★), NE : 2½ m. by B 3297 – Gweek (Seal Sanctuary★), E : 4 m. by A 394 and minor rd

at Trelowarren Southeast : 4 m. by A 394 and A 3083 on B 3293 – ✉ Helston

New Yard – at Trelowarren Estate

✉ *TR12 6AF – ✆ (01326) 221 595 – newyardrestaurant@trelowarren.com – Fax (01326) 221 595 – closed Sunday and Monday January - May and Sunday dinner*

Rest – Menu £ 14 – Carte £ 25/36

◆ Converted country house stable yard adjoining craft gallery. Terrace view from modern tables and chairs. Dinner offers full menus of locally inspired dishes; lunch is simpler.

at Gunwalloe South : 5 m. by A 394 off A 3083 – ✉ Helston

The Halzephron Inn with rm

✉ *TR12 7QB – ✆ (01326) 240 406 – halzephroninn@gunwalloe1.fsnet.co.uk – Fax (01326) 241 442 – Closed 25 December*

2 rm – †£ 50 ††£ 86 – **Rest** – Carte £ 18/27

◆ Country pub in pretty coastal setting. Gleaming copper, original paintings. Adventurous or traditional dishes using local produce. Selection of Cornish cheeses. Neat rooms.

HEMEL HEMPSTEAD – Herts. – 504 S 28 – pop. 83 118 — 12 A2

Great Britain

London 30 m – Aylesbury 16 m – Luton 10 m – Northampton 46 m

Dacorum Information Centre, Marlowes ✆ (01442) 234222

Little Hay Golf Complex Bovingdon Box Lane, ✆ (01442) 833 798 ;

Boxmoor 18 Box Lane, ✆ (01442) 242 434 .

Whipsnade Wild Animal Park★

Restaurant 65

65 High St (Old Town) ✉ HP1 5AL – ✆ (01442) 239 010 – grant@restaurant65.com – closed Sunday and Monday

Rest – Menu £ 15/25

◆ Charming 17C building in old part of town; snug restaurant with white walls, black beams and homely, relaxed feel. Well executed modern British cooking with a classical base.

ENGLAND

at Frithsden **Northwest : 4½ m. by A 4146 – ✉ Hemel Hempstead**

The Alford Arms

✉ HP1 3DD – ✆ (01442) 864 480 – inn@alfordarmsfrithseden.co.uk – Fax (01442) 876 893 – Closed 25-26 December

Rest – Carte £ 19/28

♦ Tucked away in a small hamlet, popular with cyclists and walkers. A pleasant, modern interior of terracotta and cream hues; stylish dishes with interesting combinations.

HEMINGFORD GREY – Cambs. – 504 T 27 – see Huntingdon

HENFIELD – W. Sussex – 504 T 31 – pop. 4 527 7 D2

London 47 m – Brighton 10 m – Worthing 11 m

at Wineham **Northeast : 3½ m. by A 281, B 2116 and Wineham Lane – ✉ Henfield**

Frylands without rest

(heated)

West : ¼ m. taking left turn at telephone box ✉ BN5 9BP – ✆ (01403) 710 214 – b+b@frylands.co.uk – Fax (01403) 711 449 – Closed 21 December-2 January

3 rm – †£ 30/35 ††£ 55

♦ Part Elizabethan farmhouse in 250 acres with woodlands and fishing. Fresh home-cooked breakfasts. Bedrooms exude charm and character with homely furnishings, original features.

ENGLAND

HENLADE – Somerset – see Taunton

HENLEY-IN-ARDEN – Warks. – 503 O 27 – pop. 2 797 19 C3

London 104 m – Birmingham 15 m – Stratford-upon-Avon 8 m – Warwick 8 m

Ardencote Manor H. & Country Club and Spa

rm,

Lye Green Rd, Claverdon, East : 3¾ m. by A 4189 on Shrewley rd ✉ CV35 8LT – ✆ (01926) 843 111 – hotel@ardencote.com – Fax (01926) 842 646

76 rm – †£ 90/105 ††£ 90/165

Rest ***The Lodge*** – Carte £ 30/36 **s**

♦ Secluded manor house with modern extension and spacious leisure facilities, in formal gardens and grounds. Bedrooms are generally large and traditionally furnished. Informal dining room.

The Crabmill

Preston Bagot, Claverdon, East : 1 m. on A 4189 ✉ B95 5EE – ✆ (01926) 843 342 – thecrabmill@lovelypubs.co.uk – Fax (01926) 843 989 – Closed 25 December

Rest – (closed Sunday dinner) (booking essential) Carte £ 20/28

♦ Stylish pub with a contemporary feel. Dining room has an intimate air, rustic décor and modern prints. Contemporary food with Mediterranean touches on a classic foundation.

at Tanworth-in-Arden **Northwest : 4½ m. by A 3400 and Tanworth Rd – ✉ Henley-in-Arden**

The Bell Inn with rm

The Green ✉ B94 5AL – ✆ (01564) 742 212 – thebell@realcoolbars.com

9 rm – †£ 55/70 ††£ 115 – **Rest** – (closed Sunday dinner) Menu £ 11 – Carte £ 15/25

♦ Very pleasant modern pub with rustic tones in pretty village; spacious bar. Intimate dining room serving good food with modish twists. Stylish rooms with designer touches.

HENLEY-ON-THAMES – Oxon. – 504 R 29 – pop. 10 513 11 C3

London 40 m – Oxford 23 m – Reading 9 m
to Reading (Salter Bros. Ltd) (summer only) daily (2 h 15 mn) – to Marlow (Salter Bros. Ltd) (summer only) daily (2 h 15 mn)
Kings Arms Barn, Kings Rd ✆ (01491) 578034
Huntercombe Nuffield, ✆ (01491) 641 207 .

Hotel du Vin

New St ✉ RG9 2BP – ✆ (01491) 848 400 – info@henley.hotelduvin.com – Fax (01491) 848 401
41 rm – †£ 140/145 ††£ 140/425, ☐ £13.50 – 2 suites
Rest ***Bistro*** – Menu £ 17 (lunch) – Carte approx. £ 35
◆ Former brewery premises; now an easy-going, designer styled boutique hotel. Stunning rooms: studios with outdoor terrace and bath tub or airy doubles with great amenities. Bistro with resolutely Gallic style, French influenced menus and excellent wine list.

Red Lion

Hart St ✉ RG9 2AR – ✆ (01491) 572 161 – reservations@redlionhenley.co.uk – Fax (01491) 410 039
32 rm – †£ 115/135 ††£ 125/165, ☐ £13.50 – **Rest** – Menu £ 17 (lunch) – Carte £ 25/31
◆ Hostelry since 15C; has accommodated three kings and overlooks the regatta course. Rooms are well furnished with antiques; an elegant, traditional style pervades throughout. Dining room exudes crisp, light feel.

Lenwade without rest

3 Western Rd (off St Andrews Rd) ✉ RG9 1JL – ✆ (01491) 573 468 – lenwadeuk@aol.com – Fax (01491) 411 664 – closed 24-26 December
3 rm ☐ – †£ 50/55 ††£ 70/75
◆ Late 19C home in a quiet residential area. Neatly kept throughout with modern appointments. Bedrooms are of a good size and pine furnished.

Alftrudis without rest

8 Norman Ave ✉ RG9 1SG – ✆ (01491) 573 099 – sue@alftrudis.co.uk
3 rm ☐ – †£ 50/65 ††£ 65/75
◆ Grade II listed Victorian guesthouse in private cul-de-sac. Two well-furnished, comfortable lounges. Inviting breakfast room. Well-appointed, extremely spacious rooms.

Alushta without rest

23 Queen St ✉ RG9 1AR – ✆ (01491) 636 041 – sdr@alushta.co.uk – Fax (01491) 636 042
5 rm ☐ – †£ 35/50 ††£ 65/85
◆ Centrally located guesthouse, built in late 18C. Very pleasant breakfast room: display shelves boast Russian china. Well-appointed bedrooms with thoughtful extras.

HEREFORD – Herefordshire – 503 L 27 – pop. 56 373 *Great Britain* 18 B3

London 133 m – Birmingham 51 m – Cardiff 56 m
1 King St ✆ (01432) 268430
Raven's Causeway Wormsley, ✆ (01432) 830 219 ;
Belmont Lodge Belmont, ✆ (01432) 352 666 ;
Hereford Municipal Holmer Rd, ✆ (01432) 344 376 ;
Burghill Valley Burghill Tillington Rd, ✆ (01432) 760 456 .
City★ - Cathedral★★ (Mappa Mundi★) A **A** – Old House★ A **B**
Kilpeck (Church of SS. Mary and David★★) SW : 8 m. by A 465 B

Plan on next page

Castle House

Castle St ✉ HR1 2NW – ✆ (01432) 356 321 – info@castlehse.co.uk – Fax (01432) 365 909 A **e**
15 rm ☐ – †£ 120/175 ††£ 175
Rest ***La Rive*** – Carte £ 23/37
◆ Stylish and exclusive air to this contemporarily furnished, classically proportioned Georgian house, near the cathedral. Excellent quality and attention to detail throughout. Smart restaurant overlooks gardens and Wye.

ENGLAND

HEREFORD

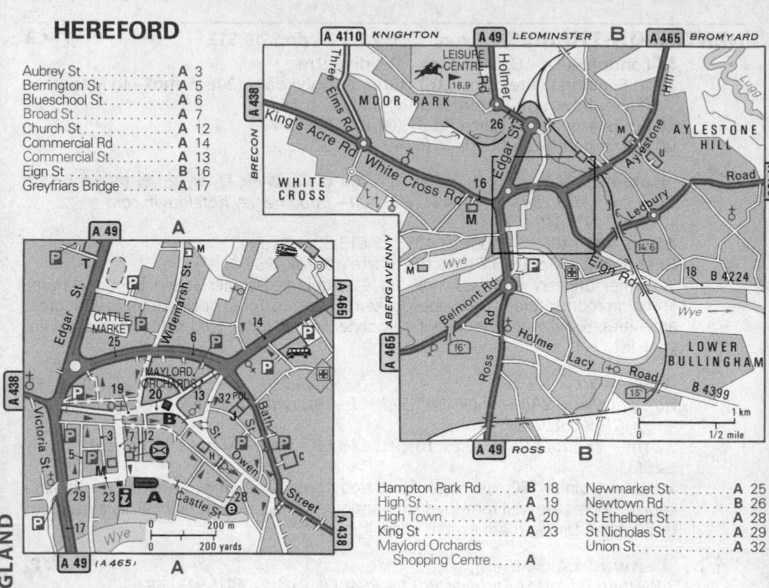

Aubrey St . . . . A 3
Berrington St . . . . A 5
Blueschool St. . . . . A 6
Broad St . . . . A 7
Church St . . . . A 12
Commercial Rd . . . . A 14
Commercial St. . . . . A 13
Eign St . . . . B 16
Greyfriars Bridge . . . . A 17
Hampton Park Rd . . . . . . B 18
High St . . . . A 19
High Town . . . . A 20
King St . . . . A 23
Maylord Orchards Shopping Centre . . . . . . A
Newmarket St. . . . . A 25
Newtown Rd . . . . B 26
St Ethelbert St . . . . A 28
St Nicholas St . . . . A 29
Union St . . . . A 32

ENGLAND

Brandon Lodge without rest

Ross Rd, South : 1 ¾ m. on A 49 ✉ HR2 8BH – ✆ (01432) 355 621 – info@brandonlodge.co.uk – Fax (01432) 355 621

10 rm ☕ – ♀£ 40/50 ♀♀£ 60/65

◆ A good value hotel with 18C origins, charmingly overseen by owner. Bedrooms in main building or adjacent annex: all are spacious, boasting a cheery warmth and good facilities.

Grafton Villa Farm without rest

Grafton, South : 2 ¼ m. on A 49 ✉ HR2 8ED – ✆ (01432) 268 689 – jennielayton@ereal.net – Fax (01432) 268 689 – closed December and January

3 rm ☕ – ♀£ 40/50 ♀♀£ 60/70

◆ Early 18C farmhouse, on a working farm with extensive grounds. Antique furnished homely bedrooms and fresh, substantial country breakfasts.

at Byford West : 7 ½ m. by A 438 - B – ✉ Hereford

Old Rectory without rest

✉ HR4 7LD – ✆ (01981) 590 218 – info@theoldrectory.uk.com – March-October

3 rm ☕ – ♀£ 45/65 ♀♀£ 66/70

◆ Rurally set Georgian-style 19C rectory with pleasant gardens. Spacious yet homely atmosphere and décor; the bedrooms are furnished in a simple, traditional style.

at Winforton Northwest : 15 m. on A 438 – ✉ Hereford

Winforton Court without rest

✉ HR3 6EA – ✆ (01544) 328 498 – Fax (01544) 328 498 – closed 20-28 December

3 rm ☕ – ♀£ 60/75 ♀♀£ 80/90

◆ Wonderfully characterful 16C house used as a circuit court by "Hanging" Judge Jeffries. Exudes personality with exposed beams, thick walls and uneven floors. Rustic rooms.

HERM – C.I. – **503** P 33 – see Channel Islands

HERMITAGE – Dorset – see Sherborne

HERSTMONCEUX – E. Sussex – 504 U 31 8 B3

London 63 m – Eastbourne 12 m – Hastings 14 m – Lewes 16 m

XX **Sundial**

Gardner St ✉ BN27 4LA – ☎ (01323) 832 217 – sundialrestaurant@hotmail.com – Fax (01323) 832 909 – Closed Sunday dinner and Monday

Rest – French Menu £ 22 – Carte £ 32/45

◆ Converted 16C cottage retaining leaded windows and a beamed ceiling. Comfortable chairs in a well spaced dining room. Menu is French with a classic, familiar style.

at Wartling Southeast : 3 ¾ m. by A 271 and Wartling rd – ✉ Herstmonceux

Wartling Place without rest

✉ BN27 1RY – ☎ (01323) 832 590 – accom@wartlingplace.prestel.co.uk

3 rm – †£ 75/105 ††£ 130/175

◆ Part Georgian house with three acres of gardens, sited in the village. Pleasantly furnished, with some antiques; two of the rooms have four-poster beds.

The Lamb Inn

Wartling Rd ✉ BN27 1RY – ☎ (01323) 832 116 – alison.farncombe@virgin.net – Fax (01323) 832 637 – Closed Sunday dinner

Rest – Carte £ 18/30

◆ Popular with locals, this early 16C pub offers a friendly welcome. Steeped in character with flag floors, fires and beams. Robust cooking uses quality, traceable ingredients.

Your opinions are important to us:
please write and let us know about your discoveries and experiences – good and bad!

HERTFORD – Herts. – 504 T 28 12 B2

London 25 m – Bishop's Stortford 16 m – Stevenage 11 m

The Hillside

45 Port Hill, Bengeo, North : ¼ m. on B 158 ✉ SG14 3EP – ☎ (01992) 554 556 – justin624@hotmail.com – Fax (01992) 583 709 – Closed Sunday dinner

Rest – Carte £ 30/45

◆ Refurbished 17C pub next to deli and farm shop. Intimate and cosy, with sofas by the fire. Dine in an airy, sunny environment. Fashionable brasserie dishes with global range.

HESSLE – Kingston-upon-Hull – 502 S 22 – see Kingston-upon-Hull

HESWALL – Mersey. – 502 K 24 – pop. 29 977 20 A3

London 212 m – Birkenhead 12 m – Chester 14 m – Liverpool 11 m

at Gayton Southeast : ½ m. on A 540 – ✉ Heswall

XX **Gem**

1 Milner Rd ✉ CH60 5RT – ☎ (0151) 342 4811 – enquiries@gemrestaurant.co.uk – Fax (0151) 342 4811 – closed 2 weeks September, Sunday and Monday

Rest – (dinner only) (booking essential) Menu £ 19 – Carte £ 26/33

◆ Personally run, friendly neighbourhood restaurant; unassuming exterior and simple, modern interior with intimate ambience. Country cooking with distinctive departures.

HETTON – N. Yorks. – 502 N 21 – see Skipton

HEXHAM – Northd. – 501 N 19 – pop. 10 682 Great Britain 24 A2

London 304 m – Carlisle 37 m – Newcastle upon Tyne 21 m
Wentworth Car Park ☎ (01434) 652220
Spital Park, ☎ (01434) 603 072 ;
De Vere Slaley Hall G. & C.C. Slaley, ☎ (01434) 673 154 ;
Tynedale Tyne Green, ☎ (01434) 608 154 .
Abbey★ (Saxon Crypt★★, Leschman chantry★)
Hadrian's Wall★★, N : 4½ m. by A 6079. Housesteads★★, NW : 12½ m. by A 6079 and B 6318

Beaumont

Beaumont St ✉ NE46 3LT – ☎ (01434) 602 331 – reservations@beaumonthotel.eclipse.co.uk – Fax (01434) 606 184
25 rm – ♦£ 80/85 ♦♦£ 110/120
Rest ***The Park*** – Menu £ 13/21 **s**
◆ Victorian building of local stone overlooking park and the town's ancient abbey - which is visible from some of the comfortable rooms. Personally run with a warm atmosphere. Park restaurant on the first floor with views of the abbey.

Hallbank

Hallgate ✉ NE46 1XA – ☎ (01434) 606 656 – Fax (01434) 605 567
8 rm – ♦£ 70 ♦♦£ 80/100 – **Rest** – (by arrangement) Menu £ 25
◆ Red-brick Georgian house close to market square, set in the shadow of the old gaol. Fully refurbished rooms exhibit a warm, classic style with good modern facilities. Dine in adjacent, informal café/bistro.

West Close House without rest

Hextol Terrace, Southwest : ½ m. off B 6305 ✉ NE46 2AD – ☎ (01434) 603 307
4 rm – ♦£ 30 ♦♦£ 70
◆ Detached house in a residential area providing a high standard of simple, good value accommodation. Polished wood floors and immaculately kept.

Dene House without rest

Juniper, South : 3¾ m. by B 6306 following signs for Dye House ✉ NE46 1SJ – ☎ (01434) 673 413 – margaret@denehouse-hexham.co.uk – closed December
3 rm – ♦£ 30/40 ♦♦£ 60
◆ Attractive stone cottage in a quiet spot with pleasant views, numerous country walks in the environs. Cosy feel throughout. Simple, homely rooms.

Valley Connection 301

Market Pl ✉ NE46 3NX – ☎ (01434) 601 234 – Fax (01434) 606 629 – closed 25 December and 1 January
Rest – Indian (dinner only) Carte £ 21/32
◆ Near Hexham Abbey; views of the market place from both floors. Old favourites interspersed with modern dishes in a tasty Indian menu.

at Slaley Southeast : 5½ m. by B 6306 – ✉ Hexham

Slaley Hall

Southeast : 2¼ m. ✉ NE47 0BY – ☎ (01434) 673 350 – slaley.hall@deverehotels.com – Fax (01434) 673 962
132 rm – ♦£ 175/195 ♦♦£ 210/235 – 10 suites – **Rest** – (bar lunch Monday-Saturday) Menu £ 30
◆ Extended Edwardian manor house, now a leisure oriented hotel, grounds with woodland and two golf courses. Spacious bedrooms with up-to-date facilities and country views. Formal restaurant offering menus based on a modern English style.

at Haydon Bridge West : 7½ m. on A 69 – ✉ Hexham

Langley Castle

Langley-on-Tyne, South : 2 m. by A 69 on A 686 ✉ NE47 5LU – ☎ (01434) 688 888 – manager@langleycastle.com – Fax (01434) 684 019
19 rm – ♦£ 100 ♦♦£ 129/249 – 1 suite – **Rest** – Menu £ 19/33
◆ Turreted stone castle in 12 acres. Tapestry style fabrics, heraldic themed ornaments, open fire. Spacious rooms in castle or converted stables. Formal restaurant with beams and stone floor; classic dishes using local produce.

HEYTESBURY – Wilts. – 503 N 30 – see Warminster

HIGH CROSBY – Cumbria – see Carlisle

HIGH ONGAR – Essex 12 B2

London 24 m – Brentwood 11 m – Chelmsford 10 m

X **The Wheatsheaf**

King St, East : 2 m. by A 414 on Blackmore rd ✉ CM5 9NS – ✆ (01277) 822 220 – Closed Sunday dinner and Monday

Rest – (booking essential) Carte £ 23/30

◆ Pretty, converted pub with large garden and terrace. Dine in four different rooms with open fires and homely ornamentation. Good value, accomplished British cuisine.

HIGH WYCOMBE – Bucks. – 504 R 29 – pop. 77 178 *Great Britain* 11 C2

London 34 m – Aylesbury 17 m – Oxford 26 m – Reading 18 m

Paul's Row ✆ (01494) 421892

18 Hazlemere G & C.C. Hazlemere Penn Rd, ✆ (01494) 719 300 ;

36 Wycombe Heights Loudwater Rayners Ave, ✆ (01494) 816 686.

Chiltern Hills★

XX **Eat-Thai**

14-15 Easton St ✉ HP11 1NT – ✆ (01494) 532 888 – Fax (01494) 532 889 – closed 25-28 December

Rest – Thai Menu £ 25 – Carte £ 20/30 **s**

◆ Modern restaurant with wood floors and well-spaced tables. Three distinct areas serving fresh, tasty dishes with ingredients flown regularly from Thailand. Attentive service.

The ✿ award is the crème de la crème. This is awarded to restaurants which are really worth travelling miles for!

HIGHCLERE – Hants. – 503 P 29 – pop. 2 409 – ✉ Newbury 6 B1

London 69 m – Newbury 5 m – Reading 25 m

The Yew Tree with rm

Hollington Cross, Andover Road, South : 1 m. on A 343 ✉ RG20 9SE – ✆ (01635) 253 360 – info@theyewtree.net – Fax (01635) 255 035

6 rm – †£ 80 ††£ 80 – **Rest** – Menu £ 18 – Carte £ 28/42

◆ 17C pub with smart front terrace, old rafters and no less than four elegant, candle-lit rear dining rooms with a classical style of modern cooking finding favour with locals.

HIGHCLIFFE – Dorset – 503 O 31 4 D3

London 112 m – Bournemouth 10 m – Salisbury 21 m – Southampton 26 m – Winchester 37 m

Lord Bute

Lymington Rd ✉ BH23 4JS – ✆ (01425) 278 884 – mail@lordbute.co.uk – Fax (01425) 279 258

13 rm – †£ 68/78 ††£ 108 – **Rest** – (Closed Sunday dinner and Monday) Menu £ 17/30 **s** – Carte £ 28/38 **s**

◆ Modern property with a traditional style. Well designed, light, airy lounge. Bedrooms are well appointed and include safes and spa baths. Formal dining room adjacent to Orangery lounge.

HIGHER BURWARDSLEY – Ches. – see Tattenhall

HIGHWORTH – Wilts – 503 O 29 – pop. 7 996 4 D1

London 85 m – Oxford 26 m – Swindon 6 m

XX **Jesmonds of Highworth** with rm rest,

Jesmond House ✉ SN6 7HJ – ☎ (01793) 762 364
– info@jesmondsofhighworth.com – Fax (01793) 861 201
10 rm – †£ 100 ††£ 100/160 – **Rest** – (closed Sunday dinner and Monday) Menu £ 23/33 – Carte £ 26/39

◆ Grade II listed red brick building; two modern dining rooms, one with glass atrium and paved terrace. Constantly evolving menus. Modern, unfussy and flavoursome cooking. Stylishly refurbished and comfortable bedrooms with contemporary fabrics and a high level of facilities.

HINCKLEY – Leics. – 502 P 26 – pop. 43 246 16 B2

London 103 m – Birmingham 31 m – Coventry 12 m – Leicester 14 m
Hinckley Library, Lancaster Rd ☎ (01455) 635106

Sketchley Grange rest,

Sketchley Lane, South : 1½ m. by B 4109 (Rugby Rd)
✉ LE10 3HU – ☎ (01455) 251 133 – reservations@sketchleygrange.co.uk
– Fax (01455) 631 384
51 rm – †£ 130 ††£ 230, ☕ £12.50 – 1 suite
Rest *The Willow* – (Closed Sunday-Monday) (dinner only and Sunday lunch) Carte £ 30/40 **s**
Rest *The Terrace Bistro* – Carte £ 19/33 **s**

◆ Privately owned, spacious hotel with good leisure and an array of conference facilities. Bedrooms are well proportioned, and furniture is comfortable and well chosen. The Willow exudes elegance and garden views. The Terrace Bistro is bright and spacious.

HINDON – Wilts. – 503 N 30 4 C2

London 103 m – Shaftesbury 7 m – Warminster 10 m

The Lamb Inn with rm

High St ✉ SP3 6DP – ☎ (01747) 820 573 – info@lambathindon.co.uk
– Fax (01747) 820 605
14 rm ☕ – †£ 70 ††£ 135 – **Rest** – Carte £ 20/25

◆ 15C former coaching inn. Attractively creeper clad with picture-strewn rich red interior. Large blackboards offer heartily traditional British menus. Characterful rooms.

HINDRINGHAM – Norfolk 15 C1

London 118 m – Fakenham 8 m – Holt 8 m

Field House without rest

Moorgate Rd ✉ NR21 0PT – ☎ (01328) 878 726
– stay@fieldhousehindringham.co.uk – closed Christmas and New Year
3 rm ☕ – †£ 70/75 ††£ 90/110

◆ Well-kept flint stone house with pretty garden and summer house. Pristine lounge with books and magazines. Extensive breakfast menus. Carefully co-ordinated rooms with extras.

HINTLESHAM – Suffolk – 504 X 27 – see Ipswich

HINTON ST GEORGE – Somerset 3 B3

Lord Poulett Arms with rm

High St ✉ TA17 8SE – ☎ (01460) 73 149
– steveandmichelle@lordpoulettarms.com
4 rm ☕ – †£ 59 ††£ 88 – **Rest** – Carte £ 18/28

◆ Beautifully restored 17C inn on delightful high street. Immense charm and character: stone floors, exposed brickwork. Accomplished, classical cooking. Immaculate rooms.

ENGLAND

HISTON – Cambs. – 504 U 27 – see Cambridge

HOCKLEY HEATH – W. Mids. – 503 – pop. 13 616 – ✉ Solihull 19 C2

London 117 m – Birmingham 11 m – Coventry 17 m

Nuthurst Grange Country House

Nuthurst Grange Lane, South : 3/4 m. by A 3400 ✉ B94 5NL – ✆ (01564) 783 972 – info@nuthurst-grange.co.uk – Fax (01564) 783 919 – closed 1 week Christmas

15 rm – £ 129 £ 129/195

Rest ***The Restaurant*** – see restaurant listing

◆ Part Edwardian manor house, overlooking M40 and convenient for Birmingham airport. Classic English country décor throughout. Spacious rooms with high level of comfort.

The Restaurant – at Nuthurst Grange Country House

Nuthurst Grange Lane, South : 3/4 m. by A 3400 ✉ B94 5NL – ✆ (01564) 783 972 – Fax (01564) 783 919

Rest – Menu £ 19/35 – Carte £ 32/38 **s**

◆ Thoroughly traditional tone in the dining room's décor which contributes to a formal ambience. Seasonal menu draws on British and French traditions.

at Lapworth Southeast : 2 m. on B 4439 – ✉ Warwick

The Boot Inn

Old Warwick Rd, on B 4439 ✉ B94 6JU – ✆ (01564) 782 464 – bootinn@hotmail.com – Fax (01564) 784 989 – Closed 25 December and 1 January

Rest – (booking essential) Carte £ 18/25

◆ Bustling modern dining pub, with traditional bucolic character at the front and spacious dining room to rear. Appealing rustic dishes supplemented by daily changing specials.

The red symbol?
This denotes the very essence of peace
– only the sound of birdsong first thing in the morning …

HOLBEACH – Lincs. – 502 U 25 – pop. 7 247 17 D2

London 117 m – Kingston-upon-Hull 81 m – Norwich 62 m – Nottingham 60 m – Peterborough 25 m

Pipwell Manor without rest

Washway Rd, Saracen's Head, Northwest : 1 1/2 m. by A 17 ✉ PE12 8AL – ✆ (01406) 423 119 – honnor@pipwellmanor.freeserve.co.uk – Fax (01406) 423 119

3 rm – £ 38 £ 55

◆ Georgian manor built on site of Cisterian Grange, close to solitude of the Wash. Garden railway for train spotters. Complimentary tea, cake on arrival. Country style rooms.

HOLBECK – Notts – 502 Q 24 – pop. 27 791 16 B1

London 160 m – Chesterfield 22 m – Worksop 6 m

Browns without rest

The Old Orchard Cottage, Holbeck Lane ✉ S80 3NF – ✆ (01909) 220 659 – browns@holbeck.fsnet.co.uk – closed 1 week Christmas

3 rm – £ 55/62 £ 72/82

◆ Cosy, comfortable, individually-decorated bedrooms in cottage dating from 1730 and named after the owners. Mature orchard and tranquil garden. Comprehensive breakfast.

ENGLAND

HOLBETON – Devon 2 C3

London 211 m – Ivybridge 6 m – Plymouth 10 m

The Dartmoor Union

Fore St ✉ PL8 1NE – ☎ (01752) 830 288 – info@dartmoorunion.co.uk – Fax (01752) 830 296

Rest – Menu £ 14 – Carte £ 22/36

◆ Hard to spot, but once inside, a conspicuous 19C log fire crackles in the bar and rose pink walls light up the restaurant. Seasonal dishes offer local flavours.

HOLFORD – Somerset – 503 K 30 – ✉ Bridgwater *Great Britain* 3 B2

London 171 m – Bristol 48 m – Minehead 15 m – Taunton 22 m

Stogursey Priory Church★★, W : 4½ m

Combe House

Southwest : ¾ m. by Youth Hostel rd ✉ TA5 1RZ – ☎ (01278) 741 382 – enquiries@combehouse.co.uk – Fax (01278) 741 322

19 rm – †£ 70 ††£ 95/135 – **Rest** – Carte £ 25/31

◆ Interesting Edwardian country house with a water wheel in pleasant Quantock Hills location. Informal relaxed ambience with plenty of books and beams. Rooms overlook garden. Restaurant with spaced beams; locally sourced produce to the fore.

HOLKHAM – Norfolk – 504 W 25 15 C1

London 124 m – King's Lynn 32 m – Norwich 39 m

The Victoria

Park Rd ✉ NR23 1RG – ☎ (01328) 711 008 – victoria@holkham.co.uk – Fax (01328) 711 009

10 rm – †£ 100/130 ††£ 120/160

Rest *The Restaurant* – see restaurant listing

◆ Trendy, stylish hotel, built in 1838, overlooking Holkham nature reserve. Bedrooms are individually styled with much of the furniture sourced from Rajasthan.

The Restaurant – at The Victoria H.

Park Rd ✉ NR23 1RG – ☎ (01328) 711 008 – victoria@holkham.co.uk – Fax (01328) 711 009

Rest – Carte £ 27/36

◆ Extensive dining areas, now including conservatory option, specialise in modish menus as well as fine fish and seafood dishes. The bar offers a buzzy alternative.

HOLMES CHAPEL – Ches. – 502 M 24 – pop. 5 669 20 B3

London 181 m – Chester 25 m – Liverpool 41 m – Manchester 24 m – Stoke-on-Trent 20 m

Cottage Restaurant and Lodge

London Rd, Allostock, North : 3 m. on A 50 ✉ WA16 9LU – ☎ (01565) 722 470 – reception@thecottageknutsford.co.uk – Fax (01565) 722 749 – closed 1 January

12 rm – †£ 89 ††£ 105 – **Rest** – (closed Sunday dinner and Bank Holidays) Menu £ 17 (lunch) – Carte £ 22/33

◆ Brick-built cottage notable for an abundant degree of rustic allure and charm. Up-to-date, spacious bedrooms are the feature of its annex extension. Characterfully beamed restaurant is part of original cottage.

HOLT – Norfolk – 504 X 25 – pop. 3 550 15 C1

London 124 m – King's Lynn 34 m – Norwich 22 m

Byfords

Shirehall Plain ✉ NR25 6BG – ☎ (01263) 711 400 – queries@byfords.org.uk – Fax (01263) 713 520 – closed 25 December

9 rm – †£ 90 ††£ 90/145 – **Rest** – Carte £ 17/26

◆ Flint-fronted Grade II listed house that boasts something different: a well-stocked deli; rustic cellar café; and stunning rooms, with Egyptian cotton and under-floor heating.

ENGLAND

HOLT – Wilts. – **503** – see Bradford-on-Avon

HONITON – Devon – **503** K 31 – **pop. 11 213** 2 **D2**

London 186 m – Exeter 17 m – Southampton 93 m – Taunton 18 m
Lace Walk Car Park ✆ (01404) 43716
All Hallows Museum★ **AC**
Ottery St Mary★ (St Mary's★) SW : 5 m. by A 30 and B 3177. Faraway Countryside Park (≤ ★) **AC**, SE : 6½ m. by A 375 and B 3174

at Yarcombe Northeast : 8 m. on A 30 – ✉ Honiton

Belfry Country H.
on A 30 ✉ EX14 9BD – ✆ (01404) 861 234 – stay@thebelfrycountryhotel.com – Fax (01404) 861 579 – Closed Christmas-New Year
6 rm – †£ 55 ††£ 80/90 – **Rest** – (Closed Tuesday) (dinner only) (booking essential for non-residents) Menu £ 28 **s**
◆ Pretty cottage, formerly the village school, opposite 14C church. Personally run and hospitable, with light, cosy bedrooms, named after poets, featuring stained glass windows. Comfy restaurant decorated with owner's world travel photos.

at Wilmington East : 3 m. on A 35 – ✉ Honiton

Home Farm
on A 35 ✉ EX14 9JR – ✆ (01404) 831 278 – info@thatchedhotel.co.uk – Fax (01404) 831 411 600
12 rm – †£ 50/60 ††£ 90/125 – **Rest** – (bar lunch) Carte £ 18/32
◆ Part 16C thatched farmhouse offering a simple and comfortable standard of accommodation. Characterful lounges and bedrooms with individual country personality. Snug, cosy dining room with inglenook.

at Gittisham Southwest : 3 m. by A 30 ✉ Honiton

Combe House
✉ EX14 3AD – ✆ (01404) 540 400 – stay@thishotel.com – Fax (01404) 46 004 – closed 2 weeks January
13 rm – †£ 139/169 ††£ 174/188 – 3 suites – **Rest** – (booking essential for non-residents) Menu £ 28/42
◆ Listed Elizabethan mansion set in glorious Devon countryside. Impressive Great Hall. Individually designed, stylish bedrooms with fine antiques and roaring fires. Confident, unfussy cooking with proud use of local produce. Friendly service.

at Payhembury Northwest : 7 m. by A 373 – ✉ Honiton

Cokesputt House
West : ¼ m. on Tale rd ✉ EX14 3HD – ✆ (01404) 841 289 – aeac.forbes@virgin.net
3 rm – †£ 42/67 ††£ 84 – **Rest** – (booking essential) (communal dining) Menu £ 29
◆ Part 17C and 18C house with gardens. Elegant antique furnished interior, in the best traditions of English country style. Charming bedrooms. Home-grown meals at welcoming communal table.

Good food and accommodation at moderate prices?
Look for the Bib symbols:
red Bib Gourmand for food, blue Bib Hotel for hotels

ENGLAND

HOOK – Hants. – **504** R 30 – **pop. 6 869** – ✉ **Basingstoke** 6 **B1**

London 47 m – Oxford 39 m – Reading 13 m – Southampton 31 m

at Rotherwick North : 2 m. by A 30 and B 3349 on Rotherwick rd – ✉ Basingstoke

Tylney Hall (heated)

South : 1½ m. by Newnham rd on Ridge Lane ✉ RG27 9AZ – ✆ (01256) 764 881 – sales@tylneyhall.com – Fax (01256) 768 141

103 rm – †£ 150 ††£ 150/195 – 9 suites – **Rest** – Menu £ 25/38 **s** – Carte £ 38/48 **s**

◆ Grand and beautifully restored 19C mansion in delightful, extensive Gertrude Jekyll gardens. Country house rooms, some with private conservatories or suites over two floors. Classically English dining room with oak panelling and garden views.

HOPE – Derbs. – **502** O 23 – ✉ **Sheffield** 16 **A1**

London 180 m – Derby 50 m – Manchester 31 m – Sheffield 15 m – Stoke-on-Trent 40 m

Underleigh House without rest

Hope Valley, North : 1 m. by Edale Rd ✉ S33 6RF – ✆ (01433) 621 372 – underleigh.house@btconnect.com – Fax (01433) 621 324 – closed 25,26 and 31 December

6 rm – †£ 55 ††£ 75/90

◆ Converted Victorian property, rurally located and personally run, well located for the Peak District. Countryside views and a welcoming country ambience.

ENGLAND

HOPE COVE – Devon – **503** I 33 – **see Salcombe**

HORLEY – Surrey – **504** T 30 – **pop. 22 582** 7 **D2**

London 27 m – Brighton 26 m – Royal Tunbridge Wells 22 m

Plan : see Gatwick

Langshott Manor

Langshott, North : by A 23 turning right at Thistle Gatwick H. onto Ladbroke Rd ✉ RH6 9LN – ✆ (01293) 786 680 – admin@langshottmanor.com – Fax (01293) 783 905

21 rm – †£ 130/140 ††£ 270/320 – 1 suite

Rest *Mulberry* – (booking essential) Menu £ 20 (lunch) – Carte dinner only £ 40/55 **s**

◆ Part Elizabethan manor house set amidst gardens of roses, vines and ponds. For centuries the home of aristocrats, now a refined and harmonious country house hotel. Country house-style dining room with intimate ambience.

Lawn without rest

30 Massetts Rd ✉ RH6 7DF – ✆ (01293) 775 751 – info@lawnguesthouse.co.uk – Fax (01293) 821 803 Y **r**

12 rm – †£ 45/50 ††£ 60/65

◆ Privately owned and personally run with home comforts and ambience. Close to the station and convenient for Gatwick airport. Chintz decorated bedrooms are pine furnished.

The Turret without rest

48 Massetts Rd ✉ RH6 7DS – ✆ (01293) 782 490 – info@theturret.com – Fax (01293) 431 492 Y **i**

10 rm – †£ 39/54 ††£ 54

◆ Victorian home, with turrets, offering a warm welcome and simple comforts with homely style. Magnolia rooms with co-ordinated soft furnishings. Courtesy airport transport.

HORNCASTLE – Lincs. – 502 T 24 – pop. 6 090 17 C1

London 143 m – Lincoln 22 m – Nottingham 62 m
14 Bull Ring ✆ (01507) 526636

XX Magpies

71-75 East St ✉ LN9 6AA – ✆ (01507) 527004 – Fax (01507) 525068 – closed January, Monday and Tuesday and Saturday lunch
Rest – Menu £ 25/32
◆ Renowned, family run restaurant in a converted 18C house. Snug, comfortable, beamed interior. Local ingredients used in accomplished, refined dishes in a modern style.

HORNDON-ON-THE-HILL – Essex – 504 V 29 13 C3

London 25 m – Chelmsford 22 m – Maidstone 34 m – Southend-on-Sea 16 m

The Bell with rm

High Rd ✉ SS17 8LD – ✆ (01375) 642463 – joanne@bell-inn.co.uk – Fax (01375) 361611 – Closed 25-26 December and bank holiday Mondays
15 rm – †£ 60 ††£ 85, ☕ £ 9.50 – **Rest** – Carte £ 22/30
◆ 16C part timbered coaching inn. Log fire in bar and beamed ceiling in restaurant. Eclectically influenced range of menus. Comfortable, individually furnished bedrooms.

Do not confuse X with ✿!
X defines comfort, while stars are awarded for the best cuisine, across all categories of comfort.

HORNINGSEA – Cambs. – see Cambridge

HORN'S CROSS – Devon – 503 H 31 – ✉ Bideford Great Britain 2 C1

London 222 m – Barnstaple 15 m – Exeter 46 m
Clovelly★★, W : 6½ m. on A 39 and B 3237 – Bideford : Bridge★★ - Burton Art Gallery★ AC - Lundy Island★★ (by ferry), NF : 7 m. on a 39 and B 3235 – Hartland : Hartland Church★ - Hartland Quay★ (✳ ★★) - Hartland Point ⩤ ★★★, W : 9 m. on A 39 and B 3248 – Great Torrington (Dartington Crystal★ AC), SE : 15 m. on A 39 and A 386 – Rosemoor★, SE : 16 m. on A 39, A 386 and B 3220

The Roundhouse without rest

West : 1 m. on A 39 ✉ EX39 5DN – ✆ (01237) 451687 – enquiries@the-round-house.co.uk – Fax (01237) 451924 – closed 25 and 26 December
3 rm ☕ – †£ 40 ††£ 65
◆ Located on site of 13C corn mill, this friendly guesthouse offers cream teas on arrival! Spacious lounge and good quality breakfasts. Comfy, clean, well-kept bedrooms.

The Hoops Inn with rm

West : ½ m. on A 39 ✉ EX39 5DL – ✆ (01237) 451222 – sales@hoopsinn.co.uk – Fax (01237) 451247
13 rm ☕ – †£ 65 ††£ 95 – **Rest** – Menu £ 25 – Carte £ 25/35
◆ Dating from 13C, this archetypal thatched Devonshire inn has timbers, thick cob walls and oak panels. Menus feature quality local produce. Comfortable rooms.

HORRINGER – Suffolk – 504 W 27 – see Bury St Edmunds

ENGLAND

HORSHAM – W. Sussex – **504** T 30 – **pop. 47 804** 7 **D2**

London 39 m – Brighton 23 m – Guildford 20 m – Lewes 25 m – Worthing 20 m

9 Causeway ✆ (01403) 211661, tourist.information@horsham.gov.uk

Fullers Mannings Heath Hammerpond Rd, ✆ (01403) 210 228 .

South Lodge

Brighton Rd, Lower Beeding, Southeast : 5 m. on A 281 ✉ RH13 6PS – ✆ (01403) 891 711 – enquiries@southlodgehotel.co.uk – Fax (01403) 892 289

36 rm – £ 195 £ 195, £17 – 3 suites – **Rest** – (booking essential for non-residents) Menu £ 18/46

◆ Victorian mansion in 93 acres of immaculate gardens and parkland, overlooking South Downs. Opulent yet relaxed antique furnished public areas. Charming individual bedrooms. Rich, refined dining room includes tapestry hung walls.

Stan's Way House

3 Stans Way, East St ✉ RH12 1HU – ✆ (01403) 255 688 – sl@stanswayhouse.co.uk – Fax (01403) 266 144 – closed 22 December-4 January, Sunday, Monday and Tuesday - Thursday lunch

Rest – Menu £ 19/29

◆ Attractive part 15C building: upstairs restaurant is in striking, vaulted room with beamed ceiling: rustic, yet modern. Relaxed service. Well-priced, modish European menus.

ENGLAND

at Rowhook Northwest : 4 m. by A 264 and A 281 off A 29 – ✉ Horsham

The Chequers Inn

✉ RH12 3PY – ✆ (01403) 790 480 – thechequers1@aol.com – Closed Sunday dinner

Rest – Carte £ 28/33

◆ Delightful 18C inn in rural hamlet with log fires, low beams and relaxed atmosphere. Neal's restaurant more formal. Aspirational cooking showcases local produce. Keen service.

HORWICH – Lancs. – **502** M 23 – ✉ **Bolton** 20 **B2**

London 217 m – Liverpool 35 m – Manchester 21 m – Preston 16 m

Whites

rm, rest,

The Reebok Stadium, (Car Park A), De Havilland Way, Southeast : 2½ m. by A 673 on A 6027 ✉ BL6 6SF – ✆ (01204) 667 788 – whites@devere-hotels.com – Fax (01204) 673 721

119 rm – £ 72/135 £ 77/145 – 6 suites

Rest *Reflections* – see restaurant listing

Rest *Brasserie at Whites* – Menu £ 20 – Carte £ 20/33 **s**

◆ Modern business hotel, uniquely part of Bolton Wanderers' football stadium. Well equipped all round with good, modern bedrooms. Corporate clients can use stadium facilities. Brasserie at Whites is a "must" for Wanderers fans.

Reflections – at Whites H.

The Reebok Stadium (car park A), De Havilland Way ✉ BL6 6SF – ✆ (01204) 667 788 – Fax (01204) 673 721 – closed Sunday-Tuesday

Rest – (dinner only and Sunday lunch) Carte £ 25/46 **s**

◆ Notable for its elevated position overlooking the pitch at the Reebok Stadium. Formal dining experience, though dishes have a distinctly modern, original style.

HOUGH-ON-THE-HILL – Lincs. – see Grantham

HOUGHTON – Cambs. – see Huntingdon

see Huntingdon

HOUGHTON CONQUEST – Beds. – 504 S 27 – see Bedford

HOVE – Brighton and Hove – 504 T 31 – see Brighton and Hove

HOVINGHAM – N. Yorks. – 502 R 21 – ✉ York 23 C2

London 235 m – Leeds 47 m – Middlesbrough 36 m – York 25 m

Worsley Arms

High St ✉ YO62 4LA – ✆ (01653) 628 234 – enquiries@worsleyarms.co.uk – Fax (01653) 628 130

20 rm – †£ 85/95 ††£ 95/135

Rest *Cricketer's Bistro* – Menu £ 30 (dinner) – Carte £ 20/29

Rest *The Restaurant* – (dinner only and Sunday lunch) Menu £ 30

◆ Part 19C coaching inn set in delightful Yorkshire stone village. Charm and character throughout the classically traditional public rooms. Comfortable individual bedrooms. Informal Cricketer's Bistro. Calm, refined Restaurant.

We try to be as accurate as possible when giving room rates. But prices are susceptible to change, so please check rates when booking.

ENGLAND

HUDDERSFIELD – W. Yorks. – 502 O 23 – pop. 146 234 22 B3

London 191 m – Bradford 11 m – Leeds 15 m – Manchester 25 m – Sheffield 26 m

3 Albion St ✆ (01484) 223200

Bradley Park Bradley Rd, ✆ (01484) 223 772 ;

Woodsome Hall Fenay Bridge, ✆ (01484) 602 971 ;

Outlane Slack Lane, ✆ (01422) 374 762 ;

Meltham Thick Hollins Hall, ✆ (01484) 850 227 ;

Fixby Hall Lightridge Rd, ✆ (01484) 426 203 ;

Crosland Heath Felks Stile Rd, ✆ (01484) 653 216 .

Plans on following pages

at Thunder Bridge Southeast : 5 ¾ m. by A 629 - B – ✉ Huddersfield

Woodman Inn with rm

✉ HD8 0PX – ✆ (01484) 605 778 – thewoodman@connectfree.co.uk – Fax (01484) 604 110

12 rm – †£ 45 ††£ 65 – **Rest** – Carte £ 15/30

◆ A collection of 19C cottage style buildings, set in Last of the Summer Wine country. Freshly prepared dishes from bar or restaurant. Compact rooms in former weavers' cottages.

at Shelley Southeast : 6 ¼ m. by A 629 - B - on B 6116 – ✉ Huddersfield

The Three Acres

rest,

Roydhouse, Northeast : 1½ m. on Flockton rd ✉ HD8 8LR – ✆ (01484) 602 606 – 3acres@globalnet.co.uk – Fax (01484) 608 411 – closed 25 December, 26 December, 1st January

20 rm – †£ 70/100 ††£ 100 – **Rest** – (closed Saturday lunch) (booking essential) Carte £ 27/44

◆ Well-established stone inn in rural location. Annex rooms more spacious and quiet; those in main house closer to the bar and dining room; all warm, modern and comfortable. Agreeably busy restaurant with open fires: fish dishes prepared at open seafood bar.

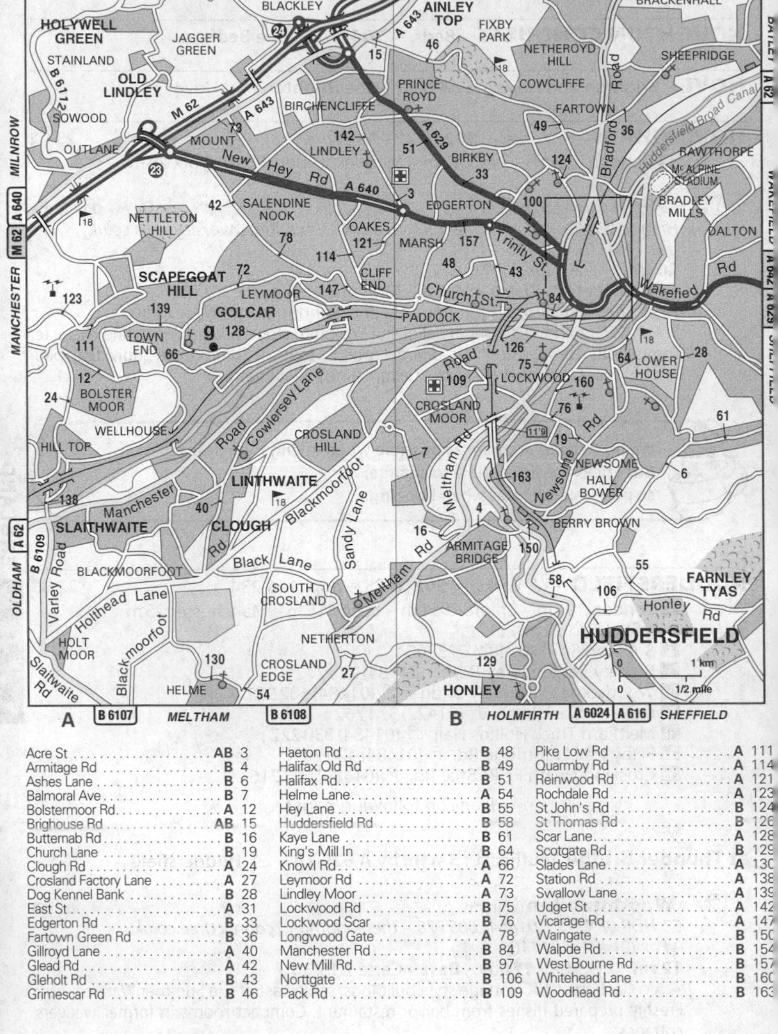

Acre St . . . . AB 3	Haeton Rd . . . . B 48	Pike Low Rd . . . . A 111
Armitage Rd . . . . B 4	Halifax Old Rd . . . . B 49	Quarmby Rd . . . . A 114
Ashes Lane . . . . B 6	Halifax Rd . . . . B 51	Reinwood Rd . . . . A 121
Balmoral Ave . . . . B 7	Helme Lane . . . . A 54	Rochdale Rd . . . . A 123
Bolstermoor Rd . . . . A 12	Hey Lane . . . . B 55	St John's Rd . . . . B 124
Brighouse Rd . . . . AB 15	Huddersfield Rd . . . . B 58	St Thomas Rd . . . . B 126
Butternab Rd . . . . B 16	Kaye Lane . . . . B 61	Scar Lane . . . . A 128
Church Lane . . . . B 19	King's Mill ln . . . . B 64	Scotgate Rd . . . . B 129
Clough Rd . . . . A 24	Knowl Rd . . . . A 66	Slades Lane . . . . A 130
Crosland Factory Lane . . . . A 27	Leymoor Rd . . . . A 72	Station Rd . . . . A 138
Dog Kennel Bank . . . . B 28	Lindley Moor . . . . A 73	Swallow Lane . . . . A 139
East St . . . . A 31	Lockwood Rd . . . . B 75	Udget St . . . . A 142
Edgerton Rd . . . . B 33	Lockwood Scar . . . . B 76	Vicarage Rd . . . . A 147
Fartown Green Rd . . . . B 36	Longwood Gate . . . . A 78	Waingate . . . . B 150
Gillroyd Lane . . . . A 40	Manchester Rd . . . . B 84	Walpde Rd . . . . B 154
Glead Rd . . . . A 42	New Mill Rd . . . . B 97	West Bourne Rd . . . . B 157
Gleholt Rd . . . . B 43	Norttgate . . . . B 106	Whitehead Lane . . . . B 160
Grimescar Rd . . . . B 46	Pack Rd . . . . B 109	Woodhead Rd . . . . B 163

at Golcar West : 3 ½ m. by A 62 on B 6111 – ✉ Huddersfield

XXX **The Weavers Shed** with rm

88 Knowl Rd, via Scar Lane ✉ HD7 4AN – ☎ (01484) 654 284 – info@weaversshed.co.uk – Fax (01484) 650 980 – closed Christmas- First week January A **g**

5 rm ☕ – †£ 80 ††£ 100 – **Rest** – (closed Saturday lunch, Sunday and Monday) Menu £ 18 (lunch) – Carte £ 34/50

◆ Converted 18C cloth finishing mill. Stone floored dining area with low beamed ceiling. Select, modern British menu supplied by an extensive kitchen garden. Smart bedrooms.

HUDDERSFIELD

Chapel Hill . . . . **C** 18
Claremont St . . . . **C** 21
Fitzwilliam St . . . . **C** 37
Gaswoors St . . . . **C** 39
Great Northern St . . . . **C** 45
Imperial Arcade . . . . **C** 60
Kingsgate Shopping Centre . . . . **C**
King St . . . . **C** 63
Lower Fitzwilliam St . . . . . **C** 79
Manchester Rd . . . . **C** 84
Market Pl. . . . . **C** 85
Market St. . . . . **C** 87
Merton St. . . . . **C** 91
New North Rd . . . . **C** 100
Northumberland St . . . . . . **C** 105
Outcote Bank . . . . **C** 108
Piazza Shopping Centre . . **C**
Portland St . . . . **C** 112
Queen St . . . . **C** 115
Queen St South. . . . . **C** 117
Railway St . . . . **C** 120
St Peter's St. . . . . **C** 125
Springwood Ave . . . . **C** 136
Spring St . . . . **C** 133
Trinity St. . . . . **C** 141
Venn St. . . . . **C** 145
Victoria Lane . . . . **C** 148
Wakefield Rd. . . . . **C** 151
Water St. . . . . **C** 156

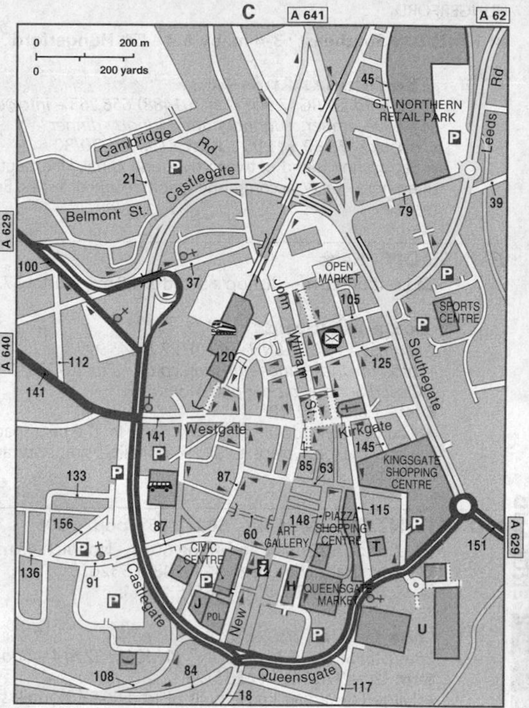

HUNGERFORD – Newbury – 503 P 29 – pop. 4 938 10 A3

London 74 m – Bristol 57 m – Oxford 28 m – Reading 26 m – Southampton 46 m

Savernake Forest★★ (Grand Avenue★★★), W : 7 m. by A 4 – Crofton Beam Engines★, SW : 8 m. by A 338 and minor roads

Fishers Farm without rest

Shefford Woodlands, North : 4 m. by A 4 and A 338 on B 4000 ✉ RG17 7AB – ✆ (01488) 648 466 – mail@fishersfarm.co.uk – Fax (01488) 648 706

3 rm – †£ 45/50 ††£ 70/80

◆ Attractive redbrick farmhouse in a rural spot on a working farm. Well-appointed sitting room. Breakfast served family style. Individually styled rooms with country views.

at Lambourn Woodlands North : 6 m. by A 338 on B 4000 – ✉ Hungerford

The Hare

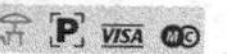

✉ RG17 7SD – ✆ (01488) 71 386 – cuisine@theharerestaurant.co.uk – Fax (01488) 71 186 – closed two weeks January, two weeks August, first week June, Sunday evening and Monday

Rest – (booking essential) Menu £ 26 (lunch) – Carte £ 32/37

◆ Contemporary pub conversion with modish interior of three dining rooms and original beams. Building a strong local reputation based on innovative cooking of a high standard.

at Kintbury **Southeast : 3 ¾ m. by A 4 – ✉ Hungerford**

The Dundas Arms with rm
Station Rd ✉ RG17 9UT – ✆ (01488) 658 263 – info@dundasarms.co.uk – Closed 25-26 December, 1 January and Monday dinner
5 rm – †£ 80 ††£ 95 – **Rest** – Carte £ 20/30
◆ Set on tiny island between river and canal. Unexceptional interior: the food's the thing here - tasty, accomplished, homecooked dishes. Bedrooms with small riverside terraces.

HUNSDON – Herts. 12 B2

London 26 m – Bishop's Stortford 8 m – Harlow 7 m

Fox and Hounds
2 High St ✉ SG12 8NH – ✆ (01279) 843 999
– info@foxandhounds-hunsdon.co.uk – Fax (01279) 841 092
– Closed Sunday dinner and Monday
Rest – Carte £ 22/40
◆ Country style décor and cosy sofas in the bar; spacious, high ceilinged dining room is the best place to sit. Seasonality, simplicity and style are bywords in the kitchen.

HUNSTANTON – Norfolk – 502 V 25 – pop. 4 505 14 B1

London 120 m – Cambridge 60 m – Norwich 45 m
Town Hall, The Green ✆ (01485) 532610
Golf Course Rd, ✆ (01485) 532 811 .

The Gables without rest
28 Austin St ✉ PE36 6AW – ✆ (01485) 532 514 – bbatthegables@aol.com
6 rm – †£ 25/40 ††£ 55/75
◆ Large Edwardian house built of traditional Norfolk stone: well located for beach and town centre. Neat guest lounge; family photos decorate hallway. Personally styled rooms.

Claremont without rest
35 Greevegate ✉ PE36 6AF – ✆ (01485) 533 171 – claremontgh@tiscali.co.uk
– mid March-mid November
7 rm – †£ 30/35 ††£ 60
◆ Classic seaside guesthouse in a Victorian building close to beach, shops and gardens. Well-kept, traditional interior and a toaster on each table at breakfast.

Neptune Inn with rm
85 Old Hunstanton Rd, Old Hunstanton, Northeast : 1 1/2 m. on A 149
✉ PE36 6HZ – ✆ (01485) 532 122 – reservations@theneptune.co.uk
– Fax (01485) 535 314 – closed 2 weeks January, 26 December, Tuesday and Wednesday lunch and Monday
7 rm – †£ 60/70 ††£ 100/110 – **Rest** – Menu £ 19 (lunch) – Carte £ 28/43
◆ Red brick 19C former coaching inn. Lounge area decorated with coastal scenes; dining room has linen laid tables. Classic dishes have modern twist; made with local ingredients.

at Ringstead **East : 3 ¾ m. by A 149 – ✉ Hunstanton**

The Gin Trap Inn with rm
6 High St ✉ PE36 5JU – ✆ (01485) 525 264 – thegintrap@hotmail.co.uk
3 rm – †£ 45 ††£ 140 – **Rest** – Carte £ 16/25
◆ Charming 17C inn with tasteful, uncluttered style, but with rural mainstays like beams and open fire. Lunchtime bar favourites; well executed gourmet evenings. Stylish rooms.

HUNSTRETE – Bath & North East Somerset – 503 M 29 – see Bristol

ENGLAND

HUNTINGDON – Cambs. – **504** T 26 – **pop. 20 600** 14 **A2**

London 69 m – Bedford 21 m – Cambridge 16 m
The Library, Princes St ✆ (01480) 388588
Hemingford Abbots Cambridge Rd, New Farm Lodge, ✆ (01480) 495 000 .

Huntingdon Marriott

Kingfisher Way, Hinchingbrooke Business Park, West : 1½ m. by A 141 at junction with A 14 ✉ PE29 6FL – ✆ (01480) 446 000 – reservations.huntingdon@marriotthotels.co.uk – Fax (01480) 451 111
146 rm – †£ 120/135 ††£ 120/135, ☕ £ 15.95 – 4 suites – **Rest** – (buffet lunch) Carte £ 22/41
◆ Purpose-built 1990s hotel, well geared to the modern business traveller. Good standard of brand furniture in public areas and well-equipped rooms which include data ports. Smart, airy dining room.

Old Bridge

1 High St ✉ PE29 3TQ – ✆ (01480) 424 300 – oldbridge@huntsbridge.co.uk – Fax (01480) 411 017
24 rm ☕ – †£ 95/110 ††£ 125/175
Rest ***Terrace*** – see restaurant listing
◆ 18C former private bank overlooking the river. All bedrooms, some very contemporary, are decorated to a good standard and bathrooms often have deep Victorian-style baths.

Terrace – at Old Bridge H.

1 High St ✉ PE29 3TQ – ✆ (01480) 424 300 – Fax (01480) 411 017
Rest – Menu £ 18 (lunch) – Carte £ 25/35
◆ Two dining areas: a formal wood panelled room and a more casual conservatory with terrace. Hearty rustic Italian dishes provide the basis for menus.

ENGLAND

at Broughton Northeast : 6 m. by B 1514 off A 141 – ✉ Huntingdon

The Crown

Bridge Rd ✉ PE28 3AY – ✆ (01487) 824 428 – simon@thecrownbrougton.co.uk – Fax (01487) 821912 – Closed 1st week January, Monday and Tuesday
Rest – Menu £ 15 – Carte £ 20/28
◆ Bay-windowed pub next to church in sleepy village. Uncluttered feel punctuated by bare tables and farmhouse chairs. Well-priced, modern meals with classic French base.

at Houghton East : 3½ m. by B 1514 off A 1123 – ✉ Huntingdon

Cheriton House without rest

Mill St ✉ PE28 2AZ – ✆ (01480) 464 004 – sales@cheritonhousecambs.co.uk – Fax (01480) 496 960
5 rm ☕ – †£ 62/75 ††£ 65/85
◆ Cream painted 19C house with lovely garden. Place your order overnight for memorable breakfast. Relaxing conservatory-lounge. Co-ordinated rooms with thoughtful touches.

at Hemingford Grey Southeast : 5 m. by A 1198 off A 14 – ✉ Huntingdon

The Willow without rest

45 High St ✉ PE28 9BJ – ✆ (01480) 494 748 – Fax (01480) 464 456
9 rm ☕ – †£ 45/70 ††£ 70
◆ Very personally run guesthouse in picturesque village location: its vivid yellow exterior makes it easy to spot. Good value, and close to The Cock. Immaculately kept bedrooms.

The Cock

47 High St ✉ PE28 9BJ – ✆ (01480) 463 609 – cock@cambscuisine.com – Fax (01480) 461 747
Rest – Menu £ 13 – Carte £ 20/35
◆ Real ale pub with spacious dining area that features a wood-burning stove and oil paintings for sale. Good choice of dishes: fresh fish or sausage selections are a speciality.

at Spaldwick West : 7½ m. by A 141 off A 14 – ✉ Huntingdon

The George Inn
5 High St ✉ PE28 0TD – ✆ (01480) 890 293 – info@georgeofspaldwick.co.uk – Fax (01480) 896 847 – closed dinner 25, 26 December and 1 January
Rest – Carte £ 20/30
◆ Built in the early 1500s, now sporting lilac and aubergine walls and an imposing fireplace. Characterful beamed restaurant: menus mix modern European with home-grown classics.

HURLEY – Berks. 11 C3

London 35 m – Maidenhead 5 m – Reading 18 m

Black Boys Inn with rm
Henley Rd, Southwest : 1½ m. on A 4130 ✉ SL6 5NQ – ✆ (01628) 824 212 – info@blackboysinn.co.uk – Closed 2 weeks Christmas, 2 weeks August, Sunday dinner and Monday
7 rm – †£ 75 ††£ 85 – **Rest** – Carte £ 25/30
◆ 16C inn: delightful modernised interior, with sage walls and central fire. Restaurant ambience. Well-priced menus: Newlyn fish, game from Hambledon Estate. Characterful rooms.

ENGLAND

HURST – Berks. – 503 Q 29 – see Reading

HURST GREEN – Lancs. – 502 M 22 – ✉ Clitheroe 20 B2

London 236 m – Blackburn 12 m – Burnley 13 m – Preston 12 m

Shireburn Arms
Whalley Rd, on B 6243 ✉ BB7 9QJ – ✆ (01254) 826 518 – sales@shireburnarmshotel.com – Fax (01254) 826 208
22 rm – †£ 50/60 ††£ 80 – 1 suite – **Rest** – Menu £ 17 – Carte £ 20/30
◆ Ivy clad 17C former farmhouse located in a charming village. Traditional cottage décor and views of the Ribble valley. Reputedly haunted by a long deceased nun. Strong showing of local ingredients in dining room; good valley outlook, too.

HURSTBOURNE TARRANT – Hants. – 503 P 30 – ✉ Andover 6 B1

London 77 m – Bristol 77 m – Oxford 38 m – Southampton 33 m

Esseborne Manor
Northeast : 1½ m. on A 343 ✉ SP11 0ER – ✆ (01264) 736 444 – info@esseborne-manor.co.uk – Fax (01264) 736 725
20 rm – †£ 98 ††£ 180 – **Rest** – Menu £ 16/22 **s** – Carte £ 24/41 **s**
◆ 100 year old country house in attractive grounds with herb garden. Smart, well-appointed bedrooms, three in garden cottages. Ferndown room boasts a spa bath and private patio. Long, narrow dining room with large windows.

HUTTON MAGNA – Durham – pop. 86 *Great Britain* 24 A3

London 258 m – Darlington 17 m – Newcastle upon Tyne 53 m – Scarborough 75 m
Raby Castle★, N : 5 m. by B 6274. Richmond★, S : 8 m. by B 6274 – Bowes Museum★, W : 8 m. by A 66

The Oak Tree Inn
✉ DL11 7HH – ✆ (01833) 627 371 – Closed 25-26 and 31 December, 1 January and Monday
Rest – (dinner only) Carte £ 24/30
◆ Part 18C inn in an unspoilt rural location. Interior beams and stone walls with homely décor. Blackboard menus offering a good range of modern pub dishes.

HUTTON-LE-HOLE – N. Yorks. – 502 R 21 23 C1

London 244 m – Scarborough 27 m – York 33 m

Burnley House without rest

YO62 6UA – (01751) 417548 – info@burnleyhouse.co.uk

6 rm – £ 50/55 £ 75/85

◆ Attractive part 16C, part Georgian house, Grade II listed in a picturesque Moors village. Brown trout in beck winding through garden. Simple, individually styled bedrooms.

HYTHE – Kent – 504 X 30 – pop. 14 766 9 D2

London 68 m – Folkestone 6 m – Hastings 33 m – Maidstone 31 m

Visitor Centre, Railway Station (01303) 266421

Sene Valley Folkestone Sene, (01303) 268 513 .

Plan : see Folkestone

Hythe Imperial rm,

Prince's Parade CT21 6AE – (01303) 267 441
– hytheimperial@qhotels.co.uk – Fax (01303) 264 610 X **d**

100 rm – £ 75/125 £ 90/135

Rest *The Princes Room* – (bar lunch Monday -Saturday) Menu 27 – Carte approx. £ 28 **s**

◆ Set in a 50 acre estate, this classic Victorian hotel retains the elegance of a former age. Wide range of bedrooms cater for everyone from families to business travellers. Spacious restaurant with classic style and menus to match.

Hythe Bay

Marine Parade CT21 6AW – (01303) 233 844 – hythebay@btinternet.com
– Fax (01303) 230 651

Rest – Seafood (buffet lunch Sunday) Carte £ 20/38

◆ Originally built as tea rooms and in a great position just feet from the beach. Bright, airy room with views out to Channel. Seafood menus - ideal for lunch on a summer's day.

If breakfast is included the symbol appears after the number of rooms.

ICKLESHAM – E. Sussex – 504 V/W 31 9 C3

London 66 m – Brighton 42 m – Hastings 7 m

Manor Farm Oast

Windmill Lane, South : ½ m. TN36 4WL – (01424) 813 787
– manor.farm.oast@lineone.net – Fax (01424) 813 787
– Closed 10 December-26 January

3 rm – £ 54/62 £ 84/94 – **Rest** – (by arrangement) Menu £ 30

◆ 19C former oast house retaining original features and surrounded by orchards. Welcoming beamed lounge with open fire. One of the comfy bedrooms is completely in the round! Home-cooked menus in circular dining room.

IGHTHAM COMMON – Kent – see Sevenoaks

ILCHESTER – Somerset – 503 L 30 – pop. 2 123 3 B3

London 138 m – Bridgwater 21 m – Exeter 48 m – Taunton 24 m – Yeovil 5 m

Ilchester Arms with rm

The Square BA22 8LN – (01935) 840 220 – Fax (01935) 841 353
– Closed 26 December and Sunday dinner

7 rm – £ 60 £ 75 – **Rest** – Carte £ 18/27

◆ Attractive-looking, ivy-covered 18C coaching inn. Relaxing, intimate public areas enhanced by flagstone flooring in bar. Hearty bistro menus. Clean and comfy bedrooms.

ENGLAND

ILFRACOMBE – Devon – 503 H 30 *Great Britain* 2 C1

London 218 m – Barnstaple 13 m – Exeter 53 m

Mortehoe★★ : St Mary's Church - Morte Point★, SW : 5½ m. on B 3343 – Lundy Island★★ (by ferry). Braunton : St Brannock's Church★, Braunton Burrows★, S : 8 m. on A 361 – Barnstaple★ : Bridge★, S : 12 m. on A 3123, B 3230, A 39, A 361 and B 3233

XX **The Quay (Atlantic Dining Room)** VISA AE

11 The Quay ✉ EX34 9EQ – ✆ (01271) 868 090 – info@11thequay.com – Fax (01271) 865 599

Rest – (closed Monday, Tuesday and Sunday dinner) Carte £ 27/40

Rest *White Hart Bar* – Menu £ 16/17 – Carte £ 18/25

◆ Handsome 18C brick harbourside building, part owned by Damien Hirst. Cool, modish interior, typified by plethora of Hirst artworks. Sea views and modern cooking in Atlantic.

ILKLEY – W. Yorks. – 502 O 22 – pop. 13 472 22 B2

London 210 m – Bradford 13 m – Harrogate 17 m – Leeds 16 m – Preston 46 m

Station Rd ✆ (01943) 602319

Myddleton, ✆ (01943) 607 277 .

Rombalds P VISA AE

11 West View, Wells Rd ✉ LS29 9JG – ✆ (01943) 603 201 – reception@rombalds.demon.co.uk – Fax (01943) 816 586 – closed 27 December-5 January

15 rm – †£ 78/100 ††£ 120/135 – 4 suites – **Rest** – Menu £ 12.95 – Carte £ 17/30 **s**

◆ Privately owned Georgian town house on edge of Moor. Elegant fixtures and fittings adorn its sitting room. Individually styled bedrooms have matching fabrics and drapes. Yorkshire produce to fore in cool blue restaurant.

XXX **Box Tree** (Simon Gueller) AC VISA

37 Church St, on A 65 ✉ LS29 9DR – ✆ (01943) 608 484 – info@theboxtree.co.uk – Fax (01943) 607 186 – closed Sunday dinner and Monday

Rest – (dinner only lunch Friday-Sunday) Menu £ 25/28 – Carte £ 45/55

Spec. Risotto of lobster with braised fennel and thyme. Veal sirloin, asparagus, Jabugo ham, morel and thyme jus. Passion fruit soufflé, passion fruit and mango sauce.

◆ Characterful 18C sandstone cottage, adorned with antiques, paintings and ornaments. Clearly defined, flavourful modern cooking served in generous portions. Charming service.

Undecided between two equivalent establishments?
Within each category, establishments are classified
in our order of preference.

ILLOGAN – Cornwall – 503 E 33 – ✉ Redruth 1 A3

London 305 m – Falmouth 14 m – Penzance 17 m – Truro 11 m

Portreath★, NW : 2 m. by B 3300 – Hell's Mouth★, SW : 5 m. by B 3301

Aviary Court P VISA

Mary's Well, Northwest : ¾ m. by Alexandra Rd ✉ TR16 4QZ – ✆ (01209) 842 256 – info@aviarycourthotel.co.uk – Fax (01209) 843 744 – closed 2 weeks Spring and 2 weeks Winter

6 rm – †£ 50 ††£ 83 – **Rest** – (dinner only) (residents only) Menu £ 18

◆ Tranquillity reigns at this cosy Cornish hotel with its neat, well-kept gardens. Traditional ambience prevails throughout with colourful furnishings and traditional rooms. Cornish ingredients dominate cuisine.

ENGLAND

ILMINGTON – Warks. – 504 O 27 *Great Britain* 19 **C3**

London 91 m – Birmingham 31 m – Oxford 34 m – Stratford-upon-Avon 9 m
Hidcote Manor Garden★★, SW : 2 m. by minor rd – Chipping Campden★★, SW : 4 m. by minor rd

Folly Farm Cottage without rest
Back St ✉ CV36 4LJ – ✆ (01608) 682 425 – bruceandpam@follyfarm.co.uk – Fax (01608) 682 425
3 rm – †£ 55 ††£ 84
◆ Welcoming, cosy guesthouse with snug interior. Notable, sunny seating area in rear garden. Spacious breakfast room. Immaculate bedrooms, where breakfast may also be taken.

The Howard Arms with rm
Lower Green ✉ CV36 4LT – ✆ (01608) 682 226 – info@howardarms.com – Fax (01608) 682 226 – Closed 25 December and dinner 31 December
3 rm – †£ 88 ††£ 145 – **Rest** – Menu £ 24 – Carte £ 25/33
◆ Cotswold stone inn facing village green. Spacious pub with various rooms and snugs. Good British pub cooking; varied blackboard menu. Bright rooms with modern facilities.

INGLETON – N. Yorks. – 502 M 21 – pop. 1 641 – ✉ Carnforth (Lancs.) 22 **A2**

London 266 m – Kendal 21 m – Lancaster 18 m – Leeds 53 m
The Community Centre ✆ (015242) 41049

Riverside Lodge
24 Main St ✉ LA6 3HJ – ✆ (015242) 41 359 – info@riversideingleton.co.uk – closed 24-25 December
7 rm – †£ 40 ††£ 60 – **Rest** – (by arrangement) Menu £ 15
◆ Pleasant 19C house close to famous pot-holing caves. Conservatory dining room with great views across Yorkshire Dales. Informal gardens. Cosy sitting room and homely bedrooms.

Pines Country House
Kendal Rd, Northwest : ¼ m. on A 65 ✉ LA6 3HN – ✆ (015242) 41 252 – pinesingleton@aol.com – closed January
7 rm – †£ 39/42 ††£ 58/64 – **Rest** – (dinner only) (by arrangement) Carte £ 16/22
◆ Spacious early Victorian house, set on busy main road, with countryside views. Homely lounge with honesty bar. Cosy, traditional bedrooms; those at back look out to the sheep. Traditional cooking in conservatory-style dining room boasting 100 year old vine.

INSTOW – Devon – 503 H 30 – see Bideford

IPSWICH – Suffolk – 504 X 27 – pop. 138 718 *Great Britain* 15 **C3**

London 76 m – Norwich 43 m
St Stephens Church, St Stephens Lane ✆ (01473) 258070, ipswich@eetb.info
Rushmere Rushmere Heath, ✆ (01473) 725 648 ;
Purdis Heath Bucklesham Rd, ✆ (01473) 727 474 ;
Fynn Valley Witnesham, ✆ (01473) 785 267 .
Sutton Hoo★, NE : 12 m. by A 12 Y and B 1083 from Woodbridge

Plan on next page

Salthouse Harbour rm,
1 Neptune Quay ✉ IP4 1AX – ✆ (01473) 226 789 – staying@salthouseharbour.co.uk – Fax (01473) 226 927 X **a**
41 rm – †£ 100/135 ††£ 130/145 – 2 suites
Rest *Brasserie* – Menu £ 15 – Carte £ 21/32
◆ Converted 7-storey warehouse overlooking the marina. Lounge with seagrass seats. Designer style bedrooms with modern facilities; some with good views; two penthouse suites. Modern brasserie with a Mediterranean touch.

ENGLAND

IPSWICH

Street	Map	No.
Argyle St	X	2
Back Hamlet	Z	3
Birkfield Drive	Z	5
Bond St	X	6
Bridgwater Rd	Z	7
Buttermarket Centre	X	9
Carr St	X	10
Chevallier St	Y	13
College St	X	15
Corn Hill	X	16
Dogs Head St	X	18
Ellenbrook Rd	Z	19
Falcon St	X	21
Fore Hamlet	Z	22
Franciscan Way	X	24
Friars St	X	25
Grey Friars Rd	X	26
Grove Lane	YZ	28
Handford Rd	X, Y	30
Lloyds Ave	X	31
Lower Orwell St	X	32
Northgate St	X	33
Orwell Pl	X	34
Quadling St	X	35
Queen St	X	37
St Helen's St	X, Y	39
St Margarets St	X	40
St Nicholas St	X	41
St Peter's St	X	42
Salthouse St	X	43
Silent St	X	46
Tavern St	X	
Tower Ramparts Centre	X	47
Upper Orwell St	X	49
Waterworks St	X	51
Westgate St	X	52
Wolsey St	X	53
Yarmouth Rd	Y	54

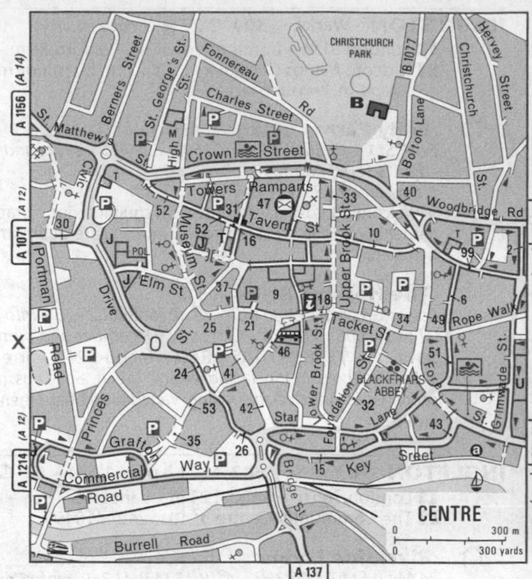

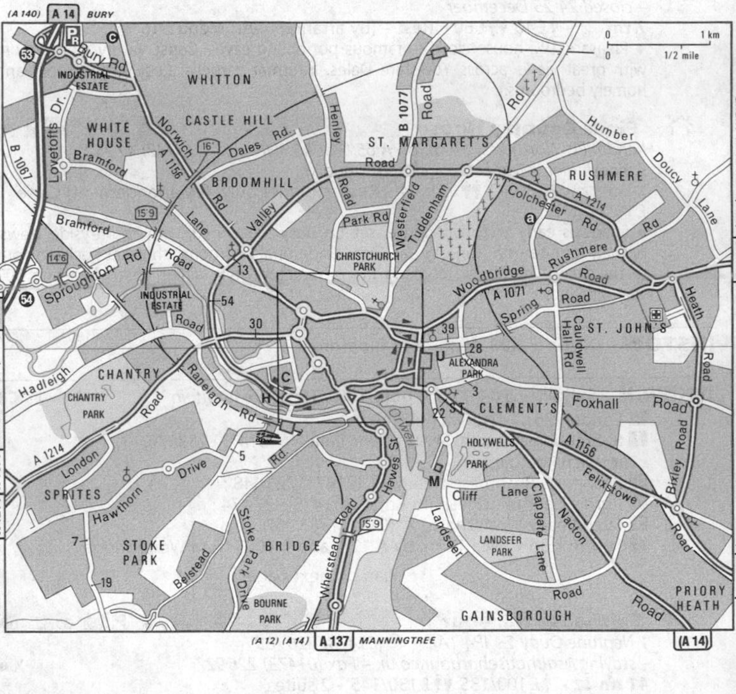

(A 140) A 14 BURY

WHITTON
CASTLE HILL
WHITE HOUSE
BROOMHILL
ST. MARGARET'S
RUSHMERE
CHRISTCHURCH PARK
CHANTRY
CHANTRY PARK
SPRITES
STOKE PARK
BRIDGE
BOURNE PARK
ALEXANDRA PARK
ST. CLEMENT'S
ST. JOHN'S
HOLYWELLS PARK
LANDSEER PARK
GAINSBOROUGH
PRIORY HEATH
INDUSTRIAL ESTATE
Bury Rd
Norwich Rd
Dales Rd.
Valley Rd
Henley Road
Westerfield Road
Tuddenham Rd
Park Rd
Colchester Rd
Humber Doucy Lane
Woodbridge Road
Rushmere Road
Spring Road
Cauldwell Hall Rd
Heath Road
Foxhall Road
Bixley Road
Felixstowe Road
Nacton Road
Clapgate Lane
Cliff Lane
Landseer Road
Hawes St
Wherstead Road
Stoke Park Drive
Belstead Road
Hawthorn Drive
London Road
Ranelagh Rd
Hadleigh Road
Sproughton Rd
Bramford Road
Bramford Lane
Lovetofts Dr.
Orwell
0 1 km
0 1/2 mile
(A 12) (A 14) A 137 MANNINGTREE
(A 14)
COLCHESTER (A 12) A 1214 A 1071 HADLEIGH (A 12) A 14

Look out for red symbols, indicating particularly pleasant establishments.

The Gatehouse
799 Old Norwich Rd ✉ IP1 6LH – ✆ (01473) 741 897 – enquiries@gatehousehotel.co.uk – Fax (01473) 744 236 Y **c**
15 rm – †£ 69/109 ††£ 109/119 – **Rest** – (dinner only) (booking essential for non-residents) Carte £ 20/29
◆ Regency style house in large garden on edge of town. Wood-panelled drawing room. Spacious rooms, including 4 singles, with individual colour schemes and attractive furniture. Smart dining room with cloth-clad tables at dinner.

Sidegate Guest House without rest
121 Sidegate Lane ✉ IP4 4JB – ✆ (01473) 728 714 – bookings@sidegateguesthouse.co.uk Y **a**
6 rm – †£ 53/58 ††£ 68
◆ Compact, friendly guesthouse in residential area. Comfy lounge with terraced doors onto garden. Neatly laid breakfast room. Well-kept, cosy rooms.

at Hintlesham West : 5 m. by A 1214 on A 1071 - Y – ✉ Ipswich

Hintlesham Hall (heated)
✉ IP8 3NS – ✆ (01473) 652 334 – reservations@hintleshamhall.com – Fax (01473) 652 463
31 rm – †£ 150 ††£ 275 – 2 suites – **Rest** – (bar lunch Saturday) Menu £ 33/34 – Carte £ 40/56
◆ Grand and impressive Georgian manor house of 16C origins set in parkland with golf course. Stuart carved oak staircase. Ornate wedding room. Individually decorated rooms. Opulent room for fine dining.

ENGLAND

IRONBRIDGE – Wrekin – **503** M 26 – **pop. 1 560** *Great Britain* 18 **B2**

London 135 m – Birmingham 36 m – Shrewsbury 18 m
The Wharfage ✆ (01952) 432166, info@ironbridge.org.uk
Ironbridge Gorge Museum★★ **AC** (The Iron Bridge★★, Coalport China Museum★★, Blists Hill Open Air Museum★★, Museum of the Gorge and Visitor Centre★)

Severn Lodge without rest
New Rd ✉ TF8 7AU – ✆ (01952) 432 147 – julia@severnlodge.com – closed 10 December-12 January
3 rm – †£ 69 ††£ 87
◆ Redbrick Georgian detached house with garden overlooking Iron Bridge, a World Heritage site. Quiet position. Cosy breakfast room. Antiques and pine furnishings in bedrooms.

The Library House without rest
11 Severn Bank ✉ TF8 7AN – ✆ (01952) 432 299 – info@libraryhouse.com
4 rm – †£ 60/65 ††£ 70/85
◆ Nicely hidden, albeit tricky to find, guesthouse with rear terrace. Homely sitting room. Cottage style breakfast room. Compact, comfy rooms, with a touch of style about them.

Bridge House without rest
Buildwas Rd, West : 2 m. on B 4380 ✉ TF8 7BN – ✆ (01952) 432 105 – Fax (01952) 432 105 – closed December and January
4 rm – †£ 55/60 ††£ 75/80
◆ Characterful 17C cottage with interesting turn of 20C machines in garden. Comfy reception room, fine collection of local objects and photos. Individually decorated rooms.

da Vinci's
26 High St ✉ TF8 7AD – ✆ (01952) 432 250 – davincis1996@aol.com – Closed 1 week Christmas and New Year, Sunday and Monday
Rest – Italian (dinner only) (booking essential) Carte £ 19/35
◆ Buzzy, personally run town centre restaurant with its rustic interior, painted boards, exposed brickwork and framed Leonardo prints. Tasty, authentic Italian cooking.

ISLE OF MAN – I.O.M. – 502 FG – see Man (Isle of)

ITTERINGHAM – Norfolk – ✉ Aylsham 15 C1

London 126 m – Cromer 11 m – Norwich 17 m

The Walpole Arms

The Common ✉ NR11 7AR – ✆ (01263) 587 258 – goodfood@thewalpolearms.co.uk – Fax (01263) 587 074 – Closed 25 December and Sunday dinner

Rest – Carte £ 21/25

◆ Charming, friendly, part 18C inn. Seasonal British menu draws intelligently on global ideas: dine at linen-clad parlour tables or in inviting, oak-beamed bar. Regional ale.

IVYCHURCH – Kent – 504 W 30 *Great Britain* 9 C2

London 67 m – Ashford 11 m – Rye 10 m

Rye Old Town★★ : Mermaid St★ - St Mary's Church (≤ ★), SW : 9 m. on A 2070 and A 259

Olde Moat House without rest

Northwest : ¾ m. on B 2070 ✉ TN29 0AZ – ✆ (01797) 344 700 – oldemoathouse@hotmail.com

3 rm – †£ 60 ††£ 70/80

◆ Blissfully characterful guesthouse with 15C origins, set in over three acres, encircled by small moat. Beamed sitting room with inglenook. Individual, homely styled rooms.

ENGLAND

Red = Pleasant. Look for the red and symbols.

IXWORTH – Suffolk – 504 W 27 – see Bury St Edmunds

JERSEY – C.I. – 503 OP 33 – see Channel Islands

JEVINGTON – E. Sussex – 504 U 31 – see Eastbourne

KEGWORTH – Derbs. – 502 Q 25 *Great Britain* 16 B2

London 123 m – Leicester 18 m – Loughborough 6 m – Nottingham 13 m

Calke Abbey★, SW : 7 m. by A 6 (northbound) and A 453 (southbound) – Derby★ - Museum and Art Gallery★, Royal Crown Derby Museum★, NW : 9 m. by A 50 – Nottingham Castle Museum★, N : 11 m. by A 453 and A 52

Kegworth House

42 High St ✉ DE74 2DA – ✆ (01509) 672 575 – info@kegworthhouse.co.uk – Fax (01509) 670 645

11 rm – †£ 75/120 ††£ 95/150 – **Rest** – (dinner only) (residents only, communal dining) Menu £ 25

◆ Georgian manor house in village, secluded in walled garden. Fine interior with original decorative features. Individually-decorated bedrooms of charm and character. Home cooking by arrangement.

KELSALE – Suffolk – 504 Y 27 – ✉ Saxmundham 15 D3

London 103 m – Cambridge 68 m – Ipswich 23 m – Norwich 37 m

Mile Hill Barn without rest

North Green, North : 1½ m. on (main) A 12 ✉ IP17 2RG – ✆ (01728) 668 519 – mail@mile-hill-barn.co.uk

3 rm – †£ 60/65 ††£ 95/100

◆ Converted 16C barn well placed for glorious Suffolk countryside. Timbered ceiling invokes rustic feel in pleasant lounge. Comfy bedrooms with pine and chintz furnishings.

KENDAL – Cumbria – 502 L 21 – pop. 28 030 Great Britain 21 B2

London 270 m – Bradford 64 m – Burnley 63 m – Carlisle 49 m – Lancaster 22 m – Leeds 72 m – Middlesbrough 77 m – Newcastle upon Tyne 104 m

Town Hall, Highgate ✆ (01539) 725758

The Heights, ✆ (01539) 723 499 .

Levens Hall and Garden★ AC, S : 4½ m. by A 591, A 590 and A 6. Lake Windermere★★, NW : 8 m. by A 5284 and A 591

Beech House without rest
40 Greenside, by All Hallows Lane ✉ LA9 4LD – ✆ (01539) 720 385 – stay@beechhouse-kendal.co.uk – Fax (01539) 724 082 – closed 24-26 December
6 rm – †£ 50/60 ††£ 80/90
◆ Tasteful and stylish semi-detached Georgian villa. Open-plan lounge; communal breakfasts. Individually decorated rooms are particularly tasteful and comfortable.

One Bridge Street
1 Bridge St ✉ LA9 7DD – ✆ (01539) 738 855 – closed 25-26 December, Sunday dinner and Monday except Bank Holidays
Rest – Menu £ 13/25
◆ Sited within a Georgian building by the River Kent. Modern ground-floor lounge; dining upstairs in two rooms. Menus boast a distinct local accent.

at Sizergh Southwest : 3 m. by A 591 – ✉ Kendal

The Strickland Arms
✉ LA8 8DZ – ✆ (01539) 561 010 – thestricklandarms@hotmail.com – Fax (01539) 561 067 – Closed 25 December
Rest – Carte £ 18/25
◆ A haven for hikers: proper refuelling guaranteed courtesy of huge portions of robust traditional fare offered in the solid surroundings of this heartily rustic hostelry.

at Brigsteer Southwest : 3 ¾ m. by All Hallows Lane – ✉ Kendal

The Wheatsheaf with rm
✉ LA8 8AN – ✆ (015395) 68 254 – wheatsheaf@brigsteer.gb.com – Fax (015395) 68 948
3 rm – †£ 70 ††£ 85 – **Rest** – (booking essential Mondays in winter) Carte £ 16/23
◆ Refurbished 18C pub with a light, airy, contemporary feel. The seasonal menu is proudly Cumbrian with smoked salmon from Cartmel Valley and shrimps from Morecombe Bay. Classically-styled, pine-furnished bedrooms.

at Crosthwaite West : 5 ¼ m. by All Hallows Lane – ✉ Kendal

The Punch Bowl Inn with rm
✉ LA8 8HR – ✆ (01539) 568 237 – info@the-punchbowl.co.uk – Fax (01539) 568 875
9 rm – †£ 85 ††£ 280 – **Rest** – Carte £ 18/33
◆ Superbly refurbished 17C inn with heart-warming rustic ambience. Dine at bar or in formal room: accomplished seasonal dishes strike the right note. Luxuriously stylish rooms.

KENILWORTH – Warks. – 503 P 26 – pop. 22 218 Great Britain 19 C2

London 102 m – Birmingham 19 m – Coventry 5 m – Leicester 32 m – Warwick 5 m

The Library, 11 Smalley Pl ✆ (01926) 748900

Castle★ AC

Chesford Grange rm,
Chesford Bridge, Southeast : 1 ¾ m. by A 452 on B 4115
✉ CV8 2LD – ✆ (01926) 859 331 – chesfordreservations@qhotels.co.uk – Fax (01926) 855 272
209 rm – †£ 120/150 ††£ 130/160 – **Rest** – (carvery lunch) Menu £ 15/25 – Carte dinner £ 20/38 **s**
◆ Sizeable hotel in 17 acres of private gardens near Warwick Castle. Characterful foyer and staircase of oak. Extensive meeting facilities and leisure club. Spacious bedrooms. Smart dining room exudes comfy air.

ENGLAND

Castle Laurels without rest
22 Castle Rd, North : ½ m. on Stonebridge rd ✉ CV8 1NG – ✆ (01926) 856 179 – reception@castlelaurels.co.uk – Fax (01926) 854 954 – Closed Christmas and Easter
12 rm – 🛉£ 45/70 🛉🛉£ 75/85
◆ Characterful Victorian house adjacent to Kenilworth Castle. Semi-panelled entrance, stained glass windows, original tiled floor. Homely sitting room and ample sized rooms.

Victoria Lodge without rest
180 Warwick Rd ✉ CV8 1HU – ✆ (01926) 512 020 – info@victorialodgehotel.co.uk – Fax (01926) 858 703 – closed 2 weeks Christmas and New Year
10 rm – 🛉£ 49/59 🛉🛉£ 70/80
◆ Personally run hotel situated close to town centre. Small sitting room with adjacent bar. Simple and homely breakfast room. Immaculately kept, ample sized rooms.

Simply Simpsons
101-103 Warwick Rd ✉ CV8 1HL – ✆ (01926) 864 567 – info@simplysimpsons.co.uk – Fax (01926) 864 510 – closed 25-26 and 31 December, last two weeks August, bank holidays, Sunday and Monday
Rest – Menu £ 18 (lunch) – Carte £ 26/34
◆ Boasts contemporary feel, typified by striking mirrors and artwork. Good value, hearty, robust classically based dishes supplemented by tried-and-tested daily specials.

ENGLAND

Bosquet
97a Warwick Rd ✉ CV8 1HP – ✆ (01926) 852 463 – rest.bosquet@aol.com – Fax (01926) 852 463 – closed 3 weeks July-August, 1 week Christmas,
Rest – French (dinner only) (lunch by arrangement) Menu £ 30 – Carte approx. £ 38
◆ Well-established French restaurant near centre of town. Contemporary interior with wooden floor and well-spaced tables accommodating stylish leather chairs.

Your opinions are important to us:
please write and let us know about your discoveries and experiences – good and bad!

KENTON – Exeter – **503** J 31 – **see Exeter**

KERNE BRIDGE – Herefordshire – **503** M 28 – **see Ross-on-Wye**

KESWICK – Cumbria – **503** K 20 – **pop. 4 984** *Great Britain* 21 **A2**

London 294 m – Carlisle 31 m – Kendal 30 m
Moot Hall, Market Sq. ✆ (017687) 72645, seatollertic@lake-district .gov.uk - at Seatoller, Seatoller Barn, Borrowdale ✆ (017687) 77294
Threlkeld Hall, ✆ (017687) 79 324 .
Derwentwater★ X – Thirlmere (Castlerigg Stone Circle★), E : 1 ½ m. X A

Plan opposite

Underscar Manor ← Derwent Water and Fells,
Applethwaite, North : 1 ¾ m. by A 591 on Underscar rd ✉ CA12 4PH – ✆ (017687) 75 000 – reception@underscarmanor.co.uk – Fax (017687) 74 904 – closed 2-4 January
11 rm (dinner included) – 🛉£ 125 🛉🛉£ 275
Rest *The Restaurant* – see restaurant listing
◆ Blissfully located Victorian Italianate manor with commanding views of Derwent Water and Fells. Two comfortable sitting rooms. Modern leisure centre. Large, well kept rooms.

KESWICK

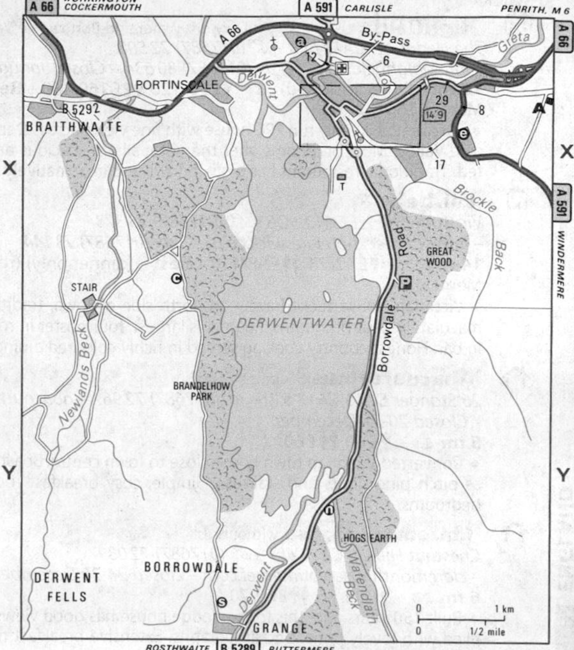

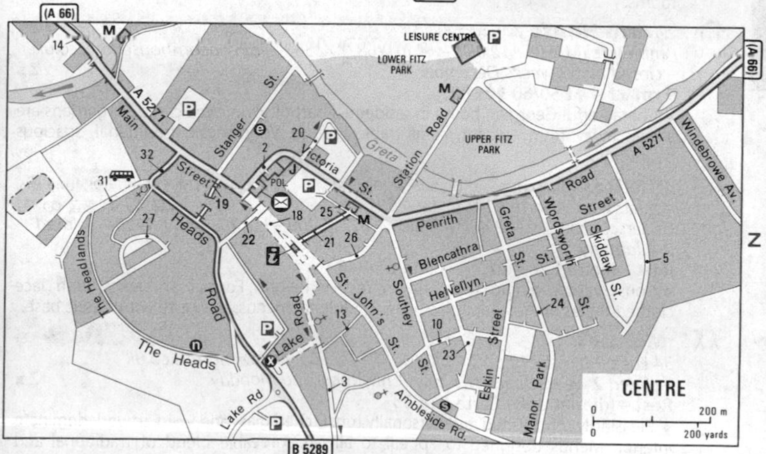

Dale Head Hall Lakeside
Lake Thirlmere,

Thirlmere, Southeast : 5 ¾ m. on A 591 ✉ *CA12 4TN*
– ✆ *(017687) 72478 – onthelakeside@daleheadhall.co.uk – Closed January*
12 rm (dinner included) – 🛉£ 130 🛉🛉£ 280/320 – **Rest** – (booking essential for non-residents) Menu £ 20/40 **s**

◆ Wonderfully set 18C house on Lake Thirlmere. The family run friendliness lends a rich country house ambience. Log fired lounges, smart rooms. Daily changing dinner menu shows a careful touch; choose lake views or a rustic 16C dining room.

Highfield ≤ Derwent Water and Borrowdale Valley, rest,
The Heads ✉ CA12 5ER – ☎ (017687) 72 508
– info@highfield.co.uk – Fax (017687) 80 634 – Closed January Z **n**
18 rm (dinner included) – £ 70/120 £ 160/180 – **Rest** – (dinner only)
Menu £ 25/35
◆ Substantial, keenly run 19C house with fine views across Derwent Water to Borrowdale Valley. Most bedrooms offer the vista; all are spacious and individually decorated. Traditional restaurant has big windows and imaginatively created dishes.

Lairbeck
Vicarage Hill ✉ CA12 5QB – ☎ (017687) 73 373
– info@lairbeckhotel-keswick.co.uk – Fax (017687) 73 144 X **a**
14 rm – £ 42/73 £ 98/110 – **Rest** – (dinner only) (residents only)
Menu £ 20
◆ Victorian house tucked away on north side of town, traditional in style, with immaculately-kept bedrooms. Room 4 is largest; four poster in room 7. Warm ambience in bar. Honest country cooking served in richly coloured dining room.

Abacourt House without rest
26 Stanger St ✉ CA12 5JU – ☎ (017687) 72 967 – abacourt@btinternet.com
– Closed 20-27 December Z **e**
5 rm – £ 60 £ 60
◆ Converted Victorian town house close to town centre. Boasts original features such as pitch pine doors and staircase. Simple, cosy breakfast room. Immaculately kept bedrooms.

ENGLAND

Claremont House without rest ≤
Chestnut Hill ✉ CA12 4LT – ☎ (017687) 72 089
– claremonthouse@btinternet.com – closed 24-26 December X **e**
6 rm – £ 35/70 £ 60/70
◆ Built 150 years ago, this former lodge house has good views over Keswick. Lounge filled with lovely prints and lithographs. Extensive breakfast menu. Spotless, homely rooms.

Acorn House without rest
Ambleside Rd ✉ CA12 4DL – ☎ (017687) 72 553 – info@acornhousehotel.co.uk
– closed first 3 weeks December Z **s**
9 rm – £ 50/60 £ 80
◆ Characterful Georgian house in residential part of town. Well cared for gardens are a step away from elegant, comfortable lounge. Very bright, traditional, spacious bedrooms.

The Restaurant – at Underscar Manor H. ≤ Derwent Water and Fells,
Applethwaite, North : 1 ¾ m. by A 591 on
Underscar rd ✉ CA12 4PH – ☎ (017687) 75 000 – Fax (017687) 74 904 – closed 2-4 January
Rest – Menu £ 28 (lunch) – Carte £ 39/48
◆ Conservatory dining room of impressive height. Formal ambience with lace clothed tables and elegant glassware. Traditional menus: à la carte with classic base.

Morrel's
34 Lake Rd ✉ CA12 5AQ – ☎ (017687) 72 666 – info@morrels.co.uk
– closed 2 weeks January, 4 days Christmas, and Monday Z **x**
Rest – (dinner only) Carte £ 18/33
◆ Pleasingly refurbished and personally run. Etched glass and vivid artwork dominate interior. Menus designed to appeal to all: an agreeable blend of traditional and modern.

at Threlkeld East : 4 m. by A 66 - X – ✉ Keswick

Scales Farm without rest
Northeast : 1 ½ m. off A 66 on Scales rd ✉ CA12 4SY – ☎ (017687) 79 660
– scales@scalesfarm.com – Fax (017687) 79 510 – closed 1 week February and Christmas
6 rm – £ 35 £ 70
◆ Converted 17C farmhouse with much rustic charm. It boasts open stove, exposed beams and solid interior walls. Comfortable, homely sitting room. Spacious cottage style rooms.

at Borrowdale South : on B 5289 – ✉ Keswick

The Lodore Falls (heated)
✉ CA12 5UX AC rest, VISA AE
– ✆ (017687) 77285 – lodorefalls@lakedistricthotels.net – Fax (017687) 77343 Y **n**
64 rm (dinner included) – †£ 107/119 ††£ 252 – 5 suites
– **Rest** – Menu £ 17/34
◆ Swiss-styled exterior, in wonderfully commanding position overlooking Derwent Water; Lodore waterfalls in grounds. Leisure oriented. Choose west facing rooms overlooking lake. Llinen-clad dining room with classic Lakeland views.

at Rosthwaite South : 6 m. on B 5289 - Y – ✉ Keswick

Hazel Bank Country House P VISA
✉ *CA12 5XB – ✆ (017687) 77248 – enquiries@hazelbankhotel.co.uk*
– Fax (017687) 77373 – closed Christmas and restricted opening in winter
8 rm (dinner included) – †£ 85/95 ††£ 170/190 – **Rest** – (dinner only) (booking essential for non-residents) (set menu only) Menu £ 33
◆ Panoramic fell views accentuate the isolated appeal of this very personally run 19C country house. Original fittings; stained glass windows. Rooms have stamp of individuality. Accomplished cuisine with daily changing set menus.

at Portinscale West : 1 ½ m. by A 66 – ✉ Keswick

Swinside Lodge Catbells and Causey Pike, P
Newlands, South : 1 ½ m. on Grange Rd ✉ CA12 5UE VISA
– ✆ (017687) 72948 – info@swinsidelodge-hotel.co.uk – Fax (017687) 73312
– closed 24-26 December X **c**
7 rm (dinner included) – †£ 128 ††£ 196 – **Rest** – (dinner only) (booking essential for non-residents) (set menu only) Menu £ 35 **s**
◆ Personally run 19C country house in beguilingly tranquil position close to extensive walks with mountain views. Two comfortable lounges; well furnished, traditional rooms. Intimate Victorian style dining room with large antique dresser.

at Braithwaite West : 2 m. by A 66 - X – ✉ Keswick

Cottage in the Wood P VISA
Whinlatter Forest, Northwest : 1 ¾ m. on B 5292 ✉ CA12 5TW
– ✆ (017687) 78409 – relax@thecottageinthewood.co.uk – Fax (017687) 78064
– Closed January and February
9 rm – †£ 70/75 ††£ 85/90 – **Rest** – (Closed Sunday and Monday) (dinner only) (set menu only) Menu £ 25 **s**
◆ Dramatically set 17C former coaching inn high up in large pine forest. Comfy, beamed lounge with fire. Smart, updated bedrooms look out over Skiddaw or the forest. Proudly local ingredients sourced for modern British cooking; mountain views.

ENGLAND

KETTERING – Northants. – **504** R 26 – **pop. 51 063** 17 **C3**
London 88 m – Birmingham 54 m – Leicester 16 m – Northampton 24 m
The Coach House, Sheep St ✆ (01536) 534381

at Rushton Northwest : 3 ½ m. by A 14 and Rushton Rd – ✉ Kettering

Rushton Hall P VISA AE
✉ *NN14 1RR – ✆ (01536) 713001 – enquiries@rushtonhall.com*
– Fax (01536) 713010
40 rm – †£ 140 ††£ 140/280 – 4 suites – **Rest** – Menu £ 20 (lunch) **s** – Carte dinner £ 35/50 **s**
◆ Hugely imposing 15C house in quadrangle boasting delightful grounds, baronial style sitting room of incredible proportions and immaculate bedrooms appointed most luxuriously. Spacious, formal dining room serving classical, wide-ranging menus.

KETTLESING – N. Yorks. – **502** P 21 – see Harrogate

KETTLEWELL – N. Yorks. – 502 N 21 — 22 A2

London 246 m – Darlington 42 m – Harrogate 30 m – Lancaster 42 m

Littlebeck without rest
The Green, take turning at the Old Smithy shop by the bridge ✉ BD23 5RD – ✆ (01756) 760 378 – stay@little-beck.co.uk – closed January
3 rm – £ 45/50 £ 68
◆ Characterful stone house from 13C with Georgian façade overlooking village maypole. Cosy lounge; extensive dales breakfast served. Attractively decorated bedrooms.

KEYSTON – Cambs. – 504 S 26 – ✉ Huntingdon — 14 A2

London 75 m – Cambridge 29 m – Northampton 24 m

The Pheasant
Village Loop Road ✉ PE28 0RE – ✆ (01832) 710 241 – thepheasant@cyberware.co.uk – Closed Sunday dinner October-April
Rest – (booking essential) Menu £ 16 – Carte £ 20/33
◆ Attractive thatched country inn with beams and open fires serving good monthly menu of eclectic dishes. Wood floors and country bric-a-brac complete the rustic feel.

Look out for red symbols, indicating particularly pleasant establishments.

KIBWORTH BEAUCHAMP – Leics. – 504 QR 26 – pop. 4 788 – ✉ Leicester — 16 B2

London 85 m – Birmingham 49 m – Leicester 6 m – Northampton 17 m

Firenze
9 Station St ✉ LE8 0LN – ✆ (0116) 279 6260 – info@firenze.co.uk – Fax (0116) 279 3646 – closed 10 days Christmas-New Year, Sunday and Bank Holidays
Rest – Italian (booking essential) Menu £ 12 (lunch) – Carte £ 29/52
◆ Modern Italian restaurant in village centre. Beamed interior; contemporary décor. Highback wood-framed chairs. Expect king prawns with pancetta or quail with sage and garlic.

KIBWORTH HARCOURT Leics. – 504 R 26 — 16 B2

Boboli
88 Main St ✉ LE8 0NQ – ✆ (0116) 279 3303 – info@firenze.co.uk – Fax (0116) 279 3646 – closed Christmas and New Year, Sunday and Bank Holidays
Rest – Italian Carte £ 23/30
◆ Stylish Italian restaurant named after gardens in Florence. Fresh, simple and seasonally-changing cooking with bold flavours. Affordable wines and cheery, prompt service.

KIDDERMINSTER – Worcs. – 503 N 26 – pop. 55 348 — 18 B2

London 139 m – Birmingham 17 m – Shrewsbury 34 m – Worcester 15 m

at Chaddesley Corbett Southeast : 4½ m. by A 448 – ✉ Kidderminster

Brockencote Hall
on A 448 ✉ DY10 4PY – ✆ (01562) 777 876 – info@brockencotehall.com – Fax (01562) 777 872 – closed 1-17 January
17 rm – £ 96/120 £ 116/190
Rest ***The Restaurant*** – see restaurant listing
◆ Reminiscent of a French château, a 19C mansion in extensive parkland. Pine and maple library, chintz furnished conservatory. Good-sized rooms, all unique in style and décor.

XXX **The Restaurant** – at Brockencote Hall

on A 448 ✉ DY10 4PY – ✆ (01562) 777876 – Fax (01562) 777872 – closed 1-17 January and Saturday lunch

Rest – French Menu £ 19/31 **s** – Carte £ 31/52 **s**

◆ Two adjacent dining rooms: impressive high ceilings, fine oak panelled walls, a formal but discreet and relaxed atmosphere and fine modern dishes from local produce.

KIDMORE END – **Oxon.** – **see Reading**

KIMBOLTON – **Herefordshire** – **503** L 27 – **see Leominster**

KINGHAM – **Oxon.** – **503** P 28 10 **A1**

London 81 m – Gloucester 32 m – Oxford 25 m

Mill House

✉ OX7 6UH – ✆ (01608) 658 188 – stay@millhousehotel.co.uk – Fax (01608) 658492

23 rm – †£ 90 ††£ 130 – **Rest** – Menu £ 18/32 – Carte dinner approx. £ 32

◆ Privately run house in 10 acres of lawned gardens with brook flowing through grounds. Spacious lounge with comfortable armchairs and books. Country house style bedrooms. Modern décor suffuses restaurant.

The Tollgate Inn with rm

Church St ✉ OX7 6YA – ✆ (01608) 658389 – info@thetollgate.com – Closed first week January, Sunday dinner and Monday

9 rm – †£ 60 ††£ 80 – **Rest** – Menu £ 16 – Carte £ 20/30

◆ 17C Grade II listed Cotswold stone former farmhouse. Sympathetically modernised interior. Global influences on restaurant style dishes. Pleasant rooms in inn or annex.

KING'S LYNN – **Norfolk** – **502** V 25 – **pop. 41 281** *Great Britain* 14 **B1**

London 103 m – Cambridge 45 m – Leicester 75 m – Norwich 44 m

The Custom House, Purfleet Quay ✆ (01553) 763044, kings-lynn.tic@west-norfolk.gov.uk

Eagles Tilney All Saints School Rd, ✆ (01553) 827 147 .

Houghton Hall★★ **AC**, NE : 14½ m. by A 148 – Four Fenland Churches★ (Terrington St Clement, Walpole St Peter, West Walton, Walsoken) SW : by A 47

XX **Maggie's**

11 Saturday Market Place ✉ PE30 5DQ – ✆ (01553) 771 483 – nickandersonchef@hotmail.com – Fax (01553) 771 483 – closed 25-30 December, Sunday and Monday

Rest – Menu £ 13/23

◆ Centrally located, in 17C house with vivid sitting room ceiling, exposed beams and bold artwork. Internationally influenced modern cooking with a distinctive seasonal base.

at Grimston East : 6 ¼ m. by A 148 – ✉ **King's Lynn**

Congham Hall

Lynn Rd ✉ PE32 1AH – ✆ (01485) 600 250 – info@conghamhallhotel.co.uk – Fax (01485) 601 191

14 rm – †£ 90/165 ††£ 170/210 – 2 suites

Rest ***Orangery*** – Menu £ 21/45 – Carte £ 21/32

◆ Immaculately peaceful cream-washed part Georgian house with herb and salad garden. Classic country house style lounges with many antiques. Elegant bedrooms of varying sizes. Pleasant, classic restaurant using herb garden produce.

KINGS MILLS – **C.I.** – **see Channel Islands**

KINGSBRIDGE – Devon – 503 I 33 – pop. 5 521 2 C3

London 236 m – Exeter 36 m – Plymouth 24 m – Torquay 21 m
The Quay ✆ (01548) 853195
Thurlestone, ✆ (01548) 560 405 .
Town★ – Boat Trip to Salcombe★★ AC
Prawle Point (≤ ★★★) SE : 10 m. around coast by A 379

at Goveton Northeast : 2½ m. by A 381 – ✉ Kingsbridge

Buckland-Tout-Saints
Goveton, Northeast : 2½ m. by A 381 ✉ TQ7 2DS – ✆ (01548) 853 055 – buckland@tout-saints.co.uk – Fax (01548) 856 261
14 rm – †£ 99/135 ††£ 145/165 – 2 suites – **Rest** – Menu £ 35 (dinner) – Carte £ 23/35
◆ Immaculate, impressive Queen Anne mansion with neat lawned gardens in rural location. Wood panelled lounge; all other areas full of antiques. Well-furnished bedrooms. Accomplished cooking in beautiful wood-panelled country house restaurant.

KINGSDON – Somerset – 503 L 30 – see Somerton

KINGSKERSWELL – Devon – 503 J 32 – ✉ Torquay 2 C2

London 199 m – Exeter 18 m – Torquay 4 m

Bickley Mill with rm
Stoneycombe, West : 2 m. ✉ TQ12 5LN – ✆ (01803) 873 201 – info@bickleymill.co.uk – Fax (01803) 875 129 – Closed 25 and 27-28 December
9 rm – †£ 55 ††£ 70 – **Rest** – Menu £ 10 – Carte £ 18/26
◆ Converted flour mill dating back to 13C boasts pleasant garden and decked terrace. Modernised interior retains rustic stone walls and exposed beams. Modern British cooking. Contemporary bedrooms.

KINGSTON BAGPUIZE – Oxon. – 503 P 28 – see Oxford

KINGSTON BLOUNT – Oxon. – see Chinnor

KINGSTON-UPON-HULL – Kingston-upon-Hull – 502 S 22 – pop. 301 416 *Great Britain* 23 D2

London 183 m – Leeds 61 m – Nottingham 94 m – Sheffield 68 m
Access Humber Bridge (toll)
Humberside Airport : ✆ (01652) 688456, S : 19 m. by A 63
to The Netherlands (Rotterdam) (P & O North Sea Ferries) daily (11 h) – to Belgium (Zeebrugge) (P & O North Sea Ferries) 3-4 weekly (13 h 45 mn)
1 Paragon St ✆ (01482) 223559King George Dock, Hedon Rd ✆ (01482) 702118
Springhead Park Willerby Rd, ✆ (01482) 656 309 ;
Sutton Park Salthouse Rd, ✆ (01482) 374 242 .
Burton Constable★ AC, NE : 9 m. by A 165 and B 1238 Z

Plan opposite

Village rest,
Henry Boot Way, Priory Park East, Southwest : 2 m. by A 63 ✉ HU4 7DY – ✆ (01482) 642 422 – village.hull@village-hotels.com – Fax (0870) 421 57 43 Z a
116 rm – †£ 149 ††£ 149
Rest *Salingers* – (Bar lunch Monday-Saturday) Carte £ 15/30 **s**
◆ Five minutes' drive from the Humber Bridge. Spacious, modern interior. Sports themed pub for snacks. Impressive state-of-the-art gym and pool area. Airy, functional rooms. Traditional British cooking in boothed restaurant.

KINGSTON-UPON-HULL

Street	Grid	No.
Bond St	X	3
Carr Lane	Y	
Commercial Rd	Y	8
County Rd North	Z	9
Dock Office Row	X	10
Dock St	X	12
Fairfax Ave	Z	13
Ferensway	XY	14
George St	X	
Grimston St	X	15
Humber Dock St	Y	16
Jameson St	Y	17
Jarratt St	X	18
Kingston Retail Park	Y	
King Edward St	Y	19
Lowgate	Y	23
Market Pl.	Y	24
Maybury Rd	Z	25
Paragon St	Y	29
Princes Quay Shopping Centre	Y	
Prince's Ave	Z	31
Prince's Dock St	Y	32
Prospect Shopping Centre	X	
Prospect St	X	
Queen St	Y	35
Queen's Dock Ave	X	36
Queen's Rd	Z	33
Reform St	X	37
Sculcoates Bridge	X	42
Southcoates Ave	Z	43
Southcoates Lane	Z	44
Waterhouse Lane	Y	47
Whitefriargate	Y	49
Wilberforce Drive	X	50
Worship St	X	52

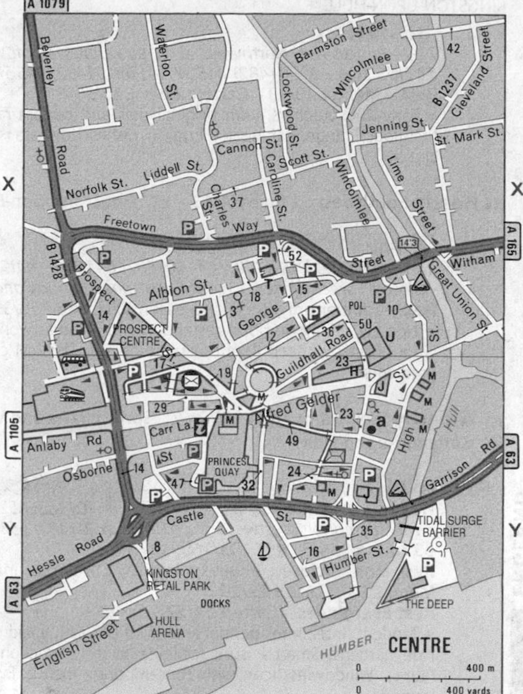

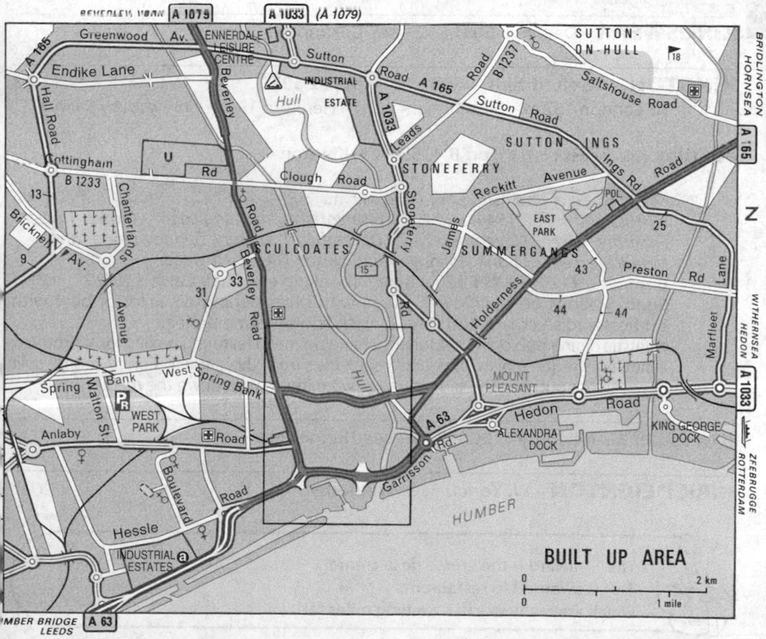

BUILT UP AREA

0 2 km
0 1 mile

X **Boars Nest** VISA MC AE

22-24 Princes Ave, Northwest : 1 m. by Ferensway off West Spring Bank Rd
✉ *HU5 3QA – ☎ (01482) 445 577 – Fax (01482) 445 577*
Rest – Menu £ 10/20 – Carte dinner £ 20/36
◆ Early 20C butchers, with original tiles and carcass rails in situ. Comfy, cluttered first-floor lounge. Eat hearty English dishes downstairs at mismatched tables and chairs.

at Hessle Southwest : 2 m. by A 63 – ✉ Kingston-upon-Hull

XX **Artisan** VISA MC AE ①

22 The Weir ✉ HU13 0RU – ☎ (01482) 644 906 – eat@artisanrestaurant.com – closed 1 week Easter, 1 week Christmas, Monday and Tuesday
Rest – (dinner only) (booking essential) Carte £ 26/35
◆ Homely, neighbourhood restaurant with vivid artwork on the walls. Formal tableware offset by cheerful, enthusiastic owner. Classical cooking utilising regional ingredients.

at Willerby West : 5 m. by A 1079 - Z - Spring Bank and Willerby Rd – ✉ Kingston-upon-Hull

Willerby Manor P VISA MC AE ①

Well Lane (via Main St) ✉ HU10 6ER – ☎ (01482) 652 616 – willerbymanor@bestwestern.co.uk – Fax (01482) 653 901 – closed 25 December
63 rm – †£ 55/85 ††£ 103/168, ☐ £ 11.25
Rest *Icon* – (closed 2 weeks August, Christmas and New Year) (dinner only) Menu £ 24 – Carte £ 22/26
Rest *Everglades* – Carte £ 14/22
◆ Modern hotel in residential area, with pleasantly laid-out landscaped grounds and rose gardens. Smart leisure facilities. Slightly functional bedrooms with colourful fabrics. Windowless Icon with contemporary menus. Everglades brasserie in hotel's lounge.

ENGLAND

KINGSWEAR – **Devon** – **503** J 32 – **see Dartmouth**

KINGTON – **Herefordshire** – **503** K 27 – **pop. 2 597** 18 **A3**

London 152 m – Birmingham 61 m – Hereford 19 m – Shrewsbury 54 m

at Titley Northeast : 3½ m. on B 4355 – ✉ Kington

The Stagg Inn (Steve Reynolds) with rm P VISA MC

✿ ✉ *HR5 3RL – ☎ (01544) 230 221 – reservations@thestagg.co.uk – Closed 1 week February, 1 week November, 25-26 December, 1 January, Sunday dinner and Monday except at Bank Holidays when closed Tuesday instead.*
6 rm ☐ – †£ 60/70 ††£ 120 – **Rest** – (booking essential) Carte £ 20/29
Spec. Scallops on cauliflower, purée with black pepper oil. Fillet of beef with set horseradish cream and potato rösti. Trio of crème brûlée.
◆ Rustic dining pub offers seasonally-changing menu featuring quality local produce, including the inn's own pigs and vegetables from the garden. Comfy rooms split between the pub and the old vicarage, two minutes walk down the road.

KINTBURY – **Newbury** – **503** P 29 – **see Hungerford**

KIRK DEIGHTON – **W. Yorks.** – **see Wetherby**

The ✿ award is the crème de la crème.
This is awarded to restaurants
which are really worth travelling miles for!

KIRKBY LONSDALE – Cumbria – 502 M 21 – pop. 2 076 – ✉ Carnforth (Lancs.) 21 B3

London 259 m – Carlisle 62 m – Kendal 13 m – Lancaster 17 m – Leeds 58 m
24 Main St ✆ (015242) 71437
Scaleber Lane Barbon, ✆ (015242) 76 365 ;
Casterton Sedbergh Rd, ✆ (015242) 71 592.

at Cowan Bridge Southeast : 2 m. on A 65 – ✉ Kirkby Lonsdale 20 B1

Hipping Hall with rm

Southeast : ½ m. on A 65 ✉ LA6 2JJ – ✆ (015242) 71 187 – info@hippinghall.com – Fax (015242) 72 452 – Closed 3 weeks January

9 rm – †£ 150 ††£ 240 – **Rest** – (Closed Saturday lunch) Menu £ 28/45

◆ Charming part 15/16C house in mature grounds with stream and flagged terrace. Modern, inventive cooking does justice to characterful hall dining room. Distinctly modish rooms.

at Nether Burrow South : 2 m. by A 65 and on a 683 – ✉ Kirkby Lonsdale

The Highwayman

✉ LA6 2RJ – ✆ (01524) 826 888 – enquiries@highwaymaninn.co.uk – Closed 25 December

Rest – Carte £ 17/24

◆ Spacious, refurbished inn with open fires, friendly service and stone terrace. Owners passionate about local, traceable produce, serving hearty, wholesome fayre.

at Tunstall (Lancs.)South : 3 ½ m. by A 65 on A 683 – ✉ Kirkby Lonsdale

The Lunesdale Arms

✉ LA6 2QN – ✆ (01524) 274 203 – info@thelunesdale.co.uk – Fax (01524) 274 229 – Closed 25-26 December

Rest – (closed Monday except Bank Holidays) Carte £ 19/25

◆ Stone-built 18C pub; now a modern dining establishment.with bright, airy interior that includes a vast fireplace and squashy sofas. Locally sourced dishes to fore.

KIRKBY STEPHEN – Cumbria – 502 M 20 – pop. 2 209 21 B2

London 296 m – Carlisle 46 m – Darlington 37 m – Kendal 28 m

Augill Castle

Northeast : 4½ m. by A 685 ✉ CA17 4DE – ✆ (01768) 341 937 – enquiries@augillcastle.co.uk – Fax (01768) 342 287 – Closed 24-26 December

12 rm – †£ 100 ††£ 140/160 – **Rest** – (Closed Sunday and Tuesday) (dinner only) (residents only, communal dining, set menu only) Menu £ 35 **s**

◆ Carefully restored Victorian folly in neo-Gothic style with extensive gardens; fine antiques and curios abound. Comfy music room and library. Individually decorated rooms. Expansive dining room with ornate ceiling and Spode tableware.

KIRKBYMOORSIDE – N. Yorks. – 502 R 21 – pop. 2 650 23 C1

London 244 m – Leeds 61 m – Scarborough 26 m – York 33 m
Manor Vale, ✆ (01751) 431 525 .

Brickfields Farm without rest

Kirby Mills, East : ¾ m. by A 170 on Kirby Mills Industrial Estate rd ✉ YO62 6NS – ✆ (01751) 433 074 – janet@brickfieldsfarm.co.uk

6 rm – †£ 50 ††£ 80/100

◆ Personally run 1850s red-brick former farmhouse set down private driveway. Rooms are very comfortably appointed in rustic style with thoughtful extra touches.

The Cornmill

Kirby Mills, East : ½ m. by A 170 ✉ YO62 6NP – ✆ (01751) 432 000 – cornmill@kirbymills.demon.co.uk – Fax (01751) 432 300

5 rm – †£ 60/70 ††£ 100/105 – **Rest** – (by arrangement) Menu £ 20 **s**

◆ Converted 18C cornmill, its millrace still visible through the glass floor of a beamed and flagged dining room. Individually decorated bedrooms in the Victorian farmhouse.

at Fadmoor Northwest : 2 ¼ m. – ✉ Kirkbymoorside

The Plough Inn
Main Street ✉ YO62 7HY – ✆ (01751) 431 515 – Fax (01751) 432 492 – Closed 25-26 December and 1 January
Rest – Menu £ 13 – Carte £ 18/28
◆ Pleasant rural pub with original tiled floor, rustic walls, scrubbed tables and real ales. Blackboard menu changes daily: traditional cooking with a modern twist.

KIRKHAM – Lancs. – **502** L 22 – pop. 10 372 – ✉ Preston 20 **A2**

London 240 m – Blackpool 9 m – Preston 7 m

at Wrea Green Southwest : 3 m. on B 5259 – ✉ Kirkham

The Villa
Moss Side Lane, Southwest : ½ m. on B 5259 ✉ PR4 2PE – ✆ (01772) 684 347 – info@the-villahotel.co.uk – Fax (01772) 687 647
25 rm – single £ 80 double £ 95 – **Rest** – Menu £ 24 – Carte £ 26/38
◆ Imposing red brick manor house with sympathetic extensions. Original house with bar and lounge, open fire, objets d'art. Purpose-built block has smart, well-furnished rooms. Dining room made up of many snugs, small rooms and conservatory; themed style.

ENGLAND

The red symbol?
This denotes the very essence of peace
– only the sound of birdsong first thing in the morning …

KIRKWHELPINGTON – Northd. – **501** N/O 18 – ✉ Morpeth *Great Britain* 24 **A2**

London 305 m – Carlisle 46 m – Newcastle upon Tyne 20 m
Wallington House★ AC, E : 3 ½ m. by A 696 and B 6342

Shieldhall
Wallington, Southeast : 2½ m. by A 696 on B 6342 ✉ NE61 4AQ – ✆ (01830) 540 387 – stay@shieldhallguesthouse.co.uk – Fax (01830) 540 490 – closed Christmas and New Year
4 rm – single £ 60 double £ 80 – **Rest** – (by arrangement) Menu £ 25
◆ Converted 18C farm buildings with gardens. Well-furnished lounge/library. Spotless rooms in former stable block: furniture constructed by cabinet-making owner!

KIRTLINGTON – Oxon. – **503** Q 28 10 **B2**

London 70 m – Bicester 11 m – Oxford 16 m

The Dashwood
South Green, Heyford Rd ✉ OX5 3HJ – ✆ (01869) 352 707 – reservations@thedashwood.co.uk – Fax (01869) 351 432 – closed last week December and first week January
12 rm – single £ 85 double £ 110/150 – **Rest** – (closed Sunday dinner to non-residents) Menu £ 15 (lunch) – Carte dinner £ 22/36
◆ Grade II listed 16C building in local soft stone. Lounge with comfy leather armchairs. Bedrooms, boasting super contemporary décor, divided between main building and barn. Exposed stone dining room: impressive menus with modern European slant.

KNAPTON – Norfolk – 504 Y 25 – see North Walsham

KNARESBOROUGH – N. Yorks. – 502 P 21 – pop. 13 380 22 B2

London 217 m – Bradford 21 m – Harrogate 3 m – Leeds 18 m – York 18 m
9 Castle Courtyard, Market Pl ℰ (01423) 866886 (summer only)
Boroughbridge Rd, ℰ (01423) 862 690 .

Dower House

Bond End ✉ HG5 9AL – ℰ (01423) 863 302 – enquiries@bwdowerhouse.co.uk – Fax (01423) 867 665
31 rm – †£ 75/95 ††£ 130/140 – **Rest** – Menu £ 17 (lunch) **s** – Carte dinner £ 25/32 **s**
◆ Part 15C, ivy clad, red brick house near town centre. Stone-floored reception and cosy bar. Small, well-equipped leisure centre. Good-sized, traditional bedrooms. Warmly toned restaurant overlooks the garden.

Newton House without rest

5-7 York Place – ℰ (01423) 863 539 – newtonhouse@btinternet.com – closed 1 week at Christmas
11 rm – †£ 50/85 ††£ 100
◆ Extended mid-18C house boasts homely lounge with soft suites and smart, comfortable, individually decorated bedrooms; those on the first floor and in the annexe are larger.

at Ferrensby Northeast : 3 m. on A 6055

The General Tarleton Inn with rm

Boroughbridge Rd ✉ HG5 0PZ – ℰ (01423) 340 284 – gti@generaltarleton.co.uk – Fax (01423) 340 288
14 rm – †£ 108 ††£ 120
Rest ***The General Tarleton Inn Pub*** – see restaurant listing
Rest – (closed Sunday dinner) (dinner only and Sunday lunch) Menu £ 33 – Carte £ 22/33
◆ Attractive stone building, an extension to original 18C coaching inn; surrounded by North Yorkshire countryside. Comfy rooms and dining room full of rustic style and ambience.

The General Tarleton Inn

Boroughbridge Rd ✉ HG5 0PZ – ℰ (01423) 340 284 – gti@generaltarleton.co.uk – Fax (01423) 340 288
Rest – Menu £ 23/33 – Carte £ 20/32
◆ Characterful, well run 18C coaching inn with stone décor, open fires and various snugs and seating areas. Robust British dishes with northern influence: excellent value.

at Coneythorpe Northeast : 4 3/4 m. by A 59

The Tiger Inn

✉ HG5 0RY – ℰ (01423) 863 632 – ifgill@btinternet.com – closed 25 December, Sunday dinner
Rest – Carte £ 21/26
◆ Refurbished pub; traditional front rooms overlook green; rear dining rooms are more formal. Well-priced menus offer robust and hearty British classics with a modern twist.

KNIPTON – Leics. 17 C2

London 125 m – Leicester 28 m – Melton Mowbray 10 m

Manners Arms

Croxton Rd ✉ NG32 1RH – ℰ (01476) 879 222 – info@mannersarms.com – Fax (01476) 879 228 – Closed 24-26 December
10 rm – †£ 55/90 ††£ 120 – **Rest** – Menu £ 18 (lunch) – Carte dinner £ 27/38
◆ Refurbished former hunting lodge originally built for sixth Duke of Rutland; a relaxing feel pervades. Locals gather round bar's roaring fire. Individually styled bedrooms. Spacious dining room offers hearty rustic cooking.

ENGLAND

KNOWLE GREEN – Lancs. – see Longridge

KNOWSLEY BUSINESS PARK – Mersey. – see Liverpool

KNOWSTONE – Devon – see South Molton

KNUTSFORD – Ches. – 502 M 24 – pop. 12 656 20 B3

London 187 m – Chester 25 m – Liverpool 33 m – Manchester 18 m – Stoke-on-Trent 30 m

Council Offices, Toft Rd (0871) 7162640

Cottons

Manchester Rd, Northwest : 1½ m. on A 50 ✉ WA16 0SU – (01565) 650 333 – cottons@shirehotels.com – Fax (01565) 755 351

109 rm – £ 155 £ 175

Rest *Magnolia* – (Closed lunch Sunday and Bank Holiday Mondays) (dinner only) Menu £ 32 **s** – Carte £ 29/35 **s**

◆ Large purpose-built hotel aimed at business travellers. Two good-sized country house style lounges and clubby bar. Smart leisure complex; comfortable, up-to-date bedrooms. French New Orleans themed dining room.

Longview

55 Manchester Rd, on A 50 ✉ WA16 0LX – (01565) 632 119 – enquiries@longviewhotel.com – Fax (01565) 652 402 – closed Christmas and New Year

29 rm – £ 62/97 £ 114/118 – 3 suites – **Rest** – (closed Sunday) (dinner only) Carte £ 17/29 **s**

◆ Bay-windowed Victorian house, family run. Open log fire in reception. At foot of stone staircase lies cellar bar with soft lighting and low ceiling. Pleasant, comfy bedrooms. Mahogany furniture and chandeliers make for relaxed dining.

Belle Epoque Brasserie with rm

60 King St ✉ WA16 6DT – (01565) 633 060 – info@thebelleepoque.com – Fax (01565) 634 150

6 rm – £ 95 £ 95 – **Rest** – (closed Sunday dinner) (dinner only and Sunday lunch) Carte £ 26/34

◆ Bustling brasserie with Art Nouveau décor. Traditional and modern dishes with international touches using local produce. Contemporary style bedrooms with modern facilities.

at Mobberley Northeast : 2½ m. by A 537 on B 5085 – ✉ Knutsford

Laburnum Cottage

Knutsford Rd, West : ¾ m. on B 5085 ✉ WA16 7PU – (01565) 872 464 – laburnum.cottage@hotelmail.co.uk – Fax (01565) 872 464

5 rm – £ 46 £ 61 – **Rest** – (by arrangement) Menu £ 17

◆ Red-brick two storey cottage guesthouse with large garden. Homely ambience, with velvet furnishings in lounge and small conservatory to rear. Good sized, individual rooms. Home cooking proudly undertaken.

Hinton

Town Lane, on B 5085 ✉ WA16 7HH – (01565) 873 484 – the.hinton@virgin.net

6 rm – £ 48 £ 62 – **Rest** – (by arrangement) Menu £ 18

◆ Bay-windowed guesthouse with rear garden. Homely lounge where you can play the organ if you wish! Simple, uncluttered bedrooms with floral theme. Local produce used in meals.

at Lach Dennis Southwest : 7 m. by A 50, B 5081 and B 5082 – ✉ Knutsford

Duke of Portland
P VISA AE

Penny's Lane ✉ CW9 7SY – ✆ (01606) 46 264 – info@dukeofportland.com – Fax (01606) 41 724

Rest – Menu £ 5/10 – Carte £ 18/24

◆ Airy, rural pub, its rustic ambience balanced by two lounges with a contemporary feel. Personally run by long-standing restaurant owners. Tasty, well-priced home-made dishes.

KYNASTON – Herefordshire – see Ledbury

LA HAULE – C.I. – **503** L 33 – see Channel Islands

LA PULENTE – C.I. – **503** P 33 – see Channel Islands

If breakfast is included the ☕ symbol appears after the number of rooms.

LA ROCQUE – C.I. – see Channel Islands

LACH DENNIS – Ches. – see Knutsford

LACOCK – Wilts. – **503** N 29 – ✉ Chippenham 4 **C2**

London 109 m – Bath 16 m – Bristol 30 m – Chippenham 3 m

Village★★ - Lacock Abbey★ AC – High St★, St Cyriac★, Fox Talbot Museum of Photography★ AC

At The Sign of the Angel
P VISA AE

6 Church St ✉ SN15 2LB – ✆ (01249) 730 230 – angel@lacock.co.uk – Fax (01249) 730 527 – closed 1 week Christmas

10 rm ☕ – †£ 76/89 ††£ 139/163 – **Rest** – (closed Monday lunch except Bank Holidays) Carte approx. £ 30

◆ Part 14C and 15C former wool merchant's house in charming National Trust village. Relaxed and historic atmosphere. Antique furnished rooms, four in the garden cottage. Tremendously characterful dining room of hotel's vintage: traditional English dishes served.

LADOCK – Cornwall – **503** F 33 1 **B2**

London 268 m – Exeter 84 m – Newquay 12 m – Penzance 37 m – Plymouth 51 m – Truro 13 m

Bissick Old Mill without rest
P VISA AE

off B 3275 ✉ TR2 4PG – ✆ (01726) 882 557 – enquiries@bissickoldmill.plus.com

4 rm ☕ – †£ 53 ††£ 75/85

◆ Charming stone-built 17C former mill. Much historic character with low beamed ceilings and stone fireplaces. Comfortable bedrooms. Breakfast room has much period charm.

LAMBOURN WOODLANDS – Berks. – see Hungerford

LANCASTER – Lancs. – **502** L 21 – **pop. 45 952** *Great Britain* 20 **A1**

London 252 m – Blackpool 26 m – Bradford 62 m – Burnley 44 m – Leeds 71 m – Middlesbrough 97 m – Preston 26 m

29 Castle Hill ✆ (01524) 32878, tourism@lancaster.gov.uk

18 Ashton Hall Ashton-with-Stodday, ✆ (01524) 752 090 ;

9 Lansil Caton Rd, ✆ (01524) 39 269 .

Castle★ AC

ENGLAND

Lancaster House
Green Lane, Ellel, South : 3¼ m. by A 6 ✉ LA1 4GJ – ✆ (01524) 844822 – lancaster@elhmail.co.uk – Fax (01524) 844766
80 rm – ♦£72/120 ♦♦£84/140 – 19 suites
Rest *The Gressingham* – Menu £14 (lunch) **s** – Carte £21/29 **s**
♦ A purpose-built hotel set amidst lawned grounds and adjacent to Lancaster University, whose conference facilities can be used. Comfortable modern decor and country views. Split-level restaurant with views towards Morecambe Bay.

LANCING – W. Sussex – **504** S 31 – **pop. 30 360** 7 **D3**
London 59 m – Brighton 4 m – Southampton 53 m

Sussex Pad
Old Shoreham Rd, East : 1 m. off A 27 ✉ BN15 0RH – ✆ (01273) 454647 – reception@sussexpadhotel.co.uk – Fax (01273) 453010 – closed 24 December-5 January
18 rm – ♦£75 ♦♦£110 – **Rest** – ✆ (01273) 454243 – Carte £25/31
♦ Pubby modern hotel against the formidable backdrop of Lancing College. Co-ordinated rooms named after grand marque Champagnes: their namesakes in plentiful supply in the bar. Dine on seafood from nearby Brighton market.

Good food and accommodation at moderate prices?
Look for the Bib symbols:
red Bib Gourmand for food, blue Bib Hotel for hotels

ENGLAND

LANGAR – Notts. – **502** R 25 16 **B2**
London 132 m – Boston 45 m – Leicester 25 m – Lincoln 37 m – Nottingham 14 m

Langar Hall
✉ NG13 9HG – ✆ (01949) 860559 – info@langarhall.co.uk – Fax (01949) 861045
10 rm – ♦£80/110 ♦♦£150/185 – 1 suite – **Rest** – Menu £20 (lunch) – Carte dinner £28/37
♦ Georgian manor in pastoral setting, next to early English church; overlooks park, medieval fishponds. Antique filled rooms named after people featuring in house's history. Elegant, candle-lit, pillared dining room.

LANGHO – Lancs. – **502** M 22 – see Blackburn

LANGTHWAITE – N. Yorks. – **502** O 20 – see Reeth

LAPWORTH – Warks. – see Hockley Heath

LASTINGHAM – N. Yorks. – **502** R 21 – **pop. 87** – ✉ **York** 23 **C1**
London 244 m – Scarborough 26 m – York 32 m

Lastingham Grange
✉ YO62 6TH – ✆ (01751) 417345 – reservations@lastinghamgrange.com – Fax (01751) 417358 – March-November
11 rm – ♦£60/120 ♦♦£100/210 – **Rest** – (light lunch Monday-Saturday) Menu 38 – Carte £20/25
♦ A delightfully traditional country house atmosphere prevails throughout this extended, pleasantly old-fashioned, 17C farmhouse. Lovely gardens; well-appointed bedrooms. Dining room with rustic fare and rose garden view.

LAVENHAM – Suffolk – 504 W 27 – ✉ Sudbury Great Britain 15 C3

London 66 m – Cambridge 39 m – Colchester 22 m – Ipswich 19 m
Lady St ✆ (01787) 248207
Town★★ – Church of St Peter and St Paul★

Swan
High St ✉ CO10 9QA – ✆ (01787) 247 477 – info@theswanatlavenham.co.uk – Fax (01787) 248 286
47 rm – †£ 60/125 ††£ 120/165 – 2 suites – **Rest** – (bar lunch Monday-Saturday) Menu £ 15/30
◆ Well-restored, part 14C, half timbered house with an engaging historical ambience. Each atmospheric bedroom is individually and stylishly decorated. Dining room has impressive timbered ceiling verging on the cavernous.

Lavenham Priory without rest
Water St ✉ CO10 9RW – ✆ (01787) 247 404 – mail@lavenhampriory.co.uk – Fax (01787) 248 472 – closed Christmas-New Year
6 rm – †£ 75 ††£ 118
◆ A Jacobean oak staircase and Elizabethan wall paintings are just two elements of this captivating part 13C former priory. Bedrooms stylishly furnished with antiques.

The Great House with rm
Market Pl ✉ CO10 9QZ – ✆ (01787) 247 431 – info@greathouse.co.uk – Fax (01787) 248 007 – closed 3 weeks January
3 rm – †£ 80/165 ††£ 96/165, £ 12.50 – 2 suites – **Rest** – French (closed Monday, Sunday dinner and Tuesday lunch) Menu £ 18 (lunch) – Carte £ 21/35
◆ Timbered house with Georgian façade in town centre, dating from 14C. Rustic-style restaurant serves good range of French dishes. Comfortable, antique furnished bedrooms.

The Angel with rm
Market Pl ✉ CO10 9QZ – ✆ (01787) 247 388 – angellav@aol.com – Fax (01787) 248 344 – Closed 25-26 December
8 rm – †£ 60 ††£ 110 – **Rest** – Carte £ 17/30
◆ 15C inn on the market square. Residents' lounge has original early 17C ceiling. Comfortable, well-kept rooms are individually furnished and some are heavily timbered.

Do not confuse X with ✿!
X defines comfort, while stars are awarded for the best cuisine, across all categories of comfort.

LEAFIELD – Oxon. – 503 P 28 – see Witney

LECHLADE – Glos. – 503 O 28 Great Britain 4 D1

London 84 m – Cirencester 13 m – Oxford 25 m
Fairford : Church of St Mary★ (stained glass windows★★), W : 4½ m. on A 417

at Southrop Northwest : 3 m. on Eastleach rd – ✉ Lechlade

The Swan
✉ GL7 3NU – ✆ (01367) 850 205 – grazzer@gmail.com – Fax (01367) 850 479 – Closed 25 December
Rest – Menu £ 17 – Carte £ 19/47
◆ Ivy covered 14C Cotswold inn. Characterful bar, popular with locals. Main dining room boasts low beamed ceiling and log fires. Modern menus with subtle Mediterranean twist.

ENGLAND

LEDBURY – Herefordshire – 503 M 27 – pop. 8 491

London 119 m – Hereford 14 m – Newport 46 m – Worcester 16 m

The Feathers

High St ✉ HR8 1DS – ☏ (01531) 635 266 – mary@feathers-ledbury.co.uk – Fax (01531) 638 955

19 rm – †£ 83 ††£ 195

Rest *Quills* – (dinner only Friday-Saturday and Sunday lunch) Carte £ 27/32

Rest *Fuggles* – Carte £ 27/32

◆ Impressive timbered 16C inn in centre of town. Much character with open fires and antique furnishings. Rooms vary in design, though they all lay claim to a stylish modernity. Intimate dining in Quills restaurant. Fuggles is decorated with hops.

The Malthouse

Church Lane ✉ HR8 1DW – ☏ (01531) 634 443 – closed 1 week January, 1 week Spring, 25 December, 1 January, Sunday and Monday

Rest – (dinner only and Saturday lunch) Carte £ 24/33

◆ Tucked away behind the butter market; rustic décor and attractive courtyard lend a classic country cottage aura. Monthly menu of carefully prepared dishes using local produce.

at Much Marcle Southwest : 4 ¼ m. on A 449 – ✉ Ledbury

Scrumpy House

Westons Cider, The Bounds, West : ¾ m. on Woolhope rd ✉ HR8 2NQ – ☏ (01531) 660 626 – matt@scrumpyhouse.co.uk – closed 27-28 December, 2-4 January and dinner Sunday-Tuesday

Rest – Menu £ 20 – Carte £ 14/32

◆ Charmingly simple eatery boasting rafters and exposed stone: the essence of rusticity. Local ingredients, like Marcle beef or home-made ice-cream, feature prominently.

at Kynaston West : 6 ½ m. by A 449, A 4172, Aylton Rd, on Fownhope Rd – ✉ Ledbury

Hall End

✉ HR8 2PD – ☏ (01531) 670 225 – khjefferson@hallend91.freeserve.co.uk – Fax (01531) 670 747 – Closed Christmas, New Year and Easter

3 rm – †£ 75 ††£ 120 – **Rest** – (booking essential) (communal dining, by arrangement) Menu £ 30

◆ Lovingly restored, personally run, part Georgian home and livery stable in the countryside. Relax in the orangery and, suitably reposed, retire to lavishly furnished bedrooms.

at Trumpet Northwest : 3 ¼ m. on A 438 – ✉ Ledbury

Verzon House

Hereford Rd ✉ HR8 2PZ – ☏ (01531) 670 381 – info@verzonhouse.com – Fax (01531) 670 830

8 rm – †£ 95/150 ††£ 160/180 – **Rest** – (closed Mondays except Bank Holidays and Sunday dinner) Menu £ 19 (lunch) – Carte dinner £ 28/40

◆ Extended Georgian redbrick house with stylish lounge bar, contemporary artwork and comfy seats. Modern bedrooms are named after cider apples; most have view over courtyard. Modern dishes served in restaurant, with decking for al fresco dining.

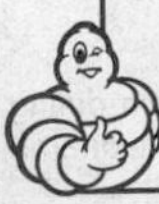

Undecided between two equivalent establishments? Within each category, establishments are classified in our order of preference.

ENGLAND

Cécile Labonne/MICHELIN

LEEDS

County: W. Yorks.
Michelin REGIONAL map: n° **502** P 22
London 204 m – Liverpool 75 m – Manchester 43 m – Newcastle upon Tyne 95 m – Nottingham 74 m

Population: 443 247
Great Britain

22 **B2**

ENGLAND

PRACTICAL INFORMATION

Tourist Information

The Arcade, City Station ✆ (0113) 242 5242, tourinfo@leeds.golf.uk

Airport

Leeds-Bradford Airport: ✆ (0113) 250 9696, NW: 8 m. by A 65 and A 658 BT

Golf Courses

36 Temple Newsam Halton Temple Newsam Rd, ✆ (0113) 264 5624 ;

18 Gotts Park Armley Armley Ridge Rd, ✆ (0113) 234 2019 ;

18 Middleton Park Middleton Ring Rd, Beeston Park, ✆ (0113) 270 0449 ;

27 Moor Allerton Wike Coal Rd, ✆ (0113) 266 1154 ;

18 Howley Hall Morley Scotchman Lane, ✆ (01924) 350 100 ;

9 Roundhay Park Lane, ✆ (0113) 266 2695.

SIGHTS

IN TOWN

City★ - Royal Armouries Museum★★★ GZ - City Art Gallery★ **AC** GY **M**

ON THE OUTSKIRTS

Kirkstall Abbey★ **AC**, NW: 3 m. by A 65 GY – Temple Newsam★ (decorative arts★) **AC**, E: 5 m. by A 64 and A 63 CU **D**

IN THE SURROUNDING AREA

Harewood House★★ (The Gallery★) **AC**, N: 8 m. by A 61 CT – Nostell Priory★, SE: 18 m. by A 61 and A 638 – Yorkshire Sculpture Park★, S: 20 m. by M 1 to junction 38 and 1 m. north off A 637 – Brodsworth Hall★, SE: 25 m. by M 1 to junction 40, A 638 and minor rd (right) in Upton

Thorpe Park H. and Spa
1150 Century Way, Thorpe Park, East : 6 m. by A 64 and A 63 on B 6120 ✉ LS15 8ZB – ✆ (0113) 264 1000 – thorpepark@shirehotels.com – Fax (0113) 264 1010 – closed 24-30 December, 1-4 January
117 rm – †£ 155 ††£ 175/220 – **Rest** – Menu £ 15/17 – Carte approx. £ 30
◆ Smart, modish hotel, close to motorways. Open-fired reception and richly toned central atrium. Fully equipped leisure centre with spa. Immaculate rooms with host of extras. Spacious, modern restaurant.

The Queens
City Sq ✉ LS1 1PJ – ✆ (0113) 243 1323 – thequeen@qhotels.co.uk – Fax (0113) 242 5154 FGZ **g**
187 rm – †£ 175 ††£ 175 – 30 suites – **Rest** – (carvery dinner) Carte £ 30/45
◆ Fully restored to stunning proportions, this 30s Art Deco hotel has many original features in situ, including ballroom and splendid bar. Impressive rooms with period fittings. Basement dining room.

Radisson SAS
No.1 The Light, The Headrow ✉ LS1 8TL – ✆ (0113) 236 6000 – info.leeds@radissonsas.com – Fax (0113) 236 6100 GY **a**
147 rm – †£ 139 ††£ 179, £12.95 – **Rest** – (in lounge) Menu £ 18/20 **s** – Carte £ 29/39 **s**
◆ Grade II listed building with Art Deco facia. Open atrium and individually styled furnishings throughout. State-of-art meeting rooms. Ultra modern, very well appointed rooms.

ENGLAND

Malmaison
1 Swinegate ✉ LS1 4AG – ✆ (0113) 398 1000 – leeds@malmaison.com – Fax (0113) 398 1002 GZ **n**
100 rm – †£ 125/160 ††£ 160/375, £13.95 – 1 suite – **Rest** – Carte £ 28/35
◆ Relaxed, contemporary hotel hides behind imposing Victorian exterior. Vibrantly and individually decorated rooms are stylishly furnished, with modern facilities to the fore. Dine in modern interpretation of a French brasserie.

Quebecs without rest
9 Quebec St ✉ LS1 2HA – ✆ (0113) 244 8989 – resquebecs@theetoncollection.com – Fax (0113) 244 9090 – closed 24-26 December FZ **a**
43 rm – †£ 170/190 ††£ 200, £15.95 – 2 suites
◆ 19C former Liberal Club, now a modish, intimate boutique hotel. Original features include oak staircase and stained glass window depicting Yorkshire cities. Stylish rooms.

42 The Calls
42 The Calls ✉ LS2 7EW – ✆ (0113) 244 0099 – hotel@42thecalls.co.uk – Fax (0113) 234 4100 – closed 3 days Christmas GZ **z**
38 rm – †£ 99/180 ††£ 155/225, £14 – 3 suites
Rest *Brasserie Forty Four* – see restaurant listing
◆ Stylish, contemporary converted quayside grain mill retaining many of the original workings. Rooms facing river have best views; all well equipped with a host of extras.

Hilton Leeds City without rest
Neville St ✉ LS1 4BX – ✆ (0113) 244 2000 – Fax (0113) 243 3577 GZ **r**
186 rm – †£ 65/157 ††£ 95/187, £17.95 – 20 suites
◆ Proximity to station, business and commercial districts make this 1970s tower block a favourite for the corporate traveller. Neat rooms have views of city.

LEEDS AND BRADFORD
0 3 km
0 2 miles
A 650 KEIGHLEY
A 647 HALIFAX
A 6036 HALIFAX
A 64 YORK
SELBY A 63
WETHERBY M 1 (A 1) U (A 1) A 642
A 639 (M 62) M 62
(A 6036) A 58 A A 641 BRIGHOUSE
MANCHESTER M 62
A 638 (A 62)
A 651
A 62 HUDDERSFIELD B
DEWSBURY A 653
A 650 (A 61)
SHEFFIELD M 1
A 61 WAKEFIELD C
T
U
LEEDS
See BRADFORD
SHIPLEY
HORSFORTH
KIRKSTALL ABBEY
SEACROFT
HALTON
PUDSEY
WHITE ROSE CENTRE
MORLEY
ROTHWELL
SHELF
Ring Road
Harrogate Rd
Scott Hall Road
Easterly Road
Wetherby Road
York Road
Otley Rd
Abbey Rd
Leeds Rd
Harrogate Rd.
Canal Rd
Toller Lane
Thornton Road
Great Horton Rd
Manchester Rd
Halifax Road
Leeds Road
Stanningley By-Pass
Stanningley Rd
Dick Lane
Roker Lane
Tong Road
Tong Lane
Tong Street
Bradford Rd
Whitehall Road
Gelderd Road
Elland Road
Dewsbury Rd
Pontefract Rd
Wakefield Rd
Whitehall Road

369

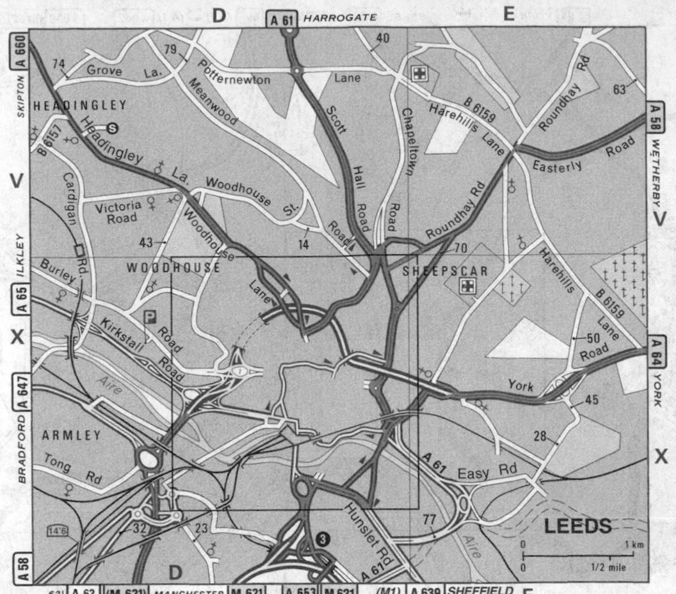

ENGLAND

Street	Grid	No.	Street	Grid	No.	Street	Grid	No.
Bradford Rd	AT	9	Huddersfield Rd	AU	41	Roseville Rd	EVX	7
Cambridge Rd	DV	14	Hyde Park Rd	AV	43	Shaw Lane	DV	7
Cleckheaton Rd	AU	16	Ivy St	EX	45	South Accommodation Rd	EX	7
Commercial Rd	BT	17	Lupton Ave	EX	51	Stainbeck Rd	DV	7
Domestic St	DX	23	New Rd Side	BT	59	Templenewsam Rd	CT	8
East Park Parade	EX	28	Oakwood Lane	EV	63	White Rose Centre	CU	
Gelderd Rd	DX	32	Pudsey Rd	BT	67			
Harrogate Rd	DV	40	Rodley Lane	BV	69			

Haley's

A/C rest, VISA AE

8 Shire Oak Rd, Headingley, Northwest : 2 m. by A 660 ✉ LS6 2DE – ✆ (0113) 278 4446 – info@haleys.co.uk – Fax (0113) 275 3342 – Closed 2 weeks December DV **s**

22 rm – £65/115 £115/135 – **Rest** – Menu £24/25 – Carte dinner £23/34

◆ Named after a prominent stonemason, this part 19C country house in a quiet area is handy for cricket fans. Antique furnished public areas. Individually styled bedrooms. Elegant, relaxed dining room with collection of original local artwork.

Bewley's

rm, A/C rest, VISA AE

City Walk, Sweet St ✉ LS11 9AT – ✆ (0113) 234 2340 – leeds@bewleyshotels.com – Fax (0113) 234 2349 – closed 24-30 December GZ **d**

334 rm – £69 £69, £6.95

Rest *The Brasserie* – (dinner only) Carte £14/27 **s**

◆ This competitively priced hotel boasts a very spacious, stylishly furnished lounge, and is ideal for both tourists or business travellers. Well-kept rooms. Bright, informal brasserie with classically based menus.

Anthony's

A/C VISA

19 Boar Lane ✉ LS1 6EA – ✆ (0113) 245 5922 – reservations@anthonysrestaurant.co.uk – closed 25 December, 1 January, Sunday and Monday GZ **a**

Rest – (booking essential) Menu £24/42

◆ Converted 19C property; ground floor lounge with red leather Chesterfields; minimalist basement dining room offers innovative menus with some intriguing combinations.

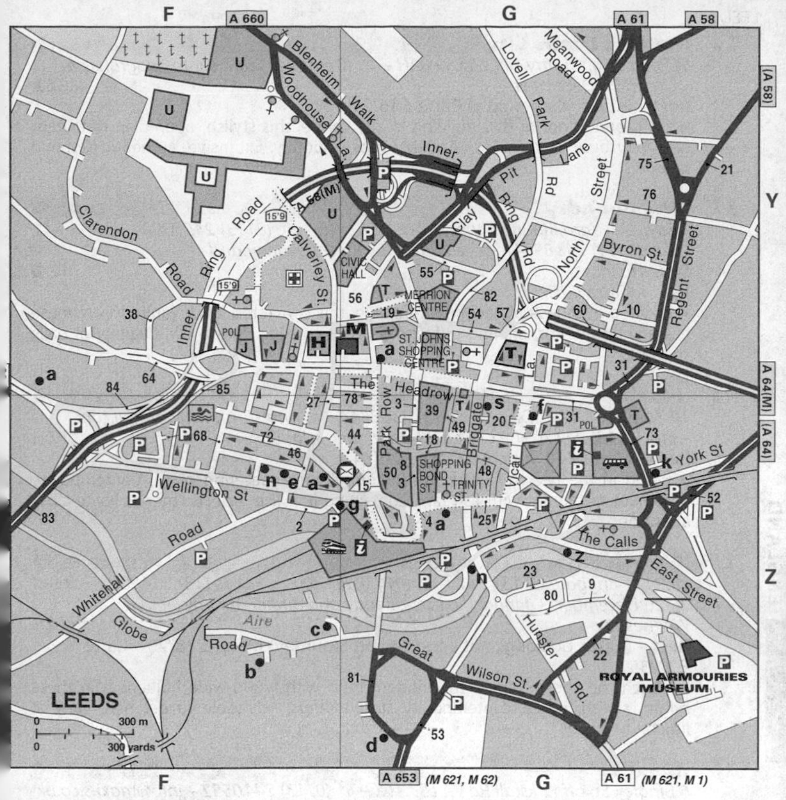

Street	Grid	No.
Aire St.	FZ	2
Albion St	GZ	3
Boar Lane	GZ	4
Bond St	GZ	8
Bowman Lane	GZ	9
Bridge St	GY	10
Briggate	GZ	
City Square	GZ	15
Commercial St	GZ	18
Cookridge St.	GY	19
County Arcade	GZ	20
Cross Stamford St	GY	21
Crown Point Rd	GZ	22
Dock St	GZ	23
Duncan St	GZ	25
Eastgate	GZ	31
East Parade	FGZ	27
Hanover Way	FY	38
Headrow Centre	GZ	39
Headrow (The)	GY	
Infirmary St	GZ	44
King St	FZ	46
Kirkgate	GZ	48
Lands Lane	GZ	49
Leeds Shopping Plaza	GZ	50
Marsh Lane	GZ	52
Meadow Lane	GZ	53
Merrion Centre	GY	
Merrion St.	GY	54
Merrion Way	GY	55
Millennium Square	GY	56
New Briggate	GY	57
New York Rd	GY	60
Park Lane	FY	64
Queen St	FZ	68
St John's Centre	GY	
St Paul's St.	FZ	72
St Peter's St	GZ	73
Sheepscar St South	GY	75
Skinner Lane	GY	76
South Parade	FGZ	78
Trinity St Shopping Centre	GZ	
Victoria Rd	GZ	81
Wade Lane	GY	82
Waterloo St	GZ	80
Wellington Rd	FZ	83
Westgate	FZ	85
West St	FZ	84

XX No.3 York Place

A/C VISA MC AE

3 York Pl ✉ LS1 2DR – ✆ (0113) 245 9922 – dine@no3yorkplace.co.uk – Fax (0113) 245 9965 – closed 25 December-4 January, Saturday lunch, Sunday and Bank Holidays FZ **e**

Rest – Menu £ 19 (lunch) – Carte £ 21/32

◆ A minimalist and discreet environment keeps the spotlight on the appealing cuisine. Classic flavours reinterpreted in a tasty range of brasserie style dishes.

XX Simply Heathcotes

A/C VISA MC AE

Canal Wharf, Water Lane ✉ LS11 5PS – ✆ (0113) 244 6611 – leeds@heathcotes.co.uk – Fax (0113) 244 0736 – closed 25-26 December and 1-2 January FZ **c**

Rest – Carte approx. £ 30

◆ Converted grain warehouse by the canal. Distinctive modern feel with rich black banquettes. Effective contemporary cooking with prominent "northern" slant.

Aagrah Leeds City
St Peter's Sq, Quarry Hill ✉ LS9 8AH – ✆ (0113) 245 5667 – info@aagrah.com – closed 25 December GZ **k**

Rest – Indian (dinner only) Carte £ 16/24 **s**

◆ On ground floor of BBC building in city centre, this stylish, open-plan restaurant gets very busy, but service invariably runs smoothly. Extensive, authentic Kashmiri menus.

The Foundry
1 Saw Mill Yard, Round Foundry ✉ LS11 5WH – ✆ (0113) 245 0390 – Fax (0113) 243 8934 – closed Saturday lunch, Sunday and Bank Holidays FZ **b**

Rest – Carte £ 26/32

◆ Located in Industrial Revolution's cradle, this converted brick vaulted warehouse has a snug interior, offering unfussy seasonal cooking with a wide variety of daily specials.

Plush
10 York Pl ✉ LS1 2DS – ✆ (0113) 234 3344 – plushrestaurant@hotmail.com – Fax (0113) 242 7051 – Closed 25 December-3 January FZ **n**

Rest – Menu £ 16 (lunch) – Carte £ 20/34

◆ Based in the heart of Leeds: a modern, vibrant gathering place. Contemporary basement restaurant with fish tank containing lion fish. Eclectic menus invite close attention.

ENGLAND

Fourth Floor – at Harvey Nichols
107-111 Briggate ✉ LS1 6AZ – ✆ (0113) 204 8000 – Fax (0113) 204 8080 – closed 25-26 December, 1 January, Easter Sunday and dinner Sunday-Wednesday GZ **s**

Rest – (lunch bookings not accepted on Saturday) Menu £ 18/20 – Carte £ 32/35

◆ Watch the chefs prepare the modern food with world-wide influences in these bright, stylish, buzzy, contemporary surroundings. Advisable to get here early at lunch.

Maxi's
6 Bingley St, off Kirkstall Rd ✉ LS3 1LX – ✆ (0113) 244 0552 – info@maxi-s.co.uk – Fax (0113) 234 3902 – Closed 25-26 December FY **a**

Rest – Chinese Carte £ 13/34

◆ Savour the taste of the Orient in this ornately decorated and busy pagoda style restaurant. Specialises in the rich flavours of Canton and hot and spicy Peking dishes.

Brasserie Forty Four – at 42 The Calls H.
44 The Calls ✉ LS2 7EW – ✆ (0113) 234 3232 – info@brasserie44.com – Fax (0113) 234 3332 – closed Sunday and Bank Holidays GZ **z**

Rest – Menu £ 17 (lunch) – Carte £ 25/28

◆ Former riverside warehouse with stylish bar; exudes atmosphere of buzzy informality. Smokehouse and char-grilled options in an eclectic range of menu dishes.

Anthony's at Flannels
Third Floor, 68 Vicar Lane ✉ LS1 7JH – ✆ (0113) 242 8732 – reservations@anthonysatflannels.co.uk – Closed 25 December, 1 January and Monday GZ **f**

Rest – (lunch only) Menu £ 17/25 – Carte £ 18/38

◆ Go to third floor of upmarket clothing store to find this sunny, stylish restaurant, adjacent to an art gallery. Friendly family service of good value, tasty, seasonal dishes.

The Mill Race
2-4 Commercial Rd, Kirkstall ✉ LS5 3AQ – ✆ (0113) 275 7555 – enquiries@themillrace-organic.com – Fax (0113) 275 0222 – closed Monday BT **r**

Rest – Organic (dinner only and Sunday lunch) Menu £ 16 – Carte £ 21/33

◆ Former neighbourhood smithy offering an intimate, comfortable dining experience, personally run by friendly owners. All meals are totally organic.

at Garforth East : 7 m. by A 63 - CT – ✉ Leeds

XX **Aagrah**

Aberford Rd, on A 642 (Garforth rd) ✉ LS25 1BA – ✆ (0113) 287 6606 – closed 25 December

Rest – Indian (dinner only) (booking essential) Carte £ 16/24 **s**

◆ Part of a family owned and personally run expanding group. Classic regional Indian cooking, specialising in the fragrant and subtly spiced dishes of the Kashmir region.

Good food and accommodation at moderate prices?
Look for the Bib symbols:
red Bib Gourmand for food, blue Bib Hotel for hotels

LEICESTER – Leicester – **502** Q 26 – **pop. 330 574** *Great Britain* 16 **B2**

London 107 m – Birmingham 43 m – Coventry 24 m – Nottingham 26 m
East Midlands Airport, Castle Donington : ✆ (0871) 9199000 NW : 22 m. by A 50 - AX - and M 1
7-9 Every St, Town Hall Sq ✆ (0116) 299 8888, info@goleicestershire.com
18 Leicestershire Evington Lane, ✆ (0116) 273 8825 ;
18 Western Park Scudamore Rd, ✆ (0116) 287 5211 ;
18 Humberstone Heights Gipsy Lane, ✆ (0116) 299 5570 ;
18 Oadby Leicester Road Racecourse, ✆ (0116) 270 0215 ;
9 Blaby Lutterworth Rd, ✆ (0116) 278 4804 .
Guildhall★ BY **B** – Museum and Art Gallery★ CY **M3** – St Mary de Castro Church★ BY **D**
National Space Centre★ N : 2 m. by A 6 - AX - turning east into Corporation Rd and right into Exploration Drive

Plans on following pages

Leicester Marriott

Smith Way, Grove Park, Enderby, Southwest : 4 m. by A 5460 off A 563 at junction 21 of M 1 ✉ LE19 1SW – ✆ (0116) 282 01 000 – Fax (0116) 282 0101 AY **z**

226 rm – †£ 129 ††£ 139, ☕ £15.50 – 1 suite –

Rest – Menu £ 16/21 **s** – Carte approx. £ 32 **s**

◆ Sleekly designed, comfortable hotel in useful location by junction 21 of M1. Coffee shop and bar. State-of-the-art gym. Standard and executive bedrooms. East meets west in contemporary restaurant; choice of buffet and eclectic à la carte.

Belmont House

De Montfort St ✉ LE1 7GR – ✆ (0116) 254 4773 – info@belmonthotel.co.uk – Fax (0116) 247 0804 – closed 24 December-2 January CY **c**

76 rm – †£ 115/120 ††£ 145, ☕ £10.95 – 1 suite

Rest ***Cherry's*** – (closed Saturday lunch, Sunday dinner and Bank Holidays) Carte £ 21/36

◆ Privately owned, centrally located and adjacent to a conservation area. Enlarged to provide a large bar and several function rooms. Spacious, comfortable bedrooms. Conservatory restaurant with formal air.

Holiday Inn Leicester City

129 St Nicholas Circle ✉ LE1 5LX – ✆ (0870) 400 90 48 – leicestercity.reservations@ihg.com – Fax (0116) 251 3169 BY **c**

187 rm ☕ – †£ 149/179 ††£ 159/189 – 1 suite –

Rest – Menu £ 20 (dinner) – Carte £ 23/27

◆ Centrally located, imposing modern hotel convenient for the ring road. Comfortable brand style bedrooms with fitted furniture and particularly good Executive rooms. Stylish modern restaurant and bar with American style menus.

ENGLAND

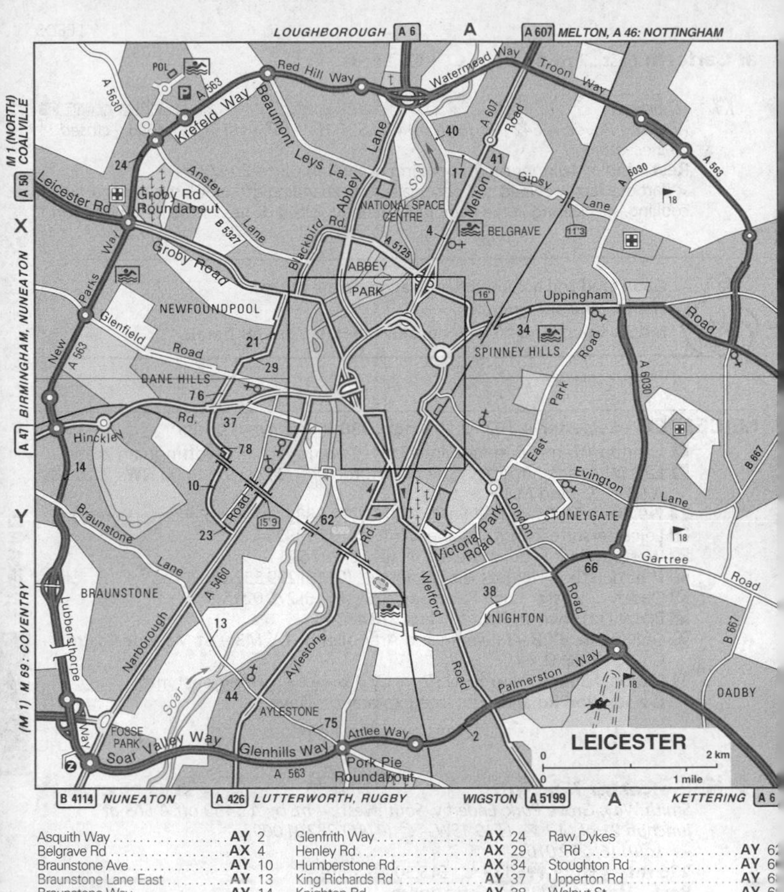

Asquith Way . . . . . AY 2
Belgrave Rd . . . . . AX 4
Braunstone Ave . . . . . AY 10
Braunstone Lane East . . . . . AY 13
Braunstone Way . . . . . AY 14
Checketts Rd . . . . . AX 17
Fosse Rd North . . . . . AX 21
Fullhurst Ave . . . . . AY 23
Glenfrith Way . . . . . AX 24
Henley Rd . . . . . AX 29
Humberstone Rd . . . . . AX 34
King Richards Rd . . . . . AY 37
Knighton Rd . . . . . AY 38
Loughborough Rd . . . . . AX 40
Marfitt St . . . . . AX 41
Middleton St . . . . . AY 44
Raw Dykes Rd . . . . . AY 62
Stoughton Rd . . . . . AY 6
Upperton Rd . . . . . AY 6
Walnut St . . . . . AY 6
Wigston Lane . . . . . AY 7
Woodville Rd . . . . . AY 7
Wyngate Drive . . . . . AY 7

XX Watsons

AC VISA MC AE

5-9 Upper Brown St ✉ LE1 5TE – ✆ (0116) 222 7770 – watsons.restaurant@virgin.net – Fax (0116) 222 7771 – closed 2 weeks Christmas, Sunday and Bank Holidays BY **x**

Rest – Menu £ 13 (lunch) – Carte £ 21/30

◆ Converted Victorian cotton mill in the centre of town. Vivid modern interior replete with chrome, glass and a cosmopolitan ambience. Wide ranging, competent, modern menu.

XX The Tiffin

AC VISA MC AE D

1 De Montfort St ✉ LE1 7GE – ✆ (0116) 247 0420 – thetiffin@msn.com – closed 24-26 December, 1 January, Saturday lunch and Sunday CY **r**

Rest – Indian (booking essential) Menu £ 10/23 – Carte £ 18/39

◆ Busy, spacious and comfortable with a gentle Eastern theme to the décor. Tasty, authentic flavour in carefully prepared Indian dishes.

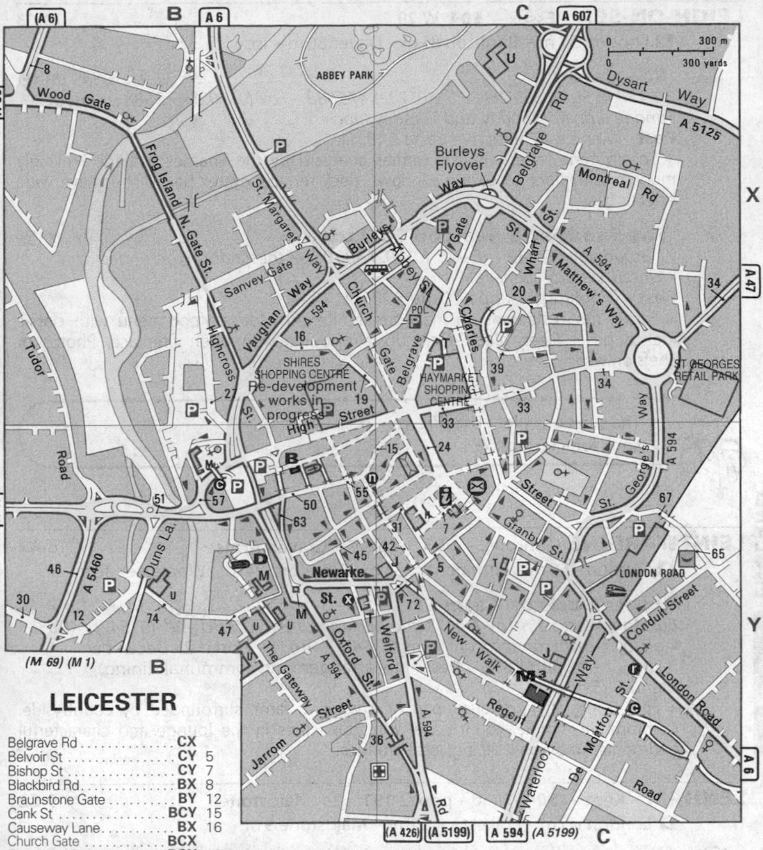

LEICESTER

Street	Grid	No.
Belgrave Rd	CX	
Belvoir St	CY	5
Bishop St	CY	7
Blackbird Rd	BX	8
Braunstone Gate	BY	12
Cank St	BCY	15
Causeway Lane	BX	16
Church Gate	BCX	
East Bond St	BCX	19
Fleet St	CX	20
Gallowtree Gate	CY	24
Great Central St	BX	27
Haymarket Shopping Centre	CX	
High St	BXY	
Hinckley Rd	BY	30
Horsefair St	CY	31
Humberstone Gate	CX	33
Humberstone Rd	CX	34
Infirmary Rd	BCY	36
Lee St	CX	39
Market St	CY	42
Market (The)	CY	43
Millstone Lane	BY	45
Narborough Rd North	BY	46
Newarke (The)	BY	47
Peacock Lane	BY	50
St Georges Retail Park	CX	
St Augustine Rd	BY	51
St Martin's	BY	55
St Nicholas Circle	BY	57
Shires Shopping Centre (The)	BX	
Southgate St	BY	63
Sparkenhoe St	CY	65
Swain St	CY	67
Welford Pl.	CY	72
Western Boulevard	BY	74

XX **The Case**

4-6 Hotel St, St Martin's ✉ LE1 5AW – ✆ (0116) 251 7675 – thecase@btconnect.com – Fax (0116) 251 7675 – Closed Sunday and Bank Holidays

BY **n**

Rest – Menu £ 13 (lunch) – Carte £ 16/29

◆ Stylish modern restaurant in a converted Victorian luggage factory. Open main dining area and a small bar. Large, modern, seasonal menu. Champagne bar adjacent.

We try to be as accurate as possible when giving room rates. But prices are susceptible to change, so please check rates when booking.

LEIGH-ON-SEA – Essex – 504 W 29 13 C3

London 37 m – Brighton 85 m – Dover 86 m – Ipswich 57 m

XX **Boatyard**

8-13 High St ✉ SS9 2EN – ☎ (01702) 475 588 – Fax (01702) 475 588 – closed Sunday dinner, Monday and Tuesday lunch

Rest – Menu £ 17 (lunch) – Carte £ 19/41

◆ Locally renowned, within a former boatyard by the Thames Estuary. Strikingly modern with floor to ceiling windows, deck terrace, oyster bar. Dishes have wide eclectic base.

X **The Sandbar & Seafood Co. Ltd**

71 Broadway ✉ SS9 1PE – ☎ (01702) 480 067 – thesandbar@btconnect.com – closed Sunday dinner

Rest – (booking essential) Carte £ 20/32

◆ Family-run restaurant on main street offering wide seafood menu with classic French base. Sleek black décor. Upstairs lounge with open fireplace. Photos of chefs on walls.

The sun's out – let's eat alfresco!
Look for a terrace:

ENGLAND

LEINTWARDINE – Shrops. – 503 L 26 – ✉ Craven Arms 18 A2

London 156 m – Birmingham 55 m – Hereford 24 m – Worcester 40 m

Upper Buckton Farm

Buckton, West : 2 m. by A 4113 and Buckton rd ✉ SY7 0JU – ☎ (01547) 540 634 – ghlloydco@btconnect.com – Fax (01547) 540 634 – closed 25 December

3 rm – †£ 60 ††£ 90 – **Rest** – (by arrangement, communal dining) Menu £ 25

◆ Fine Georgian farmhouse, part of a working farm, surrounded by countryside. Comfortable, simple, country feel with open fires in the lounge and characterful bedrooms. Traditional dining; local produce.

LENHAM – Kent – 504 W 30 – pop. 2 191 – ✉ Maidstone 9 C2

London 45 m – Folkestone 28 m – Maidstone 9 m

Chilston Park

Sandway, South : 1 ¾ m. off Broughton Malherbe rd ✉ ME17 2BE – ☎ (01622) 859 803 – chilstonpark@handpicked.co.uk – Fax (01622) 858 588

49 rm – †£ 95/115 ††£ 105/125 – **Rest** – (Closed Saturday lunch) Menu £ 18 (lunch) **s** – Carte dinner £ 33/46 **s**

◆ Part 17C mansion, set in parkland and furnished with antiques. Bedrooms are very individual and comfortable. Old stable conference facilities retain original stalls! Smart dining room and well-appointed sitting room.

LEOMINSTER – Herefordshire – 503 L 27 – pop. 10 440 *Great Britain* 18 B3

London 141 m – Birmingham 47 m – Hereford 13 m – Worcester 26 m

1 Corn Sq ☎ (01568) 615546

Ford Bridge, ☎ (01568) 612 863 .

Berrington Hall★ AC, N : 3 m. by A 49

at Kimbolton Northeast : 3 m. by A 49 on A 4112

Lower Bache House

East : 1 ¾ m. by A 4112 ✉ HR6 0ER – ☎ (01568) 750 304 – leslie.wiles@care4free.net

4 rm – †£ 50 ††£ 80 – **Rest** – (by arrangement) Menu £ 25

◆ A fine 17C farmhouse in a very quiet rural setting. Spacious, characterful, open feel throughout: bedrooms located in a charming converted granary. Converted cider barn dining room features original mill and press.

at Leysters Northeast : 5 m. by A 49 on A 4112 – ✉ Leominster

The Hills Farm without rest

✉ *HR6 0HP – ✆ (01568) 750205 – jconolly@btconnect.com – March-October*
5 rm – †£ 35/40 ††£ 64/72
◆ An attractive ivy-clad farmhouse on a working farm. The interior is delightfully comfortable, from the cosy lounge to the country-cottage rooms, three in the converted barns.

at Pudleston East : 5 m. by A 49 off A 44 – ✉ Leominster

Ford Abbey rm,

South : 1 m. on Pudleston rd ✉ HR6 0RZ – ✆ (01568) 760700 – info@fordabbey.co.uk – Fax (01568) 760264
6 rm – †£ 125/180 ††£ 125/180 – 1 suite – **Rest** – (dinner only) (booking essential for non-residents) (set menu only) Menu £ 35 **s**
◆ Sumptuous, splendid isolation: a wonderful collection of medieval and 19C farmhouses and barns. Very characterful throughout. Luxurious rooms with low beams and hideaways. Dining room exudes appeal: 15C window frame still intact.

LETCHWORTH – Herts. – 504 T 28 12 B2

London 39 m – Luton 18 m – Stevenage 7 m

at Willian South : 1 ¾ m. by A 6141 – ✉ Letchworth

The Fox

✉ *SG6 2AE – ✆ (01462) 480233 – info@foxatwillian.co.uk – Fax (01462) 676966 – Closed Sunday dinner*
Rest – Carte £ 20/27
◆ Spacious modern pub between church and pond in centre of village. Bar with plasma screen; more formal dining room. Eclectic menu with strong seafood base served throughout.

LEVINGTON – Suffolk 15 D3

London 75 m – Ipswich 5 m – Woodbridge 8 m

The Ship Inn

Church Lane ✉ IP10 0LQ – ✆ (01473) 659573 – Closed 25-26 December, dinner 31 December and 1 January
Rest – Carte £ 17/25
◆ Characterful, part 14C thatched and beamed pub with plenty of maritime curios and rustic charm. Fish a key element of dishes which range from traditional to rather innovative.

LEVISHAM – N. Yorks. – 502 R 21 – see Pickering

LEWDOWN – Devon – 503 H 32 2 C2

London 238 m – Exeter 37 m – Plymouth 29 m
Lydford★★, E : 4 m. Launceston★ - Castle★ (< ★) St Mary Magdalene★, W : 8 m. by A 30 and A 388

Lewtrenchard Manor

South : ¾ m. by Lewtrenchard rd ✉ EX20 4PN – ✆ (01566) 783222 – info@lewtrenchard.co.uk – Fax (01566) 783332
13 rm – †£ 190/220 ††£ 220/300 – 1 suite – **Rest** – (Closed Monday lunch) (booking essential for non-residents) Menu £ 22/45 **s**
◆ A grand historical atmosphere pervades this delightfully secluded 17C manor house. Plenty of personality with antiques, artworks, ornate ceilings and panelling throughout. Two elegant dining rooms with stained glass windows.

LEWES – E. Sussex – **504** U 31 – **pop. 15 988** *Great Britain* 8 **A3**

London 53 m – Brighton 8 m – Hastings 29 m – Maidstone 43 m
187 High St ✆ (01273) 483448
Chapel Hill, ✆ (01273) 473 245 .
Town★ (High St★, Keere St★) – Castle (≤ ★) **AC**
Sheffield Park Garden★ **AC**, N : 9½ m. by A 275

Shelleys

High St ✉ BN7 1XS – ✆ (01273) 472 361 – info@shelleys-hotel-lewes.com – Fax (01273) 483 152

18 rm – ♦£ 95/155 ♦♦£ 140/195 – 1 suite – **Rest** – Carte £ 15/40

◆ The great poet's family once owned this Georgian former inn. It has spacious bedrooms which are furnished and decorated in keeping with its historical connections. Smart restaurant exudes Georgian panache.

Millers without rest

134 High St ✉ BN7 1XS – ✆ (01273) 475 631 – millers134@aol.com

3 rm – ♦£ 70/75 ♦♦£ 80/85

◆ Characterful, small family home in a row of 16C houses that lead to the high street. Appealing personal feel in the individual bedrooms with books, trinkets and knick-knacks.

at East Chiltington Northwest : 5½ m. by A 275 and B 2116 off Novington Lane – ✉ Lewes

ENGLAND

The Jolly Sportsman

Chapel Lane ✉ BN7 3BA – ✆ (01273) 890 400 – info@thejollysportsman.com – Fax (01273) 890 400 – Closed 4 days at Christmas, 1 January, Sunday dinner and Monday

Rest – Menu £ 16 – Carte £ 20/29

◆ Brick and clapboard country pub with open, uncluttered interior and well cooked, contemporary dishes full of interest on regularly changing menu. Served with care.

Red = Pleasant. Look for the red and symbols.

LEYBURN – N. Yorks. – **502** O 21 – **pop. 1 844** 22 **B1**

London 251 m – Darlington 25 m – Kendal 43 m – Leeds 53 m – Newcastle upon Tyne 62 m – York 49 m
4 Central Chambers, Railway St ✆ (01969) 623069

Clyde House without rest

5 Railway St ✉ DL8 5AY – ✆ (01969) 623 941 – lucia.fisher1@btinternet.com – closed 2-31 January

5 rm – ♦£ 40 ♦♦£ 60/70

◆ Recently refurbished to a high standard, this former coaching inn dates from mid-18C and is one of the oldest buildings in town. Hearty Yorkshire breakfasts to start the day.

Dales Haven without rest

Market Pl ✉ DL8 5BJ – ✆ (01969) 623 814 – info@daleshaven.co.uk

6 rm – ♦£ 40/45 ♦♦£ 60/65

◆ Neat and tidy house in village centre. Pleasant rural views from breakfast room, which also displays artwork from local gallery. Colourful rooms include DVD and CD players.

The Sandpiper Inn with rm

Market Pl ✉ DL8 5AT – ✆ (01969) 622 206 – hsandpiper99@aol.com – Fax (01969) 625 367 – Closed 25 December and 1 January

2 rm – ♦£ 65 ♦♦£ 75 – **Rest** – (closed Monday) Carte £ 20/34

◆ Converted 16C stone house off market square. Rustic and simple with daily changing blackboard menu of tasty Yorkshire fare; good local ales. Pleasant pine furnished rooms.

at Constable Burton East : 3 ½ m. on A 684 – ✉ Leyburn

Wyvill Arms with rm

✉ DL8 5LH – ✆ (01677) 450 581
2 rm – **♦**£ 55 **♦♦**£ 75 – **Rest** – Carte £ 22/29
◆ A classic Yorkshire pub with stone bar area and good choice of ales. Seasonally changing menu with steaks a speciality: eat in bar or formal dining room. Neat, tidy bedrooms.

LEYSTERS – Herefordshire – **503** M 27 – see Leominster

LICHFIELD – Staffs. – **502** O 25 – **pop. 28 435** *Great Britain* 19 **C2**

London 128 m – Birmingham 16 m – Derby 23 m – Stoke-on-Trent 30 m
Lichfield Garrick, Castle Dyke ✆ (01543) 412112
Seedy Mill Elmhurst, ✆ (01543) 417 333 .
City★ - Cathedral★★ **AC**

Swinfen Hall

Southeast : 2 ¼ m. by A 5206 on A 38 ✉ WS14 9RE – ✆ (01543) 481 494 – info@swinfenhallhotel.co.uk – Fax (01543) 480 341 – restricted opening between Christmas and New Year
16 rm – **♦**£ 125/155 **♦♦**£ 220/230, £5 – 1 suite
Rest *Four Seasons* – (closed Saturday lunch and Sunday dinner to non-residents) Menu £ 23/42 **s**
◆ Very fine 18C house in 100 acres with beautiful façade, impressive stucco ceilings and elegant lounges furnished with taste and style. Bedrooms offer high levels of comfort. Modern menus served in superb oak-panelled restaurant with Grinling Gibbons carvings.

Thrales

40-44 Tamworth St, (corner of Backcester Lane) ✉ WS13 6JJ – ✆ (01543) 255 091 – Fax (01543) 415 352 – Closed Monday, Tuesday, Saturday lunch and Sunday dinner
Rest – Menu £ 16 (weekday dinner) – Carte £ 26/32
◆ Busy, popular restaurant with a rustic style; building has 16C origins. Wide-ranging menu of simple homely dishes using mainly local produce.

Chandlers Grande Brasserie

Corn Exchange, Conduit St ✉ WS13 6JU – ✆ (01543) 416 688 – Fax (01543) 417 887 – closed 1-5 January and Bank Holidays
Rest – Menu £ 14/17 – Carte £ 20/29
◆ On two floors in old cornmarket building. Tiled floors, prints and pin lights; a pleasant, relaxed atmosphere in which to enjoy a brasserie menu with good value lunch options.

LICKFOLD – W. Sussex – see Petworth

LIDGATE – Suffolk – **504** V 27 – see Newmarket

LIFTON – Devon – **503** H 32 – **pop. 964** 2 **C2**

London 238 m – Bude 24 m – Exeter 37 m – Launceston 4 m – Plymouth 26 m
Launceston★ - Castle★ (≤ ★) St Mary Magdalene★, W : 4 ½ m. by A 30 and A 388

Arundell Arms

Fore St ✉ PL16 0AA – ✆ (01566) 784 666 – reservations@arundellarms.com – Fax (01566) 784 494 – Accommodation closed 25-26 December
21 rm – **♦**£ 99/105 **♦♦**£ 160/200 – **Rest** – Menu £ 28/42 **s**
◆ Coaching inn, in a valley of five rivers, dating back to Saxon times. True English sporting hotel - popular with shooting parties and fishermen. Good country lodge style. English and French cuisine in opulently grand dining room.

ENGLAND

Tinhay Mill with rm

Tinhay ✉ PL16 OAJ – ✆ (01566) 784 201 – tinhay.mill@talk21.com – Fax (01566) 784 201 – closed 3 weeks February-March

5 rm – £ 60/63 £ 75/90 – **Rest** – (dinner only) Menu £ 25 – Carte £ 25/38 **s**

◆ Small converted mill: furnishings a mix of rustic and traditional, creating a cosy feel. Locally based, tasty cuisine from renowned Devonian owner/cook. Cottagey bedrooms.

LINCOLN – Lincs. – 502 S 24 – pop. 85 963 *Great Britain* 17 C1

London 140 m – Bradford 81 m – Cambridge 94 m – Kingston-upon-Hull 44 m – Leeds 73 m – Leicester 53 m – Norwich 104 m – Nottingham 38 m

Humberside Airport : ✆ (01652) 688456, N : 32 m. by A 15 - Y - M 180 and A 18

9 Castle Sq ✆ (01522) 873213

Carholme Carholme Rd, ✆ (01522) 523 725 .

City★★ - Cathedral and Precincts★★★ **AC** Y – High Bridge★★ Z **9** – Usher Gallery★ **AC** YZ **M1** – Jew's House★ Y – Castle★ **AC** Y

Doddington Hall★ **AC**, W : 6 m. by B 1003 - Z - and B 1190. Gainsborough Old Hall★ **AC**, NW : 19 m. by A 57 - Z - and A 156

Plan opposite

Bentley rm, rest,

Newark Rd, South Hykeham, Southwest : 5 ¾ m. by A 15 on B 1434 at junction with A 46 ✉ LN6 9NH – ✆ (01522) 878 000 – infothebentleyhotel@btconnect.com – Fax (01522) 878 001

80 rm – £ 88 £ 113/135 – **Rest** – (carvery lunch) Menu £ 14/20 – Carte dinner £ 28/38

◆ New purpose-built hotel. Smart, modern feel with traditional touches throughout. Well kept bedrooms including Executive and more traditional styles. Well-run leisure club. Formal or relaxed dining alternatives.

Bailhouse without rest

34 Bailgate ✉ LN1 3AP – ✆ (01522) 541 000 – info@bailhouse.co.uk – Fax (01522) 521 829 Y **c**

10 rm – £ 75 £ 175, £ 9.50

◆ Beautiful 14C building with 19C additions. Intimate, relaxing feel enhanced by unobtrusive service, enclosed garden, and rooms oozing charm, some with 14C exposed beams.

Minster Lodge without rest

3 Church Lane ✉ LN2 1QJ – ✆ (01522) 513 220 – info@minsterlodge.co.uk – Fax (01522) 513 220 – closed 1 week Christmas Y **a**

6 rm – £ 65/75 £ 90/100

◆ Converted house, close to the cathedral and castle, just by 3C Newport Arch with good access to the ring road. Immaculately kept throughout and run with a professional touch.

St Clements Lodge without rest

21 Langworthgate ✉ LN2 4AD – ✆ (01522) 521 532 – Fax (01522) 521 532 Y **u**

3 rm – £ 45 £ 60

◆ A good value house in a convenient location, a short walk from the sights. Run by hospitable owners who keep three large, pleasantly decorated bedrooms.

Wig & Mitre

30-32 Steep Hill ✉ LN2 1LU – ✆ (01522) 535 190 – email@wigandmitre.com – Fax (01522) 532 402 Y **r**

Rest – Menu £ 14 – Carte £ 23/38

◆ First floor dining area, with characterful almost medieval decor, in a building which dates back to 14C. Skilfully prepared, confident, classic cooking.

ENGLAND

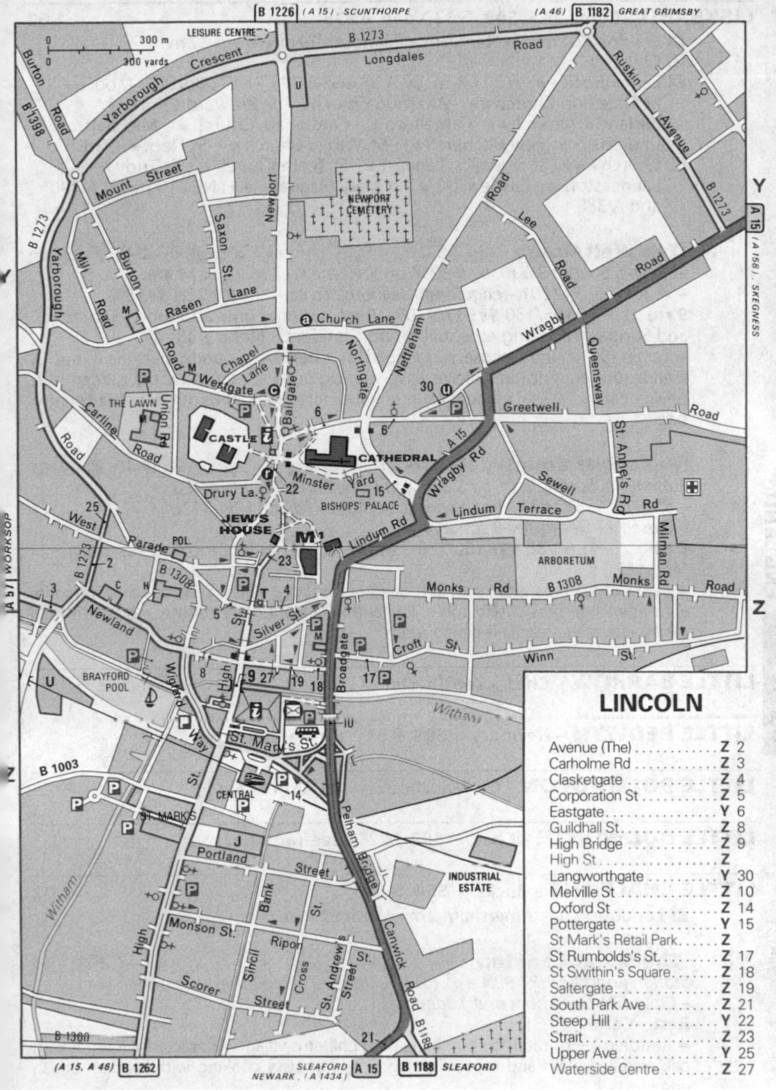

at Branston Southeast : 3 ½ m. by A 15 - Z - on B 1188 – ✉ Lincoln

Branston Hall

Lincoln Road ✉ LN41 1PD – ✆ (01522) 793 305 – info@branstonhall.com – Fax (01522) 790 734

50 rm – †£ 80/90 ††£ 180 – **Rest** – Menu £ 17/24 – Carte dinner £ 24/36

◆ Privately owned hall built in 1736, with additions. Stands in impressive grounds with lake. Bags of period charm, such as original wood panelling. Homely, comfortable rooms. Huge dining room has a formal feel and classical menus.

LISKEARD – Cornwall – **503** G 32 – pop. 8 478 1 **B2**

London 261 m – Exeter 59 m – Plymouth 19 m – Truro 37 m

Church ★

Lanhydrock ★★, W : 11 ½ m. by A 38 and A 390 – NW : Bodmin Moor ★★ - St Endellion Church ★★ - Altarnun Church ★ - St Breward Church ★ - Blisland ★ (church ★) - Camelford ★ – Cardinham Church ★ - Michaelstow Church ★ - St Kew ★ (church ★) - St Mabyn Church ★ – St Neot ★ (Parish Church ★★) - St Sidwell's, Laneast ★ - St Teath Church ★ - St Tudy ★ – Launceston ★ - Castle ★ (≤ ★) St Mary Magdalene ★, NE : 19 m. by A 390 and A 388

The Well House

(heated) VISA

St Keyne, South : 3 ½ m. by B 3254 on St Keyne Well rd ✉ PL14 4RN – ✆ (01579) 342 001 – enquiries@wellhouse.co.uk – Fax (01579) 343 891

9 rm – ♦£ 105/130 ♦♦£ 170/205 – **Rest** – (dinner only and lunch Saturday and Sunday) (booking essential for non-residents) Menu £ 38

♦ Large 19C country house surrounded by extensive grounds; personally run by friendly owner. Individual rooms have winning outlooks; those by the garden have private patios. Stylish, modern country house restaurant looks out over the country-side.

Pencubitt Country House

VISA

Station Rd, South : ½ m. by B 3254 on Lamellion rd ✉ PL14 4EB – ✆ (01579) 342 694 – hotel@pencubitt.com – Fax (01579) 342 694 – Closed 17 December-8 January

9 rm – ♦£ 60/80 ♦♦£ 100/110 – **Rest** – (dinner only) (booking essential) Menu £ 30 **s**

♦ Late Victorian mansion, with fine views of East Looe Valley. Spacious drawing room with open fire, plus sitting room, bar and veranda. Comfy rooms, most with rural views. Attractive, candlelit dining room.

ENGLAND

LITTLE BARROW – Ches. – see Chester

LITTLE BEDWYN – Newbury – **503** P 29 – see Marlborough

LITTLE BOLLINGTON – Gtr Manchester – see Altrincham

LITTLE BUDWORTH – Ches. – **502** M 24 – see Tarporley

LITTLE CHALFONT – Bucks. – **504** S 29 11 **D2**

London 33 m – Amersham 2 m – Watford 11 m

The Sugar Loaf Inn

VISA

Station Road ✉ HP7 9PN – ✆ (01494) 765 579 – info@thesugarloafinn.com – Closed 26 December and 1 January

Rest – Carte £ 20/35

♦ Restored 1930s roadside pub in heart of Chilterns village. Characterful interior with oak panelled walls and mood lighting. Fresh, unfussy cooking with modern British edge.

LITTLE LANGDALE – Cumbria – **502** K 20 – see Ambleside

LITTLE LANGFORD – Wilts. – see Salisbury

LITTLE PETHERICK – Cornwall – **503** F 32 – see Padstow

LITTLE SHELFORD – Cambs. – **504** U 27 – see Cambridge

LITTLE THETFORD – Cambs. – see Ely

LITTLE WILBRAHAM – Cambs. – see Cambridge

LITTLEBOROUGH – Gtr Manchester – 502 N 23 – see Rochdale

LITTLEHAMPTON – W. Sussex – 504 S 31 – pop. 55 716 7 C3

London 64 m – Brighton 18 m – Portsmouth 31 m
The Look and Sea Centre, 63-65 Surrey St (01903) 713480

Bailiffscourt & Spa (heated)
Climping St, Climping, West : 2 ¾ m. by A 259
BN17 5RW – (01903) 723 511 – bailiffscourt@hshotels.co.uk
– Fax (01903) 723 107
39 rm (dinner included) – £ 165 £ 245 – **Rest** – Menu £ 17/45
◆ Alluring reconstructed medieval house basking in acres of utterly peaceful grounds. Rich antiques and fine period features in an enchanting medieval ambience. Superb spa. Split-room dining area nestling amidst warmly tapestried walls.

Amberley Court without rest
Crookthorn Lane, Climping, West : 1 ¾ m. by B 2187 off A 259 BN17 5SN
– (01903) 725 131 – msimmonds06@aol.com – Fax (01903) 725 131
5 rm – £ 50/55 £ 98
◆ Converted farm barn with a tidy, homely atmosphere. Exposed beams, flourishing plants and a warm welcome. Simply decorated rooms, some in grounds, with traditional chintz.

LITTLETON – Hants. – 503 P 30 – see Winchester

ENGLAND

Undecided between two equivalent establishments? Within each category, establishments are classified in our order of preference.

Cécile Labonne/MICHELIN

LIVERPOOL

County: Mersey. **Population:** 469 017 20 **A2**
Michelin REGIONAL map: n° 502 L 23 Great Britain
London 219 m – Birmingham 103 m – Leeds 75 m – Manchester 35 m

PRACTICAL INFORMATION

Tourist Information

08 Place, 36-38 Whitechapel, (0151) 232 008, 08place@liverpool.gov.uk - Atlantic Pavilion, Albert Dock (0906) 680 6886

Airport

Liverpool John Lennon Airport: (0870) 129 8484, SE: 6 m. by A 561 BX

Ferries and Shipping Lines

Tunnel

Mersey Tunnels (toll) AX

Golf Courses

27 Allerton Municipal Allerton Rd, (0151) 428 1046 ;

18 Liverpool Municipal Kirby Ingoe Lane, (0151) 546 5435 ;

9 Bowring Roby Rd, Bowring Park, (0151) 489 1901.

ENGLAND

SIGHTS

IN TOWN

City★ – The Walker★★ DY **M3** – Liverpool Cathedral★★ (Lady Chapel★) EZ – Metropolitan Cathedral of Christ the King★★ EY – Albert Dock★ CZ (Merseyside Maritime Museum★ **AC M2** - Tate Liverpool★)

IN THE SURROUNDING AREA

Speke Hall★ **AC**, SE: 8 m. by A 561 BX

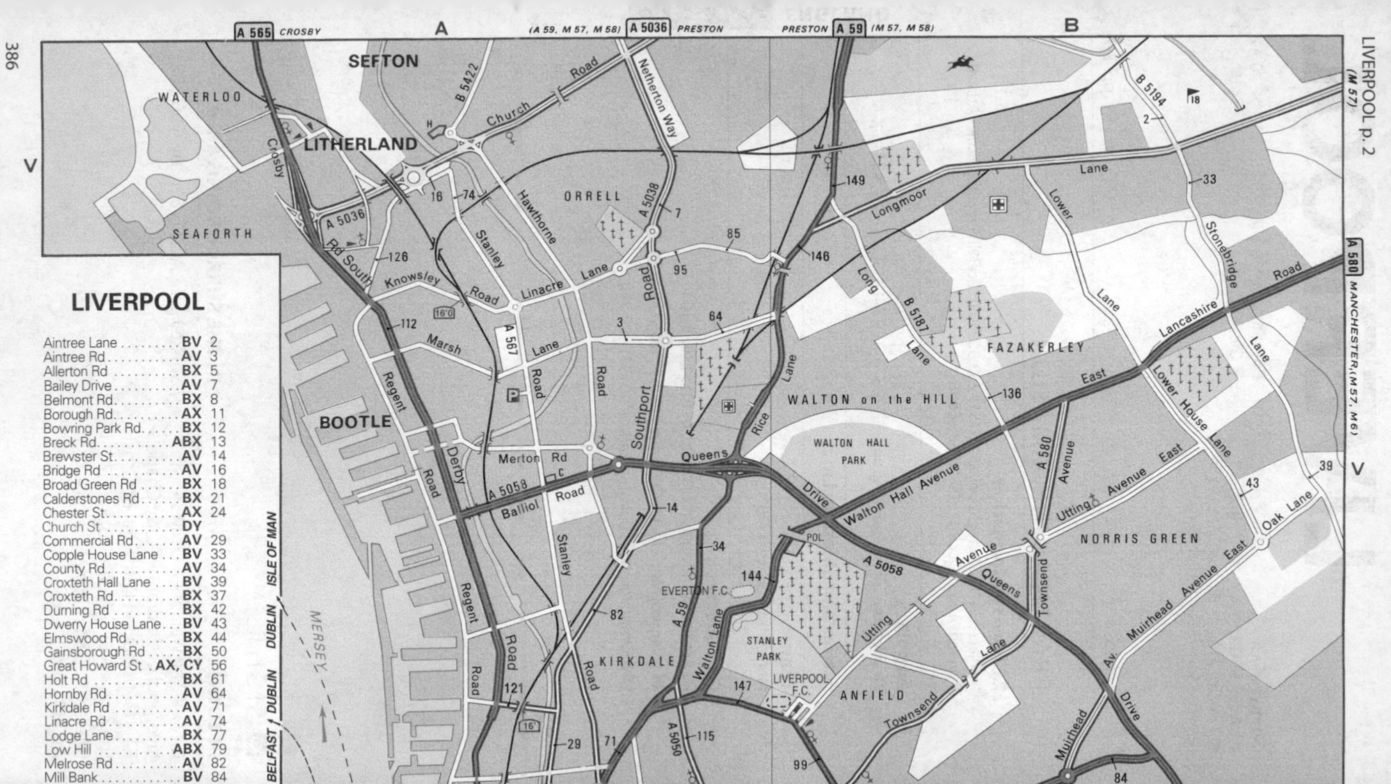

LIVERPOOL

Aintree Lane	BV	2
Aintree Rd	AV	3
Allerton Rd	BX	5
Bailey Drive	AV	7
Belmont Rd	BX	8
Borough Rd	AX	11
Bowring Park Rd	BX	12
Breck Rd	ABX	13
Brewster St	AV	14
Bridge Rd	AV	16
Broad Green Rd	BX	18
Calderstones Rd	BX	21
Chester St	AX	24
Church St	DY	
Commercial Rd	AV	29
Copple House Lane	BV	33
County Rd	AV	34
Croxteth Hall Lane	BV	39
Croxteth Rd	BX	37
Durning Rd	BX	42
Dwerry House Lane	BV	43
Elmswood Rd	BX	44
Gainsborough Rd	BX	50
Great Howard St	AX, CY	56
Holt Rd	BX	61
Hornby Rd	AV	64
Kirkdale Rd	AV	71
Linacre Rd	AV	74
Lodge Lane	BX	77
Low Hill	ABX	79
Melrose Rd	AV	82
Mill Bank	BV	84

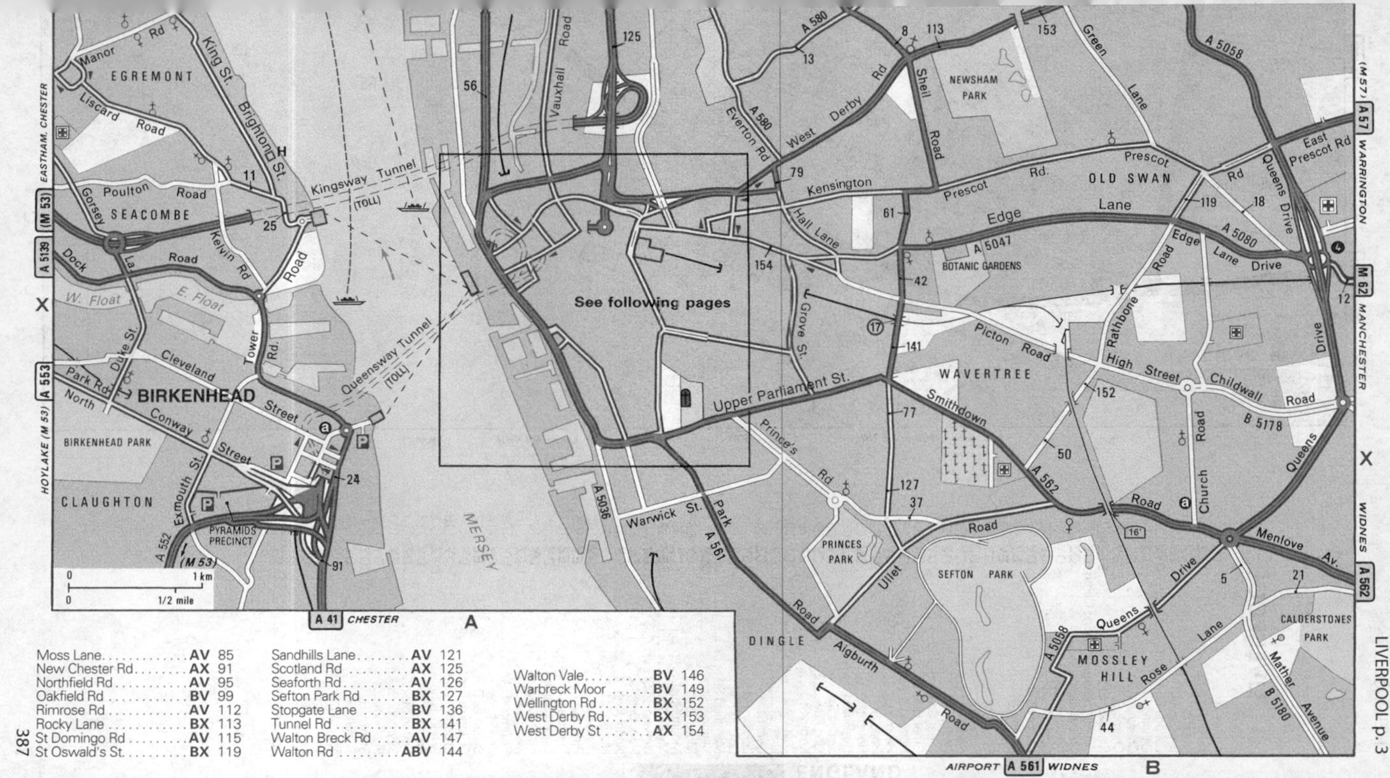

- Moss Lane .... AV 85
- New Chester Rd .... AX 91
- Northfield Rd .... AV 95
- Oakfield Rd .... BV 99
- Rimrose Rd .... AV 112
- Rocky Lane .... BX 113
- St Domingo Rd .... AV 115
- St Oswald's St. .... BX 119
- Sandhills Lane .... AV 121
- Scotland Rd .... AX 125
- Seaforth Rd .... AV 126
- Sefton Park Rd .... BX 127
- Stopgate Lane .... BV 136
- Tunnel Rd .... BX 141
- Walton Breck Rd .... AV 147
- Walton Rd .... ABV 144
- Walton Vale .... BV 146
- Warbreck Moor .... BV 149
- Wellington Rd .... BX 152
- West Derby Rd .... BX 153
- West Derby St .... AX 154

LIVERPOOL

Argyle St . . . . **DZ** 6
Blackburne Pl. . . . . **EZ** 10
Bold St. . . . . **DZ**
Brunswick Rd . . . . **EY** 19
Canada Boulevard . . . . **CYZ** 22
Canning Pl. . . . . **CZ** 23
Churchill Way . . . . **DY** 26
Church St . . . . **DY**
Clarence St . . . . **EYZ** 27
Clayton Square Shopping Centre **DY**
College Lane . . . . **DZ** 28
Commutation Row . . . . **DY** 30
Cook St . . . . **CY** 32
Crosshall St. . . . . **DY** 36
Daulby St. . . . . **EY** 40
Erskine St . . . . **EY** 45
Fontenoy St . . . . **DY** 48
Forrest St . . . . **DZ** 49
George's Dock Lane . . . . **CY** 51
Grafton St . . . . **DZ** 53
Great Charlotte St . . . . **DY** 54
Great Howard St . . . . **CY** 56
Hatton Garden . . . . **DY** 57
Haymarket . . . . **DY** 58
Hood St. . . . . **DY** 62
Houghton St. . . . . **DY** 65
Huskisson St. . . . . **EZ** 66
James St. **CY** 68
King Edward St. . . . . **CY** 69
Knight St . . . . **EZ** 72
Leece St . . . . **EZ** 73
Lime St . . . . **DY**
Liver St . . . . **CZ** 76
London Rd . . . . **DEY**
Lord St . . . . **CDY**
Mansfield St. . . . . **DEY** 80
Mathew St. . . . . **CDY** 81
Moss St. . . . . **EY** 86
Mount St . . . . **EZ** 88
Myrtle St . . . . **EZ** 89
Newington St . . . . **DZ** 92
New Quay. . . . . **CY** 93
North John St . . . . **CY** 96
Norton St. . . . . **EY** 97
Parker St . . . . **DY** 103
Prescot St . . . . **EY** 105
Prince's Rd . . . . **EZ** 107
Queen Square . . . . **DY**
Ranelagh St . . . . **DY** 108
Renshaw St . . . . **DEZ**
Richmond St. . . . . **DY** 109
Roe St . . . . **DY** 114
St James Pl. . . . . **EZ** 117
St John's Centre. . . . . **DY**
St John's Lane . . . . **DY** 118
School Lane . . . . **DYZ** 122
Scotland Pl. . . . . **DY** 123
Sefton St. **DZ** 129
Seymour St. . . . . **EY** 130
Skelhorne St. . . . . **DY** 133
Stanley St. . . . . **CDY** 135
Suffolk St. . . . . **DZ** 137
Tarleton St. . . . . **DY** 139
Victoria St . . . . **DY** 143
Water St . . . . **CY** 150
William Brown St . . . . **DY** 156
York St. . . . . **DZ** 157

ENGLAND

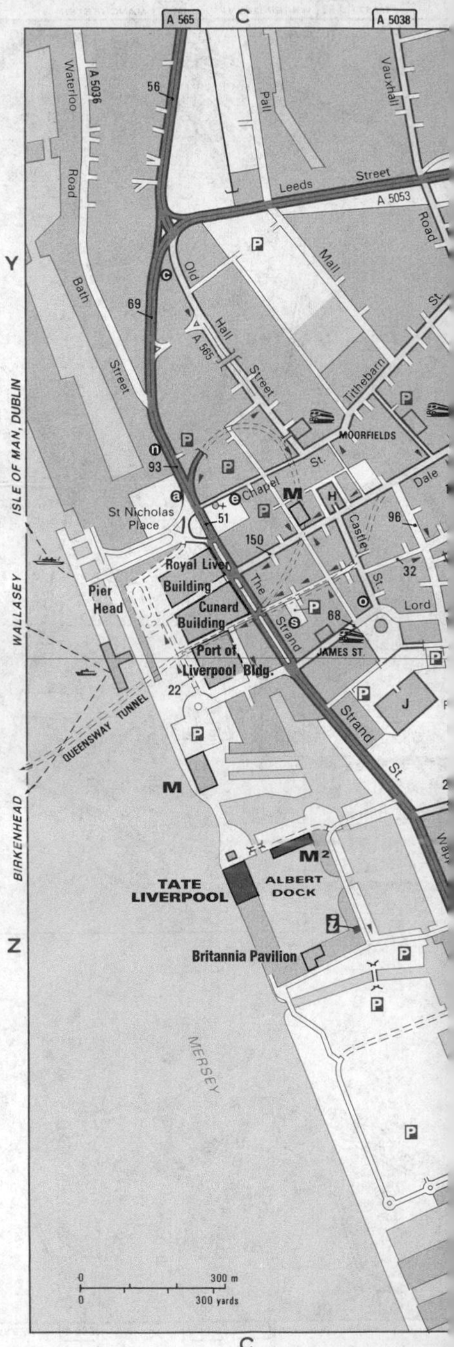

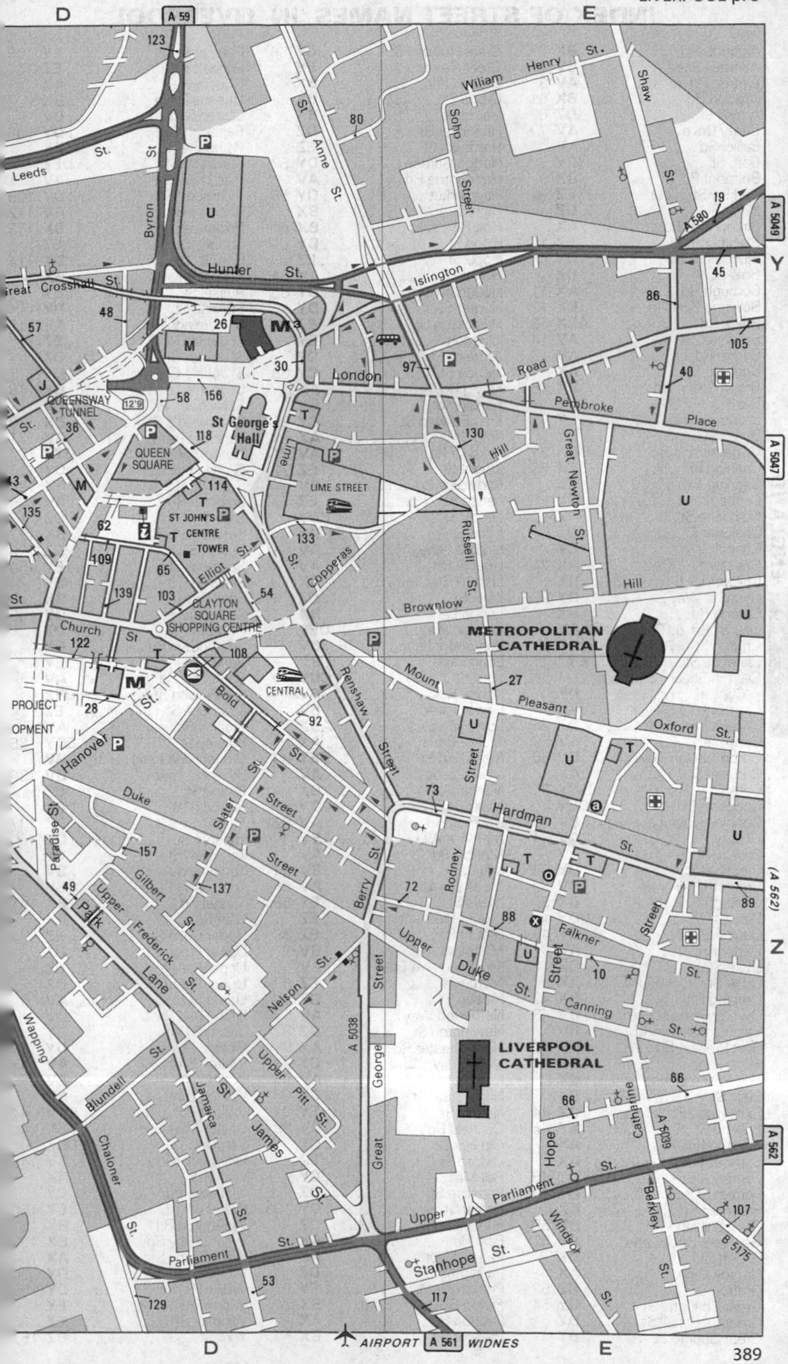

D E

A 59

Leeds St.
Byron St.
Anne St.
William Henry St.
Shaw St.
Soho Street
Hunter St.
Great Crosshall St.
Islington
London Road
Pembroke Place
QUEENSWAY TUNNEL
QUEEN SQUARE
St George's Hall
Lime St.
LIME STREET
ST JOHN'S CENTRE TOWER
Elliot St.
Copperas Hill
Great Newton St.
Russell St.
Brownlow Hill
CLAYTON SQUARE SHOPPING CENTRE
Church St.
METROPOLITAN CATHEDRAL
Mount Pleasant
Oxford St.
CENTRAL
Bold St.
Renshaw Street
Hanover St.
Duke Street
Slater St.
Hardman St.
Rodney Street
Paradise St.
Gilbert St.
Berry St.
Upper Frederick St.
Park Lane
Falkner St.
Upper Duke St.
Hope Street
Nelson St.
Canning St.
Wapping
LIVERPOOL CATHEDRAL
Great George Street
Upper Pitt St.
Jamaica St.
Blundell St.
James St.
Catharine Street
Chaloner St.
Upper Parliament St.
Parliament St.
Stanhope St.
Windsor St.
Berkley St.
A 5038
A 5039
A 580
A 5049
A 5047
(A 562)
A 562
B 5175

AIRPORT A 561 WIDNES

D E

INDEX OF STREET NAMES IN LIVERPOOL

Street	Grid	No.
Aigburth Rd	BX	
Aintree Lane	BV	2
Aintree Rd	AV	3
Allerton Rd	BX	5
Argyle St	DZ	6
Bailey Drive	AV	7
Balliol Rd	AV	
Bath St	CY	
Belmont Rd	BX	8
Berkley St	EZ	
Berry St	DZ	
Birkenhead Rd	AX	
Blackburne Pl.	EZ	10
Blundell St	DZ	
Bold St	DZ	
Borough Rd	AX	11
Bowring Park Rd	BX	12
Breck Rd	ABX	13
Brewster St	AV	14
Bridge Rd	AV	16
Brighton St	AX	
Broad Green Rd	BX	18
Brownlow Hill	DEY	
Brunswick Rd	EY	19
Byron St	DY	
Calderstones Rd	BX	21
Canning Pl.	CZ	23
Canning St	EZ	
Castle St	CY	
Catharine St	EZ	
Chaloner St	DZ	
Chapel St	CY	
Chester St	AX	24
Childwall Rd	BX	
Churchill Way	DY	26
Church Rd	BX	
Church Rd (LITHERLAND)	AV	
Church St	DY	
Clarence St	EYZ	27
Clayton Square Shopping Centre	DY	
Cleveland St	AX	
College Lane	DZ	28
Commercial Rd	AV	29
Commutation Row	DY	30
Conway St	AX	
Cook St	CY	32
Copperas Hill	DEY	
Copple House La	BV	33
County Rd	AV	34
Crosby Rd South	AV	
Crosshall St	DY	36
Croxteth Hall Lane	BV	39
Croxteth Rd	BX	37
Dale St	CDY	
Daulby St	EY	40
Derby Rd	AV	
Duke St	DZ	
Duke St. (BIRKENHEAD)	AX	
Durning Rd	BX	42
Dwerry House Lane	BV	43
East Lancashire Rd	BV	
East Prescot Rd	BX	
Edge Lane	BX	
Edge Lane Drive	BX	
Elliot St	DY	
Elmswood Rd	BX	44
Erskine St	EY	45
Everton Rd	AX	
Exmouth St	AX	
Fontenoy St	DY	48
Forrest St	DZ	49
Freeman St	AX	
Gainsborough Rd	BX	50
George's Dock Lane	CY	51
Gilbert St	DZ	
Gorsey Lane	AX	
Grafton St	DZ	53
Great Charlotte St	DY	54
Great Crosshall St	DY	
Great George St	DY	
Great Howard St	CY	56
Great Newton St	EY	
Green Lane	BX	
Grove St	BX	
Hall Lane	BX	
Hannover St	DZ	
Hardman St	EZ	
Hatton Garden	DY	57
Hawthorne Rd	AV	
Haymarket	DY	58
High St	BX	
Holt Rd	BX	61
Hood St	DY	62
Hope St	EZ	
Hornby Rd	AV	64
Houghton St	DY	65
Hunter St	DY	
Huskisson St	EZ	66
Islington	EY	
Jamaica St	DZ	
James St	CY	68
Kelvin Rd	AX	
Kensington	BX	
King Edward St	CY	69
King St	AX	
Kirkdale Rd	AV	71
Knight St	EZ	72
Knowsley Rd	AV	
Leece St	EZ	73
Leeds St	CDY	
Lime St	DY	
Linacre Lane	AV	
Linacre Rd	AV	74
Liscard Rd	AX	
Liver St	CZ	76
Lodge Lane	BX	77
London Rd	DEY	
Longmoor Lane	BV	
Long Lane	BV	
Lord St	CDY	
Lower House Lane	BV	
Lower Lane	BV	
Low Hill	ABX	79
Manor Rd	AX	
Mansfield St	DEY	80
Marsh Lane	AV	
Mather Ave	BX	
Mathew St	CDY	81
Melrose Rd	AV	82
Menlove Ave	BV	
Merton Rd	AV	
Mill Bank	BV	84
Moss Lane	AV	85
Moss St	EY	86
Mount Pleasant	EZ	
Mount St	EZ	88
Muirhead Ave	BV	
Muirhead Ave East	BV	
Myrtle St	EZ	89
Nelson St	DZ	
Netherton Way	AV	
Newington St	DZ	92
New Chester Rd	AX	91
New Quay	CY	93
Northfield Rd	AV	95
North John St	CY	96
Norton St	EY	97
Oakfield Rd	BV	99
Old Hall St	CY	
Oxford St	EZ	
Pall Mall	CY	
Paradise St	DZ	
Parker St	DY	103
Park Lane	DZ	
Park Rd	AX	
Park Rd North	AX	
Parliament St	DZ	
Pembroke Pl.	EY	
Picton Rd	BX	
Poulton Rd	AX	
Prescot Rd	BX	
Prescot St	EY	105
Prince's Rd	EZ	107
Queensway	AX	
Queens Drive	BX	
Queen Square	DY	
Ranelagh St	DY	108
Rathbone Rd	BX	
Renshaw St	DEZ	
Rice Lane	AV	
Richmond St	DY	109
Rimrose Rd	AV	112
Rocky Lane	BX	113
Rodney St	EZ	
Roe St	DY	114
Rose Lane	BX	
Russel St	EY	
St Anne St	DY	
St Domingo Rd	AV	115
St James Pl.	EZ	117
St James St	DZ	
St John's Centre	DY	
St John's Lane	DY	118
St Nicholas Pl.	CY	
St Oswald's St	BX	119
Sandhills Lane	AV	121
School Lane	DYZ	122
Scotland Pl.	DY	123
Scotland Rd	AX	125
Seaforth Rd	AV	126
Seel St	DZ	
Sefton Park Rd	BX	127
Sefton St	DZ	129
Seymour St	EY	130
Shaw St	EY	
Sheil Rd	BX	
Skelhorne St	DY	133
Slater St	DZ	
Smithdown Rd	BX	
Soho St	EY	
Southport Rd	AV	
South John St	CYZ	
Stanhope St	EZ	
Stanley Rd	AV	
Stanley St	CDY	135
Stonebridge Lane	BV	
Stopgate Lane	BV	136
Strand St	CZ	
Strand (The)	CY	
Suffolk St	DZ	137
Tarleton St	DY	139
Tithebarn St	CY	
Townsend Ave	BV	
Townsend Lane	BV	
Tunnel Rd	BX	141
Ullet Rd	BX	
Upper Duke St	EZ	
Upper Frederick St	DZ	
Upper Parliament St	EZ	
Upper Pitt St	DZ	
Utting Ave	AV	
Utting Ave East	BV	
Vauxhall Rd	CY	
Victoria St	DY	143
Walton Breck Rd	AV	147
Walton Hall Ave	BV	
Walton Lane	AV	
Walton Rd	ABV	144
Walton Vale	BV	146
Wapping	CDZ	
Warbreck Moor	BV	149
Warwick	AX	
Waterloo Rd	CY	
Water St	CY	150
Wellington Rd	BX	152
West Derby Rd	BX	153
West Derby St	AX	154
Whitechapel	DY	
William Brown St	DY	156
William Henry St	EY	
Windsor St	EZ	
York St	DZ	157

Radisson SAS
107 Old Hall St ✉ L3 9BD – ✆ (0151) 966 1500 – info.liverpool@radissonsas.com – Fax (0151) 966 1501 CY **c**
189 rm – †£ 99/140 ††£ 99/140, ☕ £15.95 – 5 suites
Rest *Filini* – Italian influences (Closed Sunday and Bank Holidays) Menu £ 13 (lunch) – Carte £ 25/36
◆ Waterfront style: sleek meeting rooms and very well equipped leisure facilities. Chic bar in two Grade II listed cottages. Modern bedrooms themed "ocean" or "urban". Spacious dining room with Italian influenced menus.

Crowne Plaza Liverpool
St Nicholas Pl, Princes Dock, Pier Head ✉ L3 1QW – ✆ (0151) 243 8000 – sales@cpliverpool.co.uk – Fax (0151) 243 8008 CY **a**
155 rm – †£ 129/149 ††£ 89/250, ☕ £14.95 – 4 suites – **Rest** – Menu £ 20/25 – Carte £ 26/38
◆ A busy conference venue within the popular dockside development. Enjoys views of the Mersey and the Liver Building. Well-appointed and very comfortable rooms. Spacious, informal ground floor brasserie.

Malmaison
7 William Jessop Way, Princes Dock ✉ L3 1QZ – ✆ (0151) 229 5000 – liverpool@malmaison.com – Fax (0151) 229 5002 CY **n**
129 rm – †£ 160 ††£ 160, ☕ £13.95 – 1 suite
Rest *Brasserie* – Menu £ 16 (lunch) – Carte £ 26/42
◆ Eye-catching building in redeveloped area of city. Smart, up-to-date bedrooms; those on the waterside have best outlook. Plum evening lounge. Look out for Beatles memorabilia. Stylish brasserie with glass-fronted wine cellar serves extensive menu of classic French dishes.

Hope Street
40 Hope St ✉ L1 9DA – ✆ (0151) 709 3000 – sleep@hopestreethotel.co.uk – Fax (0151) 709 2454 EZ **o**
41 rm – †£ 140 ††£ 140, ☕ £14.50 – 7 suites
Rest *The London Carriage Works* – see restaurant listing
◆ Converted 19C city centre property with modern, stylish interior: leather furniture prominent. Trendy basement lounge bar. Contemporary rooms with state-of-the-art facilities.

62 Castle Street
62 Castle St ✉ L2 7LQ – ✆ (0151) 702 7898 – reservations@62castlest.com – Fax (0151) 702 7899 CY **o**
20 rm – †£ 125 ††£ 125, ☕ £10 – **Rest** – Carte approx. £ 25
◆ Grade II listed Victorian building in city centre combines contemporary and period styles. Smart, spacious bedrooms, with high levels of comfort and facilities. Informal dining room serves extensive menus of international dishes.

Racquet Club
Hargreaves Buildings, 5 Chapel St ✉ L3 9AG – ✆ (0151) 236 6676 – info@racquetclub.org.uk – Fax (0151) 236 6870 – Closed Bank Holidays CY **e**
8 rm – †£ 110 ††£ 110, ☕ £12
Rest *Ziba* – see restaurant listing
◆ Ornate Victorian city centre building converted into club offering unusual accommodation. Leisure facilities are a particularly strong point. Simple, well-equipped rooms.

60 Hope Street
60 Hope St ✉ L1 9BZ – ✆ (0151) 707 6060 – info@60hopestreet.com – Fax (0151) 707 6016 – Closed 25-26 December, 1 January, Saturday lunch, Sunday and Bank Holidays EZ **x**
Rest – Carte £ 34/46
◆ Modern restaurant within an attractive Grade II Georgian house. Informal basement café-bar, brightly decorated dining room and private room above. Modern European cooking.

ENGLAND

XX **The London Carriage Works** - at Hope Street H.

40 Hope St ✉ L1 9DA – ✆ (0151) 705 2222 – eat@hopestreethotel.co.uk – Fax (0151) 709 2454 EZ **o**

Rest – Carte £ 27/47

◆ Stylish twin dining options in eponymous venue: an informal brasserie and bar, or impressive restaurant with strikingly prominent glass feature, and ambitious, seasonal menus.

XX **Simply Heathcotes**

Beetham Plaza, 25 The Strand ✉ L2 0XL – ✆ (0151) 236 3536 – liverpool@simplyheathcotes.co.uk – Fax (0151) 236 3534 – Closed 25-26 December, 1 January and Bank Holidays CY **s**

Rest – Carte £ 20/35

◆ Behind a sloping glass façade is a modish dining room where staff in emblemed shirts serve variations on the classics: hash brown of black pudding. Views of water sculpture.

XX **Ziba** - at Racquet Club

Hargreaves Buildings, 5 Chapel St ✉ L3 9AG – ✆ (0151) 236 6676 – info@racquetclub.org.uk – Fax (0151) 236 6870 – Closed Saturday lunch, Sunday and Bank Holidays CY **e**

Rest – Menu £ 20 (lunch) **s** – Carte £ 26/41 **s**

◆ Modern restaurant in old Victorian building with huge windows and artwork on walls. Small lunch menus, more extensive dinner menus, offering classic-based modern dishes.

ENGLAND

XX **Spire**

1 Church Rd ✉ L15 9EA – ✆ (0151) 734 5040 – spirerestaurant@btinternet.com – Fax (0151) 735 0058 – closed 2 weeks January, Sunday and lunch Monday and Saturday BX **a**

Rest – Menu £ 12/15 – Carte £ 24/29

◆ Glass-fronted restaurant in residential area; large mirror, abstract modern art. First floor best place to sit; window tables most popular. Unfussy modern British cooking.

X **The Side Door**

29a Hope St ✉ L1 9BQ – ✆ (0151) 707 7888 – Fax (0151) 707 7888 – Closed Sunday and Bank Holidays EZ **a**

Rest – Menu £ 17 (dinner) – Carte £ 23/27

◆ Victorian end of terrace ground floor and basement eatery with green painted brick and wood floors. Good value dishes are supplemented by a concise wine list.

at Blundellsands North : 7½ m. by A 565 - CY – ✉ Liverpool

The Blundellsands without rest

9 Elton Ave ✉ L23 8UN – ✆ (0151) 924 6947 – bsbb@blueyonder.co.uk – Fax (0151) 924 6947

4 rm ☕ – 🚹£ 45/55 🚹🚹£ 85

◆ Large semi-detached guesthouse with residential setting. Comfortable guests' lounge; the bedrooms, chintz in style, are clean, well-kept and have lots of extra touches.

at Knowsley Business Park Northeast : 8 m. by A 580 - BV – ✉ Liverpool

Suites H.

Ribblers Lane ✉ L34 9HA – ✆ (0151) 549 2222 – enquiries@suiteshotelgroup.com – Fax (0151) 549 1116

101 suites ☕ – 🚹🚹£ 109 – **Rest** – Menu £ 16 (dinner) **s** – Carte £ 21/26 **s**

◆ Adjoins a business park, with smartly designed work areas. A well-equipped, privately owned hotel, ideal for corporate clients. All rooms are comfortably furnished suites. Upbeat, vibrantly decorated dining room.

at Grassendale Southeast : 4½ m. on A 561 - BX – ✉ Liverpool

Gulshan
544-548 Aigburth Rd, on A 561 ✉ L19 3QG – ✆ (0151) 427 2273 – info@gulshan-liverpool.com
Rest – Indian (dinner only) Menu £ 17 – Carte £ 18/24
◆ A richly decorated and comfortable traditional Indian restaurant within a parade of shops. Smart and efficient service of an extensive menu of authentic dishes.

at Speke Southeast : 8¾ m. by A 561 - BX – ✉ Liverpool

Liverpool Marriott H. South rm,
Speke Aerodrome, Speke Rd, West : 1¾ m. on A 561 ✉ L24 8QD – ✆ (0151) 494 50 00 – mhrs.lplms.eventsorganiser@marriotthotels.com – Fax (0151) 494 50 50
163 rm – †£ 99/200 ††£ 99/200, ☕ £14.95 – 1 suite
Rest *Starways* – Carte £ 19/25
◆ Converted Art Deco airport terminal building, built 1937. Aviation and 1930s era the prevailing themes throughout. The modern, well-equipped bedrooms have a stylish appeal. Smart brasserie within original airport terminal; in keeping with hotel's style.

LIZARD – Cornwall – **503** E 34 1 **A3**
London 326 m – Penzance 24 m – Truro 29 m
Lizard Peninsula★ - Mullion Cove★★ (Church★) - Kynance Cove★★ - Cadgwith★ - Coverack★ – Cury★ (Church★) - Gunwalloe Fishing Cove★ - St Keverne (Church★) - Landewednack★ (Church★) – Mawgan-in-Meneage (Church★) - Ruan Minor (Church★) - St Anthony-in-Meneage★

Housel Bay Housel Cove,
Housel Bay ✉ TR12 7PG – ✆ (01326) 290 417 – info@houselbay.com – Fax (01326) 290 359 – Closed 2-16 January
21 rm ☕ – †£ 50/60 ††£ 70/140 – **Rest** – (bar lunch Monday-Saturday) Carte £ 24/30
◆ Britain's most southerly mainland hotel, with spectacular views of Atlantic and Channel: the Cornish coastal path runs through its gardens. Comfortable bedrooms. Dining room affords dramatic sea and lighthouse views.

Landewednack House (heated) 
Church Cove, East : 1 m. by A 3083 ✉ TR12 7PQ – ✆ (01326) 290 877 – luxurybandb@landewednackhouse.com – Fax (01326) 290 192
6 rm ☕ – †£ 50/75 ††£ 125/150 – **Rest** – (communal dining) Menu £ 21/38
◆ Part 17C former rectory and garden, overlooking Church Cove. Smart interiors stylishly furnished with antiques. Diners encouraged to discuss menus: best local produce to hand.

Tregullas House without rest
Housel Bay ✉ TR12 7PF – ✆ (01326) 290 351 – Closed January, February and Christmas
3 rm ☕ – †£ 28/42 ††£ 58
◆ Simple guesthouse in a charming location with mature garden and sea vista. Spotlessly kept with a cottagey style. Uncluttered bedrooms. At breakfast, take in the garden view.

LLANGARRON – Herefordshire – **503** L 28 – see Ross-on-Wye

Your opinions are important to us:
please write and let us know about your discoveries and experiences – good and bad!

ENGLAND

MICHELIN

LONDON

PRACTICAL INFORMATION

Tourist Information

Britain Visitor Centre, 1 Regent St, W1 v (020) 8846 9000

Airports

$ Heathrow v 08700 000123 12 AX Terminal: Airbus (A1) from Victoria, Airbus (A2) from Paddington Underground (Piccadilly line) frequent service daily.

Gatwick v 08700 002468 13: by A23 EZ and M23 - Terminal: Coach service from Victoria Coach Station (Flightline 777, hourly service) - Railink (Gatwick Express) from Victoria (24 h service).

London City Airportv (020) 7646 0000 11 HV

Stansted, at Bishop's Stortford v 08700 000303, NE: 34m 11 by M11 JT and A12O.

British Airways, Ticket sales and reservations, Paddington Station London, W2, v 08700 8509 8500 36 BX

Banks

Open, generally 9.30 am to 4.30 pm weekdays (except public holidays). You need ID (passport) for cashing cheques. Banks levy smaller commissions than hotels. Many `Bureaux de Change` around Piccadilly open 7 days.

Medical Emergencies

To contact a doctor for first aid, emergency medical advice and chemists night service: v 07000 372255.

Accident & Emergency: dial 999 for Ambulance, Police or Fire Services.

Post Offices

Open Monday to Friday 9am to 5.30 pm. Late collections made from Leicester Square.

Shopping

Most stores are found in Oxford Street (Selfridges, M & S), Regent Street (Hamleys, Libertys) and Knightsbridge (Harrods, Harvey Nichols). Open usually Monday to Saturday 9 am to 6 pm. Some open later (8 pm) once a week; Knightsbridge Wednesday, Oxford Street and Regent Street Thursday. Other areas worth visiting include Jermyn Street and Savile Row (mens outfitters), Bond Street (jewellers and haute couture).

Theatres

The «West End» has many major theatre performances and can generally be found around Shaftesbury Avenue. Most daily newspapers give details of performances. A half-price ticket booth is located in Leicester Square and is open Monday to Saturday 1 pm to 6.30 pm, Sunday and matinée days 12 noon to 6.30 pm. Restrictions apply.

Tipping

When a service charge is included in a bill it is not necessary to tip extra. If service is not included a discretionary 10% is normal.

Travel

As driving in London is difficult, it is advisable to take the Underground, a bus or taxi. Taxis can be hailed when the amber light is illuminated.

Congestion Charging

The congestion charge is £8 per day on all vehicles (except motor cycles and exempt vehicles) entering the central zone between 7.00 am and 6.00 pm - Monday to Friday except on Bank Holldays.

Payment can be made in advance, on the day, by post, on the Internet, by telephone (0845 900 1234) or at retail outlets.

A charge of up to £100 will be made for non-payment.

Further information is available on the Transport for London website - www. cclondon.com

Localities outside the Greater London limits are listed alphabetically throughout the guide.

Les localités situées en dehors des limites de Greater London se trouvent à leur place alphabetique dans le guide.

Alle Städte und Gemeinden außerhalb von Greater London sind in alphabetischer Reihenfolge aufgelistet.

Le località situate al di fuori dei confini della Greater London sono ordinate alfabeticamente all'interno della Guida.

SIGHTS

HISTORICAL BUILDINGS AND MONUMENTS

Palace of Westminsterz : House of Lordsy, Westminster Hallx (hammer-beam roofz), Robing Roomx, Central Lobbyx, House of Commonsx, Big Benx, Victoria Towerx 39 ALX - Tower of Londonz (Crown Jewelsz, White Tower or Keepz, St John's Chapely) - British Airways London Eye (viewsz) 32 AMV.

Banqueting Housey 31 ALV - Buckingham Palacey (Changing of the Guard, Royal Mewsy, Queen's Galleryy) 38 AIX - Kensington Palacey 27 ABV - Lincoln's Inny 32 AMT - Lloyds Buildingy 34 ARU - Royal Hospital Chelseay 37 AGZ - St James`s Palacey 30 AJV - Somerset Housey 32 AMU - South Bank Arts Centrey (Royal Festival Hallx, National Theatre Royalx, County Hallx) 32 AMV - Spencer Housey 30 AIV - The Templey (Middle Temple Hally) 32 ANU - Tower Bridgey 34 ASV.

Albert Memorialx 36 ADX - Apsley Housex 30 AHV - Burlington Housex 30 AIV - Charterhousex 19 UZD - George Innx, Southwark 33 AQV - Gray's Innx 32 AMV - Guildhallx (Lord Mayor's Show) 33 AQT - Shakespeare`s Globex 33 APV - Dr Johnson's Housex 32 ANT - Leighton Housex 35 AAX - Linley Sambourne Housex 35 AAX - London Bridgex 34 ARV - Mansion Housex (plate and insigniay) 33 AQV - The Monumentx (Q x) 34 ARU - Old Admiraltyx 31 AKV - Royal Albert Hallx 36 ADX - Royal Exchangex 34 ARU - Royal Opera Housex (Covent Garden) 31 ALU - Staple Innx 32 ANT - Theatre Royalx (Haymarket) 31 AKV - Westminster Bridgex 39 ALX.

CHURCHES

The City Churches

St Paul's Cathedralz (Dome e z) 33 APU.
St Bartholomew the Greaty (choirx) 33 APT - St Dunstan-in-the-Eastx (Towerx) 34 ARU - St Mary-at-Hilly (planx) 34 ARU - Temple Churchy 32 ANU.

All Hallows-by-the-Tower (font covery, brassesx) 34 ARU - Christ Churchx 33 APT - Cole Abbey Presbyterian Church (spirex) 33 APU - St Andrew Undershaft (monumentsx) 34 ARU - St Bridex (steepley) 32 ANU - St Clement Eastcheap (pulpitx) 34 ARU - St Edmund the King and Martyr (spirex) 34 ARU - St Giles Cripplegatex 33 AQT - St

Helen Bishopsgatex (monumentsy) 34 ART - St James Garlickhythe (spirex, sword restsx) 33 AQU - St Magnus the Martyr (towerx, sword restx) 34 ARU - St Margaret Lothburyx (spirex, woodworkx, screenx, fontx) 33 AQT - St Margaret Pattens (spirex, woodworkx) 34 ARU - St Martin-within-Ludgate (spirex, door casesx) 33 APU - St Mary Abchurchx (reredosy, spirex, domex) 33 AQU - St Mary-le-Bow (steepley) 33 AQU - St Michael Paternoster Royal (spirex) 35 AQU - St Olavex 34 ARU - St Peter upon Cornhill (screenx) 34 ARU - St Stephen Walbrookx (steeplex, domex) 33 AQU.

Other Churches

Westminster Abbeyz (Henry VII Chapelz, Chapel of Edward the Confessory, Chapter Housey, Poets' Cornerx) 39 ALX.

Southwark Cathedraly 33 AQV.

Queen's Chapelx 39 AJV - St Clement Danesx 32 AMU - St James'sx 30 AJV - St Margaret'sx 39 ALX - St Martin-in-the-Fieldsx 31 ALV - St Paul'sx (Covent Garden) 31 ALU - Westminster Roman Catholic Cathedralx 39 ALX.

PARKS

Regent's Parkz (terracesy, Zooy) 11 QZC.

Hyde Park 29 AFV - Kensington Gardensy 28 ACV (Orangeryx) 27 ABV - St James's Parky 31 AKV.

STREETS AND SQUARES

The City★★★ **33** AQT.

Bedford Squarey 31 AKT - Belgrave Squarey 37 AGX - Burlington Arcadex 30 AIV - Covent Gardeny (The Piazzay) 31 ALU - The Mally 31 AKV - Piccadillyx 30 AIV - Trafalgar Squarey 31 AKV - Whitehally (Horse Guardsx) 31 ALV.

Barbicanx 33 AQT - Bond Streetx 30 AIU - Canonbury Squarex 13 UZB - Carlton House Terracex 31 AKV - Cheyne Walkx 23 PZG - Fitzroy Squarex 18 RZD - Jermyn Streetx 30 AJV - Leicester Squarex 31 AKU - Merrick Squarex 19 VZE - Montpelier Squarex 37 AFX - Neal's Yardx 31 ALU - Piccadilly Arcadex 30 AIV - Piccadilly Circusx 31 AKU - Portman Squarex 29 AGT - Regent Streetx 30 AIU - Royal Opera Arcadex 31 AKV - St James's Squarex 31 AJV - St James's Streetx 30 AIV - Shepherd Marketx 30 AHV - Trinity Church Squarex 19 VZE - Victoria Emban kment Gardensx 31 ALV - Waterloo Placex 31 AKV.

MUSEUMS

British Museumz 31 AKL - Imperial War Museumz 40 ANY - National Galleryz 31 AKV - Science Mu-seumz 36 ADX - Tate Britainz 39 ALY - Victoria and Albert Museumz 36 ADY - Wallace Collectionz 29 AGT.

Courtauld Institute Galleriesy (Somerset House) 32 AMU - Gilbert Collectiony (Somerset House) 32 AMU - Museum of Londony 33 APT - National Portrait Galleryy 31 AKU - Natural History Museumy 36 ADY - Sir John Soane's Museumy 32 AMT - Tate Moderny (viewsz from top floors) 33 APV.

Clock Museumx (Guildhall) 33 AQT - London`s Transport Museumx 31 ALU - Madame Tussaud's Waxworksx 17 QZD - National Army Museumx 37 AGZ - Percival David Foundation of Chinese Artx 18 SZD - Wellington Museumx (Apsley House) 30 AHV.

OUTER LONDON

Blackheath 8 HX terraces and housesx, Eltham Palacex A

Brentford 5 BX Syon Parky, gardensx

Bromley 7 GXY The Crystal Palace Parkx

Chiswick 6 CV Chiswick Mally, Chiswick Housex D, Hogarth's Housex E

Dulwich 11 Picture Galleryx FX X

Greenwich 7 and 8 GHV Cutty Sarky GV F, Footway Tunnel (e y), Fan Museumx 10 GV A, National Maritime Museumy (Queen's Housey) GV M2 Royal Naval Collegey (Painted Hallx, the Chapelx) GV G, The Park and Old Royal Observatoryx (Meridian Building: collectiony) HV K, Ranger's Housex (Wernher Collection) GX N

Hampstead Kenwood Housey (Adam Libraryy, paintingsy) 2 EU P, Fenton Housey 11 PZA
Hampton Court 5 BY (The Palacez, gardensz, Fountain Courtx, The Great Vinex)
Kew 6 CX Royal Botanic Gardensz : Palm Housey, Temperate Housex, Kew Palace or Dutch Housey, Orangeryx, Pagodax, Japanese Gatewayx
Hendonx 2 Royal Air Force Museumy CT M3
Hounslow 5 BV Osterley Parky
Lewisham 7 GX Horniman Museumx M4
Richmond 5 and 6 CX Richmond Parky, Q z CX, Richmond HillQ y CX, Richmond Bridgey BX R, Richmond Greeny BX S, (Maids of Honour Rowy, Trumpeter's Housex), Asgill Housex BX B, Ham Housey BX V
Shoreditch 14 XZ Beffrye Museumx M
Tower Hamlets 7 GV Canary Wharfy B, Isle of Dogsx St Katharine Dockx 34 ASV
Twickenham 5 BX Marble Hill Housex Z, Strawberry Hillx A

The maps in this section of the Guide are based upon the Ordnance Survey of Great Britain with the permission of the Controller of Her Majesty's Stationery Office. © Crown Copyright 100000247

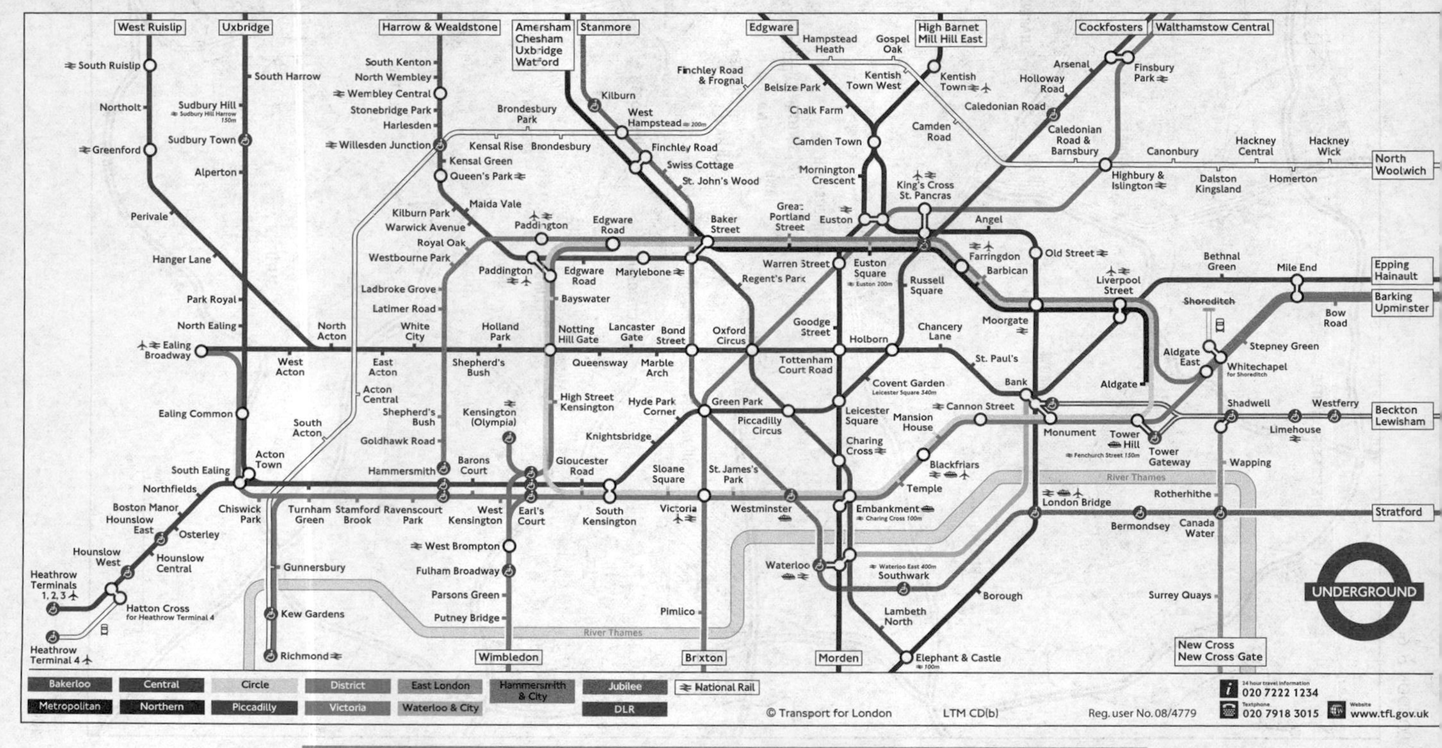
West Ruislip
Uxbridge
Harrow & Wealdstone
Amersham
Chesham
Uxbridge
Watford
Stanmore
Edgware
High Barnet
Mill Hill East
Cockfosters
Walthamstow Central
South Ruislip
South Harrow
Northolt
Sudbury Hill
Sudbury Hill Harrow 150m
Greenford
Sudbury Town
Alperton
Perivale
Hanger Lane
Park Royal
North Ealing
Ealing Broadway
West Acton
North Acton
Ealing Common
South Ealing
Acton Town
Northfields
Boston Manor
Hounslow East
Osterley
Hounslow West
Hounslow Central
Heathrow Terminals 1, 2, 3
Hatton Cross
for Heathrow Terminal 4
Heathrow Terminal 4
South Kenton
North Wembley
Wembley Central
Stonebridge Park
Harlesden
Willesden Junction
Kensal Green
Queen's Park
Kilburn Park
Maida Vale
Warwick Avenue
Royal Oak
Westbourne Park
Ladbroke Grove
Latimer Road
White City
East Acton
Acton Central
Shepherd's Bush
Goldhawk Road
Hammersmith
South Acton
Chiswick Park
Turnham Green
Stamford Brook
Ravenscourt Park
Gunnersbury
Kew Gardens
Richmond
Brondesbury Park
Kensal Rise
Brondesbury
Kilburn
West Hampstead
200m
Finchley Road & Frognal
Finchley Road
Swiss Cottage
St. John's Wood
Paddington
Edgware Road
Marylebone
Baker Street
Bayswater
Notting Hill Gate
Holland Park
Queensway
Lancaster Gate
Marble Arch
Bond Street
Oxford Circus
High Street Kensington
Kensington (Olympia)
Barons Court
West Kensington
Earl's Court
West Brompton
Fulham Broadway
Parsons Green
Putney Bridge
Wimbledon
Gloucester Road
South Kensington
Knightsbridge
Hyde Park Corner
Sloane Square
Victoria
Pimlico
Brixton
St. James's Park
Westminster
Green Park
Piccadilly Circus
Belsize Park
Hampstead Heath
Gospel Oak
Kentish Town West
Chalk Farm
Camden Town
Camden Road
Kentish Town
Mornington Crescent
Great Portland Street
Euston
King's Cross St. Pancras
Warren Street
Regent's Park
Euston Square
Euston 200m
Russell Square
Goodge Street
Tottenham Court Road
Holborn
Chancery Lane
Covent Garden
Leicester Square 340m
Leicester Square
Charing Cross
Embankment
Charing Cross 100m
Waterloo
Waterloo East 400m
Southwark
Lambeth North
Elephant & Castle
100m
Morden
Temple
Blackfriars
Mansion House
Cannon Street
St. Paul's
Bank
Monument
Borough
London Bridge
Angel
Farringdon
Barbican
Moorgate
Old Street
Liverpool Street
Aldgate
Aldgate East
Tower Hill
Fenchurch Street 150m
Tower Gateway
Arsenal
Holloway Road
Caledonian Road
Caledonian Road & Barnsbury
Finsbury Park
Highbury & Islington
Canonbury
Dalston Kingsland
Hackney Central
Homerton
Hackney Wick
North Woolwich
Bethnal Green
Mile End
Shoreditch
Whitechapel
for Shoreditch
Stepney Green
Bow Road
Epping
Hainault
Barking
Upminster
Shadwell
Limehouse
Westferry
Beckton
Lewisham
Wapping
River Thames
Rotherhithe
Bermondsey
Canada Water
Stratford
Surrey Quays
New Cross
New Cross Gate
UNDERGROUND
Bakerloo
Central
Circle
District
East London
Hammersmith & City
Jubilee
National Rail
Metropolitan
Northern
Piccadilly
Victoria
Waterloo & City
DLR
© Transport for London
LTM CD(b)
Reg. user No. 08/4779
24 hour travel information
020 7222 1234
Textphone
020 7918 3015
Website
www.tfl.gov.uk

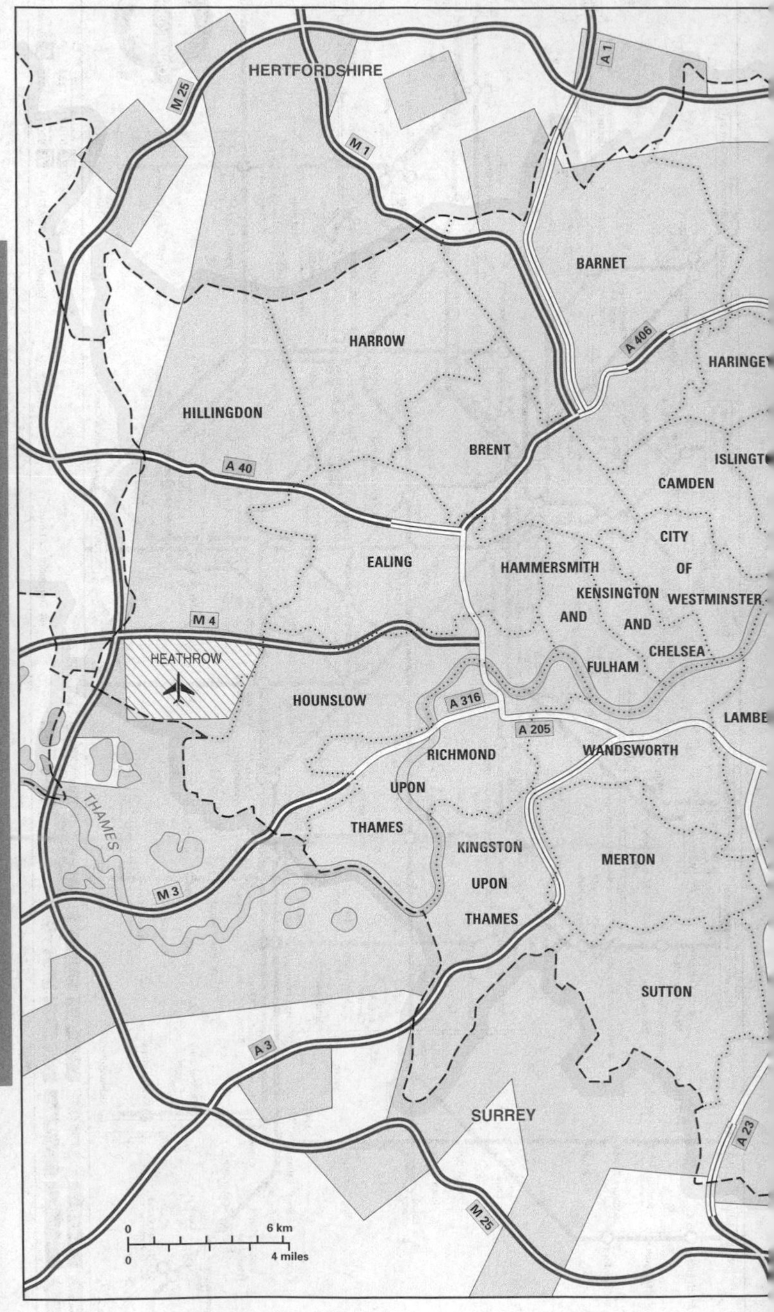
HERTFORDSHIRE
M 25
M 1
A 1
BARNET
A 406
HARROW
HARINGEY
HILLINGDON
BRENT
A 40
ISLINGTON
CAMDEN
CITY
EALING
HAMMERSMITH
OF
KENSINGTON
WESTMINSTER
AND
AND
M 4
CHELSEA
HEATHROW
FULHAM
HOUNSLOW
A 316
LAMBE
A 205
RICHMOND
WANDSWORTH
UPON
THAMES
THAMES
KINGSTON
MERTON
UPON
M 3
THAMES
SUTTON
A 3
SURREY
A 23
M 25
0
6 km
0
4 miles

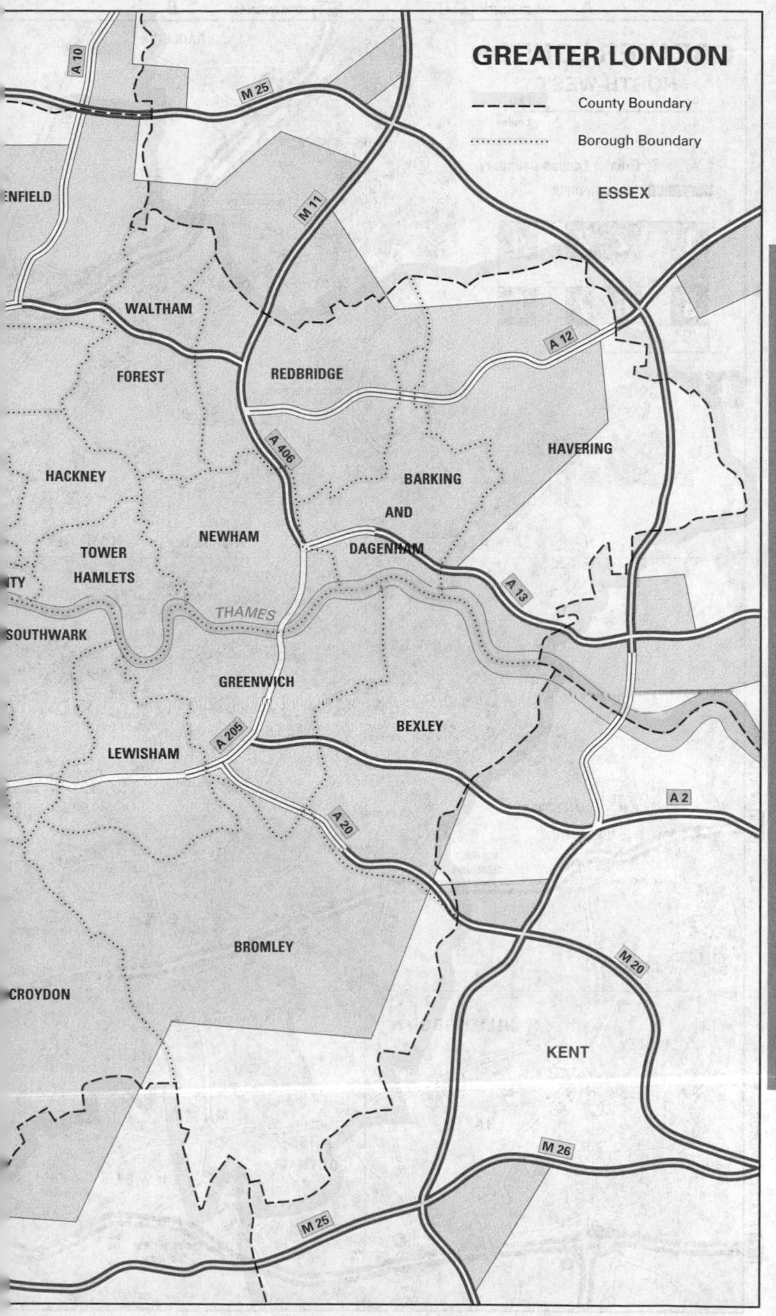
GREATER LONDON
County Boundary
Borough Boundary
ESSEX
A 10
M 25
ENFIELD
M 11
WALTHAM
FOREST
REDBRIDGE
A 12
HAVERING
A 406
HACKNEY
BARKING
AND
DAGENHAM
NEWHAM
TOWER
HAMLETS
A 13
THAMES
SOUTHWARK
GREENWICH
BEXLEY
A 205
LEWISHAM
A 2
A 20
BROMLEY
M 20
CROYDON
KENT
M 26
M 25

GREATER LONDON
NORTH-WEST

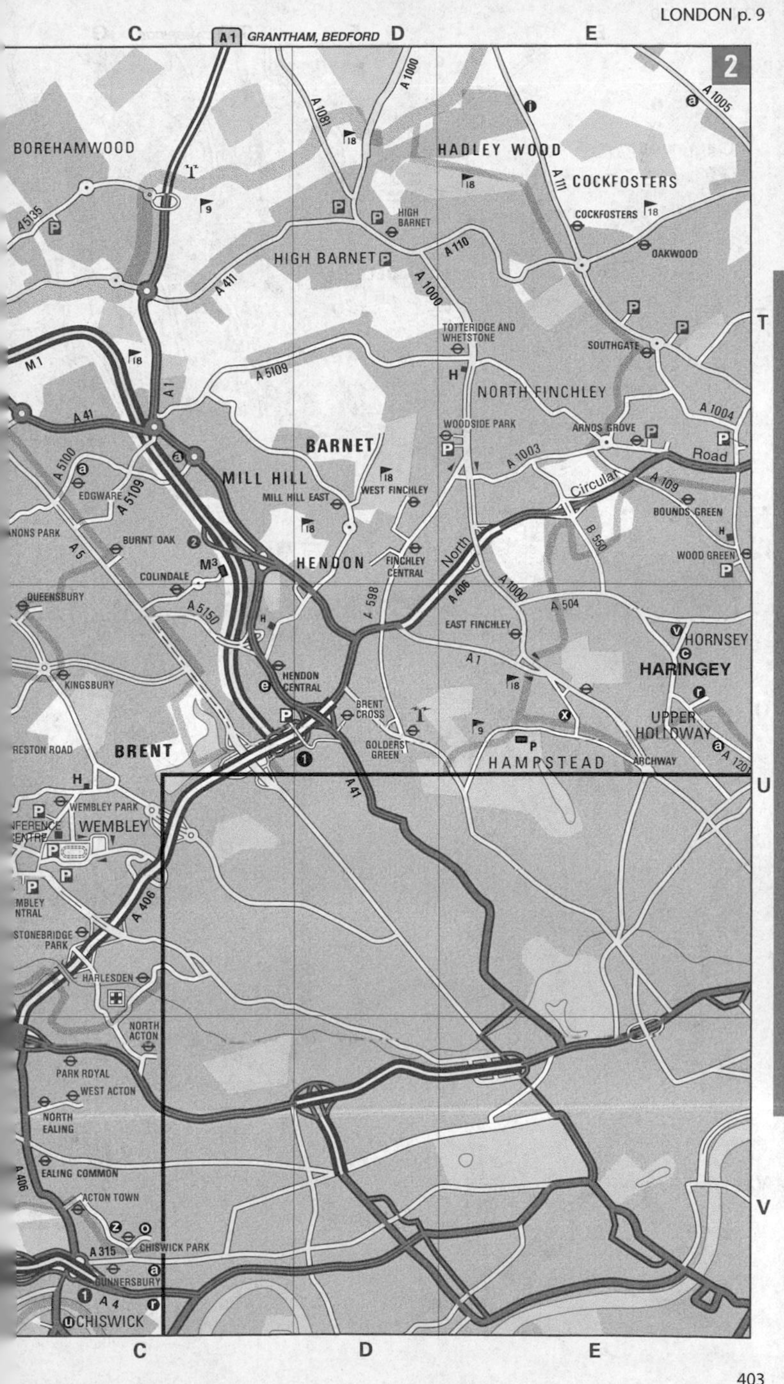
C
A 1 GRANTHAM, BEDFORD
D
E
2
A 1005
A 1000
A 1081
HADLEY WOOD
COCKFOSTERS
A 111
BOREHAMWOOD
A 5135
HIGH BARNET
COCKFOSTERS
OAKWOOD
A 110
HIGH BARNET
A 411
A 1000
T
TOTTERIDGE AND WHETSTONE
SOUTHGATE
M 1
A 5109
A 1
NORTH FINCHLEY
A 41
A 1004
WOODSIDE PARK
ARNOS GROVE
BARNET
A 1003
Road
A 5100
Circular
EDGWARE
A 5109
MILL HILL
MILL HILL EAST
WEST FINCHLEY
A 109
BOUNDS GREEN
B 550
BURNT OAK
NONS PARK
A 5
North
WOOD GREEN
HENDON
FINCHLEY CENTRAL
COLINDALE
A 1000
QUEENSBURY
A 5150
A 598
A 406
A 504
EAST FINCHLEY
HORNSEY
A 1
HARINGEY
KINGSBURY
HENDON CENTRAL
BRENT CROSS
UPPER HOLLOWAY
RESTON ROAD
BRENT
GOLDERS GREEN
HAMPSTEAD
ARCHWAY
A 41
A 1201
U
WEMBLEY PARK
WEMBLEY
NFERENCE ENTRE
MBLEY NTRAL
A 406
STONEBRIDGE PARK
HARLESDEN
NORTH ACTON
PARK ROYAL
WEST ACTON
NORTH EALING
EALING COMMON
A 406
ACTON TOWN
V
A 315
CHISWICK PARK
GUNNERSBURY
A 4
CHISWICK
C
D
E

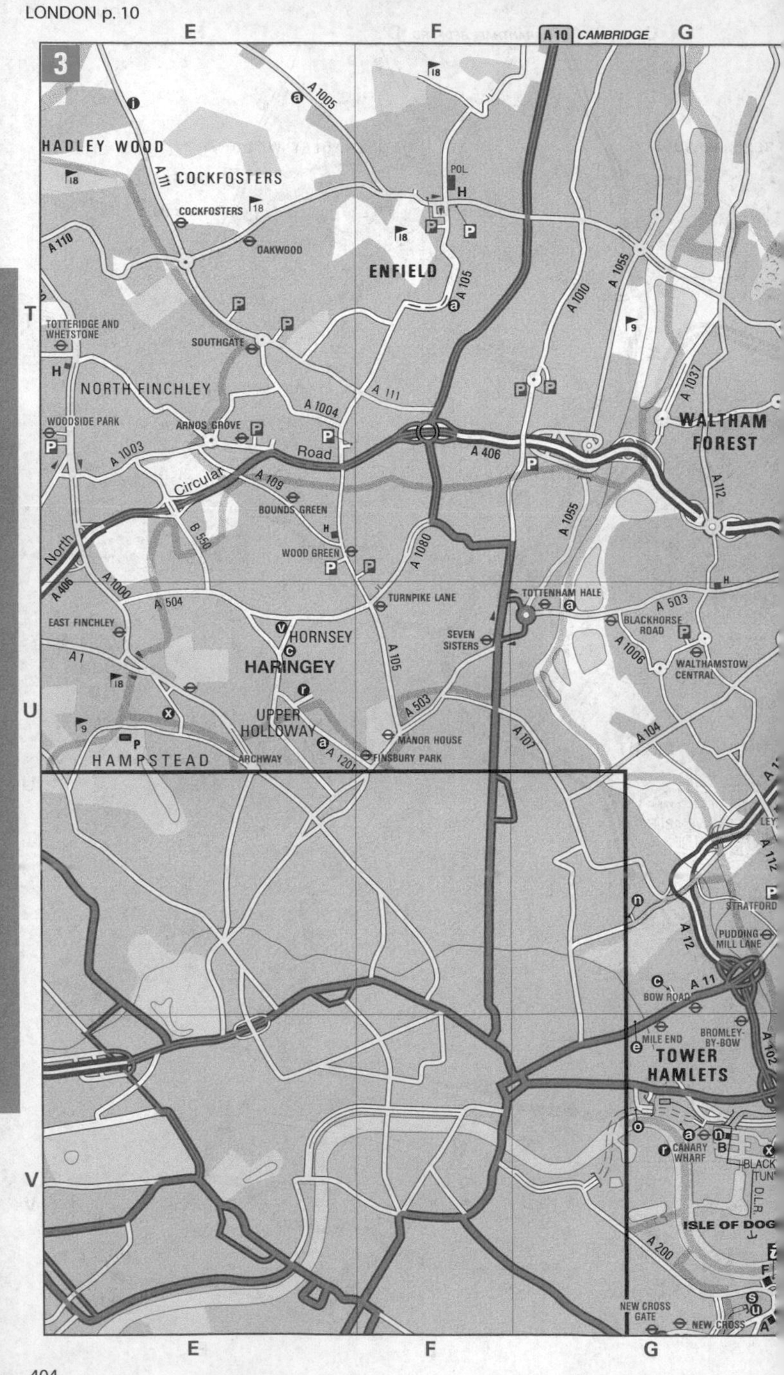

E
F
A 10 CAMBRIDGE
G
3
A 1005
HADLEY WOOD
A 111
COCKFOSTERS
POL.
COCKFOSTERS
A 110
OAKWOOD
ENFIELD
A 105
A 1010
A 1055
TOTTERIDGE AND WHETSTONE
SOUTHGATE
NORTH FINCHLEY
A 111
A 1004
A 1037
WALTHAM FOREST
WOODSIDE PARK
ARNOS GROVE
A 1003
Road
A 406
Circular
A 109
A 112
BOUNDS GREEN
B 550
A 1055
North
WOOD GREEN
A 1080
A 406
A 1000
A 504
TURNPIKE LANE
TOTTENHAM HALE
A 503
EAST FINCHLEY
HORNSEY
SEVEN SISTERS
BLACKHORSE ROAD
A 1006
A 1
HARINGEY
A 105
WALTHAMSTOW CENTRAL
A 503
UPPER HOLLOWAY
A 107
A 104
MANOR HOUSE
HAMPSTEAD
ARCHWAY
A 1201
FINSBURY PARK
LEY
A 112
STRATFORD
A 12
PUDDING MILL LANE
BOW ROAD
A 11
MILE END
BROMLEY-BY-BOW
TOWER HAMLETS
A 102
CANARY WHARF
BLACK
ISLE OF DOG
D.L.R.
A 200
NEW CROSS GATE
NEW CROSS
T
U
V
E
F
G

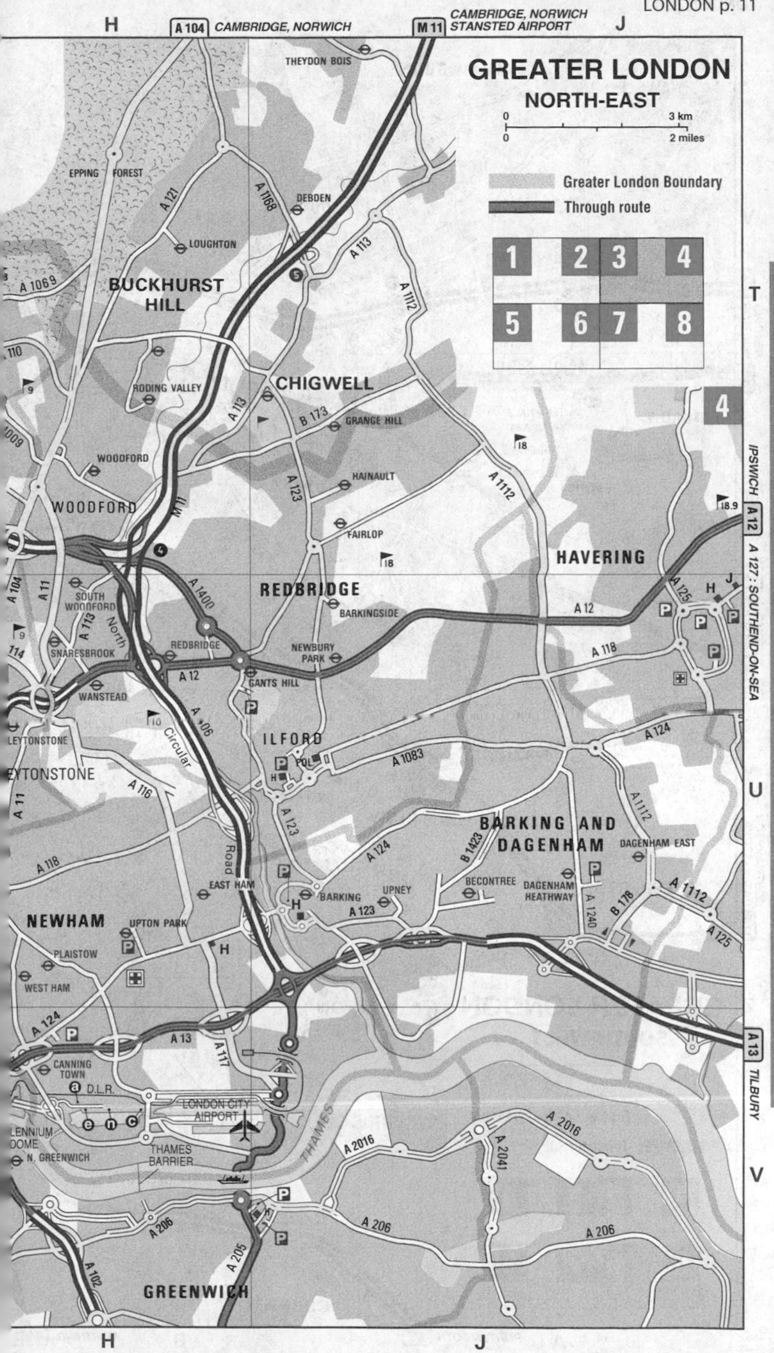
GREATER LONDON
NORTH-EAST
0 3 km
0 2 miles
Greater London Boundary
Through route
A 104 CAMBRIDGE, NORWICH
M 11 CAMBRIDGE, NORWICH STANSTED AIRPORT
H
J
T
U
V
THEYDON BOIS
EPPING FOREST
DEBDEN
LOUGHTON
BUCKHURST HILL
CHIGWELL
RODING VALLEY
GRANGE HILL
WOODFORD
HAINAULT
FAIRLOP
HAVERING
REDBRIDGE
SOUTH WOODFORD
BARKINGSIDE
REDBRIDGE
SNARESBROOK
NEWBURY PARK
GANTS HILL
WANSTEAD
LEYTONSTONE
ILFORD
North Circular Road
BARKING AND DAGENHAM
DAGENHAM EAST
BECONTREE
DAGENHAM HEATHWAY
EAST HAM
BARKING
UPNEY
NEWHAM
UPTON PARK
PLAISTOW
WEST HAM
CANNING TOWN
D.L.R.
LONDON CITY AIRPORT
THAMES BARRIER
N. GREENWICH
THAMES
GREENWICH
IPSWICH A 12
A 127 : SOUTHEND-ON-SEA
A 13 TILBURY

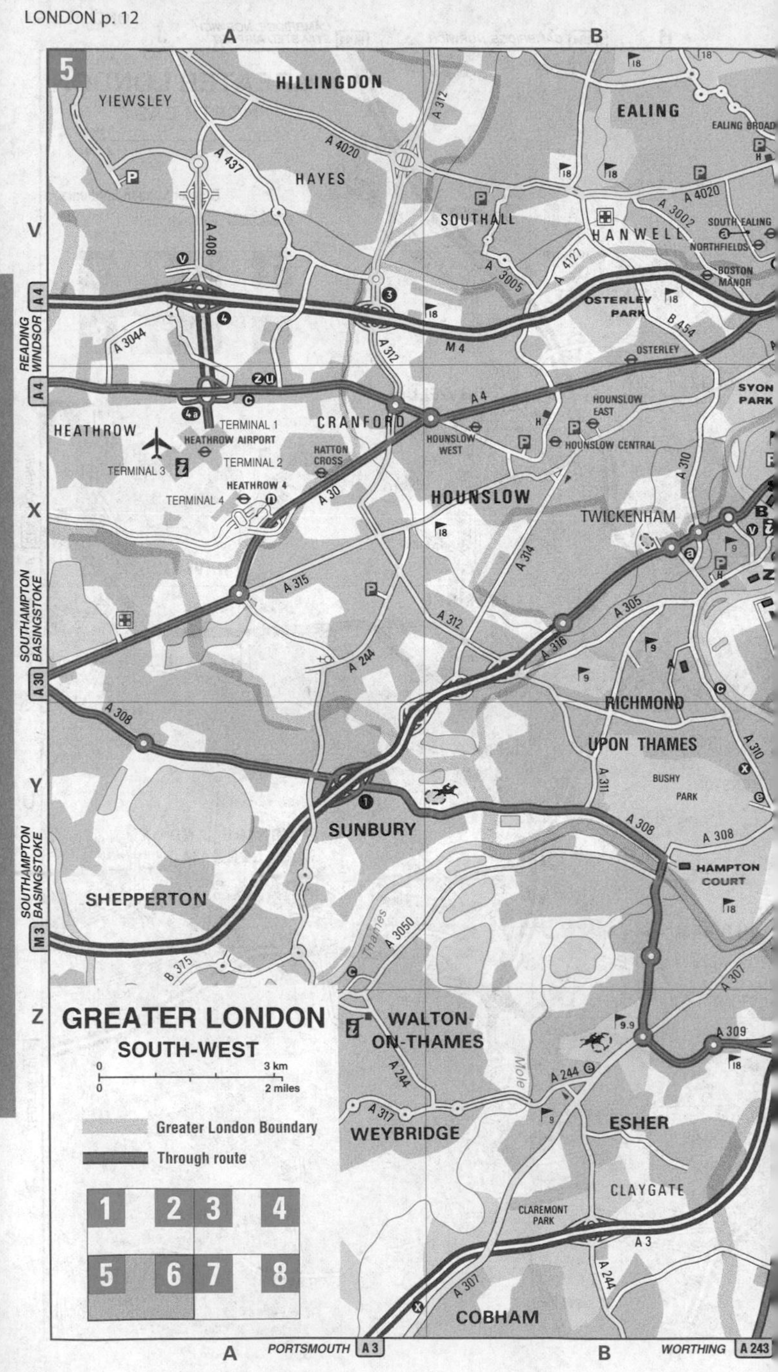
5
HILLINGDON
YIEWSLEY
EALING
HAYES
SOUTHALL
HANWELL
SOUTH EALING
NORTHFIELDS
BOSTON MANOR
OSTERLEY PARK
OSTERLEY
SYON PARK
HOUNSLOW EAST
HOUNSLOW WEST
HOUNSLOW CENTRAL
HEATHROW
HEATHROW AIRPORT
TERMINAL 1
TERMINAL 2
TERMINAL 3
TERMINAL 4
HEATHROW 4
HATTON CROSS
CRANFORD
HOUNSLOW
TWICKENHAM
RICHMOND UPON THAMES
BUSHY PARK
SUNBURY
SHEPPERTON
HAMPTON COURT
WALTON-ON-THAMES
WEYBRIDGE
ESHER
CLAYGATE
CLAREMONT PARK
COBHAM
Thames
Mole
READING WINDSOR
SOUTHAMPTON BASINGSTOKE
PORTSMOUTH A 3
WORTHING A 243
GREATER LONDON
SOUTH-WEST
3 km
2 miles
Greater London Boundary
Through route

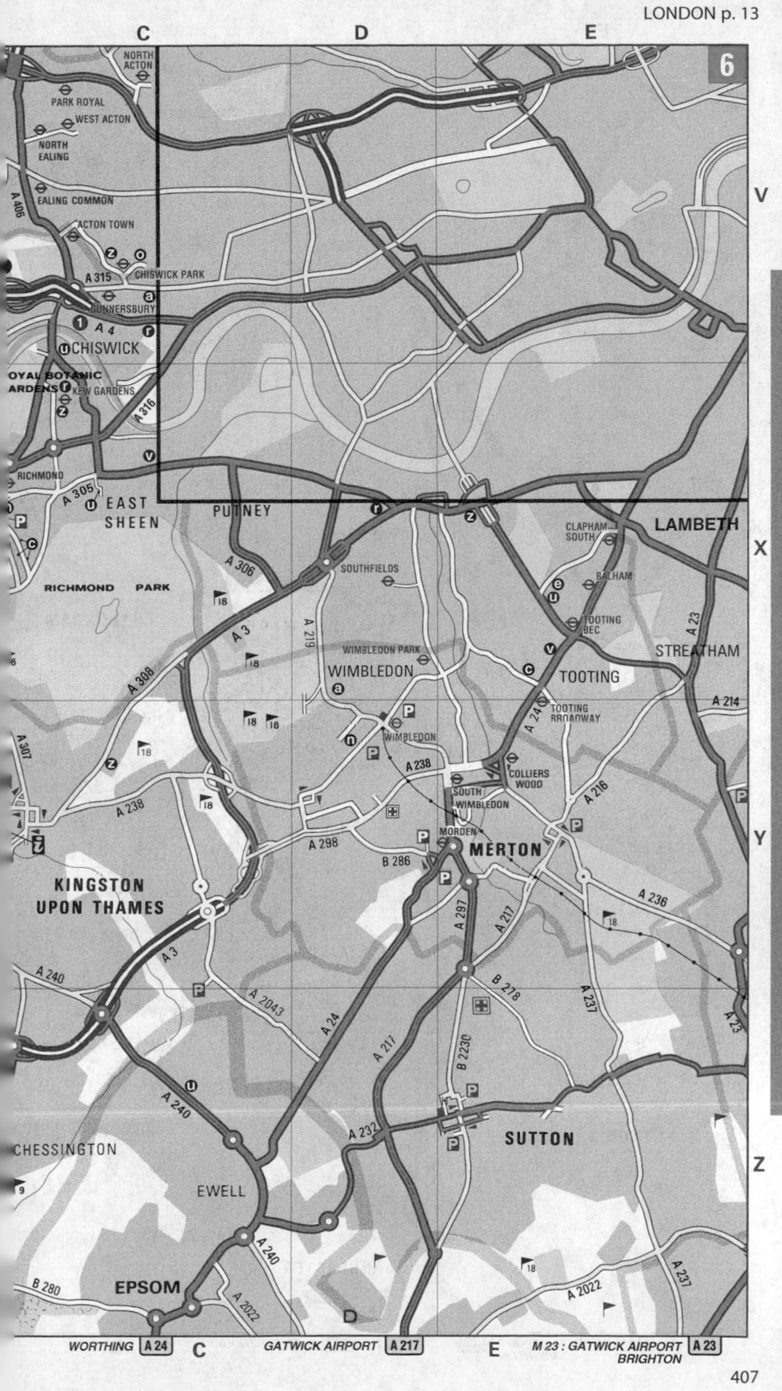
C
D
E
6
V
X
Y
Z
NORTH ACTON
PARK ROYAL
WEST ACTON
NORTH EALING
EALING COMMON
ACTON TOWN
CHISWICK PARK
GUNNERSBURY
CHISWICK
KEW GARDENS
RICHMOND
EAST SHEEN
PUTNEY
RICHMOND PARK
SOUTHFIELDS
CLAPHAM SOUTH
BALHAM
LAMBETH
TOOTING BEC
STREATHAM
WIMBLEDON PARK
WIMBLEDON
TOOTING
TOOTING BROADWAY
COLLIERS WOOD
SOUTH WIMBLEDON
MORDEN
MERTON
KINGSTON UPON THAMES
CHESSINGTON
EWELL
SUTTON
EPSOM
A 406
A 315
A 4
A 316
A 305
A 306
A 3
A 219
A 308
A 307
A 238
A 298
B 286
A 24
A 216
A 214
A 23
A 236
A 297
A 217
B 278
A 237
A 240
A 2043
B 2230
A 232
A 2022
B 280
WORTHING A 24
GATWICK AIRPORT A 217
M 23 : GATWICK AIRPORT BRIGHTON A 23

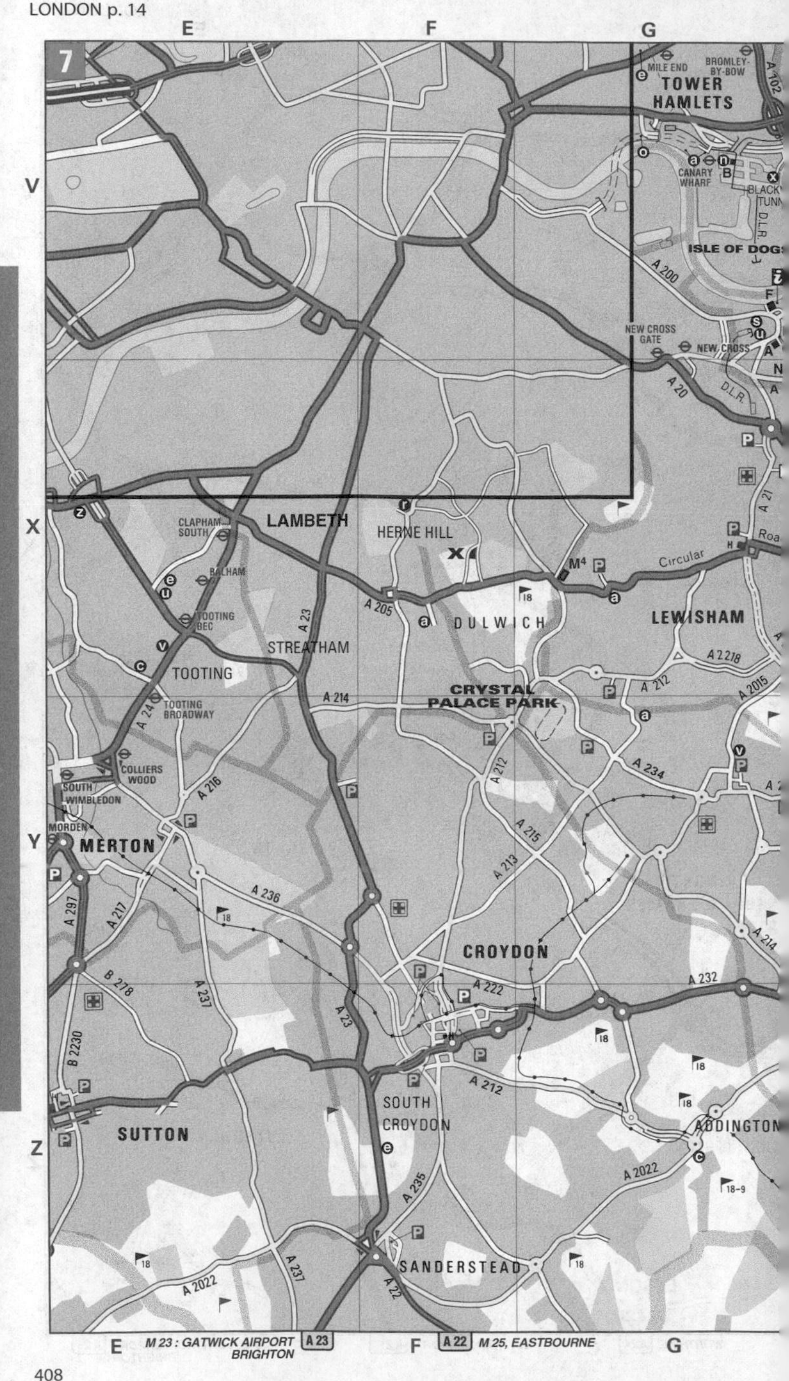
E
F
G
7
V
X
Y
Z
MILE END
BROMLEY-BY-BOW
TOWER HAMLETS
CANARY WHARF
ISLE OF DOGS
A 200
NEW CROSS GATE
NEW CROSS
A 20
D.L.R.
A 21
Circular
LAMBETH
CLAPHAM SOUTH
BALHAM
HERNE HILL
TOOTING BEC
A 205
A 23
DULWICH
LEWISHAM
STREATHAM
TOOTING
A 2218
A 214
CRYSTAL PALACE PARK
A 212
A 2015
TOOTING BROADWAY
A 24
A 234
COLLIERS WOOD
A 216
SOUTH WIMBLEDON
MORDEN
MERTON
A 215
A 213
A 236
A 297
A 217
CROYDON
A 214
B 278
A 237
A 232
A 222
B 2230
A 212
SOUTH CROYDON
SUTTON
ADDINGTON
A 2022
A 235
SANDERSTEAD
A 2022
A 22
M 23 : GATWICK AIRPORT BRIGHTON
A 23
A 22
M 25, EASTBOURNE

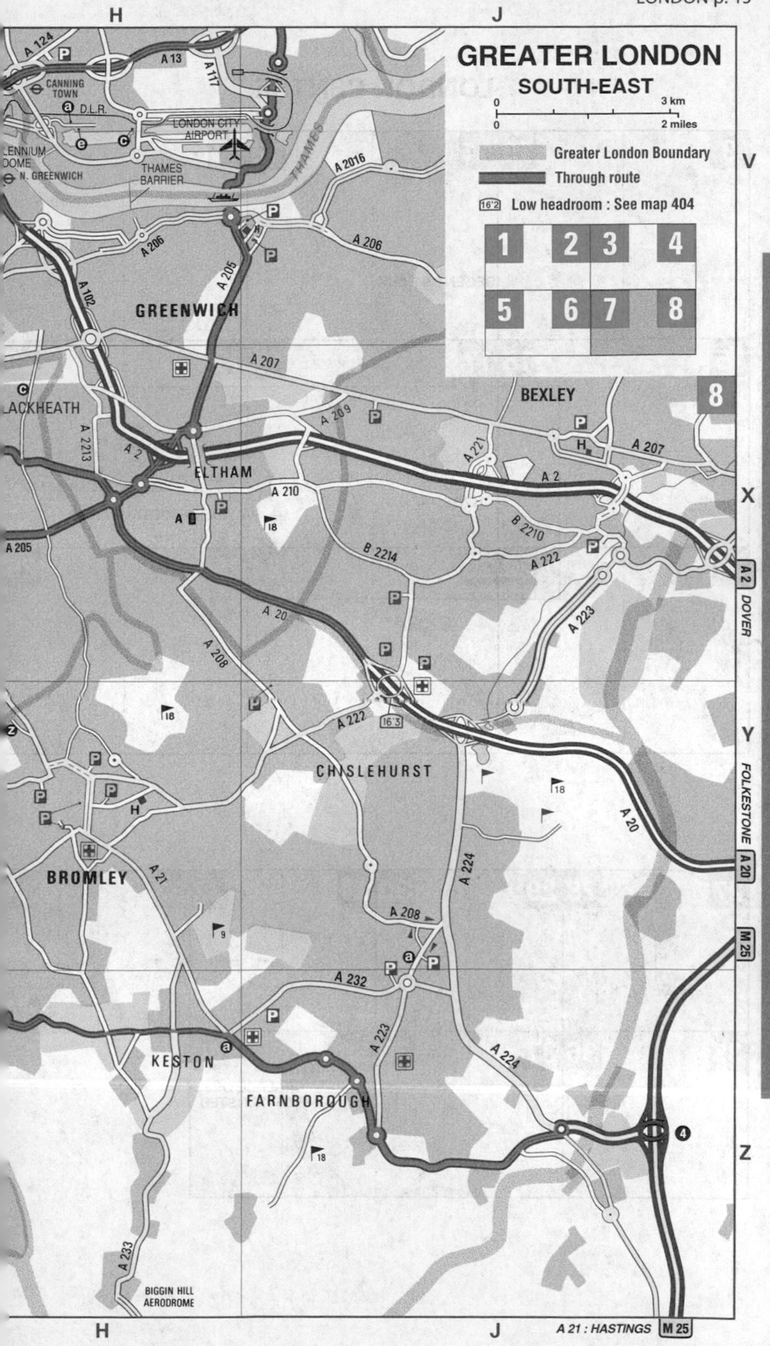

H
J
GREATER LONDON
SOUTH-EAST
0
3 km
0
2 miles
Greater London Boundary
Through route
16'2 Low headroom : See map 404
1
2
3
4
5
6
7
8
V
X
Y
Z
A 124
A 13
A 117
CANNING TOWN
D.L.R.
LONDON CITY AIRPORT
THAMES
A 2016
THAMES BARRIER
N. GREENWICH
A 206
A 205
A 102
GREENWICH
A 207
BEXLEY
A 209
A 221
A 2213
A 2
ELTHAM
A 210
B 2210
A 205
B 2214
A 222
A 223
A 20
A 208
16'3
CHISLEHURST
DOVER
FOLKESTONE
M 25
BROMLEY
A 21
A 224
A 232
KESTON
FARNBOROUGH
A 233
BIGGIN HILL AERODROME
A 21 : HASTINGS

LONDON CENTRE

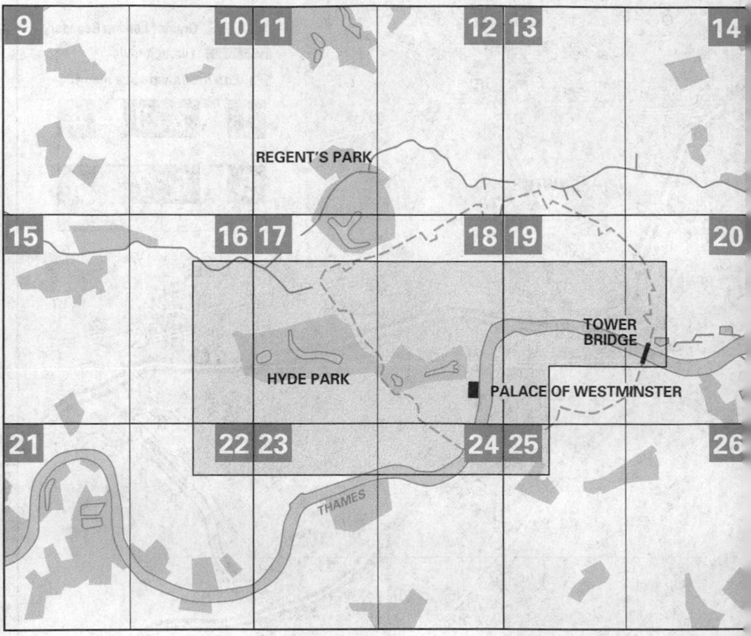

9
10 11
12 13
14
REGENT'S PARK
15
16 17
18 19
20
TOWER BRIDGE
HYDE PARK
PALACE OF WESTMINSTER
21
22 23
24 25
26
THAMES

27
28 29
30 31
32 33
34
THAMES
TOWER BRIDGE
HYDE PARK
35
36 37
38 39
40
PALACE OF WESTMINSTER

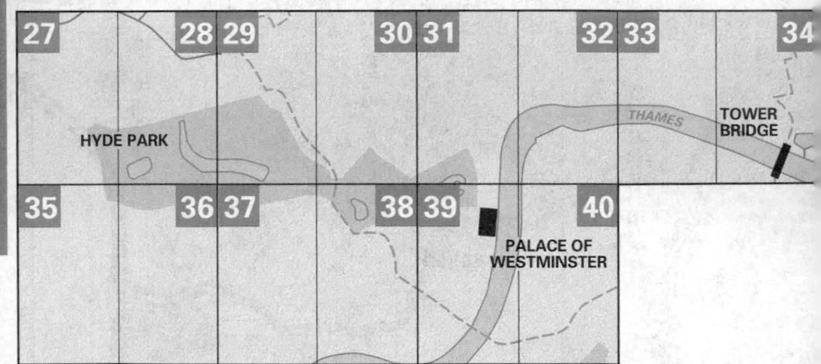

INDEX OF STREET NAMES IN LONDON CENTRE

Oxford Rd
WANDSWORTH 22 **MZH**
Parsons Green Lane 22 **NZG**
Peterborough Rd 22 **NZH**
Putney Bridge 22 **MZH**
Putney Bridge Rd 22 **MZH**
Putney High St 22 **MZH**
Putney Hill 22 **MZH** 358
Queensmill Rd 22 **MZG** 450
Rylston Rd 22 **MZG**
St Dunstan's Rd 22 **MZG**
Star Rd 22 **MZG**
Stephendale Rd 22 **OZH**
Studdridge St 22 **NZH**
Swandon Way 22 **OZH**
Vanston Pl. 22 **NZG** 207
Wandsworth Bridge 22 **OZH** 437
Wandsworth Bridge
Rd 22 **NZH**
West Cromwell Rd 22 **NZG**
Woodlaw Rd 22 **MZG**

PLAN 23

Albert Bridge 23 **QZB**
Albert Bridge Rd 23 **QZG**
Avenue (The) 23 **QZH**
Battersea Bridge 23 **PZG**
Battersea Bridge Rd 23 **PZG**
Battersea Church Rd 23 **PZG**
Battersea Park Rd 23 **QZH**
Battersea Rise 23 **PZH**
Cambridge Rd
BATTERSEA 23 **QZH** 449
Carriage Drive East 23 **QZG**
Carriage Drive North 23 **QZG**
Carriage Drive South 23 **QZG**
Cheyne Walk 23 **PZG**
Clapham Common West
Side 23 **QZH** 92
East Hill 23 **PZH** 155
Edith Grove 23 **PZG**
Elspeth Rd 23 **QZH**
Falcon Rd 23 **PZH**
Gowrie Rd 23 **QZH**
Gunter Grove 23 **OZG** 202
Imperial Rd 23 **OZG**
Latchmere Rd 23 **QZH**
Lavender Hill 23 **QZH**
Lombard Rd 23 **PZH** 266
Lots Rd 23 **OZG**
Marney Rd 23 **QZH**
Northcote Rd 23 **QZH**
North Side 23 **PZH** 316
Parade (The) 23 **QZG**
Parkgate Rd 23 **QZG**
Plough Rd 23 **PZH**
Prince of Wales Drive 23 **QZH**
St John's Hill 23 **PZH**
St John's Rd 23 **QZH**
Surrey Lane 23 **PZH**
Townmead Rd 23 **OZH**
Trinity Rd 23 **PZH** 441
Vicarage Crescent 23 **PZH** 433
Westbridge Rd 23 **PZG**
York Rd
WANDSWORTH 23 **PZH**

PLAN 24

Acre Lane 24 **SZH**
Bedford Rd 24 **SZH**
Binfield Rd 24 **SZH**
Bridgefoot 24 **SZG** 49
Cedars Rd 24 **RZH**
Clapham Common
North Side 24 **RZH** 428
Clapham High St 24 **SZH**
Clapham Manor St 24 **SZH**
Clapham Park Hill 24 **SZH**
Crescent Lane 24 **SZH**
Fentiman Rd 24 **TZG**
Jeffrey's Rd 24 **SZH**
King's Ave 24 **SZH**
Landor Rd 24 **SZH**
Landsdowne Way 24 **SZG**
Larkhall Lane 24 **SZH**
Lingham St 24 **SZH**
Long Rd 24 **RZH**
Miles St 24 **SZG** 290
North St 24 **RZH**
Old Town 24 **RZH** 426
Park Rd LAMBETH 24 **SZH**
Queenstown Rd 24 **RZH**
Queen's Circus 24 **RZG** 361
Rectory Grove 24 **RZH**
Silverthorne Rd 24 **RZH**
Triangle Place 24 **SZH**
Union Rd 24 **SZH**
Voltaire Rd 24 **SZH** 436
Wandsworth Rd 24 **SZG**
Wilkinson St 24 **TZG** 420

PLAN 25

Akerman Rd 25 **UZH**
Albany Rd 25 **VZG**
Angell Drive 25 **UZH**
Atlantic Rd 25 **UZH**
Barrington Rd 25 **UZH**
Benhill Rd 25 **VZG**
Brixton Hill 25 **UZH**
Brixton Rd 25 **UZH**
Calais St 25 **UZG**
Caldwell St 25 **UZG**
Camberwell Grove 25 **VZH**
Camberwell New Rd 25 **UZG**
Camberwell Rd 25 **VZG**
Carew St 25 **VZH**
Champion Park 25 **VZH**
Chapter Rd 25 **UZG**
Church St
Camberwell 25 **VZG**
Clapham Rd 25 **TZH**
Coldharbour Lane 25 **UZH**
Comber Grove 25 **VZG**
Denmark Hill 25 **VZH**
Denmark Rd 25 **VZH**
Dorset Rd 25 **TZG**
East St 25 **VZG**
Edmund St 25 **VZG**
Effra Rd 25 **UZH**
Elephant Rd 25 **VZF** 163
Elmington Rd 25 **VZG**
Fawnbrake Ave 25 **VZH**
Ferndene Rd 25 **VZH**
Flint St 25 **VZG**
Flodden Rd 25 **VZG**
Foxley Rd 25 **UZG**
Groveway 25 **UZH**
Grove Lane 25 **VZH**
Harleyford St 25 **UZG** 211
Herne Hill 25 **VZH**
Herne Hill Rd 25 **VZH**
Heygate St 25 **VZF**
John Ruskin St 25 **VZG**
Kellett Rd 25 **UZH**
Knatchbull Rd 25 **UZH**
Lilford Rd 25 **UZH**
Lomond Grove 25 **VZG**
Lothian Rd 25 **UZG**
Loughborough Rd 25 **UZH**
Manor Pl. 25 **VZG**
Milkwood Rd 25 **VZH**
Minet Rd 25 **UZH**
Mostyn Rd 25 **UZH**
Newington Butts 25 **UZF** 306
New Church Rd 25 **VZG**
Penton Pl. 25 **UZG**
Portland St 25 **VZG**
Railton Rd 25 **UZH**
Red Post Hill 25 **VZH**
Rodney Rd 25 **VZF**
Shakespeare Rd 25 **UZH**
Sidney Rd 25 **TZH**
Southampton Way 25 **VZG**
Stocwell Park Rd 25 **TZH**
Stocwell Rd 25 **TZH**
Sunray Ave 25 **VZH**
Thurlow St 25 **VZG**
Vassall Rd 25 **UZG**
Walworth Rd 25 **VZG**
Warner Rd 25 **VZH**
Wells Way 25 **VZG**
Wiltshire Rd 25 **UZH**
Wyndham Rd 25 **VZG**

PLAN 26

Ady's Rd 26 **XZH**
Asylum Rd 26 **YZG**
Avondale Rise 26 **XZH**
Avonley Rd 26 **YZG**
Barry Rd 26 **YZH**
Bellenden Rd 26 **XZH**
Bird In Bush Rd 26 **YZG**
Carlton Grove 26 **YZG**
Catlin St 26 **YZG**
Cheltenham Rd 26 **YZH**
Clayton Rd 26 **YZH**
Clifton Way 26 **YZG**
Cobourg Rd 26 **XZG**
Commercial Way 26 **XZG**
Consort Rd 26 **YZH**
Coopers Rd 26 **XZG**
Copeland Rd 26 **YZH**
Crystal Palace Rd 26 **XZH**
Dalwood St 26 **XZG**
Dog Kennel Hill 26 **XZH**
Dunton Rd 26 **XZG**
East Dulwich Grove 26 **XZH**
East Dulwich Rd 26 **XZH**
Evelina Rd 26 **YZH**
Galleywall Rd 26 **YZG**
Glengall Rd 26 **XZG**
Grove Hill Rd 26 **XZH**
Grove Vale 26 **XZH**
Hanover Park 26 **XZH**
Havil St 26 **XZG**
Heaton Rd 26 **YZH**
Hollydale Rd 26 **YZH**
Ilderton Rd 26 **YZG**
Kender St 26 **YZG**
Lausanne Rd 26 **YZH**
Linden Grove 26 **YZH**
Lordship Lane 26 **XZH**
Lyndhurst Grove 26 **XZH**
Lyndhurst Way 26 **XZH**
Lynton Rd 26 **YZG**
Mandela Way 26 **XZF**
Marlborough Grove 26 **XZG**
Mc Neil Rd 26 **XZH**
Meeting House Lane 26 **YZG**
Melbourne Grove 26 **XZH**
Naylord Rd 26 **YZG**
Neate St 26 **XZG**
Nunhead Grove 26 **YZH**
Nunhead Lane 26 **YZH**
Oglander Rd 26 **XZH**
Old Kent Rd 26 **XZG**
Peckham Hill St 26 **XZH**
Peckham Park Rd 26 **XZG**
Peckham Rd 26 **XZH**
Peckham Rye 26 **YZH**
Pomeroy St 26 **YZG**
Pytchley Rd 26 **XZH**
Queens Rd 26 **YZH**
Raymouth Rd 26 **YZF**
Reverdy Rd 26 **XZG**
Rolls Rd 26 **XZG**

PLAN 27

PLAN 28

PLAN 29

PLAN 30

Street	Plan	Grid	No.
Great Portland St	30	AIT	
Great Titchfield St	30	AIT	
Grosvenor Square	30	AHU	
Grosvenor St	30	AHU	
Half Moon St	30	AHV	81
Hamilton Pl.	30	AHV	205
Hanover Square	30	AIU	
Hanover St	30	AIU	
Harley St WESTMINSTER	30	AHT	
Hay's Mews	30	AHV	
Henrietta Pl.	30	AHT	
Hertford St	30	AHV	
Hill St	30	AHV	
Holles St	30	AIT	
Howland St	30	AIT	232
James St	30	AHT	
Kingly St	30	AIU	
King St ST. JAMES'S	30	AIV	
Langham St	30	AIT	
Little Portland St	30	AIT	228
Maddox St	30	AIU	
Margaret St	30	AIT	
Market Pl.	30	AIT	286
Marshall St	30	AIU	
Marylebone High St	30	AHT	
Marylebone Lane	30	AHT	287
Mortimer St	30	AIT	
Mount Row	30	AHU	
New Bond St	30	AHU	
New Cavendish St	30	AHT	
Old Bond St	30	AIV	
Old Burlington St	30	AIU	322
Old Park Lane	30	AHV	
Oxford Circus	30	AIT	
Piccadilly	30	AHV	
Piccadilly Arcade	30	AIV	
Poland St	30	AIT	
Portland Pl.	30	AIT	
Princes St	30	AQU	
Queen Anne St	30	AHT	
Queen's Walk	30	AIV	
Regent St	30	AIT	
Sackville St	30	AIU	
St George St	30	AIU	
St James's Pl.	30	AIV	116
St James's St	30	AIV	
Savile Row	30	AIU	
Shepherd Market	30	AHV	
Shepherd St	30	AHV	153
South Audley St	30	AHU	
South Molton St	30	AHU	
South St	30	AHV	
Stratton St	30	AIV	168
Thayer St	30	AHT	413
Tilney St	30	AHV	421
Vere St	30	AHU	
Vigo St	30	AIU	
Waverton St	30	AHV	178
Weighouse St	30	AHU	184
Welbeck St	30	AHT	
Wells St	30	AIT	
Weymouth St	30	AHT	
Wimpole St	30	AHT	

PLAN 31

Street	Plan	Grid	No.
Adam St	31	ALU	
Bateman St	31	AKU	18
Bayley St	31	AKT	260
Bedfordbury	31	ALU	243
Bedford Square	31	AKT	
Bedford St	31	ALU	
Berner's St	31	AJT	
Berwick St	31	AJT	26
Bloomsbury Square	31	ALT	
Bloomsbury St	31	AKT	
Bloomsbury Way	31	ALT	9
Boswell St	31	ALT	
Bow St	31	ALU	
Brewer St	31	AJU	
Broadwick St	31	AJU	
Bury Pl.	31	ALT	
Cambridge Circus	31	AKU	
Carlton Gardens	31	AKV	74
Carlton House Terrace	31	AKV	
Carting Lane	31	ALU	245
Chandos Pl.	31	ALU	
Charing Cross	31	ALV	
Charing Cross Rd	31	AKT	
Charles II St	31	AKV	
Charlotte St	31	AJT	
Cherries St	31	AKT	256
Cockspur St	31	AKV	39
Coventry St	31	AKU	
Cranbourn St	31	AKU	115
Craven St	31	ALV	
Dean St	31	AKT	
Denman St	31	AKU	133
Denmark St	31	AKT	134
Drury Lane	31	ALT	
Duke of York St	31	AJV	143
Duncannon St	31	ALV	147
D'Arblay St	31	AJU	
Earlham St	31	AKU	
Endell St	31	ALT	
Exeter St	31	ALU	
Floral St	31	ALU	
Frith St	31	AKU	
Garrick St	31	ALU	
Gerrard St	31	AKU	174
Glasshouse St SOHO	31	AJU	179
Golden Jubilee Bridge	31	ALV	
Golden Square	31	AJU	
Goodge St	31	AJT	
Gower St	31	AKT	
Great Queen St	31	ALT	
Great Russell St	31	AKT	
Great Windmill St	31	AKU	261
Greek St	31	AKU	
Hanway St	31	AKT	210
Haymarket	31	AKU	
Henrietta St	31	ALU	217
Horse Guards Ave	31	ALV	
Horse Guards Rd	31	AKV	
James St SOHO	31	AJU	
Jermyn St	31	AJV	
John Adam St	31	ALV	238
Kingsway	31	ALT	
King St STRAND	31	ALU	
Leicester Square	31	AKU	
Lexington St	31	AJU	
Lisle St	31	AKU	
Long Acre	31	ALU	
Macklin St	31	ALT	
Maiden Lane	31	ALU	83
Mall (The)	31	AKV	
Monmouth St	31	ALU	88
Museum St	31	ALT	
Neal St	31	ALU	
Newman St	31	AJT	
Newton St	31	ALT	
New Oxford St	31	AKT	
New Row	31	ALU	
Noel St	31	AJU	
Northumberland Ave	31	ALV	
Old Compton St	31	AKU	
Old Gloucester St	31	ALT	
Orange St	31	AKV	
Pall Mall	31	AJV	
Panton St	31	AKU	
Parker St	31	ALT	
Percy St	31	AKT	
Piccadilly Circus	31	AKU	
Richmond Terrace	31	ALV	234
Romilly St	31	AKU	368
Royal Opera Arcade	31	AKV	
Rupert St	31	AKU	
Russell St	31	ALU	
St Giles Circus	31	AKT	
St Giles High St	31	AKT	
St James's Square	31	AJV	
St Martins Lane	31	ALU	
Savoy Pl.	31	ALU	
Shaftesbury Ave	31	AKU	
Shelton St	31	ALU	
Shorts Gardens	31	ALU	
Soho Square	31	AKT	
Southampton Row	31	ALT	473
Southampton St	31	ALU	388
Store St	31	AKT	
Strand	31	ALV	
Tavistock St	31	ALU	
Tottenham Court Rd.	31	AKT	
Trafalgar Square	31	AKV	
Upper St Martin's Lane	31	ALU	430
Villiers St	31	ALV	
Wardour St	31	AJU	
Warwick St	31	AJU	444
Waterloo Pl.	31	AKV	
Wellington St	31	ALU	187
Whitcomb St	31	AKU	191
Whitehall	31	ALV	
Whitehall Court	31	ALV	46
Whitehall Pl.	31	ALV	
Wild St	31	ALU	
William IV St	31	ALV	467

PLAN 32

Street	Plan	Grid	No.
Aldwych	32	AMU	
Arundel St	32	AMU	
Bedford Row	32	AMT	
Belvedere Rd	32	AMV	
Bouverie St	32	ANU	
Bream's Buildings	32	ANT	47
Carey St	32	AMU	
Chancery Lane	32	AMT	
Charterhouse St	32	ANT	
Cornwall Rd	32	ANV	
Cut (The)	32	ANV	
Essex St	32	AMU	
Farringdon Rd	32	ANT	
Fetter Lane	32	ANT	
Fleet St	32	ANU	
Furnival St	32	ANT	27
Gray's Inn Rd	32	ANT	
Greville St	32	ANT	
Halton Garden	32	ANT	
Hatfields	32	ANV	
High Holborn	32	AMT	
Holborn	32	ANT	
Holborn Viaduct	32	ANT	
John Carpenter St	32	ANU	17
Kemble St	32	AMU	
Lancaster Pl.	32	AMU	
Leather Lane	32	ANT	
Lincoln's Inn Fields	32	AMT	
New Fetter Lane	32	ANT	
New Square	32	AMT	
New St Square	32	ANT	28
Portugal St	32	AMU	
Procter St	32	AMT	27
Red Lion Square	32	AMT	
Red Lion St	32	AMT	
Roupel St	32	ANV	
St Andrews St	32	ANT	37
St Bride St	32	ANT	37
Sardinia St	32	AMT	38
Savoy St	32	AMU	27
Serle St	32	AMT	
Shoe Lane	32	ANT	
Stamford St	32	ANV	
Surrey St	32	AMU	17
Temple Ave	32	ANU	
Temple Pl.	32	AMU	

Theobald's Rd...... 32 AMT
Tudor St........... 32 ANU
Upper Ground...... 32 AMV
Victoria Embankment 32 AMU
Waterloo Bridge.... 32 AMV
Waterloo Rd........ 32 ANV

PLAN 33

Aldersgate St...... 33 APT
Bankside........... 33 APV 291
Basinghall St...... 33 AQT
Blackfriars Bridge... 33 AOU
Blackfriars Rd...... 33 AOV
Borough High St.... 33 AQV
Bow Lane.......... 33 AQU
Cannon St......... 33 APU
Charterhouse Square 33 APT 475
Cheapside......... 33 AQU
Cowcross St....... 33 AOT 113
Ewer St........... 33 APV
Farringdon St...... 33 AOT
Finsbury Square.... 33 AQT 310
Fore St........... 33 AQT
Foster Lane........ 33 APT
Giltspur St........ 33 APT
Great Guilford St.... 33 APV
Great Suffolk St.... 33 APV
Gresham St........ 33 AQT
John St........... 33 APT 299
King Edward St..... 33 APT 247
King St CITY OF LONDON........ 33 AQU
Limeburner Lane.... 33 AOT 298
Little Britain....... 33 APT 264
London Wall....... 33 APT
Long Lane CITY.... 33 APT
Lothbury.......... 33 AQT
Ludgate Hill....... 33 AOU
Millennium Bridge... 33 APU
Montague St....... 33 APT 292
Moorgate......... 33 AQT
Moor Lane........ 33 AQT
Nelson Square..... 33 AOV
Newcomen St...... 33 AQV
Newgate St........ 33 APT
New Bridge St..... 33 AOU
New Change....... 33 APU
Old Bailey........ 33 AOT
Old Jewry......... 33 AQU
Park St SOUTHWARK.... 33 APV
Paternoster Square. 33 APT
Poultry........... 33 AQU
Princes St........ 33 AQU
Queen St......... 33 AQU
Queen Street Pl.... 33 AQU 301
Queen Victoria St... 33 APU
Redcross Way..... 33 AQV
Ropemaker St...... 33 AQT
St Martin's-le-Grand. 33 APT 380
St Paul's Churchyard 33 APU
St Swithin's Lane... 33 AQU 308
St Thomas St...... 33 AQV
Silk St........... 33 AQT
Southwark Bridge... 33 AQV
Southwark Bridge Rd 33 APV
Southwark St...... 33 APV
Stoney St......... 33 AQV
Sumner St........ 33 APV 169
Union St......... 33 AOV
Upper Thames St... 33 AQU
Walbrook Crescent.. 33 AQU 304
Warwick Lane...... 33 APT 294
West Smithfield.... 33 AOT
Wood St......... 33 AQT

PLAN 34

Aldgate High St.... 34 ASU
Bell Lane.......... 34 AST
Bevis Marks....... 34 ART 34
Bishopsgate....... 34 ART
Blomfield St....... 34 ART
Braham St......... 34 ASU
Brick Lane......... 34 AST
Broadgate........ 34 ART
Brushfield St...... 34 AST
Byward St........ 34 ARU
Camomile St...... 34 ART 71
Commercial St..... 34 AST
Coopers Row...... 34 ASU 318
Cornhill.......... 34 ARU 309
Crucifix Lane...... 34 ARV 125
Druid St.......... 34 ARV
Duke St Hill....... 34 ARV
Duke's Pl......... 34 AST 145
Eastcheap........ 34 ARU
East Smithfield.... 34 ASU
Eldon St.......... 34 ART
Fenchurch St...... 34 ARU
Finsbury Circus.... 34 ART
Fish Street Hill..... 34 ARU 319
Gainford St....... 34 ASV
Goodman's Yard.... 34 ASU
Goulston St....... 34 AST
Gracechurch St..... 34 ARU
Great Tower St..... 34 ARU
Harrow Pl......... 34 AST 317
Hay's Galleria Shopping Centre......... 34 ARV
Houndsditch...... 34 ART
King William St.... 34 ARU 250
Leadenhall St..... 34 ARU
Leman St......... 34 ASU
Liverpool St....... 34 ART
Lloyd's Ave....... 34 ASU
Lombard St....... 34 ARU 268
London Bridge.... 34 ARV
Lower Thames St... 34 ARU
Mansell St........ 34 ASU
Mark Lane........ 34 ARU
Middlesex St...... 34 AST
Minories......... 34 ASU
New St.......... 34 ART
Old Broad St...... 34 ART
Pepys St......... 34 ASU
Prescot St........ 34 ASU
Princelet St...... 34 AST
Princes St....... 34 AQU
Royal Mint Rd..... 34 ASU
St Botolph St...... 34 AST
St Mary Axe...... 34 ART
Shad Thames...... 34 ASV
Shorter St........ 34 ASU
Snows Fields...... 34 ARV 386
South Pl......... 34 ART 391
Spital Square...... 34 AST 399
Sun St........... 34 ART
Sun Street Passage. 34 ART
Threadneedle St.... 34 ARU
Throgmorton Ave.... 34 ART
Throgmorton St.... 34 ART 418
Tooley St........ 34 ARV
Tower Bridge...... 34 ASV
Tower Bridge Approach....... 34 ASV
Tower Bridge Rd.... 34 ASV
Tower Hill........ 34 ASU
Wentworth St...... 34 AST
Weston St........ 34 ARV 188
Whitechapel High St 34 AST
Wilson St........ 34 ART
Wormwood St..... 34 ART 472

PLAN 35

Abingdon Rd....... 35 AAX
Argyll Rd......... 35 AAX
Barkston Gardens... 35 ABY
Bolton Gardens..... 35 ABZ
Bramham Gardens.. 35 ABY
Campden Hill Rd.... 35 AAX
Collingham Gardens. 35 ABY 99
Collingham Rd..... 35 ABY 101
Cornwall Gardens... 35 ABY
Courtfield Gardens.. 35 ABY
Cromwell Crescent.. 35 AAY 119
Cromwell Rd....... 35 AAY
Eardley Crescent... 35 AAZ 151
Earl's Court Gardens 35 ABY
Earl's Court Rd..... 35 AAY
Earl's Court Square.. 35 ABZ
Edwardes Square... 35 AAY
Finborough Rd..... 35 ABZ
Holland St........ 35 AAX
Holland Walk...... 35 AAX
Hornton St........ 35 AAX
Ifield Rd......... 35 ABZ
Kensington Court... 35 ABX 241
Kensington Court Pl. 35 ABX 242
Kensington High St. 35 AAX
Kensington Rd..... 35 ABX
Kensington Square.. 35 ABX
Kenway Rd....... 35 ABY
Knaresborough Pl... 35 ABY
Lexham Gardens... 35 ABY
Lillie Rd......... 35 AAZ
Logan Pl......... 35 AAY
Longridge Rd..... 35 AAY
Marloes Rd....... 35 ABX
Melbury Rd....... 35 AAX
Nevern Pl........ 35 AAY
Nevern Square.... 35 AAY
North End Rd..... 35 AAZ
Old Brompton Rd... 35 ABZ
Pembrocke Gardens 35 AAY 342
Pembroke Rd...... 35 AAY
Penywern Rd...... 35 ABZ
Philbeach Gardens.. 35 AAZ
Phillimore Gardens.. 35 AAX
Redcliffe Gardens... 35 ABZ
Redcliffe Square... 35 ABZ
St Albans Grove.... 35 ABX
Scarsdale Villas.... 35 AAY
Seagrave Rd...... 35 AAZ
Templeton Pl...... 35 AAY 410
Trebovir Rd...... 35 AAZ
Warwick Gardens... 35 AAY
Warwick Rd...... 35 AAY
Young St........ 35 ABX

PLAN 36

Ashburn Pl....... 36 ACY
Beaufort St....... 36 ADZ
Bina Gardens..... 36 ACY
Boltons (The)...... 36 ACZ
Bute St.......... 36 ADY 59
Cale St.......... 36 ADZ
Carlyle Square..... 36 ADZ
Cathcart Rd....... 36 ACZ
Chelsea Square.... 36 ADZ
Courtfield Rd...... 36 ACY
Cranley Gardens.... 36 ACZ
Cranley Pl........ 36 ADY 215
Cromwell Pl....... 36 ADY 120
De Vere Gardens... 36 ACX
Dovehouse St...... 36 ADZ
Drayton Gardens... 36 ACZ
Elm Park Gardens... 36 ADZ
Elm Park Rd...... 36 ADZ
Elvaston Pl....... 36 ACX
Evelyn Gardens.... 36 ACZ
Exhibition Rd...... 36 ADX
Flower Walk...... 36 ACX
Foulis Terrace..... 36 ADZ 170
Fulham Rd........ 36 ADZ
Gilston Rd....... 36 ACZ
Glendower Pl...... 36 ADY 180

Street	Plan	Grid	No.
Gloucester Rd	36	**ACX**	
Grenville Pl.	36	**ACY**	
Harcourt Terrace	36	**ACZ**	477
Harrington Gardens	36	**ACY**	
Harrington Rd	36	**ADY**	
Hollywood Rd	36	**ACZ**	
Hyde Park Gate	36	**ACX**	
Kensington Gore	36	**ACX**	
King's Rd	36	**ADZ**	
Launceston Pl.	36	**ACX**	259
Little Boltons (The)	36	**ACZ**	
Manresa Rd	36	**ADZ**	
Neville Terrace	36	**ADZ**	300
Old Church St	36	**ADZ**	
Onslow Gardens	36	**ADZ**	
Onslow Square	36	**ADY**	
Palace Gate	36	**ACX**	
Park Walk	36	**ACZ**	
Pelham St	36	**ADY**	
Prince Consort Rd	36	**ADX**	
Prince's Gardens	36	**ADX**	356
Queensberry Pl.	36	**ADY**	360
Queen's Gate	36	**ACX**	
Queen's Gate Gardens	36	**ACY**	198
Queen's Gate Pl.	36	**ACY**	363
Queen's Gate Terrace	36	**ACX**	
Redcliffe Rd	36	**ACZ**	
Roland Gardens	36	**ACZ**	
South Parade	36	**ADZ**	
Stanhope Gardens	36	**ACY**	
Sumner Pl.	36	**ADY**	
Sydney Pl.	36	**ADY**	405
Thurloe Pl.	36	**ADY**	
Thurloe Square	36	**ADY**	
Tregunter Rd	36	**ACZ**	
Vale (The)	36	**ADZ**	
Victoria Grove	36	**ACX**	
Victoria Rd KENSINGTON	36	**ACX**	
Wetherby Gardens	36	**ACY**	

PLAN 37

Street	Plan	Grid	No.
Basil St	37	**AFX**	
Beauchamp Pl.	37	**AFX**	
Belgrave Square	37	**AGX**	
Bourne St	37	**AGY**	
Bray Pl.	37	**AFY**	45
Britten St	37	**AEZ**	
Brompton Rd	37	**AFX**	
Cadogan Gardens	37	**AGY**	23
Cadogan Gate	37	**AGY**	220
Cadogan Pl.	37	**AGY**	
Cadogan Square	37	**AGY**	
Cadogan St	37	**AFY**	
Carriage Rd (The)	37	**AFX**	
Chelsea Bridge Rd	37	**AGZ**	
Chelsea Embankment	37	**AGZ**	
Chelsea Manor St	37	**AFZ**	
Cheltenham Terrace	37	**AGZ**	
Chesham Pl.	37	**AGX**	
Chesham St	37	**AGY**	
Chester Row	37	**AGY**	
Cheval Pl.	37	**AFX**	
Christchurch St	37	**AFZ**	
Draycott Ave	37	**AFY**	
Draycott Pl.	37	**AFY**	
Eaton Pl.	37	**AGY**	
Egerton Gardens	37	**AFY**	160
Egerton Gardens Mews	37	**AFY**	162
Egerton Terrace	37	**AFY**	161
Elystan Pl.	37	**AFZ**	
Elystan St	37	**AEY**	
Ennismore Gardens	37	**AEX**	
Flood St	37	**AFZ**	
Franklin's Row	37	**AGZ**	
Glebe Pl.	37	**AEZ**	
Grosvenor Crescent	37	**AGX**	
Hans Crescent	37	**AFX**	
Hans Pl.	37	**AFX**	
Hans Rd	37	**AFX**	
Harriet St	37	**AGX**	214
Hasker St	37	**AFY**	
Holbein Mews	37	**AGZ**	223
Holbein Pl.	37	**AGY**	
Ixworth Pl.	37	**AEY**	
Jubilee Pl.	37	**AFZ**	
Knightsbridge	37	**AFX**	
Lennox Gardens	37	**AFY**	
Lennox Gardens Mews	37	**AFY**	263
Lower Sloane St	37	**AGY**	
Lowndes Square	37	**AGX**	
Lowndes St	37	**AGX**	
Lyall St	37	**AGY**	
Markham St	37	**AFZ**	
Milner St	37	**AFY**	
Montpelier Square	37	**AFX**	
Montpelier St	37	**AFX**	
Moore St	37	**AFY**	
Mossop St	37	**AFY**	
Oakley St	37	**AEZ**	
Ormonde Gate	37	**AGZ**	329
Pimlico Rd	37	**AGZ**	
Pont St	37	**AFY**	
Radnor Walk	37	**AFZ**	
Rawlings St	37	**AFY**	
Redesdale St	37	**AFZ**	367
Royal Hospital Rd	37	**AFZ**	
Rutland Gate	37	**AEX**	
St Leonard's Terrace	37	**AGZ**	
Shawfield St	37	**AFZ**	
Sloane Ave	37	**AFY**	
Sloane Square	37	**AGY**	
Sloane St	37	**AGX**	
Smith St	37	**AFZ**	
South Terrace	37	**AEY**	
Sydney St	37	**AEZ**	
Symons St	37	**AGY**	407
Tedworth Square	37	**AFZ**	
Tite St	37	**AFZ**	
Trevor Pl.	37	**AFX**	
Trevor Square	37	**AFX**	
Walton St	37	**AFY**	
West Halkin St	37	**AGX**	
Whiteheads	37	**AFY**	
William St	37	**AGX**	468
Wilton Pl.	37	**AGX**	

PLAN 38

Street	Plan	Grid	No.
Alderney St	38	**AIY**	
Belgrave Pl.	38	**AHX**	
Belgrave Rd	38	**AIY**	
Birdcage Walk	38	**AIX**	
Bressenden Pl.	38	**AIX**	
Buckingham Gate	38	**AIX**	
Buckingham Palace Rd	38	**AHY**	
Carlisle Pl.	38	**AIY**	
Castle Lane	38	**AIX**	
Chapel St BELGRAVIA	38	**AHX**	
Charlwood St	38	**AIZ**	
Chelsea Bridge	38	**AHZ**	
Chester Square	38	**AHY**	
Chester St	38	**AHX**	
Churchill Gardens Rd	38	**AIZ**	
Clarendon St	38	**AIZ**	
Constitution Hill	38	**AHX**	
Cumberland St	38	**AIZ**	
Denbigh St	38	**AIZ**	
Duke of Wellington Pl.	38	**AHX**	142
Eaton Square	38	**AHY**	
Ebury Bridge	38	**AHZ**	
Ebury Bridge Rd	38	**AHZ**	
Ebury St	38	**AHY**	
Eccleston Bridge	38	**AHY**	15
Eccleston Square	38	**AIY**	
Eccleston St	38	**AHY**	
Elizabeth St	38	**AHY**	
Francis St	38	**AIY**	
Gillingham St	38	**AIY**	
Gloucester St	38	**AIZ**	
Grosvenor Gardens	38	**AHX**	
Grosvenor Pl.	38	**AHX**	
Grosvenor Rd	38	**AHZ**	
Guildhouse St	38	**AIY**	20
Halkin St	38	**AHX**	
Hobart Pl.	38	**AHX**	
Hudson's Pl.	38	**AIY**	
Hugh St	38	**AIY**	
Lower Belgrave St	38	**AHY**	
Lower Grosvenor Pl.	38	**AIX**	27
Lupus St	38	**AIZ**	
Palace St	38	**AIX**	
St George's Drive	38	**AIY**	
South Eaton Pl.	38	**AHY**	
Sutherland St	38	**AHZ**	
Terminus Pl.	38	**AIY**	41
Upper Belgrave St	38	**AHX**	
Vauxhall Bridge Rd	38	**AIY**	
Victoria St	38	**AIX**	
Warwick Square	38	**AIY**	
Warwick Way	38	**AHZ**	
Wilton Rd	38	**AIY**	
Wilton St	38	**AHX**	

PLAN 39

Street	Plan	Grid	No.
Abingdon St	39	**AKY**	
Albert Embankment	39	**ALY**	
Artillery Row	39	**AKX**	8
Atterbury St	39	**ALZ**	
Aylesford St	39	**AKZ**	
Bessborough Gardens	39	**AKZ**	
Bessborough St	39	**AKZ**	30
Bridge St	39	**ALX**	
Broad Sanctuary	39	**ALX**	52
Caxton St	39	**AKX**	
Chichester St	39	**AJZ**	
Claverton St	39	**AJZ**	
Dolphin Square	39	**AJZ**	
Douglas St	39	**AKY**	
Erasmus St	39	**AKY**	
Glasshouse St LAMBETH	39	**ALZ**	10
Great College St	39	**ALX**	
Great George St	39	**AKX**	19
Great Peter St	39	**AKY**	
Great Smith St	39	**AKX**	
Greencoat Pl.	39	**AJY**	
Greycoat Pl.	39	**AKY**	20
Greycoat St	39	**AKY**	
Horseferry Rd	39	**AKY**	
Howick Pl.	39	**AJY**	
John Islip St	39	**AKZ**	
King Charles St	39	**AKX**	
Lambeth Bridge	39	**ALY**	
Marsham St	39	**AKY**	
Millbank	39	**ALZ**	
Monck St	39	**AKY**	
Montpelier Walk	37	**AFX**	
Moreton St	39	**AJZ**	
Nine Elms Lane	39	**AKZ**	
Old Pye St	39	**AKX**	
Page St	39	**AKY**	
Palmer St	39	**AKX**	
Parlament Square	39	**ALX**	
Parliament St	39	**ALX**	
Parry St	39	**ALZ**	34
Petty France	39	**AJX**	
Ponsonby Pl.	39	**AKZ**	
Rampayne St	39	**AKZ**	

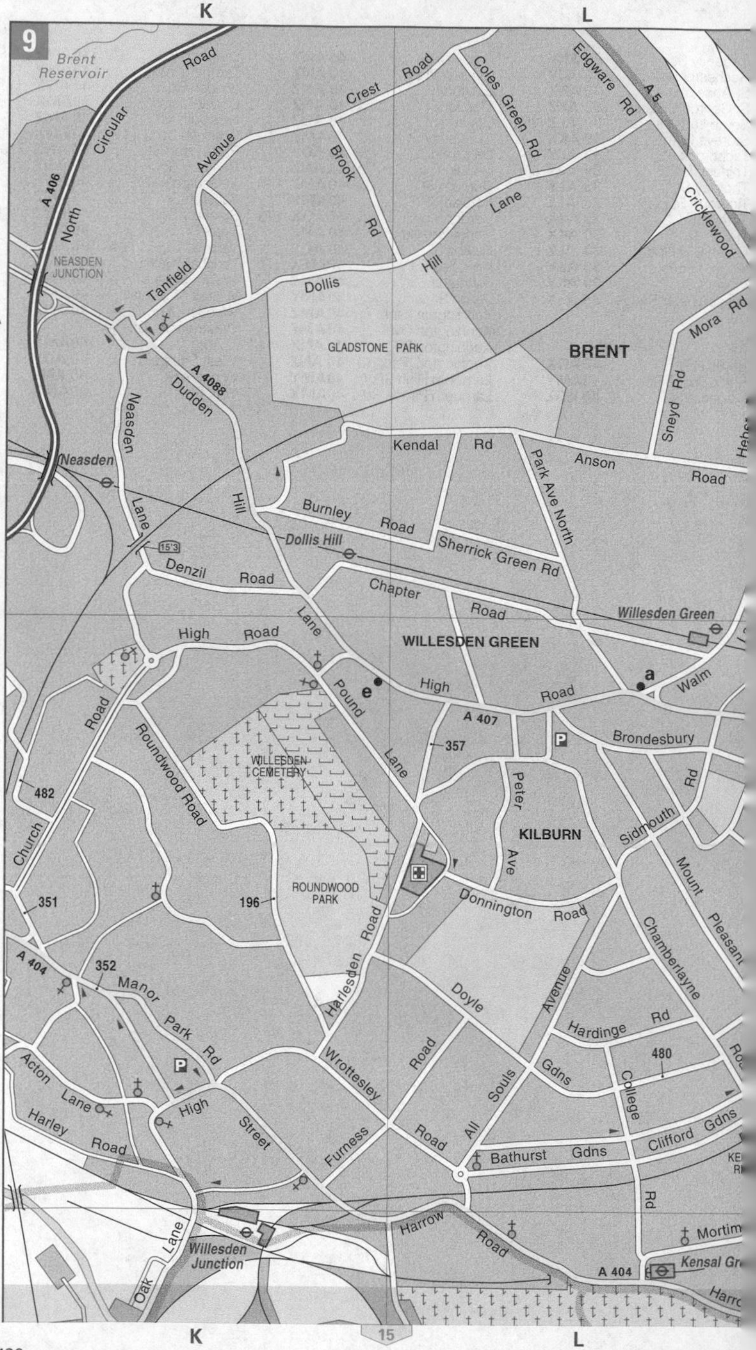

K L

9

Brent Reservoir
North Circular Road
A 406
Crest Road
Coles Green Rd
Edgware Rd
A 5
Avenue
Brook Rd
Lane
Cricklewood
NEASDEN JUNCTION
Tanfield
Dollis Hill
ZA
Mora Rd
GLADSTONE PARK
BRENT
A 4088
Dudden
Neasden
Sneyd Rd
Kendal Rd
Park Ave North
Anson Road
Neasden
Lane
Hill
Burnley Road
Sherrick Green Rd
Dollis Hill
15'3
Denzil Road
Chapter Road
Willesden Green
Lane
High Road
WILLESDEN GREEN
a
Walm
e
High Road
Pound
A 407
Road
357
Brondesbury
Roundwood Road
WILLESDEN CEMETERY
Lane
Peter Ave
Rd
482
KILBURN
Sidmouth
Church
ROUNDWOOD PARK
Mount Pleasant
351
196
Donnington Road
ZB
Harlesden Road
Chamberlayne
A 404
352
Manor Park Rd
Doyle
Avenue
Hardinge Rd
480
Acton Lane
Wrottesley Road
All Souls
Gdns
College
High Street
Harley Road
Furness
Road
Bathurst Gdns
Clifford Gdns
Rd
Harrow Road
Lane
Willesden Junction
Mortim
ZC
Oak
A 404
Kensal Gr
Harr

15

K L

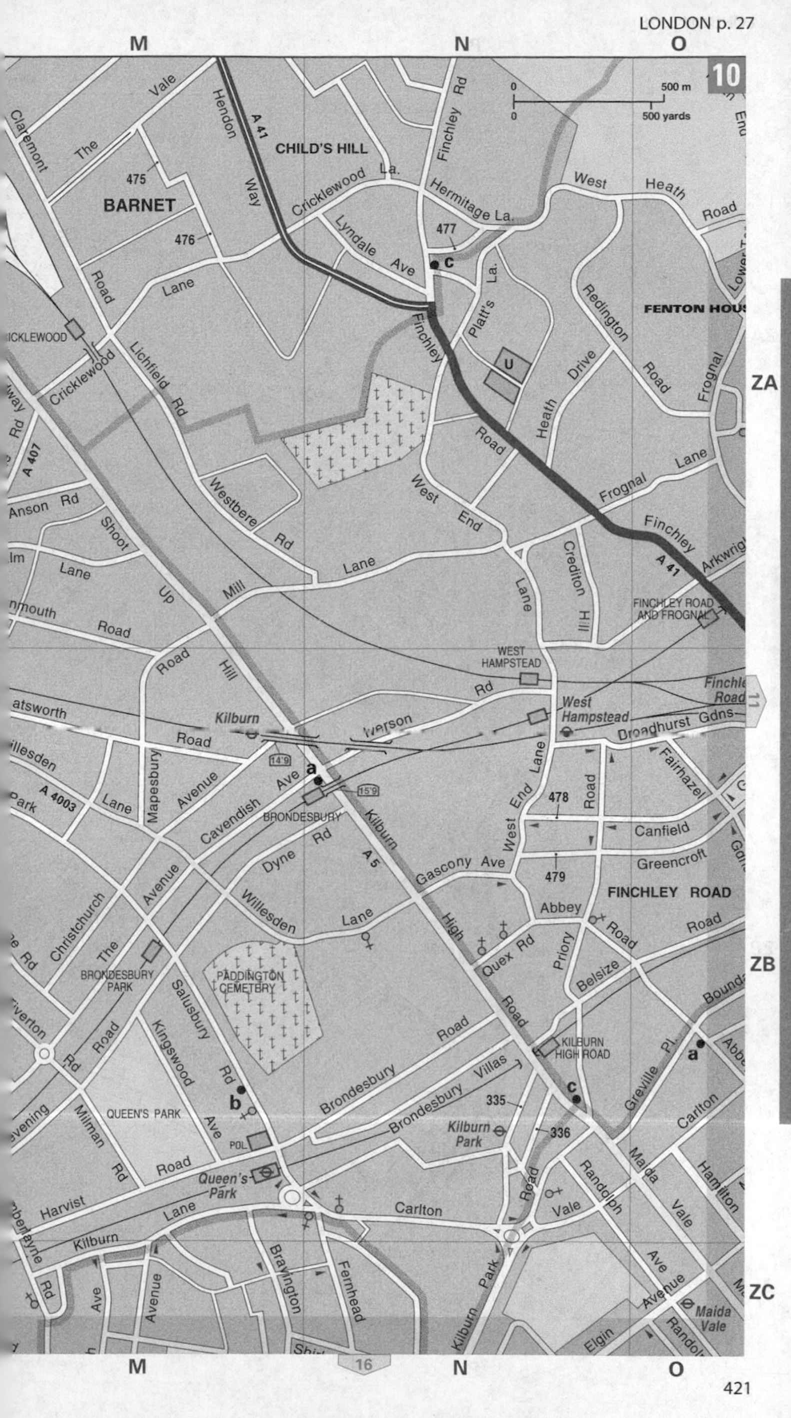
M
N
O
10
0 500 m
0 500 yards
CHILD'S HILL
BARNET
475
476
477
FENTON HOUSE
ZA
ZB
ZC
CRICKLEWOOD
FINCHLEY ROAD AND FROGNAL
WEST HAMPSTEAD
West Hampstead
Finchley Road
11
Kilburn
BRONDESBURY
478
479
FINCHLEY ROAD
PADDINGTON CEMETERY
BRONDESBURY PARK
KILBURN HIGH ROAD
QUEEN'S PARK
Queen's Park
Kilburn Park
Maida Vale
335
336
POL.
16
A 41
A 5
A 407
A 4003
Hendon Way
Finchley Rd
West Heath Road
Hermitage La.
Cricklewood La.
Lyndale Ave
Platt's La.
Redington Road
Heath Drive
Frognal
Frognal Lane
West End Lane
Crediton Hill
Mill Lane
Westbere Rd
Lichfield Rd
Shoot Up Hill
Kilburn High Road
Iverson Road
Broadhurst Gdns
Fairhazel Gdns
Canfield Gdns
Greencroft Gdns
Abbey Road
Belsize Road
Quex Rd
Priory Road
Gascony Ave
Dyne Rd
Willesden Lane
Cavendish Ave
Mapesbury Road
Christchurch Avenue
Salusbury Rd
Kingswood Ave
Brondesbury Road
Brondesbury Villas
Carlton Vale
Kilburn Lane
Harvist Road
Milman Rd
Randolph Ave
Maida Vale
Hamilton Terrace
Greville Pl.
Boundary Road
Kilburn Park Road
Elgin Avenue
Bravington Rd
Fernhead Rd
Chatsworth Road
Willesden Lane
Anson Rd
Claremont Road
The Vale
a
b
c

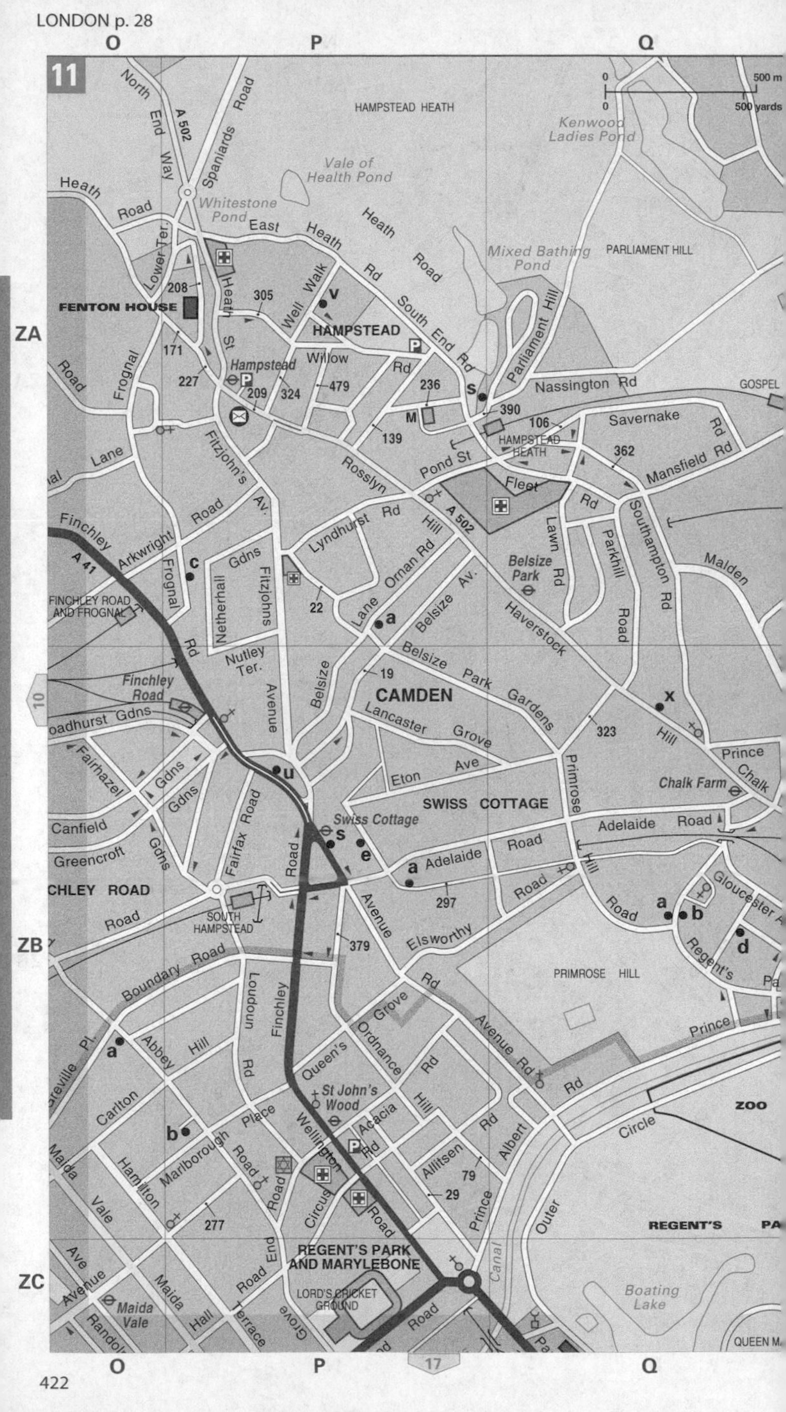
O
P
Q
11
HAMPSTEAD HEATH
Kenwood Ladies Pond
Vale of Health Pond
Whitestone Pond
Mixed Bathing Pond
PARLIAMENT HILL
FENTON HOUSE
HAMPSTEAD
Hampstead
HAMPSTEAD HEATH
Belsize Park
CAMDEN
SWISS COTTAGE
Swiss Cottage
Chalk Farm
Finchley Road
FINCHLEY ROAD AND FROGNAL
SOUTH HAMPSTEAD
PRIMROSE HILL
St John's Wood
REGENT'S PARK AND MARYLEBONE
LORD'S CRICKET GROUND
ZOO
Boating Lake
Maida Vale
QUEEN M.
ZA
ZB
ZC
10
17

R
S
T
12
Archway
Holloway
Road
Lane
Dartmouth
UPPER
HOLLOWAY
A 1
Hornsey
Tollington
Park
Tollington Way
DARTMOUTH
PARK
Park
Junction
Holloway
Seven
Sisters
Hornsey
Chetwynd Road
Hill
Tufnell
Park
Road
Tufnell
Park
Dalmeny Rd
Parkhurst
Road
A 503
ZA
Highgate
Rd
Fortess
Road
Lady Margaret Rd
Carleton Rd
Dalmeny Ave
Caledonian
Road
Hillmarton Road
Leighton Rd
Kentish
Town
A 400
Spring Place
Islip Street
Torriano Ave
Camden
Road
Hungerford Road
ISLING
Caledonian
Road
Willes Road
Busby
Place
Gaisford Street
Patshull Road
North
Road
Mackenzie
Roman
Market
Road
York
Way
A 5200
A 5203
Brewery
Road
Caledonian
CALEDONIAN
AND BARNSB
13
Wales
Road
16
Town
St
Pancras
Camden
Road
Agar
Grove
Farm
CAMDEN
ROAD
15'0
15'
15'6
Offord
366
Way
Road
Kentish
Camden
Town
Parkway
Camden
Royal
Camden
Camden
High St
Pratt
St
College
St
Pancras
Way
York
Way
Copenhagen
St
Richmon
ZB
Delancey St
Street
Outer
Crowndale Rd
Pancras
Rd
Park
Village
East
Albany
Mornington
Crescent
Hampstead
Road
Eversholt
M
455
P
KING'S
CROSS
Caledonian
Calshot St
Pentonville
BRITISH
LIBRARY
Midland
Rd
Ossulston
St
ST
PANCRAS
King's
RRACES
Circle
REGENT'S
PARK
Robert Street
EUSTON
Street
417
ZC
Road
H
Euston
Judd
Cross
ester Rd
St
Road
18

T
U
V
13
Finsbury Park
Fonthill Rd
A 503
Queen's
Blackstock
Brownswood
Road
Lordship Park
Lordship
St Thomas's
Drive
Green
CLISSOLD
PARK
Mountgrove Rd
Road
Sisters
Isledon
Rd
Road
Riversdale
Road
Lanes
Newington
Clissold Rd
Seven
Hornsey
Arsenal
Gillespie
Stoke
Clissold Cres
ZA
A 503
Park
Highbury
b
333
Park
Green
Lanes
Albion
Road
Drayton
Highbury
Park
Road
ARSENAL F.C.
Hill
HIGHBURY
Road
Caledonian
Benwell
Rd
DRAYTON PARK
Park
Highbury
New
Petherton
Holloway Road
U
Drayton
Holloway
A 105
Mildmay
ISLINGTON
Highbury
Grosvenor
Av
Highbury Place
Grove
Road
Rd
Liverpool
A 1
CANONBURY
Caledonian Road
PARADISE PARK
a
Road
Mackenzie
56
Bride Street
Highbury and Islington
Paul's
Road
Balls
Highbury
St
12
Roman
Way
56
A 1
Canonbury
Road
CANONBURY
Caledonian
A 5203
CALEDONIAN ROAD AND BARNSBURY
Road
Road
CANONBURY SQUARE
Englefield
x
Offord
a
Thornhill
Upper
A 1
H
h
Road
Essex
Halliford
a
Southgate
Road
Road
x
Barnsbury Street
Essex Road Station
POL
St
New
Downham
Road
r
k
Road
North
v
Road
Richmond
Ave
St
ZB
Hemingford
ISLINGTON
Essex
Street
Road
Road
A 1200
hagen
St
e
s
Prebend
343
St Peter's
Road
Barnsbury
Liverpool
St
350
70
Street
Eagle Wharf Rd
New
Upper
Calshot St
78
P
A 1
Shepherdess
Caledonian
345
M
Angel
Wharf Road
North
Pentonville
Road
City
Road
Road
St
Walk
Amwell
344
King's
T
City
A 501
478
P
Road
ZC
417
a
b
Avenue
John
398
Goswell
293
Central
c
East
265
Cross
Gra
St
296
U
Street
Lever
Ba
T
U
19
V

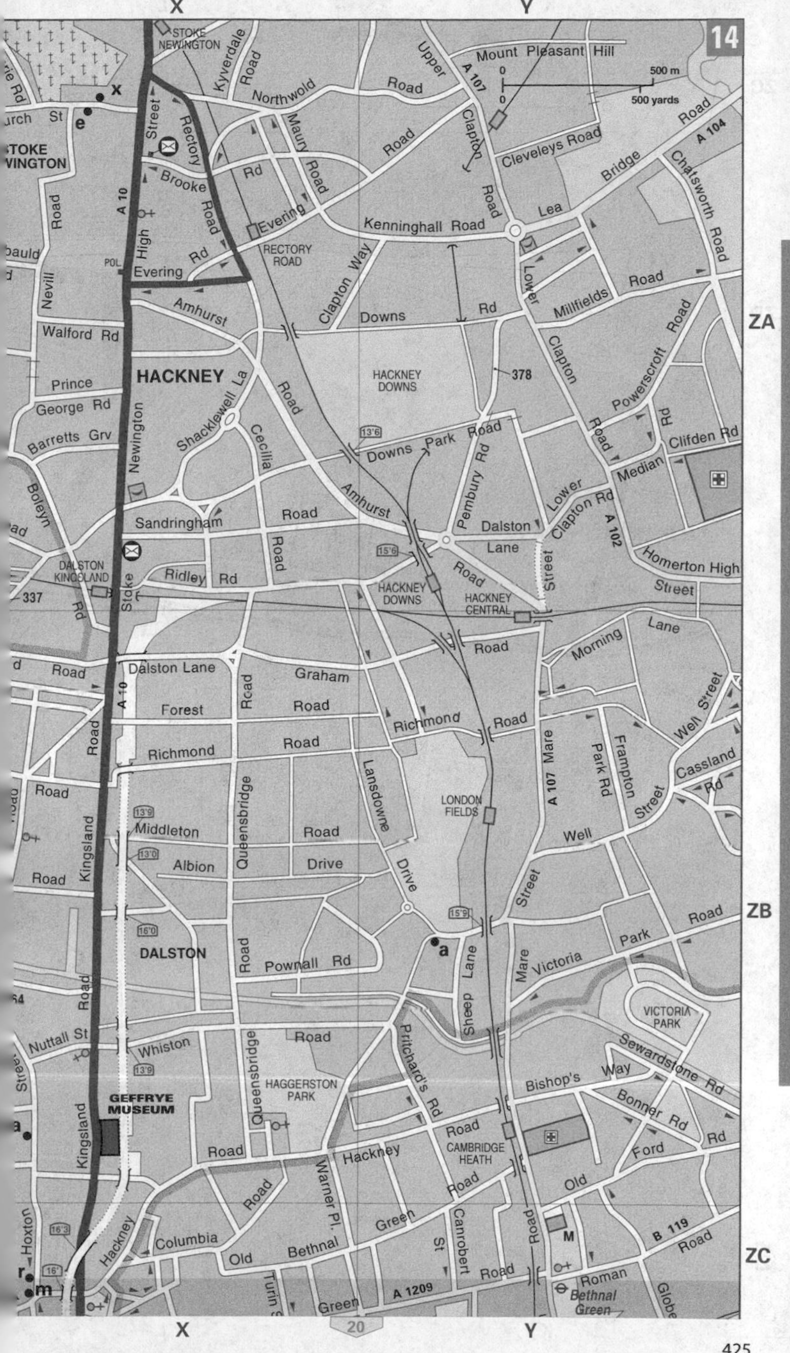
X
Y
14
STOKE NEWINGTON
Mount Pleasant Hill
A 107
500 m
500 yards
Upper Road
Kyverdale Road
Northwold Road
Maury Road
Clapton Road
Cleveleys Road
Bridge Road
A 104
Chatsworth Road
Lea
Rectory Road
Brooke Rd
Evering Rd
RECTORY ROAD
Kenninghall Road
Clapton Way
High Street
A 10
Lower Clapton
Millfields Road
Downs Rd
Amhurst Road
Nevill Road
Walford Rd
HACKNEY
HACKNEY DOWNS
378
Powerscroft Road
Prince George Rd
Barretts Grv
Shacklewell La
Cecilia Road
Downs Park Road
Pembury Rd
Clifden Rd
Median Rd
Newington
Boleyn
Sandringham Road
Dalston Lane
Lower Clapton Rd
A 102
Homerton High Street
DALSTON KINGSLAND
Ridley Rd
HACKNEY DOWNS
HACKNEY CENTRAL
337
Stoke
Dalston Lane
Graham Road
Morning Lane
Well Street
Forest Road
Richmond Road
Mare Street
A 107
Park Rd
Frampton Street
Cassland Rd
Richmond Road
Queensbridge Road
Lansdowne Drive
LONDON FIELDS
Kingsland Road
Middleton Road
Albion Drive
Well Street
ZA
ZB
ZC
DALSTON
Pownall Rd
Sheep Lane
Victoria Park Road
VICTORIA PARK
Sewardstone Rd
Nuttall St
Whiston Road
HAGGERSTON PARK
Pritchard's Rd
Bishop's Way
Bonner Rd
GEFFRYE MUSEUM
Hackney Road
CAMBRIDGE HEATH
Ford Rd
Old Road
Warner Pl.
Hoxton
Columbia Road
Old Bethnal Green Road
Carrobert St
B 119
Roman Road
Bethnal Green
A 1209
Globe
M
20

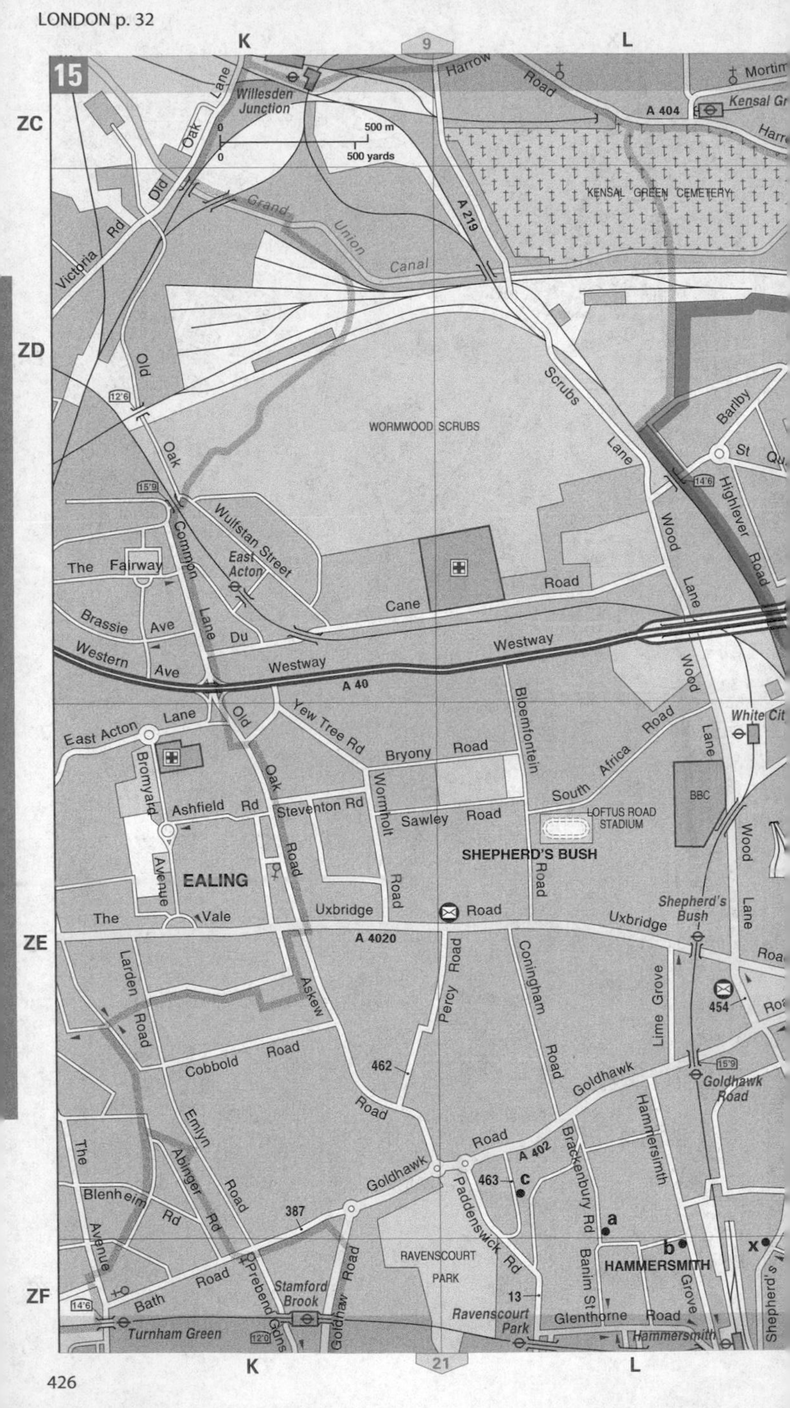
K
L
9
15
ZC
ZD
ZE
ZF
Willesden Junction
Harrow Road
Mortimer
Kensal Gr
A 404
Harr
500 m
500 yards
Oak Lane
Old Oak
KENSAL GREEN CEMETERY
Victoria Rd
Grand Union Canal
A 219
Scrubs Lane
WORMWOOD SCRUBS
Barlby
St
Highlever Road
Wood Lane
Wulfstan Street
East Acton
The Fairway
Common Lane
Cane Road
Brassie Ave
Du
Western Ave
Westway
A 40
Yew Tree Rd
East Acton Lane
Bromyard
Bryony Road
Bloemfontein Road
South Africa Road
White City
BBC
Ashfield Rd
Steventon Rd
Wormholt Road
Sawley Road
LOFTUS ROAD STADIUM
SHEPHERD'S BUSH
Avenue
EALING
The Vale
Uxbridge Road
A 4020
Shepherd's Bush
Larden Road
Askew Road
Percy Road
Coningham Road
Lime Grove
454
Cobbold Road
462
Goldhawk Road
Goldhawk Road
Emlyn Road
The Blenheim Avenue
Abinger Rd
A 402
Brackenbury Rd
Hammersmith Grove
463
c
a
b
x
387
RAVENSCOURT PARK
Paddenswick Rd
Banim St
HAMMERSMITH
Prebend Gdns
Stamford Brook
Bath Road
13
Ravenscourt Park
Glenthorne Road
Hammersmith
Shepherd's
Turnham Green
21

M
N
O
10
16
ZC
ZD
ZE
ZF
17
22
Maida Vale
Kilburn Park
Elgin Avenue
Randolph
Lauderdale Rd
Delaware Rd
Shirland Road
Bravington Road
Fernhead Road
Sixth Ave
Fifth Avenue
Kensal Rd
Ladbroke
Harrow Road
Elgin Avenue
347
340
348
Warwick Ave
Sutherland Rd
Blomfield
Grand Union Canal
BAYSWATER AND MAIDA VALE
Harrow Road
A 404
Golborne Rd
Westway
Westbourne Park
Great Western Rd
Royal Oak
Chesterton Rd
Gardens
A 40
Park Road
Westbourne
Ladbroke Grove
Lancaster Rd
Chepstow Road
Westbourne Grove
Portobello Road
Kensington Park
Ladbroke Grove
Pembridge Villas
Dawson Place
Porchester Gdns
Queensway
Bayswater
Latimer Road
107
NORTH KENSINGTON
Clarendon Road
331
Notting Hill Gate
Park Ave
St Anns Road
Cross Route
Addison Ave
Holland Park
Holland Park
371
A 40
224
KENSINGTON
HOLLAND PARK
Campden Hill
Kensington Church St
Kensington Palace Gardens
Broad Walk
ORANGERY
KENSINGTON PALACE
Holland St
Holland Villas Road
Addison Road
Abbotsbury Road
A 3220
Holland Road
Sinclair Road
Masbro Rd
Kensington Olympia
Blythe Road
326
OLYMPIA
3
Melbury Rd
LINLEY SAMBOURNE HOUSE
LEIGHTON HOUSE
Kensington High Street
High Street Kensington
Edwardes Square
Earls Court Road
Marloes Rd
KENSINGTON AND CHELSEA
POL.
Pembroke Rd.
Cromwell Road
Warwick
Green
A 315
North

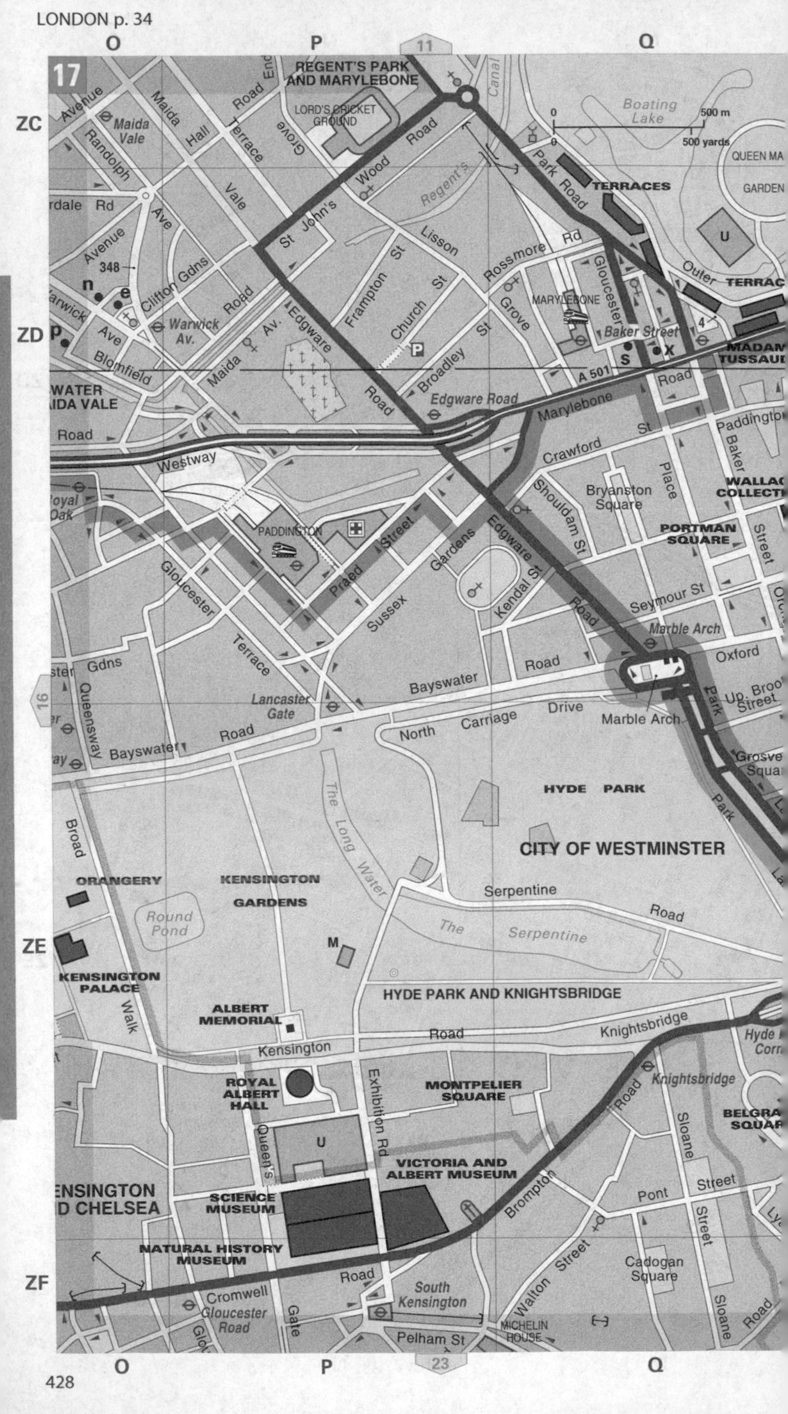
REGENT'S PARK AND MARYLEBONE
LORD'S CRICKET GROUND
TERRACES
PADDINGTON
MARYLEBONE
Baker Street
Edgware Road
Marble Arch
PORTMAN SQUARE
WALLACE COLLECTION
HYDE PARK
CITY OF WESTMINSTER
KENSINGTON GARDENS
Round Pond
The Serpentine
The Long Water
ORANGERY
KENSINGTON PALACE
ALBERT MEMORIAL
HYDE PARK AND KNIGHTSBRIDGE
ROYAL ALBERT HALL
MONTPELIER SQUARE
VICTORIA AND ALBERT MUSEUM
SCIENCE MUSEUM
NATURAL HISTORY MUSEUM
Knightsbridge
South Kensington
Gloucester Road
Lancaster Gate
MICHELIN HOUSE
Cadogan Square
Bryanston Square
Boating Lake
500 m
500 yards

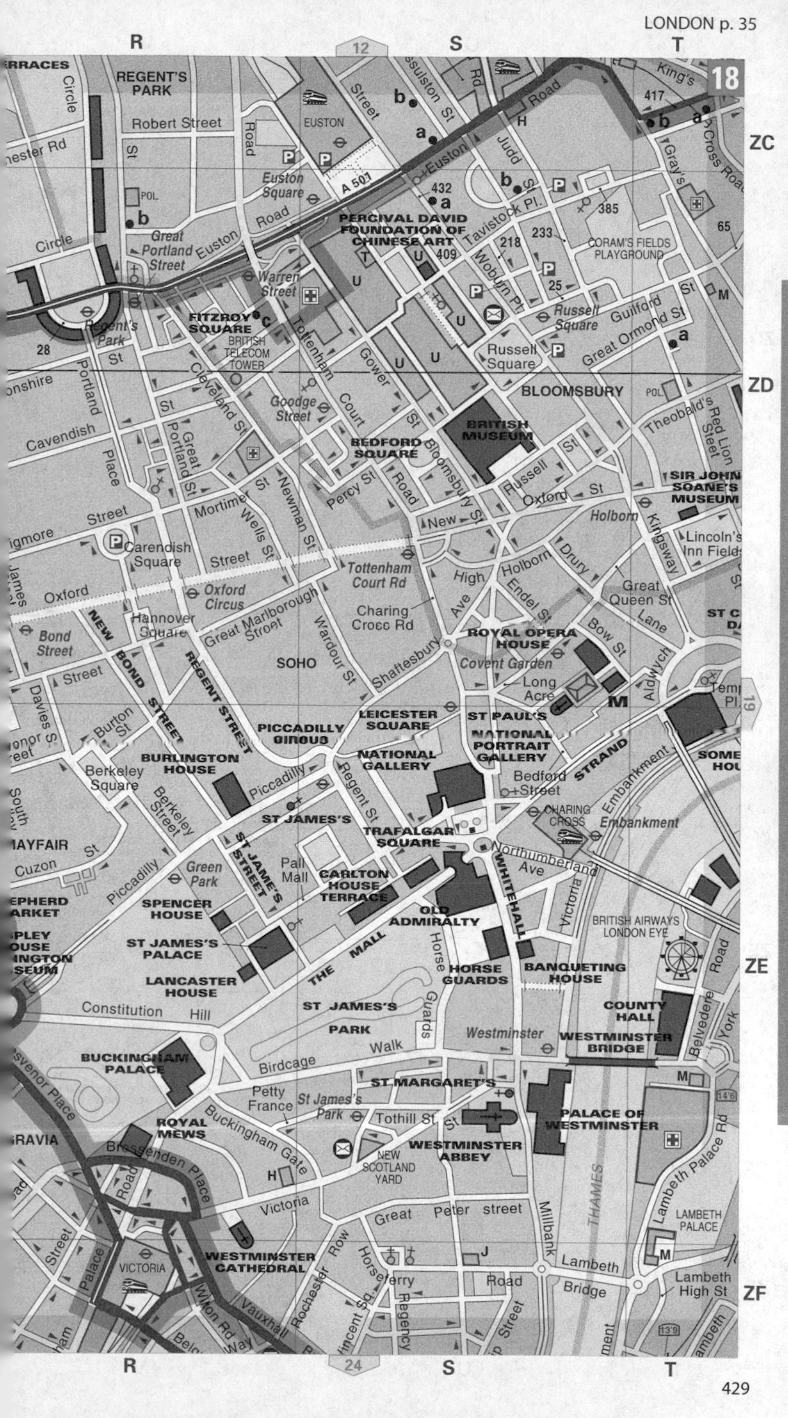
R
S
T
12
18
ZC
ZD
ZE
ZF
REGENT'S PARK
Robert Street
EUSTON
Euston Square
Euston Road
A 501
PERCIVAL DAVID FOUNDATION OF CHINESE ART
Tavistock Pl.
CORAM'S FIELDS PLAYGROUND
Great Portland Street
Warren Street
FITZROY SQUARE
BRITISH TELECOM TOWER
Tottenham
Gower
Russell Square
Guilford
Great Ormond St
BLOOMSBURY
Theobald's
Red Lion Street
Goodge Street
Cleveland St
BRITISH MUSEUM
BEDFORD SQUARE
Bloomsbury
SIR JOHN SOANE'S MUSEUM
Mortimer St
Newman St
Percy St
New Oxford St
Holborn
Kingsway
Lincoln's Inn Fields
Cavendish Square
Tottenham Court Rd
High Holborn
Drury
Great Queen St
Oxford Circus
Charing Cross Rd
Endel St
Hannover Square
Great Marlborough Street
Wardour St
ROYAL OPERA HOUSE
Bow St
NEW BOND STREET
REGENT STREET
SOHO
Shaftesbury Ave
Covent Garden
Long Acre
Aldwych
Bond Street
LEICESTER SQUARE
ST PAUL'S
PICCADILLY CIRCUS
NATIONAL PORTRAIT GALLERY
NATIONAL GALLERY
BURLINGTON HOUSE
Berkeley Square
Bedford Street
STRAND
Embankment
Piccadilly
Regent St
CHARING CROSS
ST JAMES'S
TRAFALGAR SQUARE
MAYFAIR
Northumberland Ave
Green Park
ST JAMES'S STREET
Pall Mall
CARLTON HOUSE TERRACE
WHITEHALL
SPENCER HOUSE
OLD ADMIRALTY
BRITISH AIRWAYS LONDON EYE
ST JAMES'S PALACE
THE MALL
Horse Guards
HORSE GUARDS
BANQUETING HOUSE
LANCASTER HOUSE
Constitution Hill
ST JAMES'S PARK
Birdcage Walk
Westminster
COUNTY HALL
WESTMINSTER BRIDGE
BUCKINGHAM PALACE
ST MARGARET'S
Petty France
St James's Park
Tothill St
PALACE OF WESTMINSTER
ROYAL MEWS
Buckingham Gate
WESTMINSTER ABBEY
NEW SCOTLAND YARD
THAMES
Lambeth Palace Rd
Victoria
Great Peter street
Millbank
LAMBETH PALACE
WESTMINSTER CATHEDRAL
Horseferry Road
Lambeth Bridge
Lambeth High St
VICTORIA
Vauxhall Bridge Road
24

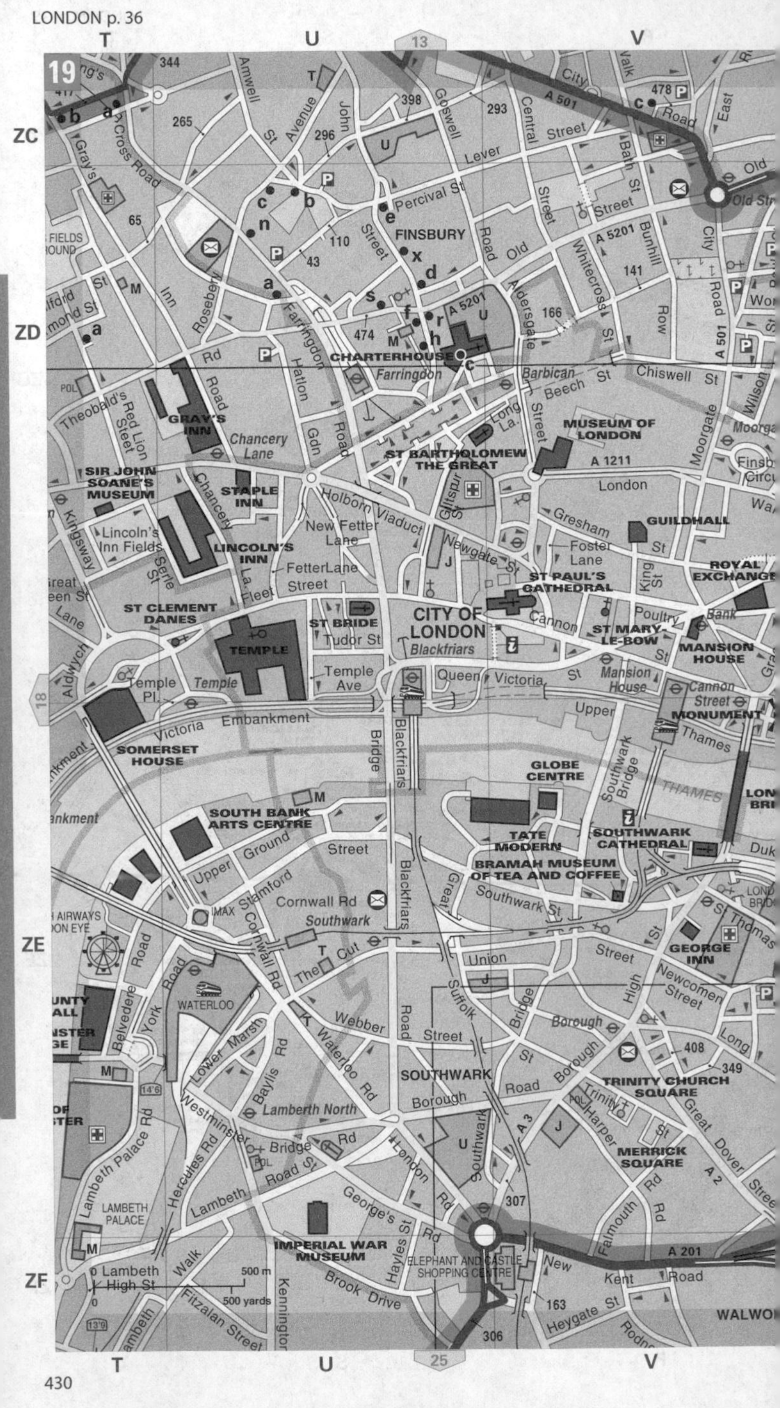
T
U
V
13
19
ZC
ZD
ZE
ZF
18
25
FINSBURY
CHARTERHOUSE
Farringdon
Barbican
MUSEUM OF LONDON
GRAY'S INN
Chancery Lane
ST BARTHOLOMEW THE GREAT
SIR JOHN SOANE'S MUSEUM
STAPLE INN
Lincoln's Inn Fields
LINCOLN'S INN
GUILDHALL
ROYAL EXCHANGE
ST PAUL'S CATHEDRAL
ST CLEMENT DANES
TEMPLE
ST BRIDE
CITY OF LONDON
Blackfriars
ST MARY-LE-BOW
MANSION HOUSE
Mansion House
Temple
Cannon Street
MONUMENT
SOMERSET HOUSE
GLOBE CENTRE
THAMES
SOUTH BANK ARTS CENTRE
TATE MODERN
SOUTHWARK CATHEDRAL
BRAMAH MUSEUM OF TEA AND COFFEE
IMAX
Southwark
GEORGE INN
WATERLOO
Borough
SOUTHWARK
TRINITY CHURCH SQUARE
Lambeth North
MERRICK SQUARE
LAMBETH PALACE
IMPERIAL WAR MUSEUM
ELEPHANT AND CASTLE SHOPPING CENTRE
WALWORTH
500 m
500 yards

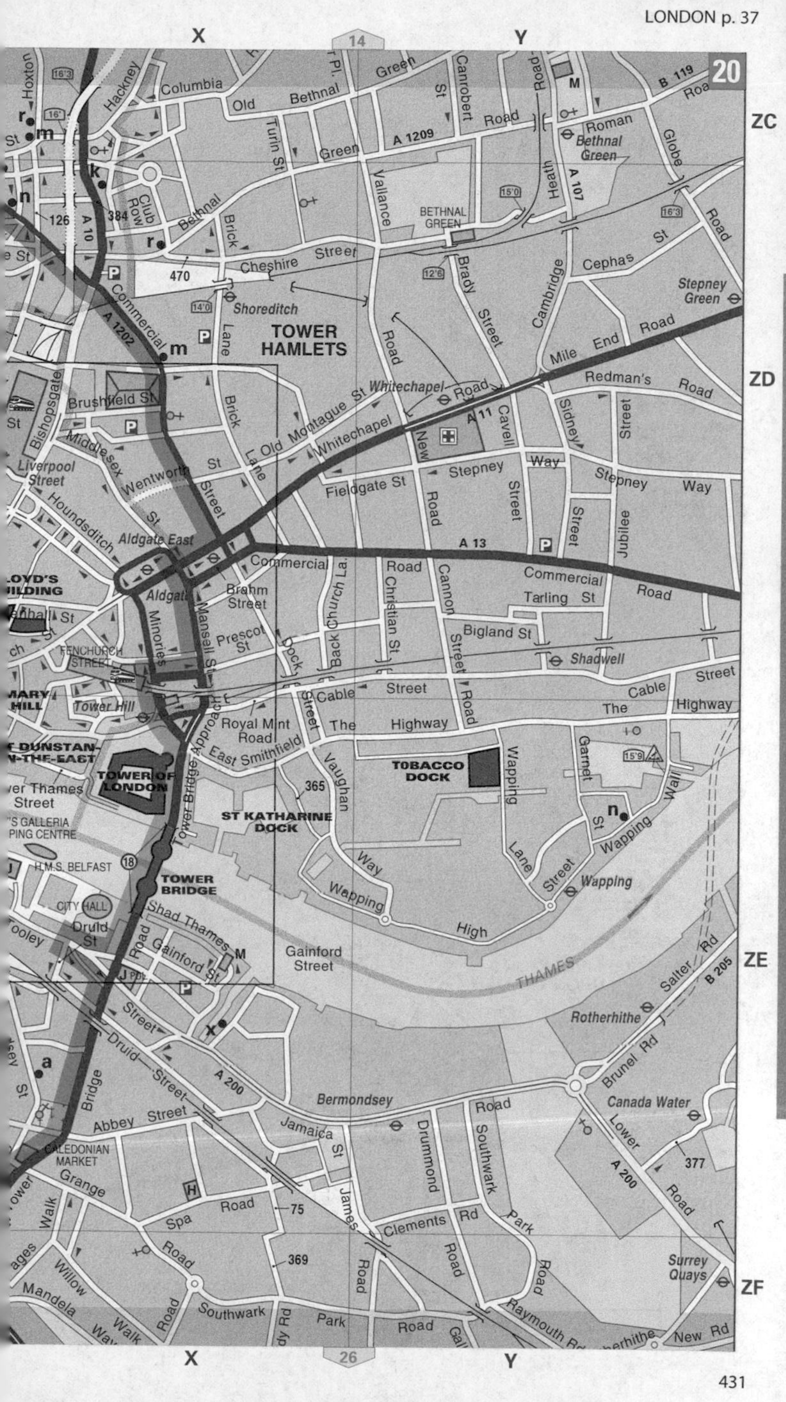
X
Y
14
20
ZC
ZD
ZE
ZF
TOWER HAMLETS
Shoreditch
Whitechapel
Aldgate East
Aldgate
Liverpool Street
Tower Hill
Stepney Green
Bethnal Green
Shadwell
Wapping
Rotherhithe
Canada Water
Surrey Quays
Bermondsey
BETHNAL GREEN
TOBACCO DOCK
ST KATHARINE DOCK
TOWER OF LONDON
TOWER BRIDGE
H.M.S. BELFAST
CITY HALL
CALEDONIAN MARKET
FENCHURCH STREET
THAMES
A 1209
A 107
A 1202
A 10
A 11
A 13
A 200
B 119
B 205
Commercial Road
Mile End Road
Whitechapel Road
Cheshire Street
The Highway
Cable Street
Wapping High Street
Jamaica Road
Southwark Park Road
Druid Street
Abbey Street
Tower Bridge Approach
East Smithfield
Royal Mint Road
X
Y
26

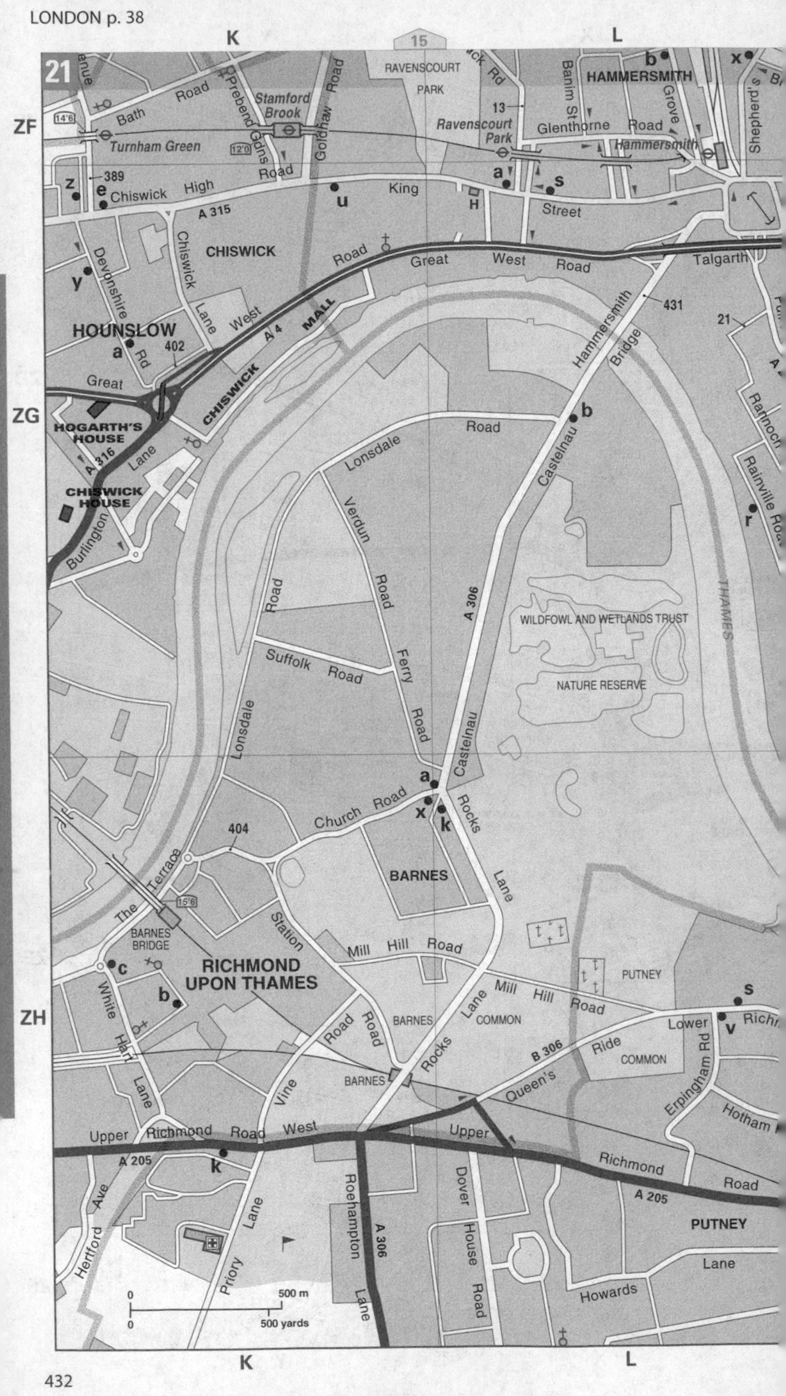
K
L
15
21
ZF
ZG
ZH
RAVENSCOURT
PARK
HAMMERSMITH
Stamford
Brook
Turnham Green
Ravenscourt
Park
Hammersmith
Bath Road
Prebend Gdns
Goldhawk Road
Glenthorne Road
Banim St
Grove
Shepherd's
Chiswick High Road
King Street
A 315
CHISWICK
Great West Road
Talgarth
HOUNSLOW
Devonshire Rd
Chiswick Lane
CHISWICK MALL
A 4
HOGARTH'S HOUSE
CHISWICK HOUSE
Burlington Lane
A 316
Hammersmith Bridge
431
Castelnau
Lonsdale Road
Verdun Road
Ferry Road
A 306
THAMES
WILDFOWL AND WETLANDS TRUST
NATURE RESERVE
Suffolk Road
Lonsdale Road
Church Road
Rocks Lane
BARNES
The Terrace
BARNES BRIDGE
Station Road
Mill Hill Road
RICHMOND UPON THAMES
White Hart Lane
BARNES COMMON
PUTNEY COMMON
Queen's Ride
B 306
Lower Richmond
Erpingham Rd
Hotham
Vine Road
BARNES
Upper Richmond Road West
Upper Richmond Road
A 205
Hertford Ave
Priory Lane
Roehampton Lane
Dover House Road
PUTNEY
Lane
Howards
Rainville Rd
Rannoch
500 m
500 yards

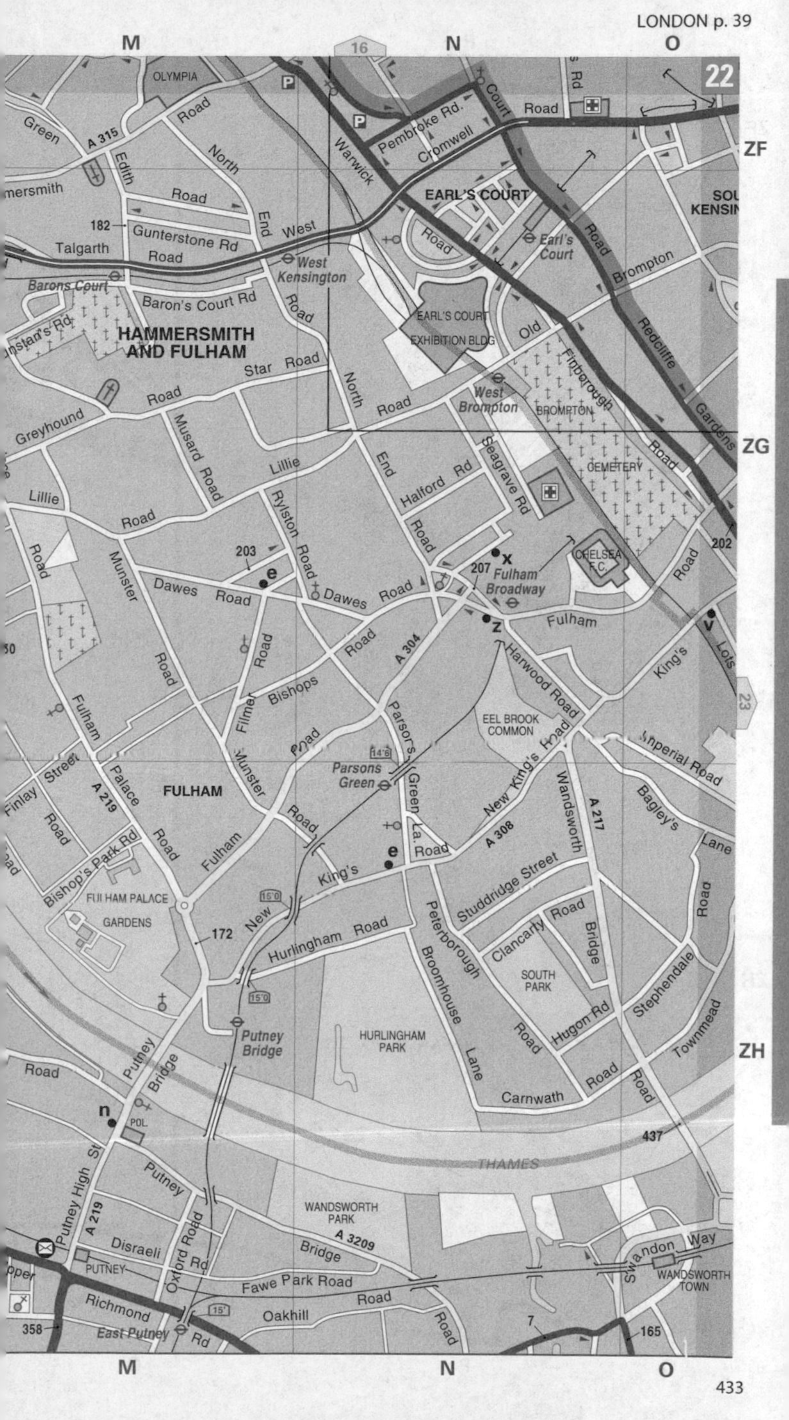

M
N
O
16
22
OLYMPIA
Road
Green
A 315
North
Edith
Warwick
Pembroke Rd.
Cromwell
Court
Road
ZF
EARL'S COURT
SOU
KENSIN
mersmith
182
Gunterstone Rd
Talgarth
Road
West
End
West Kensington
Earl's Court
Brompton
Barons Court
Baron's Court Rd
HAMMERSMITH AND FULHAM
EARL'S COURT EXHIBITION BLDG
Old
Redcliffe
Star Road
Greyhound
Musard Road
West Brompton
BROMPTON
CEMETERY
Finborough
Gardens
ZG
Lillie
Seagrave Rd
Halford Rd
Rylston Road
Munster
203
Dawes Road
207
Fulham Broadway
CHELSEA F.C.
202
Fulham
A 304
Bishops
Filmer Road
Parsons Green
Harwood Road
EEL BROOK COMMON
King's
Lots
23
Imperial Road
Finlay Street
A 219
Palace
FULHAM
New King's Road
Wandsworth
A 217
Bagley's Lane
A 308
Studdridge Street
Bishop's Park Rd
FULHAM PALACE GARDENS
172
Hurlingham Road
Peterborough
Broomhouse Lane
Clancarty Road
Bridge
SOUTH PARK
Hugon Rd
Stephendale
Townmead
Putney Bridge
HURLINGHAM PARK
ZH
Carnwath
POL
437
THAMES
Putney High St
WANDSWORTH PARK
A 3209
Disraeli Rd
Oxford Road
PUTNEY
Fawe Park Road
Swandon Way
WANDSWORTH TOWN
Richmond
Oakhill
358
East Putney
7
165

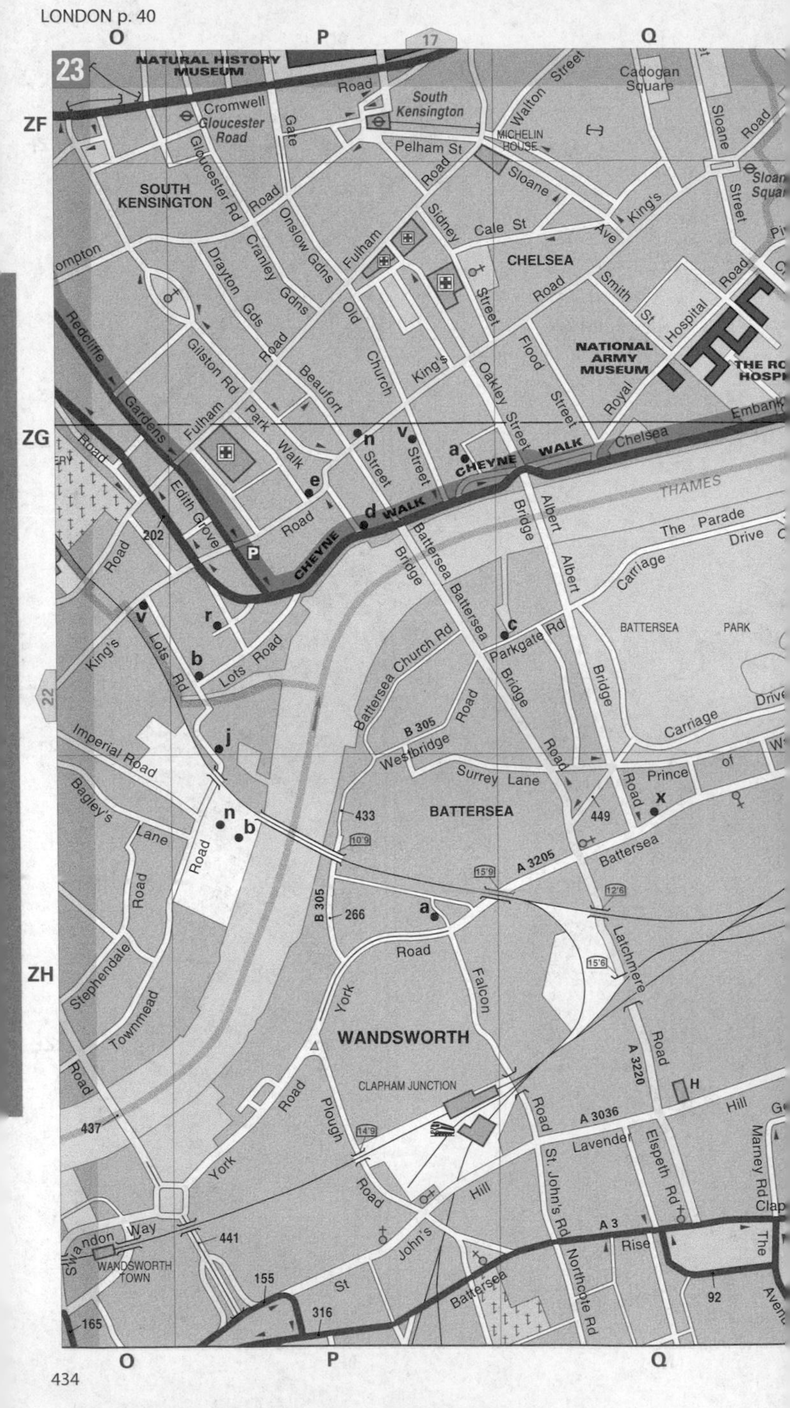
O
P
Q
17
23
NATURAL HISTORY MUSEUM
ZF
Cromwell
Gloucester Road
Gate
Road
South Kensington
Walton Street
Cadogan Square
Sloane Road
MICHELIN HOUSE
Pelham St
Sloane
SOUTH KENSINGTON
Gloucester Rd
Road
Onslow Gdns
Cranley Gdns
Drayton Gds
Road
Sidney
Cale St
King's
Ave
Sloane Square
Street
Fulham
Old Church
CHELSEA
Smith St
Road
Hospital
Street
Road
Flood Street
NATIONAL ARMY MUSEUM
Royal
Redcliffe Gardens
Gilston Rd
Beaufort
King's
Oakley Street
Fulham
Park Walk
ZG
Road
n
v
a
Street
Street
CHEYNE WALK
Chelsea Embankment
Edith Grove
e
d
THAMES
202
Road
CHEYNE WALK
Battersea Bridge
Albert Bridge
The Parade
Drive
Carriage
P
Road
Bridge
Albert
v
r
Battersea
c
Parkgate Rd
BATTERSEA PARK
King's
Lots Rd
b
Lots Road
Battersea Church Rd
Bridge
Bridge
Drive
Carriage
22
Battersea
Road
B 305
j
Imperial Road
Westbridge
Road
Prince of
Surrey Lane
Bagley's
Lane
n
b
433
BATTERSEA
Road
x
449
10'9
Battersea
A 3205
15'9
Road
Road
B 305
266
a
12'6
Latchmere
Road
15'6
Falcon
ZH
Stephendale
Townmead
York
WANDSWORTH
A 3220
Road
Road
CLAPHAM JUNCTION
H
Road
Plough
Road
A 3036
Hill
437
14'9
Lavender
Elspeth Rd
Marney Rd
York
Road
Hill
St. John's Rd
Clap
Swandon Way
441
John's
A 3
Rise
The Avenue
WANDSWORTH TOWN
155
St
Battersea
Northcote Rd
92
165
316
O
P
Q

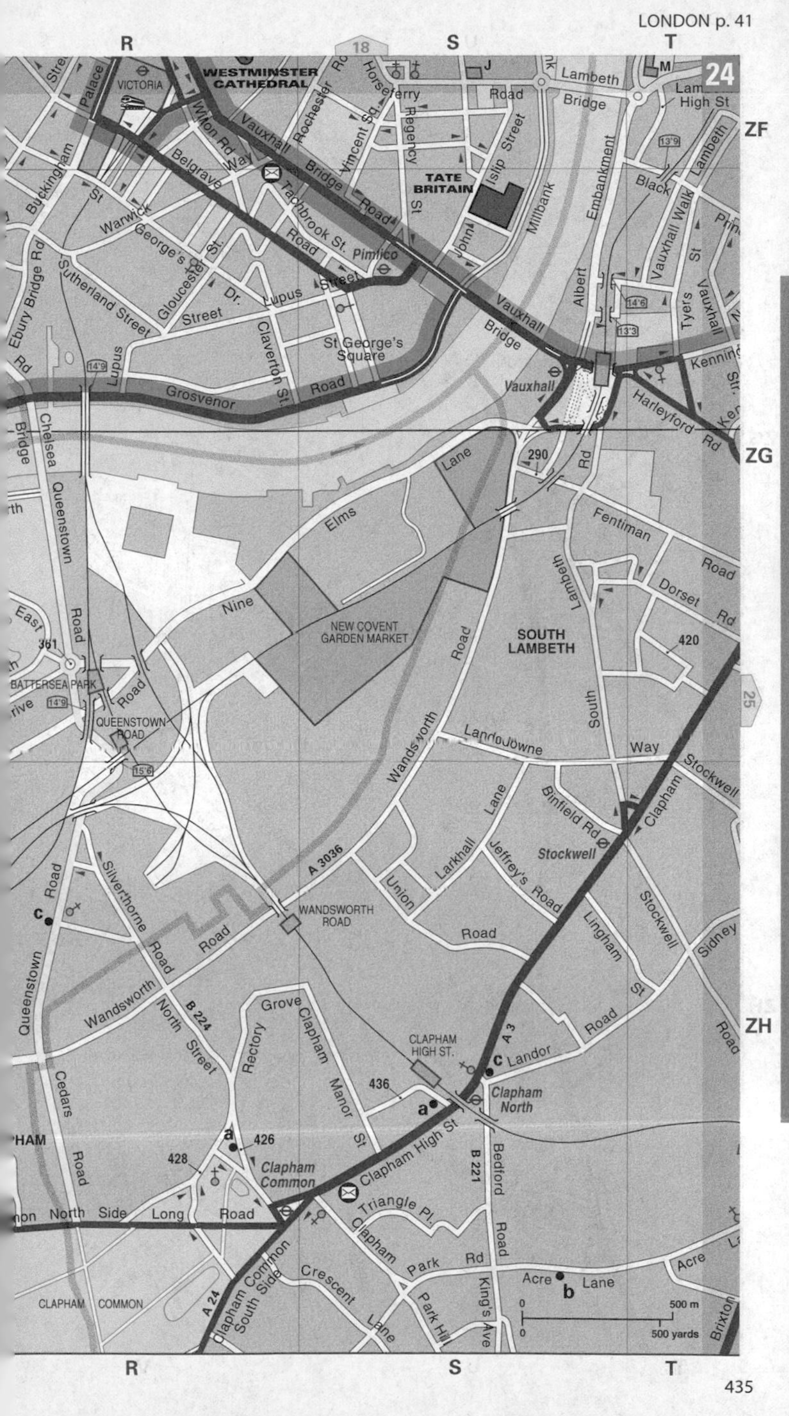
R
S
T
18
24
25
ZF
ZG
ZH
WESTMINSTER CATHEDRAL
VICTORIA
TATE BRITAIN
Pimlico
St George's Square
Vauxhall
NEW COVENT GARDEN MARKET
SOUTH LAMBETH
BATTERSEA PARK
QUEENSTOWN ROAD
WANDSWORTH ROAD
Stockwell
CLAPHAM HIGH ST.
Clapham North
Clapham Common
CLAPHAM COMMON
Vauxhall Bridge Road
Grosvenor Road
Nine Elms Lane
Wandsworth Road
Clapham High St
Clapham Road
Lambeth Bridge
Albert Embankment
Millbank
Queenstown Road
Fentiman Road
Dorset Rd
Landsdowne Way
South Lambeth Road
Larkhall Lane
Jeffrey's Road
Binfield Rd
Stockwell Road
Lingham St
Landor Road
Bedford Road
Acre Lane
Clapham Park Rd
Clapham Common South Side
Clapham Common North Side
Long Road
Silverthorne Road
North Street
Rectory Grove
Clapham Manor St
Cedars Road
Triangle Pl.
Crescent Lane
Park Hill
King's Ave
Harleyford Rd
Kennington
A 3036
A 3
A 24
B 224
B 221
290
361
420
426
428
436
0
500 m
500 yards

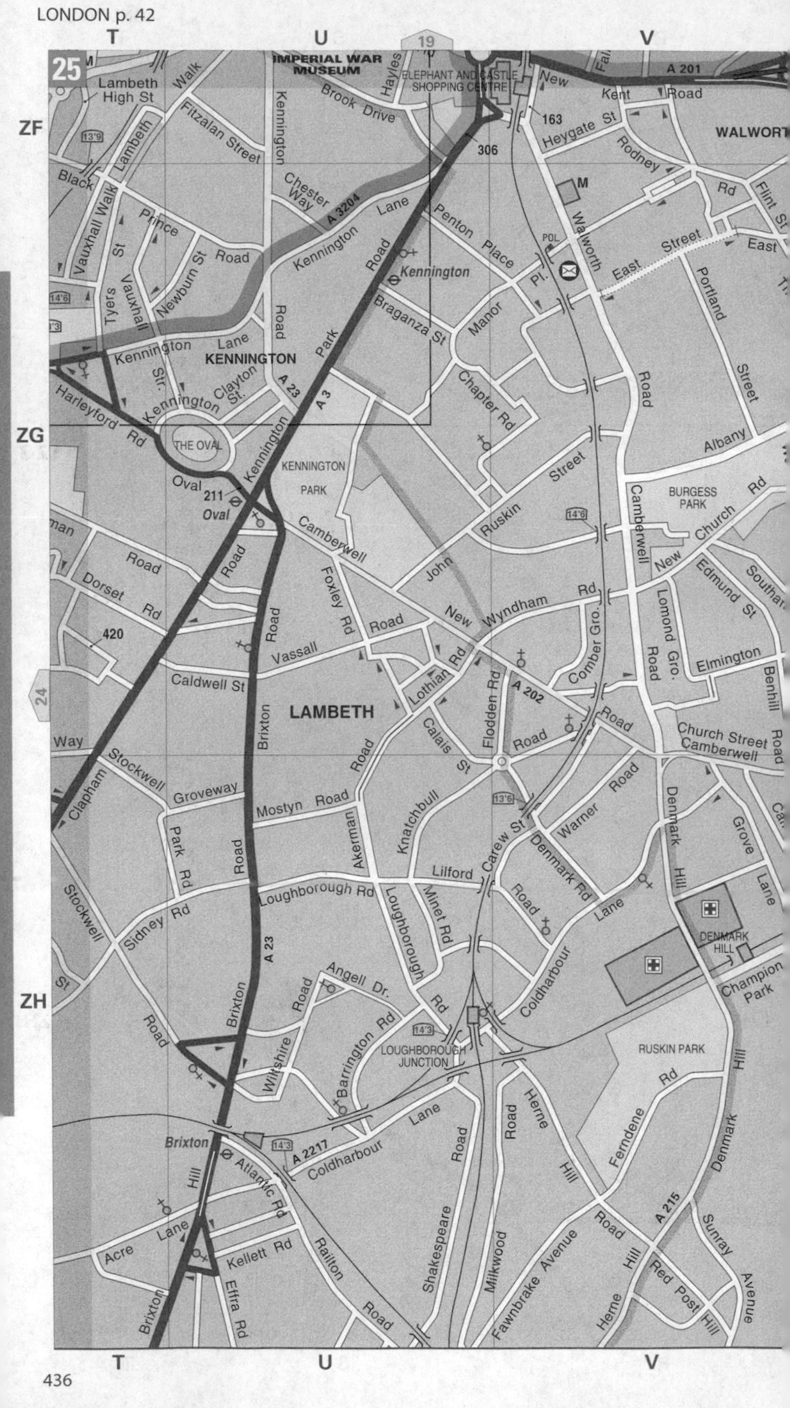
T
U
V
25
19
24
ZF
ZG
ZH
IMPERIAL WAR MUSEUM
ELEPHANT AND CASTLE SHOPPING CENTRE
WALWORTH
KENNINGTON
THE OVAL
KENNINGTON PARK
BURGESS PARK
LAMBETH
DENMARK HILL
RUSKIN PARK
LOUGHBOROUGH JUNCTION
Kennington
Oval
Brixton
Lambeth High St
Fitzalan Street
Brook Drive
Kennington Road
Chester Way
Kennington Lane
Kennington Park Road
Penton Place
Braganza St
Manor Pl.
Chapter Rd
Walworth Road
East Street
Portland Street
Albany Road
Heygate St
Rodney Rd
New Kent Road
Flint St
Black Prince Road
Vauxhall Walk
Newburn St
Tyers St
Vauxhall St.
Clayton St.
Harleyford Rd
Kennington Oval
Camberwell New Road
John Ruskin Street
Camberwell Road
New Church Rd
Edmund St
Lomond Gro.
Elmington
Benhill Road
Church Street Camberwell
Wyndham Rd
Comber Gro.
Flodden Rd
Lothian Rd
Foxley Rd
Vassall Road
Caldwell St
Dorset Rd
Brixton Road
Calais St
Stockwell Road
Groveway
Mostyn Road
Akerman Road
Knatchbull Road
Warner Road
Denmark Rd
Denmark Hill
Grove Lane
Lilford Road
Carew St
Minet Rd
Loughborough Rd
Coldharbour Lane
Park Rd
Sidney Rd
Stockwell Park Road
Clapham Road
Angell Dr.
Barrington Rd
Wiltshire Road
Champion Park
Ferndene Rd
Herne Hill
Atlantic Rd
Railton Road
Shakespeare Road
Milkwood Road
Fawnbrake Avenue
Sunray Avenue
Red Post Hill
Acre Lane
Kellett Rd
Effra Rd
Brixton Hill
A 201
A 3204
A 23
A 3
A 202
A 2217
A 215
163
306
211
420
POL
M

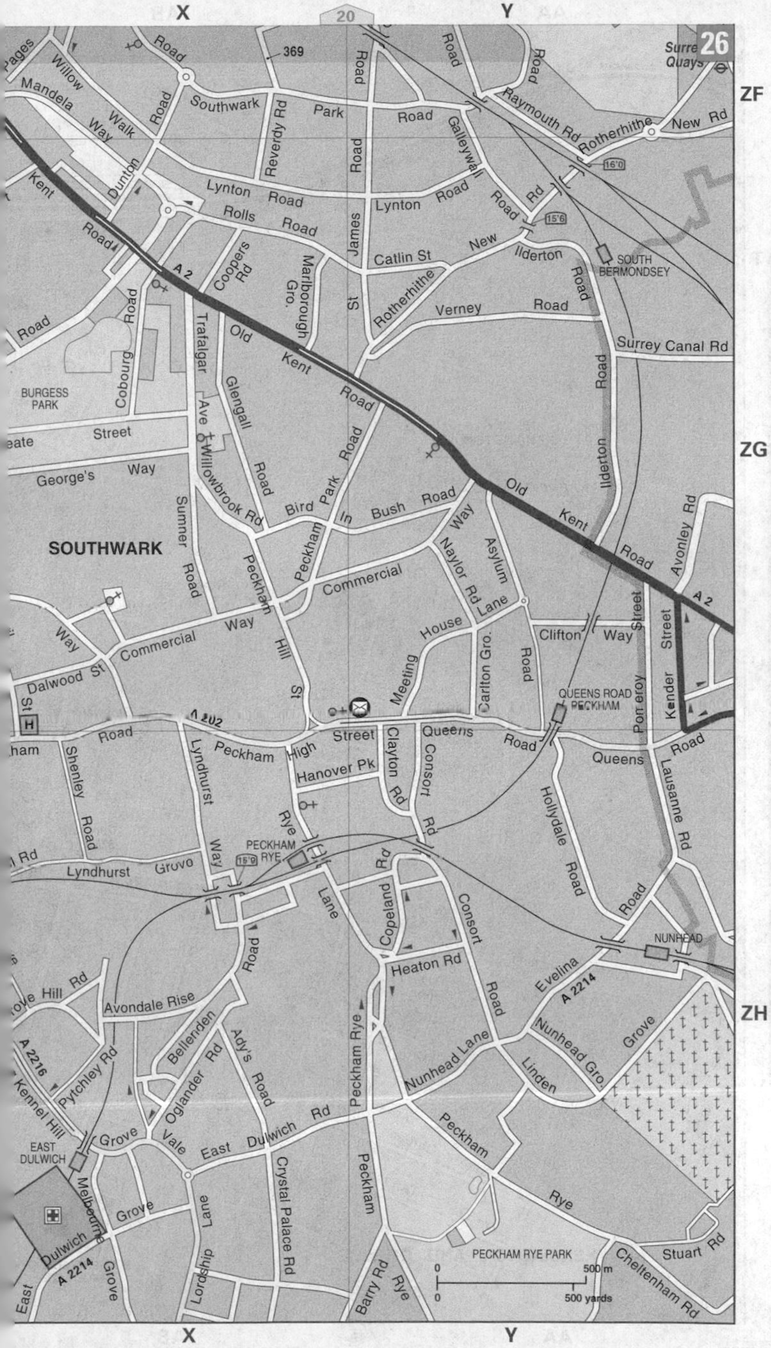

X Y
20
26
ZF
ZG
ZH
Surrey Quays
369
Pages
Willow Walk
Mandela Way
Road
Southwark Park Road
Reverdy Rd
Galleywall Road
Raymouth Rd
Rotherhithe New Rd
16'0
Dunton Road
Kent Road
Lynton Road
Rolls Road
Ilderton Rd
15'6
SOUTH BERMONDSEY
Coopers Rd
Marlborough Gro.
James St
Catlin St
New Rotherhithe
Verney Road
Surrey Canal Rd
A 2
Old Kent Road
Cobourg Road
Trafalgar Ave
Glengall Road
BURGESS PARK
Street
George's Way
Willowbrook Rd
Peckham Park Road
Bird In Bush Road
Ilderton Road
Avonley Rd
SOUTHWARK
Sumner Road
Peckham Hill St
Commercial Way
Naylor Rd
Asylum Road
Meeting House Lane
Carlton Gro.
Clifton Way
Pomeroy Street
Kender Street
Dalwood St
H
A 202
QUEENS ROAD PECKHAM
Peckham Road
Shenley Road
Lyndhurst Way
Peckham High Street
Hanover Pk
Clayton Rd
Consort Rd
Queens Road
Hollydale Road
Lausanne Rd
Rye Lane
PECKHAM RYE
15'9
Lyndhurst Grove
Copeland Rd
Consort Road
NUNHEAD
Heaton Rd
Evelina Road
A 2214
Grove Hill Rd
Avondale Rise
Bellenden Road
Peckham Rye
Nunhead Lane
Nunhead Gro
Grove
A 2216
Kennel Hill
Pytchley Rd
Oglander Rd
Ady's Road
Linden
Grove Vale
East Dulwich Rd
EAST DULWICH
Melbourne Grove
Dulwich
A 2214
East
Lordship Lane
Crystal Palace Rd
Peckham Rye
Barry Rd
PECKHAM RYE PARK
0 500 m
0 500 yards
Stuart Rd
Cheltenham Rd

AA AB

27

Grand Union Canal
Harrow Road
Bourne Terrace
BAYSWATER AND MAIDA VALE
Harrow
A 40
Westway
Westbourne Park
Great Western Road
Tavistock Rd
St Luke's Rd
Westbourne Park Road
Westbourne Park Villas
Royal Oak
Porchester
Gloucester
Westbourne Park Road
Chepstow Rd
Talbot Rd
Westbourne
Ledbury Road
Hereford Road
Westbourne Gdns
197
Talbot Road
NORTH KENSINGTON
Newton Rd
Colville Ter.
Artesian Road
Bishop's Br
Westbourne Grove
Colville Rd
Ledbury
Garway
Queensway
Inverness
Grove Villas
Kensington Gdns Sq.
Porchester
Westbourne
Chepstow Villas
Pembridge
Chepstow
Leinster Sq.
Road
Chepstow Pl.
84
Road
Portobello Road
Dawson
Place
Bayswater
Moscow
Kensington Park
Pembridge Cres.
Pembridge Square
St Petersburgh Pl.
Bark Place
Queensway
Terrace
Pembridge
Pembridge Gdns
Linden Gdns
Ossington St
Palace Court
Queensway
328
Ladbroke Square
Road
Rd
Linden Gate
Bayswater Road
Broad
Ladbroke
Hill
Notting
Notting Hill Gate
Holland Park Ave
Uxbridge St
Kensington Church
Palace Gardens
Kensington Palace Gardens
Campden Hill Square
Campden Hill
Kensington Place
ORANGERY
Aubrey Walk
Bedford Gardens
Terrace
Sheffield Terrace
Church
Palace
KENSINGTON AND CHELSEA
KENSINGTON PALACE
Holland
Campden Hill
Campden Gro.
St
T
U
V

AA 35 AB

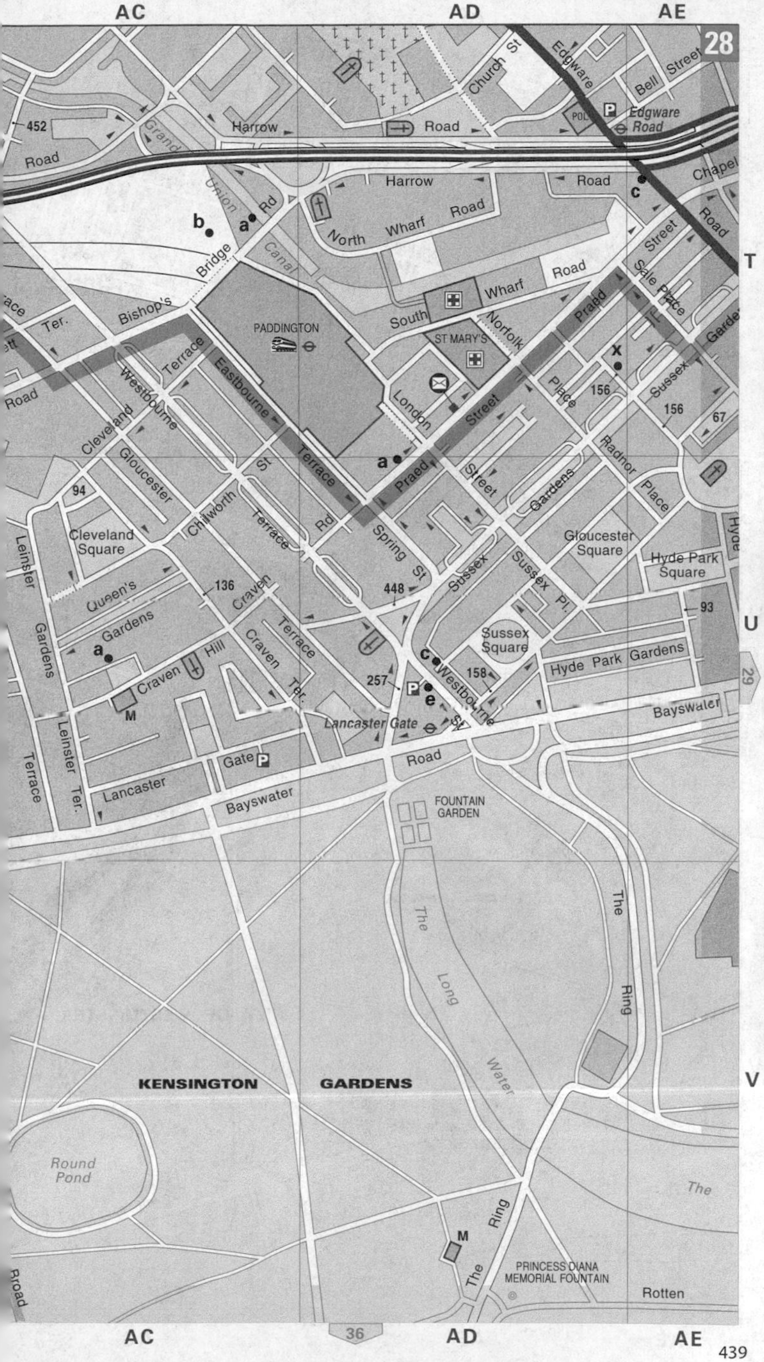

AC AD AE

28

T
U
V

452
Road
Harrow
Road
Church St
Edgware Road
Bell Street
POL
P
Edgware Road
Grand Union Canal
Harrow
Road
Road
Chapel
b
a
Rd
c
North Wharf Road
Road
Bridge
Bishop's
Street
Sale Place
Road
Wharf
Road
South
Praed
Norfolk
ST MARY'S
PADDINGTON
Ter.
Road
Terrace
Westbourne
Eastbourne
London
Street
x
Garden
Sussex
Place
156
156
67
Cleveland
Gloucester
St
Terrace
a
Praed
Street
Radnor
Place
Gardens
94
Chilworth
Rd
Terrace
Spring
Cleveland Square
Gloucester Square
Hyde Park Square
Hyde
Leinster
Queen's
136
Craven
448
St
Sussex
Sussex
Pl.
93
Gardens
a
Gardens
Craven
Hill
Craven
Terrace
Sussex Square
c
257
P
e
Westbourne
St
158
Hyde Park Gardens
29
M
Craven
Ter.
Lancaster Gate
Bayswater
Leinster
Ter.
Terrace
Gate
P
Road
Lancaster
Bayswater
FOUNTAIN GARDEN
The Long Water
The Ring
KENSINGTON GARDENS
Round Pond
The
Ring
M
The
PRINCESS DIANA MEMORIAL FOUNTAIN
Rotten
Rroad

AC 36 AD AE

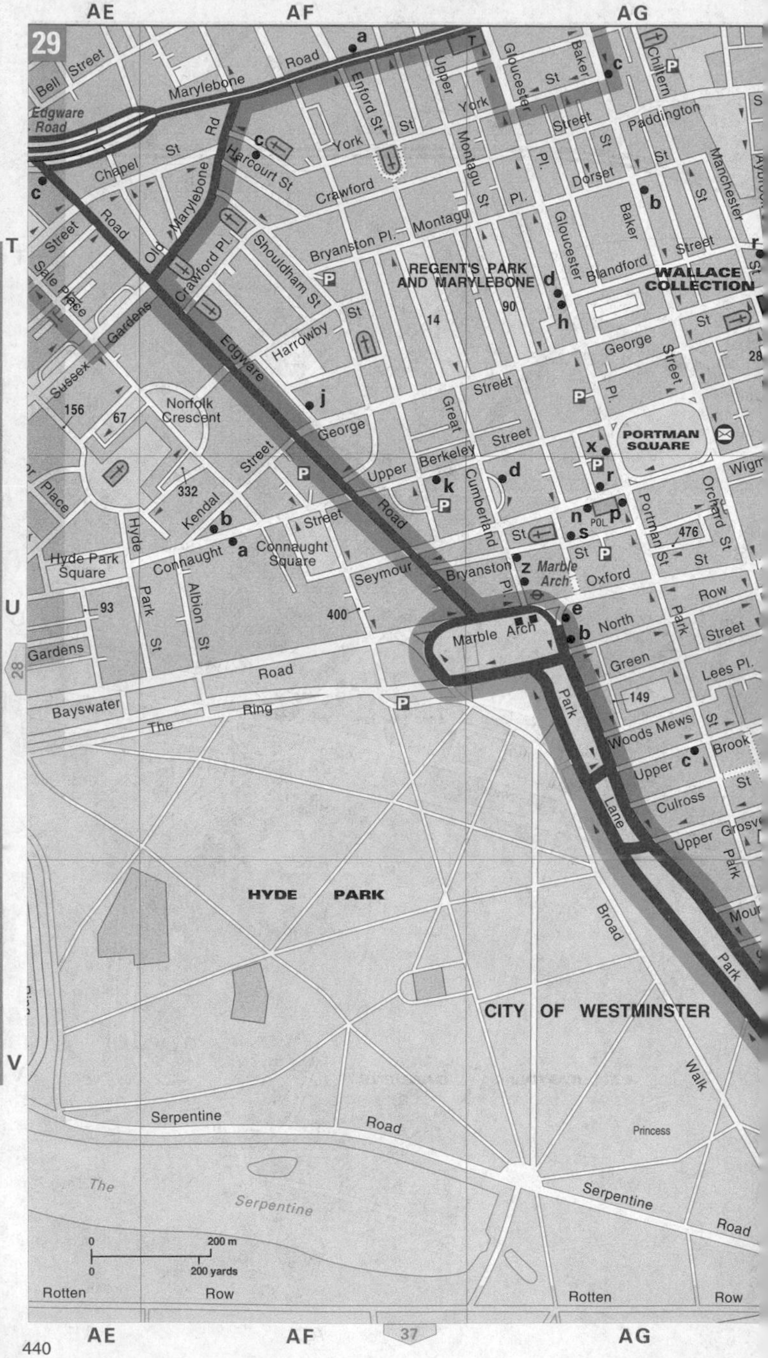

AE AF AG

29

REGENT'S PARK AND MARYLEBONE

WALLACE COLLECTION

PORTMAN SQUARE

HYDE PARK

CITY OF WESTMINSTER

Marylebone Road
Edgware Road
Old Marylebone Rd
Crawford St
York St
Harcourt St
Bryanston Pl.
Montagu St
Upper Montagu St
Gloucester Pl.
Baker St
Dorset St
Blandford Street
Paddington St
George Street
Great Cumberland Pl.
Upper Berkeley Street
Seymour Street
Connaught Square
Connaught Street
Hyde Park Square
Norfolk Crescent
Sussex Gardens
Bayswater Road
The Ring
Marble Arch
Oxford Street
North Row
Green Street
Park Lane
Upper Brook St
Woods Mews
Culross St
Upper Grosvenor St
Park Street
Orchard St
Portman St
Manchester St
Chiltern St
Serpentine Road
The Serpentine
Broad Walk
Rotten Row

0 200 m
0 200 yards

T U V

AE AF AG

37

AH
AI
AJ
30
BRITISH TELECOM TOWER
232
Marylebone High St
Weymouth
Wimpole St
Harley Street
New Cavendish Street
Portland Place
Great Portland St
Great Titchfield Street
Cleveland St
Charlotte
Goodge St
Foley St
MIDDLESEX
Berner's St
Newman St
Langham St
Welbeck
Queen Anne Street
Mortimer
Wells St
Wigmore St
Cavendish Sq.
Regent
Margaret
Eastcastle
Henrietta Pl.
Holles St
Oxford Circus
Oxford St
Vere St
James St
Argyll St
Poland
Noel St
D'Arblay St
Wardour
Princes St
Great Marlborough St
New Bond St
Regent St
Hanover Sq.
Hanover St
Bond St
South Molton St
Gilbert
Binney
Duke
Davies St
Brook St
Maddox St
Carnaby St
Marshall
Broadwick
Lexington
Kingly St
Beak
St James
Golden Sq.
Brook's Mews
MAYFAIR
Grosvenor Square
Grosvenor Street
Conduit St
Savile Row
Mount Row
Bruton Street
Adam's Row
Cork St
Vigo St
Brewer
South Audley St
Mount St
Berkeley Square
Dover St
BURLINGTON HOUSE
BURLINGTON ARCADE
Sackville St
OLD BOND ST
Farm St
Hay's Mews
Charles St
Curzon St
Bolton Street
Albemarle Street
PICCADILLY
PICCADILLY ARCADE
JERMYN ST
ST JAMES'S ST
ST JAMES SQUARE
Duke St
Bury St
King St
Pall Mall
Green Park
Queen's Walk
SHEPHERD MARKET
Hertford St
Brick St
Old Park La.
SPENCER HOUSE
GREEN PARK
QUEEN'S CHAPEL
ST JAMES PALACE
LANCASTER HOUSE
31
38
T
U
V

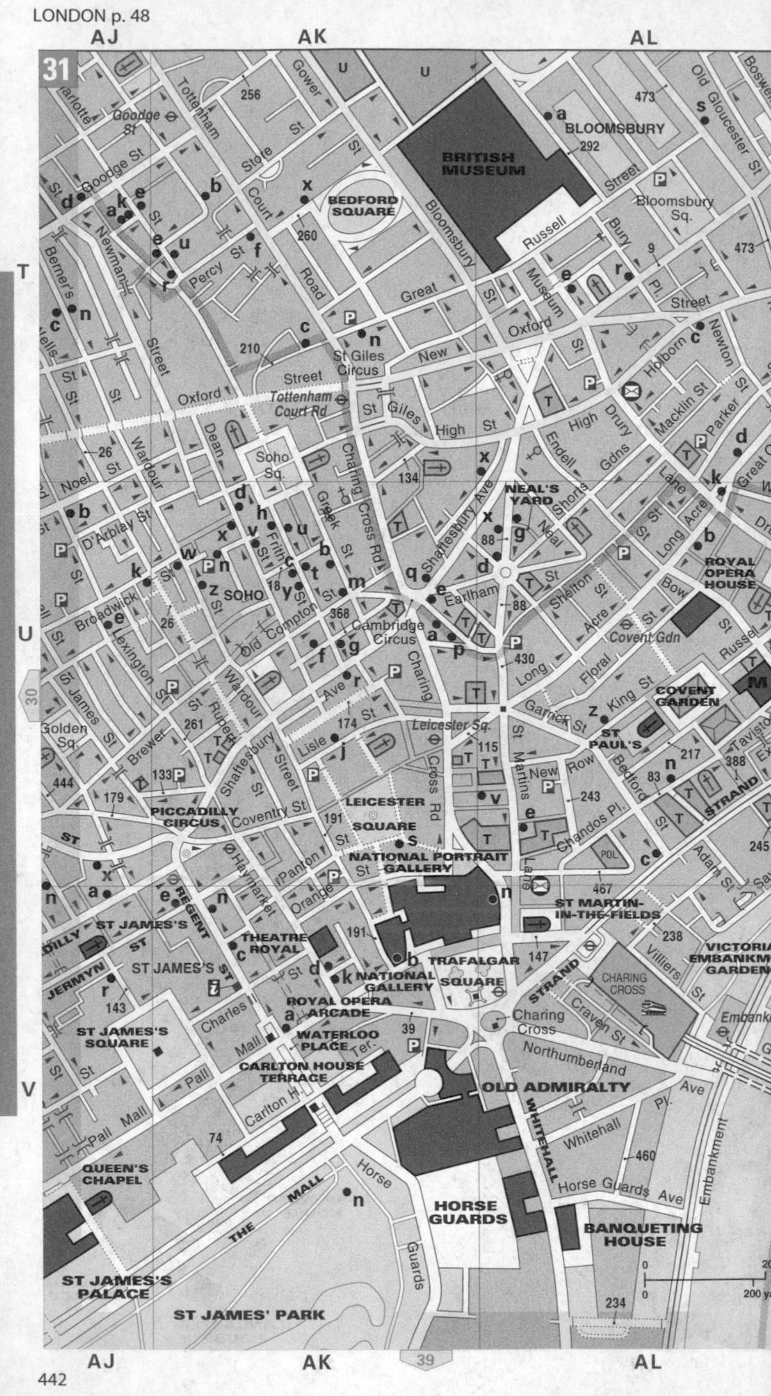
AJ
AK
AL
31
T
U
V
30
39
BRITISH MUSEUM
BLOOMSBURY
BEDFORD SQUARE
Bloomsbury Sq.
Goodge St
Tottenham Court Rd
Soho Sq.
SOHO
NEAL'S YARD
ROYAL OPERA HOUSE
Covent Gdn
COVENT GARDEN
ST PAUL'S
Cambridge Circus
St Giles Circus
Leicester Sq.
LEICESTER SQUARE
Golden Sq.
PICCADILLY CIRCUS
NATIONAL PORTRAIT GALLERY
ST MARTIN-IN-THE-FIELDS
THEATRE ROYAL
TRAFALGAR SQUARE
NATIONAL GALLERY
ROYAL OPERA ARCADE
WATERLOO PLACE
CHARING CROSS
Charing Cross
VICTORIA EMBANKMENT GARDENS
ST JAMES'S SQUARE
CARLTON HOUSE TERRACE
OLD ADMIRALTY
WHITEHALL
HORSE GUARDS
BANQUETING HOUSE
QUEEN'S CHAPEL
ST JAMES'S PALACE
ST JAMES' PARK
THE MALL
STRAND
200 yards

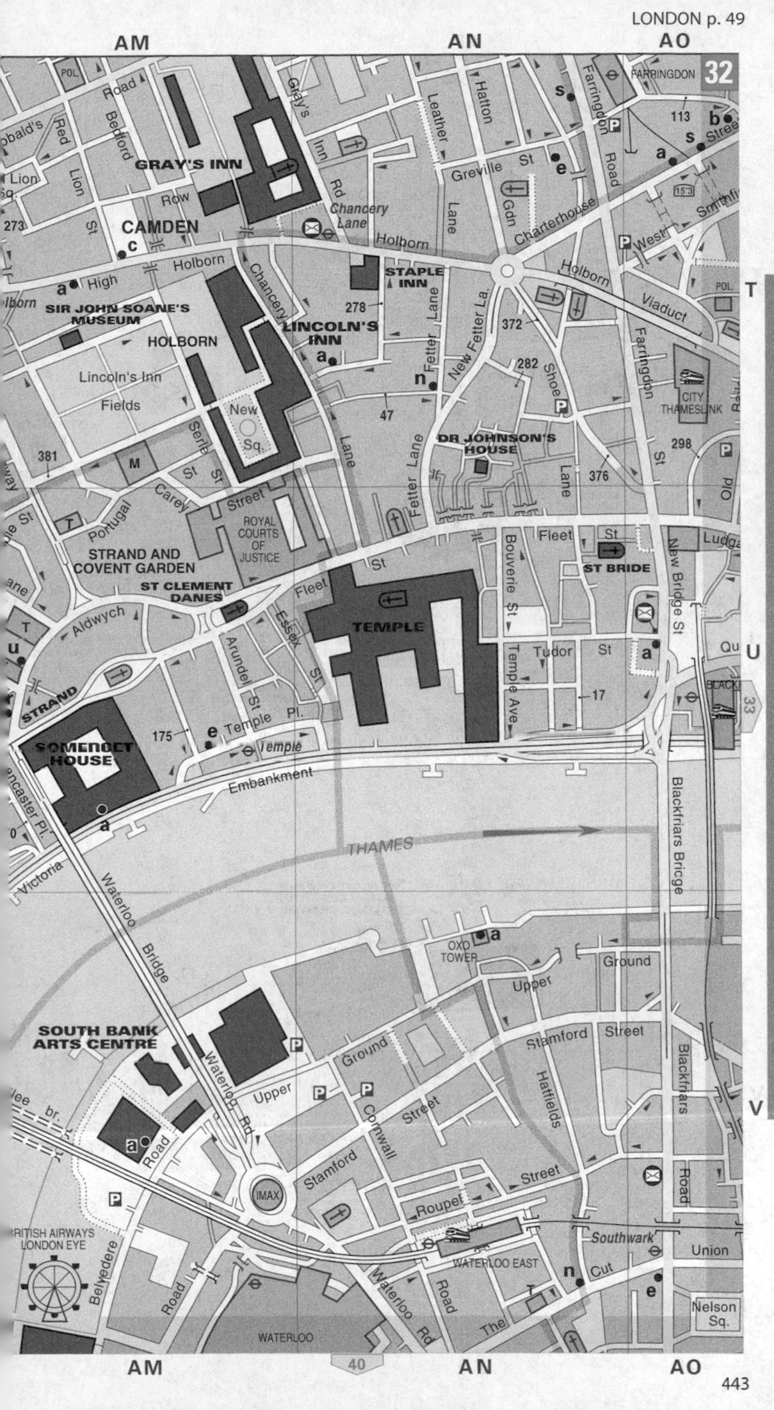
AM
AN
AO
32
FARRINGDON
GRAY'S INN
CAMDEN
SIR JOHN SOANE'S MUSEUM
HOLBORN
Lincoln's Inn Fields
New Sq.
Chancery Lane
STAPLE INN
LINCOLN'S INN
Holborn
Holborn Viaduct
Charterhouse
Greville St
Hatton Gdn
Leather Lane
Gray's Inn Rd
Farringdon Road
Farringdon St
CITY THAMESLINK
DR JOHNSON'S HOUSE
Fetter Lane
New Fetter La.
Shoe Lane
ROYAL COURTS OF JUSTICE
STRAND AND COVENT GARDEN
ST CLEMENT DANES
Carey Street
Portugal St
Serle St
Aldwych
STRAND
Fleet St
ST BRIDE
TEMPLE
Bouverie St
Tudor St
Temple Ave.
New Bridge St
Essex St
Arundel St
Temple Pl.
Temple
SOMERSET HOUSE
Embankment
Victoria
THAMES
Blackfriars Bridge
Waterloo Bridge
OXO TOWER
Upper Ground
Stamford Street
Hatfields
Blackfriars Road
SOUTH BANK ARTS CENTRE
Waterloo Rd
Cornwall
IMAX
Roupell
Southwark
Union
Cut
Nelson Sq.
WATERLOO EAST
WATERLOO
Belvedere Road
BRITISH AIRWAYS LONDON EYE
T
U
V
33
40
AM
AN
AO

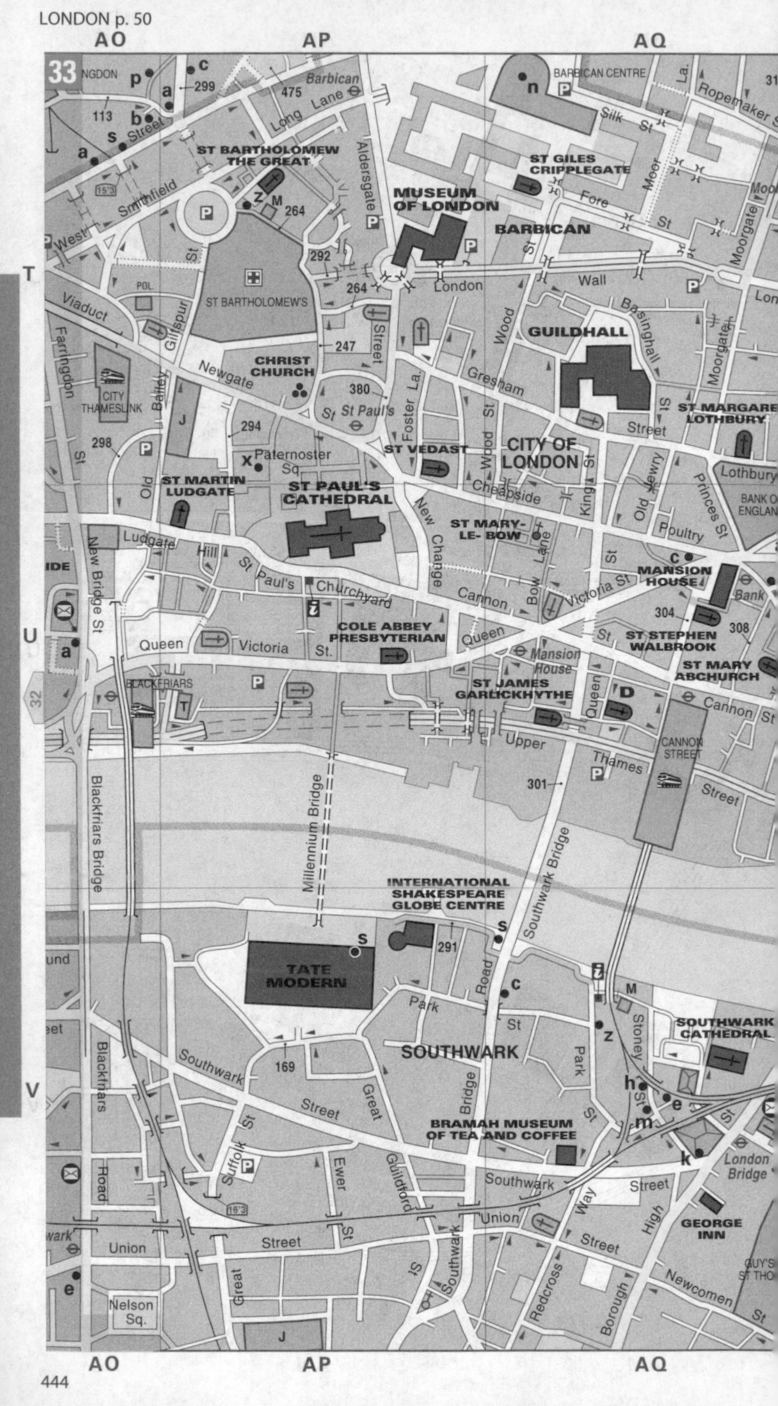
AO
AP
AQ
33
ST BARTHOLOMEW THE GREAT
MUSEUM OF LONDON
ST GILES CRIPPLEGATE
BARBICAN
BARBICAN CENTRE
ST BARTHOLOMEW'S
GUILDHALL
CHRIST CHURCH
CITY THAMESLINK
ST MARGARET LOTHBURY
ST VEDAST
CITY OF LONDON
ST MARTIN LUDGATE
ST PAUL'S CATHEDRAL
ST MARY-LE-BOW
MANSION HOUSE
BANK OF ENGLAND
COLE ABBEY PRESBYTERIAN
ST STEPHEN WALBROOK
ST MARY ABCHURCH
ST JAMES GARLICKHYTHE
BLACKFRIARS
CANNON STREET
Millennium Bridge
Blackfriars Bridge
Southwark Bridge
INTERNATIONAL SHAKESPEARE GLOBE CENTRE
TATE MODERN
SOUTHWARK
SOUTHWARK CATHEDRAL
BRAMAH MUSEUM OF TEA AND COFFEE
GEORGE INN
London Bridge
Newgate
Cheapside
Queen Victoria St.
Upper Thames Street
Southwark Street
Union Street
Borough High Street
T
U
V

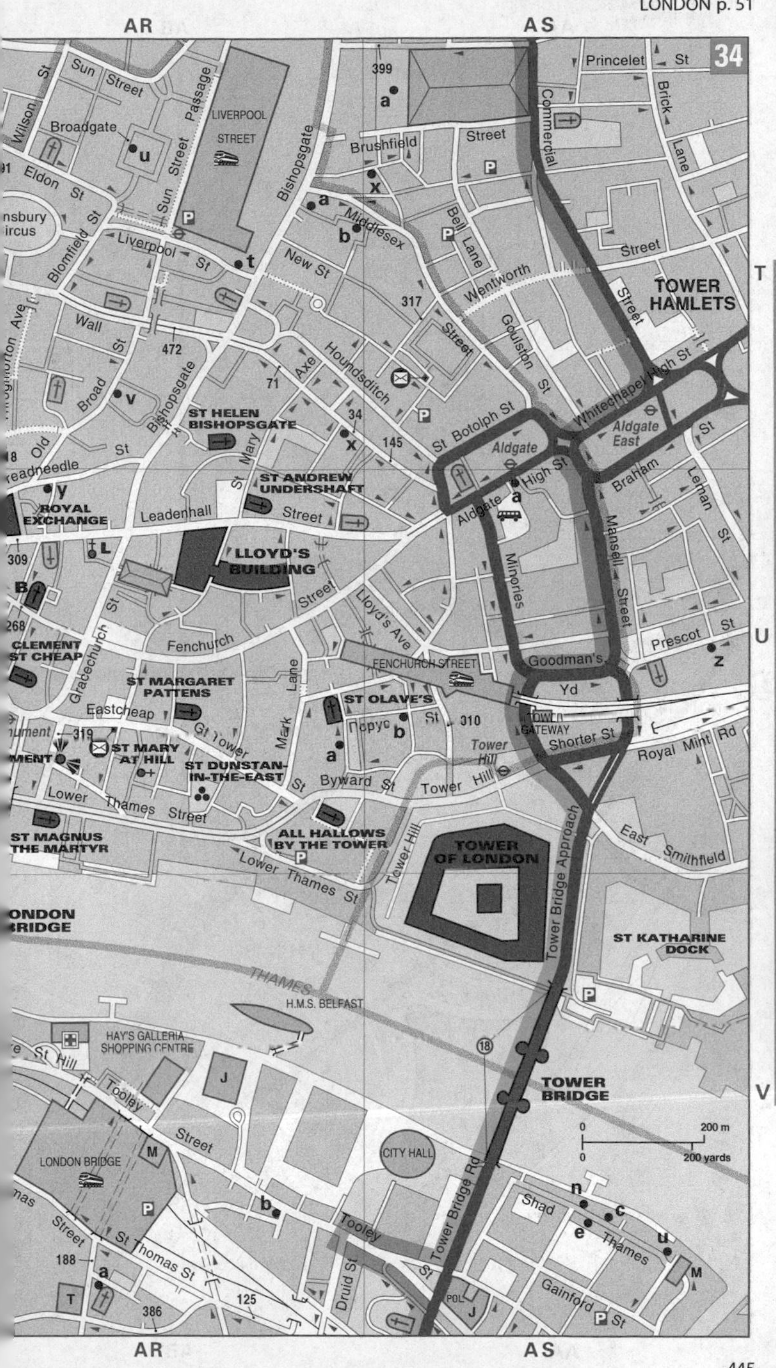
AR
AS
34
T
U
V
LIVERPOOL STREET
TOWER HAMLETS
ST HELEN BISHOPSGATE
ST ANDREW UNDERSHAFT
ROYAL EXCHANGE
LLOYD'S BUILDING
CLEMENT ST CHEAP
ST MARGARET PATTENS
FENCHURCH STREET
ST OLAVE'S
ST MARY AT HILL
ST DUNSTAN-IN-THE-EAST
ST MAGNUS THE MARTYR
ALL HALLOWS BY THE TOWER
TOWER OF LONDON
TOWER GATEWAY
ST KATHARINE DOCK
LONDON BRIDGE
THAMES
H.M.S. BELFAST
HAY'S GALLERIA SHOPPING CENTRE
TOWER BRIDGE
CITY HALL
0 200 m
0 200 yards
AR
AS

AA
27
AB
35
KENSINGTON
HOLLAND
PARK
LINLEY SAMBOURNE HOUSE
LEIGHTON HOUSE
High Street Kensington
Kensington Square
Edwardes Square
Nevern Square
Earl's Court
EARL'S COURT
Earl's Court Sq.
EARL'S COURT EXHIBITION BLDG
WEST KENSINGTON
West Brompton
BROMPTON CEMETERY
X
Y
Z
AA
AB

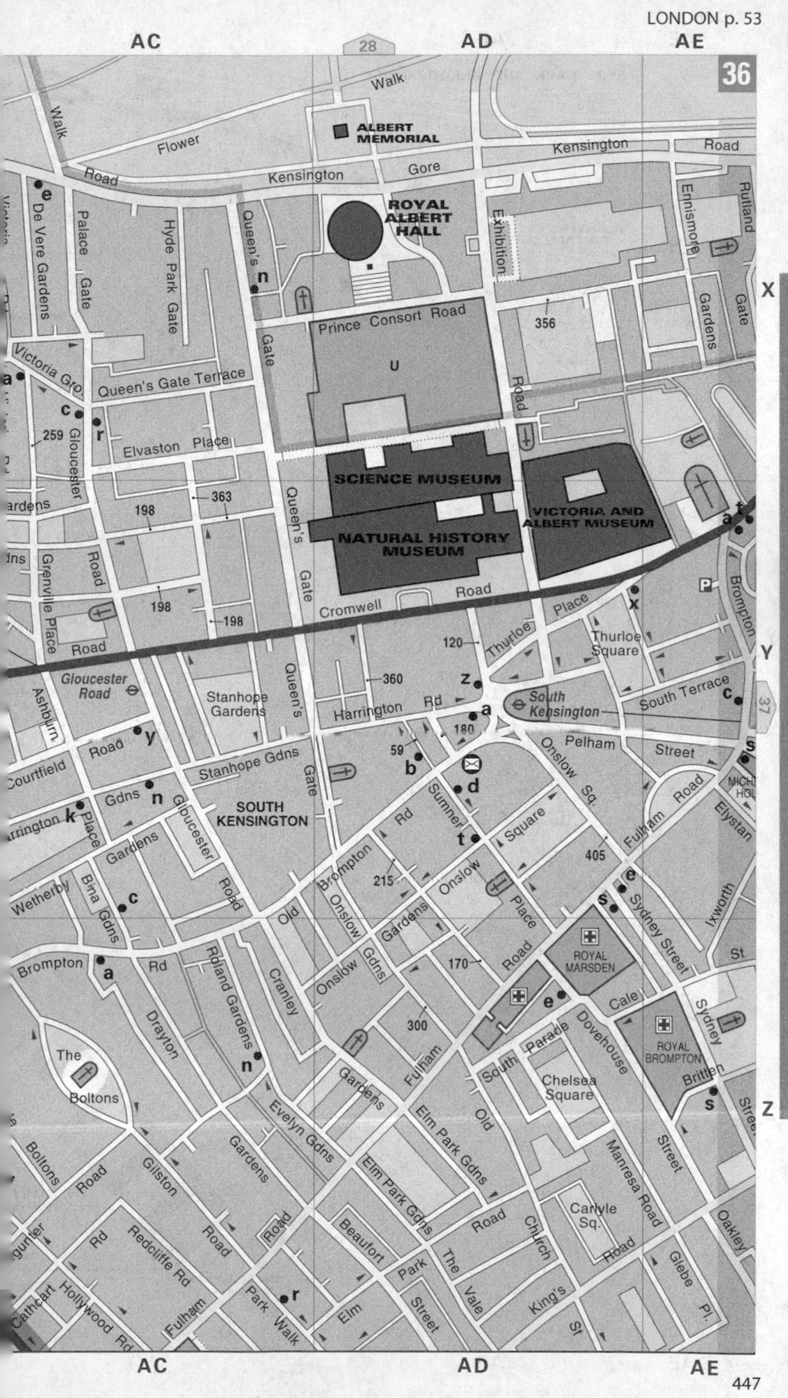
AC
AD
AE
28
36
ALBERT MEMORIAL
ROYAL ALBERT HALL
SCIENCE MUSEUM
NATURAL HISTORY MUSEUM
VICTORIA AND ALBERT MUSEUM
SOUTH KENSINGTON
ROYAL MARSDEN
ROYAL BROMPTON
Kensington Gore
Kensington Road
Prince Consort Road
Queen's Gate
Queen's Gate Terrace
Cromwell Road
Thurloe Square
South Terrace
South Kensington
Pelham Street
Harrington Rd
Stanhope Gardens
Onslow Sq.
Fulham Road
Sydney Street
Chelsea Square
Carlyle Sq.
Elm Park Gdns
King's Rd
The Boltons
Gloucester Road
X
Y
Z
37

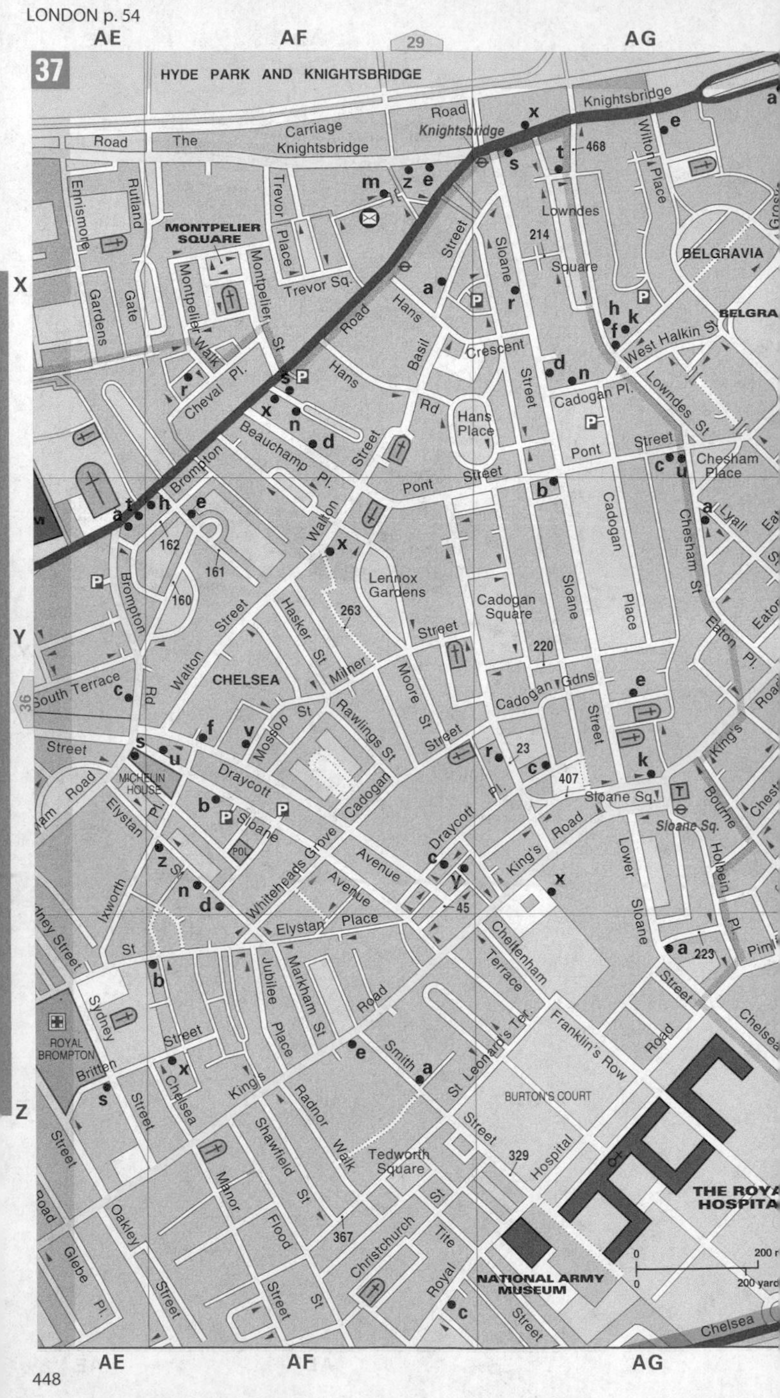
AE
AF
29
AG
37
HYDE PARK AND KNIGHTSBRIDGE
Knightsbridge
Road
The
Carriage
Knightsbridge
Road
Knightsbridge
468
Wilton Place
Ennismore
Rutland
Gate
Gardens
MONTPELIER SQUARE
Montpelier Walk
Montpelier St
Trevor Place
Trevor Sq.
Hans Road
Hans
Basil
Street
Sloane
Lowndes
214
Square
BELGRAVIA
West Halkin St
Crescent
Cheval Pl.
Hans Rd
Hans Place
Street
Cadogan Pl.
Lowndes St
Brompton
Beauchamp Pl.
Street
Pont
Chesham Place
Pont Street
Walton
Cadogan
Chesham St
Lyall
162
161
160
Brompton
Lennox Gardens
263
Sloane
Cadogan Square
Place
Hasker St
Street
Walton
Street
Eaton Pl.
South Terrace
CHELSEA
Milner
Moore St
220
Cadogan Gdns
Rd
Mossop St
Rawlings St
Street
Street
King's Road
Draycott
MICHELIN HOUSE
23
407
Sloane Sq.
Sloane Sq.
Bourne
Elystan Pl.
Sloane
POL
Cadogan
Whiteheads Grove
Avenue
Avenue
Draycott Pl.
King's
Road
Lower Sloane
Holbein Pl.
Ixworth
St
45
Elystan Place
Cheltenham Terrace
223
Sydney Street
Jubilee Place
Markham St
Road
Street
Chelsea
ROYAL BROMPTON
Britten
Street
Smith
St Leonard's Ter.
Franklin's Row
Road
Street
Chelsea
King's
Radnor Walk
BURTON'S COURT
Street
Street
Shawfield St
Tedworth Square
329
Hospital
Manor
THE ROYAL HOSPITAL
Oakley
Flood
367
St
Christchurch
Tite
Glebe Pl.
Street
Street
St
Royal
NATIONAL ARMY MUSEUM
Street
0
200
Chelsea
X
Y
Z
36
AE
AF
AG

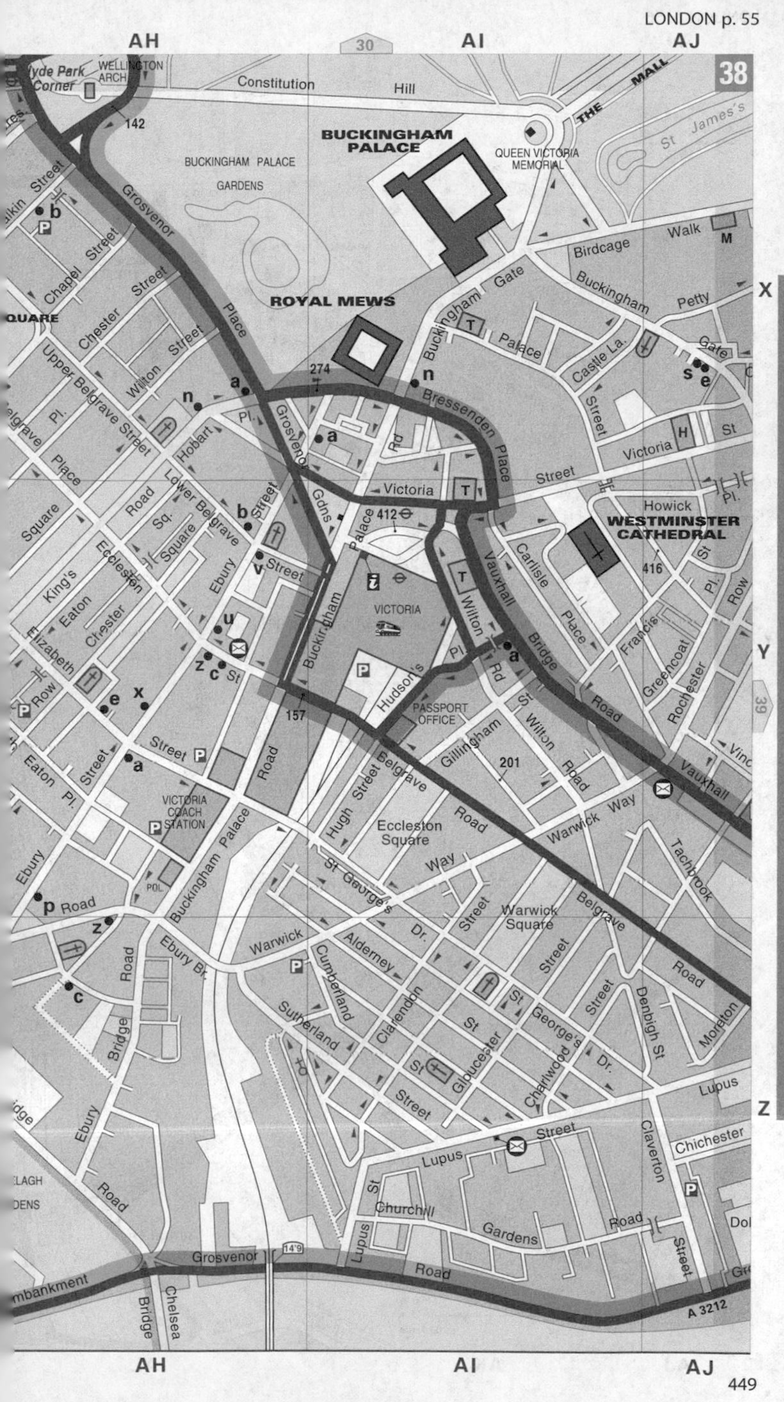
AH
AI
AJ
30
38
Hyde Park Corner
WELLINGTON ARCH
Constitution
Hill
THE MALL
BUCKINGHAM PALACE
QUEEN VICTORIA MEMORIAL
St James's
BUCKINGHAM PALACE GARDENS
ROYAL MEWS
Birdcage Walk
Buckingham Gate
Petty France
Buckingham Palace Rd
Castle La.
Bressenden Place
Victoria Street
WESTMINSTER CATHEDRAL
Howick Pl.
VICTORIA
Grosvenor Place
Grosvenor Gdns
Vauxhall Bridge Road
Wilton Rd
Hudson's Pl.
PASSPORT OFFICE
Gillingham St
Carlisle Place
Francis St
Greencoat
Rochester Row
Lower Belgrave Street
Eccleston St
Chester Square
Eaton Square
Upper Belgrave Street
Elizabeth St
Ebury Street
VICTORIA COACH STATION
Hugh Street
Belgrave Road
Eccleston Square
Warwick Way
Tachbrook St
St George's Dr.
Warwick Square
Alderney St
Cumberland St
Clarendon St
Gloucester St
Charlwood St
Denbigh St
Moreton St
Lupus Street
Sutherland St
Claverton St
Chichester St
Churchill Gardens Road
Ebury Br.
Ebury Bridge Road
Grosvenor Road
Embankment
Chelsea Bridge
A 3212
39
X
Y
Z
142
274
412
416
157
201
149

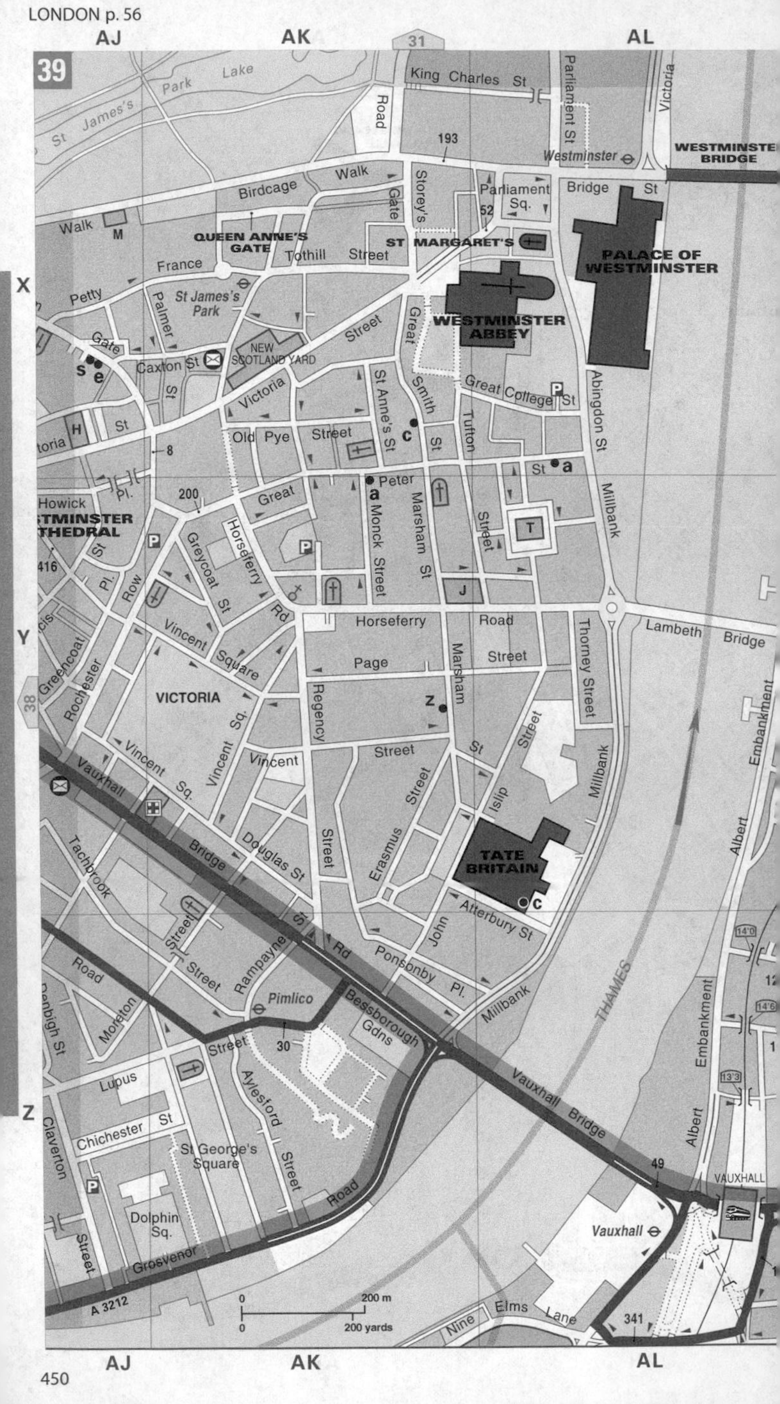
AJ
AK
31
AL
39
St James's Park Lake
King Charles St
Parliament St
Victoria
Road
193
Westminster
WESTMINSTER BRIDGE
Birdcage Walk
Gate
Storey's
Parliament Sq.
Bridge St
52
Walk
M
QUEEN ANNE'S GATE
Tothill Street
ST MARGARET'S
PALACE OF WESTMINSTER
X
France
Petty
Palmer
St James's Park
Great
WESTMINSTER ABBEY
Street
Gate
NEW SCOTLAND YARD
Caxton St
Victoria
St Anne's St
Smith
Great College St
Abingdon St
H
St
Old Pye Street
Tufton
St
8
Peter
Marsham St
St
Millbank
Howick
200
Great
Horseferry
Monck Street
Street
T
WESTMINSTER CATHEDRAL
Greycoat St
416
Pl.
Row
J
Rd
Horseferry Road
Thorney Street
Lambeth Bridge
Y
Vincent Square
Page Street
Greencoat
Rochester
38
VICTORIA
Vincent Sq.
Regency
Marsham
St
Street
Millbank
Embankment
Vincent Sq.
Vincent
Street
Vauxhall
Bridge
Islip
Street
Douglas St
Street
Erasmus
TATE BRITAIN
Albert
Tachbrook
Atterbury St
John
St
Rd
Ponsonby Pl.
Street
Street
Rampayne
Road
Pimlico
Bessborough Gdns
Millbank
THAMES
Moreton
Denbigh St
30
Street
Embankment
Lupus
Vauxhall Bridge
Aylesford
Z
Chichester St
Claverton
St George's Square
Street
Albert
49
VAUXHALL
Road
Dolphin Sq.
Vauxhall
Street
Grosvenor
A 3212
0
200 m
0
200 yards
Nine Elms Lane
341
AJ
AK
AL

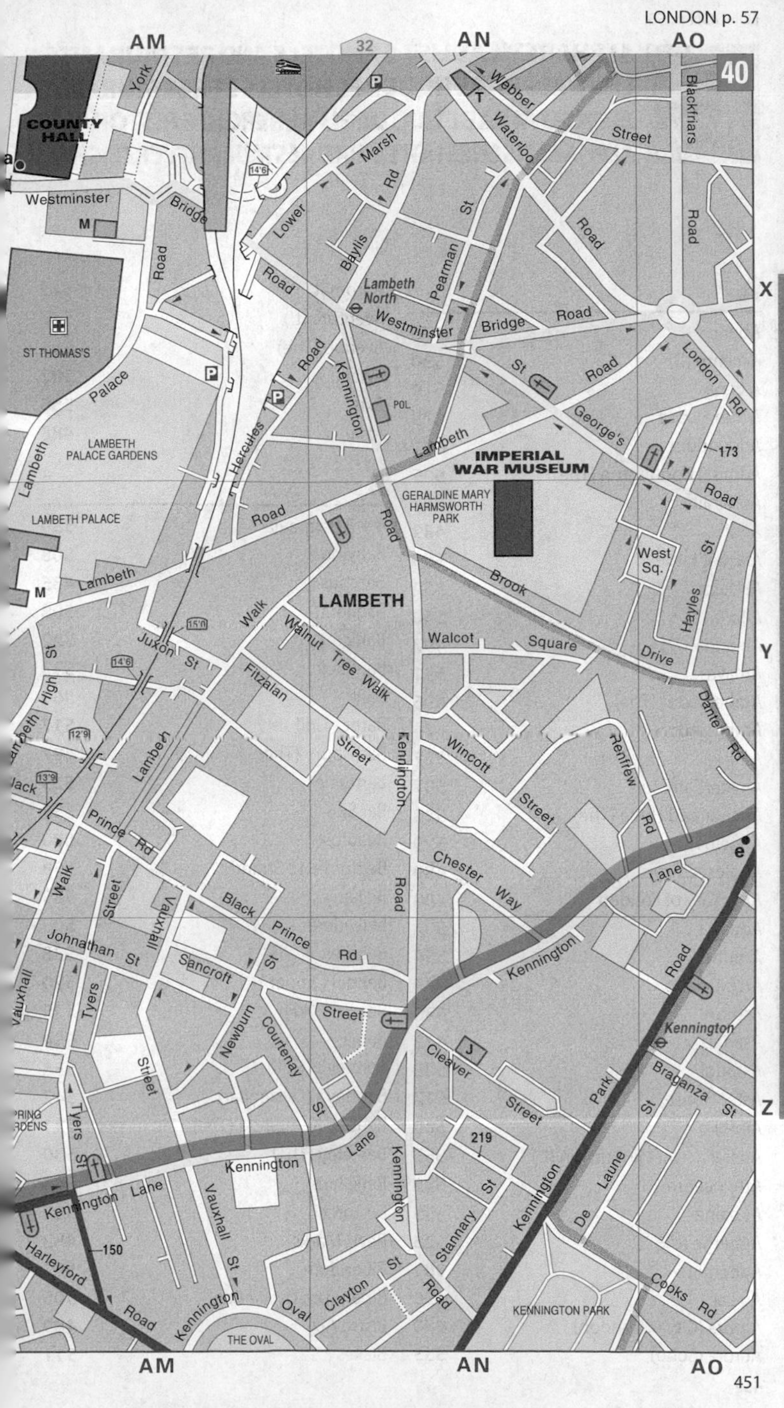
AM
AN
AO
32
40
COUNTY HALL
Westminster
Bridge
Road
York
Webber
Waterloo
Street
Blackfriars
Road
Marsh
Rd
Lower
Baylis
Lambeth North
Pearman
St
Westminster
Bridge
Road
ST THOMAS'S
Palace
LAMBETH PALACE GARDENS
LAMBETH PALACE
Lambeth
Road
Kennington
Road
POL
St
George's
Road
London
Rd
173
IMPERIAL WAR MUSEUM
GERALDINE MARY HARMSWORTH PARK
Hercules
Lambeth
West Sq.
Hayles
Brook
Drive
LAMBETH
Walk
Walnut Tree Walk
Walcot
Square
Juxon
St
High
St
Fitzalan
Street
Kennington
Wincott
Street
Renfrew
Rd
Dante
Rd
Prince
Rd
Chester
Way
Lane
Black
Prince
Rd
Walk
Street
Vauxhall
Johnathan
St
Sancroft
Street
Kennington
Road
Vauxhall
Tyers
Street
Newburn
Courtenay
St
Cleaver
Street
Kennington
Park
Braganza
St
Tyers
St
Kennington
Lane
Kennington
Kennington
Lane
150
Harleyford
Road
Vauxhall
St
Kennington
Oval
Clayton
St
Road
Stannary
St
219
Kennington
De Laune
St
Cooks
Rd
KENNINGTON PARK
THE OVAL
X
Y
Z
e
14'6
15'0
12'9
13'9
M
P
T
J

ALPHABETICAL LIST OF HOTELS AND RESTAURANTS
LISTE ALPHABÉTIQUE DES HÔTELS ET RESTAURANTS
ELENCO ALFABETICO DEGLI ALBERGHI E RISTORANTI
ALPHABETISCHES HOTEL- UND RESTAURANTVERZEICHNIS

A

B

C

D

E

F

G

O

P

Q

R

S

T

STARRED ESTABLISHMENTS
LES TABLES ÉTOILÉES
ESERCIZI CON STELLE
DIE STERNE-RESTAURANTS

✿✿✿

		Page
Gordon Ramsay	XXXX	500

✿✿

Capital Restaurant (The)	XXX	501
Gavroche (Le)	XXXX	536
Pétrus	XXXX	531
Pied à Terre	XXX	474
Square (The)	XXXX	536

✿

Amaya	XXX	531
Arbutus	X	554
Assaggi	X	529
Atelier de Joël Robuchon (L')	X	557
Aubergine	XXX	501
Benares	XXX	538
Chez Bruce	XX	527
Club Gascon	XX	481
Escargot (L')	XXX	553
Foliage	XXX	533
Glasshouse (The)	XX	518
Gordon Ramsay at Claridge's	XXXX	536
Greenhouse (The)	XXX	537
Hakkasan	XX	474
Hibiscus	XXX	537 N
Ledbury (The)	XXX	510
Locanda Locatelli	XXX	545
Maze	XXX	537
Mirabelle	XXX	537
Nahm	XX	532
Nobu	XX	540
Nobu Berkeley St	XX	541
Noisette (La)	XXXX	501
1 Lombard Street (Restaurant)	XXX	480
Quilon	XXX	559 N
Rasoi	XX	503
Rhodes Twenty Four	XXX	480
Rhodes W1 Restaurant	XXXX	545 N
Richard Corrigan at Lindsay House	XX	553
River Café	XX	488
Roussillon	XXX	560
Sketch (The Lecture Room and Library)	XXXX	536
Tamarind	XXX	538
Tom Aikens	XXX	501
Trompette (La)	XXX	492 N
Umu	XXX	539
Wild Honey	XX	541 N
Yauatcha	X	555
Zafferano	XXX	532

GOOD FOOD AT MODERATE PRICES
REPAS SOIGNÉS À PRIX MODÉRÉS
PASTI ACCURATI A PREZZI CONTENUTI
SORGFÄLTIG ZUBEREITETE, PREISWERTE MAHLZEITEN

PARTICULARLY PLEASANT HOTELS
HÔTELS AGRÉABLES
ALBERGHI AMENI
ANGENEHME HOTELS

PARTICULARLY PLEASANT RESTAURANTS
RESTAURANTS AGRÉABLES
RISTORANTI AMENI
ANGENEHME RESTAURANTS

XXXXX	Page
Ritz Restaurant (The)	550

XXXX	
Pétrus	531

XXX	
Bibendum	501
Capital Restaurant (The)	501
Oxo Tower	522
Scott's	537
Wolseley (The)	550

XX	
Caprice (Le)	550
J. Sheekey	557
Mon Plaisir	474
Rules	557

X	
Atelier de Joël Robuchon (L')	557
Oxo Tower Brasserie	522
Petersham Nurseries Café	519

RESTAURANTS CLASSIFIED ACCORDING TO TYPE
RESTAURANTS CLASSÉS SUIVANT LEUR GENRE
RISTORANTI CLASSIFICATI SECONDO IL LORO GENERE
RESTAURANTS NACH ART UND EINRICHTUNG GEORDNET

American

		Page
Automat	X	542

Asian

Champor-Champor	X	521
Cicada	X	496
Cocoon	XX	541
Crazy Bear	XX	475
E & O	XX	510
Eight over Eight	XX	504
Haiku	XX	542
Kiasu	X	530
Taman Gang	XX	540
XO	XX	473

Beef specialities

Barnes Grill	X	517
Kew Grill	XX	518
Notting Grill	X	511

British

Bentley's (Grill)	XXX	538
Brian Turner Mayfair	XXX	538
Butlers Wharf Chop House	X	521
Canteen	X	525
Great Queen Street	X (Bib)	558
Grill (The) (at Brown's)	XXXX	536
Inn the Park	X	552
Magdalen	X	521
Marquess Tavern (The)	(pub)	494
Narrow (The)	(pub) (Bib)	524
National Dining Rooms (The)	X	552
Only Running Footman (The)	(pub)	543
Paternoster Chop House	X	482
Rhodes Twenty Four	XXX ✪	480
Rivington (Greenwich)	X	484
Rivington (Shoreditch)	X	486
Roast	XX	522
Rules	XX	557
St John	X	494
St John Bread and Wine	X	525
Shepherd's	XXX	559

Chinese

Restaurant	Rating	Page
Bar Shu	X	555
China Tang	XXXX	536
Chinese Experience	X	555
Dragon Castle	XX	521
Fung Shing	X	556
Good Earth (Mill Hill)	XX	470
Good Earth (Chelsea)	XX	505
Hakkasan	XX ✿	474
Kai	XXX	539
Ken Lo's Memories of China	XX	560
Mao Tai	XX	487
Maxim	XX	483
Memories of China	XX	509
Mr Chow	XX	533
Pearl Liang	XX	529
Phoenix Palace	XX	548
Shanghai Blues	XX	477
Snazz Sichuan	XX	476
Xian	XX	472
Yauatcha	X ✿	555
Yi-Ban	XX	487

East European

Restaurant	Rating	Page
Baltic	XX	522

French

Restaurant	Rating	Page
Almeida	XX	497
Angelus	XX	529
Atelier de Joël Robuchon (L')	X ✿	557
Aubaine	X	505
Auberge (L')	XX	526
Aventure (L')	XX	547
Bistro Aix	X	489
Bleeding Heart	XX	476
Boudin Blanc (Le)	X	543
Brasserie Roux	XX ☺	551
Brula Bistrot	X ☺	520
Cercle (Le)	XX	503
Chez Kristof	XX	488
Clos Maggiore	XX	557
Club Gascon	XX ✿	481
Colombier (Le)	XX	503
Comptoir Gascon	X ☺	494
Coq d'Argent	XXX	480
French Table (The)	XX	513
Galvin	XX ☺	546
Gavroche (Le)	XXXX ✿✿	536
Lobster Pot	X	514
Ma Cuisine (Barnes)	X ☺	520
Ma Cuisine (Kew)	X ☺	518
Ma Cuisine (Twickenham)	X ☺	520
Mon Plaisir	XX	474
Morgan M	XX	493

Papillon	XX	503
Pearl	XXX	477
Petite Maison (La)	XX	542
Poissonnerie de l'Avenue	XX	503
Poule au Pot (La)	X	561
Racine	XX	503
Rhodes W1 Restaurant	XXXX ✿	545
Roussillon	XXX ✿	560
Saveur (La)	X	517
Spread Eagle	XX	484
Trouvaille (La)	XX	554
Wallace (The)	X	548

Greek

Real Greek Mezedopolio	X	486

Indian

Agni	X ☺	489
Amaya	XXX ✿	531
Benares	XXX ✿	538
Bengal Clipper	XX	520
Bengal Trader	XX	525
Bombay Brasserie	XXX	512
Café Lazeez	XX	554
Cafe Spice Namaste	XX ☺	525
Chor Bizarre	XX	541
Chutney Mary	XXX	502
Cinnamon Club (The)	XXX	559
Eriki	XX	479
Haandi	XX	470
Imli	X	555
Indian Zing	XX	488
Jamuna	XX	528
Kastoori	X ☺	527
Khan's of Kensington	XX	513
Malabar	X ☺	509
Mela	X	475
Memsaab	XXX	487
Mint Leaf	XX	551
Moti Mahal	XX	477
Painted Heron	XX	504
Planet Spice	XX	483
Porte des Indes (La)	XX	547
Quilon	XXX ✿	559
Rasa	X	486
Rasa Samudra	XX	547
Rasa Travancore	X	487
Rasoi	XX ✿	503
Red Fort	XXX	553
Tamarind	XXX ✿	538
Tangawizi	X ☺	519
3 Monkeys	XX	514
Vama	XX	504
Veeraswamy	XX	542
Zaika	XX	508

Italian

Restaurant	Comfort	Page
Accento (L')	X Bib	530
A Cena	XX	519
Al Duca	X Bib	552
Alloro	XX	540
Amici	XX	527
Arturo	X	530
Assaggi	X ✿	529
Bertorelli	X	555
Caffé Caldesi	X	548
Caldesi	XX	547
Camerino	XX	475
Cantina Del Ponte	X	521
Caraffini	XX	504
Carpaccio	XX	504
Cecconi's	XXX	539
C Garden	XX	505
Cibo	X	509
Collina (La)	XX	478
Daphne's	XX	502
Edera	XX	510
Enoteca Turi	XX	526
Florians	X	489
Franco's	XX	551
Giardinetto	XX	539
Il Convivio	XX	560
Latium	XXX	546
Locanda Locatelli	XXX ✿	545
Luciano	XXX	550
Manicomio	X	505
Metrogusto	XX Bib	497
Olivo	X	561
Passione	X	475
Pellicano	XX	504
Quadrato	XXX	524
Quirinale	XX	561
Quo Vadis	XXX	553
Riva	X	516
River Café	XX ✿	488
Santini	XXX	559
Sardo	XX	474
Sardo Canale	XX	478
Sartoria	XXX	538
Semplice	XX	539
Theo Randall	XXX	538
Timo	XX	509
Toto's	XXX	502
Trenta	XX Bib	529
Vasco and Piero's Pavilion	XX	554
Via Condotti	XX Bib	540
Zafferano	XXX ✿	532

Japanese

Restaurant	Comfort	Page
Abeno	X	476
Atami	XX	560
Chisou	X	542
Dinings	X	549

Korean

Kosher

Latin American

Lebanese

Malaysian

Mediterranean

Moroccan

North African

Polish

Scottish

Restaurant	Comfort	Page
Boisdale	XX	560
Boisdale of Bishopgate	XX	481

Seafood

Restaurant	Comfort	Page
Bentley's (Oyster Bar)	X	542
Bibendum Oyster Bar	X	505
Deep	XX	487
Fish Hook	X	492
Fishworks	X	548
J. Sheekey	XX	557
Olivomare	X	561
One-O-One	XXX	501
Scott's	XXX	537

Spanish

Restaurant	Comfort	Page
Barrafina	X	555
Cambio de Tercio	XX	513
Cigala	X	475
Fino	XX	474
L Restaurant and Bar	XX	509

Tapas

Restaurant	Comfort	Page
Tapas Brindisa	X	523

Thai

Restaurant	Comfort	Page
Bangkok	X	513
BenJa	XX (☺)	554
Blue Elephant	XX	487
Chada	XX	525
Chada Chada	X	548
Mango Tree	XX	532
Nahm	XX ✿	532
Nipa	XX	529
Saran Rom	XXX	487
Simply Thai	X	519

Turkish

Restaurant	Comfort	Page
Ozer	XX	547

Vietnamese

Restaurant	Comfort	Page
Au Lac	X	496

Boroughs and areas

Greater London *is divided, for adminitrative purposes, into 32 boroughs plus the City: these sub-divide naturally into minor areas, usually grouped around former villages or quarters, which often maintain a distinctive character.*

BARNET – Gtr London

Child's Hill – Gtr London – ✉ NW2

XX **Philpott's Mezzaluna**

424 Finchley Rd ✉ NW2 2HY – ✆ (020) 7794 0455 – Fax (020) 7794 0452 – Closed 2 weeks Easter, 25-26 December, 1 January, Saturday lunch and Monday 10 NZA **c**

Rest – Italian influences Menu £ 25/30

◆ Homely Italian restaurant, affably run by patrons. Huge lunar artefacts complement the plain walls. Weekly changing menus offer tasty, modern cuisine at moderate prices.

Edgware – Gtr London – ✉ HA8

XX **Haandi**

301-303 Hale Lane ✉ HA8 7AX ⊖ Edgware – ✆ (020) 8905 4433 – haandirestaurant@btconnect.com – Fax (020) 8905 4646 – closed 25 December 2 CT **a**

Rest – Indian Carte £ 11/24

◆ In the middle of a busy high street, this brightly lit restaurant boasts skylight, small central fountain, vivid colours and flavoursome dishes from North India.

Hendon – Gtr London – ✉ NW4

XX **Gallery**

407-411 Hendon Way ✉ NW4 3LH ⊖ Hendon Central – ✆ (020) 8202 4000 – reservations@galleryhendon.com – Fax (020) 8202 4433 – closed Sunday dinner, Monday 2 CU **e**

Rest – (dinner only & Sunday lunch) (dinner only and Sunday lunch) Menu £ 25 – Carte £ 27/42

◆ A touch of opulence on Hendon Way courtesy of quality artworks ranging from pastels to lithographs and seascapes to portraits. British ingredients prepared with French flair.

Mill Hill – Gtr London – ✉ NW7

18 100 Barnet Way Mill Hill, ✆ (020) 8959 2339 .

XX **Good Earth**

143 The Broadway ✉ NW7 4RN – ✆ (020) 8959 7011 – Fax (020) 8959 1464 – closed 23-30 December 2 CT **a**

Rest – Chinese Carte £ 28/50

◆ Smart, well-kept Chinese restaurant set slightly back from the busy A1 outside. Spacious and comfortable with efficient staff. Authentic menu; extensive vegetarian choice.

BRENT - Gtr London

Kensal Rise - Middx - ✉ NW10

The Greyhound
64-66 Chamberlayne Road ✉ NW10 3JJ ⊖ Kensal Green - ✆ (020) 8969 8080 - thegreyhound@needtoeat.co.uk - Fax (020) 8969 8081 - Closed 25-26 December, 1 January, Sunday dinner and Monday 10 MZB **a**
Rest - Carte £ 18/25
◆ Trendy gastropub, popular with locals. On one side: bar with leather sofas; on other: restaurant with reclaimed furniture, black oak floors and modern British cooking.

Kilburn - Brent - ✉ NW6

London 7 m - Luton 31 m - Watford 16 m - Slough 28 m

North London Tavern
375 Kilburn High Rd ✉ NW6 7QB - ✆ (020) 7625 6634 - northlondontavern@realpubs.co.uk - Fax (020) 7625 6635 10 NZB **a**
Rest - Carte £ 20/24
◆ Imposing former railway inn has slightly Gothic feel, with old church seats, candles and high ceilings. Cooking is satisfyingly full-bodied, with some Iberian influences.

Willesden Green - Middx - ✉ NW2/NW10

Sushi-Say
33B Walm Lane ✉ NW2 5SH ⊖ Willesden Green - ✆ (020) 8459 2971 - Fax (020) 8907 3229 - closed 25-26 December, 1 January, 1 week August and Monday 9 LZB **a**
Rest - Japanese (dinner only and lunch Saturday and Sunday) Carte £ 15/38
◆ Friendly service provided by the owner in traditional dress. From bare wooden tables, watch her husband in the open-plan kitchen carefully prepare authentic Japanese food.

The Green
110 Walm Lane ✉ NW2 4RS ⊖ Willesden Green - ✆ (020) 8452 0171 - info@thegreennw2.com - Fax (020) 8452 0774 - Closed 25 December and 1 January 9 LZA **a**
Rest - Menu £ 18 - Carte £ 16/28
◆ Large bustling bar with high ceiling conveying airy feel: light menus served here. Rear dining room: chef adds subtle Caribbean twists to modern dishes in generous portions.

Queen's Park - Middx - ✉ NW6

The Salusbury
50-52 Salusbury Road ✉ NW6 6NN - ✆ (020) 7328 3286 - thesalusbury@london.com - Closed Monday lunch 10 MZB **b**
Rest - Carte £ 24/32
◆ Half pub, half dining room with its own food store a few doors down. Italian influenced cooking with pronounced flavours and quality ingredients comes in generous portions.

The red symbol?
This denotes the very essence of peace
- only the sound of birdsong first thing in the morning ...

BROMLEY – Gtr London

Cray Valley Sandy Lane, St Paul's Cray, (01689) 837 909 .

Beckenham – Kent – BR3

Mello

2 Southend Rd BR3 1SD – (020) 8663 0994 – info@mello.uk.com – Fax (020) 8663 3674 – closed Sunday dinner 7 GY **v**

Rest – Carte £ 22/36

◆ Unassuming and welcomingly run neighbourhood restaurant; walls hung with multi-coloured modern oils. Good value, seasonally sensitive dishes enhanced by precise execution.

Bromley – Kent – BR1

Magpie Hall Lane Magpie Hall Lane, (020) 8462 7014 .

Bromley Court

Bromley Hill BR1 4JD – (020) 8461 8600 – enquiries@bromleycourthotel.co.uk – Fax (020) 8460 0899 8 HY **z**

112 rm – £ 89/109 £ 105/120 – 2 suites – **Rest** – (closed Saturday lunch) Menu £ 20/23

◆ A grand neo-Gothic mansion in three acres of well-tended garden. Popular with corporate guests for the large conference space, and the bedrooms with modems and voicemail. Conservatory or terrace dining available.

Farnborough – Kent – BR6

Chapter One

Farnborough Common, Locksbottom BR6 8NF – (01689) 854 848 – info@chaptersrestaurants.com – Fax (01689) 858 439 – closed 1st week January 8 HZ **a**

Rest – Menu £ 18 – Carte £ 23/30

◆ The mock Tudor exterior belies a stylish, light and contemporary interior. Smooth service; well executed modern European menus at a keen price.

Orpington – Kent – BR6

High Elms High Elms Rd, Downe, (01689) 858 175 .

Xian

324 High St BR6 0NG – (01689) 871 881 – Fax (01689) 829 437 – closed 1st week September and Sunday lunch 8 JY **a**

Rest – Chinese Menu £ 10/16 – Carte £ 12/23

◆ Modern, marbled interior with oriental artefacts make this personally run Chinese restaurant a firm favourite with locals. Specialises in the hotter dishes of Peking.

Penge – Gtr London – SE20

Melrose House without rest

89 Lennard Rd SE20 7LY – (020) 8776 8884 – melrosehouse@supanet.com – Fax (020) 8778 6366 – closed 24 - 26 December 7 GY **a**

9 rm – £ 40/45 £ 60/65

◆ An imposing Victorian house with a conservatory sitting room. Breakfast is taken "en famille" and the older bedrooms still have their original fireplaces.

Your opinions are important to us: please write and let us know about your discoveries and experiences – good and bad!

CAMDEN – Gtr London

Belsize Park – Camden – ✉ NW3

London 5 m – Luton 33 m – Watford 18 m – Slough 28 m

XO

29 Belsize Lane ✉ NW3 5AS ⊖ Belsize Park – ☎ (020) 7433 0888 – Fax (020) 7794 3474 – Closed 25-26 December and 1 January 11 PZA **a**

Rest – Asian Carte £ 24/33

◆ Stylish dining room with banquettes, revolving lights and mirrors. Vibrant atmosphere; popular with locals. Japanese, Korean, Thai and Chinese cooking; dishes are best shared.

Bloomsbury – Gtr London – ✉ W1/WC1/WC2

Covent Garden

10 Monmouth St ✉ WC2H 9HB ⊖ Covent Garden – ☎ (020) 7806 1000 – covent@firmdale.com – Fax (020) 7806 1100 31 ALU **x**

56 rm – †£ 264/323 ††£ 376, ☐ £19.50 – 2 suites

Rest *Brasserie Max* – (closed Sunday lunch) (booking essential) Carte £ 28/50

◆ Individually designed and stylish bedrooms, with CDs and VCRs discreetly concealed. Boasts a very relaxing first floor oak-panelled drawing room with its own honesty bar. Informal restaurant.

Montague on the Gardens

15 Montague St ✉ WC1B 5BJ ⊖ Holborn – ☎ (020) 7637 1001 – bookmt@rchmail.com – Fax (020) 7637 2516 31 ALT **a**

93 rm – †£ 159/288 ††£ 217/311, ☐ £16.50 – 6 suites

Rest *The Chef's Table* – Menu £ 6/20.50 – Carte £ 25/49.85

◆ A period townhouse with pretty hanging baskets outside. The hushed conservatory overlooks a secluded garden. The clubby bar has a Scottish golfing theme. Rich bedroom décor. Restaurant divided into two small, pretty rooms.

Mountbatten

20 Monmouth St ✉ WC2H 9HD ⊖ Covent Garden – ☎ (020) 7836 4300 – dial@radisson.com – Fax (020) 7240 3540 31 ALU **d**

149 rm ☐ – †£ 140/180 ††£ 160/180 – 2 suites

Rest *Dial* – (Closed Saturday lunch, Sunday and Bank Holidays) Menu £ 25 – Carte £ 28/34

◆ Photographs and memorabilia of the eponymous Lord Louis adorn the walls and corridors. Ideally located in the heart of Covent Garden. Compact but comfortable bedrooms. Bright, stylish restaurant.

Jurys Gt Russell St

16-22 Gt Russell St ✉ WC1B 3NN ⊖ Tottenham Court Road – ☎ (020) 7347 1000 – gtrussellstreet@jurysdoyle.com – Fax (020) 7347 1001 31 AKT **n**

169 rm – †£ 245 ††£ 245, ☐ £16 – 1 suite

Rest *Lutyens* – (bar lunch) Carte £ 34/45 **s**

◆ Neo-Georgian building by Edward Lutyens, built for YMCA in 1929. Smart comfortable interior decoration from the lounge to the bedrooms. Facilities include a business centre. Restaurant has understated traditional style.

Myhotel Bloomsbury

11-13 Bayley St, Bedford Sq ✉ WC1B 3HD ⊖ Tottenham Court Road – ☎ (020) 7667 6000 – bloomsbury@myhotels.co.uk – Fax (020) 7667 6001 31 AKT **x**

78 rm – †£ 240/276 ††£ 276/417, ☐ £18

Rest *Yo! Sushi* – Japanese Menu £ 15 (lunch) – Carte £ 26/35

◆ The minimalist interior is designed on the principles of feng shui; even the smaller bedrooms are stylish and uncluttered. Mybar is a fashionable meeting point. Diners can enjoy Japanese food from conveyor belt.

Ambassadors

12 Upper Woburn Place ✉ WC1H 0HX ⊖ Euston – ✆ (020) 7693 5400 – sales@ambassadors.co.uk – Fax (020) 7388 9930 18 SZC **a**

100 rm – †£ 245/275 ††£ 275/325

Rest *Number Twelve* – Italian influences Menu £ 15/18 – Carte £ 26/31

◆ Contemporary hotel near to Euston Station. Six floors of cleverly designed bedrooms with all mod. cons; Premier rooms the most spacious. Several well-equipped meeting rooms. Ground floor restaurant has relaxed style and offers Italian menu.

Pied à Terre (Shane Osborn)

34 Charlotte St ✉ W1T 2NH ⊖ Goodge Street – ✆ (020) 7636 1178 – info@pied-a-terre.co.uk – Fax (020) 7916 1171 – closed last week December-first week January, Saturday lunch and Sunday 31 AJT **e**

Rest – Menu £ 30/62

Spec. Seared and poached foie gras with borlotti beans and girolles. Steamed halibut with tomato fondue and courgette flower beignet. Bitter chocolate tart with stout ice cream and macadamia nut cream.

◆ Smart, low-key exterior; stylish interior with intimately-set tables; ask for a table in rear room. Elaborate, expertly-crafted classical dishes incorporate unusual combinations.

Mon Plaisir

21 Monmouth St ✉ WC2H 9DD ⊖ Covent Garden – ✆ (020) 7836 7243 – eatafrog@mail.com – Fax (020) 7240 4774 – closed 25 December-2 January, Saturday lunch, Sunday and Bank Holidays 31 ALU **g**

Rest – French Menu £ 17 – Carte £ 28/34

◆ London's oldest French restaurant and family-run for over fifty years. Divided into four rooms, all with a different feel but all proudly Gallic in their decoration.

Incognico

117 Shaftesbury Ave ✉ WC2H 8AD ⊖ Tottenham Court Road – ✆ (020) 7836 8866 – incognicorestaurant@gmail.com – Fax (020) 7240 9525 – Closed 1 week Christmas, Sunday and Bank Holidays 31 AKU **q**

Rest – Menu £ 25 – Carte £ 30/38

◆ Firmly established with robust décor of wood panelling and brown leather chairs. Downstairs bar has a window into the kitchen, from where French and English classics derive.

Sardo

45 Grafton Way ✉ W1T 5DQ ⊖ Warren Street – ✆ (020) 7387 2521 – info@sardo-restaurant.com – Fax (020) 7387 2559 – Closed Saturday lunch and Sunday 18 RZD **c**

Rest – Sardinian Carte £ 23/32

◆ Simple, stylish interior run in a very warm and welcoming manner with very efficient service. Rustic Italian cooking with a Sardinian character and a modern tone.

Hakkasan

8 Hanway Place ✉ W1T 1HD ⊖ Tottenham Court Road – ✆ (020) 7927 7000 – mail@hakkasan.com – Fax (020) 7907 1889 – closed 24-25 December 31 AKT **c**

Rest – Chinese Menu £ 40/55 – Carte £ 27/90

Spec. Crispy duck salad with pomelo, pine nut and shallot. Silver cod with Chinese honey and champagne. Chocolate fondant with passion fruit sorbet.

◆ A distinctive, modern interpretation of Cantonese cooking in an appropriately contemporary and cavernous basement. The lively, bustling bar is an equally popular nightspot.

Fino

33 Charlotte St (entrance on Rathbone St) ✉ W1T 1RR ⊖ Goodge Street – ✆ (020) 7813 8010 – info@finorestaurant.com – Fax (020) 7813 8011 – closed Saturday lunch and Sunday 31 AJT **a**

Rest – Spanish Carte £ 45/55

◆ Spanish-run basement bar with modern style décor and banquette seating. Wide-ranging menu of authentic dishes; 2 set-price selections offering an introduction to tapas.

XX **Crazy Bear**

26-28 Whitfield St ✉ W1T 2RG ⊖ Goodge Street – ✆ (020) 7631 0088 – enquiries@crazybear-london.co.uk – Fax (020) 7631 1188 – Closed Christmas, Saturday lunch, Sunday and Bank Holidays 31 AKT **b**

Rest – South East Asian Carte £ 30/40

◆ Exotic destination: downstairs bar geared to fashionable set; ground floor dining room is art deco inspired. Asian flavoured menus, with predominance towards Thai dishes.

XX **Archipelago**

110 Whitfield St ✉ W1T 5ED ⊖ Goodge Street – ✆ (020) 7383 3346 – archipelago@onetel.com – Fax (020) 7383 7181 – closed Christmas -New Year,Bank Holidays, Saturday lunch and Sunday 18 RZD **c**

Rest – Menu £ 39 – Carte £ 26/37 **s**

◆ Eccentric in both menu and décor and not for the faint hearted. Crammed with knick-knacks from cages to Buddhas. Menu an eclectic mix of influences from around the world.

XX **Camerino**

16 Percy St ✉ W1T 1DT ⊖ Tottenham Court Road – ✆ (020) 7637 9900 – info@camerinorestaurant.com – Fax (020) 7637 9696 – closed 24-26 December, Bank Holidays, Saturday lunch and Sunday 31 AKT **f**

Rest – Italian Menu £ 20 – Carte £ 20/28

◆ Personally run, wood floored restaurant where bold red drapes contrast with crisp white linen-clad tables. Menus take the authentic taste of Italy's regions for inspiration.

X **Passione**

10 Charlotte St ✉ W1T 2LT ⊖ Tottenham Court Road – ✆ (020) 7636 2833 – liz@passione.co.uk – Fax (020) 7636 2889 – Closed Christmas-New Year, Bank Holidays, Saturday lunch and Sunday 31 AKT **u**

Rest – Italian (booking essential) Carte £ 40/47

◆ Compact but light and airy. Modern Italian cooking served in informal surroundings, with friendly and affable service. Particularly busy at lunchtime.

X **Cigala**

54 Lamb's Conduit St ✉ WC1N 3LW ⊖ Holborn – ✆ (020) 7405 1717 – tasty@cigala.co.uk – Fax (020) 7242 9949 – Closed 24-26 December, 1 January and Easter 19 TZD **a**

Rest – Spanish Menu £ 18 (lunch) – Carte £ 24/37

◆ Spanish restaurant on the corner of attractive street. Simply furnished with large windows and open-plan kitchen. Robust Iberian cooking. Informal tapas bar downstairs.

X **Salt Yard**

54 Goodge St ✉ W1T 4NA ⊖ Goodge Street – ✆ (020) 7637 0657 – info@saltyard.co.uk – Fax (020) 7580 7435 – closed Sunday, Saturday lunch and Bank Holidays 31 AJT **d**

Rest – Carte £ 18/40

◆ Vogue destination with buzzy downstairs restaurant specialising in inexpensive sharing plates of tasty Italian and Spanish dishes: try the freshly cut hams. Super wine list.

X **Mela**

152-156 Shaftesbury Ave ✉ WC2H 8HL ⊖ Leicester Square – ✆ (020) 7836 8635 – info@melarestaurant.co.uk – Fax (020) 7379 0527 31 AKU **e**

Rest – Indian Menu £ 30/37 – Carte approx. £ 28

◆ Vibrantly decorated dining room with a simple style in a useful location close to Theatreland. Enjoy thoroughly tasty Indian food in a bustling, buzzy environment.

X **Acorn House**

69 Swinton St ✉ WC1X 9NT ⊖ King's Cross – ✆ (020) 7812 1842 – info@acornhouserestaurant.com – Closed 24-31 December, Sunday and Bank Holidays 18 TZC **b**

Rest – Carte £ 27/44

◆ London's first eco-friendly training restaurant, with bright earthy interior and chirpy staff. Modern European food with largely Italian influences. Fresh, natural flavours.

Abeno

47 Museum St ✉ WC1A 1LY ⊖ Tottenham Court Road – ✆ (020) 7405 3211 – okonomi@abeno.co.uk – Fax (020) 7405 3212 – Closed 24-26 and 31 December and 1 January 31 ALT **e**

Rest – Japanese Menu £ 10 (lunch) – Carte £ 17/35

◆ Specialises in okonomi-yaki: little Japanese "pancakes" cooked on a hotplate on each table. Choose your own filling and the size of your pancake.

Euston – Camden – ✉ NW1

Novotel London St. Pancras

100-110 Euston Rd ✉ NW1 2AJ ⊖ Euston – ✆ (020) 7666 9000 – h5309@accor.com – Fax (020) 7666 9025 18 SZC **a**

309 rm – †£ 185 ††£ 215, ☕ £14.50 – 3 suites – **Rest** – (bar lunch Saturday and Sunday) Menu £ 19/24 – Carte £ 23/26

◆ Halfway between Euston and Kings Cross, this hotel has good-sized bedrooms for a London hotel and those on the higher floors enjoy views over the city. Good business amenities. International menu and buffet breakfast offered in Mirrors restaurant.

Snazz Sichuan

37 Chalton St ✉ NW1 1JD ⊖ Euston – ✆ (020) 7388 0808 12 SZC **b**

Rest – Chinese (Szechuan) Carte £ 10/50

◆ Authentic Sichuan atmosphere and cooking, with gallery and traditional tea room. Menu split into hot and cold dishes; the fiery Sichuan pepper helps heat you from inside out.

Hampstead – Gtr London – ✉ NW3

Hampstead Winnington Rd, ✆ (020) 8455 0203 .

Langorf without rest

20 Frognal ✉ NW3 6AG ⊖ Finchley Road – ✆ (020) 7794 4483 – info@langorfhotel.com – Fax (020) 7435 9055 11 PZA **c**

41 rm – †£ 82/98 ††£ 95/98, ☕ £6 – 5 suites

◆ Converted Edwardian house in a quiet residential area. Bright breakfast room overlooks secluded walled garden. Fresh bedrooms, many of which have high ceilings.

The Wells

30 Well Walk ✉ NW3 1BX ⊖ Hampstead Heath – ✆ (020) 7794 3785 – info@thewellshampstead.co.uk – Fax (020) 7794 6817 – Closed 1 January 11 PZA **v**

Rest – Carte £ 20/30

◆ Attractive 18C inn with modern interior. Ground floor bar and a few tables next to open-plan kitchen; upstairs more formal dining rooms. Classically-based French cooking.

The Magdala

2A South Hill Park ✉ NW3 2SB ⊖ Belsize Park – ✆ (020) 7435 2503 – themagdala@hotmail.co.uk – Fax (020) 7435 6167 – Closed 25 December 11 PZA **s**

Rest – Carte £ 17/27

◆ Located on the edge of the Heath. Two bars popular with locals, one with open-plan kitchen. Upstairs dining room, open at weekends, offers robust cooking. Simpler lunch menu.

Hatton Garden – Gtr London – ✉ EC1

Bleeding Heart

Bleeding Heart Yard, off Greville St ✉ EC1N 8SJ ⊖ Farringdon – ✆ (020) 7242 8238 – bookings@bleedingheart.co.uk – Fax (020) 7831 1402 – closed Christmas-New Year, Saturday, Sunday and Bank Holidays 32 ANT **e**

Rest – French (booking essential) Carte £ 28/37

◆ Busy downstairs restaurant, popular with City suits. Fast-paced service, terrific wine list and well-practised cooking. Seasonally-changing French menu with traditional core.

Holborn – Gtr London – ✉ WC1/WC2

Renaissance Chancery Court

252 High Holborn ✉ WC1V 7EN ⊖ Holborn – ✆ (020) 7829 9888 – sales.chancerycourt@renaissancehotels.com – Fax (020) 7829 9889 32 AMT **a**

354 rm – 🚹£ 287/370 🚹🚹£ 287/370, ☕ £23.50 – 2 suites

Rest *Pearl* – see restaurant listing

◆ Striking building built in 1914, now an imposing place to stay. Impressive marbled lobby and grand central courtyard. Very large bedrooms with comprehensive modern facilities.

Kingsway Hall

Great Queen St ✉ WC2B 5BX ⊖ Holborn – ✆ (020) 7309 0909 – sales@kingswayhall.co.uk – Fax (020) 7309 9129 31 ALT **b**

168 rm – 🚹£ 374 🚹🚹£ 374, ☕ £15.95 – 2 suites

Rest *Harlequin* – Menu £ 20 – Carte £ 25/35

◆ Large, corporate-minded hotel. Striking glass-framed and marbled lobby. Stylish ground floor bar. Well-appointed bedrooms with an extensive array of mod cons. European menus in smart, minimalist restaurant.

Pearl – at Renaissance Chancery Court H.

252 High Holborn ✉ WC1V 7EN ⊖ Holborn – ✆ (020) 7829 7000 – info@pearl-restaurant.com – Fax (020) 7829 9889 – closed last 2 weeks August, Saturday lunch and Sunday 32 AMT **a**

Rest – French Menu £ 29/49 – Carte approx. £ 50

◆ Impressive dining room with walls clad in Italian marble; Corinthian columns. Waiters provide efficient service at well-spaced tables; original menus.

Matsuri - High Holborn

Mid City Pl, 71 High Holborn ✉ WC1V 6EA ⊖ Holborn – ✆ (020) 7430 1970 – eat@matsuri-restaurant.com – Fax (020) 7430 1971 – closed 25 December, 1 January, Sunday and Bank Holidays 32 AMT **c**

Rest – Japanese Menu £ 9/20 – Carte £ 29/42

◆ Spacious, airy Japanese restaurant. Authentic menu served in main dining room, in basement teppan-yaki bar and at large sushi counter, where chefs demonstrate their skills.

Shanghai Blues

193-197 High Holborn ✉ WC1V 7BD ⊖ Holborn – ✆ (020) 7404 1668 – info@shanghaiblues.co.uk – Fax (020) 7404 1448 – closed 25-26 December 31 ALT **c**

Rest – Chinese Menu £ 15/40 – Carte £ 30/69

◆ Set in Grade II listed former St Giles Library, this spacious, moody Chinese restaurant is offset by cool bar and mezzanine lounge. Wide range of specialities to choose from.

Asadal

227 High Holborn ✉ WC1V 7DA ⊖ Holborn – ✆ (020) 7430 9006 – info@asadal.co.uk – closed Sunday lunch 31 ALT **n**

Rest – Korean Menu £ 10 (lunch) – Carte £ 18/30

◆ A hectic, unprepossessing location, but delivers the authenticity of a modest Korean café with the comfort and service of a proper restaurant. Good quality Korean cooking.

Moti Mahal

45 Great Queen St ✉ WC2B 5AA ⊖ Covent Garden – ✆ (020) 7240 9329 – reservations@motimahal-uk.com – Fax (020) 7836 0790 – closed 25-26 December, Sunday and lunch on Bank Holidays 31 ALU **k**

Rest – Indian Menu £ 15/17 – Carte £ 39/66

◆ Elegant stone fronted restaurant. Bar with huge whisky selection; cool contemporary dining room where concise, modern Indian dishes using well prepared ingredients are served.

Primrose Hill – Gtr London – ✉ NW1

XX **Odette's**
130 Regent's Park Rd ✉ NW1 8XL ⊖ Chalk Farm – ✆ (020) 7586 8569 – odettes@vpmg.net – Fax (020) 7586 8362 – closed Christmas, Sunday dinner and Monday 11 QZB **b**
Rest – Menu £ 18 (lunch) – Carte approx. £ 40
◆ Warm, inviting restaurant on pretty main street. Balanced menu offers ambitious cooking which brings a little bit of the Welsh chef's homeland to North West London.

XX **Sardo Canale**
42 Gloucester Ave ✉ NW1 8JD ⊖ Chalk Farm – ✆ (020) 7722 2800 – info@sardocanale.com – Fax (020) 7722 0802 – Closed 25-26 December and Monday lunch 12 RZB **a**
Rest – Italian Carte £ 23/33
◆ A series of five snug but individual dining rooms in conservatory style; delightful terrace with 200 year old olive tree. Appealing Italian menus with strong Sardinian accent.

XX **La Collina**
17 Princess Rd ✉ NW1 8JR ⊖ Camden Town – ✆ (020) 7483 0192 – lacollinanw1@aol.com – Closed Bank Holidays 11 QZB **x**
Rest – Italian (dinner only and lunch Saturday-Sunday) Menu £ 24
◆ Neighbourhood restaurant over two floors: downstairs is a more intimate place to dine. Well cooked, great value Piedmontese dishes are the reason the locals keep coming back.

The Queens
49 Regent's Park Rd ✉ NW1 8XD ⊖ Chalk Farm – ✆ (020) 7586 0408 – thequeens@geronimo-inns.co.uk – Fax (020) 7586 5677 – Closed 25 December and Sunday dinner 11 QZB **a**
Rest – Carte £ 15/25
◆ One of the original "gastropubs". Very popular balcony overlooking Primrose Hill and the high street. Robust and traditional cooking from the blackboard menu.

The Engineer
65 Gloucester Ave ✉ NW1 8JH ⊖ Chalk Farm – ✆ (020) 7722 0950 – info@the-engineer.com – Fax (020) 7483 0592 – Closed 3 days at Christmas 11 QZB **z**
Rest – Carte £ 18/45
◆ Busy pub that boasts a warm, neighbourhood feel. Dining room, decorated with modern pictures, has modish appeal. Informal, chatty service. Modern cuisine.

St Pancras – Camden – ✉ WC1

London 3 m – Luton 35 m – Watford 20 m – Slough 29 m

Norfolk Arms
28 Leigh Street ✉ WC1H 9EP ⊖ Russell Square – ✆ (020) 7388 3937 – info@norfolkarms.co.uk – Closed 25 December 18 SZD **b**
Rest – Menu £ 15 – Carte £ 18/25
◆ Charming gastropub with ornate ceiling squares and raw plaster walls, where dried peppers, chillies and onions hang from the walls. Mediterranean menu, dominated by tapas.

Swiss Cottage – Gtr London – ✉ NW3

London Marriott H. Regents Park
128 King Henry's Rd ✉ NW3 3ST ⊖ Swiss Cottage – ✆ (020) 7722 7711 – Fax (020) 7586 5822 11 PZB **a**
299 rm – †£ 158/217 ††£ 158/217, ☕ £ 16.95 – 5 suites – **Rest** – Menu £ 25 (dinner) – Carte £ 22/31
◆ Large writing desks and technological extras attract the corporate market to this purpose-built group hotel. The impressive leisure facilities appeal to weekend guests. Large, open-plan restaurant and bar.

Bradley's

25 Winchester Rd ✉ NW3 3NR ⊖ Swiss Cottage – ☎ (020) 7722 3457 – ssjbradleys@aol.com – Fax (020) 7435 1392 – closed 1 week Christmas, Sunday dinner, Monday 11 PZB **e**

Rest – Menu £ 15/22 – Carte £ 24/37

◆ Warm pastel colours and modern artwork add a Mediterranean touch to this neighbourhood restaurant. The theme is complemented by the cooking of the chef patron.

Eriki

4-6 Northways Parade, Finchley Rd ✉ NW3 5EN ⊖ Swiss Cottage – ☎ (020) 7722 0606 – info@eriki.co.uk – Fax (020) 7722 8866 – closed Christmas, 1 January, Saturday lunch and lunch on Bank Holidays 11 PZB **u**

Rest – Indian Carte £ 23/26

◆ A calm and relaxing venue, in spite of the bright interior set off by vivid red walls. Obliging service of carefully presented, flavoursome dishes from southern India.

Tufnell Park – Gtr London – ✉ NW5

Junction Tavern

101 Fortess Rd ✉ NW5 1AG ⊖ Tufnell Park – ☎ (020) 7485 9400 – Fax (020) 7485 9401 – Closed 24-26 December and 1 January 12 RZA **x**

Rest – Carte £ 20/28

◆ Typical Victorian pub with wood panelling. Eat in the bar or in view of the open plan kitchen. Robust cooking using good fresh ingredients, served in generous portions.

CITY OF LONDON – Gtr London – ✉ E1/EC1/EC2/EC3/EC4

Andaz Liverpool Street

Liverpool St ✉ EC2M 7QN ⊖ Liverpool Street – ☎ (020) 7961 1234 – info.londonliv@andaz.com – Fax (020) 7961 1235 34 ART **t**

264 rm – †£ 487/511 ††£ 546 – 3 suites

Rest *Aurora* – see restaurant listing

Rest *Catch* – Seafood – ☎ (020) 7618 7200 (closed Saturday, Sunday and Bank Holidays) Carte £ 34/54 **s**

Rest *Miyako* – Japanese – ☎ (020) 7618 5000 (closed Saturday lunch, Sunday and Bank Holidays) (booking essential) Carte approx. £ 20

◆ A contemporary and stylish interior hides behind the classic Victorian façade of this railway hotel. Bright and spacious bedrooms with state-of-the-art facilities. Seafood at Catch, based within original hotel lobby. Miyako is compact Japanese restaurant.

Crowne Plaza London - The City

19 New Bridge St ✉ EC4V 6DB ⊖ Blackfriars – ☎ (0870) 400 91 90 – loncy.info@ihg.com – Fax (020) 7438 8080 32 AOU **a**

201 rm – †£ 347/423 ††£ 347/423, ☕ £ 19.50 – 2 suites

Rest *Refettorio* – Italian – ☎ (020) 7438 8052 (Closed Saturday lunch, Sunday and Bank Holidays) Menu £ 45 (dinner) **s** – Carte £ 24/39 **s**

Rest *Spicers* – ☎ (020) 7438 8051 (lunch only Monday - Saturday) Carte £ 20/26 **s**

◆ Art deco façade by the river; interior enhanced by funky chocolate, cream and brown palette. Compact meeting room; well equipped fitness centre. Sizable, stylish rooms. Modish Refettorio for Italian cuisine. British dishes with a modern twist at Spicers.

Threadneedles

5 Threadneedle St ✉ EC2R 8AY ⊖ Bank – ☎ (020) 7657 8080 – resthreadneedles@theetoncollection.com – Fax (020) 7657 8100 34 ARU **y**

68 rm – †£ 370/392 ††£ 370/392, ☕ £ 19 – 1 suite

Rest *Bonds* – see restaurant listing

◆ A converted bank, dating from 1856, with a stunning stained-glass cupola in the lounge. Rooms are very stylish and individual featuring CD players and Egyptian cotton sheets.

Apex City of London

No 1, Seething Lane ✉ EC3N 4AX ⊖ Fenchurch Street – ✆ (020) 7702 2020 – Fax (020) 7702 2020 34 ARU **a**

129 rm – †£ 287 ††£ 287, ☕ £ 10 – 1 suite

Rest *Addendum* – see restaurant listing

Rest *Addendum Bar* – Carte £ 17/27

◆ Tucked away behind Tower of London, overlooking leafy square. Smart meeting facilities, well-equipped gym and treatment rooms. Bedrooms are super sleek with bespoke extras. Open plan bar/brasserie serves interesting modern dishes; al fresco in summer.

Novotel London Tower Bridge

10 Pepys St ✉ EC3N 2NR ⊖ Tower Hill – ✆ (020) 7265 6000 – h3107@accor.com – Fax (020) 7265 6060 34 ASU **b**

199 rm – †£ 190/215 ††£ 210/235, ☕ £ 13.50 – 4 suites

Rest *The Garden Brasserie* – (buffet lunch, bar lunch Saturday-Sunday) Menu £ 20/25 – Carte £ 18/44 **s**

◆ Modern, purpose-built hotel with carefully planned, comfortable bedrooms. Useful City location and close to Tower of London which is visible from some of the higher rooms. Informally styled brasserie.

Aurora – at Andaz Liverpool Street H.

Liverpool St ✉ EC2M 7QN ⊖ Liverpool Street – ✆ (020) 7618 7000 – aurora.londonliv@andaz.com – Fax (020) 7618 5035 – closed Saturday, Sunday and Bank Holidays 34 ART **t**

Rest – Menu £ 28 (lunch) – Carte £ 38/54

◆ Vast columns, ornate plasterwork and a striking glass dome feature in this imposing dining room. Polished and attentive service of an elaborate and modern menu.

Rhodes Twenty Four

London,

24th floor, Tower 42, 25 Old Broad St ✉ EC2N 1HQ ⊖ Liverpool Street – ✆ (020) 7877 7703 – reservations@rhodes24.co.uk – Fax (020) 7877 7788 – closed Christmas-New Year, Saturday, Sunday and Bank Holidays 34 ART **v**

Rest – British Carte £ 32/58

Spec. Seared scallops with mashed potato and shallot mustard sauce. Steamed mutton and onion suet pudding with buttered carrots. Bread and butter pudding.

◆ Modern restaurant on the 24th floor of the former Natwest building with panoramic views of the city. Modern, refined cooking of classic British recipes. Booking advised.

Coq d'Argent

No.1 Poultry ✉ EC2R 8EJ ⊖ Bank – ✆ (020) 7395 5000 – coqdargent@danddlondon.com – Fax (020) 7395 5050 – closed Christmas, Easter, Saturday lunch, Sunday dinner and Bank Holidays 33 AQU **c**

Rest – French (booking essential) Menu £ 29 – Carte £ 31/47

◆ Take the dedicated lift to the top of this modern office block. Tables on the rooftop terrace have city views; busy bar. Gallic menus highlighted by popular shellfish dishes.

1 Lombard Street (Restaurant)

1 Lombard St ✉ EC3V 9AA ⊖ Bank – ✆ (020) 7929 6611 – hb@1lombardstreet.com – Fax (020) 7929 6622 – closed 22 December-3 January, Saturday, Sunday and Bank Holidays 33 AQU **r**

Rest – (booking essential at lunch) Menu £ 39/45 – Carte £ 54/62

Spec. Carpaccio of tuna with Oriental spices, ginger and lime vinaigrette. Trio of lamb with sorrel velouté and tomato compote, lamb jus. Warm strawberries in Sauternes with crème fraîche sorbet.

◆ A haven of tranquillity behind the forever busy brasserie. Former bank provides the modern and very comfortable surroundings in which to savour the accomplished cuisine.

XXX **Addendum**

No 1, Seething Lane ✉ EC3N 4AX ⊖ Fenchurch Street – ✆ (020) 7977 9500 – londonevents@apexhotels.co.uk – closed 20 December -5 January and Bank Holidays 34 ARU **a**

Rest – Menu £ 27 (lunch) – Carte £ 33/37

◆ Intimate and elegant with chocolate leather banquettes, fresh flowers and modern mirrors. Precise service of robust, earthy dishes which often rejoice in the use of offal.

XXX **Bonds** – at Threadneedles H.

5 Threadneedle St ✉ EC2R 8AY ⊖ Bank – ✆ (020) 7657 8088 – bonds@theetongroup.com – Fax (020) 7657 8089 – closed Saturday and Sunday 34 ARU **y**

Rest – Menu £ 25 (lunch) – Carte £ 31/48

◆ Modern interior juxtaposed with the grandeur of a listed city building. Vast dining room with high ceiling and tall pillars. Attentive service of hearty, contemporary food.

XX **Club Gascon** (Pascal Aussignac)

✿ *57 West Smithfield ✉ EC1A 9DS ⊖ Barbican – ✆ (020) 7796 0600 – info@clubgascon.com – Fax (020) 7796 0601 – closed 22 December-6 January, 21-24 March, Sunday, Saturday lunch and Bank Holidays* 33 APT **z**

Rest – French (booking essential) Menu £ 42 – Carte £ 38/72

Spec. Carpaccio of venison with summer truffle and crispy artichoke. Pyrenean lamb on vine shoot embers with blinis and trevise. Cherries with yoghurt coulis, almonds and griottes.

◆ Intimate restaurant on the edge of Smithfield Market. Specialises in both the food and wines of Southwest France. Renowned for its tapas-sized dishes.

XX **Sauterelle**

The Royal Exchange ✉ EC3V 3LR ⊖ Bank – ✆ (020) 7618 2483 – Closed Saturday and Sunday 33 AQU **a**

Rest – Carte £ 32/49

◆ Located on mezzanine level of Royal Exchange, a stunning 16C property with ornate columns and pillars. Typically Conran rustic French menus attract smart lunch-time diners.

XX **The Chancery**

9 Cursitor St ✉ EC4A 1LL ⊖ Chancery Lane – ✆ (020) 7831 4000 – reservations@thechancery.co.uk – Fax (020) 7831 4002 – closed 22 December-5 January, Saturday and Sunday 32 ANT **a**

Rest – Menu £ 32

◆ Near Law Courts, a small restaurant with basement bar. Contemporary interior with intimate style. Quality ingredients put to good use in accomplished, modern dishes.

XX **Lanes**

109-117 Middlesex St ✉ E1 7JF ⊖ Liverpool Street – ✆ (020) 7247 5050 – info@lanesrestaurant.co.uk – Fax (020) 7247 8071 – closed Saturday lunch, Sunday and Bank Holidays 34 ART **b**

Rest – Carte £ 33/41

◆ Busy lunchtimes and more sedate evenings at this bright destination with subterranean bar, where art displays are a regular backdrop. Modern British/European menus hold sway.

XX **Boisdale of Bishopgate**

Swedeland Court, 202 Bishopgate ✉ EC2M 4NR ⊖ Liverpool Street – ✆ (020) 7283 1763 – info@boisdale-city.co.uk – Fax (020) 7283 1664 – closed 25 December, 3 January, Saturday, Sunday and Bank Holidays 34 ART **a**

Rest – Scottish Carte £ 24/49

◆ Through ground floor bar, serving oysters and champagne, to brick vaulted basement with red and tartan décor. Menu featuring Scottish produce. Live jazz most evenings.

XX **Bevis Marks** VISA AE

Bevis Marks ✉ EC3A 5DQ ⊖ Aldgate – ✆ (020) 7283 2220 – enquiries@bevismarkstherestaurant.com – Fax (020) 7283 2221 – closed Saturday, Sunday, Friday dinner and Jewish Holidays 34 ART **x**

Rest – Kosher Carte £ 30/36

◆ Glass-roofed extension to city's oldest synagogue: limestone flooring, modern murals on wall. Regularly changing Kosher menus; influences from Mediterranean and Middle East.

XX **Searcy's** A/C VISA AE

Barbican Centre, Level 2, Silk St ✉ EC2Y 8DS ⊖ Barbican – ✆ (020) 7588 3008 – searcys@barbican.org.uk – Fax (020) 7382 7247 – closed 24-26 December, Sunday, Saturday lunch and Bank Holidays 33 AQT **n**

Rest – Carte £ 26/40

◆ Stylish modern surroundings, smooth effective service and seasonal modern British cooking. Unique location ideal for visitors to Barbican's multi-arts events.

XX **Tatsuso** A/C VISA AE

32 Broadgate Circle ✉ EC2M 2QS ⊖ Liverpool Street – ✆ (020) 7638 5863 – info.tatsuso@btinternet.com – Fax (020) 7638 5864 – closed Saturday, Sunday and Bank Holidays 34 ART **u**

Rest – Japanese (booking essential) Carte £ 34/108

◆ Dine in the busy teppan-yaki bar or in the more formal restaurant. Approachable staff in traditional costume provide attentive service of authentic and precise dishes.

XX **The White Swan** A/C VISA AE

108 Fetter Lane ✉ EC4A 1ES ⊖ Temple – ✆ (020) 7242 9696 – info@thewhiteswanlondon.com – Fax (020) 7404 2250 – Closed at Christmas and Bank Holidays 32 ANT **n**

Rest – (closed Saturday, Sunday and dinner Monday) Menu £ 27 – Carte £ 26/33

◆ Smart dining room above pub just off Fleet Street: mirrored ceilings, colourful paintings on wall. Modern, daily changing menus, are good value for the heart of London.

XX **Saki** A/C VISA AE

4 West Smithfield ✉ EC1A 9JX ⊖ Barbican – ✆ (020) 7489 7033 – info@saki-food.com – Fax (020) 7489 1658 – closed Christmas-New Year, Sunday and Bank Holidays 33 AOT **b**

Rest – Japanese Menu £ 17/58 – Carte £ 17/45

◆ Uber-stylish bar/restaurant below a Japanese deli. Incorporates a sushi bar, communal 'garden table' and impressive Japanese dishes based on seasonality and healthy eating.

X **Paternoster Chop House** A/C VISA AE

Warwick Court, Paternoster Square ✉ EC4N 7DX ⊖ St Paul's – ✆ (020) 7029 9400 – paternosterr@conran-restaurants.co.uk – Fax (020) 7029 9409 – closed Sunday dinner and Saturday 33 APT **x**

Rest – British Carte approx. £ 30

◆ A modern ambience holds sway, while there's a reassuringly resolute British classic style to the dishes. Back to basics menu relies on seasonality and sourcing of ingredients.

**The ✿ award is the crème de la crème.
This is awarded to restaurants
which are really worth travelling miles for!**

CROYDON – Gtr London

Addington – ✉ CR2

Addington Court Featherbed Lane, ✆ (020) 8657 0281 ;
The Addington 205 Shirley Church Rd, ✆ (020) 8777 1055 .

Planet Spice
88 Selsdon Park Rd ✉ CR2 8JT – ✆ (020) 8651 3300 – emdad@planet-spice.com – Fax (020) 8651 4400 – closed 26 December 7 GZ **c**
Rest – Indian Carte £ 22/27
◆ Brasserie style Indian restaurant with fresh, vibrant décor and a modern feel. Attentive and helpful service. Traditional cooking with some innovative touches.

Croydon – Surrey – ✉ CR0/CR9

Croydon Clocktower, Katharine St ✆ (020) 8253 1009

Hilton Croydon
Waddon Way, Purley Way ✉ CR9 4HH – ✆ (020) 8680 3000 – reservations.croydon@hilton.com – Fax (020) 8681 6171 7 FZ **e**
168 rm – †£ 70/129 ††£ 81/139, ☕ £ 15.95 – **Rest** – (closed Sunday) (dinner only) Carte approx. £ 20
◆ A modern hotel where the relaxing café in the open-plan lobby is open all day. Internet access is available in all bedrooms, which are decorated to a good standard. Open-plan dining room; informal char-grill concept.

EALING – Gtr London

Acton Green – Gtr London – ✉ W4

The Bollo
13-15 Bollo Lane ✉ W4 5LR ⊖ Chiswick Park – ✆ (020) 8994 6037 – thebollohousel@btconnect.com – Closed 25 December 6 CV **z**
Rest – Carte £ 20/45
◆ Attractive redbrick pub with dining area under a domed glass rotunda. Daily changing menu - mixture of traditional and eclectic dishes - served throughout the pub.

Ealing – Gtr London – ✉ W13

West Middlesex Southall Greenford Rd, ✆ (020) 8574 3450 ;
Horsenden Hill Greenford Woodland Rise, ✆ (020) 8902 4555 .

Maxim
153-155 Northfield Ave ✉ W13 9QT ⊖ Northfields – ✆ (020) 8567 1719 – Fax (020) 8932 0717 – closed 25-28 December and Sunday lunch 1 BV **a**
Rest – Chinese Menu £ 10/20 – Carte £ 17/30
◆ Decorated with assorted oriental ornaments and pictures. Well-organised service from smartly attired staff. Authentic Chinese cooking from the extensive menu.

Charlotte's Place
16 St Matthew's Rd ✉ W5 3JT ⊖ Ealing Common – ✆ (020) 8567 7541 – restaurant@charlottes.co.uk – Closed 1-2 January, 26-30 December and lunch Monday 2 CV **c**
Rest – Carte £ 24/35
◆ Friendly neighbourhood restaurant whose large windows and mirror ensure plenty of light. Modern European dishes and some brasserie classics come in decently-sized portions.

South Ealing – Gtr London – ✉ W5

The Ealing Park Tavern
222 South Ealing Rd ✉ W5 4RL ⊖ South Ealing – ✆ (020) 8758 1879 – Fax (020) 8560 5269 – Closed 25-26 December, 1 January and Monday lunch 1 BV **e**

Rest – Carte £ 24/28

◆ Victorian building with an atmospheric, cavernous interior. Characterful beamed dining room and an open-plan kitchen serving modern dishes from a daily changing menu.

ENFIELD – Gtr London

Lee Valley Leisure Edmonton Picketts Lock Lane, ✆ (020) 8803 3611.

Enfield – Middx – ✉ EN1

Whitewebbs Clay Hill Beggars Hollow, N : 1 m., ✆ (020) 8363 2951.

Oak Lodge without rest
80 Village Rd, Bush Hill Park ✉ EN1 2EU – ✆ (020) 8360 7082 – info@oaklodgehotel-enfield.co.uk 3 FT **a**

10 rm – †£ 80 ††£ 90

◆ An Edwardian house located in a residential area. Individually decorated bedrooms are compact but well equipped; the ideal antidote to faceless corporate hotels.

Hadley Wood – Herts. – ✉ EN4

West Lodge Park
off Cockfosters Rd ✉ EN4 0PY – ✆ (020) 8216 3900 – westlodgepark@bealeshotels.co.uk – Fax (020) 8216 3937 3 ET **i**

59 rm – †£ 85/115 ††£ 175, ☕ £ 15

Rest *The Cedar* – Menu £ 20/25 – Carte £ 33/42

◆ Family owned for over half a century, a country house in sweeping grounds with arboretum. Comfortable sitting rooms; neat, spacious bedrooms. Use of nearby leisure centre. Dining room boasts large windows and exposed brick walls.

GREENWICH – Gtr London

Greenwich – Gtr London – ✉ SE10

North Pole
131 Greenwich High Rd ✉ SE10 8JA ⊖ Greenwich (DLR) – ✆ (020) 8853 3020 – north-pole@btconnect.com – Fax (020) 8853 3501 7 GV **u**

Rest – (dinner only and Sunday lunch) Menu £ 20 – Carte £ 25/34

◆ Rat-pack themed former pub with popular bar: piano played most evenings. Upstairs dining room benefits from large windows and bright colours. Relaxed service; robust cooking.

Spread Eagle
1-2 Stockwell St ✉ SE10 9JN ⊖ Greenwich (DLR) – ✆ (020) 8853 2333 – Fax (020) 8293 1024 – closed 1st January 7 GV **c**

Rest – French Menu £ 20/31 **s**

◆ This converted pub is something of an institution. Cosy booth seating, wood panelling and a further upstairs room. Traditional French-influenced menu with attentive service.

Rivington
178 Greenwich High Rd ✉ SE10 8NN ⊖ Greenwich (DLR) – ✆ (020) 8293 9270 – office@rivingtongrill.co.uk – closed 25-26 December and 1 January,Monday,lunch Tuesday and Wednesday 7 GV **s**

Rest – British Carte £ 21/38

◆ Part of the Picturehouse complex; 21C rustic interior with closely set tables. Firmly English menus in bar and galleried restaurant. Banquets and market breakfasts on offer.

HACKNEY - Gtr London

Hackney - Gtr London - ✉ E8

The Empress of India
130 Lauriston Road, Victoria Park ✉ E9 7LH ⊖ Mile End - ☎ (020) 8533 5123 - info@theempressofindia.com - Fax (020) 7404 2250 - Closed 25 December 3 GU **n**
Rest - Carte £ 24/35
◆ Smart, open plan pub with mosaic flooring, red leather banquettes and eye-catching murals. Classically based dishes with Mediterranean influences range from robust to refined.

Cat & Mutton
76 Broadway Market ✉ E8 4QJ ⊖ Bethnal Green - ☎ 020 7254 5599 - catandmutton@yahoo.co.uk - Closed 25-26 December and 1 January 14 YZB **a**
Rest - (closed Sunday dinner and Monday lunch) Menu £ 15 - Carte £ 23/30
◆ 19C corner pub with vast windows, school chairs and wood-panelled ceiling. Menu on a slate board: robust gastro pub fare with ingredients from the Saturday farmers' market.

Hoxton - Gtr London - ✉ E1/EC1/EC2/N1

Crown Plaza
100 Shoreditch High St ✉ E1 6JQ ⊖ Shoreditch - ☎ (020) 7613 9800 - sales@cplondon.com - Fax (020) 7613 9811 20 XZD **k**
196 rm - †£ 294 ††£ 294, ☕ £16.95 - **Rest** - Menu £ 20 - Carte £ 26/45
◆ Purpose-built hotel on the edge of the Square Mile. Clean-lined, co-ordinated rooms with smart mod cons and king-size beds. Stylish 'Saints' bar. The Globe bar and restaurant has great views over The City.

The Hoxton
81 Great Eastern St ✉ EC2A 3HU ⊖ Old Street - ☎ (020) 7550 1000 - info@hoxtonhotels.com - Fax (020) 7550 1090 20 XZD **x**
205 rm - †£ 59/149 ††£ 59/149, ☕ £8.50
Rest ***Hoxton Grille*** - Carte £ 22/30
◆ Urban lodge: industrial styled, clean lined modernism. "No ripoffs" mantra: cheap phone rate, free internet, complimentary 'lite pret' breakfast. Carefully considered rooms. Cooking style: New York deli meets French brasserie.

Great Eastern Dining Room
54 Great Eastern St ✉ EC2A 3QR ⊖ Old Street - ☎ (020) 7613 4545 - Fax (020) 7613 4137 - closed Christmas and Sunday 20 XZD **n**
Rest - South East Asian Carte £ 24/37
◆ Half the place is a bar that's heaving in the evening. Dining area has candle-lit tables, contemporary chandeliers, and carefully prepared, seriously tasty pan-Asian cooking.

Bacchus
177 Hoxton St ✉ N1 6PJ ⊖ Old Street - ☎ (020) 7613 0477 - bookings@bacchus-restaurant.co.uk - Fax (020) 7100 1704 - closed 1 week spring, 2 weeks summer, Saturday and Sunday 14 XZB **a**
Rest - (dinner only) Menu £ 30 - Carte £ 30/45
◆ 19C former pub with retro style lounges, trendy music and buzzy atmosphere. Highly original menus with some adventurous flavour combinations; slow cooked meat a speciality.

Fifteen London
13 Westland Pl ✉ N1 7LP ⊖ Old Street - ☎ (0871) 330 15 15 - Fax (020) 7251 2749 - closed 25 December and 1 January 13 VZC **c**
Rest - Menu £ 25 (weekday lunch)/60 - Carte £ 38/60
◆ Jamie Oliver's TV restaurant. Open plan kitchen showing the trainee chefs at work. Typical menu of robust earthy flavours using carefully-sourced ingredients.

Cru

2-4 Rufus St ✉ N1 6PE ⊖ Old Street – ✆ (020) 7729 5252 – info@cru.uk.com – Fax (020) 7729 1070 – closed 25-30 December and Monday 20 XZC **m**

Rest – Carte approx. £ 23

◆ Converted 19C warehouse trendily located with artwork for sale. Bar and delicatessen leading past open kitchen to restaurant. Modern menu with Asian influences. Good value.

Hoxton Apprentice

16 Hoxton Sq ✉ N1 6NT ⊖ Old Street – ✆ (020) 7749 2828 – info@hoxtonapprentice.com – closed Monday 20 XZC **r**

Rest – Carte £ 23/34

◆ Set up as charitable enterprise in 19C former primary school; now stands on its own as accomplished restaurant where apprentices and pros cook interesting, seasonal dishes.

Real Greek Mezedopolio

15 Hoxton Market ✉ N1 6HG ⊖ Old Street – ✆ (020) 7739 8212 – admin@therealgreek.demon.co.uk – Fax (020) 7739 4910 – Closed 25-26 December, 1 January, Sunday and Bank Holidays 20 XZC **v**

Rest – Greek (bookings not accepted) Carte £ 10/16

◆ Very relaxed restaurant with emphasis on unstructured, shared eating experience. Fresh, healthy menu divided into cold and hot meze, souvlaki and large plates for 'sharers'.

Shoreditch – Gtr London – ✉ EC2

Rivington

28-30 Rivington St ✉ EC2A 3DZ ⊖ Old Street – ✆ (020) 7729 7053 – shoreditch@rivingtongrill.co.uk – closed 25-26 December 1 January and August Bank Holiday 20 XZD **e**

Rest – British Carte £ 22/51

◆ Ex-button factory with a local buzz. Airy main restaurant has school chairs, well worn floor. There's also a comfy lounge and an intimate front area. Solid English cooking.

The Princess

76-78 Paul St ✉ EC2A 4NE ⊖ Old Street – ✆ (020) 7729 9270 – theeaston@btconnect.com – Closed 24 December-8 January and Saturday lunch 19 VZD **a**

Rest – Carte £ 22/27

◆ Traditional corner pub given a gastro makeover. Dining room, above busy bar, has a stylish appeal matched by interesting international dishes underpinned by strong cooking.

The Fox

28 Paul St ✉ EC2A 4LB ⊖ Old Street – ✆ (020) 7729 5708 – thefoxpublichouse@thefoxpublichouse.com – Closed lunch Saturday and dinner Sunday 19 VZD **c**

Rest – (booking essential) Carte £ 23/26

◆ Rough and ready pub with a great menu: this is found upstairs in the rather serene, but Gothic, restaurant. No nonsense dishes with bold, seasonal, unfussy, fresh flavours.

Stoke Newington – Gtr London – ✉ N16

Rasa

55 Stoke Newington Church St ✉ N16 0AR – ✆ (020) 7249 0344 – Fax (020) 7637 0224 – closed 24-26 December, and 1 January 14 XZA **e**

Rest – Indian (dinner only and lunch Saturday and Sunday) (booking essential) Menu £ 16 – Carte £ 9/13

◆ Busy Indian restaurant, an unpretentious environment in which to sample authentic, sometimes unusual, dishes. The "Feast" offers a taste of the range of foods on offer.

X **Rasa Travancore**

56 Stoke Newington Church St ✉ N16 0NB – ✆ (020) 7249 1340
– closed 23-30 December 20 XZA **x**

Rest – Indian (dinner only) Carte approx. £ 12

◆ Friendly, knowledgable service a distinct bonus to diners getting to know Keralan cooking. Good value dishes: 'feast' menu recommended by staff offers the full experience.

HAMMERSMITH and FULHAM – Gtr London

Fulham – Gtr London – ✉ SW6

XXX **Saran Rom**

The Boulevard, Imperial Wharf, Townmead Rd ✉ SW6 2UB
⊖ Fulham Broadway – ✆ (020) 7751 3111
– info@saranrom.com 23 PZH **b**

Rest – Thai Carte £ 29/38

◆ In a recently constructed "village", with super river views. Ornately carved interior with series of rooms, including bar with Thames outlook. Authentic, fresh Thai menus.

XXX **Memories of India on the River**

7 The Boulevard, Imperial Wharf ✉ SW6 2UB ⊖ Fulham Broadway
– ✆ (020) 7736 0077 – Fax (020) 7731 5222 – Closed 25 December 35 PZH **n**

Rest – Indian Carte £ 31/48

◆ Indian fabrics adorn this slinky restaurant in a wharf complex. Vast palm useful for getting your bearings: interesting, original, well-presented Indian dishes.

XX **Yi-Ban**

5 The Boulevard, Imperial Rd, Imperial Wharf ✉ SW6 2UB ⊖ Fulham Broadway
– ✆ (020) 7731 6606 – Fax (020) 7731 7584 – closed Sunday 23 PZH **n**

Rest – Chinese Menu 25 – Carte £ 25/45

◆ Very stylish and contemporary with dark, seductice interior divided by opaque nets; cocktail bar adds to the mix. Modern Chinese dishes meet tried-and-tested favourites.

XX **Deep**

The Boulevard, Imperial Wharf ✉ SW6 2UB ⊖ Fulham Broadway
– ✆ (020) 7736 3337 – info@deeplondon.co.uk – Fax (020) 7736 7578
– Closed 2 weeks Christmas - New Year, 1 week August, Monday, Sunday dinner, Saturday lunch and Bank Holidays 23 PZH **n**

Rest – Seafood Menu £ 20 (lunch) – Carte £ 25/43

◆ Slick, modern restaurant on rejuvenated riverside wharf. Linen-clad tables; floor-to-ceiling windows. Modern seafood dishes with Scandinavian feel; large aquavit selection.

XX **Blue Elephant**

4-6 Fulham Broadway ✉ SW6 1AA ⊖ Fulham Broadway – ✆ (020) 7385 6595
– london@blueelephant.com – Fax (020) 7386 7665 – closed Christmas and Saturday lunch 22 NZG **z**

Rest – Thai (booking essential) Menu £ 15/35 – Carte £ 27/44

◆ Elaborately ornate, unrestrained décor: fountains, bridges, orchids and ponds with carp. Authentic Thai food served by attentive staff in national costumes.

XX **Mao Tai**

58 New Kings Rd, Parsons Green ✉ SW6 4LS ⊖ Parsons Green
– ✆ (020) 7731 2520 – info@maotai.co.uk – closed 25-26 December 22 NZH **e**

Rest – Chinese Carte £ 28/43

◆ A light and modern interior with wood flooring and framed artwork with an eastern theme. Well organised service. Chinese cuisine with Szechuan specialities.

The Farm

18 Farm Lane ✉ SW6 1PP ⊖ Fulham Broadway – ✆ (020) 7381 3331 – info@thefarmfulham.co.uk – Closed 25 December 22 NZG **x**

Rest – Menu £ 25/29 – Carte £ 20/45

◆ Red brick pub with leather sofas and contemporary fireplaces. Rear dining room is ultra stylish, and the menus are suitably modern British with a French accent.

Hammersmith – Gtr London – ✉ W6/W14

River Café (Ruth Rogers & Rose Gray)

Thames Wharf, Rainville Rd ✉ W6 9HA ⊖ Barons Court – ✆ (020) 7386 4200 – info@rivercafe.co.uk – Fax (020) 7386 4201 – closed Christmas-New Year and Sunday dinner 21 LZG **r**

Rest – Italian (booking essential) Carte £ 42/65

Spec. Chargrilled squid with rocket and red chilli. Wood-roasted turbot with capers, spinach and marjoram. Chocolate 'Nemesis'.

◆ An institution: seasonality and top quality produce are cornestones of the forthright Italian dishes, whose seeming simplicity belies the work that went into their creation.

Chez Kristof

111 Hammersmith Grove, Brook Green ✉ W6 0NQ ⊖ Hammersmith – ✆ (020) 8741 1177 – info@chezkristof.co.uk – closed Christmas 21 LZF **b**

Rest – French Menu £ 17 – Carte £ 23/30

◆ Well worth seeking out in Brook Green: there's a luxurious deli, delightful terrace, and unmistakable Gallic ambience to this serious French restaurant where classics reign.

Indian Zing

236 King St ✉ W6 0RF ⊖ Ravenscourt Park – ✆ (020) 8748 5959 – indianzing@aol.com – Fax (020) 8748 2332 21 LZG **a**

Rest – Indian Menu £ 16/27 – Carte £ 20/33

◆ Sophisticated, modern restaurant with crisp white walls adorned with photos of life on the subcontinent. Traditional Indian menus are jettisoned for modish, original dishes.

Snows on the Green

166 Shepherd's Bush Rd, Brook Green ✉ W6 7PB ⊖ Hammersmith – ✆ (020) 7603 2142 – info@snowsonthegreen.co.uk – Fax (020) 7602 7553 – closed Christmas, Saturday lunch, Sunday and Bank Holidays 15 LZF **x**

Rest – Menu £ 17 – Carte £ 24/27

◆ Popular neighbourhood restaurant in Brook Green, with bright, sunny feel. Wide-ranging menus have a modern Mediterranean mix; fresh, flavoursome cooking is executed with care.

The Brackenbury

129-131 Brackenbury Rd ✉ W6 0BQ ⊖ Ravenscourt Park – ✆ (020) 8748 0107 – Fax (020) 8748 6159 – closed last 2 weeks August, 25-26 December and Sunday dinner 15 LZE **a**

Rest – Menu £ 15 (lunch) – Carte £ 25/32

◆ The closely set wooden tables, pavement terrace and relaxed service add to the cosy, neighbourhood feel. Cooking is equally unfussy; modern yet robust.

Azou

375 King St ✉ W6 9NJ ⊖ Stamford Brook – ✆ (020) 8563 7266 – info@azou.co.uk – Fax (020) 8741 1425 – closed 25 December, 1 January, Bank Holidays 21 KZG **u**

Rest – North African Carte £ 15/26

◆ The North African theme is not confined to the menu; the room is decorated with hanging lanterns, screens and assorted knick-knacks. Friendly service and well priced dishes.

Agni

160 King St ✉ W6 0QU ⊖ Ravenscourt Park – ☎ (020) 8846 9191 – info@agnirestaurant.com – closed 25 December and 1 January 21 LZG **s**

Rest – Indian (closed lunch Monday-Thursday) Menu £ 13/14 – Carte £ 14/18

◆ Modest façade hides a clean, bright interior. Dishes are 'home' style from Hyderabad with biryani to the fore, and are notably good value.

Anglesea Arms

35 Wingate Rd ✉ W6 0UR ⊖ Ravenscourt Park – ☎ (020) 8749 1291 – Fax (020) 8749 1254 – Closed Christmas week 15 LZE **c**

Rest – (bookings not accepted) Carte £ 24/35

◆ The laid-back atmosphere and local feel make this pub a popular venue. Worth arriving early as bookings are not taken. Modern cooking from blackboard menu.

The Havelock Tavern

57 Masbro Rd, Brook Green ✉ W14 0LS ⊖ Kensington Olympia – ☎ (020) 7603 5374 – info@thehavelocktavern.co.uk – Closed 22-26 December, Easter Sunday and second Monday in August 16 MZE **e**

Rest – (bookings not accepted) Carte £ 19/25

◆ West London take on rusticity, with no-frills service and informal atmosphere. Food is the priority: hearty portions of British and European dishes, both tasty and nourishing.

Shepherd's Bush – Gtr London – ✉ W14

K West

rm,

Richmond Way ✉ W14 0AX ⊖ Kensington Olympia – ☎ (020) 8008 6600 – bookit@k-west.co.uk – Fax (020) 8008 6650 16 MZE **c**

214 rm – †£ 229 ††£ 412, ☕ £ 15 – 6 suites

Rest *Kanteen* – ☎ (0870) 027 4343 – Carte £ 19/30

◆ Former BBC offices, the interior is decorated in a smart, contemporary fashion. Bedrooms in understated modern style, deluxe rooms with work desks and DVD and CD facilities. Modish menus in trendy dining room.

HARINGEY – Gtr London

Crouch End – Gtr London – ✉ N4/N8

Mountview without rest

31 Mount View Rd ✉ N4 4SS – ☎ (020) 8340 9222 – mountviewbb@aol.com 3 EU **r**

3 rm ☕ – †£ 45/70 ††£ 60/80

◆ Redbrick Victorian house with a warm and stylish ambience engendered by the homely décor. One bedroom features an original fireplace and two overlook the quiet rear garden.

Florians

4 Topsfield Parade, Middle Lane ✉ N8 8RP – ☎ (020) 8348 8348 – Fax (020) 8292 2092 – closed 25-26 December and 1 January 3 EU **c**

Rest – Italian Carte £ 22/28

◆ Light room with tiled flooring and large paintings, nestling behind a busy front bar. Italian menu with blackboard daily specials. Efficient and obliging service.

Bistro Aix

54 Topsfield Parade, Tottenham Lane ✉ N8 8PT – ☎ (020) 8340 6346 – Fax (020) 8348 7236 – closed Monday 3 EU **v**

Rest – French (closed lunch Tuesday - Friday) Carte £ 19/36

◆ The simple wood furniture is complemented by plants and pictures. The owner chef's experience in France is reflected in the menu and the robust and hearty cooking.

The Queens Pub and Dining Room
26 Broadway Parade ✉ N8 9DE – ✆ (020) 8340 2031 – queens@foodandfuel.co.uk 3 EU **c**
Rest – Carte £ 20/32
◆ Classic Victorian pub with shimmering chandeliers, mahogany panelling and ornate ceilings. Menu offers a mix of modern British dishes with plenty of Mediterranean influence.

Highgate – Gtr London – ✉ N6

The Bull
13 North Hill ✉ N6 4AB ⊖ Highgate – ✆ (0845) 456 5033 – info@inthebull.biz – Fax (0845) 456 5034 2 EU **x**
Rest – (closed Monday lunch) Carte £ 30/45
◆ Grade II listed pub with large terrace and interior, spread over two floors. Appealing dishes - a mix of British and classical French - are very much reliant on the seasons.

Tottenham – Gtr London – ✉ N17

The Lock
Heron House, Hale Wharf, Ferry Lane ✉ N17 9NF ⊖ Tottenham Hale – ✆ (020) 8885 2829 – thelock06@btconnect.com – Fax (020) 8885 1618 – closed Monday 3 GU **a**
Rest – Menu £ 12 (lunch) – Carte £ 18/32
◆ An oasis of cool in N17. By the side of a lock, there's a long bar with sofas, and restaurant with wood or mosaic tables. Original touches enhance tasty French/Italian mix.

STROUD GREEN – Haringey – ✉ N4

The Old Dairy
1-3 Crouch Hill ✉ N4 4AP – ✆ (020) 7263 3337 – theolddairy@realpubs.co.uk – Fax (020) 7561 1851 – Closed 25 December 3 EU **a**
Rest – Carte £ 19/25
◆ Picture panels illustrate this listed building's former use as a dairy. Now serving modern British cooking with a hint of Europe; bold and honest, with well judged portions.

HARROW – Gtr London

Harrow Weald – Middx – ✉ HA3

Grim's Dyke
Old Redding ✉ HA3 6SH – ✆ (020) 8385 3100 – reservations@grimsdyke.com – Fax (020) 8954 4560 1 BT **a**
46 rm – †£ 100 ††£ 125/175
Rest *Gilberts* – (closed Saturday lunch) Menu £ 27 – Carte £ 30/45
◆ Victorian mansion, former country residence of W.S.Gilbert. Rooms divided between main house and lodge, the former more characterful. Over 40 acres of garden and woodland. Restaurant with ornately carved fireplace.

Pinner – Middx – ✉ HA5

Friends
11 High St ✉ HA5 5PJ ⊖ Pinner – ✆ (020) 8866 0286 – info@friendsrestaurant.co.uk – Fax (020) 8866 0286 – closed 25-26 December, Good Friday, Monday, Sunday dinner and Bank Holidays 1 BU **a**
Rest – Menu £ 22/29
◆ Pretty beamed cottage, with some parts dating back 400 years. Inside, a welcoming glow from the log fire; personal service from owners and a fresh, regularly-changing menu.

HILLINGDON – Gtr London

18 Haste Hill Northwood The Drive, ☎ (01923) 825 224 .

Heathrow Airport – Middx

London Heathrow Marriott

rm, VISA AE

Bath Rd, Hayes ✉ UB3 5AN – ☎ (0870) 400 7250
– salesadmin.heathrow@marriotthotels.com – Fax (0870) 400 7350 5 AX **z**

391 rm – †£ 182 ††£ 182, ☕ £16.95 – 2 suites
Rest *Tuscany* – Italian (Closed Sunday) (dinner only) Menu £ 39 **s** – Carte £ 30/44 **s**
Rest *Allie's grille* – Carte £ 27/39 **s**

◆ Built at the end of 20C, this modern, comfortable hotel is centred around a large atrium, with comprehensive business facilities: there is an exclusive Executive floor. Italian cuisine at Tuscany. Grill favourites at Allie's.

Crowne Plaza London - Heathrow

rm, VISA AE

Stockley Rd, West Drayton ✉ UB7 9NA
– ☎ (0870) 400 9140 – reservations.cplhr@ichotelsgroup.com
– Fax (01895) 445 122 1 AV **v**

460 rm – †£ 247 ††£ 247, ☕ £17.95 – 3 suites
Rest *Simply Nico Heathrow* – see restaurant listing
Rest *Orwell's Brasserie* – Menu £ 15/20

◆ Extensive leisure, aromatherapy and beauty salons make this large hotel a popular stop-over for travellers. Club bedrooms are particularly well-equipped. Bright, breezy Concha Grill with juice bar.

Sheraton Skyline

rm, VISA AE

Bath Rd, Hayes ✉ UB3 5BP – ☎ (020) 8759 2535 – res268-skyline@sheraton.com
– Fax (020) 8750 9150 5 AX **u**

348 rm – †£ 93/280 ††£ 145/334, ☕ £17 – 2 suites
Rest *Sage* – Menu £ 20/45 – Carte £ 32/49

◆ Well known for its unique indoor swimming pool surrounded by a tropical garden which is overlooked by many of the bedrooms. Business centre available. Classically decorated dining room.

Hilton London Heathrow Airport

rm, VISA AE

Terminal 4 ✉ TW6 3AF – ☎ (020) 8759 7755
– sales.heathrow@hilton.com – Fax (020) 8759 7579 5 AX **n**

390 rm – †£ 292 ††£ 292, ☕ £20.50 – 5 suites
Rest *Brasserie* – (closed lunch Saturday and Sunday) (buffet lunch) Menu £ 28/34 – Carte £ 30/54
Rest *Zen Oriental* – Chinese Menu £ 29/39

◆ Group hotel with a striking modern exterior and linked to Terminal 4 by a covered walkway. Good sized bedrooms, with contemporary styled suites. Spacious Brasserie in vast atrium. Zen Oriental offers formal Chinese experience.

Renaissance London Heathrow

rm, VISA AE

Bath Rd ✉ TW6 2AQ – ☎ (020) 8897 6363
– rhi.lhrbh.guestservices@renaissancehotels.com – Fax (020) 8897 1113 5 AX **c**

643 rm – †£ 85 ††£ 180, ☕ £17 – 6 suites – **Rest** – (dinner only) Menu £ 25 – Carte £ 30/34

◆ Low level façade belies the size of this easily accessible hotel. Large lounge and assorted shops in the lobby. Some of the soundproofed bedrooms have views of the runway. Open-plan restaurant with buffet or à la carte.

Simply Nico Heathrow – at Crowne Plaza London - Heathrow H.

VISA AE

Stockley Rd, West Drayton ✉ UB7 9NA
– ☎ (01895) 437 564 – heathrow.simplynico@corushotels.com
– Fax (01895) 437 565 – closed Sunday 5 AV **v**

Rest – (dinner only) Carte £ 23/44

◆ Located within the hotel but with its own personality. Mixes modern with more classically French dishes. Professional service in comfortable surroundings.

Ickenham – Middx

X **Jospens**
15 Long Lane ✉ UB10 8QU ⊖ Ickenham – ✆ (01895) 632519 – Fax (01895) 272284 – closed 1 week Christmas, 1 week August and Monday 1 AU **a**
Rest – Menu £ 14/22 **s** – Carte £ 23/30 **s**
◆ Neighbourhood restaurant with window boxes. Smart interior boasts deep lilac ceiling. Simple, well executed dishes with modern influences.

Ruislip – Middx

XXX **Hawtrey's** – at The Barn H.
West End Rd ✉ HA4 6JB ⊖ Ruislip – ✆ (01895) 679999 – info@thebarnhotel.co.uk – Fax (01895) 638379 – closed Sunday dinner 1 AU **e**
Rest – Menu £ 20/29 – Carte £ 43/49
◆ Jacobean styled baronial hall: an extension to 16C Barn Hotel. Cloth clad tables, bright chandeliers. Fine dining - modern cooking that's confident and assured.

HOUNSLOW – Gtr London

24 The Treaty Centre, High St ✆ (0845) 456 2929 (closed Sunday)
Wyke Green Isleworth Syon Lane, ✆ (020) 8560 8777 ;
Airlinks Southall Lane, ✆ (020) 8561 1418 ;
Hounslow HeathStaines Rd, ✆ (020) 8570 5271 .

Chiswick – Middx – ✉ W4

High Road House
162 Chiswick High Rd ✉ W4 1PR ⊖ Turnham Green – ✆ (020) 8742 1717 – reservation@highroadhouse.co.uk – Fax (020) 8987 8762 21 KZG **f**
14 rm – †£ 160 ††£ 160, ☕ £ 9
Rest *High Road Brasserie* – see restaurant listing
◆ Cool, sleek hotel and club, the latter a slick place to lounge around or play games. Light, bright bedrooms with crisp linen. A carefully appointed, fair-priced destination.

XXX ✿ **La Trompette**
5-7 Devonshire Rd ✉ W4 2EU ⊖ Turnham Green – ✆ (020) 8747 1836 – reception@latrompette.co.uk – Fax (020) 8995 8097 – closed 24-27 December and 1 January 21 KZG **y**
Rest – (booking essential) Menu £ 24/35 **s**
Spec. Steamed paupiette of sea bass and crab with mussels. Rump of lamb with globe artichoke and cassoulet of beans, bacon and lamb breast. Crème brûlée with plum compote.
◆ Genuine neighbourhood restaurant with pretty front terrace. Classical, flavoursome French cooking makes vibrant use of the freshest of ingredients. Exceptional wine list.

XX **High Road Brasserie**
162 Chiswick High Rd ✉ W4 1PR ⊖ Turnham Green – ✆ (020) 8742 7474 21 KZG **f**
Rest – Carte £ 28/36
◆ Confidently stylish place to eat. Marble-topped bar and Belgian tiled dining area provide sleek backdrop to well-priced, satisfying menus full of interesting brasserie dishes.

X **Fish Hook**
6-8 Elliott Rd ✉ W4 1PE ⊖ Turnham Green – ✆ (020) 8742 0766 – info@fishhook.co.uk – Fax (020) 8742 3374 – closed 23 - 26 December 21 KZG **z**
Rest – Seafood Menu £ 14 (lunch) – Carte £ 30/47
◆ Carnivores, steer clear: fish is exclusively on the menu here, either as starter or main course. Bright, simple interior. Well conceived dishes cooked with dextrous aplomb.

Sam's Brasserie

11 Barley Mow Passage ✉ W4 4PH ⊖ Turnham Green – ☎ (020) 8987 0555 – info@samsbrasserie.co.uk – Fax (020) 8987 7389 – closed 24-26 December 2 CV **a**

Rest – Menu £ 15 (lunch) – Carte £ 20/32

◆ Former paper mill by Turnham Green. 'Industrial', open plan feel with concrete and stainless steel. Robust brasserie dishes seem to be in keeping with the surroundings.

Fishworks

6 Turnham Green Terrace ✉ W4 1QP ⊖ Turnham Green – ☎ (020) 8994 0086 – chiswick@fishworks.co.uk – Fax (020) 8994 0778 – closed 25 - 28 December and 1 January 21 KZG **e**

Rest – Seafood (booking essential) Menu £ 14 (lunch) – Carte £ 26/38

◆ Well-run branded restaurant opening onto delightful rear terrace with olive trees. Daily blackboard menu of grills and popular seafood dishes.

The Devonshire House

126 Devonshire Rd ✉ W4 2JJ ⊖ Turnham Green – ☎ (020) 8987 2626 – info@thedevonshirehouse.co.uk – Fax (020) 8995 0152 – Closed 23 December-3 January and Monday 21 KZG **a**

Rest – Menu £ 14/19 – Carte £ 20/27

◆ Period pub conversion retaining original features. Leather banquettes and chairs; bare tables. Daily menu of modern cooking, slightly simpler at lunchtime. Attentive service.

ISLINGTON – Gtr London

Archway – ✉ N19

St John's

91 Junction Rd ✉ N19 5QU ⊖ Archway – ☎ (020) 7272 1587 – st.johns@virgin.net – Closed 25-26 December and 1 January 12 RZA **s**

Rest – (dinner only and lunch Friday-Sunday) Carte £ 20/32

◆ Busy front bar enjoys a lively atmosphere; dining room in a large rear room. Log fire at one end, open hatch into kitchen the other. Blackboard menu; rustic cooking.

Barnsbury – Gtr London – ✉ N1/N7

Morgan M

489 Liverpool Rd ✉ N7 8NS ⊖ Highbury and Islington – ☎ (020) 7609 3560 – Fax (020) 8292 5699 – closed 24-30 December, lunch Tuesday and Saturday, Sunday dinner and Monday 13 UZA **a**

Rest – French Menu £ 24/36 – Carte £ 36/41

◆ Simple restaurant in a converted pub. Smartly-laid tables complemented by formal service. Modern dishes based on classical French combinations.

Fig

169 Hemingford Rd ✉ N1 1DA ⊖ Caledonian Road – ☎ (020) 7609 3009 – figrestaurant@btconnect.com – closed 2 weeks Christmas - New Year, 1 week Easter, 2 weeks summer and Monday 13 UZB **a**

Rest – (dinner only) Carte £ 21/32

◆ Attractive and cosy neighbourhood restaurant with fig tree leaning over garden terrace. Original combinations move the weekly changing menu away from the modern European norm.

Canonbury – Gtr London – ✉ N1

The House

63-69 Canonbury Rd ✉ N1 2DG ⊖ Highbury and Islington – ☎ (020) 7704 7410 – info@inthehouse.biz – Fax (020) 7704 9388 – Closed 24-26 December and Monday lunch 13 UZB **h**

Rest – Carte £ 30/45

◆ This pleasant pub, on a street corner and popular with locals, has a restaurant with linen-covered tables, ceiling fans, art for sale, and modern menus with a classical base.

The Marquess Tavern

32 Canonbury Street ✉ N1 2TB ⊖ Highbury and Islington – ✆ 020 7354 2975 – info@marquesstavern.co.uk – Closed 25 December 13 VZB **x**

Rest – British Menu £ 15 – Carte £ 22/30

◆ Pillared exterior dominates a cosy corner. Stools and sofas in front bar. Far end dining area resoundingly British with all produce from the UK including wines from Cornwall.

Clerkenwell – Gtr London – ✉ EC1

Malmaison

18-21 Charterhouse Sq ✉ EC1M 6AH ⊖ Barbican – ✆ (020) 7012 3700 – london@malmaison.com – Fax (020) 7012 3702 19 UZD **o**

97 rm – †£ 276 ††£ 276, ☕ £17.95

Rest *Brasserie* – (closed Saturday lunch) Menu £ 18 (weekdays) – Carte £ 37/46

◆ Striking early 20C redbrick building overlooking pleasant square. Stylish, comfy public areas. Bedrooms in vivid, bold colours, with extras such as stereo and free broadband. Modern brasserie employing meats from Smithfield.

The Rookery without rest

12 Peters Lane, Cowcross St ✉ EC1M 6DS ⊖ Barbican – ✆ (020) 7336 0931 – reservations@rookery.co.uk – Fax (020) 7336 0932 33 AOT **p**

32 rm – †£ 206/241 ††£ 241, ☕ £9.75 – 1 suite

◆ A row of charmingly restored 18C houses. Wood panelling, stone-flagged flooring, open fires and antique furniture. Highly individual bedrooms, with Victorian bathrooms.

Smiths of Smithfield

Top Floor, 67-77 Charterhouse St ✉ EC1M 6HJ ⊖ Barbican – ✆ (020) 7251 7950 – reservations@smithsofsmithfield.co.uk – Fax (020) 7236 5666 – closed 25-26 December, 1 January and Saturday lunch 33 AOT **s**

Rest – Carte £ 32/46

Rest *The Dining Room* – Carte £ 20/24

◆ On three floors where the higher you go the more formal it becomes. Busy, bustling atmosphere and modern menu. Good views of the market from the top floor terrace. The Dining Room with mirrors and dark blue walls.

St John

26 St John St ✉ EC1M 4AY ⊖ Barbican – ✆ (020) 7251 0848 – reservations@stjohnrestaurant.com – Fax (020) 7251 4090 – closed Christmas, Easter, Saturday lunch, Sunday and Bank Holidays 33 APT **c**

Rest – British Carte £ 26/39

◆ Deservedly busy converted 19C former smokehouse. Popular bar, simple comforts. Menu specialises in offal and an original mix of traditional and rediscovered English dishes.

Vinoteca

7 St John St ✉ EC1M 4AA ⊖ Farringdon – ✆ (020) 7253 8786 – enquiries@vinoteca.co.uk – Fax (020) 7490 4282 – closed Christmas-New Year, Sunday and Bank Holidays 33 APT **a**

Rest – (booking essential at lunch) Carte £ 20/25

◆ Bold, modern dishes with perfect wine pairing in this thoroughly informal 'wine bar' eatery. Well-stocked shelves a great attraction: take out your favourite or drink within.

Comptoir Gascon

61-63 Charterhouse St ✉ EC1M 6HJ ⊖ Barbican – ✆ (020) 7608 0851 – info@comptoirgascon.com – Fax (020) 7608 0871 – closed Christmas-New Year, Sunday and Monday 33 AOT **a**

Rest – French Carte £ 22/32

◆ Half restaurant, half deli, situated opposite Smithfield. Rustic notions enhanced by exposed brick. Well priced, French based dishes form the mainstay of a simple restaurant.

Flâneur
41 Farringdon Rd ✉ EC1M 3JB ⊖ Farringdon – ✆ (020) 7404 4422 – mail@flaneur.com – Fax (020) 7831 4532 – closed 24 December-2 January and Sunday dinner 32 ANT **s**
Rest – (Sunday brunch) Menu £ 25 – Carte approx. £ 27
◆ Pleasant food store and eatery: the former has immaculately lined shelves of deli products, the latter is surrounded by succulent aromas; cooking is robust modern European.

The Coach & Horses
26-28 Ray St ✉ EC1R 3DJ ⊖ Farringdon – ✆ (020) 7278 8990 – info@thecoachandhorses.com – Fax (020) 7278 1478 – Closed 24-27 December, Saturday lunch and Sunday dinner 19 UZD **a**
Rest – Carte £ 19/27
◆ Ornate exterior in red and cream; down-to-earth interior. Daily changing menus are fiercely seasonal and carefully compiled. 'Untypical' ingredients, interesting flavours.

Finsbury – Gtr London – ✉ EC1

The Zetter
St John's Square, 86-88 Clerkenwell Rd ✉ EC1M 5RJ ⊖ Farringdon – ✆ (020) 7324 4444 – sales@thezetter.com – Fax (020) 7324 4445 19 UZD **s**
59 rm – †£ 182 ††£ 182, ☕ £16.95 – **Rest** – (closed 24 - 27 December) Carte £ 24/32
◆ Discreetly trendy modern design in the well-equipped bedrooms and rooftop studios of a converted 19C warehouse:pleasant extras from old paperbacks to flat-screen TV/DVDs. Light, informal restaurant serves modern Mediterranean dishes and weekend brunches.

The Clerkenwell Dining Room
69-73 St John St ✉ EC1M 4AN ⊖ Farringdon – ✆ (020) 7253 9000 – reservations@theclerkenwell.com – Fax (020) 7253 3322 – closed Christmas-New Year, Saturday lunch and Sunday 19 UZD **h**
Rest – Menu £ 20 – Carte £ 30/37
◆ Former pub, now a stylish modern restaurant with etched glass façade. Three adjoining dining areas with bar provide setting for contemporary British cooking.

Portal
88 St John St ✉ EC1M 4EH ⊖ Farringdon – ✆ (020) 7253 6950 – reservations@portalrestaurant.com – Fax (020) 7490 5836 – closed 23 December - 6 January, Saturday lunch, Sunday and Bank Holidays 19 UZD **r**
Rest – Carte £ 31/56
◆ Set in Grade II listed building with entrance to the 'industrial chic' restaurant via busy, bustling bar. The influence of Spain and Portugal highlighted in interesting menus.

The Larder
91-93 St John St ✉ EC1M 4NU ⊖ Farringdon – ✆ (020) 7608 1558 – info@thelarderrestaurant.com – Fax (120) 7253 9285 – Closed 24 December-2 January, Saturday lunch, Sunday and Bank Holidays 19 UZD **f**
Rest – Carte £ 19/39
◆ Large, glass-fronted restaurant with stark, noisy, industrial feel and own bakery selling breads and pastries. Unfussy food has an English accent with some European influences.

Quality Chop House
94 Farringdon Rd ✉ EC1R 3EA ⊖ Farringdon – ✆ (020) 7837 5093 – enquiries@qualitychophouse.co.uk – Fax (020) 7833 8748 – closed 25-26 December and Saturday lunch 19 UZD **n**
Rest – Carte £ 19/32
◆ On the window is etched "Progressive working class caterers". This is borne out with the individual café-style booths and a menu ranging from jellied eels to caviar.

Moro

34-36 Exmouth Market ✉ EC1R 4QE ⊖ Farringdon – ✆ (020) 7833 8336 – info@moro.co.uk – Fax (020) 7833 9338 – closed Christmas, New Year, Sunday and Bank Holidays 19 UZD **b**

Rest – (booking essential) Carte £ 26/32

♦ Daily changing menu an eclectic mix of Mediterranean, Moroccan and Spanish. Friendly T-shirted staff. Informal surroundings with bare tables and a large zinc bar.

The Ambassador

55 Exmouth Market ✉ EC1R 4QL ⊖ Farringdon – ✆ (020) 7837 0009 – clive@theambassadorcafe.co.uk – closed 24 December-2 January, Sunday dinner and Bank Holidays 19 UZD **c**

Rest – Menu £ 17 (lunch) – Carte £ 19/31

♦ Lino and melamine give a refreshing retro appeal to this cool, buzzy diner. Seasonal, honest, earthy ingredients inform all-day Eurocentric menus that tend towards the Gallic.

Medcalf

40 Exmouth Market ✉ EC1R 4QE ⊖ Farringdon – ✆ (020) 7833 3533 – mail@medcalfbar.co.uk – Fax (020) 7833 1321 – closed 24 December-2 January and Sunday dinner 19 UZD **b**

Rest – (booking essential) Carte £ 22/30

♦ Former butchers', now a 'rough-and-ready' eatery where ragged and chic charmingly collide. Precise, skilful cooking mixes a rustic style with global overtones. Very popular.

Cicada

132-136 St John St ✉ EC1V 4JT ⊖ Farringdon – ✆ (020) 7490 5898 – reservations@cicada.nu – Fax (020) 8608 1551 – closed 23 December-2 January, Saturday lunch and Sunday 19 UZD **d**

Rest – South East Asian Menu £ 25/50 – Carte £ 17/30

♦ Set in a culinary hotbed, this buzzy restaurant and vibrant bar is spacious, lively and popular for its South East Asian dishes: pop in for one course and a beer if you like.

The Peasant

240 St John St ✉ EC1V 4PH ⊖ Farringdon – ✆ (020) 7336 7726 – gapsbairs@aol.com – Fax (020) 7490 1089 – Closed 25 December -3 January 19 UZD **e**

Rest – (booking essential) Menu £ 14/18 – Carte £ 30/35

♦ Large, busy pub with half of the ground floor given over as a bar. Dining continues in the high-ceilinged room upstairs. Robust and rustic cooking with generous portions.

The Well

180 St John St ✉ EC1V 4JY ⊖ Farringdon – ✆ (020) 7251 9363 – drink@downthewell.co.uk – Fax (020) 7253 9683 – Closed 25 December 19 UZD **x**

Rest – Carte £ 22/29

♦ Rather predictable looking pub distinguished by big black canopies. Food lifts it above the average: everything from 'pie of the week' to sophisticated modern British dishes.

Highbury – Gtr London – ✉ N5

Au Lac

82 Highbury Park ✉ N5 2XE ⊖ Arsenal – ✆ (020) 7704 9187 – Fax (020) 7704 9187 13 VZA **b**

Rest – Vietnamese (dinner only and lunch Thursday and Friday) Carte £ 8/21

♦ Cosy Vietnamese restaurant, with brightly coloured walls and painted fans. Large menus with authentic dishes usefully highlighted. Fresh flavours; good value.

Islington – Gtr London – ✉ N1

Hilton London Islington

53 Upper St ✉ N1 0UY ⊖ Angel – ☎ (020) 7354 7700 – reservations.islington@hilton.com – Fax (020) 7354 7711 13 UZB **s**

184 rm – †£ 140/234 ††£ 140/234, ☕ £17.50 – **Rest** – Menu £ 21 (dinner) – Carte approx. £ 29

◆ Benefits from its location adjacent to the Business Design Centre. A purpose-built hotel with all bedrooms enjoying the appropriate creature comforts. Open-plan brasserie with small bar.

Almeida

30 Almeida St ✉ N1 1AD ⊖ Angel – ☎ (020) 7354 4777 – sharonw@danddlondon.com – Fax (020) 7354 2777 13 UZB **r**

Rest – French Menu £ 24/29

◆ Spacious, open plan restaurant with pleasant contemporary styling adjacent to Almeida Theatre. Large à la carte: a collection of classic French dishes.

Metrogusto

13 Theberton St ✉ N1 0QY ⊖ Angel – ☎ (020) 7226 9400 – Fax (020) 7226 9400 – closed 1 January, Easter, Sunday dinner and Bank Holidays 13 UZB **e**

Rest – Italian (dinner only and lunch Saturday-Sunday) Menu £ 19 (lunch) – Carte £ 25/31

◆ Relaxed neighbourhood Italian set over two rooms, with eye-catching artwork and slightly bohemian feel. Proudly run by Italian owner. Modern, carefully prepared Italian food.

Ottolenghi

287 Upper St ✉ N1 2TZ ⊖ Highbury and Islington – ☎ (020) 7288 1454 – upper@ottolenghi.co.uk – Fax (020) 7704 1456 – closed 25-26 December, 1 January and Sunday dinner 13 UZB **k**

Rest – Menu £ 15 (lunch) – Carte £ 25/31

◆ Cool, contemporary restaurant behind a smart deli. Two long tables accommodate most diners. Grazing style dishes are fresh, vibrant and tasty with a subtle Eastern spicing.

The Drapers Arms

44 Barnsbury St ✉ N1 1ER ⊖ Highbury and Islington – ☎ (020) 7619 0348 – info@thedrapersarms.co.uk – Fax (020) 7619 0413 – Closed 24-27 December, 13 UZB **x**

Rest – Carte £ 23/30

◆ Real presence to the façade of this Georgian pub tucked away in a quiet residential area. Spacious modern interior where competent, contemporary dishes are served.

The Northgate

113 Southgate Rd ✉ N1 3JS ⊖ Old Street – ☎ (020) 7359 7392 – Closed 25-26 December, and 1 January 13 VZB **a**

Rest – (dinner only and lunch Saturday and Sunday) Carte £ 19/30

◆ Corner pub with wood flooring and modern art on display. Rear dining area with a large blackboard menu offering a cross section of internationally influenced modern dishes.

The Barnsbury

209-211 Liverpool Rd ✉ N1 1LX ⊖ Highbury and Islington – ☎ (020) 7607 5519 – info@thebarnsbury.co.uk – Fax (020) 7607 3256 – Closed 25-26 December, 1 January 13 UZB **v**

Rest – Carte £ 23/33

◆ Former public house with pine tables and chairs arranged round central counter bar; art work for sale on the walls. Robust and hearty food in generous portions.

King's Cross - Gtr London - ✉ WC1

Konstam at the Prince Albert
2 Acton St ✉ WC1X 9NA ⊖ King's Cross St Pancras – ✆ (020) 7833 5040 – princealbert@konstam.co.uk – Fax (020) 7833 5045 – closed 25 December-3 January, Saturday lunch, Sunday and Bank Holidays 18 TZC **a**
Rest – Carte £ 23/32
◆ Avert your gaze from the hugely wondrous light display to enjoy interesting dishes sourced totally from within boundaries of London Transport network! Chef has own allotment.

KENSINGTON and CHELSEA (Royal Borough of) – Gtr London

Chelsea - Gtr London - ✉ SW1/SW3/SW7/SW10

Jumeirah Carlton Tower
rm,
Cadogan Pl ✉ SW1X 9PY ⊖ Knightsbridge – ✆ (020) 7235 1234 – jctinfo@jumeirah.com – Fax (020) 7235 9129 37 AGX **n**
190 rm – †£ 293 ††£ 640, ☕ £30 – 30 suites
Rest *Rib Room* – Carte £ 51/66
◆ Imposing international hotel overlooking a leafy square. Well-equipped roof-top health club has funky views. Generously proportioned rooms boast every conceivable facility. Rib Room restaurant has a clubby atmosphere.

Wyndham Grand
Chelsea Harbour ✉ SW10 0XG ⊖ Fulham Broadway – ✆ (020) 7823 3000 – Fax (020) 7352 8174 23 PZG **j**
160 suites – ††£ 558, ☕ £22.50
Rest *Aquasia* – see restaurant listing
◆ Modern, all-suite hotel within an exclusive marina and retail development. Many of the spacious and well-appointed rooms have balconies and views across the Thames.

Sheraton Park Tower
101 Knightsbridge ✉ SW1X 7RN ⊖ Knightsbridge – ✆ (020) 7235 8050 – central.london.reservations@sheraton.com – Fax (020) 7235 8231 37 AGX **t**
275 rm – †£ 470 ††£ 470, ☕ £25 – 5 suites
Rest *One-O-One* – see restaurant listing
◆ Built in the 1970s in a unique cylindrical shape. Well-equipped bedrooms are all identical in size. Top floor executive rooms have commanding views of Hyde Park and City.

Capital
22-24 Basil St ✉ SW3 1AT ⊖ Knightsbridge – ✆ (020) 7589 5171 – reservations@capitalhotel.co.uk – Fax (020) 7225 0011 37 AFX **a**
49 rm – †£ 206/335 ††£ 394/429, ☕ £18.50
Rest *The Capital Restaurant* – see restaurant listing
◆ Discreet and privately owned town house with distinct English charm. Individually decorated rooms with plenty of thoughtful touches.

Draycott without rest
26 Cadogan Gdns ✉ SW3 2RP ⊖ Sloane Square – ✆ (020) 7730 6466 – reservations@draycotthotel.com – Fax (020) 7730 0236 37 AGY **c**
31 rm – †£ 159/347 ††£ 219/347, ☕ £19.95 – 4 suites
◆ Charmingly discreet 19C house with elegant sitting room overlooking tranquil garden, for afternoon tea. Individual rooms in a country house style, named after writers or actors.

The Cadogan

75 Sloane St ✉ SW1X 9SG ⊖ Knightsbridge – ✆ (020) 7235 7141 – cadogan@thesteingroup.com – Fax (020) 7245 0994 37 AGY **b**

63 rm – †£ 300/347 ††£ 347, ☐ £20 – 2 suites

Rest *Langtry's* – (Closed Sunday dinner and Bank Holidays) Menu £ 21/35 – Carte £ 27/35

◆ An Edwardian town house, where Oscar Wilde was arrested; modernised and refurbished with a French accent. Contemporary drawing room. Stylish bedrooms; latest facilities. Discreet, stylish restaurant.

Millennium Knightsbridge

17-25 Sloane St ✉ SW1X 9NU ⊖ Knightsbridge – ✆ (020) 7235 4377 – reservations.knightsbridge@mill-cop.com – Fax (020) 7235 3705 37 AGX **r**

218 rm – †£ 176/323 ††£ 265/393, ☐ £15 – 4 suites

Rest *Mju* – Menu £ 23/27 – Carte £ 31/39

◆ Modern, corporate hotel in the heart of London's most fashionable shopping district. Executive bedrooms are well-appointed and equipped with the latest technology.

Franklin without rest

22-28 Egerton Gdns ✉ SW3 2DB ⊖ South Kensington – ✆ (020) 7584 5533 – bookings@franklinhotel.co.uk – Fax (020) 7584 5449 37 AEY **e**

46 rm – †£ 176/347 ††£ 347/464, ☐ £18.50

◆ Attractive Victorian town house in an exclusive residential area. Charming drawing room overlooks a tranquil communal garden. Well-furnished rooms in a country house style.

Knightsbridge

10 Beaufort Gdns ✉ SW3 1PT ⊖ Knightsbridge – ✆ (020) 7584 6300 – knightsbridge@firmdale.com – Fax (020) 7584 6355 37 AFX **s**

44 rm – †£ 188/229 ††£ 280/329, ☐ £16.50

Rest – (room service only)

◆ Attractively furnished town house with a very stylish, discreet feel. Every bedroom is immaculately appointed and has an individuality of its own; fine detailing throughout.

San Domenico House

29-31 Draycott Pl ✉ SW3 2SH ⊖ Sloane Square – ✆ (020) 7581 5757 – info@sandomenicohouse.com – Fax (020) 7584 1348 37 AFY **c**

15 rm – †£ 247/270 ††£ 276/300, ☐ £22.35

Rest – (room service only)

◆ Intimate and discreet Victorian town house with an attractive rooftop terrace. Individually styled and generally spacious rooms with antique furniture and rich fabrics.

Parkes without rest

41 Beaufort Gdns ✉ SW3 1PW ⊖ Knightsbridge – ✆ (020) 7581 9944 – info@parkeshotel.com – Fax (020) 7581 1999 37 AFX **x**

19 rm – †£ 159/349 ††£ 309/349, ☐ £27.50 – 14 suites

◆ Behind the portico entrance one finds a well-kept private hotel. The generally spacious and high ceilinged rooms are pleasantly decorated. Friendly and personally run.

The London Outpost of Bovey Castle without rest

69 Cadogan Gdns ✉ SW3 2RB ⊖ Sloane Square – ✆ (020) 7589 7333 – info@londonoutpost.co.uk – Fax (020) 7581 4958 – closed 23-27 December 37 AGY **r**

11 rm – †£ 235 ††£ 273/387, ☐ £16.95

◆ Classic town house in a most fashionable area. Relaxed and comfy lounges full of English charm. Bedrooms, named after local artists and writers, full of thoughtful touches.

Egerton House

17-19 Egerton Terrace ✉ SW3 2BX ⊖ South Kensington – ✆ (020) 7589 2412 – bookeg@rchmail.com – Fax (020) 7584 6540 37 AFY **e**

29 rm – †£ 276 ††£ 347/582, ☕ £24.50 – **Rest** – (room service only)

◆ Stylish redbrick Victorian town house close to the exclusive shops. Relaxed drawing room. Antique furnished and individually decorated rooms.

Beaufort without rest

33 Beaufort Gdns ✉ SW3 1PP ⊖ Knightsbridge – ✆ (020) 7584 5252 – reservations@thebeaufort.co.uk – Fax (020) 7589 2834 37 AFX **n**

29 rm – †£ 153/241 ††£ 235/317, ☕ £10.50

◆ World's largest collection of English floral watercolours adorn this 19C town house. Modern and co-ordinated rooms. Tariff includes all drinks and continental breakfast.

Myhotel Chelsea

35 Ixworth Pl ✉ SW3 3QX ⊖ South Kensington – ✆ (020) 7225 7500 – mychelsea@myhotels.com – Fax (020) 7225 7555 37 AFY **z**

44 rm – †£ 240 ††£ 276, ☕ £18 – 1 suite – **Rest** – Menu £ 15 (lunch) – Carte £ 27/35

◆ Restored Victorian property in a fairly quiet and smart side street. Conservatory breakfast room. Modern and well-equipped rooms are ideal for the corporate traveller. Smart dining room for modern menus.

Sydney House

9-11 Sydney St ✉ SW3 6PU ⊖ South Kensington – ✆ (020) 7376 7711 – info@sydneyhousechelsea.com – Fax (020) 7376 4233 – closed 24-28 December 36 ADY **s**

21 rm – †£ 125/175 ††£ 145/250, ☕ £9.95 – **Rest** – Carte £ 20/28 **s**

◆ Two usefully located Victorian town houses. Basement breakfast room; small lounge near entrance. Compact contemporary style bedrooms; one on top floor with own roof terrace.

The Sloane Square H.

Sloane Sq ✉ SW1W 8EG ⊖ Sloane Square – ✆ (020) 7896 9988 – reservations@sloanesquarehotel.co.uk – Fax (020) 7751 4211 37 AGY **k**

102 rm – †£ 160/230 ††£ 198/230, ☕ £9.50

Rest Chelsea Brasserie – see restaurant listing

◆ Redbrick hotel opened in 2007, boasts bright, contemporary décor. Sumptuous beds with crisp white linen, window seats and all mod cons.

The Levin

28 Basil St ✉ SW3 1AS – ✆ (020) 7589 6286 – reservations@thelevinhotel.co.uk – Fax (020) 7823 7826

12 rm ☕ – †£ 229/311 ††£ 229/511

Rest *Le Metro* – (Closed Sunday) Carte £ 20/26

◆ Impressive façade, contemporary interior and comfortable bedrooms in subtle art deco style, boasting marvellous champagne mini bars. Superb junior suite on top floor. Informal brasserie offers classic bistro fare; includes blackboard menu and pies of the week.

Gordon Ramsay

✿✿✿

68-69 Royal Hospital Rd ✉ SW3 4HP ⊖ Sloane Square – ✆ (020) 7352 4441 – Fax (020) 7352 3334 – Closed 1 week Christmas, Saturday and Sunday 37 AFZ **c**

Rest – (booking essential) Menu £ 40/85

Spec. Pan-fried Scottish scallops with millefeuille of potato, parmesan velouté. Roast Bresse pigeon with grilled polenta, baby golden beetroot and date sauce. Bitter chocolate cylinder with coffee granité and ginger mousse.

◆ Discreetly located, with meticulous service; ist best tables by the windows. Luxury ingredients employed in perfectly balanced classical dishes. Book 2 months in advance.

XXXX **La Noisette**

✿ *164 Sloane St ✉ SW1X 9QB ⊖ Knightsbridge – ✆ (020) 7750 5000 – lanoisette@gordonramsay.com – Fax (020) 7750 5001 – closed Saturday lunch and Sunday* 37 AGX **d**

Rest – Menu £ 21/55

Spec. Seared foie gras with coffee syrup and amaretto foam. Spit-roasted chicken from Bresse for two. White peach soufflé, verbena sorbet and palmito.

◆ From the Ramsay portfolio, with Art Deco and hazelnut meeting at the top of the stairs. Confident service of highly accomplished original/classical dishes with bold flavours.

XXX **The Capital Restaurant** – at Capital H.

✿✿ *22-24 Basil St ✉ SW3 1AT ⊖ Knightsbridge – ✆ (020) 7589 5171 – caprest@capitalhotel.co.uk – Fax (020) 7225 0011* 37 AFX **a**

Rest – (booking essential) Menu £ 30/55

Spec. Assiette 'Landaise.' Saddle of rabbit with seared calamari and tomato risotto. Iced coffee parfait with chocolate fondant.

◆ Hotel restaurant imbued with an understated elegance. Confident, precise cooking; classical dishes come with impishly ingenious touches. Enthusiastic and knowledgeable staff.

XXX **Bibendum**

Michelin House, 81 Fulham Rd ✉ SW3 6RD ⊖ South Kensington – ✆ (020) 7581 5817 – reservations@bibendum.co.uk – Fax (020) 7823 7925 – Closed 25-26 December and 1 January 37 AEY **s**

Rest – Menu £ 29 (lunch) – Carte £ 37/60

◆ A fine example of Art Nouveau architecture; a London landmark. 1st floor restaurant with striking stained glass 'Michelin Man'. Attentive service of modern British cooking.

XXX **Tom Aikens**

✿ *43 Elystan St ✉ SW3 3NT ⊖ South Kensington – ✆ (020) 7584 2003 – info@tomaikens.co.uk – Fax (020) 7584 2001 – closed two weeks August, 10 days Christmas-New Year, Saturday, Sunday and Bank Holidays* 37 AFY **n**

Rest – Menu £ 29/65

Spec. Hen's egg with truffled scambled egg, foie gras mousse and cured duck breast. Roast pork cutlet with apple purée, baby squid and pork lasagna. Apple toasted in honey with saffron ice cream.

◆ Smart restaurant; minimalist style decor with chic tableware. Highly original menu of individual and inventive dishes; smooth service. Book one month in advance.

XXX **Aubergine** (Billy Drabble)

✿ *11 Park Walk ✉ SW10 0AJ ⊖ South Kensington – ✆ (020) 7352 3449 – info@auberginerestaurant.co.uk – Fax (020) 7351 1770 – closed 2 weeks Christmas, Easter, Saturday lunch, Sunday and Bank Holidays* 36 ACZ **r**

Rest – (booking essential) Menu £ 34 (lunch)/64

Spec. Seared scallops with smoked salmon, potatoes and peas. Best end of lamb with braised sweetbreads, tomato and basil. Poached peach jelly and crumble, lemon verbena sorbet.

◆ Longstanding restaurant in heart of Chelsea, serving classic French cooking which shows off the kitchen's considerable skill. Elegant, intimate feel; immaculately laid tables.

XXX **One-O-One** – at Sheraton Park Tower H.

William St ✉ SW1X 7RN ⊖ Knightsbridge – ✆ (020) 7290 7101 – Fax (020) 7235 6196 37 AGX **t**

Rest – Seafood Menu £ 19/30 (lunch) – Carte £ 35/55

◆ Spacious, refurbished ground floor restaurant. Brittany-born chef focuses primarily on seafood; served in 'petits plats' for a lighter and more flexible eating experience.

XXX **Aquasia** – at Wyndham Grand H.
Chelsea Harbour ✉ SW10 0XG ⊖ Fulham Broadway – ✆ (020) 7300 8443 23 PZG **j**
Rest – Carte £ 26/45
◆ Modern restaurant located within Wyndham Grand hotel. Views over Chelsea Harbour. Cuisine captures the essence of the Mediterranean and Asia.

XXX **Drones**
1 Pont St ✉ SW1X 9EJ ⊖ Knightsbridge – ✆ (020) 7235 9555 – sales@whitestarline.org.uk – Fax (020) 7235 9566 – closed 26 December, 1 January, Saturday lunch and Sunday dinner 37 AGX **c**
Rest – Menu £ 19 (lunch) – Carte £ 32/45
◆ Smart exterior with etched plate-glass window. U-shaped interior with moody film star photos on walls. French and classically inspired tone to dishes.

XXX **Fifth Floor** – at Harvey Nichols
Knightsbridge ✉ SW1X 7RJ ⊖ Knightsbridge – ✆ (020) 7235 5250 – closed Christmas and Sunday dinner 37 AGX **s**
Rest – Menu £ 20/40 – Carte £ 28/44
◆ On Harvey Nichols' top floor; elevated style sporting a pink-hued oval shaped interior with green frosted glass. Chic surroundings with food to match and smooth service.

XXX **Toto's**
Walton House, Walton St ✉ SW3 2JH ⊖ Knightsbridge – ✆ (020) 7589 0075 – Fax (020) 7581 9668 – closed 3 days Christmas 37 AFY **x**
Rest – Italian Menu £ 25 (lunch) – Carte £ 35/45
◆ Converted mews house in tucked away location. Ornately decorated and bright restaurant with additional balcony area. Professional service of an extensive Italian menu.

XXX **Awana**
85 Sloane Ave ✉ SW3 3DX ⊖ South Kensington – ✆ (020) 7584 8880 – info@awana.co.uk – Fax (020) 7584 6188 – Closed 25-26 December and 1 January 37 AFY **b**
Rest – Malaysian Menu £ 15/40 – Carte £ 29/41
◆ Enter into stylish cocktail bar. Traditional Malay elements adorn restaurant. Satay chef cooks to order. Malaysian dishes authentically prepared and smartly presented.

XXX **Chutney Mary**
535 King's Rd ✉ SW10 0SZ ⊖ Fulham Broadway – ✆ (020) 7351 3113 – chutneymary@realindianfood.com – Fax (020) 7351 7694 22 OZG **v**
Rest – Indian (dinner only and lunch Saturday and Sunday) Carte £ 34/43
◆ Soft lighting and sepia etchings hold sway at this forever popular restaurant. Extensive menu of specialities from all corners of India. Complementary wine list.

XX **Chelsea Brasserie** – at The Sloane Square H.
7-12 Sloane Sq. ✉ SW1W 8EG ⊖ Sloane Square – ✆ (020) 7881 5999 – robert@chelsea-brasserie.co.uk – closed 25 December 37 AGY **k**
Rest – Carte £ 27/37
◆ Glass doors open into roomy brasserie-style restaurant, with smoky green lamps and brick walls inlaid with mirror tiles. A European menu includes some classic French dishes.

XX **Daphne's**
112 Draycott Ave ✉ SW3 3AE ⊖ South Kensington – ✆ (020) 7589 4257 – reservations@daphnes-restaurant.co.uk – Fax (020) 7225 2766 – closed 25-26 December 37 AFY **j**
Rest – Italian (booking essential) Menu £ 19 (lunch) – Carte £ 33/47
◆ Positively buzzes in the evening, the Chelsea set gelling smoothly and seamlessly with the welcoming Tuscan interior ambience. A modern twist updates classic Italian dishes.

XX **Rasoi** (Vineet Bhatia)

10 Lincoln St ✉ SW3 2TS ⊖ Sloane Square – ✆ (020) 7225 1881 – info@rasoirestaurant.co.uk – Fax (020) 7581 0220 – closed 25 -26 December, 1 January, Saturday lunch, Sunday and Bank Holidays 37 AFY **y**

Rest – Indian Menu £ 24 (lunch) – Carte £ 38/73

Spec. Grilled scallops with asparagus, curry leaf and spinach. Ginger and and chilli lobster with curry leaf and spiced cocoa powder. Chocolate samosa with Bailey's ice cream.

◆ L-shaped dining room and conservatory decorated with Indian trinkets; intimate upstairs rooms. Contemporary Indian cooking with subtle spicing and innovative flavour combinations.

XX **Racine**

239 Brompton Rd ✉ SW3 2EP ⊖ South Kensington – ✆ (020) 7584 4477 – Fax (020) 7584 4900 – closed 25 December 37 AEY **t**

Rest – French Menu £ 18/20 (lunch) – Carte £ 26/37

◆ Dark leather banquettes, large mirrors and wood floors create the atmosphere of a genuine Parisienne brasserie. Good value, well crafted, regional French fare.

XX **Papillon**

96 Draycott Ave ✉ SW3 3AD ⊖ South Kensington – ✆ (020) 7225 2555 – info@papillonchelsea.co.uk – Fax (020) 7225 2554 – closed 24-27 December, 1-4 January 37 AFY **f**

Rest – French Menu £ 17 (lunch) – Carte £ 26/46

◆ Feels like a Parisian brasserie: large arched windows, brown décor, fleur-de-lys green banquettes and leather chairs. Classic French menus please the smart Chelsea set.

XX **Nozomi**

15 Beauchamp Pl ✉ SW3 1NQ ⊖ Knightsbridge – ✆ (020) 7838 1500 – info@nazomi.co.uk – Fax (020) 7838 1001 37 AFX **d**

Rest – Japanese Carte £ 50/65

◆ DJ mixes lounge music at the front bar; up the stairs in the restaurant the feeling is minimal with soft lighting. Innovative Japanese menus provide an interesting choice.

XX **Bluebird**

350 King's Rd ✉ SW3 5UU ⊖ Sloane Square – ✆ (020) 7559 1000 – enquiries@bluebird-store.co.uk – Fax (020) 7559 1115 23 PZG **n**

Rest – Carte £ 29/44

◆ A foodstore, café and homeware shop also feature at this impressive skylit restaurant. Much of the modern British food is cooked in wood-fired ovens. Lively atmosphere.

XX **Poissonnerie de l'Avenue**

82 Sloane Ave ✉ SW3 3DZ ⊖ South Kensington – ✆ (020) 7589 2457 – info@poissonnerie.co.uk – Fax (020) 7581 3360 – closed 24-26 December and Sunday 37 AFY **u**

Rest – French Menu £ 24 (lunch) – Carte £ 27/40

◆ Long-established and under the same ownership since 1965. Spacious and traditional French restaurant offering an extensive seafood menu. An institution favoured by locals.

XX **Le Cercle**

1 Wilbraham Pl ✉ SW1X 9AE ⊖ Sloane Square – ✆ (020) 7901 9999 – info@lecercle.co.uk – Fax (020) 7901 9111 – closed 24 December-5 January, Sunday and Monday 37 AGY **e**

Rest – French Menu £ 15 (lunch) – Carte £ 20/32

◆ Discreetly signed basement restaurant down residential side street. High, spacious room with chocolate banquettes. Tapas style French menus; accomplished cooking.

XX **Le Colombier**

145 Dovehouse St ✉ SW3 6LB ⊖ South Kensington – ✆ (020) 7351 1155 – lecolombier1998@aol.com – Fax (020) 7351 5124 36 ADZ **e**

Rest – French Menu £ 16/19 (lunch) – Carte £ 28/39

◆ Proudly Gallic corner restaurant in an affluent residential area. Attractive enclosed terrace. Bright and cheerful surroundings and service of traditional French cooking.

XX **Painted Heron**

112 Cheyne Walk ✉ SW10 0DJ ⊖ Gloucester Road – ✆ (020) 7351 5232 – Fax (020) 7351 5313 – closed 25 December, 1 January and Saturday lunch 40 PZG **s**

Rest – Indian Carte £ 25/35

◆ Just off Cheyne Walk near the river. Contemporary in style, exemplified by oil paintings. Modern Indian dishes with eclectic ingredients drawn from around the sub-continent.

XX **Pellicano**

19-21 Elystan St ✉ SW3 3NT ⊖ South Kensington – ✆ (020) 7589 3718 – pellicano@btconnect.com – Fax (020) 7584 1789 37 AFY **d**

Rest – Italian Menu £ 19 (lunch) – Carte £ 22/36

◆ Dark blue canopy announces attractive neighbourhood restaurant. Contemporary interior with wood floors. Tasty and interesting modern Italian dishes; Sardinian specialities.

XX **Brasserie St Quentin**

243 Brompton Rd ✉ SW3 2EP ⊖ South Kensington – ✆ (020) 7589 8005 – reservations@brasseriestquentin.co.uk – Fax (020) 7584 6064 – Closed Christmas 37 AEY **a**

Rest – Menu £ 18 (lunch) – Carte £ 23/40

◆ Authentic Parisien brasserie, with rows of closely set tables, banquettes and ornate chandeliers. Attentive service and a lively atmosphere. French classics aplenty.

XX **Caraffini**

61-63 Lower Sloane St ✉ SW1W 8DH ⊖ Sloane Square – ✆ (020) 7259 0235 – info@caraffini.co.uk – Fax (020) 7259 0236 – closed 25 December, Easter, Sunday and Bank Holidays 37 AGZ **a**

Rest – Italian (booking essential) Carte £ 24/33

◆ The omnipresent and ebullient owner oversees the friendly service in this attractive neighbourhood restaurant. Authentic and robust Italian cooking; informal atmosphere.

XX **Vama**

438 King's Rd ✉ SW10 0LJ ⊖ Sloane Square – ✆ (020) 7565 8500 – admin@vama.co.uk – Fax (020) 7565 8501 – closed 25-26 December and 1 January 23 PZG **e**

Rest – Indian (dinner only and lunch Saturday-Sunday) (booking essential) Menu £ 12 (lunch) – Carte £ 25/45 **s**

◆ Adorned with traditional artefacts, a modern and bright restaurant. Keen and eager service of an elaborate and seasonally changing menu of Northwest Indian specialities.

XX **Carpaccio**

4 Sydney St ✉ SW3 6PP ⊖ South Kensington – ✆ (020) 7352 3435 – carpacciorest@aol.com – Fax (020) 7622 8304 – closed 25 December, Easter, last 2 weeks August, Sunday and Bank Holidays 36 ADY **e**

Rest – Italian Carte £ 27/33

◆ Fine Georgian exterior housing James Bond stills, 1920s silent Italian comedies, Ayrton Senna's Honda cockpit, witty waiters, and enjoyable, classical Trattoria style cooking.

XX **Eight over Eight**

392 King's Rd ✉ SW3 5UZ ⊖ Gloucester Road – ✆ (020) 7349 9934 – Fax (020) 7351 5157 – closed 25-26 December, 1 January and lunch Sunday and Bank Holidays 23 PZG **n**

Rest – South East Asian Carte £ 26/36

◆ Lively modern restaurant in converted theatre pub; bar in front and dining room at rear. Enthusiastic service. Eclectic Asian menu: strong flavours and unusual combinations.

XX **Good Earth**

233 Brompton Rd ✉ SW3 2EP ⊖ Knightsbridge – ✆ (020) 7584 3658 – goodearthgroup@aol.com – Fax (020) 7823 8769 – closed 22-31 December 37 AFY **h**

Rest – Chinese Menu £ 14/30 – Carte £ 27/32

◆ Ornately decorated, long-established and comfortable restaurant. Polite and efficient service. Extensive and traditional Chinese menu.

XX **C Garden**

119 Sydney St ✉ SW3 6NR ⊖ South Kensington – ✆ (020) 7352 2718 – closed 25-26 December, 1 January, Good Friday, Sunday dinner and Bank Holidays 37 AEZ **s**

Rest – Italian Menu £ 14 (lunch) – Carte £ 20/35

◆ A tent-like conservatory with fine sheltered terrace, a warm fawn and light chocolate makeover and simply prepared, good quality Italian dishes add up to a tasty concoction.

X **Bibendum Oyster Bar**

Michelin House, 81 Fulham Rd ✉ SW3 6RD ⊖ South Kensington – ✆ (020) 7589 1480 – reservations@bibendum.co.uk – Fax (020) 7823 7148 – Closed 25-26 December and 1 January 37 AEY **s**

Rest – Seafood (bookings not accepted) Carte £ 20/50

◆ Dine in either the busy bar, or in the light and relaxed foyer of this striking landmark. Concise menu of mainly cold dishes focusing on fresh seafood and shellfish.

X **Manicomio**

85 Duke of York Sq, King's Rd ✉ SW3 4LY ⊖ Sloane Square – ✆ (020) 7730 3366 – Fax (020) 7730 3377 – closed 25-26 December and 1 January 37 AGY **x**

Rest – Italian Carte £ 28/41

◆ Outside, a delightful terrace overlooks the trendy Square. Inside, a clean, modern, informal style prevails. Rustic Italian menus. Next door, a café and superbly stocked deli.

X **Aubaine**

260-262 Brompton Rd ✉ SW3 2AS ⊖ South Kensington – ✆ (020) 7052 0100 – info@aubaine.co.uk – Fax (020) 7052 0622 37 AEY **c**

Rest – French Carte £ 28/38

◆ 'Boulangerie, patisserie, restaurant'. Pass the bakery aromas to an all-day eatery with 'distressed' country feel. Well-judged menus range from croque monsieur to coq au vin.

X **Tom's Kitchen**

27 Cale St ⊖ South Kensington – ✆ (020) 7349 0202 – info@tomskitchen.co.uk – Fax (020) 7823 3652 – Closed 4 days Christmas 37 AFZ **b**

Rest – Carte £ 37/49

◆ A converted pub, whose white tiles and mirrors help to give it an industrial feel. Appealing and wholesome dishes come in man-sized portions. The eponymous Tom is Tom Aikens.

The Admiral Codrington

17 Mossop St ✉ SW3 2LY ⊖ South Kensington – ✆ (020) 7581 4005 – admiral-codrington@333holdingsltd.com – Fax (020) 7589 2452 – Closed 24-27 December 37 AFY **v**

Rest – Carte £ 24/31

◆ Aproned staff offer attentive, relaxed service in this busy gastropub. A retractable roof provides alfresco dining in the modern back room. Cosmopolitan menu of modern dishes.

Chelsea Ram

32 Burnaby St ✉ SW10 0PL ⊖ Gloucester Road – ✆ (020) 7351 4008 – bookings@chelsearam.co.uk 23 PZG **r**

Rest – Carte £ 18/24

◆ Wooden floors, modern artwork and books galore feature in this forever popular pub. Concise menu of modern British cooking with daily changing specials. Friendly atmosphere.

Swag and Tails

10-11 Fairholt St, Knightsbridge ✉ SW7 1EG ⊖ Knightsbridge – ✆ (020) 7584 6926 – theswag@swagandtails.com – Fax (020) 7581 9935 – Closed Christmas-New Year 37 AFX **r**

Rest – Carte £ 22/33

◆ Attractive Victorian pub close to Harrods and the fashionable Knightsbridge shops. Polite and approachable service of a blackboard menu of light snacks and seasonal dishes.

Builders Arms

13 Britten St ✉ SW3 3TY ⊖ South Kensington – ✆ (020) 7349 9040 – buildersarms@geronimo-inns.co.uk – Closed 25-26 December 37 AFZ **x**

Rest – (bookings not accepted) Carte £ 20/35

◆ Extremely busy modern 'gastropub' favoured by the locals. Eclectic menu of contemporary dishes with blackboard specials. Polite service from a young and eager team.

The Pig's Ear

35 Old Church St ✉ SW3 5BS ⊖ Sloane Square – ✆ 020 7352 2908 – thepigsear@hotmail.co.uk – Fax 020 7352 9321 – Closed 25-26 December, 31 December, 1 January 23 PZG **v**

Rest – Carte £ 25/30

◆ Corner pub that gets very busy, particularly for downstairs bar dining. Upstairs, more sedate wood panelled dining room. Both menus are rustic, robust and seasonal in nature.

The Phoenix

23 Smith St ✉ SW3 4EE ⊖ Sloane Square – ✆ 020 7730 9182 – thephoenix@geronimo-inns.co.uk – closed 25-26 December 37 AFZ **a**

Rest – Carte £ 22/28

◆ Tile-fronted pub with al fresco seating area, very popular in summer. Shabby chic décor that's been modernised but feels retro. Modern British repertoire on extensive menus.

The Cross Keys

1 Lawrence St ✉ SW3 5NB ⊖ South Kensington – ✆ (020) 7349 9111 – xkeys.nicole@hotmail.co.uk – Fax (020) 7349 9333 – Closed Bank Holidays 23 PZG **a**

Rest – Carte £ 21/30

◆ Hidden away near the Embankment, this 18C pub has period furniture and impressive carved stone fireplaces. Interesting, modern menus include blackboard of daily specials.

Lots Road Pub & Dining Room

114 Lots Rd ✉ SW10 0RJ ⊖ Fulham Broadway – ✆ (020) 7352 6645 – lotsroad@foodandfuel.co.uk – Fax (020) 7376 4975 23 PZG **b**

Rest – Carte £ 35/60

◆ Traditional corner pub with an open-plan kitchen, flowers at each table and large modern pictures on the walls. Contemporary menus change daily.

Earl's Court – Gtr London – ✉ SW5

K + K George

1-15 Templeton Pl ✉ SW5 9NB ⊖ Earl's Court – ✆ (020) 7598 8700 – hotelgeorge@kkhotels.co.uk – Fax (020) 7370 2285 35 AAY **s**

154 rm – †£ 200 ††£ 235 – **Rest** – Carte £ 20/31 **s**

◆ Five converted 19C houses overlooking large rear garden. Scandinavian style to rooms with low beds, white walls and light wood furniture. Breakfast room has the garden view. Informal dining in the bar.

Twenty Nevern Square without rest
Nevern Sq ✉ SW5 9PD ⊖ Earl's Court – ☎ (020) 7565 9555
– hotel@twentynevernsquare.co.uk – Fax (020) 7565 9444 35 AAY **u**
20 rm – †£ 89/140 ††£ 110/175, ☕ £13
◆ In an attractive Victorian garden square, an individually designed, privately owned town house. Original pieces of furniture and some rooms with their own terrace.

Mayflower without rest
26-28 Trebovir Rd ✉ SW5 9NJ ⊖ Earl's Court – ☎ (020) 7370 0991
– info@mayflower-group.co.uk – Fax (020) 7370 0994 35 ABY **n**
46 rm – †£ 69/99 ††£ 95/135, ☕ £9
◆ Conveniently placed, stylish establishment with a secluded rear breakfast terrace, juice bar and basement breakfast room. Individualistic rooms have Indian/ Asian influence.

Amsterdam without rest
7 and 9 Trebovir Rd ✉ SW5 9LS ⊖ Earl's Court – ☎ (020) 7370 2814
– reservations@amsterdam-hotel.com – Fax (020) 7244 7608 35 ABY **c**
19 rm ☕ – †£ 75/92 ††£ 90/96 – 8 suites
◆ Basement breakfast room and a small secluded garden. The brightly decorated bedrooms are light and airy. Some have smart wood floors; some boast their own balcony.

Rushmore without rest
11 Trebovir Rd ✉ SW5 9LS ⊖ Earl's Court – ☎ (020) 7370 3839
– rushmore-reservations@london.com – Fax (020) 7370 0274 35 ABY **a**
22 rm ☕ – †£ 65/79 ††£ 79/89
◆ Behind its Victorian façade lies an hotel popular with tourists. Individually decorated bedrooms in a variety of shapes and sizes. Piazza-styled conservatory breakfast room.

XX **Langan's Coq d'Or**
254-260 Old Brompton Rd ✉ SW5 9HR ⊖ Earl's Court – ☎ (020) 7259 2599
– admin@langansrestaurant.co.uk – Fax (020) 7370 7735
– closed Bank Holidays 35 ABZ **e**
Rest – Menu £ 23 – Carte approx. £ 27
◆ Classic, buzzy brasserie and excellent-value menu to match. Walls adorned with pictures of celebrities: look out for more from the enclosed pavement terrace. Smooth service.

Kensington – Gtr London – ✉ SW7/W8/W11/W14

Royal Garden
2-24 Kensington High St ✉ W8 4PT ⊖ High Street Kensington
– ☎ (020) 7937 8000 – sales@royalgardenhotel.co.uk
– Fax (020) 7361 1991 35 ABX **c**
376 rm – †£ 317/387 ††£ 387, ☕ £19.50 – 20 suites
Rest *Park Terrace* – Carte approx. £ 23 **s**
◆ A tall, modern hotel with many of its rooms enjoying enviable views over the adjacent Kensington Gardens. All the modern amenities and services, with well-drilled staff. Bright, spacious Park Terrace offers British, Asian and modern European cuisine. The Tenth reopening mid-2008.

The Milestone
1-2 Kensington Court ✉ W8 5DL ⊖ High Street Kensington
– ☎ (020) 7917 1000 – bookms@rchmail.com – Fax (020) 7917 1010 35 ABX **u**
52 rm – †£ 376 ††£ 376, ☕ £25 – 5 suites – **Rest** – (booking essential for non-residents) Menu £ 27 – Carte £ 43/56
◆ Elegant 'boutique' hotel with decorative Victorian façade and English feel. Charming oak panelled lounge and snug bar. Meticulously decorated bedrooms with period detail. Panelled dining room with charming little oratory for privacy seekers.

Baglioni

60 Hyde Park Gate ✉ SW7 5BB ⊖ High Street Kensington – ✆ (020) 7368 5700 – info@baglionihotellondon.com – Fax (020) 7368 5701 36 ACX **e**

53 rm – †£ 452 ††£ 452, ☕ £25 – 15 suites

Rest *Brunello* – Italian – ✆ (020) 7368 5711 – Menu £ 24 (lunch) – Carte £ 52/70

◆ Opposite Kensington Palace: ornate interior, trendy basement bar. Impressively high levels of service. Small gym/sauna. Superb rooms in cool shades boast striking facilities. Restaurant specialises in rustic Italian cooking.

Belvedere

Holland House, off Abbotsbury Rd ✉ W8 6LU ⊖ Holland Park – ✆ (020) 7602 1238 – info@belvedererestaurant.co.uk – Fax (020) 7610 4382 – closed 26 December, 1 January and Sunday dinner 16 MZE **u**

Rest – Menu £ 18/25 (lunch) – Carte £ 25/45

◆ Former 19C orangery in a delightful position in the middle of the Park. On two floors with a bar and balcony terrace. Huge vases of flowers. Modern take on classic dishes.

Babylon – at The Roof Gardens

99 Kensington High St (entrance on Derry St) ✉ W8 5SA ⊖ High Street Kensington – ✆ (020) 7368 3993 – babylon@roofgardens.virgin.co.uk – Fax (020) 7368 3995 – closed Christmas and Sunday dinner 35 ABX **n**

Rest – Menu £ 18 – Carte £ 33/54

◆ Situated on the roof of this pleasant London building affording attractive views of the London skyline. Stylish modern décor in keeping with the contemporary, British cooking.

Ribbands

147-149 Notting Hill Gate ✉ W11 3LF ⊖ Notting Hill Gate – ✆ (020) 7034 0301 – eat@ribbandsrestaurant.com – Fax (020) 7229 4259 – closed Sunday, Monday and Bank Holidays 27 AAV **a**

Rest – Menu £ 25/48 – Carte £ 39/56

◆ Coffee shop/bar at the front; step down to the serious eating areas. Range of menus to wade through. Dishes are elaborately detailed, buttressed by first-rate ingredients.

Clarke's

124 Kensington Church St ✉ W8 4BH ⊖ Notting Hill Gate – ✆ (020) 7221 9225 – restaurant@sallyclarke.com – Fax (020) 7229 4564 – closed 23 December-8 January, 1 week August, Sunday, Monday dinner and Bank Holidays 27 ABV **c**

Rest – Menu £ 43 (dinner) – Carte lunch approx. £ 29

◆ Forever popular restaurant, now serving a choice of dishes boasting trademark fresh, seasonal ingredients and famed lightness of touch. Loyal following for over 20 years.

Zaika

1 Kensington High St ✉ W8 5NP ⊖ High Street Kensington – ✆ (020) 7795 6533 – info@zaika-restaurant.co.uk – Fax (020) 7937 8854 – closed 25- December and Sunday lunch 35 ABX **r**

Rest – Indian Menu £ 20 – Carte £ 20/33

◆ A converted bank, sympathetically restored, with original features and Indian artefacts. Well organised service of modern Indian dishes.

Whits

21 Abingdon Rd ✉ W8 6AH ⊖ High Street Kensington – ✆ (020) 7938 1122 – eva@whits.co.uk – Fax (020) 7937 6121 – closed last 2 weeks August, 24-31 December, Sunday dinner and Monday 35 AAX **d**

Rest – (dinner only and Sunday lunch) Menu £ 19/24 (lunch) – Carte £ 28/37

◆ Buzzy destination: bar runs length of lower level. Most diners migrate upstairs with its modish art work, intimate tables and modern dishes: do check out the souffles!

XX **Launceston Place** A/C VISA AE

1a Launceston Pl ✉ W8 5RL ⊖ Gloucester Road – ✆ (020) 7937 6912 – lpr@egami.co.uk – Fax (020) 7938 2412 – Closed Saturday lunch and Bank Holidays 35 ACX **a**

Rest – Menu £ 15/19 – Carte £ 25/45

◆ Divided into a number of rooms, this corner restaurant is lent a bright feel by its large windows and gilded mirrors. Chatty service and contemporary cooking.

XX **Memories of China** A/C VISA AE

353 Kensington High St ✉ W8 6NW ⊖ High Street Kensington – ✆ (020) 7603 6951 – Fax (020) 7603 0848 – closed Easter and Christmas 35 AAY **v**

Rest – Chinese (booking essential) Carte £ 22/35

◆ Subtle lighting and brightly coloured high-back chairs add to the modern feel of this Chinese restaurant. Screens separate the tables. Plenty of choice from extensive menu.

XX **11 Abingdon Road** A/C VISA AE

11 Abingdon Rd ✉ W8 6AH ⊖ High Street Kensington – ✆ (020) 7937 0120 – eleven@abingdonroad.co.uk – Closed Bank Holidays 35 AAX **a**

Rest – Carte £ 20/30

◆ Part of a little 'eating oasis' off Ken High Street. Stylish frosted glass façade with a clean, white interior. Cooking's from the modern British stable with Euro accents.

XX **L Restaurant & Bar** A/C VISA AE

2 Abingdon Rd ✉ W8 6AF ⊖ High Street Kensington – ✆ (020) 7795 6969 – info@l-restaurant.co.uk – Fax (020) 7795 6699 – closed Monday lunch 35 AAX **x**

Rest – Spanish Menu £ 16 (lunch) – Carte £ 23/33

◆ Wonderfully airy glass-roofed dining room with tastefully designed wood work and mirrors. Authentic Iberian menus with an emphasis on tapas matched by good-value wine list.

XX **Timo** A/C VISA AE

343 Kensington High St ✉ W8 6NW ⊖ High Street Kensington – ✆ (020) 7603 3888 – timorestaurant@fsmail.net – Fax (020) 7603 8111 – Closed 25-26 December, Easter, Sunday and Bank Holidays 35 AAY **c**

Rest – Italian Menu £ 17 (lunch) – Carte dinner £ 29/44

◆ Modern, personally run restaurant with unadorned walls and comfortable seating in brown suede banquettes. Italian menus of contemporary dishes and daily changing specials.

X **Kensington Place** A/C VISA AE

201 Kensington Church St ✉ W8 7LX ⊖ Notting Hill Gate – ✆ (020) 7727 3184 – kpr@egami.co.uk – Fax (020) 7229 2025 – closed Christmas and 1 January 27 AAV **z**

Rest – (booking essential) Menu £ 19/25 – Carte £ 31/40

◆ A cosmopolitan crowd still head for this establishment that set the trend for large, bustling and informal restaurants. Professionally run with skilled modern cooking.

X **Cibo** VISA AE

3 Russell Gdns ✉ W14 8EZ ⊖ Kensington Olympia – ✆ (020) 7371 6271 – ciborestaurant@aol.com – Fax (020) 7602 1371 – closed Easter, 1 week Christmas, Saturday lunch, Sunday dinner and Bank Holidays 16 MZE **b**

Rest – Italian Carte £ 24/38

◆ Smoothly run Italian restaurant that combines style with the atmosphere of a neighbourhood favourite. Unaffected service with robust and tasty food.

X **Malabar** A/C VISA AE

27 Uxbridge St ✉ W8 7TQ ⊖ Notting Hill Gate – ✆ (020) 7727 8800 – feedback@malabar-restaurant.co.uk 27 AAV **e**

Rest – Indian (buffet lunch Sunday) Menu £ 21 – Carte £ 20/36 **s**

◆ Indian restaurant in a residential street. Three rooms with individual personalities and informal service. Extensive range of good value dishes, particularly vegetarian.

Wódka
12 St Albans Grove ✉ W8 5PN ⊖ High Street Kensington – ✆ (020) 7937 6513 – info@wodka.co.uk – Fax (020) 7937 8621 – closed lunch Saturday and Sunday 35 ABX **c**
Rest – Polish Menu £ 17 (lunch) – Carte £ 29/35
◆ Unpretentious Polish restaurant with rustic, authentic menu. Assorted blinis and flavoured vodkas a speciality. Simply decorated, with wooden tables and paper napkins.

North Kensington – ✉ W2/W11

The Portobello without rest
22 Stanley Gdns ✉ W11 2NG ⊖ Notting Hill Gate – ✆ (020) 7727 2777 – info@portobello-hotel.co.uk – Fax (020) 7792 9641 – closed 23-29 December 16 NZE **n**
23 rm – †£ 142/180 ††£ 310, ☕ £15
◆ An attractive Victorian town house in an elegant terrace. Original and theatrical décor. Circular beds, half-testers, Victorian baths: no two bedrooms are the same.

Guesthouse West
163-165 Westbourne Grove ✉ W11 2RS ⊖ Notting Hill Gate – ✆ (020) 7792 9800 – reception@guesthousewest.com – Fax (020) 7792 9797 27 AAU **x**
20 rm – †£ 183 ††£ 183 – **Rest** – Carte approx. £ 35
◆ Attractive Edwardian house in the heart of Notting Hill, close to its shops and restaurants. Contemporary bedrooms boast the latest in audio visual gadgetry. Chic Parlour Bar for all-day light dishes in a tapas style.

The Ledbury
127 Ledbury Rd ✉ W11 2AQ ⊖ Notting Hill Gate – ✆ (020) 7792 9090 – info@theledbury.com – Fax (020) 7792 9191 27 AAT **a**
Rest – Menu £ 25/50 – Carte £ 34/47
Spec. Flame-grilled mackerel with a mackerel tartare, avocado and shiso. Suckling pig with spring onions, mangosteen, salsify and ham beignet. Date and vanilla tart with cardamom and orange ice cream.
◆ Former pub with elegant, minimalist décor. Seasonal menu with innovative edge; flavours are pronounced and well judged; ingredients are superbly sourced.

Notting Hill Brasserie
92 Kensington Park Rd ✉ W11 2PN ⊖ Notting Hill Gate – ✆ (020) 7229 4481 – enquiries@nottinghillbrasserie.com – Fax (020) 7221 1246 – closed Sunday dinner 27 AAU **a**
Rest – Menu £ 23/30 – Carte £ 35/45
◆ Modern, comfortable restaurant with quiet, formal atmosphere set over four small rooms. Authentic African artwork on walls. Contemporary dishes with European influence.

Edera
148 Holland Park Ave ✉ W11 4UE ⊖ Holland Park – ✆ (020) 7221 6090 – Fax (020) 7313 9700 – Closed Bank Holidays 16 MZE **n**
Rest – Italian Carte £ 32/49
◆ Split level restaurant with outdoor tables. Modern Italian cooking with some unusual ingredients and combinations. Sardinian specialities include Bottarga and homemade pastas.

E&O
14 Blenheim Crescent ✉ W11 1NN ⊖ Ladbroke Grove – ✆ (020) 7229 5454 – eando@rickerrestaurants.com – Fax (020) 7229 5522 – closed 24-26 and 31 December, Sunday and Bank Holidays 16 MZD **a**
Rest – South East Asian Carte £ 24/38
◆ Mean, dark and moody: never mind the exterior, we're talking about the A-list diners. Minimalist chic meets high sound levels. Menus scour Far East: cutlery/chopstick choice.

Notting Grill

123A Clarendon Rd ✉ W11 4JG ⊖ Holland Park – ☎ (020) 7229 1500 – nottinggrill@aol.com – Fax (020) 7229 8889 – closed 24 December-3 January and Monday lunch 16 MZE **z**

Rest – Beef specialities Menu £ 19 (dinner) – Carte approx. £ 30

◆ Converted pub that retains a rustic feel, with bare brick walls and wooden tables. Specialises in well sourced, quality meats.

Bumpkin

209 Westbourne Park Rd ✉ W11 1EA – ☎ (020) 7243 9818 27 AAT **b**

Rest – (dinner only Tuesday-Saturday) Carte £ 25/40

Rest *Brasserie* – (closed Monday lunch) Carte £ 24/39

◆ Converted pea-green pub with casual, clubby feel and wholesome philosophy of cooking seasonal, carefully-sourced and organic food. Whisky tasting and private dining on top floors. First floor restaurant offers modern Mediterranean menu.

The Fat Badger

310 Portobello Road ✉ W10 5TA ⊖ Ladbroke Grove – ☎ (020) 8969 4500 – info@thefatbadger.com – Fax (020) 8969 6714 – Closed 25-26 December 16 MZD **b**

Rest – Carte £ 20/28

◆ Large rustic pub with old sofas, chandeliers, upstairs dining room and some intriguing wallpaper. Seasonal and earthy British food, with whole beasts delivered to the kitchen.

South Kensington – Gtr London – ✉ SW5/SW7

The Pelham

15 Cromwell Pl ✉ SW7 2LA ⊖ South Kensington – ☎ (020) 7589 8288 – pelham@firmdale.com – Fax (020) 7584 8444 36 ADY **z**

50 rm – †£ 200/223 ††£ 305, ☕ £21 – 2 suites

Rest *Kemps* – Menu £ 18 – Carte £ 25/33

◆ Attractive Victorian town house with a discreet and comfortable feel. Wood panelled drawing room and individually decorated bedrooms with marble bathrooms. Detailed service. Warm basement dining room.

Blakes

rest,

33 Roland Gdns ✉ SW7 3PF ⊖ Gloucester Road – ☎ (020) 7370 6701 – blakes@blakeshotels.com – Fax (020) 7373 0442 36 ACZ **n**

40 rm – †£ 205/315 ††£ 440, ☕ £25 – 12 suites – **Rest** – Carte approx. £ 80

◆ Behind the Victorian façade lies one of London's first 'boutique' hotels. Dramatic, bold and eclectic décor, with oriental influences and antiques from around the globe. Fashionable restaurant with bamboo and black walls.

The Bentley Kempinski

27-33 Harrington Gdns ✉ SW7 4JX ⊖ Gloucester Road – ☎ (020) 7244 5555 – info@thebentley-hotel.com – Fax (020) 7244 5566 36 ACY **k**

52 rm – †£ 353 ††£ 470, ☕ £22.50 – 12 suites

Rest *1880* – (closed Sunday-Monday) (dinner only) Menu £ 26/32 – Carte £ 34/53

◆ A number of stucco-fronted 19C houses were joined to create this opulent, lavish hotel decorated with marble, mosaics and ornate gold leaf. Bedrooms with gorgeous silk fabrics. 1880 for formal dining and ambitious cooking.

NH Harrington Hall

5-25 Harrington Gdns ✉ SW7 4JB ⊖ Gloucester Road – ☎ (020) 7396 9696 – book.london@nh-hotels.com – Fax (020) 7396 1719 36 ACY **n**

200 rm ☕ – †£ 115/210 ††£ 127/227

Rest *Wetherby's* – Menu £ 20 – Carte £ 21/33

◆ A series of adjoined terraced houses, with an attractive period façade that belies the size. Tastefully furnished bedrooms, with an extensive array of facilities. Classically decorated dining room.

Rembrandt
11 Thurloe Pl ✉ SW7 2RS ⊖ South Kensington – ✆ (020) 7589 8100 – rembrandt@sarova.co.uk – Fax (020) 7225 3476 36 ADY **x**
194 rm – ♦£ 235 ♦♦£ 235 – **Rest** – (carvery lunch) (booking essential) Menu £ 24 – Carte £ 20/33
◆ Built originally as apartments in the 19C, now a well-equipped hotel opposite the Victoria and Albert museum. Comfortable lounge, adjacent leisure club, well appointed rooms. Spacious dining room.

Number Sixteen without rest
16 Sumner Pl ✉ SW7 3EG ⊖ South Kensington – ✆ (020) 7589 5232 – sixteen@firmdale.com – Fax (020) 7584 8615 36 ADY **d**
42 rm – ♦£ 130/217 ♦♦£ 311, £19.50
◆ Enticingly refurbished 19C town houses in smart area. Discreet entrance, comfy sitting room and charming breakfast terrace. Bedrooms in English country house style.

The Cranley without rest
10 Bina Gardens ✉ SW5 0LA ⊖ Gloucester Road – ✆ (020) 7373 0123 – info@thecranley.com – Fax (020) 7373 9497 36 ACY **c**
38 rm – ♦£ 265 ♦♦£ 295/325, £29.50 – 1 suite
◆ Delightful Regency town house combines charm and period details with modern comforts and technology. Individually styled bedrooms; some with four-posters. Room service available.

The Rockwell
181-183 Cromwell Rd ✉ SW5 0SF – ✆ (020) 7244 2000 – enquiries@therockwell.com – Fax (020) 7244 2001 35 ABY **b**
40 rm – ♦£ 120/160 ♦♦£ 180/200, £12.50 – **Rest** – Carte £ 21/32
◆ Two Victorian houses with open, modern lobby and secluded, south-facing garden terrace. Bedrooms come in bold warm colours; 'Garden rooms' come with their own patios. Small dining room offers easy menu of modern European staples.

The Gore
190 Queen's Gate ✉ SW7 5EX ⊖ Gloucester Road – ✆ (020) 7584 6601 – reservations@gorehotel.com – Fax (020) 7589 8127 36 ACX **n**
50 rm – ♦£ 330 ♦♦£ 340/520, £16.95
Rest *190 Queensgate* – (booking essential) Menu £ 16 (lunch) – Carte £ 31/51
◆ Opened its doors in 1892; has retained its individual charm. Richly decorated with antiques, rugs and over 4,000 pictures that cover every inch of wall. 190 Queensgate boasts French-inspired décor.

Aster House without rest
3 Sumner Pl ✉ SW7 3EE ⊖ South Kensington – ✆ (020) 7581 5888 – asterhouse@btinternet.com – Fax (020) 7584 4925 36 ADY **t**
13 rm – ♦£ 146 ♦♦£ 177/211
◆ End of terrace Victorian house with a pretty little rear garden and first floor conservatory. Ground floor rooms available.

XXX **Bombay Brasserie**
Courtfield Rd ✉ SW7 4QH ⊖ Gloucester Road – ✆ (020) 7370 4040 – bombay1brasserie@aol.com – Fax (020) 7835 1669 – closed 25-26 December 36 ACY **y**
Rest – Indian (buffet lunch) Menu £ 19 (weekday lunch) – Carte £ 42/52
◆ Something of a London institution: an ever busy Indian restaurant with Raj-style décor. Ask to sit in the brighter plant-filled conservatory. Popular lunchtime buffet.

XX **L'Etranger**
36 Gloucester Rd ✉ SW7 4QT ⊖ Gloucester Road – ✆ (020) 7584 1118 – etranger@etranger.co.uk – Fax (020) 7584 8886 – closed 25-26 December, 1 January, Saturday lunch 35 ACX **c**
Rest – (booking essential) Menu £ 16.50 (lunch) – Carte £ 31/82
◆ Corner restaurant with mosaic entrance floor and bay window. Modern décor. Tables extend into adjoining wine shop. French based cooking with Asian influences.

XX **Pasha** A/C VISA MC AE DC

1 Gloucester Rd ✉ SW7 4PP ⊖ Gloucester Road – ✆ (020) 7589 7969 – info@pasha-restaurant.co.uk – Fax (020) 7581 9996 – closed 25-26 December, and 1 January 36 ACX **r**

Rest – Moroccan Menu £ 15/30 – Carte £ 22/33

◆ Relax over ground floor cocktails, then descend to mosaic floored restaurant where the rose-petal strewn tables are the ideal accompaniment to tasty Moroccan home cooking.

XX **Khan's of Kensington** A/C VISA MC AE

3 Harrington Rd ✉ SW7 3ES ⊖ South Kensington – ✆ (020) 7584 4114 – info@khansofkensington.co.uk – Fax (020) 7581 2900 – closed 25 December 36 ADY **a**

Rest – Indian Menu £ 9/17 – Carte £ 16/27

◆ Bright room with wood flooring and a large mural depicting scenes from old India. Basement bar in a colonial style. Authentic Indian cooking with attentive service.

XX **Cambio de Tercio** A/C VISA MC AE

163 Old Brompton Rd ✉ SW5 0LJ ⊖ Gloucester Road – ✆ (020) 7244 8970 – alusa@btconnect.com – Fax (020) 7373 2359 – closed 2 weeks Christmas 36 ACZ **a**

Rest – Spanish Carte £ 27/39

◆ The keen young owners have created a vibrant destination offering a mix of traditional and sophisticated Spanish cooking complemented by a well-sourced regional wine list.

X **Bangkok** A/C VISA MC

9 Bute St ✉ SW7 3EY ⊖ South Kensington – ✆ (020) 7584 8529 – Closed Christmas-New Year and Sunday 36 ADY **b**

Rest – Thai Carte £ 20/33

◆ This simple Thai bistro has been a popular local haunt for many years. Guests can watch the chefs at work, preparing inexpensive dishes from the succinct menu.

KINGSTON UPON THAMES – Gtr London

18 Home Park Hampton Wick, ✆ (020) 8977 6645.

Surbiton – Surrey – ✉ Surrey

XX **The French Table** A/C VISA MC AE

85 Maple Rd ✉ KT6 4AW – ✆ (020) 8399 2365 – Fax (020) 8390 5353 – closed 25-27 December, 1-7 January, Monday, and Sunday dinner 6 CY **a**

Rest – French Menu £ 19 (lunch) – Carte £ 29/34

◆ The lively atmosphere makes this narrow room with wooden tables and modern art a popular local. Attentive and relaxed service of a concise French-Mediterranean menu.

LAMBETH – Gtr London

Brixton – Lambeth – ✉ SW2

London 3 m – Watford 24 m – Slough 27 m – Basildon 36 m

XX **Upstairs** VISA MC

89b Acre Lane ✉ SW2 5TN ⊖ Clapham North – ✆ (020) 7733 8855 – closed 24 December-7 January, 18 August-1 September, Sunday dinner and Monday except November-December 24 SZH **b**

Rest – (dinner only) Menu £ 27/35

◆ Entrance buzzer, then narrow stairs to first floor bar and second floor restaurant. Cosy, with simple, stylish décor. A mix of French and English cooking; neat and accurate.

Clapham Common – Gtr London – ✉ SW4

XX **Trinity**
4 The Polygon ✉ SW4 0JG ⊖ Clapham Common – ✆ (020) 7622 1199 – dine@trinityrestaurant.co.uk – Fax (020) 7622 1166 – Closed 25-26 December, 1 January and Monday lunch 24 RZH **a**
Rest – Menu £ 20 (lunch) – Carte dinner £ 34/45
◆ Contemporary, stylish and bright restaurant with abstract art, crisp linen tablecloths and relaxed atmosphere. Original menu offers precise, artfully presented modern cooking.

XX **Four O Nine**
entrance on Landor Rd, 409 Clapham Rd ✉ SW9 9BT ⊖ Clapham North – ✆ (020) 7737 0722 – Closed 25-27 December and 1 January 24 SZH **c**
Rest – (dinner only) Carte £ 25/32
◆ Intimate, stylish first floor restaurant with secretive entrance. Crisp, unfussy, appetisingly-presented food, with natural flavours to the fore. French/Italian influences.

X **Tsunami**
Unit 3, 5-7 Voltaire Rd ✉ SW4 6DQ ⊖ Clapham North – ✆ (020) 7978 1610 – Fax (020) 7978 1591 – closed 25-26 December and Easter 24 SZH **a**
Rest – Japanese (dinner only and Saturday-Sunday lunch) Carte approx. £ 30
◆ Trendy, mininalist-style restaurant. Interesting Japanese menu with many dishes designed for sharing and plenty of original options. Good Sushi and Sashimi selection.

Herne Hill – Gtr London – ✉ SE24

XX **3 Monkeys**
136-140 Herne Hill ✉ SE24 9QH – ✆ (020) 7738 5500 – info@3monkeysrestaurant.com – Fax (020) 7738 5505 – Closed 25 December 7 FX **r**
Rest – Indian Menu £ 8/13 **s** – Carte £ 22/29 **s**
◆ 'New wave' Indian restaurant in a converted bank. Dining room in bright white reached via a bridge over the bar and kitchen. Menu uses influences from all over India.

Kennington – Gtr London – ✉ SE11

X **Lobster Pot**
3 Kennington Lane ✉ SE11 4RG ⊖ Kennington – ✆ (020) 7582 5556 – closed Sunday, Monday and Saturday Lunch 40 AOY **e**
Rest – French Menu £ 22/40 – Carte £ 26/45
◆ A nautical theme so bold you'll need your sea legs: fishing nets, shells, aquariums, portholes, even the sound of seagulls. Classic French seafood menu is more restrained.

Southbank – Lambeth

London Marriott H. County Hall ≤ rm, AC
Westminster Bridge Rd ✉ SE1 7PB ⊖ Westminster – ✆ (020) 7928 5200 – mhrs.lonch.salesadmin@marriotthotels.com – Fax (020) 7928 5300 40 AMX **a**
195 rm – †£ 328 ††£ 363, ☐ £21.95 – 5 suites
Rest *County Hall* – Menu £ 23 – Carte £ 29/42
◆ Occupying the historic County Hall building. Many of the spacious and comfortable bedrooms enjoy river and Parliament outlook. Impressive leisure facilities. World famous views from restaurant.

XX **Skylon** ≤ River Thames and Hungerford Bridge, AC VISA AE
1 Southbank Centre, Belvedere Rd ✉ SE1 8XX ⊖ Waterloo – ✆ (020) 7654 7800 – skylon@danddlondon.com – Fax (020) 7654 7801 32 AMV **a**
Rest – Menu £ 22/30 – Carte £ 27/38
◆ 1950s style dining flagship in Royal Festival Hall. Grill with bar, river views and easy-to-eat menu. Restaurant offers more ambitious dishes, which means higher prices.

Canteen
Southbank Centre, Belvedere Rd ✉ SE1 8XX ⊖ Waterloo – ✆ (0845) 686 1122 – rth@canteen.co.uk 32 AMV **a**
Rest – British Carte £ 30/35
♦ On ground floor of Royal Festival Hall, with booths and refectory style tables plus large outdoor terrace area. Extensive menu offers classic British food at reasonable prices.

West Dulwich

The Rosendale
65 Rosendale Rd – ✆ (020) 8670 0812 – dine@therosendale.co.uk 7 FX **a**
Rest – Carte £ 26/45
♦ Huge, high-ceilinged former coaching inn with buzzy atmosphere and smart rear terrace. Local produce well-used; even the bread and butter are homemade. Outstanding wine list.

LEWISHAM – Gtr London

Blackheath – Gtr London – ✉ SE3

Chapter Two
43-45 Montpelier Vale ✉ SE3 0TJ – ✆ (020) 8333 2666 – Fax (020) 8355 8399 8 HX **c**
Rest – Menu £ 19/24 – Carte approx. £ 24
♦ Smart and contemporary interior. Decorated in primary colours, with pine flooring. Formal service of a well-priced, well judged European-influenced modern menu.

Forest Hill – Gtr London – ✉ SE23

The Dartmouth Arms
7 Dartmouth Road ✉ SE23 3HN – ✆ (020) 8488 3117 – info@thedartmoutharms.com – Fax (020) 7771 7230 – Closed 25-26 December, 1 January GX **a**
Rest – Menu £ 18 – Carte £ 21/28
♦ Across the road from the train station, offering an appealing mix of dishes, commendable in their Britishness and inventiveness, and with a healthy regard for seasonality.

LONDON HEATHROW AIRPORT – see Hillingdon, London p. 87

MERTON – Gtr London

Wimbledon – Gtr London – ✉ SW19

Cannizaro House
West Side, Wimbledon Common ✉ SW19 4UE ⊖ Wimbledon – ✆ (020) 8879 1464 – info@cannizarohouse.com – Fax (020) 8879 7338 6 DXY **x**
43 rm – †£ 155/385 ††£ 185/475 – 2 suites – **Rest** – Carte £ 31/42
♦ Part Georgian mansion in a charming spot on the Common. Appealing drawing room popular for afternoon tea. Rooms in original house are antique furnished, some with balconies. Refined restaurant overlooks splendid formal garden.

Light House
75-77 Ridgway ✉ SW19 4ST ⊖ Wimbledon – ✆ (020) 8944 6338 – info@lighthousewimbledon.com – Fax (020) 8946 4440 – closed 25-26 December, 1 January and Sunday dinner 6 DY **n**
Rest – Menu £ 17 – Carte £ 25/30
♦ Bright and modern neighbourhood restaurant with open plan kitchen. Informal service of a weekly changing and diverse menu of progressive Italian/fusion dishes.

The Fire Stables

27-29 Church Rd ✉ SW19 5DQ ⊖ Wimbledon – ✆ (020) 8946 3197 – thefirestables@youngs.co.uk – Fax (020) 8946 1101 6 DX **a**

Rest – Menu £ 16/20 – Carte £ 25/32

◆ Modern gastropub in village centre. Open-plan kitchen. Polished wood tables and banquettes. Varied modern British dishes. Expect fishcakes, duck confit salad or risotto.

NEWHAM – Gtr London

ExCel – Gtr London – ✉ E16

Crowne Plaza Docklands rm,

Royal Victoria Dock, Western Gateway ✉ E16 1AL
⊖ Royal Victoria – ✆ (0870) 990 96 92 – sales@crowneplazadocklands.co.uk – Fax (0870) 990 96 93 8 HV **a**

205 rm – †£ 129/225 ††£ 149/225 – 5 suites

Rest *Terra* – (bar lunch) Menu £ 28 – Carte £ 27/37

◆ Spacious and stylish hotel with emphasis on the business traveller. State-of-the-art meeting rooms; snazzy, compact leisure centre. Ultra-smart, well-equipped rooms. Modish dining room with funky bar.

Ramada H. & Suites - London Docklands rm,

2 Festoon Way, Royal Victoria Dock ✉ E16 1RH
⊖ Prince Regent – ✆ (0870) 111 87 79 – bdm@ramadadocklands.co.uk – Fax (0870) 111 87 89 8 HV **c**

153 rm – †£ 89/160 ††£ 89/175, £ 13.50 – 71 suites

Rest *The Waterfront* – Menu £ 18 (weekday lunch) – Carte £ 23/34 **s**

◆ Plush, purpose-built hotel five minutes from City Airport and ExCel. Two small, well-equipped meeting rooms. The bedrooms are a strong point with impressive facilities. Modern dining room with al fresco option for fine weather.

Novotel London ExCel rm,

7 Western Gateway, Royal Victoria Dock ✉ E16 1AA
⊖ Royal Victoria – ✆ (020) 7540 9700 – h3656@accor.com – Fax (020) 7540 9710 8 HV **e**

250 rm – †£ 160 ††£ 180, £ 13.50 – 7 suites

Rest *The Upper Deck* – Carte £ 26/39 **s**

◆ Capacious purpose-built hotel adjacent to ExCel Centre. Ultra modish bar and coffee area exudes minimalism. Up-to-date meeting facilities. Well-appointed, comfortable rooms. Formal dining room with menus influenced by the seasons.

RICHMOND-UPON-THAMES – Gtr London

Barnes – Gtr London – ✉ SW13

Sonny's

94 Church Rd ✉ SW13 0DQ – ✆ (020) 8748 0393 – manager@sonnys.co.uk – Fax (020) 8748 2698 – Closed Sunday dinner and Bank Holidays 21 KZH **x**

Rest – Menu £ 16/22 – Carte £ 23/32

◆ Dine in the bright, modern and informal restaurant or the equally relaxed café-bar. Attentive service of imaginative modern dishes.

Riva

169 Church Rd ✉ SW13 9HR – ✆ (020) 8748 0434 – Fax (020) 8748 0434 – closed last 2 weeks August, 24 December-4 January, Saturday lunch and Bank Holidays 21 LZH **a**

Rest – Italian Carte £ 30/42

◆ The eponymous owner manages the polite service in this unassuming restaurant. Rustic and robust cooking uses some of Italy's finest produce. Extensive all-Italian wine list.

Barnes Grill

2-3 Rocks Lane ✉ SW13 0DB – ✆ (020) 8878 4488
– closed Monday lunch 21 LZH **k**
Rest – Beef specialities (booking essential) Carte £ 22/45
◆ Popular neighbourhood addition: eye-catching wall-mounted feather displays and mounted bull's head. Steaks, hung for 35 days, typify the heartily old-fashioned British dishes.

Ma Cuisine

7 White Hart Lane ✉ SW13 0PX – ✆ (020) 8878 4092
– info@macuisinebarnes.co.uk 21 KZH **c**
Rest – French Menu £ 16 (lunch) – Carte £ 21/27
◆ Neighbourhood restaurant with long narrow room split in two. Earthy, satisfying French classics made with quality ingredients, at philanthropic prices. Warm, welcoming service.

The Brown Dog

28 Cross Street ✉ SW13 0AP – ✆ (020) 8392 2200 – Fax (020) 8392 2200
– Closed 25-26 December, 1 January 21 KZH **B**
Rest – Menu £ 13 – Carte £ 20/30
◆ Horseshoe bar, snug lounge and separate dining room; charming décor includes cast iron fireplaces, antique furniture and space age lamps. Seasonal menu; tasty, moreish food.

The Bridge

204 Castelnau Road ✉ SW13 9DW – ✆ (020) 8563 9811
– thebridgeinbarnes@btinternet.com – Closed 25 December 21 LZG **b**
Rest – Carte £ 25/40
◆ Attractively refitted Victorian pub has characterful bar with booth seating and neatly laid dining room opening onto decked terrace. All-encompassing menu with global influences.

East Sheen – Gtr London – ✉ SW14

Redmond's

170 Upper Richmond Road West ✉ SW14 8AW – ✆ (020) 8878 1922
– pippa@redmonds.org.uk – closed 3 days Christmas, Sunday and Bank Holidays 6 CX **v**
Rest – (dinner only) Menu £ 27/32
◆ Bright, spacious and relaxed restaurant. Friendly and approachable service of modern British cooking prepared with care.

La Saveur

201 Upper Richmond Road West ✉ SW14 8QT – ✆ (020) 8876 0644
– info@brula.co.uk – closed 25-26 December and 1 January 21 KZH **k**
Rest – French Menu £ 15/17 – Carte £ 20/36
◆ Art nouveau, wood panelling and mirrors help give this restaurant its bistro feel. A menu of classic French cooking, a concise wine list and salon de thé complete the picture.

The Victoria

10 West Temple Sheen ✉ SW14 7RT – ✆ (020) 8876 4238
– reservations@thevictoria.net – Fax (020) 8878 3464
– Closed 24-27 December 6 CX **u**
Rest – Carte £ 19/25
◆ Traditional pub near Richmond Park with bright modern décor. Large conservatory, terrace and children's play area. Daily menu of interesting modern and traditional dishes.

Hampton Wick – Surrey – ✉ KT1

Chase Lodge

10 Park Rd ✉ KT1 4AS – ✆ (020) 8943 1862 – info@chaselodgehotel.com – Fax (020) 8943 9363 5 BY **e**

13 rm – †£ 78/98 ††£ 125/225 – **Rest** – Menu £ 12/18

◆ Personally-run small hotel in mid-terrace Victorian property in an area of outstanding architectural and historical interest. Individually furnished, comfortable rooms. Bright, airy conservatory restaurant.

Kew – Surrey – ✉ TW9

The Glasshouse

14 Station Parade ✉ TW9 3PZ ⊖ Kew Gardens – ✆ (020) 8940 6777 – info@glasshouserestaurant.co.uk – Fax (020) 8940 3833 – closed 24-26 December and 1 January 6 CX **z**

Rest – Menu £ 24/35 **s**

Spec. Foie gras, smoked chicken and artichoke terrine with lentils. Rump of lamb with olive oil crushed potatoes and Niçoise jus. Champagne and raspberry trifle.

◆ Relaxed contemporary neighbourhood restaurant featuring two walls of glass. The comprehensive menu offers modern European dishes; cooking is honest, earthy and well-priced.

Kew Grill

10b Kew Green ✉ TW9 3BH ⊖ Kew Gardens – ✆ (020) 8948 4433 – kewgrill@aol.com – Fax (020) 8605 3532 – closed 24-26 December and Monday lunch 6 CX **u**

Rest – Beef specialities (booking essential) Menu £ 15 (lunch) – Carte £ 25/43

◆ Just off Kew Green, this long, narrow restaurant has a Mediterranean style and feel. Grilled specialities employing top-rate ingredients: the beef is hung for 35 days.

Ma Cuisine

The Old Post Office, 9 Station Approach ✉ TW9 3QB ⊖ Kew Gardens – ✆ (020) 8332 1923 6 CX **r**

Rest – French Menu £ 16 – Carte £ 18/24

◆ Formerly Kew's post office building; features tables on the pavement, arched roof and red gingham tablecloths. Good value, classic French dishes. Truly, "le petit bistrot".

Richmond – Surrey – ✉ TW9/TW10

Old Town Hall, Whittaker Ave ✆ (020) 8940 9125

Richmond Park Roehampton Gate, ✆ (020) 8876 3205 ;

Sudbrook Park, ✆ (020) 8940 1463 .

Petersham

Nightingale Lane ✉ TW10 6UZ – ✆ (020) 8940 7471 – enq@petershamhotel.co.uk – Fax (020) 8939 1098 – closed 25-27December 6 CX **c**

60 rm – †£ 110/160 ††£ 170/300 – 1 suite

Rest *Restaurant* – see restaurant listing

◆ Extended over the years, a fine example of Victorian Gothic architecture. Impressive Portland stone, self-supporting staircase. Most comfortable rooms overlook the Thames.

Richmond Gate

158 Richmond Hill ✉ TW10 6RP – ✆ (020) 8940 0061 – richmondgate@foliohotels.com – Fax (020) 8332 0354 6 CX **c**

67 rm – †£ 69/205 ††£ 99/215, £ 15 – 1 suite

Rest *Gates On The Park* – (Closed lunch Saturday and Bank Holidays) Menu £ 23 (lunch) – Carte dinner £ 23/35 **s**

◆ Originally four elegant Georgian town houses and now a very comfortable corporate hotel. Cosy lounges have a period charm. Well-appointed deluxe rooms have thoughtful extras. Comfortable restaurant has intimate feel.

XXX **The Restaurant** – at the Petersham H.
Nightingale Lane ✉ TW10 6UZ – ✆ (020) 8939 1084 – Fax (020) 8939 1002 – closed 25-26 December 6 CX **c**
Rest – Carte £ 35/48
◆ Tables by the window have spectacular views across royal parkland and the winding Thames. Formal surroundings in which to enjoy classic and modern cooking. See the cellars.

X **Matsuba**
10 Red Lion St ✉ TW9 1RW – ✆ (020) 8605 3513 – matsuba10@hotmail.com – closed 25-26 December, 1 January and Sunday 6 CX **n**
Rest – Japanese Carte approx. £ 35
◆ Family-run restaurant with slick, contemporary interior featuring a rear sushi bar and authentic, market fresh, super value Japanese menus. Gets packed in the evenings!

X **Petersham Nurseries Café**
Church Lane (off Petersham Rd) ✉ TW10 7AG – ✆ (020) 8605 3627 – info@petershamnurseries.com – Closed Monday 6 CX **x**
Rest – Italian influences (lunch only) Carte £ 27/65
◆ Uniquely set in glasshouse (or outside, if sunny), with earthy implements and romantic Indian artefacts. Flavourful cooking with Italian influences and friendly service from welly-shod staff.

Teddington – Middx – ✉ TW11

XX **The Wharf**
22 Manor Rd ✉ TW11 8BG – ✆ (020) 8977 6333 – the.wharf@walk-on-water.co.uk – Fax (020) 8977 9444 – closed 25-26 December, 1 January, Sunday dinner and Monday 5 BX **c**
Rest – Menu £ 14/16 – Carte £ 28/35
◆ Riverside restaurant with large heated terrace opposite Teddington lock. Modern menu of good value dishes; fixed price menu in the week; modern music.

X **Simply Thai**
196 Kingston Rd ✉ TW11 9JD – ✆ (020) 8943 9747 – simplythai1@yahoo.co.uk 5 BY **x**
Rest – Thai (booking essential at lunch) Menu £ 16 – Carte £ 16/21
◆ Friendly Thai restaurant with popular local following. Extensive menus offer flavourful dishes proudly made with the best ingredients; seafood a speciality. Polite service.

Twickenham – Middx – ✉ TW1

XX **A Cena**
418 Richmond Rd ✉ TW1 2EB ⊖ Richmond – ✆ (020) 8288 0108 – Fax (020) 8940 5346 – closed Sunday dinner and Monday lunch 5 BX **e**
Rest – Italian Carte £ 27/33
◆ Smart, neighbourhood style restaurant with pleasant bar boasting extensive cocktail list and dining room festooned with mirrors. Accomplished dishes from all regions of Italy.

X **Tangawizi**
406 Richmond Rd, Richmond Bridge ✉ TW1 2EB ⊖ Richmond – ✆ (020) 8891 3737 – tangawizi-richmond@hotmail.com – Fax (020) 8891 3737 – closed 25-26 December and 1 January 5 BX **e**
Rest – Indian (dinner only) Carte £ 14/28
◆ Name means Ginger in Swahili. Sleek décor in warm purple with subtle Indian touches. Well priced, nicely balanced, slowly evolving menus take their influence from North India.

Brula Bistrot
43 Crown Rd, St Margarets ✉ TW1 3EJ – ✆ (020) 8892 0602 – info@brula.co.uk – Fax (020) 8892 7727 – closed 25-26 December and 1 January 5 BX **v**
Rest – French (booking essential) Menu £ 15/17 – Carte £ 20/36
◆ Behind the stained glass windows and the rose arched entrance, you'll find an intimate and cosy bistro. Friendly and relaxed service of a weekly changing, rustic menu.

Ma Cuisine
6 Whitton Rd ✉ TW1 1BJ – ✆ (020) 8607 9849 – closed Sunday 5 BX **a**
Rest – French Menu £ 16 – Carte £ 18/24
◆ Small neighbourhood bistro style restaurant offering good value. Classic French country cooking with blackboard specials; concise wine list.

Tapas y Vino
111 London Rd ✉ TW1 1EE – ✆ (020) 8892 5417 – info@tapasyvino.co.uk – Closed Sunday 5 BX **a**
Rest – Mediterranean Menu £ 20 (dinner) – Carte £ 12/20
◆ Simply furnished in Spanish style and serving carefully judged, satisfying tapas with influences from France, Morocco and Greece; four plates per person should be sufficient.

SOUTHWARK – Gtr London

Level 2, Tate Modern ✆ (020) 7401 5266, tourisminfo@southwark.gov.uk

Bermondsey – Gtr London – ✉ SE1

London Bridge rm,
8-18 London Bridge St ✉ SE1 9SG ⊖ London Bridge – ✆ (020) 7855 2200 – sales@londonbridgehotel.com – Fax (020) 7855 2233 33 AQV **a**
135 rm – †£ 219 ††£ 219, ☕ £ 14.95 – 3 suites
Rest *Georgetown* – (dinner only) Carte £ 26/34
◆ In one of the oldest parts of London, independently owned with an ornate façade dating from 1915. Modern interior with classically decorated bedrooms and an impressive gym. Restaurant echoing the colonial style serving Malaysian dishes.

Le Pont de la Tour
36d Shad Thames, Butlers Wharf ✉ SE1 2YE ⊖ London Bridge – ✆ (020) 7403 8403 – lepontdelatourr@danddlondon.com – Fax (020) 7940 1835 34 ASV **c**
Rest – Menu £ 25 (lunch) – Carte £ 33/57
◆ Elegant and stylish room commanding spectacular views of the Thames and Tower Bridge. Formal and detailed service. Modern menu with an informal bar attached.

Bengal Clipper
Cardamom Building, Shad Thames, Butlers Wharf ✉ SE1 2YR ⊖ London Bridge – ✆ (020) 7357 9001 – mail@bengalclipper.co.uk – Fax (020) 7357 9002 34 ASV **e**
Rest – Indian Carte £ 13/27
◆ Housed in a Thames-side converted warehouse, a smart Indian restaurant with original brickwork and steel supports. Menu features Bengali and Goan dishes. Evening pianist.

Blueprint Café Tower Bridge,
Design Museum, Shad Thames, Butlers Wharf ✉ SE1 2YD ⊖ London Bridge – ✆ (020) 7378 7031 – blueprintcafe@danddlondon.com – Fax (020) 7357 8810 – Closed 25-26 December and Sunday dinner 34 ASV **u**
Rest – Carte £ 26/35
◆ Above the Design Museum, with impressive views of the river and bridge: handy binoculars on tables. Eager and energetic service, modern British menus: robust and rustic.

X **Magdalen** [AC] VISA [MC] [AE]

152 Tooley St ✉ SE1 2TU ⊖ London Bridge – ✆ (020) 7403 1342 – info@magdalenrestaurant.co.uk – Fax (020) 7403 9950 – closed 17-31 August, 24-31 December, Saturday lunch, Sunday and Bank Holidays 34 ARV **b**

Rest – British Carte £ 25/44

◆ Appealing bistro style restaurant set over two floors, with aubergine-coloured walls and chandeliers. Seasonal menus offer precise, well-executed and simply presented cooking.

X **Village East** [AC] VISA [MC] [AE]

171 Bermondsey St ✉ SE1 3UW ⊖ London Bridge – ✆ (020) 7357 6082 – info@villageeast.co.uk – Fax (020) 7403 3360 – closed 25-26 December, and 1 January 20 XZE **a**

Rest – Menu £ 15 (lunch) – Carte £ 24/34

◆ In a glass fronted block sandwiched by Georgian townhouses, this trendy restaurant has two loud, buzzy bars and dining areas serving ample portions of modern British fare.

X **Cantina Del Ponte** VISA [MC] [AE]

36c Shad Thames, Butlers Wharf ✉ SE1 2YE ⊖ London Bridge – ✆ (020) 7403 5403 – Fax (020) 7940 1845 – closed 25-26 December 34 ASV **c**

Rest – Italian Menu £ 14/15 – Carte approx. £ 25

◆ Quayside setting with a large canopied terrace. Terracotta flooring; modern rustic style décor, simple and unfussy. Tasty, refreshing Mediterranean-influenced cooking.

X **Butlers Wharf Chop House** ← Tower Bridge, VISA [MC] [AE]

36e Shad Thames, Butlers Wharf ✉ SE1 2YE ⊖ London Bridge – ✆ (020) 7403 3403 – bwchophouse@danddlondon.com – Fax (020) 7940 1855 – closed 1-3 January 34 ASV **n**

Rest – English Menu £ 26 – Carte £ 26/38

◆ Book the terrace in summer and dine in the shadow of Tower Bridge. Rustic feel to the interior, with obliging service. Menu focuses on traditional English dishes.

X **Champor-Champor** [AC] VISA [MC] [AE]

62-64 Weston St ✉ SE1 3QJ ⊖ London Bridge – ✆ (020) 7403 4600 – mail@champor-champor.com – closed Easter, Christmas and Sunday 34 ARV **a**

Rest – Asian (dinner only) (booking essential) Carte £ 28/33

◆ Brims over with colourful Asian décor and artefacts including serene Buddha and sacred cow. Two intimate dining rooms: tasty, appealing mix of Malay, Chinese and Thai cuisine.

The Hartley [AC] VISA [MC] [AE]

64 Tower Bridge Road ✉ SE1 4TR ⊖ Borough – ✆ (020) 7394 7023 – enquries@thehartley.com – Closed 25-26 December, 1 January and Sunday dinner 20 XZE **c**

Rest – Carte £ 16/28

◆ Classic 19C red brick pub, named after former Hartley jam factory opposite: jam jars even adorn the walls! Interesting menus offer five daily changing blackboard specials.

Elephant and Castle

XX **Dragon Castle** [AC] VISA [MC] [AE]

114 Walworth Rd ✉ SE17 1JL ⊖ Elephant and Castle – ✆ (020) 7277 3388 – dragoncastle@hotmail.com 25 VZF

Rest – Chinese Carte £ 15/30

◆ Large blue building with red studded door and decoratively understated interior. Generous plates of authentic Cantonese food plus popular dim sum menu. Attentive service.

Southwark – Gtr London – ✉ SE1

Southwark Rose
43-47 Southwark Bridge Rd ✉ SE1 9HH ⊖ London Bridge – ✆ (020) 7015 1480 – info@southwarkrosehotel.co.uk – Fax (020) 7015 1481 34 AQV **c**

78 rm – †£ 180 ††£ 180, ☕ £ 12.95 – 6 suites – **Rest** – (dinner only) Carte £ 16/22

◆ Purpose built budget hotel south of the City, near the Globe Theatre. Top floor dining room with bar. Uniform style, reasonably spacious bedrooms with writing desks.

Oxo Tower
< London skyline and River Thames,

(8th floor), Oxo Tower Wharf, Barge House St ✉ SE1 9PH ⊖ Southwark – ✆ (020) 7803 3888 – oxo.reservations@harveynichols.com – Fax (020) 7803 3838 – closed 24-26 December 32 ANV **a**

Rest – Menu £ 32 – Carte £ 33/53

Rest *Oxo Tower Brasserie* – see restaurant listing

◆ Top of a converted factory, providing stunning views of the Thames and beyond. Stylish, minimalist interior with huge windows. Smooth service of modern cuisine.

Roast
The Floral Hall, Borough Market ✉ SE1 1TL ⊖ London Bridge – ✆ (020) 7940 1300 – info@roast-restaurant.com – Fax (020) 7655 2079 – closed Sunday dinner 33 AQV **e**

Rest – British Carte £ 32/50

◆ Set into the roof of Borough Market's Floral Hall. Extensive cocktail list in bar; split-level restaurant has views to St. Paul's. Robust English cooking using market produce.

Baltic
74 Blackfriars Rd ✉ SE1 8HA ⊖ Southwark – ✆ (020) 7928 1111 – info@balticrestaurant.co.uk – Fax (020) 7928 8487 – closed 25 December and 1 January 33 AOV **e**

Rest – East European Menu £ 17 – Carte £ 25/30

◆ Set in a Grade II listed 18C former coach house. Enjoy authentic and hearty east European and Baltic influenced food. Interesting vodka selection and live jazz on Sundays.

Oxo Tower Brasserie
< London skyline and River Thames,

(8th floor), Oxo Tower Wharf, Barge House St ✉ SE1 9PH ⊖ Southwark – ✆ (020) 7803 3888 – oxo.reservations@harveynichols.com – Fax (020) 7803 3838 – closed 24-26 December 32 ANV **a**

Rest – Menu £ 22 (lunch) – Carte £ 26/35

◆ Same views but less formal than the restaurant. Open-plan kitchen, relaxed service, the modern menu is slightly lighter. In summer, try to secure a table on the terrace.

Cantina Vinopolis
No.1 Bank End ✉ SE1 9BU ⊖ London Bridge – ✆ (020) 7940 8333 – cantina@vinopolis.co.uk – Fax (020) 7089 9339 – closed 23 December-3 January and Sunday dinner 33 AQV **z**

Rest – Carte £ 21/33

◆ Large, solid brick vaulted room under Victorian railway arches, with an adjacent wine museum. Modern menu with a huge selection of wines by the glass.

Tate Modern (Restaurant)
< London skyline and River Thames,

7th Floor, Tate Modern, Bankside ✉ SE1 9LS ⊖ Southwark – ✆ (020) 7401 5020 – modern.restaurant@tate.org.uk – closed 25 December 33 APV **s**

Rest – (lunch only and dinner Friday-Saturday) Carte £ 23/34

◆ Modernity to match the museum, with vast murals and huge windows affording stunning views. Canteen-style menu at a sensible price with obliging service.

Tapas Brindisa VISA AE

18-20 Southwark St, Borough Market ✉ SE1 1TJ ⊖ London Bridge – ✆ (020) 7357 8880 – office@tapasbrindisa.com – closed Sunday and Bank Holidays 33 AQV **k**

Rest – Tapas (bookings not accepted) Carte £ 18/27

◆ Primary quality Spanish produce sold in owner's shops and this bustling eatery on edge of Borough Market. Freshly prepared, tasty tapas: waiters will assist with your choice.

Wright Brothers VISA AE

11 Stoney St, Borough Market ✉ SE1 9AD ⊖ London Bridge – ✆ (020) 7403 9554 – reservations@wrightbros.eu.com – Fax (020) 7403 9558 – closed 25-26 December and Sunday 33 AQV **m**

Rest – Carte £ 23/43

◆ Classic style oyster and porter house - a large number of porter ales on offer. Simple settings afford a welcoming ambience to enjoy huge range of oysters and prime shellfish.

Brew Wharf A/C VISA AE

Brew Wharf Yard, Stoney St ✉ SE1 9AD ⊖ London Bridge – ✆ (020) 7378 6601 – Fax (020) 7940 8336 – closed Christmas-New Year 33 AQV **h**

Rest – Carte £ 19/29

◆ Bustling market eatery and micro-brewery housed in three huge railway arches. The beers and concise wine list are the reasons most people come here; menus are quite simple.

The Anchor & Hope VISA

36 The Cut ✉ SE1 8LP ⊖ Southwark – ✆ (020) 7928 9898 – anchorandhope@btconnect.com – Fax (020) 7928 4595 – Closed last 2 weeks August, 25 December-1 January, Easter, Sunday dinner and Monday lunch 32 ANV **n**

Rest – (bookings not accepted) Menu £ 30 – Carte £ 20/38

◆ Close to Waterloo, the distinctive dark green exterior lures visitors in droves. Bare floorboards, simple wooden furniture. Seriously original cooking with rustic French base.

TOWER HAMLETS – Gtr London

Bow – Tower Hamlets – ✉ E3

London 7 m – Luton 53 m – Watford 44 m – Slough 33 m

The Morgan Arms A/C VISA AE

43 Morgan St ✉ E3 5AA ⊖ Bow Road – ✆ (020) 8980 6389 – themorgan@geronimo-inns.co.uk – Closed 25-26 December and 1 January 3 GU **c**

Rest – (closed Sunday dinner) (bookings not accepted) Carte £ 22/35

◆ Characterful pub with mismatch of furniture and shabby chic appeal. Constantly evolving menu offers robust cooking with some unusual ingredients to fill your Auntie Nelly.

Canary Wharf – Gtr London – ✉ E14

Four Seasons A/C VISA AE

Westferry Circus ✉ E14 8RS ⊖ Canary Wharf – ✆ (020) 7510 1999 – sales.caw@fourseasons.com – Fax (020) 7510 1998 3 GV **a**

128 rm – †£ 411/434 ††£ 411/494, ☕ £ 22.50 – 14 suites

Rest *Quadrato* – see restaurant listing

◆ Sleek and stylish with striking river and city views. Atrium lobby leading to modern bedrooms boasting every conceivable extra. Detailed service.

Quadrato – at Four Seasons H.

Westferry Circus ✉ E14 8RS ⊖ Canary Wharf – ✆ (020) 7510 1999 – Fax (020) 7510 1998 3 GV **a**

Rest – Italian Carte £ 46/54

◆ Striking, modern restaurant with terrace overlooking river. Sleek, stylish dining room with glass-fronted open-plan kitchen. Menu of northern Italian dishes; swift service.

Ubon by Nobu ≤ River Thames and city skyline,

34 Westferry Circus ✉ E14 8RR ⊖ Canary Wharf – ✆ (020) 7719 7800 – ubon@noburestaurants.com – Fax (020) 7719 7801 – Closed Saturday lunch, Sunday and Bank Holidays 7 GV **a**

Rest – Japanese (booking essential) Carte £ 38/54

◆ Light, airy, open-plan restaurant, with floor to ceiling glass and great Thames views. Informal atmosphere. Large menu with wide selection of modern Japanese dishes.

Plateau

(4th floor) Canada Place, Canada Square ✉ E14 5ER ⊖ Canary Wharf – ✆ (020) 7715 7100 – Fax (020) 7715 7110 – Closed 25-26 December, 1 January and Sunday dinner 3 GV **n**

Rest – Carte £ 30/47

◆ Impressive open plan space with dramatic glass walls and ceilings and striking 1970s design. Rotisserie meats in the Grill; globally-influenced dishes in formal restaurant.

The Gun

27 Coldharbour ✉ E14 9NS ⊖ Blackwall (DLR) – ✆ (020) 7515 5222 – info@thegundocklands.com – Closed 25 December 7 GV **x**

Rest – Carte £ 27/32

◆ Restored historic pub with a terrace facing the Dome: tasty dishes, including Billingsgate market fish, balance bold simplicity and a bit of French finesse. Efficient service.

Limehouse – Tower Hamlets – ✉ E14

London 3 m – Watford 24 m – Slough 30 m – Basildon 28 m

The Narrow

Narrow Street ✉ E14 8DP ⊖ Limehouse (DLR) – ✆ (020) 7592 7950 – thenarrow@gordonramsay.com – Fax (020) 7592 1603 3 GV **o**

Rest – British (booking essential) Carte £ 17/26

◆ Ramsay's Grade II listed former dockmaster's house on the edge of the Thames, sympathetically restyled and serving good value old school British favourites. Spacious terrace.

Mile End – Tower Hamlets – ✉ E1

L'Oasis

237 Mile End Rd ✉ E1 4AA ⊖ Stepney Green – ✆ (020) 7702 7051 – info@loasisstepney.co.uk – Fax (020) 7265 9850 – Closed 2 weeks August, 25 December-first Monday in the New Year and Monday 3 GVU **e**

Rest – Carte £ 25/38

◆ Narrow, cavernous and bright, its original features include ornamental Victorian ceiling. Concise menus offer hearty, rustic cooking with influences from all over the world.

Spitalfields – Gtr London – ✉ E1

Les Trois Garcons

1 Club Row ✉ E1 6JX ⊖ Shoreditch – ✆ (020) 7613 1924 – info@lestroisgarcons.com – Fax (020) 7613 1924 – Closed 23 December-8 January, Sunday, and Bank Holidays 20 XZD **r**

Rest – (dinner only) Menu £ 29 – Carte £ 36/51

◆ Extraordinarily eccentric, with stuffed animals, twinkling beads, assorted chandeliers and ceiling handbags. The cooking? Original and detailed, served by bow-tied staff.

XX **Bengal Trader** A/C VISA AE

44 Artillery Lane ✉ E1 7NA ⊖ Liverpool Street – ✆ (020) 7375 0072 – mail@bengalclipper.co.uk – Fax (020) 7247 1002 – Closed Sunday 34 AST **x**

Rest – Indian Carte £ 16/21

◆ Contemporary Indian paintings feature in this stylish basement room beneath a ground floor bar. Menu provides ample choice of Indian dishes.

X **St John Bread and Wine** A/C VISA AE

94-96 Commercial St ✉ E1 6LZ ⊖ Shoreditch – ✆ (020) 7251 0848 – reservations@stjohnbreadandwine.com – Fax (020) 7247 8924 – Closed Christmas-New Year and Bank Holidays 20 XZD **m**

Rest – British Carte £ 22/26

◆ Very popular neighbourhood bakery providing wide variety of home-made breads. Appealing, intimate dining section: all day menus that offer continually changing dishes.

X **Canteen** A/C VISA AE

2 Crispin Pl ✉ E1 6DW ⊖ Liverpool Street – ✆ (0845) 686 11 22 – info@canteen.co.uk – Closed 25 December 34 AST **a**

Rest – British Carte £ 17/29

◆ All-glass modernist restaurant in 'new' Spitalfields. Sit on blond wood benches at communal refectory tables and enjoy well-sourced, well-priced classic British options.

Wapping – Gtr London – ✉ E1

X **Wapping Food** P VISA AE

Wapping Wall ✉ E1W 3ST ⊖ Wapping – ✆ (020) 7680 2080 – Closed 23 December-3 January, Sunday dinner and Bank Holidays 20 YZE **n**

Rest – Carte £ 27/32

◆ Something a little unusual; a combination of restaurant and gallery in a converted hydraulic power station. Enjoy the modern menu surrounded by turbines and TV screens.

Whitechapel – Gtr London – ✉ E1

XX **Cafe Spice Namaste** A/C VISA AE

16 Prescot St ✉ E1 8AZ ⊖ Tower Hill – ✆ (020) 7488 9242 – info@cafespice.co.uk – Fax (020) 7481 0508 – Closed Christmas-New Year, Saturday lunch, Sunday and Bank Holidays 34 ASU **z**

Rest – Indian Menu £ 30 – Carte £ 24/32

◆ A riot of colour from the brightly painted walls to the flowing drapes. Sweet-natured service adds to the engaging feel. Fragrant and competitively priced Indian cooking.

WANDSWORTH – Gtr London

Battersea – Gtr London – ✉ SW8/SW11/SW18

XX **Chada** A/C VISA AE

208-210 Battersea Park Rd ✉ SW11 4ND – ✆ (020) 7622 2209 – enquiry@chadathai.com – Fax (020) 7924 2178 – Closed Sunday and Bank Holidays 23 QZH **x**

Rest – Thai (dinner only and lunch Wednesday-Friday) Carte £ 15/29

◆ Weather notwithstanding, the Thai ornaments and charming staff in traditional silk costumes transport you to Bangkok. Carefully prepared and authentic dishes.

X **Ransome's Dock** VISA AE

35-37 Parkgate Rd ✉ SW11 4NP – ✆ (020) 7223 1611 – chef@ransomesdock.co.uk – Fax (020) 7924 2614 – Closed Christmas, August Bank Holiday and Sunday dinner 23 QZG **c**

Rest – Carte £ 21/37

◆ Secreted in a warehouse development, with a dock-side terrace in summer. Vivid blue interior, crowded with pictures. Chef patron produces reliable brasserie-style cuisine.

The Butcher & Grill

39-41 Parkgate Rd ✉ SW11 4NP – ✆ (020) 7924 3999 – info@thebutcherandgrill.com – Fax (020) 7223 7977 – Closed 25-26 December, Easter, Sunday dinner and Bank Holidays 23 QZG **c**

Rest – Menu £ 15 (lunch) – Carte £ 24/35

◆ Shop at the master butcher for prime cuts; or dine at former riverside warehouse with rear terrace. Industrial interior matched by hearty, traditional, unfussy meat dishes.

The Food Room

123 Queenstown Rd ✉ SW8 3RH – ✆ (020) 7622 0555 – info@thefoodroom.com – Fax (020) 7627 5440 – Closed 1-3 January, 25-26 December, Sunday and Monday 24 RZH **c**

Rest – Mediterranean (dinner only) Menu £ 26

◆ Attractive eatery with a relaxed feel and attentive service. Concise French/Mediterranean menus with Italian and North African flavours, utilising very good quality produce.

The Greyhound at Battersea

136 Battersea High St ✉ SW11 3JR – ✆ (020) 7978 7021 – sam@sampubs.com – Fax (020) 7978 0599 – Closed 24 December-2 January 23 PZH **a**

Rest – closed Sunday dinner and Monday Menu 31 – Carte £ 16/30

◆ Attractive tile-and-glass fronted pub with superb wine list and range of beers. Leather pouffes in stylish bar. Cosy restaurant serves concise, organically inspired menus.

Putney – ✉ SW15

Enoteca Turi

28 Putney High St ✉ SW15 1SQ ⊖ Putney Bridge – ✆ (020) 8785 4449 – enoteca@tiscali.co.uk – Fax (020) 8780 5409 – Closed 25-26 December, 1 January, Sunday and lunch Bank Holidays 22 MZH **n**

Rest – Italian Menu £ 18 – Carte £ 30/36

◆ A friendly neighbourhood Italian restaurant, overseen by the owner. Rustic cooking, with daily changing specials. Good selection of wine by the glass.

L'Auberge

22 Upper Richmond Rd ✉ SW15 2RX – ✆ (020) 8874 3593 – Closed 2 weeks Summer, 2 weeks Winter, Sunday and Monday 6 DX **r**

Rest – French (dinner only) Menu £ 16 – Carte £ 23/30

◆ Locally renowned neighbourhood restaurant. Art Nouveau prints of famous Champagne houses set tone for frequently changing, authentic French dishes; personable service assured.

The Phoenix

Pentlow St ✉ SW15 1LY – ✆ (020) 8780 3131 – thephoenix@sonnys.co.uk – Fax (020) 8780 1114 – Closed Bank Holidays 21 LZH **s**

Rest – Italian influences Menu £ 15.50 (lunch) – Carte £ 19/35

◆ Light and bright interior with French windows leading out on to a spacious terrace. Unfussy and considerate service. An eclectic element to the modern Mediterranean menu.

The Spencer Arms

237 Lower Richmond Road ✉ SW15 1HJ – ✆ (020) 8788 0640 – info@thespencerarms.co.uk – Fax (020) 8780 2216 – Closed 25 December, 1 January 21 LZH **V**

Rest – Carte £ 23/29

◆ Attractive Victorian corner pub on Putney Common. Library area with books, games and leather sofas. Rustic bar/restaurant serves concise, seasonal, daily changing menus.

Tooting – Gtr London – ✉ SW17

Kastoori
188 Upper Tooting Rd ✉ SW17 7EJ ⊖ Tooting Bec – ✆ (020) 8767 7027 – Closed 25-26 December and lunch Monday and Tuesday 6 EX **v**
Rest – Indian Carte £ 13/17
◆ Specialising in Indian vegetarian cooking with a subtle East African influence. Family-run for many years, a warm and welcoming establishment with helpful service.

Wandsworth – Gtr London – ✉ SW17/SW18

Chez Bruce (Bruce Poole)
2 Bellevue Rd ✉ SW17 7EG ⊖ Tooting Bec – ✆ (020) 8672 0114 – enquiries@chezbruce.co.uk – Fax (020) 8767 6648 – Closed 24-26 December and 1 January 6 EX **e**
Rest – (booking essential) Menu £ 24/38
Spec. Cornish crab and saffron tart. Roast cod with olive oil mash, roast tomato and grilled courgette. Hot chocolate pudding with praline parfait.
◆ Simply decorated neighbourhood restaurant serving confident classical French cooking with a touch of the Mediterranean. Animated, informal atmosphere; well organised service.

Amici
35 Bellevue Rd ✉ SW17 7EF ⊖ Balham – ✆ (020) 8672 5888 – info@amiciitalian.co.uk – Fax (020) 8672 8856 6 EX **u**
Rest – Italian Carte £ 19/30
◆ Ornate Georgian exterior; inside is a restaurant with rich wood panelling and leather chairs. Valentina Harris a consultant on clean, unfussy and spot-on Italian cooking.

Ditto
55-57 East Hill ✉ SW18 2QE – ✆ (020) 8877 0110 – will@doditto.co.uk Fax (020) 8875 0110 – Closed 26-30 December 6 EX **z**
Rest – Menu £ 26 (dinner) – Carte £ 18/26
◆ Beware: it's easy to drive past this sofa-strewn, laid-back but lively bar and restaurant. A clever, flexible menu merges Spanish, Italian and French elements.with success.

WESTMINSTER (City of) – Gtr London

Bayswater and Maida Vale – Gtr London – ✉ NW6/W2/W9

Hilton London Paddington
146 Praed St ✉ W2 1EE ⊖ Paddington – ✆ (020) 7850 0500 – sales.paddington@hilton.com – Fax (020) 7850 0600 28 ADU **a**
344 rm – †£ 328 ††£ 328, ☕ £ 19.95 – 20 suites
Rest *The Brasserie* – Carte £ 27/40
◆ Early Victorian railway hotel, sympathetically restored in contemporary style with Art Deco details. Co-ordinated bedrooms with high tech facilities continue the modern style. Contemporarily styled brasserie offering a modern menu.

Hilton London Metropole
Edgware Rd ✉ W2 1JU ⊖ Edgware Road – ✆ (020) 7402 4141 – cbs-londonmet@hilton.com – Fax (020) 7724 8866 28 AET **c**
1033 rm ☕ – †£ 140/200 ††£ 140/200 – 21 suites
Rest *Nippon Tuk* – South East Asian (closed Sunday and Monday lunch) Carte £ 22/41
Rest *Fiamma* – Carte £ 17/28
◆ One of London's most popular convention venues by virtue of both its size and transport links. Well-appointed and modern rooms have state-of-the-art facilities. Vibrant Nippon Tuk. Italian favourites at Fiamma.

Royal Lancaster

Lancaster Terrace ✉ W2 2TY ⊖ Lancaster Gate – ✆ (020) 7262 6737 – sales@royallancaster.com – Fax (020) 7724 3191 28 ADU **e**

394 rm – †£ 304 ††£ 304, ☕ £19 – 22 suites

Rest Island and **Nipa** – see restaurant listing

◆ Imposing 1960s purpose-built hotel overlooking Hyde Park. Some of London's most extensive conference facilities. Well-equipped bedrooms are decorated in traditional style.

The Hempel

31-35 Craven Hill Gdns ✉ W2 3EA ⊖ Queensway – ✆ (020) 7298 9000 – hotel@the-hempel.co.uk – Fax (020) 7402 4666 – closed 25 December 28 ACU **a**

42 rm – †£ 346/370 ††£ 370, ☕ £19.75 – 5 suites

Rest *I-Thai* – (closed Sunday and Bank Holidays) Carte £ 35/41

◆ A striking example of minimalist design. Individually appointed bedrooms are understated yet very comfortable. Relaxed ambience. Modern basement restaurant.

London Marriott H. Maida Vale

Plaza Parade ✉ NW6 5RP ⊖ Kilburn Park – ✆ (020) 7543 6000 – mhrs.lonwh.reservations@marriotthotels.com – Fax (020) 7543 2100 10 NZB **c**

226 rm – †£ 99/149 ††£ 99/149, ☕ £16.95 – 11 suites

Rest *Fratelli* – Italian (closed Sunday) (dinner only) Menu £ 18 – Carte £ 21/32 **s**

◆ A capacious hotel, away from the busier city centre streets. Well equipped with both business and leisure facilities including 12m pool. Suites have small kitchens. Informal Italian restaurant and brasserie.

Colonnade Town House without rest

2 Warrington Crescent ✉ W9 1ER ⊖ Warwick Avenue – ✆ (020) 7286 1052 – rescolonnade@theetoncollection.com – Fax (020) 7286 1057 17 OZD **e**

43 rm – †£ 164/211 ††£ 188/211, ☕ £15

◆ Two Victorian townhouses with comfortable well-furnished communal rooms decorated with fresh flowers. Stylish and comfortable bedrooms with many extra touches.

New Linden without rest

58-60 Leinster Sq ✉ W2 4PS ⊖ Bayswater – ✆ (020) 7221 4321 – newlindenhotel@mayflower-group.co.uk – Fax (020) 7727 3156 27 ABU **e**

50 rm – †£ 79/89 ††£ 89/120, ☕ £9

◆ Smart four storey white stucco façade. Basement breakfast room with sunny aspect. Bedrooms are its strength: flat screen TVs and wooden floors; two split level family rooms.

Miller's without rest

111A Westbourne Grove (entrance on Hereford Rd) ✉ W2 4UW ⊖ Bayswater – ✆ (020) 7243 1024 – enquiries@millersuk.com – Fax (020) 7243 1064 27 ABU **a**

8 rm – †£ 176 ††£ 217/270

◆ Victorian house brimming with antiques and knick-knacks. Charming sitting room provides the setting for a relaxed breakfast. Individual, theatrical rooms named after poets.

Jamuna

38A Southwick St ✉ W2 1JQ ⊖ Edgware Road – ✆ (020) 7723 5056 – info@jamuna.co.uk – Fax (020) 7706 1870 – Closed 25 December-1 January and lunch Saturday to Sunday 28 ADT **x**

Rest – Indian Menu £ 20 (lunch) – Carte £ 35/63

◆ Don't be put off by the unprepossessing nature of the area: this is a modern out of the ordinary Indian restaurant with cooking that's well presented, refined and flavoursome.

XX **Island** – at Royal Lancaster H.
Lancaster Terrace ✉ W2 2TY ⊖ Lancaster Gate – ✆ (020) 7551 6070 – eat@islandrestaurant.co.uk – Fax (020) 7551 6071 28 ADU **e**
Rest – Menu £ 21 – Carte £ 24/36
◆ Modern, stylish restaurant with buzzy open kitchen. Full length windows allow good views of adjacent Hyde Park. Seasonally based, modern menus with wide range of dishes.

XX **Trenta**
30 Connaught St ✉ W2 2AF – ✆ (020) 7262 9623 – trenta@btconnect.com – Fax (020) 7262 9636 – closed 1-14 January, Sunday, and Bank Holidays 29 AFU **b**
Rest – Italian (dinner only and lunch Thursday and Friday) Carte £ 21/26
◆ Only 7 tables on ground floor and 5 more downstairs; red and cream with comfy leather seats. Uncomplicated Italian cooking on constantly changing menu, with commendable prices.

XX **Pearl Liang**
8 Sheldon Sq., Paddington Central ✉ W2 6EZ ⊖ Paddington – ✆ (020) 7289 7000 – closed 25-26 December 28 ACT **b**
Rest – Chinese Menu £ 10 (lunch) – Carte £ 20/65 **s**
◆ Large Chinese restaurant in new development. Comfy and airy with eye-catching painting on one wall. Dim sum available until 5p.m.; extensive choice of authentic specialities.

XX **Yakitoria**
25 Sheldon Sq ✉ W2 6EY ⊖ Paddington – ✆ (020) 3214 3000 – info@yakitoriu.co.uk – Fax (020) 3214 3001 – Closed 24-26 December, 1-2 January, Saturday lunch and Sunday 28 ACT **a**
Rest – Japanese Menu £ 35 – Carte £ 29/43
◆ Funky, sleek interior accessible from platform 8 at Paddington. Appealing blend of old and new Japanese menus with a distinctive American edge. Bento boxes to take away.

XX **Nipa** – at Royal Lancaster H.
Lancaster Terrace ✉ W2 2TY ⊖ Lancaster Gate – ✆ (020) 7551 6039 – Fax (020) 7724 3191 – Closed Saturday lunch, Sunday and Bank Holidays 28 ADU **e**
Rest – Thai Menu £ 27/32 – Carte £ 21/47
◆ On the 1st floor and overlooking Hyde Park. Authentic and ornately decorated restaurant offers subtly spiced Thai cuisine. Keen to please staff in traditional silk costumes.

XX **Angelus**
4 Bathurst St ✉ W2 2SD ⊖ Lancaster Gate – ✆ (020) 7402 0083 – info@angelusrestaurant.co.uk – Fax (020) 7402 5383 – Closed 25-26 and 31 December, 1 January and Monday 28 ADU **c**
Rest – French Carte £ 27/44
◆ In the style of a French brasserie, with studded leather banquettes, huge art nouveau mirror, Murano chandeliers and lounge bar. Unfussy, French dishes; clean, precise cooking.

X **Assaggi** (Nino Sassu)
39 Chepstow Pl, (above Chepstow pub) ✉ W2 4TS ⊖ Bayswater – ✆ (020) 7792 5501 – nipi@assaggi.demon.co.uk – closed 2 weeks Christmas, Sunday and Bank Holidays 27 AAU **c**
Rest – Italian (booking essential) Carte £ 36/48
Spec. Tonno alla tartara. Pan-fried calf's liver with sage and onions. Dark chocolate flourless cake, white chocolate ice cream.
◆ Tall windows and modern artwork provide the bright surroundings, while high quality ingredients are used to create appetisingly rustic dishes with more than a hint of Sardinia.

XXX Zafferano

15 Lowndes St ✉ SW1X 9EY ⊖ Knightsbridge – ✆ (020) 7235 5800 – Fax (020) 7235 1971 – closed Christmas-New Year and Bank Holiday lunches

Rest – Italian Menu £ 30/40 37 AGX **f**

Spec. Linguini with lobster. Salt Marsh lamb with garlic purée and taggiasca olives. Fig and almond tart with vanilla ice cream.

◆ Busy, three-roomed restaurant decorated in Mediterranean colours. Classic, unfussy, flavoursome Italian cooking, where the quality of the ingredients shines through.

XX Nahm – at The Halkin H.

5 Halkin St ✉ SW1X 7DJ ⊖ Hyde Park Corner – ✆ (020) 7333 1234 – res@nahm.como.bz – Fax (020) 7333 1100 – Closed Christmas, Easter, lunch Saturday-Sunday, and Bank Holidays

Rest – Thai (booking essential) Menu £ 26/55 – Carte £ 37/39 38 AHX **b**

Spec. Crispy noodles with Asian citron. Green curry of crisp sea bass with wild ginger, coconut and pea. Fresh Thai fruits.

◆ Discreet, comfortable dining room; sleek understated décor. Sophisticated cooking showcases the harmony of Thai cooking achieved through careful combinations of textures and flavours.

XX Mango Tree

46 Grosvenor Pl ✉ SW1X 7EQ ⊖ Victoria – ✆ (020) 7823 1888 – info@mangotree.org.uk – Fax (020) 7838 9275 – closed 24-26 December and 1 January

Rest – Thai Menu £ 18/40 – Carte £ 23/51 38 AHX **a**

◆ Thai staff in regional dress in contemporarily styled dining room of refined yet minimalist furnishings sums up the cuisine: authentic Thai dishes with modern presentation.

XX Noura Brasserie

16 Hobart Pl ✉ SW1W 0HH ⊖ Victoria – ✆ (020) 7235 9444 – noura@noura.co.uk – Fax (020) 7235 9244

Rest – Lebanese Menu £ 18/60 – Carte £ 24/39 38 AHX **n**

◆ Dine in either the bright bar or the comfortable, contemporary restaurant. Authentic, modern Lebanese cooking specialises in char-grilled meats and mezzes.

Hyde Park and Knightsbridge – Gtr London – ✉ SW1/SW7

Mandarin Oriental Hyde Park

66 Knightsbridge ✉ SW1X 7LA ⊖ Knightsbridge – ✆ (020) 7235 2000 – molon-info@mohg.com – Fax (020) 7235 2001

173 rm – 🚹£ 417 🚹🚹£ 476, ☕ £ 28 – 25 suites 37 AGX **x**

Rest *Foliage* – see restaurant listing

Rest *The Park* – Menu £ 33 – Carte £ 20/47

◆ Built in 1889 this classic hotel, with striking façade, remains one of London's grandest. Many of the luxurious bedrooms enjoy Park views. Immaculate and detailed service. Smart ambience in The Park.

Knightsbridge Green without rest

159 Knightsbridge ✉ SW1X 7PD ⊖ Knightsbridge – ✆ (020) 7584 6274 – reservations@thekghotel.com – Fax (020) 7225 1635 – Closed Christmas

16 rm – 🚹£ 135/206 🚹🚹£ 176/206, ☕ £ 12 – 12 suites 37 AFX **z**

◆ Privately owned hotel, boasting peaceful sitting room with writing desk. Breakfast - sausage and bacon from Harrods! - served in the generously proportioned bedrooms.

XXX **Foliage** - at Mandarin Oriental Hyde Park H.
✿ *66 Knightsbridge ✉ SW1X 7LA ⊖ Knightsbridge – ✆ (020) 7201 3723 – molon-dine@mohg – Fax (020) 7235 4552* 37 AGX **x**
Rest – Menu £ 29/60
Spec. Foie gras jelly rolls with smoked duck salad and foie gras ice cream. Lamb with girolles, haricot blanc and jus gras. Guava sorbet with raspberry tuile and exotic fruits.
◆ Sophisticated, modern cooking features experimental combinations and unexpected flavours. View of the park through the windows reflected by earthy colours and foliage motif.

XX **Zuma**
5 Raphael St ✉ SW7 1DL ⊖ Knightsbridge – ✆ (020) 7584 1010 – info@zumarestaurant.com – Fax (020) 7584 5005 – Closed 25 December and 1 January 37 AFX **m**
Rest – Japanese Carte £ 30/96
◆ Strong modern feel with exposed pipes, modern lighting and granite flooring. A theatrical atmosphere around the Sushi bar and a varied and interesting modern Japanese menu.

XX **Mr Chow**
151 Knightsbridge ✉ SW1X 7PA ⊖ Knightsbridge – ✆ (020) 7589 7347 – mrchowuk@aol.com – Fax (020) 7584 5780 – closed 24-26 December, 1 January and Easter Monday 37 AFX **e**
Rest – Chinese Menu £ 25/40 – Carte £ 38/57
◆ Cosmopolitan Chinese restaurant with branches in New York and L.A. Well established ambience. Walls covered with mirrors and modern art. House specialities worth opting for.

Mayfair – Gtr London – ✉ W1

Dorchester rm,
Park Lane ✉ W1K 1QA ⊖ Hyde Park Corner – ✆ (020) 7629 8888 – info@thedorchester.com – Fax (020) 7629 8080 30 AHV **a**
200 rm – †£ 323/664 ††£ 611/734, ☕ £ 25.50 – 49 suites
Rest *China Tang* – see restaurant listing
Rest *The Grill* – Menu £ 28 – Carte £ 40/69
◆ A sumptuously decorated, luxury hotel offering every possible facility. Impressive marbled and pillared promenade. Rooms quintessentially English in style. Faultless service.

Claridge's
Brook St ✉ W1K 4HR ⊖ Bond Street – ✆ (020) 7629 8860 – guest@claridges.co.uk – Fax (020) 7499 2210 30 AHU **c**
143 rm – †£ 563/633 ††£ 739, ☕ £ 26 – 60 suites
Rest *Gordon Ramsay at Claridge's* – see restaurant listing
◆ The epitome of English grandeur, celebrated for its Art Deco. Exceptionally well-appointed and sumptuous bedrooms, all with butler service. Magnificently restored foyer.

Four Seasons rm,
Hamilton Pl, Park Lane ✉ W1A 1AZ ⊖ Hyde Park Corner – ✆ (020) 7499 0888 – fsh.london@fourseasons.com – Fax (020) 7493 1895 30 AHV **b**
193 rm – †£ 411/446 ††£ 493, ☕ £ 27 – 26 suites
Rest *Lanes* – Menu £ 38 (lunch) **s** – Carte £ 50/65 **s**
◆ Set back from Park Lane so shielded from the traffic. Large, marbled lobby; its lounge a popular spot for light meals. Spacious rooms, some with their own conservatory. Restaurant's vivid blue and stained glass give modern yet relaxing feel.

InterContinental
1 Hamilton Place, Park Lane ✉ *W1J 7QY* ⊖ *Hyde Park Corner* – ✆ *(020) 7409 3131* – *london@ihg.com* – *Fax (020) 7493 3476*
30 AHV **k**

399 rm – †£ 282/388 ††£ 282/388, ☕ £27 – 48 suites
Rest *Theo Randall* – see restaurant listing
Rest *Cookbook Cafe* – Menu £ 25 – Carte £ 25/34

◆ International hotel relaunched in 2007 after major refit. English style bedrooms with high tech equipment and large, open plan lobby. Cookbook Café invites visiting chefs to showcase their talents.

Le Meridien Piccadilly
21 Piccadilly ✉ *W1J 0BH* ⊖ *Piccadilly Circus* – ✆ *(020) 7734 8000* – *piccadilly.sales@lemeridien.com* – *Fax (020) 7437 3574*
31 AJV **a**

249 rm – †£ 400/435 ††£ 470, ☕ £24 – 18 suites
Rest *Terrace* – Carte £ 24/49

◆ Comfortable international hotel, in a central location. Boasts one of the finest leisure clubs in London. Individually decorated bedrooms with first class facilities. Modern cuisine in comfortable surroundings.

London Hilton
London, rm,
22 Park Lane ✉ *W1K 1BE* ⊖ *Hyde Park Corner* – ✆ *(020) 7493 8000* – *reservations.parklane@hilton.com* – *Fax (020) 7208 4142*
30 AHV **e**

395 rm – †£ 269/434 ††£ 269/434, ☕ £22 – 56 suites
Rest *Galvin at Windows* – see restaurant listing
Rest *Trader Vics* – (closed lunch Saturday and Sunday) Carte £ 32/47
Rest *Park Brasserie* – Carte £ 29/40

◆ This 28 storey tower is one of the city's tallest hotels, providing impressive views from the upper floors. Club floor bedrooms are particularly comfortable. Exotic Trader Vics with bamboo and plants. A harpist adds to the relaxed feel of Park Brasserie.

Brown's
Albemarle St ✉ *W1S 4BP* ⊖ *Green Park* – ✆ *(020) 7493 6020* – *reservations.browns@roccofortecollection.com* – *Fax (020) 7493 9381*
30 AIV **d**

105 rm – †£ 415/575 ††£ 540/725, ☕ £27 – 12 suites
Rest *The Grill* – see restaurant listing

◆ After a major refit, this urbane hotel offers a swish bar featuring Terence Donovan prints, up-to-the minute rooms and, of course, a quintessentially English lounge for tea.

London Marriott H. Park Lane
140 Park Lane ✉ *W1K 7AA* ⊖ *Marble Arch* – ✆ *(020) 7493 7000* – *Fax (020) 7493 8333*
29 AGU **b**

148 rm – †£ 347/370 ††£ 347/370, ☕ £20.95 – 9 suites
Rest *140 Park Lane* – (bar lunch Saturday) Carte £ 28/34

◆ Superbly located 'boutique' style hotel at intersection of Park Lane and Oxford Street. Attractive basement health club. Spacious, well-equipped rooms with luxurious elements. Attractive restaurant overlooking Marble Arch.

Westbury
Bond St ✉ *W1S 2YF* ⊖ *Bond Street* – ✆ *(020) 7629 7755* – *sales@westburymayfair.com* – *Fax (020) 7495 1163*
30 AIU **a**

230 rm – †£ 468 ††£ 515, ☕ £20.95 – 19 suites – **Rest** – (Closed Sunday and Saturday lunch) Menu £ 30 – Carte £ 31/54

◆ Surrounded by London's most fashionable shops; the renowned Polo bar and lounge provide soothing sanctuary. Some suites have their own terrace. Bright, fresh restaurant enhanced by modern art.

The Metropolitan

Old Park Lane ✉ *W1K 1LB* ⊖ *Hyde Park Corner* – ✆ *(020) 7447 1000*
– res.lon@metropolitan.como.bz – Fax (020) 7447 1100 30 AHV **c**
147 rm – ♦£ 440 ♦♦£ 440/763, ☕ £25 – 3 suites
Rest ***Nobu*** – see restaurant listing

◆ Minimalist interior and a voguish reputation make this the favoured hotel of pop stars and celebrities. Innovative design and fashionably attired staff set it apart.

Athenaeum

116 Piccadilly ✉ *W1J 7BJ* ⊖ *Hyde Park Corner* – ✆ *(020) 7499 3464*
– info@athenaeumhotel.com – Fax (020) 7493 1860 30 AHV **g**
145 rm – ♦£ 347 ♦♦£ 452, ☕ £22 – 12 suites
Rest ***Damask*** – Menu £ 21/24

◆ Built in 1925 as a luxury apartment block. Comfortable bedrooms with video and CD players. Individually designed suites are in an adjacent Edwardian townhouse. Conservatory roofed dining room renowned for its mosaics and malt whiskies.

Chesterfield

35 Charles St ✉ *W1J 5EB* ⊖ *Green Park* – ✆ *(020) 7491 2622*
– bookch@rchmail.com – Fax (020) 7491 4793 30 AHV **f**
103 rm – ♦£ 347/382 ♦♦£ 382, ☕ £19.50 – 4 suites – **Rest** – Menu £ 20/26 – Carte £ 31/60

◆ An assuredly English feel to this Georgian house. Discreet lobby leads to a clubby bar and wood panelled library. Individually decorated bedrooms, with some antique pieces. Classically decorated restaurant.

Washington Mayfair

5-7 Curzon St ✉ *W1J 5HE* ⊖ *Green Park* – ✆ *(020) 7499 7000*
– info@washington-mayfair.co.uk – Fax (020) 7495 6172 30 AHV **d**
166 rm – ♦£ 193/376 ♦♦£ 193/376, ☕ £19.50 – 5 suites – **Rest** – Menu £ 22 – Carte £ 29/39

◆ Successfully blends a classical style with modern amenities. Relaxing lounge with traditional English furniture and bedrooms with polished, burred oak. Piano bar annex to formal dining room.

London Marriott H. Grosvenor Square

Grosvenor Sq ✉ *W1K 6JP* ⊖ *Bond Street*
– ✆ *(020) 7493 1232 – london.regional.reservations@marriott.com*
– Fax (020) 7514 1528 30 AHU **s**
224 rm – ♦£ 280/363 ♦♦£ 280/363, ☕ £24 – 12 suites – **Rest** – Carte £ 28/31

◆ A well-appointed international group hotel that benefits from an excellent location. Many of the bedrooms specifically equipped for the business traveller. Formal dining room with its own cocktail bar.

Hilton London Green Park

Half Moon St ✉ *W1J 7BN* ⊖ *Green Park* – ✆ *(020) 7629 7522*
– reservations.greenpark@hilton.com – Fax (020) 7491 8971 30 AIV **a**
162 rm – ♦£ 292/304 ♦♦£ 304, ☕ £19.95 – **Rest** – (bar lunch) Menu £ 28

◆ A row of sympathetically adjoined townhouses, dating from the 1730s. Discreet marble lobby. Bedrooms share the same décor but vary in size and shape. Monet prints decorate light, airy dining room.

Park Lane Mews

2 Stanhope Row ✉ *W1J 7BS* ⊖ *Hyde Park Corner* – ✆ *(020) 7493 7222*
– mail@parklanemewslondon.com – Fax (020) 7629 9423 30 AHV **u**
72 rm ☕ – ♦£ 150/195 ♦♦£ 195/325 – **Rest** – Carte £ 20/27

◆ Tucked away in a discreet corner of Mayfair. This modern, group hotel manages to retain a cosy and intimate feel. Well-equipped bedrooms to meet corporate needs. Meals in cosy dining room or lounge.

XXXX **Le Gavroche** (Michel Roux) A/C VISA MC AE

✿✿ *43 Upper Brook St ✉ W1K 7QR ⊖ Marble Arch – ☎ (020) 7408 0881 – bookings@le-gavroche.com – Fax (020) 7491 4387 – closed Christmas-New Year, Sunday, Saturday lunch and Bank Holidays* 29 AGU **c**

Rest – French (booking essential) Menu £ 48 – Carte £ 60/130

Spec. Hot foie gras and crispy duck pancake flavoured with cinnamon. Roast saddle of rabbit with crispy potatoes and parmesan. Bitter chocolate and praline 'indulgence'.

◆ Long-standing, renowned restaurant with a clubby, formal atmosphere. Accomplished classical French cuisine, served by smartly attired and well-drilled staff.

XXXX **Gordon Ramsay at Claridge's** A/C VISA MC AE

✿ *Brook St ✉ W1K 4HR ⊖ Bond Street – ☎ (020) 7499 0099 – reservations@gordonramsay.com – Fax (020) 7499 3099* 30 AHU **c**

Rest – (booking essential) Menu £ 30/65

Spec. Persillade of rabbit with vegetables à la grecque, grain mustard vinaigrette. Roast John Dory with sautéed langoustines with artichokes and fennel cream. Lemon meringue with mascarpone ice cream and summer berries.

◆ A thoroughly comfortable dining room with a charming and gracious atmosphere. Serves classically-inspired food executed with a high degree of finesse.

XXXX **The Square** (Philip Howard) A/C VISA MC AE

✿✿ *6-10 Bruton St ✉ W1J 6PU ⊖ Green Park – ☎ (020) 7495 7100 – info@squarerestaurant.com – Fax (020) 7495 7150 – closed 25 December, 1 January and lunch Saturday, Sunday and Bank Holidays* 30 AIU **v**

Rest – Menu £ 30/65

Spec. Sautéed langoustines with parmesan gnocchi and truffle. Herb-crusted saddle of lamb with shallot purée and rosemary. Brillat-Savarin cheesecake with gooseberry and elderflower.

◆ Smart, popular restaurant; confortable and never overformal. Cooking is thoughtful and honest, with a dextrous balance of flavours and textures. Prompt, efficient service.

XXXX **The Grill** – at Brown's H. A/C VISA MC AE

Albemarle St ✉ W1S 4BP ⊖ Green Park – ☎ (020) 7518 4004 – Fax (020) 7518 4064 30 AIV **d**

Rest – British Menu £ 30 – Carte £ 48/54

◆ Cavernous room decorated by Olga Polizzi to reflect hotel's heritage: dark wood panelling, lime green banquettes. Well executed and unashamedly traditional English cooking.

XXXX **Sketch (The Lecture Room & Library)** A/C VISA MC AE

✿ *First Floor, 9 Conduit St ✉ W1S 2XG ⊖ Oxford Street – ☎ (0870) 777 44 88 – Fax (0870) 777 44 00 – closed 25-30 December, Sunday, Monday, Saturday lunch and Bank Holidays* 30 AIU **h**

Rest – (booking essential) Menu £ 35/65 – Carte £ 70/131

Spec. Langoustines 'addressed in five ways'. Lamb from Limousin. Pierre Gagnaire's Grand dessert.

◆ A work of animated art, full of energy, vitality and colour; an experience of true sensory stimulation. Ambitious, highly elaborate and skilled cooking; try the tasting menu.

XXXX **China Tang** – at Dorchester H. A/C VISA MC AE

Park Lane ✉ W1A 2HJ ⊖ Hyde Park Corner – ☎ (020) 7629 9988 – Fax (020) 7629 9595 – closed 25 December 30 AHV **a**

Rest – Chinese Carte £ 40/120

◆ A striking mix of Art Deco, Oriental motifs, hand-painted fabrics, mirrors and marbled table tops. Carefully prepared, traditional Cantonese dishes using quality ingredients.

XXXX **Galvin at Windows** – at London Hilton H.

22 Park Lane ✉ W1K 1BE ⊖ Hyde Park Corner – ✆ (020) 7208 4021 – Closed Saturday lunch and Sunday dinner 30 AHV **e**

Rest – Menu £ 29/75 – Carte £ 60/75

◆ On the 28th floor, so the views are spectacular. Contemporary makeover includes silk curtains and opulent gold leaf effect sculpture on ceiling. Intricate, thoughtful cooking.

XXX **Scott's**

20 Mount St ✉ W1K 2HE – ✆ (020) 7495 7309 – Fax (020) 7647 6327 – Closed 25-26 December, 1 January and August Bank holiday 30 AHU **d**

Rest – Seafood Carte £ 45/67

◆ A landmark London institution reborn. Stylish yet traditional; oak panelling juxtaposed with vibrant artwork from young British artists. Top quality seafood, kept simple.

XXX **The Greenhouse**

✿ *27a Hay's Mews ✉ W1J 5NY ⊖ Hyde Park Corner – ✆ (020) 7499 3331 – reservations@greenhouserestaurant.co.uk – Fax (020) 7499 5368 – Closed 24 December-5 January, Saturday lunch, Sunday and Bank Holidays* 30 AHV **m**

Rest – Menu £ 29/60

Spec. Scottish langoustines with pea, coconut and Moroccan mint. Roast veal chop with baby carrots and rosemary honey. 'Carré Dubuffet' chocolate biscuit with paraline ice cream.

◆ Smart, elegant restaurant broken up into sections by glass screens. Innovative selection of elaborately presented dishes, underpinned with sound French culinary techniques.

XXX **Mirabelle**

✿ *56 Curzon St ✉ W1J 8PA ⊖ Green Park – ✆ (020) 7499 4636 – sales@whitestarline.org.uk – Fax (020) 7499 5449 – Closed 26 December* 30 AIV **x**

Rest – Menu £ 23 (lunch) – Carte £ 33/55

Spec. Parfait of foie gras with truffles en gelée. Caramelised wing of skate with winkles and beurre noisette. Tarte Tatin with cinnamon.

◆ Comfortable, elegant restaurant with long, stylish bar and resident pianist. Rich, indulgent French cooking, with plenty of classic dishes, perfected over time. Formal service.

XXX **Hibiscus (Claude Bosi)**

✿ *29 Maddox St ✉ W1S 2PA ⊖ Oxford Circus – ✆ (020) 7629 2999 – closed 10 days Christmas - New Year, 1 week August, Saturday, Sunday and Bank Holiday Mondays* 30 AIU **s**

Rest – Menu £ 28 (lunch)/60

Spec. Foie gras ice cream with brioche emulsion, balsamic vinegar caramel. Roast rack of Shropshire veal with goat's cheese and anchovy jus. Iced sweet olive oil parfait, date sauce, caramelised chickpeas.

◆ Purpose built, with oak wood panelling and Welsh slate walls reminiscent of its previous incarnation in Ludlow. Shropshire ingredients feature; cooking is accomplished and original.

XXX **Maze**

✿ *10-13 Grosvenor Sq ✉ W1K 6JP ⊖ Bond Street – ✆ (020) 7107 0000 – maze@gordonramsay.com – Fax (020) 7107 0001* 30 AHU **z**

Rest – Carte £ 41/55

Spec. Cornish crab mayonnaise with avocado, sweetcorn sorbet and caviar. Butter poached chicken with maple skin and smoked mussel bread sauce. Coconut panna cotta with black olive caramel.

◆ Choose between a variety of small dishes at this sleek, contemporary restaurant. Innovative, balanced and precise, cooking has a French base and the occasional Asian influence.

XXX **Theo Randall** – at InterContinental H.

1 Hamilton Place, Park Lane ✉ W1J 7QY ⊖ Hyde Park Corner – ☎ (020) 7318 8747 – closed 25-26 December, Saturday lunch, Sunday dinner and Bank Holidays 30 AHV **k**

Rest – Italian Menu £ 23 (weekday lunch) – Carte £ 34/48

◆ Swanky ground floor restaurant with intimate lighting, stylistic flourishes and chatty service. Rustic, seasonal Italian dishes focus on the best ingredients available.

XXX ✿ **Benares** (Atul Kochhar)

12a Berkeley Square House ✉ W1J 6BS ⊖ Green Park – ☎ (020) 7629 8886 – reservations@benaresrestaurant.com – Fax (020) 7499 2430 – closed 25-26 December, 1 January, and Bank Holidays 30 AIU **q**

Rest – Indian Menu £ 30 (lunch) – Carte £ 34/68

Spec. Soft shell crab with squid salad. Seared sea bass in coconut milk and curry leaf sauce. Pistachio and star anise mousse with rum raisins.

◆ Indian restaurant where pools of water scattered with petals and candles compensate for lack of natural light. Original Indian dishes; particularly good value at lunch.

XXX **Embassy**

29 Old Burlington St ✉ W1S 3AN ⊖ Green Park – ☎ (020) 7851 0956 – embassy@embassylondon.com – Fax (020) 7734 3224 – closed Sunday, Monday and Bank Holidays 30 AIU **u**

Rest – (dinner only) Menu £ 40 – Carte £ 27/58

◆ Marble floors, ornate cornicing and a long bar create a characterful, moody dining room. Tables are smartly laid and menus offer accomplished, classic dishes.

XXX ✿ **Tamarind**

20 Queen St ✉ W1J 5PR ⊖ Green Park – ☎ (020) 7629 3561 – manager@tamarindrestaurant.com – Fax (020) 7499 5034 – closed 25-26 December, 1 January and lunch Saturday and Bank Holidays 30 AHV **h**

Rest – Indian Menu £ 22/52 – Carte £ 35/59

Spec. Salad leaves with melon, plums and kumquats in pine nut dressing. Grilled chicken in creamed tomatoes, fenugreek, ginger and honey. White chocolate and cardamom mousse with a ginger semi-freddo.

◆ Gold coloured pillars add to the opulence of this basement room. Windows allow diners the chance to watch the kitchen prepare original and accomplished Indian dishes.

XXX **Bentley's (Grill)**

11-15 Swallow St ✉ W1B 4DG ⊖ Piccadilly Circus – ☎ (020) 7734 4756 – reservations@bentleys.org – closed 25-26 December 30 AJU **n**

Rest – British Carte £ 34/49

◆ Entrance into striking bar; panelled staircase to richly decorated restaurant. Carefully sourced seafood or meat dishes enhanced by clean, crisp cooking. Unruffled service.

XXX **Sartoria**

20 Savile Row ✉ W1S 3PR ⊖ Green Park – ☎ (020) 7534 7000 – sartoriareservations@danddlondon.com – Fax (020) 7534 7070 – closed 24-28 December, 1 January and Sunday 30 AIU **b**

Rest – Italian Menu £ 25 – Carte approx. £ 35

◆ In the street renowned for English tailoring, a coolly sophisticated restaurant to suit those looking for classic Italian cooking with modern touches.

XXX **Brian Turner Mayfair** – at Millennium Mayfair H.

44 Grosvenor Sq ✉ W1K 2HP ⊖ Bond Street – ☎ (020) 7596 3444 – turner.mayfair@mill-cop.com – Fax (020) 7596 3443 – Closed 25-26 December, Saturday lunch and Sunday 30 AHU **x**

Rest – British Menu £ 29 (lunch) – Carte £ 38/65

◆ Located within the Millennium Mayfair overlooking Grosvenor Square. Restaurant on several levels with sharp modern décor. Good English dishes with modern twist.

XXX **Cecconi's**
5a Burlington Gdns ✉ W1S 3EP ⊖ Green Park – ✆ (020) 7434 1500
– giacomo@cecconis.co.uk – Fax (020) 7434 2020
– closed 25 December 30 AIU **d**
Rest – Italian Carte £ 28/48
◆ A chic bar and a stylish, modern dining venue, invariably busy; the menus call on the Italian classics with unusual touches.

XXX **Kai**
65 South Audley St ✉ W1K 2QU ⊖ Hyde Park Corner – ✆ (020) 7493 8988
– kai@kaimayfair.com – Fax (020) 7493 1456
– Closed 25-26 December and 1 January 30 AHV **n**
Rest – Chinese (booking essential) Menu £ 22 – Carte £ 38/91
◆ Marble flooring and mirrors add to the opulent feel of this smoothly run Chinese restaurant. Extensive menu offers dishes ranging from the luxury to the more familiar.

XXX **Umu**
14-16 Bruton Pl ✉ W1J 6LX ⊖ Bond Street – ✆ (020) 7499 8881
– enquiries@umurestaurant.com – Fax (020) 7499 5120 – Closed Christmas, 2 weeks August, Saturday lunch, Sunday and Bank Holidays 30 AIU **k**
Rest – Japanese Menu £ 21 (lunch) – Carte £ 34/73
Spec. Sweet shrimp with sake jelly and caviar. Grilled toro teriyaki, yuzu citrus flavoured grated radish, wasabi. White miso ice cream.
◆ Exclusive neighbourhood location: stylish, discreet interior with central sushi bar. Japanese dishes, specialising in Kyoto cuisine, employing highest quality ingredients.

XX **Semplice**
10 Blenheim St ✉ W1S 1LJ ⊖ Bond Street – ✆ (020) 7495 1509
– info@ristorantesemplice.com – Fax (020) 7493 7074 – Closed Christmas, Easter, Saturday lunch, Sunday and Bank Holidays 30 AHU **k**
Rest – Italian Menu £ 18 (lunch) – Carte £ 28/38
◆ Comfortable and stylish with custom laquered ebony, wavy gold walls and leather seating. Delicately textured, confidently presented dishes run the gamut of Italian cooking.

XX **Bellamy's**
18 Bruton Pl ✉ W1J 6LY ⊖ Bond Street – ✆ (020) 7491 2727
– info@bellamysrestaurant.co.uk – Fax (020) 7491 9990 – closed Saturday lunch, Sunday, 25 December and Bank Holidays 30 AIU **c**
Rest – Menu £ 29 – Carte £ 36/53
◆ French deli/brasserie tucked down a smart mews. Go past the caviar and cheeses into the restaurant proper for a very traditional, but well-executed, range of Gallic classics.

XX **Giardinetto**
39 40 Albemarle St ✉ W1S 4TE ⊖ Green Park – ✆ (020) 7493 7091
– info@giardinetto.co.uk – Fax (020) 7493 7096 – closed 22 December-6 January, Saturday lunch, Sunday and Bank Holidays 30 AIV **p**
Rest – Italian Carte £ 17/49
◆ Manages to mix a smart, stylish interior with a neighbourhood intimacy. Three dining areas, front being largest. Genoese chef/owner conjures up well-presented Ligurian dishes.

XX **Patterson's**
4 Mill St ✉ W1S 2AX ⊖ Oxford Street – ✆ (020) 7499 1308
– info@pattersonsrestaurant.com – Fax (020) 7491 2122 – Closed 25-26 December, Sunday, Saturday lunch and Bank Holidays 30 AIU **p**
Rest – Menu £ 20/40 – Carte £ 40/44
◆ Stylish modern interior in black and white. Elegant tables and attentive service. Modern British cooking with concise wine list and sensible prices.

XX **Alloro**

19-20 Dover St ✉ W1S 4LU ⊖ Green Park – ✆ (020) 7495 4768 – alloro@hotmail.co.uk – Fax (020) 7629 5348 – Closed Easter, 25 December, Saturday lunch, Sunday and Bank Holidays 30 AIV **r**

Rest – Italian Menu £ 29/34

◆ One of the new breed of stylish Italian restaurants with contemporary art and leather seating. A separate, bustling bar. Smoothly run with modern cooking.

XX **Hush**

8 Lancashire Court, Brook St ✉ W1S 1EY ⊖ Bond Street – ✆ (020) 7659 1500 – info@hush.co.uk – Fax (020) 7659 1501 30 AHU **v**

Rest – (Closed 25 December, 31 December, 1 January and Sunday except lunch in summer) (booking essential) Carte £ 31/47

Rest *Le Club* – (Closed Saturday lunch, Sunday and Bank Holidays) (booking essential) Menu £ 27 (lunch) – Carte £ 36/52

◆ Tucked away down a delightful mews courtyard, this brasserie - with sunny courtyard terrace - is an informal and lively little place to eat rustic Mediterranean fare. Upstairs, Le Club serves slightly more refined dining menus.

XX **Fakhreldine**

85 Piccadilly ✉ W1J 7NB ⊖ Green Park – ✆ (020) 7493 3424 – info@fakhreldine.co.uk – Fax (020) 7495 1977 – Closed 24 to 26 December 30 AIV **e**

Rest – Lebanese Menu £ 19 (lunch) – Carte £ 26/41

◆ Long-standing Lebanese restaurant with great view of Green Park. Large selection of classic mezze dishes and more modern European styled menu of original Lebanese dishes.

XX **Nobu** – at The Metropolitan H.

19 Old Park Lane ✉ W1Y 1LB ⊖ Hyde Park Corner – ✆ (020) 7447 4747 – confirmations@noburestaurants.com – Fax (020) 7447 4749 – Closed 25-26 December and 1 January 30 AHV **c**

Rest – (booking essential) Menu £ 25/70 – Carte £ 44/52

Spec. Lobster ceviche. Black cod with miso. Chocolate bento box, green tea ice cream.

◆ Its celebrity clientele has made this one of the most glamorous spots. Staff are fully conversant in the unique menu that adds South American influences to Japanese cooking.

XX **Via Condotti**

23 Conduit St ✉ W1S 2XS ⊖ Oxford Circus – ✆ (020) 7493 7050 – info@viacondotti.co.uk – Fax (020) 7409 7985 – Closed 25 December, Sunday and Bank Holidays 30 AIU **f**

Rest – Italian Menu £ 25/28

◆ Chic bar-room leads to restaurant with Italian prints and leather banquettes. Full-flavoured rustic dishes with most ingredients from Italy; chef/owner makes his own breads.

XX **Taman Gang**

141 Park Lane ✉ W1K 7AA ⊖ Marble Arch – ✆ (020) 7518 3160 – info@tamangang.com – Fax (020) 7518 3161 – closed Sunday 29 AGU **e**

Rest – South East Asian (dinner only) Menu £ 55/75

◆ Basement restaurant with largish bar and lounge area. Stylish but intimate décor. Informal and intelligent service. Pan-Asian dishes presented in exciting modern manner.

XX **Sumosan**

26 Albemarle St ✉ W1S 4HY ⊖ Green Park – ✆ (020) 7495 5999 – info@sumosan.co.uk – Fax (020) 7355 1247 – Closed 25-26 December, 1 January and lunch Saturday and Sunday 30 AIU **e**

Rest – Japanese (dinner only) Menu £ 23/70 – Carte £ 33/59

◆ A very smart interior in which diners sit in comfy banquettes and armchairs. Sushi bar to the rear with some semi-private booths. Extensive menus of Sushi and Sashimi.

XX **Wild Honey** AC VISA AE

12 St George St ✉ W1S 2FB ⊖ Oxford Circus – ☎ (020) 7758 9160 – info@wildhoneyrestaurant.co.uk – Fax (020) 7493 4549 – Closed 25-26 December and 1 January 30 AIU **w**

Rest – Menu £ 16 (lunch) – Carte £ 30/36

Spec. Warm smoked eel with fig jam and raw vegetable salad. Shin of veal with tomato and carrots. Wild honey ice cream with crushed honeycomb.

◆ High-ceilinged, oak-panelled restaurant, with banquette and booth seating; sister to Arbutus in Soho. Easy to eat, gimmick-free food with flavoursome and seasonal ingredients.

XX **Mews of Mayfair** VISA AE

10-11 Lancashire Court, New Bond St ✉ W1S 1EY ⊖ Bond Street – ☎ (020) 7518 9388 – Fax (020) 7518 9389 – closed Christmas and New Year and Sunday 30 AHU **a**

Rest – Menu £ 26/40 – Carte £ 36/54

◆ Converted mews houses once used as storage rooms for Savile Row. Ground floor bar with French windows. Pretty first floor restaurant where eclectic modern menus are served.

XX **Chor Bizarre** AC VISA AE

16 Albemarle St ✉ W1S 4HW ⊖ Green Park – ☎ (020) 7629 9802 – chorbizarrelondon@oldworldhospitality.com – Fax (020) 7493 7756 – closed 25-26 December, 1 January, Sunday lunch and Bank Holidays 30 AIV **s**

Rest – Indian Menu £ 18 (lunch) – Carte £ 24/38

◆ Translates as 'thieves market' and the décor is equally vibrant; antiques, curios, carvings and ornaments abound. Cooking and recipes chiefly from North India and Kashmir.

XX **Sketch (The Gallery)** AC VISA AE

9 Conduit St ✉ W1S 2XG ⊖ Oxford Street – ☎ (0870) 777 44 88 – info@sketch.uk.com – Fax (0870) 777 44 00 – closed 25-26 December, 1 January, Sunday and Bank Holidays 30 AIU **h**

Rest – (dinner only) (booking essential) Carte £ 34/53

◆ On the ground floor of the Sketch building: daytime video art gallery metamorphoses into evening brasserie with ambient wall projections and light menus with eclectic range.

XX **Cocoon** AC VISA AE

65 Regent St ✉ W1B 4EA ⊖ Piccadilly Circus – ☎ (020) 7494 7600 – reservations@cocoon-restaurants.com – Fax (020) 7494 7607 – closed Saturday lunch and Sunday 30 AJU **x**

Rest – Asian Carte £ 35/70

◆ Trendy restaurant, based on a prime Regent Street site. Silk nets cleverly divide long, winding room. Bold, eclectic menus cover a wide spectrum of Asian dishes.

XX **Nobu Berkeley St** AC VISA AE

15 Berkeley St ✉ W1J 8DY ⊖ Green Park – ☎ (020) 7290 9222 – nobuberkeley@noburestaurants.com – Fax (020) 7290 9223 – Closed 25-26 December, 1 January, lunch Saturday and Sunday 30 AIV **b**

Rest – Menu £ 25/60 – Carte £ 33/49

Spec. Yellowtail sashimi with jalapeño. Anti-Cucho rib-eye beef. Yuzu tart.

◆ In a prime position off Berkeley Square: downstairs 'destination' bar and above, a top quality, soft-hued restaurant. Innovative Japanese dishes with original combinations.

XX **Momo** AC VISA AE

25 Heddon St ✉ W1B 4BH ⊖ Oxford Circus – ☎ (020) 7434 4040 – info@momoresto.com – Fax (020) 7287 0404 – closed 24-26 and 31 December, 1 January and Sunday 30 AIU **n**

Rest – Moroccan Menu £ 18/45 – Carte £ 29/52

◆ Elaborate adornment of rugs, drapes and ornaments mixed with Arabic music lend an authentic feel to this busy Moroccan restaurant. Helpful service. Popular basement bar.

XX **Veeraswamy**

Victory House, 99 Regent St, entrance on Swallow St ✉ W1B 4RS ⊖ Piccadilly Circus – ✆ (020) 7734 1401 – veeraswamy@realindianfood.com – Fax (020) 7439 8434 – Closed dinner 25 December 30 AIU **t**

Rest – Indian Menu £ 20 (lunch) – Carte £ 29/52

◆ The country's oldest Indian restaurant enlivened by vivid coloured walls and glass screens. The menu also combines the familiar with some modern twists.

XX **Kiku**

17 Half Moon St ✉ W1J 7BE ⊖ Green Park – ✆ (020) 7499 4208 – Fax (020) 7409 3259 – Closed 25-26 December, Sunday and lunch Bank Holidays 30 AIV **g**

Rest – Japanese Menu £ 14/46 **s** – Carte £ 28/58 **s**

◆ Bright and fresh feel thanks to minimalistic décor of stone and natural wood. A plethora of menus, a fierce adherence to seasonality and an authentic emphasis on presentation.

XX **Haiku**

15 New Burlington Place ✉ W1S 2HX ⊖ Oxford Circus – ✆ (020) 7494 4777 – Closed Sunday 30 AIU **x**

Rest – Asian Menu £ 22/50 – Carte £ 32/54

◆ Elegant, moodily lit and set over three floors with open kitchen, the unusual theme here is 'Asian tapas,' and the menu features dishes from Japan, India, China and Thailand.

XX **La Petite Maison**

54 Brooks Mews ✉ W1K 4EG ⊖ Bond Street – ✆ (020) 7495 4774 – info@lpmlondon.co.uk – Closed Sunday 30 AHU **f**

Rest – French Mediterranean Carte £ 35/50

◆ Open plan restaurant; sister to the eponymous Nice original. Healthy French Mediterranean cooking with a seafood slant. 20 starters to choose from; sharing is encouraged.

X **Chisou**

4 Princes St ✉ W1B 2LE ⊖ Oxford Circus – ✆ (020) 7629 3931 – chisou@xln.co.uk – Fax (020) 7629 5255 – Closed Sunday 30 AIU **m**

Rest – Japanese Menu £ 15 (lunch) – Carte £ 17/55

◆ In Mayfair's Japanese quarter; simple slate flooring and polished wood tables. Cosy sushi bar to rear. Elaborate menus of modern/classic Japanese dishes. Gets very busy.

X **Bentley's (Oyster Bar)**

11-15 Swallow St ✉ W1B 4DG ⊖ Piccadilly Circus – ✆ (020) 7734 4756 – reservations@bentleys.org – Fax (020) 7758 4140 – Closed 25 December and 1 January 30 AJU **n**

Rest – Seafood Carte £ 27/39

◆ Ground floor location, behind the busy bar. White-jacketed staff open oysters by the bucket load. Interesting seafood menus feature tasty fish pies. Hearty Sunday roasts.

X **Automat**

33 Dover St ✉ W1S 4NF ⊖ Green Park – ✆ (020) 7499 3033 – info@automat-london.com – Fax (020) 7499 2682 – Closed 25 December and 1 January 30 AIV **r**

Rest – American Carte £ 25/42

◆ Buzzing New York style brasserie in three areas: a café, a 'dining car' with deep leather banquettes, and actual brasserie itself. Classic dishes from burgers to cheesecake.

X **The Cafe at Sotheby's**

34-35 New Bond St ✉ W1A 2AA ⊖ Bond Street – ✆ (020) 7293 5077 – ken.hall@sotheby's.com – Fax (020) 7293 6993 – Closed last 3 weeks August, 23 December-3 January, Saturday and Sunday 30 AIU **y**

Rest – (lunch only) (booking essential) Carte £ 29/34 **s**

◆ A velvet rope separates this simple room from the main lobby of this famous auction house. Pleasant service from staff in aprons. Menu is short but well-chosen and light.

Le Boudin Blanc
5 Trebeck St ⊖ Green Park – ✆ (020) 7499 3292
– reservations@boudinblanc.co.uk – Fax (020) 7495 6973 30 AHV **q**
Rest – French Menu £ 15 (lunch) – Carte £ 28/48
◆ Very busy restaurant with a simple bistro style; the first floor is marginally less frantic than the ground floor. Robust and satisfying French classics have authentic flavour.

The Only Running Footman
5 Charles St. ✉ W1J 5DF ⊖ Green Park – ✆ (020) 7499 2988
– info@therunningfootman.biz – Fax (020) 7491 8162 30 AHV **x**
Rest – British Carte £ 22/30
◆ Charming, historic pub whose small, atmospheric ground floor is always busy, with a first-come-first-served rule. Upstairs you can book, it's plush and the menu more ambitious.

Regent's Park and Marylebone – Gtr London – ✉ NW1/NW8/W1

Landmark London
222 Marylebone Rd ✉ NW1 6JQ ⊖ Edgware Rd
– ✆ (020) 7631 8000 – reservations@thelandmark.co.uk
– Fax (020) 7631 8080 29 AFT **a**
290 rm – †£ 211/340 ††£ 246/376, ☕ £ 28 – 9 suites
Rest *Winter Garden* – Menu £ 35 (lunch) – Carte £ 30/46
◆ Imposing Victorian Gothic building with a vast glass enclosed atrium, overlooked by many of the modern, well-equipped bedrooms. Winter Garden popular for afternoon tea.

Langham
1c Portland Pl, Regent St ✉ W1B 1JA ⊖ Oxford Circus – ✆ (020) 7636 1000
– loninfo@langhamhotels.com – Fax (020) 7323 2340 30 AIT **e**
368 rm – †£ 411 ††£ 411, ☕ £ 24.95 – 20 suites – **Rest** – Carte £ 38/61
◆ Opposite the BBC, with traditional bedrooms and impressive infinity suite. Designer-styled bar with oriental edge is named after 360ft well under hotel and specialises in rum. Contemporary new oval restaurant in mint green, yellow and powder blue.

The Cumberland
Great Cumberland Place ✉ W1A 4RF ⊖ Marble Arch – ✆ (0870) 333 92 80
– enquiries@thecumberland.co.uk – Fax (0870) 333 92 81 29 AGU **z**
1010 rm ☕ – †£ 358 ††£ 366
Rest *Rhodes W1 Restaurant* and ***Rhodes W1 Brasserie*** – see restaurant listing
◆ Fully refurbished, conference oriented hotel whose vast lobby boasts modern art, sculpture and running water panels. Distinctive bedrooms with a host of impressive extras.

Hyatt Regency London-The Churchill
30 Portman Sq ✉ W1A 4ZX ⊖ Marble Arch
– ✆ (020) 7486 5800 – london.churchill@hyattintl.com
– Fax (020) 7486 1255 29 AGT **x**
396 rm – †£ 194/447 ††£ 217/470, ☕ £ 25 – 40 suites
Rest *The Montagu* – Menu £ 23 (lunch) – Carte £ 35/47
◆ Modern property overlooking attractive square. Elegant marbled lobby. Cigar bar open until 2am for members. Well-appointed rooms have the international traveller in mind. Restaurant provides popular Sunday brunch entertainment.

Charlotte Street
15 Charlotte St ✉ W1T 1RJ ⊖ Goodge Street – ✆ (020) 7806 2000
– charlotte@firmdale.com – Fax (020) 7806 2002 31 AKT **e**
44 rm – †£ 247/282 ††£ 347, ☕ £ 19 – 8 suites
Rest *Oscar* – see restaurant listing
◆ Interior designed with a charming and understated English feel. Welcoming lobby laden with floral displays. Individually decorated rooms with CDs and mobile phones.

Sanderson

50 Berners St ✉ W1T 3NG ⊖ Oxford Circus – ☎ (020) 7300 1400
– sanderson@morganshotelgroup.com – Fax (020) 7300 1401 31 AJT **c**
150 rm – 🚹£ 264/441 🚹🚹£ 294/499, ☕ £21.50
Rest *Suka* – Malaysian Carte £ 36/84
◆ Designed by Philipe Starck: the height of contemporary design. Bar is the place to see and be seen. Bedrooms with minimalistic white décor have DVDs and striking bathrooms. Malaysian dishes designed for sharing in Suka.

The Leonard

15 Seymour St ✉ W1H 7JW ⊖ Marble Arch – ☎ (020) 7935 2010
– reservations@theleonard.com – Fax (020) 7935 6700 29 AGU **n**
19 rm – 🚹£ 116/194 🚹🚹£ 164/194, ☕ £19.50 – 20 suites – **Rest** – (Closed Sunday dinner) Carte £ 21/27
◆ Around the corner from Selfridges, an attractive Georgian townhouse: antiques and oil paintings abound. Well-appointed rooms in classic country house style. Intimate front dining room.

Montcalm

Great Cumberland Pl ✉ W1H 7TW ⊖ Marble Arch – ☎ (020) 7402 4288
– montcalm@montcalm.co.uk – Fax (020) 7724 9180 29 AGU **d**
110 rm – 🚹£ 164/293 🚹🚹£ 176/293, ☕ £18.95 – 10 suites
Rest *The Crescent* – (Closed lunch Saturday, Sunday and Bank Holidays) Menu £ 27/36
◆ Named after the 18C French general, the Marquis de Montcalm. In a charming crescent a short walk from Hyde Park. Spacious bedrooms with a subtle oriental feel.

London Marriott H. Marble Arch

134 George St ✉ W1H 5DN ⊖ Marble Arch
– ☎ (020) 7723 1277 – salesadmin.marblearch@marriott.com
– Fax (020) 7402 0666 29 AFT **j**
240 rm – 🚹£ 232/267 🚹🚹£ 232/298, ☕ £18.95
Rest *Mediterrano* – (dinner only) Carte £ 25/30 **s**
◆ Centrally located and modern. Offers comprehensive conference facilities. Leisure centre underground. An ideal base for both corporate and leisure guests. Mediterranean-influenced cooking.

Berkshire

350 Oxford St ✉ W1N 0BY ⊖ Bond Street – ☎ (020) 7629 7474
– resberk@radisson.com – Fax (020) 7629 8156 30 AHU **n**
145 rm – 🚹£ 358/386 🚹🚹£ 386, ☕ £16.50 – 2 suites
Rest *Ascots* – (Closed lunch Saturday and Sunday) (dinner only) Menu £ 25 – Carte £ 28/32
◆ Above the shops of Oxford St. Reception areas have a pleasant traditional charm. Comfortably appointed modern bedrooms have plenty of style. Personable staff. Stylish, relaxed dining room.

Durrants

26-32 George St ✉ W1H 5BJ ⊖ Bond Street – ☎ (020) 7935 8131
– enquiries@durrantshotel.co.uk – Fax (020) 7487 3510 29 AGT **e**
89 rm – 🚹£ 120 🚹🚹£ 175, ☕ £14.50 – 3 suites – **Rest** – Menu £ 22 – Carte £ 30/43
◆ First opened in 1790 and family owned since 1921. Traditionally English feel with the charm of a bygone era. Cosy wood panelled bar. Attractive rooms vary somewhat in size. Semi-private booths in quintessentially British dining room.

The Mandeville

Mandeville Pl ✉ W1U 2BE ⊖ Bond Street – ☎ (020) 7935 5599
– info@mandeville.co.uk – Fax (020) 7935 9588 30 AHT **x**
140 rm – 🚹£ 299/330 🚹🚹£ 470, ☕ £18 – 2 suites
Rest *de Ville* – (Closed Sunday) Menu £ 20/25 – Carte £ 25/37
◆ Fashionably located hotel, refurbished in 2005 with marbled reception and strikingly colourful bar. Stylish rooms have flatscreen TVs and make good use of the space available. Modern British cuisine served in splendid de Ville restaurant.

Dorset Square

39-40 Dorset Sq ✉ NW1 6QN ⊖ Marylebone – ☎ (020) 7723 7874 – reservations@dorsetsquare.co.uk – Fax (020) 7724 3328 – Closed 1 week Christmas 17 QZD **s**

37 rm – †£176 ††£282, ☕£14

Rest *The Potting Shed* – (Closed Saturday lunch and Sunday dinner) (booking essential) Menu £23/25 – Carte £23/35

◆ Converted Regency townhouses in a charming square and the site of the original Lord's cricket ground. A relaxed country house in the city. Individually decorated rooms. The Potting Shed features modern cuisine and a set business menu.

The Sumner without rest

54 Upper Berkeley St ✉ W1H 7QR ⊖ Marble Arch – ☎ (020) 7723 2244 – hotel@thesumner.com – Fax (0870) 705 8767 29 AFU **k**

20 rm ☕ – †£153 ††£165

◆ Two Georgian terrace houses in developing area of town. Comfy, stylish sitting room; basement breakfast room. Largest bedrooms, 101 and 201, have sunny, full-length windows.

Park Plaza Sherlock Holmes London

108 Baker St ✉ W1U 6LJ ⊖ Baker Street – ☎ (020) 7486 6161 – info@sherlockholmeshotel.com – Fax (020) 7958 5211 29 AGT **c**

116 rm – †£141 ††£294, ☕£16.50 – 3 suites – **Rest** – Menu £17 – Carte £27/34

◆ A stylish building with a relaxed contemporary feel. Comfortable guests' lounge with Holmes pictures on the walls. Bedrooms welcoming and smart, some with wood floors. Brasserie style dining.

Hart House without rest

51 Gloucester Pl ✉ W1U 8JF ⊖ Marble Arch – ☎ (020) 7935 2288 – reservations@harthouse.co.uk – Fax (020) 7935 8516 29 AGT **d**

15 rm ☕ – †£65/95 ††£95/125

◆ Once home to French nobility escaping the 1789 Revolution. Now an attractive Georgian, mid-terraced private hotel. Warm and welcoming service. Well kept bedrooms.

St George without rest

49 Gloucester Pl ✉ W1U 8JE ⊖ Marble Arch – ☎ (020) 7486 8586 – reservations@stgeorge-hotel.net – Fax (020) 7486 6567 29 AGT **h**

19 rm ☕ – †£80/110 ††£95/130

◆ Terraced house on a busy street, usefully located within walking distance of many attractions. Offers a warm welcome and comfortable bedrooms which are spotlessly maintained.

Rhodes W1 Restaurant – at The Cumberland H.

Great Cumberland Place ✉ W1A 4RF ⊖ Marble Arch – ☎ (020) 7479 3737 – restaurant@rhodesw1.com – Fax (020) 7479 3888 – Closed 28 December-5 January, Easter, Sunday, Monday and lunch Saturday 29 AGU **z**

Rest – French Menu £28/48

Spec. Double oyster ragoût with samphire and fresh herbs. Salt roast pigeon with asparagus, cabbage hearts and lemon cumin gravy. Caramel chocolate mousse millefeuille with lemon sorbet.

◆ Flamboyant in feel, with purples, blacks, velvets, mirrors and enormous Swarovski chandeliers à la Kelly Hoppen. Precise, polished cooking, with French flavours to the fore.

Locanda Locatelli

8 Seymour St ✉ W1H 7JZ ⊖ Marble Arch – ☎ (020) 7935 9088 – info@locandalocatelli.com – Fax (020) 7935 1149 – Closed Bank Holidays 29 AGU **r**

Rest – Italian Carte £35/56

Spec. Pan-fried scallops with a saffron viniagrette and celeriac purée. Roast monkfish with a walnut and caper sauce. Amarelli liquorice, coffee and mascarpone.

◆ Forever popular restaurant serving authentic, seasonal Italian cooking of outstanding quality, complemented by a comprehensive wine list. Best tables are the corner booths.

XXX **Latium** AC VISA MC AE D

21 Berners St, Fitzrovia ✉ W1T 3LP ⊖ Oxford Circus – ✆ (020) 7323 9123 – info@latiumrestaurant.com – Fax (020) 7323 3205 – Closed 25 December, Saturday lunch, Sunday, and Bank Holidays 31 AJT **n**

Rest – Italian Menu £ 20/29

◆ Welcoming restaurant owned by affable chef. Smart feel with well-spaced linen-clad tables, tiled floors and rural pictures. Italian country cooking in the heart of town.

XX **Texture** AC VISA MC AE

34 Portman Square ✉ W1H 7BY ⊖ Marble Arch – ✆ (020) 7224 0028 – info@texture-restaurant.co.uk – Closed 22 December-8 January, last 2 weeks August, Sunday and Monday 29 AGU **p**

Rest – Menu £ 26/45 ☸

◆ The champagne bar occupies the window space; the restaurant is in the rear. Highly skilled cooking with contrasting textures, in which the chef's Icelandic roots are evident.

XX **Rhodes W1 Brasserie** – at The Cumberland H. AC VISA MC AE D

Great Cumberland Pl ✉ W1A 4RF ⊖ Marble Arch – ✆ (020) 7479 3838 – rhodesw1@thecumberland.co.uk – Fax (020) 7479 3888 29 AGU **z**

Rest – Carte £ 25/42

◆ In the heart of the Cumberland Hotel, a very stylish dining experience with impressively high ceiling and classical Gary Rhodes dishes bringing out the best of the seasons.

XX **Galvin** AC VISA MC AE

66 Baker St ✉ W1U 7DH ⊖ Baker Street – ✆ (020) 7935 4007 – info@galvinuk.com – Fax (020) 7486 1735 – Closed 25-26 December and 1 January 29 AGT **b**

Rest – French Menu £ 16 – Carte £ 24/35

◆ A modern take on the classic Gallic bistro with ceiling fans, globe lights, rich wood panelled walls and French influenced dishes where precision and good value are paramount.

XX **Six13** AC VISA MC AE D

19 Wigmore St ✉ W1H 9LA ⊖ Bond Street – ✆ (020) 7629 6133 – inquiries@six13.com – Fax (020) 7629 6135 – Closed Jewish Holidays, Friday and Saturday 30 AHT **n**

Rest – Kosher Menu £ 28 – Carte £ 28/45

◆ Stylish and immaculate with banquette seating. Strictly kosher menu supervised by the Shama offering interesting cooking with a modern slant.

XX **Oscar** – at Charlotte Street H. AC VISA MC AE D

15 Charlotte St ✉ W1T 1RJ ⊖ Goodge Street – ✆ (020) 7907 4005 – charlotte@firmdale.com – Fax (020) 7806 2002 – Closed Sunday lunch 31 AKT **e**

Rest – (booking essential) Carte £ 29/44

◆ Adjacent to hotel lobby and dominated by a large, vivid mural of contemporary London life. Sophisticated dishes served by attentive staff: oysters, wasabi and soya dressing.

XX **The Providores** AC VISA MC AE

109 Marylebone High St ✉ W1U 4RX ⊖ Bond Street – ✆ (020) 7935 6175 – anyone@theprovidores.co.uk – Fax (020) 7935 6877 – Closed Easter and Christmas 30 AHT **y**

Rest – Carte £ 26/46

◆ Swish, stylish restaurant on first floor; unusual dishes with New World base and fusion of Asian, Mediterranean influences. Tapas and light meals in downstairs Tapa Room.

XX **La Porte des Indes** AC VISA AE

32 Bryanston St ✉ W1H 7EG ⊖ Marble Arch – ✆ (020) 7224 0055 – london.reservation@laportedesindes.com – Fax (020) 7224 1144 – Closed 25-28 December and Saturday lunch 29 AGU **s**

Rest – Indian Menu £ 15/29 – Carte £ 28/42

◆ Don't be fooled by the discreet entrance: inside there is a spectacularly unrestrained display of palm trees, murals and waterfalls. French influenced Indian cuisine.

XX **Ozer** AC VISA AE

4-5 Langham Pl, Regent St ✉ W1B 3DG ⊖ Oxford Circus – ✆ (020) 7323 0505 – info@sofra.co.uk – Fax (020) 7323 0111 30 AIT **z**

Rest – Turkish Menu £ 21 – Carte £ 15/29

◆ Behind the busy and vibrantly decorated bar you'll find a smart modern restaurant. Lively atmosphere and efficient service of modern, light and aromatic Turkish cooking.

XX **Roka** AC VISA AE

37 Charlotte St ✉ W1T 1RR ⊖ Tottenham Court Road – ✆ (020) 7580 6464 – info@rokarestaurant.com – Fax (020) 7580 0220 – Closed 25 December 31 AJT **k**

Rest – Japanese Carte £ 29/36 **s**

◆ Striking glass and steel frontage. Airy, atmospheric interior of teak, oak and paper wall screens. Authentic, flavoursome Japanese cuisine with variety of grill dishes.

XX **Rasa Samudra** VISA AE

5 Charlotte St ✉ W1T 1RE ⊖ Goodge Street – ✆ (020) 7637 0222 – Fax (020) 7637 0224 – Closed 24 December-1 January and lunch Sunday and Bank Holidays 31 AKT **r**

Rest – Indian Menu £ 23/30 – Carte £ 13/24

◆ Comfortably appointed, richly decorated and modern Indian restaurant. Authentic Keralan (south Indian) cooking with seafood and vegetarian specialities.

XX **Levant** AC VISA AE

Jason Court, 76 Wigmore St ✉ W1U 2SJ ⊖ Bond Street – ✆ (020) 7224 1111 – info@levant.co.uk – Fax (020) 7486 1216 30 AHT **c**

Rest – Lebanese Menu £ 15/29

◆ The somewhat unpromising entrance leads down to a vibrantly decorated basement. Modern Lebanese cooking featuring subtly spiced dishes.

XX **Caldesi** AC VISA AE

15-17 Marylebone Lane ✉ W1U 2NE ⊖ Bond Street – ✆ (020) 7935 9226 – tuscan@caldesi.com – Fax (020) 7935 9228 – Closed Saturday lunch and Sunday 30 AHT **e**

Rest – Italian Carte £ 35/43

◆ A traditional Italian restaurant that continues to attract a loyal clientele. Robust and authentic dishes with Tuscan specialities. Attentive service by established team.

XX **Villandry** AC VISA AE

170 Great Portland St ✉ W1W 5QB ⊖ Regent's Park – ✆ (020) 7631 3131 – contactus@villandry.com – Fax (020) 7631 3030 – Closed 25, 31 December, 1 January and Sunday dinner 30 AIT **s**

Rest – Carte £ 29/40

◆ The senses are heightened by passing through the well-stocked deli to the dining room behind. Bare walls, wooden tables and a menu offering simple, tasty dishes.

XX **L'Aventure** VISA AE

3 Blenheim Terrace ✉ NW8 0EH ⊖ St John's Wood – ✆ (020) 7624 6232 – Fax (020) 7625 5548 – Closed first week January, Easter, Sunday, Saturday lunch and Bank Holidays 11 PZB **b**

Rest – French Menu £ 19/35

◆ Behind the pretty tree lined entrance you'll find a charming neighbourhood restaurant. Relaxed atmosphere and service by personable owner. Authentic French cuisine.

XX **Phoenix Palace** A/C VISA MO AE

3-5 Glentworth St ✉ NW1 5PG ⊖ Baker Street – ✆ (020) 7486 3515 – info@phoenixpalace.uk.com – Fax (020) 7486 3401 17 QZD **x**

Rest – Chinese Menu £ 18 – Carte £ 18/26

◆ Tucked away near Baker Street; lots of photos of celebrities who've eaten here. Huge room for 200 diners where authentic, fresh, well prepared Chinese dishes are served.

X **The Wallace** VISA MO AE

Hertford House, Manchester Sq ✉ W1U 3BN ⊖ Bond St – ✆ (020) 7563 9505 – reservations@thewallacerestaurant.com 29 AGT **k**

Rest – French (lunch only and dinner Friday-Saturday) Menu £ 25 – Carte £ 29/36

◆ Situated in the Wallace Collection's delightful glass-roofed courtyard, divided by Japanese maple trees. Comprehensive selection of classic French fare; terrines a speciality.

X **Union Café** VISA MO AE

96 Marylebone Lane ✉ W1U 2QA ⊖ Bond Street – ✆ (020) 7486 4860 – unioncafe@brinkleys.com – Fax (020) 7935 1537 – Closed 25-26 December, 1 January and Sunday dinner 30 AHT **d**

Rest – Carte £ 23/32

◆ No standing on ceremony at this bright, relaxed restaurant, with its arched windows and clamour of contentment. The open kitchen at one end produces modern Mediterranean cuisine.

X **Michael Moore** VISA MO AE

19 Blandford St ✉ W1U 3DH ⊖ Baker Street – ✆ (020) 7224 1898 – info@michaelmoorerestaurant.com – Fax (020) 7224 0970 – Closed Christmas-New Year, Saturday lunch, Sunday and Bank Holidays 29 AGT **r**

Rest – Menu £ 19 (lunch) – Carte £ 30/45

◆ Warm glow emanates not just from mustard façade but also effusive welcome within. Cosy, locally renowned favourite, with global cuisine served by friendly, efficient staff.

X **Caffé Caldesi** A/C VISA MO AE

1st Floor, 118 Marylebone Lane ✉ W1U 2QF ⊖ Bond Street – ✆ (020) 7935 1144 – people@caldesi.com – Fax (020) 7935 8832 – Closed Christmas, Sunday and Bank Holidays 30 AHT **s**

Rest – Italian Carte £ 29/38

◆ Converted pub with a simple modern interior in which to enjoy tasty, uncomplicated Italian dishes. Downstairs is a lively bar with a deli counter serving pizzas and pastas.

X **Chada Chada** A/C VISA MO AE

16-17 Picton Pl ✉ W1U 1BP ⊖ Bond Street – ✆ (020) 7935 8212 – enquiry@chadathai.com – Fax (020) 7924 2178 – Closed 25 December, 1 January, and Sunday 30 AHU **b**

Rest – Thai Menu £ 13 (lunch) – Carte £ 15/29

◆ Authentic and fragrant Thai cooking; the good value menu offers some interesting departures from the norm. Service is eager to please in the compact and cosy rooms.

X **Fishworks** A/C VISA MO AE

89 Marylebone High St ✉ W1U 4QW ⊖ Baker Street – ✆ (020) 7935 9796 – marylebone@fishworks.co.uk – Fax (020) 7935 8796 30 AHT **k**

Rest – Seafood (booking essential) Carte £ 25/49

◆ Go through the fish shop to bright, unfussy restaurant where a blackboard lists the daily specials. Extensive menus offer simply prepared seafood straight from front-of-house!

Dinings
22 Harcourt St. ✉ W1H 4HH ⊖ Marylebone – ✆ (020) 7723 0666 – Fax (020) 7723 3222 – Closed 2 weeks August, Saturday lunch and Sunday AFT **c**
Rest – Japanese (booking essential) Carte £ 26/36
◆ Resembles an after-work Japanese izakaya, or pub, with chummy atmosphere and loud music. Food is a mix of small plates of delicate dishes; a mix of modern and more traditional.

The Salt House
63 Abbey Road, St John's Wood ✉ NW8 0AE ⊖ St John's Wood – ✆ (020) 7328 6626 – salthousemail@majol.co.uk – closed 25 December 11 OZB **a**
Rest – Carte £ 20/45
◆ Grand Victorian pub appearance in bottle green. Busy bar at the front; main dining room, in calm duck egg blue, to the rear. Modern menus boast a distinct Mediterranean style.

Queen's Head & Artichoke
30-32 Albany St ✉ NW1 4EA ⊖ Great Portland Street – ✆ (020) 7916 6206 – info@theartichoke.net – Closed 24 December-2 January 18 RZD **b**
Rest – Carte £ 19/25
◆ Busy, wood-panelled bar and eccentrially-styled upstairs restaurant. Modern, European influenced food mixed with a large selection of all-day international 'tapas.'

St James's – Gtr London – ✉ NW1/W1/SW1

The Ritz
150 Piccadilly ✉ W1J 9BR ⊖ Green Park – ✆ (020) 7493 8181 – enquire@theritzlondon.com – Fax (020) 7493 2687 30 AIV **c**
116 rm – †£ 306/494 ††£ 423/470, ☕ £30 – 17 suites
Rest *The Ritz Restaurant* – see restaurant listing
◆ Opened 1906, a fine example of Louis XVI architecture and decoration. Elegant Palm Court famed for afternoon tea. Many of the lavishly appointed rooms overlook the park.

Sofitel St James London
6 Waterloo Pl ✉ SW1Y 4AN ⊖ Piccadilly Circus – ✆ (020) 7747 2200 – Fax (020) 7747 2210 31 AKV **a**
179 rm – †£ 161/252 ††£ 280/400, ☕ £21 – 7 suites
Rest *Brasserie Roux* – see restaurant listing
◆ Grade II listed building in smart Pall Mall location. Classically English interiors include floral Rose Lounge and club-style St. James bar. Comfortable, well-fitted bedrooms.

Haymarket
rm,
1 Suffolk Place ✉ SW1Y 4BP ⊖ Piccadilly Circus – ✆ (020) 7470 4000 – haymarket@firmdale.com – Fax (020) 7470 4004 31 AKV **d**
47 rm – †£ 288 ††£ 364, ☕ £18.50 – 3 suites
Rest *Brumus* – Italian – ✆ (020) 7451 1012 – Carte £ 26/31
◆ Smart, spacious hotel next to Theatre Royal Haymarket with eclectic blend of modern and antique furnishings. Large, comfortable bedrooms in soothing colours. Impressive pool. Brumus bar and restaurant puts focus on Italian cooking.

Stafford
16-18 St James's Pl ✉ SW1A 1NJ ⊖ Green Park – ✆ (020) 7493 0111 – information@thestaffordhotel.co.uk – Fax (020) 7493 7121 30 AIV **u**
73 rm – †£ 317/352 ††£ 411/440, ☕ £23 – 32 suites – **Rest** – (Closed Saturday lunch) Menu £ 30 (lunch) **s** – Carte dinner £ 29/63 **s**
◆ A genteel atmosphere prevails in this elegant and discreet country house in the city. Do not miss the famed American bar. Well-appointed rooms created from 18C stables. Refined, elegant, intimate dining room.

Dukes

35 St James's Pl ✉ SW1A 1NY ⊖ Green Park – ✆ (020) 7491 4840 – bookings@dukeshotel.com – Fax (020) 7493 1264 30 AIV **f**

83 rm – 🛉£ 364/417 🛉🛉£ 505/523, ☕ £ 19.50 – 7 suites – **Rest** – Menu £ 17 – Carte £ 29/40

◆ Privately owned, discreet and quiet hotel. Traditional bar, famous for its martinis and Cognac collection. Well-kept spacious rooms in a country house style. Refined dining.

The Cavendish

81 Jermyn St ✉ SW1Y 6JF ⊖ Piccadilly Circus – ✆ (020) 7930 2111 – reservations@thecavendishlondon.com – Fax (020) 7930 3687 30 AIV **v**

227 rm – 🛉£ 152/275 🛉🛉£ 306, ☕ £ 21 – 3 suites – **Rest** – (Closed lunch Saturday, Sunday and Bank Holidays) Menu £ 20 (lunch) – Carte £ 26/35

◆ Modern hotel in heart of Piccadilly. Contemporary, minimalist style of rooms with moody prints of London; top five floors offer far-reaching views over and beyond the city. Classic-styled restaurant overlooks Jermyn Street.

22 Jermyn Street without rest

22 Jermyn St ✉ SW1Y 6HL ⊖ Piccadilly Circus – ✆ (020) 7734 2353 – office@22jermyn.com – Fax (020) 7734 0750 31 AKV **e**

5 rm – 🛉£ 258 🛉🛉£ 258 – 13 suites

◆ Exclusive boutique hotel with entrance amid famous shirt-makers' shops. Stylishly decorated bedrooms more than compensate for the lack of lounge space. Room service available.

The Ritz Restaurant – at The Ritz H.

150 Piccadilly ✉ W1V 9DG ⊖ Green Park – ✆ (020) 7493 8181 – Fax (020) 7493 2687 30 AIV **c**

Rest – Menu £ 38/65 – Carte £ 47/74 **s**

◆ The height of opulence: magnificent Louis XVI décor with trompe l'oeil and ornate gilding. Delightful terrace over Green Park. Refined service, classic and modern menu.

The Wolseley

160 Piccadilly ✉ W1J 9EB ⊖ Green Park – ✆ (020) 7499 6996 – Fax (020) 7499 6888 – Closed 25 December, 1 January, August Bank Holiday and dinner 24 and 31 December 30 AIV **q**

Rest – (booking essential) Carte £ 26/70

◆ Has the feel of a grand European coffee house: pillars, high vaulted ceiling, mezzanine tables. Menus range from caviar to a hot dog. Also open for breakfasts and tea.

St Alban

4-12 Regent St ✉ SW1Y 4PE – ✆ (020) 7499 8558 – info@stalban.net – Fax (020) 7499 6888 – Closed 25-26 December and 1 January 31 AKV **c**

Rest – Carte £ 29/41

◆ Light, airy restaurant with colourful booth seating and wonderful feeling of space. Weekly-changing modern European menu with global influences. Convenient for theatre dining.

Luciano

72-73 St James's St ✉ SW1A 1PH ⊖ Green Park – ✆ (020) 7408 1440 – info@lucianorestaurant.co.uk – Closed Sunday 30 AIV **m**

Rest – Italian Menu £ 22 (lunch) – Carte £ 25/49 **s**

◆ Art Deco, David Collins styled bar leads to restaurant sympathetic to its early 19C heritage. Mix of Italian and English dishes cooked in rustic, wholesome and earthy manner.

Le Caprice

Arlington House, Arlington St ✉ SW1A 1RJ ⊖ Green Park – ✆ (020) 7629 2239 – reservation@le-caprice.co.uk – Fax (020) 7493 9040 – Closed 24-26 December, 1 January and August Bank Holiday 30 AIV **h**

Rest – (Sunday brunch) Carte £ 35/50

◆ Still attracting a fashionable clientele and as busy as ever. Dine at the bar or in the smoothly run restaurant. Food combines timeless classics with modern dishes.

XX **Quaglino's**

16 Bury St ✉ SW1Y 6AL ⊖ Green Park – ✆ (020) 7930 6767 – quaglinos@danddlondon.com – Fax (020) 7930 2732 – Closed 25-26 December and 1 January 30 AIV **j**

Rest – (booking essential) Carte £ 25/41

◆ Descend the sweeping staircase into the capacious room where a busy and buzzy atmosphere prevails. Watch the chefs prepare everything from osso bucco to fish and chips.

XX **Mint Leaf**

Suffolk Pl ✉ SW1Y 4HX ⊖ Piccadilly Circus – ✆ (020) 7930 9020 – reservations@mintleafrestaurant.com – Fax (020) 7930 6205 – Closed lunch Saturday and Sunday 31 AKV **k**

Rest – Indian Menu £ 15 – Carte £ 33/40

◆ Basement restaurant in theatreland. Cavernous dining room incorporating busy, trendy bar with unique cocktail list and loud music. Helpful service. Contemporary Indian dishes.

XX **Brasserie Roux**

8 Pall Mall ✉ SW1Y 5NG ⊖ Piccadilly Circus – ✆ (020) 7968 2900 – h3144-fb4@accor.com – Fax (020) 7747 2251 31 AKV **a**

Rest – French Menu £ 20/25 – Carte £ 26/35

◆ Informal, smart, classic brasserie style with large windows making the most of the location. Large menu of French classics with many daily specials; comprehensive wine list.

XX **Franco's**

61 Jermyn St ✉ SW1Y 6LX ⊖ Green Park – ✆ (020) 7499 2211 – reserve@francoslondon.com – Fax (020) 7495 1375 – Closed 24 December-2 January, Sunday and Bank Holidays 30 AIV **d**

Rest – Italian (booking essential) Menu £ 25 (lunch) – Carte £ 36/45

◆ Great all day menu at 'the café'. Further in, regulars have taken to smart refurbishment. Classic/modern Italian cooking allows bold but refined flavours to shine through.

XX **The Avenue**

7-9 St James's St ✉ SW1A 1EE ⊖ Green Park – ✆ (020) 7321 2111 – avenue@egami.co.uk – Fax (020) 7321 2500 – Closed 25-26 December, Saturday lunch and Sunday 30 AIV **y**

Rest – Menu £ 22 – Carte £ 29/48

◆ The attractive and stylish bar is a local favourite. Behind is a striking, modern and busy restaurant. Appealing and contemporary food. Pre-theatre menu available.

XX **Matsuri - St James's**

15 Bury St ✉ SW1Y 6AL ⊖ Green Park – ✆ (020) 7839 1101 – dine@matsuri-restaurant.com – Fax (020) 7930 7010 – Closed Christmas and New Year 30 AIV **w**

Rest – Japanese Menu £ 35 – Carte £ 28/71

◆ Specialising in theatrical and precise teppan-yaki cooking. Separate restaurant offers sushi delicacies. Charming service by traditionally dressed staff.

XX **Noura Central**

22 Lower Regent St ✉ SW1Y 4UJ ⊖ Piccadilly Circus – ✆ (020) 7839 2020 – Fax (020) 7839 7700 31 AKV **d**

Rest – Lebanese Menu £ 18/30 – Carte £ 20/39

◆ Eye-catching Lebanese façade, matched by sleek interior design. Buzzy atmosphere enhanced by amplified background music. Large menus cover all aspects of Lebanese cuisine.

Al Duca

4-5 Duke of York St ✉ SW1Y 6LA ⊖ Piccadilly Circus – ✆ (020) 7839 3090 – info@alduca-restaurants.co.uk – Fax (020) 7839 4050 – Closed 25 December, Sunday and Bank Holidays 31 AJV **r**

Rest – Italian Menu £ 25/27

◆ Relaxed, modern, stylish restaurant. Friendly and approachable service of robust and rustic Italian dishes. Set priced menu is good value.

Inn the Park

St James's Park ✉ SW1A 2BJ ⊖ Charing Cross – ✆ (020) 7451 9999 – info@innthepark.com – Fax (020) 7451 9998 – Closed 25 December 31 AKV **n**

Rest – British Carte £ 32/52

◆ Eco-friendly restaurant with grass covered roof; pleasant views across park and lakes. Super-heated dining terrace. Modern British menus of tasty, wholesome dishes.

Portrait

3rd Floor, National Portrait Gallery, St Martin's Pl ✉ WC2H 0HE ⊖ Charing Cross – ✆ (020) 7312 2490 – portrait.restaurant@searcys.co.uk – Fax (020) 7925 0244 – Closed 25-26 December 31 ALV **n**

Rest – (lunch only and dinner Thursday and Friday) (booking essential) Carte £ 25/46

◆ On the top floor of National Portrait Gallery with rooftop local landmark views: a charming spot for lunch. Modern British/European dishes find favour with hungry tourists.

The National Dining Rooms

Sainsbury Wing, The National Gallery, Trafalgar Sq ✉ WC2N 5DN ⊖ Charing Cross – ✆ (020) 7747 2525 – enquiries@thenationaldiningrooms.co.uk – Closed Christmas 31 AKV **b**

Rest – British (lunch only and dinner Wednesday) Menu £ 30

◆ Set on the East Wing's first floor, you can tuck into cakes in the bakery or grab a prime corner table in the restaurant for great views and proudly seasonal British menus.

Soho – Gtr London – ✉ W1/WC2

The Soho

4 Richmond Mews ✉ W1D 3DH ⊖ Tottenham Court Road – ✆ (020) 7559 3000 – soho@firmdale.com – Fax (020) 7559 3003 31 AKU **n**

83 rm – 🛉£ 300 🛉🛉£ 370, ☕ £ 18.50 – 2 suites

Rest *Refuel* – Menu £ 20 – Carte £ 26/37

◆ Opened in autumn 2004: stylish hotel with two screening rooms, comfy drawing room and up-to-the-minute bedrooms, some vivid, others more muted, all boasting hi-tec extras. Contemporary bar and restaurant.

Hampshire

Leicester Sq ✉ WC2H 7LH ⊖ Leicester Square – ✆ (020) 7839 9399 – reshamp@radisson.com – Fax (020) 7930 8122 31 AKU **s**

119 rm – 🛉£ 407/436 🛉🛉£ 436, ☕ £ 19 – 5 suites

Rest *The Apex* – (dinner only) Menu £ 26 – Carte £ 22/33

◆ The bright lights of the city are literally outside and many rooms overlook the bustling Square. Inside it is tranquil and comfortable with well-appointed bedrooms. Formal yet relaxing dining room with immaculately dressed tables.

Courthouse Kempinski

19-21 Great Marlborough St ✉ W1F 7HL ⊖ Oxford Circus – ✆ (020) 7297 5555 – info@courthouse-hotel.com – Fax (020) 7297 5566 30 AIU **z**

107 rm – 🛉£ 199/352 🛉🛉£ 199/352, ☕ £ 22.50 – 5 suites

Rest *Silk* – see restaurant listing

Rest *The Carnaby* – Menu £ 16/20 – Carte £ 23/34

◆ Striking Grade II listed ex magistrates' court: interior fused imaginatively with original features; for example, the bar incorporates three former cells. Ultra stylish rooms. Informal Carnaby offers extensive French, modern and British menu.

Hazlitt's without rest
6 Frith St ✉ W1D 3JA ⊖ Tottenham Court Road – ☎ (020) 7434 1771 – reservations@hazlitts.co.uk – Fax (020) 7439 1524 31 AKU **u**
22 rm – †£ 206 ††£ 241, ☐ £9.75 – 1 suite
◆ A row of three adjoining early 18C town houses and former home of the eponymous essayist. Individual and charming bedrooms, many with antique furniture and Victorian baths.

XXX ✿ **L'Escargot**
48 Greek St ✉ W1D 4EF ⊖ Tottenham Court Road – ☎ (020) 7437 2679 – sales@whitestarline.org.uk – Fax (020) 7437 0790 31 AKU **b**
Rest – (Closed 25-26 December, 1 January, Sunday and Saturday lunch) Menu £ 18 (lunch) – Carte £ 28/30
Rest *Picasso Room* – (Closed 25-26 December, 1 January, Sunday and Monday) Menu £ 25 (lunch)/42
Spec. Tian of crab with shrimp and avocado, citrus mayonnaise. Roast rump of lamb with an onion purée. Raspberry soufflé with raspberry and lime sauce.
◆ Soho institution. Ground Floor is chic, vibrant brasserie with early-evening buzz of theatre-goers. Finely judged modern dishes. Intimate and more formal upstairs Picasso Room famed for its limited edition art.

XXX **Quo Vadis**
26-29 Dean St ✉ W1D 3LL ⊖ Tottenham Court Road – ☎ (020) 7437 9585 – sales@whitestarline.org.uk – Fax (020) 7734 7593 – Closed 24-25 December, 1 January, Saturday lunch and Sunday 31 AKU **v**
Rest – Italian Menu £ 18 (lunch) – Carte £ 25/31
◆ Stained glass windows and a neon sign hint at the smooth modernity of the interior. Modern artwork abounds. Contemporary cooking and a serious wine list.

XXX **Red Fort**
77 Dean St ✉ W1D 3SH ⊖ Tottenham Court Road – ☎ (020) 7437 2525 – info@redfort.co.uk – Fax (020) 7434 0721 – Closed lunch Saturday, Sunday and Bank Holidays 31 AKU **x**
Rest – Indian Carte £ 35/45
◆ Smart, stylish restaurant with modern water feature and glass ceiling to rear. Seasonally changing menus of authentic dishes handed down over generations.

XX ✿ **Richard Corrigan at Lindsay House**
21 Romilly St ✉ W1D 5AF ⊖ Leicester Square – ☎ (020) 7439 0450 – richardcorrigan@lindsayhouse.co.uk – Fax (020) 7437 7349 – Closed 25, 26 December, 1 January, Saturday lunch and Sunday 31 AKU **f**
Rest – Menu £ 56 (dinner) – Carte lunch £ 31/52
Spec. Ballotine of foie gras with parfait of liver, hazelnuts. Pan-roast halibut with langoustine ravioli and samphire. Peanut parfait with caramelised banana and praline ice cream.
◆ Handsome four storey house; ring the doorbell before being welcomed into one of two cosy, fabric-clad dining rooms. Modern, confidently-presented cooking boasts bold flavours.

XX **Floridita**
100 Wardour St ✉ W1F 0TN ⊖ Tottenham Court Road – ☎ (020) 7314 4000 – Fax (020) 7314 4040 – Closed 24-26 December, 1 January and Sunday 31 AKU **z**
Rest – Latin American (dinner only and lunch mid November-December) Carte £ 32/61
◆ Buzzy destination where the Latino cuisine is a fiery accompaniment to the vivacious Cuban dancing. Slightly less frenetic upstairs in the Spanish tapas and cocktail bar.

XX **Silk** – at Courthouse Kempinksi H.

19-21 Great Marlborough St ✉ W1F 7HL ⊖ Oxford Circus – ✆ (020) 7297 5567 – Fax (020) 7297 5566 – Closed Sunday-Monday 30 AIU **z**

Rest – (dinner only) Carte £ 24/36

◆ Stunningly unique former courtroom with original panelling, court benches and glass roof. Menu follows the journey of the Silk Route with Asian, Indian and Italian influences.

XX **Café Lazeez**

21 Dean St ✉ W1D 3TN ⊖ Tottenham Court Road – ✆ (020) 7434 9393 – soho@cafelazeez.com – Fax (020) 7434 0022 – Closed Sunday lunch 31 AKU **d**

Rest – Indian Carte £ 27/35

◆ In the same building as Soho Theatre; the bar hums before shows, restaurant is popular for pre- and post-theatre meals of modern Indian fare. Refined décor; private booths.

XX **Benja**

17 Beak St ✉ W1F 9RW ⊖ Oxford Circus – ✆ (020) 7287 0555 – info@krua.co.uk – Fax (020) 7287 0056 – Closed 25 December, Sunday and lunch Bank Holidays 31 AIU **i**

Rest – Thai Carte £ 19/32

◆ Named after the Thai word for 5, since there are 5 owners, 5 floors and 5 colours used to decorate. Authentic, vibrant Thai cooking. Best place to sit is spacious first floor.

XX **Vasco and Piero's Pavilion**

15 Poland St ✉ W1F 8QE ⊖ Tottenham Court Road – ✆ (020) 7437 8774 – eat@vascosfood.com – Fax (020) 7437 0467 – Closed Saturday lunch, Sunday and Bank Holidays 31 AJU **b**

Rest – Italian (booking essential at lunch) Menu £ 28 (dinner) – Carte lunch £ 26/36

◆ A long standing, family run Italian restaurant with a loyal local following. Pleasant service under the owners' guidance. Warm décor and traditional cooking.

XX **La Trouvaille**

12A Newburgh St ✉ W1F 7RR ⊖ Piccadilly Circus – ✆ (020) 7287 8488 – Fax (020) 7434 4170 – closed 25 December, Saturday lunch, Sunday and Bank Holidays 30 AIU **g**

Rest – French Menu £ 18/33

◆ Atmospheric restaurant located just off Carnaby Street. Hearty, robust French cooking with a rustic character. French wine list with the emphasis on southern regions.

XX **Stanza**

97-107 Shaftesbury Ave ✉ W1D 5DY ⊖ Leicester Square – ✆ (020) 7494 3020 – reception@stanzalondon.com – Fax (020) 7494 3050 – Closed Easter, 25 December and Sunday 31 AKU **m**

Rest – Menu £ 19 (dinner) – Carte £ 23/36

◆ Large bar with vibrant orange seats; open dining room has views of China town. Rustic seasonal cooking; the chef is from Northern England - as are many of the ingredients.

X **Arbutus** (Anthony Demetre)

✿

63-64 Frith St ✉ W1D 3JW ⊖ Tottenham Court Road – ✆ (020) 7734 4545 – info@arbutusrestaurant.co.uk – Fax (020) 7287 8624 – Closed 25-26 December and 1 January 31 AKU **n**

Rest – Menu £ 16 (lunch) – Carte £ 29/35

Spec. Braised pig's head with potato purée and caramelised onions. Bavette of beef with gratin dauphinois, red wine and shallot sauce. Vanilla panna cotta with poached rhubarb.

◆ Dining room and bar that's bright and stylish without trying too hard. Bistro classics turned on their head: poised, carefully crafted cooking - but dishes still pack a punch.

Yauatcha

15 Broadwick St ✉ W1F 0DL ⊖ Tottenham Court Road – ☎ (020) 7494 8888 – mail@yauatcha.com – Fax (020) 7494 8889 – Closed 24-25 December 31 AJU **k**

Rest – Chinese Carte £ 20/48

Spec. Prawn cheung fun; scallop shumai. Szechuan tea smoked duck with Chinese pancake, kumquat and plum sauce. White chocolate with mandarin and kumquat rice pudding.

◆ Converted 1960s post office in heart of Soho. Choose between darker, atmospheric basement or lighter, brighter ground floor. Refined Chinese dishes served on both levels.

Bertorelli

11-13 Frith St ✉ W1D 4RB ⊖ Tottenham Court Road – ☎ (020) 7494 3491 – bertorelli-soho@groupechezgerard.co.uk – Fax (020) 7439 9431 – Closed 25-26 December 31 AKU **t**

Rest – Italian Carte £ 20/40

◆ A haven of tranquillity from the bustling street below. Discreet and professionally run first floor restaurant with Italian menu. Popular ground floor café.

Alastair Little

49 Frith St ✉ W1D 5SG ⊖ Tottenham Court Road – ☎ (020) 7734 5183 – Fax (020) 7734 5206 – Closed Sunday, Saturday lunch and Bank Holidays 31 AKU **y**

Rest – (booking essential) Menu £ 38/40

◆ The eponymous owner was at the vanguard of Soho's culinary renaissance. Tasty, daily changing British based cuisine; the compact room is rustic and simple.

Bar Shu

28 Frith St ✉ W1D 5LF ⊖ Leicester Square – ☎ (020) 7287 8822 – Fax (020) 7287 8858 – Closed 25-26 December 31 AKU **g**

Rest – Chinese Carte £ 20/25

◆ Three floors decorated in carved wood and lanterns. Truly authentic Sichuan cooking typified by intense heat generated by peppers and chillies. Not for the faint hearted!

Chinese Experience

118 Shaftesbury Ave ✉ W1D 5EP ⊖ Leicester Square – ☎ (020) 7437 0377 – info@chineseexperience.com 31 AKU **r**

Rest – Chinese Menu £ 15 – Carte approx. £ 19

◆ Bright, airy restaurant: sit at long bench or chunky wood tables. Large, good value menus cover a wide range of Chinese dishes. Knowledgable service. A buzzy, informal place.

Imli

167-169 Wardour St ✉ W1F 8WR ⊖ Tottenham Court Road – ☎ (020) 7287 4243 – info@imli.co.uk – Fax (020) 7287 4245 – Closed 25 December and 1 January 31 AKU **w**

Rest – Indian Menu £ 17 (dinner) – Carte £ 11/18

◆ Long, spacious interior is a busy, buzzy place to be: not the venue to while away an evening! Good value, fresh and tasty Indian tapas style dishes prove a popular currency.

Barrafina

54 Frith St ✉ W1D 4SL – ☎ (020) 7813 8016 – info@barrafina.co.uk – Fax (020) 7813 8011 – Closed Sunday 31 AKU **c**

Rest – Spanish (Tapas) (bookings not accepted) Carte £ 19/35

◆ Centred around a counter with seating for 20, come here if you want authentic Spanish tapas served in a buzzy atmosphere. Seafood is a speciality and the Jabugo ham a must.

Aurora

49 Lexington St ✉ W1F 9AP ⊖ Piccadilly Circus – ☎ (020) 7494 0514 – Closed Sunday 31 AJU **e**

Rest – (booking essential) Carte £ 19/26

◆ An informal, no-nonsense, bohemian style bistro with a small, but pretty, walled garden terrace. Short but balanced menu; simple fresh food. Pleasant, languid atmosphere.

Closed

Fung Shing

15 Lisle St ✉ WC2H 7BE ⊖ Leicester Square – ✆ (020) 7437 1539 – Fax (020) 7734 0284 – Closed 24-26 December and lunch Bank Holidays 31 AKU **j**

Rest – Chinese Menu £ 17 – Carte £ 16/25

◆ A long-standing Chinese restaurant on the edge of Chinatown. Chatty and pleasant service. A mix of authentic, rustic dishes and the more adventurous chef's specials.

Strand and Covent Garden – Gtr London – ✉ WC2

One Aldwych

1 Aldwych ✉ WC2B 4RH ⊖ Covent Garden – ✆ (020) 7300 1000 – sales@onealdwych.com – Fax (020) 7300 1001 32 AMU **r**

96 rm – †£ 447 ††£ 447, ☐ £29.50 – 9 suites

Rest *Axis* – see restaurant listing

Rest *Indigo* – (Closed Sunday, Easter and Christmas) Menu £ 18 – Carte £ 28/51

◆ Decorative Edwardian building, former home to the Morning Post newspaper. Now a stylish and contemporary address with modern artwork, a screening room and hi-tech bedrooms. All-day restaurant looks down on fashionable bar.

Swissôtel The Howard

Temple Pl ✉ WC2R 2PR ⊖ Temple – ✆ (020) 7836 3555 – reservations.london@swissotel.com – Fax (020) 7379 4547 32 AMU **e**

177 rm – †£ 188/316 ††£ 723, ☐ £23.50 – 12 suites

Rest *Jaan* – see restaurant listing

◆ Cool elegance is the order of the day at this handsomely appointed hotel. Many of the comfortable rooms enjoy balcony views of the Thames. Attentive service.

The Waldorf Hilton

Aldwych ✉ WC2B 4DD ⊖ Covent Garden – ✆ (020) 7836 2400 – enquiry.waldorflondon@hilton.com – Fax (020) 7836 4648 32 AMU **u**

289 rm – †£ 198/421 ††£ 198/421, ☐ £22 – 10 suites

Rest *Homage* – (Closed lunch Saturday and Sunday) Menu £ 20 – Carte £ 29/44

◆ Impressive curved and columned façade: an Edwardian landmark. Basement leisure club. Ornate meeting rooms. Two bedroom styles: one contemporary, one more traditional. Large, modish brasserie with extensive range of modern menus.

St Martins Lane

45 St Martin's Lane ✉ WC2N 4HX ⊖ Charing Cross – ✆ (020) 7300 5500 – sml@morganshotelgroup.com – Fax (020) 7300 5501 31 ALU **e**

202 rm – †£ 252/393 ††£ 276/417, ☐ £20.50 – 2 suites

Rest *Asia de Cuba* – Asian Carte £ 53/83

◆ The unmistakable hand of Philippe Starck evident at this most contemporary of hotels. Unique and stylish, from the starkly modern lobby to the state-of-the-art rooms. 350 varieties of rum and tasty Asian dishes at fashionable Asia de Cuba.

The Ivy

1-5 West St ✉ WC2H 9NQ ⊖ Leicester Square – ✆ (020) 7836 4751 – Fax (020) 7240 9333 – Closed 24-26 December, 1 January and August Bank Holiday 31 AKU **p**

Rest – Carte £ 30/54

◆ Wood panelling and stained glass combine with an unpretentious menu to create a veritable institution. A favourite of 'celebrities', so securing a table can be challenging.

Axis

1 Aldwych ✉ WC2B 4RH ⊖ Covent Garden – ✆ (020) 7300 0300 – axis@onealdwych.com – Fax (020) 7300 0301 – Closed 24 December-4 January, Easter, Sunday, Saturday lunch and Bank Holidays 31 AMU **r**

Rest – Menu £ 18 (lunch) – Carte £ 28/37

◆ Lower-level room overlooked by gallery bar. Muted tones, black leather chairs and vast futuristic mural appeal to the fashion cognoscenti. Globally-influenced menu.

XXX **Jaan** – at Swissôtel The Howard
Temple Pl ✉ WC2R 2PR ⊖ Temple – ✆ (020) 7300 1700 – jaan.london@swissotel.com – Fax (020) 7240 7816 – Closed Saturday lunch and Sunday and bank holidays 32 AMU **e**
Rest – Menu £ 24/38 – Carte £ 33/49
◆ Bright room on the ground floor of the hotel with large windows overlooking an attractive terrace. Original cooking - modern French with Cambodian flavours and ingredients.

XX **J. Sheekey**
28-32 St Martin's Court ✉ WC2 4AL ⊖ Leicester Square – ✆ (020) 7240 2565 – reservations@j-sheekey.co.uk – Fax (020) 7497 0891 – Closed 25-26 December, 1 January and August Bank Holiday 31 ALU **v**
Rest – Seafood (booking essential) Carte £ 25/51
◆ Festooned with photographs of actors and linked to the theatrical world since opening in 1890. Wood panels and alcove tables add famed intimacy. Accomplished seafood cooking.

XX **Rules**
35 Maiden Lane ✉ WC2E 7LB ⊖ Leicester Square – ✆ (020) 7836 5314 – info@rules.co.uk – Fax (020) 7497 1081 – closed 4 days Christmas 31 ALU **n**
Rest – British (booking essential) Carte £ 35/53
◆ London's oldest restaurant boasts a fine collection of antique cartoons, drawings and paintings. Tradition continues in the menu, specialising in game from its own estate.

XX **Clos Maggiore**
33 King St ✉ WC2E 8JD ⊖ Leicester Square – ✆ (020) 7379 9696 – enquiries@closmaggiore.com – Fax (020) 7379 6767 – Closed 25-26 December, Saturday and Sunday lunch and Bank Holidays 31 ALU **z**
Rest – French Menu £ 20 (lunch) – Carte £ 46/56
◆ Walls covered with flowering branches create delightful woodland feel to rear dining area with retractable glass roof. Seriously accomplished, original, rustic French cooking.

XX **Admiralty**
Somerset House, The Strand ✉ WC2R 1LA ⊖ Temple – ✆ (020) 7845 4646 – info@theadmiraltyrestaurant.com – Fax (020) 7845 4658 – Closed 24-27 December, dinner Sunday and Bank Holiday Mondays 32 AMU **a**
Rest – Menu £ 16 (lunch) – Carte £ 26/37
◆ Interconnecting rooms with bold colours and informal service contrast with its setting within the restored Georgian splendour of Somerset House. 'Cuisine de terroir'.

XX **Le Deuxième**
65a Long Acre ✉ WC2E 9JH ⊖ Covent Garden – ✆ (020) 7379 0033 – Fax (020) 7379 0066 – Closed 24-25 December 31 ALU **b**
Rest – Menu £ 16 – Carte £ 29/30
◆ Caters well for theatregoers: opens early, closes late. Buzzy eatery, quietly decorated in white with subtle lighting. Varied international menu: Japanese to Mediterranean.

X ✿ **L'Atelier de Joël Robuchon**
13-15 West St ✉ WC2H 9NE ⊖ Leicester Square – ✆ (020) 7010 8600 – info@joelrobuchon.co.uk – Fax (020) 7010 8601 31 AKU **a**
Rest – French (Closed 24-26 December and 1-2 January) Carte £ 33/75
Rest *La Cuisine* – French (Closed 24-26 December, 1-2 January and Saturday lunch) Carte £ 33/100
Spec. Fresh mackerel tart with parmesan shavings and olives. Free range quail stuffed with foie gras, truffled mashed potatoes. Araguani chocolate, white chocolate ice cream and Oreo cookie.
◆ Entrance into trendy atelier with counter seating; upstairs the more structured La Cuisine has wonderfully delicate, precise modern French cooking. Cool top floor lounge bar.

Le Café du Jardin

28 Wellington St ✉ WC2E 7BD ⊖ Covent Garden – ✆ (020) 7836 8769 – info@lecafedujardin.com – Fax (020) 7836 4123 – Closed 25-26 December 31 ALU **f**

Rest – Menu £ 16 – Carte £ 28/34

◆ Divided into two floors with the downstairs slightly more comfortable. Light and contemporary interior with European-influenced cooking. Ideally placed for the Opera House.

Bedford & Strand

1a Bedford St ✉ WC2E 9HH ⊖ Charing Cross – ✆ (020) 7836 3033 – Closed 25-26 and 31 December, 1 January, Saturday lunch, Sunday and Bank Holidays 31 ALU **c**

Rest – (booking essential) Menu £ 16 – Carte £ 24/53

◆ Basement bistro/wine bar with simple décor and easy-going atmosphere; kitchen sources well and has a light touch with Italian, French and British dishes.

Great Queen Street

32 Great Queen St ✉ WC2B 5AA ⊖ Holborn – ✆ (020) 7242 0622 – Fax (020) 7404 9582 – Closed Monday lunch and Sunday 31 ALT **d**

Rest – British (booking essential) Carte £ 20/30

◆ Simply decorated, with ruby red walls. The menu is a model of British understatement; the cooking, confident and satisfying with laudably low prices and generous portions.

Victoria – Gtr London – ✉ SW1

i Victoria Station Forecourt ✆ (09068) 663344

The Goring

15 Beeston Pl, Grosvenor Gdns ✉ SW1W 0JW ⊖ Victoria – ✆ (020) 7396 9000 – reception@goringhotel.co.uk – Fax (020) 7834 4393 38 AIX **a**

65 rm – †£ 327/393 ††£ 386/434, ☕ £ 23 – 6 suites – **Rest** – British (Closed Saturday lunch) Menu £ 33/44

◆ Opened in 1910 as a quintessentially English hotel. The fourth generation of Goring is now at the helm. Many of the attractive rooms overlook a peaceful garden. Elegantly appointed restaurant provides memorable dining experience.

Crowne Plaza London - St James

45 Buckingham Gate ✉ SW1E 6AF ⊖ St James's Park – ✆ (020) 7834 6655 – sales@cplonsj.co.uk – Fax (020) 7630 7587 39 AJX **e**

323 rm – †£ 323 ††£ 388, ☕ £ 16 – 19 suites

Rest Quilon and **Bank** – see restaurant listing

Rest ***Bistro 51*** – Menu £ 18/22 – Carte £ 30/36

◆ Built in 1897 as serviced accommodation for visiting aristocrats. Behind the impressive Edwardian façade lies an equally elegant interior. Quietest rooms overlook courtyard. Bright and informal café-style restaurant.

51 Buckingham Gate

51 Buckingham Gate ✉ SW1E 6AF ⊖ St James's Park – ✆ (020) 7769 7766 – info@51-buckinghamgate.co.uk – Fax (020) 7828 5909 39 AJX **s**

86 suites – ††£ 423/628, ☕ £ 21.75

Rest Quilon and **Bank** – see restaurant listing

◆ Canopied entrance leads to luxurious suites: every detail considered, every mod con provided. Colour schemes echoed in plants and paintings. Butler and nanny service.

41 without rest

41 Buckingham Palace Rd ✉ SW1W 0PS ⊖ Victoria – ✆ (020) 7300 0041 – book41@rchmail.com – Fax (020) 7300 0141 38 AIX **n**

27 rm – †£ 264/382 ††£ 288/415, ☕ £ 25 – 1 suite

◆ Discreet appearance; exudes exclusive air. Leather armchairs; bookcases line the walls. Intimate service. State-of-the-art rooms where hi-tec and fireplace merge appealingly.

The Rubens at The Palace

39 Buckingham Palace Rd ✉ SW1W 0PS ⊖ Victoria – ✆ (020) 7834 6600 – bookrb@rchmail.com – Fax (020) 7828 5401 38 AIX **n**

170 rm – †£ 155/300 ††£ 172/320, ☕ £18.50 – 2 suites – **Rest** – (dinner only) Menu £ 35 – Carte £ 35/47

◆ Traditional hotel with an air of understated elegance. Tastefully furnished rooms: the Royal Wing, themed after Kings and Queens, features TVs in bathrooms. Smart carvery restaurant.

Park Plaza Victoria

rm,

239 Vauxhall Bridge Rd ✉ SW1V 1EQ ⊖ Victoria – ✆ (020) 7769 9999 – info@vpp.com – Fax (020) 7769 9998 38 AIY **a**

299 rm – †£ 294/306 ††£ 294/435, ☕ £16

Rest *J.B.'s* – (Closed lunch Saturday and Sunday) Carte £ 27/38

◆ Conveniently located for Victoria station. Spacious modern interior filled with modish artwork. State-of-the-art meeting rooms. Well-equipped rooms boast a host of facilities. Appealing dining room offers modern European cuisine.

B + B Belgravia without rest

64-66 Ebury St ✉ SW1W 9QD ⊖ Victoria – ✆ (020) 7259 8570 – info@bb-belgravia.com – Fax (020) 7259 8591 38 RZF **x**

17 rm ☕ – †£ 97/107 ††£ 107

◆ Two houses, three floors, and, considering the location, some of the best value accommodation in town. Sleek, clean-lined rooms. Breakfast overlooking little garden terrace.

The Cinnamon Club

30-32 Great Smith St ✉ SW1P 3BU ⊖ St James's Park – ✆ (020) 7222 2555 – info@cinnamonclub.com – Fax (020) 7222 1333 – Closed Sunday 39 AKX **c**

Rest – Indian Menu £ 22 (lunch) – Carte £ 35/48

◆ Housed in former Westminster Library: exterior has ornate detail, interior is stylish and modern. Walls are lined with books. New Wave Indian cooking with plenty of choice.

Quilon – at Crowne Plaza London - St James H.

41 Buckingham Gate ✉ SW1 6AF ⊖ St James's Park – ✆ (020) 7821 1899 – info@quilonrestaurant.co.uk – Fax (020) 7233 9597 – Closed 25 December and Saturday lunch 39 AJX **e**

Rest – Indian Menu £ 18 – Carte £ 34/47

Spec. Crab cakes with curry leaves, ginger and green chillies. Char-grilled lobster, prawn, fish and scallops with a mild sauce. Spiced chocolate dessert.

◆ Original, vibrant and well balanced Indian dishes, many of which originate from the South West coast. Excellent use of spices, appealing seafood specialities and graceful service.

Santini

29 Ebury St ✉ SW1W 0NZ ⊖ Victoria – ✆ (020) 7730 4094 – info@santini-restaurant.com – Fax (020) 7730 0544 38 AHY **v**

Rest – Italian Carte £ 35/55

◆ Discreet, refined and elegant modern Italian restaurant. Assured and professional service. Extensive selection of modern dishes and a more affordable set lunch menu.

Shepherd's

Marsham Court, Marsham St ✉ SW1P 4LA ⊖ Pimlico – ✆ (020) 7834 9552 – admin@langansrestaurants.co.uk – Fax (020) 7233 6047 – Closed Saturday, Sunday and Bank Holidays 39 AKY **z**

Rest – British (booking essential) Menu £ 33

◆ A truly English restaurant where game and traditional puddings are a highlight. Popular with those from Westminster - the booths offer a degree of privacy.

XXX ✿ **Roussillon** (Alex Gauthier) — A/C VISA MC AE

16 St Barnabas St ✉ SW1W 8PE ⊖ Sloane Square – ✆ (020) 7730 5550 – alexis@roussillon.co.uk – Fax (020) 7824 8617 – Closed Saturday lunch and Sunday — 38 AHZ **c**

Rest – French Menu £ 35/55 ✿

Spec. Black truffle risotto, veal jus. Highland venison with pumpkin, poached pear and celeriac, tuffle purée. Louis XV, crunchy praline and chocolate.

◆ Tucked away in a smart residential area. Cooking clearly focuses on the quality of the ingredients. Seasonal menu with inventive elements and a French base.

XX **Atami** — A/C VISA MC AE

37 Monck St (entrance on Great Peter St) ✉ SW1P 2BL ⊖ Pimlico – ✆ (020) 7222 2218 – mail@atami-restaurant.com – Fax (020) 7222 2788 – Closed Saturday lunch and Sunday — 39 AKY **a**

Rest – Japanese Menu £ 23 (lunch) – Carte £ 25/37

◆ Clean, modern lines illuminated by vast ceiling orbs induce a sense of calm. Menus true to Japanese roots feature sushi and sashimi turning down interesting modern highways.

XX **Il Convivio** — A/C VISA MC AE

143 Ebury St ✉ SW1W 9QN ⊖ Sloane Square – ✆ (020) 7730 4099 – comments@etruscarestaurants.com – Fax (020) 7730 4103 – closed 25 December and Sunday — 38 AHY **a**

Rest – Italian Menu £ 22 (lunch) – Carte approx. £ 34

◆ A retractable roof provides alfresco dining to part of this comfortable and modern restaurant. Contemporary and traditional Italian menu with home-made pasta specialities.

XX **Bank** — A/C VISA MC AE

45 Buckingham Gate ✉ SW1E 6BS ⊖ St James's Park – ✆ (020) 7630 6644 – reservations.westminster@bankrestaurants.com – Fax (020) 7630 5665 – Closed Saturday lunch, Sunday and Bank Holidays — 39 AJX **e**

Rest – (booking essential at lunch) Carte £ 29/45

◆ The understated entrance belies the vibrant contemporary interior. One of Europe's longest bars has a lively atmosphere. Conservatory restaurant, modern European cooking.

XX **Boisdale** — A/C VISA MC AE

15 Eccleston St ✉ SW1W 9LX ⊖ Victoria – ✆ (020) 7730 6922 – info@boisdale.co.uk – Fax (020) 7730 0548 – closed Christmas and Sunday — 38 AHY **c**

Rest – Scottish Carte £ 29/48

◆ Popular haunt of politicians; dark green, lacquer red panelled interior. Run by a Scot of Clanranald, hence modern British dishes with Scottish flavour.

XX **Rex Whistler** — A/C VISA MC AE

Tate Britain, Millbank ✉ SW1P 4RG ⊖ Pimlico – ✆ (020) 7887 8825 – tate.restaurant@tate.org.uk – Fax (020) 7887 8902 – Closed 25 December — 39 ALY **c**

Rest – (lunch only) (booking essential) Carte £ 31/38 ✿

◆ Continue your appreciation of art when lunching in this basement room decorated with original Rex Whistler murals. Forever busy, it offers modern British fare.

XX **Ken Lo's Memories of China** — A/C VISA MC AE

65-69 Ebury St ✉ SW1W 0NZ ⊖ Victoria – ✆ (020) 7730 7734 – Fax (020) 7730 2992 – Closed 25-26 December, Sunday lunch and Bank Holidays — 38 AHY **u**

Rest – Chinese Menu £ 19/30 – Carte £ 29/35

◆ An air of tranquillity pervades this traditionally furnished room. Lattice screens add extra privacy. Extensive Chinese menu: bold flavours with a clean, fresh style.

XX **Quirinale** VISA MC AE

North Court, 1 Great Peter St ⊖ Westminster – ✆ (020) 7222 7080 – info@quirinale.co.uk – Closed August, 1week Christmas, Saturday and Sunday 39 ALX **a**

Rest – Italian Carte £ 28/38

◆ Light and bright Italian restaurant with contemporary, minimalist feel typified by cream leather banquettes. Seasonally-changing menu encompasses all things Italian.

X **Olivo** A/C VISA MC AE

21 Eccleston St ✉ SW1W 9LX ⊖ Victoria – ✆ (020) 7730 2505 – maurosanna@oliveto.fsnet.co.uk – Fax (020) 7823 5377 – Closed Bank Holidays, lunch Saturday and Sunday 38 AHY **z**

Rest – Italian Menu £ 21 (lunch) – Carte £ 26/30

◆ Rustic, informal Italian restaurant. Relaxed atmosphere provided by the friendly staff. Simple, non-fussy cuisine with emphasis on best available fresh produce.

X **La Poule au Pot** A/C VISA MC AE

231 Ebury St ✉ SW1W 8UT ⊖ Sloane Square – ✆ (020) 7730 7763 – Fax (020) 7259 9651 – Closed 25-26 December 38 AHY **p**

Rest – French Menu £ 17 – Carte £ 27/41

◆ The subdued lighting and friendly informality make this one of London's more romantic restaurants. Classic French menu with extensive plats du jour.

X **Olivomare** A/C VISA MC AE

10 Lower Belgrave St ✉ SW1W 0LJ ⊖ Victoria – ✆ (020) 7730 9022 – maurosanna@oliveto.fsnet.co.uk – Fax (020) 7823 5377 – Closed Sunday and Bank Holidays 38 AHY **b**

Rest – Seafood Carte £ 29/36

◆ Chic minimalist décor with magic-eye mural of intertwined fish. The food is robust and full-flavoured; seafood is the theme, with a subtle Sardinian subtext. Assured service.

The Ebury A/C VISA MC AE

11 Pimlico Rd ✉ SW1W 8NA ⊖ Sloane Square – ✆ (020) 7730 6784 – info@theebury.co.uk – Fax (020) 7730 6149 – Closed 25-26 December 38 AHZ **z**

Rest – Carte £ 25/30

◆ Victorian corner pub restaurant with walnut bar, simple tables and large seafood bar. Friendly service. Wide-ranging menu from snacks to full meals.

The Thomas Cubitt VISA MC AE

44 Elizabeth Street ✉ SW1W 9PA ⊖ Sloane Square – ✆ (020) 7730 6060 – reservations@thethomascubitt.co.uk – Fax (020) 7730 6055 – Closed 24 December-1 January 38 RZF **e**

Rest – (booking essential) Menu £ 25 – Carte £ 23/40

◆ Georgian pub refurbished and renamed after master builder. He'd approve of elegant, formal dining room. Carefully supplied ingredients underpin tasty, seasonal English dishes.

The ✿ award is the crème de la crème. This is awarded to restaurants which are really worth travelling miles for!

LONG COMPTON – Warks. – see Shipston-on-Stour

LONG CRENDON – Bucks. – 503 – pop. 2 383 – ✉ Aylesbury 11 C2

London 50 m – Aylesbury 11 m – Oxford 15 m

Angel with rm

47 Bicester Rd ✉ HP18 9EE – ✆ (01844) 208 268 – angelrestaurant@aol.co.uk – Fax (01844) 202 497 – Closed Sunday dinner

3 rm – £ 65 £ 85 – **Rest** – Menu £ 20 (lunch) – Carte £ 30/45

◆ Characterful former pub with low ceilings, leather furnished lounge bar and airy conservatory. Oft-changing menus offer tasty modern British cooking, with well-chosen wine list. Stylish bedrooms, all individually decorated. 3 is the cosiest, 4 the biggest.

LONG MELFORD – Suffolk – 504 W 27 – pop. 2 734 *Great Britain* 15 C3

London 62 m – Cambridge 34 m – Colchester 18 m – Ipswich 24 m

Melford Hall★ AC

Black Lion

Church Walk, The Green ✉ CO10 9DN – ✆ (01787) 312 356 – enquiries@blacklionhotel.net – Fax (01787) 374 557

9 rm – £ 99 £ 170 – 1 suite – **Rest** – Carte £ 23/36

◆ 17C inn overlooking the village green and beyond to the Tudor Melford Hall. Individual rooms have a mix of furnishings with much use of antique pine. Stylish restaurant with walled garden terrace.

Scutchers

Westgate St, on A 1092 ✉ CO10 9DP – ✆ (01787) 310 200 – eat@scutchers.com – Fax (01787) 375 700 – Closed Christmas, 10 days March, 10 days August, Sunday and Monday

Rest – Menu £ 20 – Carte £ 24/40

◆ Former medieval Hall House now contains an informal and unpretentious restaurant serving a range of creative modern dishes using good quality ingredients.

LONG SUTTON – Somerset – 503 L 30 – ✉ Langport 3 B3

London 132 m – Bridgwater 16 m – Yeovil 10 m

The Devonshire Arms with rm

✉ TA10 9LP – ✆ (01458) 241 271 – mail@thedevonshirearms.com – Fax (01458) 241 037 – Closed 25 December

9 rm – £ 65/75 £ 120 – **Rest** – (closed Sunday dinner October-May) (bookings not accepted) Menu £ 15 – Carte £ 22/33

◆ Contemporary styling typified by wood floors and leather sofas in this creeper-clad, 17C former hunting lodge. Food ranges from satisfying bar classics to the more refined. Luxurious bedrooms with bold, modern colour schemes and up-to-date facilities.

LONGHORSLEY – Northd. – 501 – see Morpeth

LONGRIDGE – Lancs. – 502 M 22 – pop. 7 491 20 A2

London 241 m – Blackburn 12 m – Burnley 18 m

The Longridge Restaurant

104-106 Higher Rd, Northeast : ½ m. by B 5269 following signs for Jeffrey Hill ✉ PR3 3SY – ✆ (01772) 784 969 – longridge@heathcotes.co.uk – Fax (01772) 785 713 – Closed Saturday lunch and Monday

Rest – Menu £ 25 (lunch) – Carte £ 35/52

◆ Former pub with stylish black and grey décor, sumptuous bar, comfy seats and elegant dining room. Modern, seasonal cooking boasts decidedly Lancastrian bias. Friendly service.

ENGLAND

Thyme
1-3 Inglewhite Rd ✉ PR3 3JR – ✆ (01772) 786888 – Fax (01772) 784138 – Closed 2-3 January and Monday except December
Rest – Menu £ 11 (lunch) – Carte £ 23/32
◆ Modern restaurant near roundabout; wooden floors and modern lighting; artwork on the walls. Locally sourced produce used as much as possible. Good value, especially at lunch.

at Knowle Green East : 2 ¼ m. by A 5269 on B 6243 – ✉ Longridge

Oak Lea without rest
Clitheroe Rd, East : ½ m. on B 6243 ✉ PR3 2YS – ✆ (01254) 878486 – tandm.mellor@tiscali.co.uk – Fax (01254) 878486 – Restricted opening in winter
3 rm – †£ 31/32 ††£ 52/54
◆ Neat little guesthouse in the heart of the Ribble Valley with fine all-round views. Conservatory with access to mature garden. Pleasantly furnished bedrooms.

LONGTOWN – Cumbria – 501 21 A1

London 326 m – Carlisle 9 m – Newcastle upon Tyne 61 m

Bessiestown Farm
Catlowdy, Northeast : 8 m. by Netherby St on B 6318 ✉ CA6 5QP – ✆ (01228) 577219 – info@bessiestown.co.uk – Fax (01228) 577019 – Closed 25 December
6 rm (dinner included) – †£ 45/48 ††£ 75/120 – **Rest** – (by arrangement) Menu £ 18
◆ Comfortable, warm accommodation in homely, modern farmhouse conversion in a rural location on a working farm. Décor has a traditional British tone, well-kept throughout. Home-cooked food served in airy dining room.

LOOE – Cornwall – 503 G 32 – pop. 5 280 1 B2

London 264 m – Plymouth 23 m – Truro 39 m
The Guildhall, Fore St ✆ (01503) 262072
Bin Down, ✆ (01503) 240 239 ;
Whitsand Bay Hotel Torpoint Portwrinkle, ✆ (01503) 230 276.
Town★ – Monkey Sanctuary★ **AC**

Barclay House
St Martins Rd, East Looe, East : ½ m. by A 387 on B 3253 ✉ PL13 1LP – ✆ (01503) 262929 – info@barclayhouse.co.uk – Fax (01503) 262632 – Closed Christmas and 7-14 January
10 rm – †£ 50/75 ††£ 120/140
Rest *The Restaurant* – see restaurant listing
◆ Smart but relaxed and welcoming hotel near harbour. Gardens overlooking estuary. Snug sitting room and bar. Individually decorated bedrooms.

Beach House without rest
Hannafore, Southwest : 3/4 m. by Quay Rd ✉ PL13 2DH – ✆ (01503) 262598 – enquiries@thebeachhouselooe.com – Fax (01503) 262298 – closed Christmas
5 rm – †£ 60 ††£ 110
◆ Large detached house with front garden. Immaculate bedrooms: three have sea vistas; 'Fistral' with balcony is best. Breakfast room upstairs; arched window with views over bay.

Bucklawren Farm without rest
St Martin-by-Looe, Northeast : 3 ½ m. by A 387 and B 3253 turning right onto single track road signposted to Monkey Sanctuary ✉ PL13 1NZ – ✆ (01503) 240738 – bucklawren@btopenworld.com – Fax (01503) 240481 – March-October
6 rm – †£ 30/50 ††£ 57/66
◆ Characterful farmhouse within 500 acre working farm. Large conservatory overlooks pleasant garden. Spotlessly kept interior with simple, country house-style bedrooms.

ENGLAND

XX **The Restaurant** – at Barclay House

St Martins Rd, East Looe, East : ½ m. by A 387 on B 3253 ✉ PL13 1LP – ✆ (01503) 262 929 – info@barclayhouse.co.uk – Fax (01503) 262 632 – Closed Christmas, 7-14 January, Sunday and Monday

Rest – (dinner only) Menu £ 30 – Carte £ 25/40

◆ Extensive views of estuary. Matching mustard coloured walls and table cloths. Attentive well-informed service. Eclectic menu using fresh local produce, particularly seafood.

X **Trawlers on the Quay**

The Quay, East Looe ✉ PL13 1AH – ✆ (01503) 263 593 – info@trawlersrestaurant.co.uk – Closed Christmas, Sunday and Monday except Bank Holidays

Rest – (dinner only) Carte £ 26/32

◆ Personally run restaurant in a pretty setting on the quay. Faux marble table tops; clean, neutral décor. Balanced menu of local seafood and meat dishes. Home-made bread, too.

at Talland Bay Southwest : 4 m. by A 387 – ✉ Looe

Talland Bay (heated)

✉ PL13 2JB – ✆ (01503) 272 667 – reception@tallandbayhotel.co.uk – Fax (01503) 272 940

20 rm – †£ 75/130 ††£ 150/195 – 3 suites

Rest ***Terrace*** – Menu £ 17/33

◆ 16C house in secluded position with lovely gardens. Well chosen fabrics and furniture create a warm and comfortable environment. Many rooms with sea views. Modern fine dining from interesting menu.

ENGLAND

LORTON – Cumbria – 502 K 20 – see Cockermouth

LOUGHBOROUGH – Leics. – 502 – pop. 55 258 16 B2

London 117 m – Birmingham 41 m – Leicester 11 m – Nottingham 15 m

Town Hall, Market Pl ✆ (01509) 218113

Lingdale Woodhouse Eaves Joe Moore's Lane, ✆ (01509) 890 703 .

at Quorndon Southeast : 3 m. by A 6 – ✉ Loughborough

Quorn Country H.

66 Leicester Rd ✉ LE12 8BB – ✆ (01509) 415 050 – reservations@quorncountryhotel.co.uk – Fax (01509) 415 557

28 rm – †£ 125 ††£ 140/180 – 2 suites

Rest ***Shires*** – Menu £ 25 (dinner) – Carte £ 14/30

Rest ***Orangery*** – Carte £ 14/21 **s**

◆ Personally run hotel based around a listed 17C building, once a private club. Very comfortable and appealingly traditional, individually decorated bedrooms. Classic, intimate, traditionally styled Shires. Spacious Orangery features hanging plants and rural art.

at Belton West : 6 m. by A 6 on B 5324 – ✉ Loughborough

The Queen's Head with rm

2 Long St ✉ LE12 9TP – ✆ (01530) 222 359 – enquiries@thequeenshead.org – Fax (01530) 224 860 – Closed 25 December, 1 January and Sunday dinner

6 rm – †£ 65 ††£ 110 – **Rest** – Menu £ 17 – Carte £ 18/35

◆ Early 19C pub, with extension, now embraces a sleek modernity. Restaurant boasts chocolate suede chairs. Serious dining menus evolve constantly. Modish, bright, airy rooms.

at Woodhouse Eaves South : 4 ½ m. by A 6 via Woodhouse – ✉ Loughborough

The Woodhouse

43 Maplewell Rd ✉ LE12 8RG – ☎ (01509) 890318 – paul@thewoodhouse.co.uk – Fax (01509) 890718 – Closed lunch Saturday and Monday and Sunday dinner
Rest – Menu £ 16/17 **s** – Carte £ 30/38 **s**
◆ Bright, boldly coloured restaurant with exotic floral arrangements and artwork. Modern European cooking with a classic French base and innovative edge. Enthusiastic team.

Houghton's at the Pear Tree

8 Church Hill ✉ LE12 8RT – ☎ (01509) 890243 – david@houghtonspeartree.co.uk – Fax (01509) 890243 – Closed 25-26 December, 1 January, Sunday dinner and Monday
Rest – Menu £ 16 – Carte £ 21/34
◆ Oldest pub in the village given modern new look. Upstairs dining room overlooks village rooftops. Classic bar menu; more ambitious à la carte. Attentive service. Decked terrace.

LOUTH – Lincs. – 502 – pop. 15 930 17 D1

London 156 m – Boston 34 m – Great Grimsby 17 m – Lincoln 26 m
The New Market Hall, off Cornmarket ☎ (01507) 609289

Brackenborough Arms

Cordeaux Corner, Brackenborough, North : 2 m. by A 16 ✉ LN11 0SZ – ☎ (01507) 609 169 – reception@brackenborough.co.uk – Fax (01507) 609413
24 rm – †£ 72/87 ††£ 87 – **Rest** – Carte £ 20/35
◆ Family owned hotel run with a warm and personal style. Public areas have a relaxed feel and bedrooms are spacious, individually designed and boast a host of extras. Homely dining.

LOVINGTON – Somerset – 503 M 30 – see Castle Cary

LOW FELL – Tyne and Wear – see Gateshead

LOWER HARDRES – Kent – 504 X 30 – see Canterbury

LOWER ODDINGTON – Glos. – see Stow-on-the-Wold

LOWER SLAUGHTER – Glos. – 503 – see Bourton-on-the-Water

LOWER SWELL – Glos. – see Stow-on-the-Wold

LOWER VOBSTER – Somerset – pop. 2 222 – ✉ Radstock 4 C2

London 119 m – Bath 16 m – Frome 5 m

The Vobster Inn

✉ BA3 5RJ – ☎ (01373) 812920 – info@vobsterinn.co.uk – Fax (01373) 812920 – Closed Sunday dinner,25-26 December, 1 week in February
Rest – Carte £ 18/25
◆ Sit on the terrace or in the restaurant to sample cooking from the regularly-changing menus. Choose from classic British or Spanish dishes, made using locally sourced produce.

Your opinions are important to us: please write and let us know about your discoveries and experiences – good and bad!

ENGLAND

LOWER WHITLEY – Ches. – 502 M 24 20 A3

London 199 m – Liverpool 25 m – Manchester 24 m – Warrington 7 m

Chetwode Arms with rm

Street Lane ✉ WA4 4EN – ✆ (01925) 730 203 – claudia.d@btinternet.com – Fax (01925) 730 203 – Closed 25 December and 1 January

3 rm – †£ 50/100 ††£ 70 – **Rest** – Carte £ 20/40

◆ Redbrick 17C coaching inn and lawned garden. Variety of panelled rooms and snugs. Large menus and blackboard specials of classic British dishes. Simple, homely bedrooms.

LOWESTOFT – Suffolk – 504 Z 26 – pop. 62 907 *Great Britain* 15 D2

London 116 m – Ipswich 43 m – Norwich 30 m

East Point Pavillion, Royal Plain ✆ (01502) 533600, touristinfo@wavernly.gov.uk

Rookery Park Carlton Colville, ✆ (01502) 509 190 .

Norfolk Broads★

at Oulton Broad West : 2 m. by A 146 – ✉ Lowestoft

Ivy House

Ivy Lane, Southwest : 1½ m. by A 146 ✉ NR33 8HY – ✆ (01502) 501 353 – michelin@ivyhousecountryhotel.co.uk – Fax (01502) 501 539 – Closed 2 weeks Christmas-New Year

19 rm – †£ 98/115 ††£ 130/165 – 1 suite

Rest *The Crooked Barn* – see restaurant listing

◆ Converted farm in rural seclusion down an unmade lane. Well kept gardens and grounds. Spacious bedrooms, in converted barns, have bright, fresh décor.

The Crooked Barn – at Ivy House

Ivy Lane, Southwest : 1½ m. by A 146 ✉ NR33 8HY – ✆ (01502) 501 353 – michelin@ivyhousecountryhotel.co.uk – Fax (01502) 501 539 – Closed 2 weeks Christmas-New Year

Rest – Menu £ 18/30 – Carte £ 29/44 **s**

◆ Thatched part 18C former hay loft, the focus of Ivy House Farm's characterful setting. Delightful crooked beamed interior. Modern British fare using fresh, local produce.

LOWICK – Northants. 17 C3

London 92 m – Leicester 39 m – Peterborough 23 m

The Snooty Fox

16 Main St ✉ NN14 3BH – ✆ (01832) 733 434 – the.snooty.fox@btinternet.com – Closed dinner 25-26 December and 1 January

Rest – Menu £ 15/13 – Carte £ 18/25

◆ Locally renowned stone-built village inn. Main bar with appealing blackboard menu and elegant dining room. Noteworthy, accomplished rotisserie.

LUDLOW – Shrops. – 503 L 26 – pop. 9 548 *Great Britain* 18 B2

London 162 m – Birmingham 39 m – Hereford 24 m – Shrewsbury 29 m

Castle St ✆ (01584) 875053

Town★ Z – Castle★ **AC** – Feathers Hotel★ – St Laurence's Parish Church★ (Misericords★) **S**

Stokesay Castle★ **AC**, NW : 6½ m. by A 49

Plan opposite

Overton Grange

Old Hereford Rd, South : 1 ¾ m. by B 4361 ✉ SY8 4AD – ✆ (01584) 873 500 – info@overtongrangehotel.com – Fax (01584) 873 524

14 rm – †£ 95/140 ††£ 140/240 – **Rest** – (booking essential for non-residents) (lunch by arrangement) Menu £ 33/43

◆ Edwardian country house with good views of the surrounding countryside. Comfortable lounges. Attentive service and well-kept, individual rooms. Accomplished, inventive modern cuisine with a French base.

ENGLAND

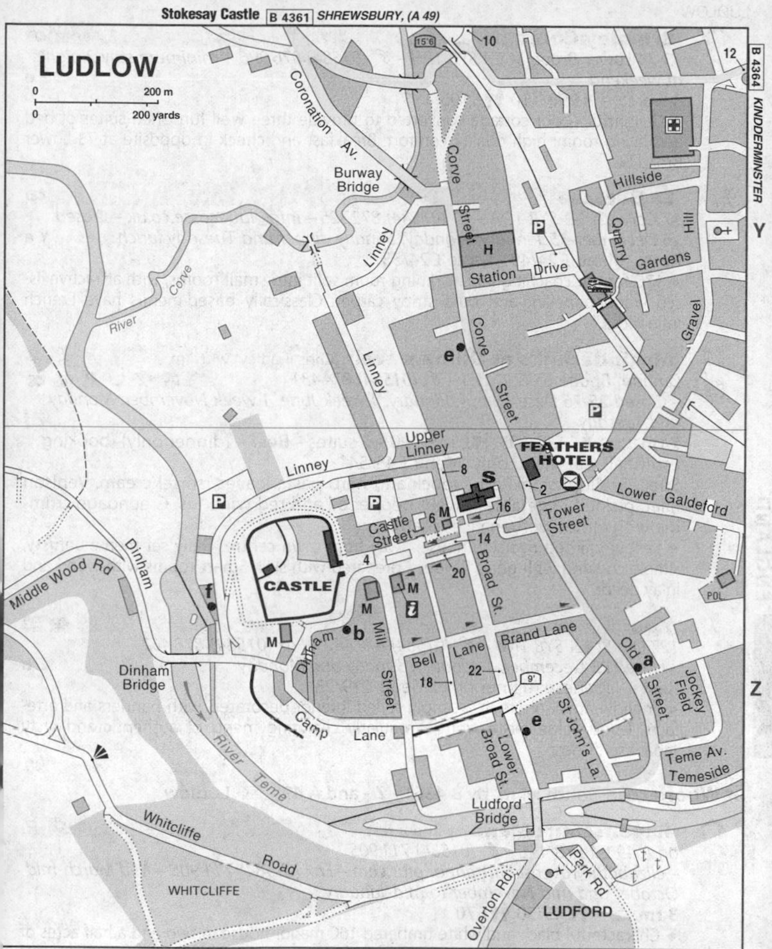

Bull Ring .... Z 2
Castle Square .... Z 4
Church St................... Z 6
College St.................. Z 8

Fishmore Rd .... Y 10
Henley Rd .... Y 12
High St..................... Z 14
King St .... Z 16

Lower Raven Lane .... Z 18
Market St................... Z 20
Silk Mill .... Z 22

Dinham Hall

Dinham ✉ SY8 1EJ – ✆ (01584) 876 464 – info@dinhamhall.co.uk – Fax (01584) 876 019 Z **b**

13 rm ☕ – 🚹£ 95/160 👫£ 190 – **Rest** – Menu £ 39 (dinner) – Carte lunch £ 29/34

◆ 18C manor house, with pretty walled garden, situated by Ludlow Castle in the heart of charming medieval town. Period furnishings and individual rooms. Crisp, bright décor and creative menu.

Bromley Court without rest
73-74 Lower Broad St ✉ SY8 1PH – ✆ (01584) 876 996 – minimum stay 2 nights at weekend Z **e**
3 rm – £ 90/110 £ 105/115
◆ Delightful Tudor cottage converted to provide three well-furnished suites of bed and living room: high quality comfort. Breakfast and check-in opposite at 73 Lower Broad St.

La Becasse
17 Corve St ✉ SY8 1DA – ✆ (01584) 872 325 – info@labecasse.co.uk – Closed 26 December-15 January, Monday, Sunday dinner and Tuesday lunch Y **e**
Rest – Menu £ 24/49 – Carte £ 24/55
◆ 17C former coaching inn; its dining room split into small rooms, with attractive listed wood panelling and bold stripy carpet. Classically based menus have French influences.

Mr Underhill's at Dinham Weir (Chris Bradley) with rm
Dinham Bridge ✉ SY8 1EH – ✆ (01584) 874 431 – Closed 25-26 December, 1 January, 1 week June, 1 week November, Monday and Tuesday Z **f**
7 rm – £ 135/195 £ 145/190 – 2 suites – **Rest** – (dinner only) (booking essential) (set menu only) Menu £ 45/54
Spec. Scallop, smoked haddock and herb pasta leaves, sorrel cream. Venison fillet, pickled vegetables, sweet pepper oil and red wine jus. Greengage crumble with lemon verbena ice cream.
◆ Yellow painted riverside house, away from town centre. Daily set menu: unfussy, simple cooking with good flavours, prepared with skill. Smart rooms with wood and inlay décor.

ENGLAND

Koo
127 Old St ✉ SY8 1NU – ✆ (01584) 878 462 – Fax (01584) 878 462 – closed 25 December, 1 January, Sunday and Monday Z **a**
Rest – Japanese (dinner only) Menu £ 19/23
◆ Friendly atmosphere in a simply styled interior decorated with banners and artefacts. Good value meals from a regularly changing menu of authentic and tasty Japanese dishes.

at Woofferton South : 4 m. by B 4361 - Z - and A 49 – ✉ Ludlow

Ravenscourt Manor without rest
on A 49 ✉ SY8 4AL – ✆ (01584) 711 905 – elizabeth@ravenscourtmanor.plus.com – Fax (01584) 711 905 – Mid March-mid October and mid-November to mid-January
3 rm – £ 45/50 £ 70
◆ Characterful black and white timbered 16C manor house in two and a half acres of lawned gardens. Friendly welcome; comfy lounge. Individually decorated, period style rooms.

at Brimfield South : 4 ½ m. by B 4361 - Z - and A 49 – ✉ Ludlow

The Roebuck Inn with rm
✉ SY8 4NE – ✆ (01584) 711 230 – info@theroebuckinn.co.uk – Closed Sunday dinner
3 rm – £ 55 £ 79 – **Rest** – (booking essential) Carte £ 23/28
◆ Country pub filled with rustic objects and curios. Well prepared, locally sourced, traditional-style food in bar and formal dining room. Warm, homely bedrooms.

at Orleton South : 5 ½ m. by B 4361 - Y – ✉ Ludlow

Line Farm without rest
Tunnel Lane, Southeast : ¾ m. ✉ SY8 4HY – ✆ (01568) 780 400 – Fax (01568) 780 995 – February-October
3 rm – £ 70/75
◆ Purpose-built house in a relaxing location on a working farm. Pleasant views across a pretty garden to open countryside from each of the comfortable bedrooms.

at Bromfield Northwest : 2½ m. on A 49 - Y - ✉ Ludlow

XX **The Clive** with rm rm, P VISA AE
✉ *SY8 2JR – ✆ (01584) 856 565 – info@theclive.co.uk – Fax (01584) 856 661 – Closed 25-26 December*
15 rm – †£ 50 ††£ 75 – **Rest** – Carte £ 18/34
◆ Large converted pub with modern décor in vivid colours. Restaurant, bar, café and bistro areas. Menu of internationally inspired traditional dishes. Very good modern bedrooms.

LUXBOROUGH – Somerset – **503** J 30 – ✉ **Watchet** 3 **A2**
London 205 m – Exeter 42 m – Minehead 9 m – Taunton 25 m

The Royal Oak Inn of Luxborough with rm P VISA
Exmoor National Park ✉ TA23 0SH – ✆ (01984) 640 319 – info@theroyaloakinnluxborough.co.uk – Fax (01984) 641 561 – Closed 25 December
11 rm – †£ 55/65 ††£ 95 – **Rest** – Carte £ 15/30
◆ Rural inn with bags of character and lots of real ale. Home-cooked food, including fresh fish and game, served in numerous beamed rooms. Tastefully furnished bedrooms.

LYDDINGTON – Rutland – see Uppingham

LYDFORD – Devon – **503** H 32 – **pop. 1 734** – ✉ **Okehampton** 2 **C2**
London 234 m – Exeter 33 m – Plymouth 25 m
Village★★
Dartmoor National Park★★

Moor View House P
Vale Down, Northeast : 1½ m. on A 386 ✉ EX20 4BB – ✆ (01822) 820 220 – Fax (01822) 820 220
4 rm – †£ 45/50 ††£ 70/80 – **Rest** – (by arrangement, communal dining) Menu £ 25
◆ Victorian country house with attractive garden. Relaxed and friendly atmosphere with real fires; traditionally furnished with antique pieces. Thoughtful, personal touches. Dine with fellow guests at antique table.

The Dartmoor Inn with rm P VISA AE
Moorside, East : 1 m. on A 386 ✉ EX20 4AY – ✆ (01822) 820 221 – info@dartmoorinn.co.uk – Fax (01822) 820 494 – Closed Sunday dinner and Monday
3 rm – †£ 115 ††£ 125 – **Rest** – Carte £ 18/35
◆ Pleasant service and a relaxed ambience amidst gently rustic surroundings. Modern menu using local ingredients influenced by Mediterranean and local styles. Smart rooms.

LYME REGIS – Dorset – **503** L 31 – **pop. 4 406** 3 **B3**
London 160 m – Dorchester 25 m – Exeter 31 m – Taunton 27 m
Guildhall Cottage, Church St ✆ (01297) 442138
Timber Hill, ✆ (01297) 442 963 .
Town★ – The Cobb★

Alexandra 
Pound St ✉ DT7 3HZ – ✆ (01297) 442 010 – enquiries@hotelalexandra.co.uk – Fax (01297) 443 229 – Closed Christmas and January
26 rm (dinner included) – †£ 75/110 ††£ 175/185 – **Rest** – Menu £ 21/33 – Carte lunch £ 18/26
◆ A busy, family run hotel with traditional style at the top of the town. Set in manicured gardens with views of the sea. Comfortable lounge and south facing conservatory. Tasty, home-cooked menus.

ENGLAND

LYMINGTON – Hants. – 503 – pop. 14 227 6 A3

London 103 m – Bournemouth 18 m – Southampton 19 m – Winchester 32 m

to the Isle of Wight (Yarmouth) (Wightlink Ltd) frequent services daily (30 mn)

St Barb Museum and Visitor Centre, New St (01590) 689000

Stanwell House

15 High St ✉ SO41 9AA – ✆ (01590) 677 123 – sales@stanwellhousehotel.co.uk – Fax (01590) 677 756

23 rm – †£ 99 ††£ 135 – 4 suites

Rest *Bistro* – Menu £ 13 (lunch) **s** – Carte dinner £ 29/38 **s**

◆ Privately owned hotel with individual style in Georgian building. Rich décor verges on the gothic with sumptuous silks, crushed velvets and an eclectic mix of furniture. Atmospheric Bistro in dramatic, rich colours.

The Mill at Gordleton

rest,

Silver St, Hordle, Northwest : 3½ m. by A 337 and Sway Rd ✉ SO41 6DJ – ✆ (01590) 682 219 – info@themillatgordleton.co.uk – Fax (01590) 683 073 – Closed 25 December

6 rm – †£ 90 ††£ 130 – 1 suite – **Rest** – (Closed Sunday dinner) Menu £ 16 – Carte £ 24/40

◆ Delightfully located part 17C water mill on edge of New Forest, in well-kept gardens. Comfortable, traditionally styled interior with a pubby bar and clean-lined rooms. Terrace available for alfresco dining.

ENGLAND

Efford Cottage without rest

Everton, West : 2 m. on A 337 ✉ SO41 0JD – ✆ (01590) 642 315 – effordcottage@aol.com – Fax (01590) 641 030 – Restricted opening in winter

3 rm – †£ 50/65 ††£ 55/75

◆ Family run guesthouse in Georgian cottage with garden. Traditional-style interiors include a spacious drawing room with large windows and well-equipped bedrooms.

Egan's

24 Gosport St ✉ SO41 9BG – ✆ (01590) 676 165 – johnegan@dsl.pipex.com – Closed 26 December-8 January, Sunday and Monday

Rest – (booking essential) Menu £ 14 (lunch) – Carte dinner £ 24/32

◆ Bustling bistro style restaurant near the High Street. Warm yellow walls give it a Mediterranean feel. Pleasant, efficient service. Fresh, simple cooking with modern elements.

at Downton West : 3 m. on A 337 – ✉ Lymington

The Olde Barn without rest

Christchurch Rd, East : ½ m. on A 337 ✉ SO41 0LA – ✆ (01590) 644 939 – julie@theoldbarn.co.uk – Fax (01590) 644 939

3 rm – †£ 45/60 ††£ 60/70

◆ Unsurprisingly, a converted 17C barn with large, chintzy lounge and wood burner. Some bedrooms in barn annex: a mix of modern style and exposed brick, all spotlessly clean.

LYNDHURST – Hants. – 503 *Great Britain* 6 A2

London 95 m – Bournemouth 20 m – Southampton 10 m – Winchester 23 m

New Forest Museum and Visitor Centre, Main Car Park (023) 8028 2269

Dibden Golf Centre Main Rd, ✆ (023) 8020 7508 ;

New Forest Southampton Rd, ✆ (023) 8028 2752 .

New Forest★★ (Bolderwood Ornamental Drive★★, Rhinefield Ornamental Drive★★)

Crown

9 High St ✉ SO43 7NF – ✆ (023) 8028 2922 – reception@crownhotel-lyndhurst.co.uk – Fax (023) 8028 2751

37 rm – †£ 73/145 ††£ 145/165 – 1 suite – **Rest** – (bar lunch Monday-Saturday) Carte £ 21/31

◆ Extended house with 19C façade in the middle of town - a classically English hotel. Spacious public areas include a wood panelled bar. Bedrooms vary in shapes and sizes. "Decidedly fattening" puddings a dining room speciality.

Beaulieu

Beaulieu Rd, Southeast : 3½ m. on B 3056 ✉ SO42 7YQ – ✆ (023) 8029 3344 – beaulieu@newforesthotels.co.uk – Fax (023) 8029 2729

23 rm – †£ 80/85 ††£ 130/140 – **Rest** – (dinner only) Menu £ 22

◆ Small country hotel in terrific location deep in New Forest, giving some rooms great views. Traditional interior and well-equipped rooms. Dining room is divided into partitioned areas.

Ormonde House

Southampton Rd ✉ SO43 7BT – ✆ (023) 8028 2806 – enquiries@ormondehouse.co.uk – Fax (023) 8028 2004 – Closed Christmas

25 rm – †£ 40/65 ††£ 70/120 – **Rest** – (dinner only) (by arrangement, residents only) Menu £ 21

◆ Privately owned hotel on edge of the New Forest. Decorated in warm pastel colours throughout, including the well-kept bedrooms. Public areas include conservatory lounge. Locally sourced menus.

LYNMOUTH – Devon – 503 I 30 – see Lynton

LYNTON – Devon – 503 I 30 2 C1

London 206 m – Exeter 59 m – Taunton 44 m

Town Hall, Lee Rd ✆ (01598) 752225, info@lyntourism.co.uk

Town★ (≤ ★)

Valley of the Rocks★, W : 1 m. – Watersmeet★, E : 1½ m. by A 39. Exmoor National Park★★ – Doone Valley★, SE : 7½ m. by A 39 (access from Oare on foot)

Lynton Cottage

≤ bay and Countisbury Hill,

North Walk Hill ✉ EX35 6ED – ✆ (01598) 752 342 – mail@lyntoncottage.co.uk – Fax (01598) 754 016 – Closed 2 December-12 January

16 rm – †£ 44/72 ††£ 78/104 – **Rest** – (bar lunch) Menu £ 30

◆ Stunning vistas of the bay and Countisbury Hill from this personally run, cliff top hotel. All bedrooms to a good standard - superior rooms command the best views. Outside the restaurant, stunning sea views. Inside, local art on the walls.

Hewitt's - Villa Spaldi

≤ bay and Countisbury Hill,

North Walk ✉ EX35 6HJ – ✆ (01598) 752 293 – hewitts.hotel@talk21.com – Fax (01598) 752 489 – 12 March-12 October

7 rm – †£ 65/95 ††£ 165/185 – 1 suite – **Rest** – (Closed Monday) Menu £ 39 (dinner) **s** – Carte £ 34/39 **s**

◆ Splendid 19C Arts & Crafts house in tranquil wooded cliffside setting. Stained glass window by Burne Jones and library filled with antiques. Stylish rooms with sea views. Oak panelled dining room; charming service.

Highcliffe House

≤ bay and Countisbury Hill,

Sinai Hill ✉ EX35 6AR – ✆ (01598) 752 235 – info@highcliffehouse.co.uk – Closed December-January

7 rm – †£ 60/90 ††£ 120 – **Rest** – (Closed Monday-Thursday) (dinner only) (residents only) Menu £ 28

◆ Intimate, friendly atmosphere in former Victorian gentleman's residence. Authentic period-style rooms with panoramic views and ornate antique beds. Modern dining room has lovely views from panoramic windows.

Victoria Lodge without rest

30-31 Lee Rd ✉ EX35 6BS – ✆ (01598) 753 203 – info@victorialodge.co.uk – Fax (01598) 753 203 – March-October

8 rm – †£ 60 ††£ 140

◆ Large 19C house decorated with period photographs, prints and Victoriana. Traditional décor in communal areas and bedrooms which are comfortable and inviting.

ENGLAND

St Vincent

Market St, Castle Hill ✉ EX35 6JA – ✆ (01598) 752 244 – welcome@st-vincent-hotel.co.uk – Fax (01598) 752 244 – Easter-October
5 rm – ♦£ 65 ♦♦£ 75 – **Rest** – (Closed Monday) (dinner only) (booking essential for non-residents) Menu £ 27
◆ Grade II listed building with charming Belgian owners 200 metres from Coastal Path. Lovely Edwardian lounge with crackling fire. Neat, simple, clean bedrooms. Cloth-clad dining room: owners proud of French/Mediterranean menus.

at Lynmouth

Tors

< Lynmouth and bay, (heated) VISA AE

✉ EX35 6NA – ✆ (01598) 753 236 – torshotel@torslynmouth.co.uk – Fax (01598) 752 544 – Closed 4 January-16 February
31 rm – ♦£ 76/79 ♦♦£ 112/152 – **Rest** – (bar lunch) Menu £ 30 **s**
◆ Perched above Lynmouth and the bay, affording splendid views. Unashamedly traditional: spacious lounges and popular bar. Well-appointed, bright rooms in light tones. Traditional restaurant; tea served on the terrace.

Shelley's without rest

8 Watersmeet Rd ✉ EX35 6EP – ✆ (01598) 753 219 – info@shelleyshotel.co.uk – Fax (01598) 753 219 – March-October
11 rm – ♦£ 70 ♦♦£ 100/110
◆ Centrally located hotel named after eponymous poet who honeymooned here in 1812. Stylish public areas. Very comfortable bedrooms with good views of picturesque locale.

Bonnicott House

Watersmeet Rd ✉ EX35 6EP – ✆ (01598) 753 346 – stay@bonnicott.com
8 rm – ♦£ 46/86 ♦♦£ 108/192 – **Rest** – (October-April) (dinner only) Menu £ 23 **s**
◆ Former 19C rectory in elevated setting. Spacious lounge with log fire: large windows offer good views to sea. Bright rooms, two with four poster, all with sherry decanter. Fresh, traditional meals cooked on the Aga.

Rising Sun

Harbourside ✉ EX35 6EG – ✆ (01598) 753 223 – reception@specialplace.co.uk – Fax (01598) 753 480 – Closed 25 December
14 rm – ♦£ 60/85 ♦♦£ 150/160 – 1 suite – **Rest** – (bar lunch) Carte £ 28/34 **s**
◆ Part 14C thatched and whitewashed harbourside smuggler's inn. Warm, intimate style. Pubby bar with tiled floor and exposed beams. Well furnished, individually styled rooms. Balanced modern meals making good use of local game and seafood.

The Heatherville

Tors Park, by Tors Rd ✉ EX35 6NB – ✆ (01598) 752 327 – Fax (01598) 752 634 – March-October
6 rm – ♦£ 50 ♦♦£ 90 – **Rest** – (by arrangement) Menu £ 25
◆ Victorian house perched above the town. Well kept throughout with bright, warm décor. Rooms with bold fabrics and woodland views: room 6 has the best outlook. Home-cooked meals employ fresh, local produce.

Sea View Villa

6 Summer House Path ✉ EX35 6ES – ✆ (01598) 753 460 – reservations@seaviewvilla.co.uk – Fax (01598) 753 496 – Closed 3 January-7 February and first 2 weeks November
5 rm – ♦£ 30/70 ♦♦£ 100/110 – **Rest** – (by arrangement, communal dining) Menu £ 30
◆ Grade II listed Georgian house a stone's throw from harbour. Luxurious interior filled with owners' mementoes. Stylish rooms furnished with taste; all boast enviable sea view. Dinner party style evening meals with fellow guests.

at Martinhoe West : 4 ¼ m. via Coast rd (toll) – ✉ Barnstaple

Old Rectory

✉ *EX31 4QT – ✆ (01598) 763 368 – info@oldrectoryhotel.co.uk*
– Fax (01598) 763 567 – March-October
8 rm (dinner included) – †£ 110/135 ††£ 175/225 – **Rest** – (dinner only) (residents only) Menu £ 33 **s**

◆ Built in 19C for rector of Martinhoe's 11C church. Quiet country retreat in charming three acre garden with cascading brook. Bright and co-ordinated bedrooms. Classic country house dining room.

LYTHAM ST ANNE'S – Lancs. – 502 L 22 – pop. 41 327 — 20 A2

London 237 m – Blackpool 7 m – Liverpool 44 m – Preston 13 m
67 St Annes Rd West ✆ (01253) 725610, touristinfo@flyde.gov.uk
Fairhaven AnsdellLytham Hall Park, ✆ (01253) 736 741 ;
St Annes Old Links Highbury Rd, ✆ (01253) 723 597 .

at Lytham

Clifton Arms

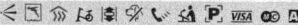

West Beach ✉ FY8 5QJ – ✆ (01253) 739 898
– welcome@cliftonarms-lytham.com – Fax (01253) 730 657
45 rm (dinner included) – †£ 60/100 ††£ 120/165 – 3 suites
Rest – (bar lunch Monday-Saturday) Menu £ 28 – Carte £ 20/36

◆ Former coaching inn with strong associations with local championship golf course. Traditional country house public areas. Cottage-style rooms, front ones with great views. Restaurant's popular window tables overlook Lytham Green.

at St Anne's

The Grand

South Promenade ✉ FY8 1NB – ✆ (01253) 721 288 – book@the-grand.co.uk
– Fax (01253) 714 459 – Closed 24-26 December
53 rm – †£ 80/135 ††£ 100/160, £ 5.50 – 2 suites
Rest *The Bay* – (bar lunch Monday-Saturday) Carte £ 19/32 **s**

◆ Impressive, turreted Victorian hotel on promenade. Warm, country house-style décor. Spacious rooms, most with good views, turret rooms have particularly good aspect. Rich crimson restaurant overlooks the sea.

Glendower

North Promenade ✉ FY8 2NQ – ✆ (01253) 723 241
– glendower@bestwestern.co.uk – Fax (01253) 640 069 – Closed 25-26 December
61 rm – †£ 50/120 ††£ 80/140
Rest *The Clifton* – (bar lunch) Menu £ 21

◆ Family owned hotel consisting of 19C buildings overlooking the beach and Irish Sea. Comfortable, traditional style throughout. Choose the west facing rooms for best views. Comfortable, welcoming restaurant.

XX **Greens Bistro**

3-9 St Andrews Road South - Lower Ground Floor ✉ FY8 1SX – ✆ (01253) 789 990 – info@greensbistro.co.uk – Closed 1 week January, 1 week October, 25-26 December, Sunday and Monday
Rest – (dinner only) Carte £ 22/26 **s**

◆ Worth the effort to find, this simple, pleasant bistro, hidden beneath some shops, has linen clad tables, friendly service, and good value, well executed modern British menus.

The ✿ award is the crème de la crème.
This is awarded to restaurants
which are really worth travelling miles for!

ENGLAND

MACCLESFIELD – Ches. – 502 N 24 – pop. 50 688 — 20 B3

London 186 m – Chester 38 m – Manchester 18 m – Stoke-on-Trent 21 m
Town Hall ✆ (0871) 7162640
The Tytherington Club, ✆ (01625) 506 000 ;
Shrigley Hall Pott Shrigley Shrigley Park, ✆ (01625) 575 757 .

Chadwick House without rest
55 Beech Lane, North : ¼ m. on A 538 ✉ SK10 2DS – ✆ (01625) 615 558 – chadwickhouse@ntlworld.com – Fax (01625) 610 265
14 rm – £ 40 £ 55
◆ Two converted terraced houses away from the town centre. Bedrooms vary in shapes and sizes and all are traditionally decorated and pine furnished.

MADINGLEY – Cambs. – 504 U 27 – see Cambridge

MAGHAM DOWN – E. Sussex – see Hailsham

The red symbol?
This denotes the very essence of peace
– only the sound of birdsong first thing in the morning …

MAIDEN NEWTON – Dorset – 503 M 31 — 4 C3

London 144 m – Exeter 55 m – Taunton 37 m – Weymouth 16 m

Le Petit Canard
Dorchester Rd ✉ DT2 0BE – ✆ (01300) 320 536 – craigs@le-petit-canard.co.uk – Fax (01300) 321 286 – Closed Monday and dinner Sunday
Rest – (dinner only) (Sunday lunch by arrangement) Menu £ 30/35
◆ Pleasant stone-built cottage in middle of charming village. Plenty of candles, well-spaced tables and soft music. English dishes with French and Oriental touches.

MAIDENCOMBE – Devon – 503 J 32 – see Torquay

MAIDENHEAD – Windsor & Maidenhead – 504 R 29 – pop. 58 848 — 11 C3

London 33 m – Oxford 32 m – Reading 13 m
to Marlow, Cookham and Windsor (Salter Bros. Ltd) (summer only) (3 h 45 mn)
The Library, St Ives Rd ✆ (0871) 7161962
Bird Hills Hawthorn Hill Drift Rd, ✆ (01628) 771 030 ;
Shoppenhangers Rd, ✆ (01628) 624 693 .

Plan opposite

Fredrick's (heated)
Shoppenhangers Rd ✉ SL6 2PZ – ✆ (01628) 581 000 – reservations@fredricks-hotel.co.uk – Fax (01628) 771 054 – Closed Christmas-New Year — X c
33 rm – £ 245 £ 325 – 1 suite
Rest *Fredrick's* – see restaurant listing
◆ Redbrick former inn with well-equipped spa facilities. Ornate, marble reception with smoked mirrors. Conservatory with wicker chairs. Very comfy, individually styled rooms.

Holiday Inn Maidenhead rm,
Manor Lane, off Shoppenhangers Rd ✉ SL6 2RA – ✆ (0870) 400 9053 – reservations-maidenhead@ihg.com – Fax (01628) 506 001 — X n
197 rm – £ 155/175 £ 165/185 – **Rest** – Menu £ 22 (dinner) – Carte £ 23/29
◆ 1970s purpose-built hotel. Convenient for M4 motorway. Ideal for business guests with extensive conference facilities and spacious, well-equipped leisure centre.

MAIDENHEAD

Bad Godesberg Way . . . . . Y 2
Belmont Park Ave . . . . V 3
Blackamoor Lane . . . . V 5
Boyn Hill Ave . . . . Z 6
Braywick Rd . . . . Z 7
Bridge St . . . . Y 9
College Rd . . . . V 13
Cookham Rd . . . . Y 14
Crescent (The) . . . . Y 15
Ferry Rd . . . . X 17
Frascati Way . . . . YZ 18
Furze Platt Rd . . . . V 20
Grenfell Pl. . . . . Z 21
Gringer Hill . . . . V 22
Harrow Lane . . . . V 24
High St . . . . Y
High St BRAY-ON-THAMES . . . . X 25
King's Grove . . . . Z 27
Linden Ave. . . . . V 28
Lower Cookham Rd . . . . . . V 29
Manor Lane . . . . X 31
Market St . . . . Y 32
Nicholson's Walk Shopping Centre . . . . . YZ
Norreys Drive . . . . X 35
Oldfield Rd . . . . V 36
Ray Mill Rd West . . . . V 39
Ray St. . . . . V 38
St Ives Rd. . . . . Y 41
St Mark Rd . . . . V 42
Stafferton Way . . . . Z 43
Upper Bray Rd. . . . . X 45

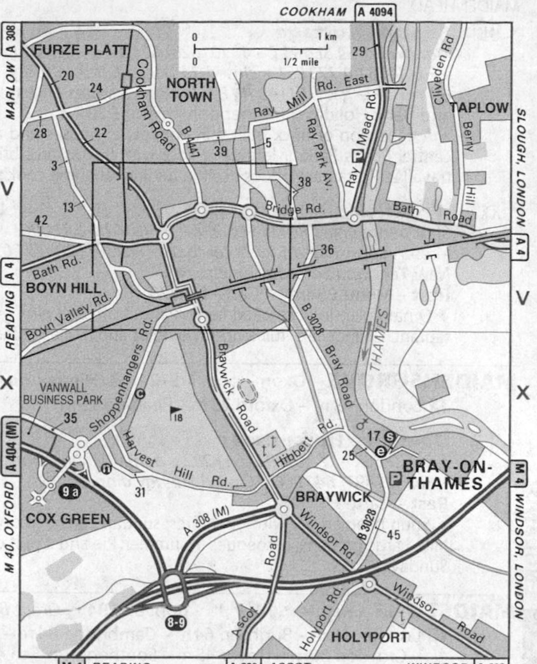

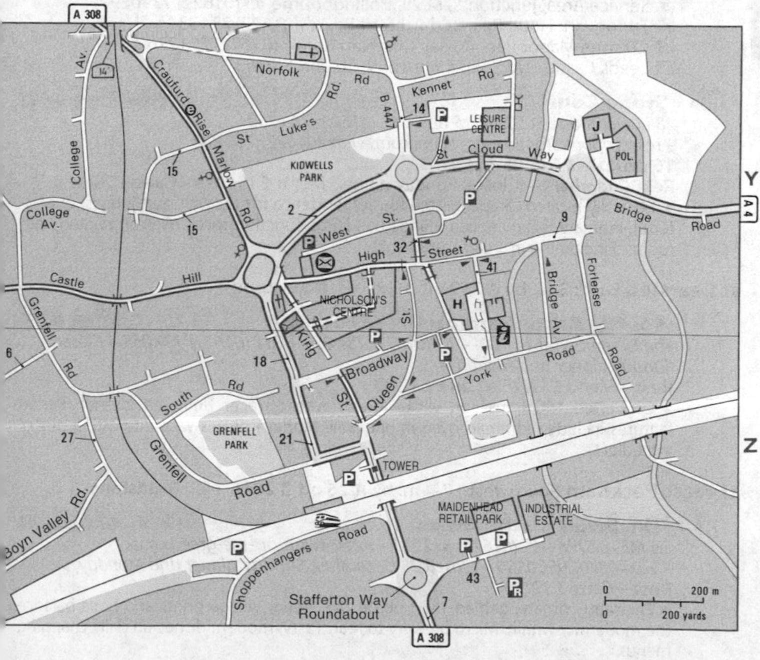

A 308
Craufurd Rise
Marlow Rd
College Av.
College
Norfolk Rd
St Luke's Rd.
B 4447
Kennet Rd
LEISURE CENTRE
St Cloud Way
J
POL.
KIDWELLS PARK
Y
Bridge Road
A 4
West St.
High Street
Castle Hill
NICHOLSON'S CENTRE
King St.
Bridge Av.
Forlease Road
H
Grenfell Rd
Broadway
Queen St.
York Road
South Rd
GRENFELL PARK
Grenfell Road
TOWER
Z
Boyn Valley Rd.
MAIDENHEAD RETAIL PARK
INDUSTRIAL ESTATE
Shoppenhangers Road
Stafferton Way Roundabout
200 m
200 yards
A 308

Walton Cottage
Marlow Rd ✉ SL6 7LT – ✆ (01628) 624394 – res@waltoncottagehotel.co.uk – Fax (01628) 773851 – closed 24 December-2 January Y **e**
69 rm – £ 110/145 £ 150/180 – 3 suites – **Rest** – (Closed Friday-Sunday and Bank Holidays) (dinner only) Menu £ 20
◆ A collection of brick built, bay-windowed houses and annexed blocks near town centre. Poet's Parlour lounge is cosy with beams and brick. Aimed at the business traveller. Restaurant prides itself in traditional home cooking.

Fredrick's – at Fredrick's H.
Shoppenhangers Rd ✉ SL6 2PZ – ✆ (01628) 581000 – reservations@fredricks-hotel.co.uk – Fax (01628) 771054 – Closed Christmas-New Year and Saturday lunch X **c**
Rest – Menu £ 34/44 – Carte £ 47/70
◆ Ornate paintings, smoked mirrors and distressed pine greet diners in this large restaurant. Chandeliers, full-length windows add to classic feel. Elaborate British menus.

MAIDENSGROVE – Oxon – pop. 1 572 – ✉ Henley-on-Thames 11 **C3**

London 43 m – Oxford 23 m – Reading 15 m

The Five Horseshoes
✉ RG9 6EX – ✆ (01491) 641282 – admin@thefivehorseshoes.co.uk – Fax (01491) 641086 – Closed Sunday dinner
Rest – Carte £ 17/27
◆ Snug beamed bar with open fires; suntrap conservatory with southerly views over hills. Large gardens; barbeques in summer. Pie and a pint on Fridays; hog roasts some Sundays.

MAIDSTONE – Kent – 504 V 30 – pop. 89 684 *Great Britain* 8 **B2**

London 36 m – Brighton 64 m – Cambridge 84 m – Colchester 72 m – Croydon 36 m – Dover 45 m – Southend-on-Sea 49 m
Town Hall, High St ✆ (01622) 602169, tic@maidstone.gov.ukMotorway Service Area, junction 8, M 20, Hollingbourne ✆ (01622) 739029
Tudor Park Hotel Bearsted Ashford Rd, ✆ (01622) 734334 ;
Cobtree Manor Park Boxley Chatham Rd, ✆ (01622) 753276 .
Leeds Castle★ AC, SE : 4½ m. by A 20 and B 2163

Stone Court
28 Lower Stone St ✉ ME15 6LX – ✆ (01622) 769769 – reservations.stonecourt@ohiml.com – Fax (01622) 769888
16 rm – £ 75/85 £ 95
Rest *Chambers* – (Closed Sunday dinner) Menu £ 13/28 **s** – Carte £ 28/36 **s**
◆ Centrally located, Grade II listed former residence for Crown Court judges. Characterful, intimate, oak-panelled lounge bar. Large function room. Well-appointed bedrooms. Fine dining in smart restaurant.

at Bearsted East : 3 m. by A 249 off A 20 – ✉ Maidstone

Soufflé Restaurant on the Green
The Green ✉ ME14 4DN – ✆ (01622) 737065 – Fax (01622) 737065 – Closed Sunday dinner and Monday
Rest – Menu £ 17/25 – Carte £ 32/37
◆ Converted 16C house on village green with terrace. Timbered interior. Period features include old bread oven in one wall. Modern dishes with interesting mix of ingredients.

at West Peckham Southwest : 7¾ m. by A 26 off B 2016 – ✉ Maidstone

The Swan on the Green
✉ ME18 5JW – ✆ (01622) 812271 – info@swan-on-the-green.co.uk – Fax (0870) 0560556 – Closed 25 December, Sunday dinner and Monday
Rest – Carte £ 22/29
◆ Pleasantly ornate, gabled 16C pub on the green. Village prints and hops balance the modernity within. Micro brewery to rear. Tasty, modern dishes on daily changing menus.

ENGLAND

LES OUVRIERS DU PARADIS / UNITED

LOUIS ROEDERER
CHAMPAGNE

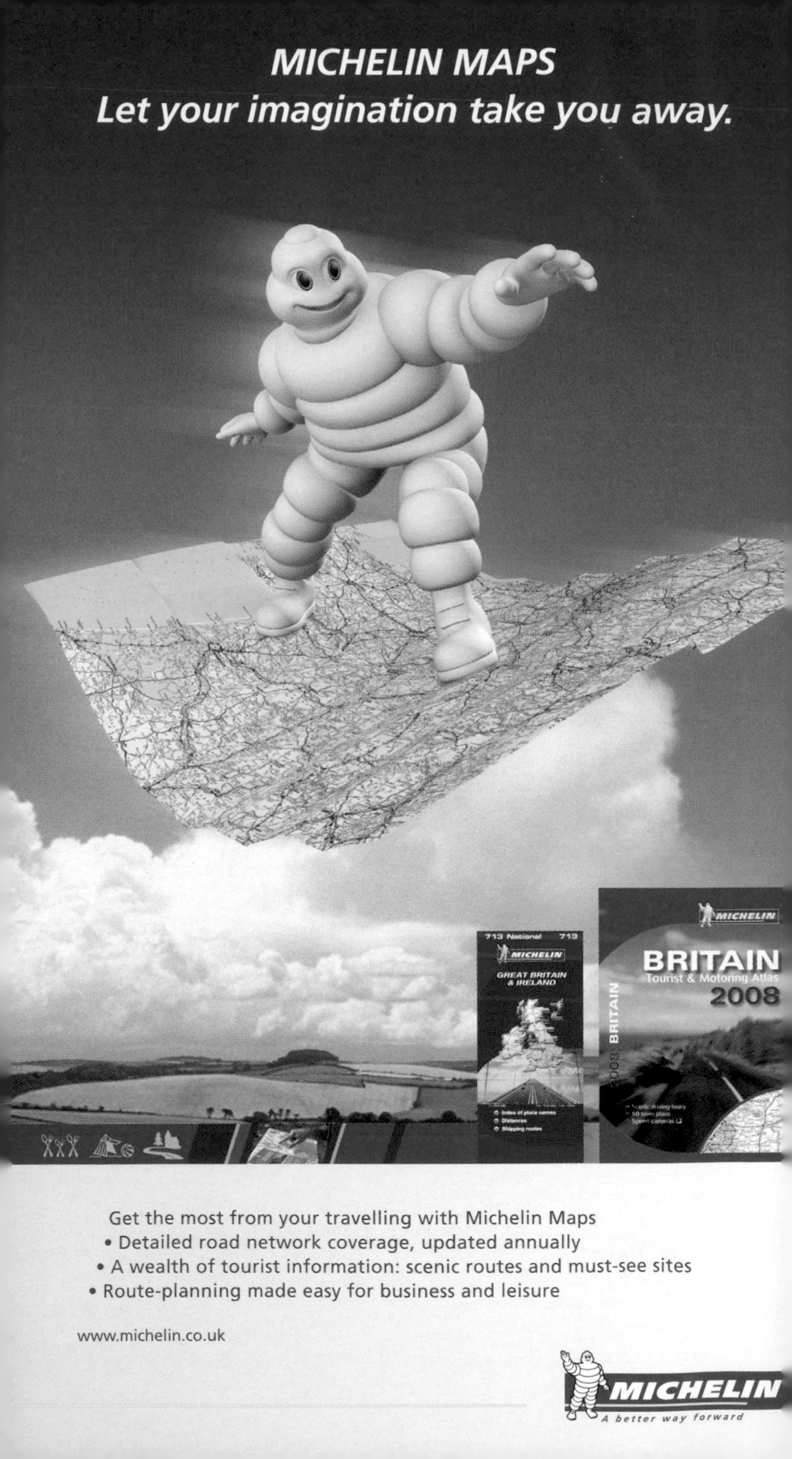

MICHELIN MAPS

Let your imagination take you away.

713 National 713

MICHELIN

GREAT BRITAIN & IRELAND

MICHELIN

BRITAIN

Tourist & Motoring Atlas

2008

Get the most from your travelling with Michelin Maps

- Detailed road network coverage, updated annually
- A wealth of tourist information: scenic routes and must-see sites
- Route-planning made easy for business and leisure

www.michelin.co.uk

MALDON - Essex - 504 W 28 - pop. 20 731 — 13 C2

London 42 m - Chelmsford 9 m - Colchester 17 m
Coach Lane ✆ (01621) 856503
Forrester Park Great Totham Beckingham Rd, ✆ (01621) 891 406 ;
Bunsay Downs Woodham Walter Little Baddow Rd, ✆ (01245) 412 648 .

Five Lakes

Colchester Rd, Tolleshunt Knights, Northeast : 8¼ m. by B 1026 ✉ CM9 8HX - ✆ (01621) 868888 - enquiries@fivelakes.co.uk - Fax (01621) 869696
190 rm - †£ 165/185 ††£ 235, ☕ £13.95 - 4 suites
Rest *Camelot* - (closed Sunday-Monday) (dinner only) Menu £ 28 **s** - Carte £ 28/35 **s**
Rest *Bejerano's Brasserie* - ✆ (01621) 862411 - Menu £ 19 **s**
◆ Massive, purpose-built hotel in 320 acres with two golf courses, imposing lobby with fountain and extensive leisure and conference facilities. Modern, well-equipped rooms. Relax in fine dining Camelot. Informal Bejerano's with adjoining Sports Bar and terrace.

MALMESBURY - Wilts. - 503 N 29 - pop. 5 094 — 4 C2

London 108 m - Bristol 28 m - Gloucester 24 m - Swindon 19 m
Town Hall, Market Lane ✆ (01666) 823748
Town★ - Market Cross★★ - Abbey★

Whatley Manor

Easton Grey, West : 2¼ m. on B 4040 ✉ SN16 0RB - ✆ (01666) 822888 - reservations@whatleymanor.com - Fax (01666) 826120
15 rm ☕ - ††£ 285/850 - 8 suites
Rest *Le Mazot* - see restaurant listing
Rest *The Dining Room* - (closed Monday-Tuesday) (dinner only) (booking essential for non-residents) Menu £ 65/80 **s**
Spec. Pan-fried foie gras with pea purée, Sauternes jelly and smoked bacon. Caramelised veal kidney with braised snails and potato crisps. Pressed pink grapefruit, coconut bonbons and pineapple sorbet.
◆ Extended Cotswold stone manor in its own grounds. Luxurious décor; superb hydrotherapy treatment spa. Elegant, well-appointed, stylish bedrooms in varying sizes. Refined, well-judged and accomplished cooking in The Dining Room overlooking terrace and gardens.

The Old Bell

Abbey Row ✉ SN16 0BW - ✆ (01666) 822344 - info@oldbellhotel.com - Fax (01666) 825145
31 rm ☕ - †£ 85/95 ††£ 200
Rest *The Restaurant* - see restaurant listing
◆ Part 13C former abbots hostel with gardens. Elegant public areas with hugely characterful bar and lounge. Handsome, well-kept rooms in coach-house or inn.

Le Mazot - at Whatley Manor

Easton Grey, West : 2¼ m. on B 4040 ✉ SN12 0RB - ✆ (01666) 822888 - lemazot@whatleymanor.com - Fax (01666) 826120
Rest - Menu £ 22 **s** - Carte £ 29/36 **s**
◆ Wood carving and alpine tones recreate a Swiss ambience. Interesting modern menus prevail. Disarmingly relaxed and intimate with assured, friendly service.

The Restaurant - at The Old Bell

Abbey Row ✉ SN16 0BW - ✆ (01666) 822344 - info@oldbellhotel.com - Fax (01666) 825145
Rest - Carte £ 23/34
◆ Charming restaurant with accomplished modern cooking; local ingredients are very much to the fore. Outside terrace with peaceful garden allows for relaxed summer dining.

ENGLAND

at Crudwell North : 4 m. on A 429 – ✉ Malmesbury

The Rectory (heated) P VISA
✉ SN16 9EP – ☎ (01666) 577 194 – info@therectoryhotel.com
– Fax (01666) 577 853
11 rm – †£ 95 ††£ 165 – 1 suite
Rest – Menu £ 19 (lunch) – Carte £ 26/30
♦ 17C stone-built former Rectory with formal garden and mature trees. Personally run. Comfortable, individually-styled bedrooms with many modern extras, some with spa baths. Airy oak-panelled dining room; modern seasonal cooking.

at Charlton Northeast : 2½ m. on B 4040 – ✉ Chichester

The Horse and Groom with rm P VISA
The Street, on B 4040 ✉ *SN16 9DL* – ☎ *(01666) 823 904*
– info@horseandgroominn.com
5 rm – †£ 80 ††£ 90
Rest – Carte £ 17/35
♦ Pretty, grade II listed 16C coaching inn with stone floor, open fire, dining room and lawned garden with outside bar. Well-judged, flavourful British cooking. Welcoming feel.

ENGLAND

MALPAS – Ches. – 502 20 A3

London 177 m – Birmingham 60 m – Chester 15 m – Shrewsbury 26 m – Stoke-on-Trent 30 m

at Tilston NW : 3 m. on Tilston Rd – ✉ Malpas

Tilston Lodge without rest P
Tilston, Northwest : 3 m. on Tilston Rd ✉ *SY14 7DR* – ☎ *(01829) 250 223*
– Fax (01829) 250 223 – Closed 25 December
3 rm – †£ 45/50 ††£ 80/85
♦ A former Victorian hunting lodge with delightful gardens and grounds, personally run in a very pleasant style by the charming owner. Cosy, individually appointed bedrooms.

MALVERN WELLS – Worcs. – 503 – see Great Malvern

MAN (Isle of) – I.O.M. – 502 F/G 21 – pop. 76 315 *Great Britain* 20 B1

from Douglas to Belfast (Isle of Man Steam Packet Co. Ltd) (summer only) (2 h 45 mn) – from Douglas to Republic of Ireland (Dublin) (Isle of Man Steam Packet Co. Ltd) (2 h 45 mn/4 h) – from Douglas to Heysham (Isle of Man Steam Packet Co.) (2 h/3 h 30 mn) – from Douglas to Liverpool (Isle of Man Steam Packet Co. Ltd) (2 h 30 mn/4 h)
Laxey Wheel★★ - Snaefell★ (✳ ★★★) - Cregneash Folk Museum★

Douglas – I.O.M. – pop. 25 347 20 B1

Ronaldsway Airport : ☎ (01624) 821600, SW : 7 m.
Sea Terminal Buildings ☎ (01624) 686801
Douglas Municipal Pulrose Park, ☎ (01624) 675 952 ;
King Edward Bay Onchan Groudle Rd, ☎ (01624) 620 430 .

Sefton rm, P VISA AE
Harris Promenade ✉ *IM1 2RW* – ☎ *(01624) 645 500* – *info@seftonhotel.co.im*
– Fax (01624) 676 004
97 rm – †£ 95/110 ††£ 105/110, £ 9.95 – 3 suites
Rest *The Gallery* – (lunch residents only) Menu £ 14 – Carte £ 25/39
♦ Enviable promenade position: behind the 19C façade lies a stunning atrium with water features and flora; marble reception. The well-appointed bedrooms overlook the bay. Modish, bright eatery with modern Manx art on the walls.

The Regency
Queens Promenade ✉ *IM2 4NN – ☎ (01624) 680680 – regency@iom-1.net – Fax (01624) 680690*
35 rm – £66/140 ££110/160 – 3 suites
Rest *Five Continents* – Menu £23 **s**
◆ Grand-looking, four storey hotel with appealing traditional style. Sea front position with good views over Douglas Bay. Rooms equipped with latest technology. Wood-panelled restaurant with sea outlook.

Mount Murray H. & Country Club rm,
Santon, Southwest : 4 3/4 m. by A 5 ✉ *IM4 2HT – ☎ (01624) 661111 – hotel@mountmurray.com – Fax (01624) 611116*
100 rm – £105/130 ££130
Rest *Charlotte's Bistro* – Menu £15/24 **s** – Carte £24/37 **s**
◆ Surrounded by vast grounds and golf course. Large sports bar and two lounges. Extensive leisure and conference facilities. Comfortable, modern rooms. Large, formal Murray's overlooks golf course.

Admirals House without rest
12 Loch Promenade ✉ *IM1 2LX – ☎ (01624) 629551 – enquiries@admiralhouse.com – Fax (01624) 675021*
26 rm – £95 ££110
◆ Impressively situated Victorian building on promenade and only two minutes from ferry terminal. Split-level café-bar. Particularly large, modern bedrooms.

Penta without rest
Queens Promenade ✉ *IM9 4NE – ☎ (01624) 680680 – penta@iom-1.net – Fax (01624) 680690*
22 rm – £49/65 ££57/70
◆ Victorian property with bay windows on the town's main promenade. By way of contrast, spacious and up-to-date bedrooms which include a computer in each room.

Ciappelli's
12-13 Loch Promenade ✉ *IM1 2LX – ☎ (01624) 677442 – enquiries@ciappellis.com – Fax (01624) 671305 – Closed Saturday lunch and Sunday*
Rest – Carte £38/57
◆ Sleek promenade destination. Funky basement bar. Split level restaurant enhanced by wall-hung glassware. Immaculate tables; smooth service; locally inspired seasonal dishes.

Port Erin – I.O.M. – pop. 3 369 20 **B1**

Rowany Cottier without rest Port Erin Bay,
Spaldrick ✉ *IM9 6PE – ☎ (01624) 832287 – rowanycottier@manx.net*
5 rm – £40/55 ££70/85
◆ Detached house with spectacular views over Port Erin Bay. Homely lounge with open fires. Oak floor and pine tables in breakfast room. Bright, colourful bedrooms.

Port St Mary – I.O.M. – pop. 1 941 20 **B1**

Aaron House without rest
The Promenade ✉ *IM9 5DE – ☎ (01624) 835702 – Fax (01624) 837731 – Closed Christmas-New Year*
5 rm – £49/98 ££98/108
◆ High degree of hospitality guaranteed in this imposing 19C property - owner wears Victorian dresses. Substantial breakfasts. Very comfortable rooms with winning touches.

Ramsey – I.O.M. – pop. 7 322 20 **B1**

The River House without rest
North : 1/4 m. turning left after bridge before Bridge Inn on Bowring Rd ✉ *IM8 3DA – ☎ (01624) 816412 – closed February*
3 rm – £50/75 ££77/97
◆ Part Georgian house in delightful location along riverside. Peaceful ambience. Country house style lounge. Scrubbed wood breakfast room. Individually styled bedrooms.

ENGLAND

N. Boyd/Robert HARDING

MANCHESTER

County: Gtr Manchester
Michelin REGIONAL map: n° 502 N 23
London 202 m – Birmingham 86 m – Glasgow 221 m – Leeds 43 m – Liverpool 35 m – Nottingham 72 m

Population: 394 269
Great Britain

20 **B2**

PRACTICAL INFORMATION

Tourist Information

Manchester Visitor Centre, Town Hall Extension, Lloyd St ✆ (0871) 222 8223, manchester-visitor-centre@notes.manchester.gov.uk

Manchester Airport, International Arrivals Hall, Terminal 1 ✆ (0161) 436 3344 - Manchester Airport, International Arrivals Hall, Terminal 2 ✆ (0871) 222 8223 - Salford T.I.C., Pier 8, Salford Quays ✆ (0161) 848 8601 - Portland St ✆ (0845) 600 6040

Airport

Manchester International Airport: ✆ (0161) 489 3000, S: 10 m. by A 5103 - AX - and M 56

Golf Courses

Heaton Park Prestwich, ✆ (0161) 654 9899 ;

Houldsworth Park Stockport Houldsworth St, Reddish, ✆ (0161) 442 1712 ;

Chorlton-cum-Hardy Barlow Hall Rd, Barlow Hall, ✆ (0161) 881 3139 ;

William Wroe Flixton Pennybridge Lane, ✆ (0161) 748 8680.

ENGLAND

SIGHTS

SEE

City★ - Castlefield Heritage Park★ CZ – Town Hall★ CZ – Manchester Art Gallery★ CZ **M2** – Cathedral★ (stalls and canopies★) CY – Museum of Science and Industry★ CZ **M** – Urbis★ CY – Imperial War Museum North★ , Trafford Park AX **M**

ENV.

Whitworth Art Gallery★ , S: 1 ½ m

EXC.

Quarry Bank Mill★ , S: 10 m. off B 5166, exit 5 from M 56

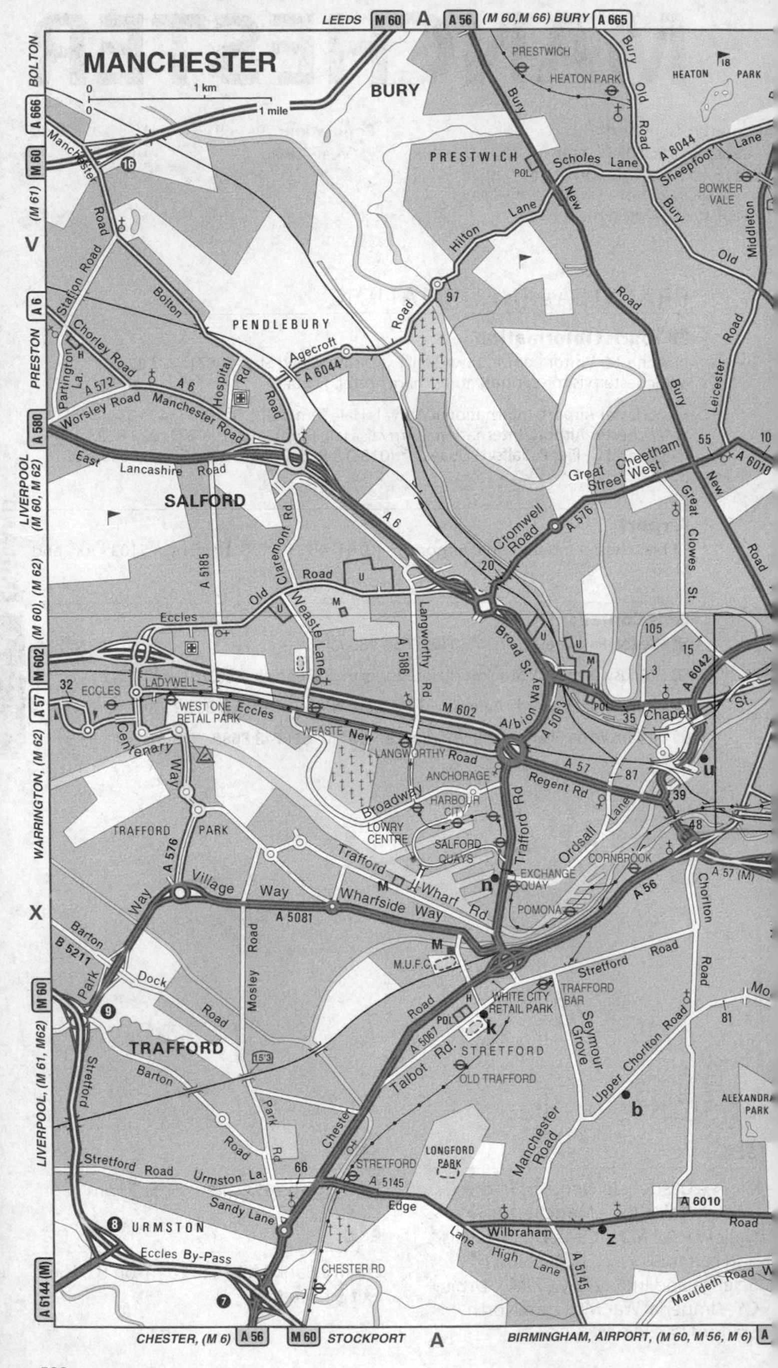
MANCHESTER
0 1 km
0 1 mile
LEEDS M 60 A A 56 (M 60, M 66) BURY A 665
BOLTON
A 666
M 60
(M 61)
V
PRESTON A 6
LIVERPOOL (M 60, M 62) A 580
WARRINGTON, (M 60), (M 62) M 602
WARRINGTON, (M 62) A 57
X
LIVERPOOL, (M 61, M62) M 60
A 6144 (M)
CHESTER, (M 6) A 56 M 60 STOCKPORT A BIRMINGHAM, AIRPORT, (M 60, M 56, M 6)
BURY
PRESTWICH
HEATON PARK
HEATON PARK
Bury Old Road
PRESTWICH
POL
Scholes Lane
A 6044
Sheepfoot Lane
BOWKER VALE
Bury Old
Middleton
Bury New Road
Hilton Lane
97
Agecroft Road
A 6044
PENDLEBURY
Manchester Road
16
Station Road
Bolton Road
Chorley Road
Partington La.
A 572
A 6
Worsley Road
Manchester Road
Hospital Rd
Road
East Lancashire Road
SALFORD
Claremont Rd
Old Road
A 5185
Great Cheetham Street West
55
A 6010
Leicester Road
Bury New Road
Cromwell Road
A 576
20
Great Clowes St.
Broad St.
Albion Way
A 5063
A 6
Eccles
Weaste Lane
Langworthy Rd
A 5186
M 602
105
15
3
A 6042
POL
35 Chapel St.
32
ECCLES
LADYWELL
WEST ONE RETAIL PARK
Eccles New Road
WEASTE
LANGWORTHY Road
ANCHORAGE
A 57
Regent Rd
87
39
48
u
Centenary Way
Broadway
HARBOUR CITY
LOWRY CENTRE
SALFORD QUAYS
Trafford Rd
Ordsall Lane
CORNBROOK
A 57 (M)
TRAFFORD PARK
A 576
Village Way
Trafford Wharf Rd
M
n
EXCHANGE QUAY
A 56
Chorlton Road
A 5081
Wharfside Way
POMONA
Barton
B 5211
Park
Dock Road
Mosley Road
M
M.U.F.C.
Stretford Road
TRAFFORD BAR
WHITE CITY RETAIL PARK
Seymour Grove
9
TRAFFORD
15'3
Road
POL
A 5067
k
Talbot Rd.
STRETFORD
OLD TRAFFORD
Upper Chorlton Road
81
b
ALEXANDRA PARK
Stretford
Barton Road
Park Rd
Chester
LONGFORD PARK
Manchester Road
Stretford Road
Urmston La.
66
STRETFORD
A 5145
A 6010
Sandy Lane
Edge Lane
Wilbraham Road
z
8 URMSTON
High Lane
A 5145
Eccles By-Pass
7
CHESTER RD
Mauldeth Road W.

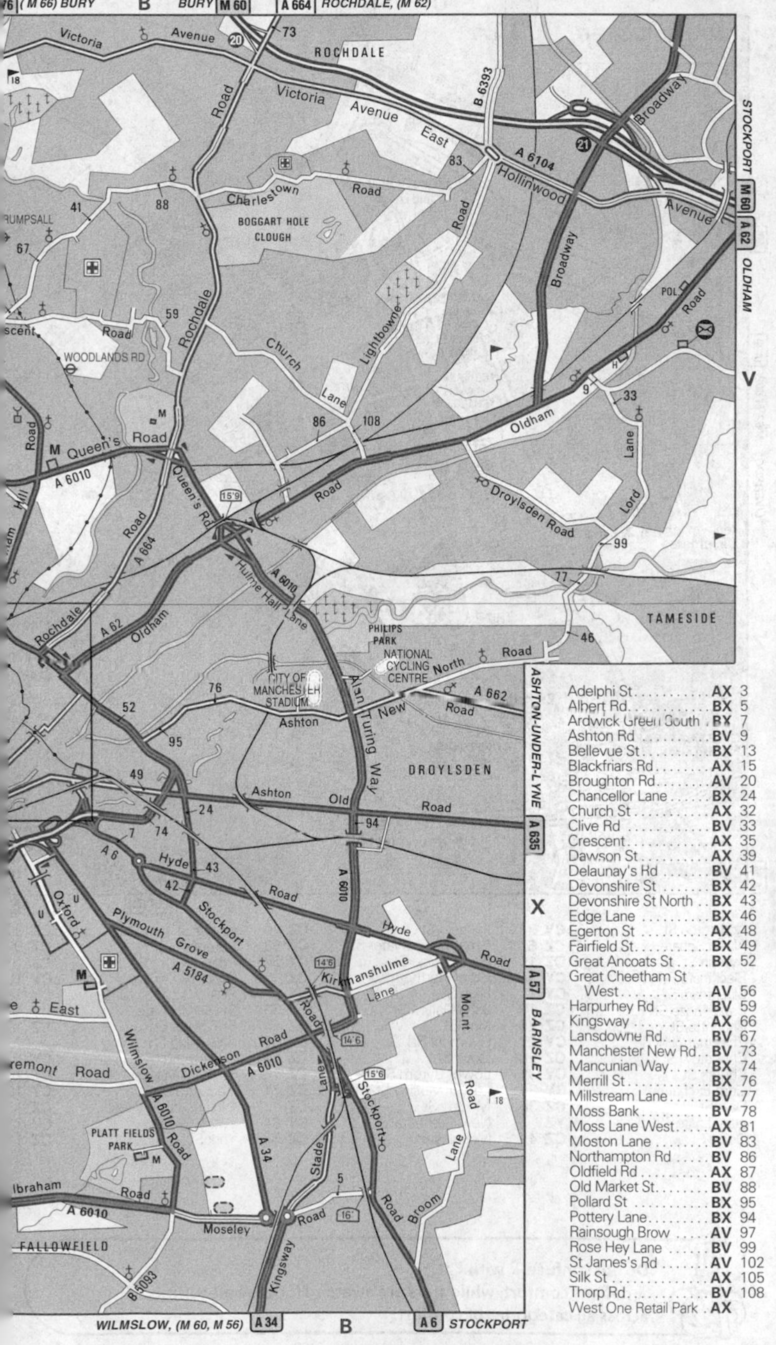

(M 66) BURY
B
BURY M 60
A 664 ROCHDALE, (M 62)
STOCKPORT M 60
A 62 OLDHAM
V
ASHTON-UNDER-LYNE A 635
X
A 57 BARNSLEY
WILMSLOW, (M 60, M 56) A 34
B
A 6 STOCKPORT
ROCHDALE
Victoria Avenue
Victoria Avenue East
B 6393
A 6104
Hollinwood Avenue
Broadway
Charlestown Road
BOGGART HOLE CLOUGH
RUMPSALL
WOODLANDS RD
Rochdale Road
Church Lane
Lightbowne
Queen's Road
A 6010
Queen's Rd
A 664
Oldham Road
Droylsden Road
Lord Lane
Hulme Hall Lane
TAMESIDE
PHILIPS PARK
NATIONAL CYCLING CENTRE
CITY OF MANCHESTER STADIUM
North Road
A 662
New Road
Ashton
Alan Turing Way
DROYLSDEN
A 62
Ashton Old Road
A 6
Hyde Road
Stockport
Oxford
Plymouth Grove
A 5184
Kirkmanshulme Lane
Mount Road
Wilmslow
Dickenson Road
A 6010
remont Road
East
PLATT FIELDS PARK
A 34
Stade Lane
Stockport Road
Broom Lane
lbraham Road
Moseley Road
Kingsway
FALLOWFIELD
B 5093

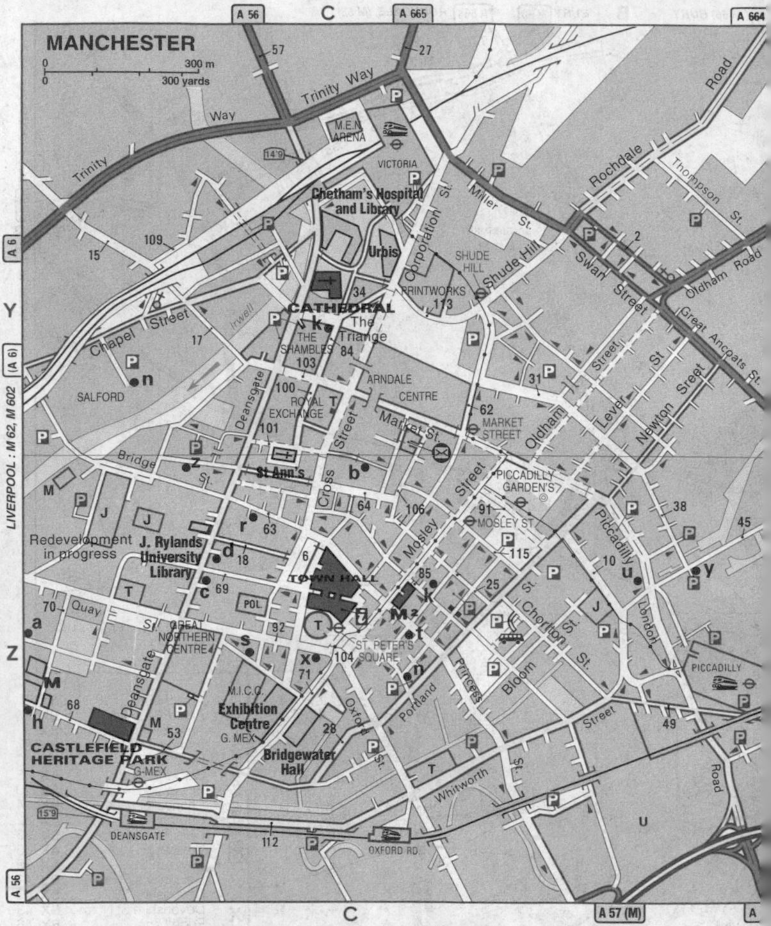

MANCHESTER

0 — 300 m
0 — 300 yards

Street	Grid	No.
Addington St	CY	2
Albert Square	CZ	6
Aytoun St.	CZ	10
Blackfriars Rd	CY	15
Blackfriars St	CY	17
Brazennoze St.	CZ	18
Charlotte St	CZ	25
Cheetham Hill Rd	CY	27
Chepstow St	CZ	28
Church St	CY	31
Corn Exchange	CY	34
Dale St	CZ	38
Deansgate	CYZ	
Ducie St.	CZ	45
Fairfield St	CZ	49
Great Bridgewater St	CZ	53
Great Ducie St	CY	57
Great Northern centre	CZ	
High St	CY	62
John Dalton St	CZ	63
King St	CZ	64
Liverpool Rd	CZ	68
Lloyd St	CZ	69
Lower Byrom St	CZ	70
Lower Mosley St	CZ	71
Mosley St	CZ	
New Cathedral St	CY	84
Nicholas St	CZ	85
Parker St	CZ	91
Peter St	CZ	92
Princess St	CZ	
St Ann's Square	CY	10
St Ann's St	CY	10
St Mary's Gate	CY	10
St Peter's Square	CZ	10
Shambles Shopping Centre (The)	CY	
Spring Gardens	CZ	10
Viaduct St	CY	10
Whitworth St West	CZ	1
Withy Grove	CY	1
York St	CZ	1

Do not confuse X with ✿!
X defines comfort, while stars are awarded for the best cuisine, across all categories of comfort.

The Lowry
50 Dearmans Pl, Chapel Wharf, Salford ✉ *M3 5LH* – ✆ *(0161) 827 4000*
– enquiries.lowry@roccofortecollection.com – Fax (0161) 827 4001 CY **n**
158 rm – †£ 265 ††£ 285, ☕ £17.50 – 7 suites
Rest ***River*** – see restaurant listing
◆ Stylish contemporary design with a minimalist feel. Smart spacious bedrooms have high levels of comfort and facilities; some overlook River Irwell. State-of-the-art spa.

The Midland
16 Peter St ✉ *M60 2DS* – ✆ *(0161) 236 3333 – midlandsales@qhotels.co.uk*
– Fax (0161) 932 4100 CZ **x**
298 rm – †£ 250 ††£ 250, ☕ £15 – 14 suites
Rest ***The French*** – see restaurant listing
Rest ***The Colony*** – Menu £ 19 (lunch) – Carte dinner £ 23/32
◆ Edwardian splendour on a vast scale in the heart of the city. Period features and a huge open lobby combine with up-to-date facilities to create a thoroughly grand hotel. Brasserie menus take pride of place at the restaurant.

Radisson Edwardian
Free Trade Hall, Peter St ✉ *M2 5GP* – ✆ *(0161) 835 9929*
– Fax (0161) 835 9979 CZ **s**
233 rm – †£ 167/209 ††£ 188/240, ☕ £16.50 – 30 suites
Rest ***Opus One*** – Menu £ 25 – Carte £ 25/33.50
◆ Smart, modern hotel incorporating impressive façade of Free Trade Hall. Grand surroundings of stone, marble and sculptures. Conference and leisure facilities. Stylish rooms. Chic fine dining, with strong Japanese influences, in Opus One.

ENGLAND

Malmaison
Piccadilly ✉ *M1 3AQ* – ✆ *(0161) 278 1000 – manchester@malmaison.com*
– Fax (0161) 278 1002 CZ **u**
154 rm – †£ 99/155 ††£ 99/155, ☕ £13.95 – 13 suites
Rest ***Brasserie*** – Menu £ 15.95/19.95 – Carte £ 24/41
◆ A more modern brand of hotel that combines contemporary design and fresh décor with an informal and unstuffy atmosphere. Bedrooms are bright, stylish and hi-tech. Bright, characterful brasserie.

Arora International
18-24 Princess St ✉ *M1 4LY* – ✆ *(0161) 236 8999*
– manchesterreservations@arorainternational.com – Fax (0161) 236 3222
– closed 25 December CZ **t**
141 rm – †£ 119/175 ††£ 119/209, ☕ £13.50
Rest ***Obsidian*** – Menu £ 17 – Carte £ 20/45
◆ Part owned by Sir Cliff Richard, this Grade II listed building has been refurbished with distinctive modern décor throughout. Very comfy rooms, four with a "Cliff" theme! Stylish basement dining room with eclectic mix of dishes.

Great John Street without rest
Great John St ✉ *M3 4FD* – ✆ *(0161) 831 3211 – info@greatjohnstreet.co.uk*
– Fax (0161) 831 3212 CZ **a**
30 rm – †£ 235/395 ††£ 235/395, ☕ £14.95
◆ Revamped 19C school featuring many stylish, elegant touches. Rooftop terrace with champagne bar, hot tub, and city views. State-of-art rooms boast duplex style and vivid hues.

Marriott Manchester Victoria and Albert
Water St ✉ *M3 4JQ* – ✆ *(0161) 832 1188*
– Fax (0161) 834 2484 AX **u**
143 rm – †£ 139/159 ††£ 139/159, ☕ £16.95 – 4 suites – **Rest** – (bar lunch) Carte £ 25/30
◆ Restored 19C warehouses on the banks of the River Irwell, with exposed brick and original beams and columns. Bedrooms take their themes from Granada Television productions. Restaurant proud of its timbered warehouse origins.

Novotel Manchester Centre

21 Dickinson St ✉ M1 4LX – ✆ (0161) 235 2200 – h3145@accor.com – Fax (0161) 235 2210 CZ **n**

164 rm – †£ 89/149 ††£ 89/149, ☕ £ 12 – **Rest** – (Closed Saturday and Sunday lunch) Carte £ 25/31 **s**

◆ The open-plan lobby boasts a spacious, stylish bar and residents can take advantage of an exclusive exercise area. Decently equipped, tidily appointed bedrooms. Compact dining room with grill-style menus.

The French – at The Midland H.

Peter St ✉ M60 2DS – ✆ (0161) 236 3333 – midlandsales@qhotels.co.uk – Fax (0161) 932 4100 – Closed 2 weeks August, Sunday and Monday CZ **x**

Rest – (dinner only) Carte £ 37/51 **s**

◆ As grand as the hotel in which it is housed, with gilded paintings, large mirrors and heavy drapes. Attentively formal service, classically French-based cooking.

River – at The Lowry H.

50 Dearmans Pl, Chapel Wharf, Salford ✉ M3 5LH – ✆ (0161) 827 4003 – enquiries.lowry@roccofortecollection.com – Fax (0161) 827 4001 CY **n**

Rest – Menu £ 25 (lunch) **s** – Carte £ 42/45 **s**

◆ Matching its surroundings, this is a stylish modern restaurant serving, in a precise manner, classic dishes that have stood the test of time. Irwell views, for good measure.

ENGLAND

Wings

1 Lincoln Sq ✉ M2 5LN – ✆ (0161) 834 9000 – wing@wingsrestaurant.co.uk CZ **d**

Rest – Chinese Menu £ 28 – Carte £ 25/57

◆ Chinese restaurant hidden off busy square, its smart exterior exuding an up-to-date feel. Carefully prepared, top quality dishes washed down with wide range of champagnes.

Second Floor - Restaurant – at Harvey Nichols

21 New Cathedral St ✉ M1 1AD – ✆ (0161) 828 8898 – secondfloor.reservations@harveynichols.com – Fax (0161) 828 8815 – Closed 25-26 December, 1 January, Easter Sunday and dinner Sunday and Monday CY **k**

Rest – Carte £ 31/44

◆ Central location on second floor of famous department store. Well-designed restaurant with immaculate linen-clad tables. Brasserie style cooking.

Pacific

58-60 George St ✉ M1 4HF – ✆ (0161) 228 6668 – info@pacificrestaurant.co.uk – Fax (0161) 236 0191 CZ **k**

Rest – Chinese and Thai Menu £ 10 (lunch) – Carte £ 24/41

◆ Located in Chinatown: Chinese cuisine on first floor, Thai on the second; modern décor incorporating subtle Asian influences. Large menus boast high levels of authenticity.

Simply Heathcotes

Jackson Row, Deansgate ✉ M2 5WD – ✆ (0161) 835 3536 – manchester@heathcotes.co.uk – Fax (0161) 835 3534 – Closed Bank Holidays CZ **c**

Rest – Menu £ 30 – Carte approx. £ 26

◆ Contemporary interior, with live jazz in the wine bar, contrasts with the original oak panels of this Victorian former register office. Robust menu is equally à la mode.

Koreana

Kings House, 40a King St West ✉ M3 2WY – ✆ (0161) 832 4330 – alexkoreana@aol.com – Fax (0161) 832 2293 – Closed 25-26 December, 1 January, Sunday, lunch Saturday and Bank Holidays CZ **z**

Rest – Korean Carte £ 12/27

◆ Family run basement restaurant, bustling yet still relaxed, offers authentic, balanced Korean cuisine. Novices are guided gently through the menu by staff in national dress.

Palmiro

197 Upper Chorlton Rd, South : 2 m. by A 56 off Chorlton Rd ✉ M16 0BH – ✆ (0161) 860 7330 – bookings@palmiro.net – Fax (0161) 861 7464 – Closed 25 December and 1 January AX **b**

Rest – Italian Menu £ 12 (lunch) **s** – Carte £ 21/26 **s**

◆ Spartan interior with grey mottled walls and halogen lighting: a highly regarded neighbourhood Italian eatery boasting good value rustic dishes cooked with maximum simplicity.

Brasserie Blanc

55 King St ✉ M2 4LQ – ✆ (0161) 832 1000 – manchester@brasserieblanc.com – Fax (0161) 832 1001 – Closed 25-26 December and 1 January CZ **b**

Rest – Menu £ 14/18 – Carte approx. £ 26

◆ Busy, group-owned brasserie with large bar and polished tables. Extensive menus of classic and modern British dishes as well as regional French options. Attentive service.

The Restaurant Bar and Grill

14 John Dalton St ✉ M2 6JR – ✆ (0161) 839 1999 – manchester@rbgltd.co.uk – Fax (0161) 835 1886 CZ **r**

Rest – Carte £ 33/40

◆ Stylish ground floor lounge bar and lively first floor eatery. Extensive international repertoire from an open kitchen. Very busy with business community at lunch.

Second Floor - Brasserie – at Harvey Nichols

21 New Cathedral St ✉ M1 1AD – ✆ (0161) 828 8898 – secondfloor.reservations@harveynichols.com – Fax (0161) 828 8815 – closed 25-26 December, 1 January, Easter and dinner Sunday and Monday CY **k**

Rest – Carte £ 25/32

◆ Open and lively restaurant with minimalist décor. Wide range of cocktails available at the large bar. Attractive menu with a European eclectic mix of dishes.

The Ox

71 Liverpool Rd, Castlefield ✉ M3 4NQ – ✆ (0161) 839 7740/60 – gmtheox@baabar.co.uk – Closed 25 December and 1 January CZ **h**

Rest – Menu £ 14 – Carte £ 18/27

◆ Central, homely pub, ideal after local museum trip. Cooking style is eclectic, featuring many well-tried or original dishes. Spot a celebrity from nearby Granada TV studios!

at Didsbury South : 5½ m. by 5103 - AX - on A 5145 – ✉ Manchester

Didsbury House

Didsbury Park, South : 1½ m. on A 5145 ✉ M20 5LJ – ✆ (0161) 448 2200 – info@didsburyhouse.co.uk – Fax (0161) 448 2525

23 rm – †£ 110/130 ††£ 110/130, ☕ £ 14.50 – 4 suites – **Rest** – (room service only)

◆ Grade II listed 19C house: grand wooden staircase, superb stained glass window. Otherwise, stylish and modern with roof-top hot tubs. Spacious, individually designed rooms.

Eleven Didsbury Park

11 Didsbury Park, South : ½ m. by A 5145 ✉ M20 5LH – ✆ (0161) 448 7711 – enquiries@didsburyhouse.co.uk – Fax (0161) 448 8282

20 rm – †£ 140 ††£ 140, ☕ £ 14.50 – **Rest** – (room service only)

◆ The cool contemporary design in this Victorian town house creates a serene and relaxing atmosphere. Good-sized bedrooms decorated with flair and style. Personally run.

Café Jem&I

1c School Lane ✉ M20 6SA – ✆ (0161) 445 3996 – jemosullivan@aol.com – Fax (0161) 448 8661 – Closed 25-26 December, 1 January, Monday lunch and Bank Holidays

Rest – Carte £ 26/32

◆ Simple, unpretentious cream coloured building tucked away off the high street. Open-plan kitchen; homely, bistro feel. Good value, tasty modern classics.

ENGLAND

at West Didsbury South : 5 ½ m. by A 5103 - AX - and A 5145 – ✉ Manchester

Rhubarb
167 Burton Rd ✉ M20 2LN – ☎ (0161) 448 8887 – info@rhubarbrestaurant.co.uk – Closed 25 December
Rest – (dinner only and Sunday lunch) Carte £ 22/34
◆ An eye-catching exterior draws in a loyal local following. Yes, there are rhubarb walls, but the cooking, not so locally inspired, features tasty dishes from far and wide.

at Manchester Airport South : 9 m. by A 5103 - AX - off M 56 – ✉ Manchester

Radisson SAS Manchester Airport
Chicago Ave ✉ M90 3RA – ☎ (0161) 490 5000 – sales.manchester.airport@radissonsas.com – Fax (0161) 490 5100
354 rm – †£ 159 ††£ 159, ☕ £ 17.95 – 6 suites
Rest *Phileas Fogg* – (dinner only) Carte £ 29/38 **s**
Rest *Runway Brasserie* – Carte £ 16/28 **s**
◆ Vast, modern hotel linked to airport passenger walkway. Four room styles with many extras. Ideal for business clients or travellers. Phileas Fogg is curved restaurant with eclectic menus and runway views. All-day Runway with arrivals/departures info.

ENGLAND

Hilton Manchester Airport
Outwood Lane (Terminal One) ✉ M90 4WP – ☎ (0161) 435 3000 – reservations.manchester@hilton.com – Fax (0161) 435 3040
224 rm – †£ 136/153 ††£ 136/153, ☕ £ 17.95 – 1 suite – **Rest** – (bar lunch) Menu £ 30 – Carte £ 33/40 **s**
◆ Popular with corporate travellers for its business centre and location 200 metres from the airport terminal. Comfortable, soundproofed bedrooms. Restaurant exudes pleasant, modern style.

Etrop Grange
Thorley Lane ✉ M90 4EG – ☎ (0161) 499 0500 – etropgrange@foliohotels.com – Fax (0161) 499 0790
62 rm – †£ 99/149 ††£ 99/149, ☕ £ 13.50 – 2 suites – **Rest** – Menu £ 20/30 – Carte £ 30/43 **s**
◆ Sympathetically extended Georgian house that retains a period feel. Rooms vary in size; all are pleasantly decorated with some boasting four-posters, others cast-iron beds. Intimate, traditionally styled dining room.

Bewley's
Outwood Lane, (Terminal Three) ✉ M90 4HL – ☎ (0161) 498 0333 – man@bewleyshotels.com – Fax (0161) 498 0222
365 rm – †£ 79 ††£ 79, ☕ £ 6.95 – **Rest** – (bar lunch) Carte £ 19/24 **s**
◆ Good value, four-storey, purpose-built group hotel with modern, open lobby. Brightly decorated bedrooms that all have either one double bed and sofa or two double beds. Appealing, popular dishes in restaurant or lobby café.

Moss Nook
Ringway Rd, Moss Nook, East : 1 ¼ m. on Cheadle rd ✉ M22 5WD – ☎ (0161) 437 4778 – Fax (0161) 498 8089 – Closed 2 weeks Christmas, Saturday lunch, Sunday and Monday
Rest – Menu £ 20/37 – Carte £ 32/44
◆ Decorated in a combination of Art Nouveau, lace and panelling. Long-standing owners provide polished and ceremonial service; cooking is robust and classically based.

at Trafford Park Southwest : 2 m. by A 56 and A 5081 – ✉ Manchester

Old Trafford Lodge without rest
Lancashire County Cricket Club, Talbot Rd, Old Trafford ✉ M16 0PX – ✆ (0161) 874 3333 – lodge@lccc.co.uk – Fax (0161) 874 3399 – closed 24 December-1 January AX **k**
68 rm – †£ 54/74 ††£ 54/74
◆ Purpose-built lodge within Lancashire County Cricket Club; half the rooms have balconies overlooking the ground. Good value accommodation in smart, colourful bedrooms.

at Salford Quays Southwest : 2 ¼ m. by A 56 off A 5063 – ✉ Manchester

Copthorne Manchester rm, rest,
Clippers Quay ✉ M50 3SN – ✆ (0161) 873 7321 – roomsales.manchester@mill-cop.com – Fax (0161) 877 8112 AX **n**
166 rm – ††£ 270, ☕ £ 15.75
Rest *Chandlers* – (Closed Sunday-Monday) (dinner only) Menu £ 38/43
Rest *Clippers* – (bar lunch Saturday-Sunday) Carte £ 15/30
◆ Part of the redeveloped Quays, overlooking the waterfront, with a Metrolink to the City. Connoisseur bedrooms are particularly well-appointed. Chandlers offers diners enjoyable waterfront views. Informal, pleasantly busy Clippers with open kitchen.

at Chorlton-Cum-Hardy Southwest : 5 m. by A 5103 - AX - on A 6010 – ✉ Manchester

Abbey Lodge without rest
501 Wilbraham Rd ✉ M21 0UJ – ✆ (0161) 862 9266 – info@abbey-lodge.co.uk AX **z**
4 rm – †£ 40/55 ††£ 60/65, ☕ £ 6
◆ Attractive Edwardian house boasting many original features including stained glass windows. Owners provide charming hospitality and pine fitted rooms are immaculately kept.

Marmalade
60 Beech Road, Chorlton cum Hardy ✉ M21 9EG – ✆ (0161) 862 9665 – jqmarmalade@tiscali.co.uk – Fax (0161) 861 7788 – closed 25-26 December
Rest – (closed lunch Monday-Wednesday) Menu £ 12/14 – Carte £ 20/27
◆ Three tier cake stands, crutches and antique suitcases define this eye-catching pub. Food's a serious matter: cracking local menus. Yes, homemade marmalade's on offer, too.

at Trafford Centre Southwest : 5 ¼ m. by A 56 - AX - and A 5081 – ✉ Manchester

Tulip Inn rm, rest,
Old Park Lane, on B 5214 ✉ M17 8PG – ✆ (0161) 755 3355 – info@tulipinnmanchester.co.uk – Fax (0161) 755 3344
161 rm – †£ 99 ††£ 104, ☕ £ 8.95 – **Rest** – (dinner only) Carte £ 15/28 **s**
◆ Large, modern hotel within a stone's throw of the Trafford Centre and M60. Good value accommodation. Bedrooms are notably spacious, well-equipped and up-to-date. Relaxed, informal bistro.

MANSFIELD – Notts. – **502** Q 24 16 **B1**
London 143 m – Chesterfield 12 m – Worksop 14 m

No.4 Wood Street
No.4 Wood St ✉ NG18 1QA – ✆ (01623) 424 824 – Closed 26 December, 1 January, Monday, Sunday dinner and Saturday lunch
Rest – Menu £ 19 – Carte £ 23/41
◆ Solid brick restaurant hidden away in town centre. Relax in lounge bar with comfy armchairs before enjoying well-executed, modern, seasonal dishes in rustic dining room.

ENGLAND

MARAZION – Cornwall – 503 D 33 – ✉ Penzance 1 A3

London 318 m – Penzance 3 m – Truro 26 m
Praa Sands Penzance, ✆ (01736) 763 445 .
St Michael's Mount★★ (≤ ★★) – Ludgvan★ (Church★) N : 2 m. by A 30 – Chysauster Village★, N : 2 m. by A 30 – Gulval★ (Church★) W : 2½ m – Prussia Cove★, SE : 5½ m. by A 30 and minor rd

Mount Haven ≤ St Michael's Mount and bay, P VISA
Turnpike Rd, East : ¼ m. ✉ TR17 0DQ – ✆ (01736) 710 249 – reception@mounthaven.co.uk – Fax (01736) 711 658 – closed 16 December - 10 February
18 rm – £ 65/95 £ 90/150 – **Rest** – (bar lunch) Menu £ 25 – Carte £ 25/33
◆ Small hotel overlooking St Michael's Bay. Spacious bar and lounge featuring Indian crafts and fabrics. Contemporary rooms with modern amenities, some with balcony and view. Bright attractive dining room; menu mixes modern and traditional.

at St. Hilary East : 2½ m. by Turnpike Rd, on B 3280 – ✉ Penzance

Ennys without rest (heated) P VISA
Trewhella Lane, St Hilary, East : 2½ m. by Turnpike Rd, on B 3280 ✉ TR20 9BZ – ✆ (01736) 740 262 – ennys@ennys.co.uk – Fax (01736) 740 055 – 20 March-October
5 rm – £ 65/85 £ 105/120
◆ Blissful 17C manor house on working farm. Spacious breakfast room and large farmhouse kitchen for afternoon tea. Modern country house style lounge. Elegant, classical rooms.

at Perranuthnoe Southeast : 1¾ m. by A 394 – ✉ Penzance

Ednovean Farm without rest ≤ St Michaels Mount and Bay, P VISA AE
✉ TR20 9LZ – ✆ (01736) 711 883 – info@ednoveanfarm.co.uk – Closed Christmas
3 rm – £ 75/95 £ 80/100
◆ Very spacious, characterful converted 17C granite barn offering peace, tranquillity and Mounts Bay views. Fine choice at breakfast on oak table. Charming, individual rooms.

Good food and accommodation at moderate prices?
Look for the Bib symbols:
red Bib Gourmand for food, blue Bib Hotel for hotels

MARDEN – Wilts. – see Devizes

MARKET DRAYTON – Shrops. – 502 M 25 18 B1

London 159 m – Nantwich 13 m – Shrewsbury 21 m

Goldstone Hall ≤ P VISA
South : 4½ m. on A 529 ✉ TF9 2NA – ✆ (01630) 661 202 – info@goldstonehall.com – Fax (01630) 661 585
12 rm – £ 88 £ 132/165 – **Rest** – Menu £ 23/32 **s**
◆ 16C red-brick country house that's been extensively added to over the ages. Five acres of formal garden: PG Wodehouse enjoyed its shade! Modern rooms with huge beds. Contemporary twists on daily changing menus.

ENGLAND

MARKET HARBOROUGH – Leics. – 504 R 26 – pop. 20 127 16 B3

London 88 m – Birmingham 47 m – Leicester 15 m – Northampton 17 m
Council Offices, Adam and Eve St ✆ (01858) 828282
Great Oxendon Rd, ✆ (01858) 463 684 .

at Thorpe Langton North : 3 ¾ m. by A 4304 via Great Bowden – ✉ Market Harborough

The Bakers Arms

Main St ✉ LE16 7TS – ✆ (01858) 545 201 – Fax (01858) 545 924 – Closed Sunday dinner and Monday

Rest – (dinner only and lunch Saturday and Sunday) (booking essential) Carte £ 21/31

◆ Atmospheric thatched pub with deep red walls, exposed timbers and pew seats. Scrubbed wooden tables add to the relaxed feel. Tasty, well-priced, tried-and-tested dishes.

MARKINGTON – N. Yorks. – 502 P 21 – see Ripon

MARLBOROUGH – Wilts. – 503 O 29 – pop. 7 713 4 D2

London 84 m – Bristol 47 m – Southampton 40 m – Swindon 12 m
The Library, High St ✆ (01672) 513989
The Common, ✆ (01672) 512 147 .
Town★
Savernake Forest★★ (Grand Avenue★★★), SE : 2 m. by A 4 – Whitehorse (⋞ ★), NW : 5 m – West Kennett Long Barrow★, Silbury Hill★, W : 6 m. by A 4. Ridgeway Path★★ – Avebury★★ (The Stones★, Church★), W : 7 m. by A 4 – Crofton Beam Engines★ **AC**, SE : 9 m. by A 346 – Wilton Windmill★ **AC**, SE : 9 m. by A 346, A 338 and minor rd

Coles

27 Kingsbury Hill ✉ SN8 1JA – ✆ (01672) 515 004 – Fax (01672) 512 069 – Closed 25-26 December, 1 January, Sunday and Bank Holidays

Rest – Carte £ 24/28

◆ Shots of 70s film stars adorn a busy, bay-windowed former pub which retains its firelit bar. Friendly staff and elaborate but robust cuisine with an array of daily specials.

at Ramsbury Northeast : 7 ¼ m. by A 346 – ✉ Marlborough

The Bell

The Square ✉ SN8 2PE – ✆ (01672) 520 230 – bookings@thebellramsbury.com – closed Sunday dinner

Rest – Carte £ 18/33

◆ Black and white pub with two distinct sides: busy bar with open fire and sofas, and long dining room featuring eye-catching abstract artwork. Classic, unfussy British cooking.

at Little Bedwyn East : 9 ½ m. by A 4 – ✉ Marlborough

The Harrow at Little Bedwyn (Roger Jones)

✉ SN8 3JP – ✆ (01672) 870 871 – dining@harrowinn.co.uk – closed 14-31 August, 22 December-18 January, Sunday dinner, Monday and Tuesday

Rest – Menu £ 30 – Carte £ 42/55

Spec. Pan-fried black pudding, foie gras and scallops. Fillet of sole with leek, pea and garlic risotto. Rhubarb and ginger compote with vanilla ice cream.

◆ Cosy former village pub, whose extensive range of menus offer accomplished, unfussy dishes which allow the quality of the produce to shine through. An impressive wine list.

ENGLAND

MARLDON – Devon – 503 J 32 2 C2

London 193 m – Newton Abbott 7 m – Paignton 3 m

Church House Inn

Village Rd ✉ TQ3 1SL – ✆ (01803) 558 279 – Fax (01803) 664 185

Rest – Carte £ 22/30

◆ Tricky to find, but worth the effort. Characterful interior of beams and flags, and lots of informal areas to enjoy tasty, locally based dishes that are all home made.

MARLOW – Bucks. – 504 R 29 – pop. 17 552 11 C3

London 35 m – Aylesbury 22 m – Oxford 29 m – Reading 14 m

to Henley-on-Thames (Salter Bros. Ltd) (summer only) (2 h 15 mn) – to Maidenhead, Cookham and Windsor (Salter Bros. Ltd) (summer only)

31 High St ✆ (01628) 483597

Danesfield House

< Terraced gardens and River Thames, rest,

Henley Rd, Southwest : 2½ m. on A 4155 ✉ SL7 2EY – ✆ (01628) 891 010 – sales@danesfieldhouse.co.uk – Fax (01628) 890 408

83 rm – †£ 240 ††£ 275, ☕ £9.50 – 1 suite

Rest *Oak Room* – Menu £ 30/55

Rest *Orangery* – Menu £ 29

◆ Stunning house and gardens in Italian Renaissance style with breathtaking views of Thames. Grand lounge with country house feel. Comfy rooms; state-of-art health spa. Intimate Oak Room restaurant. Orangery is a charming terrace brasserie.

ENGLAND

Crowne Plaza Marlow

rm,

Fieldhouse Lane, East : 2 m. by A 4155 off Parkway Rd ✉ SL7 1GJ – ✆ (0870) 444 89 40 – enquiries@crowneplazamarlow.co.uk – Fax (0870) 444 89 50

162 rm ☕ – †£ 99/205 ††£ 99/205 – 6 suites

Rest *Glaze* – (closed lunch Saturday and Sunday) Menu £ 35 – Carte £ 20/27

Rest *Agua* – Carte £ 14/21

◆ Purpose built hotel near business park. Spacious lobby, leisure club and meeting rooms. Bedrooms well equipped with large desk. Glaze with conservatory overlooking the artificial lake. More informal Agua.

Compleat Angler

< River Thames, rm,

Marlow Bridge, Bisham Rd ✉ SL7 1RG – ✆ (0870) 400 81 00 – general.compleatangler@macdonald-hotels.co.uk – Fax (01628) 486 388

61 rm ☕ – †£ 250 ††£ 300 – 3 suites

Rest Dean Timpson at The Compleat Angler – see restaurant listing

Rest *Bowaters* – Carte £ 30/35

◆ Picturesque riverside hotel; spectacular view of Marlow weir. Rooms are very comfortable; those on river side have four-poster beds and balcony. Bowaters offers British menu in informal conservatory.

Dean Timpson at The Compleat Angler

< River Thames and Marlow Weir,

Marlow Bridge, Bisham Rd ✉ SL7 1RG – ✆ (01628) 481 971 – enquiries@deantimpson.co.uk – Fax (01628) 486 388

Rest – (closed Sunday, Monday and lunch Tuesday) Menu £ 25 – Carte £ 41/51

◆ Refurbished restaurant with enviable outlook and elegant, rustic feel. Modern European cooking uses quality ingredients.

The Vanilla Pod

31 West St ✉ SL7 2LS – ✆ (01628) 898 101 – allmail@thevanillapod.co.uk – Fax (01628) 898 108 – Closed Easter, 2 weeks September, 23 December-6 January, Sunday and Monday

Rest – (booking essential) Menu £ 20/40

◆ Attractive townhouse – former home of T. S. Eliot – boasts refurbished restaurant with loyal following. Classic cooking with French accent makes use of seasonal ingredients.

The Hand and Flowers (Tom Kerridge) with rm
126 West St ✉ SL7 2BP – ☎ (01628) 482 277 – Closed dinner 23-26, 30 December, 1 January and lunch 31 December
4 rm – †£ 140 ††£ 190 – **Rest** – (booking essential) Carte £ 25/38
Spec. Parmesan and smoked haddock omelette. Canon of lamb, slow cooked shoulder and crushed swede. Praline parfait with pineapple sorbet and nougat.
◆ Row of pretty period cottages with exposed beams and flint walls. Classically based cooking is well sourced, finely balanced and full of richly appealing flavours. Comfortable bedrooms now available.

The Royal Oak
Frieth Rd, Bovingdon Green, West : 1 ¼ m. by A 4155 ✉ SL7 2JF – ☎ (01628) 488 611 – info@royaloakmarlow.co.uk – Fax (01628) 478 680 – Closed 25-26 December
Rest – Carte £ 19/29
◆ Characterful pub with redbrick exterior and smart interior. Full-length window area at back faces spacious garden terrace. Modern menus plus specials board.

MARPLE – Gtr Manchester – 502 N 23 – pop. 18 475 — 20 B3

London 190 m – Chesterfield 35 m – Manchester 11 m

Springfield without rest
99 Station Rd ✉ SK6 6PA – ☎ (0161) 449 0721 – Fax (0161) 449 0766
8 rm – †£ 55 ††£ 75
◆ Part Victorian house with sympathetic extensions. Useful for visits to Peak District. Two homely lounges, one with good views to Derbyshire hills. Individually styled rooms.

MARSDEN – W. Yorks. – 502 O 23 – pop. 3 499 – ✉ Huddersfield — 22 A3

London 195 m – Leeds 22 m – Manchester 18 m – Sheffield 30 m

Olive Branch with rm
Manchester Rd, Northeast : 1 m. on A 62 ✉ HD7 6LU – ☎ (01484) 844 487 – mail@olivebranch.uk.com – Closed first 2 weeks January
3 rm – †£ 55 ††£ 70, £ 12.50 – **Rest** – Seafood (closed Monday-Tuesday and lunch Saturday) Menu £ 15/19 – Carte £ 25/35
◆ In a secluded valley, a part 16C drovers inn, run with real warmth. Open fire and wide-ranging menus in smart restaurant with outside decking; seafood specials. Modern rooms.

MARSH BENHAM – West Berks. – see Newbury

MARSTON MONTGOMERY – Derbs. – see Ashbourne

MARTINHOE – Devon – see Lynton

MARTOCK – Somerset – 503 L 31 – pop. 4 309 — 3 B3

London 148 m – Taunton 19 m – Yeovil 6 m
Village★ - All Saints★★
Montacute House★★ AC, SE : 4 m. – Muchelney★★ (Parish Church★★), NW : 4½ m. by B 3165 – Ham Hill (≤ ★★), S : 2 m. by minor roads. Barrington Court★ AC, SW : 7½ m. by B 3165 and A 303

The Hollies
Bower Hinton, South : 1 m. on B 3165 ✉ TA12 6LG – ☎ (01935) 822 232 – info@thehollieshotel.com – Fax (01935) 822 249
33 rm – †£ 83/88 ††£ 93/98 – 3 suites – **Rest** – (dinner only) Carte £ 24/33
◆ Impressive former 17C farmhouse in small village near grand Montacute House. Separate annex has large, well-equipped, up-to-date bedrooms with good comforts and facilities. Characterful oak beamed, boothed restaurant and lounge in the farmhouse.

ENGLAND

MARTON – N. Yorks. – 502 R 21 – see Pickering

see Pickering

MARTON – Shrops. *Great Britain* 18 A1

London 174 m – Birmingham 57 m – Shrewsbury 16 m

Powis Castle★★★, NW : 7 m. by B 4386 and A 490

The Sun Inn

SY21 8JP – (01938) 561 211 – info@suninn.biz – *Closed Sunday dinner and Tuesday lunch*

Rest – Menu £ 16 – Carte £ 18/30

◆ Rural pub where keen young owners serve good value, tasty, traditional dishes heavily influenced by local ingredients. Choose to eat in bar or beech-furnished dining room.

MASHAM – N. Yorks. – 502 P 21 – Ripon 22 B1

London 231 m – Leeds 38 m – Middlesbrough 37 m – York 32 m

Swinton Park

Swinton, Southwest : 1 m HG4 4JH
– (01765) 680 900 – enquiries@swintonpark.com
– Fax (01765) 680 901

26 rm – £ 160 £ 270 – 4 suites

Rest *Samuels* – Menu £ 23/42

◆ 17C castle with Georgian and Victorian additions, on a 20,000 acre estate and deer park. Luxurious, antique filled lounges. Very comfortable, individually styled bedrooms. Grand dining room with ornate gold leaf ceiling and garden views.

ENGLAND

Bank Villa

on A 6108 HG4 4DB – (01765) 689 605 – bankvilla@btopenworld.com

6 rm – £ 45/60 £ 85/95 – **Rest** – (by arrangement) Carte £ 22/25

◆ Stone-built Georgian villa with Victorian additions. Two lounges and conservatory; delightful, "sun-trap" stepped garden. Cosy, cottagey rooms: some are in the eaves! Home-cooked menus in pastel dining room/tea room.

Vennell's

7 Silver St HG4 4DX – (01765) 689 000 – info@vennellsrestaurant.co.uk – Closed 26-30 December, Sunday dinner, Monday and lunch Tuesday-Thursday

Rest – Menu £ 20 (lunch) **s** – Carte approx. £ 27 **s**

◆ Smart restaurant with comfy basement bar; linen-clad dining room enhanced by local artwork. Warm service of good value, seasonal dishes prepared with flair and a flourish.

MATFEN – Northd. – 501 O 18 24 A2

London 309 m – Carlisle 42 m – Newcastle upon Tyne 24 m

Matfen Hall

NE20 0RH – (01661) 886 500 – info@matfenhall.com
– Fax (01661) 886 055

53 rm – £ 115 £ 170

Rest *Library and Print Room* – (dinner only and Sunday lunch) Menu £ 35

◆ 19C country mansion built by Thomas Ruckman, master of Gothic design. Set in 500 acres with superb Grand Hall, fine paintings, plush drawing room and mix of bedroom styles. Characterful Library dining room has display of original books.

Do not confuse X with ✿!
X defines comfort, while stars are awarded for the best cuisine, across all categories of comfort.

MATLOCK – Derbs. – **502** P 24 – **pop. 11 265** *Great Britain* 16 **B1**

London 153 m – Derby 17 m – Manchester 46 m – Nottingham 24 m – Sheffield 24 m

Crown Sq ✆ (01629) 583388 - The Pavilion, Matlock Bath ✆ (01629) 55082

Hardwick Hall★★ **AC**, E : 12½ m. by A 615 and B 6014 – Crich Tramway Village★ **AC**, S : 12 m. by A 6 and B 5036

at Birchover **Northeast : 7½ m. by A 6 – ✉ Matlock**

The Druid Inn

Main St ✉ DE4 2BL – ✆ (01629) 650302 – Closed Monday October-March and Sunday dinner

Rest – Menu £ 16 – Carte £ 25/35

◆ Family-run inn with rustic bar and airy dining room with open kitchen. Tasty, wholesome cooking includes pub favourites and more modern dishes. Own brand of beer; Druid Ale.

MAWNAN SMITH – Cornwall – **503** E 33 – **see Falmouth**

MEDBOURNE – Leics. – **504** R 26 16 **B2**

London 93 m – Corby 9 m – Leicester 16 m

XX **Horse & Trumpet** with rm

Old Green ✉ LE16 8DX – ✆ (01858) 565 000 – info@horseandtrumpet.com – Fax (01858) 565 551 – closed 1 week January, Sunday dinner and Monday

4 rm – †£ 75 ††£ 75 – **Rest** – Menu £ 20 – Carte £ 30/43

◆ 18C thatched inn with bowling green. Stylish well-furnished bedrooms. Linen clad tables in the dining rooms; al fresco eating in courtyard. Modern menu using local produce.

ENGLAND

MELKSHAM – Wilts. – **503** N 29 – **pop. 14 372** 4 **C2**

London 113 m – Bristol 25 m – Salisbury 35 m – Swindon 28 m

Church St ✆ (01225) 707424

Corsham Court★★ **AC**, NW : 4½ m. by A 365 and B 3353 – Lacock★★ (Lacock Abbey★ **AC**, High Street★, St Cyriac★, Fox Talbot Museum of Photography★ **AC**) N : 3½ m. by A 350

at Whitley **Northwest : 2 m. by A 365 on B 3353 – ✉ Melksham**

The Pear Tree Inn with rm

Top Lane, by First Lane ✉ SN12 8QX – ✆ (01225) 709 131 – enquiries@thepeartreeinn.com – Fax (01225) 702 276 – Closed 25-26 December, 1 January

8 rm – †£ 75 ††£ 105 – **Rest** – Menu £ 16 – Carte £ 25/30

◆ Characterful Bath stone pub with lovely gardens and terrace. Modish restaurant to rear: assured, tasty cooking. Very smart, modern, stylish bedrooms in house and conversion.

MELLOR – Lancs. – **see Blackburn**

MELLOR BROOK – Blackburn – **see Blackburn**

MELLS – Som – **503** M 30 – **pop. 2 222** 4 **C2**

London 117 m – Bath 16 m – Frome 3 m

The Talbot Inn with rm

Selwood St ✉ BA11 3PN – ✆ (01373) 812 254 – enquiries@talbotinn.com – Fax (01373) 813 599 – Closed 25 December

8 rm – †£ 75 ††£ 145 – **Rest** – Carte £ 25/30

◆ 15C stone-built coaching inn boasting cobbled courtyard and walled garden with pétanque piste and vine-covered pergola. Intimate main bar and large tythe barn with mural. Bright, pretty bedrooms.

MELTON MOWBRAY – Leics. – 502 R 25 – pop. 25 554 16 B2

London 113 m – Leicester 15 m – Northampton 45 m – Nottingham 18 m
7 King St ☎ (01664) 480992
Thorpe Arnold Waltham Rd, ☎ (01664) 562 118 .

Stapleford Park

East : 5 m. by B 676 on Stapleford rd ✉ LE14 2EF – ☎ (01572) 787 000 – reservations@stapleford.co.uk – Fax (01572) 787 001 – Closed February
55 rm – †£ 195 ††£ 250/275
Rest *Grinling Gibbons Dining Room* – (dinner only) (booking essential) Menu £ 47/58
Rest *Pavilion Brasserie* – Menu £ 24/35
◆ Astoundingly beautiful stately home in 500 glorious acres, exuding a grandeur rarely surpassed. Extensive leisure facilities; uniquely designed rooms of sumptuous elegance. Ornate rococo dining room a superb example of master craftsman's work. Smart brasserie.

Quorn Lodge

46 Asfordby Rd, West : ½ m. on A 6006 ✉ LE13 0HR – ☎ (01664) 566 660 – quornlodge@aol.com – Fax (01664) 480 660
19 rm – †£ 45/65 ††£ 70/80
Rest *The Laurels* – Menu £ 10/17 – Carte £ 12/22
◆ Former hunting lodge, privately owned, situated just outside town centre. Spacious sitting room and bar leads on to small conference room. Spacious, neatly kept rooms. Homely restaurant with pretty garden to rear.

ENGLAND

at Stathern North : 8 m. by A 607 – ✉ Melton Mowbray

Red Lion Inn

2 Red Lion St ✉ LE14 4HS – ☎ (01949) 860 868 – info@theredlioninn.co.uk – Fax (01949) 861 579 – Closed dinner 25 December, 1 January, Sunday dinner and Monday
Rest – (booking essential) Menu £ 14 – Carte £ 26/33
◆ Rural pub with a predominant "country" feel: solid stone floors, wooden antiques, rustic ornaments, solid fireplaces, skittle alley. Daily changing, modern menus.

MERIDEN – W. Mids. – 503 – see Coventry

MEVAGISSEY – Cornwall – 503 F 33 – pop. 2 221 1 B3

London 287 m – Newquay 21 m – Plymouth 44 m – Truro 20 m
Town★★
NW : Lost Gardens of Heligan★

Trevalsa Court Country House

School Hill, East : ½ m. on B 3273 (St Austell rd) ✉ PL26 6TH – ☎ (01726) 842 468 – stay@trevalsa-hotel.co.uk – Fax (01726) 844 482
12 rm – †£ 75/128 ††£ 100/220 – **Rest** – (dinner only) Menu £ 34 – Carte £ 31/42
◆ Charming 1930s building with lovely garden which has access to Polstreath Beach. Homely morning room; quirky, 'Continental'-style bar. Autumnal shades enhance tasteful rooms. Oak-panelled dining room with daily menu, devised using best available produce.

Kerryanna without rest

(heated)

Treleaven Farm ✉ PL26 6SA – ☎ (01726) 843 558 – enquiries@kerryanna.co.uk – Fax (01726) 843 558 – May-September
3 rm – †£ 70 ††£ 75
◆ Purpose-built bungalow within farm providing pleasant ambience. Useful for Lost Gardens of Heligan. Spacious front sitting room. Immaculately kept, sizeable, chintz bedrooms.

MICKLEHAM – Surrey – 504 T 30 7 D1

London 21 m – Brighton 32 m – Guildford 14 m – Worthing 34 m

The King William IV

Byttom Hill, North : ½ m. by A 24 ✉ RH5 6EL – ✆ (01372) 372 590 – iduke@another.com – Closed Sunday lunch

Rest – Carte £ 13/26

◆ Once a beer house for Lord Beaverbrook's staff, this part 19C hillside pub looks over Mole Valley from lounge and terrace. Large blackboard menu: wholesome and homely.

MICKLETON – Glos. – 503 – see Chipping Campden

MIDDLE WINTERSLOW – Wilts. – see Salisbury

MIDDLEHAM – N. Yorks. – 502 O 21 22 B1

London 233 m – Kendal 45 m – Leeds 47 m – Newcastle upon Tyne 63 m – York 45 m

Waterford House

19 Kirkgate ✉ DL8 4PG – ✆ (01969) 622 090 – info@waterfordhousehotel.co.uk – Fax (01969) 624 020 – Closed Christmas-New Year

5 rm – †£ 75/85 ††£ 90/115 – **Rest** – (Closed Sunday) (dinner only) (residents only) Menu £ 33 **s**

◆ Elegant Georgian house, just off cobbled market square, with neat walled garden. Drawing room boasts cluttered charm. Individually appointed rooms with thoughtful touches. Formal restaurant: home cooked menus use much local produce.

The White Swan

AC rest,

Market Pl ✉ DL8 4PE – ✆ (01969) 622 093 – whiteswan@easynet.co.uk – Fax (01969) 624 551 – Closed dinner 25 December

17 rm – †£ 55 ††£ 99 – **Rest** – Menu £ 14 – Carte £ 15/25

◆ Former coaching inn in bustling village market place. Traditional flagged floor bar with wood-burning stove and inglenook. Stylish, modern bedrooms. Spacious brasserie restaurant serving tried and tested dishes.

Middleham Grange without rest

Market Pl ✉ DL8 4NR – ✆ (01969) 622 630 – tammi.t@tiscali.co.uk – Fax (01969) 625 437 – Closed Christmas-New Year

3 rm – †£ 60/80 ††£ 80

◆ Beautifully restored part-Georgian manor house. Comfy period style lounge; bright breakfast room in conservatory overlooking garden. Snug bedrooms exude a classical style.

at Carlton-in-Coverdale Southwest : 4 ½ m. by Coverham rd – ✉ Leyburn

Abbots Thorn

✉ DL8 4AY – ✆ (01969) 640 620 – abbots.thorn@virgin.net – February-November

3 rm – †£ 44/54 ††£ 54/60 – **Rest** – (by arrangement, communal dining) Menu £ 18

◆ Well priced, comfortable, quiet guesthouse in attractive rural village. Handy for visits to Moors. Cosy sitting room. Sizeable bedrooms which are homely and well-kept. Fresh, local produce to fore at dinner.

Foresters Arms with rm

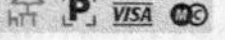

✉ DL8 4BB – ✆ (01969) 640 272 – chambersmic@hotmail.co.uk – Fax (01969) 640 272 – Closed Sunday dinner, Monday, Tuesday lunch and Wednesday lunch November-April

3 rm – †£ 65 ††£ 79 – **Rest** – Menu £ 15 – Carte £ 20/26

◆ Compact 17C stone-built inn. Flagged floor bar with beams and open fire. Timbered restaurant where modern dishes utilise fresh, local produce. Pleasant, cottagey rooms.

MIDDLETON – N. Yorks. – see Pickering

MIDDLETON-IN-TEESDALE – Durham – 502 N 20 – pop. 1 143 24 A3

London 447 m – Carlisle 91 m – Leeds 124 m – Middlesbrough 70 m – Newcastle upon Tyne 65 m

Market Pl ✆ (01833) 641001

Grove Lodge

Hude, Northwest : ½ m. on B 6277 ✉ DL12 0QW – ✆ (01833) 640 798

3 rm – ♦£ 42/45 ♦♦£ 70 – **Rest** – Carte £ 16/28

◆ Victorian former shooting lodge perched on a hill where the two front facing rooms have the best views. Neat and friendly house, traditionally decorated. Home-cooked dinners are proudly served.

MIDDLEWICH – Ches. – 502 M 24 20 B3

London 176 m – Crewe 13 m – Northwich 7 m

Kinderton's with rm — AC rest, P VISA

Kinderton St ✉ CW10 0JE – ✆ (01606) 834 325 – kinderton@tiscali.co.uk – Fax (01606) 832 323 – Closed 25-27 December and 1-3 January

12 rm – ♦£ 65 ♦♦£ 65 – **Rest** – Menu £ 12 (lunch) – Carte £ 19/33

◆ Personally run restaurant in pleasantly refurbished hotel with garden and terrace. The simple, modern style is complemented by good value, appealing menus. Comfy bedrooms.

ENGLAND

MIDHURST – W. Sussex – 504 R 31 – pop. 6 120 7 C2

London 57 m – Brighton 38 m – Chichester 12 m – Southampton 41 m

North St ✆ (01730) 817322

Spread Eagle — P VISA AE

South St ✉ GU29 9NH – ✆ (01730) 816 911 – spreadeagle@hshotels.co.uk – Fax (01730) 815 668

37 rm (dinner included) – ♦£ 150/160 ♦♦£ 205/235 – 2 suites

Rest – Menu £ 23/37 **s**

◆ 15C hostelry boasting lovely characterful bar with uneven oak flooring and roaring fire. Many antiques. Good leisure facilities. Rooms have country house décor and style. A very traditional ambience pervades restaurant.

at Bepton Southwest : 2 ½ m. by A 286 on Bepton rd – ✉ Midhurst

Park House — (heated) rm, P VISA

Bepton ✉ GU29 0JB – ✆ (01730) 819 000 – reservations@parkhousehotel.com – Fax (01730) 819 099

14 rm – ♦£ 110/145 ♦♦£ 110/290 – 1 suite – **Rest** – (dinner only) (booking essential) Menu £ 32

◆ Comfortable, privately owned country house. Charming lounge with chintz armchairs, antique paintings, heavy drapes. Bar with honesty policy. Rooms are bright and colourful. Classical dining room with antique tables and chairs.

at Elsted Southwest : 5 m. by A 272 on Elsted rd – ✉ Midhurst

Three Horseshoes — P VISA

✉ GU29 0JY – ✆ (01730) 825 746

Rest – Carte £ 20/25

◆ Lovely, informal 16C drovers inn with wood burners, stone floors and low ceiling. Honest pub cooking, fresh and tasty. Expect cottage or fish pie with a little extra twist.

at Stedham West : 2 m. by A 272 – ✉ Midhurst

Nava Thai at The Hamilton Arms — P VISA AE

School Lane ✉ GU29 0NZ – ✆ (01730) 812 555 – hamiltonarms@hotmail.com – Fax (01730) 817 459 – Closed first week January and Monday

Rest – Thai Menu £ 20 – Carte £ 20/35

◆ Busy Thai restaurant in bustling pub. Mahogany tables, wicker chairs. Thai royalty adorns the walls. Lanterns lighten your way. Colourful cooking, fragrant and flavoursome.

MIDSOMER NORTON – Somerset – 503 M 30 4 C2

London 125 m – Bath 11 m – Wells 12 m

XX **The Moody Goose at the Old Priory** with rm

Church Sq ✉ BA3 2HX – ☎ (01761) 416 784 – info@theoldpriory.co.uk – Fax (01761) 417 851 – Closed Sunday-Monday and Bank Holidays except Good Friday

7 rm – †£ 85/95 ††£ 115/135 – **Rest** – Menu £ 20/25 – Carte dinner £ 37/41

◆ 12C former priory, by a church, with enviable walled garden. Flagged floors, beams and vast fireplaces create impressive interior. Interesting modern cooking. Comfy rooms.

MILFORD-ON-SEA – Hants. – 503 P 31 – pop. 4 229 – ✉ Lymington 6 A3

London 109 m – Bournemouth 15 m – Southampton 24 m – Winchester 37 m

Westover Hall ← Christchurch Bay, Isle of Wight and The Needles,

Park Lane ✉ SO41 0PT – ☎ (01590) 643 044 – info@westoverhallhotel.com – Fax (01590) 644 490

11 rm (dinner included) – †£ 130/165 ††£ 230/360 – 1 suite

Rest – Menu £ 20/40 – Carte £ 23/44

◆ Characterful 19C family-owned mansion in stunning spot overlooking Christchurch Bay. Very comfortable sitting room. Magnificent hall and minstrels gallery. Sumptuous rooms. Ornate dining room: decorative ceiling, stained glass, panelling.

We try to be as accurate as possible when giving room rates. But prices are susceptible to change, so please check rates when booking.

MILLBROOK – Cornwall – 503 H 32 2 C2

London 235 m – Liskeard 16 m – Plymouth 23 m

at Freathy West : 3 m. by B 3247, Whitsand Bay Rd and Treninnow Cliff Rd – ✉ Millbrook

X **The View** ← Whitsand Bay and Rame Head,

East : 1 m. ✉ PL10 1JY – ☎ (01752) 822 345 – Closed February, Monday except Bank Holidays and Tuesday

Rest – Seafood Carte £ 27/31

◆ Converted café: best views are from front terrace. Basic interior smartened up in evenings. Interesting, understated, seafood oriented menus: cooking is clean and delicious.

MILLOM – Cumbria – 502 K 21 – pop. 6 103 *Great Britain* 21 A3

London 299 m – Barrow-in-Furness 22 m – Ulverston 17 m

Hard Knott Pass★★, N : 23 m. by A 595 and minor rd (eastbound)

Underwood

The Hill, North : 2 m. on A 5093 ✉ LA18 5EZ – ☎ (01229) 771 116 – enquiries@underwoodhouse.co.uk – Fax (01229) 719 900 – Closed 2 weeks March-April

7 rm – †£ 45/60 ††£ 120 – **Rest** – (dinner only) (booking essential)(residents only) Menu £ 25

◆ Built in classic Lakeland grey, a Victorian former vicarage boasting two comfortable lounges and a large indoor pool. Well-kept, spacious double rooms with countryside views. Pleasant dining room overlooks gardens; tasty home cooking.

MILTON – Oxon. – see Banbury

MILTON ABBOT – Devon – **503** H 32 – see Tavistock

MILTON BRYAN – Beds. – **504** S 28 – see Woburn

MILTON KEYNES – Milton Keynes – **504** R 27 – pop. 184 506 11 **C1**

London 56 m – Bedford 16 m – Birmingham 72 m – Northampton 18 m – Oxford 37 m

askvic@powernet.com

18 Abbey Hill Two Mile Ash Monks Way, ✆ (01908) 563 845 ;

18 Windmill Hill Bletchley Tattenhoe Lane, ✆ (01908) 631 113 ;

27 Wavendon Golf Centre Wavendon Lower End Rd, ✆ (01908) 281 811.

MILTON KEYNES

Street	Grid	No.
Avebury Boulevard	EFY	
Boundary (The)	FZ	3
Boycott Ave	EZ	4
Bradwell Common Boulevard	DEY	
Bradwell Rd	DZ	
Brearley Ave	EFZ	
Brill Pl.	DY	
Burnham Drive	DY	
Century Ave	EFZ	
Chaffron Way (H7)	FZ	
Childs Way (H6)	EFZ	
Conniburrow Boulevard	EY	
Dansteed Way (H4)	DY	
Deltic Ave	DY	6
Dexter Ave	FZ	7
Elder Gate	DZ	9
Evans Gate	EZ	
Fishermead Boulevard	FZ	
Food Centre	FY	
Fulwoods Drive	FZ	10
Gibsons Green	DY	
Glovers Lane	DY	12
Grafton Gate	DEZ	
Grafton St (V6)	DY, EZ	
Ibstone Ave	DEY	13
Kirkstall Pl.	EZ	
Leys Rd.	DZ	
Loughton Rd	DY	
Mallow Gate	EY	15
Marlborough St (V8)	FY	
Mayditch Pl.	DY	
Midsummer Boulevard	EFY	
Oldbrook Boulevard	EFZ	
Patriot Drive	DY	16
Pitcher Lane	DZ	
Portway (H5)	EFY	
Precedent Drive	DY	18
Quinton Drive	DY	
Saxon Gate (V7)	EY	
Saxon St (V7)	EY, FZ	
Secklow Gate	FY	
Silbury Boulevard	EFY	
The Centre : MK	EFY	
Walgrave Drive	DY	19
Witan Gate	EZ	

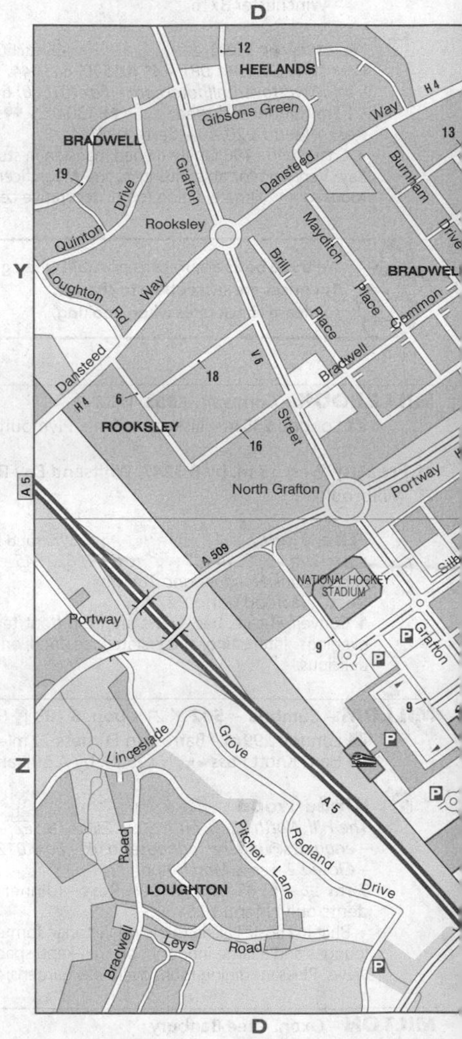

Holiday Inn Milton Keynes

500 Saxon Gate West, Central Milton Keynes
✉ *MK9 2HQ – ✆ (0870) 400 9057*
– reservations-miltonkeynes@ichotelsgroup.com
– Fax (01908) 698 693

rm, VISA AE EYZ **a**

164 rm – †£ 170 ††£ 170, ☕ £14.95 – 2 suites
Rest – Menu £ 20/32 – Carte £ 15/25

◆ Commercial business hotel, with public areas set in modern atrium. Opposite main shopping area. Good leisure club with above average sized pool. Well-kept, clean rooms. Informal, family-friendly restaurant.

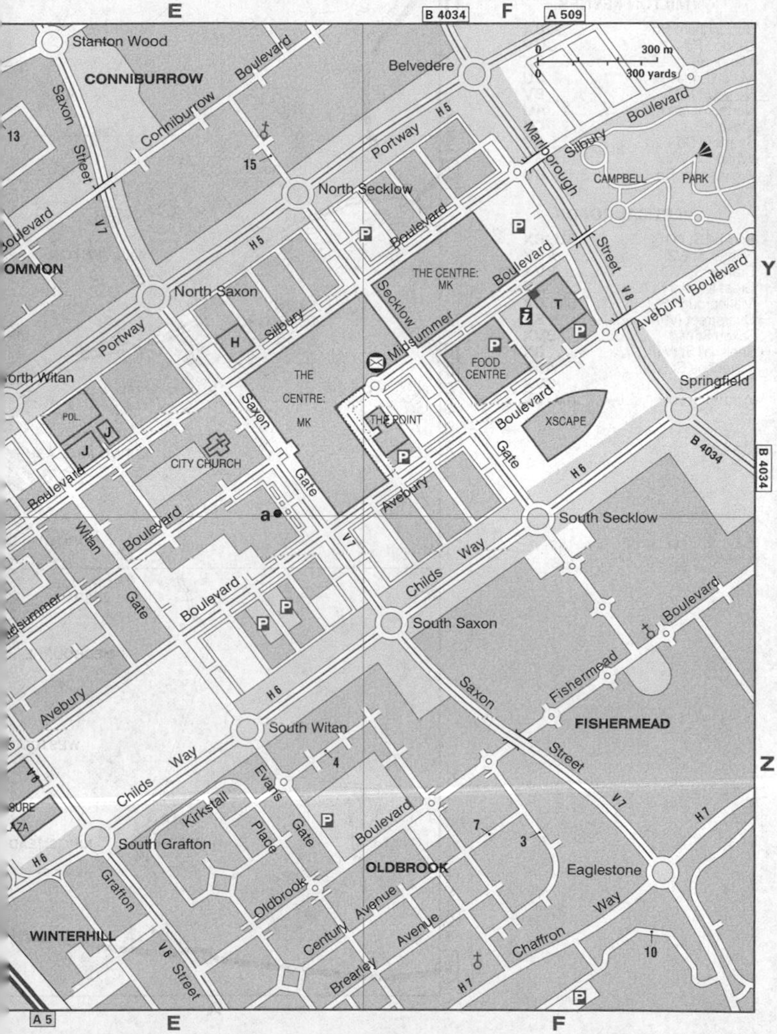

HORIZONTAL ROADS

Bletcham Way (H10) . . . . **CX**
Chaffron Way (H7) . . . . **BX, CV**
Childs Way (H6) . . . . **BX, CV**
Dansteed Way (H4) . . . . **ABV**
Groveway (H9) . . . . **CVX**
Millers Way (H2) . . . . **AV**
Monks Way (H3) . . . . **ABV**
Portway (H5) . . . . **BCV**
Ridgeway (H1) . . . . **AV**
Standing Way (H8) . . . . **BX, CV**

MILTON KEYNES

Buckingham Rd . . . . **BX**
London Rd. . . . . **CUV**
Manor Rd . . . . **CX**
Marsh End Rd . . . . **CU**
Newport Rd . . . . **BV**
Northampton Rd . . . . **AU**
Stoke Rd. **CX**
Stratford Rd . . . . **AV**
Whaddon Way . . . . **BX**
Wolverton Rd. . . . . **BU**

VERTICAL ROADS

Brickhill St (V10) . . . . **BU, CX**
Fulmer St (V3) . . . . **ABX**
Grafton St (V6). . . . . **BVX**
Great Monks St (V5) . . . . **AV**
Marlborough St (V8) . . . . . . **BV, CX**
Overstreet (V9). . . . . **BV**
Saxon St (V7). . . . . **BVX**
Snelshall St (V1) . . . . **BX**
Tattenhoe St (V2). . . . . **ABX**
Tongwell St (V11) . . . . **CVX**
Watling St (V4) . . . . **AV, BX**

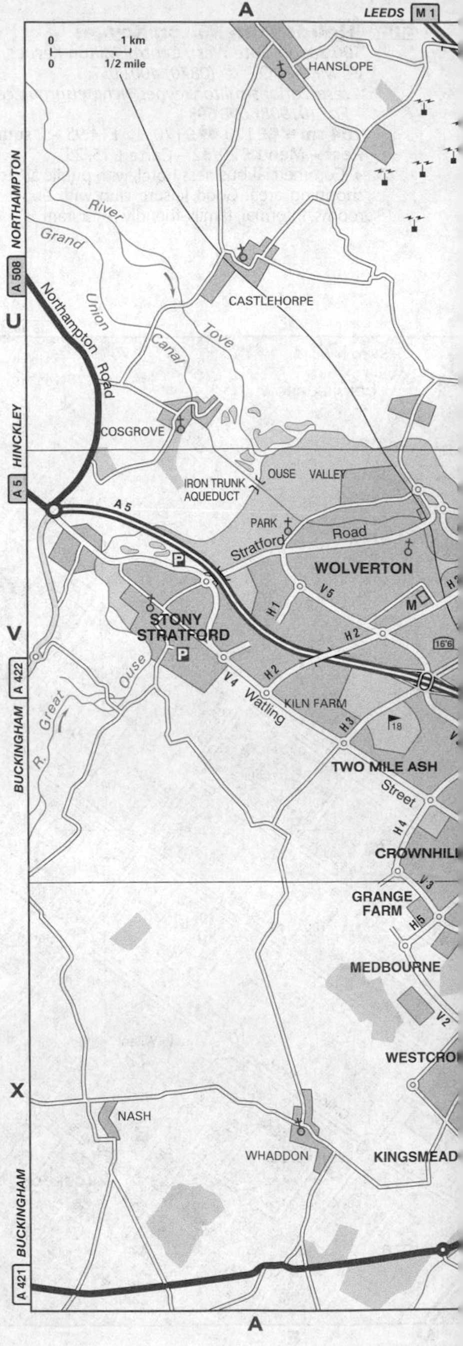

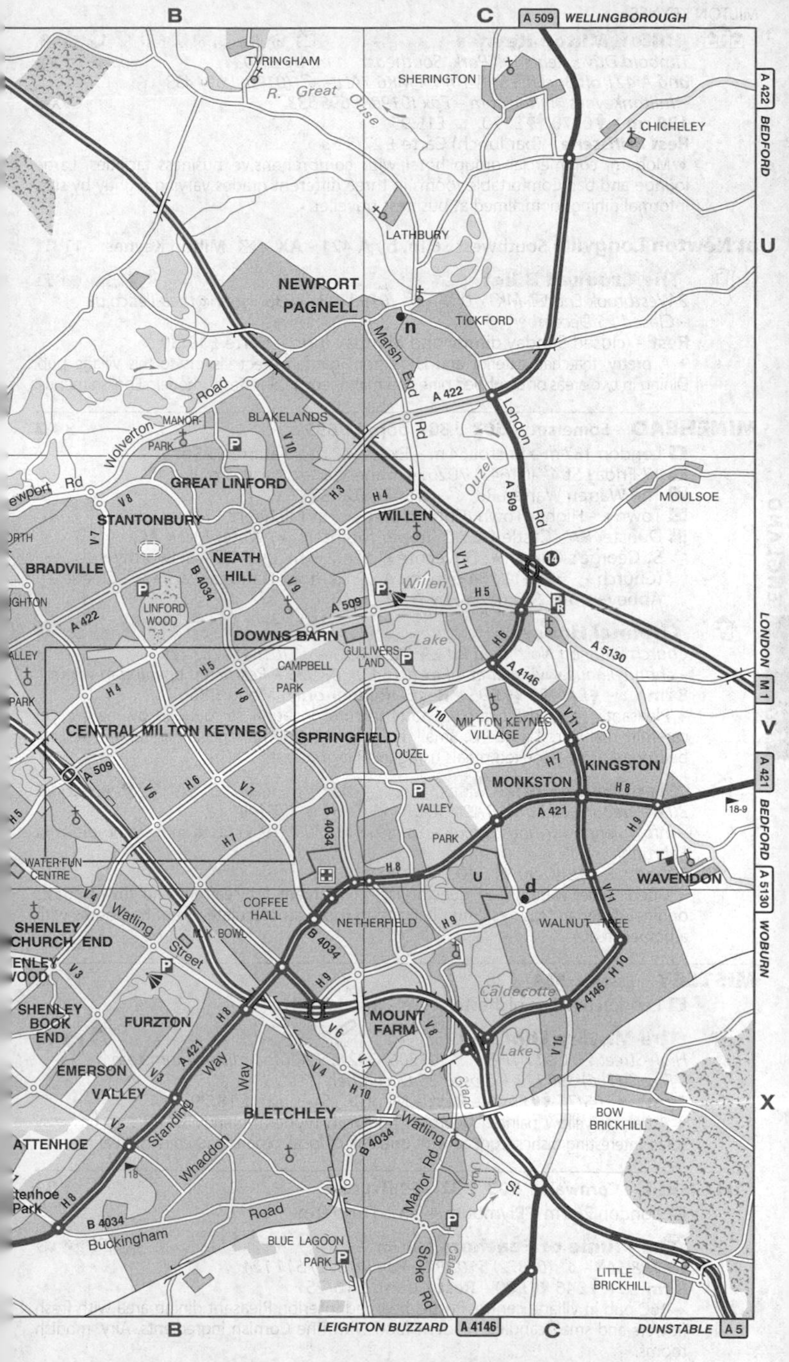
B
C
A 509 WELLINGBOROUGH
A 422 BEDFORD
TYRINGHAM
R. Great Ouse
SHERINGTON
CHICHELEY
LATHBURY
U
NEWPORT PAGNELL
n
TICKFORD
Marsh End Rd
A 422
London A 509 Rd
Wolverton Road
MANOR PARK
BLAKELANDS
V 10
Ouzel
GREAT LINFORD
Newport Rd
MOULSOE
H 3
H 4
WILLEN
V 8
STANTONBURY
V 7
NEATH HILL
14
BRADVILLE
B 4034
V 9
V 11
Willen
H 5
LINFORD WOOD
A 422
A 509
DOWNS BARN
Lake
H 6
LONDON M 1
A 5130
GULLIVERS LAND
CAMPBELL PARK
H 5
H 4
V 8
A 4146
CENTRAL MILTON KEYNES
SPRINGFIELD
V 10
MILTON KEYNES VILLAGE
V 11
V
A 509
OUZEL
H 7
KINGSTON
MONKSTON
A 421 BEDFORD
V 6
H 6
V 7
H 8
H 5
B 4034
VALLEY
A 421
H 9
18-9
PARK
H 7
WATER FUN CENTRE
T
WAVENDON
A 5130 WOBURN
H 8
U
d
V 4
COFFEE HALL
V 11
Watling
NETHERFIELD
H 9
WALNUT TREE
SHENLEY CHURCH END
M.K. BOWL
B 4034
Street
SHENLEY WOOD
V 3
H 9
Caldecotte
A 4146 - H 10
SHENLEY BROOK END
FURZTON
H 8
MOUNT FARM
V 8
V 6
Lake
V 10
EMERSON
Way
Way
V 4
V 7
Grand
V 3
A 421
VALLEY
H 10
X
BLETCHLEY
Standing
BOW BRICKHILL
V 2
B 4034
Watling
ATTENHOE
Whaddon
18
Manor Rd
Union
St.
Attenhoe Park
H 8
Road
B 4034
Buckingham
BLUE LAGOON PARK
Stoke Rd
Canal
LITTLE BRICKHILL
B
LEIGHTON BUZZARD
A 4146
C
DUNSTABLE
A 5

Hilton Milton Keynes

rm, rest,

Timbold Drive, Kents Hill Park, Southeast : 4 m. by B 4034 and A 421 off Brickhill St (V10) ✉ MK6 7AH – ✆ (01908) 694 433 – miltonkeynes@hilton.com – Fax (01908) 695 533 CVX **d**

138 rm – †£ 170 ††£ 170, ☕ £15.95

Rest *Britisserie* – (bar lunch) Carte £ 27/32 **s**

◆ Modern, commercial group hotel with comprehensive business facilities. Large lounge and bar. Comfortable rooms in three different grades varying slightly by size. Informal dining room aimed at business traveller.

at Newton Longville Southwest : 6 m. by A 421 - AX – ✉ Milton Keynes 11 C1

The Crooked Billet

2 Westbrook End ✉ MK17 0DF – ✆ (01908) 373 936 – john@thebillet.co.uk – Closed 25 December

Rest – (closed Sunday dinner and Monday lunch) Carte £ 19/30

◆ A pretty, thatched exterior and large front garden greet visitors to this village pub. Dining in two areas on scrubbed pine and mahogany tables. Tasty, modern English menus.

MINEHEAD – Somerset – 503 J 30 – pop. 11 699 3 A2

London 187 m – Bristol 64 m – Exeter 43 m – Taunton 25 m

17 Friday St ✆ (01643) 702624, mineheadtic@visit.org.uk

The Warren Warren Rd, ✆ (01643) 702 057 .

Town★ - Higher Town (Church Steps★, St Michael's★)

Dunster★★ - Castle★★ **AC** (upper rooms ≤ ★) Water Mill★ **AC**, St George's Church★, Dovecote★, SE : 2½ m. by A 39 – Selworthy★ (Church★, ≤ ★★) W : 4½ m. by A 39. Exmoor National Park★★ – Cleeve Abbey★★ **AC**, SE : 6½ m. by A 39

Channel House

Church Path, off Northfield Rd ✉ TA24 5QG – ✆ (01643) 703 229 – channel.house@virgin.net – Fax (01643) 708 925 – Restricted opening in winter

8 rm ☕ – †£ 60/95 ††£ 95 – **Rest** – (dinner only) Menu £ 25

◆ Pleasantly located Edwardian hotel in rural location surrounded by mature yet carefully manicured gardens. Small, homely style lounge and fair sized, immaculate bedrooms. Home-cooked meals using local ingredients.

Glendower House without rest

30-32 Tregonwell Rd ✉ TA24 5DU – ✆ (01643) 707 144 – info@glendower-house.co.uk – Fax (01643) 708 719 – closed mid December-mid February

12 rm ☕ – †£ 40/50 ††£ 80

◆ Good value, warmly run guesthouse, convenient for seafront and town; boasts original Victorian features. Snug bar/sitting room. Immaculately kept bedrooms with a homely feel.

MISTLEY – Essex – 504 X 28 13 D2

London 69 m – Colchester 11 m – Ipswich 14 m

The Mistley Thorn with rm

High Street ✉ CO11 1HE – ✆ (01206) 392 821 – info@mistleythorn.com – Fax (01206) 390 122 – Closed 25 December

5 rm – †£ 65/75 ††£ 105 – **Rest** – Menu £ 15 – Carte £ 18/29

◆ Attractive yellow painted Georgian pub with modern interior: sitting area has cosy sofas. Interesting dishes, cooked with care, full of local, organic ingredients. Neat rooms.

MITCHELL – Cornwall – 503 E 32 – ✉ Truro 1 B2

London 265 m – Plymouth 47 m – Truro 9 m

The Plume of Feathers with rm

✉ TR8 5AX – ✆ (01872) 510 387 – Fax (01872) 511 124

8 rm ☕ – †£ 46 ††£ 80 – **Rest** – Carte £ 16/25

◆ 16C pub in village centre. Rustic, beamed interior. Pleasant dining area with fresh flowers and small candles. Modern food with fine Cornish ingredients. Airy, modish rooms.

ENGLAND

MITTON – Lancs. – see Whalley

MOBBERLEY – Ches. – 502 N 24 – see Knutsford

MOCCAS – Herefordshire – 503 L 27 18 A3

Moccas Court

✉ HR2 9LH – ✆ (01981) 500 019 – bencmaster@btconnect.com – Fax (01981) 500 098 – Closed January-15 March

5 rm – †£ 112/148 ††£ 145/195 – **Rest** – (dinner only) (by arrangement, communal dining, set menu only) Menu £ 35 **s**

◆ Breathtakingly beautiful Grade I listed Georgian house in 100 acres of grounds on terraced banks over the Wye. Antique filled interior; bedrooms furnished to high standard. Estate sourced produce served in ornate Round Room.

MODBURY – Devon – 503 I 32 – pop. 1 454 2 C2

London 211 m – Plymouth 13 m – Torquay 28 m – Paignton 25 m

White Hart with rm

Church St ✉ PL21 0QW – ✆ (01548) 831 561 – info@whitehart-inn.co.uk – Closed 25 December, 1 January and Monday

5 rm – †£ 35 ††£ 50 – **Rest** – Menu £ 13 – Carte £ 21/30

◆ Whitewashed coaching inn serving seasonal, rustic cooking with a refined edge. Modern bar, dining room with glass-topped well; first floor Assembly Rooms with chandeliers. Simply furnished bedrooms.

ENGLAND

MONK FRYSTON – N. Yorks. – 502 Q 22 – ✉ Lumby 22 B2

London 190 m – Kingston-upon-Hull 42 m – Leeds 13 m – York 20 m

Monk Fryston Hall

Main St ✉ LS25 5DU – ✆ (01977) 682 369 – reception@monkfrystonhallhotel.co.uk – Fax (01977) 683 544

29 rm – †£ 85 ††£ 140 – **Rest** – Menu £ 28 (dinner) – Carte lunch £ 17/22

◆ Very characterful, possibly haunted, manor house dating from the 1300s with many later additions. Spacious grounds. Baronial style hall with antiques. Imposing rooms. Comfortable dining room with baronial touches.

MONKS ELEIGH – Suffolk – 504 W 27 15 C3

London 72 m – Cambridge 47 m – Colchester 17 m – Ipswich 16 m – Norwich 49 m

The Swan

The Street ✉ IP7 7AU – ✆ (01449) 741 391 – swan@monkseleigh.com – Closed 25-26 December and 1 January

Rest – (closed Monday-Tuesday) Carte £ 15/35

◆ Charming, friendly ambience in 16C whitewashed village inn with thatched roof. Daily changing blackboard menus of modern British pub food using fresh local ingredients.

MONTACUTE – Somerset – 503 – see Yeovil

Undecided between two equivalent establishments? Within each category, establishments are classified in our order of preference.

MORETONHAMPSTEAD – Devon – 503 I 32 – ✉ Newton Abbot 2 C2

London 213 m – Exeter 13 m – Plymouth 30 m
Bovey Castle North Bovey, ✆ (01647) 445 009 .
Dartmoor National Park★★

The White Hart

Station Rd ✉ TQ13 8NF – ✆ (01647) 441 340
– enquiries@whitehartdartmoor.co.uk – Fax (01647) 441 341
28 rm – £ 70/85 £ 118/140 – **Rest** – (bar lunch) Carte £ 26/31
◆ 17C Grade II listed former coaching inn in the town. Charming country furnished residents lounge. Pleasant 'locals' bar. Attractively refurbished rooms are strong point. Clothed dining room with Glorious Devon posters on the wall.

Moorcote without rest

Northwest : ¼ m. on A 382 ✉ TQ13 8LS – ✆ (01647) 440 966
– moorcote@smartone.co.uk – March-November
4 rm – £ 48 £ 54
◆ Perched on hill above Moretonhampstead, this Victorian guesthouse has mature gardens and well-kept bedrooms with stunning views of Dartmoor. Cosy breakfast room and lounge.

Great Sloncombe Farm without rest

Northwest : 1½ m. by A 382 ✉ TQ13 8QF – ✆ (01647) 440 595
– hmerchant@sloncombe.freeserve.co.uk – Fax (01647) 440 595
3 rm – £ 35 £ 64/70
◆ Cottagey part 13C farmhouse on vast working farm. Atmospheric beamed lounge with woodburning stove. Airy pine-furnished rooms. Pleasant breakfast room with rustic feel.

ENGLAND

Your opinions are important to us:
please write and let us know about your discoveries and experiences – good and bad!

MORETON-IN-MARSH – Glos. – 503 O 28 – pop. 3 198 4 D1

Great Britain

London 86 m – Birmingham 40 m – Gloucester 31 m – Oxford 29 m
Chastleton House★★, SE : 5 m. by A 44

Manor House

rest,
High St ✉ GL56 0LJ – ✆ (01608) 650 501 – info@manorhousehotel.info
– Fax (01608) 651 481
34 rm – £ 115/135 £ 135/245 – 2 suites
Rest *Mulberry* – (light lunch) Menu £ 33
◆ Part 16C manor house in town centre. Walled lawns to rear. Two country house style low-beamed lounges with open fires. Sympathetically styled rooms; luxurious fabrics. Contemporary restaurant with bold style and cooking.

at Bourton-on-the-Hill West : 2 m. on A 44 – ✉ Moreton-in-Marsh

Horse & Groom with rm

✉ GL56 9AQ – ✆ (01386) 700 413 – greenstocks@horseandgroom.info
– Fax (01386) 700 413 – Closed 25 December, Sunday dinner and Monday lunch,
5 rm – £ 70 £ 125 – **Rest** – (booking essential) Carte £ 18/28
◆ Attractive 18C former coaching inn of yellowing local stone. Big, welcoming, beamed bar. 'Proper' English cooking on menus that change up to twice a day. Large, comfy rooms.

MORPETH – Northd. – 501 O 18 – pop. 13 555 24 B2

London 301 m – Edinburgh 93 m – Newcastle upon Tyne 15 m
The Chantry, Bridge St ✆ (01670) 511323
The Common, ✆ (01670) 504 942 .

at Eshott North : 6 m. by A 1 – ✉ Morpeth

Eshott Hall
by unmarked drive just before entering village ✉ NE65 9EP – ✆ (01670) 787 777 – thehall@eshott.co.uk – Fax (01670) 787 999 – Closed Christmas - New Year
6 rm – £79 £128 – **Rest** – (by arrangement, communal dining) Menu £33
◆ Impressive Georgian mansion in a private drive with mature grounds. A smart country house feel is evident all around. Popular for weddings. Rooms exude spotless quality. Owner cooks and serves at an antique table.

at Longhorsley Northwest : 6 ½ m. by A 192 on A 697 – ✉ Morpeth

Linden Hall rm,
North : 1 m. on A 697 ✉ NE65 8XF – ✆ (01670) 500 000 – lindenhall@macdonald-hotels.co.uk – Fax (01670) 500 001
50 rm – £85/214 £99/228
Rest *Dobson* – (dinner only and Sunday lunch) Menu £18/33
Rest *Linden Tree* – ✆ (01670) 500 033 – Carte £18/29 **s**
◆ Imposing, ivy clad Georgian house in extensive grounds. Numerous lounges refurbished with contemporary edge and a real fire. Well-kept, modernised, stylish rooms. Formal dining in comfy Dobson. Modish Linden Tree.

ENGLAND

Thistleyhaugh Farm
Northwest : 3 ¾ m. by A 697 and Todburn rd taking first right turn ✉ NE65 8RG – ✆ (01665) 570 629 – thistleyhaugh@hotmail.com – Fax (01665) 570 629 – Closed Christmas-New Year
5 rm (dinner included) – £55/70 £75 – **Rest** – (by arrangement, communal dining) Menu £20
◆ Attractive Georgian farmhouse on working farm in a pleasant rural area. The River Coquet flows through the grounds. Comfortable, cosy bedrooms in traditional style. Communal dining overlooking garden.

MORSTON – Norfolk – see Blakeney

MORTEHOE – Devon – 503 H 30 – see Woolacombe

MOTCOMBE – Dorset – 503 N 30 – see Shaftesbury

MOULSFORD – Oxon. 10 B3

London 53 m – Newbury 16 m – Reading 13 m

The Beetle & Wedge Boathouse
Ferry Lane ✉ OX10 9JF – ✆ (01491) 651 381 – boathouse@beetleandwedge.co.uk – Fax (01491) 651 376 – Closed 25 December
Rest – (booking essential) Carte £28/34
◆ Beautifully located by the Thames and enhanced by lovely terrace. Two dining options: bare-brick char-grill or conservatory dining room. Daily changing, wide-ranging menus.

MOULTON – N. Yorks. – 502 P 20 – ✉ Richmond 22 B1

London 243 m – Leeds 53 m – Middlesbrough 25 m – Newcastle upon Tyne 43 m

Black Bull Inn
✉ DL10 6QJ – ✆ (01325) 377 289 – sarah@blackbullinn.demon.co.uk – Fax (01325) 377 422 – Closed 24-26 December and Sunday
Rest – Seafood Menu £19 – Carte £35/45
◆ Old country pub with variety of dining areas, including an original Brighton Belle Pullman carriage from 1932 and conservatory with huge grapevine. Seafood a speciality.

MOUSEHOLE – Cornwall – 503 D 33 – ✉ Penzance 1 A3

London 321 m – Penzance 3 m – Truro 29 m

Village★

Penwith★★ – Lamorna (The Merry Maidens and The Pipers Standing Stone★) SW : 3 m. by B 3315. Land's End★ (cliff scenery★★★) W : 9 m. by B 3315

The Old Coastguard

The Parade ✉ TR19 6PR – ✆ (01736) 731 222 – bookings@oldcoastguardhotel.co.uk – Fax (01736) 731 720 – Closed 25 December

14 rm (dinner included) – †£ 110/265 ††£ 270/330 – **Rest** – Menu £ 40

◆ Creamwash hotel in unspoilt village with good views of Mounts Bay. Spacious lounge has sun terrace overlooking water. Modern rooms: Premier variety are best for the vista. Watch the bay as you eat freshly caught seafood.

Cornish Range with rm

6 Chapel St ✉ TR19 6SB – ✆ (01736) 731 488 – info@cornishrange.co.uk

3 rm – ††£ 80/100 – **Rest** – Seafood (booking essential) Carte £ 21/34

◆ Converted 18C pilchard processing cottage hidden away in narrow street. Cottagey inner filled with Cornish artwork. Excellent local seafood dishes. Very comfortable rooms.

MUCH MARCLE – Herefordshire – 503 M 28 – see Ledbury

MUCH WENLOCK – Shrops. – 502 M26 – pop. 1 959 *Great Britain* 18 B2

London 154 m – Birmingham 34 m – Shrewsbury 12 m – Worcester 37 m

The Museum, High St ✆ (01952) 727679 (summer only)

Priory★ AC

Ironbridge Gorge Museum★★ AC (The Iron Bridge★★ - Coalport China Museum★★ - Blists Hill Open Air Museum★★ – Museum of the Gorge and Visitor Centre★) NE : 4½ m. by A 4169 and B 4380

Raven

Barrow St ✉ TF13 6EN – ✆ (01952) 727 251 – enquiry@ravenhotel.com – Fax (01952) 728 416 – closed 25 December

20 rm – †£ 85 ††£ 120

Rest *The Restaurant* – Menu £ 31 – Carte £ 22/32

◆ Hotel spread across range of historic buildings with 17C coaching inn at its heart. Pleasant inner courtyard and conservatory. Good sized bedrooms with chintz fabrics. Dining room exudes homely rustic charm.

at Brockton Southwest : 5 m. on B 4378 – ✉ Much Wenlock

The Feathers at Brockton

✉ TF13 6JR – ✆ (01746) 785 202 – kayiatou@hotmail.com – Fax (01746) 785 202 – Closed 26-28 December and Monday except Bank Holiday Monday

Rest – Menu £ 15 – Carte £ 19/30

◆ Characterful part 16C pub near Wenlock Edge: whitewashed stone walls, beams and vast inglenooks. Constantly changing blackboard menus provide plethora of interesting dishes.

MUDEFORD – Dorset – 503 O 31 – see Christchurch

MULLION – Cornwall – 503 E 33 – pop. 1 834 – ✉ Helston 1 A3

London 323 m – Falmouth 21 m – Penzance 21 m – Truro 26 m

Mullion Cove★★ (Church★) – Lizard Peninsula★

Kynance Cove★★, S : 5 m. – Cury★ (Church★), N : 2 m. by minor roads. Helston (The Flora Day Furry Dance★★) (May), N : 7½ m. by A 3083 – Culdrose (Flambards Village Theme Park★) AC, N : 6 m. by A 3083 – Wendron (Poldark Mine★), N : 9½ m. by A 3083 and B 3297

ENGLAND

Mullion Cove ← Mullion Cove and Mount's Bay, P VISA AE
Southwest : 1 m. by B 3296 ✉ TR12 7EP – ✆ (01326) 240 328
– enquiries@mullion-cove.co.uk – Fax (01326) 240 998
– Closed 6 January-8 February
32 rm (dinner included) – †£ 96/212 ††£ 180/240
Rest *Atlantic View* – (dinner only and Sunday lunch) Menu £ 30
Rest *Bistro* – (dinner only and Sunday lunch) Carte £ 14/33
◆ Dramatic Victorian hotel, personally run, standing in spectacular position on cliffs above Mullion Cove. Terrific views along coastline. Comfortable, modern rooms. Cream painted, welcoming Atlantic View. Bistro with terrace perfect for lunch.

MUNSLOW – Shrops. – 503 L 26 18 B2

London 166 m – Ludlow 10 m – Shrewsbury 21 m

The Crown Country Inn with rm P VISA AE
on B 4378 ✉ SY7 9ET – ✆ (01584) 841 205 – info@crowncountry-inn.co.uk
– Fax (01584) 841 255 – Closed Christmas, Sunday dinner and Monday
3 rm – †£ 50 ††£ 75 – **Rest** – Menu £ 17 – Carte £ 22/30
◆ Hugely characterful, heavily beamed bar, crackling fire and hops hanging from the rafters. Well executed dishes served here or in linen clad restaurant. Simple, comfy rooms.

MURCOTT – Oxon – pop. 1 293 – ✉ Kidlington 10 B2

London 70 m – Oxford 14 m – Witney 20 m

The Nut Tree P VISA
✉ OX5 2RE – ✆ (01865) 331 253 – Closed Sunday dinner and Monday
Rest – Menu £ 15 – Carte £ 26/36
◆ Thatched 16C inn with low beamed ceilings and formally laid tables. Confident chef uses quality ingredients to produce attractive, flavoursome dishes. Enthusiastic service.

MYLOR BRIDGE – Cornwall – 503 E 33 – see Falmouth

NAILSWORTH – Glos. – 503 N 28 – pop. 5 276 4 C1

London 110 m – Bristol 30 m – Swindon 28 m

Egypt Mill P VISA
✉ GL6 0AE – ✆ (01453) 833 449 – reception@egyptmill.com
– Fax (01453) 839 919
28 rm – †£ 80 ††£ 110 – **Rest** – Carte £ 23/30
◆ Hugely characterful former 16C mill on the Frome, once used for cloth manufacture. Bedrooms are in three blocks; some with original features and river views. Comfy bistro style restaurant with watery vistas; mill workings surround diners.

NANTWICH – Ches. – 502 M 24 – pop. 13 447 20 A3

London 176 m – Chester 20 m – Liverpool 45 m – Manchester 40 m
– Stoke-on-Trent 17 m
Church House, Church Walk ✆ (01270) 610983
Alvaston Hall Middlewich Rd, ✆ (01270) 628 473 .

Rookery Hall ← rm, P VISA AE
Worleston, North : 2½ m. by A 51 on B 5074 ✉ CW5 6DQ – ✆ (01270) 610 016
– rookery@handpicked.co.uk – Fax (01270) 626 027
68 rm – †£ 135/145 ††£ 155/165, £12.50 – 2 suites
Rest – (bar lunch Monday-Friday) (booking essential) Menu £ 32
– Carte £ 33/46
◆ Originally built in 1816 in Georgian style; enjoys a peacefully set, smart country house ambience. The individually decorated bedrooms offer a very good level of comfort. Wood panelled restaurant with polished tables.

ENGLAND

The Limes without rest
5 Park Rd, on A 530 (Whitchurch rd) ✉ CW5 7AQ – ✆ (01270) 624081 – thelimesparkroad@aol.com – Fax (01270) 624081 – Easter-October
3 rm – 🚹£50 🚹🚹£60
◆ Redbrick Victorian house in Queen Anne style. The large bedrooms have been individually decorated and benefit from a warm personality. Friendly and personally run.

Oakland House without rest
252 Newcastle Rd, Blakelow, Shavington, East : 2½ m. by A 51 on A 500 ✉ CW5 7ET – ✆ (01270) 567134 – enquiries@oaklandhouseonline.co.uk
9 rm – 🚹£39 🚹🚹£54
◆ Private guesthouse with family photos adding personal touch. Homely lounge, warmly decorated breakfast room and conservatory. Comfy rooms in house and converted outbuildings.

NATIONAL EXHIBITION CENTRE – W. Mids. – 503 O 26 – see Birmingham

NAWTON – N. Yorks. – see Helmsley

NAYLAND – Suffolk – 504 W 28 15 C3

London 64 m – Bury St Edmunds 24 m – Cambridge 54 m – Colchester 6 m – Ipswich 19 m

The White Hart Inn with rm
11 High St ✉ CO6 4JF – ✆ (01206) 263382 – nayhart@aol.com – Fax (01206) 263638 – Closed 2 weeks after New Year
6 rm – 🚹£66/87 🚹🚹£129 – **Rest** – Menu £18 – Carte £23/37 **s**
◆ Accomplished food served in terracotta tiled dining room of part 15C coaching inn. Floodlit cellars and comfortable beamed bedrooms.

NEAR SAWREY – Cumbria – 502 L 20 – see Hawkshead

NETHER BURROW – Cumbria – see Kirkby Lonsdale

NETTLEBED – Oxon. – 504 R 29 11 C3

London 44 m – Oxford 20 m – Reading 10 m

White Hart
28 High St ✉ RG9 5DD – ✆ (01491) 641245 – info@whitehartnettlebed.com – Fax (01491) 649018
12 rm – 🚹£90/125 🚹🚹£95/145
Rest ***Bistro*** – (Closed Sunday dinner) Carte £24/35
◆ Recently refurbished part 17C inn boasts spacious, modern bedrooms, all uniquely styled with a certain "designer" appeal, some in original hotel, others in adjacent new block. Minimalist Bistro.

NETTLETON SHRUB – Wilts. – 503 N 29 – see Castle Combe

The ✿ award is the crème de la crème. This is awarded to restaurants which are really worth travelling miles for!

NEW MILTON – Hants. – **503** P 31 – **pop. 26 681** 6 **A3**

London 106 m – Bournemouth 12 m – Southampton 21 m – Winchester 34 m

Barton-on-Sea Milford Rd, ✆ (01425) 615 308 .

Chewton Glen (heated) rm,

Christchurch Rd, West : 2 m. by A 337 and Ringwood Rd on Chewton Farm Rd ✉ BH25 6QS – ✆ (01425) 275 341 – reservations@chewtonglen.com – Fax (01425) 272 310

48 rm – £ 295/320 £ 295/517, £ 20 – 10 suites

Rest *Marryat Room and Conservatory* – Menu £ 25/65 **s** – Carte £ 47/61 **s**

◆ A byword in luxury: 19C house where Captain Marryat wrote novels. Sherry and shortbread await in huge rooms of jewel colours; balconies overlook grounds. Scented steam room. Accomplished cooking in cool smooth conservatory and bright dining room.

NEW ROMNEY – Kent – **504** W 31 9 **C2**

London 71 m – Brighton 60 m – Folkestone 17 m – Maidstone 36 m

Romney Bay House

Coast Rd, Littlestone, East : 2¼ m. off B 2071 ✉ TN28 8QY – ✆ (01797) 364 747 – Fax (01797) 367 156 – Closed 1 week Christmas

10 rm – £ 60 £ 160 – **Rest** – (Closed Sunday, Monday and Thursday) (dinner only) (booking essential for non-residents) (set menu only) Menu £ 40

◆ Beach panorama for late actress Hedda Hopper's house, built by Portmeirion architect Clough Williams-Ellis. Individual rooms; sitting room with telescope and bookcases. Enjoy drinks on terrace before conservatory dining.

The red symbol?
This denotes the very essence of peace
– only the sound of birdsong first thing in the morning ...

NEWARK-ON-TRENT – Notts. – **502** R 24 – **pop. 35 454** 17 **C1**

 *Great Britain*

London 127 m – Lincoln 16 m – Nottingham 20 m – Sheffield 42 m

Kelwick Coddington, ✆ (01636) 626 282 .

St Mary Magdalene★

Grange

73 London Rd, South : ½ m. on Grantham rd (B 6326) ✉ NG24 1RZ – ✆ (01636) 703 399 – info@grangenewark.co.uk – Fax (01636) 702 328 – Closed 25 December-7 January

19 rm – £ 79/110 £ 110/200

Rest *Cutlers* – (dinner only and Sunday lunch) Carte £ 22/29

◆ Situated in a residential area but not far from town centre, this small hotel is fitted with functional, simply decorated bedrooms and miniature pulpit-style bar. Compact dining room boasts cadlelit dinners.

XX Reeds

13-15 Castlegate ✉ NG24 1AL – ✆ (01636) 704 500 – food@reedrestaurants.com – Fax (01636) 611 139 – Closed 1 January and Sunday dinner

Rest – Menu £ 14 (lunch) – Carte £ 23/36

◆ Intimate, brick vaulted, Georgian house cellar with original ceiling meat hooks in situ. Mix of linen-clad and plain tables. Seasonal ingredients to the fore in varied menus.

at Caunton Northwest : 7 m. by A 616 – ✉ Newark-on-Trent

Caunton Beck

Main St ✉ NG23 6AB – ✆ (01636) 636 793 – email@cauntonbeck.com – Fax (01636) 636 828

Rest – Menu £ 14 – Carte £ 23/34

◆ Welcoming modern pub, with stone-floored bar, beamed ceilings, flower-filled front terrace and restaurant serving classic pub dishes. Popular weekend breakfast destination.

NEWBIGGIN – Cumbria – 502 L 19 – see Penrith

Look out for red symbols, indicating particularly pleasant establishments.

NEWBURY – Newbury – 503 Q 29 – pop. 33 273 10 B3

London 67 m – Bristol 66 m – Oxford 28 m – Reading 17 m – Southampton 38 m

The Wharf ✆ (01635) 30267, tourism@westberks.gov.uk

Newbury and Crookham Greenham Common Bury's Bank Rd, ✆ (01635) 40 035 ;

Donnington Valley Old Oxford Rd, ✆ (01635) 568 140.

ENGLAND

NEWBURY

Street	Grid	No.
Almond Ave	BY	3
Andover Rd	BZ	4
Bartholomew St	BZ	6
Bone Lane	BZ	10
Carnegie Rd	BZ	13
Castle Grove	BY	15
Cheap St	BZ	16
Chesterfield Rd	BZ	18
Craven Rd	BZ	24
Dolman Rd	BY	25
Donnington Link	BY	27
Greenham Hill	BZ	31
Greenham Rd	BZ	33
Hambridge Rd	BZ	36
Kennett Shopping Centre	BZ	
Kiln Rd	BY	40
Kings Rd	BZ	
London Rd	BY	
Love Lane	BY	
Maple Crescent	BY	43
Market St	BZ	45
Mill Lane	BZ	
Newtown Rd	BZ	48
New Rd	BZ	46
Northbrook St	BYZ	
Northcroft Lane	BZ	
Old Bath Rd	BY	
Oxford Rd	BY	
Park Way	BYZ	50
Pound St	BZ	
Queens Rd	BZ	
Racecourse Rd	BZ	
Rockingham Rd	BZ	52
St Johns Rd	BZ	
Sandleford Link	BZ	54
Shaw Hill	BY	
Shaw Rd	BY	
Station Rd	BZ	
Strawberry Hill	BY	58
Western Ave	BY	
West St	BZ	66
Wharf St	BZ	67

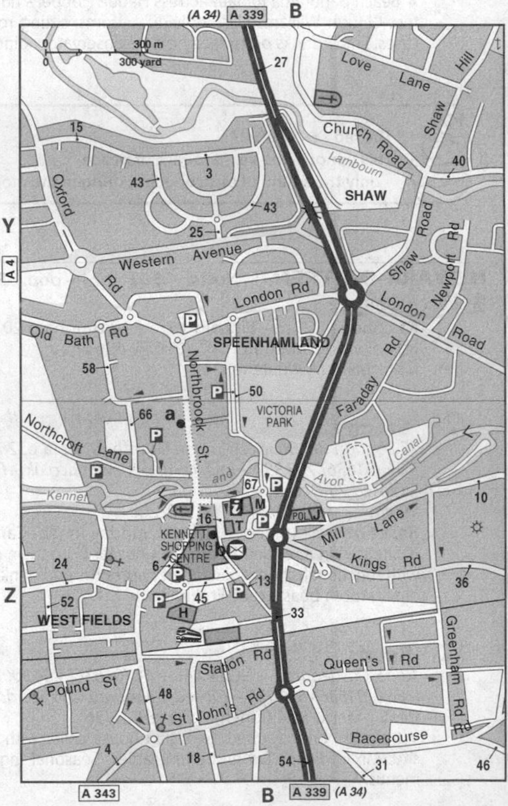

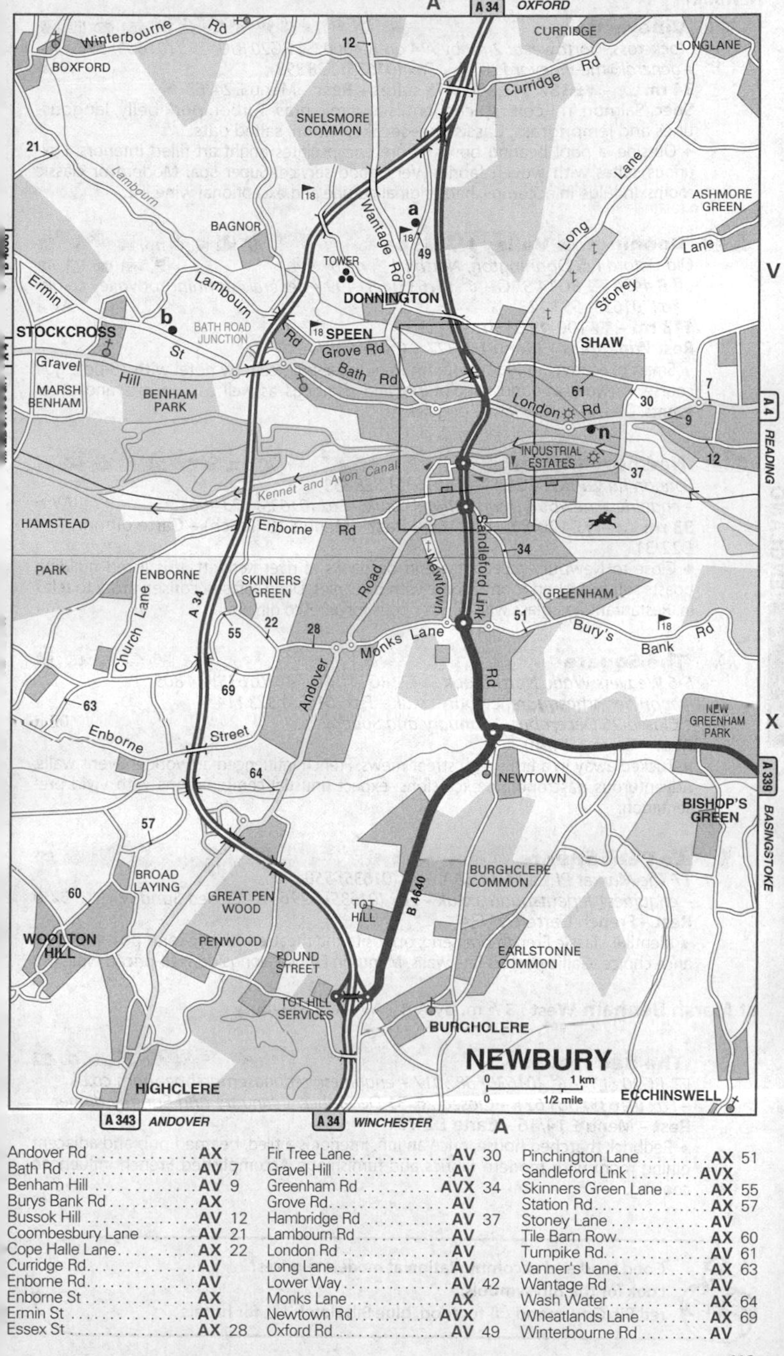

Andover Rd . . . . AX
Bath Rd . . . . AV 7
Benham Hill . . . . AV 9
Burys Bank Rd . . . . AX
Bussok Hill . . . . AV 12
Coombesbury Lane . . . . AV 21
Cope Halle Lane . . . . AX 22
Curridge Rd . . . . AV
Enborne Rd . . . . AV
Enborne St . . . . AX
Ermin St . . . . AV
Essex St . . . . AX 28
Fir Tree Lane . . . . AV 30
Gravel Hill . . . . AV
Greenham Rd . . . . AVX 34
Grove Rd . . . . AV
Hambridge Rd . . . . AV 37
Lambourn Rd . . . . AV
London Rd . . . . AV
Long Lane . . . . AV
Lower Way . . . . AV 42
Monks Lane . . . . AX
Newtown Rd . . . . AVX
Oxford Rd . . . . AV 49
Pinchington Lane . . . . AX 51
Sandleford Link . . . . AVX
Skinners Green Lane . . . . AX 55
Station Rd . . . . AX 57
Stoney Lane . . . . AV
Tile Barn Row . . . . AX 60
Turnpike Rd . . . . AV 61
Vanner's Lane . . . . AX 63
Wantage Rd . . . . AV
Wash Water . . . . AX 64
Wheatlands Lane . . . . AX 69
Winterbourne Rd . . . . AV

Vineyard

Stockcross, Northwest : 2 m. by A 4 on B 4000 ✉ RG20 8JU – ☏ (01635) 528 770 – general@the-vineyard.co.uk – Fax (01635) 528 398 AV **b**

34 rm – ♦£ 187 ♦♦£ 300 – 15 suites – **Rest** – Menu £ 24/68

Spec. Salmon 'mi-cuit', spiced lentils and foie gras. Turbot, pork belly, langoustines and lemongrass. Cassis cheesecake, lemon, salted oats.

♦ Outside, a pool bearing bowls of fire encapsulates bright art-filled interiors. Luxurious suites with woven fabrics. Very good service. Super spa. Modern or classic rooms. Indulge in accomplished original cuisine and exceptional wine list.

Donnington Valley H. & Spa

Old Oxford Rd, Donnington, North : 1 ¾ m. by A 4 off B 4494 ✉ RG14 3AG – ☏ (01635) 551 199 – general@donningtonvalley.co.uk – Fax (01635) 551 123 AV **a**

113 rm – ♦£ 190 ♦♦£ 190, £ 15

Rest *Winepress* – Menu £ 23/27 – Carte £ 37/45

♦ Smart executive and family rooms in purpose-built country hotel with 18-hole golf course. Artwork abounds: sculptures and paintings as well as concerts and other events. Dine in conservatory or gallery.

Newbury Manor

London Rd ✉ RG14 2BY – ☏ (01635) 528 838 – enquiries@newbury-manor-hotel.co.uk – Fax (01635) 523 406 AV **n**

33 rm – ♦£ 120 ♦♦£ 120/165 – **Rest** – Menu £ 18 (lunch) – Carte dinner £ 22/31

♦ Close to Newbury racecourse and on banks of river Kennett, this listed building boasts soft furnished rooms, some with balconies. Deep sofas in conservatory to relax in. Restaurant has glass wall which opens for alfresco dining.

The Square

5-6 Weavers Walk, Northbrook St ✉ RG14 1AL – ☏ (01635) 44 805 – enquiries@thesquarenewbury.co.uk – Fax (01635) 523 114 – Closed 26 December, 1 January and Sunday BZ **a**

Rest – Carte £ 24/40

♦ Tucked away in a little high street mews. French influenced artwork enlivens walls. Adventurous gastronomic excursions: expect unusual combinations with vivid presentation.

Le Petit Square

17 The Market Pl ✉ RG14 5AA – ☏ (01635) 550 770 – enquiries@lepetitsquare.co.uk – Fax (01635) 529 669 – Closed Sunday BZ **b**

Rest – French Carte £ 21/34

♦ Identikit classic French brasserie: opposite the theatre with pre- and post-performance choice. Gallic posters line walls. Menus in French alongside well-priced wine list.

at Marsh Benham West : 3 ½ m. by A 4 - AV – ✉ Newbury

The Red House

✉ RG20 8LY – ☏ (01635) 582 017 – enquiries@redhousemarshbenham.co.uk – Fax (01635) 581 621 – Closed 26, 31 December, 1 January and Sunday dinner

Rest – Menu £ 14/16 – Carte £ 21/31

♦ Redbrick thatched house, once an inn. Interior is a tiled, beamed pub and adjacent dining room with modern fabrics and furnishings. Accomplished French influenced cooking.

ENGLAND

Good food and accommodation at moderate prices?
Look for the Bib symbols:
red Bib Gourmand for food, blue Bib Hotel for hotels

NEWBY BRIDGE – Cumbria – 502 L 21 – ✉ Ulverston

London 270 m – Kendal 16 m – Lancaster 27 m
Lake Windermere★★

Lakeside

Lakeside, Northeast : 1 m. on Hawkshead rd
✉ LA12 8AT – ✆ (015395) 30 001 – reservations@lakesidehotel.co.uk – Fax (015395) 31 699 – Closed 23 December-21 January
74 rm – ♦£ 150/195 ♦♦£ 170/215 – 3 suites
Rest *Lakeview* – Menu £ 28/48
Rest *John Ruskins Brasserie* – (dinner only) Menu £ 35
◆ Delightfully situated on the shores of Lake Windermere. Plenty of charm and character. Work out at the state-of-the-art leisure centre then sleep in fitted, modern bedrooms. Lakeview offers smart ambience. Bright, informal John Ruskins Brasserie.

The Knoll

Lakeside, Northeast : 1 ¼ m. on Hawkshead rd ✉ LA12 8AU – ✆ (015395) 31 347 – info@theknoll-lakeside.co.uk – Fax (015395) 30 850 – closed 25-26 December
8 rm – ♦£ 56/92 ♦♦£ 124 – **Rest** – (closed Sunday-Monday) (dinner only) (booking essential for non-residents) Menu £ 26/30 **s**
◆ Late Victorian country house close to popular lakeside, with welcoming owners, comfortable lounge and contemporary bedrooms; room 4 is the best. Extensive breakfast menu. Linen clad dining room; local produce proudly used.

NEWBY WISKE – N. Yorks. – 502 P 21 – see Northallerton

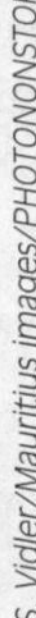
S. Vidler/Mauritius images/PHOTONONSTOP

NEWCASTLE UPON TYNE

County: Tyne and Wear
Michelin REGIONAL map: n° 501
London 276 m – Edinburgh 105 m – Leeds 95 m

Population: 189 863
Great Britain

24 **B2**

Access Tyne Tunnel (toll)

PRACTICAL INFORMATION

Tourist Information

132 Grainger St ✆ (0191) 277 8000, tourist.info@newcastle.gov.uk

Guild Hall Visitors Centre, Quayside

Newcastle International Airport ✆ (0191) 214 4422

Airport

Newcastle Airport: ✆ (0871) 882 1121, NW: 5 m. by A 696 AV

Ferries and Shipping Lines

to Norway (Bergen, Haugesund and Stavanger) (Fjord Line) (approx 26 h) – to The Netherlands (Amsterdam) (DFDS Seaways A/S) daily (15 h)

Tunnel

Tyne Tunnel (toll)

Golf Courses

Broadway East Gosforth, ✆ (0191) 285 6710 ; City of Newcatle Gosforth Three Mill Bridge, ✆ (0191) 285 1775 ; Wallsend Bigges Main Rheydt Ave, NE: by A1058, ✆ (0191) 262 1973 ; Wickham Fellside Rd, Hollinside Park, ✆ (0191) 488 7309.

ENGLAND

SIGHTS

IN TOWN

City★ – Grey Street★ CZ – Quayside★ CZ : Composition★ , All Saints Church★ (interior★) – Castle Keep★ **AC** CZ – Laing Art Gallery and Museum★ **AC** CY **M1** – Museum of Antiquities★ CY **M2** – LIFE Interactive World★ CZ – Gateshead Millennium Bridge★ CZ

ON THE OUTSKIRTS

Hadrian's Wall★★ , W: by A 69 AV

IN THE SURROUNDING AREA

Beamish: North of England Open-Air Museum★★ **AC**, SW: 7 m. by A 692 and A 6076 AX – Seaton Delaval Hall★ **AC**, NE: 11 m. by A 189 - BV - and A 190

NEWCASTLE-UPON-TYNE

Street	Grid	No.
Adelaide Terrace	AX	2
Atkinson Rd	AX	3
Bath St	BX	4
Bensham Rd	AX	6
Benton Bank	BV	8
Buddle St	BV	13
Byker Bridge	BV	15
Church Ave	AV	16
Church Rd	AV	18
Clayton Rd	BV	21
Coldwell Lane	BX	22
Coldwell St	BX	24
Condercum Rd	AX	26
Fossway	BV	31
Haddrick's Mill Rd	BV	36
High St West	BV	37
Jesmond Dene Rd	BV	39
Killingworth Rd	BV	42
Lobley Hill Rd	AX	45
Matthew Bank	BV	49
Neptune Rd	BV	51
Redheugh Bridge	AX	62
Red Hall Drive	BV	61
Saltwell Rd	BX	69
Shipdon Rd	AX	71
Springfield Rd	AV	72
Station Rd	BX	73
Stephenson Rd	BV	74
Sunderland Rd	BX	76
Sutton St	BV	77
Swalwell Bank	ABX	79
Waverdale Ave	BV	83
West Farm Ave	BV	87
Whickham Bank	AX	89
Windy Nook Rd	BX	91

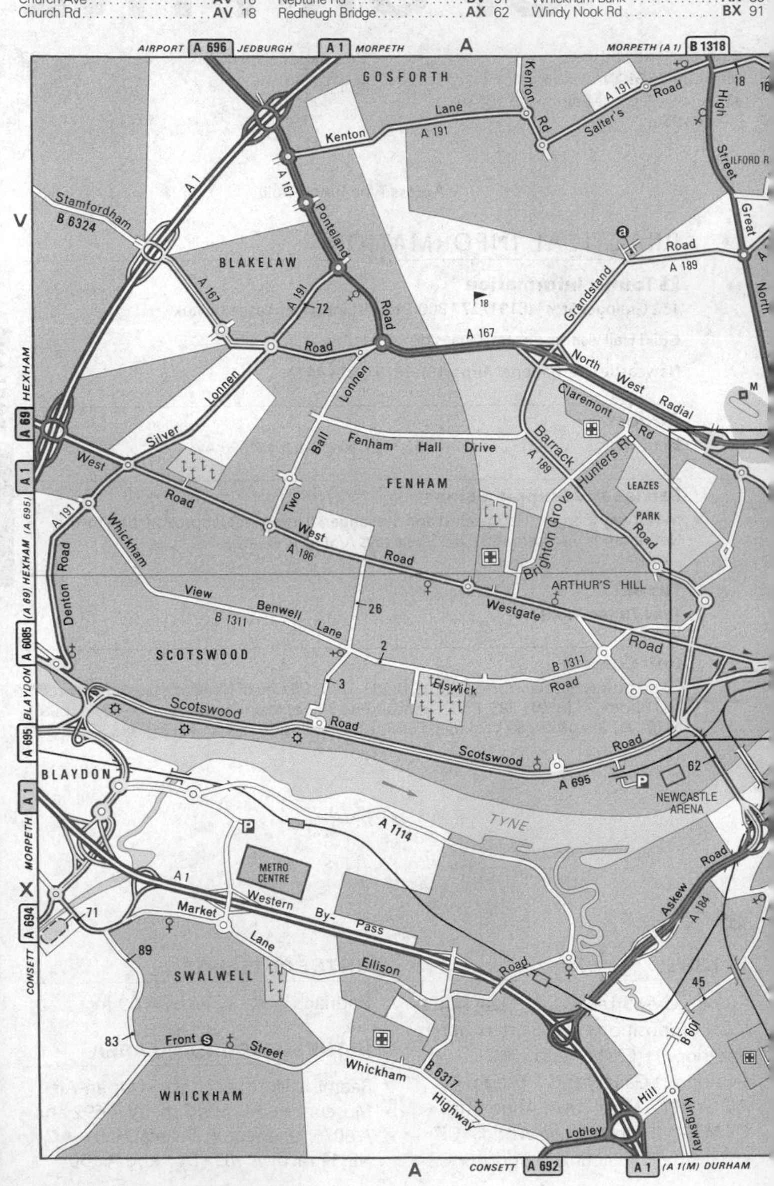

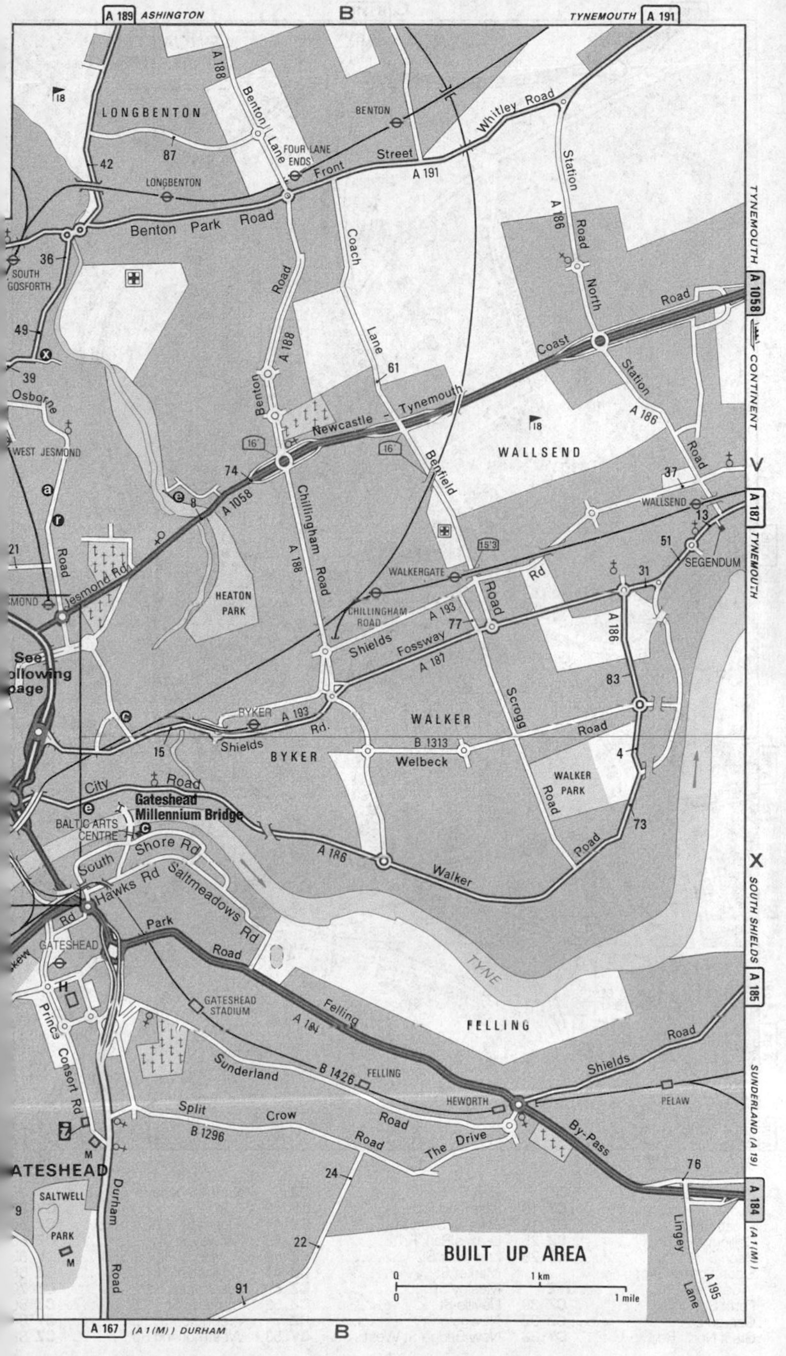
A 189 ASHINGTON
B
TYNEMOUTH A 191
LONGBENTON
BENTON
FOUR LANE ENDS
Front Street
A 191
Whitley Road
Benton Park Road
Station Road
North Road
Coach Lane
Benton Road
A 188
Coast Road
A 1058
Newcastle - Tynemouth
WALLSEND
Station Road
A 186
SOUTH GOSFORTH
Osborne
WEST JESMOND
Jesmond Rd
HEATON PARK
Chillingham Road
Benfield Road
WALKERGATE
CHILLINGHAM ROAD
WALLSEND
SEGENDUM
Shields Fossway
A 193
A 187
BYKER
WALKER
Scrogg Road
Welbeck
B 1313
Shields Rd.
City Road
Gateshead Millennium Bridge
BALTIC ARTS CENTRE
South Shore Rd
Hawks Rd
Saltmeadows Rd
Walker Road
A 186
WALKER PARK
Park Road
GATESHEAD
TYNE
GATESHEAD STADIUM
Felling
A 184
FELLING
Sunderland Road
B 1426
FELLING
HEWORTH
PELAW
Shields Road
By-Pass
Princes Consort Rd
Split Crow Road
B 1296
The Drive
GATESHEAD
SALTWELL PARK
Durham Road
Lingey Lane
A 195
BUILT UP AREA
1 km
1 mile
See following page
A 167 (A 1(M)) DURHAM
TYNEMOUTH A 1058 CONTINENT
V
A 187 TYNEMOUTH
X
SOUTH SHIELDS A 185
SUNDERLAND (A 19)
A 184 (A 1(M))

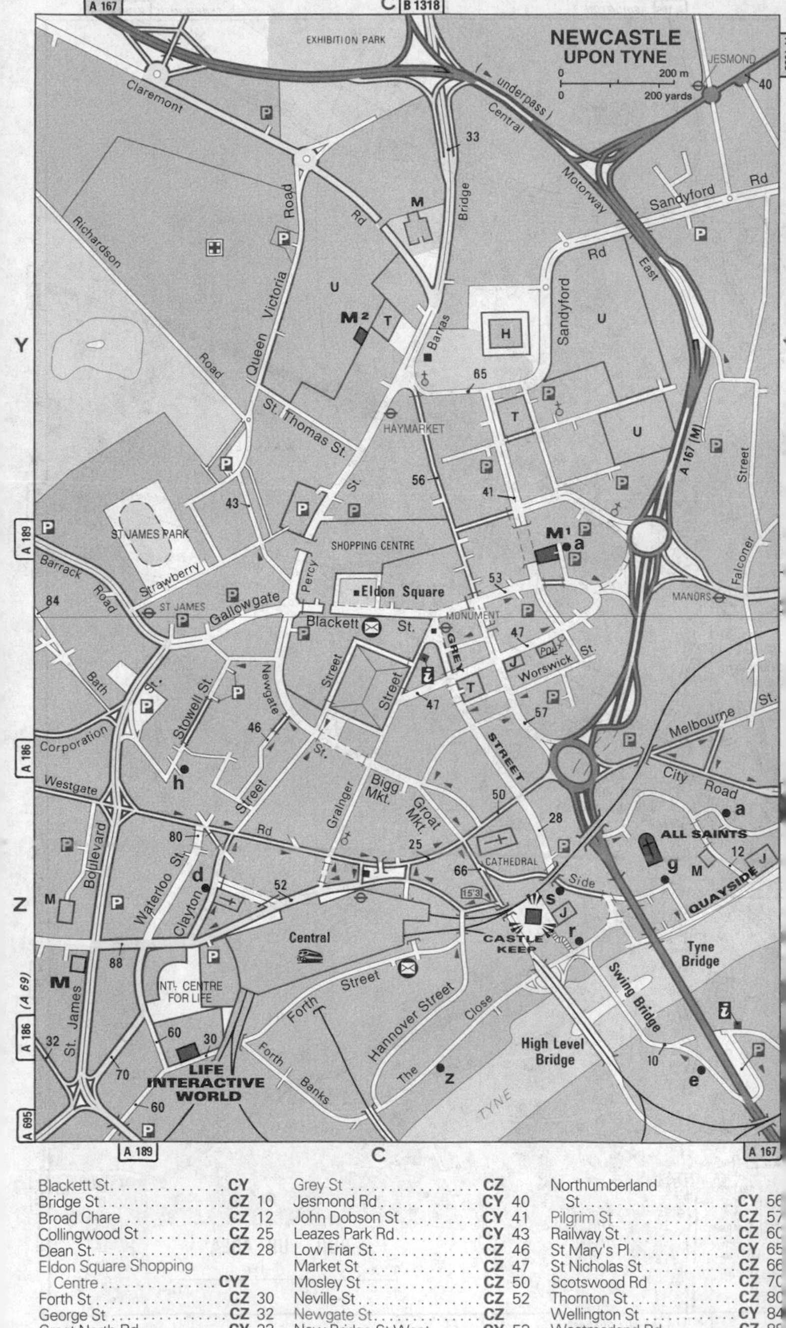

NEWCASTLE UPON TYNE
0 200 m
0 200 yards
A 167
C
B 1318
EXHIBITION PARK
JESMOND
40
underpass
Central
Motorway
East
Claremont
Rd
33
Bridge
Sandyford
Rd
Richardson
Road
Queen Victoria
M
U
M²
T
Barras
H
Sandyford
U
65
St. Thomas St.
HAYMARKET
T
U
A 167 (M)
Street
Falconer
56
41
43
St.
ST JAMES PARK
SHOPPING CENTRE
M¹
a
Y
A 189
Barrack
Road
Strawberry
Percy
Eldon Square
53
MANORS
84
ST JAMES
Gallowgate
Blackett
St.
MONUMENT
GREY
47
J
Worswick
St.
Bath
St.
Stowell St.
Newgate
Street
Street
T
47
57
St.
Melbourne
A 186
Corporation
46
STREET
City
Road
h
Westgate
St.
Bigg Mkt.
Groat Mkt.
50
a
Grainger
Boulevard
80
Rd
25
28
ALL SAINTS
12
Waterloo St.
d
Clayton
52
CATHEDRAL
66
g
M
J
Z
M
Side
QUAYSIDE
s
J
Central
CASTLE KEEP
r
Tyne Bridge
88
(A 69)
M
INTL CENTRE FOR LIFE
Street
Forth
Hannover Street
Close
Swing Bridge
A 186
St. James
32
60
30
Forth
Banks
The
z
High Level Bridge
10
e
70
LIFE INTERACTIVE WORLD
TYNE
60
A 695
A 189
C
A 167

Copthorne H. Newcastle rm, rest,
The Close, Quayside ✉ *NE1 3RT* – ✆ *(0191) 222 0333*
– sales.newcastle@mill-cop.com – Fax (0191) 260 3033 CZ **z**
156 rm – †£ 200 ††£ 200, ☕ £15.75
Rest *Harry's* – (Closed Saturday lunch) Menu £ 11/22 – Carte £ 27/34
◆ Modern hotel beside the Tyne. Bright and airy lounges within an imposing atrium. Well-appointed rooms have river views; ask for one with a balcony. Ornately decorated Le Rivage overlooks the Tyne.

Jesmond Dene House rm,
Jesmond Dene Rd, Northeast: 1½ m. by B 1318 and A 189
✉ *NE2 2EY* – ✆ *(0191) 212 3000 – info@jesmonddenehouse.co.uk*
– Fax (0191) 212 3001 BV **x**
40 rm – †£ 140/150 ††£ 165/375, ☕ £16 – **Rest** – Menu £ 22 (lunch) – Carte £ 31/46
◆ Stylishly refurbished 19C Grade II listed house in tranquil city dene.Two very smart lounges, one with cocktail bar. Eclectic range of modish rooms with hi-tech feel. Formal dining room with conservatory style extension overlooks garden.

Malmaison rm,
Quayside ✉ *NE1 3DX* – ✆ *(0191) 245 5000 – newcastle@malmaison.com*
– Fax (0191) 245 4545 BX **e**
120 rm – †£ 105/160 ††£ 105/160, ☕ £14 – 2 suites
Rest *Brasserie* – (bar lunch Saturday) Menu £ 17 (lunch) – Carte £ 22/41
◆ Unstuffy and contemporary hotel hides within this quayside former Co-operative building. Vibrantly and individually decorated rooms; some overlook Millennium Bridge. Brasserie has modern interpretation of French style.

ENGLAND

New Northumbria
61-73 Osborne Rd, Jesmond ✉ *NE2 2AN* – ✆ *(0191) 281 4961*
– reservations@newnorthumbriahotel.co.uk – Fax (0191) 281 8588 BV **a**
57 rm ☕ – †£ 65/85 ††£ 75/125
Rest *Scalini's* – Italian Menu £ 9 (lunch) **s** – Carte £ 12/21 **s**
Rest *Louis* – ✆ (0191) 281 5284 – Menu £ 14 (lunch) **s** – Carte £ 24/40 **s**
◆ Welcoming hotel with bright yellow exterior and metro access to city. Bustling bar: its lively location gives immediate access to buzzy nightspots. Well-equipped, comfy rooms. Scalini's with Italian specialities. Smart, stylish Louis.

Waterside without rest
48-52 Sandhill, Quayside ✉ *NE1 3JF* – ✆ *(0191) 230 0111*
– enquiries@watersidehotel.com – Fax (0191) 230 1615
– Closed 25-26 December CZ **r**
24 rm ☕ – †£ 80 ††£ 80
◆ Grade II listed quayside conversion close to most of the city's attractions. Compact yet well-furnished and cosy bedrooms. Top floor rooms benefit from air-conditioning.

Fisherman's Lodge
Jesmond Dene, Jesmond ✉ *NE7 7BQ* – ✆ *(0191) 281 3281*
– info@fishermanslodge.co.uk – Fax (0191) 281 6410 – Closed 25-26 December, Sunday and Monday BV **e**
Rest – Menu £ 23/50
◆ Attractive Victorian house secreted in a narrow wooded valley yet close to city centre. Series of well-appointed, stylish rooms. Modern British cooking with seafood bias.

Black Door
32 Clayton Street West ✉ *NE1 5DZ* – ✆ *(0191) 261 6295 – Fax (0191) 260 5422*
– closed 1 January, 25-26 December CZ **d**
Rest – (dinner only) Menu £ 43
◆ Set in Georgian terrace, with smart and contemporary interior. There's a wood floored lounge with leather sofas and a cosy dining room serving intriguing modern combinations.

XX **Café 21**

Trinity Gardens ✉ NE1 2HH – ✆ (0191) 222 0755 – bh@cafetwentyone.co.uk – Fax (0191) 221 0761 – Closed 25-26 December, 1 January and Bank holidays CZ **a**

Rest – Menu £ 17 – Carte £ 31/37

◆ Busy restaurant on ground floor of office block in redevelopment area of city. Open plan layout; warm, stylish décor. Flavoursome, bistro-style dishes have European influences.

XX **Amer's**

34 Osborne Rd, Jesmond ✉ NE2 2AJ – ✆ (0191) 281 5377 – jesmondhotel@aol.com – Fax (0191) 212 0783 – Closed 24-26 December, Bank Holidays, Sunday and lunch Saturday and Monday BV **d**

Rest – (booking essential) Carte £ 16/33

◆ Popular ground floor restaurant in smart location. Cosy, stylish lounge/bar sets you up for good value dishes that are modern in style and prepared with skill and flair.

XX **Brasserie Black Door**

The Biscuit Factory, 16 Stoddart St ✉ NE2 1AN – ✆ (0191) 260 5411 – Fax (0191) 260 5422 – Closed 25 December, 1 January and Sunday dinner BV **c**

Rest – Menu £ 17 (lunch) – Carte dinner £ 25/37

◆ Art gallery restaurant set in a 1930s former biscuit factory. Through modish lounge to airy dining space with industrial ambience, wall art and recognisable brasserie dishes.

XX **Grainger Rooms**

7 Higham Place ✉ NE1 8AF – ✆ (0191) 232 4949 – info@graingerrooms.co.uk – Closed 25 December, Sunday and Bank Holidays CY **a**

Rest – Menu £ 16/33 – Carte £ 16/33

◆ Red brick Georgian townhouse with first floor dining, eye-catching chandeliers and rustic photos. Hearty, flavoursome British cooking uses excellent produce. Polite service.

XX **Vujon**

29 Queen St, Quayside ✉ NE1 3UG – ✆ (0191) 221 0601 – mahtab@vujon.com – Fax (0191) 221 0602 – Closed Sunday lunch CZ **g**

Rest – Indian Menu £ 23 – Carte £ 19/36

◆ A friendly and authentic Indian restaurant can be found behind the striking Victorian façade with modern etched windows. Menu of traditional and more contemporary dishes.

X **Blackfriars**

Friars St ✉ NE1 4XN – ✆ (0191) 261 5945 – info@blackfriarsrestaurant.co.uk – Closed Sunday dinner and Bank Holidays CZ **h**

Rest – Menu £ 13 – Carte £ 24/34

◆ Late 13C stone built monks' refectory still serving food in a split level beamed restaurant. Relaxed atmosphere with friendly informal service. Interesting and original menu.

at Gosforth North : 2½ m. by B 1318 - AV – ✉ Newcastle upon Tyne

Newcastle Marriott H. Gosforth Park

High Gosforth Park, North : 2 m. on B 1318 at junction with A 1056 ✉ NE3 5HN – ✆ (0191) 236 4111 – nclgf.salesoffice.northeast@marriotthotels.com – Fax (0191) 236 8192

173 rm – †£ 99 ††£ 99, ☕ £ 14.95 – 5 suites

Rest *Chats* – (dinner only and Sunday lunch) Menu £ 20/27 **s** – Carte £ 32/40 **s**

Rest *Park* – (dinner only and Sunday lunch) Menu £ 20/30 **s** – Carte £ 32/40 **s**

◆ Ideal for both corporate and leisure guests. Extensive conference and leisure facilities. Well-equipped bedrooms with up-to-date décor. Close to the racecourse and the A1. Relaxed Park overlooks the grounds. Informal Chats for light snacks.

ENGLAND

Open Kitchen

3rd Floor, Gosforth Squash Club, Moor Court Annexe, Southwest : 1 ¼ m. by B 1318, A 189 and Kenton Rd on Westfield Rd ✉ NE3 4YD – ☎ (0191) 285 2909 – eat@theopenkitchen.co.uk – Closed 24-26 December and 1-2 January, AV **a**

Rest – (dinner only and Sunday lunch) (booking essential) Carte £ 23/36

◆ Intimate restaurant on top floor of a squash club. Kitchen is, indeed, on show behind the bar. Polite, knowledgable service underpins original cooking using Fairtrade produce.

at Seaton Burn North : 8 m. by B 1318 - AV – ✉ Newcastle upon Tyne

Horton Grange

Northwest : 3 ½ m. by Blagdon rd on Ponteland rd ✉ NE13 6BU – ☎ (01661) 860 686 – enquiries@horton-grange.co.uk – Fax (01661) 860 308

9 rm – †£ 95 ††£ 135 – **Rest** – (booking essential) Menu £ 18/23 – Carte dinner £ 23/39

◆ Attractive, personally run Edwardian country house with contemporary edge. Bedrooms in main house have more character and space than those in annex. Dine in pleasant conservatory overlooking ornamental garden.

at Cobalt Business Park Northeast : 8 m. by A 1058 - BV -, A 19 off A 191 – ✉ Newcastle upon Tyne

Village

Cobalt Business Park, West Allotment ✉ NE27 0BY – ☎ (0191) 270 1414 – village.newcastle@village-hotels.com – Fax (0191) 270 1515

157 rm – †£ 151 ††£ 161 – **Rest** – (dinner only and Sunday lunch) Carte £ 16/31

◆ A modern hotel on business park with an excellent, extensive and well-equipped leisure club. Bright, light and airy modern bedrooms. Popular menus in the grill restaurant, the village pub or the cafe in the leisure club.

at Ponteland Northwest : 8 ¼ m. by A 167 on A 696 - AV – ✉ Newcastle upon Tyne

Cafe Lowrey

33-35 Broadway, Darras Hall Estate, Southwest : 1 ½ m. by B 6323 and Darras Hall Estate rd ✉ NE20 9PW – ☎ (01661) 820 357 – Fax (01661) 820 357 – Closed 25-26 December, 1 January, Monday, dinner Sunday and Bank Holidays

Rest – (dinner only and lunch Saturday and Sunday) (booking essential) Carte £ 19/38

◆ Small restaurant in shopping parade with wooden chairs and cloth-laid tables. Blackboard menus offering modern British cooking using local produce.

NEWICK – E. Sussex – **504** U 31 – pop. 2 129 8 **A2**

London 57 m – Brighton 14 m – Eastbourne 20 m – Hastings 34 m – Maidstone 30 m

Newick Park

(heated), rm,

Southeast : 1 ½ m. following signs for Newick Park ✉ BN8 4SB – ☎ (01825) 723 633 – bookings@newickpark.co.uk – Fax (01825) 723 969

15 rm – †£ 125 ††£ 285 – 1 suite – **Rest** – (booking essential for non-residents) Menu £ 21/39

◆ Georgian manor in 200 acres; views of Longford river and South Downs. Stately hallway and lounge. Unique rooms, some with original fireplaces, all with Egyptian cotton sheets. Dine in relaxed formality on high-back crimson chairs.

272

20-22 High St ✉ BN8 4LQ – ☎ (01825) 721 272 – twoseventwo@hotmail.co.uk – Closed 25-26 December, 1 January, Monday, Sunday dinner and Tuesday lunch

Rest – Menu £ 15 (lunch) – Carte £ 24/38

◆ Well-run restaurant with an easy-going, relaxed feel. Chairs from Italy, modern art on walls. Frequently changing menus offer a winning blend of British and European flavours.

ENGLAND

NEWMARKET – Suffolk – 504 V 27 – pop. 16 947 14 B2

London 64 m – Cambridge 13 m – Ipswich 40 m – Norwich 48 m
Palace House, Palace St ✆ (01638) 667200
Links Cambridge Rd, ✆ (01638) 663 000 .

Rutland Arms

High St ✉ CB8 8NB – ✆ (01638) 664 251 – reservations.rutlandarms@ohiml.com – Fax (01638) 666 298

46 rm – £ 45/135 £ 65/170 – **Rest** – (bar lunch Monday-Saturday) Carte £ 18/33

◆ Constructed round a central courtyard, this Georgian coaching inn has warm interiors of patterned carpets and wallpapers. Bedrooms are similarly traditional. Rustic dining room with racing theme.

at Lidgate Southeast : 7 m. on B 1063 – ✉ Newmarket

The Star Inn

The Street ✉ CB8 9PP – ✆ (01638) 500 275 – Fax (01638) 500 275 – Closed 25-26 December, 1 January and Sunday dinner

Rest – Spanish Menu £ 13 – Carte £ 25/30

◆ Pink washed part 16C inn, oozing charm with beams and inglenooks, in pretty village. Original, predominantly Iberian menus: local game cooked in a hearty, fresh Spanish style.

at Six Mile Bottom Southwest : 6 m. on A 1304 – ✉ Newmarket

Swynford Paddocks

✉ CB8 0UE – ✆ (01638) 570 234 – events@swynfordpaddocks.com – Fax (01638) 570 283

15 rm – £ 110/135 £ 110/195 – **Rest** – Carte £ 26/40

◆ Hotel in pastures with a past: Lord Byron stayed here, penning poetry and having an affair with half-sister: their portraits on stairs. Elegant rooms. Softly lit, oak-panelled restaurant.

ENGLAND

Red = Pleasant. Look for the red and symbols.

NEWPORT – Shrops. – 502 M 25 18 B1

London 148 m – Stafford 12 m – Telford 9 m

The Fox

Pave Lane, Chetwynd Aston, South : 1½ m. by Wolverhampton rd (A 41) ✉ TF10 9LQ – ✆ (01952) 815 940 – fox@brunningandprice.co.uk – Fax (01952) 815 941 – Closed 26 December

Rest – Carte £ 18/27

◆ Updated pub with lawned garden and terrace. Light, airy interior: walls filled with old pictures and posters. Big tables predominate for family get-togethers. Modern menus.

NEWPORT PAGNELL – Milton Keynes – 504 R 27 – pop. 14 739 11 C1

London 57 m – Bedford 13 m – Luton 21 m – Northampton 15 m – Oxford 46 m

Plan : see Milton Keynes

Robinsons

18-20 St John St ✉ MK16 8HJ – ✆ (01908) 611 400 – info@robinsonsrestaurant.co.uk – Fax (01908) 216 900 – Closed 26 December, 1 January, Saturday lunch, Sunday and Bank Holidays CU **n**

Rest – Menu £ 19 (dinner) – Carte £ 28/32

◆ A bright façade defines sunny nature of Mediterranean style cuisine. An upbeat eatery in which to sample an eclectic blend of dishes which range from modern to traditional.

NEWQUAY – Cornwall – **503** E 32 – **pop. 19 562** 1 **A2**

▶ London 291 m – Exeter 83 m – Penzance 34 m – Plymouth 48 m – Truro 14 m
✈ Newquay Airport : ✆ (01637) 860600 Y
ℹ Municipal Offices, Marcus Hill ✆ (01637) 854020, info@newquay.co.uk
⛳18 Tower Rd, ✆ (01637) 872091 ; ⛳9 Treloy, ✆ (01637) 878554 ;
⛳18 Merlin Mawgan Porth, ✆ (01841) 540222 .
Penhale Point and Kelsey Head★ (⩽ ★★), SW : by A 3075 Y – Trerice★ AC, SE : 3 ½ m. by A 392 - Y - and A 3058. St Agnes - St Agnes Beacon★★ (✻ ★★), SW : 12½ m. by A 3075 - Y - and B 3285

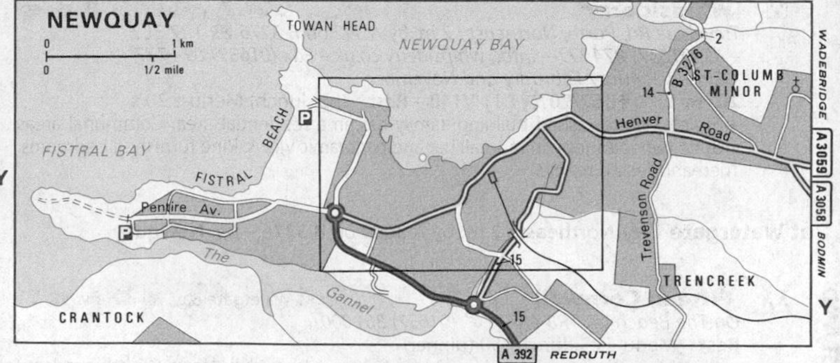

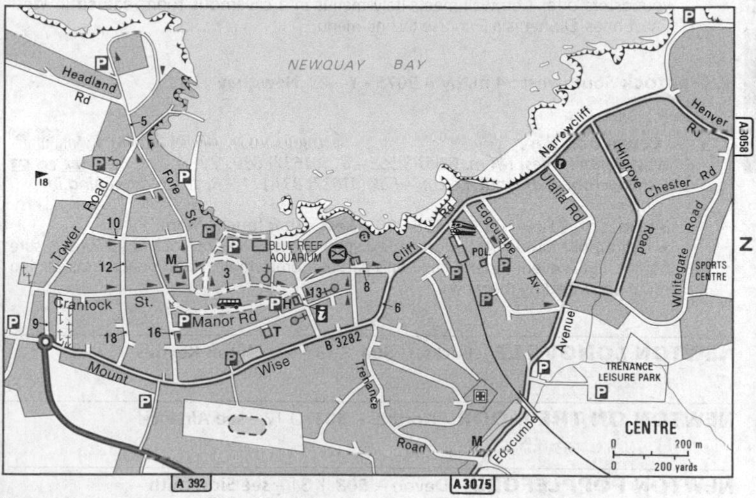

Alexandra Rd	**Y** 2	Fore St	**Z**	Porth Way	**Y** 14
Bank St.	**Z** 3	Higher Tower Rd	**Z** 9	St George Rd	**Z** 16
Beacon Rd	**Z** 5	Hope Terrace	**Z** 10	St John's Rd.	**Z** 18
Berry Rd	**Z** 6	Jubilee St	**Z** 12	Trevemper Rd	**Y** 15
East St	**Z** 8	Marcus Hill	**Z** 13		

Trebarwith

⩽ bay and coast,

Trebarwith Crescent ✉ *TR7 1BZ* – ✆ *(01637) 872288*
– enquiry@trebarwith-hotel.co.uk – Fax (01637) 875431 – April-October Z **a**

41 rm – †£ 39/80 ††£ 78/160 – **Rest** – (bar lunch) Menu £ 18 **s** – Carte £ 30/43

◆ Superb bay and coastline views from this renowned seaside hotel. Has its own cinema, plus evening discos and dances. You'll get the stunning vistas from traditional bedrooms. Dine by the sea beneath Wedgewood-style ceiling.

The Bristol

Narrowcliff ✉ TR7 2PQ – ✆ (01637) 870275 – info@hotelbristol.co.uk – Fax (01637) 879347 – Closed Christmas and New Year Z **r**

73 rm – ♦£ 80/115 ♦♦£ 140/150 – 1 suite – **Rest** – (bar lunch Monday-Saturday) Menu £ 15/23 **s** – Carte dinner £ 25/33 **s**

◆ Classic Victorian seaside hotel, well established and family run. Wide range of bedrooms from singles to family suites. Extensive conference facilities. Large windowed dining room overlooks Atlantic.

Whipsiderry

(heated)

Trevelgue Rd, Porth, Northeast : 2 m. by A 392 off B 3276 ✉ TR7 3LY – ✆ (01637) 874777 – info@whipsiderry.co.uk – Fax (01637) 874777 – Closed January-February and November

20 rm – ♦£ 57/70 ♦♦£ 114/140 – **Rest** – (bar lunch) Menu £ 20 **s**

◆ Simple, whitewashed building; family run, in a residential area. Communal areas include two lounges with a small bar and panoramic views. Pine furnished bedrooms. Tried-and-tested menus.

at Watergate Bay **Northeast : 3 m. by A 3059 on B 3276 – ✉ Newquay**

Fifteen Cornwall

Watergate Bay,

On The Beach ✉ TR8 4AA – ✆ (01637) 861000

Rest – Menu £ 25 (lunch)/50 (dinner)

◆ Phenomenally successful converted café in a golden idyll. Jamie Oliver's academy youngsters offer Cornwall-meets-Italy menus in a cavernous room bathed in West Coast hues. Dinner is a 5 course tasting menu.

at Crantock **Southwest : 4 m. by A 3075 - Y – ✉ Newquay**

Crantock Bay

Crantock Bay,

West Pentire, West : ¾ m. ✉ TR8 5SE – ✆ (01637) 830229 – stay@crantockbayhotel.co.uk – Fax (01637) 831111 – Restricted opening in winter

31 rm – ♦£ 69/105 ♦♦£ 138/210 – **Rest** – (bar lunch) Menu £ 24

◆ Delightfully sited hotel affording exceptional views of Crantock Bay. Good leisure facilities, gala evenings and children's parties. Comfortable, traditional rooms. Dining room enhanced by the views.

NEWTON LONGVILLE – **Bucks.** – **504** R 28 – **see Milton Keynes**

NEWTON ON THE MOOR – **Northd.** – **501** O 17 – **see Alnwick**

NEWTON POPPLEFORD – **Devon** – **503** K 31 – **see Sidmouth**

NOMANSLAND – Wilts. – 503 P 31 – ✉ Salisbury 4 D3

London 96 m – Bournemouth 26 m – Salisbury 13 m – Southampton 14 m – Winchester 25 m

Les Mirabelles

Forest Edge Rd ✉ SP5 2BN – ✆ (01794) 390205 – Fax (01794) 390106 – Closed 25 December-mid January, 1 week May-June, Sunday and Monday

Rest – French Carte £ 24/34

◆ Unpretentious little French restaurant overlooking the village common. Superb wine list. Extensive menu of good value, classic Gallic cuisine.

ENGLAND

NORTHALLERTON – N. Yorks. – 502 P 20 – pop. 15 517 22 B1

London 238 m – Leeds 48 m – Middlesbrough 24 m – Newcastle upon Tyne 56 m – York 33 m

Applegarth ✆ (0871) 7161924

at Staddlebridge Northeast : 7 ½ m. by A 684 on A 19 at junction with A 172 – ✉ Northallerton

McCoys Bistro at The Tontine with rm

on southbound carriageway (A 19) ✉ DL6 3JB – ✆ (01609) 882 671 – enquiries@mccoysatthetontine.co.uk – Fax (01609) 882 660 – closed 25-26 December and 1-3 January

6 rm – ♦£ 95 ♦♦£ 120 – **Rest** – (booking essential) Menu £ 17 (lunch) – Carte £ 28/45

◆ Yorkshire meets France in long-standing restaurant with mirrors, wood panelling, framed memorabilia. Snug bar to plot coups in. Large bedrooms, unique in decorative style.

at Newby Wiske South : 2 ½ m. by A 167 – ✉ Northallerton

Solberge Hall

Northwest : 1 ¼ m. on Warlaby rd ✉ DL7 9ER – ✆ (01609) 779 191 – reservations@solbergehall.co.uk – Fax (01609) 780 472

23 rm – ♦£ 80/90 ♦♦£ 120 – 1 suite

Rest – Menu £ 15/28

Rest *Silks* – Carte £ 22/32

◆ Tranquil grounds surround this graceful Georgian house, situated in the heart of the countryside. Popular for weddings; bedrooms in main house or stable block. Local ingredients well employed in flavoursome menus.

ENGLAND

Undecided between two equivalent establishments? Within each category, establishments are classified in our order of preference.

NORTHAMPTON – Northants. – 504 R 27 – pop. 189 474 16 B3

Great Britain

London 69 m – Cambridge 53 m – Coventry 34 m – Leicester 42 m – Luton 35 m – Oxford 41 m

Sessions House ✆ (01604) 622677, northampton.tic@northamptonshireenterprise.ltd.uk

27 Delapre Nene Valley Way, Eagle Drive, ✆ (01604) 764 036 ;

18 Collingtree Park Windingbrook Lane, ✆ (01604) 700 000 .

All Saints, Brixworth★, N : 7 m. on A 508 Y

Plan on next page

Northampton Marriott

Eagle Drive, Southeast : 2 m. by A 428 off A 45 ✉ NN4 7HW – ✆ (01604) 768 700 – Fax (01604) 769 011 Z a

120 rm – ♦£ 135 ♦♦£ 135/185, £15 –

Rest – (Closed Saturday lunch) Menu £ 15 (lunch) **s** – Carte dinner £ 20/40 **s**

◆ Modern hotel in riverside setting. Neat trim rooms, very practical, with well-lit work desks, some have disabled facilities and sofa beds. Silverstone race track is nearby. Pleasing dining room with bright brasserie feel.

NORTHAMPTON

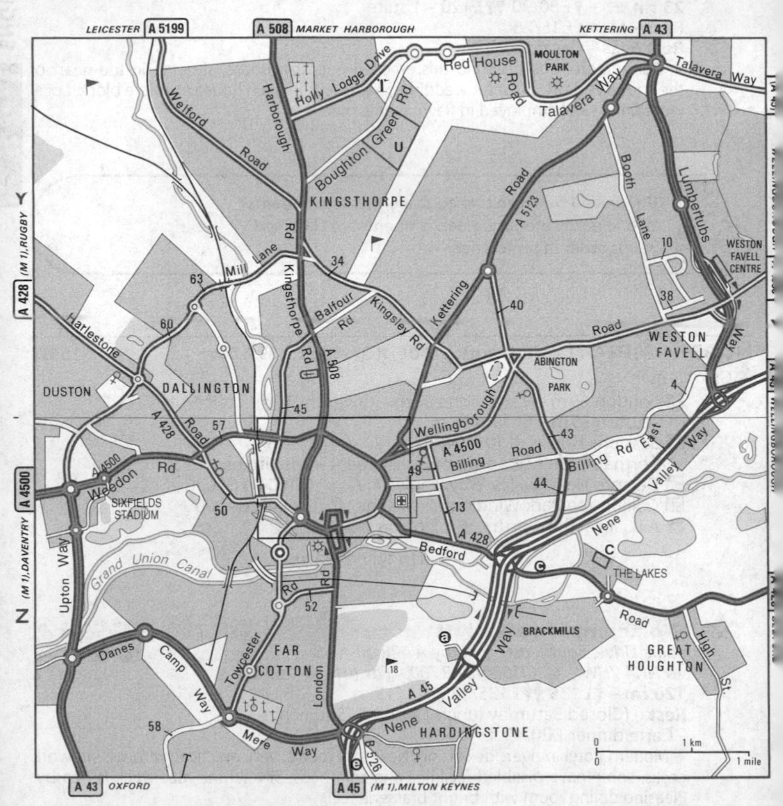

Holiday Inn Northampton
Bedford Rd, Southeast : 1 ½ m. on A 428 ✉ NN4 7YF – ✆ (01604) 622 777 – Fax (01604) 604 544 Z c
104 rm – †£ 110/130 ††£ 130/150, ☕ £13.95 – **Rest** – ✆ (0870) 400 72 14 – Menu £ 10/18 **s** – Carte £ 20/29 **s**
◆ Purpose-built, modern hotel. Smart interior with a branded style. Comfortable bedrooms are simply appointed and well-kept. Suited to business and leisure travellers. Relaxing restaurant and adjacent lounge.

NORTH BOVEY – Devon – 503 I 32 – ✉ Newton Abbot 2 C2

London 214 m – Exeter 13 m – Plymouth 34 m – Torquay 21 m
Dartmoor National Park★★

Bovey Castle
West : 1 m. on B 3212 ✉ TQ13 8RE – ✆ (01647) 445 000 – enquiries@boveycastle.com – Fax (01647) 445 020
61 rm ☕ – †£ 175/250 ††£ 250/875 – 25 suites
Rest *Palm Court* – (dinner only and Sunday lunch) (booking essential for non-residents) Menu £ 39 – Carte approx. £ 53 **s**
Rest *Bistro* – Carte £ 23/39
◆ Stunningly opulent property: castle and sporting estate set in beautiful grounds with incomparable leisure facilities, awesome Cathedral Room and sumptuous, stylish bedrooms. Formal, cloth-clad Palm Court. Relaxed Club House includes a golf shop!

The Gate House without rest 

just off village green, past "Ring of Bells" public house ✉ TQ13 8RB – ✆ (01647) 440 479 – srw.gatehouse@virgin.net – Fax (01647) 440 479 – Closed 24-26 December
3 rm ☕ – †£ 50 ††£ 76
◆ 15C white Devon hallhouse; picturebook pretty with thatched roof, pink climbing rose. Country style rooms; some have views of moor. Large granite fireplace in sitting room.

Look out for red symbols, indicating particularly pleasant establishments.

NORTH CERNEY – Glos. – 503 – see Cirencester

NORTH CHARLTON – Northd. – 501 O 17 – see Alnwick

NORTH HINKSEY – Oxon. – 504 Q 28 – see Oxford

NORTH KILWORTH – Leics. 16 B3

London 95 m – Leicester 20 m – Market Harborough 9 m

Kilworth House
Lutterworth Rd, West : ½ m. on A 4304 ✉ LE17 6JE – ✆ (01858) 880 058 – info@kilworthhouse.co.uk – Fax (01858) 880 349
41 rm – †£ 140 ††£ 200, ☕ £14 – 3 suites
Rest *The Wordsworth* – (dinner only) Carte £ 29/51
Rest *The Orangery* – Carte £ 22/30
◆ 19C extended house set in 38 acres of parkland, with original staircase, stained glass windows and open air theatre. Individually appointed rooms, some with commanding views. Ornate Wordsworth with courtyard vista. Light meals in beautiful Orangery.

NORTH NEWINGTON – Oxon. – see Banbury

NORTHREPPS – Norfolk – 504 Y 25 – see Cromer

ENGLAND

NORTH WALSHAM – Norfolk – 503 Y 25 – pop. 11 845 *Great Britain* 15 **D1**

London 125 m – Norwich 16 m
Blicking Hall★★ **AC**, W : 8½ m. by B 1145, A 140 and B 1354

Beechwood

20 Cromer Rd NR28 0HD – (01692) 403 231
– enquiries@beechwood-hotel.co.uk – Fax (01692) 407 284
17 rm – £ 72 £ 90/160 – **Rest** – (dinner only and Sunday lunch)
Menu £ 20/34 **s**
◆ Privately owned, peacefully set, part 19C hotel where Agatha Christie once stayed. Attentive service, as typified by tea and biscuits on arrival. Thoughtfully appointed rooms. Handsome dining room with flowers.

at Knapton Northeast : 3 m. on B 1145 – North Walsham

White House Farm without rest

NR28 0RX – (01263) 721 344 – info@whitehousefarmnorfolk.co.uk
3 rm – £ 55 £ 70
◆ 18C brick and flint farmhouse. Spacious lounge with many books. Breakfast of local produce. Comfortable, modern, well-kept bedrooms.

The ✿ award is the crème de la crème.
This is awarded to restaurants
which are really worth travelling miles for!

ENGLAND

NORTON – Shrops. – see Telford

NORTON ST PHILIP – Somerset – 503 N 30 – Bath 4 **C2**

London 113 m – Bristol 22 m – Southampton 55 m – Swindon 40 m

Bath Lodge without rest

East : 1 ¼ m. by A 366 on A 36 BA2 7NH – (01225) 723 040
– info@bathlodge.com – Fax (01225) 723 737
7 rm – £ 60/85 £ 130/145
◆ Grade II listed lodge with a charming exterior of towers and battlements once served as a gatehouse to the Farleigh estate. Country house décor, spacious, comfortable rooms.

The Plaine without rest

BA2 7LT – (01373) 834 723 – enquiries@theplaine.co.uk
– Fax (01373) 834 101
3 rm – £ 55/75 £ 60/95
◆ 16C stone cottages opposite George Inn on site of original market place. Beams, stone walls denote historic origins. Four-posters, pine furnishings in bedrooms. Family run.

NORWICH – Norfolk – 504 Y 26 – pop. 174 047 *Great Britain* 15 **D2**

London 109 m – Kingston-upon-Hull 148 m – Leicester 117 m – Nottingham 120 m
Norwich Airport : (01603) 411923, N : 3½ m. by A 140 V
The Forum, Millennium Plain (01603) 727927
Royal Norwich Hellesdon Drayton High Rd, (01603) 425 712 ;
Marriott Sprowston Manor Hotel Wroxham Rd, (0870) 400 72 29 ;
Costessy Park Costessey, (01603) 746 333 ;
Bawburgh Marlingford Rd, Glen Lodge, (01603) 740 404 .
City★★ - Cathedral★★ Y – Castle (Museum and Art Gallery★ **AC**) Z – Market Place★ Z
Sainsbury Centre for Visual Arts★ **AC**, W : 3 m. by B 1108 X. Blicking Hall★★ **AC**, N : 11 m. by A 140 - V - and B 1354 – NE : Norfolk Broads★

Plan on next page

Marriott Sprowston Manor H. & Country Club

rm, rest,

Wroxham Rd, Northeast : 3¼ m. on A 1151 ✉ NR7 8RP – ✆ (01603) 410871 – Fax (01603) 423911

93 rm – ☨£ 99/350 ☨☨£ 99/350 – 1 suite

Rest *Manor* – (Closed Sunday dinner) (dinner only and Sunday lunch) Menu £ 25 – Carte £ 20/55

◆ Part Elizabethan manor house set in 10 acres of parkland and golf course. Pleasant lounge. Extensive leisure facilities. Many of the bedrooms overlook the picturesque grounds. Restaurant with Gothic arched windows, ancient mahogany columns and oil paintings.

St Giles House

rm,

41-45 St Giles St ✉ NR2 1JR – ✆ (01603) 275180 – info@stgileshouse.com YZ **o**

22 rm – ☨£ 120 ☨☨£ 350, £14.95 – 1 suite – **Rest** – Carte £ 28/36

◆ Boutique hotel with impressive façade in heart of old town. Superb art deco interior with open plan bar/lounge. Individually decorated bedrooms boast modern facilities. Brasserie style menu.

Beeches

2-6 Earlham Rd ✉ NR2 3DB – ✆ (01603) 621167 – beeches@mjbhotels.com – Fax (01603) 620151 VX **e**

42 rm – ☨£ 74/79 ☨☨£ 81/95 – 1 suite – **Rest** – (dinner only and Sunday lunch) Menu £ 25

◆ Personally run series of Grade II listed properties overlooking terraced Victorian gardens. Spacious rooms may have Cathedral views. Popular with business guests. Dining room with Plantation Garden outlook.

Annesley House

6 Newmarket Rd ✉ NR2 2LA – ✆ (01603) 624553 – annesleyhouse@bestwestern.co.uk – Fax (01603) 621577 Closed 22 December 3 January Z **c**

26 rm – ☨£ 90/100 ☨☨£ 115 – **Rest** – (light lunch) Menu £ 25

◆ A relaxed atmosphere prevails at this established hotel set in a pair of Georgian houses. Some of the generously proportioned bedrooms overlook the feature water garden. Conservatory restaurant.

Catton Old Hall without rest

Lodge Lane, Old Catton, North : 3¼ m. by Catton Grove Rd and St Faiths Rd ✉ NR6 7HG – ✆ (01603) 419379 – enquiries@catton-hall.co.uk – Fax (01603) 400339

7 rm – ☨£ 75/85 ☨☨£ 100/120

◆ 17C flint fronted farmhouse in a residential area. Antique furnished lounge with log fire. Individually and attractively furnished rooms have plenty of thoughtful extras.

Beaufort Lodge without rest

62 Earlham Rd ✉ NR2 3DF – ✆ (01603) 627928 – beaufortlodge@aol.com VX **a**

4 rm – ☨£ 55/60 ☨☨£ 70

◆ A pretty Victorian terraced house within walking distance of the Market Place. Comfortable, good-sized bedrooms in modern pine. Spacious breakfast room and bright conservatory.

Arbor Linden Lodge without rest

557 Earlham Rd ✉ NR4 7HW – ✆ (01603) 451303 – info@guesthousenorwich.com – Fax (01603) 479793 X **r**

6 rm – ☨£ 40/45 ☨☨£ 60

◆ Close to both university and hospitals. Friendly and family run guesthouse. Enjoy a relaxed breakfast in the conservatory. Clean, comfortable bedrooms.

ENGLAND

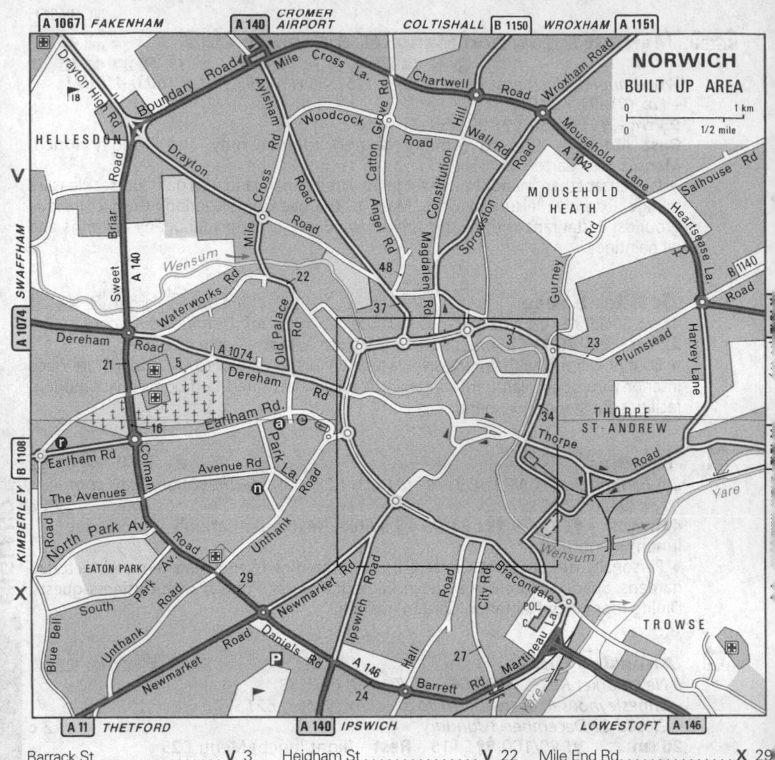

Barrack St	V 3	Heigham St	V 22	Mile End Rd	X 29
Bowthorpe Rd	V 5	Ketts Hill	V 23	Riverside Rd	V 34
Farrow Rd	V 16	Lakenham Rd	X 24	St Augustine's St	V 37
Guardian Rd	V 21	Long John Hill	X 27	Waterloo Rd	V 48

XX **By Appointment** with rm

25-29 St Georges St ✉ NR3 1AB – ✆ (01603) 630 730 – puttii@tiscali.co.uk – Fax (01603) 630 730 – Closed 25 December Y **a**

5 rm – †£ 70/85 ††£ 130 – **Rest** – (Closed Sunday-Monday) (dinner only) Carte £ 33/36

◆ Pretty, antique furnished restaurant. Interesting, traditional dishes off blackboard with theatrical service. Characterful bedrooms include a host of thoughtful extras.

X **Tatler's**

21 Tombland ✉ NR3 1RF – ✆ (01603) 766 670 – info@tatlers.com – Fax (01603) 766 625 – Closed Sunday and Bank Holidays Y **n**

Rest – Menu £ 12 (lunch) – Carte £ 30/34

◆ Georgian townhouse near cathedral comprising small rooms on several floors set off by period detail. Relaxed atmosphere. Modern menu; inventive cooking using local produce.

X **St Benedicts**

9 St Benedicts St ✉ NR2 4PE – ✆ (01603) 765 377 – jayner@talktalk.net – Fax (01603) 624 541 – Closed 25-31 December, Sunday and Monday Y **v**

Rest – Menu £ 10/17 – Carte £ 20/24

◆ Informal and personally run bistro. Interesting menus of both traditional British and adventurous heart-warming dishes. Booking advisable for dinner.

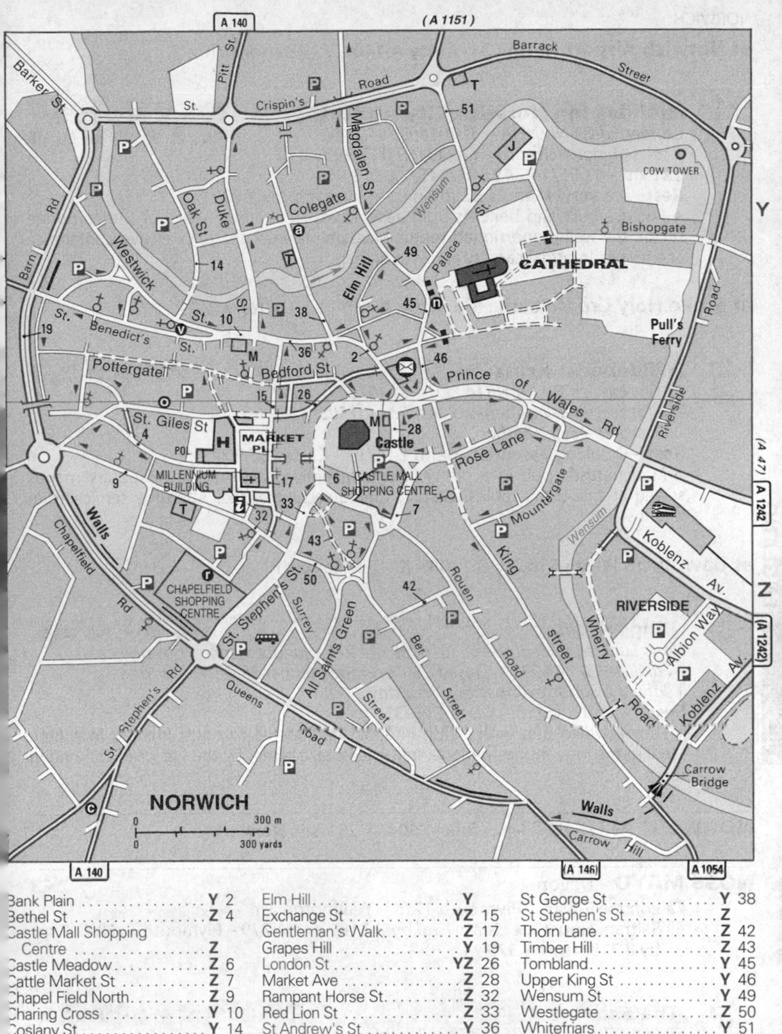

1 Up at the Mad Moose Arms

2 Warwick St, off Dover St ✉ NR2 3LD – ✆ (01603) 627 687 – madmoose@animalinns.co.uk – closed 25 December and Sunday dinner X **n**

Rest – (dinner only and Sunday lunch) Menu 21 – Carte £ 17/26

◆ Enjoy the relaxed atmosphere in this converted Victorian pub. Friendly service, occasional live music. Rustic and modern food guarantees great choice in the menus.

Mackintosh's Canteen

Unit 410, Chapelfield Plain ✉ NR2 1SZ – ✆ (01603) 305 280 – info@mackintoshscanteen.co.uk – Fax (01603) 305 281 Z **r**

Rest – Carte £ 21/35

◆ Stylish and modern; an oasis for shoppers. Bright and airy upstairs with leather banquettes, open kitchen and floor to ceiling windows. Modern cooking; interesting specials.

at Norwich Airport North : 3 ½ m. by A 140 - V – ✉ Norwich

Holiday Inn Norwich City Airport
Cromer Rd ✉ NR6 6JA – ✆ (01603) 410 544 – sales@hinorwich.com – Fax (01603) 789 935
121 rm – £ 95/145 £ 95/145, ☕ £ 13.95 –
Rest – (carvery) Menu £ 22 (dinner) – Carte approx. £ 22 **s**
◆ Purpose built and benefits from easy access to terminal. Aimed at the corporate sector, the well-proportioned rooms have ample work space. Extensive conference and leisure. Informal carvery and lounge bar.

at Stoke Holy Cross South : 5 ¾ m. by A 140 - X – ✉ Norwich

Wildebeest Arms
82-86 Norwich Rd ✉ NR14 8QJ – ✆ (01508) 492 497 – wildebeestl@animalinns.co.uk – Fax (01508) 494 946 – Closed 25-26 December
Rest – (booking essential) Menu £ 16/19 – Carte £ 25/32
◆ Modern-rustic pub in a pretty village. Inventive, seasonal, contemporary menus served at tree-trunk tables. Garden dining recommended. Attentive service from bright staff.

ENGLAND

at Bawburgh West : 5 m. by B 1108 - X – ✉ Norwich

Kings Head
Harts Lane ✉ NR9 3LS – ✆ (01603) 744 977 – jandncatering@hotmail.co.uk – Fax (01603) 744 990 – Closed 26 December, dinner 25 December and 1 January, Sunday dinner and Monday
Rest – Menu £ 15/18 – Carte £ 23/35
◆ Family-owned pub with stylish interior, its timbered bar most inviting in winter. Modern menu with international influences: take a seat by the fire or in the dining room.

NORWICH AIRPORT – Norfolk – 504 X 25 – see Norwich

NOSS MAYO – Devon 2 C3

London 242 m – Plymouth 12 m – Yealmpton 3 m
Saltram House★★, NW : 7 m. by B 3186 and A 379 – Plymouth★, NW : 9 m. by B 3186 and A 379

The Ship Inn
✉ PL8 1EW – ✆ (01752) 872 387 – ship@nossmayo.com – Fax (01752) 873 294
Rest – Carte £ 20/30
◆ On two floors with a terrific terrace; beside the water in delightful coastal village. Oldest part dates from 1700s. Extensive menus from the simple to the adventurous.

The red symbol?
This denotes the very essence of peace
– only the sound of birdsong first thing in the morning ...

London 135 m – Birmingham 50 m – Leeds 74 m – Leicester 27 m – Manchester 72 m

Nottingham East Midlands Airport, Castle Donington : (0871) 9199000 SW : 15 m. by A 453 AZ

1-4 Smithy Row (0115) 915 5330, touristinfo@nottinghamcity.gov.uk - at West Bridgford: County Hall, Loughborough Rd (0115) 977 4401

Bulwell Forest Hucknall Rd, (0115) 977 0576 ;
Wollaton Park, (0115) 978 7574 ;
Mapperley Central Ave, Plains Rd, (0115) 955 6672 ;
Nottingham City Bulwell Lawton Drive, (0115) 927 6916 ;
Beeston Fields Beeston, (0115) 925 7062 ;
Ruddington Grange Ruddington Wilford Rd, (0115) 984 6141 ;
Edwalton, (0115) 923 4775 ;
Cotgrave Place G. & C.C. Stragglethorpe, (0115) 933 3344 .

Castle Museum★ (alabasters★) **AC**, CZ **M**

Wollaton Hall★ **AC**, W : 2½ m. by Ilkeston Rd, A 609 AZ **M.** Southwell Minster★★, NE : 14 m. by A 612 BZ - Newstead Abbey★ **AC**, N : 11 m. by A 60, A 611 - AY - and B 683 – Mr Straw's House★, Worksop, N : 20 m. signed from B 6045 (past Bassetlaw Hospital) – St Mary Magdalene★, Newark-on-Trent, NE : 20 m. by A 612 BZ

Plan on next page

Park Plaza

rm, VISA

41 Maid Marian Way NG1 6GD – (0115) 947 7200 – info@parkplazanottingham.com – Fax (0115) 947 7300 CY **v**

177 rm – £ 155 £ 155, £ 12 – 1 suite

Rest *Chino Latino* – Pan Asian (Closed Sunday and Bank Holidays) Carte £ 32/54 **s**

◆ Converted city centre office block with stylish and contemporary decor. Choice of meeting rooms. Spacious stylish bedrooms with many extras. Formal Chino Latino Japanese restaurant.

Welbeck

rm, VISA

Talbot St NG1 5GS – (0115) 841 1000 – info@welbeck-hotel.co.uk – Fax (0115) 841 1001 – Closed Christmas CY **s**

96 rm – £ 115 £ 115, £ 9.75 – **Rest** – (Closed Sunday dinner) Menu £ 15 (lunch) – Carte £ 15/30

◆ Bright modern hotel in city centre close to theatre. Colourful cushions and pared-down style in bedrooms. Three conference rooms for hire. Fifth floor dining room gives fine views of city.

Hart's

VISA

Standard Hill, Park Row NG1 6FN – (0115) 988 1900 – ask@hartsnottingham.co.uk – Fax (0115) 947 7600 CZ **e**

30 rm – £ 120 £ 120, £ 13.50 – 2 suites

Rest *Harts* – see restaurant listing

◆ Stylish modern hotel. Breakfast in contemporary style bar serving light snacks. Modern bedrooms; ground floor rooms open onto patio; good views from higher floors.

Lace Market

VISA

29-31 High Pavement NG1 1HE – (0115) 852 3232 – stay@lacemarkethotel.co.uk – Fax (0115) 852 3223 – closed 24-27 December DZ **a**

42 rm – £ 95/119 £ 119/239, £ 14.95

Rest *Merchants* – see restaurant listing

◆ Located in old lacemaking quarter, but nothing lacy about interiors; crisp rooms with minimalist designs, unpatterned fabrics. A stylish place to rest one's head.

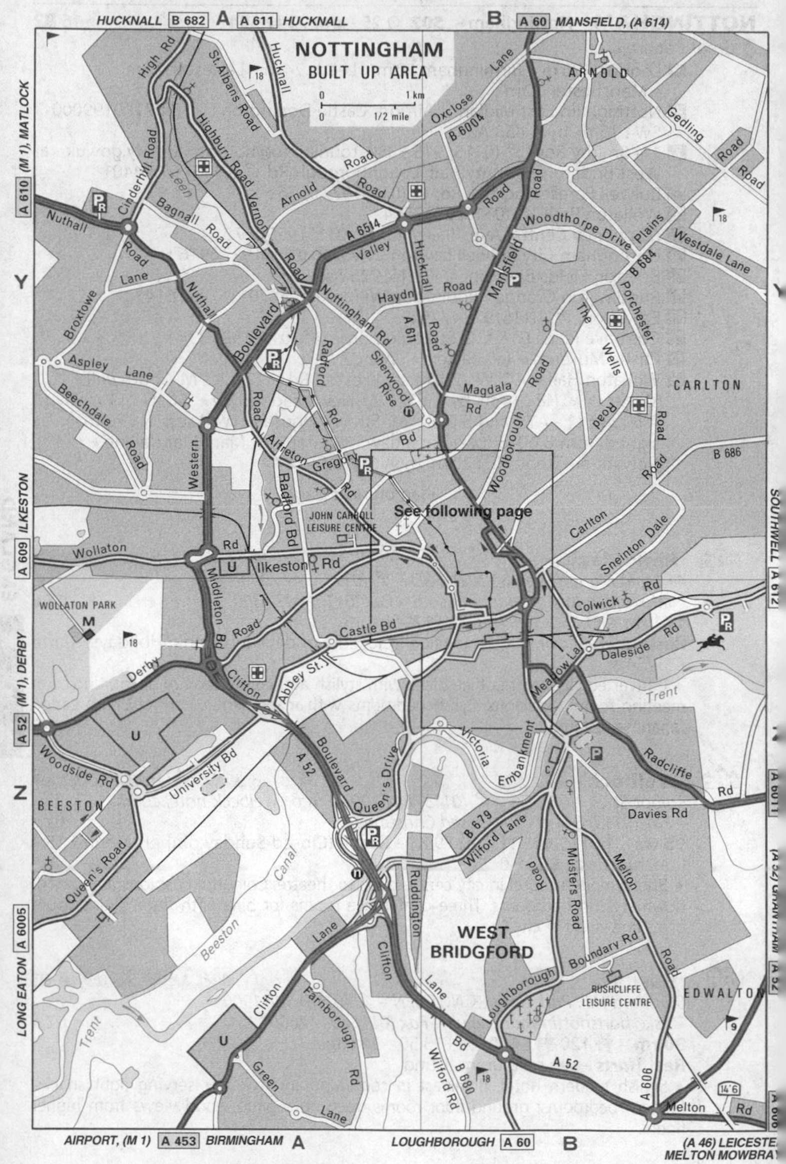

Greenwood Lodge City without rest

5 Third Ave, Sherwood Rise ✉ *NG7 6JH – ✆ (0115) 962 1206*
– pdouglas71@aol.com – Fax (0115) 962 1206 – Closed 24-28 December AY **n**

6 rm – †£ 45/60 ††£ 90

♦ Regency house with elegant reception offset by paintings, antiques. Conservatory breakfast room from which to view birdlife. Period beds, lovely fabrics in pretty rooms.

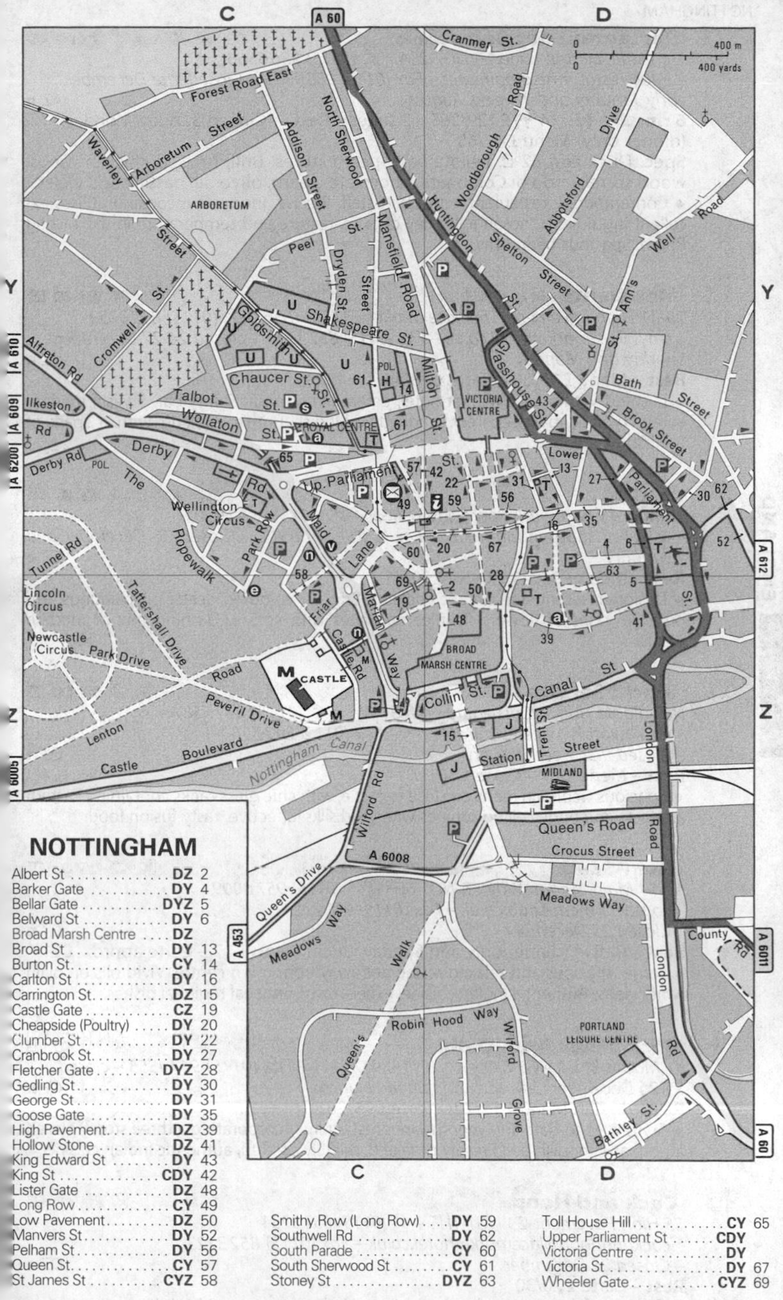

NOTTINGHAM

Albert St . . . . DZ 2
Barker Gate . . . . DY 4
Bellar Gate . . . . DYZ 5
Belward St . . . . DY 6
Broad Marsh Centre . . . . DZ
Broad St . . . . DY 13
Burton St. . . . . CY 14
Carlton St . . . . DY 16
Carrington St. . . . . DZ 15
Castle Gate . . . . CZ 19
Cheapside (Poultry) . . . . . DY 20
Clumber St . . . . DY 22
Cranbrook St. . . . . DY 27
Fletcher Gate . . . . DYZ 28
Gedling St . . . . DY 30
George St . . . . DY 31
Goose Gate . . . . DY 35
High Pavement . . . . DZ 39
Hollow Stone . . . . DZ 41
King Edward St . . . . DY 43
King St . . . . CDY 42
Lister Gate . . . . DZ 48
Long Row . . . . CY 49
Low Pavement . . . . DZ 50
Manvers St . . . . DY 52
Pelham St . . . . DY 56
Queen St. . . . . CY 57
St James St . . . . CYZ 58
Smithy Row (Long Row) . . . . DY 59
Southwell Rd . . . . DY 62
South Parade . . . . CY 60
South Sherwood St . . . . CY 61
Stoney St . . . . DYZ 63
Toll House Hill . . . . CY 65
Upper Parliament St . . . . . . CDY
Victoria Centre . . . . DY
Victoria St . . . . DY 67
Wheeler Gate . . . . CYZ 69

Restaurant Sat Bains with rm

Trentside, Lenton Lane ✉ NG7 2SA – ☎ (0115) 986 6566 – info@restaurantsatbains.net – Fax (0115) 986 0343 – Closed late December-early January and 2 weeks August AZ **n**

6 rm – †£ 114 ††£ 129/265 – 2 suites – **Rest** – (Closed Sunday-Monday) (dinner only) Menu £ 47/65

Spec. Duck egg 62°C, Bellota ham, pea textures. Brill, braised chicken wings, wood sorrel, lardo di Colonnata. Chocolate cream, olive oil, pastille and violets.

◆ Contemporary restaurant with smart staff. Precise, innovative cooking utilises excellent ingredients; go on a journey of taste, texture and temperature in the Tasting Room. Spacious bedrooms.

Merchants – at Lace Market H.

29-31 High Pavement, The Lace Market ✉ NG1 1HE – ☎ (0115) 852 3232 – stay@lacemarkethotel.co.uk – Fax (0115) 852 3223 – closed 24-27 December, Sunday and Monday DZ **a**

Rest – Menu £ 15/30 – Carte £ 28/46

◆ Located within Lace Market hotel, entered via trendy Saints bar. Stylish, modern eatery typified by deep red banquettes. Modish British cooking with a spark of originality.

Hart's

Standard Court, Park Row ✉ NG1 6GN – ☎ (0115) 988 1900 – ask@hartsnottingham.co.uk – Fax (0115) 911 0611 – Closed 26 December and 1 January CZ **e**

Rest – Menu £ 16/23 – Carte £ 30/41

◆ Designer setting for vibrant cooking. Brightly coloured seats, oil paintings, impressive vases of flowers. Truffles on plates with coffee. Dashing mix of modern meals.

World Service

Newdigate House, Castlegate ✉ NG1 6AF – ☎ (0115) 847 5587 – info@worldservicerestaurant.com – Fax (0115) 847 5584 – Closed first week January CZ **n**

Rest – Menu £ 17 – Carte £ 30/37

◆ Spacious Georgian mansion close to castle, with chic glass tanks containing Eastern artefacts and huge ceiling squares with vivid silks. Effective, tasty fusion food.

Mem-Saab

12-14 Maid Marian Way ✉ NG1 6HS – ☎ (0115) 957 0009 – contact@mem-saab.co.uk – Fax (0115) 941 2724 – Closed 25 December CY **n**

Rest – Indian (dinner only and Sunday lunch) Menu £ 17 – Carte approx. £ 21

◆ Large, spacious and relaxed restaurant away from town centre. Vivid oils on plain white walls. Authentic Indian cuisine: expect tasty, unusual regional dishes.

4550 Miles from Delhi

41 Mount St ✉ NG1 6HE – ☎ (0115) 947 5111 – Fax (0115) 947 4555 – closed 25-26 December, Saturday and Sunday lunch CY **n**

Rest – Indian Menu £ 17/22 – Carte £ 15/26

◆ Stylish, up-to-date and very spacious restaurant incorporating a three storey glazed atrium and modish bar. Freshly prepared, skilfully cooked, authentic Indian cuisine.

Cock and Hoop

25 High Pavement ✉ NG1 1HE – ☎ (0115) 852 3231 – cockandhoop@lacemarkethotel.co.uk – Fax (0115) 852 3223 – Closed 25 December DZ **a**

Rest – Carte £ 20/30

◆ Characterful pub in redeveloped Lace Market quarter, with mullioned windows, panelled walls, zinc-topped bar and vaulted ceiling. Pub favourites come in satisfying portions.

ENGLAND

at Plumtree **Southeast : 5 ¾ m. by A 60 - BZ - off A 606 – ✉ Nottingham**

XX **Perkins**

Old Railway Station, Station Rd ✉ NG12 5NA – ✆ (0115) 937 3695 – info@perkinsrestaurant.co.uk – Fax (0115) 937 6405 – Closed 1-4 January, Sunday dinner and Monday
Rest – Carte £ 24/32
◆ Longstanding restaurant named after owners; once a railway station. Dine in conservatory or relax in bar, a former waiting room. Classical cooking makes use of local ingredients.

at Beeston **Southwest : 4 ¼ m. on A 6005 - AZ – ✉ Nottingham**

Village H. & Leisure Club rm, rest,

Brailsford Way, Chilwell Meadows, Chilwell Retail Park, Southwest : 2 ¾ m. by A 6005 ✉ NG9 6DL – ✆ (0115) 946 4422 – village.nottingham@village-hotels.com – Fax (0115) 946 4428
135 rm – †£ 79/119 ††£ 89/129 – **Rest** – (dinner only and Sunday lunch) Carte £ 19/37 **s**
◆ Modern hotel with impressive leisure facilities: large pool, toning tables, cardio vascular area, gym, squash courts. After exercising, unwind in neat, comfortable rooms. A couple of traditionally based restaurant alternatives.

at Sherwood Business Park **Northwest : 10 m. by A 611 - AY - off A 608 – ✉ Nottingham**

Dakota rm,

Lakeview Drive ✉ NG15 0DA – ✆ (0870) 442 27 27 – enquiries@dakotahotels.co.uk – Fax (01623) 727 677
92 rm – †£ 99 ††£ 99, £ 9.95
Rest *Grill* – (bar lunch Saturday) Carte £ 25/30
◆ Hard-to-miss hotel just off the M1 - it's a big black cube! Lobby with plush sofas, bookshelves and Dakota aircraft montage. Spacious rooms with kingsize beds and plasma TVs. Modern British grill style menus.

at Stapleford **Southwest : 5 1/2 m. by A 52 - AZ - ✉ Nottingham**

XX **Crème**

12 Toton Lane ✉ NG9 7HA – ✆ (0115) 939 7422 – Fax (0115) 939 7453 – Closed last week June, 1st week July, 26 December-2 January, Saturday lunch, Sunday dinner and Monday
Rest – Menu £ 15 (lunch) – Carte £ 23/35
◆ Smart, well run restaurant offering well-presented, modern British cooking served by friendly staff. Long lounge area with comfy sofas; airy, formally-laid dining room.

NOTTINGHAM EAST MIDLANDS AIRPORT – Leics. – 16 **B2**
502 P/Q 25 – ✉ **Derby**

London 125 m – Birmingham 40 m – Derby 13 m – Leicester 24 m – Nottingham 15 m

Thistle East Midlands Airport rm,

✉ DE74 2SH – ✆ (0870) 333 9132 – reservations.eastmidlandsairport@thistle.co.uk – Fax (0870) 333 9232
164 rm – †£ 235 ††£ 235, £ 14.95 – **Rest** – (Closed Sunday lunch) Menu £ 15/25 – Carte £ 26/32 **s**
◆ Spacious and carefully designed modern, purpose-built hotel on the airport doorstep. Rooms are smart and bright with contemporary furnishings. Light, airy dining room; popular menu suiting all tastes.

NUNEATON – Warks – **503** P 26 – **pop. 119 132** 19 **D2**

London 102 m – Birmingham 25 m – Coventry 17 m

Leathermill Grange

Leathermill Lane, Caldecote, Northwest : 3½ m. by B 4114 on B 4111
✉ CV10 0RX – ✆ (01827) 714637 – davidcodd@leathermillgrange.co.uk
– Fax (01827) 716422 – Closed Christmas-New Year and mid July-mid August
3 rm – †£ 60 ††£ 90 – **Rest** – (by arrangement, communal dining)
Menu £ 25

◆ Imposing Victorian farmhouse in peaceful rural spot. Spacious, spotless bedrooms - one four poster. Homebaking and tea on arrival. Guest lounge and conservatory with garden view. Meals homecooked on Aga use fruit and vegetables grown in garden. Fine tableware.

OAKHAM – Rutland – **502** R 25 – **pop. 9 620** *Great Britain* 17 **C2**

London 103 m – Leicester 26 m – Northampton 35 m – Nottingham 28 m
Rutland County Museum, Catmose St ✆ (01572) 758441
Oakham Castle ★
Rutland Water ★, E : by A 606 – Normanton Church ★ **AC**, SE : 5 m. by A 603 and minor road East

Barnsdale Lodge rm, VISA AE

The Avenue, Rutland Water, East : 2½ m. on A 606 ✉ LE15 8AH
– ✆ (01572) 724678 – reservations@barnsdalelodge.co.uk – Fax (01572) 724961
44 rm – †£ 75/105 ††£ 85/125
Rest *Restaurant* – Menu £ 15 (lunch) – Carte £ 22/30

◆ Privately owned, converted farmhouse with mature gardens. Ample, modern rooms, a large bar flagged in York stone and extensive meeting facilities in renovated stables. Flavours of the season to fore in the Restaurant.

The Whipper-In VISA AE

Market Pl ✉ LE15 6WT – ✆ (01572) 756971 – whipper.in@brook-hotels.co.uk
– Fax (01572) 757759
24 rm – †£ 75/128 ††£ 85 – **Rest** – Menu £ 20 (dinner) – Carte £ 21/33

◆ 17C inn on market square with coaching yard and traditional feel. Bedrooms in understated country style, named after local hunts. Firelit lounge with inviting armchairs. Formal dining in restaurant.

Lord Nelson's House H. and Nicks Restaurant with rm

Market Pl ✉ LE15 6DT – ✆ (01572) 723199 VISA AE
– simon@nicksrestaurant.co.uk – Fax (01572) 723199 – closed 25-26 December, Monday and Sunday dinner
4 rm – †£ 80 ††£ 95 – **Rest** – Carte £ 27/45 **s**

◆ Imaginative modern interiors in 17C town house: choose nautical dark wood, zebra-skin throws or an elegant chaise longue. Classic seasonal dishes with a flavourful flourish.

at Hambleton East : 3 m. by A 606 – ✉ Oakham

Hambleton Hall ← Rutland Water, (heated)

✉ LE15 8TH – ✆ (01572) 756991 VISA AE
– hotel@hambletonhall.com – Fax (01572) 724721
16 rm – †£ 170/200 ††£ 300/365, £ 14 – 1 suite – **Rest** – Menu £ 35/40
– Carte £ 58/78

Spec. Seared scallops with orange and carrot velouté flavoured with vanilla. Fillet of beef with slow roast onion and petit chou farci. Poached peach with raspberries and lavender.

◆ Beautiful Victorian manor house with gardens, still run by its founding family. Lovingly appointed period interiors and immaculate, antique filled bedrooms. Daily changing, seasonal menus offer accomplished classical dishes. Faultless service.

ENGLAND

Finch's Arms with rm
Ketton Rd ✉ LE15 8TL – ✆ (01572) 756 575 – finchsarms@talk21.com – Fax (01572) 771 142 – Closed 25 December
6 rm – ♦£65 ♦♦£75 – **Rest** – Menu £ 14/16 – Carte £ 14/20
◆ Sandstone pub overlooking Rutland Water: rustic interior, flagged floors, rattan chairs. Real ales accompany tasty modern menus, brimming with Asian flavours. Cosy bedrooms.

OAKSEY – Wilts. – **503** N 29 4 **C1**
London 98 m – Cirencester 8 m – Stroud 20 m

The Wheatsheaf at Oaksey
Wheatsheaf Lane ✉ SN16 9TB – ✆ (01666) 577 348 – Closed Sunday dinner and Monday
Rest – (closed Monday) Carte £ 16/25
◆ Rurally set traditional pub in the heart of the country. Rafters; exposed stone walls covered with farming implements above inglenook. Assured, ambitious, modern cooking.

If breakfast is included the symbol appears after the number of rooms.

OBORNE – Dorset – **503** M 31 – **see Sherborne**

OCKLEY – Surrey – **504** S 30 7 **D2**
London 31 m – Brighton 32 m – Guildford 23 m – Lewes 36 m – Worthing 29 m
Gatton Manor Hotel G. & C.C. Standon Lane, ✆ (01306) 627 555 .

Bryce's
Old School House, Stane St, on A 29 ✉ RH5 5TH – ✆ (01306) 627 430 – bryces.fish@virgin.net – Fax (01306) 628 274 – Closed 25-26 December, January, February and Sunday dinner in November
Rest – Seafood Menu £ 29 – Carte £ 29/35
◆ Busy, redbrick former school, locally renowned for flavourful, home-smoked and market-fresh seafood from Thai fricassee to swordfish mille feuille. Attentive, dapper staff.

ODIHAM – Hants. – **504** R 30 – **pop. 2 908** – ✉ **Hook** 7 **C1**
London 51 m – Reading 16 m – Southampton 37 m – Winchester 25 m

George
100 High St ✉ RG29 1LP – ✆ (01256) 702 081 – reception@georgehotelodiham.com – Fax (01256) 704 213 – closed 25-26 December
28 rm – ♦£65/125 ♦♦£100/125
Rest *Cromwell's* – Seafood (closed Saturday lunch, Sunday dinner and Bank Holidays) Carte £ 28/35
Rest *Next door at the George* – Carte £ 22/30
◆ 15C inn at the heart of the town; cosy lounge bar and comfortable rooms. Those in the main building have greater rural character than more recent, if smartly fitted ones. Cromwells is impressively oak-panelled. Informality rules Next door at the George.

St John
83 High St ✉ RG29 1LB – ✆ (01256) 702 697 – reuben.evans@st-john-restaurant.co.uk – Fax (01256) 702 697 – closed 25-28 December and Sunday
Rest – Menu £ 19 – Carte £ 22/35
◆ Refurbished and stylish restaurant boasts vivid artwork, suspended arcs of wood from the ceiling and comfy leather banquettes. Eclectic menus with classical base.

ENGLAND

Grapevine
121 High St ✉ RG29 1LA – ✆ (01256) 701 122 – grapevine701122@tiscali.co.uk – closed 1 week Christmas, Saturday lunch, Sunday and Bank Holidays
Rest – Carte £ 19/33
◆ Bright, airy, relaxed neighbourhood restaurant. Local produce used to good effect in generous modern British dishes, plus flavourful, more elaborate blackboard specialities.

OLD BURGHCLERE – Hants. – 504 Q 29 – ✉ Newbury 6 B1
London 77 m – Bristol 76 m – Newbury 10 m – Reading 27 m – Southampton 28 m

Dew Pond
✉ RG20 9LH – ✆ (01635) 278 408 – Fax (01635) 278 580 – closed 2 weeks August 2 weeks Christmas, Sunday and Monday
Rest – (dinner only) Menu £ 32
◆ This traditionally decorated cottage, set in fields and parkland, overlooks Watership Down and houses a collection of local art. Tasty Anglo-gallic menu.

Red = Pleasant. Look for the red and symbols.

ENGLAND

OLD WARDEN – Beds. – 504 S 27 – see Biggleswade

OLDHAM – Gtr Manchester – 502 N 23 – pop. 103 544 20 B2
London 212 m – Leeds 36 m – Manchester 7 m – Sheffield 38 m
12 Albion St ✆ (0161) 627 1024
Crompton and Royton Royton High Barn, ✆ (0161) 624 2154 ;
Werneth Garden Suburb Green Lane, ✆ (0161) 624 1190 ;
Lees New Rd, ✆ (0161) 624 4986 .

Plan : see Manchester

Smokies Park
rm, rest,
Ashton Rd, Bardsley, South : 2 ¾ m. on A 627 ✉ OL8 3HX – ✆ (0161) 785 5000 – reservations@smokies.co.uk – Fax (0161) 785 5010
72 rm – †£ 100 ††£ 110/170 – 1 suite
Rest *Cosi Fan Tutti* – Italian (dinner only and Sunday lunch) Menu £ 24 – Carte £ 24/31 s
◆ Purpose-built hotel in the southern suburbs. Executive rooms in particular are modern and handsomely equipped. Regular music in the nightclub or more relaxing lounge bar. Trattoria styling in airy restaurant.

Dinnerstone
99-101 High St, Uppermill, Saddleworth, East : 4 m. on A 669 ✉ OL3 6BD – ✆ (01457) 875 544 – bookings@dinnerstone.co.uk – Fax (01457) 875 190 – closed 1-3 January, 26-27 December and Monday
Rest – Modern Menu £ 13 (lunch) – Carte £ 18/31
◆ Airy modern restaurant in centre of busy village with semi-open kitchen, vibrant art and relaxed feel. Large menu has Mediterranean base yet retains its Northern accent.

The White Hart Inn with rm
51 Stockport Rd, Lydgate, East : 3 m. by A 669 on A 6050 ✉ OL4 4JJ – ✆ (01457) 872 566 – bookings@thewhitehart.co.uk – Fax (01457) 875 190
12 rm – †£ 90/100 ††£ 140 – **Rest** – (booking essential) Menu £ 16/40 – Carte £ 24/32
◆ Busy pub with old timber, open fires and exposed brick. Eat hearty, modern dishes in brasserie or linen-clad restaurant. Private dining and function rooms also available. Comfortable bedrooms, named after local dignitaries, housed in the original building.

OLTON – W. Mids. – 502 O 26 – see Solihull

OMBERSLEY – Worcs. – 503 N 27 – pop. 2 089 18 B3

London 148 m – Birmingham 42 m – Leominster 33 m

Bishopswood Rd, (01905) 620 747 .

The Venture In

Main St WR9 0EW – (01905) 620 552 – Fax (01905) 620 552 – closed 1 week Christmas, 2 weeks February, 2 weeks August, Sunday dinner and Monday

Rest – Menu £ 25/35

◆ Charming, restored Tudor inn, traditional from its broad inglenook to its fringed Victorian lights. Modern, flavourful menu, well judged and locally sourced. Friendly staff.

ORFORD – Suffolk – 504 Y 27 – Woodbridge 15 D3

London 103 m – Ipswich 22 m – Norwich 52 m

The Crown and Castle

IP12 2LJ – (01394) 450 205 – info@crownandcastle.co.uk

20 rm – £ 72/80 £ 140/155

Rest The Trinity – see restaurant listing

◆ 19C redbrick hotel with garden and terrace standing proudly next to 12C Orford Castle. Cosy lounges with soft suites and sofas. Stylish modern rooms, some facing the Ness.

The Trinity – at The Crown and Castle H.

IP12 2LJ – (01394) 450 205 – info@crownandcastle.co.uk

Rest – (booking essential) Menu £ 24/32 (weekdays) – Carte Saturday dinner £ 28/35

◆ Relaxed, stylish restaurant featuring brick fireplaces, abstract artwork and red banquettes. Classic combinations make vibrant use of local produce. Friendly service.

King's Head Inn with rm

Front Street IP12 2LW – (01394) 450 271

4 rm – £ 70 £ 90 – **Rest** – Carte £ 17/23

◆ 16C pub with traditional décor of heraldic prints and banners. Wooden tables, open fired stove, large dining room. Honest, down to earth food and classic puddings. Spacious, well-furnished and comfortable bedrooms.

ORLETON – Shrops. – 503 L 23 – see Ludlow

OSMOTHERLEY – N. Yorks. – 502 Q 20 – Northallerton 22 B1

London 245 m – Darlington 25 m – Leeds 49 m – Middlesbrough 20 m – Newcastle upon Tyne 54 m – York 36 m

The Golden Lion with rm

6 West End DL6 3AA – (01609) 883 526 – Closed 25 December

3 rm – £ 60 £ 90 – **Rest** – Carte £ 16/27

◆ Unpretentious, beamed, firelit alehouse; plant-filled upper dining room; large menu of satisfying, full-flavoured cooking, Yorkshire beers and sprightly, engaging service.

OSWESTRY – Shrops. – 502 K 25 – pop. 16 660 18 A1

London 182 m – Chester 28 m – Shrewsbury 18 m

Mile End Services (01691) 662488

Aston Park, (01691) 610 535 ;

Llanymynech Pant, (01691) 830 983 .

The Walls

Welsh Walls SY11 1AW – (01691) 670 970 – info@the-walls.co.uk – Fax (01691) 653 820 – closed 26-28 December, 1-3 January

Rest – Menu £ 18 – Carte £ 19/36

◆ Built in 1841 as a school; now a buzzy restaurant. High ceiling with wooden rafters; original wood flooring. Friendly atmosphere. Varied menu offers some adventurous options.

ENGLAND

at Trefonen **Southwest : 2 ½ m. on Trefonen rd – ✉ Oswestry**

The Pentre — Tanat Valley,
Southwest : 1 ¾ m. by Treflach rd off New Well Lane ✉ SY10 9EE – ✆ (01691) 653 952 – helen@thepentre.com – closed 1 week Christmas
3 rm – †£ 50 ††£ 80 – **Rest** – (communal dining) Menu £ 21
◆ Restored 16C farmhouse with superb views over Tanat Valley. Heavily timbered inglenook and wood-burning stove in lounge. Sloping floors enhance rooms of tremendous character. Home-cooked dinners served with fellow guests.

at Rhydycroesau **West : 3 ¼ m. on B 4580 – ✉ Oswestry**

Pen-Y-Dyffryn Country H.
✉ SY10 7JD – ✆ (01691) 653 700 – stay@peny.co.uk
12 rm – †£ 86/99 ††£ 142/150 – **Rest** – (dinner only) (booking essential for non-residents) Menu £ 35
◆ Peaceful 19C listed rectory in five-acre informal gardens near Offa's Dyke. Cosy lounge, friendly ambience; good-sized, individually styled rooms, four in the coach house. Home-cooked dishes utilising organic ingredients.

ENGLAND

Good food and accommodation at moderate prices?
Look for the Bib symbols:
red Bib Gourmand for food, blue Bib Hotel for hotels

OULTON BROAD – Suffolk – **504** Z 26 – see Lowestoft

OUNDLE – Northants. – **504** S 26 – pop. 5 219 – ✉ Peterborough 17 **C3**

London 89 m – Leicester 37 m – Northampton 30 m
14 West St ✆ (01832) 274333
Benefield Rd, ✆ (01832) 273 267 .

at Fotheringhay **North : 3 ¾ m. by A 427 off A 605 – ✉ Peterborough (Cambs.)**

Castle Farm without rest
Fotheringhay, North : 3 ¾ m. by A 427 off A 605 ✉ PE8 5HZ – ✆ (01832) 226 200 – Fax (01832) 226 200
5 rm – †£ 43 ††£ 67
◆ Wisteria-clad, gabled 19C house in the Nene Valley; lawned gardens beside the river. Ample, pine furnished rooms, two in the adjacent wing; intimate lounge with open fire.

The Falcon Inn
Fotheringhay, North : 3 ¾ m. by A 427 off A 605 ✉ PE8 5HZ – ✆ (01832) 226 254 – falcon@cyberware.co.uk – Fax (01832) 226 046
Rest – Carte £ 12/35
◆ Popular village inn: pretty bouquets, framed prints and airy, spacious conservatory. Mediterranean flavours to the fore in robust dishes from the modern British menu.

OVERSTRAND – Norfolk – **504** Y 25 – see Cromer

OVINGTON – Hants. – see Winchester

London 59 m – Birmingham 63 m – Brighton 105 m – Bristol 73 m – Cardiff 107 m – Coventry 54 m – Southampton 64 m

Access Swinford Bridge (toll)

to Abingdon Bridge (Salter Bros. Ltd) (summer only) daily (2 h)

15-16 Broad St ✆ (01865) 726871, tic@oxford.gov.uk

City★★★ - Christ Church★★ (Hall★★ **AC**, Tom Quad★, Tom Tower★, Cathedral★ **AC** - Choir Roof★) BZ – Merton College★★ **AC** BZ - Magdalen College★★ BZ – Ashmolean Museum★★ BY **M1** – Bodleian Library★★ (Ceiling★★, Lierne Vaulting★) **AC** BZ **A1** – St John's College★ BY - The Queen's College★ BZ – Lincoln College★ BZ - Trinity College (Chapel★) BY – New College (Chapel★) **AC**, BZ – Radcliffe Camera★ BZ **P1** – Sheldonian Theatre★ **AC**, BZ **T** – University Museum of National History★ BY **M4** – Pitt Rivers Museum★ BY **M3**

Iffley Church★ AZ **A.** Woodstock : Blenheim Palace★★★ (Park★★★) **AC**, NW : 8 m. by A 4144 and A 34 AY

Plan on next page

Randolph

rm, VISA MC AE

Beaumont St ✉ OX1 2LN – ✆ (0870) 400 82 00 – sales.randolph@macdonald-hotels.co.uk – Fax (01865) 791 678 BY **n**

142 rm – ♦£ 144/290 ♦♦£ 159/305 – 9 suites

Rest *The Restaurant at the Randolph* – Menu £ 32 (dinner) – Carte £ 32/42

◆ Grand Victorian edifice. Lounge bar: deep burgundy, polished wood and chandeliers. Handsome rooms in a blend of rich fabrics; some, more spacious, have half-tester beds. Spacious, linen-clad Restaurant.

Malmaison

rm, rest, VISA MC AE

3 Oxford Castle ✉ OX1 1AY – ✆ (01865) 268 400 – oxford@malmaison.com – Fax (01865) 268 402 BZ **a**

91 rm – ♦£ 150/200 ♦♦£ 150/220, £13.95 – 3 suites

Rest *Brasserie* – (Sunday brunch) Carte £ 27/34

◆ Unique accommodation by castle: this was a prison from 13C to 1996! Former visitors' room now moody lounge. Stunning rooms in converted cells or ex-house of correction! Brasserie in old admin area: modern British menu with fine French edge.

Old Bank

rm, VISA MC AE

92-94 High St ✉ OX1 4BN – ✆ (01865) 799 599 – info@oldbank-hotel.co.uk – Fax (01865) 799 598 BZ **s**

41 rm – ♦£ 170 ♦♦£ 185/210, £12.95 – 1 suite

Rest *Quod* – Menu £ 14 (weekday lunch) – Carte £ 23/34

◆ Elegantly understated, clean-lined interiors and the neo-Classical façade of the city's first bank - an astute combination. Rooms in modern wood and leather with CD players. Lively Italian-influenced brasserie.

Old Parsonage

VISA MC AE

1 Banbury Rd ✉ OX2 6NN – ✆ (01865) 310 210 – info@oldparsonage-hotel.co.uk – Fax (01865) 311 262 BY **e**

30 rm – ♦£ 140 ♦♦£ 160/225, £14 – **Rest** – Menu £ 16 (weekday lunch) – Carte £ 24/41

◆ Part 17C house, creeper-clad and typically Oxfordian; dedicated staff; pristine rooms: antiques, modern and traditional fabrics and, in some cases, views of the roof garden. Meals in cosy lounge bar with antique prints and paintings.

Eastgate without rest

VISA MC AE

73 High St ✉ OX1 4BE – ✆ (0870) 400 82 01 – events.eastgate@macdonald-hotels.co.uk – Fax (01865) 794 163 BZ **c**

63 rm – ♦£ 119 ♦♦£ 149/159, £13.95

◆ Near the botanical gardens and the Boathouse's punt moorings, a former coaching inn offering comfortable, traditionally styled rooms decorated in plaid and floral patterns.

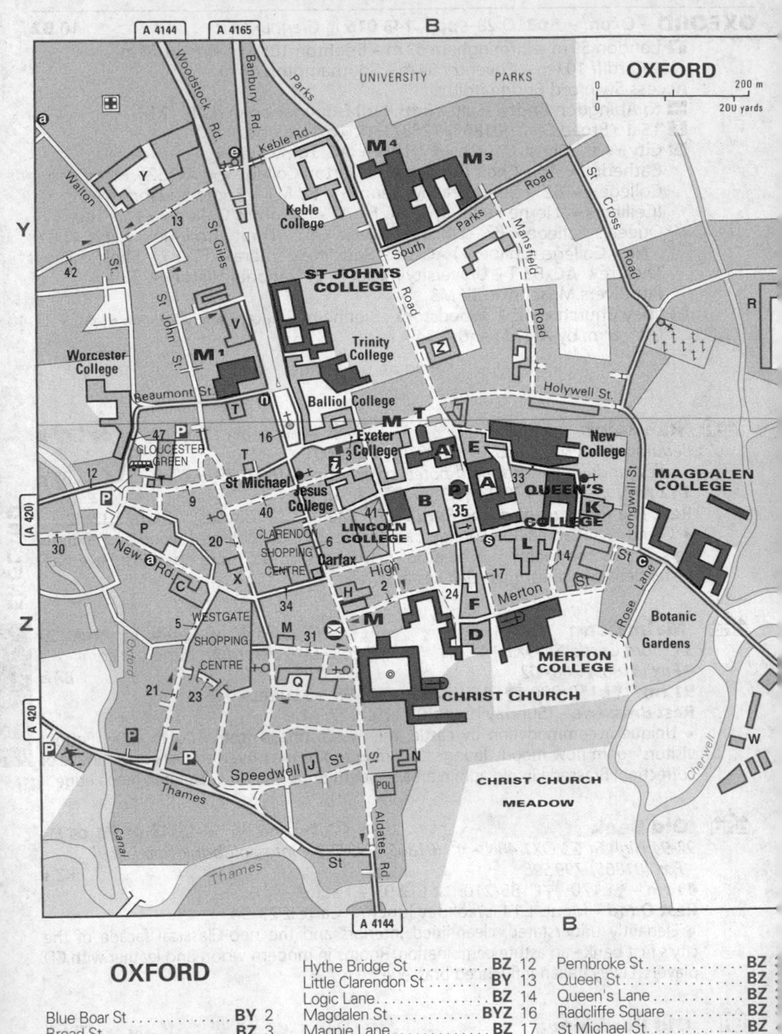

OXFORD

Blue Boar St	BY	2
Broad St	BZ	3
Castle St	BZ	5
Clarendon Shopping Centre	BZ	
Cornmarket St.	BZ	6
George St	BZ	9
High St.	BZ	
Hythe Bridge St	BZ	12
Little Clarendon St	BY	13
Logic Lane	BZ	14
Magdalen St.	BYZ	16
Magpie Lane	BZ	17
New Inn Hall St.	BZ	20
Norfolk St	BZ	21
Old Greyfriars St	BZ	23
Oriel Square	BZ	24
Park End St	BZ	30
Pembroke St.	BZ	
Queen St.	BZ	
Queen's Lane	BZ	
Radcliffe Square	BZ	
St Michael St.	BZ	
Turl St.	BZ	
Walton Crescent.	BY	
Westgate Shopping Centre	BZ	
Worcester St.	BZ	

COLLEGES

All Souls	BZ	A
Balliol	BY	
Brasenose	BZ	B
Christ Church	BZ	
Corpus Christi	BZ	D
Exeter	BZ	
Hertford	BZ	E
Jesus	BZ	
Keble	BY	
Lady Margaret Hall	AY	Z
Linacre	BZ	N
Lincoln	BZ	
Magdalen	BZ	
Merton	BZ	
New	BZ	
Nuffield	BZ	P
Oriel	BZ	F
Pembroke	BZ	Q
Queen's	BZ	
St Anne's	AY	K
St Anthony's	AY	L
St Catherine's	BY	R
St Cross	BY	V
St Edmund Hall	BZ	K
St Hilda's	BZ	W
St Hugh's	AY	P
St John's	BY	
St Peter's	BZ	X
Sommerville	BY	Y
Trinity	BY	
University	BZ	L
Wadham	BY	Z
Wolfson	AY	X
Worcester	BY	

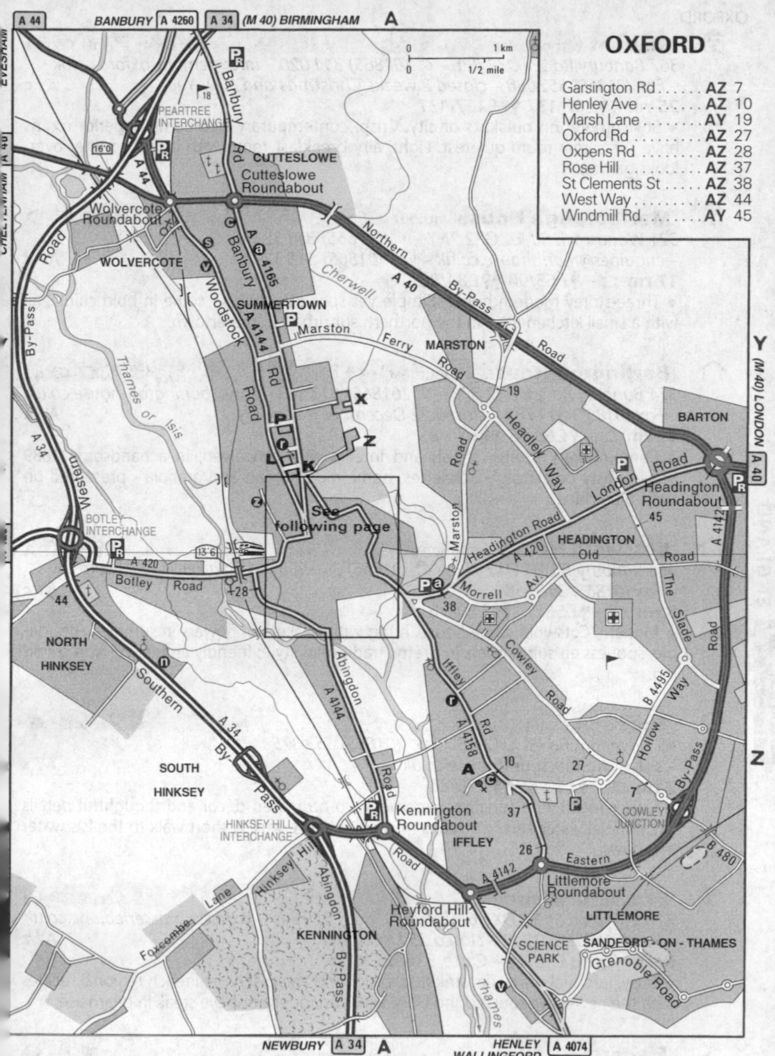

Hawkwell House

Church Way, Iffley ✉ *OX4 4DZ – ☎ (01865) 749 988*
– reservations@hawkwellhousehotel.co.uk – Fax (01865) 748 525 AZ **c**

66 rm – †£ 65/130 ††£ 85/150

Rest *Arezzo* – Carte £ 20/28

◆ Victorian in origin, a group-owned hotel in a quiet suburb. Co-ordinated and smartly fitted modern rooms, suited to business travel. Bright lounge bar in checks and tartans. Airy, atmospheric conservatory restaurant.

Remont without rest

367 Banbury Rd ✉ OX2 7PL – ✆ (01865) 311 020 – info@remont-oxford.co.uk – Fax (01865) 552 080 – closed 2 weeks Christmas and New Year AY **c**

25 rm – †£ 82/137 ††£ 117/137

◆ Stylish hotel on outskirts of city. Crisp, contemporary bedrooms; superior rooms have sofas; rear room quietest. Light, airy breakfast room with buffet counter overlooks garden.

Marlborough House without rest

321 Woodstock Rd ✉ OX2 7NY – ✆ (01865) 311 321 – enquiries@marlbhouse.co.uk – Fax (01865) 515 329 AY **v**

17 rm ☕ – †£ 65/90 ††£ 84/98

◆ Three-storey modern house. Simple yet spacious rooms - some in bold chintz, all with a small kitchenette - in the northern suburb of Summertown.

Burlington House without rest

374 Banbury Rd ✉ OX2 7PP – ✆ (01865) 513 513 – stay@burlington-house.co.uk – Fax (01865) 311 785 – closed 22 December-2 January AY **a**

12 rm ☕ – †£ 60/65 ††£ 70/85

◆ Contemporary rooms, stylish and intelligently conceived, in a handsome 1889 house. Tasty breakfasts - omelettes, home-made bread and granola - presented on Delft-blue china.

Cotswold House without rest

363 Banbury Rd ✉ OX2 7PL – ✆ (01865) 310 558 – d.r.walker@talk21.com – Fax (01865) 310 558 AY **c**

8 rm ☕ – †£ 55/67 ††£ 80/90

◆ Modern, Cotswold stone house, hung with baskets of flowers in summer. Affordable, spotless en suite rooms in pretty, traditional style; friendly ambience. Non smoking.

Chestnuts without rest

45 Davenant Rd ✉ OX2 8BU – ✆ (01865) 553 375 – stay@chestnutsguesthouse.co.uk AY **s**

7 rm ☕ – †£ 50/65 ††£ 75/85

◆ Under friendly personal management; co-ordinated décor and thoughtful details like mineral water and bathrobes in ensuite bedrooms. A short walk to the Isis water meadows.

Brasserie Blanc

71-72 Walton St ✉ OX2 6AG – ✆ (01865) 510 999 – oxford@brasserieblanc.co.uk – Fax (01865) 510 700 – closed 25 December AY **z**

Rest – Menu £ 13/18 – Carte £ 18/35

◆ Busy, informal brasserie; striking interior and sharp service; French regional recipes with the new-wave touch: John Dory with coriander or ribeye steak in béarnaise.

Fishers

36-37 St Clements ✉ OX4 1AB – ✆ (01865) 243 003 – dining@fishers-oxford.co.uk – closed one week Christmas and Monday lunch AZ **a**

Rest – Seafood Carte £ 21/31

◆ Informal, bright restaurant near Magdalen Bridge. Tables covered with fish and chip style paper. Market-oriented dishes include Mediterranean and Pacific Rim influences.

Branca

111 Walton St ✉ OX2 6AJ – ✆ (01865) 556 111 – info@brancarestaurants.com – Fax (01865) 556 501 – Closed 24-26 December BY **a**

Rest – Italian Carte £ 21/27

◆ Modern restaurant with casual, friendly feel and minimalist décor. Vibrant, simple, fresh Italian influenced dishes: antipasti taster plates, pasta and pizza are specialities.

at Stanton St John **Northeast : 5 ½ m. by A 420 and Barton crematorium rd on B 4027 – ✉ Oxford**

The Talkhouse with rm

Wheatley Rd ✉ OX33 1EX – ✆ (01865) 351 648 – talkhouse@fullers.co.uk – Fax (01865) 351 085

4 rm – †£ 75 ††£ 85 – **Rest** – Menu £ 16 – Carte £ 20/28

◆ Attractive, partly thatched country pub. Characterful, modernised interior with open fires and heavy beams. Generous portions of classic pub dishes. Refurbished bedrooms enclose suntrap terrace.

at Sandford-on-Thames **Southeast : 5 m. by A 4158 – ✉ Oxford**

Oxford Thames Four Pillars rm, AC rest, P VISA AE

Henley Rd ✉ OX4 4GX – ✆ (01865) 334 444 – thames@four-pillars.co.uk – Fax (01865) 334 400 AZ **v**

62 rm – †£ 105/125 ††£ 125/218

Rest ***The River Room*** – Menu £ 15 (lunch) – Carte approx. £ 25

◆ Modern sandstone hotel around a 13C barn, though the pool is more reminiscent of a Roman bath; spacious lounge with medieval style chandelier, spotless, comfortable rooms. Restaurant overlooks lawned grounds and river.

at Toot Baldon **Southeast : 5 ½ m. by B 480 - AZ – ✉ Oxford**

The Mole Inn

✉ OX44 9NG – ✆ (01865) 340 001 – info@themoleinn.com – Fax (01865) 343 011 – Closed 25 December

Rest – Carte £ 20/30

◆ Much refurbished pub in tiny hamlet. Beams galore, stone tiles, cosy lounge with leather sofas, pine/oak tables. Tasty, assured menus: rustic and earthy or appealingly modish.

at Great Milton **Southeast : 12 m. by A 40 off A 329 - AY – ✉ Oxford**

Le Manoir aux Quat' Saisons (Raymond Blanc)

Church Rd ✉ OX44 7PD – ✆ (01844) 278 881 – lemanoir@blanc.co.uk – Fax (01844) 278 847 – closed 1-11 January AC P VISA AE

25 rm – †£ 395/680 ††£ 395/680, £ 16 – 7 suites – **Rest** – French Menu £ 49 (lunch) – Carte £ 87/98

Spec. Ceviche of scallops and tuna, fennel and ginger, orange dressing. Pan-fried sea bream with squid, cod brandade, bouillabaisse. Pistachio soufflé with cocoa sorbet.

◆ Refined elegance at every turn, resulting in picture perfect harmony. Sumptuous lounges and rooms, classic and modern, surrounded by Japanese, ornamental and kitchen gardens. Virtuoso classic French menu of precision and flair, inspired by the seasons.

at Kingston Bagpuize **Southwest : 10 m. by A 420 - AY - off A 415 – ✉ Oxford**

Fallowfields Country House P VISA AE

Faringdon Rd ✉ OX13 5BH – ✆ (01865) 820 416 – stay@fallowfields.com – Fax (01865) 821 275 – closed 27-29 December

10 rm – †£ 98 ††£ 120/170

Rest ***Wellingtonia*** – Menu £ 20/25 – Carte £ 24/47

◆ Elephants are everywhere - in paintings, wood and china - in this privately run 19C manor. Cosy lounge, fireside chintz armchairs. Canopy beds in thoughtfully appointed rooms. Classically elegant restaurant views sweeping lawns.

ENGLAND

at North Hinksey Southwest : 3 ½ m. by A 420 – ✉ **Oxford**

The Fishes
North Hinksey Village ✉ OX2 0NA – ✆ (01865) 249 796 – fishes@peachpubs.com – Closed 25 December AZ **n**

Rest – Carte £ 20/28

◆ Red brick pub with lively atmosphere, conservatory-style extension and pretty gardens for riverside picnics. Robust dishes make use of local ingredients. Well-chosen wine list.

at Wytham Northwest : 3 ¼ m. by A 420 - AY - off A 34 (northbound carriageway) – ✉ **Oxford**

The White Hart
✉ OX2 8QA – ✆ (01865) 244 372 – enquiries@thewhitehartoxford.co.uk – Fax (01865) 248 595

Rest – (closed dinner 25 December) Menu £ 10/13 – Carte £ 20/30

◆ Mellow 18C inn located in a pretty hamlet. Delightful courtyard terrace; inside are roaring fires, flagged floors, scrubbed pine tables. Menus mix classics with contemporary.

OXHILL – Warks. – 503 P 27 — 19 C3

London 90 m – Banbury 11 m – Birmingham 37 m

ENGLAND

Oxbourne House
✉ CV35 0RA – ✆ (01295) 688 202 – graememcdonald@msn.com

3 rm – †£ 40/50 ††£ 75 – **Rest** – (by arrangement, communal dining) Menu £ 25

◆ Late 20C house oozing charm, individuality and fine rural views; splendid gardens. Antiques abound, complemented by the finest soft furnishings. Stylishly appointed bedrooms. Spacious dining room: plenty of ingredients grown in house grounds.

PADIHAM – Blackburn – 502 N 22 — 20 B2

London 230 m – Burnley 6 m – Clitheroe 8 m

at Fence Northeast : 3 m. by A 6068 – ✉ **Burnley**

Fence Gate Inn
Wheatley Lane Road ✉ BB12 9EE – ✆ (01282) 618 101 – info@fencegate.co.uk – Fax (01282) 615 432

Rest – Carte £ 23/28

Rest *The Topiary* – Wheatley Lane Rd – Carte £ 25/33

◆ High on the moors, a cavernous 17C inn renowned for locally sourced ingredients such as tasty home-made sausages. Bar or brasserie dining: service with a sense of humour.

PADSTOW – Cornwall – 503 F 32 – pop. 2 449 — 1 B2

London 288 m – Exeter 78 m – Plymouth 45 m – Truro 23 m

Red Brick Building, North Quay ✆ (01841) 533449, padstowtic@visit.org.uk

Trevose Constantine Bay, ✆ (01841) 520 208 .

Town★ - Prideaux Place★

Trevone (Cornwall Coast Path★★) W : 3 m. by B 3276 – Trevose Head★ (≤ ★★) W : 6 m. by B 3276. Bedruthan Steps★, SW : 7 m. by B 3276 – Pencarrow★, SE : 11 m. by A 389

The Metropole
≤ Camel Estuary, (heated)

Station Rd ✉ PL28 8DB – ✆ (01841) 532 486 – info@the-metropole.co.uk – Fax (01841) 532 867

58 rm – †£ 92/132 ††£ 144/176 – **Rest** – (bar lunch Monday-Saturday) Menu £ 30 – Carte £ 18/30

◆ Grand 19C hotel perched above this quaint fishing town. Exceptional views of Camel Estuary. Well-furnished sitting room. Comfortable bedrooms in smart, co-ordinated style. Traditional dining; local produce.

Old Custom House Inn Camel Estuary and harbour, rest,
South Quay PL28 8BL – (01841) 532 359
– oldcustomhouse@smallandfriendly.co.uk – Fax (01841) 533 372
24 rm – £65/120 £90/125
Rest ***Pescadou*** – (booking essential) Carte approx. £25
◆ Listed, slate-built former grain store and exciseman's house: spacious and comfortable throughout. Front and side rooms have views of the quayside and Camel Estuary. Seafood emphasis in bustling, glass-fronted restaurant.

Woodlands Country House without rest
Treator, West : 1¼ m. on B 3276 PL28 8RU
– (01841) 532 426 – info@woodlands-padstow.co.uk – Fax (01841) 533 353
– closed 16 December - 31 January
9 rm – £57/65 £100/124
◆ Personally run Victorian country house with well-kept garden. Large lounge in classic traditional style; views sweeping down to Trevone Bay. Co-ordinated bedrooms.

Treverbyn House without rest
Station Rd PL28 8DA – (01841) 532 855 – Fax (01841) 532 855
– closed 23 December - February
5 rm – £68 £90/100
◆ Something of a grand style with views of the Camel Estuary. Large rooms retain open fireplaces and have comfortable, uncluttered décor: Turret rooms are the ones to ask for.

Althea Library without rest
27 High St PL28 8BB – (01841) 532 717 – enquiries@althealibrary.co.uk
– Fax (01841) 532 717 – closed two weeks January, one week June, Christmas
4 rm – £86
◆ Grade II listed former school library with very friendly feel. Neat terrace; homely breakfast room/lounge with food cooked on the Aga. Cosy, individually styled beamed rooms.

ENGLAND

The Seafood with rm rest,
Riverside PL28 8BY – (01841) 532 700 – reservations@rickstein.com
– Fax (01841) 532 942 – closed 2 January-7 February,1 May, and 24-26 December
20 rm – £125 £260 – **Rest** – Seafood (booking essential) Carte £35/60
◆ Bold artwork and a buzz of enthusiasm animate Rick Stein's converted granary and conservatory. Flavourful Cornish seafood. Stylish rooms in a cool modern palette.

St Petroc's with rm
4 New St PL28 8EA – (01841) 532 700 – reservations@rickstein.com
– Fax (01841) 532 942 – closed 24-26 December and 1 May
10 rm – £125 £195 – **Rest** – (booking essential) Carte £30/36
◆ Handsome white-fronted house on a steep hill, where confidently prepared modern dishes with local, seasonal produce take centre stage. Stylish, individual bedrooms.

No.6
6 Middle St PL28 8AP – (01841) 532 093
– enquiries@number6inpadstow.co.uk – Fax (01841) 533 941 – closed January, 23-27 December, Sunday and Monday
Rest – (dinner only) Menu £45 – Carte £38/45
◆ Targeting the top end of the market, this converted cottage has striking black and white floors, early evening as well as ambitious menus featuring elaborate, complex dishes.

Rick Stein's Café with rm
10 Middle St PL28 8AP – (01841) 532 700 – reservations@rickstein.com
– Fax (01841) 532 942 – closed 24-26 December, 1 May and dinner Sunday and Monday November-February
3 rm – £90 £115 – **Rest** – (booking essential) Menu £22 – Carte £25/33
◆ Contemporary, unfussy bistro with modern, well-priced Mediterranean influenced cuisine employing the best local and seasonal ingredients. Well-appointed bedrooms.

Margot's
11 Duke St ✉ PL28 8AB – ✆ (01841) 533 441 – enquiries@margots.co.uk – Closed Sunday
Rest – (booking essential at dinner) Menu £ 25 (dinner) – Carte £ 25/30
◆ Informal bistro-style restaurant with a friendly welcoming atmosphere. Varied menu capitalises on finest, fresh, local ingredients and bold, characterful flavours.

at Little Petherick South : 3 m. on A 389 – ✉ Wadebridge

Molesworth Manor without rest
✉ PL27 7QT – ✆ (01841) 540 292 – molesworthmanor@aol.com – February-October
9 rm – †£ 60/75 ††£ 82
◆ Part 17C and 19C former rectory. Charming individual establishment with inviting country house atmosphere amid antique furniture and curios. Rooms furnished in period style.

Old Mill House without rest
✉ PL27 7QT – ✆ (01841) 540 388 – enquiries@theoldmillhouse.com – Fax (01841) 540 406 – February - November
7 rm – †£ 75/80 ††£ 110/115
◆ Rural curios on display in a listed, family owned 16C cornmill with working water wheel. Homely, individually decorated rooms, some overlooking the millrace and neat garden.

ENGLAND

at St Issey South : 3 ½ m. on A 389 – ✉ Wadebridge

Olde Tredore House without rest
North : ¼ m. off A 389 ✉ PL27 7QS – ✆ (01841) 540 291 – closed Christmas and New Year
3 rm – †£ 65/70 ††£ 65/70
◆ Large, grand house in a tranquil and secluded location. Well-furnished guest areas and bedrooms all in traditional country house style.

at Constantine Bay West : 4 m. by B 3276 – ✉ Padstow

Treglos rm, rest, VISA
✉ PL28 8JH – ✆ (01841) 520 727 – stay@tregloshotel.com – Fax (01841) 521 163 – March-November
39 rm (dinner included) – †£ 91/159 ††£ 182/212 – 3 suites – **Rest** – (bar lunch Monday-Saturday) Menu £ 28
◆ An extensive, family run building surrounded by garden. Facilities include games rooms, children's play area and a lounge bar. Consistently decorated, bright, neat bedrooms. Smart attire the code in very comfortable dining room.

PAIGNTON – Torbay – **503** J 32 – **pop. 47 398** 2 **C2**

London 226 m – Exeter 26 m – Plymouth 29 m
The Esplanade (08707) 070 010, tourist.board@torbay.gov.uk
Torbay★ - Kirkham House★ **AC** Y B
Paignton Zoo★★ **AC**, SW : ½ m. by A 3022 AY (see Plan of Torbay) – Cockington★, N : 3 m. by A 3022 and minor roads

Plan of Built up Area : see Torbay

Plan opposite

Redcliffe Torbay, (heated) rest, VISA Y **n**
4 Marine Drive ✉ TQ3 2NL – ✆ (01803) 526 397 – redclfe@aol.com – Fax (01803) 528 030
68 rm – †£ 56/118 ††£ 112/128 – **Rest** – (bar lunch Monday-Saturday) Menu £ 18 (dinner) – Carte £ 22/26
◆ Smoothly run family owned hotel, handily set on the seafront, a favourite of auther Dick Francis. Children's play area and putting green options. Airy, pine furnished rooms. Admire the sea views from spacious, neat restaurant.

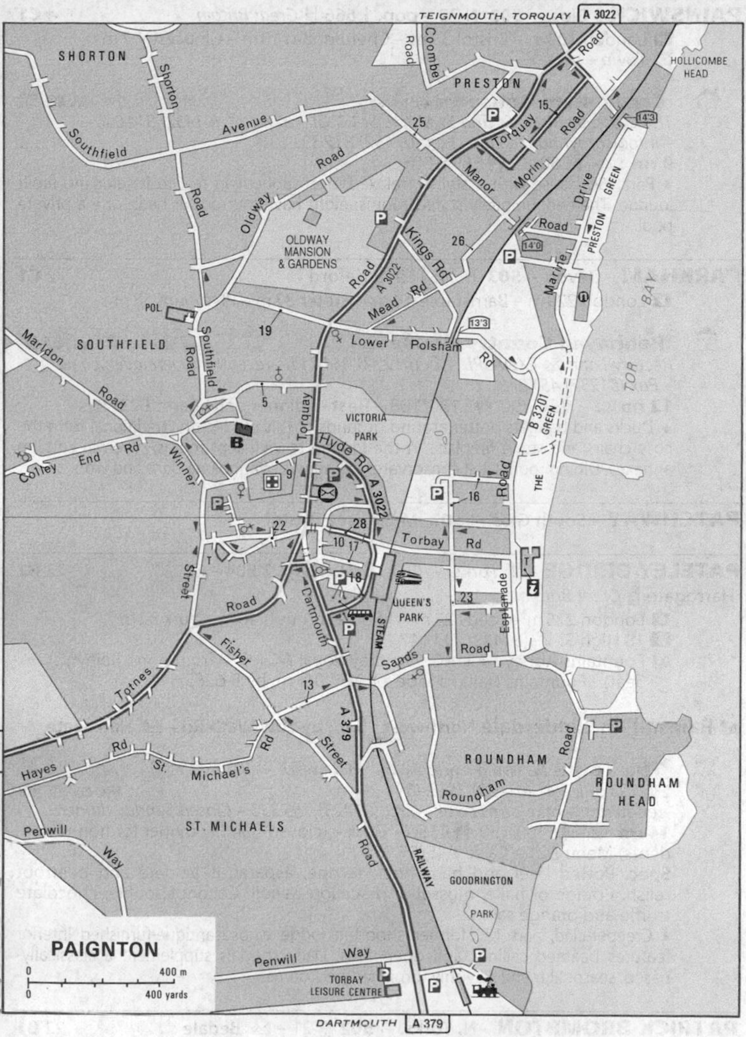

PAIGNTON

Cecil Rd . . . . Y 5
Church St . . . . Y 9
Commercial Rd . . . . Z 10
Elmsleigh Rd . . . . Z 13
Eugene Rd . . . . Y 15
Garfield Rd . . . . Y 16
Gerston Rd . . . . Z 17
Great Western Way . . . . Z 18
Higher Polsham Rd . . . . Y 19
Hyde Rd . . . . Y
Palace Ave . . . . Z 22
Queen's Rd . . . . Z 23
Torbay Rd . . . . Z
Torquay Rd . . . . Y
Upper Manor Rd . . . . Y 25
Upper Morin Rd . . . . Y 26
Victoria Rd . . . . Z 28

**The ✿ award is the crème de la crème.
This is awarded to restaurants
which are really worth travelling miles for!**

PAINSWICK – Glos. – 503 N 28 – pop. 1 666 *Great Britain* 4 C1

London 107 m – Bristol 35 m – Cheltenham 10 m – Gloucester 7 m

Town★

Cardynham House without rest

The Cross, by Bisley St and St Marys St ✉ GL6 6XX – ☎ (01452) 814 006 – info@cardynham.co.uk – Fax (01452) 812 321

9 rm – £ 50/85 £ 89/100

◆ Part 15C house with a stylish, relaxed, even Bohemian feel to its elegant, firelit lounge. Themed, uniquely styled rooms: eight have four-poster beds, one a private pool.

PARKHAM – Devon – 503 H 31 – ✉ Bideford 2 C1

London 229 m – Barnstaple 14 m – Exeter 87 m – Plymouth 58 m

Penhaven Country House

Rectory Lane ✉ EX39 5PL – ☎ (01237) 451 711 – reception@penhaven.co.uk – Fax (01237) 451 878

12 rm – £ 65/90 £ 130/180 – **Rest** – (dinner only) Carte £ 23/26 **s**

◆ Ducks and badgers potter around grounds of this old rectory, traditional from the cosy chairs and stone fireplace in the lounge to well-kept rooms, seven in cottage annexes. Dining room's tall conservatory windows overlook gardens and woods.

ENGLAND

PATCHWAY – South Glos. – 503 M 29 – see Bristol

PATELEY BRIDGE – N. Yorks. – 502 O 21 – pop. 2 504 – ✉ Harrogate *Great Britain* 22 B2

London 225 m – Leeds 28 m – Middlesbrough 46 m – York 32 m

18 High St ☎ (01423) 711147

Fountains Abbey★★★ AC - Studley Royal AC (< ★ from Anne Boleyn's Seat) - Fountains Hall (Fa½ade★), NE : 8½ m. by B 6265

at Ramsgill-in-Nidderdale Northwest : 5 m. by Low Wath Rd – ✉ Harrogate

XX **The Yorke Arms** (Frances Atkins) with rm

✉ HG3 5RL – ☎ (01423) 755 243 – enquiries@yorke-arms.co.uk – Fax (01423) 755 330 – Closed Sunday dinner

14 rm – £ 100/150 £ 380 – **Rest** – (closed Sunday dinner for non-residents) Menu £ 21 – Carte £ 45/55

Spec. Potted beef and ham hock terrine, asparagus velouté and beetroot relish. Potage of hake, mussel and scallop ravioli. Coconut soufflé, chocolate truffle and orange salad.

◆ Creeper-clad, part 17C former shooting lodge whose antique-furnished interior features beamed ceilings and open fires. Daily specials supplement a classically-based, seasonal menu. Lavishly furnished bedrooms.

PATRICK BROMPTON – N. Yorks. – 502 P 21 – ✉ Bedale 22 B1

London 242 m – Newcastle upon Tyne 58 m – York 43 m

Elmfield House

Arrathorne, Northwest : 2¼ m. by A 684 on Richmond rd ✉ DL8 1NE – ☎ (01677) 450 558 – stay@elmfieldhouse.co.uk – Fax (01677) 450 557

7 rm – £ 52 £ 78 – **Rest** – (dinner only) (booking essential) (residents only) Menu £ 19

◆ Spacious, neatly fitted accommodation in a peaceful, personally run hotel, set in acres of gardens and open countryside. Try your luck at the adjacent fishing lake. Tasty, home-cooked meals.

PATTISWICK – Essex – see Coggeshall

PAULERSPURY – Northants. – 503 R 27 – see Towcester

PAXFORD – Glos. – **503** O 27 – see Chipping Campden

PAYHEMBURY – Devon – see Honiton

PEASMARSH – E. Sussex – **504** W 31 – see Rye

PEMBRIDGE – Herefordshire – **503** L 27 18 **A3**

London 162 m – Hereford 15 m – Leominster 7 m

Lowe Farm

West : 3 ¼ m. by A 44 following signs through Marston village ✉ HR6 9JD – ✆ (01544) 388 395 – wiliams-family@lineone.net – Fax (01544) 388 395 – closed Christmas

5 rm – †£ 40 ††£ 80 – **Rest** – (by arrangement) Menu £ 21

◆ Working farm: farmhouse dates from 13C; renovated barn from 14C with pleasant lounge and countryside views. Rooms in house and barn are cosy, comfortable and of a good size. Dining room boasts chunky pine tables, exposed brick and beams.

Look out for red symbols, indicating particularly pleasant establishments.

PENN – Bucks – **504** R/S 29 – **pop. 3 779** 11 **D2**

London 31 m – High Wycombe 4 m – Oxford 36 m

The Old Queen's Head

Hammersley Lane ✉ HP10 8EY – ✆ (01494) 813 371 – info@oldqueensheadpenn.co.uk – Fax (01494) 816 145 – Closed 25-26 December and Sunday dinner

Rest – Carte £ 19/28

◆ Attractive part 17C pub with flagged floors, low beams and brick fireplaces. Mix of traditional and more modern dishes served in generous portions. Garden with picnic tables.

PENRITH – Cumbria – **501** L 19 – **pop. 14 471** 21 **B2**

London 290 m – Carlisle 24 m – Kendal 31 m – Lancaster 48 m

Robinsons School, Middlegate ✆ (01768) 867466, pen.tic@eden.gov.uk - Rheged, Redhills, Penrith ✆ (01768) 860034

Salkeld Rd, ✆ (01768) 891 919 .

North Lakes rm,

Ullswater Rd, South : 1 m. by A 592 at junction 40 of M 6 ✉ CA11 8QT – ✆ (01768) 868 111 – nlakes@shirehotels.com – Fax (01768) 868 291

VISA AE

84 rm – †£ 122/127 ††£ 160/165

Rest *The Martindale* – (bar lunch Saturday and Sunday) Menu £ 19/25 – Carte £ 29/36

◆ Practically located, ideal for business traveller, with comprehensive leisure club. Sleek, contemporary coffee bar. Stylish bedrooms; Junior suites the most spacious. Extended restaurant with stylish, comfortable lounge area. Speciality hors d'oeuvres buffet.

Brooklands without rest VISA

2 Portland Place ✉ CA11 7QN – ✆ (01768) 863 395 – enquiries@brooklandsguesthouse.com – Fax (01768) 863 395 – closed 1 week Christmas

7 rm – †£ 35/50 ††£ 75

◆ Traditonal Victorian terraced house a minute's walk from the shops: many original features restored. Pleasantly furnished breakfast room. Locally made pine enhances bedrooms.

ENGLAND

at Temple Sowerby East : 6 ¾ m. by A 66 – ✉ Penrith

Temple Sowerby House
✉ CA10 1RZ – ✆ (01768) 361 578 – stay@templesowerby.com – Fax (01768) 361 958 – closed 24 January - 10 February, one week Christmas
12 rm – †£ 90/100 ††£ 120/140 – **Rest** – (dinner only) Carte £ 27/35
◆ Listed building with Georgian frontage, run with enthusiasm and charm. Refurbished bedrooms are stylishly decorated and include spa baths and body jet showers. Dining room overlooks walled garden. Menu offers concise, modern selection, cooked using fine seasonal produce.

at Yanwath Southwest : 2 ½ m. by A 6 and B 5320 – ✉ Penrith

The Yanwath Gate Inn
✉ CA10 2LF – ✆ (01768) 862 386 – enquiries@yanwathgate.com – Fax (01768) 899 892
Rest – Carte £ 28/43
◆ An erstwhile toll gate, with cosy,characterful candlelit bar and oak-panelled restaurant. Local ales and locally sourced produce; balanced cooking displays finesse.

at Newbiggin West : 3 ½ m. by A 66 – ✉ Penrith

The Old School
✉ CA11 0HT – ✆ (01768) 483 709 – info@theold-school.com – Fax (01768) 483 709 – closed 4-18 June, 21-28 December
3 rm – †£ 35/45 ††£ 65/70 – **Rest** – (by arrangement, communal dining) Menu £ 20
◆ Well sited off two major roads, this 19C former school house has been tastefully converted with an open-fired lounge and rooms individually decorated to a high standard.

ENGLAND

PENZANCE – Cornwall – 503 D 33 – pop. 20 255 — 1 A3

London 319 m – Exeter 113 m – Plymouth 77 m – Taunton 155 m
Access Access to the Isles of Scilly by helicopter, British International Heliport (01736) 364296, (01736) 363871
to the Isles of Scilly (Hugh Town) (Isles of Scilly Steamship Co. Ltd) (summer only) (approx. 2 h 40 mn)
Station Rd ✆ (01736) 362207
Town★ - Outlook★★★ – Western Promenade (≤ ★★★) YZ – National Lighthouse Centre★ **AC** Y – Chapel St★ Y – Maritime Museum★ **AC** Y **M1** – Penlee House Gallery and Museum★, **AC**
St Buryan★★ (church tower★★), SW : 5 m. by A 30 and B 3283 - Penwith★★ – Trengwainton Garden★★, NW : 2 m. – Sancreed - Church★★ (Celtic Crosses★★) - Carn Euny★, W : 3 ½ m. by A 30 Z – St Michael's Mount★★ (≤ ★★), E : 4 m. by B 3311 - Y - and A 30 – Gulval★ (Church★), NE : 1 m. - Ludgvan★ (Church★), NE : 3 ½ m. by A 30 - Chysauster Village★, N : 3 ½ m. by A 30, B 3311 and minor rd – Newlyn★ - Pilchard Works★, SW : 1 ½ m. by B 3315 Z - Lanyon Quoit★, NW : 3 ½ m. by St Clare Street – Men-an-Tol★, NW : 5 m. by B 3312 - Madron Church★, NW : 1 ½ m. by St Clare Street Y. Morvah (≤ ★★), NW : 6 ½ m. by St Clare Street Y – Zennor (Church★), NW : 6 m. by B 3311 Y – Prussia Cove★, E : 8 m. by B 3311 - Y - and A 394 – Land's End★ (cliff scenery★★★), SW : 10 m. by A 30 Z – Porthcurno★, SW : 8 ½ m. by A 30, B 3283 and minor rd

Plan opposite

Hotel Penzance (heated) rest,
Britons Hill ✉ TR18 3AE – ✆ (01736) 363 117 – enquiries@hotelpenzance.com – Fax (01736) 350 970 — Y c
24 rm – †£ 57/95 ††£ 102/170
Rest ***Bay*** – (dinner only and lunch in summer) (booking essential for non-residents) Menu £ 15/27 – Carte £ 28/47
◆ Well-established hotel with modern interior in elevated spot with views to St. Michaels Mount. Comfortable lounge. Bedrooms are immaculately kept and equipped with mod cons. Bright, modern restaurant with local artwork and bar.

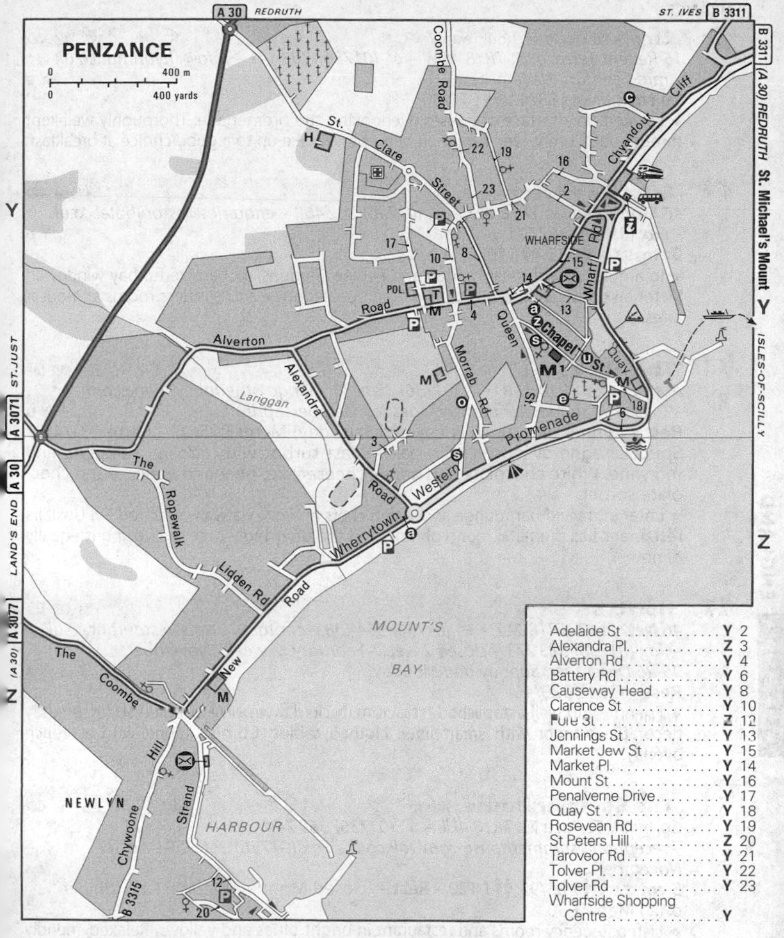

The Abbey without rest — P VISA

Abbey St ✉ TR18 4AR – ✆ (01736) 366 906 – hotel@theabbeyonline.com – Fax (01736) 351 163 – closed 25 December — Y **u**

6 rm – †£ 75/150 ††£ 150/180 – 2 suites

◆ Powder blue painted 17C house with lovely Victorian gardens. Attractive antique furnishings include historical pictures. Country house atmosphere and characterful bedrooms.

Beachfield — VISA AE

The Promenade ✉ TR18 4NW – ✆ (01736) 362 067 – office@beachfield.co.uk – Fax (01736) 331 100 – closed Christmas-New Year — Z **a**

18 rm – †£ 55/75 ††£ 109/139 – **Rest** – (bar lunch) Menu £ 23 **s** – Carte £ 20/30 **s**

◆ Classic seaside hotel with good views. Well-kept public areas include traditional lounge. Comfy bedrooms are well maintained and have a neat, bright feel. Traditional, varied menus, featuring fish specials.

Chy-An-Mor without rest
15 Regent Terrace ✉ TR18 4DW – ☎ (01736) 363 441 – info@chyanmor.co.uk – mid February-November Y **e**
10 rm ☕ – 🚹£ 35/42 🚹🚹£ 70/80
◆ Located on a terrace of houses overlooking the promenade. Thoroughly well kept throughout. Comfy, well-furnished bedrooms. Wake up to a good choice at breakfast.

Estoril without rest
46 Morrab Rd ✉ TR18 4EX – ☎ (01736) 362 468 – enquiries@estorilhotel.co.uk – Fax (01736) 367 471 Y **o**
9 rm ☕ – 🚹£ 35 🚹🚹£ 70
◆ In a quiet suburb near Morrab and Penlee Gardens, a characterful bay windowed Victorian house with a comfortable, traditional lounge and spotless rooms at modest rates.

The Abbey (Ben Tunnicliffe)
Abbey St ✉ TR18 4AR – ☎ (01736) 330 680 – kinga@theabbeyonline.com – Closed January, Monday and Tuesday October-April Y **u**
Rest – (dinner only lunch Friday and Saturday) Menu £ 25/27 – Carte £ 31/41
Spec. Lasagne of lobster with basil. Roast turbot with girolles, samphire and red wine. White chocolate and honey cheesecake, poached apricots and chocolate sorbet.
◆ Enter into vivid bar/lounge and watch chefs at work via wall-mounted TV! Upstairs restaurant has dramatic mono photos, and the unerringly precise cooking is equally of note.

Harris's
46 New St ✉ TR18 2LZ – ☎ (01736) 364 408 – contact@harrissrestaurant.co.uk – Fax (01736) 333 273 – closed 2 weeks February, 2 weeks November, 25-26 December, Sunday and Monday Y **a**
Rest – Carte £ 29/46
◆ Friendly and well-established restaurant, tucked away on a cobbled street. Brightly decorated interior with smart linen clothed tables. Cornish menu with a French overlay.

The Summer House with rm
Cornwall Terrace ✉ TR18 4HL – ☎ (01736) 363 744 – reception@summerhouse-cornwall.com – Fax (01736) 360 959 – Easter - November Z **s**
5 rm ☕ – 🚹£ 85/95 🚹🚹£ 120 – **Rest** – (closed Monday-Wednesday) (dinner only) Menu £ 30
◆ Listed Regency rooms and restaurant in bright blues and yellows. Relaxed, friendly ambience. Mediterranean influenced seafood; modern and flavourful. Leafy patio garden.

The Lime Tree
Trevelyan House, 16 Chapel St ✉ TR18 4AQ – ☎ (01736) 332 555 – bookings@the-lime-tree.co.uk – Fax (01736) 332 555 – closed Sunday, Monday and bank holidays Y **s**
Rest – (light lunch) Carte £ 27/31
◆ Central three-storey Georgian townhouse comprising two dining rooms, comfy lounge and tiny lunchtime roof terrace. Adventurous dinner menus and good value lunches of interest.

Bakehouse
Old Bakehouse Lane, Chapel St ✉ TR18 4AE – ☎ (01736) 331 331 – carrjasper@aol.com – closed Sunday Y **z**
Rest – (dinner only) (booking essential) Carte £ 20/39
◆ Penzance's original bakery, now a stylish restaurant on two floors, with old bakers oven in situ downstairs. Modern menus boast good choice of local seafood and produce.

ENGLAND

at Drift Southwest : 2 ½ m. on A 30 - Z – ✉ Penzance

Rose Farm without rest

Chyenhal, Buryas Bridge, Southwest : ¾ m. on Chyenhal rd ✉ TR19 6AN – ✆ (01736) 731 808 – penny@rosefarmcornwall.co.uk – Fax (01736) 731 808 – closed 24-25 December

3 rm – †£ 40/45 ††£ 60/70

◆ In the heart of the countryside, a tranquil working farm. Cosy, rustic farmhouse ambience with neatly kept bedrooms including large barn room.

PERRANUTHNOE – Cornwall – 503 D 33 – see Marazion

PERSHORE – Worcs. – 503 N 27 – pop. 7 104 19 C3

London 106 m – Birmingham 33 m – Worcester 8 m

The Barn without rest

Pensham Hill House, Pensham, Southeast : 1 m. by B 4084 ✉ WR10 3HA – ✆ (01386) 555 270 – ghorton@pensham-barn.co.uk – Fax (01386) 552 894

3 rm – †£ 50 ††£ 85

◆ Stylish barn renovation in enviable hillside location. Attractive open-plan lounge and breakfast area with exposed roof timbers. Rooms individually styled to a high standard.

Belle House

Bridge St ✉ WR10 1AJ – ✆ (01386) 555 055 – mail@belle-house.co.uk – Fax (01386) 555 377 – closed first 2 weeks January, 1 week August, 25-26 December, Sunday and Monday

Rest – Menu £ 26

◆ 16C and 18C high street building with some very characterful parts, including heavily beamed bar. Accomplished cooking on modern menus using carefully sourced ingredients.

Do not confuse X with ✿!
X defines comfort, while stars are awarded for the best cuisine, across all categories of comfort.

ENGLAND

PETERBOROUGH – Peterborough – 502 T 26 – pop. 136 292 14 A2

Great Britain

London 85 m – Cambridge 35 m – Leicester 41 m – Lincoln 51 m

3-5 Minster Precinct ✆ (0871) 7162618

Thorpe Wood Nene Parkway, ✆ (01733) 267 701 ;

Peterborough Milton Milton Ferry, ✆ (01733) 380 489 ;

Orton Meadows Ham Lane, ✆ (01733) 237 478 .

Cathedral★★ **AC** Y

Plan on next page

Orton Hall rm,

The Village, Orton Longueville, Southwest : 2½ m. by Oundle Rd (A 605) ✉ PE2 7DN – ✆ (01733) 391 111 – reception@ortonhall.co.uk – Fax (01733) 231 912 BX **c**

77 rm – †£ 80/100 ††£ 170, £12.50

Rest *The Huntly* – (dinner only and Sunday lunch) Menu £ 28 **s**

◆ Smartly run, part 17C house in 20 acres, once the seat of the Marquess of Huntly. Spacious, comfortable rooms: State rooms particularly impressive. Pub in former stables. Pleasantly set dining room offers richly varied cuisine.

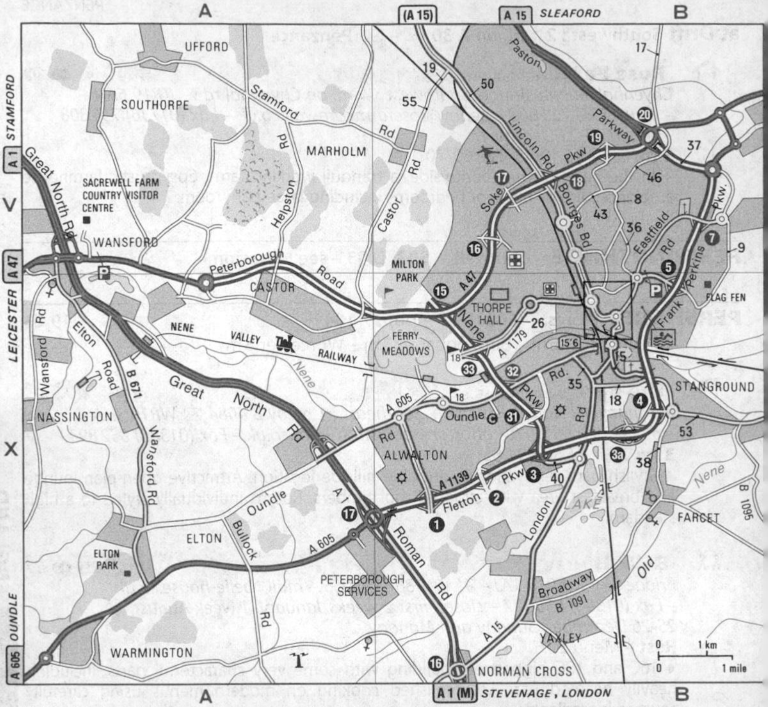

PETERBOROUGH

Street	Grid	No.
Bridge St	Z	
Cattle Market Rd	Y	2
Church St	YZ	
City Rd	Y	3
Cowgate	Y	5
Cross St	Z	6
Dogsthorpe Rd	BV	8
Edgerley Drain Rd	BV	9
Embankment Rd	Z	12
Exchange St	Y	13
Fletton Ave	BX	15
Geneva St	Y	16
Guntons Rd	BV	17
High St	BX	18
Hurn Rd	BV	19
Longthorpe Parkway	BX	26
Long Causeway	Y	25
Market Way	Y	28
Midgate	Y	29
New Rd	BX	35
Park Rd	BV	36
Paston Parkway	BV	37
Peterborough Rd	BX	38
Phorpres Way	BX	40
Queensgate Shopping Centre	Y	
Rivergate	Z	42
Rivergate Shopping Centre	Z	
St Paul's Rd	BV	43
Thorpe Rd	Y	45
Welland Rd	BV	46
Wentworth St	Z	48
Werrington Parkway	BV	50
Wheelyard	Y	52
Whittlesey Rd	BX	53
Woodcroft Rd	BV	55

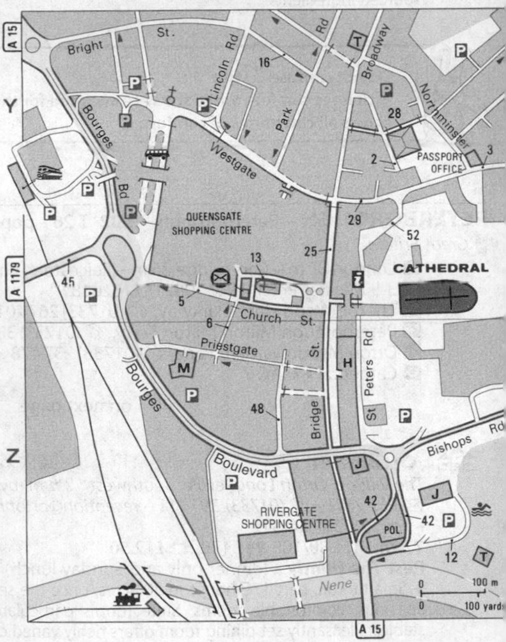

PETERSFIELD – Hants. – 504 R 30 7 C2

London 60 m – Brighton 45 m – Portsmouth 21 m – Southampton 34 m

Langrish House

Langrish, West : 3½ m. by A 272 ✉ GU32 1RN – ☎ (01730) 266 941 – frontdesk@langrishhouse.co.uk – Fax (01730) 260 543 – closed 4-11 January

13 rm – †£ 72/81 ††£ 145/155 – **Rest** – (lunch by arrangement) Menu £ 19/30 **s**

◆ Peaceful country house in wooded grounds, dating from 17C and family owned for seven generations. Characterful lounge in old Civil War cellars. Bright bedroom décor. Modish cuisine, proudly served.

XXX **JSW** (Jake Watkins) with rm

20 Dragon St ✉ GU31 4JJ – ☎ (01730) 262030 – closed 2 weeks January, 2 weeks July, Sunday and Monday

3 rm – ††£ 85/110 – **Rest** – Menu £ 27/43

Spec. Scallops with cauliflower and ceps. Slow cooked suckling pig belly with summer vegetables and Jersey Royals. Honeycomb parfait with Valrhona chocolate.

◆ Sympathetically restored, stylish 17C coaching inn with attractive enclosed rear courtyard for summer dining. Contemporary cooking: flavourful, well-sourced and confident. Comfortable bedrooms.

PETERSTOW – Herefordshire – 503 M 28 – see Ross-on-Wye

PETWORTH – W. Sussex – 504 S 31 – pop. 2 298 *Great Britain* 7 C2

London 54 m – Brighton 31 m – Portsmouth 33 m

Osiers London Rd, ☎ (01798) 344 097.

Petworth House★★ AC

Old Railway Station without rest

South : 1½ m. off A 285 ✉ GU28 0JF – ☎ (01798) 342 346 – info@old-station.co.uk – Fax (01798) 343 066 – closed 24-26 and 1 January

10 rm – †£ 57/107 ††£ 150/160

◆ Elegant converted 1894 waiting room and ticket hall, full of charming details from the age of steam. Six rooms in handsome Pullman carriages. Summer breakfast on platform.

XX **The Grove Inn**

Grove Lane, South : ½ m. by High St and Pulborough rd ✉ GU28 0HY – ☎ (01798) 343 659 – steveandvaleria@tiscali.co.uk – closed 2 weeks January, 31 December, Sunday dinner and Monday

Rest – (light lunch) Carte £ 25/32

◆ Restored farmhouse: conservatory bar and beamed restaurant. Dinner menu with modern influence, simpler lunch menu. Attentive service.

Badgers with rm

Coultershaw Bridge, South : 1½ m. on A 285 ✉ GU28 0JF – ☎ (01798) 342 651 – Closed 25 December

3 rm – †£ 80 ††£ 80 – **Rest** – (closed Sunday dinner in winter) Carte £ 23/34

◆ Lovely pub next to Old Railway Station. Beautiful oak panelled bar has old photos and 'badger and honey' theme. Log fire; intimate alcove. Eclectic, robust menus. Comfy rooms.

at Halfway Bridge West : 3 m. on A 272 – ✉ Petworth

The Halfway Bridge Inn with rm

✉ GU28 9BP – ☎ (01798) 861 281 – enquiries@halfwaybridge.co.uk – Closed 25 December

6 rm – †£ 65/90 ††£ 130 – **Rest** – Carte £ 12/25

◆ Affable staff, balanced cooking and fine local ales in an instantly likeable 17C coaching inn. Brick interior festooned with hops, warmed by stoves and log fires. Comfy rooms.

at Lickfold Northwest : 6 m. by A 272 – ✉ Petworth

The Lickfold Inn
✉ GU28 9EY – ☎ (01798) 861 285 – thelickfoldinn@aol.com – Closed 25-26 December, Sunday dinner and Monday except Bank Holiday Monday
Rest – Menu £ 12/15 – Carte £ 22/33
◆ Handsome, oak-beamed pub in a quiet Downs village. Cosy ambience and easy-going, helpful staff. Concise modern repertoire, with a Mediterranean twist, from wood-fired ovens.

PHILLEIGH – Cornwall – ✉ Truro 1 B3

London 273 m – Falmouth 26 m – Truro 14 m

Roseland Inn
✉ TR2 5NB – ☎ (01872) 580 254 – Closed 25 December
Rest – Carte £ 21/31
◆ Family run, rurally set 16C inn with lovely rustic interior. Exposed beams, solid stone floor and open fires aid relaxation. Wide-ranging menu with Cornish base.

PICKERING – N. Yorks. – 502 R 21 – pop. 6 616 23 C1

London 237 m – Middlesbrough 43 m – Scarborough 19 m – York 25 m
The Ropery ☎ (01751) 473791

ENGLAND

White Swan Inn
Market Pl ✉ YO18 7AA – ☎ (01751) 472 288 – welcome@white-swan.co.uk – Fax (01751) 475 554
20 rm – †£ 95/100 ††£ 130/185 – 1 suite – **Rest** – Carte £ 21/35
◆ Long-standing former coaching halt in a popular market town. Lovely lounge and comfortable bedrooms - the new ones in the courtyard are very stylish with contemporary touches. Traditional dining room offers lengthy menu.

17 Burgate without rest
17 Burgate ✉ YO18 7AU – ☎ (01751) 473 463 – info@17-burgate.co.uk – Fax (01751) 473 463 – closed 24 and 25 December
5 rm – †£ 65/75 ††£ 90
◆ Painstakingly restored 17C town house, the décor smoothly spanning 400 years. Sitting room bar; sizzling breakfasts; superbly appointed rooms, two with larger seating areas.

Bramwood
19 Hall Garth ✉ YO18 7AW – ☎ (01751) 474 066 – bramwood@fsbdial.co.uk
8 rm – †£ 40/55 ††£ 75 – **Rest** – (by arrangement) Menu £ 20
◆ Georgian town house with sheltered garden. Personally run with curios of rural life dotted around a firelit lounge. Cosy bedrooms in homely, cottagey style.

Old Manse
Middleton Rd ✉ YO18 8AL – ☎ (01751) 476 484 – info@oldmansepickering.co.uk – Fax (01751) 477 124
10 rm – †£ 45/60 ††£ 86/96 – **Rest** – (by arrangement) Menu £ 19
◆ A welcoming ambience and modestly priced rooms, spacious and spotless, make this personally run house an ideal base for touring the moors. Secluded rear garden and orchard. Informal conservatory dining room.

at Levisham Northeast : 6½ m. by A 169 – ✉ Pickering 23 C1

The Moorlands Country House
✉ YO18 7NL – ☎ (01751) 460 229 – ronaldoleonardo@aol.com – Fax (01751) 460 470 – Closed December. March-November, minimum 2 night stay
7 rm – †£ 80/140 ††£ 140/180 – **Rest** – (by arrangement) Menu £ 25 – Carte £ 16/40
◆ Restored 19C house with attractive gardens in the heart of the North York Moors National Park. There are fine views to be enjoyed here. Rooms furnished to high standard. Traditional, home-cooked meals in pretty dining room.

at Marton West : 5 ¼ m. by A 170 – ✉ Pickering

The Appletree

✉ YO62 6RD – ✆ (01751) 431 457 – appletreeinn@supanet.com – Fax (01751) 430 190 – Closed 2 weeks January and 25 December

Rest – (closed Monday-Tuesday) Carte £ 17/25

◆ Large, part 18C inn in quiet village. Plenty of recently added beams. Small, comfy, sofa-strewn lounge. The modern British cooking provides originality and interest.

at Middleton Northwest : 1 ½ m. on A 170 – ✉ Pickering

The Leas

Nova Lane, North : 1 m. via Church Lane ✉ YO18 8PN – ✆ (01751) 472 129 – enquiries@cottageleashotel.co.uk – Fax (01751) 474 930

17 rm – †£ 45/55 ††£ 68/88 – **Rest** – (lunch by arrangement) Carte £ 22/34

◆ Get away from it all to an extended period house in the hills above Middleton. Large lounge with open fire. Simple, sizeable rooms looking to quiet, unspoilt fields. Bistro menus in heavily wood-furnished restaurant.

at Sinnington Northwest : 4 m. by A 170 – ✉ York

Fox and Hounds with rm

Main St ✉ YO62 6SQ – ✆ (01751) 431 577 – foxhoundsinn@easynet.co.uk – Fax (01751) 432 791 – Closed 25-26 December

10 rm – †£ 49/69 ††£ 120 – **Rest** – Carte £ 20/28

◆ At the heart of this sleepy village on the river Seven, an extended coaching house, beamed and panelled in ancient oak. Well-proportioned, cottagey rooms; hearty breakfasts. Modern restaurant or rustic bar offer dining options.

ENGLAND

PICKHILL – N. Yorks. – 502 P 21 – ✉ Thirsk — 22 B1

London 229 m – Leeds 41 m – Middlesbrough 30 m – York 34 m

Nags Head Country Inn

✉ YO7 4JG – ✆ (01845) 567 391 – reservations@nagsheadpickhill.co.uk – Fax (01845) 567 212

14 rm – †£ 55 ††£ 80 – 1 suite – **Rest** – Carte £ 18/28

◆ Atmospheric 300 year old inn in an ancient hamlet, an easy drive to Thirsk and Ripon races. Neat rooms in soft floral fabrics. Over 800 ties on display in the rustic bar. Rural restaurant adorned with bookshelves and patterned rugs.

PILLERTON PRIORS – Warks. – 503 P 27 – see Stratford-upon-Avon

PILTDOWN – E Sussex – pop. 1 517 — 8 A2

London 41 m – Brighton 21 m – Uckfield 3 m

The Peacock Inn

Shortbridge ✉ TN22 3XA – ✆ (01825) 762 463 – matthewarnold@aol.com – Closed 25-26 December

Rest – Carte £ 18/30

◆ Quintessentially English pub in heart of Sussex countryside, with black and white timbered exterior and neatly trimmed yew trees. Characterful beamed rooms; traditional menus.

PLUCKLEY – Kent – 504 W 30 — 9 C2

London 53 m – Folkestone 25 m – Maidstone 18 m

The Dering Arms

Station Rd, South : 1 ½ m. on Bethersden rd ✉ TN27 0RR – ✆ (01233) 840 371 – jim@deringarms.com – Fax (01233) 840 498 – Closed 25-29 December and 1 January

Rest – Seafood (closed Sunday dinner and Monday) Carte £ 20/35

◆ Well-established, personally run 19C gabled lodge; informal, flagged bar hung with hunting trophies. Robust dishes, seafood specials, farm ciders and a real "local" feel.

PLUMTREE – Notts. – see Nottingham

PLUSH – Dorset – 503 M 31 — 4 C3

London 142 m – Bournemouth 35 m – Salisbury 44 m – Taunton 52 m – Weymouth 15 m – Yeovil 23 m

The Brace of Pheasants

DT2 7RQ – (01300) 348 357 – bennett.family@btinternet.com – Fax (01300) 348 959 – Closed 25 December

Rest – (closed Sunday dinner in winter) Carte £ 20/30

◆ Secluded 16C inn, once two thatched cottages and smithy; Robust modern and classic dishes in a spacious bar or more formal parlour. Rear garden, woods and bridleways beyond.

PLYMOUTH – Plymouth – 503 H 32 – pop. 243 795 — 2 C2

London 242 m – Bristol 124 m – Southampton 161 m

Access Tamar Bridge (toll) AY

Plymouth City (Roborough) Airport : (01752) 204090, N : 3 ½ m. by A 386 ABY

to France (Roscoff) (Brittany Ferries) 1-3 daily (6 h) – to Spain (Santander) (Brittany Ferries) 2 weekly (approx 24 h)

Plymouth Mayflower, 3-5 The Barbican (01752) 304849 - Plymouth Discovery Centre, Crabtree (01752) 266030

Staddon Heights Plymstock, (01752) 402 475 ;

Elfordleigh Hotel G. & C.C. Plympton Colebrook, (01752) 348 425 .

Town★ - Smeaton's Tower (≤ ★★) **AC** BZ **T1** – Plymouth Dome★ **AC** BZ – Royal Citadel (ramparts ≤ ★★) **AC** BZ – City Museum and Art Gallery★ BZ **M1**

Saltram House★★ **AC**, E : 3 ½ m. BY **A** - Tamar River★★ – Anthony House★ **AC**, W : 5 m. by A 374 – Mount Edgcumbe (≤ ★) **AC**, SW : 2 m. by passenger ferry from Stonehouse AZ. NE : Dartmoor National Park★★ – Buckland Abbey★★ **AC**, N : 7 ½ m. by A 386 ABY

Plan opposite

Holiday Inn

≤ city and Plymouth Sound, rm,

Armada Way PL1 2HJ – (01752) 639 988 – hiplymouth@qmh-hotels.com – Fax (01752) 673 816 — BZ **s**

211 rm – ♦£ 119/129 ♦♦£ 119/129 – **Rest** – (dinner only and Sunday lunch) Menu £ 15/20 – Carte £ 20/31 **s**

◆ Substantial purpose-built hotel enjoys a panorama of the city skyline and the Plymouth Sound. Neatly laid-out, well-equipped bedrooms; extensive leisure club. Modern restaurant on top floor to make most of view.

Copthorne H. Plymouth

rm, rest,

Armada Way, (via Western Approach southbound) PL1 1AR – (01752) 224 161 – sales.plymouth@mill-cop.com – Fax (01752) 670 688 — BZ **e**

135 rm – ♦£ 72/127 ♦♦£ 72/127, £ 15.75 – **Rest** – (bar lunch Monday-Saturday) Menu £ 20 (dinner) – Carte £ 24/31

◆ Popular with business travellers, a group-owned hotel in easy reach of the station. Smartly kept accommodation - quieter corner rooms look across the gardens or the city. Bentley's offers spacious, modern comforts.

Bowling Green without rest

9-10 Osborne Pl, Lockyer St, The Hoe PL1 2PU – (01752) 209 090 – info@bowlingreenhotel.co.uk – Fax (01752) 209 092 — BZ **r**

12 rm – ♦£ 45/58 ♦♦£ 68

◆ Georgian house, half overlooking Hoe, near site of Drake's legendary game. High-ceilinged rooms in pine and modern fabrics; some have power showers. Stroll to promenade.

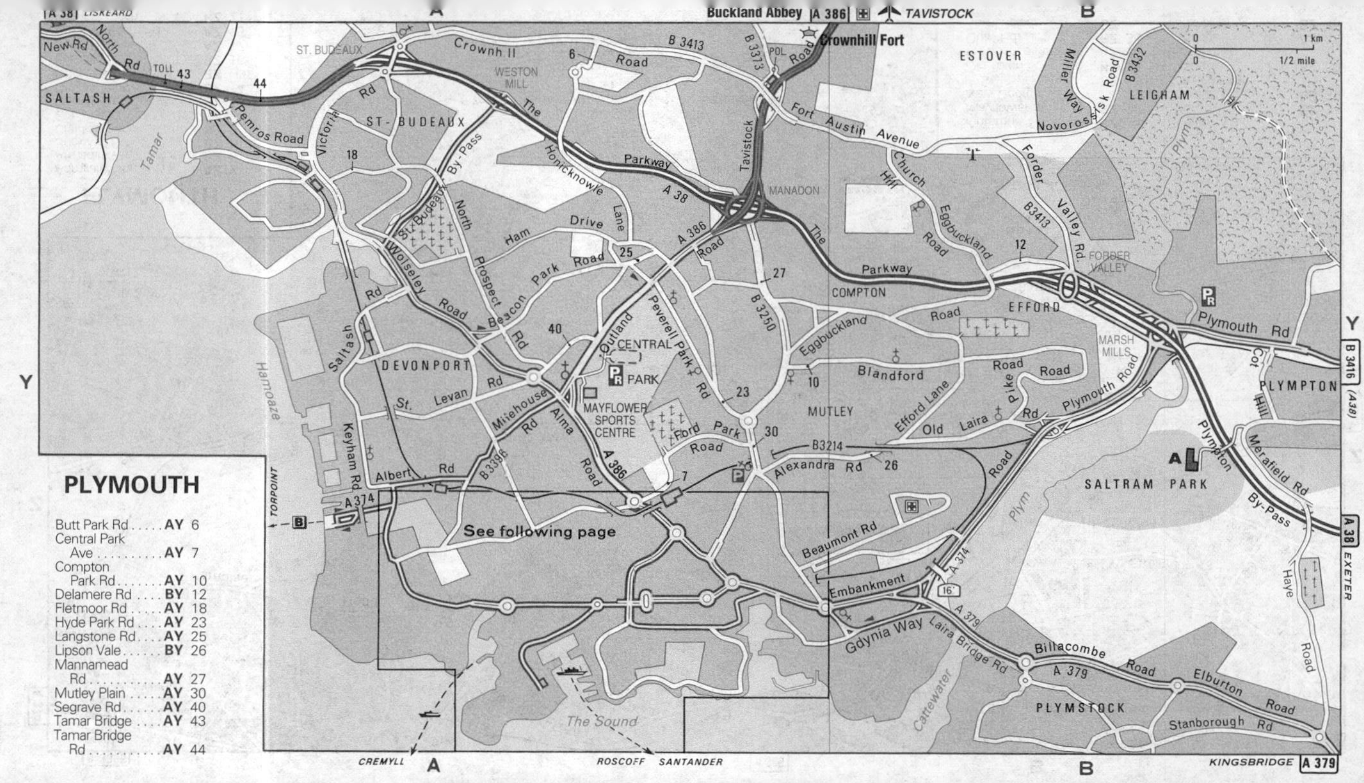

PLYMOUTH

Butt Park Rd	AY	6
Central Park Ave	AY	7
Compton Park Rd	AY	10
Delamere Rd	BY	12
Fletmoor Rd	AY	18
Hyde Park Rd	AY	23
Langstone Rd	AY	25
Lipson Vale	BY	26
Mannamead Rd	AY	27
Mutley Plain	AY	30
Segrave Rd	AY	40
Tamar Bridge	AY	43
Tamar Bridge Rd	AY	44

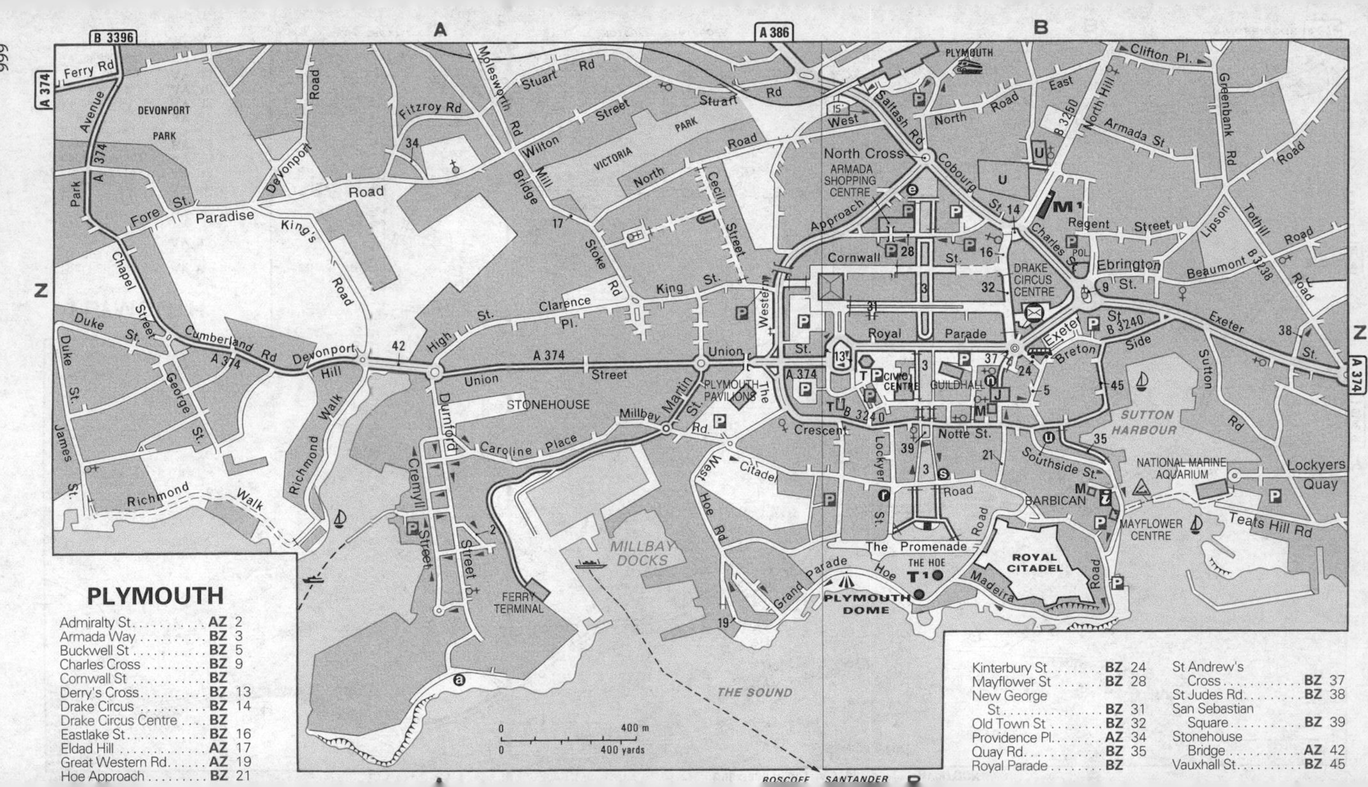
PLYMOUTH
Admiralty St. . . . . AZ 2
Armada Way . . . . BZ 3
Buckwell St . . . . BZ 5
Charles Cross . . . . BZ 9
Cornwall St . . . . BZ
Derry's Cross. . . . . BZ 13
Drake Circus . . . . BZ 14
Drake Circus Centre . . . . BZ
Eastlake St. . . . . BZ 16
Eldad Hill . . . . AZ 17
Great Western Rd. . . . . . AZ 19
Hoe Approach . . . . BZ 21
Kinterbury St . . . . BZ 24
Mayflower St . . . . BZ 28
New George St. . . . . BZ 31
Old Town St . . . . BZ 32
Providence Pl. . . . . AZ 34
Quay Rd. . . . . BZ 35
Royal Parade . . . . BZ
St Andrew's Cross. . . . . BZ 37
St Judes Rd. . . . . BZ 38
San Sebastian Square. . . . . BZ 39
Stonehouse Bridge . . . . AZ 42
Vauxhall St. . . . . BZ 45
A
B
Z
A 374
B 3396
A 386
B 3250
B 3238
B 3240
Ferry Rd
Avenue
Park
DEVONPORT PARK
Devonport Road
Fore St.
Paradise Road
King's Road
Chapel Street
Duke St.
Cumberland Rd
Devonport Hill
George St.
James St.
Richmond Walk
Molesworth Rd
Stuart Rd
Fitzroy Rd
Wilton Street
Mill Bridge
VICTORIA PARK
North Road
Stuart Rd
West
Saltash Rd
North Cross
ARMADA SHOPPING CENTRE
Approach
Cobourg St.
Cecil Street
Stoke Rd
King St.
Clarence Pl.
High St.
Union Street
STONEHOUSE
Durnford Street
Cremyll Street
Caroline Place
Millbay Rd.
Martin St.
PLYMOUTH PAVILIONS
The Crescent
Western
Cornwall St.
Royal Parade
CIVIC CENTRE
GUILDHALL
DRAKE CIRCUS CENTRE
Notte St.
Lockyer St.
Citadel Road
West Hoe Rd
Grand Parade
The Promenade
THE HOE
Hoe Road
PLYMOUTH DOME
Madeira Road
ROYAL CITADEL
BARBICAN
Southside St.
MAYFLOWER CENTRE
NATIONAL MARINE AQUARIUM
SUTTON HARBOUR
Sutton Rd
Lockyers Quay
Teats Hill Rd
Exeter St.
Breton Side
Ebrington St.
Regent Street
Charles St.
Beaumont Road
Lipson Road
Tothill Road
Greenbank Rd
Armada St.
North Hill
East
Clifton Pl.
PLYMOUTH
FERRY TERMINAL
MILLBAY DOCKS
THE SOUND
400 m
400 yards
ROSCOFF
SANTANDER

XX **Tanners**

Prysten House, Finewell St ✉ PL1 2AE – ✆ (01752) 252 001 – enquiries@tannersrestaurant.co.uk – Fax (01752) 252 105 – closed 24-26 and 31 December, first week January, Sunday and Monday BZ **n**

Rest – (booking essential) Menu £ 19/32 **s** – Carte £ 26/36 **s**

◆ Characterful 15C house, reputedly Plymouth's oldest building: mullioned windows, tapestries, exposed stone and an illuminated water well. Modern, interesting cooking.

XX **Artillery Tower**

Firestone Bay ✉ PL1 3QR – ✆ (01752) 257610 – closed 2 weeks in Summer, 2 weeks at Christmas, Sunday and Monday AZ **a**

Rest – (booking essential at lunch Tuesday-Friday only) Menu £ 29/37

◆ Uniquely located in 500 year-old circular tower, built to defend the city. Courteous service of mostly well executed local dishes: blackboard fish specialities.

X **Barbican Kitchen**

Black Friars Distillery, 60 Southside St ✉ PL1 2LQ – ✆ (01752) 604 448 – info@barbicankitchen.com – Fax (01752) 604 445 – closed 25-26, 31 December, and 1 January BZ **u**

Rest – Carte £ 16/27

◆ Set within the famous Plymouth Gin Distillery, this stylish restaurant, in vivid lime green and lilac, is split between two upper rooms, offering good value brasserie fare.

at Plympton St Maurice East : 6 m. by A 374 on B 3416 - BY – ✉ Plymouth

ENGLAND

St Elizabeth's House

Longbrook St – ✆ (01752) 344 840 – enquiries@stelizabeths.co.uk – Fax (01752) 331 391

13 rm – †£ 135 ††£ 151 – 2 suites – **Rest** – Menu £ 14 (lunch) – Carte approx. £ 32

◆ Immaculate cream-washed former convent, now a stylish boutique hotel; lounge is dressed in period décor while light bedrooms are contemporary, with up-to-date facilities. Formal dining room offers classically based cooking with a modern twist.

Hotels and restaurants change every year, so change your Michelin guide every year!

PLYMPTON ST MAURICE Devon – see PLYMOUTH

POLPERRO – Cornwall – **503** G 33 – ✉ **Looe** 1 **B2**

London 271 m – Plymouth 28 m

Village★

Trenderway Farm without rest

Northeast : 2 m. by A 387 ✉ PL13 2LY – ✆ (01503) 272 214 – trenderwayfarm@hotmail.com – Fax (01503) 272 991 – closed Christmas and New Year

6 rm – †£ 40/60 ††£ 70/90

◆ Charming 16C farmhouse on working farm with converted outbuildings: modish ambience in a traditional setting. Breakfast over the lake. Stylish rooms with modern fabrics.

PONTELAND – Tyne and Wear – **501** O 19 – see Newcastle upon Tyne

POOLE – Poole – **503** O 31 – pop. 144 800 4 **C3**

London 116 m – Bournemouth 4 m – Dorchester 23 m – Southampton 36 m – Weymouth 28 m

to France (Cherbourg) (Brittany Ferries) 1-2 daily May-October (4 h 15 mn) day (5 h 45 mn) night – to France (St Malo) (Brittany Ferries) daily (8 h) – to France (St Malo) (Condor Ferries Ltd)

Welcome Centre, Enefco House, Poole Quay ✆ (01202) 253253

Parkstone Links Rd, ✆ (01202) 707 138 ;

The Bulbury Club Lytchett Matravers Bulberry Lane, ✆ (01929) 459 574 .

Town★ (Waterfront **M1** , Scaplen's Court **M2**)

Compton Acres★★, (English Garden ≤ ★★★) **AC**, SE : 3 m. by B 3369 BX (on Bournemouth town plan) – Brownsea Island★ (Baden-Powell Stone ≤ ★★) **AC**, by boat from Poole Quay or Sandbanks BX (on Bournemouth town plan)

Plan of Built up Area : see Bournemouth BX

Plan opposite

The Haven
≤ Ferry, Old Harry Rocks and Poole Bay, (heated)

161 Banks Rd, Sandbanks, Southeast : 4 ¼ m. on B 3369 ✉ BH13 7QL – ✆ (01202) 707 333 – enquiries@havenhotel.co.uk – Fax (01202) 708 796 BX **c**

rest, VISA AE

76 rm – ♦£ 100/170 ♦♦£ 320/480 – 2 suites

Rest *La Roche* – see restaurant listing

Rest *Seaview* – (dinner only) Menu £ 19/30 **s**

♦ Sweeping white façade and heated seawater pool. Smart modern rooms. Lounge on site of Marconi's laboratory has fireside leather wing chairs. Candlelit Seaview overlooks bay.

Harbour Heights
≤ Poole Harbour, VISA AE

Haven Rd, Sandbanks, Southeast : 3 m. by B 3369 ✉ BH13 7LW – ✆ (01202) 707 272 – enquiries@harbourheights.net – Fax (01202) 708 594 BX **n**

38 rm – ♦£ 135/165 ♦♦£ 210/260

Rest *harbar bistro* – Menu £ 27 (lunch) – Carte £ 32/56

♦ 1920s hotel stylishly updated in 2003; walls decorated with vibrant modern art. Swanky, smart bedrooms boast modern interiors and all mod cons: request room with a sea view. Bistro-styled restaurant with very popular terrace.

Thistle Poole
≤ VISA AE

The Quay ✉ BH15 1HD – ✆ (0870) 333 9143 – poole@thistle.co.uk – Fax (0870) 333 9243 **e**

70 rm – ♦£ 94/134 ♦♦£ 104/164 – **Rest** – (bar lunch Monday-Saturday) Menu £ 15 **s** – Carte £ 34/37 **s**

♦ Purpose-built, redbrick, group hotel on the quay; informal bar; neatly laid-out rooms - half of which have views over the water - in sober blue fabrics and pine furniture. Fine outlook from wide-windowed restaurant.

La Roche – at Haven H.
≤ Ferry, Old Harry Rocks and Poole Bay, VISA AE

161 Banks Rd, Sandbanks, Southeast : 4 ¼ m. on B 3369 ✉ BH13 7QL – ✆ (01202) 707 333 – Fax (01202) 708 796 – closed Sunday dinner and Monday BX **c**

Rest – Carte £ 26/39 **s**

♦ Perched at the side of the Haven, overlooking the bay. Watch the fishing boats from wonderful adjacent terrace. Eclectic menus with seafood base and tasty local ingredients.

Isabel's
VISA AE

32 Station Rd, Lower Parkstone ✉ BH14 8UD – ✆ (01202) 747 885 – isabels@onetel.com – Fax (01202) 747 885 – closed 26 December, 1 January, Sunday and Monday BX **a**

Rest – (dinner only) (booking essential) Menu £ 30 – Carte £ 26/32

♦ Long-established neighbourhood restaurant; old shelves recall its origins as a Victorian pharmacy. Intimate wooden booths. Classically inspired menu with a rich Gallic tone.

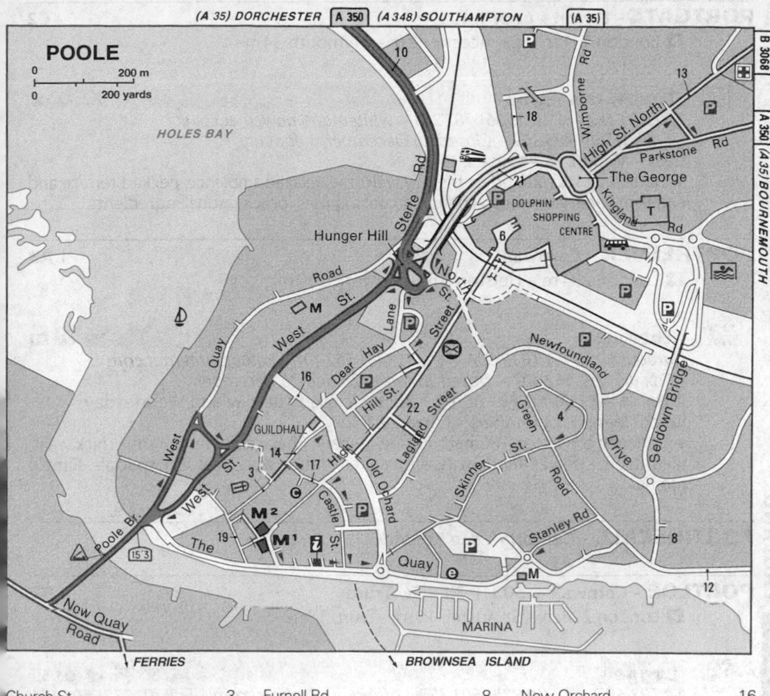

Church St	3	Furnell Rd	8	New Orchard	16
Dolphin Quay Shopping Centre		High St	9	New St	17
Emerson Rd	4	Holes Bay Rd	10	Serpentine Rd	18
Falkland Square	6	Labrador Drive	12	Thames St	19
Fishermans Rd	7	Longfleet Rd	13	Towngate Bridge	21
		Market St	14	Westons Lane	22

POOLEY BRIDGE – Cumbria – **501** L 20 – see Ullswater

PORLOCK – Somerset – **503** J 30 – ✉ **Minehead** 3 **A2**

▶ London 190 m – Bristol 67 m – Exeter 46 m – Taunton 28 m

Village★ - Porlock Hill (≤ ★★) – St Dubricius Church★

Dunkery Beacon★★★ (≤ ★★★), S : 5 ½ m. – Exmoor National Park★★ - Selworthy★ (≤ ★★, Church★), E : 2 m. by A 39 and minor rd - Luccombe★ (Church★), E : 3 m. by A 39 – Culbone★ (St Beuno), W : 3 ½ m. by B 3225, 1 ½ m. on foot – Doone Valley★, W : 6 m. by A 39, access from Oare on foot

Oaks ≤ Porlock Bay, P VISA

✉ *TA24 8ES – ☎ (01643) 862 265 – info@oakshotel.co.uk – Fax (01643) 863 131 – March-October and Christmas-New Year*

8 rm – †£ 90 ††£ 135 – **Rest** – (dinner only) (booking essential for non-residents) Menu £ 33

◆ Traditionally styled Edwardian country house in pretty gardens, very well run by most hospitable owners. Stunning rural views. Cosy, individual rooms in co-ordinated colours. Neat dining room: all land produce from a 20 mile radius.

PORT ERIN – Isle of Man – **502** F 21 – see Man (Isle of)

PORT ST MARY – I.O.M. – **502** F/G 21 – see Man (Isle of)

PORTGATE – Devon – pop. 1 453 2 C2

London 211 m – Launceston 8 m – Plymouth 34 m

The Harris Arms

✉ EX20 4PZ – ☎ (01566) 783 331 – whiteman@powernet.co.uk
– Fax (01566) 783 359 – Closed 26 December, 1 January
Rest – Menu £ 15 – Carte £ 19/25

◆ Traditional 16C pub offers friendly welcome, relaxed ambience, decked terrace and excellent wine list. Robust, confident cooking uses local, seasonal ingredients.

PORTHLEVEN – Cornwall 1 A3

London 284 m – Helston 3 m – Penzance 12 m

Kota with rm

Harbour Head ✉ TR13 9JA – ☎ (01326) 562 407 – kota@btinternet.com
– Fax (01326) 562 407 – closed January, 25 and 26 December
2 rm – †£ 50/60 ††£ 65/90 – **Rest** – (closed Tuesday and Wednesday lunch) Menu £ 13 (dinner) – Carte £ 22/32

◆ Cottagey converted 18C harbourside granary. Characterful restaurant - thick walls, tiled floors - serves modern Asian inspired dishes with local fish specials. Simple rooms.

PORTINSCALE – Cumbria – see Keswick

PORTLOE – Cornwall – 503 F 33 – ✉ Truro 1 B3

London 296 m – St Austell 15 m – Truro 15 m

Lugger

✉ TR2 5RD – ☎ (01872) 501 322 – office@luggerhotel.com – Fax (01872) 501 691
22 rm – †£ 170/225 ††£ 295/355 – **Rest** – (light lunch) Menu £ 20/38 – Carte approx. £ 21

◆ Former inn in a beautiful location within pretty Cornish cove. Stylish public areas. The bedrooms are created with a tasteful palette in strikingly contemporary vein. Restaurant enjoys blissful outlook over the cove.

PORTSCATHO – Cornwall – 503 F 33 – ✉ Truro 1 B3

London 298 m – Plymouth 55 m – Truro 16 m

St Just-in-Roseland Church★★, W : 4 m. by A 3078 – St Anthony-in-Roseland (≤ ★★) S : 3½ m

Rosevine

Rosevine, North : 2 m. by A 3078 ✉ TR2 5EW – ☎ (01872) 580 206
– info@rosevine.co.uk – Fax (01872) 580 230 – closed January
7 rm – †£ 135/280 ††£ 150/400, £ 10 – 10 suites – **Rest** – (bar lunch) Carte £ 19/35

◆ Surrounded by attractive gardens, this family owned hotel offers traditional, homely comforts. Rooms are well looked after and a friendly air prevails. Pretty restaurant makes use of local ingredients.

Driftwood

≤ Gerrans Bay,

Rosevine, North : 2 m. by A 3078 ✉ TR2 5EW – ☎ (01872) 580 644
– info@driftwoodhotel.co.uk – Fax (01872) 580 801 – closed mid December to mid February
15 rm – †£ 173/205 ††£ 240/310 – **Rest** – (dinner only) (booking essential) Menu £ 40 s

◆ Stylish décor and a neutral, contemporary feel make this an enviable spot to lay one's head. Attractive decking affords fine sea views. Smart bedrooms with pristine style. Distinctive modern dining room with fine vistas.

ENGLAND

PORTSMOUTH and SOUTHSEA – Portsmouth – **503** Q 31 6 **B3**

– **pop. 187 056** *Great Britain*

London 78 m – Brighton 48 m – Salisbury 44 m – Southampton 21 m

to France (St Malo) (Brittany Ferries) daily (8 h 45 mn) day (10 h 45 mn) night – to France (Caen) (Brittany Ferries) 2-4 daily (6 h) day (6 h 45 mn) night – to France (Cherbourg) (Brittany Ferries) 2 daily (5 h) day, (7 h) night – to France (Le Havre) (LD Lines) daily (5 h 30 mn/7 h 30 mn) – to France (Cherbourg) (Brittany Ferries) 1-2 daily (2 h 45 mn) – to France (Caen) (Brittany Ferries) 2-4 daily (3 h 45 mn) – to Spain (Bilbao) (P & O European Ferries Ltd) 1-2 weekly (35 h) – to Guernsey (St Peter Port) and Jersey (St Helier) (Condor Ferries Ltd) daily except Sunday (10 hrs) – to the Isle of Wight (Fishbourne) (Wightlink Ltd) frequent services daily (35 mn)

to the Isle of Wight (Ryde) (Wightlink Ltd) frequent services daily (15 mn) – from Southsea to the Isle of Wight (Ryde) (Hovertravel Ltd) frequent services daily (10 mn)

The Hard (023) 9282 6722, tic@portsmouthcc.gov.uk.

Great Salterns Burrfields Rd, Portsmouth Golf Centre, (023) 9266 4549 ;

Crookhorn Lane Waterlooville Widley, (023) 9237 2210 ;

Southwick Park Southwick Pinsley Drive, (023) 9238 0131 .

City★ – Naval Portsmouth BY : H.M.S. Victory★★★ **AC**, The Mary Rose★★, Royal Naval Museum★★ **AC** – Old Portsmouth★ BYZ : The Point (≤ ★★) - St Thomas Cathedral★ – Southsea (Castle★ **AC**) AZ – Royal Marines Museum, Eastney★ **AC**, AZ **M1**

Portchester Castle★ **AC**, NW : 5½ m. by A 3 and A 27 AY

Plan on next page

ENGLAND

Beaufort

71 Festing Rd, Southsea ✉ PO4 0NQ – (023) 9282 3707 – enq@beauforthotel.co.uk – Fax (023) 9287 0270 AZ **n**

20 rm – ♦£ 45/70 ♦♦£ 70/85 – **Rest** – (dinner only) Menu £ 20 **s**

◆ Privately owned Southsea hotel, a few minutes from the water. Sizeable and well-kept bedrooms in smart modern décor. Cosy sitting room with leather chesterfields. Sprays of flowers brighten traditional dining room.

Upper Mount House without rest

The Vale, Clarendon Rd ✉ PO5 2EQ – (023) 9282 0456 – Fax (023) 9282 0456 – closed 2 weeks Christmas CZ **e**

16 rm – ♦£ 38/55 ♦♦£ 62/70

◆ Privately managed, gabled Victorian villa, set in a quiet suburb. Handsomely sized rooms in varying styles, some with four poster beds, all simply appointed.

Fortitude Cottage without rest

51 Broad St, Old Portsmouth ✉ PO1 2JD – (023) 9282 3748 – info@fortitudecottage.co.uk – Fax (023) 9282 3748 – closed December BY **c**

4 rm – ♦£ 45/85 ♦♦£ 85/95

◆ Pretty little quayside townhouse named after an 18C battleship. Watch yachts rounding the Point from a cosy bow windowed lounge. Simple, well-priced rooms, charming owners.

8 Kings Road

8 Kings Rd, Southsea ✉ PO5 3AH – (08451) 303 234 – info@8kingsroad.co.uk – Fax (02392) 862 729 – closed 25-26 December, 1 January, Sunday dinner and Monday CZ **c**

Rest – Menu £ 17 (lunch) – Carte £ 29/34

◆ High ceilinged former bank with vast windows, marble floors, mezzanine and chandelier-style lighting. Quality ingredients well prepared and presented in modern French dishes.

Tang's

127 Elm Grove, Southsea ✉ PO5 1LJ – (023) 9282 2722 – Fax (023) 9283 8323 – closed Monday AZ **c**

Rest – Chinese (dinner only) Menu £ 17 – Carte £ 11/20

◆ Smooth presentation at every turn at this neighbourhood Chinese restaurant - rattan chairs, neat linen, impeccably attired staff and authentic, delicately composed cuisine.

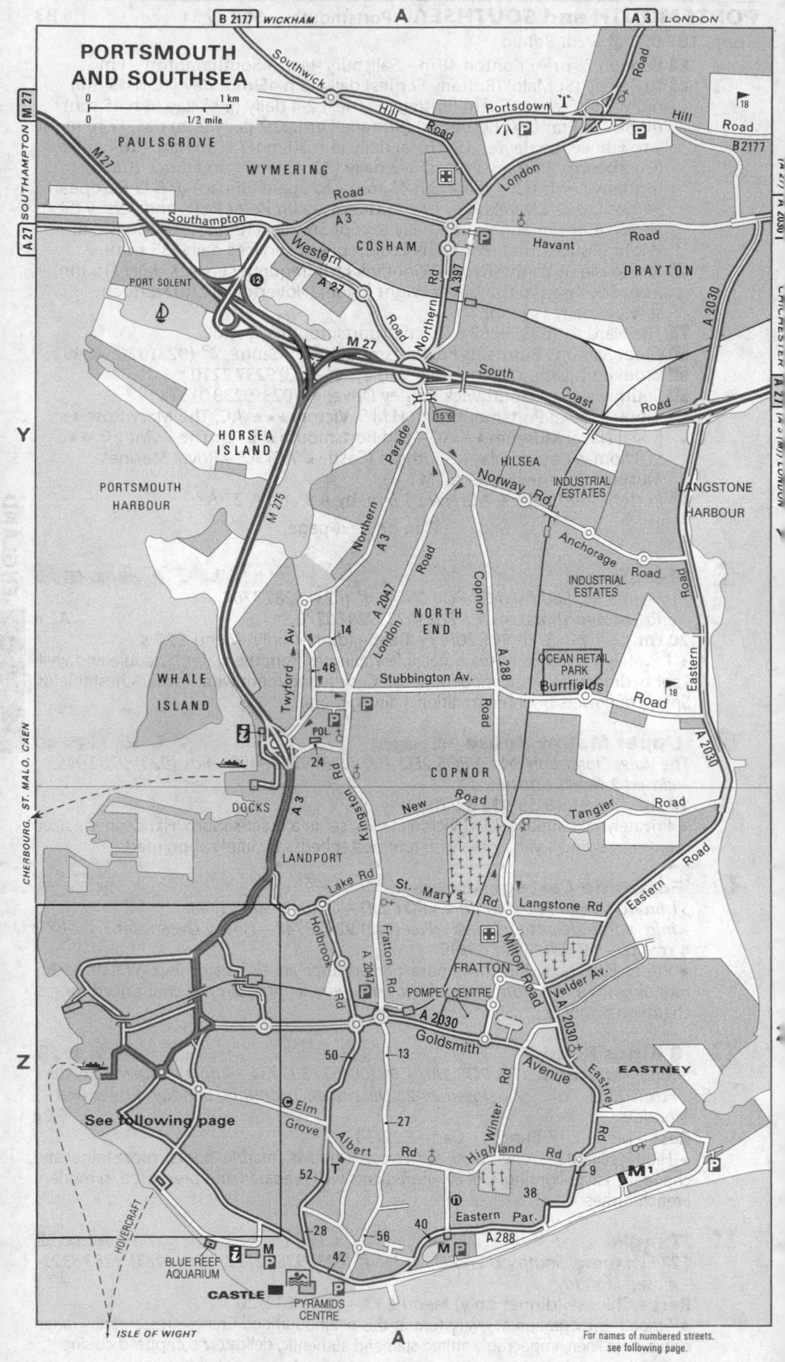
PORTSMOUTH AND SOUTHSEA
0 1 km
0 1/2 mile
B 2177 WICKHAM
A
A 3 LONDON
M 27
A 27 SOUTHAMPTON
Southwick
Hill
Road
Portsdown
Hill
Road
B 2177
PAULSGROVE
WYMERING
Road
Southampton
A 3
London
Road
COSHAM
Havant
Road
DRAYTON
Western
A 27
Road
Northern
Rd
A 397
PORT SOLENT
M 27
South
Coast
Road
A 2030
CHICHESTER
A 27
Y
HORSEA ISLAND
PORTSMOUTH HARBOUR
M 275
Parade
Northern
A 3
HILSEA
Norway Rd.
INDUSTRIAL ESTATES
Anchorage
Road
INDUSTRIAL ESTATES
LANGSTONE HARBOUR
Road
A 2047
London
Road
Copnor
NORTH END
A 288
OCEAN RETAIL PARK
Burrfields
Road
Eastern
14
46
Twyford
Av.
Stubbington Av.
Road
WHALE ISLAND
POL
24
Rd
Kingston
COPNOR
A 2030
CHERBOURG, ST. MALO, CAEN
DOCKS
A 3
New
Road
Tangier
Road
LANDPORT
Lake Rd
St. Mary's
Rd
Langstone Rd
Eastern
Road
Holbrook
Rd
A 2047
Fratton
Rd
Milton Road
FRATTON
POMPEY CENTRE
Velder Av.
A 2030
A 2030
Goldsmith
Avenue
Z
50
13
Winter
Rd
Eastney
EASTNEY
See following page
Elm
Grove
27
Albert
Rd
Highland
Rd
Rd
9
M1
52
38
Eastern
Par.
40
28
56
42
A 288
HOVERCRAFT
BLUE REEF AQUARIUM
M
CASTLE
PYRAMIDS CENTRE
ISLE OF WIGHT
A
For names of numbered streets, see following page.

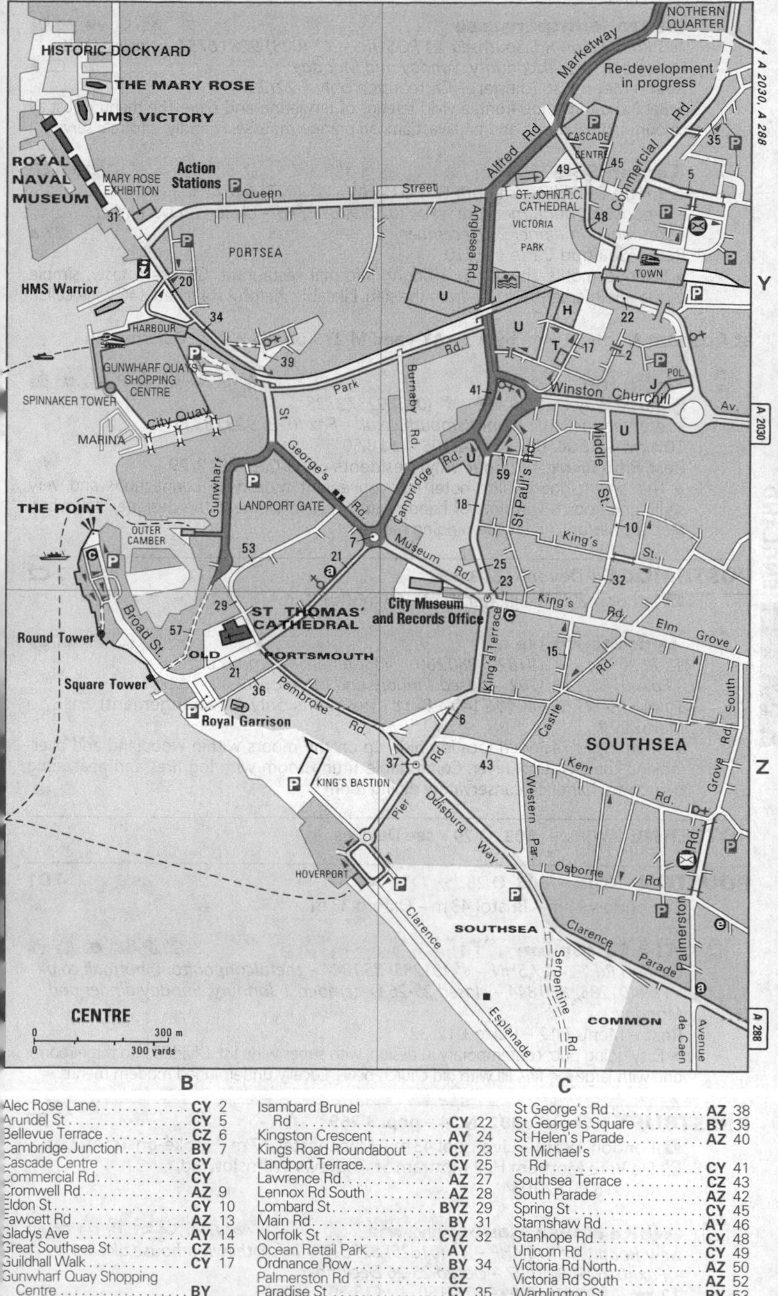

Alec Rose Lane	CY	2
Arundel St	CY	5
Bellevue Terrace	CZ	6
Cambridge Junction	BY	7
Cascade Centre	CY	
Commercial Rd	CY	
Cromwell Rd	AZ	9
Eldon St	CY	10
Fawcett Rd	AZ	13
Gladys Ave	AY	14
Great Southsea St	CZ	15
Guildhall Walk	CY	17
Gunwharf Quay Shopping Centre	BY	
Hampshire Terrace	CY	18
Hard (The)	BY	20
High St	BYZ	21
Isambard Brunel Rd	CY	22
Kingston Crescent	AY	24
Kings Road Roundabout	CY	23
Landport Terrace	CY	25
Lawrence Rd	AZ	27
Lennox Rd South	AZ	28
Lombard St	BYZ	29
Main Rd	BY	31
Norfolk St	CYZ	32
Ocean Retail Park	AY	
Ordnance Row	BY	34
Palmerston Rd	CZ	
Paradise St	CY	35
Penny St	BZ	36
Pier Road Roundabout	CZ	37
Pompey Centre	AZ	
St George's Rd	AZ	38
St George's Square	BY	39
St Helen's Parade	AZ	40
St Michael's Rd	CY	41
Southsea Terrace	CZ	43
South Parade	AZ	42
Spring St	CY	45
Stamshaw Rd	AY	46
Stanhope Rd	CY	48
Unicorn Rd	CY	49
Victoria Rd North	AZ	50
Victoria Rd South	AZ	52
Warblington St	BY	53
Waverley Rd	AZ	56
White Hart Rd	BYZ	57
Wiltshire St	CY	59

Bistro Montparnasse
103 Palmerston Rd, Southsea ✉ PO5 3PS – ☎ (023) 9281 6754 – closed 25-26 December, 1 week January, Sunday and Monday CZ **a**
Rest – Menu £ 30 (dinner) – Carte lunch only £ 22/29
◆ Behind a trim shop front, a vivid interior of tangerine and blue. The menu is just as colourful: tuna, prawn and papaya, Campari orange mousse. Friendly, informal service.

Lemon Sole
123 High St, Old Portsmouth ✉ PO1 2HW – ☎ (023) 9281 1303 – lemonsole@btinternet.com – Fax (023) 9281 1345 – closed 26 December, 1 January and dinner 25 December BY **a**
Rest – Seafood Carte £ 25/30
◆ Seafood motifs abound in a bright, informal restaurant. Choose a tasty, simple recipe and market-fresh fish from the slab. Likeable, helpful staff. Part 14C wine cellar.

at Cosham North : 4½ m. by A 3 - AY - and M 275 on A 27 – ✉ Portsmouth

Tulip Inn rm,
Binnacle Way ✉ PO6 4FB – ☎ (023) 9237 3333 – reservations@tulipinnportsmouth.co.uk – Fax (023) 9237 3335
108 rm – †£ 64/105 ††£ 64/105, £ 8.50
Rest *Bibo Bistro* – (dinner only) (residents only) Carte £ 19/29
◆ This smart, good value hotel has convenient motorway connections and very stylish bedrooms with lots of handy extras to complement the designer flourishes. Modern bar/grill with wide-ranging menus.

ENGLAND

POSTBRIDGE – Devon – **503** I 32 2 **C2**
London 207 m – Exeter 21 m – Plymouth 21 m

Lydgate House
✉ PL20 6TJ – ☎ (01822) 880 209 – lydgatehouse@email.com – Fax (01822) 880 202 – closed January and Monday
7 rm – †£ 50/95 ††£ 140 – **Rest** – (residents only, by arrangement) Menu £ 29
◆ In an idyllic secluded location high up on the moors within woodland and overlooking the East Dart River. Comfortable sitting room with log fires and neat, snug bedrooms. Candlelit conservatory dining room.

POTTERNE – Wilts. – **503** O 29 – **see Devizes**

POULTON – Glos. – **503** O 28 4 **D1**
London 91 m – Bristol 43 m – Oxford 33 m

The Falcon Inn
London Rd ✉ GL7 5HN – ☎ (01285) 850 844 – thefalconpoulton@hotmail.co.uk – Fax (01285) 850 844 – closed 25-26 December, 1 Janaury, Sunday dinner and Monday
Rest – Menu £ 12 – Carte £ 12/32
◆ Easy going pub, contemporary in design, with super wine list. Divided into three rooms, one with large log fire, all with old church pews. Locally underpinned modern menus.

PRESTBURY – Ches. – **502** N 24 – **pop. 3 269** 20 **B3**
London 184 m – Liverpool 43 m – Manchester 17 m – Stoke-on-Trent 25 m
18 De Vere Mottram Hall Mottram St Andrews Wilmslow Rd, ☎ (01625) 820 064 .

White House Manor without rest
New Road ✉ SK10 4HP – ☎ (01625) 829 376 – info@thewhitehouse.uk.com – Fax (01625) 828 627 – closed 25-26 December
12 rm – †£ 50/110 ††£ 125/150, £ 13.50
◆ Privately run 18C redbrick house with stylish, unique and individually decorated rooms which provide every luxury. Breakfast in your room or in the conservatory.

The Bridge

The Village ✉ SK10 4DQ – ☎ (01625) 829 326 – reception@bridge-hotel.co.uk – Fax (01625) 827 557 – closed 1-3 January
23 rm – †£ 50/90 ††£ 90, ☕ £ 9.75 – **Rest** – (closed Sunday evening) Menu £ 13/28 – Carte £ 31/41
◆ Dating back to the 1600s, a sympathetically extended hotel on the river Bollin. Classic, subtly co-ordinated décor in rooms, more characterful in the old timbered house. Live music at weekends in the beamed, galleried hall of the restaurant.

PRESTON – **502** L 22 – **pop. 184 836** 20 **A2**

London 226 m – Blackpool 18 m – Burnley 22 m – Liverpool 30 m – Manchester 34 m – Stoke-on-Trent 65 m
The Guildhall, Lancaster Rd ☎ (01772) 253731
Fulwood Fulwood Hall Lane, ☎ (01772) 700 011 ;
Ingol Tanterton Hall Rd, ☎ (01772) 734 556 ;
Aston & Lea Tudor Ave, Blackpool Rd, ☎ (01772) 735 282 ;
Penwortham Blundell Lane, ☎ (01772) 744 630 .

The Park

209 Tulketh Rd, Northwest : 2 ¼ m. by A 6 off ✉ PR2 1ES – ☎ (01772) 726 250 – theparkhotelpreston@hotmail.com – Fax (01772) 723 743 – Closed 24 December-2 January
16 rm ☕ – †£ 50/65 ††£ 75/85 – **Rest** – (Closed Friday-Sunday) (dinner only) Menu £ 19 **s**
◆ Built in 1903, a turreted, redbrick villa in a quiet suburb. Original hall - antique tiling and stained glass. Traditional rooms with greater personality in the old house. Light dining room dominated by black marble fireplace.

Winckley Square Chop House

23 Winckley Sq ✉ PR1 3JJ – ☎ (01772) 252 732 – preston@heathcotes.co.uk – Fax (01772) 203 433 – closed 25-26 December and 1 January and Bank Holiday Mondays
Rest – Menu £ 18 – Carte £ 23/39
Rest *Olive Press* – Carte £ 17/28
◆ Chic and contemporary restaurant with a cuisine style that handsomely matches the surroundings. Robust, balanced, classic British cooking with some regional input. Spacious basement bar-bistro serving pizzas and pastas.

Inside Out

100 Higher Walton Rd, Walton-le-Dale, Southeast : 1 ¾ m. by A 6 on A 675 ✉ PR5 4HR – ☎ (01772) 251 366 – Fax (01772) 258 918 – closed 25-26 December, first 2 weeks January, one week in October, Saturday lunch and Monday
Rest – Menu £ 16/18 – Carte £ 23/34
◆ Inside - a chic and stylish restaurant; 'out' - a lovely decked terrace with heaters overlooking a garden. Well sourced, quality ingredients assembled with love and flair.

at Broughton North : 3 m. on A 6 – ✉ Preston

Preston Marriott

418 Garstang Rd ✉ PR3 5JB – ☎ (01772) 864 087 – frontdesk.preston@marriotthotels.co.uk – Fax (01772) 861 327
149 rm – †£ 102/114 ††£ 102/114, ☕ £ 14.95
Rest – (dinner only lunch Saturday and Sunday) Menu £ 24 – Carte £ 26/35
Rest *Broughton Brasserie* – (dinner only and Sunday lunch) Menu £ 24 (dinner) – Carte £ 26/35
◆ Sympathetically extended 19C redbrick house in wooded grounds offers airy modern accommodation: more traditional comfort in original house rooms. Up-to-date leisure club. Easy-going lounge/restaurant. Formal, linen-clad Broughton Brasserie.

PUDLESTON – Herefordshire – see Leominster

ENGLAND

PULFORD – Ches. – **502** L 24 – see Chester

PULHAM MARKET – Norfolk – **504** X 26 – **pop. 919** – ✉ **Diss** 15 **C2**

London 106 m – Cambridge 58 m – Ipswich 29 m – Norwich 16 m

Old Bakery without rest

Church Walk ✉ IP21 4SL – ✆ (01379) 676 492 – jean@theoldbakery.net – Fax (01379) 676 492

3 rm – £ 50/55 £ 66/70

◆ Characterful Elizabethan house on village green: spacious timbered rooms hold antiques or comfy armchairs; toiletries by local herbalist. Pretty garden with summer house.

PURTON – Wilts. – **503** O 29 – **pop. 3 328** – ✉ **Swindon** 4 **D2**

London 94 m – Bristol 41 m – Gloucester 31 m – Oxford 38 m – Swindon 5 m

Pear Tree at Purton

Church End, South : ½ m. by Church St on Lydiard Millicent rd ✉ SN5 4ED – ✆ (01793) 772 100 – stay@peartreepurton.co.uk – Fax (01793) 772 369 – closed 26-31 December

15 rm – £ 115 £ 150 – 2 suites – **Rest** – (closed lunch Saturday) Menu £ 20/35 **s**

◆ Personally run, extended 16C sandstone vicarage in mature seven-acre garden. Spacious flower-filled lounge. Rooms with traditional comforts and thoughtful extras. Conservatory restaurant overlooks wild flower borders.

ENGLAND

QUITHER – Devon – see Tavistock

QUORNDON – Leics. – **502** Q 25 – **see Loughborough**

RADNAGE – Bucks. – see Stokenchurch

RAINHAM – Essex – **504** U 29 9 **C1**

London 14 m – Basildon 16 m – Dartford 9 m

The Barn

507 Lower Rainham Rd, North : 1 ¾ m. by Station Rd ✉ ME8 7TN – ✆ (01634) 361 363 – info@thebarnrestaurant.co.uk – closed 25 December, Saturday lunch and Sunday dinner

Rest – Menu £ 15 (lunch) – Carte £ 33/43

◆ Rurally set, heavily beamed 17C barn with beamed dining room and cosy upstairs lounge. Elaborate cooking uses locally sourced, seasonal produce. Ideal for special occasions.

RAMSBOTTOM – Gtr Manchester – **502** N 23 – **pop. 17 352** 20 **B2**

London 223 m – Blackpool 39 m – Burnley 12 m – Leeds 46 m – Liverpool 39 m – Manchester 13 m

ramsons

18 Market Pl ✉ BL0 9HT – ✆ (01706) 825 070 – chris@ramsons.org.uk – closed two weeks May, one week January, one week September, Sunday dinner, Monday and Tuesday

Rest – Italian influences Menu £ 25/40

◆ Passionately run and slightly quirky, this well-regarded eatery offers mostly Italian influenced cooking utilising refined ingredients. Accompanying fine wine list.

RAMSBURY – Wilts. – **503** P 29 – **see Marlborough**

RAMSEY – Isle of Man – **502** G 21 – **see Man (Isle of)**

RAMSGILL-IN-NIDDERDALE – N. Yorks. – **502** O 21 – **see Pateley Bridge**

RAWTENSTALL – Lancs. – **502** N 22 — 20 **B2**

London 232 m – Accrington 9 m – Burnley 12 m

The Dining Room

8-12 Burnley Rd ✉ BB4 8EW – ☎ (01706) 210 567 – thediningroom@hotmail.co.uk – closed 25 December, 1 January and Tuesday

Rest – (booking essential) Menu £ 15/25 – Carte £ 32/39

◆ Bland façade hides slick, neutral interior. Semi-split level dining room hosts good value, understated, seasonal cooking where texture, balance and flavours gel seamlessly.

RAYLEIGH – Essex – **504** V 29 – **pop. 30 629** — 13 **C3**

London 35 m – Chelmsford 13 m – Southend-on-Sea 6 m

at Thundersley South : 1 ¼ m. on A 129 – ✉ Rayleigh

The Woodmans Arms

Rayleigh Rd ✉ SS7 3TA – ☎ (01268) 775 799 – thewoodman@hotmail.co.uk – Fax (01268) 590 689

Rest – Carte £ 18/27

◆ Updated 19C pub in gastronomic desert. Cosy lounge with comfy leather sofas. Dining areas, separated by screens, serve impressive range of dishes - eg: Thai, French, British.

READING – Reading – **503** Q 29 – **pop. 232 662** — 11 **C3**

London 43 m – Brighton 79 m – Bristol 78 m – Croydon 47 m – Luton 62 m – Oxford 28 m – Portsmouth 67 m – Southampton 46 m

Access Whitchurch Bridge (toll)

to Henley-on-Thames (Salter Bros. Ltd) (summer only)

Church House, Chain St ☎ (0871) 7162670

Calcot Park Calcot Bath Rd, ☎ (0118) 942 7124 .

Plan on next page

Crowne Plaza Reading

Caversham Bridge, Richfield Ave ✉ RG1 8BD – ☎ (0118) 925 9988 – info@cp-reading.co.uk – Fax (0118) 939 1665 — X **e**

122 rm – †£ 98/175 ††£ 98/185 – 2 suites – **Rest** – Menu £ 27 (dinner) – Carte £ 23/29 **s**

◆ Modern purpose-built hotel just out of centre on banks of Thames. Spacious public areas with large windows which look towards river. Executive rooms boast extra touches. Bright restaurant with terrace and atrium roof.

Millennium Madejski

Madejski Stadium, South : 1 ½ m. by A 33 ✉ RG2 0FL – ☎ (0118) 925 3500 – reservations.reading@mill-cop.com – Fax (0118) 925 3501 — X **v**

201 rm – †£ 69/160 ††£ 69/160, ☕ £ 15.75 – 11 suites

Rest *Cilantro* – (closed Sunday) (dinner only) Menu £ 48

Rest *Le Café* – (closed Saturday lunch - except match days) Menu £ 13/25 – Carte £ 25/30

◆ Purpose-built hotel, in modern retail park; part of the Madejski sports stadium. Imposing Atrium lounge-bar and marble floored lobby. Stylish, inviting rooms. Impressively smart Cilantro. Informal Le Café is open plan to Atrium lounge.

The Forbury

26 The Forbury ✉ RG1 3EJ – ☎ (0800) 078 97 89 – info@theforburyhotel.co.uk – Fax (0118) 959 0806 — Y **c**

24 rm – †£ 230/260 ††£ 230/260, ☕ £ 16.50

Rest *Cerise* – Menu £ 18 – Carte £ 30/40

◆ Former civic hall overlooking Forbury Square Gardens; now a very stylish town house hotel. Eye-catching artwork features in all the stunningly individualistic bedrooms. Stylish basement cocktail bar/restaurant where clean, crisp, modern cooking holds sway.

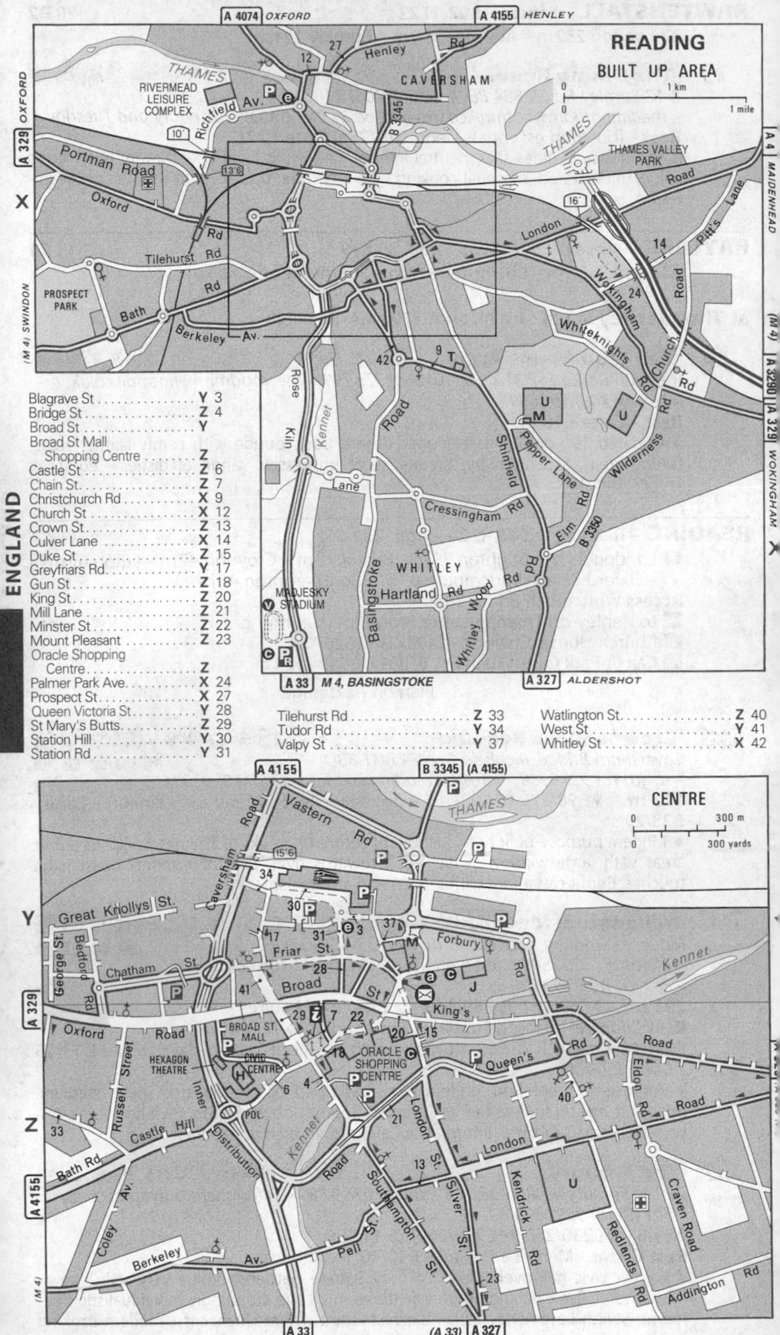
READING
BUILT UP AREA
0 1 km
0 1 mile
A 4074 OXFORD
A 4155 HENLEY
A 329 OXFORD
A 4 MAIDENHEAD
(M 4) SWINDON
(M 4)
A 3290
A 329 WOKINGHAM
A 33 M 4, BASINGSTOKE
A 327 ALDERSHOT
CAVERSHAM
THAMES
RIVERMEAD LEISURE COMPLEX
THAMES VALLEY PARK
PROSPECT PARK
WHITLEY
MADJESKY STADIUM
Portman Road
Oxford Rd
Tilehurst Rd
Bath Rd
Berkeley Av.
Richfield Av.
Henley Rd
London Road
Wokingham Road
Pitt's Lane
Whiteknights Rd
Church Rd
Wilderness Rd
Pepper Lane
Elm Rd
B 3350
B 3345
Shinfield Rd
Cressingham Rd
Hartland Rd
Whitley Wood Rd
Basingstoke Road
Rose Kiln Lane
Kennet
Blagrave St Y 3
Bridge St Z 4
Broad St Y
Broad St Mall Shopping Centre Z
Castle St Z 6
Chain St Z 7
Christchurch Rd X 9
Church St X 12
Crown St Z 13
Culver Lane X 14
Duke St Z 15
Greyfriars Rd Y 17
Gun St Z 18
King St Z 20
Mill Lane Z 21
Minster St Z 22
Mount Pleasant Z 23
Oracle Shopping Centre Z
Palmer Park Ave. X 24
Prospect St X 27
Queen Victoria St Y 28
St Mary's Butts Z 29
Station Hill Y 30
Station Rd Y 31
Tilehurst Rd Z 33
Tudor Rd Y 34
Valpy St Y 37
Watlington St. Z 40
West St Y 41
Whitley St X 42
CENTRE
0 300 m
0 300 yards
A 4155
B 3345 (A 4155)
A 329
A 4155
A 33
(A 33) A 327
THAMES
Kennet
Vastern Rd
Caversham Road
Great Knollys St.
George St.
Bedford Rd
Chatham St.
Friar St.
Broad St
Forbury Rd
King's Rd
Oxford Road
BROAD ST. MALL
HEXAGON THEATRE
CIVIC CENTRE
POL.
ORACLE SHOPPING CENTRE
Queen's Rd
Inner Distribution Road
Russell Street
Castle Hill
Bath Rd
Coley Av.
Berkeley Av.
Pell St.
Southampton St.
London St.
Silver St.
London Road
Kendrick Rd
Eldon Rd
Redlands Rd
Craven Road
Addington Rd

Malmaison

Great Western Rd ✉ RG1 1JX – ☎ (0118) 956 2300 – Fax (0118) 956 2302 Y **e**
75 rm – †£ 150 ††£ 175, ☕ £ 13.95
Rest ***Brasserie*** – Menu £ 17 – Carte £ 31/37
◆ Modernised Victorian railway hotel with contemporary furnishings, busy cafe and smart bar. Spacious, stylish bedrooms boast high level of facilities. Railway theme throughout. Industrial feel Brasserie serves contemporary, French influenced cooking.

Forbury's

1 Forbury Sq, The Forbury ✉ RG1 3BB – ☎ (0118) 957 4044 – forburys@btconnect.com – Fax (0118) 956 9191 – closed 25-26 December, 1-2 January, Sunday Y **a**
Rest – Menu £ 18/20 – Carte £ 32/36
◆ Modern eatery near law courts. Relaxing area of comfy leather seats. Spacious dining room enhanced by bold prints of wine labels. Eclectic menus with Gallic starting point.

LSQ2

Lime Sq., 220 South Oak Way, Green Park, South : 2 m. by A 33 ✉ RG2 6UP – ☎ (0118) 987 3702 – reading@lsq2.co.uk – closed Sunday and Bank holidays X **c**
Rest – Carte £ 27/38
◆ Head towards the wind turbine by the M4 to find this buzzy restaurant with floor-to-ceiling glass serving 'corporate' style lunch menus and modern British dishes for dinner.

London Street Brasserie

2-4 London St ✉ RG1 4SE – ☎ (0118) 950 5036 – Fax (0118) 950 5031 Z **c**
Rest – (booking essential) Carte £ 25/37
◆ Lively and modern: a polite, friendly team serve appetising British classics and international dishes. Deck terrace and first-floor window tables overlook the river Kennett.

at Kidmore End North : 5 m. by A 4155 - X - off B 481 – ✉ Reading

The New Inn with rm

Chalkhouse Green Rd ✉ RG4 9AU – ☎ (0118) 972 3115 – thenewinn@4cinns.co.uk – Fax (0118) 972 4733
6 rm ☕ – †£ 65/110 ††£ 220 – **Rest** – (closed Sunday dinner) Carte £ 15/29
◆ 16C inn with rough floorboards, beams and open fires and delightful canopied terrace. Smart, updated restaurant serves adventurous fare. Stylish, comfy, well-equipped rooms.

at Hurst East : 5 m. by A 329 - X - on B 3030 – ✉ Reading

The Castle at Hurst

Church Hill ✉ RG10 0SJ – ☎ (0118) 934 0034 – info@castlerestaurant.co.uk – Fax (0118) 934 0334 – closed dinner 26 December and 1 January
Rest – Carte £ 20/29
◆ Charming 16C monk's wash-house. Part panelled dining room with wattle and daub on display and a cosy snug. Classical French menu enhanced by modern interpretations.

at Shinfield South : 4 ¼ m. on A 327 - X – ✉ Reading

L'Ortolan (Alan Murchison)

Church Lane ✉ RG2 9BY – ☎ (0118) 988 8500 – info@lortolan.com – Fax (0118) 988 9338 – Closed 20 December-6 January, Sunday and Monday
Rest – Menu £ 24/49
Spec. Foie gras terrine with pain d'épices. Pan-fried sea bass and scallops, fennel purée, artichokes and red wine. Cherry soufflé, clafoutis and espuma.
◆ Pretty red brick former vicarage with lawned gardens and stylish lounge and conservatory. Bright, comfortable dining room; classically based cooking with original touches.

ENGLAND

REDDITCH – Worcs. – 503 O 27 – pop. 74 803 19 C2

London 111 m – Birmingham 15 m – Cheltenham 33 m – Stratford-upon-Avon 15 m
Civic Square, Alcester St ✆ (01527) 60806
Abbey Park G. & C.C. Dagnell End Rd, ✆ (01527) 406 600 ;
Lower Grinsty Callow Hill Green Lane, ✆ (01527) 543 079 ;
Pitcheroak Plymouth Rd, ✆ (01527) 541 054 .

Old Rectory

Ipsley Lane, Ipsley ✉ B98 0AP – ✆ (01527) 523 000 – ipsleyoldrectory@aol.com – Fax (01527) 517 003 – closed 25 December-1 January
10 rm – †£ 105 ††£ 136 – **Rest** – (closed Saturday-Sunday) (dinner only) (booking essential for non-residents) Menu £ 24
◆ Converted early Georgian rectory surrounded by pleasant mature gardens creating a quiet and secluded haven. Smart, traditional interior décor and individually styled rooms. Charming Georgian style conservatory restaurant.

REDHILL – Surrey – 504 T 30 – pop. 50 436 7 D2

London 22 m – Brighton 31 m – Guildford 20 m – Maidstone 34 m
Redhill & Reigate Pendleton Rd, Clarence Lodge, ✆ (01737) 770 204 ;
Canada Ave, ✆ (01737) 770 204 .

Nutfield Priory

Nutfield, East : 2 m. on A 25 ✉ RH1 4EL – ✆ (01737) 824 400 – nutfieldpriory@handpicked.co.uk – Fax (01737) 824 410
59 rm – †£ 120 ††£ 140/320, £ 14.50 – 1 suite
Rest *Cloisters* – (closed Saturday lunch) Menu £ 25/36 – Carte £ 36/55
◆ Restored Victorian mansion boasting intricate stonework, stained glass and neo-Gothic cloisters. Tasteful country house décor throughout including the comfortable rooms. Characterful dining room with stained glass and views across countryside.

Undecided between two equivalent establishments? Within each category, establishments are classified in our order of preference.

REDWORTH – Durham – see Darlington

REETH – N. Yorks. – 502 O 20 – ✉ Richmond 22 B1

London 253 m – Leeds 53 m – Middlesbrough 36 m – Newcastle upon Tyne 61 m
Hudson House, The Green ✆ (01748) 884059

The Burgoyne

On The Green ✉ DL11 6SN – ✆ (01748) 884 292 – enquiries@theburgoyne.co.uk – Fax (01748) 884 292 – closed 2 January-8 February
8 rm – †£ 103/125 ††£ 128/180 – 1 suite – **Rest** – (dinner only) (booking essential for non-residents) Menu £ 33
◆ Late Georgian hotel overlooking the green with views of the Dales. A charming, personally run, traditionally furnished house with well-appointed, individually styled rooms. Deep green dining room complements surrounding fells.

at Langthwaite Northwest : 3 ¼ m. on Langthwaite rd – ✉ Reeth

The Charles Bathurst Inn with rm

✉ DL11 6EN – ✆ (01748) 884 567 – info@cbinn.co.uk – Fax (01748) 886 233 – Closed 25 December
19 rm – †£ 93 ††£ 115 – **Rest** – Carte £ 20/35
◆ 18C inn sited high in the hills. Open fires provide appealing atmosphere. Fresh, locally sourced menus mixing classic with modern. Large, timbered rooms with country views.

ENGLAND

at Whaw Northwest : 5 ¼ m. by Langthwaite rd on Tan Hill rd – ✉ Reeth

Chapel Farm

✉ DL11 6RT – ☎ (01748) 884 062 – chapelfarmbb@aol.com
3 rm – †£ 40 ††£ 60 – **Rest** – (by arrangement, communal dining) Menu £ 16
◆ Restored, peaceful 18C lead miners' cottages in remote hamlet: dales are literally outside the front door. Beamed lounge with open fire. Attractive rural styled bedrooms.

REIGATE – Surrey – 504 T 30 – pop. 50 436 7 D2

London 26 m – Brighton 33 m – Guildford 20 m – Maidstone 38 m

Tony Tobin @ The Dining Room

59a High St ✉ RH2 9AE – ☎ (01737) 226 650 – Fax (01737) 226 650 – closed 23 December-4 January, Saturday lunch, Sunday dinner and Bank Holidays
Rest – Menu £ 20 (lunch) – Carte £ 37/45
◆ Top floor of a building on the High Street with a smart modern interior. Busy, bustling atmosphere. International menus with a modern style of cooking.

The Westerly

2-4 London Rd ✉ RH2 9AN – ☎ (01737) 222 733 – info@thewesterly.co.uk – closed 2 weeks August, 2 weeks Christmas, Tuesday lunch, Saturday lunch, Sunday and Monday
Rest – (booking essential at dinner) Menu £ 20 (lunch) – Carte £ 25/30
◆ Modern, simply decorated restaurant. Skilful kitchen, passionate about the seasons; intelligent menu and understated, wholesome cooking at honest prices. Welcoming service.

La Barbe

71 Bell St ✉ RH2 7AN – ☎ (01737) 241 966 – restaurant@labarbe.co.uk – Fax (01737) 226 387 – closed Christmas and Bank Holidays Saturday lunch and Sunday dinner
Rest – French Menu £ 23/30
◆ Friendly bistro with Gallic atmosphere and welcoming ambience. Regularly changing menus offer good choice of traditional French cuisine - classical and provincial in style.

RETFORD – Notts. – 502 R 24 – pop. 21 314 16 B1

London 148 m – Lincoln 23 m – Nottingham 31 m – Sheffield 27 m
40 Grove St (01777) 860780

The Barns without rest

Morton Farm, Babworth, Southwest : 2 ¼ m. by A 6420 ✉ DN22 8HA – ☎ (01777) 706 336 – enquiries@thebarns.co.uk – closed Christmas and New Year
6 rm – †£ 38/40 ††£ 62/80
◆ Privately owned and run converted part 18C farmhouse on a quiet country road. Informal, old-fashioned, cottage décor throughout. Beams within and lawned gardens without.

RHYDYCROESAU – Shrops. – 502 K 25 – see Oswestry

RIBCHESTER – Lancs – 502 M 22 – pop. 1 535 20 B2

London 229 m – Blackburn 7 m – Manchester 41 m

The White Bull with rm

Church Street ✉ PR3 3XP – ☎ (01254) 878 303 – enquiries@whitebullribchester.co.uk
3 rm – †£ 55 ††£ 70 – **Rest** – Carte £ 14/23
◆ Stone pub dating from 1707 with spacious dining room, open fired bar and garden overlooking Roman bath remains. Hearty British pub dishes all homemade using best produce. Individually decorated, comfortable, characterful bedrooms.

ENGLAND

London 243 m – Leeds 53 m – Middlesbrough 26 m – Newcastle upon Tyne 44 m
Friary Gardens, Victoria Rd (01748) 850252
Bend Hagg, (01748) 825 319 ; Catterick Leyburn Rd, (01748) 833 268 .
Town ★ - Castle ★ AC – Georgian Theatre Royal and Museum ★
The Bowes Museum ★, Barnard Castle, NW : 15 m. by B 6274, A 66 and minor rd (right) – Raby Castle ★, NE : 6 m. of Barnard Castle by A 688

Millgate House without rest
3 Millgate DL10 4JN – (01748) 823 571
– oztim@millgatehouse.demon.co.uk – Fax (01748) 850 701
4 rm – £ 65/110 £ 110
◆ Georgian townhouse with fine elevated views of river Swale and Richmond Castle. Award winning terraced garden. Antique furnished interior. Bedrooms are tastefully restrained.

West End without rest
45 Reeth Rd, West : ½ m. on A 6108 DL10 4EX – (01748) 824 783
– westend@richmond.org – closed December and January
5 rm – £ 35/48 £ 70
◆ Fine mid 19C house, away from town centre, with gardens. Homely lounge with plenty of maps and walking guides. Simple, neat and tidy rooms. Adjacent self-catering cottages.

at Downholme Southwest : 5 ½ m. on A 6108 – Richmond

Walburn Hall without rest
South : 1 ½ m. on A 6108 DL11 6AF – (01748) 822 775
– walburnhall@farmersweekly.net – Fax (01748) 822 152 – February-November
3 rm – £ 45/50 £ 70/90
◆ Mary Queen of Scots reputedly stayed in this part 14C fortified farmhouse. Cottage-style lounge; dining room serves traditional Yorkshire breakfasts. Beamed bedrooms.

at Whashton Northwest : 4 ½ m. by Ravensworth rd – Richmond

Whashton Springs Farm without rest
South : 1 ½ m. on Richmond rd DL11 7JS – (01748) 822 884
– whashtonsprings@btconnect.com – Fax (01748) 826 285 – closed Christmas-New Year
8 rm – £ 36 £ 70
◆ A working farm with a spacious, pleasantly converted, period farmhouse; surrounded by attractive countryside. Cottagey rooms, some in converted stable block.

at Dalton Northwest : 6 ¾ m. by Ravensworth rd and Gayles rd – Richmond

The Travellers Rest
DL11 7HU – (01833) 621 225 – annebabsa@aol.com
– Closed 25-26 December, 1 January, Sunday dinner and Monday
Rest – (dinner only and Sunday lunch) Carte £ 17/27
◆ Characterful country inn in tiny hamlet. Blackboard menu offers a wide-ranging menu where traditional meets the up-to-date. Linen-laid restaurant also available.

RIDGEWAY – Derbs. – see Sheffield (S. Yorks.)

RINGSTEAD – Norfolk – 504 V 25 – see Hunstanton

Your opinions are important to us:
please write and let us know about your discoveries and experiences – good and bad!

ENGLAND

RINGWOOD – Hants. – 503 O 31 – pop. 13 387 6 A2

London 102 m – Bournemouth 11 m – Salisbury 17 m – Southampton 20 m
The Furlong ✆ (01425) 470896

Moortown Lodge without rest

244 Christchurch Rd, South : 1 m. on B 3347 ✉ BH24 3AS – ✆ (01425) 471 404 – enquiries@moortownlodge.co.uk – Fax (01425) 476 527
7 rm – †£ 68 ††£ 94
◆ House dating from the 1760s, located on the edge of the New Forest. Family run, traditional atmosphere with a cosy lounge and chintz-furnished rooms of varying sizes.

RIPLEY – N. Yorks. – 502 P 21 – ✉ Harrogate 22 B2

London 213 m – Bradford 21 m – Leeds 18 m – Newcastle upon Tyne 79 m

The Boar's Head

✉ HG3 3AY – ✆ (01423) 771 888 – reservations@boarsheadripley.co.uk – Fax (01423) 771 509
25 rm – †£ 105/125 ††£ 125/150
Rest *The Restaurant* – Menu £ 20/40
Rest *The Bistro* – Carte £ 18/27
◆ 18C coaching inn within estate village of Ripley Castle, reputedly furnished from castle's attics. Comfy, unique rooms, some in courtyard or adjacent house. The Restaurant, in deep burgundy, has period paintings. The Bistro boasts impressive flagged floors.

RIPLEY – Surrey – 504 S 30 – pop. 1 697 7 C1

London 28 m – Guildford 6 m

Drake's (Steve Drake)

The Clock House, High St ✉ GU23 6AQ – ✆ (01483) 224 777 – Fax (01483) 222 940 – Closed Christmas, 2 weeks August, 10 days January, Sunday and Monday
Rest – Menu £ 24/43
Spec. Duck and beetroot cannelloni with langoustine and horseradish froth. Poached and roast pigeon, crushed celeriac, pickled rhubarb and maple jus. Passion fruit panna cotta, caramelised peaches, lemon verbena ice cream.
◆ Georgian restaurant's red brick façade dominated by large clock. Relaxing, open plan dining room with local gallery art on walls. Precise, classical cooking. Formal service.

RIPON – N. Yorks. – 502 P 21 – pop. 16 468 *Great Britain* 22 B2

London 222 m – Leeds 26 m – Middlesbrough 35 m – York 23 m
Minster Rd ✆ (01765) 604625
Ripon City Palace Rd, ✆ (01765) 603 640 .
Town★ - Cathedral★ (Saxon Crypt) **AC**
Fountains Abbey★★★ **AC** :- Studley Royal **AC** (≤ ★ from Anne Boleyn's Seat) - Fountains Hall (Fa½ade★), SW : 2 ½ m. by B 6265 – Newby Hall (Tapestries★) **AC**, SE : 3 ½ m. by B 6265

The Old Deanery

Minster Rd ✉ HG4 1QS – ✆ (01765) 600 003 – reception@theolddeanery.co.uk – Fax (01765) 600 027 – closed 25-26 December
11 rm – †£ 95 ††£ 140 – **Rest** – (closed Sunday dinner) Menu £ 15/25 – Carte £ 26/31 **s**
◆ Eponymously named hotel opposite cathedral. Stylish interior blends seamlessly with older charms. Afternoon tea in secluded garden. 18C oak staircase leads to modern rooms. Appealing seasonal cooking in spacious dining room.

ENGLAND

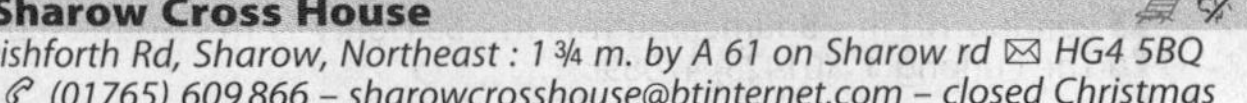

Sharow Cross House

Dishforth Rd, Sharow, Northeast : 1 ¾ m. by A 61 on Sharow rd ✉ HG4 5BQ – ✆ (01765) 609 866 – sharowcrosshouse@btinternet.com – closed Christmas and New Year

3 rm – †£ 50/65 ††£ 70/80 – **Rest** – (by arrangement) Menu £ 21

◆ Idyllically set 19C house, built for mill owner. Capacious hall with welcoming fire. Spacious bedrooms: the master room is huge and offers Cathedral views on clear days.

at Aldfield Southwest : 3 ¾ m. by B 6265 – ✉ Ripon

Bay Tree Farm without rest

✉ HG4 3BE – ✆ (01765) 620 394 – val@btfarm.entadsl.com – Fax (01765) 620 394

6 rm – †£ 45/65 ††£ 75/90

◆ Comfortable and characterful farmhouse conversion with pleasant gardens. Homely rooms, some beamed, in 17C stone barn; all accommodation boasts serene views over pasture.

at Markington Southwest : 5 m. by A 61 – ✉ Harrogate

Hob Green

Southwest : ½ m. ✉ HG3 3PJ – ✆ (01423) 770 031 – info@hobgreen.com – Fax (01423) 771 589

11 rm – †£ 90/95 ††£ 115/135 – 1 suite – **Rest** – Menu £ 17/28 – Carte £ 29/40

◆ 18C country house in a rural position surrounded by extensive parkland. A true country house hotel furnished with antiques and curios. Each room unique and characterful. Dining room with country views; garden produce prominently used.

ENGLAND

RISHWORTH – W. Yorks. – see Sowerby Bridge

ROADE – Northants. – 504 R 27 – pop. 2 254 — 16 B3

London 66 m – Coventry 36 m – Leicester 42 m – Northampton 5 m

Roade House with rm

16 High St ✉ NN7 2NW – ✆ (01604) 863 372 – info@roadehousehotel.co.uk – Fax (01604) 862 421 – closed 1 week Christmas-New Year

10 rm – †£ 75 ††£ 83 – **Rest** – (closed Sunday, lunch Saturday and Bank Holiday Monday's) Menu £ 25/33

◆ Personally run converted schoolhouse with comfortable bedrooms. Uncluttered, beamed dining room. Classic, seasonally based dishes with modern international elements.

ROCHDALE – Gtr Manchester – 502 N 23 – pop. 95 796 — 20 B2

London 224 m – Blackpool 40 m – Burnley 11 m – Leeds 45 m – Liverpool 40 m – Manchester 12 m

The Clock Tower, Town Hall ✆ (01706) 356592

18 Bagslate Edenfield Rd, ✆ (01706) 643 818 ;

18 Marland Bolton Rd, Springfield Park, ✆ (01706) 649 801 ;

27 Castle Hawk Castleton Chadwick Lane, ✆ (01706) 640 841 .

Hindle Pastures

Highgate Lane, Whitworth, North : 2½ m. by A 671 off Tonacliffe Rd ✉ OL12 0TS – ✆ (01706) 643 310 – hindlepastures@tiscali.co.uk

3 rm – †£ 30/45 ††£ 50/65 – **Rest** – (by arrangement, communal dining) Menu £ 15 **s**

◆ Superbly located barn high in the Pennines with views over four counties. Special attention paid to extensive breakfasts with freshly laid eggs. Brightly decorated rooms. Open plan dining room; imaginative meals served with fellow guests.

Nutters
Edenfield Rd, Norden, West : 3½ m. on A 680 ✉ OL12 7TT – ✆ (01706) 650 167 – enquiries@nuttersrestaurant.com – Fax (01706) 650 167 – closed 2-3 January and Monday
Rest – Menu £ 16/35 – Carte £ 26/36
◆ Views of the lyrical gardens contrast with a menu of often complex modern British dishes with international twists and influences. Best views at either end of the room.

at Littleborough Northeast : 4½ m. by A 58 on B 6225 – ✉ Rochdale

Hollingworth Lake without rest
164 Smithybridge Rd ✉ OL15 0DB – ✆ (01706) 376 583 – Fax (01706) 374 054
5 rm – £ 33/38 £ 50
◆ A short distance from country park, lake and the moors. A comfortable, friendly, good value house with well equipped, attractively furnished bedrooms.

ROCHESTER – Medway – 504 V 29 – pop. 17 125 – ✉ Chatham 8 B1

Great Britain

London 30 m – Dover 45 m – Maidstone 8 m – Margate 46 m
95 High St ✆ (01634) 843666, visitor.centre@medway.gov.uk
Castle★ AC – Cathedral★ AC
World Naval Base★★, Chatham, NE : 2 m. of the Cathedral. Leeds Castle★, SE : 11 m. by A 229 and M 20

Bridgewood Manor rm, rest,
Bridgewood Roundabout, Southeast : 3 m. by A 2 and A 229 on Walderslade rd ✉ ME5 9AX – ✆ (01634) 201 333 – bridgewoodmanor@qhotels.co.uk – Fax (01634) 201 330
96 rm – £ 70/139 £ 80/178 – 4 suites
Rest *Squires* – (closed Saturday lunch) Menu £ 19 (lunch) – Carte £ 25/37
◆ Purpose-built hotel with central courtyard and fitted modern interior. Bedrooms have a well-kept, comfortable feel. Geared to business travellers. Imposingly formal Squires.

**The ✿ award is the crème de la crème.
This is awarded to restaurants
which are really worth travelling miles for!**

ROCK – Cornwall – 503 F 32 – pop. 3 433 – ✉ Wadebridge 1 B2

London 266 m – Newquay 24 m – Tintagel 14 m – Truro 32 m
Pencarrow★, SE : 8½ m. by B 3314 and A 389

St Enodoc (heated)
✉ PL27 6LA – ✆ (01208) 863 394 – info@enodoc-hotel.co.uk – Fax (01208) 863 970 – closed mid December - mid February except New Year
16 rm – £ 100/185 £ 130/235 – 4 suites
Rest *Restaurant* – (light lunch) Carte £ 29/41
◆ A refreshingly modern take on the seaside hotel; neutral fabrics, sandwashed pine and contemporary oil paintings in stylish rooms, many facing the Camel Estuary.

L'Estuaire
Rock Rd ✉ PL27 6JS – ✆ (01208) 862 622 – Fax (01208) 862 622 – Closed Christmas, 2 weeks January, 2 weeks November and Monday-Tuesday except Bank Holidays
Rest – French Menu £ 23 (lunch) – Carte £ 27/49
◆ Oddly shaped building has been a dance hall and garage in its day! Now a family run restaurant, its tastefully restrained interior is matched by serious modern French menus.

ROCKBEARE – Devon – see Exeter

ENGLAND

ROGATE – W. Sussex – 504 R 30 – ✉ Petersfield (Hants.) 7 C2

London 63 m – Brighton 42 m – Guildford 29 m – Portsmouth 23 m – Southampton 36 m

Mizzards Farm without rest (heated) P

Southwest : 1 m. by Harting rd ✉ GU31 5HS – ☎ (01730) 821 656 – francis@mizzards.co.uk – Fax (01730) 821 655 – closed Christmas and New Year

3 rm – £ 50/60 £ 86

◆ 17C farmhouse with delightful landscaped gardens, which include a lake, bordered by river Rother. Views of woods and farmland. Fine fabrics and antiques in appealing rooms.

ROMALDKIRK – Durham – 502 N 20 – see Barnard Castle

ROMFORD – Essex – 504 U 29 – pop. 13 200 12 B3

London 18 m – Brentwood 7 m – Watford 41 m

Coach House P VISA AE

33 Main Rd ✉ RM1 3DL – ☎ (01708) 751 901

36 rm – £ 120/150 £ 120/150, £ 10.50

Rest *I Paparazzi* – Italian (closed Sunday evening) Carte £ 23/42

◆ Victorian house retains original charm and character. Delightful bar decorated with horseracing memorabilia. Feature bedrooms in main house; more modern in adjacent block. Wide-ranging Italian menu served in conservatory extension.

Look out for red symbols, indicating particularly pleasant establishments.

ROMSEY – Hants. – 503 P 31 – pop. 17 386 *Great Britain* 6 A2

London 82 m – Bournemouth 28 m – Salisbury 16 m – Southampton 8 m – Winchester 10 m

13 Church St ☎ (01794) 512987

Dunwood Manor Awbridge Danes Rd, ☎ (01794) 340 549 ;

Nursling, ☎ (023) 8073 4437 ;

Wellow East Wellow Ryedown Lane, ☎ (01794) 322 872 .

Abbey★ (interior★★)

Broadlands★ AC, S : 1 m

Ranvilles Farm House without rest P

Ower, Southwest : 2 m. on A 3090 (southbound carriageway) ✉ SO51 6AA – ☎ (023) 8081 4481 – info@ranvilles.com – Fax (023) 8081 4481

4 rm – £ 30/40 £ 55/70

◆ Attractive part 16C farmhouse set within five acres of garden and fields. Welcoming country style décor and furniture throughout, including the well-kept bedrooms.

Highfield House P

Newtown Rd, Awbridge, Northwest : 3½ m. by A 3090 (old A 31) and A 27 ✉ SO51 0GG – ☎ (01794) 340 727 – highfield-house@btinternet.com – Fax (01794) 340 727

3 rm – £ 50 £ 70 – **Rest** – (by arrangement, communal dining) Menu £ 18

◆ Modern house with gardens, in a tranquil location just out of Awbridge village. Accommodation is comfortable with good facilities. Real fires in the guest lounge. Communal dining with garden views.

The Three Tuns P VISA AE

58 Middlebridge St ✉ SO51 8HL – ☎ (01794) 512 639 – Closed Monday lunch

Rest – Menu £ 12/15 – Carte £ 15/23

◆ 18C town centre pub with period feel supplied by beams and log fire, though rest of interior is understated. Modern, well-judged cooking using first-rate ingredients.

ENGLAND

ROSS-ON-WYE – Herefordshire – 503 M 28 – pop. 10 085 18 B3

Great Britain

London 118 m – Gloucester 15 m – Hereford 15 m – Newport 35 m
Swan House, Edde Cross St ✆ (01989) 562768
Market House★ – Yat Rock (≤ ★)
SW : Wye Valley★ – Goodrich Castle★ AC, SW : 3½ m. by A 40

The Chase

Gloucester Rd ✉ HR9 5LH – ✆ (01989) 763 161 – res@chasehotel.co.uk – Fax (01989) 768 330 – closed 24-29 December

36 rm – †£ 85 ††£ 179 – **Rest** – Menu £ 17/25 – Carte £ 22/38

◆ Elegant Georgian country house, close to town centre. Original architectural features such as impressive tiled reception area. Range of room styles with traditional décor. Restaurant exudes airy, period feel.

Wilton Court

Wilton Lane, West : ¾ m. by B 4260 (A 49 Hereford) ✉ HR9 6AQ – ✆ (01989) 562 569 – info@wiltoncourthotel.com – Fax (01989) 768 460

10 rm – †£ 80/110 ††£ 100/140

Rest *Mulberry* – (dinner only and Sunday lunch) Menu £ 18 (lunch) – Carte £ 29/38

◆ Attractive, part-Elizabethan house on the banks of the river Wye. 16C wood panelling in situ in bar and two of the bedrooms: others have a distinctly William Morris influence. Light, airy conservatory restaurant boasts Lloyd Loom furniture and garden views.

Bridge House with rm

Wilton ✉ HR9 6AA – ✆ (01989) 562 655 – info@bridge-house-hotel.com – Fax (01989) 567 652

9 rm – †£ 80 ††£ 120 – **Rest** – Menu £ 17 (lunch) – Carte approx. £ 34

◆ On the banks of the Wye, boasting a kitchen garden supplying ingredients for the owners' passionate belief in home cooking. Also, a homely bar and well-maintained bedrooms.

The Lough Pool at Sellack

Sellack, Northwest : 3¼ m. by B 4260 and A 49 on Hoarwithy rd ✉ HR9 6LX – ✆ (01989) 730 236 – david@loughpool.co.uk – Fax (01989) 730 548 – Closed January-February, Monday and dinner Sunday October-November

Rest – Carte £ 21/30

◆ Ancient beams and wattle walls in this personally run 16C inn. Seasonal cooking, served at scrubbed farmhouse tables, is well-priced, unfussy and full of local flavour.

at Glewstone Southwest : 3¼ m. by A 40 – ✉ Ross-on-Wye

Glewstone Court

✉ HR9 6AW – ✆ (01989) 770 367 – glewstone@aol.com – Fax (01989) 770 282 – closed 24-27 December

8 rm – †£ 60/80 ††£ 120/135 – **Rest** – Carte £ 24/32

◆ Part Georgian and Victorian country house with impressive cedar of Lebanon in grounds. Sweeping staircase leads to uncluttered rooms. Family run with charming eccentricity. Antique-strewn dining room.

at Llangarron Southwest : 5½ m. by A 40 – ✉ Ross-on-Wye

Trecilla Farm without rest

✉ HR9 6NQ – ✆ (01989) 770 647 – info@trecillafarm.co.uk – closed Christmas and New Year

3 rm – ††£ 75/105

◆ 16C farmhouse with babbling brook. Beautiful lounge typifies smart, country house style. Breakfast locations dependent on time of year. Book the four-poster room if possible!

ENGLAND

at Peterstow West : 2 ½ m. on A 49 – ✉ Ross-on-Wye

Pengethley Manor (heated) P VISA AE
Northwest : 1 ½ m. on A 49 ✉ HR9 6LL – ☎ (01989) 730 211
– reservations@pengethleymanor.co.uk – Fax (01989) 730 238
22 rm – †£ 65/115 ††£ 105/120 – 3 suites
Rest *Georgian Restaurant* – Menu £ 25 (dinner) – Carte £ 23/34
♦ Fine period house set in a prominent position affording country views. Grounds include vineyard and giant chess set. Rooms vary in size and all are comfy and characterful. Spacious dining room with country house feel.

at Kerne Bridge South : 3 ¾ m. on B 4234 – ✉ Ross-on-Wye

Lumleys without rest P
✉ HR9 5QT – ☎ (01600) 890 040 – helen@lumleys.force9.co.uk
3 rm – †£ 35/50 ††£ 70
♦ Welcoming and personally run guesthouse in sympathetically converted Victorian house. Ideally located for Wye valley and Forest of Dean. Pine decorated cottage style rooms.

ROSTHWAITE – Cumbria – 502 K 20 – see Keswick

ROTHBURY – Northd. – 501 O 18 – pop. 1 963 – ✉ Morpeth 24 A2

Great Britain

London 311 m – Edinburgh 84 m – Newcastle upon Tyne 29 m
National Park Centre, Church House, Church St ☎ (01669) 620887
Cragside House★ (interior★) AC

Farm Cottage without rest P VISA
Thropton, West : 2 ¼ m. on B 6341 ✉ NE65 7NA – ☎ (01669) 620 831
– joan@farmcottageguesthouse.co.uk – Fax (01669) 620 831
– closed 24 December - 2 January
5 rm – †£ 45/65 ††£ 70/80
♦ 18C stone cottage and gardens; owner was actually born here. Two comfy lounges filled with family prints and curios. Individually styled rooms with plenty of extra touches.

Thropton Demesne Farmhouse without rest P
Thropton, West : 2 ¼ m. on B 6341 ✉ NE65 7LT – ☎ (01669) 620 196
– thropton-demesne@yahoo.co.uk – Easter-October
5 rm – †£ 50 ††£ 60
♦ Early 19C stone-built former farmhouse; unbroken Coquet Valley views. Lounge defined by quality décor. Artwork on walls by owner. Individually styled rooms with lovely vistas.

Lee Farm without rest P
South : 3 ¼ m. by B 6342 on The Lee rd ✉ NE65 8JQ – ☎ (01665) 570 257
– enqs@leefarm.co.uk – Fax (01665) 570 257 – March - November
3 rm – †£ 45/55 ††£ 70/75
♦ Family-run house in a peaceful valley; firelit lounge, trim, pretty rooms in pastel tones, breakfasts at a communal table. Guests are free to explore the livestock farm.

ROTHERFIELD PEPPARD – Oxon – pop. 2 105 – ✉ Henley-on-Thames 11 C3

London 41 m – Henley-on-Thames 4 m – Oxford 22 m

The Greyhound P VISA
Gallowstree Rd ✉ RG9 5HT – ☎ (01189) 722 227
– greyhound@awtrestaurants.com – Fax (01189) 242 975
Rest – (booking essential) Carte £ 20/39
♦ Characterful 17C pub on edge of picturesque village. Small bar, more formal dining and barn extension with exposed timbers and animal heads. Aberdeen Angus steak a speciality.

ENGLAND

ROTHERHAM – S. Yorks. – **502** P 23 – pop. 117 262 — 22 **B3**

London 166 m – Kingston-upon-Hull 61 m – Leeds 36 m – Sheffield 6 m
Central Library, Walker Pl ☎ (01709) 823611
Thrybergh Park, ☎ (01709) 850 466 ;
Grange Park Kimberworth Upper Wortley Rd, ☎ (01709) 558 884 ;
Phoenix Brinsworth Pavilion Lane, ☎ (01709) 363 788 .

Courtyard by Marriott

rm, rest, VISA

West Bawtry Rd, South : 2 ¼ m. on A 630 ✉ S60 4NA – ☎ (01709) 830 630 – reservations@rotherham.kewgreen.co.uk – Fax (01709) 786 005

102 rm – £ 129 £ 129 – 2 suites

Rest *Capistrano* – (dinner only and Sunday lunch) Carte £ 20/27

◆ Modern purpose-built hotel out of town centre. Uniform rooms have a bright tone. Features, such as work desks and ergonomic chairs, are well suited to business travellers. Restaurant boasts smoked glass conservatory extension.

at Bramley East : 4 ½ m. by A 6021 off A 631 – ✉ Rotherham

Elton

rm, rest, VISA

Main St, ✉ S66 2SF – ☎ (01709) 545 681 – bestwestern.eltonhotel@btinternet.com – Fax (01709) 549 100 – closed 25 December

29 rm – £ 55/90 £ 80/110 – **Rest** – Menu £ 13/23 – Carte £ 13/26

◆ Solid stone house with extensions, in the centre of village. Traditionally styled public areas include conservatory lounge. Extension rooms have a more modern style. Richly styled dining room with warm burgundy walls.

The red symbol?
This denotes the very essence of peace
– only the sound of birdsong first thing in the morning …

ENGLAND

ROTHERWICK – Hants. – see Hook

ROUGHAM GREEN – Suffolk – see Bury St Edmunds

ROWDE – Wilts. – **503** N 29 – see Devizes

ROWHOOK – W. Sussex – see Horsham

ROWSLEY – Derbs. – **502** P 24 – ✉ Matlock *Great Britain* — 16 **A1**

London 157 m – Derby 23 m – Manchester 40 m – Nottingham 30 m
Chatsworth★★★ (Park and Garden★★★) AC, N : by B 6012

East Lodge

rm, rest, VISA

✉ DE4 2EF – ☎ (01629) 734 474 – info@eastlodge.com – Fax (01629) 733 949

12 rm – £ 110/150 £ 250 – **Rest** – Menu £ 19/33

◆ Elegant 17C country house set in ten acres of well kept grounds, once the lodge to Haddon Hall. Rooms are each individually decorated and superior rooms have garden views. Simple dining room with terrace.

The Peacock

VISA

Bakewell Rd ✉ DE4 2EB – ☎ (01629) 733 518 – reception@thepeacockatrowsley.com – Fax (01629) 732 671

16 rm – £ 75/175 £ 145/210, £ 6.25 – **Rest** – Menu £ 22 – Carte £ 35/46

◆ Characterful, antique furnished, 17C house with gardens leading down to the river Derwent. Rooms, a variety of shapes and sizes, are antique or reproduction furnished. Restaurant divided between three smart rooms.

ROWTON – Ches. – **502** – see Chester

ROYAL LEAMINGTON SPA – Warks. – 503 P 27 – pop. 61 595 19 D3

London 99 m – Birmingham 23 m – Coventry 9 m – Leicester 33 m – Warwick 3 m
The Royal Pump Rooms, The Parade ☎ (01926) 742762
Leamington and County Whitnash Golf Lane, ☎ (01926) 425 961 .

ROYAL LEAMINGTON SPA

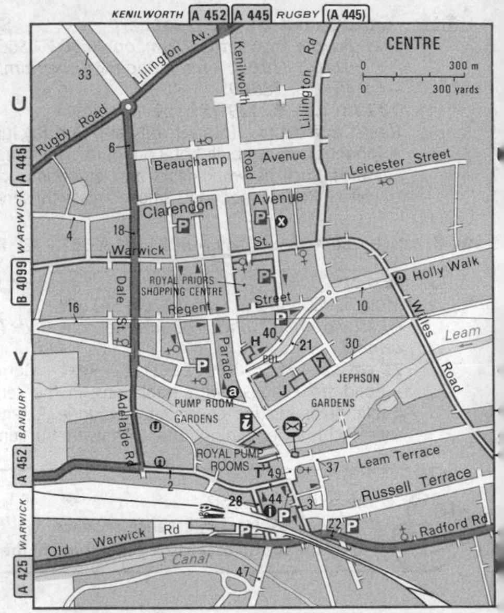

ENGLAND

Mallory Court rm,
Harbury Lane, Bishop's Tachbrook, South : 2¼ m. by B 4087 (Tachbrook Rd)
✉ CV33 9QB – ☎ (01926) 330 214 – reception@mallory.co.uk
– Fax (01926) 451 714
30 rm – †£ 95/145 ††£ 155
Rest ***The Brasserie at Mallory*** – see restaurant listing
Rest – (closed Saturday lunch) (booking essential) Menu £ 28/40 – Carte £ 40/55
Spec. Sweetbread and wild mushroom cannelloni, asparagus, leek and bacon. Poached and roast pigeon, cep flavoured sauce. Rhubarb crumble brûlée, ginger advocaat ice cream.
◆ Part Edwardian country house in Lutyens style; extensive landscaped gardens. Finest quality antiques and furnishings throughout public areas and individually styled bedrooms. Refined country house style dining in elegant, comfortable restaurant.

Episode
64 Upper Holly Walk ✉ CV32 4JL – ☎ (01926) 883 777
– leamington@episodehotels.co.uk – Fax (01926) 330 467 U **o**
32 rm – †£ 75/95 ††£ 95/105 – **Rest** – Menu £ 15 (lunch) – Carte £ 21/36
◆ Characterful Victorian house with spacious and well-decorated interior featuring high ceilings and parquet flooring. Good comfort levels in the sizeable bedrooms. Bistro dining room has smart, elegant, period feel.

Adams without rest
22 Avenue Rd ✉ CV31 3PQ – ☎ (01926) 450 742 – bookings@adams-hotel.co.uk
– Fax (01926) 313 110 – closed Christmas and New Year V **n**
14 rm – †£ 69/80 ††£ 90
◆ Delightful house of the Regency period with plenty of charm and character: original features include ceiling mouldings. Immaculate and similarly attractive bedrooms.

York House without rest
9 York Rd ✉ CV31 3PR – ✆ (01926) 424671 – reservations@yorkhousehotel.biz – Fax (01926) 832272 – closed 2 weeks Christmas V **u**
8 rm – 🚹£ 35/52 🚹🚹£ 68
◆ Victorian house on a pleasant parade, retains characterful fittings such as stained glass windows. Views of River Leam. Simply furnished rooms in period style.

The Brasserie at Mallory – at Mallory Court H.
Harbury Lane, Bishop's Tachbrook, South : 2¼ m. by B 4087 (Tachbrook Rd) ✉ CV33 9QB – ✆ (01926) 453939 – thebrasserie@mallory.co.uk – Fax (01926) 451714 – closed Sunday dinner
Rest – (booking essential) Carte £ 21/32
◆ In hotel annex; step into bar with eye-catching Art Deco style. Conservatory dining room overlooks pretty walled garden and terrace. Modern British cooking in a buzzy setting.

Restaurant 23
23 Dormer Place ✉ CV32 5AA – ✆ (01926) 422422 – info@restaurant23.co.uk – Fax (01926) 422246 – closed 2 weeks August, 1-14 January, Sunday and Monday V **a**
Rest – Menu £ 16 (lunch) – Carte £ 31/34
◆ Ever spoken to a working chef in a restaurant? You can here, in elegantly appointed surroundings, where classically based, seasonal, modern dishes are concocted by the owner.

ENGLAND

Oscar's
39 Chandos St ✉ CV32 4RL – ✆ (01926) 452807 – enquiries@oscarsfrenchbistro.co.uk – closed Sunday-Monday U **x**
Rest – (booking essential) Menu £ 15/24
◆ Bustling, informal and unpretentious, set in three rooms on two floors; upstairs smoking area. Good value, accomplished French bistro cooking; notable steak specialities.

The Emperors
Bath Place ✉ CV31 3BP – ✆ (01926) 313030 – Fax (01926) 435966 – closed 25-26 December, 1 January, Bank Holiday Mondays and Sunday V **i**
Rest – Chinese Carte £ 19/26 **s**
◆ Large warehouse conversion adjacent to railway station. Decorated with traditional war banners and framed oriental prints. Authentic, tasty Chinese cuisine.

at Weston under Wetherley **Northeast : 4½ m. by A 445 on B 4453 – ✉ Royal Leamington Spa**

Wethele Manor Farm without rest
✉ CV33 9BZ – ✆ (01926) 831772 – simonmoreton@wethelemanor.com – Fax (01926) 315359
9 rm – 🚹£ 65/85 🚹🚹£ 90/95
◆ Lovingly restored manor house with individually furnished, characterful bedrooms, low beams and uneven boards. Breakfast room incorporates an old well. Welcoming feel.

Good food and accommodation at moderate prices?
Look for the Bib symbols:
red Bib Gourmand for food, blue Bib Hotel for hotels

ROYAL TUNBRIDGE WELLS – Kent – 504 U 30 – pop. 60 095 8 B2

Great Britain

London 36 m – Brighton 33 m – Folkestone 46 m – Hastings 27 m – Maidstone 18 m

The Old Fish Market, The Pantiles ✆ (01892) 515675

Langton Rd, ✆ (01892) 523 034 .

The Pantiles★ B 26 – Calverley Park★ B

ROYAL TUNBRIDGE WELLS

Benhall Mill Rd . . . . A 3
Bishop's Down . . . . A 4
Calverley Rd . . . . B
Crescent Rd . . . . B 9
Fir Tree Rd . . . . A 10
Grosvenor Rd . . . . B 12
Hall's Hole Rd . . . . A 13
High Rocks Lane . . . . A 16
High St . . . . B 14
Hungershall Park Rd . . . . A 17
Lansdowne Rd . . . . B 18
Lower Green Rd . . . . A 20
Major York's Rd . . . . A 21
Monson Rd . . . . B 22
Mount Ephraim . . . . A, B 23
Mount Ephraim Rd . . . . B 24
Mount Pleasant Rd . . . . B 25
Pantiles (The) . . . . B 26
Prospect Rd . . . . A 27
Royal Victoria Pl. Shopping Centre . . . . B
Rusthall Rd . . . . A 28
St John's Rd . . . . B 29
Tea Garden Lane . . . . A 30
Vale Rd . . . . B 33
Victoria Rd . . . . B 34
Warwick Park . . . . B 35

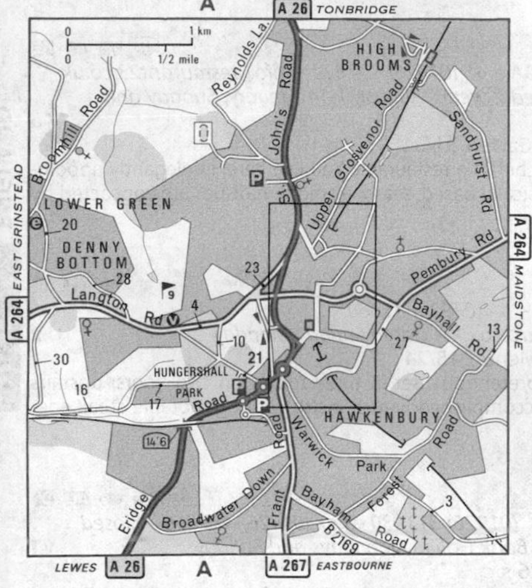

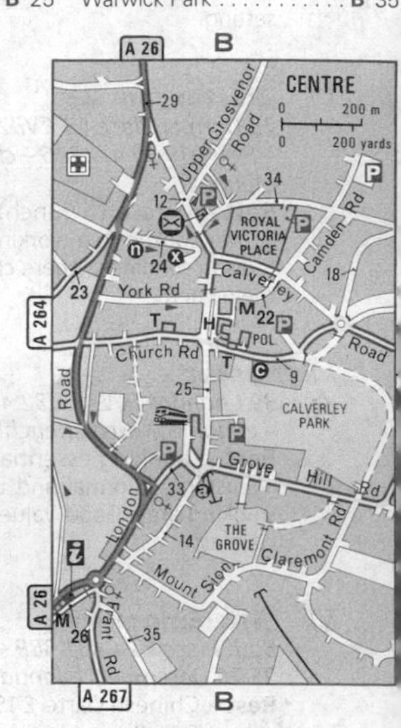

Hotel du Vin

Crescent Rd ✉ *TN1 2LY* – ✆ *(01892) 526 455*
– *info@tunbridgewells.hotelduvin.com* – *Fax (01892) 512 044* B c

34 rm – 🛉£ 105/195 🛉🛉£ 105/195, ☕ £13.50

Rest *Bistro* – see restaurant listing

◆ Delightful Georgian house with a contemporarily styled interior themed around wine; provides a stylish, comfortable feel throughout. Occasional wine-based events.

Spa

Mount Ephraim ✉ *TN4 8XJ* – ✆ *(01892) 520 331* – *reservations@spahotel.co.uk* – *Fax (01892) 510 575* A v

67 rm – 🛉£ 105/120 🛉🛉£ 150, ☕ £13.50 – 3 suites

Rest *Chandelier* – (Closed Saturday lunch) Menu £ 32/47

◆ Classic Georgian mansion set in 14 acres of gardens and parkland with lakes. An old-fashioned, English style of hospitality. Comfortable, well-furnished bedrooms. Dining options in formal restaurant or lounge.

Danehurst without rest
41 Lower Green Rd, Rusthall, West : 1 ¾ m. by A 264 ✉ TN4 8TW – ☎ (01892) 527739 – info@danehurst.net – Fax (01892) 514804 – closed 1-14 February, 25 December A **e**
4 rm – †£ 60/70 ††£ 100
◆ Victorian family home, with koi carp in the garden, located in residential area of town. Mix of homely furniture and furnishings and a conservatory breakfast room.

Thackeray's
85 London Rd ✉ TN1 1EA – ☎ (01892) 511921 – reservations@thackeraysrestaurant.co.uk – Fax (01892) 527561 – Closed Monday and Sunday dinner B **n**
Rest – Menu £ 17/29 – Carte £ 40/49 **s**
◆ Grade II listed 17C house with handsome Oriental terrace. Modern interior contrasts pleasingly with façade. The classically based cooking employs first rate ingredients.

Signor Franco
5a High St ✉ TN1 1UL – ☎ (01892) 549199 – Fax (01892) 541378 – closed Sunday and Bank Holidays B **a**
Rest – Italian Carte £ 24/39
◆ On first floor in high street. Several dining areas with good-sized, well-spaced tables. Classic Italian feel in the broad range of dishes and the welcoming ambience.

Bistro – at Hotel du Vin
✉ TN1 2LY – ☎ (01892) 526455 – Fax (01892) 512044 B **c**
Rest – (booking essential) Carte approx. £ 29
◆ Classically styled with dark wood floors and furniture and wine memorabilia. Terrace for lunch. Interesting modern menu. Informal and efficient service.

Blanc Brasserie
Fiveways, Lime Hill Rd ✉ TN1 1LJ – ☎ (01892) 559170 – tunbridgewells@brasserieblanc.com – Fax (01892) 559171 – closed 25 December B **x**
Rest – Carte £ 20/38
◆ Simple, modern décor: banquette seats and full-length glass windows. Extensive selection of menus with a French base, prepared with trademark Blanc expertise.

at Speldhurst North : 3 ½ m. by A 26 - A – ✉ Royal Tunbridge Wells

George & Dragon
Speldhurst Hill ✉ TN3 0NN – ☎ (01892) 863125 – julian@leefe-griffiths.freeserve.co.uk – Fax (01892) 863216 – Closed Sunday dinner
Rest – Carte £ 20/30
◆ Locally renowned black-and-white fronted pub where fresh Kentish ingredients from small, local suppliers are proudly employed in good value dishes with a classic French base.

ROYSTON – Herts. – 504 T 27 12 B1

The Cabinet at Reed
High St, South : 3 m. by A 10 ✉ SG8 8AH – ☎ (01763) 848366 – thecabinet@btconnect.com – Fax (01763) 849407 – Closed Sunday dinner
Rest – Menu £ 19/25 – Carte £ 27/35
◆ 16C clapperboard country pub with a smart, contemporary restaurant and welcoming ambience. Interesting choice of modern British dishes; good wine list, many by the glass.

ENGLAND

ROZEL BAY – C.I. – **503** P 33 – see Channel Islands

RUAN-HIGH-LANES – Cornwall – **503** F 33 – see Veryan

RUNSWICK BAY – N. Yorks. – ✉ **Whitby** 23 **C1**

London 285 m – Middlesbrough 24 m – Whitby 9 m

Cliffemount

✉ TS13 5HU – ☎ (01947) 840 103 – info@cliffemounthotel.co.uk – Fax (01947) 841 025

20 rm – †£ 48/65 ††£ 130 – **Rest** – Carte £ 17/33 **s**

◆ Enviably located hotel which has benefitted hugely from refurbishment. Cosy bar with blackboard menu. Balanced mix of luxurious or cosy bedrooms, 10 of which have balconies. Light, airy dining room boasts fantastic views of bay. Strong seafood base.

RUSHLAKE GREEN – E. Sussex – **504** U 31 – ✉ **Heathfield** 8 **B2**

London 54 m – Brighton 26 m – Eastbourne 13 m

Stone House

Northeast corner of the green ✉ TN21 9QJ – ☎ (01435) 830 553 – Fax (01435) 830 726 – closed last week February, first week March, 24 December-3 January

5 rm – †£ 135/165 ††£ 195/245 – 1 suite – **Rest** – (dinner only lunch May-August) (residents only.) Menu £ 25

◆ Charming part 15C, part Georgian country house surrounded by parkland. All interiors delightfully furnished with antiques and fine art. Garden produce features on menu.

RUSHTON – Northants. – see Kettering

ENGLAND

Good food without spending a fortune?
Look out for the Bib Gourmand

RYE – E. Sussex – **504** W 31 – **pop. 4 195** *Great Britain* 9 **C2**

London 61 m – Brighton 49 m – Folkestone 27 m – Maidstone 33 m

The Heritage Centre, Strand Quay ☎ (01797) 226696, ryetic@rother.gov.uk

Old Town★★ : Mermaid Street★, St Mary's Church (≤ ★)

The George in Rye

98 High St ✉ TN31 7JT – ☎ (01797) 222 114 – Fax (01797) 224 065

24 rm – †£ 95/125 ††£ 225 – **Rest** – Menu £ 16 (lunch) – Carte £ 24/32

◆ Part 16C coaching inn; appealing mix of contemporary design and original features. Variously-sized bedrooms have state-of-the-art TVs and quality linen. Pleasant courtyard. Trendy restaurant offers Mediterranean dishes made with locally sourced produce and good choice of wines by glass.

Mermaid Inn

Mermaid St ✉ TN31 7EY – ☎ (01797) 223 065 – info@mermaidinn.com – Fax (01797) 225 069

31 rm – †£ 85/110 ††£ 220 – **Rest** – Menu £ 23/39 – Carte approx. £ 45

◆ Historic inn dating from 15C. Immense character from the timbered exterior on a cobbled street to the heavily beamed, antique furnished interior warmed by roaring log fires. Two dining options: both exude age and character.

Rye Lodge
Hilders Cliff ✉ TN31 7LD – ✆ (01797) 223 838 – info@ryelodge.co.uk – Fax (01797) 223 585
18 rm – £70 £200 – **Rest** – (dinner only) Menu £30
◆ Family run house located close to historic town centre yet with Romney Marsh in sight. Welcoming guest areas and comfortable, smartly fitted rooms, three in the courtyard. Enjoy dining in candlelight.

Jeake's House without rest
Mermaid St ✉ TN31 7ET – ✆ (01797) 222 828 – stay@jeakeshouse.com – Fax (01797) 222 623
11 rm – £79 £100
◆ Down a cobbled lane, a part 17C house, once a wool store and a Quaker meeting place. Welcoming atmosphere amid antiques, sloping floors and beams. Pretty, traditional rooms.

Oaklands without rest
Udimore Rd, Southwest : 1 ¼ m. on B 2089 ✉ TN31 6AB – ✆ (01797) 229 734 – info@oaklands-rye.co.uk – Fax (01797) 229 734 – Closed Christmas-New Year
3 rm – £50/60 £75/84
◆ Restored Edwardian guest house with countryside views and welcoming hosts. Stylish breakfast room with old Arabic door as table. Spotless bedrooms include two four posters.

Durrant House without rest
2 Market St ✉ TN31 7LA – ✆ (01797) 223 182 – info@durranthouse.com – Fax (01797) 226 940 – Closed January
5 rm – £78 £105
◆ Grade I listed house of unknown age. Neat breakfast room with daily breakfast specials. Bright lounge looks down East Street. Carefully appointed, immaculate modern rooms.

Little Orchard House without rest
West St ✉ TN31 7ES – ✆ (01797) 223 831 – info@littleorchardhouse.com – Fax (01797) 223 831 – minimum 2 night stay at weekends
3 rm – £60/70 £100/120
◆ Charming cottage in quiet street, rebuilt 1745. Surrounded by peaceful garden. Pleasantly cluttered atmosphere with paintings and objets d'art in communal areas and rooms.

Flushing Inn
4 Market St ✉ TN31 7LA – ✆ (01797) 223 292 – j.e.flynn@btconnect.com – closed first two weeks January, first two weeks June, Monday and Tuesday
Rest – Seafood Menu £19 (lunch) – Carte £27/43
◆ A neighbourhood institution, this 15C inn with heavily timbered and panelled dining area features a superb 16C fresco. The seafood oriented menu has a local, traditional tone.

Webbes at The Fish Café
17 Tower St ✉ TN31 7AT – ✆ (01797) 222 226 – info@thefishcafe.com – Fax (01797) 229 260 – closed 1-15 January, Monday
Rest – Seafood (closed Monday dinner November-Easter) (booking essential at dinner) Carte £26/31
◆ Large converted warehouse: terracotta painted ground floor for seafood lunches and eclectic options. Dinner upstairs features more serious piscine menus. Tangible buzziness.

ENGLAND

Landgate Bistro

VISA MC AE DC

5-6 Landgate ✉ TN31 7LH – ✆ (01797) 222 829 – info@landgatebistro.co.uk – closed 1 week August, 24-25 & 31 December, 1 January, Sunday and Monday and Tuesday after Bank Holiday

Rest – (dinner only) Carte £ 18/28 **s**

◆ Well established, personally run, unpretentious bistro: a local favourite. Classic and modern cooking is fresh and tasty with good choice seafood reassuringly to the fore.

Globe Inn

VISA MC AE

10 Military Rd, North : 1/4 m. off A 268 ✉ TN31 7NX – ✆ (01797) 227 918 – info@theglobe-inn.com – closed Sunday dinner and Monday

Rest – (booking essential) Carte £ 26/35

◆ Modern pub boasts leather sofas and displays of homemade goodies as well as quirky forties furnishings and décor. Modern British menu uses local produce. Homely puddings.

at Camber Southeast : 4 ¼ m. by A 259 – ✉ Rye

The Place

AC rest, P VISA MC AE

New Lydd Rd, Camber Sands ✉ TN31 7RB – ✆ (01797) 225 057 – enquiries@theplacecambersands.co.uk – Fax (01797) 227 003

18 rm – †£ 83/93 ††£ 90/100 – **Rest** – Carte £ 20/31

◆ Immaculately whitewashed, converted former seaside motel located over the dunes. Smart, stylish rooms with a good level of facilities and charming extra touches. Informal brasserie style restaurant with emphasis on local ingredients.

at Peasmarsh Northwest : 4 m. on A 268 – ✉ Rye

Flackley Ash

rm, P VISA MC AE DC

London Rd, on A 268 ✉ TN31 6YH – ✆ (01797) 230 651 – enquiries@flackleyashhotel.co.uk – Fax (01797) 230 510

41 rm ☐ – †£ 87 ††£ 184 – 4 suites – **Rest** – (bar lunch Monday-Saturday) Menu £ 29 – Carte £ 29/39

◆ Extended Georgian country house of red brick. Traditional style throughout with comfortable lounge and bar areas. Each well-equipped bedroom is of a unique size and shape. Dining room has sunny conservatory extension.

SAFFRON WALDEN – Essex – 504 U 27 – pop. 14 313 12 B1

▶ London 43 m – Bishop's Stortford 12 m – Cambridge 18 m

the restaurant

VISA MC AE

Victoria House, 2 Church St ✉ CB10 1JW – ✆ (01799) 526 444 – reservations@trocs.co.uk – Closed Sunday and Monday

Rest – (dinner only) Menu £ 17 (weekdays) – Carte £ 21/32 **s**

◆ Stylishly converted cellar with an informal feel: candles light the brick and flint walls and etched glass tables. Original, contemporary menu; relaxed style and service.

Dish

AC VISA MC AE

13a King St ✉ CB10 1HE – ✆ (01799) 513 300 – dishrestaurant@btinternet.com – Fax (01799) 531 699 – Closed 25-27 December, 1-3 January and Sunday dinner

Rest – Menu £ 15 (lunch) – Carte £ 25/31

◆ First floor restaurant within characterful beamed house in town centre. Modern oil paintings exude jazzy theme. Classically based dishes take on adventurous note at dinner.

ENGLAND

ST AGNES – Cornwall – 503 E 33 – pop. 2 759 1 A2

London 302 m – Newquay 12 m – Penzance 26 m – Truro 9 m
Perranporth Budnic Hill, ☎ (01872) 573 701 .
St Agnes Beacon★★ (※ ★★)
Portreath★, SW : 5½ m

Rose-in-Vale Country House (heated)
Mithian, East : 2 m. by B 3285 ✉ TR5 0QD – ☎ (01872) 552 202 – reception@rose-in-vale-hotel.co.uk – Fax (01872) 552 700
19 rm – †£ 60/100 ††£ 100/135
Rest *The Valley* – (Closed lunch Monday-Wednesday) Menu £ 25 **s**
◆ Handsome Georgian manor clad in climbing roses; outdoor pool and peaceful gardens with summer house and dovecote. Classically styled lounge bar and library; well-kept rooms. Neat, formal dining room with local specials.

Luxury pad or humble abode?
and denote categories of comfort.

ST ALBANS – Herts. – 504 T 28 – pop. 82 429 *Great Britain* 12 A2

London 27 m – Cambridge 41 m – Luton 10 m
Town Hall, Market Pl ☎ (01727) 864511
Batchwood Hall Batchwood Drive, ☎ (01727) 833 349;
Redbourn Kinsbourne Green Lane, ☎ (01582) 793 493.
City★ - Cathedral★ BZ – Verulamium★ (Museum★ **AC** AY)
Hatfield House★★ **AC**, E : 6 m. by A 1057

Plan on next page

Sopwell House
Cottonmill Lane, Southeast : 1½ m. by A 1081 and Mile House Lane ✉ AL1 2HQ – ☎ (01727) 864 477 – enquiries@sopwellhouse.co.uk – Fax (01727) 844 741
127 rm – †£ 99/185 ††£ 169/185 – 2 suites
Rest *The Restaurant* – (Closed Saturday and Monday lunch) Menu £ 30 – Carte £ 24/42
Rest *Bejerano's Brasserie* – Carte £ 9/34
◆ Everything denotes peace and seclusion: pretty gardens, leather furnished lounge, modern spa with Japanese treatments, pool and gym. Modern rooms and apartments. Seasonal modern cooking in The Restaurant. Bejerano's Brasserie has swimming pool views.

St Michael's Manor rm,
St Michael's Village, Fishpool St ✉ AL3 4RY – ☎ (01727) 864 444 – reservations@stmichaelsmanor.com – Fax (01727) 848 909 – closed 25 December and 1 January AY **d**
29 rm – †£ 145 ††£ 180/250 – 1 suite – **Rest** – (closed dinner 25 December and 1 January) Menu £ 20 – Carte £ 29/39
◆ This part 16C, part William and Mary manor house overlooks a lake. Elegant bedrooms are named after trees; some are suites with sitting rooms, all are luxurious and stylish. Conservatory dining room with splendid vistas.

Comfort rm, rest,
Ryder House, Holywell Hill ✉ AL1 1HG – ☎ (01727) 848 849 – admin@gb055.u-net.com – Fax (01727) 812 210 BZ **b**
60 rm – †£ 79 ††£ 79, £ 8.95 – **Rest** – (Closed Sunday) (dinner only) Carte £ 14/20
◆ Built by Samuel Ryder, donor of golf's Ryder cup. Defined by Edwardian features: stained glass dome and carved fireplace. The bedrooms, though, are of practical bent. Meals served in restaurant or your room.

ENGLAND

Ardmore House

54 Lemsford Rd ✉ AL1 3PR – ✆ (01727) 859313 – info@ardmorehousehotel.co.uk – Fax (01727) 859313 CY **a**

40 rm – †£65/95 ††£78/125

Rest *Belvedere* – (Closed Saturday lunch and Sunday dinner) Carte £23/41

◆ Edwardian residence with Victorian annex: this is a traditional, family owned hotel. Homely bedrooms have the feel of a lounge, boasting sofas and wall lamps. Traditional dining room with menu to match.

Sukiyaki

6 Spencer St ✉ AL3 5EG – ✆ (01727) 865009 – closed 2 weeks in summer, 1 week Christmas, Sunday and Monday BY **e**

Rest – Japanese Menu £8/20 – Carte £15/19

◆ A pared-down style, minimally decorated restaurant with simple, precise helpings of Japanese food. No noodles or sushi, expect instead sukiyaki (a beef dish), and tempura.

A 1081 HARPENDEN, LUTON

Street	Grid	No.
Abbey Mill Lane	AZ	
Albert St.	BZ	
Alma Rd	CZ	
Avenue Rd	CY	
Beaconsfield Rd	CYZ	
Belmont Hill	BZ	
Branch Rd	AY	
Bricket Rd	BCYZ	5
Britton Ave	BY	6
Carlisle Ave	BCY	8
Catherine St	BY	
Chequer St	BZ	10
Church Crescent	ABY	11
Cottonmill Lane	BCZ	13
Dalton St	BY	15
Drovers Way	BY	16
Etna Rd	BY	18
Fishpool St	AYZ	
Folly Ave	BY	20
Folly Lane	ABY	
Grange St	BY	
Grimston Rd	CZ	21
Grosvenor Rd	CZ	22
Hall Pl. Gardens	CY	
Hatfield Rd	CY	
High St	BZ	
Hillside Rd	CY	
Holywell Hill	BZ	
Lattimore Rd	CZ	
Lemsford Rd	CY	
London Rd	BCZ	
Lower Dagnall St	BYZ	26
Maltings Shopping Centre	BZ	
Manor Rd	CY	
Market Pl.	BZ	29
Marlborough Rd	CZ	28
Mount Pleasant	AY	
New England St	AY	
Normandy Rd	BY	
Old London Rd	CZ	
Portland St	AY	
Ridgemont Rd	CZ	
Russell Ave	BY	35
St Peter's Rd	CY	37
St Peter's St	BCY	
Sopwell Lane	BZ	
Spencer St	BY	39
Spicer St College	BYZ	40
Station Way	CZ	
Thorpe Rd	BZ	42
Upper Dagnall St	BYZ	44
Upper Lattimore Rd	CYZ	
Upper Marlborough Rd	CYZ	46
Verulam Rd	ABY	
Victoria St	BCZ	
Watson's Walk	CZ	48
Welclose St	AYZ	49
Worley Rd	BY	

(M25) POTTERS BAR A 1081

ST ANNE – C.I. – **503** Q 33 – **see Channel Islands**

ST ANNE'S – Lancs. – **502** K 22 – **see Lytham St Anne's**

ST AUBIN – C.I. – **503** P 33 – **see Channel Islands**

The ✿ award is the crème de la crème.
This is awarded to restaurants
which are really worth travelling miles for!

ST AUSTELL – Cornwall – **503** F 32 – pop. 22 658 1 **B2**

London 281 m – Newquay 16 m – Plymouth 38 m – Truro 14 m
Carlyon Bay, ✆ (01726) 814 250 .
Holy Trinity Church★
St Austell Bay★★ (Gribbin Head★★) E : by A 390 and A 3082 – Carthew : Wheal Martyn China Clay Heritage Centre★★ **AC**, N : 2 m. by A 391 – Mevagissey★★ - Lost Gardens of Heligan★, S : 5 m. by B 3273 – Charlestown★, SE : 2 m. by A 390 – Eden Project★★, NE : 3 m. by A 390 at St Blazey Gate. Trewithen★★★ **AC**, NE : 7 m. by A 390 – Lanhydrock★★, NE : 11 m. by A 390 and B 3269 – Polkerris★, E : 7 m. by A 390 and A 3082

Poltarrow Farm without rest

St Mewan, Southwest : 1 ¾ m. by A 390 ✉ PL26 7DR – ✆ (01726) 67 111 – enquire@poltarrow.co.uk – Fax (01726) 67 111 – closed Christmas and New Year
5 rm – †£ 70 ††£ 70
◆ Tucked away down a tree-lined drive stands this working farm equipped with indoor pool, elegant sitting room and conservatory serving Cornish breakfasts. Rooms have views.

at Tregrehan East : 2 ½ m. by A 390 – ✉ St Austell 1 **B2**

Anchorage House

Nettles Corner, Boscundle ✉ PL25 3RH – ✆ (01726) 814 071 – info@anchoragehouse.co.uk – Fax (01726) 813 462 – Closed Christmas and January
4 rm – †£ 85/120 ††£ 140/150 – **Rest** – (by arrangement, communal dining) Menu £ 35
◆ Intriguing mix of modern and period styles in welcoming house set in peaceful position. Antique beds in spacious rooms plus extras: flowers, fruit, hot water bottles.

at Carlyon Bay East : 2 ½ m. by A 3601 – ✉ St Austell

Carlyon Bay

Carlyon Bay, (heated) rest,
✉ PL25 3RD – ✆ (01726) 812 304 – reservations@carlyonbay.com – Fax (01726) 814 938
86 rm – †£ 90/120 ††£ 230/300, £ 16 – **Rest** – Menu £ 18/35 – Carte £ 45/55
◆ With superb views across bay and well-positioned pool as suntrap, this family friendly hotel has golf course access and lays on programmes for children. Spacious, neat rooms. Dining room with live music and handsome vistas.

Porth Avallen

Carlyon Bay,
Sea Rd ✉ PL25 3SG – ✆ (01726) 812 802 – info@porthavallen.co.uk – Fax (01726) 817 097
28 rm – †£ 59/94 ††£ 148/170 – **Rest** – (bar lunch) Menu £ 34 (dinner) **s** – Carte £ 23/33 **s**
◆ Built as a family home in 1928; enjoys a commanding position overlooking Carlyon Bay. Warmly decorated interiors with wood panelling, rich coloured carpets and furnishings. Restaurant with fine sea views.

at Charlestown Southeast : 2 m. by A 390 – ✉ St Austell

T' Gallants without rest

6 Charlestown Rd ✉ PL25 3NJ – ✆ (01726) 70 203 – enquiries@tgallants.co.uk
8 rm – †£ 45 ††£ 65
◆ Georgian house in quiet fishing port. Benches in walled garden for sunning yourself. Good value accommodation: try and book Room 5, which boasts four poster and the best view.

Revival

✉ PL25 3NJ – ✆ (01726) 879 053 – info@cornwall-revival.co.uk – closed 2 weeks January, Monday and Sunday except lunch in summer.
Rest – Carte £ 26/30
◆ Once a cooperage; reputedly Charlestown's second oldest building, it overlooks 19C tall ships in the harbour. Local, seasonal ingredients used to good effect on all-day menus.

ST BLAZEY – Cornwall – 503 F 32 – pop. 9 256 1 B2

London 276 m – Newquay 21 m – Plymouth 33 m – Truro 19 m

Eden Project★★, NW; 1 ½ m. by A 390 and minor roads

Nanscawen Manor House without rest (heated)

Prideaux Rd, West : ¾ m. by Luxulyan rd ✉ PL24 2SR – ✆ (01726) 814 488 – keith@nanscawen.com

3 rm – †£ 86 ††£ 72/120

◆ Sumptuous country house, until 1520 the home of Nanscawen family. Conservatory breakfast room set in fragrant gardens. Welcoming bedrooms; outdoor spa bath.

ST BRELADE'S BAY – C.I. – 503 P 33 – see Channel Islands

ST HELIER – C.I. – 503 P 33 – see Channel Islands

ST ISSEY – Cornwall – 503 F 32 – see Padstow

ST IVES – Cornwall – 503 D 33 1 A3

London 319 m – Penzance 10 m – Truro 25 m

The Guildhall, Street-an-Pol ✆ (01736) 796297, ivtic@penwith.gov.uk

Tregenna Castle H., ✆ (01736) 795 254;

West Cornwall Lelant, ✆ (01736) 753 401.

Town★★ - Barbara Hepworth Museum★★ **AC** Y **M1** – Tate St Ives★★ (≤ ★★) - St Nicholas Chapel (≤ ★★) Y – Parish Church★ Y **A**

S : Penwith★★ Y. St Michael's Mount★★ (≤ ★★) S : 10 m. by B 3306 - Y - B 3311, B 3309 and A 30

Plan on next page

The Garrack

Burthallan Lane ✉ TR26 3AA – ✆ (01736) 796 199 – mich@garrack.com – Fax (01736) 798 955 – Closed Christmas Y **a**

18 rm – †£ 75/160 ††£ 180/199

Rest *The Restaurant* – (dinner only) Menu £ 26 – Carte £ 25/51

◆ Well-established hotel with pleasant gardens close to Tate. Plenty of homely touches. Spacious pool and sauna. Individually designed bedrooms, many with feature beds. Very popular dining room serves Cornish specialities.

Pedn-Olva ≤ Harbour and bay,

West Porthminster Beach ✉ TR26 2EA – ✆ (01736) 796 222 – pednolva@smallandfriendly.co.uk – Fax (01736) 797 710 Y **c**

31 rm – †£ 55/75 ††£ 150/220

Rest *The Lookout* – (bar lunch) Carte £ 27/32

◆ Meaning "lookout on the headland" in Cornish; boasts commanding views of harbour and bay. Sheltered sun terrace and pool. Neutral décor typified by simple bedrooms. Restaurant offers diners splendid outlook.

Blue Hayes without rest

Trelyon Ave ✉ TR26 2AD – ✆ (01736) 797 129 – info@bluehayes.co.uk – Fax (01736) 799 098 – March to October Y **u**

6 rm – †£ 120/135 ††£ 160/190

◆ 19C house with super view from terrace over the harbour; access to coast path from garden. Hi-tech interior. Single course supper available. Well-appointed bedrooms.

Primrose Valley

Porthminster Beach ✉ TR26 2ED – ✆ (01736) 794 939 – info@primroseonline.co.uk – Fax (01736) 794 939 – closed December and January Y **r**

10 rm – †£ 90/145 ††£ 125/175 – **Rest** – (by arrangement in summer only)

◆ Edwardian villa with unrivalled proximity to beach. Stylish café bar and lounge; relaxing front patio. Local suppliers ensure good breakfast choice. Individually styled rooms. Summer-time meals arranged with the owners.

ENGLAND

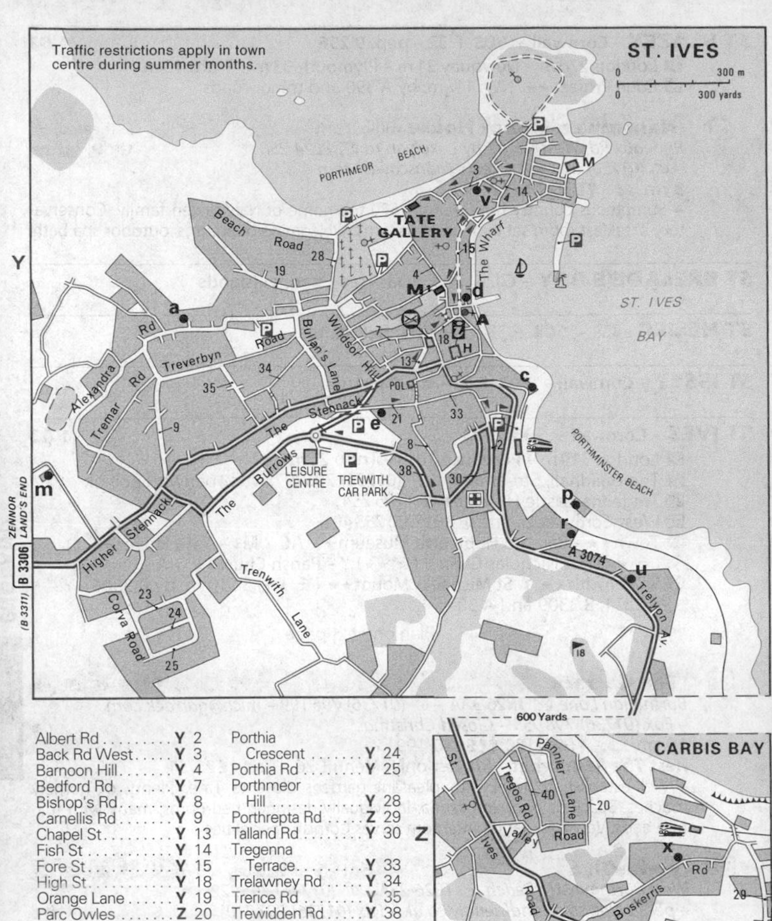

Old Vicarage without rest

Parc-an-Creet ✉ TR26 2ES – ✆ (01736) 796 124 – stay@oldvicarage.com – restricted opening in Winter — Y m

7 rm ☕ – 🚹£57 🚹🚹£76

◆ Former vicarage built of granite and slate retains Victorian charm and character, especially in bar lounge furnished in red velvet, gilt and mahogany. Rooms in uniform style.

Pebble without rest

4 Parc Ave ✉ TR26 2DN – ✆ (01736) 794 168 – info@pebble-hotel.co.uk – restricted opening in winter — Y e

7 rm ☕ – 🚹£40/85 🚹🚹£90/125

◆ Small family run hotel; superb views of harbour and bay. Make yourself at home in lounge stocked with local information books. Simply furnished bedrooms in cottage style.

XX **Alba**

Old Lifeboat House, The Wharf ✉ TR26 1LF – ✆ (01736) 797 222 – Fax (01736) 798 937 – closed 25-26 December Y **d**

Rest – Seafood Menu £ 17 – Carte £ 27/34

◆ Ideally situated in centre of town, on both floors of Old Lifeboat House; good harbour views. Modern feel; artwork on walls. Tasty, extensive menus with a modern slant.

X **Porthminster Cafe** ← St Ives Bay and town,

Porthminster Beach ✉ TR26 2EB – ✆ (01736) 795 352 – p.minster@btopenworld.com – Fax (01736) 795 352 – Closed 25 December Y **p**

Rest – Seafood Carte £ 29/43

◆ 1930s beach house on Porthminster sands. Super views: large terrace for al fresco dining. Colourful local artwork on walls. Seafood oriented dishes plus eclectic dinner menus.

X **Blue Fish**

Norway Lane ✉ TR26 1LZ – ✆ (01736) 794 204 – bluefishrest@btconnect.com – restricted opening in winter Y **v**

Rest – Seafood Carte £ 25/36

◆ Welcoming, family run eatery in the centre of town with a charming sunny terrace affording views of the town. Local and Mediterranean seafood in a simple, relaxed style.

at Carbis Bay South : 1 ¾ m. on A 3074 – ✉ St Ives

Boskerris

Boskerris Rd ✉ TR26 2NQ – ✆ (01736) 795 295 – reservations@boskerrishotel.co.uk – closed December and January Z **x**

15 rm – †£ 70/90 ††£ 140/190 – **Rest** – (dinner only) Menu £ 25

◆ Hotel with panoramic views of Carbis Bay and coastline. Lounge, separate TV room and bar serving light lunches. Outdoor pool overlooking the sea. Restaurant serving local fish, produce and herbs from hotel garden.

We try to be as accurate as possible when giving room rates. But prices are susceptible to change, so please check rates when booking.

ST JUST – Cornwall – 503 C 33 – pop. 1 890 1 A3

London 325 m – Penzance 7 m – Truro 35 m

Cape Cornwall G. & C.C., ✆ (01736) 788 611 .

Church★

Penwith★★ – Sancreed - Church★★ (Celtic Crosses★★), SE : 3 m. by A 3071 – St Buryan★★ (Church Tower★★), SE : 5 ½ m. by B 3306 and A 30 – Land's End★ (cliff scenery★★★), S : 5 ½ m. by B 3306 and A 30 – Cape Cornwall★ (← ★★), W : 1 ½ m. - Morvah (← ★★), NE : 4 ½ m. by B 3306 – Geevor Tin Mine★ AC, N : 3 m. by B 3306 – Carn Euny★, SE : 3 m. by A 3071 - Wayside Cross★ - Sennen Cove★ (← ★), S : 5 ½ m. by B 3306 and A 30. Porthcurno★, S : 9 ½ m. by B 3306, A 30 and B 3315

Boscean Country

Northwest : ½ m. by Boswedden Rd ✉ TR19 7QP – ✆ (01736) 788 748 – boscean.hotel@yahoo.com – Restricted opening in winter

12 rm – †£ 49/80 ††£ 70/110 – **Rest** – (dinner only) (residents only) Carte £ 19/27

◆ Originally a doctor's residence; this Edwardian house is surrounded by 3 acres of walled gardens, a haven for wildlife. Wealth of oak panelling indoors; most rooms have views.

ENGLAND

ST KEVERNE – Cornwall – 503 E 33 1 A3

London 302 m – Penzance 26 m – Truro 28 m

Old Temperance House without rest

The Square ✉ TR12 6NA – ✆ (01326) 280 986 – info@oldtemperancehouse.co.uk – Closed January and February

4 rm – †£ 50/55 ††£ 80/90

◆ 'Roses round the door' charm, in idyllic spot on pretty square. Spotlessly neat lounge. Excellent, out-of-the-ordinary breakfasts. Fresh, bright, carefully co-ordinated rooms.

ST LAWRENCE – C.I. – see Jersey

ST LAWRENCE – I.O.W. – 503 Q 32 – see Wight (Isle of)

ST MARGARET'S AT CLIFFE – Kent – 504 Y 30 – see Dover

ST MARTIN Guernsey – C.I. – 503 P 33 – see Channel Islands

ST MARTIN'S – Cornwall – 503 B 34 – see Scilly (Isles of)

ENGLAND

ST MARY'S – Cornwall – 503 B 34 – see Scilly (Isles of)

ST MAWES – Cornwall – 503 E 33 – ✉ Truro 1 B3

London 299 m – Plymouth 56 m – Truro 18 m

Town★ - Castle★ AC (< ★)

St Just-in-Roseland Church★★, N : 2½ m. by A 3078

Tresanton < St Mawes bay, St Anthony's Head and lighthouse,

27 Lower Castle Rd ✉ TR2 5DR – ✆ (01326) 270 055 – info@tresanton.com – Fax (01326) 270 053 – Closed 2 weeks early January

VISA AE

27 rm – †£ 158/216 ††£ 240/310 – 2 suites – **Rest** – Seafood (booking essential for non-residents) Menu £ 30/39

◆ Enduringly trendy former 1940s yachtsman's club with cinema. Watercolours on pale walls; gleaming crisp rooms with views; contemporary lounge and attentive service. Dining room boasts open terrace with harbour views and modern seafood dishes.

Idle Rocks < harbour and estuary, VISA AE

Harbourside, 1 Tredenham Rd ✉ TR2 5AN – ✆ (01326) 270 771 – reception@idlerocks.co.uk – Fax (01326) 270 062

33 rm – †£ 68/103 ††£ 136/266

Rest *The Water's Edge* – (light lunch) Carte £ 30/45

◆ Fine waterfront hotel with splendid views of the harbour and fishermen's cottages. Deep comfortable chairs in lounge and bright bedrooms, many with sea views. Restaurant with terrace overlooks the sea.

Rising Sun VISA

The Square ✉ TR2 5DJ – ✆ (01326) 270 233 – info@risingsunstmawes.co.uk – Fax (01326) 270 198

8 rm – †£ 70/90 ††£ 140/160 – **Rest** – (bar lunch Monday-Saturday) Menu £ 36 – Carte £ 18/25

◆ Renovated 17C house on harbour. Immaculately furnished bedrooms with a stylish feel. Lively, open-fired bar. A friendly place to rest your head. Buzzy conservatory restaurant with seascapes on the walls.

ST MAWGAN – Cornwall – 503 F 32 – ✉ Newquay 1 B2

London 262 m – Plymouth 41 m – St Austell 3 m

The Falcon Inn with rm

✉ *TR8 4EP* – ☎ *(01637) 860 225* – *enquiries@thefalconinn-newquay.co.uk* – *Fax (01637) 860 884* – *Closed 25 December*

3 rm – †£ 44 ††£ 84 – **Rest** – Carte £ 9/18

◆ Characterful 16C pub with cosy terrace. Warm interior in keeping with age of property: well maintained rustic décor. Popular menus, with seafood the highlight. Comfy rooms.

ST PETER – C.I. – 503 P 33 – see Channel Islands

ST PETER PORT – C.I. – 503 P 33 – see Channel Islands

Undecided between two equivalent establishments? Within each category, establishments are classified in our order of preference.

ST SAVIOUR – C.I. – 503 P 33 – see Channel Islands

SALCOMBE – Devon – 503 I 33 – pop. 1 893 2 C3

London 243 m – Exeter 43 m – Plymouth 27 m – Torquay 28 m

Council Hall, Market St ☎ (01548) 843927, info@salcombeinformation.co.uk

Sharpitor (Overbecks Museum and Garden★) (≤ ★★) **AC**, S : 2 m. by South Sands Z. Prawle Point (≤ ★★★) E : 16 m. around coast by A 381 - Y - and A 379

Plan on next page

Marine ≤ estuary,

Cliff Rd ✉ *TQ8 8JH* – ☎ *(01548) 844 444* – *bookings@marinehotelsalcombe.com* – *Fax (01548) 843 109* Y **e**

52 rm – †£ 75/195 ††£ 150/290 – 1 suite – **Rest** – (dinner only and Sunday lunch) Menu £ 17/30 – Carte £ 33/40

◆ Spectacular position on water's edge overlooking the estuary. Hotel makes the most of this; many bedrooms have balconies whilst centrally located rooms share the best views. Bright, roomy restaurant looks onto the water.

Tides Reach ≤ estuary,

South Sands ✉ *TQ8 8LJ* – ☎ *(01548) 843 466* – *enquire@tidesreach.com* – *Fax (01548) 843 954* – *February-November* Z **x**

32 rm – †£ 70/90 ††£ 130/320 – **Rest** – (bar lunch) Menu £ 38

◆ Traditional, personally run hotel set in pleasant sandy cove on Salcombe Estuary. Lilac and green rooms boast floral fabrics and flowers; many have balconies and a fine view. Restaurant overlooks attractive gardens and pond.

Restaurant 42 ≤

Fore St ✉ *TQ8 8JG* – ☎ *(01548) 843 408* – *jane@restaurant42.demon.co.uk* – *Fax (01548) 842 854* – *closed mid November-mid March* Y **n**

Rest – (dinner only) Carte approx. £ 30

◆ Things you may not know about 42: it has a delightful terrace/garden; fabulous views of the estuary; comfy lounge with squashy sofas; and interesting use of local ingredients.

ENGLAND

SALCOMBE

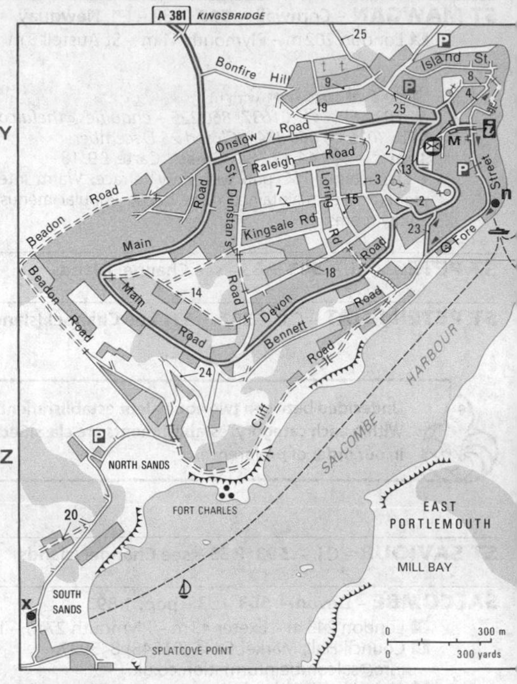

at Soar Mill Cove Southwest : 4 ¼ m. by A 381 - Y - via Malborough village – ✉ Salcombe

Soar Mill Cove (heated)
✉ TQ7 3DS – ☎ (01548) 561 566 – info@soarmillcove.co.uk
– *Fax (01548) 561 223 – closed 2 January-1 February*
22 rm – ♦£ 80/150 ♦♦£ 160/300 – **Rest** – (booking essential for non-residents) Menu £ 29 – Carte £ 20/32
♦ Family run local stone and slate hotel on one level in delightful and secluded coastal setting; rooms have terraces and chintz furnishings. Geared for families. Classically styled dining room.

at Hope Cove West : 4 m. by A 381 - Y - via Malborough village – ✉ Kingsbridge

Lantern Lodge
by Grand View Rd ✉ TQ7 3HE – ☎ (01548) 561 280
– lanternlodge@hopecove.wanadoo.co.uk – Fax (01548) 561 736
– March-mid November
14 rm – ♦£ 105/128 ♦♦£ 140/170 – **Rest** – (dinner only) (booking essential for non-residents) Menu £ 20
♦ Named after its lantern window, reputedly designed to guide sailors home, this welcoming, traditional clifftop hotel overlooks Hope Cove. Front bedrooms have views. Pretty dining room with small, adjacent bar.

Your opinions are important to us:
please write and let us know about your discoveries and experiences – good and bad!

SALE – Gtr Manchester – 502 N 23 – pop. 55 234 – ✉ Manchester 20 B3

London 212 m – Liverpool 36 m – Manchester 6 m – Sheffield 43 m
Sale Lodge Golf Rd, ☎ (0161) 973 1638 .

Cornerstones without rest
230 Washway Rd ✉ M33 4RA – ☎ (0161) 283 6909
– info@cornerstonesguesthouse.com – closed Christmas-New Year
9 rm – 🛉£ 30/38 🛉🛉£ 56, ☕ £6
◆ Built in 1871 for the Lord Mayor, this restored Victorian house is family run. A medley of rooms: spacious with varied décor and fabrics. Homely breakfast room.

SALFORD QUAYS – Gtr Manchester – see Manchester

SALISBURY – Wilts. – 503 O 30 – pop. 43 355 4 D3

London 91 m – Bournemouth 28 m – Bristol 53 m – Southampton 23 m
Fish Row ☎ (01722) 334956
Salisbury & South Wilts. Netherhampton, ☎ (01722) 742 645 ;
High Post Great Durnford, ☎ (01722) 782 356 .
City★★ - Cathedral★★★ **AC** Z – Salisbury and South Wiltshire Museum★ **AC** Z **M2** – Close★ Z : Mompesson House★ **AC** Z **A** – Sarum St Thomas Church★ Y **B** – Redcoats in the Wardrobe★ Z **M1**
Wilton Village★ (Wilton House★★ **AC**, Wilton Carpet Factory★ **AC**), W : 3 m. by A 30 Y – Old Sarum★ **AC**, N : 2 m. by A 345 Y – Woodford (Heale House Garden★) **AC**, NW : 4½ m. by Stratford Rd Y. Stonehenge★★★ **AC**, NW : 10 m. by A 345 - Y - and A 303 – Wardour Castle★ **AC**, W : 15 m. by A 30 Y

Plan on next page

White Hart
1 St John's St ✉ SP1 2SD – ☎ (01722) 327 476 – H6616@accor.com
– Fax (01722) 412 761 Z **s**
68 rm – 🛉£ 60/130 🛉🛉£ 100/180, ☕ £12.95
Rest ***Squire's*** – (closed lunch Saturday and Bank Holidays) (bar lunch) Menu £ 11/28 – Carte £ 17/27 **s**
◆ The elegant portico façade of this 17C hotel hints at formality whilst interior is relaxed and comfortable with plenty of sofas and armchairs in lounge and plush bedrooms. Dine al fresco on foliage-filled terrace.

Milford Hall
206 Castle St ✉ SP1 3TE – ☎ (01722) 417 411
– reservations@milfordhallhotel.com – Fax (01722) 419 444
– closed 24-26 December Y **a**
35 rm – 🛉£ 112 🛉🛉£ 115, ☕ £10
Rest ***Brasserie at 206*** – Carte £ 14/28 **s**
◆ A Georgian house, built 1780s; four period rooms in main building and in extension a variety of modern rooms, some with sofa beds. A predominantly commercial establishment. Outside decking for terrace dining.

Grasmere House rm,
70 Harnham Rd ✉ SP2 8JN – ☎ (01722) 338 388 – info@grasmerehotel.com
– Fax (01722) 333 710 Z **a**
38 rm – 🛉£ 76/100 🛉🛉£ 126/156 – **Rest** – Menu £ 23 (dinner) – Carte £ 25/34 **s**
◆ A deep redbrick house built for Salisbury merchants in 1896 and set in lawned gardens that go down to the rivers Avon and Nadder. Canopied beds in smartly furnished rooms. Conservatory restaurant with splendid views.

Cricket Field House without rest
Wilton Rd, West : 1¼ m. on A 36 ✉ SP2 9NS – ☎ (01722) 322 595
– cricketfieldcottage@btinternet.com – Fax (01722) 322 595
14 rm ☕ – 🛉£ 60/75 🛉🛉£ 75/95
◆ Personally run extended house overlooking the County Cricket Ground. Bedrooms are prettily decorated with pictures and floral touches; majority of rooms are in the annex.

ENGLAND

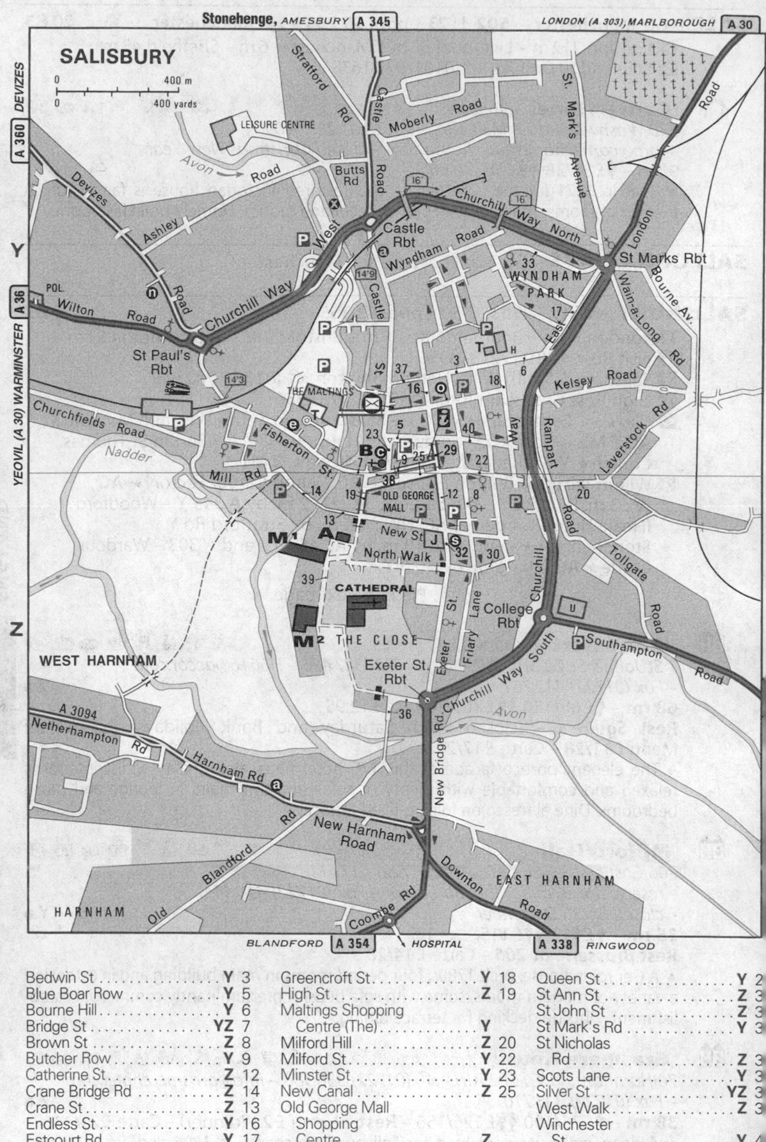

Bedwin St	Y	3	Greencroft St	Y	18	Queen St	Y	2
Blue Boar Row	Y	5	High St	Z	19	St Ann St	Z	3
Bourne Hill	Y	6	Maltings Shopping Centre (The)	Y		St John St	Z	3
Bridge St	YZ	7	Milford Hill	Z	20	St Mark's Rd	Y	3
Brown St	Z	8	Milford St	Y	22	St Nicholas Rd	Z	3
Butcher Row	Y	9	Minster St	Y	23	Scots Lane	Y	3
Catherine St	Z	12	New Canal	Z	25	Silver St	YZ	3
Crane Bridge Rd	Z	14	Old George Mall Shopping Centre	Z		West Walk	Z	3
Crane St	Z	13				Winchester St	Y	4
Endless St	Y	16						
Estcourt Rd	Y	17						

Old House without rest

161 Wilton Rd, West : 1 m. on A 36 ✉ SP2 7JQ – ✆ (01722) 333 433 – Fax (01722) 335 551

7 rm ☕ – 🚹£ 35/55 🚹🚹£ 55/90

◆ 17C house with homely rooms and character: cosy lounge, basement bar, stone flagged breakfast room, spacious bedrooms, antique artefacts. There's a rather nice garden, too.

Websters without rest

11 Hartington Rd, (off A 360 Devizes Rd) ✉ SP2 7LG – ✆ (01722) 339 779 – enquiries@websters-bed-breakfast.com – closed New Year Y **n**

5 rm – †£ 40/60 ††£ 55/65

◆ Secluded Victorian terrace house, with own parking, close to town centre. Friendly owner. Cosy breakfast room. Homely style bedrooms, immaculately kept; very good value.

Malvern without rest

31 Hulse Rd ✉ SP1 3LU – ✆ (01722) 327 995 – malvern-gh@madasafish.com – Fax (01722) 327 995 Y **x**

3 rm – †£ 50 ††£ 60

◆ A terrace house in a cul-de-sac which backs onto the river Avon, a short walk from city centre. Well-sized bedrooms, in homely decorative style. A non smoking establishment.

Anokaa

60 Fisherton St ✉ SP2 7RB – ✆ (01772) 414 142 – enquiry@anokaa.com – Fax (01772) 414 142 – closed 25-26 December Y **e**

Rest – Indian (buffet lunch) Menu £ 7/25 – Carte £ 15/38

◆ Lives up to being "something out of the ordinary", with eye-catching interior and staff in silky full-length gowns. Indian dishes mix modern and classical styles with aplomb.

The Haunch of Venison

1 Minster St ✉ SP1 1TB – ✆ (01722) 411 313 – oneminsterst@aol.com – Fax (01722) 341 774 – Closed dinner 25 December and Sunday -Tuesday Y **c**

Rest – Menu £ 10 – Carte £ 10/25

◆ Immensely charming and characterful 14C inn: check out 'The House of Lords' with its mummified hand! Bags of individuality in main dining room: eclectic menus; hearty fare.

The Gastrobistro at the Pheasant Inn

19 Salt Lane ✉ SP1 1DT – ✆ (01722) 414 926 – gastrobistro@aol.com – Closed 26 December and 1 January Y **o**

Rest – Menu £ 7 – Carte £ 100

◆ Black and white timbered pub in heart of city. Distinctive 17C character takes in inglenooks and ancient beams. Gregarious Gallic owner; simply presented dishes have French accent.

at Middle Winterslow Northeast : 6 ½ m. by A 30 - Y – ✉ Salisbury

The Beadles

Middleton ✉ SP5 1QS – ✆ (01980) 862 922 – winterbead@aol.com – Fax (01980) 863 565 – April to November

3 rm – †£ 50/55 ††£ 70/75 – **Rest** – (by arrangement) Menu £ 25

◆ Recently built from 100-year old bricks and Georgian in style; geese clack in garden. Flower-filled rooms with extra touches: pictures, reading lamps, comfortable chairs. Recently built from 100-year old bricks and Georgian in style; geese clack in garden. Flower-filled rooms with extra touches: pictures, reading lamps, comfortable chairs.

at Whiteparish Southeast : 7 ½ m. by A 36 - Z - on A 27 – ✉ Salisbury

Newton Farmhouse without rest

Southampton Rd, Southwest : 1 ½ m. on A 36 ✉ SP5 2QL – ✆ (01794) 884 416 – lizzie@newtonfarmhouse.com – Fax (01794) 884 105

8 rm – †£ 50/70 ††£ 100

◆ Step back in time in this 16C farmhouse, gifted to Nelson's family after Battle of Trafalgar. Original bread oven in inglenook fireplace, oak beams and well. Cottagey rooms.

ENGLAND

at Burcombe West : 5 ¼ m. by A 36 - Y - off A 30 – ✉ Salisbury

The Ship Inn
Burcombe Lane ✉ SP2 0EJ – ☎ (01722) 743 182 – theshipburcombe@mail.com – Closed first 2 weeks January
Rest – Carte £ 20/32
♦ Attractive part 17C pub: a tributary of river Nadder gurgles along at garden's end. Beams, open fires, plus sprinkling of modernity. Ample choice menus with seasonal variety.

at Teffont West : 10 ¼ m. by A 36 - Y - and A 30 on B 3089 – ✉ Salisbury

Howard's House
Teffont Evias ✉ SP3 5RJ – ☎ (01722) 716 392 – enq@howardshousehotel.co.uk – Fax (01722) 716 820 – closed Christmas
9 rm – †£ 100 ††£ 155 – **Rest** – (closed lunch Monday, Friday and Saturday) (booking essential for non-residents) Menu £ 25/26 – Carte £ 26/42
♦ Personally run, part 17C dower house boasting fine gardens in a quaint, quiet village. Comfortable lounge and pleasant bedrooms with village/ garden vistas. Garden herbs and vegetables grace accomplished cooking.

ENGLAND

at Stapleford Northwest : 7 m. by A 36 - Y - on B 3083 – ✉ Salisbury

Elm Tree Cottage without rest
Chain Hill ✉ SP3 4LH – ☎ (01722) 790 507 – jaw.sykes@virgin.net – restricted opening in winter
3 rm – †£ 35/50 ††£ 67/70
♦ Pretty, redbrick, quintessentially English cottage; the lounge boasts inglenook fireplace. Conservatory overlooks garden. Self-contained, chintz rooms with cottagey décor.

at Little Langford Northwest : 8 m. by A 36 - Y - and Great Wishford rd – ✉ Salisbury

Little Langford Farmhouse without rest
✉ SP3 4NP – ☎ (01722) 790 205 – bandb@littlelangford.co.uk – Fax (01722) 790 086 – Restricted opening in winter
3 rm – †£ 55/60 ††£ 68/75
♦ An unusual Victorian Gothic farmhouse with turret, crenellations and lancet windows. Period style interiors throughout. Spacious, well-furnished bedrooms with rural views.

SANDFORD-ON-THAMES – Oxon. – see Oxford

SANDGATE – Kent – **504** X 30 – see Folkestone

SANDIWAY – Ches. – 502 M 24 – ✉ Northwich 20 A3
London 191 m – Liverpool 34 m – Manchester 22 m – Stoke-on-Trent 26 m

Nunsmere Hall
Tarporley Rd, Southwest : 1½ m. by A 556 on A 49 ✉ CW8 2ES – ☎ (01606) 889 100 – reservations@nunsmere.co.uk – Fax (01606) 889 055
36 rm – †£ 160/185 ††£ 220/260, £19.50
Rest ***Crystal*** – Menu £ 27 (lunch) – Carte £ 37/51
♦ Secluded, on a wooded peninsular, originally built in 1900. Deep-seated sofas and sumptuous drawing rooms. Tasteful, individually furnished bedrooms exude quality and comfort. Dine in the classical style on imaginative and accomplished cuisine.

SANDSEND – N. Yorks. – **502** R/S 20 – see Whitby

SANDWICH – Kent – **504** Y 30 – **pop. 4 398** *Great Britain* 9 **D2**

London 72 m – Canterbury 13 m – Dover 12 m
Guildhall ✆ (01304) 613565
Town★

The Bell at Sandwich

The Quay ✉ CT13 9EF – ✆ (01304) 613 388 – reservations@sandwich.theplacehotels.co.uk – Fax (01304) 615 308 – Accommodation closed 25-26 December
34 rm – †£ 95/115 ††£ 115/199
Rest *The Place Brasserie* – Menu £ 18 (lunch) – Carte £ 26/34
◆ Situated by River Stour with original Victorian fittings in situ. Refurbishment has resulted in stunning transformation of bedrooms: now cool, elegant, stylish and welcoming. Pleasant brasserie with strong seafood base.

SANDY – Beds. – **504** T 27 – **pop. 10 887** 12 **A1**

London 49 m – Bedford 8 m – Cambridge 24 m – Peterborough 35 m
5 Shannon Court, High St ✆ (01767) 682728

Highfield Farm without rest

Tempsford Rd, North : 2 m. by B 1042 on A 1 (southbound carriageway) ✉ SG19 2AQ – ✆ (01767) 682 332 – margaret@highfield-farm.co.uk
8 rm – †£ 55/75 ††£ 75/90
◆ Working arable farm with gardens and 300 acres of land. Light, airy breakfast room, homely lounge and immaculately kept bedrooms, three of which are outside in coach house.

SANDYPARK – Devon – **503** I 31 – **see Chagford**

SAPPERTON – Glos. – **503** N 28 – **see Cirencester**

SARK – C.I. – **503** P 33 – **see Channel Islands**

SATWELL – Oxon – **pop. 1 163** 11 **C3**

London 43 m – Oxford 24 m – Reading 8 m

The Lamb

✉ RG9 4QZ – ✆ (01491) 628 482 – thelamb@awtrestaurants.com – Fax (01491) 628 257 – Closed dinner 25-26 December and 1 January
Rest – (bookings not accepted) Carte £ 17/25
◆ 17C timbers, low ceilings, quarry tiled floors and inglenook. Candlelight contributes to the cosy, informal ambience. Old photos decorate. Serves generous, heart-warming classics.

SAUNTON – Devon – **503** H 30 – ✉ **Braunton** 2 **C1**

London 230 m – Barnstaple 8 m – Exeter 48 m
Saunton Braunton, ✆ (01271) 812 436 .
Braunton★ - St Brannock's Church★, E : 2½ m. on B 3231 – Braunton Burrows★, E : ½ m. on B 3231

Saunton Sands ← Saunton Sands and Bideford Bay, (heated)

✉ EX33 1LQ – ✆ (01271) 890 212 – reservations@sauntonsands.com – Fax (01271) 890 145
rest,
90 rm – †£ 89/149 ††£ 178/300 – **Rest** – Menu £ 20/33 – Carte £ 27/35 **s**
◆ Imposing and busy 1930s seaside hotel in a prominent elevated position. Airy, spacious deluxe rooms have sea vistas. Families are well catered for; staffed crêche available. Classic dining room has sweeping sea views.

SAWDON – N. Yorks. – **see Scarborough**

ENGLAND

SAWLEY – Lancs. 20 B2

London 242 m – Blackpool 39 m – Leeds 44 m – Liverpool 54 m

Spread Eagle

BB7 4NH – (01200) 441 202 – Fax (01200) 441 973 – *closed 1 week January, Sunday dinner and Monday*
Rest – Carte £ 20/30
♦ Former pub overlooking the Ribble and surrounding countryside; this busy restaurant serves well-priced dishes with a modern twist and strong local influences.

SAXMUNDHAM – Suffolk – 504 Y 27 – pop. 2 712 – Ipswich 15 D3

London 95 m – Aldeburgh 7 m – Ipswich 20 m

The Bell

31 High St IP17 1AF – (01728) 602 331 – thebell@saxhighstreet.fsnet.co.uk – Fax (01728) 602 331
10 rm – £ 45 £ 75, £ 5.95 – **Rest** – (closed 1 week in spring, 1 week in autumn, Sunday and Monday except Bank Holidays) Menu £ 16/19 – Carte £ 25/29 **s**
♦ 17C former coaching inn, retaining much original visual character. Striking wall mural in hall. Local ale flows in cosy public bar. Spacious bedrooms offer stylish comforts. Accomplished cooking in smart dining room.

SCALBY – N. Yorks. – 502 S 21 – see Scarborough

SCARBOROUGH – N. Yorks. – 502 S 21 – pop. 38 364 *Great Britain* 23 D1

London 253 m – Kingston-upon-Hull 47 m – Leeds 67 m – Middlesbrough 52 m

Brunswick Pavilion, Westborough (01723) 373333 - Harbourside, Sandside (01723) 383637 (except November-Easter Sunday only)

Scarborough North Cliff North Cliff Ave, Burniston Rd, NW : 2 m. by A 165, (01723) 360 786 ;

Scarborough South Cliff Deepdale Ave, S : 1 m. by A 165, off Filey Rd, (01723) 374 737 .

Robin Hood's Bay★, N : 16 m. on A 171 and minor rd to the right (signposted) – Whitby Abbey★, N : 21 m. on A 171 – Sledmere House★, S : 21 m. on A 645, B 1249 and B 1253 (right)

Plan opposite

Beiderbecke's

1-3 The Crescent YO11 2PW – (01723) 365 766 – info@beiderbeckes.com – Fax (01723) 367 433 Z **s**
26 rm – £ 65/90 £ 130/150 – 1 suite – **Rest** – (dinner only) Menu £ 21 – Carte £ 25/32
♦ Named after the jazz musician. Although housed in a restored Georgian building, the rooms' décor is balanced between period style and contemporary feel with bright colours. Themed restaurant with nightclub feel.

The Royal

St Nicholas St YO11 2HE – (01723) 364 333 – royalhotel@englishrosehotels.co.uk – Fax (01723) 500 618 Z **a**
118 rm – £ 60/115 £ 110/170 – **Rest** – Menu £ 18/25 **s** – Carte £ 27/45 **s**
♦ Make-up recently re-applied to one of the town's grand old ladies; 1830s elegance exemplified by unforgettable main staircase. Mix of original or contemporary bedroom styles. Formal ambience in grand dining room.

The Crown Spa H.

7-11 Esplanade YO11 2AG – (01723) 357 400 – info@crownspahotel.com – Fax (01723) 357 404 Z **i**
85 rm – £ 70/180 £ 140/180 – 1 suite
Rest *Taste* – (dinner only) Menu £ 25 – Carte £ 19/28 **s**
Rest *Taste Café Bar* – Carte £ 18/30 **s**
♦ 19C landmark - the town's first resort hotel, on the esplanade overlooking the bay. Spacious lounges in the classic style. Large bedrooms, many with fine sea views. Popular Taste serves family favourites. Informal dining in Taste Café Bar.

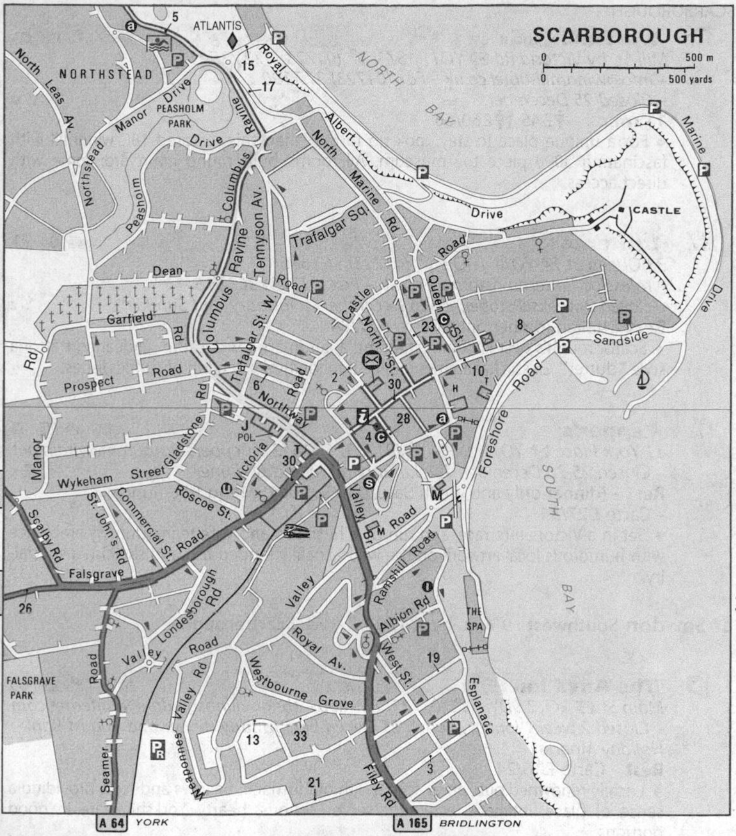

Street	Grid	No.
Aberdeen Walk	Y	2
Avenue Victoria	Z	3
Brunswick Pavillon Shopping Centre	Z	4
Burniston Rd	Y	5
Cambridge St	Y	6
Eastborough	Y	8
Falsgrave Rd	Z	
Newborough	Y	10
Oriel Crescent	Z	13
Peasholm Gap	Y	15
Peasholm Rd	Y	17
Prince of Wales Terrace	Z	19
Queen Margaret's Rd	Z	21
St Thomas St	Y	23
Stepney Rd	Z	26
Vernon Rd	Z	28
Victoria Rd	YZ	
Westborough	YZ	30
Westbourne Rd	Z	33

Ox Pasture Hall

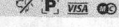

Lady Edith's Drive, Raincliffe Woods, West : 3 ¼ m. by A 171 following signs for Raincliffe Woods ✉ YO12 5TD – ✆ (01723) 365 295 – oxpasturehall@btconnect.com – Fax (01723) 355 156

22 rm ☕ – 🚹£ 110/150 🚹🚹£ 180 – **Rest** – (bar lunch) Menu £ 18/26 – Carte £ 32/40 **s**

◆ Deep in the countryside, yet close to the sea. A charming part-17C farmhouse: most bedrooms offer pleasant views, some around an attractive wisteria-clad courtyard. Dining room has uniform feel.

Alexander

33 Burniston Rd ✉ YO12 6PG – ✆ (01723) 363 178 – enquiries@alexanderhotelscarborough.co.uk – March-October Y **a**

10 rm ☕ – 🚹£ 33/44 🚹🚹£ 68/70 – **Rest** – (closed Sunday) (dinner only) (residents only) Menu £ 17 **s**

◆ Red-brick 1930s house situated close to North Bay attractions. Smartly furnished lounge. Bedrooms vary in size and are all pleasantly decorated and comfortable.

Windmill without rest
Mill St, by Victoria Rd ✉ YO11 1SZ – ✆ (01723) 372 735
– info@windmill-hotel.co.uk – Fax (01723) 377 190
– Closed 25 December Z **u**
11 rm – £45 £60/66
◆ For a unique place to stay, look no further than this restored 18C windmill with fascinating 3000 piece toy museum. All rooms built round courtyard; some with direct access.

Lanterna
33 Queen St ✉ YO11 1HQ – ✆ (01723) 363 616
– ralessio@lanterna-ristorante.co.uk – Fax (01723) 363 616
– closed 2 weeks October, 25-26 December, 1 January and Sunday Y **c**
Rest – Italian (dinner only) Carte £27/84
◆ Scarborough's best known restaurant: a landmark for decades. Endearing trattoria style "clutter". Classic Italian menu, plus a renowned selection of truffle dishes.

Pepper's
11 York Place ✉ YO11 2NP – ✆ (01723) 500 642 – peppers.restaurant@virgin.net
– Closed 25-26 December, 1-2 January and Sunday dinner Z **c**
Rest – (dinner only and lunch Saturday-Sunday) Menu £18 (lunch)
– Carte £27/34
◆ Set in a Victorian terrace, and run by a husband and wife team. Unfussy ambience with humorous local artwork on the walls. Locally landed fish and shellfish a speciality.

ENGLAND

at Sawdon Southwest : 9 ¾ m. by A 170 - Z – ✉ Scarborough

The Anvil Inn
Main St ✉ YO13 9DY – ✆ (01723) 859 896 – theanvilinnsawdon@btinternet.com
– Closed 2 weeks January, lunch 25 December, Sunday dinner and August Bank Holiday Monday
Rest – Carte £16/24
◆ Locally renowned pub, an ex-forge with old furnace, bellows and tools providing a sense of place. Intimate restaurant serves serious, hearty Yorkshire fare in good portions.

at Scalby Northwest : 3 m. by A 171 - Z – ✉ Scarborough

Wrea Head Country House
Barmoor Lane, North : 1 m. by A 171 ✉ YO13 0PB
– ✆ (01723) 378 211 – sales@englishrosehotels.co.uk
– Fax (01723) 371 780
19 rm – £58/98 £100/150 – 1 suite – **Rest** – Menu £15/28 – Carte dinner £28/40
◆ Close to North York Moors National Park and flanked by gardens, this Victorian manor promises a peaceful stay: oak panelling, stained glass, spacious rooms. Elegant dining room renowned for its local produce.

SCAWTON – **N. Yorks.** – **502** Q 21 – **see Helmsley**

The ✿ award is the crème de la crème.
This is awarded to restaurants
which are really worth travelling miles for!

SCILLY (Isles of) – Cornwall – 503 A/B 34 1 A1

Access Helicopter service from St Mary's and Tresco to Penzance : ✆ (01736) 363871

St Mary's Airport : ✆ (01720) 422677, E : 1 ½ m. from Hugh Town

from Hugh Town to Penzance (Isles of Scilly Steamship Co. Ltd) (summer only) (2 h 40 mn)

Hugh Town, St Mary's ✆ (01720) (Scillonia) 422536

Islands★ - The Archipelago (≤ ★★★)

St Agnes : Horsepoint★

Bryher – Cornwall – pop. 78 – ✉ Scillonia 1 A1

Watch Hill (≤ ★) – Hell Bay★

Hell Bay ≤ (heated) VISA

✉ TR23 0PR – ✆ (01720) 422 947 – contactus@hellbay.co.uk – Fax (01720) 423 004 – closed 2 January-mid February

11 rm (dinner included) – †£ 130/550 ††£ 280/580 – 14 suites – ††£ 280/580 – **Rest** – (bar lunch) (booking essential for non-residents) Menu £ 35

◆ Totally renovated, with a charming style that's relaxed, modern, comfy and colourful. Courtyard terraces, a vast lounge/bar and clean-lined rooms add to an idyllic appeal. Dining room with garden views and daily changing menu.

Bank Cottage without rest ≤

✉ TR23 0PR – ✆ (01720) 422 612 – macmace@homecall.co.uk – Fax (01720) 422 612 – March-November

4 rm – †£ 96 ††£ 96

◆ A modern guesthouse in lush sub-tropical gardens, complete with koi fish pond. A peaceful haven with floral bedrooms and a cosy little boxroom where you can buy seafood.

St Martin's Cornwall – pop. 113 1 A1

St Martin's Head (≤ ★★)

St Martin's on the Isle ≤ Tean Sound and islands, VISA AE

✉ TR25 0QW – ✆ (01720) 422 092 – stay@stmartinshotel.co.uk – Fax (01720) 422 298 – mid March-late October

27 rm (dinner included) – †£ 140/204 ††£ 280/370 – 3 suites

Rest Tean – see restaurant listing

Rest *Bistro* – (closed Monday dinner) Carte approx. £ 28

◆ Set on the quayside with unrivalled views of white beaches and blue sea; a truly idyllic island setting. Snooze peacefully in snug bedrooms. Bistro, with terrace and eclectic menu, is perfect for lunch.

XXX **Tean** – at St Martin's on the Isle H. ≤ Tean Sound and Islands, VISA AE

✉ TR25 0QW – ✆ (01720) 422 092 – stay@stmartinshotel.co.uk – Fax (01720) 422 298 – mid March-late October

Rest – (dinner only) (booking essential) Menu £ 45 **s**

Spec. Brill and lemon poached lobster with potato salad and lobster vinaigrette. Best end of lamb, cannelloni of leg, pea and mint purée, rosemary jus. Vanilla panna cotta with poached rhubarb and jelly, raspberry salad.

◆ Confident kitchen produces skilfully prepared, seasonal dishes which make the best of local produce, including home grown vegetables and herbs. Fantastic views.

St Mary's – Cornwall – pop. 1 607 1 A1

, ✆ (01720) 422692.

Gig racing★★ - Garrison Walk★ (≤ ★★) – Peninnis Head★ – Hugh Town - Museum★

Star Castle ≤ VISA AE

The Garrison ✉ TR21 0JA – ✆ (01720) 422 317 – info@star-castle.co.uk – Fax (01720) 422 343 – Closed 2 January-11 February

34 rm (dinner included) – †£ 65/200 ††£ 110/296 – 4 suites

Rest *Castle Dining Room* – (dinner only) Menu £ 25 **s**

Rest *Conservatory* – Seafood (April-October) Menu £ 25

◆ Elizabethan castle built in 1593 in the shape of an eight pointed star, surrounded by dry moat. There are harbour views; palms, echiums in garden. Airy rooms; subtle colours. Medieval wall tapestry highlight of Castle Dining Room. Seafood menus in Conservatory.

ENGLAND

Atlantic ≤ St Mary's Harbour, ♿ rm, VISA MC

Hugh St, Hugh Town ✉ TR21 0PL – ✆ (01720) 422 417 – atlantichotel@staustellbrewery.co.uk – Fax (01720) 423 009 – Closed 2 January-12 February

25 rm (dinner included) – †£ 99/119 ††£ 178/230 – **Rest** – Carte £ 21/24

◆ A traditional white hotel with views of St Mary's harbour and bobbing boats. Cottage charm in older rooms - low ceilings, floral fabrics; modern rooms in extension. Scillian ingredients in dining room with harbour views.

Evergreen Cottage without rest

Parade, Hugh Town ✉ TR21 0LP – ✆ (01720) 422 711 – evergreen.scilly@btinternet.com – Closed Christmas-New Year and 2 weeks February

5 rm – †£ 30/50 ††£ 60/75

◆ A 300-year old captain's cottage; very pleasant, with window boxes, a few minutes walk from the quay. Plenty of local literature in low beamed lounge. Compact, tidy rooms.

Tresco – Cornwall – pop. 167 – ✉ New Grimsby 1 A1

Island★ - Abbey Gardens★★ AC (Lighthouse Way ≤ ★★)

The Island ≤ St Martin's and islands, ⚓ (heated) VISA MC

Old Grimsby ✉ TR24 0PU – ✆ (01720) 422 883 – islandhotel@tresco.co.uk – Fax (01720) 423 008 – March-October

45 rm (dinner included) – †£ 130/255 ††£ 260/500 – 3 suites – **Rest** – Menu £ 40 (dinner) – Carte £ 19/32

◆ A heated pool, sub-tropical gardens, panoramic views to be had at this luxurious hotel. Enthusiastic owners collect art for interiors. Well appointed garden rooms. Light, welcoming dining room boasts sea vistas and friendly staff.

New Inn ≤ (heated) VISA MC

✉ TR24 0QQ – ✆ (01720) 423 006 – newinn@tresco.co.uk – Fax (01720) 423 200

16 rm – †£ 70/150 ††£ 105 – **Rest** – (booking essential for non-residents) Carte £ 19/32

◆ This stone built former inn makes a hospitable stopping off point. Friendly, bustling ambience in lounges and bars; very pleasant garden terrace. Comfortable bedrooms. Bistro-style dining room's more refined cooking a good alternative to bar menu.

ENGLAND

SEAHAM – Durham – 501 P/Q 19 – pop. 21 153 24 B2

London 284 m – Carlisle 77 m – Leeds 84 m – Middlesbrough 24 m – Newcastle upon Tyne 17 m

Seaham Hall ≤ ♿ rm, AC P VISA MC AE

Lord Byron's Walk, North : 1 ¼ m. by B 1287 ✉ SR7 7AG – ✆ (0191) 516 1400 – reservations@seaham-hall.com – Fax (0191) 516 1410

16 rm – †£ 225/575 ††£ 225/575 – 3 suites

Rest *The White Room* – (booking essential for non-residents) Menu £ 20/48

Spec. Seared scallops, celeriac, truffle, apple and lovage. Roast venison, chorizo, shallots and watercress. Saffron panna cotta, apricot sorbet.

◆ Imposing 17C and 19C mansion with ultra-modern technology in spacious rooms. Contemporary sculpture and décor. Unique Oriental spa has relaxing, Far Eastern ambience. Crisp linen and fine china define restaurant. Accomplished modern cooking uses luxury ingredients.

SEAHOUSES – Northd. – 501 P 17 *Great Britain* 24 B1

London 328 m – Edinburgh 80 m – Newcastle upon Tyne 46 m

Car Park, Seafield Rd ✆ (01665) 720884 (Easter-October)

Beadnell Rd, ✆ (01665) 720 794.

Farne Islands★ (by boat from harbour)

Olde Ship P VISA MC

9 Main St ✉ NE68 7RD – ✆ (01665) 720 200 – theoldeship@seahouses.co.uk – Fax (01665) 721 383 – February-November

13 rm – †£ 50/114 ††£ 100/114 – 5 suites – **Rest** – (bar lunch Monday-Saturday) Menu £ 21 – Carte £ 19/22

◆ Built in 1745 as a farmhouse but has left origins far behind, proudly proclaiming nautical links. Harbour views and marine artefacts throughout. Cosy, comfortable rooms. Dine in characterful bar at lunch or classic dining room for dinner.

SEASALTER – Kent – 504 X 29 – see Whitstable

SEATON BURN – Tyne and Wear – 502 P 18 – see Newcastle upon Tyne

SEAVIEW – I.O.W. – 503 Q 31 – see Wight (Isle of)

SEDLESCOMBE – E. Sussex – 504 V 31 – ✉ Battle 8 B3

London 56 m – Hastings 7 m – Lewes 26 m – Maidstone 27 m

Brickwall (heated) P VISA AE

The Green ✉ TN33 0QA – ☎ (01424) 870 253 – info@brickwallhotel.com – Fax (01424) 870 785

25 rm – ♦£ 70/75 ♦♦£ 100/140 – **Rest** – Menu £ 30 (dinner) – Carte lunch £ 17/25

◆ Part Tudor mansion at top of village green, built for local ironmaster in 1597. Well placed for beauty spots. Range of rooms include family, four-poster and ground floor. Dining room boasts characterful low beamed ceiling.

SEMINGTON – Wilts. – 503 N 29 – see Trowbridge

SETTLE – N. Yorks. – 502 N 21 – pop. 3 621 22 A2

London 238 m – Bradford 34 m – Kendal 30 m – Leeds 41 m

Town Hall, Cheapside ☎ (01729) 825192

Giggleswick, ☎ (01729) 825 288 .

ENGLAND

Falcon Manor P VISA

Skipton Rd ✉ BD24 9BD – ☎ (01729) 823 814 – enquiries@thefalconmanor.com – Fax (01729) 822 087

19 rm – ♦£ 85/110 ♦♦£ 110

Rest *Ingfield* – (dinner only and Sunday lunch) Menu £ 25

◆ Built in 1842 as a rectory; sits on the fringe of Dales National Park. A grand hall with chandelier and sweeping wooden staircase leads to traditionally furnished rooms. Elegant dining room: ornate ceiling, large leaded window.

Husband's Barn without rest P

Stainforth, North : 2 m. on B 6479 ✉ BD24 9PB – ☎ (01729) 822 240 – Fax (01729) 822 240 – Restricted opening in winter

3 rm – ♦£ 45/50 ♦♦£ 60/70

◆ Recently converted barn, surrounded by attractive dales scenery. Comfy beamed lounge with open fire. Light, airy breakfast room with views. Bedrooms have exposed rafters.

Little House VISA

17 Duke St ✉ BD24 9DJ – ☎ (01729) 823 963 – closed 2 weeks January, 1 week September, Sunday except May to September, Monday and Tuesday

Rest – (dinner only) (booking essential) Carte £ 20/28

◆ Former 19C gate house, a 'little house' of stone that was once a cobblers. Well-kept, rustic style within a compact space. Traditional and classic styles of cooking prevail.

SEVENOAKS – Kent – 504 U 30 – pop. 26 699 *Great Britain* 8 B1

London 26 m – Guildford 40 m – Maidstone 17 m

Buckhurst Lane ☎ (01732) 450305, tic@sevenoakstown.gov.uk

Woodlands Manor Tinkerpot Lane, ☎ (01959) 523 806 ;

Darenth Valley Shoreham Station Rd, ☎ (01959) 522 944 .

Knole★★ AC, SE : ½ m. – Ightham Mote★★ AC, E : 5 m. by A 25

Sun Do A/C VISA AE

61 High St ✉ TN13 1JF – ☎ (01732) 453 299 – Fax (01732) 454 860 – closed 25-26 December

Rest – Chinese Menu £ 9 (lunch) – Carte approx. £ 28 **s**

◆ Meaning "Happiness", with attentive staff and oriental setting, you can expect authentic Chinese food here. Extensive choice, including various set menus.

at Ightham Common Southeast : 5 m. by A 25 on Common Rd – ✉ Sevenoaks

Harrow Inn
Common Rd ✉ TN15 9EB – ✆ (01732) 885912 – Fax (01732) 885912 – Closed 26 December, 1 January and Bank Holiday Monday
Rest – Carte £ 20/34
◆ Attractive 17C stone and brick inn on sleepy narrow lane. Oozing character: flags, beams, open fire. Appealing and inventive dishes are enhanced by honest, rustic cooking.

SHAFTESBURY – Dorset – 503 N 30 – pop. 6 665 4 C3

London 115 m – Bournemouth 31 m – Bristol 47 m – Dorchester 29 m – Salisbury 20 m
8 Bell St ✆ (01747) 853514
Gold Hill★ (≤ ★) – Local History Museum★ AC
Wardour Castle★ AC, NE : 5 m

Royal Chase
Royal Chase Roundabout, Southeast : at junction of A 30 with A 350 ✉ SP7 8DB – ✆ (01747) 853355 – royalchasehotel@btinternet.com – Fax (01747) 851969
33 rm – †£ 95 ††£ 120
Rest ***Byzant*** – Carte £ 18/31
◆ Located in "Thomas Hardy" country and once a training school for the Order of Missionary Priests. Possesses a Turkish steam room, indoor pool. Individually styled bedrooms. Cosy, atmospheric dining room.

The Retreat without rest
47 Bell St ✉ SP7 8AE – ✆ (01747) 850372 – info@the-retreat.org.uk – Closed January
10 rm ☕ – †£ 40/60 ††£ 80
◆ Georgian townhouse in good location - central but not noisy. Spotlessly clean throughout. Individually decorated bedrooms; several overlook the rear, so particularly quiet.

La Fleur de Lys with rm
Bleke St ✉ SP7 8AW – ✆ (01747) 853717 – info@lafleurdelys.co.uk – Fax (01747) 853130 – Closed Sunday dinner and lunch Monday-Tuesday
7 rm ☕ – †£ 75/85 ††£ 110/135 – **Rest** – Menu £ 29 (dinner) – Carte £ 30/40
◆ Owners relocated to this address in 2003: smart restaurant in an 1870s ivy-covered house. Comfy bar with plenty of sofas. Well-kept bedrooms, named after grape varieties.

at Donhead St Andrew East : 5 m. by A 30 – ✉ Shaftesbury

Forester Inn
Lower Street ✉ SP7 9EE – ✆ (01747) 828038 – possums1@btinternet.com – Fax (01747) 828038
Rest – Carte £ 15/25
◆ Attractive thatched pub with 13C origins. Lovely rustic bar with beams and inglenooks. Dine in barn style extension where much locally sourced produce enhances modern dishes.

at Compton Abbas South : 4 m. on A 350 – ✉ Shaftesbury

Old Forge without rest
Chapel Hill ✉ SP7 0NQ – ✆ (01747) 811881 – theoldforge@hotmail.com – Fax (01747) 811881
3 rm ☕ – †£ 40/70 ††£ 65/75
◆ Thatched cottage dating from 1700; once a wheelwright, carriage builder. Tradition continues in car restoration business. Rooms all slightly different; pretty, characterful.

at Motcombe Northwest : 2½ m. by B 3081 – ✉ **Shaftesbury**

Coppleridge Inn
North : 1 m. on Mere rd ✉ SP7 9HW – ✆ (01747) 851 980 – thecoppleridgeinn@btinternet.com – Fax (01747) 851 858
10 rm – †£ 50 ††£ 85 – **Rest** – Carte £ 17/25
◆ A converted 18C farmhouse in 15 acres of meadow. Bedrooms, in a separate courtyard, with views, are a particular strength - bright and airy. Magnificent barn for functions.

SHALDON – Devon – **503** J 32 – **pop. 1 628** 2 **D2**
London 188 m – Exeter 16 m – Torquay 7 m – Paignton 13 m

ODE
21 Fore St ✉ TQ14 0DE – ✆ (01626) 873 977 – info@odetruefood.co.uk – Closed 25 December, 1 January, Sunday dinner and Monday
Rest – Organic (dinner only and lunch Saturday and Sunday and lunch Thursday and Friday in summer) (booking essential) Carte £ 30/42
◆ Intimate restaurant in glass-fronted Georgian house. Menus use good quality, local organic produce; dishes have some innovative twists and Asian influences. Charming service.

SHANKLIN – I.O.W. – **503** Q 32 – **see Wight (Isle of)**

SHEDFIELD – Hants. – **503** Q 31 – **pop. 3 558** – ✉ **Southampton** 6 **B2**
London 75 m – Portsmouth 13 m – Southampton 10 m
27 Marriott Meon Valley H. & C.C. Sandy Lane, off A 334, ✆ (01329) 833 455 .

Marriott Meon Valley H. & Country Club
Sandy Lane, off A 334 rm, rest,
✉ SO32 2HQ – ✆ (01329) 833 455 – Fax (01329) 834 411
113 rm – †£ 119/129 ††£ 129/164, £ 14.95
Rest *Treetops* – (dinner only and Sunday lunch) Menu £ 28 – Carte £ 26/43
Rest *The Long Weekend* – (Closed 25 December) Carte £ 16/34
◆ Set in 225 acres of Hampshire countryside with extensive leisure facilities: championship golf course, all weather tennis courts, cardiovascular suite. Well-equipped rooms. Treetops overlooks the golf course. The Long Weekend is sports oriented brasserie.

SHEFFIELD – S. Yorks. – **502** P 23 – **pop. 439 866** *Great Britain* 22 **B3**
London 174 m – Leeds 36 m – Liverpool 80 m – Manchester 41 m – Nottingham 44 m
1 Tudor Square ✆ (0114) 221 1900
18 Tinsley Park Darnall High Hazel Park, ✆ (0114) 203 7435 ;
18 Beauchief Municipal Abbey Lane, ✆ (0114) 236 7274 ;
18 Birley Wood Birley Lane, ✆ (0114) 264 7262 ;
18 Concord Park Shiregreen Lane, ✆ (0114) 257 7378 ;
18 Abbeydale Dore Twentywell Lane, ✆ (0114) 236 0763 ;
18 Lees Hall Norton Hemsworth Rd, ✆ (0114) 255 4402.
Cutlers' Hall★ CZ **A** – Cathedral Church of SS. Peter and Paul CZ **B** : Shrewsbury Chapel (Tomb★)
Magna★ **AC**, NE : 3 m. by A 6178 - BY - and Bessemer Way

Plan on next page

Mercure St Paul's H & Spa
119 Norfolk St ✉ S1 2JE – ✆ (0870) 122 65 85 – h6628@accor.com – Fax (0870) 122 65 86 CZ **c**
159 rm – †£ 185 ††£ 185, £ 14.95 – 2 suites
Rest *Canteen & Grill* – Carte £ 28/41
Rest *Zucca* – Italian (Closed 25-26 December) Carte £ 21/36
◆ Two minutes from lovely Winter Gardens; boasts palm-filled atrium entrance and distinctive, designer touches throughout. State-of-the-art gym. Sleek and spacious rooms. Italian dishes in Zucca. Steaks to the fore in Canteen & Grill.

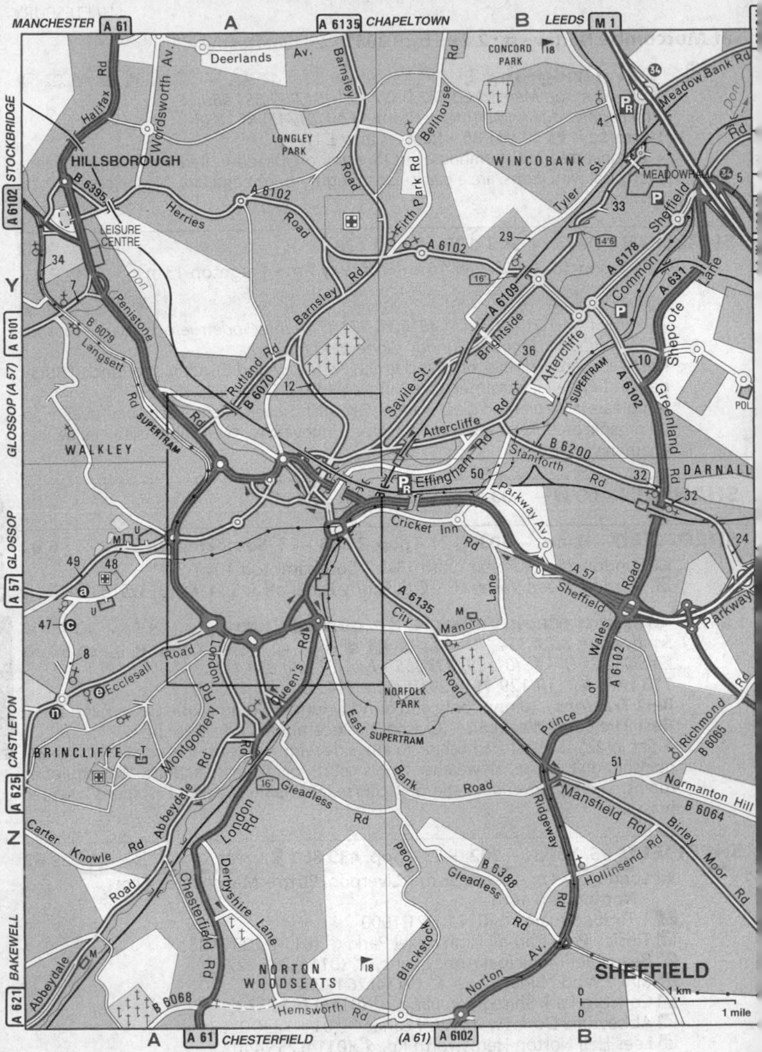

SHEFFIELD

Barrow Rd . . . . **BY** 4	Holywell Rd . . . . **BY** 29	Newhall Rd . . . . **BY** 3
Bawtry Rd . . . . **BY** 5	Main Rd . . . . **BZ** 32	Westbourne Rd . . . . **AZ** 4
Bradfield Rd . . . . **AY** 7	Meadowhall Shopping Centre . . . . **BY**	Western Bank . . . . **AZ** 4
Brocco Bank . . . . **AZ** 8	Meadow Hall Rd . . . . **BY** 33	Whitham Rd . . . . **AZ** 4
Broughton Lane . . . . **BY** 10	Middlewood Rd . . . . **AY** 34	Woodbourn Rd . . . . **BYZ** 5
Burngreave Rd . . . . **AY** 12		Woodhouse Rd . . . . **BZ** 5
Handsworth Rd . . . . **BZ** 24		

A good night's sleep without spending a fortune?
Look for a Bib Hotel

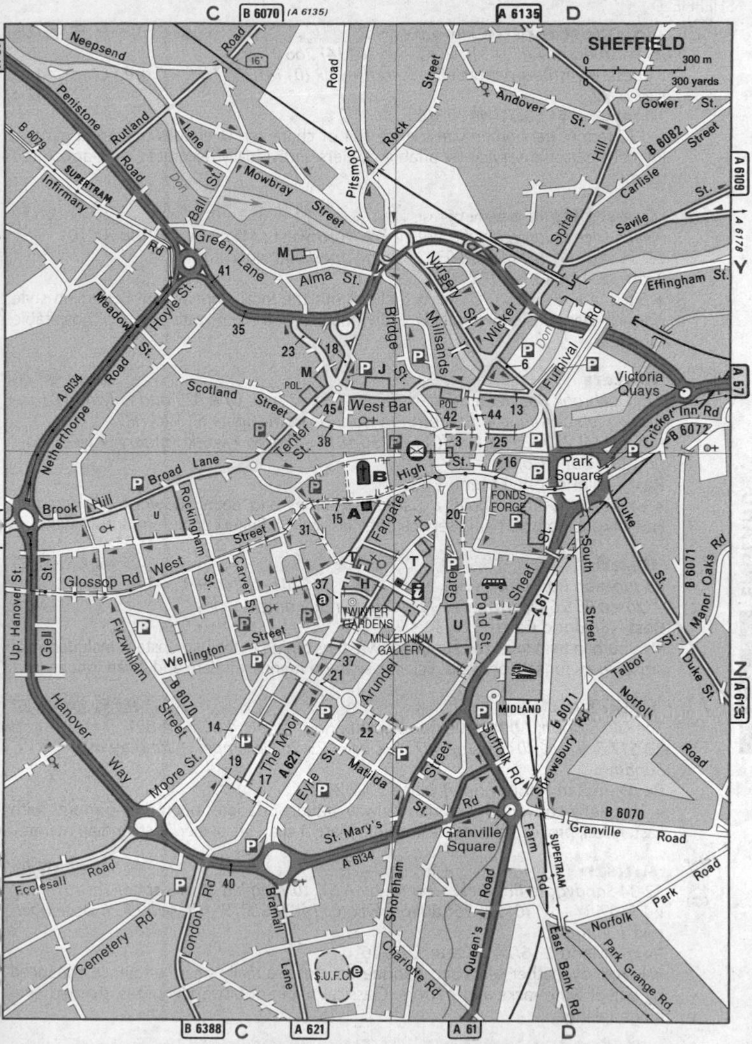

SHEFFIELD

Luxury pad or humble abode?
and denote categories of comfort.

The Westbourne without rest
25 Westbourne Rd ✉ S10 2QQ – ☎ (0114) 266 0109 – guests@westbournehousehotel.com – Fax (0114) 266 7778 – Closed Christmas-New Year AZ **c**
10 rm – †£50/70 ††£75/85
◆ 19C former gentleman's residence full of character. Overlooks tree-lined garden. Friendly, personal service by affable owners. Individually decorated, well-appointed rooms.

Quarry House without rest
Rivelin Glen Quarry, Rivelin Valley Rd, Northwest : 4½ m. by A 61 on A 6101 ✉ S6 5SE – ☎ (0114) 234 0382 – penelopeslack@aol.com
3 rm – †£40/80 ††£80
◆ Sited in a disused 19C quarry - check out the local stonemason! Bohemian style prevails; thespians stay regularly. Individually styled rooms with plenty of hospitable touches.

Rafters
220 Oakbrook Rd, Nether Green, Southwest : 2½ m. by A 625 and Fulwood rd, turning left at mini roundabout, on right at traffic lights ✉ S20 7ED – ☎ (0114) 230 4819 – Fax (0114) 230 4819 – Closed 1 week January, 1 week August and Bank Holidays.
Rest – (dinner only) Menu £33
◆ Discreetly located above a parade of shops and definitely worth seeking out. Friendly and approachable service of a classically influenced modern British menu.

ENGLAND

Bluefin
85 Junction Rd, Hunters Bar ✉ S11 8XA – ☎ (0114) 266 0805 – Closed 25-26 December, 1 January, Sunday and Monday AZ **n**
Rest – Seafood Carte £20/30 **s**
◆ Suburban twin level restaurant: downstairs dining in the bar, upstairs includes local artists' work for sale on walls. Eclectic seafood menus: modern and Asian influences.

Delhi Junction
The Old Station, Abbeydale Road South, Southwest : 4 m. on A 621 ✉ S17 3LB – ☎ (0114) 262 0675 – closed 25-26 December, 1 January and Sunday
Rest – Indian (dinner only) Carte £14/22 **s**
◆ Pleasantly converted Victorian railway station. Spacious, open dining rooms with Easten feel; proceedings orchestrated by larger-than-life owner. Tasty Indian menus.

Artisan
32-34 Sandygate Rd, West : 2¼ m. by A 57, turning left at Crosspool Tavern ✉ S10 5RY – ☎ (0114) 266 6096 – Fax (0114) 266 0279 – Closed 25-26 December and 1 January
Rest – Menu £16/24 – Carte £22/36
◆ Burgundy leather seats and banquettes create a really smart ambience enhanced by lots of wine racks and mirrors. Classical menu of bistro favourites; themed evenings aplenty.

Catch
(first floor) 32-34 Sandygate Rd, West : 2¾ m. by A 57 turning left at Crosspool Tavern ✉ S10 5RY – ☎ (0114) 266 6096 – Closed 25-26 December, 1 January and Sunday
Rest – Seafood Menu £16 (lunch) – Carte £23/36
◆ Intimate eatery; chef goes to market every day to select the best, freshest fish and seafood available, written up on daily blackboard menu. Fruits de mer are a speciality.

Thyme Cafe
490-492 Glossop Rd ✉ S10 2QA – ☎ (0114) 267 0735 – Fax (0114) 267 6758 – Closed 25-26 December and Bank Holidays AZ **a**
Rest – (bookings not accepted) Carte £19/27
◆ Snug, though bustling, bistro located outside city centre. Rustic interior with wooden school chairs and church pews. Appealing range of hearty dishes, ordered from the bar.

Nonna's
535-541 Ecclesall Rd ✉ S11 8PR – ✆ (0114) 268 6166 – info@nonnas.co.uk – Fax (0114) 266 6122 – Closed 25 December and 1 January AZ **e**
Rest – Italian Carte £ 24/33
◆ Take a walk through the deli before sitting down to savour the robust and authentic Italian dishes in busy surroundings. Speciality home-made pastas.

at Chapeltown North : 6 m. on A 6135 - AY – ✉ Sheffield

Greenhead House
84 Burncross Rd ✉ S35 1SF – ✆ (0114) 246 9004 – Fax (0114) 246 9004 – closed 2 weeks Easter, 2 weeks August, Christmas-New Year, Sunday-Tuesday, lunch Wednesday, Thursday and Saturday
Rest – (booking essential) Menu 44
◆ Cosy and attractive restaurant in country house style where hospitable owners offer traditional, tasty and home-cooked fare. A local favourite for many a year.

at Ridgeway Southeast : 6 ¾ m. by A 6135 (signed Hyde Park) - BZ - on B 6054 turning right at Ridgeway Arms – ✉ Sheffield 22 **B3**

Old Vicarage (Tessa Bramley)
Ridgeway Moor, on Marsh Lane rd ✉ S12 3XW – ✆ (0114) 247 5814 – eat@theoldvicarage.co.uk – Closed first two weeks August, Christmas, Sunday, Monday and Bank Holidays
Rest – (lunch by arrangement) Menu £ 40/55
Spec. Brill, ox cheek, star anise, onion marmalade and horseradish. Tarragon lamb, porcini and caramelised sweetbreads. Strawberry and mint soufflé.
◆ Victorian vicarage in mature gardens. Traditional, homely lounge; abstract art in more modern dining room. Innovative cooking makes vibrant use of local/home grown ingredients.

Red = Pleasant. Look for the red and symbols.

ENGLAND

SHEFFORD – Beds. – 504 S 27 – pop. 3 319 12 **A1**

London 48 m – Bedford 10 m – Luton 16 m – Northampton 37 m

The Black Horse with rm
Ireland, Northwest : 1 ¾ m. by Northbridge St and B 658 on Ireland rd ✉ SG17 5QL – ✆ (01462) 811 398 Fax (01462) 817 238 – Closed 25-26 December, 1 January and Sunday dinner
2 rm – †£ 55 ††£ 55 – **Rest** – Menu £ 20/26 – Carte £ 20/30
◆ Part 18C brick and timbered pub with garden and chalet-style bedrooms. Confident cooking, interesting menus based round old favourites. Eat in traditional bar or restaurant.

SHELF – W. Yorks. – 502 O 22 – see Halifax

SHELLEY – W. Yorks. – 502 O 23 – see Huddersfield

SHEPSHED – Leics – 503 Q 25 – pop. 12 882 16 **B2**

London 111 m – Derby 21 m – Leicester 15 m

The Grange Courtyard without rest
Forest St ✉ LE12 9DA – ✆ (01509) 600 189 – linda.lawrence@thegrangecourtyard.co.uk – Fax (01509) 603 834 – Closed 23 December-3 January and 1-3 June
20 rm – †£ 60 ††£ 70/80
◆ Well-kept, Grade II listed building near to Donnington Park. Tastefully converted courtyard cottages; immaculate bedrooms. Guest lounge with honesty bar. Family style breakfast.

SHEPTON MALLET – Somerset – 503 M 30 – pop. 8 830 4 C2

London 127 m – Bristol 20 m – Southampton 63 m – Taunton 31 m
The Mendip Gurney Slade, ✆ (01749) 840 570 .
Town★ - SS. Peter and Paul's Church★
Downside Abbey★ (Abbey Church★) N : 5½ m. by A 37 and A 367. Longleat House★★★ **AC**, E : 15 m. by A 361 and B 3092 – Wells★★ - Cathedral★★★, Vicars' Close★, Bishop's Palace★ **AC** (≤ ★★) W : 6 m. by A 371 – Wookey Hole★ (Caves★ **AC**, Papermill★) W : 6½ m. by B 371 – Glastonbury★★ - Abbey★★ (Abbot's Kitchen★) **AC**, St John the Baptist★★, Somerset Rural Life Museum★ **AC** – Glastonbury Tor★ (≤ ★★★) SW : 9 m. by B 3136 and A 361 - Nunney★, E : 8½ m. by A 361

Charlton House

rm, rest, P

East : 1 m. on A 361 (Frome rd) ✉ BA4 4PR VISA AE
– ✆ (01749) 342 008 – enquiry@charltonhouse.com – Fax (01749) 346 362
26 rm – £ 180/210 £ 375/465 – **Rest** – Menu £ 28/53
♦ Grand 17C house owned by founders of Mulberry Company; a smart, boutique style prevails touched by informality. Antiques in luxury bedrooms: Adam and Eve carved four-poster. Well used local produce to the fore in conservatory dining room.

SHERBORNE – Dorset – 503 M 31 – pop. 7 606 4 C3

London 128 m – Bournemouth 39 m – Dorchester 19 m – Salisbury 36 m – Taunton 31 m
3 Tilton Court, Digby Rd ✆ (01935) 815341
Higher Clatcombe, ✆ (01935) 812 274.
Town★ - Abbey★★ – Castle★ **AC**
Sandford Orcas Manor House★ **AC**, NW : 4 m. by B 3148 – Purse Caundle Manor★ **AC**, NE : 5 m. by A 30. Cadbury Castle (≤ ★★) N : 8 m. by A 30 – Parish Church★, Crewkerne, W : 14 m. on A 30

ENGLAND

Eastbury

P VISA AE

Long St ✉ DT9 3BY – ✆ (01935) 813 131 – enquiries@theeastburyhotel.co.uk – Fax (01935) 817 296
23 rm – £ 68/88 £ 160 – **Rest** – (bar lunch) Carte £ 30/33
♦ Traditional town house, a former gentleman's residence, built in 1740 with peaceful walled garden. Well-kept rooms named after country flowers. 15C abbey is nearby. Bright restaurant looking onto garden.

The Green

VISA AE

On The Green ✉ DT9 3HY – ✆ (01935) 813 821 – Closed 2 weeks February, 1 week June, 1 week September, Sunday, Monday and Bank Holidays
Rest – Carte £ 21/30
♦ Pretty Grade II listing at the top of the hill in town centre with stone floor and inglenook. A bistro feel predominates; dishes are traditional with a strong seasonal base.

at Corton Denham North : 3 ¾ m. by B 3145 – ✉ Sherborne

The Queen's Arms with rm

P VISA AE

✉ DT9 4LR – ✆ (01963) 220 317 – relax@thequeens-arms.com
5 rm – £ 60/70 £ 120 – **Rest** – Carte £ 18/26
♦ The essence of this pub is relaxed informality, engendered by sofas and armchairs inside, and an attractively sunny rear terrace. Locally inspired dishes; luxurious bedrooms.

at Oborne Northeast : 2 m. by A 30 – ✉ Sherborne

The Grange

P VISA AE

✉ DT9 4LA – ✆ (01935) 813 463 – reception@thegrange.co.uk – Fax (01935) 817 464
18 rm – £ 90 £ 105/150 – **Rest** – (Closed Sunday dinner) (light lunch) Menu £ 32
♦ A 200-year old country house in floodlit gardens. Rooms are a treat: five modern, five traditional, all large; some have patio access; some have balconies. Friendly owner. Dorset and Somerset ingredients zealously used in dining room.

at Hermitage South : 7½ m. by A 352 – ✉ Sherborne

Almshouse Farm without rest

✉ *DT9 6HA – ✆ (01963) 210296 – Fax (01963) 210296 – Easter-October*

3 rm – £30 £64

◆ Part 16C former monastery, now a working farm, surrounded by rural landscape. Original features include inglenook fireplace in cosy breakfast room. Pretty, neat bedrooms.

at Alweston Southeast : 2½ m. by A 352 A 3030 – ✉ Sherborne

Munden House without rest

Munden Lane ✉ DT9 5HU – ✆ (01963) 23150 – admin@mundenhouse.demon.co.uk – Fax (01963) 23153

9 rm – £50/65 £85/105

◆ Peacefully located guesthouse: originally a small complex of stone cottages. Modern country house furnishings. Breakfast room with 300 year old fireplace. Elegant bedrooms.

Good food and accommodation at moderate prices?
Look for the Bib symbols:
red Bib Gourmand for food, blue Bib Hotel for hotels

ENGLAND

SHERE – Surrey – **504** S 30 – see Guildford

SHERINGHAM – Norfolk – **504** X 25 – **pop. 7 143** 15 **C1**

London 136 m – Cromer 5 m – Norwich 27 m

The Dales Country House

Lodge Hill, Upper Sheringham, Southwest : 1¼ m. by A 149 on B 1157 ✉ NR26 8TJ – ✆ (01263) 824555 – dales@mackenziehotels.com – Fax (01263) 822647

18 rm – £91 £164

Rest *Upchers* – Menu £15 (lunch) – Carte £22/38

◆ Substantial 19C country house whose rich décor affords much comfort. Famous gardens conveniently adjacent. Original oak staircase in situ. Smart bedrooms overlook the grounds. Wood-panelled restaurant with superb oak-carved inglenook.

SHERWOOD BUSINESS PARK – Nottingham – see Nottingham

SHILTON – W. Mids. – **503** P 26 – see Coventry

SHINCLIFFE – Durham – see Durham

SHINFIELD – Reading – **504** R 29 – see Reading

SHIPLEY – W. Yorks. – **502** O 22 – **pop. 28 162** 22 **B2**

London 216 m – Bradford 4 m – Leeds 12 m

Northcliffe High Bank Lane, ✆ (01274) 584085 ;

Bingley Beckfoot Lane, Cottingley Bridge, ✆ (01274) 568652 .

Aagrah

Ground Floor, 4 Saltaire Rd ✉ BD18 3HN – ✆ (01274) 530880 – info@aagrah.com – Fax (01274) 599105 – Closed 25 December

Rest – Indian (dinner only) Carte £16/25 **s**

◆ Spacious, modern first floor buffet/carvery with cooking and char-grilling to order. Sit at funky red leather seats. Cuisine includes delicious Dahi dishes from Kashmir.

SHIPSTON-ON-STOUR – Warks. – 503 P 27 – pop. 4 456 19 C3

London 85 m – Oxford 30 m – Stratford-upon-Avon 12 m

at Long Compton South : 5 m. on A 3400 – pop. 1 994 – ✉ Shipston-on-Stour

The Red Lion with rm

on A 3400 ✉ CV36 5JS – ✆ (01608) 684 221 – info@redlion-longcompton.co.uk – Fax (01608) 684 968

5 rm ☕ – †£ 50 ††£ 80 – **Rest** – Menu £ 12 – Carte £ 18/30

◆ 18C coaching inn of golden stone, tastefully madeover, with cosy, intimate feel. Seasonal menu of British favourites. Smiley service and a friendly atmosphere. Comfortable bedrooms stylishly furnished in cool linen shades.

SHIPTON GORGE – Dorset – see Bridport

SHOBDON – Herefordshire – 503 L 27 – ✉ Leominster 18 A3

London 158 m – Birmingham 55 m – Hereford 18 m – Shrewsbury 37 m – Worcester 33 m

The Paddock without rest

✉ HR6 9NQ – ✆ (01568) 708 176 – thepaddock@talk21.com – Fax (01568) 708 829 – Restricted opening in Winter

4 rm ☕ – †£ 40 ††£ 60/65

◆ Well-priced, ground floor accommodation in this pleasant, village centre bungalow. All rooms are comfy and immaculately kept. Well run by hospitable owner.

ENGLAND

SHOTTLE – Derbs. – see Belper

SHREWSBURY – Shrops. – 502 L 25 – pop. 67 126 *Great Britain* 18 B2

London 164 m – Birmingham 48 m – Chester 43 m – Derby 67 m – Gloucester 93 m – Manchester 68 m – Stoke-on-Trent 39 m

The Music Hall, The Square ✆ (01743) 281200, tic@shrewsburytourism.co.uk

18 Condover, ✆ (01743) 872 977 ;

9 Meole Brace, ✆ (01743) 364 050 .

Abbey★ D

Ironbridge Gorge Museum★★ **AC** (The Iron Bridge★★ - Coalport China Museum★★ - Blists Hill Open Air Museum★★ – Museum of the Gorge and Visitor Centre★) SE : 12 m. by A 5 and B 4380

Plan opposite

Prince Rupert rm, rest, P VISA

Butcher Row ✉ SY1 1UQ – ✆ (01743) 499 955 – post@prince-rupert-hotel.co.uk – Fax (01743) 357 306 **n**

68 rm – †£ 79/95 ††£ 105, ☕ £10.50 – 2 suites

Rest *Royalist* – (Closed Sunday dinner and Monday) Carte £ 21/30 **s**

Rest *Chambers* – Carte £ 21/27 **s**

◆ 12C home of Prince Rupert, in the shadow of the cathedral. A collection of old buildings, some 15C, affords tremendous character. Rooms vary in age: the oldest are the best. Baronial style Royalist. Olde Worlde atmosphere of Chambers.

Pinewood House without rest

Shelton Park, The Mount, Northwest : 1½ m. on A 458 ✉ SY3 8BL – ✆ (01743) 364 200 – Closed 1 week November and 24-26 December

3 rm ☕ – †£ 45/48 ††£ 58/64

◆ A Regency house surrounded by wooded gardens. A homely, intimate atmosphere pervades the drawing room with its sofas, fresh flowers whilst bedrooms are charmingly decorated.

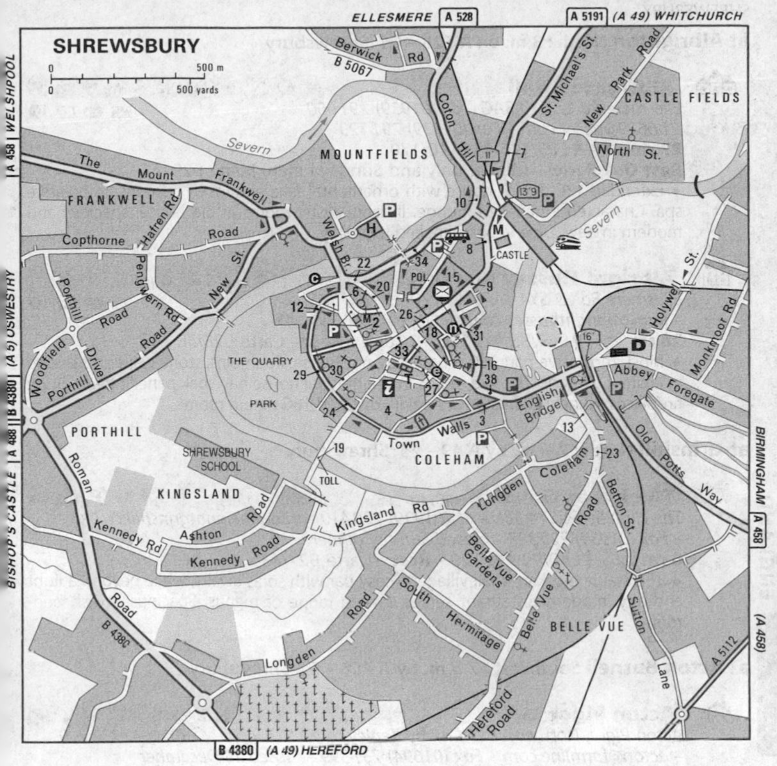

Barker St	2	Coleham Head	13	Pride Hill	26
Beeches Lane	3	Darwin Centre	15	Princess St	27
Belmont	4	Dogpole	16	St Chad's Terrace	29
Bridge St	6	High St	18	St John's Hill	30
Castle Foregate	7	Kingsland Bridge	19	St Mary's St	31
Castle Gates	8	Mardol	20	Shoplatch	33
Castle St	9	Mardol Quay	22	Smithfield Rd	34
Chester St	10	Moreton Crescent	23	Wyle Cop	38
Claremont Bank	12	Murivance	24		

Tudor House without rest

2 Fish St ✉ SY1 1UR – ✆ (01743) 351 735
– enquire@tudorhouseshrewsbury.co.uk – Fax (01743) 351 735 **e**

5 rm ☕ – †£69/95 ††£89/120

◆ On a picturesque medieval street in a historic part of Shrewsbury, this compact 15C house retains its antiquated charm in its cosy sitting room and simple bedrooms.

The Armoury

VISA MO AE

Victoria Quay, Welsh Bridge ✉ SY1 1HH – ✆ (01743) 340525
– armoury@brunningandprice.co.uk – Closed 25 December and dinner 1 January **c**

Rest – Carte £20/30

◆ Former 18C riverside warehouse with huge open-plan interior; sturdy brick walls full of old pictures and bookshelves. Daily changing menus offer an eclectic range of dishes.

at Albrighton North : 3 m. on A 528 – ✉ Shrewsbury

Albrighton Hall rm,

Ellesmere Rd ✉ SY4 3AG – ✆ (01939) 291 000 – h6629@accor.com – Fax (01939) 291 123

87 rm – ♦£ 85/115 ♦♦£ 110/170

Rest *Oak Room* – (dinner only and Sunday lunch) Menu £ 29

◆ Extended 17C manor house with ornamental lake and lovely gardens. Impressive spa. Characterful panelled lounge. Individualistic rooms in old house; spacious and modern in new. Dine in oak-panelled formality.

Albright Hussey Manor rm,

Ellesmere Rd ✉ SY4 3AF – ✆ (01939) 290 571 – info@albrighthussey.co.uk – Fax (01939) 291 143

28 rm – ♦£ 69/85 ♦♦£ 130 – 1 suite – **Rest** – Carte £ 25/38

◆ Most impressive part 16C moated manor house. Fountains, stone walls and bridge in lawned gardens. The five rooms in the original house have oak panelling and huge fireplaces. Hugely characterful, heavily beamed 16C dining room.

at Grinshill North : 7 ¾ m. by A 49 – ✉ Shrewsbury

XX **The Inn at Grinshill** with rm

The High St ✉ SY4 3BL – ✆ (01939) 220 410 – info@theinnatgrinshill.co.uk – Fax (01939) 220 327 – Closed Sunday dinner

6 rm – ♦£ 60/90 ♦♦£ 120 – **Rest** – Carte £ 27/43 **s**

◆ 18C stable block in small village: a cosy bar with sofas awaits, while beyond a light and airy, modern restaurant serves a wide range of menus. Spacious, stylish bedrooms.

at Acton Burnell Southeast : 7 ½ m. by A 458 – ✉ Shrewsbury

Acton Pigot (heated)

Acton Pigot, Northeast : 1 ¾ m. by Kenley rd ✉ SY5 7PH – ✆ (01694) 731 209 – acton@farmline.com – Fax (01694) 731 399 – Closed 25 December

3 rm – ♦£ 45 ♦♦£ 70 – **Rest** – (by arrangement, communal dining) Menu £ 20

◆ 17C farmhouse on working farm. Wealth of pursuits includes heated pool, fishing lake and tennis court. Age of house handsomely apparent in guest areas. Pleasant, cosy rooms. Huge oak dining table for dinner with fellow guests; adventurous cooking.

SHURDINGTON – Glos. – 503 N 28 – see Cheltenham

SIBFORD GOWER – Oxon. – see Banbury

SIDFORD – Devon – 503 K 31 – see Sidmouth

SIDMOUTH – Devon – 503 K 31 – pop. 12 066 — 2 D2

London 176 m – Exeter 14 m – Taunton 27 m – Weymouth 45 m

Ham Lane ✆ (01395) 516441

Cotmaton Rd, ✆ (01395) 513 023 .

Bicton★ (Gardens★) AC, SW : 5 m

Victoria (heated) rest,

The Esplanade ✉ EX10 8RY – ✆ (01395) 512 651 – info@victoriahotel.co.uk – Fax (01395) 579 154

62 rm – ♦£ 95/260 ♦♦£ 160/325, £ 15 – 3 suites – **Rest** – Menu £ 20/35

◆ An imposing Edwardian house on Esplanade; most rooms are south facing with coastal views. Sun lounge, games room, dancing every Saturday night are among its attractions. Menus run on traditional lines.

ENGLAND

Riviera rest, VISA AE

The Esplanade ✉ EX10 8AY – ☎ (01395) 515201 – enquiries@hotelriviera.co.uk – Fax (01395) 577775 – Closed 2 January-7 February

26 rm (dinner included) – †£109/163 ††£218/350 – **Rest** – Menu £25/36 – Carte £42/50

◆ An established seafront hotel with fine Regency façade and bow fronted windows. Peach and pink bedrooms with floral touches and friendly staff make for a comfortable stay. Formal dining salon affords views across Lyme Bay.

Belmont rest, VISA AE

The Esplanade ✉ EX10 8RX – ☎ (01395) 512555 – reservations@belmont-hotel.co.uk – Fax (01395) 579101

50 rm – †£90/210 ††£130/220, £15 – **Rest** – Menu £17/33 **s** – Carte £43/50 **s**

◆ A former 19C family summer residence situated on seafront with attendant views. Spacious lounge; traditional bedrooms. Guests can use leisure facilities at Victoria hotel. Stylish dining room with resident pianist.

Old Farmhouse P

Hillside Rd, off Salcombe Rd ✉ EX10 8JG – ☎ (01395) 512284 – April-October

7 rm – †£28/62 ††£56/68 – **Rest** – (by arrangement) Menu £13

◆ Utterly charming 16C ex-cider mill and farmhouse with low ceilings, heavy beams, numerous inglenooks, cosy lounge and pleasant rooms that boast rafters and sloping roofs. Dinner served in rustic dining room.

at Sidford North : 2 m. – ✉ Sidmouth

XX **Salty Monk** with rm P VISA

Church St, on A 3052 ✉ EX10 9QP – ☎ (01395) 513174 – saltymonk@btconnect.com – Closed 2 weeks November and 2 weeks January

5 rm – †£70/75 ††£110/180 – **Rest** – (dinner only and lunch Thursday-Saturday) (booking essential) Menu £36 – Carte lunch £23/33

◆ Former 16C salt house where monks stayed en route to Exeter Cathedral. Fine lounge with deep leather armchairs. Modern cooking in conservatory restaurant. Pleasant bedrooms.

at Newton Poppleford Northwest : 4 m. by B 3176 on A 3052 – ✉ Sidmouth

XX **Moores'** VISA

6 Greenbank, High St ✉ EX10 0EB – ☎ (01395) 568100 – mooresrestaurant@aol.com – Closed 3 weeks January, Christmas, Sunday dinner and Monday

Rest – Menu £19/25 **s**

◆ Two pretty 18C cottages set back from the main road are the setting for this busy, personally run restaurant with conservatory extension. Modern, locally sourced dishes.

SINGLETON – Lancs. – **502** L 22 – see Blackpool

SINNINGTON – N. Yorks. – **502** R 21 – see Pickering

SISSINGHURST – Kent – **504** V 30 – see Cranbrook

Do not confuse X with ✿!
X defines comfort, while stars are awarded for the best cuisine, across all categories of comfort.

ENGLAND

SITTINGBOURNE – Kent – 504 W 29 9 C1

London 44 m – Canterbury 18 m – Maidstone 15 m – Sheerness 9 m

Hempstead House (heated)

London Rd, Bapchild, East : 2 m. on A 2 ✉ ME9 9PP – ✆ (01795) 428020 – info@hempsteadhouse.co.uk – Fax (01795) 436362

27 rm – £80/120 £90/130

Rest *Lakes* – Menu £18/25 – Carte £27/37

◆ Part Victorian manor, a former estate house for surrounding farmland. Original sitting room in situ; outdoor heated pool. Cheerful, individually designed, modern bedrooms. Sunny restaurant with terrace.

SIX MILE BOTTOM – Cambs. – see Newmarket (Suffolk)

SIZERGH – Cumbria – see Kendal

SKELWITH BRIDGE – Cumbria – 502 K 20 – see Ambleside

SKIPTON – N. Yorks. – 502 N 22 – pop. 14 313 *Great Britain* 22 A2

London 217 m – Kendal 45 m – Leeds 26 m – Preston 36 m – York 43 m

35 Coach St ✆ (01756) 792809

off NW Bypass, ✆ (01756) 793922 .

Castle★ AC

Carlton House without rest

46 Keighley Rd ✉ BD23 2NB – ✆ (01756) 700921 – carltonhouse@rapidial.co.uk – Fax (01756) 700921

5 rm – £25/40 £55

◆ Victorian terraced house near centre of town. Pleasantly furnished in sympathetic style. Attractive dining room serves full English breakfast. Individually decorated bedrooms.

The Bull

Broughton, West : 3 m. on A 59 ✉ BD23 3AE – ✆ (01756) 792065 – janeneil@thebullatbroughton.co.uk – Fax (01756) 792065 – Closed Sunday dinner

Rest – Menu £10 – Carte £18/27

◆ Set on busy main road, this delightful country pub has open log fire and its own specially brewed beer. Intimate dining room serving varied, tasty menus full of local produce.

at Hetton North : 5 ¾ m. by B 6265 – ✉ Skipton

Angel Inn and Barn Lodgings with rm

✉ BD23 6LT – ✆ (01756) 730263 – info@angelhetton.co.uk – Fax (01756) 730363 – Closed 2 weeks January, 25 December and Sunday dinner

5 rm – £115/140 £130/155

Rest – (dinner only and Sunday lunch) (booking essential) Menu £35 – Carte £27/32

◆ Well regarded restaurant with stone walls, beams and roaring log fire. Fine quality, locally sourced produce. Bedrooms with antique furniture and modern appointments.

The Angel Inn

✉ BD23 6LT – ✆ (01756) 730263 – info@angelhetton.co.uk – Fax (01756) 730363 – Closed 1st week January, 25-26 December

Rest – (booking essential) Menu £23/35 – Carte £27/33

◆ Ancient beams and inglenooks in hugely characterful pubby part of renowned 18C inn. Fine modern British cooking. Shares rooms with restaurant in converted farm-buildings.

at Elslack West : 5 m. by A 59 and A 56 – ✉ Skipton

The Tempest Arms
✉ BD23 3AY – ✆ (01282) 842 450 – info@tempestarms.co.uk – Fax (01282) 843 331 – closed 25 December, dinner 1 January
21 rm – †£ 60 ††£ 80 – **Rest** – Carte £ 19/22
◆ Extended 18C stone inn with characterful beams and traditional feel. Smart bedrooms; those in annexed block are best - spacious, most with balconies, two with outdoor hot tubs. Open plan bar and dining room. Huge choice on menus.

SLALEY – Northd. – **501** N 19 – see Hexham

SLAPTON – Devon – **503** J 33 2 **C3**

London 223 m – Dartmouth 7 m – Plymouth 29 m
Dartmouth★★, N : 7 m. by A 379 – Kingsbridge★, W : 7 m. by A 379

The Tower Inn with rm
Church Rd ✉ TQ7 2PN – ✆ (01548) 580 216 – towerinn@slapton.org – Closed Sunday dinner
3 rm – †£ 45 ††£ 75 – **Rest** – Carte £ 20/30
◆ Built in 1347 as cottages for men working on local chantry. Beams, flag floors, stone walls: all very characterful. Surprisingly modern menus. Simple annex bedrooms.

SLOUGH – Slough – **504** S 29 – **pop. 126 276** 11 **D3**

London 29 m – Oxford 39 m – Reading 19 m

Heathrow/Windsor Marriott
Ditton Rd, Langley, Southeast : 2½ m. on A 4 ✉ SL3 8PT – ✆ (0870) 400 72 44 – mhrs.lhrsl.conferenceandevents@marriotthotels.co.uk – Fax (0870) 400 73 44
381 rm – †£ 169/189 ††£ 169/189, £14.95 – 1 suite – **Rest** – (Closed Saturday lunch) (buffet lunch) Menu £ 18 (lunch) **s** – Carte £ 22/33 **s**
◆ A five-storey hotel, 15 minutes from Heathrow airport, with well-equipped leisure club. Bedrooms are furnished with good quality fabrics; Executive rooms have private lounge. All-day restaurant option.

Copthorne
400 Cippenham Lane, Southwest : 1¼ m. by A 4 on A 355 off M 4 junction 6 ✉ SL1 2YE – ✆ (01753) 516 222 – event.slough@mill-cop.com – Fax (01753) 516 237
217 rm – †£ 190 ††£ 210, £15.95 – 2 suites
Rest *Zig Zag* – (closed lunch Saturday and Sunday and bank holidays) Carte £ 24/35 **s**
Rest *Turner's Grill* – (closed Saturday lunch, Sunday and Bank holidays) Carte £ 26/40 **s**
◆ The marble floored reception leads to split-level lounge, bar, leisure club. Rooms with mini-bars; some overlook Windsor Castle. Good business facilities in Executive rooms. Turner's Grill for British classics. Zig Zag is informal modern eatery.

Holiday Inn Slough/Windsor
Church St, Chalvey, Southwest : 1¼ m. by A 4 on A 355 off M 4 junction 6 ✉ SL1 2NH – ✆ (0870) 400 72 15 – reservations@slough.kewgreen.co.uk – Fax (0870) 400 73 15
150 rm – †£ 60/159 ††£ 89/199, £13.95 – **Rest** – (bar lunch) Carte £ 18/28 **s**
◆ Modern hotel, ideal for leisure and business travellers, close to Windsor Castle. All mod cons and services readily available. Executive rooms have work area. Smart mezzanine level restaurant.

ENGLAND

SNAINTON – N. Yorks. – 502 S 21 23 C2

London 241 m – Pickering 8 m – Scarborough 10 m

Coachman Inn with rm

Pickering Road West, West : ½ m. by A 170 on B 1258 ✉ YO13 9PL – ✆ (01723) 859 231 – james@coachmaninn.co.uk – Fax (01723) 850 008 – Closed 25 December, Monday and lunch Tuesday

2 rm – †£ 50 ††£ 66 – **Rest** – Carte £ 20/30

◆ Georgian former coaching inn, with cosy firelit bar and cloth-clad dining room. Traditional cooking keeps up to date with modern influences and uses seasonal, local produce. Classically-furnished, spacious bedrooms.

SNAPE – Suffolk – 504 Y 27 15 D3

London 113 m – Ipswich 19 m – Norwich 50 m

The Crown Inn with rm

Bridge Rd ✉ IP17 1SL – ✆ (01728) 688 324 – Closed 25 December and dinner 26 December

3 rm – †£ 70 ††£ 80 – **Rest** – Carte £ 19/28

◆ 15C inn with antique settle, log fire and exposed beams. Agricultural artefacts and paintings fill the small dining rooms where seasonal dishes are served. Comfortable rooms.

ENGLAND

SNETTISHAM – Norfolk – 504 V 25 – pop. 2 145 14 B1

London 113 m – King's Lynn 13 m – Norwich 44 m

The Rose and Crown with rm

Old Church Rd ✉ PE31 7NE – ✆ (01485) 541 382 – info@roseandcrownsnettisham.co.uk – Fax (01485) 543 172

16 rm – †£ 70/80 ††£ 110 – **Rest** – Carte £ 16/25

◆ Cosy, rustic pub in centre of town: open fires, antique furniture, bustling ambience. Original menus with Asiatic and Italian influences. Vibrant, well-maintained rooms.

SOAR MILL COVE – Devon – see Salcombe

SOLIHULL – W. Mids. – 503 O 26 – pop. 94 753 19 C2

London 109 m – Birmingham 7 m – Coventry 13 m – Warwick 13 m

Central Library, Homer Rd ✆ (0121) 704 6130

XX The Town House

727 Warwick Rd ✉ B91 3DA – ✆ (0121) 704 1567 – reservations@thetown-house.com – Fax (0121) 705 9315 – closed 1 January

Rest – Menu £ 16 (weekdays) – Carte £ 24/33

◆ Once a salubrious nightclub with town centre location. Stylish open-plan interior boasts large dining area with leather banquettes. Soundly prepared modern dishes.

XX Shimla Pinks

44 Station Rd ✉ B91 3RX – ✆ (0121) 704 0344 – Fax (0121) 643 3325

Rest – Indian (dinner only) Carte £ 20/23

◆ Well regarded Indian cuisine in distinctly modern surroundings. A popular venue: regulars return for the original, interesting cooking that ventures away from the traditional.

X Metro Bar and Grill

680-684 Warwick Rd ✉ B91 3DX – ✆ (0121) 705 9495 – Fax (0121) 705 4754 – closed 25-26 December and Sunday

Rest – Carte £ 20/28

◆ Locally renowned town centre bar/restaurant that combines buzzy informality with appealing range of brasserie dishes. Dine alongside busy bar: don't expect a quiet night out!

at Olton **Northwest : 2½ m. on A 41 – ✉ Solihull**

XX **Rajnagar**

256 Lyndon Rd ✉ B92 7QW – ✆ (0121) 742 8140 – info@rajnagar.com – Fax (0121) 743 3147

Rest – Indian (dinner only) Menu £ 15 – Carte £ 14/21

◆ A busy, modern neighbourhood favourite, privately owned, offering authentic, regional specialities of Indian cuisine. Service is flexible and friendly.

SOMERLEYTON – Suffolk — 15 D2

London 134 m – Great Yarmouth 10 m – Norwich 20 m

The Duke's Head

Slugg's Lane, West : ¾ m. off B 1074 ✉ NR32 5QR – ✆ (01502) 730 281 – dukeshead@somerleyton.co.uk

Rest – Carte £ 25/40

◆ Part of the Somerleyton Estate; boasts a super sundrenched terrace "down by the river". Appetizing modern dishes employ tasty fresh cooking with ingredients from the estate.

SOMERTON – Somerset – 503 L 30 – pop. 4 133 — 3 B2

London 138 m – Bristol 32 m – Taunton 17 m

Town★ - Market Place★ (cross★) – St Michael's Church★

Long Sutton★ (Church★★) SW : 2½ m. by B 3165 – Huish Episcopi (St Mary's Church Tower★★) SW : 4½ m. by B 3153 – Lytes Cary★, SE : 3½ m. by B 3151 – Street - The Shoe Museum★, N : 5 m. by B 3151. Muchelney★★ (Parish Church★★) SW : 6½ m. by B 3153 and A 372 – High Ham (≤ ★★, St Andrew's Church★), NW : 9 m. by B 3153, A 372 and minor rd – Midelney Manor★ **AC**, SW : 9 m. by B 3153 and A 378

Lynch Country House without rest

4 Behind Berry ✉ TA11 7PD – ✆ (01458) 272 316 – the-lynch@talk21.com – Fax (01458) 272 590

9 rm – †£ 60/70 ††£ 100

◆ Stands on a crest overlooking the Cary Valley. The grounds of this Regency house are equally rich with unusual shrubs, trees and lake. Antique four-poster; spotless rooms.

at Kingsdon **Southeast : 2½ m. by B 3151 – ✉ Somerton**

Kingsdon Inn

✉ TA11 7LG – ✆ (01935) 840 543 – enquiries@kingsdoninn.co.uk – Closed 25 December

Rest – Menu £ 14 – Carte £ 12/23

◆ Thatched inn with bags of character. Modernised interior retains beams, wood-burning stove, colourful scatter cushions. Daily changing menus full of traditional favourites.

SONNING-ON-THAMES – Wokingham – 504 R 29 — 11 C3

London 48 m – Reading 4 m

XXX **French Horn** with rm — ≤ River Thames and gardens, rm, rm

✉ RG4 6TN – ✆ (01189) 692 204 – info@thefrenchhorn.co.uk – Fax (01189) 442 210 – Closed 26-28 and dinner 25 December

16 rm – †£ 125 ††£ 170 – 5 suites – **Rest** – (booking essential) Carte £ 35/59 **s**

◆ Personally run former 19C coaching inn. Warm, comfy lounges with open fires. Accomplished cooking of classics; professional service in formal environment. Individual rooms.

ENGLAND

SOUTHAMPTON – Southampton – **503** P 31 – pop. 234 224 6 **B2**

Great Britain

London 87 m – Bristol 79 m – Plymouth 161 m

Access Itchen Bridge (toll) AZ

Southampton/Eastleigh Airport : ✆ (0870) 040 0009, N : 4 m. BY

to the Isle of Wight (East Cowes) (Red Funnel Ferries) frequent services daily (55 mn)

to Hythe (White Horse Ferries Ltd) frequent services daily (12 mn) – to the Isle of Wight (Cowes) (Red Funnel Ferries) frequent services daily (approx. 22 mn)

9 Civic Centre Rd ✆ (023) 8083 3333, city.information@southampton.gov.uk

27 Southampton Municipal Bassett Golf Course Rd, ✆ (023) 8076 8407;

18 Stoneham Bassett Monks Wood Close, ✆ (023) 8076 9272;

18 Chilworth Golf Centre Chilworth Main Rd, ✆ (023) 8074 0544.

Old Southampton AZ : Bargate ★ **B** - Tudor House Museum ★ **M1**

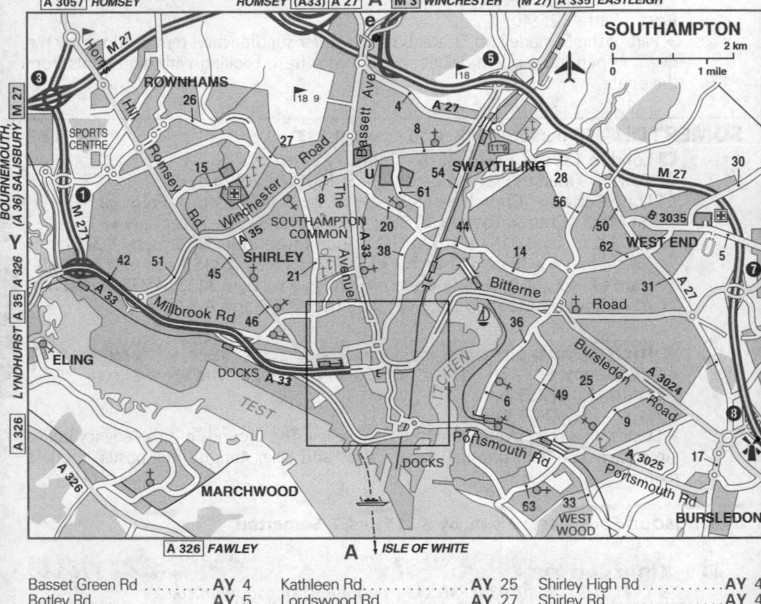

Basset Green Rd . . . . . AY 4	Kathleen Rd. . . . . AY 25	Shirley High Rd . . . . . AY 4
Botley Rd. . . . . AY 5	Lordswood Rd . . . . . AY 27	Shirley Rd . . . . . AY 4
Bridge Rd . . . . . AY 6	Lords Hill Way. . . . . AY 26	Spring Rd. . . . . AY 4
Burgess Rd . . . . . AY 8	Mansbridge Rd . . . . . AY 28	Swaything Rd . . . . . AY 5
Butts Rd . . . . . AY 9	Moorgreen Rd . . . . . AY 30	Tebourba Way. . . . . AY 5
Cobden Ave . . . . . AY 14	Moor Hill . . . . . AY 31	Thomas Lewis Way . . . . . AY 5
Coxford Rd . . . . . AY 15	Newtown Rd . . . . . AY 33	Townhill Way. . . . . AY 5
Hamble Lane . . . . . AY 17	Peartree Ave . . . . . AY 36	Welbeck Ave. . . . . AY 6
Highfield Lane. . . . . AY 20	Portswood Rd. . . . . AY 38	Westend Rd . . . . . AY 6
Hill Lane. . . . . AY 21	Redbridge Rd . . . . . AY 42	Weston Lane . . . . . AY 6
Kane's Hill . . . . . AY 24	St Denys Rd . . . . . AY 44	

De Vere Grand Harbour
rm, rest,

West Quay Rd ⊠ *SO15 1AG – ✆ (023) 8063 3033*
– grandharbour@devere-hotels.com – Fax (023) 8063 3066 VISA AE AZ **a**

169 rm – †£ 139 ††£ 149/229 – 4 suites

Rest *Allerton's* – (Closed Sunday-Monday) (dinner only) (booking essential) Menu £ 43

Rest *Number 5* – Menu £ 29 – Carte £ 23/33 **s**

◆ Modern and stylish. The split-level pavilion leisure club boasts a Finnish sauna, Turkish steam room and bar. Well furnished rooms; some with balconies and king-size beds. Allerton's is arcaded, with screens. Chic, informal Number 5.

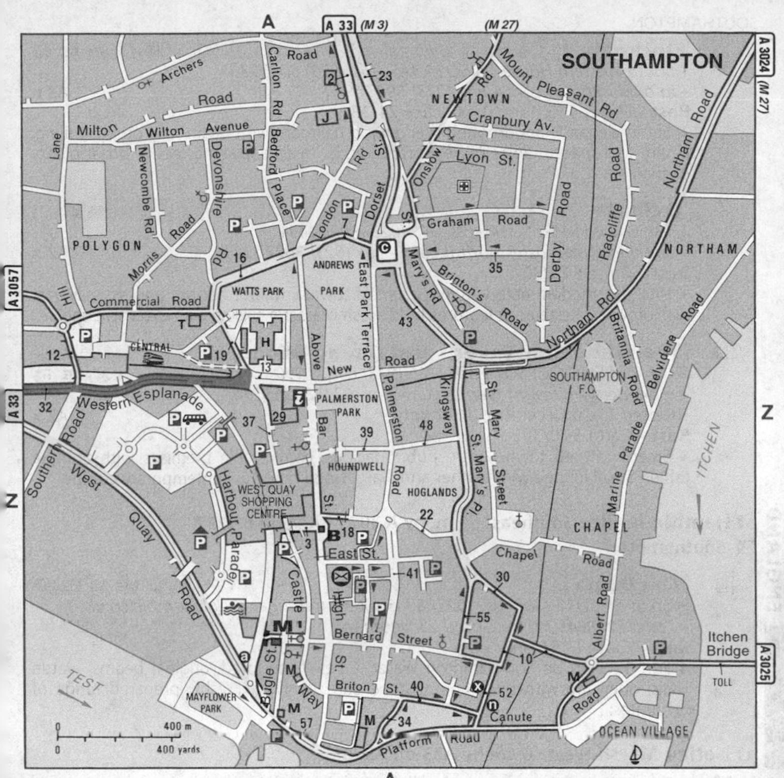

Above Bar St. . . . . **AZ**
Avenue (The). . . . . **AZ** 2
Bargate St . . . . **AZ** 3
Brunswick Pl. . . . . **AZ** 7
Central Bridge . . . . **AZ** 10
Central Station Bridge . . . . . **AZ** 12
Civic Centre Rd. . . . . **AZ** 13
Cumberland Pl. . . . . **AZ** 16
Hanover Buildings . . . . **AZ** 18
Havelock Rd . . . . **AZ** 19
High St . . . . **AZ**
Houndwell Pl. . . . . **AZ** 22
Inner Ave. . . . . **AZ** 23
Marlands Shopping Centre . . . . **AZ** 29
Marsh Lane. . . . . **AZ** 30
Mountbatten Way . . . . **AZ** 32
Orchard Pl. . . . . **AZ** 34
Oxford Ave . . . . **AZ** 35
Portland Terrace . . . . **AZ** 37
Pound Tree Rd . . . . **AZ** 39
Queen's Terrace. . . . . **AZ** 40
Queen's Way . . . . **AZ** 41
St Andrew's Rd . . . . **AZ** 43
South Front . . . . **AZ** 48
Terminus Terrace . . . . **AZ** 52
Threefield Lane. . . . . **AZ** 55
Town Quay . . . . **AZ** 57
West Quay Shopping Centre . . . . **AZ**

Hilton Southampton

Bracken Pl, Chilworth ✉ SO16 3RB – ✆ (023) 8070 2700 – Fax (023) 8076 7233 — VISA MC AE D — AY **e**

133 rm – 🚹£ 69/164 🚹🚹£ 79/174 – 2 suites – **Rest** – (booking essential at lunch) Menu £ 19/26 – Carte £ 28/36

◆ A purpose-built hotel with smart marbled lobby and individual reception desks. Extensive leisure facilities and good size bedrooms, well furnished to a high standard. Informal, family-oriented restaurant.

Jurys Inn

1 Charlotte Pl ✉ SO14 0TB – ✆ (023) 8037 1111 – jurysinnsouthampton@jurysdoyle.com – Fax (023) 8037 1100 – closed 24-26 December — AZ **c**

270 rm – 🚹£ 95/109 🚹🚹£ 95/109, ☕ £ 9.95

Rest *Innfusion* – (bar lunch) Menu £ 20 – Carte £ 21/32 **s**

◆ Up-to-date hotel, handily placed close to city centre. Well-equipped conference facilities; spacious coffee shop/bar. Good value, ample sized accommodation. Modern dining room with modish menus.

Dockgate 4
1 South Western House ✉ SO14 3AS – ✆ (023) 8033 9303 – info@dockgate4.com – Fax (023) 8033 6999 AZ **n**
Rest – Menu £ 13 (lunch) – Carte £ 24/38
◆ Set in elegantly apportioned Wedgwood ballroom with beautifully ornate ceiling. Smart, well-spaced tables mirror surroundings. Tasty, appealing menus boast plenty of choice.

Oxfords
35-36 Oxford St ✉ SO14 3DS – ✆ (023) 8022 4444 – bookings@oxfordsrestaurant.com – Fax (023) 8022 2284 AZ **x**
Rest – Carte £ 25/30
◆ Well-run, modern eatery in lively part of town. Entrance bar has impressively vast wall of wines. Restaurant features bold, fresh brasserie cuisine with extensive choice.

The White Star Tavern and Dining Rooms
28 Oxford Street ✉ SO14 3DJ – ✆ (023) 8082 1990 – manager@whitestartavern.co.uk – Fax (023) 8036 9274 – Closed 25-26 December, 1 January AZ **x**
Rest – Carte £ 20/30
◆ Smartly attired town centre pub. Spacious, comfortable premises with antique tables. Small lounge with leather armchairs. Good range of contemporary cuisine.

at Hamble-le-Rice Southeast : 5 m. by A 3025 - A - and B 3397 – ✉ Southampton

The Bugle
High St ✉ SO31 4AH – ✆ (023) 8045 3000 – manager@buglehamble.co.uk – Fax (023) 8045 3051 – closed 25 December
Rest – Carte £ 15/25 **s**
◆ Part 12C inn on Southampton Water. Carefully restored: original beams, wattle walls, open fire with brick lining, stone and oak floor. Freshly prepared range of favourites.

at Netley Marsh West : 6 ½m by A33 off A336

Hotel TerraVina (heated)
174 Woodlands Rd ✉ SO40 7GL Southampton – ✆ (023) 8029 3784 – info@hotelterravina.co.uk – Fax (023) 8029 3627
11 rm – †£ 130 ††£ 200, ☕ £12.50 – **Rest** – Carte £ 27/36 **s**
◆ Attractive Victorian house with extensions beautifully clad in cedar, and friendly, hands-on Anglo-French owners. Comfy, boutique-style bedrooms; some with terraces. Classic British and French dishes; precise, well judged cooking. Superb wine list and cellars. Wonderful colonial style roofed terrace.

SOUTH CADBURY – Somerset – 503 M 30 – see Castle Cary

SOUTH DALTON – East Riding – see Beverley

SOUTHEND-ON-SEA – Southend – 504 W 29 – pop. 160 257 13 C3

London 39 m – Cambridge 69 m – Croydon 46 m – Dover 85 m
Southend-on-Sea Airport : ✆ (01702) 608100, N : 2 m
Western Esplanade ✆ (01702) 215120
18 Belfairs Leigh-on-Sea Eastwood Road North, ✆ (01702) 525 345 ;
18 Ballards Gore G. & C.C. Gore Rd, Canewdon, ✆ (01702) 258 917 ;
27 The Essex Golf Complex Eastern Ave, Garon Park, ✆ (01702) 601 701 .

Beaches without rest
192 Eastern Esplanade, Thorpe Bay ✉ SS1 3AA – ✆ (01702) 586 124 – mark@beachesguesthouse.co.uk
7 rm – †£ 40/65 ††£ 75/85
◆ A sunny guesthouse on Thorpe Bay with panorama of Thames Estuary. Continental buffet breakfast. Individually styled rooms: four have sea views; two have balconies.

Pebbles without rest

190 Eastern Esplanade, Thorpe Bay ✉ SS1 3AA – ✆ (01702) 582 329 – res@mypebbles.co.uk – Fax (01702) 582 329

5 rm – †£ 45 ††£ 65 – 1 suite

◆ Friendly guesthouse on the Esplanade overlooking estuary; away from bustle of town but within easy walking distance. Rooftop garden and sea views from most bedrooms.

Atlantis without rest

63 Alexandra Rd ✉ SS1 1EY – ✆ (01702) 332 538 – atlantisguesthouse@eurotelbroadband.com – Fax (01702) 392 736 – closed 25-26 December

10 rm – †£ 45 ††£ 65/75

◆ Centrally located Victorian terraced house; pretty cloth-clad dining room with good traditional breakfast choice. Thoughtfully decorated bedrooms are all very well maintained.

Fleur de Provence

52 Alexandra St ✉ SS1 1BJ – ✆ (01702) 352 987 – marcel@fleurdeprovence.co.uk – Fax (01702) 431 123 – Closed 1-15 January, 26-29 December, Sunday and Bank Holidays

Rest – French Menu £ 15/20 – Carte £ 34/45

◆ Personally run restaurant, a classical French inspiration with a modern edge underpinning flavourful menus. Friendly service and continental style; well regarded in the area.

Paris

719 London Rd, Westcliff-on-Sea ✉ SS0 9ST – ✆ (01702) 344 077 – info@parisrestaurant.net – Fax (01702) 349 238 – closed Sunday dinner and Monday

Rest – (booking essential at lunch) Menu £ 19 – Carte £ 32/36

◆ Unprepossessing façade conceals a modern restaurant with well-spaced, well-sized tables waited on by attentive staff. Ambitious cooking on good choice of daily changing menus.

SOUTH LEIGH – Oxon. – 503 P 28 – see Witney

SOUTH MOLTON – Devon – 503 I 30 2 C1

London 197 m – Barnstaple 11 m – Bristol 81 m

Kerscott Farm

Ash Mill, Southeast : 5 m. by A 361 on B 3227 ✉ EX36 4QG – ✆ (01769) 550 262 – kerscott.farm@virgin.net – Fax (01769) 550 910 – closed Christmas and New Year

3 rm – †£ 40/45 ††£ 60/64 – **Rest** – (communal dining) Menu £ 15

◆ Beautiful, personally run 14C/17C farmhouse with fine views to Exmoor. Watch out for lambs and geese. Bags of internal character: beams and vast inglenooks. Charming rooms. Communal farmhouse dinners using farm's own produce.

at Knowstone Southeast : 9½ m. by A 361 – ✉ South Molton

The Masons Arms Inn (Mark Dodson)

✉ EX36 4RY – ✆ (01398) 341 231 – dodsonmasonsarms@aol.com – Closed Sunday dinner and Monday

Rest – (booking essential) Menu £ 30 – Carte £ 25/36

Spec. Smoked haddock risotto with poached egg and grain mustard. Roulade of pork belly, red cabbage and apple compote. Amaretto parfait with vanilla plums and pistachio biscuit.

◆ Delightful, thatched 13C inn, with beams, vast fireplace and exquisite ceiling mural in restaurant. Superb, flavourful, modern dishes, employing quality seasonal ingredients.

ENGLAND

SOUTH NORMANTON – Derbs. – 502 Q 24 – pop. 14 044 16 B1

London 130 m – Derby 17 m – Nottingham 15 m – Sheffield 31 m

Renaissance Derby/Nottingham

Carter Lane East, on A 38 ✉ DE55 2EH – ☎ (01773) 812 000 – Fax (01773) 580 032

157 rm – £ 97 £ 107/147 – **Rest** – (Closed Saturday) Menu £ 16/23 **s** – Carte £ 19/33 **s**

◆ Located close to M1; a modern hotel offering comfortable, well-equipped rooms; those away from motorway are quieter. Usefully, newspapers, toiletries available at reception. Capacious restaurant.

SOUTHPORT – Mersey. – 502 K 23 – pop. 91 404 20 A2

London 221 m – Liverpool 25 m – Manchester 38 m – Preston 19 m

112 Lord St ☎ (01704) 533333

Southport Municipal Golf Links Park Road West, ☎ (01704) 535 286.

Cambridge House

4 Cambridge Rd, Northeast : 1½ m. on A 565 ✉ PR9 9NG – ☎ (01704) 538 372 – info@cambridgehousehotel.co.uk – Fax (01704) 547 183

16 rm – £ 55/75 £ 95/115 – **Rest** – (dinner only and Sunday lunch) Menu £ 20 – Carte £ 20/25 **s**

◆ Personally run Victorian town house; lavishly furnished lounge and cosy bar. Very comfortably appointed period rooms in original house; large, more modern style in extension. Regency-style dining room with elegant chairs.

The Waterford without rest

37 Leicester St ✉ PR9 0EX – ☎ (01704) 530 559 – reception@waterford-hotel.co.uk – Fax (01704) 542 630 – April-October

8 rm – £ 55 £ 85

◆ Pleasantly located close to the promenade, this personally run seaside hotel features a cosy bar for residents and decently sized, neatly decorated bedrooms.

Lynwood without rest

11A Leicester St ✉ PR9 0ER – ☎ (01704) 540 794 – info@lynwoodhotel.com – Fax (01704) 500 724 – closed Christmas

9 rm – £ 35/45 £ 70/90

◆ Only a couple of minutes' walk from busy Lord Street, this 19C terraced house retains period style in its lounge and neat breakfast room. Pleasantly individual bedrooms.

Warehouse Brasserie

30 West St ✉ PR8 1QN – ☎ (01704) 544 662 – info@warehousebrasserie.co.uk – Fax (01704) 500 074 – closed 25 December, 1 January and Sunday

Rest – Menu £ 16 (lunch) – Carte £ 20/30

◆ Former warehouse, now a sleek modern restaurant with Salvador Dali prints and buzzy atmosphere. The open-plan kitchen offers modern cooking with interesting daily specials.

SOUTHROP – Glos. – 503 O 28 – see Lechlade

We try to be as accurate as possible when giving room rates. But prices are susceptible to change, so please check rates when booking.

ENGLAND

SOUTHWOLD – Suffolk – 504 Z 27 – pop. 3 858 15 D2

London 108 m – Great Yarmouth 24 m – Ipswich 35 m – Norwich 34 m
69 High St ✆ (01502) 724729
The Common, ✆ (01502) 723234 .

Swan

Market Pl ✉ IP18 6EG – ✆ (01502) 722 186 – swan.hotel@adnams.co.uk – Fax (01502) 724 800

40 rm – £ 91/116 £ 162 – 2 suites – **Rest** – Menu £ 25/35 – Carte approx. £ 24 **s**

◆ Restored coaching inn by Adnams Brewery. Antique filled interiors: 17C portrait of local heiress in hallway. Vintage rooms in main house; garden rooms built round the green. Tall windows define elegant restaurant.

The Crown

90 High St ✉ IP18 6DP – ✆ (01502) 722 275 – crown.hotel@adnams.co.uk – Fax (01502) 727 263

14 rm – £ 83/90 £ 146 – 1 suite – **Rest** – Carte £ 21/33

◆ Whitewashed inn combines a smart bar with buzzy dining area and locally popular real ale pub. Unfussy rooms are furnished in contemporary style. Smart, elegant restaurant with impressive wine list.

Northcliffe without rest

20 North Parade ✉ IP18 6LT – ✆ (01502) 724 074 – northcliffe.southwold@virgin.net – restricted opening in Winter

6 rm – £ 55/90 £ 100

◆ Keenly run 19C house commands fine clifftop views; contemporary en suite rooms: ask for one facing the sea. Model boats and nautical curios decorate a cosy, firelit lounge.

The Randolph with rm

41 Wangford Rd, Reydon, Northwest : 1 m. by A 1095 on B 1126 ✉ IP18 6PZ – ✆ (01502) 723 603 – reception@therandolph.co.uk – Fax (01502) 722 194

10 rm – £ 50/65 £ 120 – **Rest** – Carte £ 16/21

◆ Renovated in bright contemporary style, a substantial turn of 20C inn named in honour of Randolph Churchill. Heartwarming, modern food. Spacious rooms with distinctive décor.

SOWERBY BRIDGE – W. Yorks. – 502 O 22 – pop. 9 901 – ✉ Halifax 22 A2

London 211 m – Bradford 10 m – Burnley 35 m – Manchester 32 m – Sheffield 40 m

The Millbank

Mill Bank, Southwest : 2 ¼ m. by A 58 ✉ HX6 3DY – ✆ (01422) 825 588 eat@themillbank.com – Closed 2 weeks October and first week January

Rest – (closed Monday lunch) (booking essential) Menu £ 12 – Carte £ 21/35

◆ A stone inn, now a modernised dining pub with wooden and flagstone floors. Smart conservatory from which views of valley can be savoured over interesting modern cooking.

at Rishworth Southwest : 4 m. by A 58 and A 672 – ✉ Sowerby Bridge

The Old Bore

Oldham Rd, South : ½ m. on A 672 ✉ HX6 4QU – ✆ (01422) 822 291 – chefhessel@aol.com – Closed first 2 weeks January, Monday and Tuesday

Rest – Menu £ 12 – Carte £ 22/32

◆ Remotely set pub with delightful side terrace, characterful bar and smartly dressed dining rooms. High quality local ingredients employed to create classical British dishes.

ENGLAND

SPALDING – Lincs. – 502 T 25 17 C2

London 108 m – Peterborough 23 m – Stamford 19 m

at Surfleet Seas End North : 5 ¾ m. by A 16 – ✉ Spalding

The Ship Inn with rm

154 Reservoir Rd ✉ PE11 4DH – ☎ (01775) 680 547 – info@shipinnsurfleet.com – Fax (01775) 680 541 – Closed Sunday dinner, Monday and lunch October-April

4 rm – †£ 55 ††£ 70 – **Rest** – Menu £ 9/12 – Carte £ 15/25

◆ Hearty pub meals served in either spacious downstairs bar or first floor restaurant; terrace affords views over the jetty and fens. Opportunity to join the Pie Club. Large, simply furnished bedrooms.

SPALDWICK – Cambs. – 504 S 26 – see Huntingdon

SPARSHOLT – Hants. – 503 P 30 – see Winchester

SPEEN – Bucks. – 504 R 28 – ✉ Princes Risborough 11 C2

London 41 m – Aylesbury 15 m – Oxford 33 m – Reading 25 m

Old Plow (Restaurant)

Flowers Bottom, West : ½ m. by Chapel Hill and Highwood Bottom ✉ HP27 0PZ – ☎ (01494) 488 300 – Fax (01494) 488 702 – closed Christmas-New Year, August, Monday, Saturday lunch, Sunday dinner and Bank Holidays except Good Friday

Rest – Menu £ 30/34

Rest *Bistro* – see restaurant listing

◆ A fine, oak beamed restaurant at back of the bistro; more formal in style with linen table cover and high-back chairs. Set menus show French influence with classic sauces.

Bistro – at Old Plow

Flowers Bottom, West : ½ m. by Chapel Hill and Highwood Bottom ✉ HP27 0PZ – ☎ (01494) 488 300 – Fax (01494) 488 702 – closed Christmas-New Year, August, Monday, Saturday lunch, Sunday dinner and Bank Holidays except Good Friday

Rest – (booking essential) Menu £ 15 – Carte £ 24/39

◆ A cosy little bistro: low ceiling, tiled floors; log fire in the lounge. Blackboards announce simple à la carte menus; includes separate Brixham fish board. Affable owners.

SPEKE – Mersey. – 502 L 23 – see Liverpool

SPELDHURST – Kent – 504 U 30 – see Royal Tunbridge Wells

SPENNYMOOR – Durham – 501 P 19 – pop. 17 207 – ✉ Darlington 24 B3

London 275 m – Durham 6 m – Leeds 75 m – Newcastle upon Tyne 24 m

Whitworth Hall

Whitworth Hall Country Park, Northwest : 1 ½ m. by Middlestone Moor rd on Brancepeth rd ✉ DL16 7QX – ☎ (01388) 811 772 – enquiries@whitworthhall.co.uk – Fax (01388) 818 669

29 rm – †£ 70/90 ††£ 90/135

Rest *Library* – (dinner only and Sunday lunch) Carte £ 22/35

Rest *Silver Buckles Brasserie* – Menu £ 12 (lunch) – Carte £ 19/36

◆ Part 19C country house, sympathetically converted; fine views over deer park and vineyard. Orangery lounge; larger rooms, in the original house, are in period style. The Library handsomely set in eponymous room. Conservatory dining in Silver Buckles Brasserie.

SPRIGG'S ALLEY – Oxon. – see Chinnor

STADDLEBRIDGE – N. Yorks. – see Northallerton

STADHAMPTON – Oxon. – 503 Q 28 10 B2

London 53 m – Aylesbury 18 m – Oxford 10 m

XX **Crazy Bear** with rm

Bear Lane, off Wallingford rd ✉ OX44 7UR – ✆ (01865) 890 714 – enquiries@crazybeargroup.co.uk – Fax (01865) 400 481

17 rm – £ 80 £ 325

Rest – Menu £ 16/16 – Carte approx. £ 35

Rest *Thai Thai* – (closed Sunday lunch) (booking essential) Menu £ 27 – Carte approx. £ 35

◆ Crazy by name, crazy by nature: reception is a red London bus and barside acivities are overseen by large stuffed bear. Uniquely designed bedrooms are zany and luxurious. Modern British menu served in restaurant with leather walls, huge mirrors and chandeliers. Alternatively, Thai Thai serves authentic Thai cuisine.

STAFFORD – Staffs. – 502 N 25 – pop. 63 681 19 C1

London 142 m – Birmingham 26 m – Derby 32 m – Shrewsbury 31 m – Stoke-on-Trent 17 m

Market St ✆ (0871) 7161932

Stafford Castle Newport Rd, ✆ (01785) 223 821 .

Moat House rm, rest,

Lower Penkridge Rd, Acton Trussell, South: 3 ¾ m. by A 449 ✉ ST17 0RJ – ✆ (01785) 712 217 – info@moathouse.co.uk – Fax (01785) 715 344 – closed 25 December and 1 January

40 rm – £ 125 £ 140 – 1 suite

Rest *The Conservatory* – Menu £ 17 (lunch) – Carte approx. £ 17

◆ Timbered 15C moated manor house with modern extensions and lawned gardens, within sight of the M6. Characterful rustic bar. Colourful rooms with individual style. Bright, airy conservatory restaurant overlooks canal.

The Swan rm, rest,

46-46A Greengate St ✉ ST16 2JA – ✆ (01785) 258 142 – info@theswanstafford.co.uk – Fax (01785) 225 372 – closed 25 December

32 rm – £ 80 £ 95

Rest *The Brasserie at The Swan* – Carte £ 22/30

◆ Part 17C coaching inn with modern décor throughout. Convenient central location. Stylish reception. Well-equipped bedrooms with good facilities. Light, airy brasserie is open all day.

ENGLAND

STAINES – Middx. – 504 S 29 – pop. 50 538 7 C1

London 26 m – Reading 25 m

Mercure Thames Lodge rm, rest,

Thames St ✉ TW18 4SJ – ✆ (01784) 464 433 – h6620@accor.com – Fax (01784) 454 858

78 rm – £ 170 £ 170, £ 13.95

Rest *The Brasserie* – Menu £ 22

◆ Once used as a stopover for horse-pulled barges, this riverside hotel has moorings on the Thames. A mix of rooms: some with traditional décor, some more modern in style. Terrace brasserie overlooks river.

STAITHES – N. Yorks. – 502 R 20 – ✉ Saltburn (Cleveland) 23 C1

London 269 m – Middlesbrough 22 m – Scarborough 31 m

X **Endeavour** with rm

1 High St ✉ TS13 5BH – ✆ (01947) 840 825 – endeavour.restaurant@virgin.net – closed Sunday and Monday except Bank Holidays

4 rm – £ 80/95 £ 80/95 – **Rest** – Seafood (dinner only) Menu £ 19 – Carte £ 25/35 **s**

◆ Named after Captain Cook's sailing ship: a compact former fisherman's cottage serving tasty menus, with emphasis on locally caught fish. Neat, well-appointed bedrooms.

STAMFORD – Lincs. – 502 S 26 – pop. 19 525 *Great Britain* 17 C2

London 92 m – Leicester 31 m – Lincoln 50 m – Nottingham 45 m
The Arts Centre, 27 St Mary's St ☎ (01780) 755611
Town★★ - St Martin's Church★ – Lord Burghley's Hospital★ – Browne's Hospital★ AC
Burghley House★★ AC, SE : 1½ m. by B 1443

The George of Stamford

71 St Martin's ✉ PE9 2LB – ☎ (01780) 750 750
– reservations@georgehotelofstamford.com – Fax (01780) 750 701
46 rm – †£ 85/110 ††£ 235 – 1 suite
Rest – Menu £ 19 (lunch) – Carte £ 34/50 **s**
Rest *Garden Lounge* – Carte £ 26/51 **s**
◆ Historic inn, over 900 years old. Crusading knights stayed here en route to Jerusalem. Walled garden and courtyard with 17C mulberry tree. Original bedrooms; designer décor. Oak panelled dining room exudes elegance. Garden Lounge with leafy courtyard.

Jim's Yard

3 Ironmonger St, off Broad St ✉ PE9 1PL – ☎ (01780) 756 080
– jim@jimsyard.biz – Fax (01780) 480 848 – closed 20 July-4 August, 21 December-5 January, Sunday and Monday
Rest – Menu £ 17 (lunch) – Carte £ 23/29
◆ Two 18C houses in a courtyard: conservatory or first-floor dining options. Smart tableware enhances enjoyment of great value menus employing well-executed, classic cooking.

ENGLAND

at Collyweston Southwest : 3½ m. on A 43 – ✉ Stamford

The Collyweston Slater with rm

87-89 Main Road ✉ PE9 3PQ – ☎ (01780) 444 288
– info@colllywestonslater.co.uk – Fax (01780) 444 270 – Closed 25-26 December
5 rm – †£ 60/70 ††£ 100 – **Rest** – Menu £ 15 – Carte £ 20/30
◆ Light and modern country pub with intimate, rustic bar and friendly staff. Wholesome cooking blends the traditional and the more modern. Bedrooms are named after English vineyards.

at Clipsham Northwest : 9½ m. by B 1081 off A 1 – ✉ Stamford

The Olive Branch & Beech House (Sean Hope) with rm

Main St ✉ LE15 7SH – ☎ (01780) 410 355 rm,
– info@theolivebranchpub.com – Fax (01780) 410 000 – Closed dinner 25 December, lunch 26 and 31 December and 1 January
6 rm – †£ 75 ††£ 150 – **Rest** – (booking essential) Menu £ 19 – Carte £ 22/34
Spec. Artichoke and beetroot risotto. Roast lamb with rosemary gratin potatoes. Apple crumble with saffron and sultanas, vanilla ice cream.
◆ Soundly judged, flavoursome cooking, varied and modern, in cosy firelit pub with simple pews and sepia prints. Rooms, over the road in Georgian house, are sassy and stylish.

STANDISH – Gtr Manchester – 502 M 23 – pop. 14 350 – ✉ Wigan 20 A2

London 210 m – Liverpool 25 m – Manchester 21 m – Preston 15 m

at Wrightington Bar Northwest : 3½ m. by A 5209 on B 5250 – ✉ Wigan

The Mulberry Tree

9 Wood Lane ✉ WN6 9SE – ☎ (01257) 451 400 – mulberrytree@btconnect.com
– Fax (01257) 451 400 – closed 26 December and 1 January
Rest – Menu £ 13/17 – Carte £ 22/31
◆ Hugely spacious roadside pub with open bar and more formal, linen-clad dining area. Range of menus offer extensive choice of generously proportioned dishes. Warm atmosphere.

STANNERSBURN – Northd. – **501** M 18 – ✉ **Hexham** 24 **A2**

London 363 m – Carlisle 56 m – Newcastle upon Tyne 46 m

The Pheasant Inn with rm

Falstone ✉ NE48 1DD – ☎ (01434) 240382 – enquiries@thepheasantinn.com – Fax (01434) 240382 – Closed 25-26 December, Monday-Tuesday November to mid-March

8 rm – †£ 45/60 ††£ 85 – **Rest** – Carte £ 15/24

◆ Set in Northumberland National Park, near Kielder reservoir; epitome of a traditional inn. Pine dining room serves homecooked local fare. Cottagey rooms in converted stables.

STANSTED AIRPORT – Essex – **504** U 28 – ✉ **Stansted Mountfitchet** 12 **B2**

London 37 m – Cambridge 29 m – Chelmsford 18 m – Colchester 29 m

Stansted International Airport : ☎ (0870) 0000303

Radisson SAS rm,

Waltham Close ✉ CM24 1PP – ☎ (01279) 661012 – info.stansted@radissonsas.com – Fax (01279) 661013

484 rm – †£ 140 ††£ 140, £ 14.95 – 16 suites

Rest *New York Grill Bar* – Carte £ 28/40 **s**

Rest *Wine Tower* – Carte £ 18/30 **s**

Rest *Filini* – Italian Carte £ 17/28 **s**

◆ Impressive hotel just two minutes from main terminal; vast open atrium housing 40 foot wine cellar. Extensive meeting facilities. Very stylish bedrooms in three themes. Small, formal New York Grill Bar. Impressive Wine Tower. Filini for Italian dishes.

Hilton London Stansted Airport rm, rest,

Round Coppice Rd ✉ CM24 1SF – ☎ (01279) 680800 – reservations.stansted@hilton.com – Fax (01279) 680890

237 rm – †£ 99/145 ††£ 99/145, £ 17.95 – 2 suites –

Rest – (closed lunch Saturday, Sunday and Bank Holidays) Menu £ 21 (dinner) – Carte £ 33/41

◆ Bustling hotel whose facilities include leisure club, hairdressers and beauty salon. Modern rooms, with two of executive style. Transport can be arranged to and from terminal. Restaurant/bar has popular menu; sometimes carvery lunch as well.

STANSTED MOUNTFITCHET – Essex – **504** U 28 – **see Bishop's Stortford (Herts.)**

STANTON – Suffolk – **504** W 27 – **pop. 2 073** 15 **C2**

London 88 m – Cambridge 38 m – Ipswich 40 m – King's Lynn 38 m – Norwich 39 m

The Leaping Hare

Wyken Vineyards, South : 1 ¼ m. by Wyken Rd ✉ IP31 2DW – ☎ (01359) 250287 – Fax (01359) 253022 – closed 25 December-5 January

Rest – (lunch only and dinner Friday and Saturday) (booking essential) Menu £ 20 (lunch) – Carte £ 23/28

◆ 17C long barn in working farm and vineyard. Hare-themed pictures and tapestries decorate a beamed restaurant and café. Tasty dishes underpinned by local, organic produce.

STANTON SAINT QUINTIN – Wilts. – **503** N 29 – **see Chippenham**

STANTON ST JOHN – Oxon. – **503** Q 28 – **see Oxford**

STANTON WICK – Bath & North East Somerset – **503** M 29 – **see Bristol**

STANWICK – Northants. 17 C3

The Courtyard without rest

West St ✉ *NN9 6QY – ✆ (01933) 622 233 – bookings@thecourtyard.me.uk – Fax (01933) 622 276*

10 rm – 🚹£ 55 🚹🚹£ 75

◆ Main house with cosy, traditional bedrooms, lounge opening onto courtyard and carefully-maintained garden. Newly converted stable block houses bright, contemporary bedrooms.

STAPLEFORD – 504 Q 25 – see Nottingham

STAPLEFORD – Wilts. – 503 O 30 – see Salisbury

STATHERN – Leics. – see Melton Mowbray

STAVERTON – Devon – 503 I 32 – pop. 682 – ✉ Totnes 2 C2

London 220 m – Exeter 20 m – Torquay 33 m

Kingston House

Northwest : 1 m. on Kingston rd ✉ *TQ9 6AR – ✆ (01803) 762 235 – info@kingston-estate.com – Fax (01803) 762 444 – closed 24 December-7 January*

3 rm – 🚹£ 110/120 🚹🚹£ 180/200 – **Rest** – (dinner only) (residents only, set menu only) Menu £ 38 **s**

◆ A spectacular Georgian mansion in sweeping moorland. Unique period details include painted china closet, marquetry staircase, authentic wallpapers. Variety of antique beds.

STAVERTON – Northants. – 504 Q 27 – see Daventry

STEDHAM – W. Sussex – 504 R 31 – see Midhurst

STEPPINGLEY – Beds 12 A1

London 44 m – Luton 12 m – Milton Keynes 13 m

The French Horn

Church End ✉ *MK45 5AU – ✆ (01525) 712 051 – manager@thefrenchhorn.com – Fax (01717) 334 305*

Rest – (closed Sunday dinner) (booking essential) Carte £ 30/50

◆ Refurbished late 18C pub with restaurant in pretty hamlet. Characterful front bar and smart restaurant where contemporary style and well-regarded seasonal menus hold sway.

STEVENAGE – Herts. – 504 T 28 – pop. 81 482 *Great Britain* 12 B2

London 36 m – Bedford 25 m – Cambridge 27 m

Aston Lane, ✆ (01438) 880 424 ;

Chesfield Downs Graveley Jack's Hill, ✆ (08707) 460 020 .

Knebworth House★ AC, S : 2½ m

Novotel Stevenage

(heated) rm, rest,

Knebworth Park, Southwest : 1½ m. by A 602 at junction 7 of A 1(M) ✉ *SG1 2AX – ✆ (01438) 346 100 – h0992@accor.com – Fax (01438) 723 872*

100 rm – 🚹£ 54/99 🚹🚹£ 99, ☕ £ 12 – **Rest** – Carte £ 20/37 **s**

◆ Modern hotel not far from Knebworth Park and Hatfield House. Large rooms with family facilities, some with sofa beds. Outdoor playground available and babysitting on request. Dining room with open kitchen area.

ENGLAND

STEYNING – W. Sussex – 504 T 31 – pop. 9 501 7 D2

London 52 m – Brighton 12 m – Worthing 10 m

The Old Tollgate
rm,

The Street, Bramber, Southwest : 1 m. ✉ BN44 3WE – ✆ (01903) 879 494 – info@oldtollgatehotel.com – Fax (01903) 813 399

36 rm – †£ 82 ††£ 135, ☕ £9.95 – 2 suites – **Rest** – (carvery) Menu £ 19/24 **s**

◆ Once travellers had to stop here to pay toll; now it is a pleasant hotel offering hospitality and resting place. Spic and span rooms; pine furnishings. Renowned three-roomed carvery restaurant.

Springwells without rest
(heated)

9 High St ✉ BN44 3GG – ✆ (01903) 812 446 – contact@springwells.co.uk – Fax (01903) 879 823 – Closed Christmas-New Year

11 rm ☕ – †£ 60 ††£ 60/120

◆ Built in 1772, a picturesque former merchant's house in the heart of town. Tidy accommodation in pretty chintz; four-poster rooms on the first floor face the High Street.

at Ashurst North : 3 ½ m. on B 2135 – ✉ Steyning

The Fountain Inn

✉ BN44 3AP – ✆ (01403) 710 219

Rest – Carte £ 16/32

◆ Former farmhouse dating from 1572, now an attractive pub with garden and pond. Interior oozes charm with low ceilings and beams galore. Freshly prepared traditional fare.

Red = Pleasant. Look for the red ✗ and ⌂ symbols.

STILTON – Cambs. – 504 T 26 – pop. 2 500 – ✉ Peterborough 14 A2

London 76 m – Cambridge 30 m – Northampton 43 m – Peterborough 6 m

Bell Inn

Great North Rd ✉ PE7 3RA – ✆ (01733) 241 066 – reception@thebellstilton.co.uk – Fax (01733) 245 173 – closed 25-26 December, Saturday lunch and Sunday dinner

22 rm ☕ – †£ 73/80 ††£ 130

Rest *Village Bar* – see restaurant listing

◆ A swinging red bell pub sign hangs outside this part 16C inn with garden. Deluxe bedrooms are individually styled; some retain original rafters and stonework.

Village Bar – at Bell Inn

Great North Rd ✉ PE7 3RA – ✆ (01733) 241 066 – reception@thebellstilton.co.uk Fax (01733) 245 173 – Closed dinner 25-26 December

Rest – Menu 27 – Carte £ 21/32

◆ As one would expect, Stilton cheese is used to full effect in this rustic bar, appearing in soups, dumplings, quiche and dressings. Blackboard specials to tickle taste-buds.

STOCKBRIDGE – Hants. – 503 P 30 6 B2

London 75 m – Salisbury 14 m – Southampton 19 m – Winchester 9 m

The Greyhound with rm

31 High St ✉ SO20 6EY – ✆ (01264) 810 833 – thegreyhouse-inn@hotmail.com – Closed 25-26 and 31 December, 1 January, Sunday dinner and Monday

8 rm ☕ – †£ 90 ††£ 120 – **Rest** – Menu £ 22 – Carte £ 25/40

◆ Characterful, low-beamed, yellow brick pub with aged wooden tables beside Test on smart high street.Contemporary dishes of carefully sourced ingredients. Sleek, airy bedrooms.

ENGLAND

at Longstock **North : 1 ½ m. on A 3057 – Stockbridge – ✉ Stockbridge**

The Peat Spade Inn with rm

Village Street ✉ SO20 6DR – ✆ (01264) 810612 – info@peatspadeinn.co.uk – Fax (01264) 811 078 – Closed 25-26 December, 1 January and Sunday dinner

6 rm – †£ 110 ††£ 110 – **Rest** – (booking essential) Carte £ 23/35

◆ The ultimate hunting and fishing pub, with lovely local ambience. Country pursuits theme reflected in the décor. Serves proper pub dishes, locally sourced. Residents' lounge. Stylish bedrooms with all modern comforts and amenities.

STOCKTON-ON-TEES – Stockton-on-Tees – 502 P 20 – pop. 80 060 24 B3

London 251 m – Leeds 61 m – Middlesbrough 4 m – Newcastle upon Tyne 39 m

Durham Tees Valley Airport : ✆ (08712) 242426, SW : 6 m. by A 1027, A 135 and A 67

Stockton Central Library, Church Road ✆ (01642) 521830

Eaglescliffe Yarm Rd, ✆ (01642) 780 098 ;

Knotty Hill Golf Centre Sedgefield, ✆ (01740) 620 320 ;

Norton Junction Rd, ✆ (01642) 676 385 .

at Eaglescliffe **South : 3 ½ m. on A 135 – ✉ Stockton-on-Tees**

ENGLAND

Parkmore

636 Yarm Rd, ✉ TS16 0DH – ✆ (01642) 786 815 – enquiries@parkmorehotel.co.uk – Fax (01642) 790 485

54 rm – †£ 75/85 ††£ 95/120, ☕ £8.95 – 1 suite

Rest *J's @ 636* – Menu £ 18 (lunch) **s** – Carte £ 25/43 **s**

◆ Built in 1896 for shipbuilding family; combines a sense of the old and new. Rooms are furnished in modern style; leisure and conference facilities also available. Dining room specialises in steak options.

STOKE BY NAYLAND – Suffolk – 504 W 28 15 C3

London 70 m – Bury St Edmunds 24 m – Cambridge 54 m – Colchester 11 m – Ipswich 14 m

The Crown

✉ CO6 4SE – ✆ (01206) 262 001 – thecrown@eoinns.co.uk – Fax (01206) 264 026 – Closed 25-26 December

Rest – (booking essential) Carte £ 18/35

◆ 16C pub with smart terrace, huge garden and 21C style: spacious rooms offer variety of cool dining options. Locally renowned menus: a seasonal, modern take on classic dishes.

The Angel Inn with rm

Polstead St ✉ CO6 4SA – ✆ (01206) 263 245 – the.angel@tiscali.co.uk – Fax (01206) 263 373 – Closed Sunday

7 rm ☕ – †£ 60 ††£ 95 – **Rest** – Carte £ 17/28

◆ 16C timbered inn, its original well is the dining room centrepiece; Speciality griddle dishes are well worth tucking into. Traditional rooms available.

STOKE CANON – Devon – 503 J 31 – see Exeter

STOKE D'ABERNON – Surrey – 504 S 30 – see Cobham

STOKE HOLY CROSS – Norfolk – 504 X 26 – see Norwich

Undecided between two equivalent establishments? Within each category, establishments are classified in our order of preference.

STOKE POGES – Bucks. – 504 S 29 – pop. 4 112 11 D3

London 30 m – Aylesbury 28 m – Oxford 44 m
Park Rd, ✆ (01753) 643 332 .

Stoke Park Club
rest,

Park Rd ✉ SL2 4PG – ✆ (01753) 717 171 – info@stokeparkclub.com – Fax (01753) 717 181 – closed 24-26 December and 3-21 January

21 rm – †£ 285 ††£ 285, £ 18

Rest *The Park* – (dinner only and Sunday lunch) (residents only) Menu £ 40

◆ A palatial hotel, all pillars, balconies and cupola with golf course where James Bond played Goldfinger in film. Rooms are impressive: antiques, marble baths, heated floors. Snug, plush chairs in relaxed brasserie with French posters on walls.

Stoke Place
rm,

Stoke Green, South : ½ m. by B 416 ✉ SL2 4HT – ✆ (01753) 534 790 – enquiries@stokeplace.co.uk – Fax (01753) 512 743

29 rm – †£ 225 ††£ 275

Rest *Garden Room* – Carte £ 24/36

◆ 17C extended Queen Anne mansion in 22 acres with lake and geese. Boutique makeover has particularly benefitted Gloucester and Queen Anne rooms with their cool, sleek lines. Chic Garden Room restaurant serves fresh, local modern menus.

**Your opinions are important to us:
please write and let us know about your discoveries and experiences – good and bad!**

STOKE ROW – Oxon. 11 C3

London 45 m – Henley-on-Thames 6 m – Reading 10 m

The Cherry Tree Inn with rm

✉ RG9 5QA – ✆ (01491) 680 430 – info@thecherrytreeinn.com – Closed 25-26 December, 1 January and Sunday dinner

4 rm †£ 95 ††£ 95 – **Rest** – Carte £ 25/35

◆ 17C inn with an impressive 21C refurbishment: bags of charm and character typified by low ceiling and beams. Platefuls of good value dishes offering eclectic mix. Plush rooms.

STOKE SUB HAMDON – Somerset – 503 L 31 – see Yeovil

STOKEINTEIGNHEAD – Devon – see Torquay

STOKENCHURCH – Bucks – 504 R 29 – pop. 5 038 11 C2

London 42 m – High Wycombe 10 m – Oxford 18 m

at Radnage Northeast : 1 ¾ m. by A 40 – ✉ Stokenchurch

The Three Horseshoes Inn with rm

Bennett End, North : 1 ¼ m. by Town End rd ✉ HP14 4EB – ✆ (01494) 483 273 – threehorseshoes@btconnect.com – Closed Sunday dinner and Monday

6 rm – †£ 75 ††£ 145 – **Rest** – Menu £ 18 (lunch) – Carte £ 23/30

◆ Attractive red brick pub with tiny front bar, rear restaurant and telephone box in duck pond. Good value, precisely cooked British dishes; well presented and locally sourced. Comfortable bedrooms have character beds and modern bathrooms. Molières is best.

STOKENHAM – Devon – 503 I 33 – ✉ Kingsbridge 2 C3

London 225 m – Plymouth 26 m – Salcombe 11 m
Kingsbridge★, W : 5 m. by A 379. Dartmouth★★, N : 9 m. by A 379

The Tradesman's Arms

✉ TQ7 2SZ – ☎ (01548) 580 313 – nick@thetradesmansarms.com – Fax (01548) 580 657

Rest – (booking essential) Carte £ 18/25

◆ Charming, personally run part-14C thatched inn with beamed bar and stone fireplace in delightful coastal village. Lots of character; neat garden. Local fish and game feature.

STOKESLEY – N. Yorks. – 502 Q 20 – pop. 4 725 – ✉ Middlesbrough 23 C1

Great Britain

London 239 m – Leeds 59 m – Middlesbrough 8 m – Newcastle upon Tyne 49 m – York 52 m
Great Ayton (Captain Cook Birthplace Museum★ AC), NE : 2½ m. on A 173

Chapter's with rm

AC rest, VISA

27 High St ✉ TS9 5AD – ☎ (01642) 711 888 – enquiries@chaptershotel.co.uk – Fax (01642) 713 387 – Closed 1 week January, 1 week September, 25-26 December and 1 January

13 rm – †£ 66/85 ††£ 89/95 – **Rest** – (Closed Sunday dinner and Monday lunch) Carte £ 24/35

◆ Solid, mellow brick Victorian house with colour washed rooms. Bistro style dining with strong Mediterranean colour scheme. Eclectic menu: classics and more modern dishes.

STON EASTON – Somerset – 503 M 30 – ✉ Bath (Bath & North East Somerset) 4 C2

London 131 m – Bath 12 m – Bristol 11 m – Wells 7 m

Ston Easton Park

✉ BA3 4DF – ☎ (01761) 241 631 – info@stoneaston.co.uk – Fax (01761) 241 377

21 rm – †£ 155/220 ††£ 250/355 – 1 suite

Rest ***The Cedar Tree*** – (booking essential for non-residents) Menu £ 23/45

◆ Aristocratic Palladian mansion; grounds designed by Humphrey Repton, through which river Norr flows. Lavish rooms: Grand Saloon with Kentian plasterwork. 18C style bedrooms. Formal restaurant served by a Victorian kitchen garden.

STONESFIELD – Oxon – 504 P 28 – pop. 1 764 10 B2

London 70 m – Oxford 15 m – Witney 8 m

The White Horse

The Ridings ✉ OX29 8EA – ☎ (01993) 891 063 – info@thewhitehorse.uk.com – Closed Sunday dinner, Monday

Rest – Menu £ 10/13 – Carte £ 21/34

◆ Modernised dining pub with central bar, smart oak-floored dining room and lounge with leather sofas and open fires. Some ambitiously original dishes served on à la carte.

STORRINGTON – W. Sussex – 504 S 31 – pop. 7 727 7 C2

London 54 m – Brighton 20 m – Portsmouth 36 m

Old Forge

6 Church St ✉ RH20 4LA – ☎ (01903) 743 402 – enquiry@oldforge.co.uk – Fax (01903) 742 540 – Closed 2 weeks in spring and autumn, Saturday lunch, Sunday dinner and Monday-Wednesday

Rest – Menu £ 18/34

◆ Appealing whitewashed and brick cottages with three dining rooms bearing all hallmarks of flavoursome traditional cuisine. Array of cheeses; fine wine from small producers.

ENGLAND

STOURPORT-ON-SEVERN – Worcs. – 503 N 26 – pop. 18 899 — 18 B2

London 137 m – Birmingham 21 m – Worcester 12 m

Stourport Manor

Hartlebury Rd, East : 1 ¼ m. on B 4193 ✉ DY13 9JA – ☎ (01299) 289 955 – stourport@menzieshotels.co.uk – Fax (01299) 878 520

66 rm – †£ 60/125 ††£ 60/125, ☕ £ 14.95 – 2 suites

Rest *The Brasserie* – Menu £ 14/22 – Carte £ 26/33 **s**

◆ Gracious country house, once home to former prime minister, Stanley Baldwin. Lovely, warm-hued lounge; wide-ranging indoor leisure facilities. Bedrooms are nicely spacious. Brasserie overlooks the garden; wide ranging menus.

STOURTON – Wilts. — 4 C2

London 112 m – Shaftesbury 12 m – Wincanton 10 m

The Spread Eagle Inn with rm

Church Lawn ✉ BA12 6QE – ☎ (01747) 840 587 – enquiries@spreadeagleinn.com – Fax (01747) 840 954 – Closed 25 December

5 rm ☕ – †£ 70 ††£ 110 – **Rest** – Menu £ 17 – Carte £ 20/25

◆ Located within the stunning grounds of Stourhead House, this 18C pub has a front bar and two rear burgundy rooms, serving locally sourced menus. Simple, well-kept rooms.

STOWMARKET – Suffolk – 504 W 27 – pop. 15 248 — 15 C3

London 95 m – Ipswich 14 m – Colchester 35 m – Clacton-on-Sea 40 m

at Buxhall West : 3 ¾ m. by B 115 – ✉ **Stowmarket**

The Buxhall Crown

Mill Road ✉ IP14 3DW – ☎ (01449) 736 521 – trevor@thebuxhallcrown.co.uk – Closed 25-26 December, Sunday dinner and Monday

Rest – Carte £ 25/45

◆ Cosy and characterful, with wattle and daub walls, heavy wood beams and an inglenook fireplace. Good use of local produce, including particularly nice beef. Popular terrace.

STOW-ON-THE-WOLD – Glos. – 503 – pop. 2 074 *Great Britain* — 4 D1

London 86 m – Birmingham 44 m – Gloucester 27 m – Oxford 30 m

Hollis House, The Square ☎ (01451) 831082

Chastleton House★★, NE : 6 ½ m. by A 436 and A 44

Wyck Hill House

rm, rest,

South : 2 ¼ m. by A 429 on A 424 ✉ GL54 1HY – ☎ (01451) 831 936 – enquiries@wyckhillhouse.com – Fax (01451) 832 243

46 rm ☕ – †£ 99/135 ††£ 99/135 – 8 suites – **Rest** – Menu £ 33 – Carte £ 30/45

◆ Handsome 18C mansion set in 100-acre grounds above Windrush Valley. Panelled drawing rooms; quiet and characterful rooms in the old wing, coach house and modern orangery. Conservatory restaurant with wold views.

Grapevine

Sheep St ✉ GL54 1AU – ☎ (01451) 830 344 – enquiries@vines.co.uk – Fax (01451) 832 278

22 rm ☕ – †£ 85/95 ††£ 150/160

Rest *The Conservatory* – Menu £ 20/33 – Carte £ 17/24

Rest *Lavigna* – Carte £ 18/22

◆ Among the antique shops, two extended 17C houses. Rooms in bright, modern décor with a nod to tradition, half with beams and bare stone. Timbered bar; sepia photos of Stow. In Conservatory black grapes hang from spreading vine. Easy-going, informal Lavigna.

The Royalist

Digbeth St ✉ GL56 1BN – ☎ (01451) 830670 – enquiries@theroyalisthotel.com – Fax (01451) 870048
14 rm – †£60/95 ††£120/180
Rest *Eagle & Child* – see restaurant listing
Rest *947 AD* – Menu £25/35
◆ Historic high street inn - reputedly England's oldest. Comfortable, stylish rooms, individual in shape and décor and quieter at the rear. Two-room bar in exposed stone. Intimate, beamed restaurant offers fine dining: inglenook fireplace.

Fosse Manor

Fosse Way, South : 1 ¼ m. on A 429 ✉ GL54 1JX – ☎ (01451) 830354 – enquiries@fossemanor.co.uk – Fax (01451) 832486
19 rm – †£95 ††£225 – **Rest** – Carte £20/33
◆ Former coaching inn on the main road. Contemporary public areas with informal feel. Up-to-date bedrooms, some of which are set in the coach house. Lunch available in bar. Classically proportioned dining room with menu of Mediterranean favourites.

Crestow House without rest (heated)

at junction of A 429 on B 4068 Lower Swell rd ✉ GL54 1JX – ☎ (01451) 830969 – fsimonetti@btinternet.com – closed 25 December and February
4 rm – †£50 ††£80
◆ Victorian manor house with conservatory, garden and pool. Breakfast served in family style. Well-appointed rooms larger at front or smaller at rear overlooking the garden.

ENGLAND

Number Nine without rest

9 Park St ✉ GL54 1AQ – ☎ (01451) 870333 – enquiries@number-nine.info
3 rm – †£45/50 ††£60/75
◆ Ivy-clad 18C Cotswold stone house run by friendly owners on the high street. Winding staircase leads to the large bedrooms which occupy each floor.

The Old Butchers

7 Park St ✉ GL54 1AQ – ☎ (01451) 831700 – louise@theoldbutchers.com – Fax (01451) 831388 – closed 1 week May and 1 week October
Rest – Carte £20/29
◆ Former butcher's shop of Cotswold stone: closely set tables in a very busy, modern restaurant. Daily changing, affordable, modish menus feature prominent use of local produce.

Eagle & Child – at The Royalist H.

Digbeth St ✉ GL54 1BN – ☎ (01451) 830670 – stay@theroyalisthotel.co.uk – Fax (01451) 870048
Rest – Carte £22/27
◆ Stone pub attached to an inn; conservatory to the rear. Atmospheric dining room: soft lighting, flagstones, beams. Robust cooking: plenty of choice.

at Upper Oddington East : 2 m. by A 436 – ✉ Stow-on-the-Wold

Horse & Groom Village Inn with rm

✉ GL56 0XH – ☎ (01451) 830584 – info@horseandgroom.uk.com – Closed 2 weeks January
8 rm – †£70 ††£98 – **Rest** – Carte £19/30
◆ Part 16C former coaching inn in rural hamlet. Long, split-level interior with beams and open fires. Modern pub food from a regularly changing menu. Cottage-style bedrooms.

at Lower Oddington East : 3 m. by A 436 – ✉ Stow-on-the-Wold 4 D1

The Fox Inn with rm

✉ GL56 0UR – ☎ (01451) 870555 – info@foxinn.net – Fax (01451) 870669 – Closed 25 December
3 rm – †£95 ††£95 – **Rest** – (booking essential) Carte £18/30
◆ 16C ivy dressed pub in a charming village. Flag floors, beams, fireplaces, nooks, crannies, books and candlelight. Hearty English fare. Sumptuously decorated rooms.

at Daylesford East : 3 ½ m. by A 436 – ✉ Stow-on-the-Wold

The Cafe at Daylesford Organic

✉ *GL56 0YG – ✆ (01608) 731 700 – enquiries@daylesfordorganic.com – Fax (01608) 731 701*
Rest – Organic (lunch only) (bookings not accepted) Carte £ 22/27
◆ Beautifully designed farm shop, spa, yoga centre and two-floor café, which becomes very busy as customers tuck into tasty dishes whose ingredients are all organically sourced.

at Bledington Southeast : 4 m. by A 436 on B 4450 – ✉ Kingham

The Kings Head Inn with rm

The Green ✉ OX7 6XQ – ✆ (01608) 658 365 – kingshead@orr-ewing.com – Fax (01608) 658 902 – Closed 25-26 December
12 rm ☕ – 🚹£ 50 🚹🚹£ 125 – **Rest** – Carte £ 18/29
◆ 15C inn on the green, oozing style, charm and personality: stone floors, beams, open fires. Confident cooking with good flavour combinations. Timbered or modern annex rooms.

at Lower Swell West : 1 ¼ m. on B 4068 – ✉ Stow-on-the-Wold 4 **D1**

Rectory Farmhouse without rest

by Rectory Barns Rd ✉ GL54 1LH – ✆ (01451) 832 351 – rectory.farmhouse@cw-warwick.co.uk – closed Christmas and New Year
3 rm ☕ – 🚹£ 58/60 🚹🚹£ 87/93
◆ 17C former farmhouse of Cotswold stone. Bedrooms are very comfortable and decorated in distinctive cottage style. Communal breakfast at family table.

ENGLAND

STRATFORD-UPON-AVON – Warks. – 503 P 27 – pop. 22 187 19 **C3**

Great Britain

London 96 m – Birmingham 23 m – Coventry 18 m – Leicester 44 m – Oxford 40 m

Bridgefoot ✆ (0870) 1607930, stratfordtic@shakespeare-country.co.uk

Tiddington Rd, ✆ (01789) 205 749 ;

Welcombe Hotel Warwick Rd, ✆ (01789) 413 800 ;

Stratford Oaks Snitterfield Bearley Rd, ✆ (01789) 731 980 .

Town★★ - Shakespeare's Birthplace★ **AC**, AB

Mary Arden's House★ **AC**, NW : 4 m. by A 3400 A. Ragley Hall★ **AC**, W : 9 m. by A 422 A

Plan on next page

Ettington Park

Alderminster, Southeast : 6 ¼ m. on A 3400 ✉ CV37 8BU – ✆ (01789) 450 123 – ettingtonpark@handpicked.co.uk – Fax (01789) 450 472
43 rm ☕ – 🚹£ 110/130 🚹🚹£ 129/179 – 5 suites – **Rest** – (dinner only) Menu £ 30 – Carte £ 39/45
◆ Imposing, corporate friendly, Gothic mansion with sympathetic extensions in attractive grounds. Ornate ceilings, classic country house feel. Comfy, well-equipped bedrooms. Oak-panelled dining room with medieval feel.

Welcombe H. Spa and Golf Club

Warwick Rd, Northeast : 1 ½ m. on A 439 ✉ CV37 0NR – ✆ (01789) 295 252 – welcombe@menzieshotels.co.uk – Fax (01789) 414 666
73 rm ☕ – 🚹£ 180 🚹🚹£ 180 – 5 suites
Rest *Trevelyan* – Menu £ 22 (lunch) **s** – Carte £ 35/45 **s**
◆ Jacobean house built 1869; sweeping Italian gardens and gracious, oak panelled interiors. Grand rooms in main house with many antique features. Golf course overlooks Avon. Savour views of gardens, fountain and waterfall from restaurant.

STRATFORD-UPON-AVON

Banbury Rd . . . . **B** 2
Bell Court Shopping Centre . . . . **A** 39
Benson Rd. . . . . **B** 3
Bridge Foot . . . . **B** 6
Bridge St . . . . **B** 8
Chapel Lane . . . . **A** 13
Chapel St. . . . . **A** 14
Church St . . . . **A** 16
Clopton Bridge . . . . **B** 18
College Lane . . . . **A** 19
Ely St . . . . **A** 22
Evesham Pl. . . . . **A** 24
Great William St . . . . **A** 25
Greenhill St . . . . **A** 27
Guild St . . . . **A** 28
Henley St. . . . . **A** 29
High St. . . . . **A** 31
Rother St . . . . **A** 32
Scholars Lane . . . . **A** 33
Sheep St. . . . . **AB** 35
Tiddington Rd . . . . **B** 38
Trinity St. . . . . **A** 40
Warwick Rd. . . . . **B** 42
Waterside . . . . **B** 43
Windsor St . . . . **A** 45
Wood St . . . . **A** 47

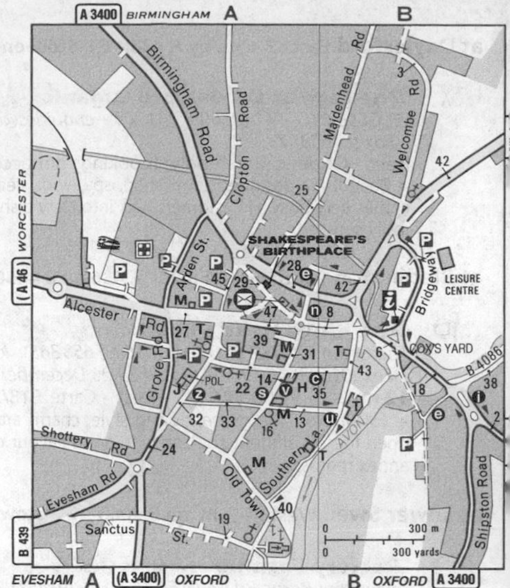

ENGLAND

Alveston Manor

Clopton Bridge ✉ *CV37 7HP – ✆ (0870) 400 81 81*
– sales.alvestonmanor@macdonald-hotels.co.uk – Fax (01789) 414 095 B **i**
109 rm – 🛉£ 75/98 🛉🛉£ 98/250, ☕ £ 15.95 – 4 suites
Rest *The Manor Grill* – (bar lunch) Menu £ 28 – Carte £ 35/46
◆ Part Elizabethan manor where "A Midsummer's Night Dream" was first performed beneath the cedar tree in the grounds. Richly decorated period rooms; modern rooms in extension. Seasoned oak panelling in medieval dining room.

Thistle Stratford-Upon-Avon

Waterside ✉ *CV37 6BA – ✆ (01789) 294 949*
– reservations.stratforduponavon@thistle.co.uk – Fax (0870) 333 92 46 B **u**
63 rm – 🛉£ 175 🛉🛉£ 205, ☕ £ 12.95
Rest *Bards* – Menu £ 15/18 **s** – Carte £ 20/30 **s**
◆ A compact hotel opposite the renowned RSC and birthplace of the bard. Themed weekends such as murder mysteries are popular. Well-equipped bedrooms. Bustling restaurant with a formal, elegant style.

Stratford Manor

rest,
Warwick Rd, Northeast : 3 m. on A 439 ✉ *CV37 0PY*
– ✆ (01789) 731 173 – stratfordmanor@marstonhotels.com
– Fax (01789) 731 131
104 rm – 🛉£ 80/179 🛉🛉£ 80/179, ☕ £ 14.50 – **Rest** – (closed Saturday lunch) Menu £ 29 **s**
◆ Three miles from Stratford and Warwick, this modern, well located hotel enjoys 21 acres of surrounding countryside. Murals, arresting meeting room and ample bedrooms within. Popular restaurant with traditional palette.

The Shakespeare

Chapel St ✉ *CV37 6ER – ✆ (01789) 294 997 – h6630@accor.com*
– Fax (01789) 415 411 A **v**
73 rm ☕ – 🛉£ 80/160 🛉🛉£ 90/160 – 1 suite
Rest *David Garrick* – ✆ (0870) 400 8182 (dinner only and Sunday lunch) Menu £ 27 – Carte £ 22/35 **s**
◆ Exudes atmosphere with gabled façade, leaded windows; this 18C inn was once a writers' watering hole. Afternoon tea served in vintage lounge; rooms with modern furnishings. Medieval styled restaurant; abundance of tried-and-tested dishes.

Cherry Trees without rest
Swan's Nest Lane ✉ CV37 7LS – ✆ (01789) 292 989 – gotocherrytrees@aol.com – Fax (01789) 292 989 B e
3 rm – †£ 65 ††£ 85/110
◆ Friendly welcome to this chalet style guest house. Luxurious bedrooms with every detail taken care of include four poster room with own garden. Breakfast cooked to order.

Victoria Spa Lodge without rest
Bishopton Lane, Northwest : 2 m. by A 3400 on Bishopton Lane turning left at roundabout with A 46 ✉ CV37 9QY – ✆ (01789) 267 985 – ptozer@victoriasspalodge.demon.co.uk – Fax (01789) 204 728 – closed Christmas and New Year
7 rm – †£ 55 ††£ 70
◆ Built as spa, hotel and pump room; Queen Victoria stayed as one of its many guests, testified by the gables which bear her coat of arms. Pristine rooms are among its charms.

The Payton without rest
6 John St ✉ CV37 6UB – ✆ (01789) 266 442 – info@payton.co.uk – Fax (01789) 266 442 – closed 24 December-2 January A e
5 rm – †£ 55/65 ††£ 60/75
◆ Pretty, white Grade II listed Georgian town house built in 1832 in quiet conservation area. Pale, pastel coloured bedrooms and small neat breakfast room.

Malbec
6 Union St ✉ CV37 6QT – ✆ (01789) 269 106 – eatmalbec@aol.com – Fax (01789) 269 106 – closed one week October, 25 December-2 January, Sunday and Monday A n
Rest – Menu £ 15 (lunch) – Carte £ 24/28 **s**
◆ Pleasant modern restaurant with atmospheric barrel ceiling in intimate basement. Good value set menus: accomplished à la carte with season's larder bolstering a classic base.

Lambs
12 Sheep St ✉ CV37 6EF – ✆ (01789) 292 554 – eat@lambsrestaurant.co.uk – Fax (01789) 293 372 – closed 25-26 December, Sunday dinner, Monday lunch B c
Rest – Menu £ 20 – Carte £ 22/34
◆ 16C town house with zesty bistro-style cooking in old-world surrounds of white wattle walls, rafters and well-spaced wooden tables.

at Alveston **East : 2 m. by B 4086 - B – ✉ Stratford-upon-Avon**

The Baraset Barn
1 Pimlico Lane, on B 4086 ✉ CV37 7RF – ✆ (01789) 295 510 – barasetbarn@lovelypubs.co.uk – Fax (01789) 292 961 – Closed 25 December and Sunday dinner
Rest – Menu £ 10/20 – Carte £ 25/45
◆ 200 year-old pub given a sumptuous contemporary makeover. Decked terrace; stylish lounge conservatory; Main dining in barn or mezzanine: bold, freshly prepared modern cooking.

at Pillerton Priors **Southeast : 7 m. on A 422 - B – ✉ Stratford-upon-Avon**

Fulready Manor without rest
South : ¾ m. on Halford rd ✉ CV37 7PE – ✆ (01789) 740 152 – stay@fulreadymanor.co.uk – Fax (01789) 740 247
3 rm – †£ 115/150 ††£ 115/150
◆ Peaceful guest house in 120 acres of arable farmland. Warm welcome and delightful drawing room. Luxurious, uniquely-styled bedrooms with sumptuous furnishings and comforts.

ENGLAND

at Ardens Grafton Southwest : 5 m. by A 46 - A – ✉ Stratford-upon-Avon

The Golden Cross
Wixford Road, South : ¼ m. ✉ B50 4LG – ☎ (01789) 772 420 – pat@thegoldencross.net – Fax (01798) 491 358 – closed Sunday dinner
Rest – Menu £ 13 – Carte £ 20/25
◆ Solid stone floor, exposed beams, open fire, scrubbed wooden furnishing: all the winning ingredients for a welcoming pub. Freshly prepared dishes with tasty seasonal base.

at Billesley West : 4 ½ m. by A 422 - A - off A 46 – ✉ Stratford-upon-Avon

Billesley Manor
✉ B49 6NF – ☎ (01789) 279 955 – info@billesleymanor.co.uk – Fax (01789) 764 145
70 rm – †£ 89/159 ††£ 189/259, ☐ £13.50 – 2 suites
Rest ***The Stuart*** – Menu £ 25/38
◆ Topiary garden and ornamental pond complements lovely 16C manor. The oak panelled interior evokes its past: Shakespeare reputedly used the library. Modern and period rooms. Original 16C oak panelling in restaurant.

STREATLEY – Newbury – **503** Q 29 – **pop. 3 924** – ✉ **Goring** 10 **B3**
Great Britain

London 56 m – Oxford 16 m – Reading 11 m
Goring & Streatley Rectory Rd, ☎ (01491) 873 229.
Basildon Park★ **AC**, SE : 2 ½ m. by A 329 – Mapledurham★ **AC**, E : 6 m. by A 329, B 471 and B 4526. Ridgeway Path★★

The Swan at Streatley ← River Thames,
High St ✉ RG8 9HR – ☎ (01491) 878 800 – sales@swan-at-streatley.co.uk – Fax (01491) 872 554
44 rm ☐ – †£ 110/150 ††£ 138/160 – 1 suite
Rest ***Cygnetures*** – Menu £ 19/27 – Carte £ 34/45
◆ Attractive riverside views to be savoured from large windows of most bedrooms, some having patios and balconies. Hotel's business nature benefits from Thames-side location. Nautically themed restaurant overlooking the water.

STRETE – Devon – see Dartmouth

STRETTON – Ches. – **502** M 23 – see Warrington

STRETTON – Staffs. – **502** P 25 – see Burton-upon-Trent

STROUD – Glos. – **503** N 28 – **pop. 32 052** 4 **C1**

London 113 m – Bristol 30 m – Gloucester 9 m
Subscription Rooms, George St ☎ (0871) 7162676
Minchinhampton, ☎ (01453) 833 840 ;
Painswick, ☎ (01452) 812 180.

at Brimscombe Southeast : 2 ¼ m. on A 419 – ✉ Stroud

Burleigh Court
Burleigh Lane, South : ½ m. by Burleigh rd via The Roundabouts ✉ GL5 2PF – ☎ (01453) 883 804 – info@burleighcourthotel.co.uk – Fax (01453) 886 870 – closed 25-26 December
18 rm ☐ – †£ 85 ††£ 125 – **Rest** – Carte £ 28/40
◆ 18C manor house on edge of a steep hill overlooking Golden Valley. Swimming pool in closeted garden of hidden pathways and stone walls. Homely bedrooms with views. Regency style dining room overlooks terraced gardens.

STUCKTON – Hants. – see Fordingbridge

STUDLAND – Dorset – 503 O 32 4 C3

London 135 m – Bournemouth 25 m – Southampton 53 m – Weymouth 29 m

Shell Bay ← Poole Harbour and Brownsea Island, VISA AE

Ferry Rd, North : 3 m. or via car ferry from Sandbanks ✉ BH19 3BA – ✆ (01929) 450 363 – Fax (01929) 450 570 – March-October and weekends only in winter

Rest – Seafood Carte £ 21/32

◆ Hut-like appearance, but in a spectacular location with views of Poole Harbour and Brownsea Island. Inside, large windows and mirrors make the most of this. Seafood emphasis.

STURMINSTER NEWTON – Dorset – 503 N 31 – pop. 2 317 4 C3

London 123 m – Bournemouth 30 m – Bristol 49 m – Salisbury 28 m – Taunton 41 m

Mill★ AC

Plumber Manor with rm VISA AE

Southwest : 1 ¾ m. by A 357 on Hazelbury Bryan rd ✉ DT10 2AF – ✆ (01258) 472 507 – book@plumbermanor.com – Fax (01258) 473 370 – closed February

16 rm – †£ 95/115 ††£ 115/175 – **Rest** – (dinner only and Sunday lunch) Menu £ 25/28

◆ Secluded 18C manor house owned by the same family since it was first built. Three dining rooms where assured, popular dishes are served. Well-kept rooms, some with antiques.

SUDBURY – Suffolk – 504 W 27 – pop. 11 933 15 C3

London 68 m – Ipswich 22 m – Cambridge 45 m – Chelmsford 30 m

Hitchcock's VISA

10 Station Rd ✉ CO10 2SS – ✆ (01787) 377 037 – Fax (01787) 377 037 – closed first week January and Monday

Rest – Italian influences (lunch only and dinner Thursday-Saturday) Carte £ 18/27

◆ 150 year old former coal merchants; now a passionately run restaurant and deli, with cheese room. Cooking is simple and precise and uses only the finest local ingredients.

SUMMERCOURT – Cornwall – 503 F 32 – ✉ Newquay 1 B2

London 263 m – Newquay 9 m – Plymouth 45 m

Viners VISA

Carvynick, Northwest : 1 ½ m. of the junction of A 30 and A 3058 ✉ TR8 5AF – ✆ (01872) 510 544 – Fax (01872) 510 468 – Closed 4 weeks in winter

Rest – (closed Sunday dinner late October-Whitsun and Monday dinner mid September-mid July) (dinner only and Sunday lunch) Menu £ 17 – Carte £ 25/34

◆ 17C pub with grey stone exterior and rustic interior boasting original beams. Welcoming ambience. Buzzy restaurant offers old favourites as well as more ambitious dishes.

The ✿ award is the crème de la crème.
This is awarded to restaurants
which are really worth travelling miles for!

SUNDERLAND

Street	Map	No.
Albion Pl.	B	2
Barnes Park Rd	A	3
Bedford St	B	4
Borough Rd	B	5
Bridge St	B	6
Charlton Rd	A	8
Chester Rd.	B	10
Crowtree Rd	B	11
Dame Dorothy St	A	12
Derwent St	B	13
Fawcett St	B	
Harbour View	A	14
High St West	B	15
Holmeside	B	
John St	B	16
Kayll Rd	A	17
Livingstone Rd.	B	18
New Durham Rd	B	19
Ormonde St	A	21
Pallion Rd	A	22
Park Lane	B	23
Queens Rd	A	24
Roker Terrace	A	25
St Luke's Terrace	A	26
St Mary's Way	B	27
Shields Rd	A	29
Southwick Rd	B	30
Station Rd	A	32
The Bridges	B	
Trimdon St	A	35
Vine Pl.	B	36
Wessington Way	A	38

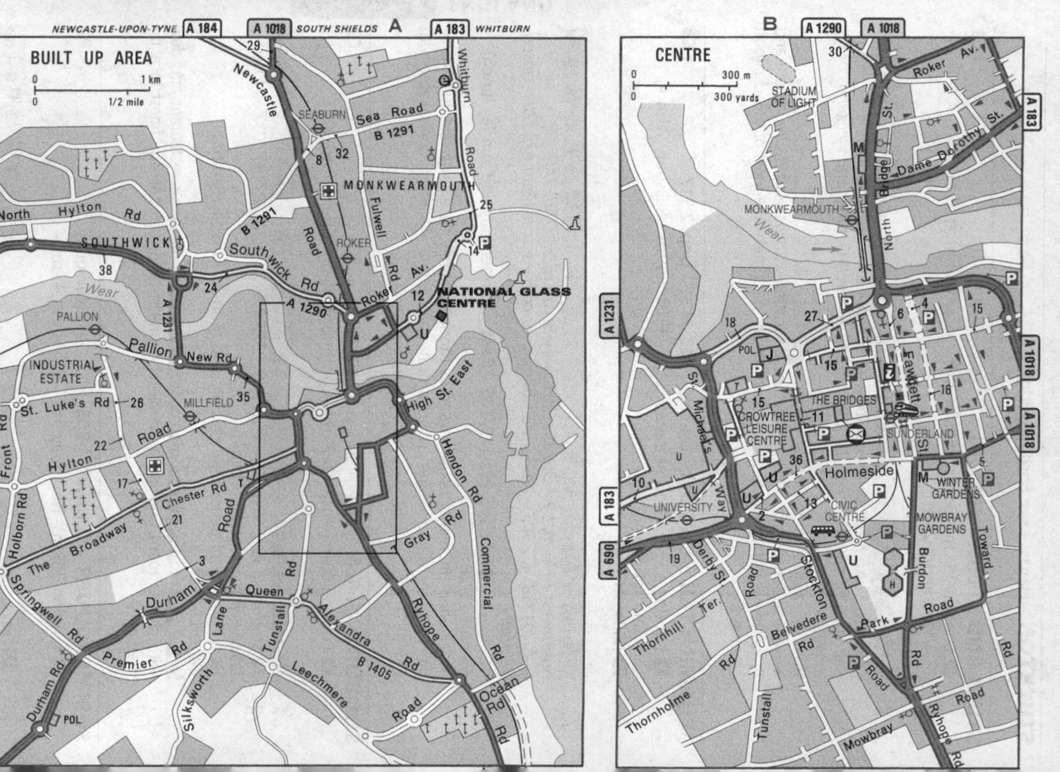

SUNDERLAND – Tyne and Wear – **501** P 19 – **pop. 280 807** 24 **B2**

Great Britain

London 272 m – Leeds 92 m – Middlesbrough 29 m – Newcastle upon Tyne 12 m

50 Fawcett St ✆ (0191) 553 2000, tourist.info@sunderland.gov.uk

Whitburn South Shields Lizard Lane, ✆ (0191) 529 2144 .

National Glass Centre★ A

Plan on preceding page

Sunderland Marriott rm, rest,

Queens Parade, Seaburn ✉ SR6 8DB – ✆ (0870) 400 72 87
– mhrs.nclsl.reservations@marriotthotels.com – Fax (0870) 400 73 87 A **e**

82 rm – ♀£ 135 ♀♀£ 195 – **Rest** – Carte £ 21/37 **s**

◆ Overlooks Whitburn Sands. A smart, contemporary, branded commercial hotel. Equally modern bedrooms with stylish, comfortable facilities. Restaurant and bar dining alternatives.

SUNNINGDALE – Berks. – **504** S 29 11 **D3**

Bluebells

Shrubbs Hill, London Rd, Northeast : ¾ m. on A 30 ✉ SL5 0LE
– ✆ (01344) 622 722 – info@bluebells-restaurant.com – Fax (01344) 620 990
– closed 25-30 December and Monday

Rest – Menu £ 20 (lunch) – Carte £ 32/47

◆ Smart, well-manicured façade matched by sophisticated interior of deep green. Large rear terrace, deck and garden. Modern British cooking with original starting point.

SUNNINGHILL – Windsor & Maidenhead – **504** S 29 – **see Ascot**

SURFLEET SEAS END – Lincs. – **see Spalding**

SUTTON COLDFIELD – W. Mids. – **503** O 26 – **pop. 105 452** 19 **C2**

London 124 m – Birmingham 8 m – Coventry 29 m – Nottingham 47 m – Stoke on Trent 40 m

Pype Hayes Walmley Eachelhurst Rd, ✆ (0121) 351 1014 ;

Boldmere Monmouth Dr., ✆ (0121) 354 3379 ;

110 Thornhill Rd, ✆ (0121) 580 7878 ;

The Belfry Wishaw Lichfield Rd, ✆ (01675) 470 301 .

Plan : see Birmingham pp. 4 and 5

The Belfry rm, rest,

Wishaw, East : 6½ m. by A 453 on A 446
✉ B76 9PR
– ✆ (01675) 470 301 – enquiries@thebelfry.com – Fax (01675) 470 256

311 rm – ♀£ 118/138 ♀♀£ 118/158 – 13 suites

Rest *French Restaurant* – (dinner only and Sunday lunch) Carte £ 28/50 **s**

Rest *Atrium* – (dinner only and Sunday lunch) Menu £ 25 **s**

◆ Famed for championship golf course, this large hotel has an unashamedly leisure oriented slant, including a superb AquaSpa. Sizeable rooms; superior variety overlook courses. Formal French Restaurant has golfing vistas. Atrium dominated by glass dome ceiling.

Moor Hall rm,

Moor Hall Drive, Northeast : 2 m. by A 453 and Weeford Rd ✉ B75 6LN
– ✆ (0121) 308 3751 – mail@moorhallhotel.co.uk
– Fax (0121) 308 8974 DT **r**

82 rm – ♀£ 120 ♀♀£ 120

Rest *Oak Room* – (closed Saturday lunch and Sunday dinner) Menu £ 13/26 **s** – Carte approx. £ 26 **s**

Rest *Country Kitchen* – (dinner only and lunch Saturday and Sunday, carvery rest.) Carte approx. £ 15 **s**

◆ Imposing, commercially oriented manor house featuring 19C/early 20C fixtures and fittings, set in quiet parkland. Fine range of rooms: some look over sunken gardens. Refined Oak Room. Carvery at Country Kitchen.

ENGLAND

The Cock Inn

Bulls Lane, Wishaw, East : 7 m. by A 453 off A 446 following signs to Grove End
✉ B76 9QL – ✆ (0121) 313 3960
Rest – (closed Sunday dinner) Carte £ 18/32
◆ Modern, spacious pub adorned by wood carvings and log fires; separate cigar bar adds an air of exclusivity. Seasonally changing, robust modern cooking with eclectic twists.

SUTTON GAULT – **Cambs.** – **504** U 26 – **see Ely**

SUTTON-ON-THE-FOREST – **N. Yorks.** – **502** P 21 23 **C2**

London 230 m – Kingston-upon-Hull 50 m – Leeds 52 m – Scarborough 40 m – York 12 m

The Blackwell Ox Inn with rm

Huby Rd ✉ YO61 1DT – ✆ (01347) 810 328 – info@blackwelloxinn.co.uk – Fax (01347) 812 738 – Closed 1 January
6 rm – †£ 95 – **Rest** – (Closed lunch 24 and 31 December, dinner 25 December and Sunday dinner) Menu £ 12/14 **s** – Carte £ 17/27 **s**
◆ Stylish destination in very pleasant village. Open-fired bar with cosy sofas. Two comfy, snug dining rooms: tasty menus with Spanish and French accent. Individual rooms.

ENGLAND

Rose & Crown

Main St ✉ YO61 1DP – ✆ (01347) 811 333 – ben-w@btconnect.com – Fax (01347) 811 333 – Closed first 2 weeks January
Rest – (closed Sunday dinner and Monday) (booking essential) Carte £ 23/27
◆ Lovely enclosed rear terrace and garden. Rustic bar ambience made all the warmer by roaring fires. Modern menu plus blackboard specials with imaginative, stylish twists.

SWANAGE – **Dorset** – **503** O 32 – **pop. 11 097** 4 **C3**

London 130 m – Bournemouth 22 m – Dorchester 26 m – Southampton 52 m

The White House, Shore Rd ✆ (0870) 4420680

Isle of Purbeck Studland, ✆ (01929) 450 361.

Town★

St Aldhelm's Head★★ (⩽ ★★★), SW : 4 m. by B 3069 – Durlston Country Park (⩽ ★★), S : 1 m. – Studland (Old Harry Rocks★★, Studland Beach (⩽ ★), St Nicholas Church★), N : 3 m. – Worth Matravers (Anvil Point Lighthouse ⩽ ★★), S : 2 m. – Great Globe★, S : 1 ¼ m. Corfe Castle★ (⩽ ★★) **AC**, NW : 6 m. by A 351 – Blue Pool★, NW : 9 m. by A 351 and minor roads – Lulworth Cove★, W : 18 m. by A 351 and B 3070

Cauldron Bistro

5 High St ✉ BH19 2LN – ✆ (01929) 422 671 – closed 2 weeks January, last week November, first week December and Monday-Wednesday
Rest – (light lunch) Carte £ 24/44
◆ Quaint and cosy; boothed tables, mix and match furniture. Quality ingredients, local fish, generous portions cooked with care. Unusual vegetarian dishes.

SWAY – **Hants.** – **503** P 31 – **see Brockenhurst**

SWINBROOK – **Oxon.** – **503** P 28 – **see Burford**

The red symbol?
This denotes the very essence of peace
– only the sound of birdsong first thing in the morning …

SWINDON – Swindon – 503 O 29 – pop. 155 432 4 D2

- London 83 m – Bournemouth 69 m – Bristol 40 m – Coventry 66 m – Oxford 29 m – Reading 40 m – Southampton 65 m
- 37 Regent St ✆ (01793) 530328
- Broome Manor Pipers Way, ✆ (01793) 532 403 ;
- Shrivenham Park Shrivenham Penny Hooks, ✆ (01793) 783 853 ;
- The Wiltshire Wootton Bassett Vastern, ✆ (01793) 849 999 ;
- Wrag Barn G & C.C. Highworth Shrivenham Rd, ✆ (01793) 861 327 .
- Great Western Railway Museum★ **AC** – Railway Village Museum★ **AC** Y **M**
- Lydiard Park (St Mary's★) W : 4 m. U. Ridgeway Path★★, S : 8½ m. by A 4361 – Whitehorse (⩽ ★)E : 7½ m. by A 4312, A 420 and B 400 off B 4057

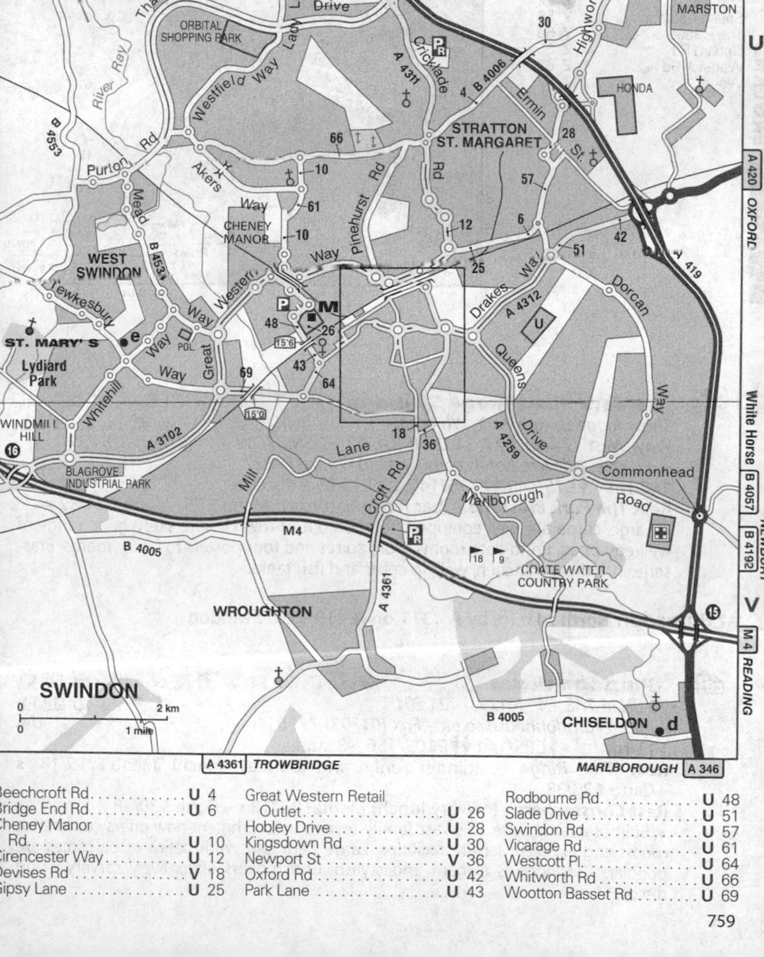

Beechcroft Rd. . . . U 4	Great Western Retail Outlet . . . U 26	Rodbourne Rd. . . . U 48
Bridge End Rd. . . . U 6	Hobley Drive . . . U 28	Slade Drive . . . U 51
Cheney Manor Rd. . . . U 10	Kingsdown Rd . . . U 30	Swindon Rd . . . U 57
Cirencester Way . . . U 12	Newport St . . . V 36	Vicarage Rd . . . U 61
Devises Rd . . . V 18	Oxford Rd . . . U 42	Westcott Pl. . . . U 64
Gipsy Lane . . . U 25	Park Lane . . . U 43	Whitworth Rd . . . U 66
		Wootton Basset Rd . . . U 69

SWINDON

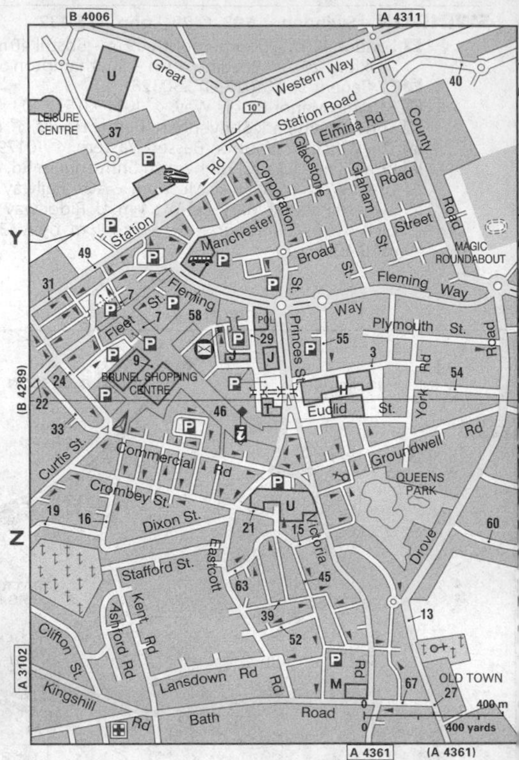

De Vere Shaw Ridge Swindon
rm, rest,

Shaw Ridge Leisure Park, Whitehill Way, West : 2 ¾ m. by A 3102 off B 4553 ✉ *SN5 7DW – ☎ (01793) 878 785 – dvs.sales@devere-hotels.com – Fax (01793) 877 822* U **e**

148 rm – †£ 75/140 ††£ 75/140, ☕ £ 12.95 – 4 suites

Rest *The Park Brasserie* – (bar lunch Saturday) Menu £ 15 – Carte £ 24/32 **s**

◆ Large, corporate, well-equipped hotel on out-of-town leisure site; a good range of well-equipped, up-to-date rooms, from suites and four-posters to family rooms. Brasserie with theatre kitchen, walk-in cellar and fish tanks.

at Blunsdon North : **4 ½ m. by A 4311 on A 419** – ✉ **Swindon**

Blunsdon House
rm, rest,

✉ *SN26 7AS – ☎ (01793) 721 701 – info@blunsdonhouse.co.uk – Fax (01793) 721 056* U **a**

111 rm ☕ – †£ 85/140 ††£ 105/150 – 3 suites

Rest *The Ridge* – (dinner only and Sunday lunch) Menu £ 15/18 **s** – Carte £ 30/38

Rest *Christophers* – (carvery lunch) Menu £ 15/18 **s** – Carte £ 30/38

◆ Built as a farmhouse, this vast family-owned establishment now offers conference rooms and excellent leisure facilities. Large bedrooms with patios or balconies are popular. The Ridge is elegant and stylish. Christophers offers lively carvery - and discos!

at Chiseldon South : 6 ¼ m. by A 4259, A 419 and A 346 on B 4005 – ✉ Swindon

Chiseldon House
New Rd ✉ SN4 0NE – ✆ (01793) 741 010 – info@chiseldonhousehotel.co.uk – Fax (01793) 741 059 V **d**
21 rm – †£ 65/90 ††£ 95/110
Rest ***Orangery*** – Menu £ 17/23 – Carte £ 16/25 **s**
◆ The gardens are one of the strongest aspects of this extended Georgian house. Rooms are a particularly good size with all mod cons. Close to motorway and easily accessible. Ornate, split-level restaurant decorated with murals.

SYMONDS YAT WEST – Herefordshire – **503** M 28 – ✉ 18 **B3**
Ross-on-Wye *Great Britain*

London 126 m – Gloucester 23 m – Hereford 17 m – Newport 31 m
Town★ – Yat Rock (≤ ★)
S : Wye Valley★

Norton House without rest
Whitchurch ✉ HR9 6DJ – ✆ (01600) 890 046 – enquiries@norton-house.com – Fax (01600) 890 045 – closed 25-26 December
3 rm – †£ 45/50 ††£ 35/45
◆ Built of local stone, this 18C farmhouse of 15C origins boasts quaint interiors. Rooms with antique beds in patchwork quilts and flowers. Tea, cake on arrival.

TADCASTER – N. Yorks. – **502** Q 22 – **pop. 6 548** 22 **B2**
London 206 m – Harrogate 16 m – Leeds 14 m – York 11 m

Hazlewood Castle
Paradise Lane, Hazlewood, Southwest : 2 ¾ m. by A 659 off A 64 ✉ LS24 9NJ – ✆ (01937) 535 353 – info@hazlewood-castle.co.uk – Fax (01937) 530 630
12 rm – †£ 155 ††£ 195 – 9 suites
Rest ***Restaurant Anise*** – Carte £ 17/23
◆ Impressive part 13C fortified manor house in parkland. Panelled entrance hall, ornate lounges. Extensive conference facilities. Spacious rooms, individually styled. Dine in former orangery.

Aagrah
York Rd, Steeton, Northeast : 2½ m. on A 64 (westbound carriageway) ✉ LS24 8EG – ✆ (01937) 530 888 – Closed 25 December
Rest – Indian (dinner only) (booking essential) Carte £ 13/23 **s**
◆ Tasty and authentic Kashmiri specialities in a spacious, busy Indian restaurant with ornaments and friezes inspired by the subcontinent. Large menus and quality ingredients.

at Colton Northeast : 3 m. by A 659 and A 64 – ✉ Tadcaster

Ye Old Sun Inn
Main Street ✉ LS24 8EP – ✆ (01904) 744 261 – kelly.mccarthy@btconnect.com – Closed 1-21 January, 26 December and Monday
Rest – Menu £ 15 – Carte £ 17/25
◆ Homely, rustic pub with solar theme and deli serving homemade goodies. Spacious gardens and decked terrace. Classically-based, seasonal cooking with international flavours.

TALLAND BAY – Cornwall – **503** G 32 – see Looe

TANGMERE – W. Sussex – **504** R 31 – see Chichester

TANWORTH-IN-ARDEN – Warks. – **503** O 26 – see Henley-in-Arden

ENGLAND

TAPLOW – Windsor & Maidenhead – 504 R 29 — 11 C3

London 33 m – Maidenhead 2 m – Oxford 36 m – Reading 12 m

Cliveden
National Trust Gardens, parterre and River Thames,

North : 2 m. by (heated)

Berry Hill ✉ SL6 0JF – ✆ (01628) 668 561 – info@clivedenhouse.co.uk – Fax (01628) 661 837

32 rm – £ 240/600 £ 240/600 – 7 suites – £ 495/1000

Rest *Waldo's* – see restaurant listing

Rest *Terrace* – Menu £ 35/59

◆ Breathtakingly stunning 19C stately home in National Trust gardens. Ornate, sumptuous public areas, filled with antiques. Exquisitely appointed rooms the last word in luxury. View parterre and Thames in top class style from Terrace.

Taplow House

Berry Hill ✉ SL6 ODA – ✆ (01628) 670 056 – reception@taplowhouse.com – Fax (01628) 783 985

31 rm – £ 90/195 £ 110/195, £ 12.50 – 1 suite

Rest *Stroks* – (Closed Saturday lunch and Bank Holiday Mondays) Menu £ 20 (lunch) – Carte approx. £ 34

◆ Part 16C mansion with Europe's tallest tulip tree, planted by Elizabeth I. Set in mature woodland. Warm, cosy décor throughout. Plush suites and sofas. Well-equipped rooms. Intimate dining room, overlooking lawned gardens.

ENGLAND

Waldo's – at Cliveden H.

North : 2 m. by Berry Hill ✉ SL6 0JF – ✆ (01628) 668 561 – info@clivedenhouse.co.uk – Fax (01628) 661 837 – Closed Sunday and Monday

Rest – (dinner only) (booking essential) Menu £ 68

◆ Exquisitely upholstered restaurant, seamlessly weaving into the grand tapestry of Cliveden. Superbly prepared ingredients contribute to seasonal menus served with flair.

TARPORLEY – Ches. – 502 L/M 24 – pop. 2 634 — 20 A3

London 186 m – Chester 11 m – Liverpool 27 m – Shrewsbury 36 m

Portal G & C.C. Cobblers Cross Lane, ✆ (01829) 733 933 ;

Portal Premier Forest Rd, ✆ (01829) 733 884 .

The Swan

50 High St ✉ CW6 0AG – ✆ (01829) 733 838 – Fax (01829) 732 932 – Accommodation closed 25 December

16 rm – £ 71/85 £ 96/145 – **Rest** – Menu £ 12 (lunch) – Carte £ 22/33

◆ 16C former coaching inn with hanging baskets, located in pleasant village. Original beams, open fires and oak panelling adorn guest areas. Bedrooms retain period feel of inn. Informality the key to relaxed dining room.

at Cotebrook Northeast : 2½ m. on A 49 – ✉ Tarporley

Fox and Barrel

Forrest Road ✉ CW6 9DZ – ✆ (01829) 760 529 – Fax (01829) 760 192 – closed 25 December

Rest – Carte £ 20/35

◆ Wood floors, beamed ceiling and character aplenty. Busy and friendly pub offers an extensive menu of hearty traditional fare. Book early for the Monday live Jazz evenings.

at Little Budworth Northeast : 3½ m. on A 49 – ✉ Tarporley

Cabbage Hall

Forest Road ✉ CW6 9ES – ✆ (01829) 760 292 – Fax (01829) 760 292 – closed Monday

Rest – Carte £ 25/40

◆ Sleek former pub in 11 acres of land. Beautiful interior with gilded mirrors and startling copies of Picasso and Van Gogh. Impressively comprehensive range of bistro dishes.

at Bunbury South : 3 ¼ m. by A 49 – ✉ Tarporley

Dysart Arms

Bowes Gate Rd, by Bunbury Mill rd ✉ CW6 9PH – ✆ (01829) 260 183
– dysart-arms@brunningandprice.co.uk – Fax (01829) 261 286
– closed 25 and 31 December
Rest – Carte £ 18/31
◆ Characterful village pub, in the shadow of impressive Bunbury Church. Open fire, beams and lots of clutter. Interesting, original, hearty British food.

at Willington Northwest : 3 ½ m. by A 51 – ✉ Tarporley

Willington Hall

✉ CW6 0NB – ✆ (01829) 752 321 – enquiries@willingtonhall.co.uk
– Fax (01829) 752 596 – closed 25-26 December
10 rm – 🚹£ 80 🚹🚹£ 130 – **Rest** – (closed Sunday dinner) Menu £ 26 (dinner) – Carte £ 24/29
◆ Imposing 19C country house with ornate façade in mature grounds; many original features remain, including vast hall and impressive staircase. Most rooms have rural outlook. Intimate dinners served in classically proportioned surroundings.

Good food and accommodation at moderate prices?
Look for the Bib symbols:
red Bib Gourmand for food, blue Bib Hotel for hotels

ENGLAND

TARR STEPS – Somerset – 503 J 30 — 3 A2

London 191 m – Taunton 31 m – Tiverton 20 m
Tarr Steps ★★ (Clapper Bridge ★★)

Tarr Farm Inn with rm

✉ TA22 9PY – ✆ (01643) 851 507 – enquiries@tarrfarm.co.uk
– Fax (01643) 851 111 – Closed 1-9 February
9 rm – 🚹£ 90 🚹🚹£ 150 – **Rest** – Carte £ 16/38
◆ On beautiful Exmoor, overlooking ancient clapper bridge. Hugely characterful, beamed interior. Accomplished, modish menus in intimate restaurant. Bedrooms exude luxury.

TATTENHALL – Ches. – 502 L 24 – pop. 1 860 — 20 A3

London 200 m – Birmingham 71 m – Chester 10 m – Liverpool 29 m – Manchester 38 m – Stoke-on-Trent 30 m

Higher Huxley Hall

North : 2 ¼ m. on Huxley rd ✉ CH3 9BZ – ✆ (01829) 781 484
– info@huxleyhall.co.uk – Closed 25 December - 7 January
5 rm – 🚹£ 55/65 🚹🚹£ 100 – **Rest** – (by arrangement, communal dining) Menu £ 30
◆ This historic manor house, sited on a former farm, dates from 13C and is attractively furnished with antiques. Bedrooms are comfortable and well equipped. Homely, communal dining room serving local produce.

at Higher Burwardsley Southeast : 1 m. – ✉ Tattenhall

The Pheasant Inn with rm

Cheshire plain,
✉ CH3 9PF – ✆ (01829) 770 434
– info@thepheasantinn.co.uk – Fax (01829) 771 097
12 rm – 🚹£ 65 🚹🚹£ 130 – **Rest** – Carte £ 20/28
◆ Appealing part-timber pub with superb views over Cheshire Plain. Accomplished, original food on offer. Attractively stylish rooms in adjacent, converted sandstone barn.

TAUNTON – Somerset – **503** K 30 – **pop. 58 241** 3 **B3**

London 168 m – Bournemouth 69 m – Bristol 50 m – Exeter 37 m – Plymouth 78 m – Southampton 93 m – Weymouth 50 m

Paul St ✆ (01823) 336344

Taunton Vale Creech Heathfield, ✆ (01823) 412 220;

Vivary Vivary Park, ✆ (01823) 289 274;

Taunton and Pickeridge Corfe, ✆ (01823) 421 876.

Town ★ - St Mary Magdalene ★ V – Somerset County Museum ★ **AC** V **M** – St James' ★ U – Hammett St ★ V **25** – The Crescent ★ V – Bath Place ★ V **3**

Trull (Church ★), S : 2½ m. by A 38 – Hestercombe Gardens ★, N : 5 m. by A 3259 BY and minor roads to Cheddon Fitzpaine. Bishops Lydeard ★ (Church ★), NW : 6 m. – Wellington : Church ★, Wellington Monument (≤ ★★), SW : 7½ m. by A 38 – Combe Florey ★, NW : 8 m. – Gaulden Manor ★ **AC**, NW : 10 m. by A 358 and B 3227

Plan opposite

The Castle

Castle Green ✉ TA1 1NF – ✆ (01823) 272 671 – reception@the-castle-hotel.com – Fax (01823) 336 066 V **a**

44 rm – †£ 115/139 ††£ 185/265 – **Rest** – (Closed Sunday dinner) Menu £ 30/47

◆ Traditionally renowned, family owned British hotel: afternoon tea a speciality. 12C origins with Norman garden. Wisteria-clad and castellated. Individually styled rooms. Classic British cooking uses top quality West Country produce.

Meryan House

Bishop's Hull Rd, West : ¾ m. by A 38 ✉ TA1 5EG – ✆ (01823) 337 445 – meryanhousehotel@yahoo.co.uk – Fax (01823) 322 355 AZ **c**

12 rm – †£ 56/68 ††£ 85 – **Rest** – (Closed Sunday) (dinner only) (booking essential for non-residents) Menu £ 22

◆ Privately owned extended house on town outskirts. Comfortable sitting room has adjacent patio garden and small bar with jukebox. Well-kept, individually styled rooms. Intimate dining room with large inglenook.

The Willow Tree

3 Tower Lane ✉ TA1 4AR – ✆ (01823) 352 835 – closed January, August, Sunday and Monday V **c**

Rest – (dinner only) Menu £ 25/30

◆ Converted 17C town house in central location. Exposed beams and large inglenook fireplaces. Friendly service. Appealing menu of modern seasonal cooking with a classical base.

Brazz

Castle Bow ✉ TA1 1NF – ✆ (01823) 252 000 – taunton@brazz.co.uk – Fax (01823) 336 066 – Closed 25 December V **e**

Rest – Carte £ 19/28

◆ Bright and breezy bistro style eatery to rear of The Castle hotel. Large, bustling bar area. Main restaurant has large aquarium, concave ceiling and brasserie favourites.

The Sanctuary

Middle St ✉ TA1 1SJ – ✆ (01823) 257 788 – Fax (01823) 257 788 – Closed 10 days Christmas and New Year, Bank Holidays, Saturday lunch and Sunday U **a**

Rest – Carte £ 20/33

◆ Long-standing, popular eatery of exposed brick and beams tucked away down a side street. Search out charming little landscaped roof terrace. Simple and eclectic modern menus.

at West Monkton Northeast : 3½ m. by A 38 - BY – ✉ Taunton

Springfield House without rest

Walford Cross, on A 38 ✉ TA2 8QW – ✆ (01823) 412 116 – tina.ridout@btopenworld.com – Closed 21 December-2 January

5 rm – †£ 40 ††£ 65

◆ Guesthouse with annex of quite recent vintage with attractive, spacious gardens. Main building has simple breakfast room and conservatory lounge. Cottage style bedrooms.

TAUNTON

Street	Grid	No.
Bath Pl.	V	3
Billetfield	V	6
Billet St.	V	4
Birch Grove	U	7
Bishop's Hull Rd	AZ	9
Bridge St	U	12
Bridge (The)	U	10
Burton Pl.	V	13
Cann St	V	15
Cleveland St	U	16
Comeytrowe Lane	AZ	18
Corporation St	V	19
County Walk Shopping Centre	V	
Duke St	V	21
East St	V	
Fore St	V	22
Hamilton Rd	BZ	24
Hammet St	V	25
High St	V	
Hurdle Way	V	27
Ilminster Rd	BZ	28
Magdalene St	V	30
Middleway	AZ	31
North St	V	33
Obridge Viaduct	BY	34
Old Market Shopping Centre	V	
Portland St	U	36
Priory Ave	U	37
Shoreditch Rd	BZ	39
Shuttern	V	40
Silver St South	V, Z	42
Upper High St	V	43
Upper Wood St	U	44
Victoria Parkway	BYZ	45
Wellington New Rd	AZ	46
Wilton St	V	48
Winchester St	U	49
Wood St	U	51

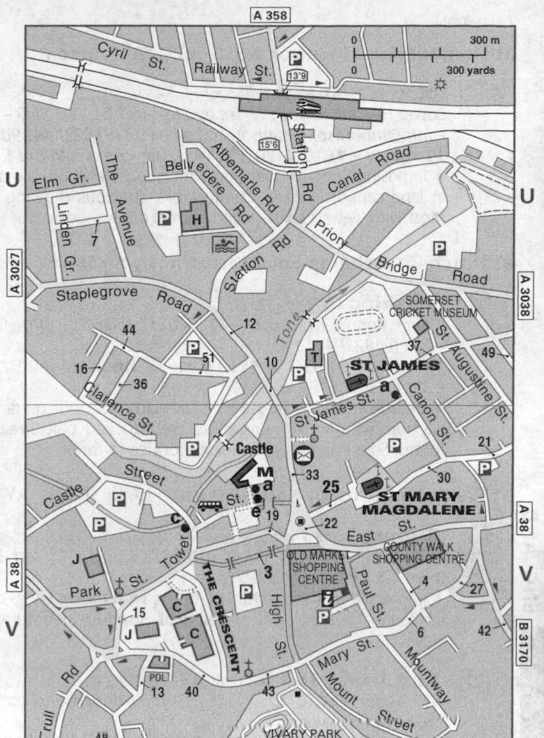

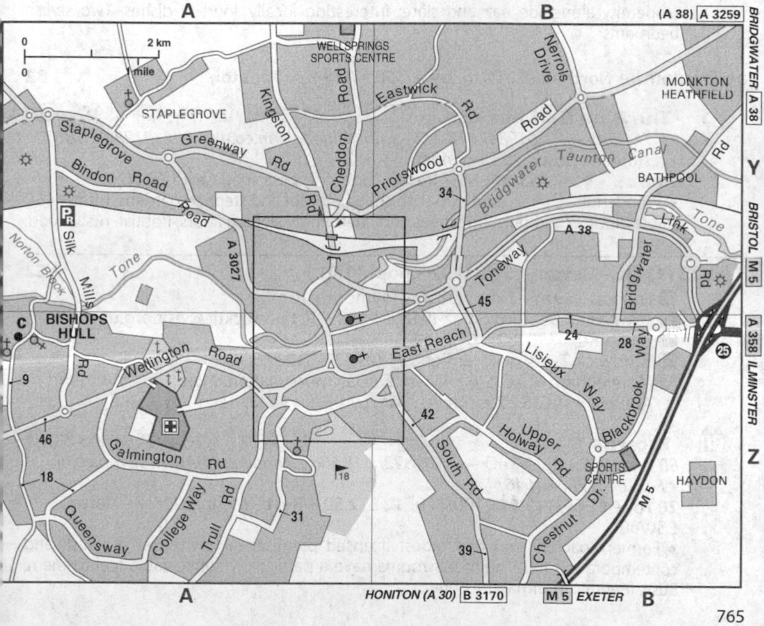

A B

(A 38) A 3259

BRIDGWATER A 38

2 km
1 mile
WELLSPRINGS SPORTS CENTRE
Nerrols Drive
MONKTON HEATHFIELD
STAPLEGROVE
Kingston Rd
Cheddon Road
Eastwick Rd
Road
Staplegrove Greenway
Taunton Canal
Y
Bindon Road
Priorswood
Bridgwater
BATHPOOL
Road
34
Rd
BRISTOL M 5
Silk Mills
Norton Brook
Tone
A 3027
A 38
Link
Tone
Toneway
Bridgwater Way
Rd
45
C
BISHOPS HULL
East Reach
24
28
A 358 ILMINSTER
25
Rd
Wellington Road
Lisieux Way
9
Blackbrook
46
42
Upper Holway Rd
Galmington Rd
South Rd
Z
18
18
SPORTS CENTRE
HAYDON
Queensway
College Way
Trull Rd
31
Chestnut Dr.
M 5
39

A
HONITON (A 30) B 3170
M 5 EXETER
B

at Henlade East : 3 ½ m. on A 358 - BZ – ✉ Taunton

Mount Somerset
Lower Henlade, South : ½ m. by Stoke Rd ✉ TA3 5NB – ☎ (01823) 442 500 – info@mountsomersethotel.co.uk – Fax (01823) 442 900
11 rm – †£ 105/120 ††£ 145/205 – **Rest** – Menu £ 28/37
◆ Imposing Regency mansion with good views of Vale of Taunton. Exotic peacocks in landscaped gardens. Comfortable, spacious drawing rooms. Elegant bedrooms, most with views. Oak panelled, formal dining room.

at Hatch Beauchamp Southeast : 6 m. by A 358 - BZ – ✉ Taunton

Farthings
Village Road ✉ TA3 6SG – ☎ (01823) 480 664 – info@farthingshotel.co.uk – Fax (01823) 481 118
11 rm – †£ 65/175 ††£ 130/175 – **Rest** – Menu £ 28/32 – Carte dinner £ 31/44
◆ Georgian country house with pleasant, spacious gardens in pretty village. Personally run, with small lounge and well-stocked bar. Sizeable, individually decorated rooms. Smart dining room; local produce to fore.

at West Bagborough Northwest : 10 ½ m. by A 358 - AY – ✉ Taunton

Tilbury Farm without rest — Vale of Taunton,
East : ¾ m. ✉ TA4 3DY – ☎ (01823) 432 391 – Closed 26-30 December
3 rm – †£ 40 ††£ 60/75
◆ Impressively characterful 18C house with terrific views of Vale of Taunton. Welcoming lounge boasts log fire. Well-kept, spacious bedrooms all with beams and good views.

The Rising Sun Inn with rm
✉ TA4 3EF – ☎ (01823) 432 575 – jon@brinkmancatering.co.uk – closed Monday except Bank Holidays
2 rm – †£ 55 ††£ 85 – **Rest** – (closed Sunday dinner) Carte £ 15/21
◆ 16C pub, rebuilt after a fire, seemingly tumbling off the edge of the Quantocks! Modernity alongside oak and slate; interesting locally sourced dishes. Two stylish bedrooms.

at Triscombe Northwest : 11 m. by A 358 - AY – ✉ Taunton 3 **B2**

The Blue Ball Inn with rm — rm,
✉ TA4 3HE – ☎ (01984) 618 242 – info@blueballinn.co.uk – Fax (01984) 618 371 – restaurant closed 25 December
2 rm – †£ 40/53 ††£ 85 – **Rest** – (booking essential) Carte £ 23/25
◆ Wonderfully characterful pub with thatched roof and stepped gardens: former 15C stable block. Wood burning stoves and charmingly sloping floors. Robust, rustic food.

TAVISTOCK – Devon – 503 H 32 – pop. 11 018 2 **C2**

London 239 m – Exeter 38 m – Plymouth 16 m
Town Hall, Bedford Sq ☎ (01822) 612938, tavistocktic@visit.org.uk
Down Rd, ☎ (01822) 612 344 ;
Hurdwick Tavistock Hamlets, ☎ (01822) 612 746 .
Morwellham★ **AC**, SW : 4 ½ m. E : Dartmoor National Park★★ – Buckland Abbey★★ **AC**, S : 7 m. by A 386 – Lydford★★, N : 8 ½ m. by A 386

Browns
80 West St ✉ PL19 8AQ – ☎ (01822) 618 686 – enquiries@brownsdevon.co.uk – Fax (01822) 618 646
20 rm – †£ 69/119 ††£ 100/129, £12.50 – **Rest** – Menu £ 22/37 – Carte £ 30/40
◆ Former coaching inn and oldest licensed premises in town; now a stylish and contemporary hotel. The mews rooms have a particularly comfortable feel to them. Busy, friendly, informal brasserie.

ENGLAND

April Cottage
12 Mount Tavy Rd ✉ PL19 9JB – ✆ (01822) 613 280 – aprilcottage12@hotmail.co.uk
3 rm – £ 45/55 £ 60/64 – **Rest** – Menu £ 17 **s**
◆ Compact but homely Victorian cottage. Meals taken in rear conservatory overlooking River Tavy. Curios adorn small lounge. Carefully furnished rooms with varnished pine.

at Gulworthy West : 3 m. on A 390 – ✉ **Tavistock**

The Horn of Plenty with rm — Tamar Valley and Bodmin Moor,
Northwest : 1 m. by Chipshop rd ✉ PL19 8JD – ✆ (01822) 832 528 – enquiries@thehornofplenty.co.uk – Fax (01822) 834 390 – Closed 24-26 December
10 rm – £ 150 £ 250 – **Rest** – Menu £ 27/45
◆ Stylish, contemporary restaurant featuring local artwork, in enchanting, creeper-clad country house. Classic cooking uses local ingredients. Polite service. Modern country house style bedrooms; those in annex have terrace.

at Quither Northwest : 5 ¾ m. by Chillaton rd on Quither rd – ✉ **Tavistock** 2 **C2**

Quither Mill
✉ PL19 0PZ – ✆ (01822) 860 160 – quither.mill@virgin.net – Fax (01822) 860 160 – closed Christmas-New Year
3 rm – £ 55 £ 80 – **Rest** – (communal dining) Menu £ 25
◆ 18C converted water mill in peaceful rural location. Characterful stone appearance. Fine antiques. Utter peacefulness pervades beamed, country style rooms. Communal dining room employing fine china and silver.

at Milton Abbot Northwest : 6 m. on B 3362 – ✉ **Tavistock**

Hotel Endsleigh
Southwest : 1 m. ✉ PL19 0PQ – ✆ (01822) 870 000 – mail@hotelendsleigh.com – Fax (01822) 870 578 – Closed 7-20 January
13 rm – £ 200 £ 300/400 – 3 suites – **Rest** – Menu £ 30/39 **s**
◆ Painstakingly restored Regency lodge in magnificent Devonian gardens and grounds. Stylish lounge and refined bedrooms are imbued with an engaging, understated elegance. Interesting, classically based dishes served in two minimalist dining rooms.

at Chillaton Northwest : 6 ¼ m. by Chillaton rd – ✉ **Tavistock**

Tor Cottage without rest — (heated)
Southwest : ¼ m. by Tavistock rd, turning right at bridle path sign, down unmarked track for ½ m. ✉ PL16 0JE – ✆ (01822) 860 248 – info@torcottage.co.uk – Fax (01822) 860 126 – Closed 2 weeks Christmas and New Year
5 rm – £ 94 £ 140
◆ Lovely cottage and peaceful gardens in 18 hillside acres. Terrace or conservatory breakfast. Individual rooms, most spread around garden, with tremendous attention to detail.

TEFFONT – Wilts. – see Salisbury

TEIGNMOUTH – Devon – **503** J 32 – **pop. 14 799** 2 **D2**

London 216 m – Exeter 16 m – Torquay 8 m
The Den, Sea Front ✆ (01626) 215666

Britannia House without rest
26 Teign St ✉ TQ14 8EG – ✆ (01626) 770 051 – gillettbritannia@aol.com – Fax (01626) 879 903 – Closed January
3 rm – £ 50/60 £ 70/80
◆ Intimate 17C Grade II listed townhouse enhanced by many original features. Tuck into an organic breakfast and relax in walled garden or cosy upstairs lounge. Homely rooms.

Thomas Luny House without rest
Teign St, follow signs for the Quays, off the A 381 ✉ TQ14 8EG – ✆ (01626) 772976 – alisonandjohn@thomas-luny-house.co.uk
4 rm – †£65 ††£80/92
◆ Personally run Georgian house with sheltered walled garden. Smart breakfast room with antique pieces. Well furnished drawing room. Stylish, individually appointed bedrooms.

TELFORD – Wrekin – 502 M 25 – pop. 138 241 *Great Britain* 18 B2

London 152 m – Birmingham 33 m – Shrewsbury 12 m – Stoke-on-Trent 29 m
Management Suite, The Telford Centre ✆ (01952) 238008
Telford Sutton Heights Great Hay, ✆ (01952) 429977 ;
Wrekin Wellington, ✆ (01952) 244032 ;
The Shropshire Muxton Muxton Grange, ✆ (01952) 677866 .
Ironbridge Gorge Museum★★ AC (The Iron Bridge★★, Coalport China Museum★★, Blists Hill Open Air Museum★★, Museum of the River and Visitor Centre★) S : 5 m. by B 4373. Weston Park★★ AC, E : 7 m. by A 5

at Norton South : 7 m. on A 442 – ✉ Shifnal

Hundred House with rm
Bridgnorth Rd ✉ TF11 9EE – ✆ (01952) 730353 – reservations@hundredhouse.co.uk – Fax (01952) 730355 – accommodation closed 25-26 December
10 rm – †£59 ††£135 – **Rest** – Carte £22/35
◆ Characterful, family run redbrick inn with herb garden. Carefully sourced dishes, robust and original. Sizable rooms in 19C style, some with canopied beds and swings.

at Bratton Northwest : 6 ¾ m. by A 442 and B 5063 (following signs for Admaston) off the B 4394 – ✉ Telford

Dovecote Grange without rest
Bratton Rd ✉ TF5 0BT – ✆ (01952) 243739 – mandy@dovecotegrange.co.uk – Fax (01952) 243739
5 rm – †£39/55 ††£59/70
◆ Attractive guesthouse, garden and terrace enjoying views over the local fields. Combined lounge and breakfast area with modern leather furniture. Large, comfy, modish rooms.

Look out for red symbols, indicating particularly pleasant establishments.

TEMPLE SOWERBY – Cumbria – 502 M 20 – see Penrith

TENBURY WELLS – Worcs. – 503 M 27 – pop. 3 316 18 B2

London 144 m – Birmingham 36 m – Hereford 20 m – Shrewsbury 37 m – Worcester 28 m

Cadmore Lodge
St Michaels, Southwest : 2 ¾ m. by A 4112 ✉ WR15 8TQ – ✆ (01584) 810044 – reception.cadmore@cadmorelodge.com – Fax (01584) 810044
15 rm – †£65 ††£90 – **Rest** – (bar lunch only on Monday) Menu £15/23 – Carte £15/24
◆ Family run hotel in pleasant location. Lakeside setting. Plenty of outdoor activities, including golf and fishing. Well-planned rooms: some larger ones have antique furniture. Restaurant overlooks the lake.

ENGLAND

TENTERDEN – Kent – 504 W 30 – pop. 6 977 9 C2

London 57 m – Folkestone 26 m – Hastings 21 m – Maidstone 19 m
Town Hall, High St ✆ (01580) 763572 (summer only)

Little Silver Country H.

Ashford Rd, St Michaels, North : 2 m. on A 28 ✉ TN30 6SP – ✆ (01233) 850321 – enquiries@little-silver.co.uk – Fax (01233) 850647

16 rm – †£ 60 ††£ 95/135 – **Rest** – (light lunch) Carte £ 19/28

◆ Extended mock-Tudor country house hotel with smart gardens. Large function room ideal for weddings. Cosy conservatory breakfast room. Clean and spacious bedrooms. Dining room with table lamps, candelabra and Kentish watercolours.

TETBURY – Glos. – 503 N 29 – pop. 5 250 *Great Britain* 4 C1

London 113 m – Bristol 27 m – Gloucester 19 m – Swindon 24 m
33 Church St ✆ (01666) 503552, tourism@tetbury.com
Westonbirt, ✆ (01666) 880242 .
Westonbirt Arboretum★ AC, SW : 2½ m. by A 433

Calcot Manor

(heated)

Calcot, West : 3½ m. on A 4135 ✉ GL8 8YJ – ✆ (01666) 890391 – reception@calcotmanor.co.uk – Fax (01666) 890394

34 rm – †£ 180 ††£ 205/245 – 1 suite

Rest *The Gumstool Inn* – see restaurant listing

Rest *Conservatory* – (booking essential) Menu £ 23 (lunch) – Carte £ 33/40

◆ Impressive Cotswold farmhouse, gardens and meadows with converted ancient barns and stables. Superb spa. Variety of luxuriously appointed rooms with contemporary flourishes. Stylish Conservatory serves interesting modern dishes.

Snooty Fox

Market Pl ✉ GL8 8DD – ✆ (01666) 502436 – res@snooty-fox.co.uk – Fax (01666) 503479

12 rm – †£ 60/149 ††£ 70/210 – **Rest** – Carte £ 18/30

◆ Stone built former 17C wool factory, with extensions, opposite Tudor market place. Characterful bar with inglenook. Individualistic rooms with superior drapes and fabrics. Cosy wood panelled bistro with all-day menu.

The Trouble House

Cirencester Rd, Northeast : 2 m. on A 433 ✉ GL8 8SG – ✆ (01666) 502206 – enquiries@troublehouse.co.uk – Closed Christmas-New Year, Sunday dinner and Monday

Rest – Carte £ 28/37

◆ A country haven of low-beamed bars, open fires and chunky furniture, in a warm, cosy atmosphere. Robust, hearty classics are cooked with care using fine local ingredients.

The Gumstool Inn – at Calcot Manor H.

Calcot, West : 3½ m. on A 4135 ✉ GL8 8YJ – ✆ (01666) 890391 – reception@calcotmanor.co.uk – Fax (01666) 890394

Rest – (booking essential) Carte £ 20/50

◆ Cheerful, flagstoned pub incorporated into Calcot Manor. Low ceiling creates atmosphere. Large menus with daily blackboard specials. Classic pub dishes.

at Willesley Southwest : 4 m. on A 433 – ✉ Tetbury

Beaufort House without rest

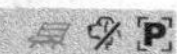

✉ GL8 8QU – ✆ (01666) 880444 – beauforthouseuk@aol.com

4 rm – †£ 75 ††£ 90

◆ Part 17C former inn and staging post with an attractive and secluded rear garden, overlooked by comfortable lounge and little breakfast room. Elegantly refurbished bedrooms.

ENGLAND

TETSWORTH – Oxon – **504** Q/R 28 – **pop. 709** – ✉ **Thame** 11 **C2**

London 47 m – Aylesbury 15 m – Oxford 12 m

The Swan

High St ✉ OX9 7AB – ✆ (01844) 281 182 – restaurant@theswan.co.uk – Closed Sunday dinner

Rest – (booking essential) Carte £ 30/40

◆ Creeper clad former coaching inn which doubles as antiques centre. Exposed timbers, informal atmosphere. Modern cooking with lots of choice and a touch of sophistication.

TEWKESBURY – **Glos.** – **503** N 28 – **pop. 9 978** *Great Britain* 4 **C1**

London 108 m – Birmingham 39 m – Gloucester 11 m

64 Barton St ✆ (01684) 295027

Tewkesbury Park Hotel Lincoln Green Lane, ✆ (01684) 295 405 .

Town★ – Abbey★★ (Nave★★, vault★)

St Mary's, Deerhurst★, SW : 4 m. by A 38 and B 4213

Alstone Fields Farm without rest

Stow Rd, Teddington Hands, East : 5 m. by A 438 and A 46 on B 4077 ✉ GL20 8NG – ✆ (01242) 620 592 – janeandrobin@yahoo.co.uk – Closed 25 December

6 rm – †£ 45 ††£ 70

◆ Farmhouse in well-tended garden. Communal breakfast room with view; local ingredients and fruit from the garden. Bright, clean, chintzy rooms, two on the ground floor.

at Corse Lawn Southwest : 6 m. by A 38 and A 438 on B 4211 – ✉ Gloucester

Corse Lawn House

✉ GL19 4LZ – ✆ (01452) 780 771 – enquiries@corselawn.com – Fax (01452) 780 840 – Closed 24-26 December

17 rm – †£ 93 ††£ 150 – 2 suites

Rest ***The Restaurant*** – see restaurant listing

Rest ***Bistro*** – Menu £ 24/31 **s** – Carte £ 28/38 **s**

◆ Elegant Queen Anne Grade II listed house, set back from village green and fronted by former "coach wash". Two comfortable lounges and classic country house style rooms. Informal brasserie style eatery in atmospheric bar.

The Restaurant – at Corse Lawn House H.

✉ GL19 4LZ – ✆ (01452) 780 771 – Fax (01452) 780 840 – Closed 24-26 December

Rest – Menu £ 24/31 **s** – Carte £ 28/38 **s**

◆ Formal restaurant with period décor and framed prints, nicely set overlooking rear garden. Extensive à la carte and set menu. Classic style of dishes; quality wine list.

THAXTED – Essex – **504** V 28 – **pop. 2 066** 13 **C2**

London 44 m – Cambridge 24 m – Colchester 31 m – Chelmsford 20 m

Crossways without rest

32 Town St ✉ CM6 2LA – ✆ (01371) 830 348 – info@crosswaysthaxted.co.uk

3 rm – †£ 42 ††£ 63

◆ 16C house in picturesque, largely timbered village. Breakfast room is tea room during day. Small lounge with fireplace and beams. Rooms in keeping with age of property.

THIRSK – N. Yorks. – **502** P 21 – **pop. 9 099** 22 **B1**

London 227 m – Leeds 37 m – Middlesbrough 24 m – York 24 m

49 Market Pl ✆ (0871) 7161924

Thornton-Le-Street, ✆ (01845) 522 170 .

Golden Fleece

42 Market Pl ✉ YO7 1LL – ✆ (01845) 523 108 – reservations@goldenfleecehotel.com – Fax (01845) 523 996

23 rm – †£ 65/75 ††£ 100 – **Rest** – (bar lunch Monday-Saturday) Carte approx. £ 19 **s**

◆ Sizeable Grade II listed 16C coaching inn located in centre of market town. Dick Turpin was a regular visitor. Spacious, comfortable lounge. Well-kept, inviting rooms. Yorkshire flavours are a staple of restaurant.

ENGLAND

Spital Hill
York Rd, Southeast : 1 ¾ m. on A 19, entrance between 2 white posts ✉ YO7 3AE – ✆ (01845) 522 273 – spitalhill@spitalhill.entadssl.com – Fax (01845) 524 970
3 rm – †£ 59/65 ††£ 98/102 – **Rest** – (by arrangement, communal dining) Menu £ 30
◆ Expansive early Victorian house surrounded by nearly two acres of secluded gardens. Fully tiled entrance hall and comfortable sitting room. Spacious rooms, warmly furnished. Communal dining at mealtimes.

Laburnum House without rest
31 Topcliffe Rd, Southwest : ¾ m. by A 61 on Wetherby rd ✉ YO7 1RX – ✆ (01845) 524 120 – mid March-October
3 rm – ††£ 60
◆ Modern house on the road into this busy market town, famous for its connection with vet and author James Herriot. Spacious, well-maintained bedrooms at affordable rates.

at Topcliffe Southwest : 4 ½ m. by A 168 – ✉ Thirsk

Angel Inn
Long St ✉ YO7 3RW – ✆ (01845) 577 237 – res@angelinn.co.uk – Fax (01845) 578 000 – Accommodation closed 25-26 December
15 rm – †£ 55/65 ††£ 80 – **Rest** – Carte £ 17/27
◆ Enlarged hostelry dating back to early 17C in tiny village. Spacious lounge and characterful bar. Popular with business travellers. Sizeable bedrooms have pine furniture. Bright décor enlivens dining room.

at Asenby Southwest : 5 ¼ m. by A 168 – ✉ Thirsk

Crab Manor
Dishforth Rd ✉ YO7 3QL – ✆ (01845) 577 286 – info@crabandlobster.co.uk – Fax (01845) 577 109
14 rm – †£ 100 ††£ 150 – 2 suites
Rest *Crab and Lobster* – see restaurant listing
◆ Part Georgian manor filled with quality objects and Victoriana. Highly individual bedrooms, themed around world famous hotels. Some rooms have outdoor hot tubs.

Crab and Lobster
Dishforth Rd ✉ YO7 3QL – ✆ (01845) 577 286 – Fax (01845) 577 109
Rest – Seafood Menu £ 15 (lunch) – Carte £ 20/35
◆ Atmospheric and individual eating place filled with memorabilia. Choose the informal bar or formal Pavilion restaurant. Seafood oriented menus with blackboard specials.

THORNBURY – South Glos. – 503 M 29 – pop. 11 969 – ✉ Bristol 4 C1

London 128 m – Bristol 12 m – Gloucester 23 m – Swindon 43 m

Thornbury Castle
Castle St ✉ BS35 1HH – ✆ (01454) 281 182 – info@thornburycastle.co.uk – Fax (01454) 416 188
22 rm – †£ 100/155 ††£ 295 – 3 suites – **Rest** – Menu £ 25/43
◆ 16C castle built by Henry VIII with gardens and vineyard. Two lounges boast plenty of antiques. Rooms of stately comfort; several bathrooms resplendent in marble. Restaurant exudes formal aura.

Red = Pleasant. Look for the red X and symbols.

THORNHAM MAGNA – Suffolk – 504 X 27 – ✉ Eye 15 C2

London 96 m – Cambridge 47 m – Ipswich 20 m – Norwich 30 m

Thornham Hall

✉ *IP23 8HA – ✆ (01379) 783 314 – hallrestaurant@aol.com – Fax (01379) 788 347*

3 rm – †£ 55 ††£ 100 – **Rest** – (by arrangement, communal dining) Menu £ 15/18 – Carte £ 15/22

◆ 20C incarnation of former Tudor, Georgian and Victorian homes. House party atmosphere. Lovely paintings throughout. Comfortable, welcoming rooms. Dining room of character in converted coach house.

at Yaxley West : 2 m. on A 140 – ✉ Eye

The Bull Auberge with rm

Ipswich Rd ✉ IP23 8BZ – ✆ (01379) 783 604 – deestenhouse@fsmail.net – Fax (01379) 788 486 – Closed Saturday lunch, Sunday and Monday

4 rm – †£ 80/120 ††£ 80/120 – **Rest** – (dinner only) Menu £ 23 (dinner) – Carte £ 23/35

◆ 15C inn by busy road; rustic origins enhanced by brick walls, beams and open fire. Original, well presented, modern menus prepared with care. Stylish, well appointed rooms.

THORNTON – Lancs. – 502 K 22 – see Blackpool

THORNTON HOUGH – Mersey. – 502 – ✉ Wirral 20 A3

London 215 m – Birkenhead 12 m – Chester 17 m – Liverpool 12 m

Thornton Hall

on B 5136 ✉ CH63 1JF – ✆ (0151) 336 3938 – reservations@thorntonhallhotel.com – Fax (0151) 336 7864

62 rm – †£ 119 ††£ 119, £13.50 – 1 suite

Rest *The Italian Room* – (bar lunch Saturday) Menu £ 30 (dinner) – Carte £ 26/33

◆ Family owned, extended manor house with lawned gardens in rural location. Atmospheric wood panelled lounges with heavy drapes. Excellent leisure club. Spacious bedrooms. Rich, warmly decorated dining room with chandelier.

THORPE LANGTON – Leics. – see Market Harborough

THORPE MARKET – Norfolk – 504 X 25 – ✉ North Walsham 15 D1

London 130 m – Norwich 21 m

Elderton Lodge

Gunton Park, South : 1 m. on A 149 ✉ NR11 8TZ – ✆ (01263) 833 547 – enquiries@eldertonlodge.co.uk – Fax (01263) 834 673

11 rm – †£ 65 ††£ 120 – **Rest** – Menu £ 17 (lunch) – Carte dinner £ 21/31

◆ Late 18C former shooting lodge on large estate and deer park. Tranquil air. Favoured retreat of Lillie Langtry. Modern bedrooms are individually styled and comfortable. Local ingredients used widely in restaurant; particularly good value lunches.

THRELKELD – Cumbria – 502 K 20 – see Keswick

THUNDER BRIDGE – W. Yorks. – see Huddersfield

THUNDERSLEY – Essex – 504 V 29 – see Rayleigh

THURSFORD GREEN – Norfolk 15 C1

London 120 m – Fakenham 7 m – Norwich 29 m

Holly Lodge

The Street ✉ NR21 0AS – ✆ (01328) 878 465 – info@hollylodgeguesthouse.co.uk – Closed January

3 rm – †£ 60/70 ††£ 100/110 – **Rest** – Menu £ 18

◆ Stylishly furnished 18C house set in delightful garden. Welcome includes Pimms by the pond or afternoon tea. Excellent breakfast. Well appointed bedrooms in converted stables. Home-cooked evening meals.

THWING – East Riding 23 D2

London 228 m – Bridlington 10 m – York 16 m

The Falling Stone

Main St ✉ YO25 3DS – ✆ (01262) 470 403 – Closed Monday-Tuesday

Rest – (dinner only and lunch Saturday-Sunday) Carte £ 18/30

◆ A relaxed local, typified by owners' friendly mastif. Snug rooms with low-level sofas. Fine selection of local beers. Rustic dining room specialises in classical French fare.

TICEHURST – E. Sussex – 504 V 30 – pop. 3 118 – ✉ Wadhurst 8 B2

London 49 m – Brighton 44 m – Folkestone 38 m – Hastings 15 m – Maidstone 24 m

36 Dale Hill, ✆ (01580) 200 112 .

King John's Lodge

(heated)

Sheepstreet Lane, Etchingham, South : 2 m. by Church St ✉ TN19 7AZ – ✆ (01580) 819 232 – kingjohnslodge@aol.com – Fax (01580) 819 562 – Closed Christmas-New Year

4 rm – †£ 60 ††£ 90 – **Rest** – (by arrangement, communal dining) Menu £ 29

◆ Part Tudor hunting lodge with Jacobean additions and stunning gardens. King John II imprisoned here in 1350. Cosy sitting rooms with log fire. Cottagey bedrooms. Communal dining room exudes great rustic charm.

TITLEY – Herefordshire – 503 L 27 – see Kington

TIVERTON – Devon – 503 J 31 – pop. 16 772 2 D2

London 191 m – Bristol 64 m – Exeter 15 m – Plymouth 63 m

Hornhill without rest

Exeter Hill, East : ½ m. by A 396 and Butterleigh rd ✉ EX16 4PL – ✆ (01884) 253 352 – hornhill@tinyworld.co.uk – Fax (01884) 253 352

3 rm – †£ 38 ††£ 60

◆ Georgian house on hilltop boasting pleasant views of the Exe Valley. Well-furnished drawing room with real fire. Attractively styled bedrooms with antiques.

TODMORDEN – W. Yorks. – 502 N 22 22 A2

London 217 m – Burnley 10 m – Leeds 35 m – Manchester 22 m

The Old Hall

Hall St, off A 6033 ✉ OL14 7AD – ✆ (01706) 815 998 – Fax (01706) 810 669 – Closed first week January, Sunday dinner, Monday and Tuesday following Bank Holidays

Rest – (dinner only and Sunday lunch) Carte £ 24/29

◆ Impressive example of an Elizabethan manor house. Three rooms in which to dine: one boasts a vast fireplace and period grandeur. Sound cooking with global twists.

TOOT BALDON – Oxon. – see Oxford

TOPCLIFFE – N. Yorks. – 502 P 21 – see Thirsk

ENGLAND

TOPSHAM – Devon – **503** J 31 – ⊠ Exeter 2 **D2**

The Galley with rm
41 Fore St ⊠ EX3 0HU – ✆ (01392) 876 078 – fish@galleyrestaurant.co.uk – Fax (01392) 876 333 – Closed Christmas-New Year, Sunday and Monday
4 rm – †£ 95 ††£ 150/200 – **Rest** – Seafood Menu £ 29 – Carte £ 36/40
◆ Idiosyncratic and gloriously eccentric, every nook and cranny filled with bric-a-brac or foody paraphernalia. Original, tasty, locally sourced piscine dishes. Comfy bedrooms.

TORQUAY – Torbay – **503** J 32 – **pop. 62 968** 2 **C2**

London 223 m – Exeter 23 m – Plymouth 32 m
Vaughan Parade ✆ (0906) 6801268, torquay.tic@torbay.gov.uk
St Marychurch Petitor Rd, ✆ (01803) 327 471 .
Torbay★ – Kent's Cavern★ **AC** CX **A**
Paignton Zoo★★ **AC**, SE : 3 m. by A 3022 - Cockington★, W : 1 m. AX

The Imperial ← Torbay, (heated) rm, rest,
Park Hill Rd ⊠ TQ1 2DG – ✆ (01803) 294 301 – cg.iman@paramount-hotels.co.uk – Fax (01803) 298 293 CZ **a**
135 rm – †£ 192 ††£ 204 – 17 suites
Rest *Regatta* – (dinner only) Menu £ 30 – Carte £ 30/34
◆ Landmark hotel's super clifftop position is part of Torquay skyline. Palm Court lounge has classic style. Excellent leisure facilities. Rooms provide stunning bay views. Regatta's style emulates cruise liner luxury.

The Palace (heated)
Babbacombe Rd ⊠ TQ1 3TG – ✆ (01803) 200 200 – info@palacetorquay.co.uk – Fax (01803) 299 899 CX **u**
135 rm – †£ 69/94 ††£ 168 – 6 suites – **Rest** – (dinner only) Menu £ 27 – Carte £ 27/39 **s**
◆ Large, traditional hotel in 25 acres of gardens with sub-tropical woodland and charming terraces. Well-furnished lounge. Excellent leisure facilities. Comfortable rooms. Spacious restaurant exudes air of fine dining.

The Osborne ← (heated)
Hesketh Crescent, Meadfoot ⊠ TQ1 2LL – ✆ (01803) 213 311 – enq@osborne-torquay.co.uk – Fax (01803) 296 788 CX **n**
32 rm – †£ 65/110 ††£ 130/230
Rest *Langtry's* – (dinner only and Sunday lunch) Menu £ 27 **s** – Carte £ 30/39 **s**
Rest *The Brasserie* – Carte £ 17/25 **s**
◆ Smart hotel situated within elegant Regency crescent. Charming terrace and garden with views over Torbay. Well-appointed rooms: those facing sea have telescope and balcony. Langtry's has classic deep green décor. Informal Brasserie with terrace.

Corbyn Head ←
Seafront ⊠ TQ2 6RH – ✆ (01803) 213 611 – info@corbynhead.com – Fax (01803) 296 152 BX **a**
45 rm – †£ 30/110 ††£ 60/172
Rest *Orchid* – see restaurant listing
Rest *Harbour View* – (booking essential at lunch) Menu £ 19/25
◆ Boasts sea views across Torbay. Pleasant, enthusiastic staff. Very large, comfy sitting room and cosy bar. Bright, airy bedrooms, prettily created from a pastel palette. A friendly atmosphere pervades the main Harbour View dining room.

Marstan without rest (heated)
Meadfoot Sea Rd ⊠ TQ1 2LQ – ✆ (01803) 292 837 – enquiries@marstanhotel.co.uk – Fax (01803) 299 202 – Closed January CX **a**
9 rm – †£ 55/90 ††£ 120/130
◆ Substantial 19C house in quiet area; given a 21C edge with hot tub, sun deck and pool. Opulent interior with gold coloured furniture and antiques. Room décor of high standard.

ENGLAND

Colindale

20 Rathmore Rd, Chelston ✉ TQ2 6NY – ☎ (01803) 293 947 – rathmore@blueyonder.co.uk – Closed 1 week Christmas BZ **a**

8 rm – £ 37/47 £ 68/70 – **Rest** – (by arrangement) Menu £ 18

◆ Yellow hued 19C terraced house with pretty front garden. Particularly attractive sitting room with deep sofas and books. Welsh dresser in breakfast room. Immaculate bedrooms. Homecooked dishes have a French accent.

Cranborne House without rest

58 Belgrave Rd ✉ TQ2 5HY – ☎ (01803) 298 046 – info@cranbornehotel.co.uk BY **i**

10 rm – £ 40/60 £ 80/90

◆ Victorian house close to shops and seafront. Light, airy, pastel hued dining room; rear 'clubby' bar dotted with Victoriana. Tasteful rooms boast bathrobes.

Kingston House without rest

75 Avenue Rd ✉ TQ2 5LL – ☎ (01803) 212 760 – stay@kingstonhousehotel.co.uk – Fax (01803) 201 425 – Closed 25-26 December BY **n**

5 rm – £ 64/68 £ 64/68

◆ Sunny yellow Victorian house enhanced by vivid summer floral displays; run by friendly Italian husband and wife. Convivial sitting room; bedrooms of individual character.

Fairmount House

Herbert Rd, Chelston ✉ TQ2 6RW – ☎ (01803) 605 446 – stay@fairmounthousehotel.co.uk – Fax (01803) 605 446 AX **a**

8 rm – £ 26/33 £ 58/76 – **Rest** – (dinner only) Menu £ 15 **s**

◆ Yellow-hued Victorian house above picturesque Cockington Valley. Small bar in conservatory. Spotless, chintz bedrooms: two have doors leading onto secluded rear garden. Wide ranging menu.

The Orchid – at Corbyn Head H.

Seafront ✉ TQ2 6RH – ☎ (01803) 296 366 – dine@orchidrestaurant.net – Closed Sunday, Monday and Tuesday lunch BX **a**

Rest – Menu £ 26/38

◆ On first floor of hotel; benefits from plenty of windows making most of sea view. Immaculate linen cover. Elaborate, modern dishes using top quality ingredients.

The Room in the Elephant

3-4 Beacon Terrace ✉ TQ1 2BH – ☎ (01803) 200 044 – info@elephantrestaurant.co.uk – Fax (01803) 202 717 – Closed first 2 weeks January, Sunday and Monday CZ **e**

Rest – (dinner only) Menu £ 40/50 **s**

Spec. Scallops with peanut dusted veal sweetbreads and almond milk foam. John Dory on parsnip purée with a verjus and spring onion butter. Sweet Cicely and star anise panna cotta, mandarin and carrot sorbet.

◆ Overlooking the harbour, with bohemian style bar for pre-dinner drinks. Refined, confident cooking makes use of quality local produce; classically based dishes; modern touches.

The Brasserie

Ground Floor, 3-4 Beacon Terrace ✉ TQ1 2BH – ☎ (01803) 200 044 – info@elephantrestaurant.co.uk – Fax (01803) 202 717 – Closed 2 weeks January, Sunday dinner and Monday CZ **e**

Rest – Menu £ 18/20 **s** – Carte £ 23/32 **s**

◆ Smart split level restaurant with slight colonial feel, on ground floor of Victorian property. Large choice of classic brasserie dishes made using local produce. Polite service.

Number 7

Beacon Terrace ✉ TQ1 2BH – ☎ (01803) 295 055 – enquiries@no7-fish.com – Closed 2 weeks Christmas-New Year, first 2 weeks February, first week November, Tuesday lunch, Sunday and Monday in winter CZ **e**

Rest – Seafood Carte £ 24/33

◆ On harbour front in centre of town: modest, friendly, family run restaurant specialising in simply prepared fresh fish, mostly from Brixham. Fishing themes enhance ambience.

ENGLAND

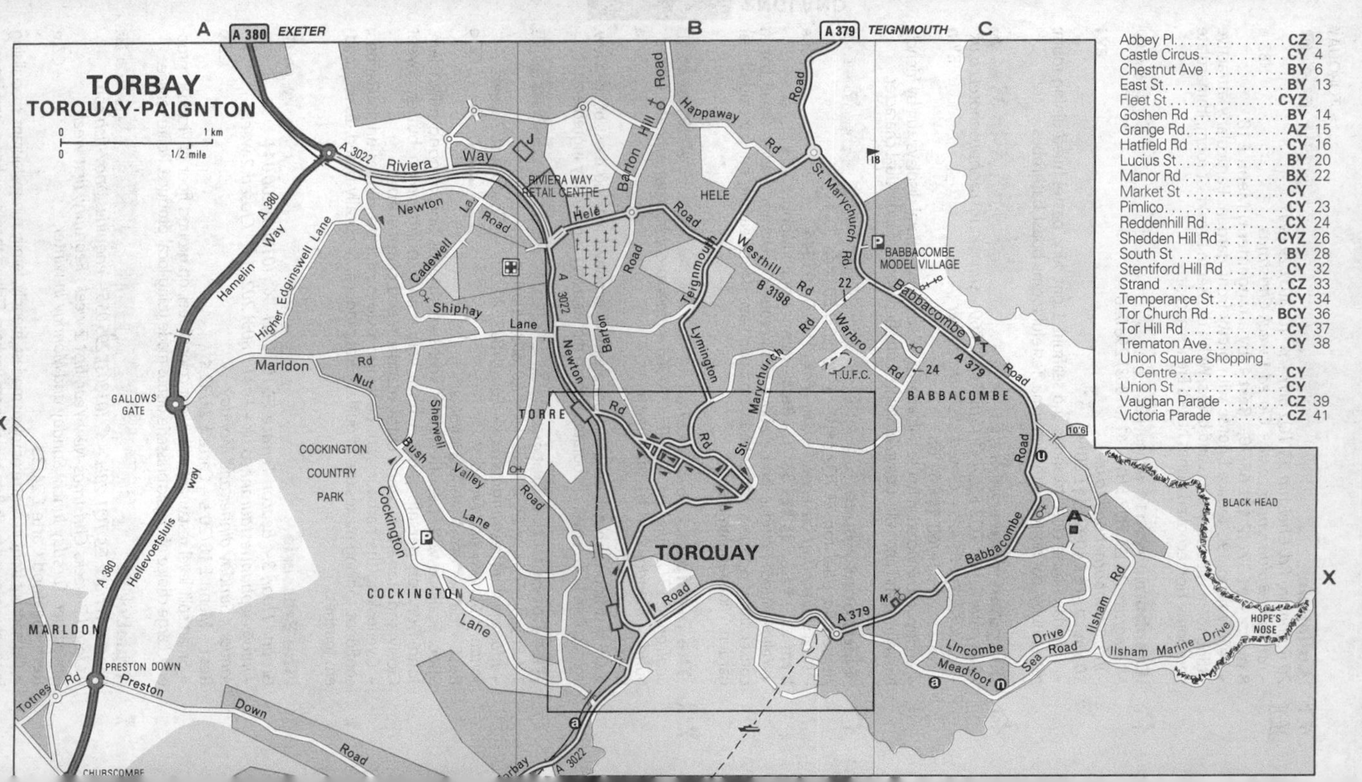
TORBAY
TORQUAY-PAIGNTON
0 1 km
0 1/2 mile
A
B
C
X
X
A 380 EXETER
A 379 TEIGNMOUTH
A 3022
Riviera
Way
A 380
Hamelin
Way
Higher Edginswell Lane
Newton
La
Road
Cadewell
Shiphay
Lane
RIVIERA WAY RETAIL CENTRE
Hele
Road
Barton
Hill
Road
Happaway
Rd
HELE
Road
Teignmouth
Westhill
B 3198
Rd
St. Marychurch
Rd.
BABBACOMBE MODEL VILLAGE
Babbacombe
Road
A 379
Warbro
Rd
T.U.F.C.
22
24
BABBACOMBE
Lymington
Marychurch
St.
Rd
Newton
Rd
Barton
Road
Marldon
Rd
Nut
GALLOWS GATE
COCKINGTON COUNTRY PARK
Bush
Sherwell
Valley
Road
Lane
Cockington
COCKINGTON
Lane
TORRE
TORQUAY
Road
A 379
Babbacombe
Road
BLACK HEAD
HOPE'S NOSE
Ilsham
Rd
Ilsham Marine Drive
Lincombe
Drive
Sea Road
Meadfoot
Hellevoetsluis
Way
A 380
MARLDON
PRESTON DOWN
Preston
Totnes
Rd
Down
Road
CHURSCOMBE
Torbay
A 3022

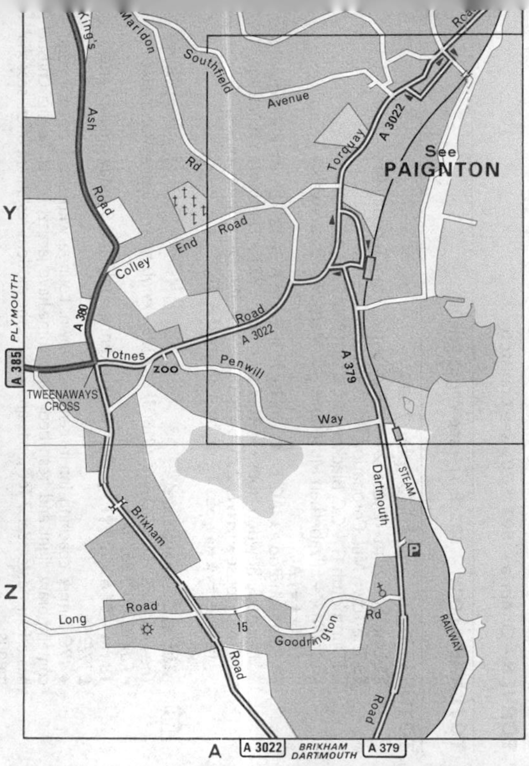
See
PAIGNTON
King's
Ash
Road
Marldon
Southfield
Avenue
Torquay
A 3022
Rd
Colley
End
Road
A 380
PLYMOUTH
A 385
Totnes
ZOO
TWEENAWAYS
CROSS
Penwill
Way
A 379
Dartmouth
STEAM
RAILWAY
Brixham
Road
Long
Road
15
Goodrington
Rd
A 3022
BRIXHAM
DARTMOUTH
A 379
A
Y
Z

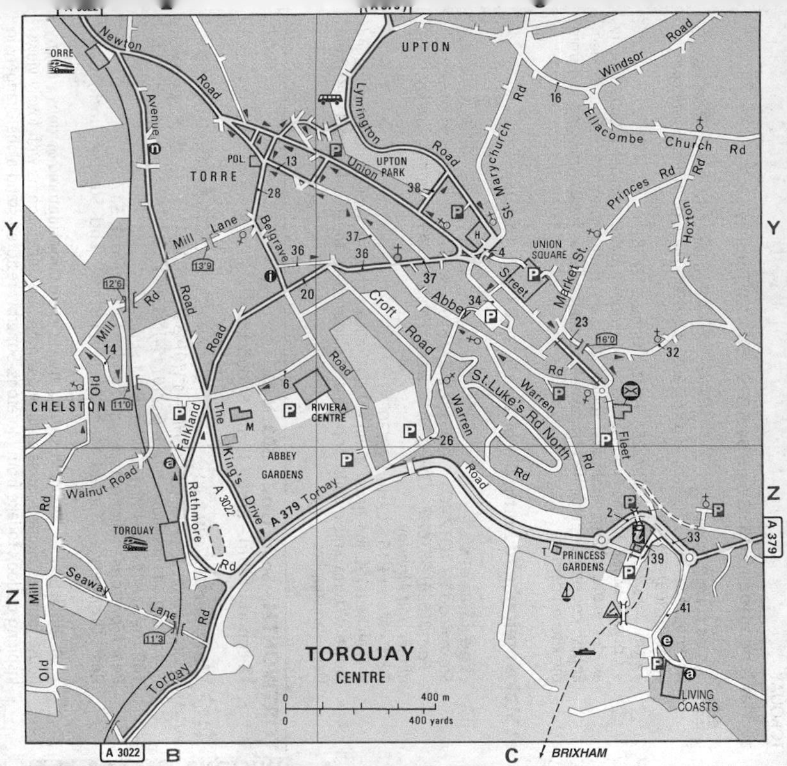
TORQUAY
CENTRE
TORRE
Newton
Road
Avenue
UPTON
Lymington
Road
UPTON
PARK
Union
Windsor
Road
16
Ellacombe
Church
Rd
St. Marychurch
Rd
Princes
Rd
Hoxton
Rd
POL
13
28
TORRE
38
H
4
UNION
SQUARE
Street
Market St.
Mill
Lane
13'9
Belgrave
36
37
36
37
Abbey
34
Croft
Road
20
12'6
Rd
Road
Road
23
16'0
32
Mill
14
Old
11'0
CHELSTON
Falkland
The
King's
Drive
6
RIVIERA
CENTRE
M
ABBEY
GARDENS
Road
26
Warren
Rd
St.Luke's Rd North
Warren
Rd
Rd
Fleet
Walnut Road
Rd
A 3022
Rathmore
Rd
A 379 Torbay
Road
TORQUAY
PRINCESS
GARDENS
2
33
39
A 379
41
Mill
Seaway
Lane
11'3
Rd
Old
Torbay
LIVING
COASTS
400 m
400 yards
0
0
A 3022
B
C
BRIXHAM
Y
Z

at Maidencombe North : 3 ½ m. by A 379 - BX – ✉ Torquay

Orestone Manor (heated)

Rockhouse Lane ✉ TQ1 4SX – ✆ (01803) 328 098 – info@orestonemanor.com – Fax (01803) 328 336

12 rm – †£ 99 ††£ 190/225 – **Rest** – Menu £ 18/38

◆ Country house in the woods! Terrace overlooks mature gardens. Conservatory exudes exotic charm. Individual rooms. Pleasant dining with interesting modern English cooking underpinned by tasty local seafood plus herbs, fruit and veg from the kitchen garden.

at Stokeinteignhead North : 5 ¾ m. by A 379 - BX – ✉ Torquay

The Chasers

Stoke Road ✉ TQ12 4QS – ✆ (01626) 873 670 – enquiries@thechasers.co.uk – Fax (01626) 873 670 – Closed last 2 weeks February,26 December, Sunday dinner and Monday

Rest – Menu £ 16 – Carte £ 22/30

◆ Thatched 16C inn given a vibrant 21C gastro style makeover including framed foodie pictures and menus. Top class cooking: chef's touch brings out best from Devonian supplies.

ENGLAND

TORTWORTH – South Glos. – 503 M 29 4 C1

London 128 m – Bristol 19 m – Stroud 18 m

Tortworth Court rm,

Wotton-under-Edge ✉ GL12 8HH – ✆ (01454) 263 000 – tortworth@four-pillars.co.uk – Fax (01454) 263 001

189 rm – †£ 65/149 ††£ 69/149 – 1 suite

Rest *Moretons* – (dinner only and Sunday lunch) Menu £ 17/25

Rest *Orangery* – (Closed Monday) (dinner only and Sunday lunch) Carte £ 25/44

◆ 19C hotel built in the Gothic style with arboretum and sculptured gardens. Country house lounges abound. Glass ceilinged atrium bar. Comfy rooms with lovely views. Inspiring outlook to lake from Moretons. Superbly restored stand-alone Orangery in the grounds.

TORVER – Cumbria – 502 K 20 – see Coniston

TOTLAND – I.O.W. – 503 P 31 – see Wight (Isle of)

TOTNES – Devon – 503 I 32 – pop. 7 929 2 C2

London 224 m – Exeter 24 m – Plymouth 23 m – Torquay 9 m

The Town Mill, Coronation Rd ✆ (01803) 863168

Dartmouth G & C.C. Blackawton, ✆ (01803) 712 686.

Town★ – Elizabethan Museum★ - St Mary's★ – Butterwalk★ – Castle (< ★★★) AC

Paignton Zoo★★ AC, E : 4 ½ m. by A 385 and A 3022 – British Photographic Museum, Bowden House★ AC, S : 1 m. by A 381 – Dartington Hall (High Cross House★), NW : 2 m. on A 385 and A 384. Dartmouth★★ (Castle < ★★★), SE : 12 m. by A 381 and A 3122

Royal Seven Stars

The Plains ✉ TQ9 5DD – ✆ (01803) 862 125 – enquiry@royalsevenstars.co.uk – Fax (01803) 867 929

18 rm – †£ 69/99 ††£ 99/130 – **Rest** – (dinner only and Sunday lunch) Carte £ 17/29

◆ 17C former coaching inn in centre of town. Lounge with smart colonial edge, contemporary, light and fresh bedrooms; some have jacuzzi baths, Agatha Christie has a four poster. Bar 7 for tapas and coffee; the modern restaurant offers seasonal menus.

at Stoke Gabriel Southeast : 4 m. by A 385 – ✉ **Totnes**

XX **Wills**

2-3 The Plains ✉ TQ9 5DR – ✆ (01803) 865 192 – philsil@btconnect.com – Closed 25 December, Sunday dinner and Monday

Rest – Carte £ 19/35

◆ Smart Regency townhouse restaurant, named after local explorer William Wills. Bold Georgian décor and antique chairs for dining. Modern British dishes.

The Steam Packet Inn with rm

St Peter's Quay ✉ TQ9 5EW – ✆ (01803) 863 880 – steampacket@buccaneer.co.uk – Fax (01803) 862 754

4 rm – †£ 60 ††£ 80 – **Rest** – Carte £ 16/24

◆ 19C inn delightfully set in the quay in the centre of town. Rustic bar is cosy, but most people come for conservatory, terrace and River Dart. Versatile menus. Sleek bedrooms.

TOWCESTER – Northants. – 503 R 27 – pop. 8 073 16 B3

London 70 m – Birmingham 50 m – Northampton 9 m – Oxford 36 m

Whittelbury Park G. & C.C. Whittlebury, ✆ (01327) 850 000 ;

Farthingstone Hotel Farthingstone, ✆ (01327) 361 291 .

at Paulerspury Southeast : 3 ¼ m. by A 5 – ✉ **Towcester**

XX **Vine House** with rm

100 High St ✉ NN12 7NA – ✆ (01327) 811 267 – info@vinehousehotel.com – Fax (01327) 811 309 – Closed 1 week Christmas- New Year, lunch Monday and Sunday

6 rm – †£ 65/95 ††£ 95/105 – **Rest** – Menu £ 30

◆ Converted 17C stone building with cottage garden in old village. Pleasantly rustic sitting room, bar with log fire. Quality cooking with traditional base. Converted 17C stone building with cottage garden in old village. Pleasantly rustic sitting room, bar with log fire. Quality cooking with traditional base.

TRAFFORD CENTRE – Gtr Manchester – see Manchester

TRAFFORD PARK – Gtr Manchester – see Manchester

TREFONEN – Shrops. – 502 K 25 – see Oswestry

TREGREHAN – Cornwall – 503 F 32 – see St Austell

TRELOWARREN – Cornwall – see Helston

TRESCO – Cornwall – 503 B 34 – see Scilly (Isles of)

TRING – Herts. – 504 S 28 – pop. 11 835 12 A2

London 38 m – Aylesbury 7 m – Luton 14 m – Oxford 31 m

Pendley Manor

Cow Lane, East : 1½ m. by B 4635 off B 4251 ✉ HP23 5QY – ✆ (01442) 891 891 – info@pendley-manor.co.uk – Fax (01442) 890 687

73 rm – †£ 130/140 ††£ 140/170 – **Rest** – Menu £ 28/31

◆ Attractive manor house in 35 acres of parkland. Good outdoor leisure facilities. Charming, wicker furnished lounge in the modern conservatory. Spacious, functional rooms. Smart, comfy air pervades dining room.

TRISCOMBE – Somerset – 503 K 30 – see Taunton

ENGLAND

TROUTBECK – Cumbria – **502** L 20 – see Windermere

TROWBRIDGE – Wilts. – **503** N 30 – **pop. 34 401** 4 **C2**

London 115 m – Bristol 27 m – Southampton 55 m – Swindon 32 m
St Stephen's Pl (01225) 777054, visittrowbridge@westwiltshire.gov.uk
Westwood Manor★, NW : 3 m. by A 363 – Farleigh Hungerford★ (St Leonard's Chapel★) **AC**, W : 4 m. Longleat House★★★ **AC**, SW : 12 m. by A 363, A 350 and A 362 - Bratton Castle (≤ ★★) SE : 7½ m. by A 363 and B 3098 – Steeple Ashton★ (The Green★) E : 6 m. – Edington (St Mary, St Katherine and All Saints★) SE : 7½ m

Old Manor rm, P VISA AE

Trowle Common, Northwest : 1 m. on A 363 ✉ BA14 9BL – (01225) 777 393 – romanticbeds@oldmanorhotel.com – Fax (01225) 765 443 – Closed 23 December-2 January

19 rm – ♦£ 70/90 ♦♦£ 90/130 – **Rest** – (Bar lunch) Menu £ 25

◆ Attractive Grade II listed Queen Anne house with 15C origins. Lovely gardens and pleasant lounges: wealth of beams adds to charm. Most bedrooms - some four poster - in annex. Spacious restaurant with welcoming ambience.

Red or White AC P VISA

Evolution House, 46 Castle St ✉ BA14 8AY – (01225) 781 666 – info@redorwhite.biz – Fax (01225) 776 505 – Closed 25 December, Bank Holidays and Sunday

Rest – Carte £ 18/27

◆ Modern personally-run restaurant at the rear of wine shop where you choose what to drink with your meal. Seasonal food cooked with flair; good value for lunch.

ENGLAND

at Semington Northeast : 2½ m. by A 361 – ✉ **Trowbridge**

The Lamb on the Strand P VISA AE

99 The Strand, East : 1½ m. on A 361 ✉ BA14 6LL – (01380) 870 263 – philip@cbcc.fsworld.co.uk – Fax (01380) 871 203 – Closed 25-26 December, 1 January and Sunday dinner

Rest – (booking essential) Carte £ 17/20

◆ Attractive ivy-clad pub with 18C origins. Spacious bar affords plenty of seating while dining area has exposed bricks and tasty, original dishes on blackboard menu.

Do not confuse ✗ with ✿!
✗ defines comfort, while stars are awarded for the best cuisine, across all categories of comfort.

TRUMPET – Herefordshire – see Ledbury

TRURO – Cornwall – **503** E 33 – **pop. 20 920** 1 **B3**

London 295 m – Exeter 87 m – Penzance 26 m – Plymouth 52 m
Municipal Buildings, Boscawen St (01872) 274555
Treliske, (01872) 272 640 ;
Killiow Park Kea Killiow, (01872) 270 246 .
Royal Cornwall Museum★★ **AC**
Trelissick Garden★★ (≤ ★★) **AC**, S : 4 m. by A 39 – Feock (Church★) S : 5 m. by A 39 and B 3289. Trewithen★★★, NE : 7½ m. by A 39 and A 390 – Probus★ (tower★ - garden★) NE : 9 m. by A 39 and A 390

Royal rm, P VISA AE

Lemon St ✉ TR1 2QB – (01872) 270 345 – reception@royalhotelcornwall.co.uk – Fax (01872) 242 453 – Closed 24-28 December

34 rm – ♦£ 80/100 ♦♦£ 110/125

Rest *Mannings* – (Closed Sunday lunch) Carte £ 30/44

◆ The name came after Prince Albert stayed in 1846: the Royal Arms stands proudly above the entrance. Comfortable, stylish lounges; modern bedrooms. Cuisine with global influences.

XX Tabb's

85 Kenwyn St ✉ TR1 3BZ – ✆ (01872) 262 110 – info@tabbs.co.uk – Closed 2 weeks January, 25 December, lunch Saturday, Sunday and Monday
Rest – Carte £ 28/37
◆ Stylish restaurant with lilac walls, flint floors and well-spaced, cloth-covered tables. Hearty, well-constructed dishes show good understanding of flavours. Relaxed atmosphere.

X Saffron

5 Quay St ✉ TR1 2HB – ✆ (01872) 263 771 – saffronrestaurant@btconnect.com – Closed 25-26 December, Bank Holidays, Sunday and Monday dinner January-May
Rest – Menu £ 20 (dinner) – Carte £ 27/35
◆ Bright exterior with colourful hanging baskets and attractive brightly coloured interior with a rustic tone. Varied Cornish menus to be enjoyed at any hour of the day.

TUNBRIDGE WELLS – Kent – 504 U 30 – see Royal Tunbridge Wells

TUNSTALL – Cumbria – see Kirkby Lonsdale

TURNERS HILL – W. Sussex – 504 T 30 – pop. 1 534 7 D2

London 33 m – Brighton 24 m – Crawley 7 m

Alexander House

East St, East : 1 m. on B 2110 ✉ RH10 4QD – ✆ (01342) 714 914 – info@alexanderhouse.co.uk – Fax (01342) 717 328
36 rm – †£ 155/190 ††£ 380/450 – 2 suites
Rest *Alexanders* – (Closed Monday dinner) (dinner only and Sunday lunch) Menu £ 22/40 – Carte £ 37/51
Rest *Reflections Brasserie* – Carte £ 24/38
◆ Set in extensive gardens, a stunning, classically comfortable country house, once owned by the family of poet Percy Shelley. Luxuriously appointed rooms in rich chintz. Sumptuous Alexanders. Informal air at Reflections.

TURVILLE – Bucks. – ✉ Henley-on-Thames 11 C2

London 45 m – Oxford 22 m – Reading 17 m

The Bull & Butcher

✉ RG9 6QU – ✆ (01491) 638 283 – info@thebullandbutcher.com – Fax (01491) 638 836
Rest – Carte £ 20/27
◆ Small pub in charming 'Vicar of Dibley' village. Flagstone flooring, log fires and scrubbed pine. Slightly different modern and traditional menus served in all dining areas.

TWO BRIDGES – Devon – 503 I 32 – ✉ Yelverton 2 C2

London 226 m – Exeter 25 m – Plymouth 17 m
Dartmoor National Park★★

Prince Hall

East : 1 m. on B 3357 ✉ PL20 6SA – ✆ (01822) 890 403 – info@princehall.co.uk – Fax (01822) 890 676 – Closed January
9 rm – †£ 80/160 ††£ 190/250 – **Rest** – (dinner only) (booking essential for non-residents) Menu £ 35 **s**
◆ Unique 18C country house, traditional in style, set alone in heart of Dartmoor. Magnificent view over West Dart River to rolling hills. Individually styled rooms. Local dishes proudly served in rustic restaurant.

ENGLAND

TYNEMOUTH – Tyne and Wear – **501** P 18 – **pop. 17 056** 24 **B2**

London 290 m – Newcastle upon Tyne 8 m – Sunderland 7 m

Grand

Grand Parade ✉ NE30 4ER – ✆ (0191) 293 6666 – Fax (0191) 293 6665
45 rm – ♦£ 85 ♦♦£ 165 – **Rest** – (Closed Sunday dinner and Bank Holiday Monday dinner) Menu £ 15/23 – Carte £ 27/32 **s**
◆ Impressive Victorian hotel built as home for Duchess of Northumberland. Commanding views over coastline. Atmospheric lounges and bars. Well-equipped rooms with fine views. Classical dining room with imposing drapes, floral displays and ceiling cornices.

Martineau Guest House without rest

57 Front St ✉ NE30 4BX – ✆ (0191) 296 0746 – martineau.house@ukgateway.net
3 rm – ♦£ 45/70 ♦♦£ 70
◆ 18C Georgian stone terraced house in main street, named after Harriet Martineau. Breakfast in open plan kitchen. Homely spacious individually styled rooms, two with view.

Sidney's

3-5 Percy Park Rd ✉ NE30 4LZ – ✆ (0191) 257 8500 – bookings@sidneys.co.uk – Fax (0191) 257 9800 – Closed 25-26 December, Sunday and Bank Holidays
Rest – (booking essential) Menu £ 15 (lunch) – Carte £ 20/36
◆ Fine painted, wood floored, busy little restaurant with two dining areas. The modern British cooking is interesting with plenty of variety and choice.

ENGLAND

UCKFIELD – E. Sussex – **504** U 31 – **pop. 15 374** 8 **A2**

London 45 m – Brighton 17 m – Eastbourne 20 m – Maidstone 34 m

Horsted Place

Little Horsted, South : 2½ m. by B 2102 and A 22 on A 26 ✉ TN22 5TS – ✆ (01825) 750 581 – hotel@horstedplace.co.uk – Fax (01825) 750 459 – Closed first week January
15 rm – ♦£ 130/175 ♦♦£ 130/175 – 5 suites – **Rest** – (Closed Saturday lunch) Menu £ 19 (lunch) – Carte approx. £ 36
◆ Imposing country house from the height of the Victorian Gothic revival; handsome Pugin-inspired drawing rooms and luxurious bedrooms overlook formal gardens and parkland. Pristine restaurant with tall 19C archways and windows.

Buxted Park

Buxted, Northeast : 2 m. on A 272 ✉ TN22 4AY – ✆ (01825) 733 333 – buxtedpark@handpicked.co.uk – Fax (01825) 732 770
rm,
43 rm – ♦£ 190 ♦♦£ 190 – 1 suite
Rest *Orangery* – Menu £ 28 – Carte £ 38/49
◆ 18C Palladian mansion in 300 acres with ornate public areas exuding much charm: spacious, period lounges. Rooms, modern in style, in original house or garden wing. Beautiful all-glass Orangery restaurant with large terrace.

UFFINGTON – Oxon. – **503** P 29 10 **A2**

London 75 m – Oxford 29 m – Reading 32 m – Swindon 17 m

The Craven

Fernham Rd ✉ SN7 7RD – ✆ (01367) 820 449 – carol@thecraven.co.uk
5 rm – ♦£ 30/55 ♦♦£ 75/105 – **Rest** – (by arrangement, communal dining) Menu £ 25
◆ 17C thatched hostelry; some rooms in brewhouse, stables. Quaint features: winding passageways, antique weighing machine in bathroom, four-poster with Victorian pillowslips. Dine in huge scarlet-walled kitchen with pretty china on dresser.

ULLINGSWICK – Herefordshire – 503 M 27 – ✉ Hereford 18 B3

London 134 m – Hereford 12 m – Shrewsbury 52 m – Worcester 19 m

Three Crowns Inn

Bleak Acre, East : 1¼ m. ✉ *HR1 3JQ – (01432) 820 279 – info@threecrownsinn.com – Fax (08700) 515 338 – Closed 25-26 December, Monday and Bank Holidays*

Rest – Menu £ 13/15 – Carte £ 15/25

◆ Pleasant part-timbered pub on a quiet country road: hops hang from the beams. Eclectic assortment of benches and pews. Rustic, robust dishes on daily changing menus.

ULLSWATER – Cumbria – 502 L 20 – ✉ Penrith 21 B2

London 296 m – Carlisle 25 m – Kendal 31 m – Penrith 6 m

Beckside Car Park, Glenridding, Penrith (017684) 82414

at Pooley Bridge on B 5320 – ✉ Penrith

Sharrow Bay Country House

Ullswater and fells,

South : 2 m. on Howtown rd ✉ *CA10 2LZ* rest,

– (017684) 86 301 – info@sharrowbay.co.uk – Fax (017684) 86 349

20 rm – £ 135/210 £ 350/420 – 4 suites – **Rest** – (booking essential) Menu £ 40/53

Spec. Braised belly pork, foie gras, black pudding, apple and sage sauce. Fillet of brill, shrimp risotto and scallops with Noilly Prat and lemon sauce. Strawberry and lemongrass jelly, pink champagne granita.

◆ Victorian country house in idyllic spot on shores of Lake Ullswater. Richly appointed, antique-filled interior. Traditional bedrooms blend luxury and old-fashioned charm. Richly flavoured, classical cooking. Personable service.

at Watermillock on A 592 – ✉ Penrith

Rampsbeck Country House

Ullswater and fells,

✉ *CA11 0LP – (017684) 86 442 – enquiries@rampsbeck.co.uk – Fax (017684) 86 688 – Closed 4 January-9 February*

18 rm – £ 80/120 £ 260 – 1 suite

Rest ***The Restaurant*** – see restaurant listing

◆ Personally run country house with peaceful gardens and homely guest areas. Very comfortable deluxe bedrooms, some with balconies; standard rooms more traditionally furnished.

Leeming House

on A 592 ✉ *CA11 0JJ – (0870) 400 81 31 – leeminghouse@macdonald-hotels.co.uk – Fax (017684) 86 443*

40 rm – £ 110/185 £ 125/200

Rest ***Regency*** – (dinner only) Menu £ 40

◆ Built as private residence in 19C for local family; in stepped gardens leading down to Lake Ullswater. A rural retreat with croquet lawn; appropriately styled country rooms. Georgian dining room brightened by mirrors and chandelier.

The Restaurant – at Rampsbeck Country House H.

Ullswater and fells,

✉ *CA11 0LP – (017684) 86 442 – Fax (017684) 86 688 – Closed 4 January-9 February*

Rest – (booking essential) (lunch by arrangement Monday-Saturday) Menu £ 28/40 **s**

◆ Refurbished house retains traditional character, with polished silver, fresh flowers and lake views. Seasonal menu combines modern with more traditional. Unobtrusive service.

If breakfast is included the symbol appears after the number of rooms.

ENGLAND

ULVERSTON – Cumbria – 502 K 21 – pop. 11 210 21 A3

London 278 m – Kendal 25 m – Lancaster 36 m
Coronation Hall, County Sq ✆ (01229) 587120

XX **The Bay Horse** with rm ≤ Morecambe Bay, P VISA AE
Canal Foot, East : 2¼ m. by A 5087, turning left at Morecambe Rd and beyond Industrial area, on the coast ✉ LA12 9EL – ✆ (01229) 583 972 – reservations@thebayhorsehotel.co.uk – Fax (01229) 580 502 – Closed Monday lunch
9 rm – ♦£ 80 ♦♦£ 123 – **Rest** – (booking essential) Carte £ 20/40
♦ Well-established inn by Ulverston Sands. Smart conservatory, flavourful seasonal menu and friendly staff. Cosy rooms, some equipped with binoculars and birdwatching guides.

UPPER ODDINGTON – Glos. – see Stow-on-the-Wold

UPPER SLAUGHTER – Glos. – 503 O 28 – see Bourton-on-the-Water

UPPINGHAM – Rutland – 504 R 26 – pop. 3 947 17 C2

London 101 m – Leicester 19 m – Northampton 28 m – Nottingham 35 m

X **Lake Isle** with rm AC rest, P VISA AE
16 High St East ✉ LE15 9PZ – ✆ (01572) 822 951 – info@lakeislehotel.com – Fax (01572) 824 400
12 rm – ♦£ 55/65 ♦♦£ 75/100 – **Rest** – (Closed Sunday dinner and Monday lunch) (light lunch) Carte £ 20/35
♦ Converted 18C shop; old scales, pine dresser and tables. Simple, well-judged seasonal menu, fine half-bottle cellar. Rooms in pretty cottage style, named after wine regions.

at Lyddington South : 2 m. by A 6003 – ✉ Uppingham

Old White Hart with rm P VISA
51 Main Street ✉ LE15 9LR – ✆ (01572) 821 703 – mail@oldwhitehart.co.uk – Fax (01572) 821 965 – closed 25 December and Sunday
6 rm – ♦£ 60 ♦♦£ 90 – **Rest** – Menu £ 13 – Carte £ 21/34
♦ Very pleasant 17C pub in pretty village; rural memorabilia within and huge petanque court without. Tasty, carefully prepared dishes. Welcoming rooms with a country feel.

UPTON SCUDAMORE – Wilts. – 503 N 30 – see Warminster

UPTON-UPON-SEVERN – Worcs. – 503 N 27 – pop. 1 789 18 B3

London 116 m – Hereford 25 m – Stratford-upon-Avon 29 m – Worcester 11 m
4 High St ✆ (01684) 594200, upton.tic@malvernhills.gov.uk

Tiltridge Farm and Vineyard without rest P VISA
Upper Hook Rd, West : 1½ m. by A 4104 and Greenfields Rd following B&B signs ✉ WR8 0SA – ✆ (01684) 592 906 – info@tiltridge.com – Fax (01684) 594 142 – Closed Christmas and New Year
3 rm – ♦£ 40 ♦♦£ 65
♦ Extended 17C farmhouse at the entrance to a small vineyard. Homely lounge, dominated by a broad inglenook fireplace, and spacious bedrooms, one with original timbers.

ENGLAND

at Hanley Swan **Northwest : 3 m. by B 4211 on B 4209 – ✉ Upton-upon-Severn**

Yew Tree House without rest

✉ WR8 0DN – ✆ (01684) 310 736 – info@yewtreehouse.co.uk – Fax (01684) 311 709 – Closed 24 December-1 January

3 rm – †£ 40/50 ††£ 70/80

◆ Imposing cream coloured Georgian guesthouse, built in 1780, in centre of pleasant village. One mile from Three Counties Showground. Cosy lounge; individually styled rooms.

URMSTON – Gtr Manchester – 502 M 23 — 20 B2

London 204 m – Manchester 9 m – Sale 4 m

Isinglass

46 Flixton Rd ✉ M40 1AB – ✆ (0161) 749 8400 – isinglass@btconnect.com – Closed 25-27 December, 1 January and Monday

Rest – (dinner only and Sunday lunch) Menu £ 14 – Carte £ 18/30

◆ Hidden away in Manchester suburb, this is a neighbourhood favourite. Very personally run, with warm rustic interior. Unusual dishes underpinned by a strong Lancastrian base.

We try to be as accurate as possible when giving room rates. But prices are susceptible to change, so please check rates when booking.

ENGLAND

UTTOXETER – Staffs. – 503 O 25 – pop. 12 023 — 19 C1

London 150 m – Birmingham 41 m – Stafford 16 m

at Beamhurst **Northwest : 3 m. on A 522 – ✉ Uttoxeter**

Gilmore at Strine's Farm

✉ ST14 5DZ – ✆ (01889) 507 100 – paul@restaurantgilmore.com – Fax (01889) 507 238 – Closed 1 week January, 1 week Easter, 1 week August, 1 week November, Monday, Tuesday, Sunday dinner and lunch Saturday and Wednesday

Rest – (booking essential) Menu £ 24/35

◆ Personally run converted farmhouse in classic rural setting. Three separate, beamed, cottage style dining rooms. New approach to classic dishes: fine local ingredients used.

VAZON BAY – C.I. – 503 P 33 – see Channel Islands

VENTNOR – I.O.W. – 503 Q 32 – see Wight (Isle of)

VERYAN – Cornwall – 503 F 33 – ✉ Truro — 1 B3

London 291 m – St Austell 13 m – Truro 13 m

Village★

Nare ← Carne Bay, (heated) rest,

Carne Beach, Southwest : 1 ¼ m. ✉ TR2 5PF – ✆ (01872) 501 111 – office@narehotel.co.uk – Fax (01872) 501 856

35 rm – †£ 105/240 ††£ 306/380 – 4 suites

Rest *The Dining Room* – (dinner only and Sunday lunch) Menu £ 41

Rest *Quarterdeck* – ✆ (01872) 500 000 – Carte £ 19/55

◆ On the curve of Carne Bay, surrounded by National Trust land; superb beach. Inside, owner's Cornish art collection in evidence. Most rooms have patios and balconies. The Dining Room boasts high windows and sea views; dinner dress code. Informal Quarterdeck.

at Ruan High Lanes West : 1 ¼ m. on A 3078 – ✉ Truro

The Hundred House

✉ TR2 5JR – ☎ (01872) 501 336 – enquiries@hundredhousehotel.co.uk – Fax (01872) 501 151
10 rm – †£ 85/143 ††£ 170/190
Rest *Fish in the Fountain* – (dinner only) (booking essential for non-residents) Menu £ 30 **s**
◆ Personally run small hotel: its period furnished hallway with fine staircase, ornate wallpaper sets tone of care and attention to detail. Mirrors, flowers, fine china abound. Comfortable dining room serves West Country fare.

VIRGINSTOW – Devon – 503 H 31 — 2 C2

London 227 m – Bideford 25 m – Exeter 41 m – Launceston 11 m – Plymouth 33 m

Percy's

Coombeshead Estate, Southwest : 1 ¼ m. on Tower Hill rd ✉ EX21 5EA – ☎ (01409) 211 236 – info@percys.co.uk – Fax (01409) 211 460
8 rm – †£ 110/170 ††£ 150/210
Rest Percy's – see restaurant listing
◆ Rural location surrounded by 130 acres of land and forest which include woodland trails and animals. Airy, modern rooms in granary or bungalow boast range of charming extras.

ENGLAND

XX Percy's

Coombeshead Estate, Southwest : 1 ¼ m. on Tower Hill rd ✉ EX21 5EA – ☎ (01409) 211 236 – info@percys.co.uk – Fax (01409) 211 460
Rest – (dinner only) Menu £ 40
◆ Modern rear extension with deep sofas alongside chic ash and zinc bar. Restaurant has an understated style. Locally sourced, organic produce and homegrown vegetables.

WADDESDON – Bucks. – 504 R 28 – pop. 1 865 – ✉ Aylesbury — 11 C2

Great Britain

London 51 m – Aylesbury 5 m – Northampton 32 m – Oxford 31 m
Chiltern Hills★
Waddesdon Manor★★, S : ½ m. by a 41 and minor rd – Claydon House★, N : by minor rd

XX The Five Arrows with rm

High St ✉ HP18 0JE – ☎ (01296) 651 727 – bookings@thefivearrowshotel.fsnet.co.uk – Fax (01296) 658 596
11 rm – †£ 75/120 ††£ 150 – 1 suite – **Rest** – Menu £ 20 (lunch) **s** – Carte £ 20/36 **s**
◆ Beautiful 19C inn on Rothschild estate, an influence apparent in pub crest and wine cellar. Striking architecture, stylish dining, relaxed ambience, Anglo-Mediterranean menu. Individually decorated bedrooms - some four posters - divided between main house and courtyard, the latter being smaller but quieter.

WAKEFIELD – W. Yorks. – 502 P 22 – pop. 76 886 *Great Britain* — 22 B3

London 188 m – Leeds 9 m – Manchester 38 m – Sheffield 23 m
Wood St ☎ (01924) 305000, tic@wakefield.gov.uk
18 City of Wakefield Horbury Rd, Lupset Park, ☎ (01924) 367 442 ;
18 28 Woodthorpe Lane Sandal, ☎ (01924) 258 778 ;
9 Painthorpe House Crigglestone Painthorpe Lane, ☎ (01924) 254 737 .
Nostell Priory★ AC, SE : 4 ½ m. by A 638

XX Aagrah

108 Barnsley Rd, Sandal, South : 1 ¼ m. on A 61 ✉ WF1 5NX – ☎ (01924) 242 222 – Fax (01924) 240 562
Rest – Indian (dinner only) (booking essential) Carte £ 15/20
◆ Ornate Eastern curios and furnishings catch the eye in this ever-lively restaurant; good choice of genuine Indian dishes; friendly service from a smartly dressed team.

WALBERTON – W. Sussex – see Arundel

WALCOTT – Norfolk – ✉ Norwich 15 **D1**

London 134 m – Cromer 12 m – Norwich 23 m

Holly Tree Cottage without rest

Walcott Green, South : 2 m. by B 1159 and Stalham rd taking 2nd left after Lighthouse Inn ✉ NR12 0NS – (01692) 650 721 – May-September

3 rm – £ 40 £ 60

◆ A hospitable couple keep this traditional Norfolk flint cottage in excellent order. Snug lounge with wood-fired stove and neat rooms overlooking fields. Good breakfasts.

WALLASEY – Mersey. – **502** K 23 – **pop. 58 710** – ✉ **Wirral** 20 **A2**

London 222 m – Birkenhead 3 m – Liverpool 4 m

Wallasey Bayswater Rd, (0151) 691 1024 .

Grove House AC rest, P VISA AE

Grove Rd ✉ CH45 3HF – (0151) 639 3947 – reception@thegrovehouse.co.uk – Fax (0151) 639 0028

14 rm – £ 70/75 £ 90, £ 8.95 – **Rest** – (Closed Bank Holidays) (dinner only and Sunday lunch) Carte £ 18/33

◆ Part Victorian house in a residential street. Meeting room with conservatory. Bedrooms in different shapes and sizes: quieter rear accommodation overlooks garden. Oak-panelled dining room.

ENGLAND

Undecided between two equivalent establishments?
Within each category, establishments are classified in our order of preference.

WALLINGFORD – Oxon. – **503** Q 29 – **pop. 8 019** *Great Britain* 10 **B3**

London 54 m – Oxford 12 m – Reading 16 m

Town Hall, Market Pl (01491) 826972

Ridgeway Path ★★

North Moreton House without rest (heated) P

North Moreton, West : 4 m. by A 4130 ✉ OX11 9AT – (01235) 813 283 – miles-katie@hotmail.com – Fax (01235) 511 305

3 rm – £ 48/50 £ 65/70

◆ Grade II listed house in mature lawned gardens with fine 17C barn. Spacious, individually decorated bedrooms. Breakfast on local organic produce at vast antique table.

WALTON – W. Yorks. – **502** Q 22 – see Wetherby

WANTAGE – Oxon. – **503** – **pop. 17 913** 10 **B3**

London 71 m – Oxford 16 m – Reading 24 m – Swindon 21 m

Vale and Downland Museum, 19 Church St (01235) 760176

The Boar's Head with rm P VISA AE

Church St, East : 2½ m. by A 417 ✉ OX12 8QA – (01235) 833 254 – info@boarsheadardington.co.uk

3 rm – £ 75/105 £ 130 – **Rest** – Menu £ 23 – Carte £ 24/45

◆ Pretty, timbered pub: pine tables, hunting curios and rural magazines. Locally-grown salad, modern British dishes, good wine and ale draw the locals. Bright modern bedrooms.

WARE – Herts. – 504 T 28 – pop. 17 193 12 B2

London 24 m – Cambridge 30 m – Luton 22 m
Whitehill Dane End, (01920) 438 495.

Marriott Hanbury Manor H. & Country Club

Thundridge rm, rest,
North : 1 ¾ m. by A 1170 on A 10 SG12 0SD – (01920) 487 722 – Fax (01920) 487 692
156 rm – £ 179 £ 179, £ 17.50 – 5 suites
Rest *Zodiac* – (Closed Sunday dinner and Monday) Menu £ 25/35 – Carte £ 44/57
Rest *Oakes* – Carte £ 31/42
◆ 1890s neo-Jacobean mansion, a former convent, in 220 acres. Tea in firelit, oak-beamed hall. Classically luxurious rooms; many overlook golf course and lake. Walled garden. Formal, fine dining Zodiac. Mediterranean menus in spacious Oakes.

Jacoby's

Churchgate House, 15 West St SG12 9EE – (01920) 469 181 – info@jacobys.co.uk – Fax (01920) 469 182 – Closed Sunday dinner and Monday
Rest – Menu £ 10 – Carte £ 20/35
◆ Carefully renovated 15C Grade II listed timber framed house with tremendous character. Front bar with leather armchairs. Twin level dining: British or Mediterranean classics.

ENGLAND

WAREHAM – Dorset – 503 N 31 – pop. 2 568 4 C3

London 123 m – Bournemouth 13 m – Weymouth 19 m
Holy Trinity Church, South St (01929) 552740
Town★ – St Martin's★★
Blue Pool★ AC, S : 3 ½ m. by A 351 – Bovington Tank Museum★ AC, Woolbridge Manor★, W : 5 m. by A 352. Moreton Church★★, W : 9 ½ m. by A 352 – Corfe Castle★ (★★) AC, SE : 6 m. by A 351 – Lulworth Cove★, SW : 10 m. by A 352 and B 3070 – Bere Regis★ (St John the Baptist Church★), NW : 6 ½ m. by minor rd

Springfield Country H.

(heated)
Grange Rd, South : 1 ¼ m. by South St and West Lane BH20 5AL – (01929) 552 177 – enquiries@thespringfield.co.uk – Fax (01929) 551 862 – Closed 24 December-1 January
60 rm – £ 89/109 £ 120/180
Rest *Millview* – (bar lunch) Menu £ 25 – Carte £ 21/32
Rest *Springers* – (Closed Friday-Sunday) (dinner only) Carte £ 21/32
◆ Privately owned hotel in sight of the Purbeck Hills. Neatly laid-out rooms; landscaped gardens. Comprehensive spa treatments and a state-of-the-art gym. Regional flavours abound in Millview. Informal, unfussy Springers.

Priory

Church Green BH20 4ND – (01929) 551 666 – reservations@theprioryhotel.co.uk – Fax (01929) 554 519
16 rm – £ 172 £ 260 – 2 suites – **Rest** – Menu £ 39 (dinner) – Carte lunch £ 28/33
◆ Charming, privately run part 16C priory, friendly and discreetly cosy. Well-equipped rooms. Manicured four-acre gardens lead down to River Frome: luxury suites in boathouse. Charming restaurant beneath stone vaults of undercroft.

Gold Court House

St John's Hill BH20 4LZ – (01929) 553 320 – info@goldcourthouse.co.uk – Fax (01929) 553 320
3 rm – £ 45 £ 70 – **Rest** – (winter only) (by arrangement, communal dining) Menu £ 18
◆ Affable hosts are justly proud of this pretty 1760s house on a quiet square. Classically charming sitting room and bedrooms; well-chosen books and antiques. Dine communally while viewing delightful courtyard garden.

WAREN MILL – Northd. – 501 O 17 – see Bamburgh

WARGRAVE – Windsor & Maidenhead – 504 R 29 – pop. 2 876 11 C3

London 37 m – Henley-on-Thames 4 m – Oxford 27 m

St George & Dragon

High Street ✉ RG10 8HY – ✆ (0118) 940 5021 – pubs@simon-king.co.uk – Closed 25-26 December

Rest – Carte £ 15/31

◆ Modernised yet still characterful beamed pub with lovely decked terrace overlooking Thames. Text-book modern interior. Stone-fired oven provides range of modern dishes.

WARKWORTH – Northd. – 502 P 17 24 B2

London 316 m – Alnwick 7 m – Morpeth 24 m

Roxbro House without rest

5 Castle Terrace ✉ NE65 0UP – ✆ (01665) 711 416 – info@roxbrohouse.co.uk – Closed 23-30 December

3 rm – †£ 40 ††£ 80

◆ A discreet style enhances this 19C stone house in the shadow of Warkworth castle. Stylish lounge in harmony with very smart boutique bedrooms, two of which face the castle.

Your opinions are important to us:
please write and let us know about your discoveries and experiences – good and bad!

ENGLAND

WARMINSTER – Wilts. – 503 N 30 – pop. 17 486 4 C2

London 111 m – Bristol 29 m – Exeter 74 m – Southampton 47 m

Central Car Park ✆ (01985) 218548

Longleat House★★★ AC, SW : 3 m. Stonehenge★★★ AC, E : 18 m. by A 36 and A 303 – Bratton Castle (≤ ★★) NE : 6 m. by A 350 and B 3098

Bishopstrow House (heated)

Southeast : 1½ m. on B 3414 ✉ BA12 9HH – ✆ (01985) 212 312 – info@bishopstrow.co.uk – Fax (01985) 216 769

29 rm – †£ 79/99 ††£ 179/199 – 3 suites

Rest *The Mulberry* – Menu £ 17/40 – Carte £ 18/33

◆ Dignified, ivy-clad Georgian manor; 22-acre gardens along the river Wylye. Large modern rooms. Clubby, panelled bar with log fire; popular leisure club for the more active. Wall lanterns lend a warm feel to restaurant, which overlooks the garden.

at Upton Scudamore North : 2½ m. by A 350 – ✉ Warminster

The Angel Inn with rm

✉ BA12 0AG – ✆ (01985) 213 225 – mail@theangelinn.co.uk – Fax (01985) 218 182 – Closed 25-26 December, 1 January

10 rm – †£ 75 ††£ 85 – **Rest** – Carte £ 20/30

◆ Refurbished 16C inn with a warm personal style. Sunny rear terrace. Rustic interior of scrubbed wood and pine. Fish specials highlight of appealing menus. Immaculate rooms.

at Heytesbury Southeast : 3 ¾ m. by B 3414 – ✉ Warminster

The Angel Inn with rm

High St ✉ BA12 0ED – ✆ (01985) 840 330

8 rm – †£ 60 ††£ 75 – **Rest** – Beef specialities (Closed 25 December) Menu £ 18 – Carte £ 25/35

◆ 17C village inn with a delightful courtyard terrace. Dine at well-spaced tables in an elegant restaurant or the friendly real-ale bar. Cosy, well-appointed bedrooms.

WARRINGTON – Warrington – **502** M 23 – **pop. 80 661** 20 **A3**

London 195 m – Chester 20 m – Liverpool 18 m – Manchester 21 m – Preston 28 m
The Market Hall, Academy Way ✆ (01925) 632571
Hill Warren Appleton, ✆ (01925) 261 775 ;
Walton Hall Higher Walton Warrington Rd, ✆ (01925) 266 775 ;
Birchwood Kelvin Close, ✆ (01925) 818 819 ;
Leigh Broseley Lane, Kenyon Hall, ✆ (01925) 763 130 ;
Alder Root Winwick Alder Root Lane, ✆ (01925) 291 919 .

at Stretton South : 3 ½ m. by A 49 on B 5356 – ✉ Warrington

Park Royal
rm, rest,
Stretton Rd ✉ WA4 4NS – ✆ (01925) 730 706 – stay@qhotels.co.uk – Fax (01925) 730 740
143 rm – £ 85/149 £ 95/159 – 3 suites
Rest *Topiary in the Park* – Menu £ 22 (dinner) – Carte lunch £ 22/36 **s**
◆ Busy, well-equipped business hotel with motorway access. Well-appointed rooms in co-ordinated patterns, facing open countryside at rear. Excellent leisure centre and café-bar. Traditionally formal restaurant.

WARTLING – E. Sussex – **504** V 31 – see Herstmonceux

WARWICK – Warks. – **503** P 27 – **pop. 23 350** *Great Britain* 19 **C3**

London 96 m – Birmingham 20 m – Coventry 11 m – Leicester 34 m – Oxford 43 m
The Court House, Jury St ✆ (01926) 492212
Warwick Racecourse, ✆ (01926) 494 316.
Town★ - Castle★★ **AC** Y – Leycester Hospital★ **AC** Y **B** – Collegiate Church of St Mary★ (Tomb★) Y **A**

Plan opposite

Charter House without rest
87 West St ✉ CV34 6AH – ✆ (01926) 496 965 – sheila@penon.gotadsl.co.uk – Closed Christmas Y **c**
3 rm – £ 56/65 £ 85/95
◆ Timbered 15C house not far from the castle. Comfortable, delicately ordered rooms with a personal touch: pretty counterpanes and posies of dried flowers. Tasty breakfasts.

Park Cottage without rest
113 West St ✉ CV34 6AH – ✆ (01926) 410 319 – janet@parkcottagewarwick.co.uk – Fax (01926) 497 994 Y **e**
7 rm – £ 50/58 £ 70/85
◆ Between the shops and restaurants of West Street and the River Avon, a listed part Tudor house offering a homely lounge and sizeable, traditionally appointed bedrooms.

Saffron
Unit 1, Westgate House, Market St ✉ CV34 4DE – ✆ (01926) 402 061 – Closed 25-26 December Y **n**
Rest – Indian (dinner only) Carte £ 13/30
◆ Split-level dining room hung with sitars and prints from the subcontinent. Piquant seafood and Goan dishes are the specialities of a freshly prepared Indian repertoire.

Art Kitchen
7 Swan St ✉ CV34 4BJ – ✆ (01926) 494 303 – reservations@theartkitchen.com – Fax (01926) 494 304 – Closed 25 December- mid January Y **r**
Rest – Thai Menu £ 13 (lunch) – Carte £ 16/24
◆ Unpretentious town centre restaurant with upstairs dining area featuring artwork for sale by owners' daughter. Authentic Thai cooking with attention paid to originality.

WARWICK-ROYAL LEAMINGTON SPA

Birmingham Rd . . . . Z 7
Bowling Green St . . . . Y 9
Brook St . . . . Y 12
Butts (The) . . . . Y 13
Castle Hill . . . . Y 15
Church St . . . . Y 17
High St . . . . Y 23
Jury St . . . . Y
Lakin Rd . . . . Y 25
Linen St . . . . Y 26
Market Pl . . . . Y 29
Old Square . . . . Y 35
Old Warwick Rd . . . . Z 36
Radford Rd . . . . Z 39
Rock (The) . . . . Y 32
St John's Rd . . . . Y 42
St Nicholas Church St . . . . Y 43
Shires Retail Park . . . . Z
Smith St . . . . Y
Swan St . . . . Y 46
Theatre St . . . . Y 48
West St . . . . Y 50

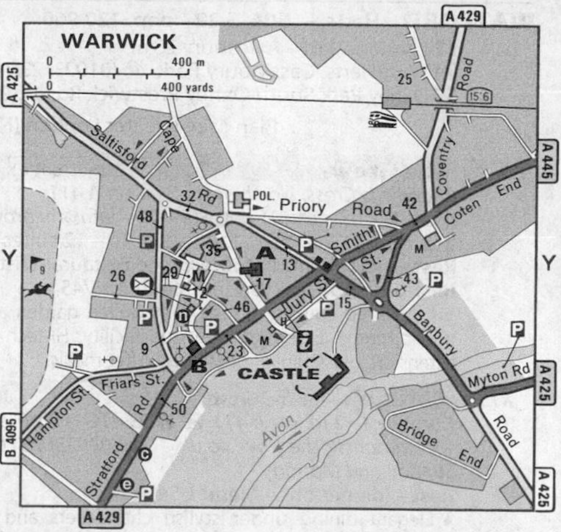

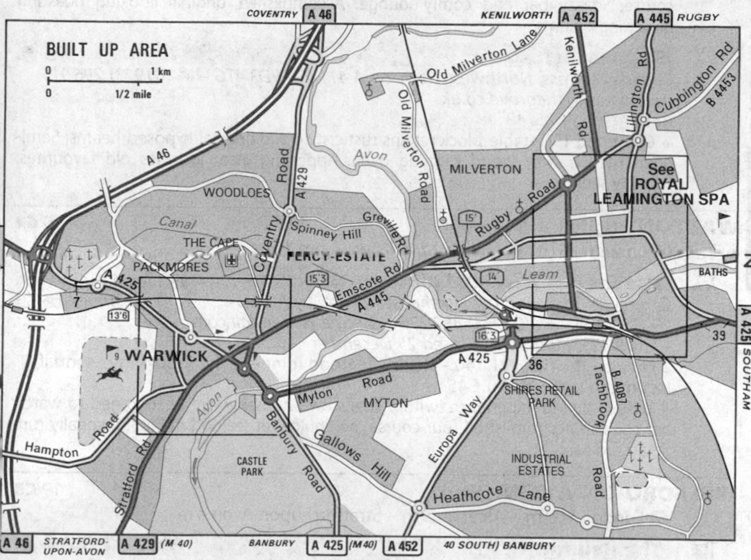

BUILT UP AREA
0 1 km
0 1/2 mile
COVENTRY A 46
KENILWORTH A 452
A 445 RUGBY
Old Milverton Lane
Old Milverton Road
Kenilworth Rd
Lillington Rd
Cubbington Rd
B 4453
A 46
Avon
MILVERTON
WOODLOES
Coventry Road
A 429
See ROYAL LEAMINGTON SPA
Rugby Road
Canal
Spinney Hill
Greville Rd
THE CAPE
PACKMORES
PERCY ESTATE
Emscote Rd
A 445
Leam
BATHS
Z
A 425
7
WARWICK
A 425
36
39
SOUTHAM
Myton Road
MYTON
SHIRES RETAIL PARK
Tachbrook Road
B 4087
Avon
Banbury Road
Gallows Hill
Europa Way
Hampton Road
Stratford Rd
CASTLE PARK
INDUSTRIAL ESTATES
Heathcote Lane
A 46 STRATFORD-UPON-AVON
A 429 (M 40)
BANBURY A 425 (M40)
A 452 40 SOUTH) BANBURY

For a pleasant stay in a charming hotel, look for the red ⌂ ... ⌂⌂⌂ symbols.

WATERGATE BAY – Cornwall – **503** E 32 – see Newquay

WATERMILLOCK – Cumbria – **502** L 20 – see Ullswater

WATFORD – Herts. – **504** S 29 – **pop. 120 960** 12 **A2**

London 21 m – Aylesbury 23 m
West Herts. Cassiobury Park, (01923) 236 484 ;
Oxhey Park South Oxhey Prestwick Rd, (01923) 248 213 .

Plan : see Greater London (North-West) 2

The Grove (heated) rm,
Chandler's Cross, Northwest : 2 m. on A 411
WD3 4TG – (01923) 807 807 – info@thegrove.co.uk – Fax (01923) 221 008
215 rm – £ 280 £ 280, £23.50 – 12 suites
Rest *Colette's* and ***Stables*** – see restaurant listing
Rest *Glasshouse* – (buffet) Menu £ 30/45
◆ Converted country house with walled garden and golf course. Modern décor in public rooms. Extensive new spa facility. Hi-tech bedrooms and suites in modern extension. Glasshouse for stylish buffet meals.

Colette's – at The Grove
Northwest : 2 m. on A 411 WD3 4TG – (01923) 296 015
– restaurants@thegrove.co.uk – Fax (01923) 221 008 – Closed 13-23 August, Sunday and Monday
Rest – (dinner only) Menu £ 54
◆ Elegant dining under stylish chandeliers and original artwork; overlooks golf course. Snazzy bar and comfy lounge. Accomplished, original cooking boasting luxury ingredients.

Stables – at The Grove
Chandler's Cross, Northwest : 2 m. on A 411 WD3 4TG – (01923) 296 015
– restaurant@thegrove.co.uk
Rest – Carte £ 35/48
◆ Converted 19C stable block retains rustic style and original exposed beams. Semi-open kitchen with wood burning oven. Appealing menu includes old favourites. Friendly service.

ENGLAND

WATTON – Norfolk – **504** W 26 15 **C2**

London 95 m – Norwich 22 m – Swaffham 10 m

The Café at Brovey Lair with rm (heated) rest,
Carbrooke Rd, Ovington, Northeast : 1 ¾ m. by A 1075
IP25 6SD – (01953) 882 706 – thecafe@broveylair.com
– Fax (01953) 885 365 – Closed 25 December
2 rm – £ 125 £ 140 – **Rest** – Seafood (dinner only) (booking essential) (set menu only) Menu £ 45
◆ Unique dining experience, within chef's own house: you're encouraged to watch her cook an accomplished four-course, no choice set seafood menu. Personally run. Smart rooms.

WELFORD-ON-AVON – Warks. 19 **C3**

London 109 m – Alcester 9 m – Stratford-upon-Avon 4 m

The Bell Inn
Binton Rd CV37 8EB – (01789) 750 353 – info@thebellwelford.co.uk
– Fax (01789) 750 893
Rest – Carte £ 20/28
◆ Part 17C inn in neat village near Stratford. Attractive dining terrace. Flagged and beamed bar with open fire. Eclectic mix of dishes: local suppliers printed on back of menu.

WELLINGHAM – Norfolk 15 **C1**

London 120 m – King's Lynn 29 m – Norwich 28 m

Manor House Farm without rest
PE32 2TH – (01328) 838 227 – libby.ellis@btconnect.com
– Fax (01328) 838 348
3 rm – £ 50/65 £ 80/100
◆ Idyllic setting beside church, surrounded by gardens and working farm. Family style breakfast; home grown bacon and sausage. Charming rooms in the house or comfortable annexe.

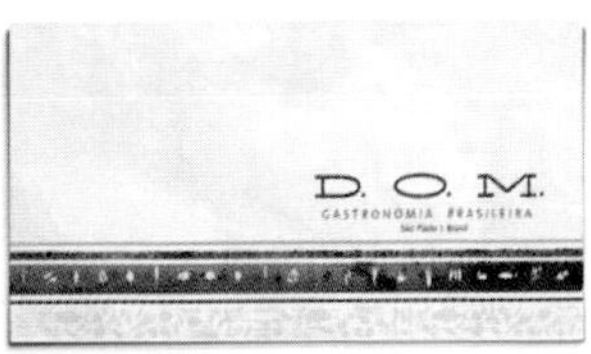

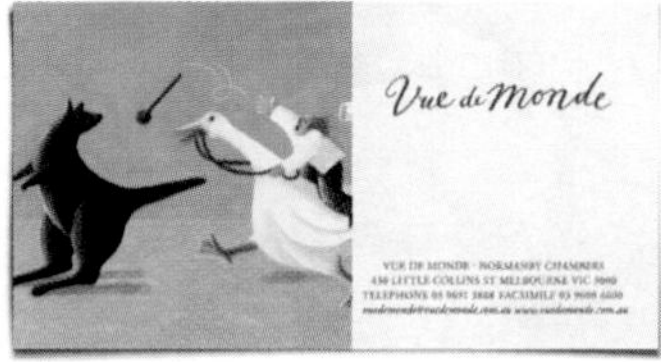

To enhance great foods they choose great waters.

The delicate complex flavours of the finest cuisine are best appreciated by an educated palate. And in the same way that the right wine can release the nuances of a dish, the right water can subtly cleanse the palate, enhancing the pleasure and experience of both. To discover why S.Pellegrino and Acqua Panna are seen on all the best tables, go to WWW.FINEDININGWATERS.COM

ACQUA PANNA AND S.PELLEGRINO. FINE DINING WATERS.

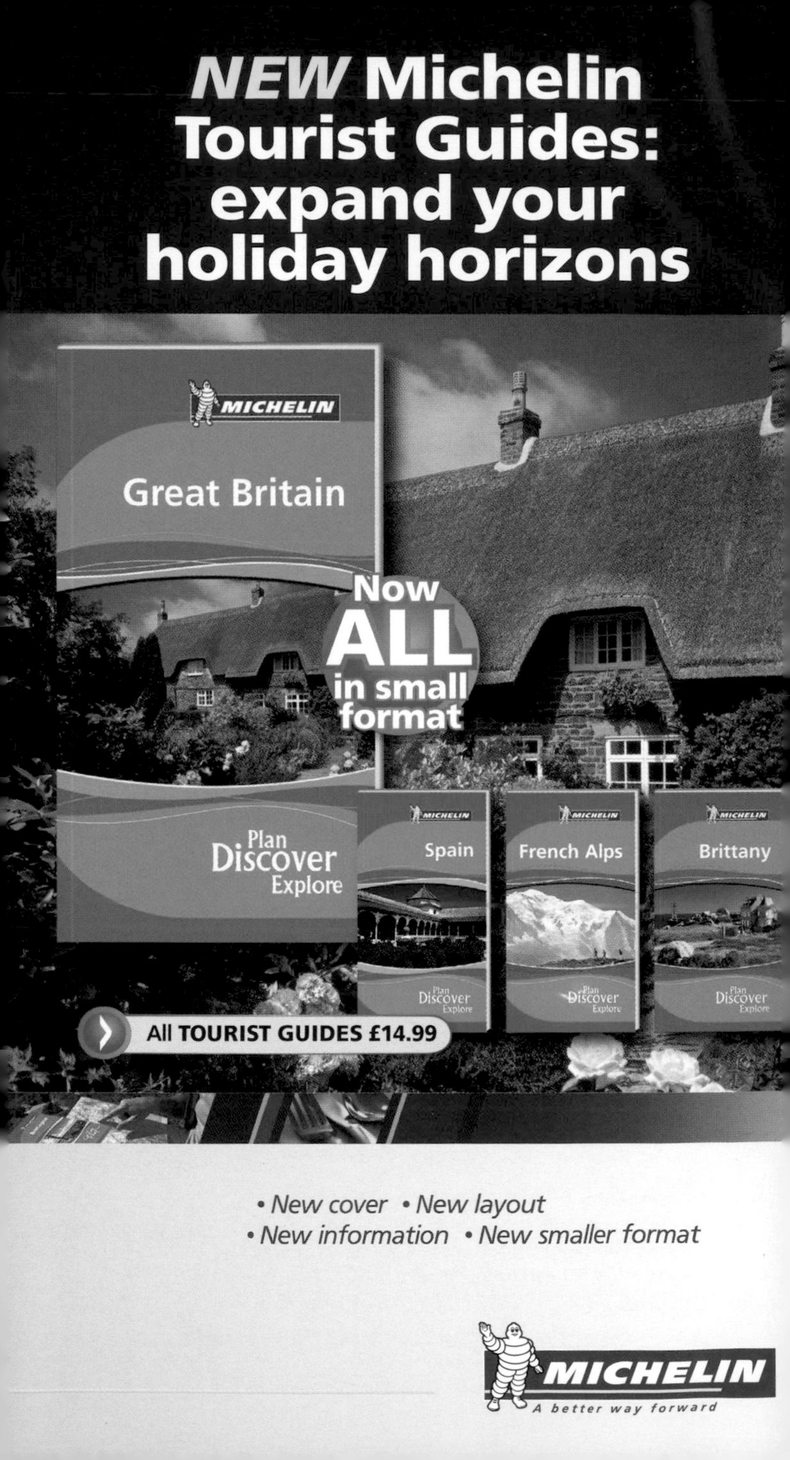

NEW Michelin Tourist Guides: expand your holiday horizons

MICHELIN

Great Britain

Now ALL in small format

Plan Discover Explore

Spain

French Alps

Brittany

All TOURIST GUIDES £14.99

• *New cover* • *New layout*
• *New information* • *New smaller format*

WELLINGTON – Somerset – 503 K 31 – pop. 10 599 — 3 B3

London 176 m – Barnstaple 42 m – Exeter 32 m – Taunton 10 m

Bindon Country House
(heated)

Langford Budville, Northwest : 4½ m. by B 3187 via Langford Budville village following signs for Wiveliscombe ✉ TA21 0RU – ✆ (01823) 400 070 – stay@bindon.com – Fax (01823) 400 071

12 rm – ♦£ 115/145 ♦♦£ 145/225

Rest *The Wellesley* – Menu £ 17/35

◆ A rural idyll; splendid part 17C house with distinctive Flemish gables, rose garden; personally run with tasteful style. Individually designed rooms in refined, quiet colours. Fine views from restaurant; accomplished cooking in modern style.

WELLS – Somerset – 503 M 30 – pop. 10 406 — 4 C2

London 132 m – Bristol 20 m – Southampton 68 m – Taunton 28 m

Town Hall, Market Pl ✆ (01749) 672552, wells.tic@ukonline.co.uk

East Horrington Rd, ✆ (01749) 675 005.

City★★ – Cathedral★★★ – Bishop's Palace★ (≤ ★★) **AC** – St Cuthbert★

Glastonbury★★ - Abbey★★ (Abbot's Kitchen★) **AC**, St John the Baptist★★, Somerset Rural Life Museum★ **AC**, Glastonbury Tor★ (≤ ★★★), SW : 5½ m. by A 39 – Wookey Hole★ (Caves★ **AC**, Papermill★), NW : 2 m. Cheddar Gorge★★ (Gorge★★, Caves★, Jacob's Ladder ✻ ★) - St Andrew's Church★, NW : 7 m. by A 371 – Axbridge★★ (King John's Hunting Lodge★, St John the Baptist Church★), NW : 8½ m. by A 371

The Swan
rm,

11 Sadler St ✉ BA5 2RX – ✆ (01749) 836 300 – info@swanhotelwells.co.uk – Fax (01749) 836 301

49 rm – ♦£ 90/102 ♦♦£ 134/170 – **Rest** – Carte £ 23/35

◆ Refurbished to a very good standard, this friendly former posting inn faces the Cathedral's west front. Two relaxing, firelit lounges; stylish individually decorated rooms. Restaurant boasts framed antique clothing and oak panelling.

Beryl without rest
(heated)

East : 1¼ m. by B 3139 off Hawkers Lane ✉ BA5 3JP – ✆ (01749) 678 738 – stay@beryl-wells.co.uk – Fax (01749) 670 508 – Closed 23-25 December

10 rm – ♦£ 65/85 ♦♦£ 120/130

◆ Neo-gothic former hunting lodge in formal gardens run in idiosyncratic style. Impeccable antique-filled drawing room. Traditional rooms, larger on first floor. Charming hosts.

Littlewell Farm without rest

Coxley, Southwest : 1½ m. on A 39 ✉ BA5 1QP – ✆ (01749) 677 914 – enquiries@littlewellfarm.co.uk

5 rm – ♦£ 35/45 ♦♦£ 58

◆ Restored 18C farmhouse set in a broad lawned garden. Cosy, attractively furnished sitting room and pristine, individually decorated bedrooms. Breakfasts at communal table.

The Old Spot

12 Sadler St ✉ BA5 2SE – ✆ (01749) 689 099 – Closed 1 week Christmas, Monday, Sunday dinner and Tuesday lunch

Rest – Menu £ 18/27

◆ Restaurant's rear leads straight onto stunning Cathedral grounds. Relaxing interior "spot on" for enjoying gloriously unfussy, mouth-wateringly tasty dishes. Good value, too.

at Wookey Hole Northwest : 1 ¾ m. by A 371 – ✉ Wells

Glencot House

Glencot Lane ✉ BA5 1BH – ✆ (01749) 677 160 – relax@glencothouse.co.uk – Fax (01749) 670 210 – Closed 25 December

15 rm – ♦£ 175 ♦♦£ 260/285 – **Rest** – (booking essential for non-residents) Menu £ 14/30 **s**

◆ Set in mature gardens by the river Axe, a 19C mansion in Jacobean style. Preserved walnut panelling, carved ceilings and comfortable rooms with decorative touches. Dining room with mullioned windows, chandelier, river views.

at Easton **Northwest : 3 m. on A 371 – ✉ Wells**

Beaconsfield Farm without rest
on A 371 ✉ BA5 1DU – ✆ (01749) 870 308 – carol5ll@aol.com – Closed 20 December-New Year
3 rm – 🚹£ 65 🚹🚹£ 70/75
◆ In the foothills of the Mendips, a renovated farmhouse offering well-fitted, cottage-style rooms. Generous breakfasts in the parlour overlooking the four-acre grounds.

WELLS-NEXT-THE-SEA – Norfolk – 504 W 25 – pop. 2 451 — 15 C1

London 122 m – Cromer 22 m – Norwich 38 m

The Crown
The Buttlands ✉ NR23 1EX – ✆ (01328) 710 209 – reception@thecrownhotelwells.co.uk – Fax (01328) 711 432
12 rm – 🚹£ 70/110 🚹🚹£ 110/155
Rest *Restaurant* – (dinner only) Menu £ 35
Rest *Bar* – (bookings not accepted) Carte £ 21/32
◆ 16C coaching inn with smart Georgian façade, overlooking the village green. Bedrooms are contemporary in style; service is informal and friendly. Light, airy Restaurant with bright décor. Modern conservatory Bar with terrace.

The Globe Inn with rm
The Buttlands ✉ NR23 1EU – ✆ (01328) 710 206 – globe@holkham.co.uk – Fax (01328) 713 249
7 rm – 🚹£ 65/90 🚹🚹£ 125 – **Rest** – Carte £ 17/22
◆ Updated Georgian pub with terrace facing town green. Sleek, modern bar. Large dining room: excellent local photos enliven walls. Modern British cooking. Stylish rooms.

ENGLAND

WELWYN – Herts. – 504 T 28 – pop. 10 700 — 12 B2

London 31 m – Bedford 31 m – Cambridge 31 m

Tewin Bury Farm rest,
Southeast : 3½ m. by A 1000 on B 1000 ✉ AL6 0JB – ✆ (01438) 717 793 – hotel@tewinbury.co.uk – Fax (01438) 840 440 – Closed 25-26 December
32 rm – 🚹£ 114 🚹🚹£ 141 – **Rest** – Menu £ 21 (dinner) – Carte £ 24/27
◆ Consisting of a range of converted farm buildings on 400-acre working farm. 17C tythe barn used as function room located next to river. Individual rooms have beamed ceilings. Restaurant located in timbered farm building.

White Hart
2 Prospect Place ✉ AL6 9EN – ✆ (01438) 715 353 – bookings@thewhitehartotel.net – Fax (01438) 714 448
13 rm – 🚹£ 110 🚹🚹£ 110 – **Rest** – (Closed Sunday dinner) Carte £ 17/34
◆ Family-run converted 17C inn with snug bar filled with photos of yesteryear. Some contemporary bedrooms, others more traditional; those in courtyard are most spacious. Charming dining room with impressive high ceiling serves traditional English dishes.

WELWYN GARDEN CITY – Herts. – 504 T 28 — 12 B2

London 22 m – Luton 21 m
Panshanger Golf Complex Old Herns Lane, ✆ (01707) 333 312 .

Auberge du Lac
Brocket Hall, West : 3 m. by A 6129 on B 653 ✉ AL8 7XG – ✆ (01707) 368 888 – auberge@brocket-hall.co.uk – Fax (01707) 368 898 – Closed 1-10 January, Sunday dinner, Monday and Bank Holidays
Rest – Menu £ 30/55
◆ Part 18C former hunting lodge with lakeside terrace in the grounds of Brocket Hall - an idyllic setting for confident, classic cooking with a firm French base.

WENDLING – Norfolk – 504 W 25 – see East Dereham

WENTBRIDGE – W. Yorks. – **502** Q 23 – ✉ **Pontefract** 22 **B3**

London 183 m – Leeds 19 m – Nottingham 55 m – Sheffield 28 m

Wentbridge House

Old Great North Rd ✉ WF8 3JJ – ☎ (01977) 620 444 – info@wentbridgehouse.co.uk – Fax (01977) 620 148 – Closed 25 December

42 rm – †£ 100 ††£ 190/220

Rest *Fleur de Lys* – (dinner only and Sunday lunch) Carte £ 29/42

Rest *Wentbridge Brasserie* – (dinner only and Sunday lunch) Carte £ 23/30

◆ Once owned by the late Queen Mother's family, a part 18C bay-windowed house decorated in traditional colours. Sizeable rooms, some overlooking the lawned grounds. Fleur de Lys adjacent to smart firelit bar. Informal Wentbridge Brasserie.

WEOBLEY – Herefordshire – **503** L 27 – ✉ **Hereford** 18 **A3**

London 145 m – Brecon 30 m – Hereford 12 m – Leominster 9 m

Broxwood Court (heated) rm,

Broxwood, Northwest : 3 ¼ m. by A 4112, Broxwood rd on Lyonshall rd ✉ HR6 9JJ – ☎ (01544) 340 245 – mikeanne@broxwood.kc3.co.uk – Fax (01544) 340 573 – Closed 21 December - 6 January

5 rm – †£ 50/65 ††£ 100 – **Rest** – (by arrangement, communal dining) Menu £ 30

◆ 1950s house set in wonderfully tranquil location: vast grounds and formally laid-out gardens. Spacious drawing room, cosy library. Individually styled rooms with views.

The Salutation Inn with rm

Market Pitch ✉ HR4 8SJ – ☎ (01544) 318 443 – salutationinn@btinternet.com – Fax (01544) 318 216 – Closed 2 weeks after New Year, 25 December and lunch Sunday

3 rm – †£ 50/58 ††£ 90 – **Rest** – Carte £ 15/30

◆ In the heart of this pretty village, a charming, part 16C former cider house with a rustic real ale bar. Traditionally decorated bedrooms, two in the next door cottage. Attractive dining room.

WEST BAGBOROUGH – Somerset – **503** K 30 – see Taunton

WEST BURTON – N. Yorks. – **502** O 21 – ✉ **Leyburn** 22 **A1**

London 260 m – Carlisle 81 m – Darlington 34 m – Kendal 40 m – Leeds 62 m – York 58 m

The Grange without rest

✉ DL8 4JR – ☎ (01969) 663 348 – info@thegrange-yorkshiredales.co.uk

4 rm – †£ 45/50 ††£ 70/80

◆ 19C house: preserved tiling, staircase and antiques. Well-proportioned bedrooms, firelit drawing room. Mature riverside gardens. Impressive mahogany breakfast table.

WESTBURY – Wilts. – **503** N 30 4 **C2**

London 111 m – Trowbridge 5 m – Warminster 4 m

Garden House with rm rest,

26 Edward St, North : 4 m. by A 350 ✉ BA13 3BD – ☎ (01373) 859 995 – reception@thegardenhotel.co.uk – Fax (01373) 858 586 – Closed 24 December - 4 January

11 rm – †£ 65/75 ††£ 110 – **Rest** – (Closed Sunday dinner, Monday lunch and Bank Holidays) (dinner only and Sunday lunch) Carte £ 17/29 **s**

◆ Very personally run former post office in centre of town, with lovely enclosed rear garden. Modern, tasty menus with strong seasonal base. Cosy bedrooms.

WEST DIDSBURY – Gtr Manchester – see Manchester

ENGLAND

WEST END – Surrey – 504 S 29 – pop. 4 135 – ✉ Guildford 7 C1

London 37 m – Bracknell 7 m – Camberley 5 m – Guildford 8 m – Woking 6 m

The Inn @ West End

42 Guildford Road, on A 322 ✉ GU24 9PW – ☎ (01276) 858652 – greatfood@the-inn.co.uk

Rest – Menu £ 12/19 – Carte £ 25/30

◆ Well-prepared modern British standards and good-value lunches in this smartly renovated Victorian roadside pub; occasional wine tastings from a diverse cellar.

WESTFIELD – E. Sussex – 504 V 31 – pop. 1 509 8 B3

London 66 m – Brighton 38 m – Folkestone 45 m – Maidstone 30 m

The Wild Mushroom

Woodgate House, Westfield Lane, Southwest : ½ m. on A 28 ✉ TN35 4SB – ☎ (01424) 751 137 – info@wildmushroom.co.uk – Fax (01424) 753 405 – Closed first 2 weeks January, Christmas, Monday, Saturday lunch and Sunday dinner

Rest – (dinner only) (booking essential) Menu £ 19 – Carte £ 24/34 **s**

◆ Bustling and hospitable with modern interior and conservatory lounge. Flavourful, well-priced dishes from a varied, interesting menu. Loyal local following: be sure to book.

ENGLAND

WEST KIRBY – Wirral – 502 K 23 *Great Britain* 20 A3

London 219 m – Chester 19 m – Liverpool 12 m

Liverpool★ - Cathedrals★★, The Walker★★, Merseyside Maritime Museum★ and Albert Dock★, E : 13½ m. by A 553

Hillbark

Royden Park, Frankby, East : 2 ¾ m. by A 540 and B 5139 off Hillbark Rd ✉ CH48 1NP – ☎ (0151) 624 2400 – enquiries@hillbarkhotel.co.uk – Fax (0151) 625 4040

17 rm – 🛉£ 175 🛉🛉£ 175 – 2 suites

Rest *Yellow Room* – (Closed Sunday-Monday) Carte £ 50/65

Rest *Hillbark Grill* – Carte £ 26/37 **s**

◆ Impressive black and white timbered late Victorian house in tranquil lawned gardens. Antique furniture in country house style bedrooms; best views over Dee Estuary. Formal fine dining in Italiante Yellow Room. Hillbark grill specialises in steak.

Peel Hey without rest

Frankby Rd, Frankby, East : 2 ¼ m. by A 540 on B 5139 ✉ CH48 1PP – ☎ (0151) 677 9077 – enquiries@peelhey.com – Fax (0151) 625 4115

9 rm – 🛉£ 65/85 🛉🛉£ 85/115, £7.25

◆ Modernised 19C house that offers a good standard of accommodation. Attractive, comfortable rooms.

WESTLETON – Suffolk – 504 Y 27 – ✉ Saxmundham 15 D2

London 97 m – Cambridge 72 m – Ipswich 28 m – Norwich 31 m

Pond House without rest

The Hill ✉ IP17 3AN – ☎ (01728) 648 773 – minimum stay 2 nights

3 rm – 🛉£ 40 🛉🛉£ 60

◆ A welcoming atmosphere prevails in this neatly maintained 1700s cottage beside the village green. Simple, pine furnished bedrooms. Convenient for Minsmere Nature Reserve.

The ✿ award is the crème de la crème. This is awarded to restaurants which are really worth travelling miles for!

WEST LULWORTH – Dorset – 503 N 32 – ✉ Wareham 4 C3

London 129 m – Bournemouth 21 m – Dorchester 17 m – Weymouth 19 m
Lulworth Cove★

Gatton House without rest
Main Rd ✉ BH20 5RL – ✆ (01929) 400 252 – avril@gattonhouse.co.uk – Fax (01929) 400 252 – March-September
8 rm – †£ 52/62 ††£ 64/84
♦ Follow the winding garden path to a smart gabled house in the middle of this pleasant village. Comfy accommodation in co-ordinated décor; neat front-facing breakfast room.

WEST MALLING – Kent – 504 V 30 – pop. 2 144 8 B1

London 35 m – Maidstone 7 m – Royal Tunbridge Wells 14 m
Addington Maidstone, ✆ (01732) 844 785 .

Scott House without rest
37 High St ✉ ME19 6QH – ✆ (01732) 841 380 – mail@scott-house.co.uk – Fax (01732) 522 367 – Closed Christmas-New Year
5 rm – †£ 69 ††£ 89
♦ Comfy rooms in period style and a relaxing first-floor lounge share this part Georgian town house with a fine interior décor shop, run by the same warm husband and wife team.

The Swan
35 Swan St ✉ ME19 6JU – ✆ (01732) 521 910 – info@theswanwestmalling.co.uk – Fax (01732) 522 898 – Closed 26 December and 1 January
Rest – Menu £ 16 – Carte £ 24/37
♦ Radically renovated 16C pub in modern pine. Stylish lounge: leopard-print carpet, purple cushions. Modish menu at sensible prices; informal, very efficient service.

WEST MONKTON – Somerset – 503 K 30 – see Taunton

WESTON-SUPER-MARE – North Somerset – 503 K 29 – pop. 78 044 3 B2

London 147 m – Bristol 24 m – Taunton 32 m
Beach Lawns ✆ (01934) 888800
Worlebury Monks Hill, ✆ (01934) 625 789 .
Seafront (≤ ★★) BZ
Axbridge★★ (King John's Hunting Lodge★, St John the Baptist Church★) SE : 9 m. by A 371 - BY - and A 38 – Cheddar Gorge★★ (Gorge★★, Caves★, Jacob's Ladder ✻ ★) – Clevedon★ (≤ ★★, Clevedon Court★), NE : 10 m. by A 370 and M 5 – St Andrew's Church★, SE : 10½ m. by A 371

Plan on next page

The Beachlands rm,
17 Uphill Road North ✉ BS23 4NG – ✆ (01934) 621 401 – info@beachlandshotel.com – Fax (01934) 621 966 – Closed 24-31 December AZ **c**
23 rm – †£ 60/90 ††£ 110/120 – **Rest** – (bar lunch Monday-Saturday) Menu £ 21
♦ Well-established and family run, convenient for beach and golf course. Rooms in traditional prints; some, south-facing, have veranda doors giving on to a secluded garden. Formal dining room overlooks pleasant gardens.

Queenswood rest,
Victoria Park, off Upper Church Rd ✉ BS23 2HZ – ✆ (01934) 416 141 – Fax (01934) 621 759 – Closed 10 December-10 January BZ **s**
19 rm – †£ 50/75 ††£ 75/100 – **Rest** – (bar lunch) Menu £ 20 **s**
♦ Sizeable, 19C-style house, well kept by friendly, long-standing owners. Red velour lounge sofas and neat rooms in the time-honoured tradition of the British seaside holiday. Tried-and-tested menus.

ENGLAND

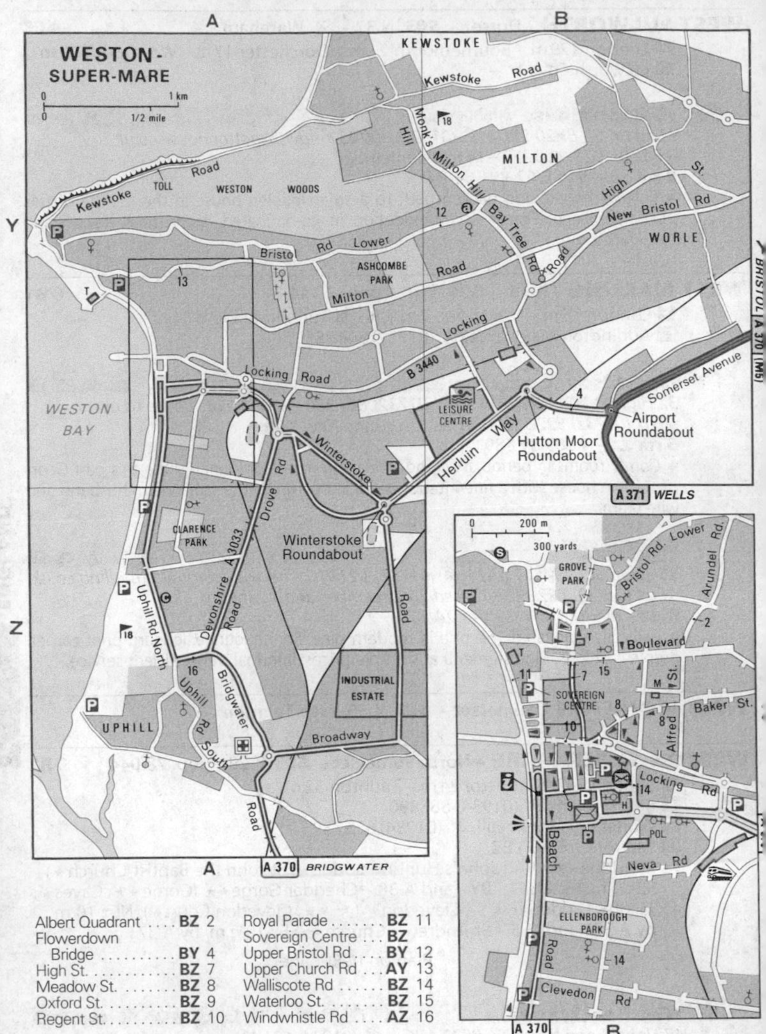

Albert Quadrant	BZ 2	Royal Parade	BZ 11
Flowerdown Bridge	BY 4	Sovereign Centre	BZ
High St.	BZ 7	Upper Bristol Rd	BY 12
Meadow St.	BZ 8	Upper Church Rd	AY 13
Oxford St.	BZ 9	Walliscote Rd	BZ 14
Regent St.	BZ 10	Waterloo St.	BZ 15
		Windwhistle Rd	AZ 16

XX **Duets** VISA MC

103 Upper Bristol Rd ✉ BS22 8ND – ✆ (01934) 413 428
– Closed 2 weeks August, first week January, Sunday dinner, Monday and Tuesday BY **a**

Rest – (dinner only and Sunday lunch) Menu £ 18/25 – Carte £ 29/32

◆ Diligent and unfussy service sets the tone in this traditionally styled restaurant, deservedly a neighbourhood favourite. Ably judged cooking on a tasty classical base.

WESTON UNDER WETHERLEY – Warks. – see Royal Leamington Spa

WESTON UNDERWOOD – Derbs. – see Derby

WESTOW – N. Yorks. 23 **C2**

London 224 m – Malton 8 m – York 15 m

The Blacksmiths Inn with rm — rm, P, VISA

Main St ✉ YO60 7NE – ✆ (01653) 618 365 – info@blacksmithsinn.co.uk – Fax (01653) 618 394 – Closed 1 week January, Monday and Tuesday

6 rm – †£ 40 ††£ 70 – **Rest** – (dinner only and Sunday lunch) Carte £ 15/30

◆ Fully refurbished country dining pub; log-burning stove, beams and flagged floor. Ingredients from local Manor Farm proudly used in winningly modish menus with daily specials.

WEST PECKHAM – Kent – see Maidstone

WEST STOKE – W. Sussex – see Chichester

WEST TANFIELD – N. Yorks. – 502 P 21 – ✉ Ripon 22 **B2**

London 237 m – Darlington 29 m – Leeds 32 m – Middlesbrough 39 m – York 36 m

The Bruce Arms with rm — P, VISA, AE

Main St ✉ HG4 5JJ – ✆ (01677) 470 325 – info@bruce-arms.com – Fax (01677) 470 925 – Closed Monday

2 rm – †£ 35 ††£ 70 – **Rest** – Carte £ 22/30

◆ Stone-built village pub: log fire, local ales, leather sofas. Vine covered, decked terrace. Well-spaced candlelit pub tables. Satisfying blackboard menu. Rustic bedrooms.

WEST WITTON – N. Yorks. – 502 O 21 – ✉ Leyburn 22 **B1**

London 241 m – Kendal 39 m – Leeds 60 m – Newcastle upon Tyne 65 m – York 53 m

Ivy Dene without rest — P

✉ DL8 4LP – ✆ (01969) 622 785 – info@ivydeneguesthouse.co.uk – Fax (01969) 622 785 – Closed 1 December-6 January

4 rm – †£ 56 ††£ 56/60

◆ Cosy, cottage-style rooms, one with four-poster bed, others with brass bedsteads, in this 300-year-old house. Firelit sitting room with a collection of clocks and antiques.

WETHERBY – W. Yorks. – 502 P 22 – pop. 10 562 *Great Britain* 22 **B2**

London 208 m – Harrogate 8 m – Leeds 13 m – York 14 m

The Library, 17 Westgate ✆ (01937) 582151

Linton Linton Lane, ✆ (01937) 580 089 .

Harewood House★★ (The Gallery★) AC, SW : 5 ½ m. by A 58 and A 659

Wood Hall — P, VISA, AE

Trip Lane, Linton, Southwest : 3 m. by A 661 and Linton Rd ✉ LS22 4JA – ✆ (01937) 587 271 – enquiries@woodhall.co.uk – Fax (01937) 584 353

44 rm – †£ 99/130 ††£ 135/195 – **Rest** – (bar lunch Monday-Saturday) Menu £ 35 – Carte £ 39/53

◆ Peacefully set part Jacobean and Georgian manor in 100 acres of woods and gardens. Refurbished contemporary public areas; well-appointed bedrooms. Popular wedding venue. Elegant dining room with candelabras and tall sash windows.

at Walton East : 4 m. by B 1224 – ✉ Wetherby

The Fox and Hounds — P, VISA, AE

Hall Park Road ✉ LS23 7DQ – ✆ (01937) 842 192 – Closed Sunday dinner

Rest – (booking essential) Menu £ 14 – Carte £ 20/28

◆ Hidden away in a sleepy village. Snug bar with stuffed fox in basket, framed sepia prints and dried flowers. Wide-ranging, homemade menus from rustic bread to ice-cream.

at Kirk Deighton **Northwest : 1 ½ m. on B 6164 – ✉ Wetherby**

The Bay Horse Inn

Main St ✉ LS22 4DZ – ✆ (01937) 580 058 – Fax (01937) 582 443 – Closed 25-26 December, 1 January, Sunday dinner and Monday lunch
Rest – (booking essential) Menu £ 14 – Carte £ 18/35
◆ Pub exuding real country character: fishing rods on ceiling, sepia prints, solid stone floors. Buy home-made jams and pickles. Eat tasty dishes with strong Yorkshire accent.

WEYMOUTH – Dorset – 503 M 32 – pop. 48 279 — 4 C3

London 142 m – Bournemouth 35 m – Bristol 68 m – Exeter 59 m – Swindon 94 m
to Guernsey (St Peter Port) and Jersey (St Helier) (Condor Ferries Ltd)
The King's Statue, The Esplanade ✆ (01305) 785747, tic@weymouth.gov.uk
Links Rd, ✆ (01305) 773 981 .
Town★ – Timewalk★ **AC** – Nothe Fort (≤ ★) **AC** – Boat Trip★ (Weymouth Bay and Portland Harbour) **AC**
Chesil Beach★★ – Portland★ - Portland Bill (✳ ★★) S : 2½ m. by A 354. Maiden Castle★★ (≤ ★) N : 6½ m. by A 354 – Sub-Tropical Gardens★ **AC**, St Catherine's Chapel★) NW : 9 m. by B 3157

Moonfleet Manor

Northwest : 4½ m. by B 3157 ✉ DT3 4ED – ✆ (01305) 786 948 – info@moonfleetmanor.co.uk – Fax (01305) 774 395
34 rm – †£ 145/190 ††£ 300/440 – 2 suites – **Rest** – (bar lunch Monday-Saturday) Menu £ 34
◆ Georgian in origin, an extended country house with stunning coastal views. Well equipped rooms, cosy lounges hung with oils. Games room and special facilities for families. Subtle Mediterranean styling imbues restaurant.

Chandlers without rest

4 Westerhall Rd ✉ DT4 7SZ – ✆ (01305) 771 341 – info@chandlershotel.com – Fax (01305) 830 122 – Closed 24-26 December
10 rm – †£ 55/80 ††£ 90/150
◆ Large Victorian house with unexpected air of tranquility. Spacious lounge, pleasant breakfast room and stylish, contemporary bedrooms with high ceilings and Swedish style.

Bay View without rest

35 The Esplanade ✉ DT4 8DH – ✆ (01305) 782 083 – info@bayview-weymouth.co.uk – Fax (01305) 782 083 – February-November
8 rm – †£ 40/45 ††£ 50/60, £7.50
◆ Generously sized en suite rooms, many with four-poster beds or broad bay windows, in a sizeable townhouse with views over the bay. Neatly kept basement lounge.

Perry's

4 Trinity Rd, The Old Harbour ✉ DT4 8TJ – ✆ (01305) 785 799 – Fax (01305) 787 002 – Closed 25-26 December, lunch Monday and Saturday and dinner Sunday and Monday in winter
Rest – Seafood Menu £ 20 (lunch) – Carte £ 24/34
◆ Simple, family-run local favourite by the old harbour. Friendly staff, tasty cooking and plenty of seafood specials: shellfish soup, Portland crab, citrus-dressed bass.

The red symbol?
This denotes the very essence of peace – only the sound of birdsong first thing in the morning …

ENGLAND

WHALLEY – Lancs. – 502 M 22 – pop. 3 230 – ✉ Blackburn 20 B2

London 233 m – Blackpool 32 m – Burnley 12 m – Manchester 28 m – Preston 15 m

Long Leese Barn Clerkhill, ✆ (01254) 822 236.

at Mitton Northwest : 2½ m. on B 6246 – ✉ Whalley

The Three Fishes

Mitton Road ✉ BB7 9PQ – ✆ (01254) 826 888 – Fax (01254) 826 026 – Closed 25 December

Rest – (bookings not accepted) Carte £ 16/22

◆ Huge, 140 cover modern dining pub, once a coaching inn. Lancashire and north-west England regional specialities dominate the menu. Perenially busy: remember, you can't book!

WHASHTON – N. Yorks. – see Richmond

WHAW – N. Yorks. – 502 O 20 – see Reeth

WHICKHAM – Tyne and Wear – 501 O/P 19 – see Gateshead

WHITBY – N. Yorks. – 502 S 20 – pop. 13 594 *Great Britain* 23 C1

London 257 m – Middlesbrough 31 m – Scarborough 21 m – York 45 m

Langborne Rd ✆ (01947) 602674

Low Straggleton Sandsend Rd, ✆ (01947) 600 660.

Abbey★

Bagdale Hall

1 Bagdale ✉ YO21 1QL – ✆ (01947) 602 958 – Fax (01947) 820 714

14 rm – †£ 60/70 ††£ 90/160 – **Rest** – (dinner only) Carte approx. £ 25

◆ Tudor manor with fine fireplaces in carved wood and 19C Delft tiles; panelled rooms with mullioned windows; four-posters in period style bedrooms. Annex for more modern rooms. Dining room boasts timbered ceiling and massive wooden fireplace.

Cross Butts Stable

rm,

Guisborough Rd, West : 1¾ m. on A 171 (Teeside rd) ✉ YO21 1TL – ✆ (01947) 820 986 – info@cross-butts.co.uk – Fax (01947) 825 665

9 rm – †£ 55/85 ††£ 85/160 – **Rest** – Carte £ 20/29

◆ Extended farmhouse on working farm personally run by a welcoming family. Superb bedrooms, set round courtyard with water feature, have flag floors and warm, sumptuous aura. Smart, informal restaurant areas over two floors: a mix of suites, sofas and tables.

Green's

13 Bridge St ✉ YO22 4BG – ✆ (01947) 600 284 – info@greensofwhitby.com – Closed 25-26 December and 1 January

Rest – Seafood (dinner only and lunch Friday-Sunday) (booking essential) Menu £ 40 (dinner) – Carte £ 25/39

◆ Set in town centre, close to quayside, with a rustic, informal ambience. Constantly changing seafood menus are simply cooked and employ much produce freshly landed at Whitby.

at Briggswath Southwest : 3½ m. by A 171 (Teesdie rd), A 169 on B 1410 ✉ Whitby

The Lawns without rest

73 Carr Hill Lane ✉ YO21 1RS – ✆ (01947) 810 310 – lorton@onetel.com – Fax (01947) 810 310 – Closed Christmas-New Year

3 rm – †£ 68 ††£ 68

◆ Sizeable, converted house above a south-facing garden and verge of evergreens. Stripped wooden floors, understated décor. Spotless rooms. Fine views of moors and Esk valley.

The Olde Ford without rest
1 Briggswath ✉ YO21 1RU – ☎ (01947) 810704 – gray.theoldeford@btinternet.com – Closed 3 weeks January, 14-30 June and 22-28 December
3 rm – †£45 ††£55/60
◆ Appealing little stone cottage on the banks of the river Esk: former village post office. Traditional Yorkshire breakfasts. All rooms look out over garden and river.

at Dunsley West : 3 ¼ m. by A 171 – ✉ Whitby

Dunsley Hall Country House
✉ YO21 3TL – ☎ (01947) 893437 – reception@dunsleyhall.com – Fax (01947) 893505
26 rm – †£95/120 ††£149/198 – **Rest** – (bar lunch Monday-Saturday) Menu £17 – Carte £26/36
◆ Behind pillared gates, a personally run late Victorian house: intricately oak panelled lounge with leather furnished bar. Comfortable, period styled rooms with country views. Dining room boasts Whitby seafood.

at Sandsend Northwest : 3 m. on A 174 – ✉ Whitby

Estbek House with rm
East Row ✉ YO21 3SY – ☎ (01947) 893424 – info@estbekhouse.co.uk – Fax (01947) 893623 – Closed 3 January-1 February
4 rm – †£60/70 ††£100/130 – **Rest** – Seafood (dinner only) Carte £28/43
◆ This personally run Regency house, adjacent to beach, boasts delightful terrace, basement bar, smart restaurant serving local, wild seafood, and utterly charming rooms.

Good food and accommodation at moderate prices?
Look for the Bib symbols:
red Bib Gourmand for food, blue Bib Hotel for hotels

ENGLAND

WHITCHURCH – Shrops. – 502 L 25 18 B1

London 168 m – Nantwich 11 m – Wrexham 15 m

at Burleydam East : 4 ¼ m. on A 525 – ✉ Whitchurch

The Combermere Arms
✉ SY13 4AT – ☎ (01948) 871223 – combermere.arms@brunningandprice.co.uk – Fax (01948) 661371
Rest – Carte £18/27
◆ Rurally located pub with smart terrace ideal for al fresco refreshment. Interior skylights lend an open, airy feel. Informal, eclectic menus. Some vast tables for big parties.

WHITEHAVEN – Cumbria – 502 J 20 21 A2

London 332 m – Carlisle 39 m – Keswick 28 m – Penrith 47 m

Zest
Low Rd, South : ½ m. on B 5345 (St Bees) ✉ CA28 9HS – ☎ (01946) 692848 – Fax (01946) 66984 – Closed 25 December-2 January and Sunday-Tuesday
Rest – (dinner only) Carte £17/32
◆ Don't be put off by the unprepossessing exterior: inside is a smart, stylish eatery and bar with brown leather sofas. Eclectic range of modern menus with numerous influences.

WHITEPARISH – Wilts. – 503 P 30 – see Salisbury

WHITEWELL – Lancs. – **502** M 22 – ✉ **Clitheroe** 20 **B2**

London 281 m – Lancaster 31 m – Leeds 55 m – Manchester 41 m – Preston 13 m

The Inn at Whitewell

Forest of Bowland ✉ BB7 3AT – ✆ (01200) 448 222 – reception@innatwhitewell.com – Fax (01200) 448 298

23 rm – †£74 ††£98 – 1 suite – **Rest** – (bar lunch) Carte £20/35

◆ Once home to the Royal Keeper of the Forest, a popular inn with considerable charm, full of eyecatching curios. Stylish rooms with CD players; some have real peat fires. Intimate dining room overlooks river Hodder and Trough of Bowland.

WHITLEY – Wilts. – see Melksham

WHITSTABLE – Kent – **504** X 29 – **pop. 30 195** 9 **C1**

London 68 m – Dover 24 m – Maidstone 37 m – Margate 12 m

7 Oxford St ✆ (01227) 275482, whitstableinformation@canterbury.gov.uk

Continental

29 Beach Walk, East : ½ m. by Sea St and Harbour St ✉ CT5 2BP – ✆ (01227) 280 280 – jamie@hotelcontinental.co.uk – Fax (01227) 284 114

30 rm – †£63 ††£100/145 – **Rest** – (bar lunch) Carte £20/32

◆ Laid-back, privately owned hotel with an unadorned 30s-style façade overlooking the sea; simply furnished, plain-walled rooms - picture windows and warm colours. Split-level bistro with "no frills" approach.

Whitstable Oyster Fishery Co.

Royal Native Oyster Stores, The Horsebridge ✉ CT5 1BU – ✆ (01227) 276 856 – Fax (01227) 770 829 – Closed 25-26 and 31 December and Monday except Bank Holidays

Rest – Seafood (booking essential) Carte £30/40

◆ Relaxed and unfussy converted beach warehouse; seafood on display in open kitchen; oysters and moules-frites draw a trendy young set at weekends. Arthouse cinema upstairs.

Jo Jo's

209 Tankerton Rd, East : 1½ m. by Sea St and Harbour St ✉ CT5 2AT – ✆ (01227) 274 591 – Closed December- January, Monday-Tuesday and Sunday dinner

Rest – (booking essential) Carte £18/25

◆ Charmingly laid back eatery with snug interior and mix of bar stools and rustic wooden tables. There's a simple terrace, too. Appealing mix of tapas and meze to graze over.

at Seasalter Southwest : 2 m. by B 2205 – ✉ **Whitstable**

The Sportsman (Steve Harris)

Faversham Rd, Southwest : 2 m. following coast rd ✉ CT5 4BP – ✆ (01227) 273 370 – Closed 25-26 December

Rest – (closed Sunday dinner and Monday) Carte £19/29

Spec. Crab risotto. Roast Barnsley chop, spinach, potato cake and lamb jus. Jasmine tea junket, tropical fruit soup.

◆ Set between shingle and marsh on the coastal road, serving confident, unfussy and fantastically flavoursome cooking, made from ingredients very much rooted in the locality.

WHITTLE-LE-WOODS – Lancs. – **502** M 23 – see Chorley

Hotels and restaurants change every year, so change your Michelin guide every year!

WHITTLESFORD – Cambs. – **504** U 27 14 **B3**

London 50 m – Cambridge 11 m – Peterborough 46 m

The Tickell

1 North Rd ✉ CB2 4NZ – ✆ (01223) 833 128 – Fax (01223) 835 907 – Closed 25-26 December, Sunday dinner and Monday

Rest – Menu £ 30 – Carte £ 20/38

◆ Richly ornate 300 year-old exterior with conservatory and terrace. Quirky feel pervades: emerald green walls, yellow ceiling. Rich, classic meals from the Gallic repertoire.

WHITWELL-ON-THE-HILL – N. Yorks. – **502** R 21 – ✉ York 23 **C2**

London 240 m – Kingston-upon-Hull 47 m – Scarborough 29 m – York 13 m

The Stone Trough Inn

Kirkham Abbey, East : 1 ¾ m. by A 64 on Kirkham Priory rd ✉ YO60 7JS – ✆ (01653) 618 713 – info@stonetroughinn.co.uk – Fax (01653) 618 819 – Closed 2-5 January, 25 December

Rest – (closed Monday) Carte £ 23/30

◆ Friendly rustic pub, two minutes from the striking ruins of Kirkham Abbey. Wide-ranging menu on a sound local base: satisfying and full of flavour. Warm, attentive service.

WICKFORD – Essex – **504** V 29 – see Basildon

WIGGINTON – Oxon. – see Banbury

WIGHT (Isle of) – I.O.W. – **503** P/Q 31 – pop. 124 577 *Great Britain* 6 **B3**

from East Cowes to Southampton (Red Funnel Ferries) frequent services daily (1 h) – from Yarmouth to Lymington (Wightlink Ltd) frequent services daily (30 mn) – from Fishbourne to Portsmouth (Wightlink Ltd) frequent services daily (35 mn)

from Ryde to Portsmouth (Hovertravel Ltd) frequent services daily (10 mn) – from Ryde to Portsmouth (Wightlink Ltd) frequent services daily (15 mn) – from East Cowes to Southampton (Red Funnel Ferries) frequent services daily (22 mn)

Island★★

Osborne House, East Cowes★★ **AC** – Carisbrooke Castle, Newport★★ **AC** (Keep ≤ ★) – Brading★ (Roman Villa★ **AC**, St Mary's Church★, Nunwell House★ **AC**) – Shorwell : St Peter's Church★ (wall paintings★)

Brighstone 6 **B3**

The Lodge without rest

Main Rd ✉ PO30 4DJ – ✆ (01983) 741 272 – thelodgeb@hotmail.com – Fax (01983) 741 272 – restricted opening in winter

7 rm – ♦£ 45/60 ♦♦£ 50/70

◆ Victorian country house set in two and a half acres: quiet location. Real fire centrepiece of large sitting room. Completely co-ordinated rooms of varnished pine.

Freshwater – I.O.W. – pop. 7 317 – ✉ Isle of Wight 6 **A3**

Newport 13 m

Sandpipers

Coastguard Lane (via public car park), Freshwater Bay, South : 1 ½ m. by A 3055 ✉ PO40 9QX – ✆ (01983) 758 500 – info@sandpipershotel.com

26 rm – ♦£ 35/70 ♦♦£ 70/180 – **Rest** – Carte £ 18/40

◆ Detached Victorian house with a friendly, family run atmosphere. Close to the cliffs, beach and Afton nature reserve. Good sized, modern-style rooms. Garden conservatory restaurant set around variety of water features.

ENGLAND

The Red Lion

Church Pl, via Hooke Hill ✉ PO40 9BP – ✆ (01983) 754 925 – info@redlion-wight.co.uk – Fax (01983) 754 483 – Closed 25 December
Rest – Carte £ 20/28
◆ Bustling part 14C pub with much charm. Located at the top of a hill and next to the church. Stone floors, open fires and a couple of sofas. Blackboard menu of seasonal fare.

St Lawrence – I.O.W. – ✉ Isle of Wight — 6 B3

▶ Newport 16 m

Little Orchard without rest

Undercliffe Drive, West : 1 m. on A 3055 ✉ PO38 1YA – ✆ (01983) 731 106
3 rm ☕ – 🚹£ 42 🚹🚹£ 60
◆ A pretty, detached stone cottage with secluded rear garden and some views of the sea. Large, welcoming lounge with piano. Simple, comfortable bedrooms.

Seaview – I.O.W. – pop. 2 181 – ✉ Isle of Wight — 6 B3

Priory Bay

Priory Drive, Southeast : 1½ m. by B 3330 ✉ PO34 5BU – ✆ (01983) 613 146 – enquiries@priorybay.co.uk – Fax (01983) 616 539
18 rm ☕ – 🚹£ 70/135 🚹🚹£ 200/270 – 2 suites
Rest *The Restaurant* – Menu £ 30
◆ Medieval priory with Georgian additions, surrounded by woodland. High ceilinged drawing room and bar area with leaded windows. Characterful rooms. Main Restaurant has views of the garden.

Seaview rest,

High St ✉ PO34 5EX – ✆ (01983) 612 711 – reception@seaviewhotel.co.uk – Fax (01983) 613 729
23 rm ☕ – 🚹£ 100/200 🚹🚹£ 120/345 – 1 suite
Rest *The Restaurant and Sunshine Room* – (in bar Sunday dinner except Bank Holidays) (booking essential) Carte approx. £ 31
◆ Victorian hotel with smart genuine style. Integral part of the community, on street leading to seafront. Bold modern bedrooms and nautically styled, welcoming public areas. Twin eateries, full of clocks and rare model ship collection.

Shanklin – I.O.W. – pop. 17 305 – ✉ Isle of Wight — 6 B3

▶ Newport 9 m
🅘 67 High St ✆ (01983) 813818
18 The Fairway Lake Sandown, ✆ (01983) 403 217 .

Rylstone Manor

Rylstone Gdns ✉ PO37 6RG – ✆ (01983) 862 806 – rylstone.manor@btinternet.com – Fax (01983) 862 806 – Closed January
9 rm ☕ – 🚹£ 55 🚹🚹£ 110/125 – **Rest** – (dinner only) Menu £ 20 **s**
◆ Part 19C former gentleman's residence set in the town's cliff-top gardens. Interior has a comfortable period feel. Well furnished, individually styled bedrooms. Characterful Victorian hued dining room.

Foxhills without rest

30 Victoria Ave ✉ PO37 6LS – ✆ (01983) 862 329 – info@foxhillsofshanklin.co.uk – Fax (01983) 866 666 – Closed January and 24-26 December
8 rm ☕ – 🚹£ 54/108 🚹🚹£ 88/108
◆ Attractive house in leafy avenue with woodland to the rear. Bright lounge with fireplace. Bedrooms in pastel shades. Unusual jacuzzi, spa and beauty treatments.

ENGLAND

Grange Bank
Grange Rd ✉ PO37 6NN – ✆ (01983) 862 337 – grangebank@btinternet.com – March-October
9 rm – £ 28/43 £ 55/65 – **Rest** – (dinner only) (booking essential) (residents only, unlicensed) Menu £ 12
◆ Extended Victorian house near high street. Comfortable, simple and immaculately kept with friendly, domestic ambience. Good value accommodation.

Totland – I.O.W. – pop. 7 317 – ✉ Isle of Wight 6 A3

Newport 13 m

Sentry Mead
Madeira Rd ✉ PO39 0BJ – ✆ (01983) 753 212 – info@sentrymead.co.uk – Fax (01983) 754 710 – Closed 7-21 November and 25-27 December
13 rm (dinner included) – £ 70/115 £ 140/170 – **Rest** – (bar lunch Monday-Saturday) Menu £ 23 – Carte £ 21/31
◆ Detached Victorian house with quiet garden 100 yards from beach. Traditional interiors include bar area and conservatory lounge. Comfortable rooms furnished with light wood. Popular menus in dining room.

Ventnor – I.O.W. – pop. 5 978 – ✉ Isle of Wight 6 B3

Newport 10 m
34 High St, ✆ (01983) 813818 (summer only)
Steephill Down Rd, ✆ (01983) 853 326 .

at Bonchurch – ✉ Isle of Wight 6 B3

ENGLAND

Royal
Belgrave Rd ✉ PO38 1JJ – ✆ (01983) 852 186 – enquiries@royalhoteliow.co.uk – Fax (01983) 855 395 – Closed 2 weeks January
55 rm – £ 100/160 £ 155/175 – **Rest** – (bar lunch Monday-Saturday) Menu £ 35 (dinner) **s** – Carte lunch £ 28/34 **s**
◆ Largest hotel on the island, a Victorian property, in the classic style of English seaside hotels. Traditional décor throughout the public areas and comfortable bedrooms. Light lunches in conservatory; classic meals in capacious dining room.

Wellington ← Ventnor and English Channel,
Belgrave Rd ✉ PO38 1JH – ✆ (01983) 856 600 – enquiries@thewellingtonhotel.net – Fax (01983) 856 611
28 rm – £ 80/90 £ 110/120 – **Rest** – (dinner only) Carte £ 23/36 **s**
◆ Totally refurbished Victorian hotel with commanding town and sea views. Modish lines throughout. Most rooms have a balcony; all are imbued with a stunning sense of modernity. Spacious dining room with dramatic views and beautiful decked terrace.

The Hambrough with rm ← rest,
Hambrough Rd ✉ PO38 1SQ – ✆ (01983) 856 333 – info@thehambrough.com – Fax (01983) 857 260
7 rm – £ 109/135 £ 149/200 – **Rest** – (Closed Tuesday and Sunday dinner) Menu £ 18/39
◆ Victorian house with contrastingly modish bar and avant-garde restaurant. Well-conceived menus enjoy contemporary starting point. State-of-the-art rooms with neutral hues.

The Pond Café
Bonchurch ✉ PO38 1RG – ✆ (01983) 855 666 – info@thepondcafe.com – Fax (01983) 855 666 – closed Monday
Rest – Carte £ 18/27 **s**
◆ Intimate restaurant, with duck pond, in sleepy hamlet. Cosy sunlit terrace. Island's larder utilised to the full for seasonal dishes in unfussy, halogen lit surroundings.

Yarmouth – I.O.W. – ✉ Isle of Wight 6 **A3**

▶ Newport 10 m

The George

Quay St ✉ PO41 0PE – ☎ (01983) 760 331 – res@thegeorge.co.uk – Fax (01983) 760 425

18 rm – ♦£ 95/130 ♦♦£ 255 – 1 suite

Rest ***The Brasserie*** – see restaurant listing

◆ 17C quayside hotel in shadow of Yarmouth Castle. Flagged central hall and extensive wood panelling. Traditionally decorated bedrooms; best are 'balcony suites' with views of Solent.

The Brasserie – at The George H.

Quay St ✉ PO41 0PE – ☎ (01983) 760 331 – Fax (01983) 760 425

Rest – Carte £ 26/40

◆ Informal brasserie restaurant overlooks terrace and garden, with views out to sea. Mediterranean-influenced menu.

The sun's out – let's eat alfresco!

Look for a terrace:

WILLERBY – East Riding – **502** S 22 – **see Kingston-upon-Hull**

WILLESLEY – Glos. – **503** N 29 – **see Tetbury**

WILLIAN – Herts. – **see Letchworth**

WILLINGTON – Ches. – **see Tarporley**

WILMINGTON – Devon – **503** K 31 – **see Honiton**

WILMINGTON – E. Sussex – **504** U 31 – **see Eastbourne**

WILMINGTON – Kent – **504** V 29 – **see Dartford**

WILMSLOW – Ches. – **502** N 24 – **pop. 34 087** 20 **B3**

▶ London 189 m – Liverpool 38 m – Manchester 12 m – Stoke-on-Trent 27 m

Great Warford Mobberley, ☎ (01565) 872 148 .

Holiday Inn Manchester Airport

Oversley Ford, Altrincham Rd, Northwest : 2 ¾ m. on A 538 ✉ SK9 4LR – ☎ (01625) 889 988 – Fax (01625) 531 876

126 rm – ♦£ 54/189 ♦♦£ 54/189, £13.95

Rest ***The Terrace*** – (bar lunch) Carte £ 20/26 **s**

◆ Group hotel, at first sight suggestive of a large cream-painted villa. Bright rooms, busy meeting suites plus coffee shop and extensive leisure club for relaxing time-outs. Bright modern décor. Extensive menu of popular dishes to suit all tastes.

Stanneylands

Stanneylands Rd, North : 1 m. by A 34 ✉ SK9 4EY – ☎ (01625) 525 225 – enquiries@stanneylandshotel.co.uk – Fax (01625) 537 282

55 rm – ♦£ 110/125 ♦♦£ 125, £12.95 – 1 suite

Rest ***The Restaurant*** – (residents only Sunday dinner) Menu £ 18/28 – Carte £ 28/33

◆ Attractive 19C redbrick hotel standing in mature grounds; exudes pleasant, country house style. Two characterful lounges and comfortable, traditional bedrooms. Comfy oak-panelled surroundings for diners.

ENGLAND

Marigold House without rest
132 Knutsford Rd, Southwest : 1 m. on B 5086 ✉ SK9 6JH – ✆ (01625) 584 414 – closed Christmas
3 rm – £ 38 £ 50
◆ 18C former farmhouse, 10 minutes from Manchester Airport; flagged floors throughout with log fires and antiques. Oak beams in bedrooms. Communal breakfast at superb oak table.

WIMBORNE MINSTER – Dorset – 503 O 31 – pop. 14 884 4 C3

London 112 m – Bournemouth 10 m – Dorchester 23 m – Salisbury 27 m – Southampton 30 m
29 High St ✆ (01202) 886116, wimbornetic@eastdorsetdc.gov.uk
Town★ - Minster★ – Priest's House Museum★ **AC**
Kingston Lacy★★ **AC**, NW : 3 m. by B 3082

Les Bouviers with rm
Arrowsmith Rd, Canford Magna, South : 2¼ m. by A 349 and A 341 ✉ BH21 3BD – ✆ (01202) 889 555 – info@lesbouviers.co.uk – Fax (01202) 639 428
6 rm – £ 85/105 £ 120/140, £ 12.50 – **Rest** – (Closed Sunday dinner) Menu £ 20/30
◆ Plush yet homely restaurant affording views to acres of mature grounds. Formal feel lightened by personable service. Complex dishes with modern twists. Stylish bedrooms.

WINCANTON – Somerset – 503 M 30 4 C3

London 118 m – Bruton 5 m – Glastonbury 20 m

Holbrook House
West : 2¼ m. on A 371 ✉ BA9 8BS – ✆ (01963) 824 466 – enquiries@holbrookhouse.co.uk – Fax (01963) 32 681
19 rm – £ 100/140 £ 310 – 2 suites
Rest ***Cedar*** – (Closed Sunday dinner) Menu £ 18/35 – Carte £ 29/37
◆ Substantial 19C country house in mature grounds. Dramatic proportions prevail, but intimate spaces - like the wood-panelled bar - gel seamlessly. Smart spa; individual rooms. Classic dining room overlooks gardens.

WINCHCOMBE – Glos. – 503 O 28 – pop. 3 682 4 D1

London 100 m – Birmingham 43 m – Gloucester 26 m – Oxford 43 m
Town Hall, High St ✆ (01242) 602925

Isbourne Manor House without rest
Castle St ✉ GL54 5JA – ✆ (01242) 602 281 – felicity@isbourne-manor.co.uk – Fax (01242) 602 281 – Closed Christmas
3 rm – £ 60/65 £ 95/100
◆ Wisteria-clad Georgian and Elizabethan manor. Cosy drawing room: antique furniture and open fire. One room has a four-poster bed, one a roof top terrace. Riverside garden.

Westward without rest
Sudeley Lodge, East : 1½ m. by Castle St on Sudeley Lodge/Parks/Farm rd ✉ GL54 5JB – ✆ (01242) 604 372 – jimw@haldon.co.uk – Fax (01242) 604 640 – Closed Christmas-New Year
3 rm – £ 55/70 £ 100
◆ Secluded, personally run 18C farmhouse: elegant, wood-floored drawing room and charming sitting room, bedrooms share fine views of 550-acre estate and mature gardens.

ENGLAND

XX **Wesley House** with rm

High St ✉ GL54 5LJ – ☎ (01242) 602 366 – enquiries@wesleyhouse.co.uk – Fax (01242) 609 046

5 rm – †£ 65/130 ††£ 80/200 – **Rest** – (Closed Sunday dinner) Menu £ 25/35

◆ Hugely characterful part 15C house: dine amongst the beams or in the stylish glass-roofed extension. Tasty modern British cooking with original twists. Smilingly quaint rooms.

XX **5 North St** (Marcus Ashenford)

5 North St ✉ GL54 5LH – ☎ (01242) 604 566 – marcusashenford@yahoo.co.uk – Fax (01242) 603 788 – Closed 2 weeks January, 1 week August, Sunday dinner, Tuesday lunch and Monday

Rest – Menu £ 24/40

Spec. Roast lobster, pasta, gingered vegetables with a champagne and lemon grass sauce. Duck breast, sweet and sour legs, lentils, celeriac purée, cassis sauce. Chocolate marquise, raspberry sorbet and vanilla tuiles.

◆ Personally run, cosy, 17C timbered restaurant with low-beamed ceiling and a pleasantly relaxed, friendly atmosphere. Good value menus offer flavoursome and refined cooking.

X **Wesley House Bar & Grill**

20 High St ✉ GL54 5LJ – ☎ (01242) 602 366 – enquiries@wesleyhouse.co.uk – Fax (01242) 609 046

Rest – Tapas Menu £ 13 (lunch) – Carte £ 14/29

◆ Located on busy high street, this is a buzzy place to be, with trendy bar, comfy lounge, and wood-floored dining area serving authentic Spanish tapas beneath the big mirrors.

The White Hart Inn with rm

High St ✉ GL54 5LJ – ☎ (01242) 602 359 – info@wineandsausage.com – Fax (01242) 602 703

8 rm – †£ 75 ††£ 115 – **Rest** – Carte £ 18/27

◆ Whitewashed former coaching inn with rustic feel. Hearty homemade dishes; sausages have their own menu. Friendly, chatty atmosphere and service. Well-stocked wine shop. Comfortable bedrooms have a traditional feel; the rear rooms are quieter.

Undecided between two equivalent establishments? Within each category, establishments are classified in our order of preference.

ENGLAND

WINCHELSEA – E. Sussex – **504** W 31 *Great Britain* 9 **C3**

London 64 m – Brighton 46 m – Folkestone 30 m

Town★ – St Thomas Church (effigies★)

Strand House

Tanyard's Lane, East : ¼ m. on A 259 ✉ TN36 4JT – ☎ (01797) 226 276 – info@thestrandhouse.co.uk – Fax (01797) 224 806

10 rm (dinner included) – †£ 50/70 ††£ 75/120 – **Rest** – (by arrangement) Menu £ 25

◆ 14C and 15C half-timbered house of low beams and inglenook fireplaces: carefully tended rear garden shaded by tall trees, snug lounge; well-kept rooms in traditional style. Simple homecooking.

WINCHESTER – Hants. – **503** P 30 – **pop. 41 420** *Great Britain* 6 **B2**

London 72 m – Bristol 76 m – Oxford 52 m – Southampton 12 m
Guildhall, The Broadway (01962) 840500, tourism@winchester.gov.uk
City★★ - Cathedral★★★ **AC** B – Winchester College★ **AC** B **B** – Castle Great Hall★ B **D** – God Begot House★ B **A**
St Cross Hospital★★ **AC** A

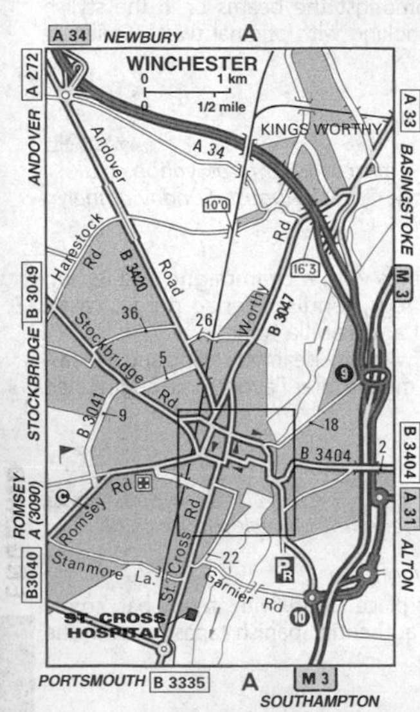

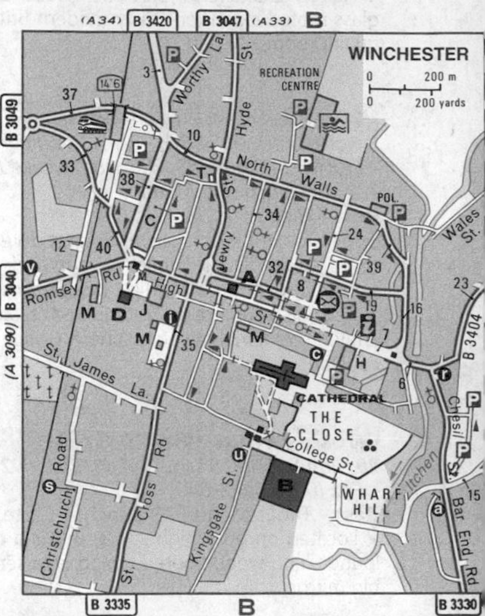

Alresford Rd . . . . **A** 2
Andover Rd . . . . **B** 3
Bereweeke Rd . . . . **A** 5
Bridge St . . . . **B** 6
Broadway (The) . . . . **B** 7
Brooks Shopping Centre . . . **B** 8
Chilbolton Ave . . . . **A** 9
City Rd . . . . **B** 10
Clifton Terrace . . . . **B** 12
Eastgate St . . . . **B** 16
Easton Lane . . . . **A** 18
East Hill . . . . **B** 15
Friarsgate . . . . **B** 19
High St . . . . **B**
Kingsgate Rd . . . . **A** 22
Magdalen Hill . . . . **B** 23
Middle Brook St . . . . **B** 24
Park Rd . . . . **A** 26
St George's St . . . . **B** 3
St Paul's Hill . . . . **B** 3
St Peter's St . . . . **B** 3
Southgate St . . . . **B** 3
Stockbridge Rd . . . . **B** 3
Stoney Lane . . . . **A** 3
Sussex St . . . . **B** 3
Union St . . . . **B** 3
Upper High St . . . . **B** 4

Mercure Wessex rest, VISA AE

Paternoster Row SO23 9LQ – (01962) 861 611 – h6619-gm@accor.com – Fax (01962) 849617 B **c**
93 rm – £65/104 £65/104, £12.95 – 1 suite
Rest *Walkers* – (bar lunch) Menu £ 17/28 **s**
◆ Smartly run group hotel. Enviable cathedral view from the lounge - a pleasant spot for tea - and many of the rooms, all well appointed and decorated in traditional patterns. Wide windowed restaurant with floodlit views of cathedral by night.

Hotel du Vin VISA AE

14 Southgate St SO23 9EF – (01962) 841 414 – info.winchester@hotelduvin.com – Fax (01962) 842 458 B **i**
24 rm – £ 135/205 £ 135/205, £13.95
Rest *Bistro* – see restaurant listing
◆ Elegant bedrooms, each with CD player, mini bar and distinct décor reflecting its wine house sponsors, in a 1715 redbrick house. Smart Champagne bar with inviting sofas.

Giffard House without rest VISA AE

50 Christchurch Rd SO23 9SU – (01962) 852 628 – giffardhotel@aol.com – Fax (01962) 856 722 – Closed 28 December-2 January B **s**
13 rm – £69/81 £115
◆ Imposing part Victorian, part Edwardian house. Spacious breakfast room and comfortable sitting room with large fireplace. Immaculate rooms with good facilities.

Dawn Cottage without rest
Romsey Rd ✉ SO22 5PQ – ☎ (01962) 869 956 – dawncottage@hotmail.com – Fax (01962) 869 956 – Closed Christmas A **c**
3 rm – ♦£ 50/55 ♦♦£ 70
◆ Attractive, spotlessly kept cottage; friendly hosts. Simply decorated rooms; all have views across the Itchen Valley. Secluded rear garden flanked by tall trees.

Chesil Rectory
Chesil St ✉ SO23 0HU – ☎ (01962) 851 555 – info@chesilrectory.co.uk – Fax (01962) 869 704 – Closed 2 weeks Christmas, 2 weeks August, Sunday, Monday and lunch Tuesday B **r**
Rest – Menu £ 23/49 **s**
◆ Formal white linen blends well with a part 15C interior of low beams and leaded windows. Attentive service; modern cooking in marked contrast with the surroundings.

Bistro – at Hotel du Vin
14 Southgate St ✉ SO23 9EF – ☎ (01962) 841 414 – Fax (01962) 842 458 B **i**
Rest – (booking essential) Menu £ 18 (lunch) – Carte £ 25/35
◆ Oenophile memorabilia covers panelled cream walls; hops crown tall sash windows. Terrace under broad sunshades. Classic modern flavours set off the carefully chosen wines.

The Wykeham Arms with rm
75 Kingsgate St ✉ SO23 9PE – ☎ (01962) 853 834 – wykehamarms@accommodating-inns.co.uk – Fax (01962) 854 411 – Closed 25 December B **u**
14 rm – ♦£ 62/105 ♦♦£ 150 **Rest** – (closed Sunday dinner) (booking essential) Menu £ 16 – Carte £ 19/31
◆ 18C inn; cosy snugs off a bar crammed with tankards, sporting curios and old school desks. Full-flavoured cooking. Cottage-style rooms, larger in annex: a city institution.

ENGLAND

at Easton Northeast : 4 m. by A 3090 - A - off B 3047 – ✉ Winchester

The Chestnut Horse
✉ SO21 1EG – ☎ (01962) 779 257 – Fax (01962) 779 037 – Closed Sunday dinner in winter
Rest – Menu £ 16 – Carte £ 21/32
◆ Characterful 16C pub in rural village near M3. Welcoming interior with log fires, beams and hanging pots and jugs. Two dining rooms serve tasty, classic pub favourites.

at Ovington East : 5 ¾ m. by B 3404 - A - and A 31 – ✉ Winchester

The Bush Inn
✉ SO24 0RE – ☎ (01962) 732 764 – thebushinn@wadworth.co.uk – Fax (01962) 735 130 – Closed 25 December
Rest – (closed Sunday dinner) Menu £ 10/15 – Carte £ 19/30
◆ 17C country inn, hidden down winding country road along river Itchen, with delightful garden and engaging rural décor. Four intimate dining rooms serve tasty country dishes.

at Littleton Northwest : 2 ½ m. by B 3049 - A – ✉ Winchester

The Running Horse with rm
88 Main Road ✉ SO22 6QS – ☎ (01962) 880 218 – runninghorseinn@btconnect.com – Fax (01962) 886 596 – Closed 25 December and Monday
9 rm – ♦£ 65 ♦♦£ 75 – **Rest** – Carte £ 20/30
◆ Yellow hued hostelry boasting a rear restaurant with stone floors, wicker chairs and a sophisticated range of dishes. Two terraces for summer dining. Smart rooms.

at Sparsholt Northwest : 3 ½ m. by B 3049 - A – ✉ Winchester

Lainston House

✉ *SO21 2LT – ✆ (01962) 776 088 – enquiries@lainstonhouse.com – Fax (01962) 776 672*
48 rm – 🚹£ 170/435 🚹🚹£ 170/435, ☕ £19.95 – 2 suites
Rest *Avenue* – Menu £ 32/40 **s** – Carte £ 44/52 **s**
◆ Charming 17C manor with pretty grounds, parks and old herb garden. Traditionally styled lounge, cedar-panelled bar and up-to-date gym. Rooms, some more modern, vary in size. Dark wood dining room overlooks lawn.

Plough Inn

Main Road ✉ SO21 2NW – ✆ (01962) 776 353 – Fax (01962) 776 400 – Closed 25 December
Rest – (booking essential) Carte £ 20/30
◆ Friendly, unassuming pub - book early for a varied blackboard menu combining the modern and traditional, all served at pine tables. Real ales.

WINDERMERE – Cumbria – 502 L 20 – pop. 7 941 *Great Britain* 21 A2

London 274 m – Blackpool 55 m – Carlisle 46 m – Kendal 10 m
Victoria St ✆ (015394) 46499
Lake Windermere★★ – Brockhole National Park Centre★ **AC**, NW : 2 m. by A 591

Plan opposite

Langdale Chase

< Lake Windermere and mountains, rest,
Northwest : 3 m. on A 591 ✉ LA23 1LW – ✆ (015394) 32 201 – sales@langdalechase.co.uk – Fax (015394) 32 604
28 rm ☕ – 🚹£ 80/104 🚹🚹£ 90/198 – 1 suite – **Rest** – Menu £ 19/34 **s**
◆ Substantial 19C house with beautiful gardens and wonderful lakeside setting boasting a wealth of ornate Victoriana and superbly preserved carvings. Pleasantly styled rooms. Formal dining in a classic room; sweeping views across the lake.

Holbeck Ghyll

< Lake Windermere and mountains,
Holbeck Lane, Northwest : 3 ¼ m. by A 591 ✉ LA23 1LU – ✆ (015394) 32 375 – stay@holbeckghyll.com – Fax (015394) 34 743 – Closed first 2 weeks January
21 rm (dinner included) ☕ – 🚹£ 160/270 🚹🚹£ 290/370 – 2 suites – **Rest** – (booking essential at lunch) Menu £ 28/50
Spec. Cannelloni of smoked salmon with crab. Fillet of veal with broad beans and baby leeks. Apricot délice, beignet and sorbet.
◆ Charming Victorian hunting lodge with pleasant gardens and stunning views. Individually decorated bedrooms combine country house style with a contemporary edge. Cooking is confident and precise; appealing menus are complemented by an exceptional wine list.

Cedar Manor

Ambleside Rd ✉ LA23 1AX – ✆ (015394) 43 192 – info@cedarmanor.co.uk – Fax (015394) 45 970 Y **i**
10 rm (dinner included) ☕ – 🚹🚹£ 160/170 – 1 suite – **Rest** – (Closed 25-26 December) (dinner only) Menu £ 25 – Carte £ 25/31
◆ 1860s house, its mature garden shaded by an ancient cedar. Sizeable bedrooms, including the Coniston Room with views of Langdale Pike and lounge with ornate stained glass. Locally sourced menus.

Glenburn

New Rd ✉ LA23 2EE – ✆ (015394) 42 649 – glen.burn@virgin.net – Fax (015394) 88 998 Y **u**
16 rm ☕ – 🚹£ 59/69 🚹🚹£ 92/124 – **Rest** – (dinner only) (booking essential) Menu £ 19 – Carte £ 16/27
◆ Well-placed for exploring the central Lakes, a privately run hotel offering homely rooms in soft-toned décor plus a small bar and lounge with an open fire. Neatly set dining room with peach and white linen.

ENGLAND

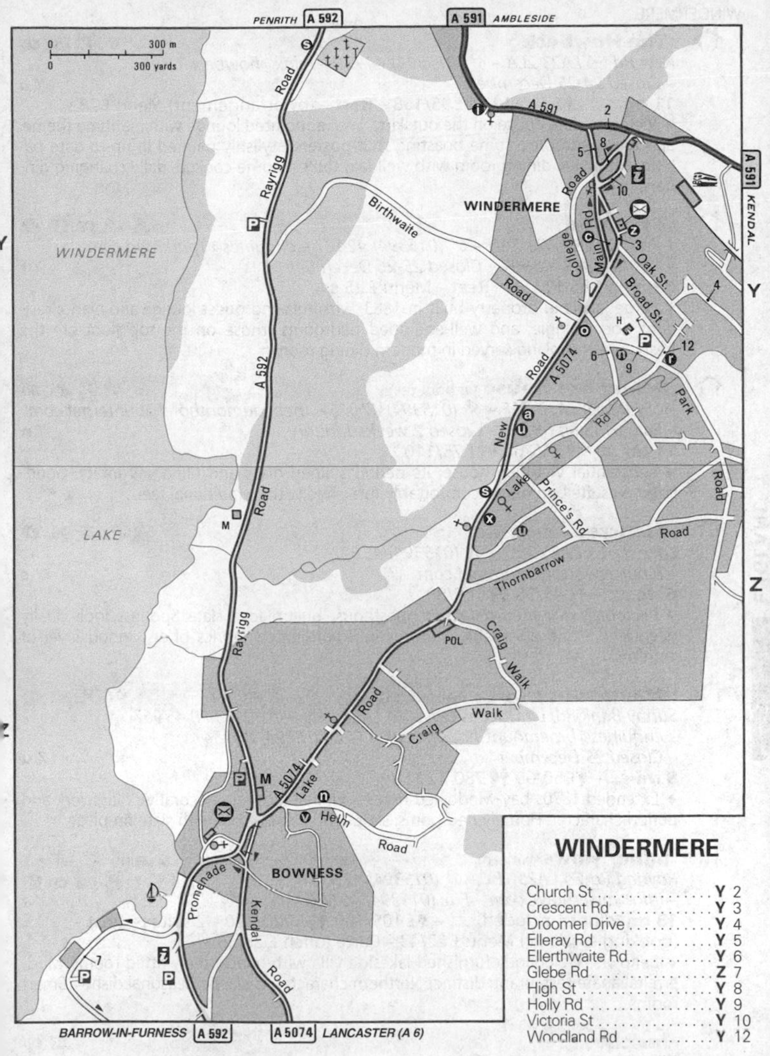

Newstead without rest

New Rd ✉ LA23 2EE – ✆ (015394) 44485 – info@newstead-guesthouse.co.uk – Fax (015394) 88904 – closed 1 week Christmas Y **a**

9 rm – †£ 45/65 ††£ 50/90

◆ A warm welcome is assured at this restored Victorian residence. Original features aplenty; fireplaces in all the cosy, spotless bedrooms. Hearty breakfasts a speciality.

Fir Trees without rest

Lake Rd ✉ LA23 2EQ – ✆ (015394) 42272 – enquiries@fir-trees.com – Fax (015394) 42512 Z **x**

9 rm – †£ 50/60 ††£ 68/92

◆ Built in 1888 as gentleman's residence and retains original pine staircase. Contrastingly modern, stylish and individually decorated bedrooms. Broad-windowed breakfast room.

The Howbeck
New Rd ✉ LA23 2LA – ✆ (015394) 44 739 – relax@howbeck.co.uk – Closed 24-25 December Y **o**
11 rm – £ 71/119 £ 95/158 – **Rest** – (by arrangement) Menu £ 28 **s**
◆ Victorian slate house on the outskirts. Well appointed lounge with maritime theme. Spacious bedrooms, some boasting four-posters, stylishly painted in up-to-date palette. Attractive dining room with well-laid tables: home-cooked, daily changing dinners.

1 Park Rd
1 Park Rd ✉ LA23 2AN – ✆ (015394) 42 107 – enquiries@1parkroad.com – Fax (015394) 48 997 – Closed 25-26 December Y **r**
6 rm – £ 85 £ 96 – **Rest** – Menu £ 25 **s**
◆ Large lakeland property built in 1883, with relaxing guest lounge and piano; resident dog, Maggie, and well-equipped bedrooms (those on the top floor are the best). Fresh cooking served in modern dining room.

Beaumont House without rest
Holly Rd ✉ LA23 2AF – ✆ (015394) 47 075 – thebeaumonthotel@btinternet.com – Fax (015394) 88 311 – Closed 2 weeks January Y **n**
11 rm – £ 45/60 £ 75/110
◆ Substantial Victorian house, its period stained glass and tiling still intact. Good-sized en suite bedrooms, comfortably furnished with a traditional feel.

Glencree without rest
Lake Rd ✉ LA23 2EQ – ✆ (015394) 45 822 – h.butterworth@btinternet.com Z **s**
6 rm – £ 45/55 £ 60/80
◆ Personally managed, detached guesthouse built of local slate. Spotless, individually decorated - and affordable - rooms in co-ordinated fabrics offer a good level of comfort.

Braemount House without rest
Sunny Bank Rd, by Queens Drive ✉ LA23 2EN – ✆ (015394) 45 967 – enquiries@braemount-house.co.uk – Fax (015394) 88 154 – Closed 25 December Z **u**
8 rm – £ 50/60 £ 80/120
◆ Extended 1870s bay-windowed house: original tiles and decorative glasswork add period character. Homely bedrooms; simple breakfast room with slate fireplace.

Miller Howe with rm — ≤ Lake Windermere and mountains, AC rest,
Rayrigg Rd ✉ LA23 1EY – ✆ (015394) 42 536 – info@millerhowe.com – Fax (015394) 45 664 Y **s**
13 rm (dinner included) – £ 105/180 £ 220/320 – 2 suites – **Rest** – (booking essential) Menu £ 22/43 – Carte lunch £ 23/35
◆ Renowned, elegantly furnished lakeside villa with handsomely fitted rooms. Modern Italianate restaurant; distinct Northern character to classic, seasonal dishes. Smart rooms.

Jerichos
Birch St ✉ LA23 1EG – ✆ (015394) 42 522 – enquiries@jerichos.co.uk – Fax (015394) 42 522 – Closed last 2 weeks November-first week December, 25-26 December, 1 January, Monday and Sunday January-March Y **z**
Rest – (dinner only) Carte £ 30/34
◆ Personally run restaurant with open kitchen; well-spaced tables, elegant glassware and framed Beryl Cook prints. Local produce enhances rich, complex blend of modern flavours.

Francine's
27 Main Rd ✉ LA23 1DX – ✆ (015394) 44 088 – Fax (015394) 44 088 – Closed 2 weeks January, 2 weeks November, Tuesday dinner and Monday Y **c**
Rest – (booking essential at dinner) Carte £ 27/45
◆ Unpretentious bistro/coffee house with light décor, well-spaced tables and an informal feel, offers traditional French-influenced cooking. Eponymous owner bakes the cakes.

ENGLAND

at Bowness-on-Windermere South : 1 m. - Z - ✉ Windermere

Gilpin Lodge

Crook Rd, Southeast : 2½ m. by A 5074 on B 5284 ✉ LA23 3NE – ✆ (015394) 88 818 – hotel@gilpinlodge.co.uk – Fax (015394) 88 058

20 rm (dinner included) – £ 175 £ 290/360 – **Rest** – (booking essential for non-residents) Menu £ 25/43 – Carte lunch £ 15/25

◆ Extended country house with comfortable, classically-styled sitting room and terrace for afternoon tea. Most bedrooms have contemporary décor; private hot tubs in Garden suites. Four individually styled dining rooms. Cooking combines classic technique and modern influences.

Storrs Hall

South : 2 m. on A 592 ✉ LA23 3LG – ✆ (015394) 47 111 – storrshall@elhmail.co.uk – Fax (015394) 47 555

29 rm – £ 113 £ 304 – 1 suite

Rest *The Terrace* – Menu £ 20/40 **s**

◆ Oils, antiques and fine fabrics fill an elegant Georgian mansion. Traditional orangery, 19C bar in dark wood and stained glass and comfortable, individually decorated rooms. Ornate dining room overlooks lawns and lake.

Linthwaite House

Lake Windermere and fells,

Crook Rd, South : ¾ m. by A 5074 on B 5284 ✉ LA23 3JA – ✆ (015394) 88 600 – stay@linthwaite.com – Fax (015394) 88 601

27 rm – £ 130/210 £ 180/310 – **Rest** – (light lunch Monday Saturday) Menu £ 18/48 **s** – Carte lunch £ 14/23 **s**

◆ Set in superb elevated position with stunning views of Lake Windermere. Chic, modern rooms. Cane chairs and louvred blinds give conservatory teas an almost colonial feel. Refined modern cooking in restaurant boasting vast mirror collection!

Lindeth Howe

rm,

Storrs Park, South : 1 ¼ m. by A 592 off B 5284 ✉ LA23 3JF – ✆ (015394) 45 759 – hotel@lindeth-howe.co.uk – Fax (015394) 46 368 – Closed 2 weeks January

36 rm – £ 60/115 £ 120/240

Rest *The Dining Room* – (light lunch Monday-Saturday) Menu £ 16/38 **s**

◆ Once owned by Beatrix Potter, this extended and updated house surveys a broad sweep of Lakeland scenery. Smart, spacious rooms in traditional style, some with useful extras. Spacious dining room with wonderful fell views.

Fayrer Garden House

rest,

Lyth Valley Rd, South : 1 m. on A 5074 ✉ LA23 3JP – ✆ (015394) 88 195 – lakescene@fayrergarden.com – Fax (015394) 45 986 – Closed 2-19 January

29 rm (dinner included) – £ 81/131 £ 254/280

Rest *The Terrace* – (dinner only) (booking essential for non-residents) Menu £ 35

◆ Extensive house with five acres of grounds and beautiful gardens. Clubby bar and pleasantly homely lounge. Cosy rooms show the owners' feel for thoughtful detail. Wonderful views to be gained from The Terrace.

Lindeth Fell

Lake Windermere and mountains,

Lyth Valley Rd, South : 1 m. on A 5074 ✉ LA23 3JP – ✆ (015394) 43 286 – kennedy@lindethfell.co.uk – Fax (015394) 47 455 – Closed 2-26 January

14 rm – £ 45/90 £ 120/170 – **Rest** – Menu £ 18/35

◆ In landscaped gardens with bowls and croquet lawns, a privately owned 1907 house with neat, bright rooms, oak-panelled hall and curios and watercolours in the drawing room. Elegantly set dining room with superb Lakeland views.

ENGLAND

Angel Inn rest,
Helm Rd ✉ LA23 3BU – ☎ (015394) 44080 – rooms@the-angelinn.com – Fax (015394) 46003 – Closed 25 December Z **v**
14 rm – ♦£55/70 ♦♦£105/165 – **Rest** – Carte £18/30
◆ Homely, good-sized rooms in an enlarged early 18C cottage, set in a secluded spot yet close to town. Cosy, unpretentious bar, its armchairs centred on an open fire. Dining room has columned archway and landscape murals.

Oakbank House without rest
Helm Rd ✉ LA23 3BU – ☎ (015394) 43386 – enquiries@oakbankhousehotel.co.uk – Fax (015394) 47965 – Closed 24-27 December Z **n**
12 rm – ♦£50/75 ♦♦£50/100
◆ Privately run house off the main street. Affordable bedrooms, stylish and individually decorated. Ferns and chandeliers lend grandeur to substantial Cumbrian breakfasts.

Low House without rest
South : 1 m. by A 5074 and B 5284 on Heathwaite rd ✉ LA23 3NA – ☎ (015394) 43156 – info@lowhouse.co.uk
3 rm – ♦£50/80 ♦♦£80/120
◆ Charming 17C country house with fine furnishings, log burner, organic breakfasts and welcoming feel. Bedrooms boast top comforts and one can borrow the boat or the Bentley.

Fair Rigg without rest
Ferry View, South : ½ m. on A 5074 ✉ LA23 3JB – ☎ (015394) 43941 – stay@fairrigg.co.uk
6 rm – ♦£50/65 ♦♦£70/88
◆ 19C property with pleasing views over the lake to the hills. Hearty Cumbrian breakfasts guaranteed, accompanied by the fine vista. Original fireplaces enhance comfy rooms.

ENGLAND

at Troutbeck North : 4 m. by A 592 - Y – ✉ Windermere

Broadoaks
Bridge Lane, South : 1 m. on Windermere rd ✉ LA23 1LA – ☎ (015394) 45566 – trev@broadoaksf9.co.uk – Fax (015394) 88766
14 rm – ♦£65/73 ♦♦£110/220 – **Rest** – Menu £15/35 – Carte £18/30
◆ Extended 19C manor in mature 10-acre garden. Victoriana fills the panelled hall and a handsome Music Room with Bechstein piano. Individual rooms, many with four-poster beds. Imposing period fireplace is dining room's focal point.

The Queen's Head with rm
North : ¾ m. on A 592 ✉ LA23 1PW – ☎ (01539) 432174 – feast@queensheadhotel.com – Fax (01539) 431398 – Closed 25 December
15 rm – ♦£68/75 ♦♦£120 – **Rest** – Menu £19 – Carte £22/30
◆ 17C posting inn with charm to spare: beamed, panelled interior, unique four-poster bar. Tasty blackboard menu; real ale. Cosy rooms, many have antique beds and furniture.

at Winster South : 4 m. on A 074 – ✉ Windermere

Brown Horse Inn with rm
on A 5074 ✉ LA23 3NR – ☎ (01539) 443443 – steve@thebrownhorseinn.co.uk
9 rm – ♦£70 ♦♦£90 – **Rest** – Carte £18/25
◆ Traditional 1850s coaching inn with real fires and candlelit tables. Robust, flavourful dishes classically prepared with prime local produce. Wine tastings and race nights. Light modern bedrooms are simply decorated yet comfortable.

Your opinions are important to us: please write and let us know about your discoveries and experiences – good and bad!

WINDLESHAM – Surrey – 504 S 29 – pop. 4 103 7 C1

London 40 m – Reading 18 m – Southampton 53 m

The Brickmakers

Chertsey Rd, East : 1 m. on B 386 ✉ GU20 6HT – ✆ (01276) 472 267 – thebrickmakers@4cinns.co.uk

Rest – Menu £ 26 – Carte £ 20/26

◆ Appropriately redbrick pub with bright, modern dining room and conservatory. Tasty menu with a new-British slant plus daily fish specials. Friendly staff; good ale.

WINDSOR – Windsor & Maidenhead – 504 S 29 – pop. 30 568 *Great Britain* 11 D3

London 28 m – Reading 19 m – Southampton 59 m

to Marlow, Maidenhead and Cookham (Salter Bros. Ltd) (summer only)

24 High St ✆ (0871) 7161962, windsor.tic@86wm.gov.uk

Town★ – Castle★★★ : St George's Chapel★★★ **AC** (stalls★★★), State Apartments★★ **AC**, North Terrace (≤ ★★) Z – Eton College★★ **AC** (College Chapel★★, Wall paintings★) Z

Windsor Park★ **AC** Y

Plan on next page

Oakley Court

Windsor Rd, Water Oakley, West : 3 m. on A 308 ✉ SL4 5UR – ✆ (01753) 609 988 – reservations@oakleycourt.com – Fax (01753) 609 939

118 rm – 🛉£ 180 🛉🛉£ 190/290

Rest *The Oakleaf* – (Closed Saturday lunch) Menu £ 30 – Carte £ 33/60 **s**

◆ Impressive part Gothic mansion on banks of river Thames. Spacious public areas in classic country house style. Many bedrooms in annex, most characterful ones in main house. Large dining room provides pleasant views of gardens and river.

The Castle

18 High St ✉ SL4 1LJ – ✆ (01753) 851 577 – h6618@accor.com – Fax (01753) 856 930 Z **c**

104 rm – 🛉£ 155/240 🛉🛉£ 165/250 – 4 suites

Rest *Eighteen* – Menu £ 22/35

◆ Former inn built by monks, now a terraced property with Georgian façade. Décor in traditional style. Modern rooms in converted stables, more characterful ones in old building. Very comfortable Eighteen with modern menus.

Sir Christopher Wren's House

Thames St ✉ SL4 1PX – ✆ (01753) 861 354 – reservations@windsor.wrensgroup.com – Fax (01753) 442 490 Z **e**

90 rm – 🛉£ 85/230 🛉🛉£ 97/290, £ 11.50 – 5 suites

Rest *Strok's* – Carte £ 32/48 **s**

◆ Built by Wren as his family home in 1676, he supposedly haunts his old rooms. On banks of Thames close to station and Windsor Castle. Antique furnished in original building. Restaurant has views of Thames and elegant dining terrace.

Royal Adelaide

46 Kings Rd ✉ SL4 2AG – ✆ (01753) 863 916 – royaladelaide@meridianleisure.com – Fax (01753) 830 682 Z **v**

42 rm – 🛉£ 115/160 🛉🛉£ 135/160 – **Rest** – Menu £ 23 (dinner) – Carte £ 24/34 **s**

◆ Three adjoining Georgian houses with light blue painted façade. Just outside town centre. Rooms vary in shapes and sizes, all in individual traditional style. Dining room offers daily changing, international menus.

The Christopher

110 High St, Eton ✉ SL4 6AN – ✆ (01753) 852 359 – sales@thechristopher.co.uk – Fax (01753) 830 914 Z **a**

33 rm – 🛉£ 116/185 🛉🛉£ 185/210, £ 11.95 – **Rest** – Carte £ 17/28

◆ Refurbished 17C former coaching inn close to Eton College and perfect for walking to the castle. Contemporary bedrooms split between main building and mews annex. Simple homecooking.

ENGLAND

WINDSOR

Bexley St . . . . Z 2
Bolton Rd . . . . Y 3
Castle Hill . . . . Z 4
Charles St . . . . Z 5
Claremont Rd . . . . Z 6
Clarence Crescent . . . . Z 7
Clewer Crescent Rd . . . . Z 8
Datchet Rd . . . . Z 9
Goswell Rd . . . . Z 10
Grove Rd . . . . Z 12
High St . . . . Z 13
High St DATCHET . . . . Y 14
Horton Rd . . . . Y 16
Keats Lane . . . . Z 17
King Edward Court
Centre . . . . Z
Peascod St . . . . Z 19
Ragstone Rd . . . . Y 20
River St . . . . Z 21
Sheet St Rd . . . . Y 22
Stovell Rd . . . . Z 23
Thames Ave . . . . Z 24
Thames St . . . . Z 25
Trinity Pl . . . . Z 27
Windsor Bridge . . . . Z 28
Windsor Rd . . . . Y 29

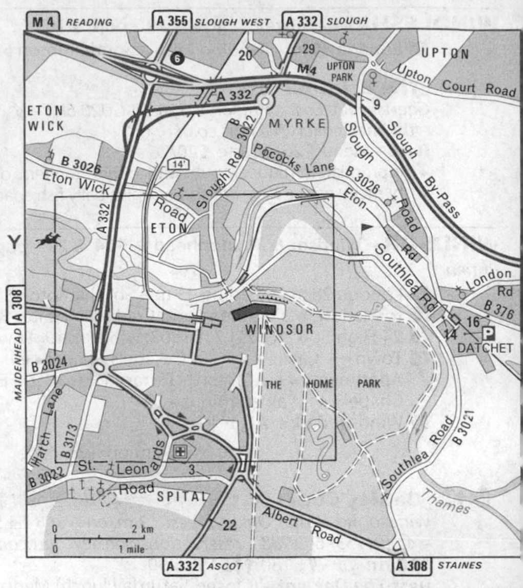

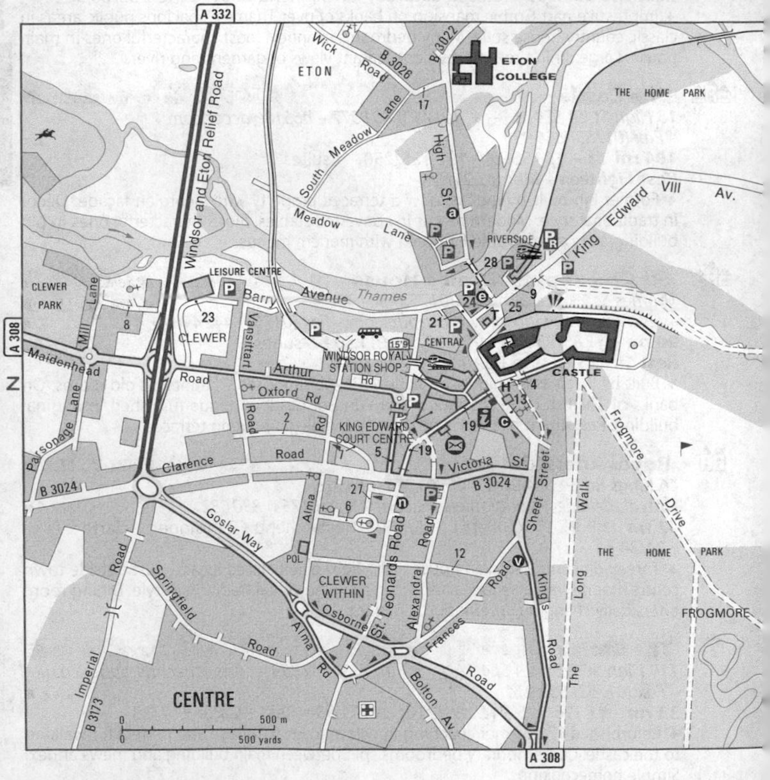

Al Fassia

27 St Leonards Rd ✉ SL4 3BP – ☎ (01753) 855 370 – Fax (01753) 855 370 – Cosed 25 December and 1 January Z **n**

Rest – Moroccan (booking essential) Menu £ 13/17 – Carte £ 18/23

◆ The name means "a lady from Fez" and the food has an authentic fresh Moroccan flavour with subtle spicing and fragrant flavours. Friendly and well run.

WINEHAM – W. Sussex – 504 T 31 – see Henfield

WINFORTON – Herefordshire – 503 K 27 – see Hereford

WINGHAM – Kent – 504 X 30 – pop. 1 618 9 D2

London 67 m – Canterbury 7 m – Dover 16 m

at Goodnestone South : 2 m. by B 2046 – ✉ Wingham

The Fitzwalter Arms

The Street ✉ CT3 1PJ – ☎ (01304) 840 303 – Closed 25 December and Sunday dinner

Rest – Carte £ 16/24

◆ Striking brick pub with castellated exterior and mullioned windows. Darts, billiards and open fire in characterful beamed bar create feel of village local. Large beer garden.

WINSFORD – Somerset – 503 J 30 – ✉ Minehead 3 A2

London 194 m – Exeter 31 m – Minehead 10 m – Taunton 32 m

Village ★

Exmoor National Park ★★

The Royal Oak Inn

Exmoor National Park ✉ TA24 7JE – ☎ (01643) 851 455 – enquiries@royaloak-somerset.co.uk – Fax (01643) 851 009

12 rm – †£ 65/116 ††£ 136 – **Rest** – (in bar Monday-Saturday lunch and Sunday dinner) Carte £ 20/25

◆ Attractive part 12C thatched inn overlooking the village green. Quaint cottage atmosphere, especially in those rooms in the main house; annex rooms of more recent vintage. Out-and-out English cooking prevails.

Karslake House

Halse Lane ✉ TA24 7JE – ☎ (01643) 851 242 – enquiries@karslakehouse.co.uk – Fax (01643) 851 242 – Closed February-March and 1 week Christmas

6 rm – †£ 75 ††£ 115 – **Rest** – (Closed Sunday-Monday) (dinner only) Menu £ 30

◆ Personally run 15C malthouse with lovely gardens. Good home-cooked fare on varied menus with fine use of local produce. Welcoming accommodation including four-poster comfort.

WINSTER – Cumbria – 502 L 20 – see Windermere

WINSTER – Derbs – 502 P 24 – pop. 1 787 16 A1

London 153 m – Derby 25 m – Matlock 4 m

The Dower House without rest

Main St ✉ DE4 2DH – ☎ (01629) 650 931 – fosterbig@aol.com – Closed 25-26 December and 1 January

4 rm – †£ 75 ††£ 95

◆ Attractive stone house dating from 16C, with lovely walled garden, cosy lounge and spacious, well-kept bedrooms; choose the four poster for its view of the historic village.

WINTERBOURNE STEEPLETON – Dorset – 503 M 31 – see Dorchester

ENGLAND

WINTERINGHAM – North Lincolnshire – 502 S 22 – ✉ Scunthorpe 23 C3

London 176 m – Kingston-upon-Hull 16 m – Sheffield 67 m

XXXX Winteringham Fields with rm

1 Silver St ✉ DN15 9ND – ✆ (01724) 733 096 – wintfields@aol.com – Fax (01724) 733 898 – Closed 2 weeks Christmas-NewYear

8 rm – £ 105 £ 215, ☕ £12.50 – 2 suites – **Rest** – (Closed Sunday-Monday) (booking essential for non-residents) Menu £ 39/79 – Carte £ 49/79 **s** ✿

◆ 16C house with beamed ceilings, and original range with fire. Cosy, cottagey atmosphere. Carefully executed menu, served in choice of dining rooms. Characterful bedrooms.

WITCOMBE – Glos. – see Cheltenham

WITNEY – Oxon. – 503 P 28 – pop. 22 765 10 B2

London 69 m – Gloucester 39 m – Oxford 13 m

26A Market Sq ✆ (01993) 775802

The Fleece with rm

11 Church Green ✉ OX28 4AZ – ✆ (01993) 892 270 – thefleece@peachpubs.com – Closed 25 December

10 rm – £ 80 £ 90 – **Rest** – Carte £ 18/19

◆ Modernised dining pub in pretty setting. Front room has leather sofas. Open plan rear restaurant serves flavourful dishes from classic menu. Polite, efficient service. Comfortable bedrooms boast eye-catching decor; those at front overlook village green.

ENGLAND

at Barnard Gate East : 3 ¼ m. by A 40 – ✉ Eynsham

The Boot Inn

✉ OX29 6XE – ✆ (01865) 881 231 – info@theboot-inn.com

Rest – Carte £ 20/30

◆ Friendly pub in Cotswold stone. Snug interior with memorabilia and boot collection, including footwear from Bee Gees and Stanley Matthews. Traditional menu, informal service.

at South Leigh Southeast : 3 m. by A 40 – ✉ Witney

XX Mason Arms

✉ OX29 6XN – ✆ (01993) 702 485 – Closed 3 weeks August, 1 week Christmas, 1 week Spring, Sunday dinner and Monday

Rest – Carte £ 20/50

◆ Privately owned 15C thatched inn with unique style and much individuality. Dimly lit, with intimate atmosphere. French influenced traditional cooking and extensive wine list.

at Leafield Northwest : 5 ¾ m. by B 4022 (Charlbury Rd) – ✉ Witney

The Navy Oak

Lower End ✉ OX29 9QQ – ✆ (01993) 878 496 – thenavyoak@aol.com – Closed 1st week in January and Monday

Rest – Carte £ 19/28

◆ Experienced, friendly owners serving good value, well-presented restaurant-style dishes in firelit bar or more formal dining rooms. Gastronomic evenings held regularly.

The ✿ award is the crème de la crème. This is awarded to restaurants which are really worth travelling miles for!

WIX – Essex – **504** X 28 – ✉ Manningtree 13 **D2**

London 70 m – Colchester 10 m – Harwich 7 m – Ipswich 16 m

Dairy House Farm without rest

Bradfield Rd, Northwest : 1 m. ✉ CO11 2SR – ✆ (01255) 870 322 – bridgetwhitworth@btinternet.com – Fax (01255) 870 186

3 rm – £ 38/40 £ 60

◆ Victorian farmhouse, delightfully secluded in 700 acres of working arable and fruit farmland. Friendly and welcoming. Simple, comfortable style and well-kept throughout.

WOBURN – Beds. – **504** S 28 – ✉ Milton Keynes *Great Britain* 12 **A2**

London 49 m – Bedford 13 m – Luton 13 m – Northampton 24 m – Oxford 47 m

Woburn Abbey★★

Inn at Woburn rm, rest,

George St ✉ MK17 9PX – ✆ (01525) 290 441 – enquiries@theinnatwoburn.com – Fax (01525) 290 432

52 rm – £ 115/135 £ 135/165, £ 11 – 5 suites – **Rest** – Menu £ 13 (lunch) – Carte £ 17/30

◆ 18C coaching inn, part of Woburn Estate with its abbey and 3000 acre park. Pleasant modern furnishings and interior décor. Tastefully decorated rooms: book a Cottage suite. Brasserie open throughout the day.

Paris House

Woburn Park, Southeast : 2¼ m. on A 4012 ✉ MK17 9QP – ✆ (01525) 290 692 – info@parishouse.co.uk – Fax (01525) 290 471 – Closed 25-27 December, Sunday dinner and Monday

Rest – Menu £ 25/57

◆ Built 1878 for Paris Exhibition, dismantled and rebuilt on Woburn Estate, this striking timbered house provides an august setting for classic French-inspired cuisine.

The Birch

20 Newport Rd, North : ½ m. on A 5130 ✉ MK17 9HX – ✆ (01525) 290 295 – etaverns@aol.com – Fax (01525) 290 899 – Closed 25-26 December, 1 January and Sunday dinner

Rest – (booking essential) Carte £ 20/28

◆ Established modern dining pub. Stylish décor in the smart restaurant and bar. Modern menu specialising in meat and fish from an open grill. Attentive service.

at Milton Bryan Southeast : 2½ m. by A 4012 – ✉ Woburn

The Red Lion

Toddington Rd ✉ MK17 9HS – ✆ (01525) 210 044 – paul@redlion-miltonbryan.co.uk – Closed 25-26 December, 1 January and Sunday dinner

Rest – Carte £ 18/30

◆ Open fires and exposed beams define the lovely old world charm of this tastefully furnished pub. Carefully sourced ingredients underpin tasty, home cooked dishes.

WOLD NEWTON – East Riding 23 **D2**

London 229 m – Bridlington 25 m – Scarborough 13 m

Wold Cottage without rest

South : ½ m. on Thwing rd ✉ YO25 3HL – ✆ (01262) 470 696 – katrina@woldcottage.com – Fax (01262) 470 696

5 rm – £ 45/60 £ 80/120

◆ Georgian former farmhouse set in many rural acres; a country house style prevails with antique furniture in all areas. Spacious, individually named rooms: two in barn annex.

WOLVERHAMPTON – W. Mids. – 502 N 26 – pop. 254 623 19 C2

London 132 m – Birmingham 15 m – Liverpool 89 m – Shrewsbury 30 m

18 Queen Sq ✆ (01902) 312051, wolverhampton.tic@dial.pipex.com

Plan of Enlarged Area : see Birmingham pp. 4 and 5

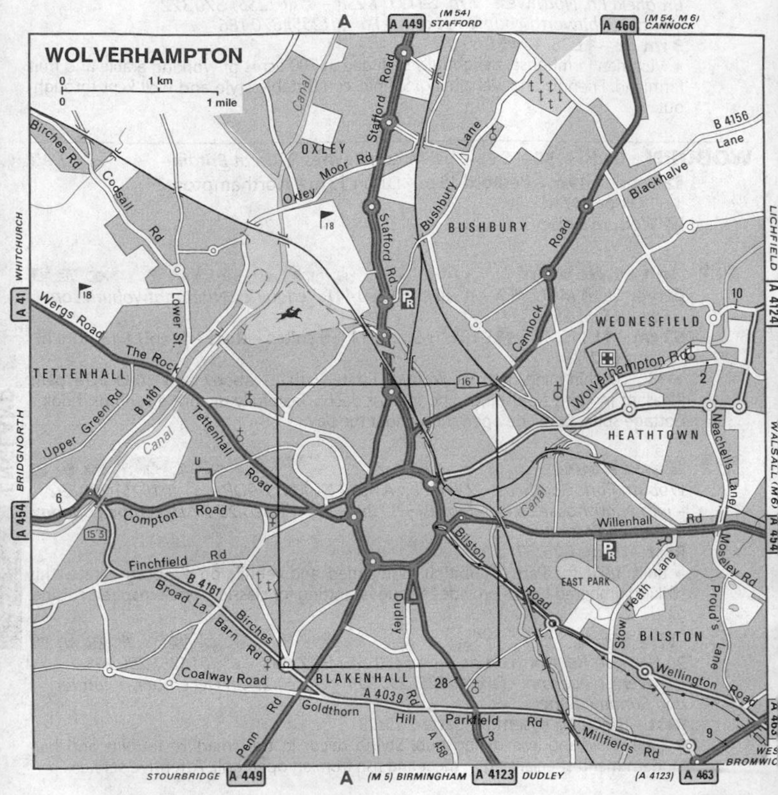

Birmingham New Rd	A 3	Lichfield St	B 12	St Johns Retail Park	B		
Bridgnorth Rd	A 6	Mander Centre	B	Salop St	B 22		
Cleveland St	B 7	Market St	B 14	School St	B 25		
Darlington St	B	Princess St	B 15	Thompson Ave	A 28		
Garrick St	B 8	Queen Square	B 17	Victoria St	B 30		
High St	A 9	Railway Drive	B 20	Wulfrun Centre	B		
Lichfield Rd	A 10						

Novotel

(heated) & rm, VISA AE

Union St ✉ WV1 3JN – ✆ (01902) 871 100 – h1188@accor.com – Fax (01902) 870 054 B **a**

132 rm – †£ 49 ††£ 125

Rest *The Garden Brasserie* – (dinner only) Carte £ 18/31 **s**

◆ Conveniently located in the centre of town near to train station. Purpose-built lodge hotel with well fitted modern furnishings. Suitable for business and leisure stopovers. Large windows give bright feel to restaurant.

Bilash

AC VISA AE

No 2 Cheapside ✉ WV1 1TU – ✆ (01902) 427 762 – mbilash.co.uk – Fax (01902) 311 991 – Closed 25-26 December and Sunday B **c**

Rest – Indian Menu £ 12/20 – Carte £ 30/48

◆ In a pleasant square, and easily identified by its bright yellow façade and modish interior. Family owned; well established, locally renowned Indian/Bangladeshi cooking.

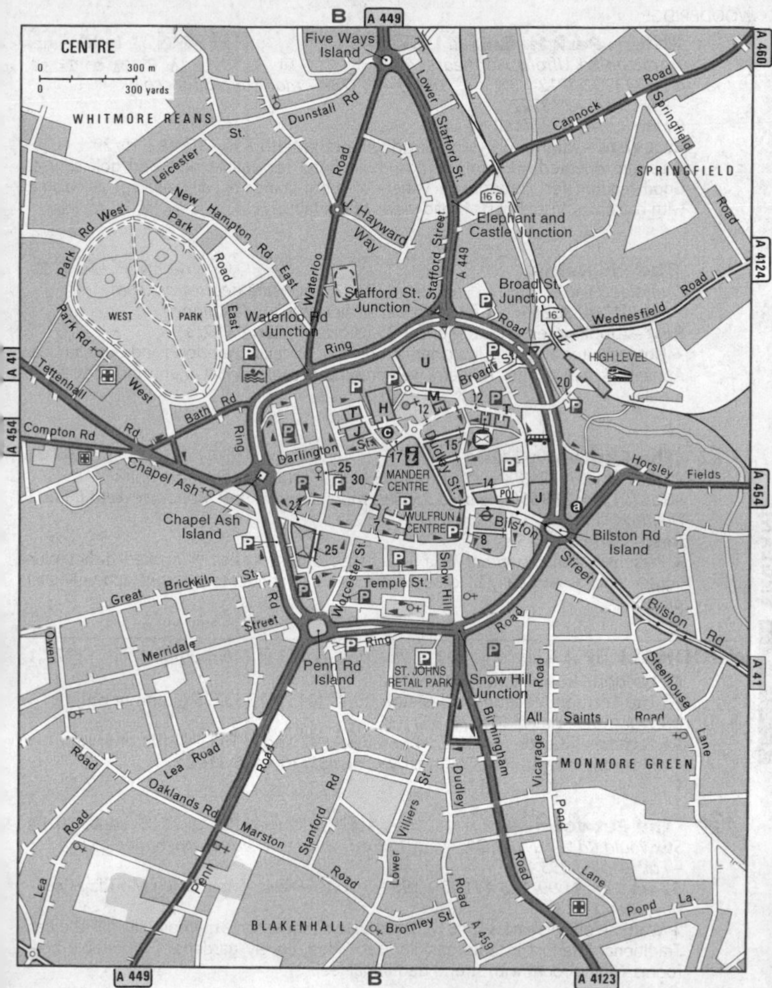

WOOBURN COMMON – Bucks. – see Beaconsfield

WOODBRIDGE – Suffolk – 504 X 27 – pop. 10 965 15 D3

London 81 m – Great Yarmouth 45 m – Ipswich 8 m – Norwich 47 m
Cretingham Grove Farm, ✆ (01728) 685 275 ;
Seckford Great Bealings Seckford Hall Rd, ✆ (01394) 388 000.

Seckford Hall rm, rest,

Southwest : 1 ¼ m. by A 12 ✉ IP13 6NU – ✆ (01394) 385 678 – reception@seckford.co.uk – Fax (01394) 380 610 – Closed 25 December

VISA AE

32 rm – ♦£ 85/115 ♦♦£ 140 – 7 suites – **Rest** – (Closed Monday lunch) Carte £ 30/35 **s**

◆ Reputedly once visited by Elizabeth I, a part Tudor country house set in attractive gardens. Charming traditionally panelled public areas. Comfortable bedrooms. Local lobster proudly served in smart dining room.

Ufford Park H. Golf & Leisure

rm, AC rest,

Yarmouth Rd, Ufford, Northeast : 2 m. on B 1438 ✉ IP12 1QW – ✆ (0844) 477 3737 – mail@uffordpark.co.uk – Fax (0844) 477 3727

87 rm – †£ 120/140 ††£ 140

Rest *Vista* – (dinner only and Sunday lunch) Menu £ 20 – Carte £ 15/29

◆ Leisure oriented, modern, purpose-built hotel set amidst park and golf course. Good modern feel throughout. Variety of room standards, all well-kept and some with balconies. Vista boasts broad views of the fairways.

The Riverside

Quayside ✉ IP12 1BH – ✆ (01394) 382 587 – riversidetheatre@aol.com – Fax (01394) 382 656 – Closed 25 December and Sunday dinner

Rest – (booking essential) Menu £ 25 (dinner) – Carte £ 22/33

◆ Not just a restaurant, but a cinema too! Floor to ceiling windows and busy terrace. Appealing menus offer modern, well-presented cooking. Set menu includes ticket for film.

The Captain's Table

3 Quay St ✉ IP12 1BX – ✆ (01394) 383 145 – eat@captainstable.co.uk – Fax (01394) 388 508 – Closed 25 December, Sunday and Monday except Bank Holidays

Rest – Carte £ 18/25 **s**

◆ Personally run restaurant in a 16C house offers classically inspired dishes plus lighter lunches and daily blackboard specials, all confident, generous and very well priced.

ENGLAND

WOODHALL SPA – Lincs. – 502 T 24 – pop. 4 133 *Great Britain* 17 **C1**

London 138 m – Lincoln 18 m

The Cottage Museum, Iddesleigh Rd ✆ (01526) 353775 (summer only)

Woodhall Spa, ✆ (01526) 351 835 .

Tattershall Castle★ **AC**, SE : 4 m. by B 1192 and A 153 – Battle of Britain Memorial Flight, RAF Coningsby★, SE : 3½ m. on B 1192

The Petwood

rm,

Stixwould Rd ✉ LN10 6Q9 – ✆ (01526) 352 411 – reception@petwood.co.uk – Fax (01526) 353 473

52 rm – †£ 99/123 ††£ 170/193 – 1 suite – **Rest** – (bar lunch Monday-Friday) Menu £ 23

◆ Wartime officers' mess for 617 "Dambusters" Squadron - memorabilia fills the bar. Traditional interiors include panelled reception. Lovely gardens. Comfortable bedrooms. Dining room with strong traditional feel.

WOODHOUSE EAVES – Leics. – 503 Q 25 – see Loughborough

WOODSTOCK – Oxon. – 503 P 28 – pop. 2 589 *Great Britain* 10 **B2**

London 65 m – Gloucester 47 m – Oxford 8 m

Oxfordshire Museum, Park St ✆ (01993) 813276

Blenheim Palace★★★ (Park★★★) **AC**

Bear

rm,

Park St ✉ OX20 1SZ – ✆ (0870) 400 82 02 – bear@macdonald-hotels.co.uk – Fax (01993) 813 380

47 rm – †£ 164/230 ††£ 164/230, £15.95 – 7 suites – **Rest** – Menu £ 22/30 – Carte £ 32/41

◆ Characterful part 16C inn. Original personality and charm; oak beams, open fires and stone walls. Particularly comfortable contemporarily furnished rooms. Dining room exudes an elegant air.

Feathers
Market St ✉ OX20 1SX – ☎ (01993) 812 291 – enquiries@feathers.co.uk – Fax (01993) 813 158
16 rm ☕ – †£ 85/119 ††£ 165/195 – 4 suites – **Rest** – (Closed Sunday dinner) (booking essential) Menu £ 25/38 – Carte £ 25/45
♦ Restored 17C houses in centre of charming town. Much traditional allure with highly individual, antique furnished bedrooms. High levels of comfort and style throughout. Stylish restaurant offers formal dining experience.

The Kings Arms
19 Market St ✉ OX20 1SU – ☎ (01993) 813 636 – stay@kingshotelwoodstock.co.uk – Fax (01993) 813 737
15 rm ☕ – †£ 75 ††£ 140/150 – **Rest** – Carte £ 24/32
♦ Centrally located, modernised hotel with an informal feel and café style bar with leather bucket seats. Contemporary bedrooms are named after kings. Restaurant with glass roof serves brasserie style dishes.

The Townhouse without rest
15 High St ✉ OX20 1TE – ☎ (01993) 810 843 – info@woodstock-townhouse.com – Fax (01993) 810 864
5 rm ☕ – †£ 55 ††£ 80
♦ Charming town house in the centre of this attractive market town. Friendly owner and bright bedrooms with all amenities. Breakfast is served in the garden conservatory.

The Laurels without rest
40 Hensington Rd ✉ OX20 1JL – ☎ (01993) 812 583 – stay@laurelsguesthouse.co.uk – Fax (01993) 810 041 – Closed 15 December-25 January
3 rm ☕ – †£ 55/65 ††£ 70/75
♦ Fine Victorian house just off the town centre. Personally run home with pretty guest rooms and private room facilities.

ENGLAND

If breakfast is included the ☕ symbol appears after the number of rooms.

WOOFFERTON – Shrops. – see Ludlow

WOOKEY HOLE – Somerset – 503 L 30 – see Wells

WOOLACOMBE – Devon – 503 H 30 2 C1

London 237 m – Barnstaple 15 m – Exeter 55 m
The Esplanade ☎ (01271) 870553
Exmoor National Park★★ - Mortehoe★★ (St Mary's Church★, Morte Point - vantage point★) N : ½ m. – Ilfracombe : Hillsborough (< ★★) AC, Capstone Hill★ (< ★), St Nicholas' Chapel (< ★) AC, NE : 5 ½ m. by B 3343 and A 361. Braunton★ (St Brannock's Church★, Braunton Burrows★), S : 8 m. by B 3343 and A 361

Woolacombe Bay (heated) rest,
South St ✉ EX34 7BN – ☎ (01271) 870 388 – woolacombe.bayhotel@btinternet.com – Fax (01271) 870 613 – Closed 2 January-8 February
63 rm ☕ – †£ 75/102 ††£ 150/204
Rest *Doyles* – (dinner only) Menu £ 30
Rest *Maxwell's* – (lunch only and dinner during summer and school holidays) Carte approx. £ 15
♦ Large, traditional, family oriented Victorian seaside hotel with gardens and beach access. Activities from board games to health suite. Well-kept, bright bedrooms. Classic Doyles dining room. Informal Maxwell's bistro.

at Mortehoe North : ½ m. – ✉ **Woolacombe**

Watersmeet ← Morte Bay, (heated) & rm, P VISA
The Esplanade ✉ EX34 7EB – ☎ (01271) 870 333 – info@watersmeethotel.co.uk – Fax (01271) 870 890
29 rm (dinner included) – †£ 62/201 ††£ 124/266 – **Rest** – Menu £ 17/36
◆ Edwardian house on the National Trust's rugged North Atlantic coastline. Superb views of Morte Bay. Smart country house style, large lounges and steps to the beach. Stylish restaurant offers tremendous sea views.

Cleeve House & rm, P VISA
✉ EX34 7ED – ☎ (01271) 870 719 – info@cleevehouse.co.uk – Fax (01271) 870 719 – March-October
6 rm – †£ 55/57 ††£ 80/84 – **Rest** – (by arrangement) Menu £ 19 – Carte £ 22/25
◆ Bright and welcoming feel in décor and atmosphere. Very comfortable lounge and individually styled bedrooms with co-ordinated fabrics. Rear rooms with great country views. Neat dining room; walls hung with local artwork.

WOOLAVINGTON – Somerset – 503 L 30 – see Bridgwater

WOOLER – Northd. – 502 N 17 24 A1

London 330 m – Alnwick 17 m – Berwick-on-Tweed 17 m

ENGLAND

Firwood without rest P VISA
Middleton Hall, South : 1 ¾ m. by Earle rd on Middleton Hall rd ✉ NE71 6RD – ☎ (01668) 283 699 – welcome@firwoodhouse.co.uk
3 rm – †£ 60 ††£ 70/74
◆ Victorian former hunting lodge in the Cheviot. Homely lounge and open-fired breakfast rooms boast bay windows with country views. Good sized rooms with individual style.

WOOLHAMPTON – Berks. – 503 Q 29 *Great Britain* 10 B3

London 56 m – Newbury 8 m – Thatcham 4 m
Basildon Park★, NE : 10 m. by A 4, A 340 and A 417

The Angel P VISA
Bath Rd ✉ RG7 5RT – ☎ (0118) 971 3301 – mail@thea4angel.com – Closed 1 week Christmas and Monday
Rest – Carte £ 16/30
◆ Technicolored interior, vividly dressed with elaborate vases and rows of bottles. Fireplaces divide rooms. Well-spaced tables. Interesting dishes from modern British range.

WOOLSTHORPE-BY-BELVOIR – Lincs. – 502 R 25 – see Grantham

WORCESTER – Worcs. – 503 N 27 – pop. 94 029 *Great Britain* 18 B3

London 124 m – Birmingham 26 m – Bristol 61 m – Cardiff 74 m
The Guildhall, High St ☎ (01905) 726311
Perdiswell Park Bilford Rd, ☎ (01905) 754 668 .
City★ – Cathedral★★ – Royal Worcester Porcelain Works★ (Museum of Worcester Porcelain★) M
The Elgar Trail★

Plan opposite

Diglis House ← P VISA AE
Severn St ✉ WR1 2NF – ☎ (01905) 353 518 – diglishouse@yahoo.com – Fax (01905) 767 772 o
25 rm – †£ 90 ††£ 130 – 1 suite – **Rest** – (bar lunch Monday-Saturday) Carte £ 16/22
◆ Georgian house on banks of river Severn. Close to Royal Worcester factory. Attractive bar terrace. Characterful rooms in main house, those in annex more modern. Conservatory dining room with river outlook.

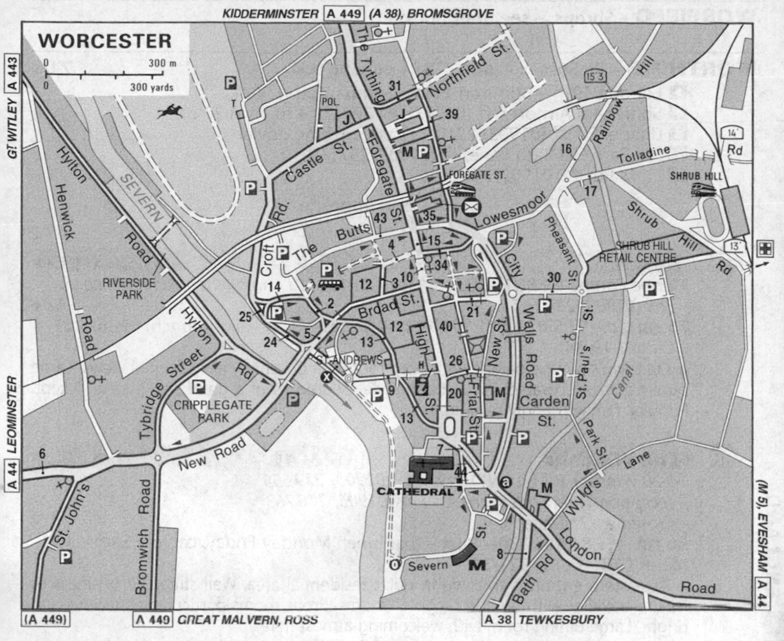

All Saints Rd	2	Deansway	13	Pump St	26
Angel Pl.	3	Dolday	14	St Martin's Gate	30
Angel St	4	Foregate (The)	15	St Mary's St	31
Bridge St.	5	High St		St Nicholas St.	34
Broad St		Lowesmoor Pl.	16	Sansome St	35
Bromyard Rd	6	Lowesmoor Terrace	17	Sansome Walk	39
College St.	7	Lychgate Shopping Centre	20	Shambles (The)	40
Commandery Rd	8	Mealcheapen St.	21	Shaw St	43
Copenhagen St	9	North Parade	24	Shrub Hill Retail Centre	
Cross (The)	10	North Quay	25	Sidbury	44
Crown Gate Centre	12				

XX **Glasshouse**

Sidbury ✉ WR1 2HU – ☎ (01905) 611 120 – eat@theglasshouse.co.uk – Closed 25 December, Bank Holidays and Sunday dinner c

Rest – Carte £ 26/41

◆ Leather furnished lounge. Stylish chocolate and blue hued dining areas; the first floor has glass wall and views of city. Brasserie style menu offers modern British dishes.

XX **Brown's**

24 Quay St ✉ WR1 2JJ – ☎ (01905) 26 263 – Fax (01905) 25 768 – Closed Monday x

Rest – Menu £ 25/40 – Carte £ 19/28

◆ Converted riverside corn mill. Spacious, open interior as befits the building's origins. Impressive collection of modern artwork. Mainly British dishes are renowned locally.

at Bransford West : 4 m. by A 44 on A 4103 – ✉ Worcester

Bear and Ragged Staff

Station Rd, Southeast : ½ m. on Powick rd ✉ WR6 5JH – ☎ (01886) 833 399 – mail@bear.uk.com – Fax (01886) 833 106 – Closed dinner 25 December and 1 January

Rest – Carte £ 19/35

◆ Two oak trees dominate the front of this traditional pub in quiet country lane. Huge blackboard menus offer plenty of interest: vegetables travel from rear garden to kitchen.

WORFIELD – Shrops. – see Bridgnorth

WORTHING – W. Sussex – 504 S 31 – pop. 96 964 7 D3

London 59 m – Brighton 11 m – Southampton 50 m
Shoreham Airport : (01273) 467373, E : 4 m. by A 27 BY
Chapel Rd (01903) 221066, tic@worthing.gov.uk
Hill Barn Hill Barn Lane, (01903) 237 301;
Links Rd, (01903) 260 801.

Plan opposite

Beach

Marine Parade ✉ BN11 3QJ – (01903) 234 001 – info@thebeachhotel.co.uk – Fax (01903) 234 567 AZ **e**

75 rm – £ 53/79 £ 100/140 – 4 suites – **Rest** – (light lunch) Menu £ 21 – Carte £ 19/34

♦ On town's marine parade with front rooms all boasting clear Channel views. Large public areas decorated in Art Deco style. Bedrooms of a good size and well kept. Popular, family-friendly restaurant.

The Windsor

14-20 Windsor Rd ✉ BN11 2LX – (01903) 239 655 – reception@thewindsor.co.uk – Fax (01903) 210 763 – Closed 24-31 December BY **i**

30 rm – £ 84 £ 130 – **Rest** – (bar lunch Monday-Friday, carvery Saturday) Menu £ 18 – Carte £ 21/30

♦ At eastern entrance to town in quiet residential area. Well suited to business or leisure traveller with a wide range of rooms. Front rooms particularly spacious and bright. Large dining room with welcoming atmosphere.

Berkeley

rm, rest,

86-95 Marine Parade ✉ BN11 3QD – (01903) 820 000 – reservations@berkeleyhotel-worthing.co.uk – Fax (01903) 821 234 BZ **a**

80 rm – £ 55/90 £ 75/135 – **Rest** – (bar lunch Monday-Saturday) Menu £ 22 (dinner) – Carte £ 22/27 **s**

♦ Overlooking the Channel and well located for visiting the famous South Downs. First floor rooms boast original Victorian splendour of high ceilings and larger windows. Dining room boasts pleasant sea views.

Chatsworth

rm, rest,

Steyne ✉ BN11 3DU – (01903) 236 103 – hotel@chatsworthworthing.co.uk – Fax (01903) 823 726 BZ **x**

98 rm – £ 75/105 £ 100/140 – **Rest** – (dinner only) Menu £ 17

♦ In a Georgian terrace overlooking Steyne Gardens and ideally located for a range of the town's resort activities. Attentive service and good sized bedrooms. Simple, uncluttered dining room.

Beacons without rest

18 Shelley Rd ✉ BN11 1TU – (01903) 230 948 – thebeacons@btconnect.com BZ **e**

8 rm – £ 40/45 £ 72/78

♦ Friendly traditional home providing classic English seaside accommodation. In the centre of town close to parks. Ideal base for visiting historic Arundel and Chichester.

XX The Parsonage

6-10 High St, Tarring ✉ BN14 7NN – (01903) 820 140 – parsonage.bookings@ntlworld.com – Fax (01903) 523 233 – Closed 26 December-4 January, Sunday and Bank Holidays AY **c**

Rest – Menu £ 21 – Carte £ 25/38

♦ Within one of Tarring high street's original 15C cottages. Exposed beams and framed photographs. Good international cuisine and a friendly, comfortable atmosphere.

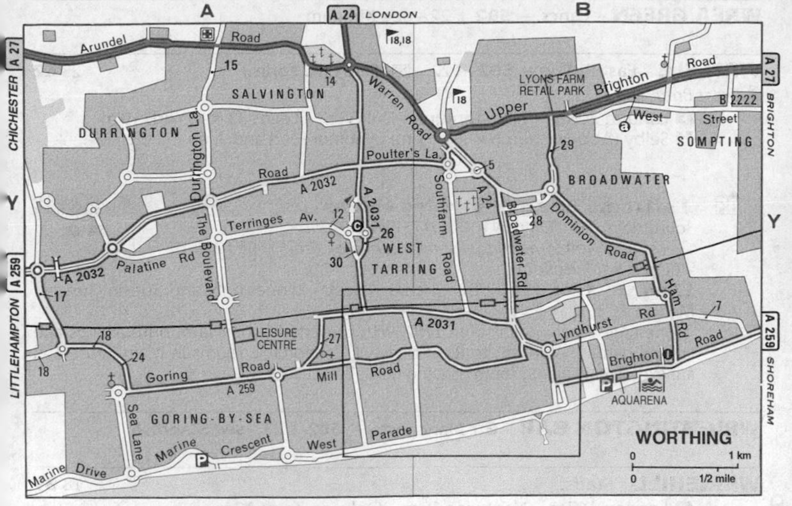

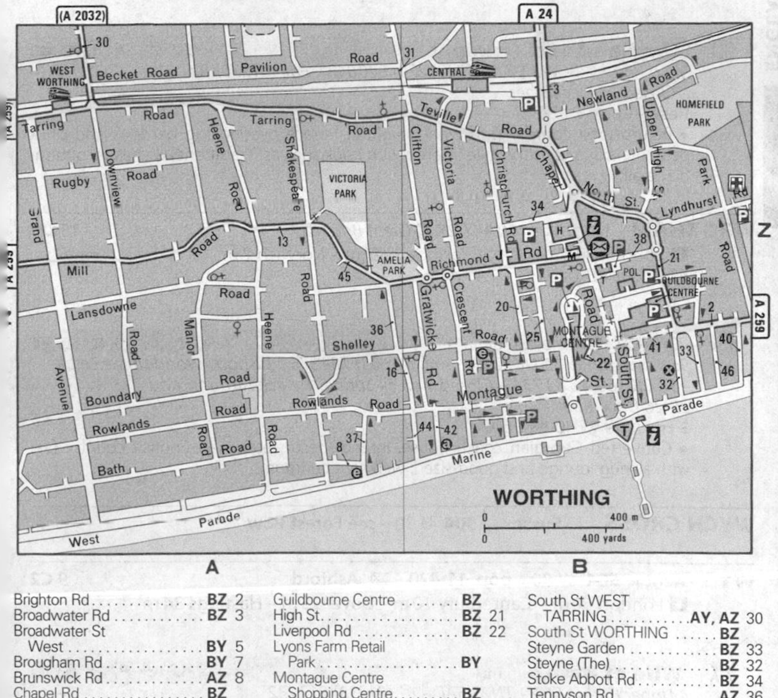

Brighton Rd	BZ	2
Broadwater Rd	BZ	3
Broadwater St West	BY	5
Brougham Rd	BY	7
Brunswick Rd	AZ	8
Chapel Rd	BZ	
Church Rd	AY	12
Cowper Rd	AZ	13
Crockhurst Hill	AY	14
Durrington Hill	AY	15
Eriswell Rd	ABZ	16
Goring St	AY	17
Goring Way	AY	18
Grafton Rd	BZ	20
Guildbourne Centre	BZ	
High St	BZ	21
Liverpool Rd	BZ	22
Lyons Farm Retail Park	BY	
Montague Centre Shopping Centre	BZ	
Montague St	BZ	
Mulberry Lane	AY	24
Portland Rd	BZ	25
Rectory Rd	AY	26
Reigate Rd	AY	27
Sompting Ave	BY	28
Sompting Rd	BY	29
South Farm Rd	ABZ	31
South St WEST TARRING	AY, AZ	30
South St WORTHING	BZ	
Steyne Garden	BZ	33
Steyne (The)	BZ	32
Stoke Abbott Rd	BZ	34
Tennyson Rd	AZ	36
Thorn Rd	AZ	37
Union Pl	BZ	38
Warwick Rd	BZ	40
Warwick St	BZ	41
Western Pl	BZ	44
West St	BZ	42
Wykeham Rd	AZ	45
York Rd	BZ	46

WREA GREEN – Lancs. – 502 L 22 – see Kirkham

WRESSLE – East Riding – 502 R 22 – ✉ Selby (N. Yorks.) 23 C2

Great Britain

London 208 m – Kingston-upon-Hull 31 m – Leeds 31 m – York 19 m

Selby (Abbey Church★), W : 5 m. by minor road and A 63

Loftsome Bridge Coaching House

South : ½ m. ✉ YO8 6EN – ☎ (01757) 630070
– reception@loftsomebridge-hotel.co.uk – Fax (01757) 633900
– Closed Bank Holidays

17 rm – 🚹£ 52 🚹🚹£ 77/82 – 1 suite – **Rest** – (dinner only and Sunday lunch) Menu £ 26 **s**

◆ One-time coaching inn from 1782, with converted former farm outbuildings and lawned garden. Adjacent to River Derwent. Comfortable rooms in main house and annexes. Smart dining room echoing house's light style.

WRIGHTINGTON BAR – Gtr Manchester – 502 L 23 – see Standish

WRINEHILL – Staffs. 18 B1

London 167 m – Nantwich 10 m – Stoke-on-Trent 10 m

The Hand and Trumpet

Main Road ✉ CW3 9BJ – ☎ (01270) 820048 – Fax (01270) 821911
– Closed 25 December

Rest – Carte £ 25/35

◆ Refurbished country pub with delightful terrace overlooking gardens and duck pond. Relaxing country style interior with book shelves. Traditional dishes recognisable to all.

WROXHAM – Norfolk – 504 Y 25 *Great Britain* 15 D1

London 118 m – Great Yarmouth 21 m – Norwich 7 m

Norfolk Broads★

Coach House without rest

96 Norwich Rd ✉ NR12 8RY – ☎ (01603) 784376 – bishop@worldonline.co.uk
– Fax (01603) 783734 – Closed 1 week Spring, 1 week Autumn and 25-26 December

3 rm – 🚹£ 40 🚹🚹£ 60

◆ Converted Georgian coach house. Interior décor retains an English country feel with a snug lounge and good-sized, well-kept bedrooms.

WYCH CROSS – E. Sussex – 504 U 30 – see Forest Row

WYE – Kent – 504 W 30 – pop. 11 420 – ✉ Ashford 9 C2

London 60 m – Canterbury 10 m – Dover 28 m – Hastings 34 m

Wife of Bath with rm

4 Upper Bridge St ✉ TN25 5AF – ☎ (01233) 812232
– reservations@wifeofbath.com

5 rm – 🚹£ 65 🚹🚹£ 95 – **Rest** – (Closed Monday, Tuesday lunch and Sunday dinner) Carte £ 25/33

◆ A lovely timber-framed house built in 1760. Fine cloth tables. Well chosen menu of satisfying dishes. Full or Continental breakfast after staying in comfy, soft-toned rooms.

WYMONDHAM – Norfolk – 504 X 26 15 C2

London 102 m – Cambridge 55 m – King's Lynn 49 m – Norwich 12 m

Old Thorn Barn without rest

Corporation Farm, Wymondham Rd, Hethel, Southeast : 3½ m. on B 1135 (following signs to Mulbarton) ✉ NR14 8EU – ✆ (01953) 607 785 – enquiries@oldthornbarn.co.uk – Fax (01953) 601 909

10 rm – †£ 33/56 ††£ 52/56

◆ Simple, rural guesthouse sited on farm and utilising former outbuildings as bedrooms with hand-built wood furniture. Rustic lounge and breakfast area with wood-burning stove.

WYTHAM – Oxon. – see Oxford

YANWATH – Cumbria – see Penrith

YARCOMBE – Devon – 503 K 31 – see Honiton

YARM – Stockton-on-Tees – 502 P 20 – pop. 8 929 24 B3

London 242 m – Middlesbrough 8 m – Newcastle upon Tyne 47 m

Crathorne Hall

Crathorne, South : 3½ m. by A 67 ✉ TS15 0AR – ✆ (01642) 700 398 – crathornehall@handpicked.co.uk – Fax (01642) 700 814

36 rm – †£ 105/115 ††£ 165 – 1 suite

Rest *Leven* – (dinner only and Sunday lunch) Menu £ 35 – Carte £ 35/44

◆ One of the last stately homes of the Edwardian period. Plenty of original features such as wood panelling and ornate fireplaces. Antique furnished bedrooms and public areas. Formal dining room with an air of classic elegance and tables clothed in crisp linen.

Judges Country House

Kirklevington Hall, Kirklevington, South : 1½ m. on A 67 ✉ TS15 9LW – ✆ (01642) 789 000 – enquiries@judgeshotel.co.uk – Fax (01642) 787 692

21 rm – †£ 129/163 ††£ 179/194 – **Rest** – Menu £ 18/44 – Carte £ 44/54

◆ Former Victorian judge's residence surrounded by gardens. Welcoming panelled bar and spacious lounge filled with antiques and curios. Attractive rooms with a host of extras. Conservatory dining room overlooks the gardens.

YARMOUTH – I.O.W. – 503 P 31 – see Wight (Isle of)

YARPOLE – Herefordshire 18 B2

The Bell Inn

Green Lane ✉ HR6 0BD – ✆ (01568) 780 359 – Closed Monday except Bank Holidays

Rest – Menu £ 15 – Carte £ 17/25

◆ Traditional country pub: black and white timbered façade, original stone cider press, roaring fire. Converted barn dining room for robust amalgam of classic and modern dishes.

Good food and accommodation at moderate prices?
Look for the Bib symbols:
red Bib Gourmand for food, blue Bib Hotel for hotels

ENGLAND

YATTENDON – Newbury – 503 Q 29 – ✉ Newbury 10 B3

London 61 m – Oxford 23 m – Reading 12 m

The Royal Oak with rm

The Square ✉ RG18 0UG – ✆ (01635) 201 325 – info@royaloakyattendon.com – Fax (01635) 201 926 – Closed 1 January

5 rm – †£ 110 ††£ 130 – **Rest** – (booking essential) Menu £ 15 – Carte £ 26/35

◆ Personally run part 16C former coaching inn in attractive village. Quintessentially English style. Classic or modern dishes in beamed bar or cosy restaurant. Chintzy bedrooms.

at Frilsham South : 1 m. by Frilsham rd on Bucklebury rd – ✉ Yattendon

The Pot Kiln

✉ RG18 0XX – ✆ (01635) 201 366 – info@potkiln.co.uk – Closed 25 December

Rest – Carte £ 25/30

◆ 350-year old pub: tiny, wonderfully characterful bar with centuries-old benches. Micro-brewery to rear. Totally local food: owner shoots game; veg from garden and woods.

Do not confuse ✗ with ✿!
✗ defines comfort, while stars are awarded for the best cuisine, across all categories of comfort.

ENGLAND

YAXLEY – Suffolk – see Thornham Magna

YEALMPTON – Devon – 503 H/I 32 2 C2

London 211 m – Ivybridge 7 m – Plymouth 8 m

✗✗ **The Seafood** – at Rose & Crown

Market St ✉ PL8 2EB – ✆ (01752) 880 502 – info@theroseandcrown.co.uk – Fax (01752) 881 058 – Closed Sunday dinner and Monday

Rest – Seafood Menu £ 13 (lunch) – Carte £ 18/30

◆ Converted barn opposite Rose & Crown, with local black and white fishing photos on walls. Fittingly, the delicious seafood dishes are interesting and ambitious.

Rose & Crown

Market St ✉ PL8 2EB – ✆ (01752) 880 223 – info@theroseandcrown.co.uk – Fax (01752) 881 058 – closed 25 December

Rest – Menu £ 10 – Carte £ 18/27

◆ Neat exterior and smart rear walled terrace and water feature. Big leather sofas and long benches in open-plan interior where modern dishes make use of seafood proximity.

YEOVIL – Somerset – 503 M 31 – pop. 41 871 3 B3

London 136 m – Exeter 48 m – Southampton 72 m – Taunton 26 m

Hendford ✆ (01935) 845946, yeoviltic@southsomerset.gov.ukat Cart Gate : Picnic Site ✆ (01935) 829333

Sherborne Rd, ✆ (01935) 422965 .

St John the Baptist★

Monacute House★★ **AC**, W : 4 m. on A 3088 – Fleet Air Arm Museum, Yeovilton★★ **AC**, NW : 5 m. by A 37 – Tintinhull House Garden★ **AC**, NW: 5½ m. – Ham Hill (≤ ★★) W : 5½ m. by A 3088 – Stoke sub Hamdon (parish church★) W : 5¼ m. by A 3088. Muchelney★★ (parish church★★) NW : 14 m. by A 3088, A 303 and B 3165 – Lytes Cary★, N : 7½ m. by A 37, B 3151 and A 372 – Sandford Orcas Manor House★, NW : 8 m. by A 359 – Cadbury Castle (≤ ★★) NE : 10½ m. by A 359 – East Lambrook Manor★ **AC**, W : 12 m. by A 3088 and A 303

Lanes
West Coker, Southwest : 3 m. on A 30 ✉ BA22 9AJ – ☎ (01935) 862555 – stay@laneshotel.net – Fax (01935) 864260
28 rm – £ 93 £ 130 – **Rest** – (Closed Saturday lunch) Carte £ 17/31
◆ 18C stone former rectory in walled grounds. Stylish modern interior with chocolate and red leather predominant. Stretch out in relaxed lounge. Airy, modish bedrooms. Modern classics and lots of glass in the Brasserie.

at Barwick South : 2 m. by A 30 off A 37 – ✉ Yeovil

Little Barwick House with rm
✉ BA22 9TD – ☎ (01935) 423902 – reservations@barwick7.fsnet.co.uk – Fax (01935) 420908 – Closed 2 weeks Christmas
6 rm – £ 80/126 £ 138/154 – **Rest** – (Closed Sunday dinner, Monday and Tuesday lunch) (booking essential) Menu £ 24/37
◆ Dignified Georgian dower house in a secluded spot. Though cosy rooms are available, the focus is on the restaurant with its menu of satisfying regionally based menus.

at Montacute Northwest : 5 m. by A 3088 – ✉ Yeovil

Phelips Arms
The Borough ✉ TA15 6XB – ☎ (01935) 822557 – info@phelips.co.uk – closed Sunday dinner and Monday
Rest – Carte £ 15/25
◆ Sand coloured 17C pub with traditional décor and furnishings. Modern, interesting menus, underpinned by accomplished cooking, have an eclectic range.

at Stoke sub Hamdon Northwest : 5 ½ m. by A 3088 – ✉ Yeovil

The Priory House
1 High St ✉ TA14 6PP – ☎ (01935) 822826 – reservations@theprioryhouserestaurant.co.uk – Fax (01935) 825822 – Closed last 2 weeks May, first 2 weeks November, Sunday, Monday and Bank Holidays
Rest – (dinner only and Saturday lunch) Menu £ 22 **s** – Carte £ 31/36 **s**
◆ Village centre restaurant that sticks firmly to traditions with tried and tested classics to the fore: a quiet and relaxing experience. Swallow a cider brandy after dinner!

YORK – N. Yorks. – **502** Q 22 – **pop. 137 505** *Great Britain* 23 **C2**

London 203 m – Kingston-upon-Hull 38 m – Leeds 26 m – Middlesbrough 51 m – Nottingham 88 m – Sheffield 62 m

The De Grey Rooms, Exhibition Sq ☎ (01904) 621756, tic@york.tourism.co.uk.

Strensall Lords Moor Lane, ☎ (01904) 491840 ;

Heworth Muncastergate Muncaster House, ☎ (01904) 424618 .

City★★★ – Minster★★★ (Stained Glass★★★, Chapter House★★, Choir Screen★★) CDY – National Railway Museum★★★ CY – The Walls★★ CDXYZ – Castle Museum★ **AC** DZ **M2** – Jorvik Viking Centre★ **AC** DY **M1** – Fairfax House★ **AC** DY **A** – The Shambles★ DY **54**

Plan on next page

Middlethorpe Hall
Bishopthorpe Rd, South : 1 ¾ m. ✉ YO23 2GB – ☎ (01904) 641241 – info@middlethorpe.com – Fax (01904) 620176
21 rm – £ 125/180 £ 185/250, £6.95 – 8 suites – **Rest** – (booking essential for non-residents) Menu £ 24/42 **s**
◆ Impressive William and Mary country house dating from 1699. Elegantly and carefully restored; abundantly furnished with antiques. Most characterful rooms in main house. Wood-panelled, three-roomed restaurant with period feel.

ENGLAND

YORK

Street	Grid	No.
Bishopgate St.	CZ	3
Bishophill Senior	CZ	4
Blake St	CY	5
Campleshon Rd	AZ	7
Church St.	DY	8
Clifford St.	DY	10
Colliergate	DY	12
Coney St.	CY	13
Cromwell Rd.	CZ	15
Davygate	CY	16
Deangate	DY	18
Duncombe Pl.	CY	20
Fawcett St	DZ	21
Fetter Lane	CY	22
Goodramgate	DY	25
High Ousegate	DY	26
High Petergate	CY	28
Knavesmire Rd	AZ	29
Leeman Rd.	AY, CY	30
Lendal	CY	32
Lord Mayor's Walk	DX	33
Low Petergate	DY	35
Melrosegate	BY	36
Museum St	CY	39
Parliament St	DY	42
Pavement	DY	43
Peasholme Green	DY	45
Penley's Grove St	DX	46
Queen St	CZ	49
St Helen's Rd	AZ	50
St Leonard's Pl.	CY	52
St Maurice's Rd	DXY	53
Shambles (The)	DY	54
Station Rd.	CY	55
Stonebow (The)	DY	56
Stonegate	CY	58
Tower St.	DZ	59
University Rd	BZ	60

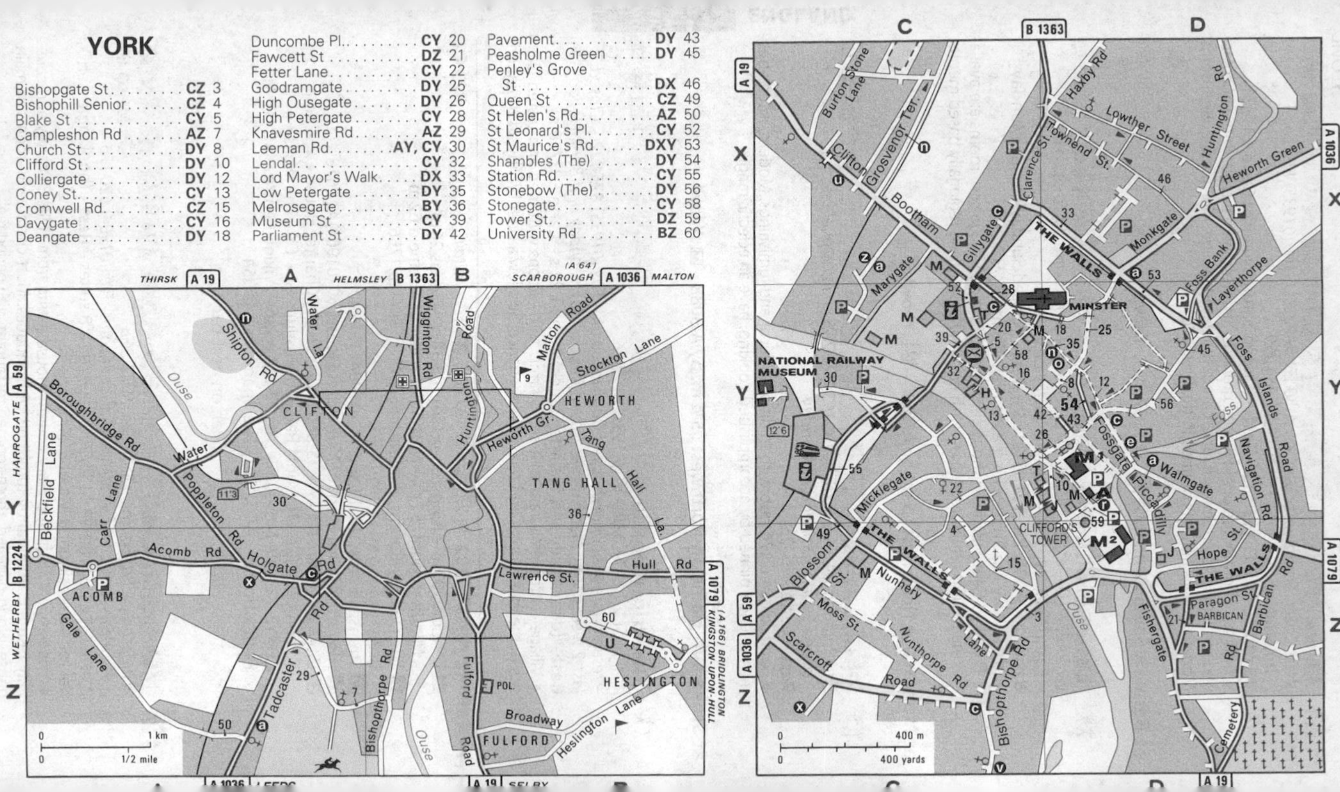

The Grange

Clifton ⊠ YO30 6AA – ☎ (01904) 644 744 – info@grangehotel.co.uk – Fax (01904) 612 453 CX **u**

29 rm – £ 128/138 £ 195 – 1 suite

Rest *The Ivy Brasserie* – (Closed Sunday dinner) (dinner only and Sunday lunch) Carte £ 24/40

Rest *The Cellar Bar* – (Closed Sunday lunch) Carte £ 24/40

◆ Elegant Regency town house with stylish period furniture throughout. Comfortable lounges and marble columned entrance hall. Excellently kept rooms vary in shapes and sizes. Ivy Brasserie boasts grand ceiling mural. Cellar Bar exudes much character.

Marriott

Tadcaster Rd ⊠ YO24 1QQ – ☎ (01904) 701 000 – york@marriotthotels.co.uk – Fax (01904) 702 308 AZ **a**

148 rm – £ 99 £ 99 – 3 suites

Rest *Ridings* – (bar lunch) Menu £ 25 **s**

◆ Large, group owned property on the edge of the racecourse with purpose-built extensions. Grandstand rooms, featuring large balconies and terraces, overlook course. Dining room with racecourse outlook.

York Pavilion

45 Main St, Fulford, South : 1½ m. on A 19 ⊠ YO10 4PJ – ☎ (01904) 622 099 – help@yorkpavilionhotel.com – Fax (01904) 626 939

63 rm – £ 89/125 £ 99/130

Rest *Langtons Brasserie* – Menu £ 17 (lunch) – Carte £ 21/34

◆ Georgian house on main road in suburbs. Wood panelled reception and period-style lounge. Older, more individual rooms in main house and uniform, chintzy style in extension. Informal dining.

Dean Court

rest,

Duncombe Pl ⊠ YO1 7EF – ☎ (01904) 625 082 – info@deancourt-york.co.uk – Fax (01904) 620 305 CY **c**

36 rm – £ 75/105 £ 120/230 – 1 suite

Rest *DCH* – Menu £ 17 (lunch) – Carte £ 28/35

◆ Built in the 1850s to house clerics visiting the Minster, visible from most rooms. Now a very modern feel pervades the public areas. Aforementioned rooms more traditional. Minster outlook from smart restaurant.

Monkbar

St Maurice's Rd ⊠ YO31 7JA ☎ (01904) 638 086 – sales@monkbarhotel.co.uk – Fax (01904) 629 195 DX **a**

99 rm – £ 95/110 £ 110/175 – **Rest** – Menu £ 13/25 **s** – Carte dinner £ 26/33 **s**

◆ Purpose-built and close to impressive Monkbar Gate. Modern décor throughout. Two room types: traditional, cottage-style in annex and uniform, modern rooms in main building. Restaurant exudes medieval atmosphere.

Holmwood House without rest

114 Holgate Rd ⊠ YO24 4BB – ☎ (01904) 626 183 – holmwood.house@dial.pipex.com – Fax (01904) 670 899 – Closed 24-26 December AZ **x**

14 rm – £ 60/70 £ 80/120

◆ Informal atmosphere in well-kept terraced Victorian property. Individually decorated bedrooms include William Morris styling. Bright basement breakfast room.

Alexander House without rest

94 Bishopthorpe Rd ⊠ YO23 1JS – ☎ (01904) 625 016 – info@alexanderhouseyork.co.uk – Closed mid-December-mid-January CZ **v**

4 rm – £ 59/75 £ 69/85

◆ Classic Victorian terraced house, immaculately refurbished by experienced owners. Delightful sitting room with porcelain and artworks. Hearty breakfasts. Attractive bedrooms.

The Hazelwood without rest
24-25 Portland St ✉ YO31 7EH – ☎ (01904) 626 548
– reservations@thehazelwoodyork.com – Fax (01904) 628 032 CX **c**
14 rm ☕ – 🚹£ 50/105 🚹🚹£ 110/120
◆ Two 19C town houses with characterful basement sitting room featuring original cooking range. Welcoming breakfast room in blue. Individual bedrooms, some with four posters.

Crook Lodge without rest
26 St Mary's, Bootham ✉ YO30 7DD – ☎ (01904) 655 614
– crooklodge@hotmail.com – Fax (01904) 625 915 CX **z**
6 rm ☕ – 🚹£ 45/70 🚹🚹£ 75/85
◆ Privately owned, attractive Victorian redbrick house in quiet location. Basement breakfast room with original cooking range. Some rooms compact, all pleasantly decorated.

Acer without rest
52 Scarcroft Hill ✉ YO24 1DE – ☎ (01904) 653 839 – info@acerhotel.co.uk
– Fax (01904) 677 017 – Closed Christmas-New Year CZ **x**
5 rm ☕ – 🚹£ 55 🚹🚹£ 90
◆ Terraced Victorian house with a creeper covered exterior. Warm welcome into homely and immaculately kept surroundings. Individually styled, traditionally appointed rooms.

ENGLAND

Apple House without rest
74-76 Holgate Rd ✉ YO24 4AB – ☎ (01904) 625 081
– pamelageorge1@yahoo.co.uk – Fax (01904) 628 918
– Closed 23 December-5 January AZ **c**
10 rm ☕ – 🚹£ 35/70 🚹🚹£ 60/80
◆ 19C terraced house that's been refurbished to a neat and tidy standard. Rooms vary in shape and size; all have good modern facilities. A friendly address to lay your head.

Bronte Guesthouse without rest
22 Grosvenor Terrace ✉ YO30 7AG – ☎ (01904) 621 066
– enquiries@bronte-guesthouse.com – Fax (01904) 653 434 CX **n**
6 rm ☕ – 🚹£ 38/55 🚹🚹£ 70/80
◆ Cosy little Victorian terraced house with pretty exterior, decorated in keeping with period nature of property. Charming breakfast room has antique furnishings. Comfy rooms.

The Heathers without rest
54 Shipton Rd, Clifton-Without, Northwest : 1½ m. on A 19 ✉ YO30 5RQ
– ☎ (01904) 640 989 – reservations@heathers-guest-house.co.uk
– Fax (01904) 640 989 – Closed 24-26 December AY **n**
6 rm ☕ – 🚹£ 60/86 🚹🚹£ 76/120
◆ A personally run guesthouse in an extended 1930s property overlooking meadowland. Bedrooms, which vary in size, are colourfully decorated and well furnished.

Melton's
7 Scarcroft Rd ✉ YO23 1ND – ☎ (01904) 634 341 – Fax (01904) 635 115
– Closed 2 weeks Christmas, Monday lunch and Sunday CZ **c**
Rest – (booking essential) Menu £ 21 (lunch) – Carte £ 27/33
◆ Glass fronted restaurant with mural decorated walls and neighbourhood feel. Smart, crisp tone in both service and table cover. Good modern British food with some originality.

J. Baker's

7 Fossgate ✉ YO1 9TA – ☎ (01904) 622 688 – info@jbakers.co.uk – Fax (01904) 671 931 – Closed 1-9 January, Sunday and Monday DY **c**

Rest – (light lunch) Menu £ 27 **s**

◆ Contemporary restaurant in city centre. Spacious first floor 'chocolate' lounge for coffee and truffles. Modern dining room matched by good value, funky, cutting edge dishes.

Blue Bicycle

34 Fossgate ✉ YO1 9TA – ☎ (01904) 673 990 – info@thebluebicycle.com – Fax (01904) 677 688 – Closed 24-26 December and 1-2 January DY **e**

Rest – (booking essential) Carte £ 31/42

◆ Delightfully cluttered, atmospheric restaurant full of objets d'art, ornaments and pictures. Wood floors and heavy, old, pine tables. Bustling and busy; British cuisine.

31 Castlegate

31 Castlegate ✉ YO1 9RN – ☎ (01904) 621 404 – Closed 25-26 December, 1 January and Monday DY **r**

Rest – Menu £ 12 (lunch) – Carte £ 21/27

◆ Superbly located former home of Georgian architect. Impressive period décor in situ. First floor, high ceilinged dining room for well-priced, tasty dishes on eclectic menus.

Vanilla Black

26 Swinegate ✉ YO1 8AZ – ☎ (01904) 676 750 – Closed 1 week January, 1 week June, 1 week October, 25-26 December, Sunday, Monday and lunch Tuesday DY **o**

Rest – Vegetarian (light lunch) Carte £ 22/24

◆ Vegetarian restaurant with eye-catching exterior, close to the Minster. Spacious interior dotted with scrubbed wooden tables. Very interesting dishes with host of influences.

The Tasting Room

13a Swinegate Court East ✉ YO1 8AJ – ☎ (01904) 627 879 – bookings@thetastingroom.co.uk – Closed 25 December, Sunday, Monday and Bank Holidays DY **n**

Rest – Carte £ 20/26

◆ Near the Minster with outdoor tables in good weather. Refurbished in 2005: smart fabrics and mood lighting. Simple, tasty, approachable cooking based upon a few good flavours.

Melton's Too

25 Walmgate ✉ YO1 9TX – ☎ (01904) 629 222 – greatfood@meltonstoo.co.uk – Fax (01904) 636 677 – Closed 25-26 December and 1 January DY **a**

Rest – Carte £ 21/28

◆ Café-bistro 'descendant' of Melton's restaurant. Located in former saddlers shop with oak beams and exposed brick walls. Good value eclectic dishes, with tapas a speciality.

at Escrick South : 5 ¾ m. on A 19 - BZ – ✉ York

Parsonage Country House

Main St ✉ YO19 6LF – ☎ (01904) 728 111 – reservations@parsonagehotel.co.uk – Fax (01904) 728 151

50 rm – †£ 75/95 ††£ 95/140 – **Rest** – (Closed Saturday lunch) Menu £ 16/25 **s** – Carte dinner £ 25/40 **s**

◆ Ivy-clad former parsonage with gardens; dating from 1848 and located adjacent to the parish church of St. Helen. Main house rooms most characterful, all are well appointed. Dining room with palpable country house feel.

ENGLAND

at York Business Park **Northwest : 3 ¾ m. by A 59 - AY - on A 1237 – ✉ York**

XX **Maxi's**

Ings Lane, Nether Poppleton ✉ YO26 6RA – ✆ (01904) 783 898 – info@maxi-s.co.uk – Fax (01904) 783 818 – Closed 25-26 December

Rest – Chinese Carte £ 18/20

◆ Purpose-built property with an ornate exterior. Chinese theme throughout including a feature pagoda in the dining room. Authentic food and attentive, friendly service.

ZENNOR – Cornwall – 503 D 33 — 1 A3

London 305 m – Penzance 11 m – St Ives 5 m

The Gurnard's Head with rm

Treen, West : 1 ½ m. on B 3306 ✉ TR26 3DE – ✆ (01736) 796 928 – enquiries@gurnardshead.co.uk – closed January-February

7 rm – †£ 50/53 ††£ 93 – **Rest** – (restricted lunch Monday) Carte £ 20/28

◆ Roughly textured, mustard hued pub. Shelves of books give it a shabby chic edge. Eat in restaurant or bar: clever, satisfying, carefully balanced combinations. Smart rooms.

ENGLAND

Q. Forir/MICHELIN

Towns
from A to Z

Villes
de A à Z

Città
de A a Z

Städte
von A bis Z

Scotland

ABERDEEN – Aberdeen – **501** N 12 – **pop. 184 788** *Scotland* 28 **D1**

Edinburgh 130 m – Dundee 67 m

Aberdeen Airport, Dyce : ✆ (0870) 0400006, NW : 7 m. by A 96 X

to Shetland Islands (Lerwick) and via Orkney Islands (Stromness) (P and O Scottish Ferries) 1-2 daily

Provost Ross's House, Shiprow (01224) 288828

Hazelhead Hazelhead Park, ✆ (01224) 321 830;

Royal Aberdeen Bridge of Don Balgownie, ✆ (01224) 702 571;

Balnagask St Fitticks Rd, ✆ (01224) 871 286;

King's Links Golf Rd, ✆ (01224) 632 269;

Portlethen Badentoy Rd, ✆ (01224) 781 090;

Murcar Bridge of Don, ✆ (01224) 704 354;

Auchmill West Heatheryfold Bomyview Rd, ✆ (01224) 715 214.

City★★ - Old Aberdeen★★ X – St Machar's Cathedral★★ (West Front★★★, Heraldic Ceiling★★★) X **A** – Art Gallery★★ (Macdonald Collection★★) Y **M** – Mercat Cross★★ Y **B** – King's College Chapel★ (Crown Spire★★★, medieval fittings★★★) X **D** – Provost Skene's House★ (painted ceilings★★) Y **E** – Maritime Museum★ Z **M1** – Marischal College★ Y **U**

Brig o' Balgownie★, by Don St X. SW : Deeside★★ - Crathes Castle★★ (Gardens★★★) **AC**, SW : 16 m. by A 93 X – Dunnottar Castle★★ **AC** (site★★★), S : 18 m. by A 90 X – Pitmedden Garden★★, N : 14 m. by A 90 on B 999 X – Castle Fraser★ (exterior★★) **AC**, W : 16 m. by A 944 X - Fyvie Castle★, NW : 26½ m. on A 947

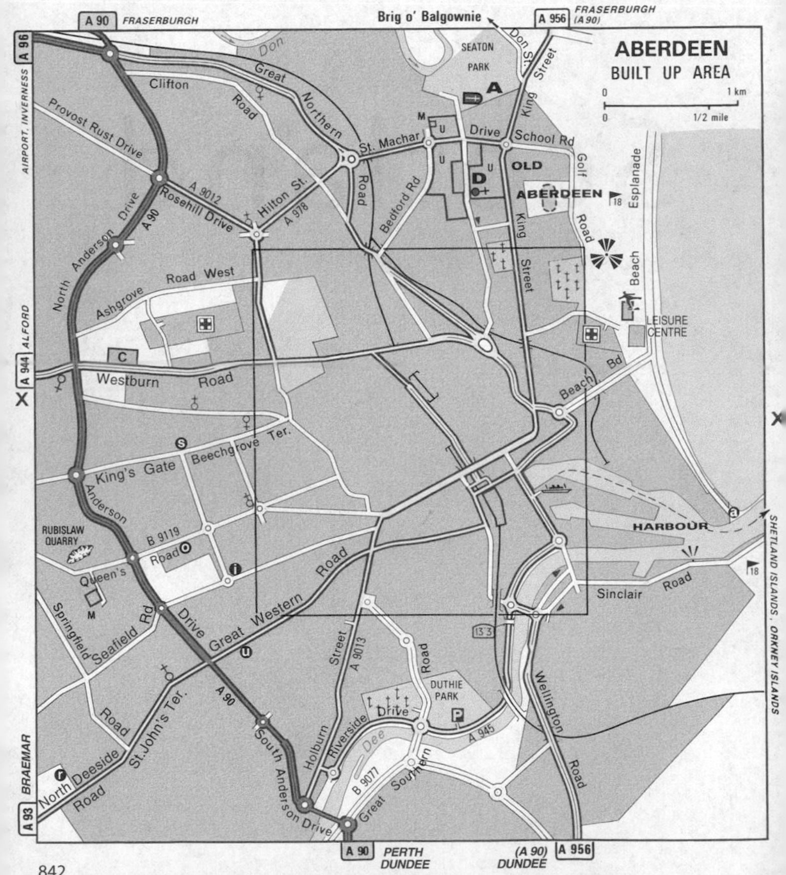

The Marcliffe H and Spa

North Deeside Rd ✉ AB15 9YA – ✆ (01224) 861 000 – enquiries@marcliffe.com – Fax (01224) 868 860 X **r**

40 rm – £ 150/195 £ 245/295 – 2 suites

Rest *Conservatory* – Carte £ 31/45 **s**

◆ Family owned and professionally run modern country house set amidst 8 acres of pleasant grounds. Spacious, individually decorated rooms with antique furniture. Light, airy conservatory dining.

Mercure Ardoe House H. and Spa

South Deeside Rd, Blairs, Southwest : 5 m. on B 9077 ✉ AB12 5YP – ✆ (01224) 860 600 – H6626-re@accor.com – Fax (01224) 860 644

107 rm – £ 200 £ 220 – 2 suites

Rest *Blairs* – Menu £ 34 – Carte £ 29/42

◆ Imposing 18C Scottish baronial style mansion with annexes. Country house character aligned to excellent leisure facilities. Modern bedrooms, many overlooking the grounds. Formal, wood-panelled Blairs.

Simpson's

59 Queen's Rd ✉ AB15 4YP – ✆ (01224) 327 777 – reservations@simpsonshotel.co.uk – Fax (01224) 327 700 – Closed 24 December-3 January X **o**

48 rm – £ 150 £ 175 – 2 suites

Rest *Brasserie* – Carte £ 17/30

◆ Period granite façade belies vibrantly decorated and contemporary interior. Family owned and relaxed "boutique" hotel. Stylish and modern bedrooms with business facilities. Roman bath house styled brasserie.

Skene House Holburn without rest

6 Union Grove ✉ AB10 6SY – ✆ (01224) 580 000 – holburn@skene-house.co.uk – Fax (01224) 585 193 Z **v**

39 suites – £ 108/159, £ 8

◆ Row of five granite former tenements. Not your conventional hotel, but a number of serviced apartments. Each suite benefits from its own kitchen. Ideal for long stays.

The Mariner

349 Great Western Rd ✉ AB10 6NW – ✆ (01224) 588 901 – info@themarinerhotel.co.uk – Fax (01224) 571 621 – Closed 26 December X **u**

25 rm – £ 80 £ 110

Rest *Atlantis* – Seafood (Closed Saturday lunch) (bar lunch Saturday) Menu £ 18 – Carte £ 22/38

◆ A nautical theme prevails through the ground floor of this commercial hotel. Spacious, colourfully decorated bedrooms with extensive facilities. More seclusion in annex rooms. Long established restaurant with wood panelling and maritime themed décor.

Atholl

54 King's Gate ✉ AB15 4YN – ✆ (01224) 323 505 – info@atholl-aberdeen.co.uk – Fax (01224) 321 555 – closed 1 January X **s**

34 rm – £ 85/110 £ 125/140 – **Rest** – Carte £ 15/29

◆ Baronial style hotel set in leafy suburbs; well run by friendly staff. Traditional lounge bar; well-priced, up-to-date rooms. A useful address for visitors to the city. Dining room specialises in tried-and-tested Scottish cooking.

Carmelite

Stirling St – ✆ (01224) 589 101 – info@carmelitehotel.com – Fax (01224) 574 288 Z **c**

50 rm – £ 55/125 £ 65/325, £ 12 – **Rest** – Carte £ 22/29

◆ Boutique hotel on site of former monastery. Refurbished first floor bedrooms have contemporary style; top two floors are more traditional, while luxury suites are the largest. Traditional restaurant serving simple, flavoursome food.

SCOTLAND

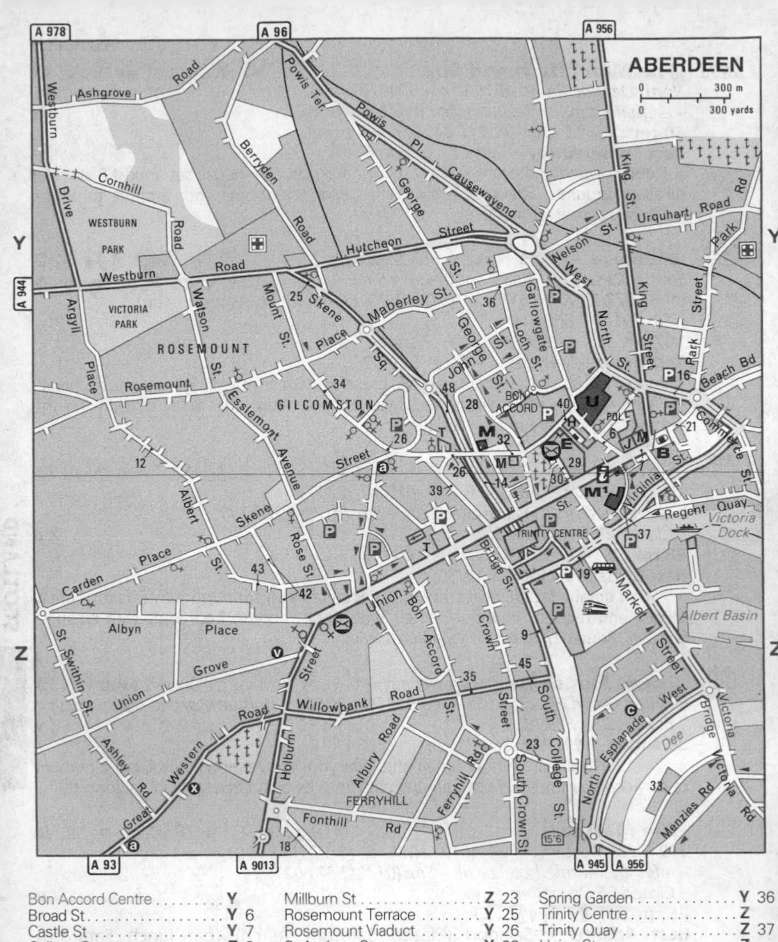

Bon Accord Centre . . . . Y
Broad St . . . . Y 6
Castle St . . . . Y 7
College St. . . . . Z 9
Craigie Loanings . . . . Y 12
Denburn Rd. . . . . YZ 14
East North St. . . . . Y 16
George St . . . . Y
Great Southern Rd . . . . Z 18
Guild St. . . . . Z 19
Justice St . . . . Y 21

Millburn St . . . . Z 23
Rosemount Terrace . . . . Y 25
Rosemount Viaduct . . . . Y 26
St Andrew St. . . . . Y 28
St Nicholas Centre . . . . Y 29
St Nicholas St . . . . YZ 30
School Hill . . . . YZ 32
South Esplanade
West. . . . . Z 33
South Mount St. . . . . Y 34
Springbank Terrace . . . . Z 35

Spring Garden . . . . Y 36
Trinity Centre . . . . Z
Trinity Quay . . . . Z 37
Union St . . . . Z
Union Terrace. . . . . Z 39
Upperkirkgate . . . . Y 40
Victoria St. . . . . Z 42
Waverley Pl. . . . . Z 43
Wellington
Pl. Z 45
Woolmanhill. . . . . Y 48

Penny Meadow without rest

189 Great Western Rd ✉ AB10 6PS – ✆ (01224) 588 037
– frances@pennymeadow.freeserve.co.uk – Fax (01224) 573 639 Z **x**

3 rm – £45 £65

◆ Attractive Victorian house built of local granite. Welcoming service by owners. Light and airy bedrooms have some thoughtful touches and are well-appointed.

Silver Darling < Aberdeen Harbour and Bay,

Pocra Quay, North Pier ✉ AB11 5DQ – ✆ (01224) 576 229 – Fax (01224) 588 119
– Closed 2 weeks Christmas-New Year, Saturday lunch and Sunday X **a**

Rest – Seafood Carte £ 37/47

◆ Former customs house attractively set at port entrance; panoramic views across harbour and coastline. Attentive service of superb quality seafood prepared in imaginative ways.

XX **The Eating Room**

239 Great Western Rd ✉ AB10 6PS – ✆ (01224) 212 125 – info@eatingroom.com – Closed 25-26 December, 1-2 January, Sunday and Monday Z **a**

Rest – Carte £ 21/31

◆ Small, contemporary restaurant in a granite house. Neatly laid, polished lacquered tables. Modern cooking style incorporates complex twists with feel for Asian flavours.

XX **Nargile**

77-79 Skene St ✉ AB10 1QD – ✆ (01224) 636 093 – Fax (01224) 636 202 – closed 25-26 December and 1 January Y **a**

Rest – Turkish (dinner only and lunch in December) Menu £ 22 – Carte £ 18/23

◆ Traditionally decorated Turkish restaurant with subdued lighting from Turkish lamps. Open-plan kitchen allows the diner to watch the chefs prepare the authentic dishes.

X **Rendezvous at Nargile**

106-108 Forest Ave ✉ AB15 4UP – ✆ (01224) 323 700 – nargile@freeserve.co.uk – Fax (01224) 312 202 – Closed 25-26 December and 1-2 January X **I**

Rest – Turkish/Mediterranean Menu £ 22/25 – Carte £ 18/33 **s**

◆ Corner restaurant with contemporary décor. Mediterranean - predominantly Turkish - menu from snacks to a full a la carte meal; fixed price menu between 5-7pm.

Your opinions are important to us: please write and let us know about your discoveries and experiences – good and bad!

SCOTLAND

ABERDEEN AIRPORT – Aberdeenshire – 501 N 12 – see Aberdeen

ABERFELDY – Perth and Kinross – 501 I 14 28 C2

▶ Edinburgh 75 m – Dunkeld 17 m – Pitlochry 14 m

at Fortingall West : 8 m. by B 846 and Fortingall rd

Fortingall Hotel

✉ PH15 2NQ – ✆ (01887) 830 367 – hotel@fortingallhotel.com – closed 2 weeks in February

10 rm – 🚹£ 95 🚹🚹£ 140 – **Rest** – Carte £ 20/33

◆ Refurbished arts and crafts style house on private estate. Bedrooms, named after local estates, have a contemporary style with a touch of tweed; those at front boasting views. Daily-changing menu served in antique-furnished restaurant.

ABERLADY East Lothian – 501 L 15 – see GULLANE

ABERLOUR – Aberdeenshire – 501 K 11 *Scotland* 28 C1

▶ Edinburgh 192 m – Aberdeen 60 m – Elgin 15 m – Inverness 55 m

Rothes Blackhall, ✆ (01340) 831 443 .

Dufftown (Glenfiddich Distillery★), SE : 6 m. by A 95 and A 941

Dowans

Southwest : ¾ m. by A 95 ✉ AB38 9LS – ✆ (01340) 871 488 – enquiries@dowanshotel.com – Fax (01340) 871 038

19 rm – 🚹£ 55/68 🚹🚹£ 140 – **Rest** – Carte £ 19/35 **s**

◆ Welcoming, informal establishment with classic Scottish country house style. Inviting public areas. Comfortably smart rooms, refurbished in 2006; best views from the front. Two roomed restaurant.

ABOYNE – Aberdeenshire – 501 L 12 – pop. 2 202 Scotland 28 D1

Edinburgh 131 m – Aberdeen 30 m – Dundee 68 m
Formanston Park, ✆ (013398) 86 328 .
Craigievar Castle★ AC, NE : 12 m. by B 9094, B 9119 and A 980

Struan Hall without rest

Ballater Rd ✉ AB34 5HY – ✆ (013398) 87 241 – struanhall@zetnet.co.uk – Fax (013398) 87 241 – April-September

3 rm – †£ 40/47 ††£ 79

◆ An agreeable and welcoming guesthouse with attractive garden. Well kept throughout. Large sitting room and antique breakfast table. Simple, comfy bedrooms.

The Candlestick-Maker

Charleston Rd ✉ AB34 5EJ – ✆ (013398) 86 060 – enquiries@thecandlestick-maker.com – Closed first 3 weeks February, 1-3 January, Sunday dinner and Monday

Rest – Menu £ 20 (lunch) – Carte dinner £ 23/41

◆ Simply decorated, candlelit restaurant overlooking the village green; formerly a butchers and a bakers, hence the name. Traditional British cooking, with European influences.

ACHILTIBUIE – Highland – 501 D 9 30 C1

SCOTLAND

Edinburgh 243 m – Inverness 84 m – Ullapool 25 m

Summer Isles

< Summer Isles,

✉ IV26 2YG – ✆ (01854) 622 282 – info@summerisleshotel.co.uk – Fax (01854) 622 251 – 22 March-15 October

10 rm – †£ 88/160 ††£ 139/202 – 3 suites

Rest *Summer Isles Bar* – see restaurant listing

Rest – (booking essential)(set menu only at dinner)(light seafood lunch) Menu £ 52 **s**

Spec. Stilton soufflé with herb leaf salad. Grilled turbot and mussels steamed in white wine and saffron. White chocolate flan with crisp chocolate and Bailey's base.

◆ Exceedingly well run with a fine setting and superb views of Summer Isles. Very comfy lounges and real fire. Superb duplex suite and cosy log cabin rooms. Pleasant restaurant boasts exacting cooking to a very high standard; local seafood to the fore.

Summer Isles (Bar) – at Summer Isles H.

✉ IV26 2YG – ✆ (01854) 622 282 – info@summerisleshotel.co.uk – Fax (01854) 622 251 – Closed mid-October to mid-March

Rest – Seafood (bookings not accepted) Carte £ 18/35 **s**

◆ Simple, informal bar with outside seating for sunny days and snug interior for more bracing weather. Seafood oriented blackboard menu and puddings from the restaurant.

AIRD UIG – Western Isles Outer Hebrides – see Lewis and Harris (Isle of)

ALLOWAY – South Ayrshire – 501 – see Ayr

ALTNAHARRA – Highland – 501 G 9 – ✉ Lairg Scotland 30 C1

Edinburgh 239 m – Inverness 83 m – Thurso 61 m
Ben Loyal★★, N : 10 m. by A 836 – Ben Hope★ (< ★★★) NW : 14 m

Altnaharra

✉ IV27 4UE – ✆ (01549) 411 222 – office@altnaharra.co.uk – Fax (01549) 411 233 – April-October

14 rm (dinner included) – †£ 105/150 ††£ 210/260 – **Rest** – (dinner only) Menu £ 29 **s**

◆ Refurbished rural hunting lodge with abundance of local wildlife. Stylishly decorated, cosy interiors include a cocktail bar and library. Simple, good-sized bedrooms. Local, seasonal menus in smart, formally set restaurant oozing charm and character.

ALYTH – Perth. and Kinross – 501 J 14 – pop. 2 301 28 C2

Edinburgh 63 m – Aberdeen 69 m – Dundee 16 m – Perth 21 m
Pitcrocknie, ☎ (01828) 632 268 .

Lands of Loyal

Loyal Rd, North : ½ m. by B 952 ✉ PH11 8JQ – ☎ (01828) 633 151 – enq@landsofloyal.com – Fax (01828) 633 313

16 rm – †£ 83 ††£ 145 – **Rest** – Menu £ 13 (lunch) – Carte £ 22/33 **s**

◆ Victorian mansion with an impressive reproduction salon from the SS Mauritania. Individually decorated bedrooms blend a pleasant traditional style with antiques. Appealing restaurant spans three different rooms.

Tigh Na Leigh

22-24 Airlie St ✉ PH11 8AJ – ☎ (01828) 632 372 – bandcblack@yahoo.co.uk – Fax (01828) 632 279 – Closed 29 December-12 February and restricted opening 15 November-28 December

5 rm – †£ 40/68 ††£ 110/200 – **Rest** – (dinner only) (booking essential) Menu £ 21

◆ Extremely spacious, modern bedrooms - two with jacuzzi baths - in this comfortable, contemporary conversion, which retains many original features. Look out for Tom, the cat. Dining room overlooks walled garden, church and carp pond. Daily-changing dinner menu and small wine list.

Look out for red symbols, indicating particularly pleasant establishments.

ANNBANK – South Ayrshire – 501 G 17 25 B2

Edinburgh 84 m – Ayr 6 m – Dumfries 54 m – Dumfries 38 m

Enterkine

Southeast : ½ m. on B 742 (Coylton rd) ✉ KA6 5AL – ☎ (01292) 520 580 – mail@enterkine.com – Fax (01292) 521 582

6 rm – †£ 60/120 ††£ 140/180 – 1 suite – **Rest** – (booking essential) Menu £ 19/30

◆ 1930s country house surrounded by extensive gardens and woodlands. Spacious, comfortable lounges. Luxurious bedrooms; one with large roof terrace. Charming library. Formal restaurant with views over River Ayr serves modern cooking; popular with non-residents.

ANSTRUTHER – Fife – 501 L 15 – pop. 3 442 *Scotland* 28 D2

Edinburgh 46 m – Dundee 23 m – Dunfermline 34 m
Scottish Fisheries Museum, Harbourhead ☎ (01333) 311073 (April-October)
Marsfield Shore Rd, ☎ (01333) 310 956 .
Scottish Fisheries Museum★★ **AC**
The East Neuk★★ – Crail★★ (Old Centre★★, Upper Crail★) NE : 4 m. by A 917. Kellie Castle★ **AC**, NW : 7 m. by B 9171, B 942 and A 917

The Spindrift

Pittenweem Rd ✉ KY10 3DT – ☎ (01333) 310 573 – info@thespindrift.co.uk – Fax (01333) 310 573 – Closed 5-28 January, 2 weeks November and Christmas

8 rm – †£ 40/50 ††£ 60/76 – **Rest** – (by arrangement) Menu £ 20 **s**

◆ Victorian house originally owned by tea clipper captain whose bedroom replicates a master's cabin. Comfortable period style throughout and local kippers for breakfast. 19C style dining room reflects house's age.

The Grange without rest

45 Pittenweem Rd ✉ KY10 3DT – ☎ (01333) 310 842 – grange@pamela-rae.com – Fax (01333) 310 842 – March-November

4 rm – †£ 33/60 ††£ 70/75

◆ Spacious Edwardian house on main road into this delightful coastal village. Snug lounges including charming sun room. Neatly kept, traditional bedrooms.

XX **Cellar**

24 East Green ✉ KY10 3AA – ✆ (01333) 310 378 – Fax (01333) 312 544 – Closed Christmas, Sunday, Monday in Winter and lunch mid week except in Summer
Rest – Seafood (booking essential) Menu £ 23/39
◆ Located through an archway on quiet back streets. Warm ambience with fires and exposed brick and stone. Bold, original cooking, more elaborate at dinner.

APPLECROSS – Highland – 501 C 11 29 B2

Applecross Inn ← Islands of Raasay and Skye, rm,

Shore St ✉ IV54 8LR – ✆ (01520) 744 262 – applecrossinn@globalnet.co.uk – Fax (01520) 744 400 – Closed 25 December and 1 January
7 rm – †£ 70 ††£ 100 – **Rest** – (booking essential) Carte £ 20/26
◆ An unforgettable coastal road journey of 24 miles ends at this cosy row of stone fishermen's cottages with lots of windows to enjoy the stupendous views. Smart, comfy rooms. Blackboard menus feature local seafood.

X **The Potting Shed**

Applecross Walled Garden, Northeast : ½ m. ✉ IV54 8ND – ✆ (01520) 744 440 – mail@eatinthewalledgarden.co.uk – restricted opening January-mid February
Rest – (Closed Sunday dinner) (lunch only and dinner Wednesday-Saturday) Carte £ 17/28
◆ Lovely 17C walled kitchen garden whose restaurant has grown from a tearoom. Its simple structure belies its tasty dishes, fresh from owner's fishing boat or the garden itself.

SCOTLAND

The ✿ award is the crème de la crème. This is awarded to restaurants which are really worth travelling miles for!

ARBROATH – Angus – 501 M 14 28 D2

Edinburgh 72 m – Dundee 17 m – Montrose 12 m

The Old Vicarage without rest

2 Seaton Rd, Northeast : ¾ m. by A 92 and Hayshead Rd ✉ DD11 5DX – ✆ (01241) 430 475 – loris@theoldvicaragebandb.co.uk
3 rm – †£ 45/50 ††£ 60/70
◆ Detached 19C house, of large proportions, clothed in Victorian style throughout. Eye-catching dolls house in lounge. Antique furnished rooms: ask for view of Arbroath Abbey.

ARCHIESTOWN – Moray – 501 K 11 – ✉ Aberlour (Aberdeenshire) 28 C1

Edinburgh 194 m – Aberdeen 62 m – Inverness 49 m

Archiestown

The Square ✉ AB38 7QL – ✆ (01340) 810 218 – jah@archiestownhotel.co.uk – Fax (01340) 810 239 – Closed 3 January-8 February and 23-28 December
11 rm – †£ 40/75 ††£ 80/120
Rest ***Bistro*** – Carte £ 27/36
◆ Privately owned little hotel appealing to all with its characterful, comfortable lounges and nearby golf and distilleries. Comfy, individual rooms, prettily decorated. Informal bistro with daily changing menu.

ARDEONAIG – Perth and Kinross – 501 H 14 – see Killin (Stirling)

ARDHASAIG – Western Isles Outer Hebrides – **501** Z 10 – see Lewis and Harris (Isle of)

ARDRISHAIG – Argyll and Bute – **501** D 15 – ✉ Lochgilphead 27 **B2**
Edinburgh 132 m – Glasgow 86 m – Oban 40 m

Allt-na-Craig
Tarbert Rd, on A 83 ✉ PA30 8EP – ☎ (01546) 603 245 – information@allt-na-craig.co.uk – Fax (01546) 603 255 – Closed Christmas
5 rm – †£ 45/65 ††£ 90 – **Rest** – (by arrangement) Menu £ 22
◆ Spacious, modernised Victorian house with lovely gardens, once the childhood home of author Kenneth Grahame. Front bedrooms have good views over loch. Simple, traditional dining room where breakfasts and evening meals are served.

ARDUAINE – Argyll and Bute – **501** D 15 – ✉ **Oban** *Scotland* 27 **B2**
Edinburgh 142 m – Oban 20 m
Loch Awe★★, E : 12 m. by A 816 and B 840

Loch Melfort ← Asknish bay and Islands of Jura, Shuna and Scarba,
✉ PA34 4XG – ☎ (01852) 200 233 – reception@lochmelfort.co.uk – Fax (01852) 200 214 – Closed 2 January-mid February
25 rm – †£ 50/89 ††£ 100/138 – **Rest** – Seafood (bar lunch) Menu £ 27 – Carte £ 17/24
◆ Next to Arduaine Gardens and with glorious, captivating views of the Sound of Jura, the hotel has spacious public areas including a bistro bar. Largest rooms in main house. Formal atmosphere in the main restaurant with a focus on quality local seafood.

ARRAN (Isle of) – North Ayrshire – **501** *Scotland* 25 **A2**
from Brodick to Ardrossan (Caledonian MacBrayne Ltd) 4-6 daily (55 mn) – from Lochranza to Kintyre Peninsula (Claonaig) (Caledonian MacBrayne Ltd) frequent services daily (30 mn) – from Brodick to Isle of Bute (Rothesay) (Caledonian MacBrayne Ltd) 3 weekly (2 h 5 mn)
Island★★ - Brodick Castle★★ AC

Brodick – North Ayrshire – pop. 822 25 **A2**
The Pier ☎ (01770) 302140
Brodick, ☎ (01770) 302 349;
Machrie Bay, ☎ (01770) 850 232.

Kilmichael Country House
Glen Cloy, West : 1 m. by Shore Rd, taking left turn opposite Golf Club ✉ KA27 8BY – ☎ (01770) 302 219 – enquiries@kilmichael.com – Fax (01770) 302 068 – Easter-October
4 rm – †£ 95 ††£ 120/190 – 3 suites – **Rest** – (Closed Tuesday) (dinner only) (booking essential) Menu £ 40 **s**
◆ Reputedly the oldest house on the Isle of Arran, in peaceful location with immaculate lawned grounds. Comfortable country house style and individually decorated bedrooms. Welcoming owners. Restaurant housed in extension. Daily-changing menus.

Alltan without rest
Knowe Rd, West : ½ m. by Shore Rd taking left at Golf Club ✉ KA27 8BY – ☎ (01770) 302 937 – alltanarran@yahoo.co.uk – Restricted opening in winter
3 rm – †£ 76 ††£ 76
◆ Friendly, modern guest house outside village. Comfortable rear lounge with wood-burning stove overlooks garden and river. Raised decked balcony with wrought iron furniture.

Dunvegan House
Shore Rd ✉ KA27 8AJ – ☎ (01770) 302 811 – dunveganhouse1@hotmail.com – Fax (01770) 302 811 – Closed Christmas and New Year
9 rm – †£ 35/45 ††£ 70/80 – **Rest** – Menu £ 22 **s**
◆ Close to ferry terminal on Brodick seafront with view out over bay. Small lawned garden, comfortable lounge and simple, homely bedrooms with pastel décor. Dining room to front.

Kilmory – N Ayrshire – pop. 65

London 460 m – Edinburgh 105 m – Ayr 38 m – Troon 32 m

Lagg

Lagg, on A 841 ✉ KA27 8PQ – ✆ (01770) 870 255 – info@lagghotel.com – Fax (01770) 870 250 – 19 March-3 November

13 rm – £ 45/60 £ 90/110 – **Rest** – (bar lunch) Carte £ 23/36 **s**

◆ Extended 18C inn with acres of grounds and a river. Traditional lounges with open fires and a characterful, beamed bar. Antique furnished bedrooms. Smartly refurbished restaurant with brushed purple velvet walls.

Lamlash – North Ayrshire – pop. 900 – ✉ Brodick

18 Lamlash, ✆ (01770) 600 296 .

Lilybank without rest

Shore Rd ✉ KA27 8LS – ✆ (01770) 600 230 – colin369.richardson@virgin.net – Fax (01770) 600 230 – April-October

7 rm – £ 30/50 £ 65

◆ Whitewashed shoreside cottage with lawned garden. Unpretentious, with homely lounge and comfy breakfast room overlooking Holy Island. Simple bedrooms; front has best view.

Lochranza – North Ayrshire

9 Lochranza, ✆ (0177083) 0273 .

Apple Lodge

✉ KA27 8HJ – ✆ (01770) 830 229 – Fax (01770) 830 229 – Closed Christmas and New Year, minimum 3 night stay

4 rm – £ 52 £ 78/84 – **Rest** – (by arrangement) Menu £ 23

◆ Extended period house with small garden and pleasing views, in centre of quiet village. Homely cottage-style decor with antique furniture and a welcoming atmosphere. Food is home-cooked and uses island and home produce in good, hearty, varied dishes.

Whiting Bay – North Ayrshire

18 Whiting Bay Golf Course Rd, ✆ (01770) 700 487 .

Royal Arran without rest

Shore Rd ✉ KA27 8PZ – ✆ (01770) 700 286 – royalarran@btinternet.com – Easter-October

4 rm – £ 45/89 £ 99

◆ Large, late Victorian house revitalised by owners. Comfy lounge and breakfast room with homely touches and ornaments. Nicely-sized bedrooms - front one has excellent view.

ASCOG – Argyll and Bute – **501** E 16 – see Bute (Isle of)

AUCHENCAIRN – Dumfries and Galloway – **501** I 19 – ✉ Castle Douglas 25 **B3**

Edinburgh 94 m – Dumfries 21 m – Stranraer 60 m

Balcary Bay Balcary Bay and Solway Firth, rm,

Southeast : 2 m. on Balcary rd ✉ DG7 1QZ – ✆ (01556) 640 217 – reservations@balcary-bay-hotel.co.uk – Fax (01556) 640 272 – closed 3 December-January

20 rm – £ 70 £ 150 – **Rest** – (lunch by arrangement) Menu £ 33

◆ Perched on the eponymous bay with magnificent views of Auchencairn Bay and Solway Firth. Comfortable, family run hotel. Bedrooms have bay or garden views. Restaurant decorated in keeping with the hotel's traditional style; window tables much in request.

SCOTLAND

Balcary Mews without rest — Balcary Bay and Solway Firth,

Balcary Bay, Southwest : 2 m. on Balcary rd ✉ DG7 1QZ – ✆ (01556) 640 276 – pamelavaughan@yahoo.com – Fax (01556) 640 276 – Closed Christmas-New Year

3 rm – ♦£ 45/46 ♦♦£ 70

◆ Well-priced, smuggler-built 18C property with lovely views. Warm welcome enhances overall homely feel, typified by comfy lounge overlooking pretty garden. Quality rooms.

AUCHTERARDER – Perth and Kinross – 501 I 15 – pop. 3 945 — 28 C2

Scotland

- Edinburgh 55 m – Glasgow 45 m – Perth 14 m
- 111 High St ✆ (0845) 2255121 (closed half day Wednesday October-March), auchterardertic@perthshire.co.uk
- Ochil Rd, ✆ (01764) 662 804 ;
- Dunning Rollo Park, ✆ (01764) 684 747.
- Tullibardine Chapel★, NW : 2 m

Gleneagles — rm,

Southwest : 2 m. by A 824 on A 823 ✉ PH3 1NF – ✆ (01764) 662 231 – resort.sales@gleneagles.com – Fax (01764) 662 134

216 rm – ♦£ 295/370 ♦♦£ 410/520 – 16 suites

Rest *Andrew Fairlie at Gleneagles* – see restaurant listing

Rest *Strathearn* – (dinner only and Sunday lunch) Menu £ 52 **s**

Rest *Deseo* – Carte £ 30/50 **s**

◆ World famous for its championship golf courses and extensive leisure facilities. Graceful art deco and country house décor within impressive grandeur of early 20C mansion. Strathearn is elegant art deco dining room. Deseo offers Mediterranean dishes in informal atmosphere.

Andrew Fairlie at Gleneagles

Southwest : 2 m. by A 824 on A 823 ✉ PH3 1NF – ✆ (01764) 694 267 – andrew.fairlie@gleneagles.com – Fax (01764) 694 163 – Closed 3 weeks January and Sunday

Rest – (dinner only) Menu £ 65 **s**

Spec. King scallop, caramelised garlic and lemongrass velouté. Lamb loin, roast kidney and confit shoulder. Citrus soufflé, millefeuille, sorbet and salad.

◆ Discreet, minimalist restaurant, decorated with still life, food themed oil paintings. Precise, well-presented cooking utilises prime Scottish ingredients. Welcoming staff.

If breakfast is included the symbol appears after the number of rooms.

AVIEMORE – Highland – 501 I 12 – pop. 2 397 *Scotland* — 30 D3

- Edinburgh 129 m – Inverness 29 m – Perth 85 m
- Grampian Rd ✆ (01479) 810363, aviemoretic@host.co.uk
- Town★
- The Cairngorms★★ (≤ ★★★) - ✻ ★★★ from Cairn Gorm, SE : 11 m. by B 970 – Landmark Visitor Centre (The Highlander★) **AC**, N : 7 m. by A 9 – Highland Wildlife Park★ **AC**, SW : 7 m. by A 9

Corrour House

Inverdruie, Southeast : 1 m. on B 970 ✉ PH22 1QH – ✆ (01479) 810 220 – enquiries@corrourhouse.co.uk – Fax (01479) 811 500 – Closed mid November-30 December

8 rm – ♦£ 40/55 ♦♦£ 70/100 – **Rest** – (dinner only) (booking essential for non-residents) Carte approx. £ 29

◆ Victorian dower house in charming setting surrounded by neat lawned garden. Rooms are comfortably furnished with reproduction furniture - those on top floor have best views. Good sized dining room with a slightly more modern feel than the rest of the house.

SCOTLAND

The Old Minister's Guest House without rest

Rothiemurchus, Southeast : 1 m. on B 970 ✉ PH22 1QH – ✆ (01479) 812 181 – kate@theoldministershouse.co.uk – Fax (0871) 661 9324 – Closed 1-28 December, 1 week spring and 1 week autumn

4 rm – †£ 42/80 ††£ 76/84

◆ Early 20C house on outskirts of town, recently vacated by minister. River at bottom of pretty garden. Nicely-laid breakfast room. Spacious bedrooms, finished to high standard.

Look out for red symbols, indicating particularly pleasant establishments.

AYR – South Ayrshire – **501** G 17 – **pop. 46 431** *Scotland* 25 **A2**

Edinburgh 81 m – Glasgow 35 m

22 Sandgate ✆ (01292) 288688

Belleisle Doonfoot Rd, Belleisle Park, ✆ (01292) 441 258;

Dalmilling Westwood Ave, ✆ (01292) 263 893;

Doon Valley Patna Hillside, ✆ (01292) 531 607.

Alloway★ (Burns Cottage and Museum★ **AC**) S : 3 m. by B 7024 BZ. Culzean Castle★ **AC** (setting★★★, Oval Staircase★★) SW : 13 m. by A 719 BZ

Plan opposite

Western House

Ayr Racecourse, 2 Craigie Rd ✉ KA8 0HA – ✆ (0870) 055 55 10 – info@westernhousehotel.co.uk – Fax (0870) 055 55 15 BZ **a**

48 rm – †£ 80/190 ††£ 80/190 – 1 suite

Rest *The Jockey Club* – Carte £ 16/24

◆ Built in 1920 and designed by Lutyens on Ayr racecourse. Contemporary bedrooms named after racecourses – those in main house the most spacious; some overlook the golf course. Modern restaurant with horseracing theme offers classically based dishes.

Fairfield House

12 Fairfield Rd ✉ KA7 2AS – ✆ (01292) 267 461 – manager@fairfieldhotel.co.uk – Fax (01292) 261 456 AY **a**

44 rm – †£ 75/115 ††£ 105/125

Rest *Martins Bar & Grill* – Menu £ 13 (lunch) – Carte £ 18/37

◆ Former holiday retreat for Glasgow tea merchant, refurbished in contemporary browns and beiges. Bedrooms in main house have sea view. Those in extension well-equipped but smaller. Restaurant offers traditional cooking, popular with locals.

Ellisland

19 Racecourse Rd ✉ KA7 2TD – ✆ (01292) 260 111 – ellisland@costley-hotels.co.uk – Fax (01292) 260 124 BZ **e**

7 rm – †£ 85 ††£ 120 – 2 suites – **Rest** – Carte £ 18/22

◆ Victorian house furnished in reds and greens and hung with modern art; tartan carpet lines the corridors. Terrace with fountain and manicured lawns. Smart, spacious bedrooms. Traditional menu served in restaurant and conservatory. Lighter snacks in lounge.

Carrick Lodge

46 Carrick Rd ✉ KA7 2RE – ✆ (01292) 262 846 – reservations@murdochhospitality.co.uk – Fax (01292) 611 101 BZ **n**

7 rm – †£ 60 ††£ 90 – **Rest** – Menu £ 15/19 – Carte £ 18/31

◆ Victorian building close to town centre, refurbished to a high standard. Family-run; warm, welcoming feel and smiley staff. Contemporary bedrooms named after local areas. Traditional Scottish dishes on menu.

SCOTLAND

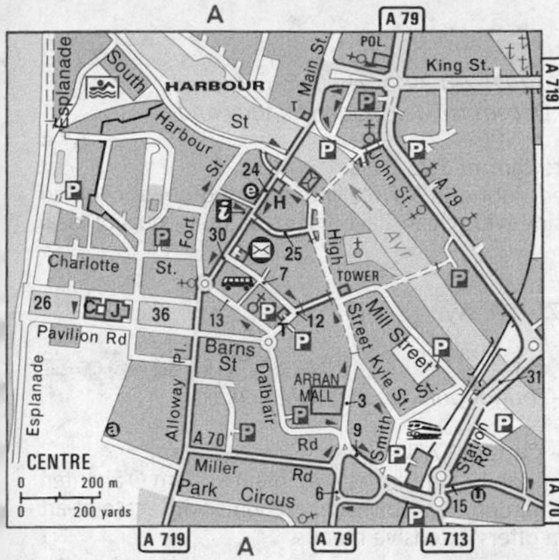

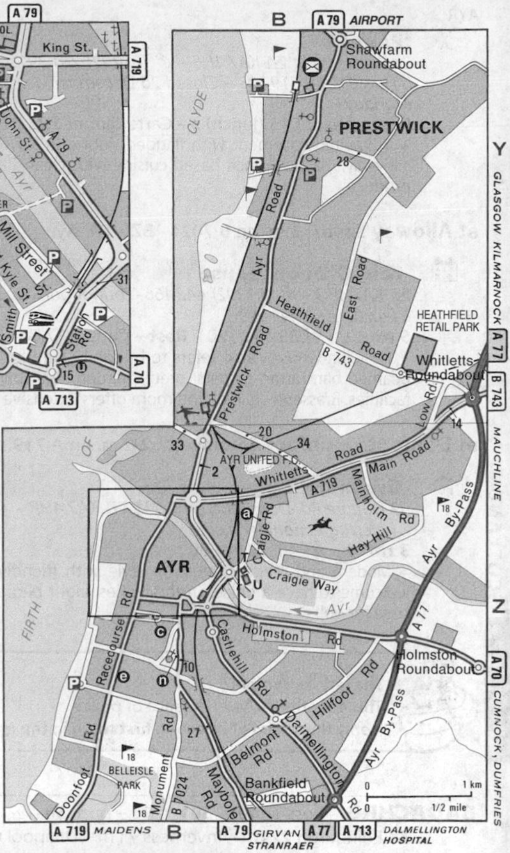

AYR AND PRESTWICK

Street	Grid	No.
Allison St.	BZ	2
Alloway St	AY	3
Arran Mall	AY	
Beresford Terrace	AY	6
Boswell Park	AY	7
Burns' Statue Square	AY	9
Carrick Rd	BZ	10
Carrick St	AY	12
Fullarton St	AY	13
Heathfield Retail Park	BY	
High Rd	BYZ	14
High St	AY	
Holmston Rd	AY	15
Mac Call's Ave	BZ	20
Newmarket St	AY	25
New Bridge St	AY	24
St Germain-en-Laye (Pl. de)	AY	26
St Leonard's Rd	BZ	27
St Quivox Rd	BY	28
Sandgate	AY	30
Victoria Bridge	AY	31
Waggon Rd	BZ	33
Walker Rd	BZ	34
Wellington Square	AY	36

No.26 The Crescent without rest
26 Bellevue Crescent ✉ KA7 2DR – ☎ (01292) 287 329 – carrie@26crescent.freeserve.co.uk – Fax (01292) 286 779 – Closed Christmas and New Year
BZ **c**
5 rm ☕ – 👤£ 45/50 👥£ 65/70
◆ Superior, well-priced guest house with mix of traditional and modern décor. Comfortable and well-run, with individually-furnished bedrooms – best one at front has four poster.

Coila without rest
10 Holmston Rd ✉ KA7 3BB – ☎ (01292) 262 642 – hazel@coila.co.uk – Closed Christmas and New Year
AY **u**
4 rm ☕ – 👤£ 35/45 👥£ 50/70
◆ Spotlessly-kept house proudly decorated with owners' personal ornaments and family photos. Warm, homely lounge. Good-sized bedrooms with king-size beds and modern facilities.

Fouters

2a Academy St ✉ KA7 1HS – ✆ (01292) 261 391 – chef@fouters.co.uk – Fax (01292) 619 323 – Closed 26 December, 1 January, Sunday and Monday AY **e**

Rest – Menu £ 13 (lunch) **s** – Carte dinner £ 25/37 **s**

◆ In vaulted basement with flagged floor and low ceiling, accessed down cobbled alleyway. Classic French based cuisine with clean flavours, made using quality local produce.

at Alloway South : 3 m. on B 7024 - BZ – ✉ Ayr

Brig O'Doon House

✉ KA7 4PQ – ✆ (01292) 442 466 – brigodoon@costleyhotels.co.uk – Fax (01292) 441 999

5 rm – £ 85 £ 120 – **Rest** – Carte £ 17/31

◆ Busy inn whose name refers to bridge behind hotel – as in Burn's Tam O'Shanter. Beamed bar, tartan carpets, pretty garden. Refurbished bedrooms with state-of-art facilities. Brasserie-style dining room offers extensive menus.

at Dunfoot/Doonfoot Southwest : 2½ m. on A 719 - BZ – ✉ Ayr

Greenan Lodge without rest

39 Dunure Rd, Doonfoot, on A 719 ✉ KA7 4HR – ✆ (01292) 443 939 – helen@greenanlodge.com

3 rm – £ 40/45 £ 60

◆ Modern and Mediterranean in style with friendly owner. Roomy lounge; guests welcome to have a tinkle on the ivories. Light bedrooms with flat screen TVs. Good base for golf.

SCOTLAND

The red symbol?
This denotes the very essence of peace
– only the sound of birdsong first thing in the morning …

BADACHRO – Ross-shire – 501 C 10 – pop. 58 – ✉ Gairloch 29 B2

Edinburgh 224 m – Inverness 71 m – Ullapool 61 m

Badachro Inn

✉ IV21 2AA – ✆ (01445) 741 255 – lesley@badachroinn.com – Fax (01445) 741 319 – Closed 25 December and lunch Monday-Friday January-March

Rest – Carte £ 12/35

◆ Nestled in secluded inlet on South shore of Loch Gairloch. Cosily rustic atmosphere with beamed bar, open fire and maritime charts on walls. Menus make good use of local catch.

BALLACHULISH – Highland – 501 E 13 *Scotland* 30 C3

Edinburgh 117 m – Inverness 80 m – Kyle of Lochalsh 90 m – Oban 38 m

Albert Rd ✆ (01855) 811866

Glen Coe★★, E : 6 m. by A 82

Isles of Glencoe ← Loch Leven and the Pap of Glencoe,

✉ PH49 4HL – ✆ (01855) 811 602 – reservations.glencoe@foliohotels.com – Fax (01855) 811 770 rm,

59 rm (dinner included) – £ 208 £ 208 – **Rest** – Menu £ 20 (dinner) **s** – Carte £ 20/36 **s**

◆ Family-friendly modern hotel in peninsular with fine views to Glencoe. Relax in extensive grounds. Spacious lounge and bar. Leisure facilities. Well-equipped rooms with views. Conservatory restaurant is a bistro by day and offers casual fine dining by night.

Ballachulish House

West : 2½ m. by A 82 off A 828 ✉ PH49 4JX – ☎ (01855) 811 266 – mclaughlins@btconnect.com – Fax (01855) 811 498

8 rm (dinner included) – £ 80/120 £ 195/221 –

Rest – (booking essential for non-residents) Menu £ 25/48 **s**

Spec. Velouté of artichokes with girolles and truffle. Roast duck, pomme dauphinoise, foie gras and cherry sauce. Strawberry parfait and salad, raspberry sorbet.

♦ Cosy, whitewashed 17C house with walled garden, country house style and colourful history that inspired Stevenson's "Kidnapped". Comfortable bedrooms with loch views. Precise, well presented, flavourful cooking served in formal dining room at 8 p.m.

Ardno House without rest — Loch Linnhe and Morven Hills,

Lettermore, Glencoe, West : 3½ m. by A 82 on A 828 ✉ PH49 4JD – ☎ (01855) 811 830 – pam@ardnohouse.co.uk

3 rm – £ 50 £ 60

♦ Purpose-built guesthouse with fine view of Loch Linnhe and the Morven Hills. Personally run and providing good value, comfortable accommodation. Spacious bedrooms.

Lyn Leven

West Laroch ✉ PH49 4JP – ☎ (01855) 811 392 – macleodcilla@aol.com – Fax (01855) 811 600 – Closed 25 December

12 rm – £ 30/50 £ 56/64 – **Rest** – (by arrangement) Menu £ 9

♦ Spacious bungalow with attractive gardens a mile from Glencoe overlooking Loch Leven. Comfortable lounge and rooms offering good standard of homely accommodation. Traditional dining room with panoramic views.

BALLANTRAE – South Ayrshire – 501 E 18 – ✉ Girvan — 25 A2

Edinburgh 115 m – Ayr 33 m – Stranraer 18 m

Glenapp Castle

South : 1 m. by A 77 taking first right turn after bridge ✉ KA26 0NZ – ☎ (01465) 831 212 – enquiries@glenappcastle.com – Fax (01465) 831 000 – Closed 2 January-14 March and Christmas

14 rm (dinner included) – £ 255/275 £ 435/475 – 3 suites –

Rest – (light lunch) (booking essential for non-residents) (set menu only) Menu £ 55

Spec. Roast scallops with ceps. Loin of lamb with artichokes, girolles and Madeira jus. Caramel mousse in tuile, mango and lime sorbet and kalamansi jelly.

♦ Magnificent Baronial castle in extensive grounds; built as home for Deputy Lord Lieutenant of Ayrshire. Spacious, antique-furnished bedrooms with tall Victorian windows. Well prepared and presented cooking uses much local produce. Professional service.

Cosses Country House

East : 2¼ m. by A 77 (south) taking first turn left after bridge ✉ KA26 0LR – ☎ (01465) 831 363 – staying@cossescountryhouse.com – Fax (01465) 831 598 – Restricted opening in winter

3 rm – £ 55 £ 80/100 – **Rest** – (by arrangement, communal dining) Menu £ 30

♦ Very well run former shooting lodge, dating from 1670. Warm lounge with log fire; afternoon tea and homemade cakes served on arrival. Thoughtful extras provided in bedrooms. Set three course menu uses home grown produce.

Good food and accommodation at moderate prices?
Look for the Bib symbols:
red Bib Gourmand for food, blue Bib Hotel for hotels

SCOTLAND

BALLATER – Aberdeenshire – 501 K 12 – pop. 1 446

Edinburgh 111 m – Aberdeen 41 m – Inverness 70 m – Perth 67 m
Station Square ☎ (013397) 55306, ballater@agtb.org
Victoria Rd, ☎ (013397) 55 567 .

Darroch Learg
Dee Valley and Grampians,

Braemar Rd ✉ AB35 5UX – ☎ (013397) 55 443 – enquiries@darrochlearg.co.uk – Fax (013397) 55 252 – Closed last 3 weeks January and Christmas

12 rm (dinner included) – £ 105/145 £ 190/275

Rest *The Conservatory* – see restaurant listing

◆ Country house hotel: enjoy superb views from its elevated position. Plush lounges with soft suites, open fires and antiques. Enticing bedrooms: upper floors have best outlook.

Balgonie Country House

Braemar Pl, West : ½ m. by A 93 ✉ AB35 5NQ – ☎ (013397) 55 482 – balgoniech@aol.com – Fax (013397) 55 497 – Closed 6 January-20 March

9 rm – £ 60/85 £ 100/150 – **Rest** – (booking essential for non-residents) (lunch by arrangement) Menu £ 25/40

◆ Personally run, peaceful Edwardian style country house with relaxed atmosphere in mature gardens with fine hill views. Individually furnished bedrooms boast admirable outlook. Restaurant renowned for its use of fine Scottish produce and accomplished cooking.

The Auld Kirk

Braemar Rd ✉ AB35 5RX – ☎ (01339) 755 762 – info@theauldkirk.com – Fax (0707) 515 84 00

6 rm – £ 63/65 £ 95/105 – **Rest** – (Closed Sunday and lunch in winter) Menu £ 32 (dinner) **s** – Carte lunch £ 20/32 **s**

◆ Hotel in former church with bar, lounge and breakfast room refurbished in contemporary style. Well equipped bedrooms currently being redecorated to similar standard. Restaurant in former side chapel has vaulted ceiling and chandeliers and serves traditional menu.

Moorside House without rest

26 Braemar Rd ✉ AB35 5RL – ☎ (013397) 55 492 – info@moorsidehouse.co.uk – Fax (013397) 55 492 – March-October

9 rm – £ 45 £ 60

◆ Detached Victorian pink stone guesthouse on main road just outside town centre. Neat garden. Vividly coloured breakfast room. Sizeable, well-furnished rooms.

Morvada House without rest

28 Braemar Rd ✉ AB35 5RL – ☎ (013397) 56 334 – morvada@aol.com – Fax (013397) 56 092 – February-November

5 rm – £ 40/60 £ 55/60

◆ Attractive stone built house. Personally run. Notable for its collection of Russel Flint pictures. Immaculately kept, individually decorated rooms, some with mountain views.

The Conservatory – at Darroch Learg H.

Braemar Rd ✉ AB35 5UX – ☎ (013397) 55 443 – enquiries@darrochlearg.co.uk – Fax (013397) 55 252 – Closed Christmas and last 3 weeks January

Rest – (dinner only and Sunday lunch) Menu £ 43 **s**

◆ Attractive conservatory restaurant with a fine view from its garden location: comfortable dining enhanced by attentive service. Notably impressive wine list.

The Green Inn with rm

9 Victoria Rd ✉ AB35 5QQ – ☎ (013397) 55 701 – info@green-inn.com – Closed first 2 weeks January and first 2 weeks November

3 rm – £ 50/60 £ 70/90, £ 10 – **Rest** – (dinner only) Menu £ 37

◆ Former temperance hall, opposite the green, boasting comfy lounges and pleasant conservatory. Interesting, well sourced and accomplished modern British cooking. Cosy rooms.

SCOTLAND

BALLOCH – West Dunbartonshire – **501** G 15 – ✉ **Alexandria** 25 **B1**
Scotland

Edinburgh 72 m – Glasgow 20 m – Stirling 30 m
The Old Station Building, Balloch Rd ✆ (08707) 200607 (April-October), info@balloch.visitscotland.com
N : Loch Lomond★★

De Vere Deluxe Cameron House ← Loch Lomond, rm, rest, VISA AE
Loch Lomond, Northwest : 1½ m. by A 811 on A 82 ✉ G83 8QZ – ✆ (01389) 755565 – reservations@cameronhouse.co.uk – Fax (01389) 759522
123 rm – †£ 149/339 ††£ 149/349 – 12 suites
Rest Lomonds – see restaurant listing
Rest *Camerons Grill* – (dinner only) Carte £ 32/55
◆ Extensive Victorian house superbly situated on shores of Loch Lomond. Impressive leisure facilities. Luxurious rooms with four posters and panoramic views. Camerons Grill has a contemporary feel.

Lomonds – at De Vere Deluxe Cameron House ← Loch Lomond, AC VISA AE
Loch Lomond, Northwest : 1½ m. by A 811 on A 82 ✉ G83 8QZ – ✆ (01389) 755565 – reservations@cameronhouse.co.uk – Fax (01389) 759522
Rest – (Closed Sunday and Monday) Carte £ 35/53
◆ Intimate restaurant with views of the mountains and loch; plush, contemporary styling, comfy central banquettes, formal service and well-presented, modern cooking.

BALLYGRANT – **Argyll and Bute** – **501** B 16 – **see Islay (Isle of)**

BALMEDIE – Aberdeenshire – **501** N 12 28 **D1**

Edinburgh 137 m – Aberdeen 7 m – Peterhead 24 m

Cock and Bull VISA AE
Ellon Rd, Blairton, North : 1 m. on A 90 ✉ AB23 8XY – ✆ (01358) 743249 – info@thecockandbull.co.uk – Fax (01358) 742466 – Closed 25-26 December and 1-4 January
Rest – Carte £ 16/33
◆ Whitewashed 19C pub and conservatory with North Sea views. Bar and restaurant have bags of atmosphere, courtesy of characterful artefacts. Hearty dishes cover wide range.

BALTASOUND – **Shetland Islands** – **501** R 1 – **see Shetland Islands (Island of Unst)**

BANAVIE – **Highland** – **501** E 13 – **see Fort William**

BANCHORY – Aberdeenshire – **501** M 12 – **pop. 6 034** *Scotland* 28 **D2**

Edinburgh 118 m – Aberdeen 17 m – Dundee 55 m – Inverness 94 m
Bridge St ✆ (01330) 822000 (Easter-October)
Kinneskie, ✆ (01330) 822365 ;
Torphins, ✆ (013398) 82115.
Crathes Castle★★ (Gardens★★★) AC, E : 3 m. by A 93 – Cairn o'Mount Road★ (← ★★), S : by B 974. Dunnottar Castle★★ (site★★★) AC, SW : 15½ m. by A 93 and A 957 – Aberdeen★★, NE : 17 m. by A 93

Raemoir House ← VISA AE
North : 2½ m. on A 980 ✉ AB31 4ED – ✆ (01330) 824884 – hotel@raemoir.com – Fax (01330) 822171 – Closed 25-29 December
20 rm – †£ 95/125 ††£ 155/225 – **Rest** – Menu £ 35 (dinner) – Carte lunch £ 18/32
◆ Enviably located 18C Highland mansion with 17C "ha-hoose" (hall house) as popular alternative to main house. Country house ambience: antiques abound. Very comfortable rooms. The "Oval" dining room luxuriates with Victorian tapestry walls.

SCOTLAND

Banchory Lodge
Dee St ✉ AB31 5HS – ✆ (01330) 822 625 – enquiries@banchorylodge.co.uk – Fax (01330) 825 019
22 rm – ♦£ 90 ♦♦£ 160/200 – **Rest** – (bar lunch) Menu £ 21 – Carte £ 20/29
◆ Part 16C former coaching inn delightfully situated on River Dee. Country house style accentuated by antiques and china. Individually decorated bedrooms. Dee views and floral displays enhance the attraction of the dining room.

The Old West Manse without rest
71 Station Rd, on A 93 ✉ AB31 5YD – ✆ (01330) 822 202 – westmanse@btinternet.com – Fax (01330) 822 202
3 rm – ♦£ 45/50 ♦♦£ 65/70
◆ Immaculately distinctive guesthouse just outside village. Bright yellow exterior, lovely gardens and homely lounge with warm décor. Spotlessly kept, bright bedrooms.

BARRA (Isle of) – Western Isles – 501 X 12/13 – ✉ Castlebay 29 A3

Castlebay – Western Isles 29 A3

Castlebay ← Kisimul Castle and Island of Vatersay,
✉ HS9 5XD – ✆ (01871) 810 223 – info@castlebayhotel.com – Fax (01871) 810 455 – Closed 25 December
12 rm (dinner included) – ♦£ 49/89 ♦♦£ 95/130 –
Rest – (bar lunch) Carte £ 17/29
◆ Personally run, early 20C hotel situated in prominent position overlooking Kisimul Castle and Isle of Vatersay. Cosy sitting room and spacious bar. Homely, well-kept rooms. Linen-clad dining room with excellent bay view and traditional fare.

Grianamul without rest
✉ HS9 5XD – ✆ (01871) 810 416 – macneilronnie@aol.com – Fax (01871) 810 319 – April-September
3 rm – ♦£ 54 ♦♦£ 54
◆ Purpose-built guesthouse, convenient for local amenities; adjacent to heritage centre. Comfortable, homely lounge. Very sunny breakfast room. Sizeable, well-kept rooms.

North Bay – Western Isles 29 A3

Heathbank
✉ HS9 5YQ – ✆ (01871) 890 266 – info@barrahotel.co.uk – Fax (01871) 890 266
5 rm – ♦£ 48/70 ♦♦£ 76/80 – **Rest** – (bar lunch) (booking essential) Carte £ 13/27 **s**
◆ Former 19C schoolhouse on a quiet road. Relax in ample space, including a terrace to admire the landscape. Airy bedrooms, in light lemon hues with DVDs, are the strong point. Home-cooked menus in bar and intimate dining room.

BEAULY – Highland – 501 G 11 – pop. 1 164 30 C2

Edinburgh 169 m – Inverness 13 m – Wick 125 m

Lovat Arms
High St ✉ IV4 7BS – ✆ (01463) 782 313 – info@lovatarms.com – Fax (01463) 782 862
28 rm – ♦£ 45/51 ♦♦£ 65/105 – **Rest** – (bar lunch Monday-Saturday) Carte £ 16/27
◆ Stylish, family owned hotel in village centre with distinctive Scottish feel: full tartan décor abounds. Spacious sitting room, busy bar. Smart rooms with clan influence. All-enveloping tartan curtains dominate warmly hued dining room.

Red = Pleasant. Look for the red ✗ and symbols.

SCOTLAND

BELLANOCH – Argyll and Bute – 501 D 15 Scotland 27 B2

Edinburgh 134 m – Arduaine 16 m – Oban 34 m

Crinan★, W : 2 m. by B 841. Auchindrain Township Open Air Museum★, E : 25 m. by B 841 and A 83

Bellanoch House

Bellanoch Bay, Crinan Canal ✉ PA31 8SN – ✆ (01546) 830 149 – stay@bellanochhouse.co.uk

3 rm – †£ 55/60 ††£ 90/100 – **Rest** – (by arrangement) Menu £ 30

◆ Former church and school-house with gardens. Stylish lounge boasts stone fireplace from Italy. Owners' family paintings on walls. Airy rooms; front two with good views. Home-cooked food served in dining area.

BENDERLOCH – Argyll and Bute – 501 D 14 – see Connel

BISHOPTON – Renfrewshire – 501 G 16 25 B1

Edinburgh 59 m – Dumbarton 9 m – Glasgow 13 m

Mar Hall

Earl of Mar Estate, Northeast : 1 m. on B 815 ✉ PA7 5NW – ✆ (0141) 812 9999 – info@marhall.com – Fax (0141) 812 9997

VISA AE

50 rm – †£ 135 ††£ 290, £ 16 – 3 suites

Rest *Cristal* – (dinner only and Sunday lunch) Carte £ 23/38

◆ 19C Gothic mansion set in parkland. Spacious and stylish; ideal weekend break location. Impressive Aveda spa with well-equipped gym. Contemporary bedrooms. Elaborate fine dining with exceptional levels of service in The Cristal.

SCOTLAND

BLAIR ATHOLL – Perth and Kinross – 501 I 13 28 C2

Edinburgh 79 m – Inverness 83 m – Perth 35 m

Blair Atholl Invertilt Rd, ✆ (01796) 481 407.

The Loft

AC P VISA AE

Golf Course Rd ✉ PH18 5TE – ✆ (01796) 481 377 – enquiries@theloftrestaurant.co.uk – Fax (01796) 481 511 – Closed 6 January-mid February, 25-26 December, Tuesday in winter and Monday

Rest – Carte £ 21/27

◆ Modern restaurant set on first floor of former hayloft, with beamed ceilings in situ. Bright décor; lots of natural light. Good value, freshly prepared modern menus.

BLAIRGOWRIE – Perth and Kinross – 501 J 14 – pop. 7 965 Scotland 28 C2

Edinburgh 60 m – Dundee 19 m – Perth 16 m

26 Wellmeadow ✆ (01250) 872960, blairgowrietic@perthshire.co.uk

Scone Palace★★ AC, S : 12 m. by A 93

Kinloch House

P VISA AE

West : 3 m. on A 923 ✉ PH10 6SG – ✆ (01250) 884 237 – reception@kinlochhouse.com – Fax (01250) 884 333 – Closed 2 weeks Christmas

17 rm – †£ 100/225 ††£ 180/290 – 1 suite – **Rest** – Menu £ 28/50

◆ Wonderfully tranquil, ivy-clad 19C country house set in its own grounds. Appealingly traditional lounges. Conservatory and leisure centre. Large, smart, well-furnished rooms. Restaurant with bright yellow décor and Scottish influenced cooking.

Heathpark House without rest

P VISA

Coupar Angus Rd, Rosemount, Southeast : ¾ m. on A 923 ✉ PH10 6JT – ✆ (01250) 870 700 – lori@forsyth12.freeserve.co.uk – Fax (01250) 870 700 – Closed 25-26 December

3 rm – †£ 40 ††£ 70

◆ Substantial Victorian guesthouse in a quiet residential spot with mature gardens. Spacious lounge; breakfasts taken in welcoming dining room. Large, individually styled rooms.

Gilmore House without rest

Perth Rd, Southwest : ½ m. on A 93 ✉ PH10 6EJ – ☎ (01250) 872 791 – jill@gilmorehouse.co.uk – Fax (01250) 872 791 – Closed December

3 rm – †£ 27/35 ††£ 48/55

◆ Traditional stone-built guesthouse only a few minutes' walk from town, keenly run by owners. Comfortable front lounge and breakfast room. Cosy bedrooms with tartan flourishes.

Laurels

Golf Course Rd, Southwest : 1 ¼ m. on A 93 ✉ PH10 6LH – ☎ (01250) 874 920 – laurel-blairgowrie@talk21.com – Fax (01250) 874 920 – Closed mid November-mid January

6 rm – †£ 24/30 ††£ 48 – **Rest** – (by arrangement) Menu £ 14

◆ Stone built extended cottage just out of town centre and useful base for touring Perthshire. Comfortable, homely lounge with soft velvet suites. Simple, spotless rooms.

BOAT OF GARTEN – Highland – 501 I 12

30 **D2**

Edinburgh 133 m – Inverness 28 m – Perth 89 m

Boat of Garten, ☎ (01479) 831 282 .

SCOTLAND

The Boat

✉ PH24 3BH – ☎ (01479) 831 258 – info@boathotel.co.uk – Fax (01479) 831 414 – April-November

24 rm – †£ 40/70 ††£ 90/150 – 1 suite

Rest *Capercaillie* – (dinner only) Menu £ 35 **s**

Rest *The Osprey Bar* – (dinner only) Carte £ 14/28 **s**

◆ An evocative hiss of steam from adjacent Strathspey railway line adds character to this 19C hotel, run by keen, friendly young team. Pleasant traditional or modern rooms. Vivid artwork in comfy Capercaillie. Busy Osprey bar/bistro overlooks the trains.

BONNYRIGG – Lothian – 501 K 16

26 **C1**

Edinburgh 8 m – Galashiels 27 m – Glasgow 50 m

Dalhousie Castle

Southeast : 1 ¼ m. on B 704 ✉ EH19 3JB – ☎ (01875) 820 153 – info@dalhousiecastle.co.uk – Fax (01875) 821 936

36 rm – †£ 150/160 ††£ 195/220

Rest *Dungeon* – (dinner only) (booking essential for non-residents) Menu £ 38

Rest *The Orangery* – Carte £ 26/32

◆ 13C castle on the banks of the South Esk with spacious, medieval style rooms and historically-themed bedrooms. Popular venue for weddings, with falconry centre in grounds. Barrel-vaulted Dungeon restaurant features suits of armour. The Orangery overlooks river and parkland, and offers a less formal menu.

BORGIE – Highland – 501 H 8

30 **C1**

Edinburgh 262 m – Inverness 93 m – Thurso 31 m

Borgie Lodge

✉ KW14 7TH – ☎ (01641) 521 332 – info@borgielodgehotel.co.uk – Fax (01641) 521 889

8 rm – †£ 50/65 ††£ 80/95 – **Rest** – (bar lunch) Menu £ 32 **s**

◆ Small, detached hotel in peaceful Highland setting. Simple "locals" bar and residents lounge with coal fire and deep sofas. Rooms with characterful older style furnishings. Cosy dining room.

BOWMORE – Argyll and Bute – 501 B 16 – see Islay (Isle of)

BRAE – Shetland Islands – 501 P 2 – see Shetland Islands (Mainland)

BRAEMAR – Aberdeenshire – **501** J 12 *Scotland* 28 **C2**

Edinburgh 85 m – Aberdeen 58 m – Dundee 51 m – Perth 51 m

The Mews, Mar Rd (013397) 41600

Cluniebank Rd, (013397) 41 618 .

Lin O'Dee★, W : 5 m

Callater Lodge without rest

9 Glenshee Rd AB35 5YQ – (013397) 41 275
– hampsons@hotel-braemar.co.uk – Closed November-December

6 rm – £32/50 £60

◆ Stone house in large garden on the road to Glenshee. Lounge with leather chairs and library with inglenook. Pleasant spacious bedrooms, some with view across the valley.

BREASCLETE – Western Isles Outer Hebrides – **501** Z 9 – see Lewis and Harris (Isle of)

BRIDGEND OF LINTRATHEN – Angus – **501** K 13 – Kirriemuir 28 **C2**

Edinburgh 70 m – Dundee 20 m – Pitlochry 37 m

XX **The Steading** with rm

(at Lochside Lodge and Roundhouse restaurant) DD8 5JJ
– (01575) 560 340 – enquiries@lochsidelodge.com – Fax (01575) 560 251
– Closed 3 weeks January, 1 week October, 23-27 December, Sunday dinner and Monday

6 rm – £70/85 £120 – **Rest** – Menu £19 – Carte £16/37

◆ Converted farmstead in tiny hamlet at gateway to Angus Glens by Loch Lintrathen. Elaborate modern cooking in former grain grinding room. Comfy rooms in hayloft conversion.

BROADFORD – Highland – **501** C 12 – see Skye (Isle of)

BRODICK – North Ayrshire – **501** E 17 – see Arran (Isle of)

BRORA – Highland – **501** I 9 – pop. 1 140 30 **D2**

Edinburgh 234 m – Inverness 78 m – Wick 49 m

Golf Rd, (01408) 621 417 .

Royal Marine rm,

Golf Rd KW9 6QS – (01408) 621 252 – info@highlandescape.com
– Fax (01408) 621 181

22 rm – £85/105 £150 – **Rest** – Carte £25/37

◆ Originally a laird's home. Traditional lounge with log fire. Good leisure facilities plus snooker room and unlimited golf. Spacious bedrooms with antique furnishings. Cuisine reflects Highland location.

Glenaveron without rest

Golf Rd KW9 6QS – (01408) 621 601 – glenaveron@hotmail.com
– Closed Christmas and New Year

3 rm – £45/55 £64/70

◆ Agreeable looking, detached, stone guesthouse with gardens. Spick and span lounge. Pleasant communal breakfast room. Very spacious rooms with superior pine furnishings.

BROUGHTY FERRY – Dundee – **501** L 14 – see Dundee

BUNCHREW – Highland – see Inverness

BUNESSAN – Argyll and Bute – **501** B 15 – see Mull (Isle of)

BURRAY – Orkney Islands – **501** L 7 – see Orkney Islands

BUTE (Isle of) – Argyll and Bute – 501 E 16 – pop. 7 354 27 B3

from Rothesay to Wemyss Bay (Mainland) (Caledonian MacBrayne Ltd) frequent services daily (35 mn) – from Rhubodach to Colintraive (Mainland) (Caledonian MacBrayne Ltd) frequent services daily (5 mn)

Ascog – Argyll and Bute 27 B3

Balmory Hall without rest

Balmory Rd ✉ PA20 9LL – ✆ (01700) 500669 – enquiries@balmoryhall.com – Fax (01700) 500669 – Closed December-8 February

4 rm – 🚹£ 80 🚹🚹£ 160

◆ Impressive, carefully restored mid 19C Italianate mansion. Columned hall and well-furnished lounge. Tastefully furnished bedrooms. Breakfast at an antique table.

Rothesay – Argyll and Bute 27 B3

Isle of Bute Discovery Centre, Winter Garden ✆ (08707) 200619, info@rothesay.visitscotland.com

18 Canada Hill, ✆ (01700) 503 554 ;

9 Sithean Academy Rd, ✆ (01700) 504 369 ;

9 Port Bannatyne Bannatyne Mains Rd, ✆ (01700) 503 554 .

Cannon House

5 Battery Pl ✉ PA20 9DP – ✆ (01700) 502819 – cannon.house@btinternet.com – Fax (01700) 505 725 – Closed January-mid March

7 rm – 🚹£ 45/50 🚹🚹£ 100 – **Rest** – (dinner only) (booking essential for non-residents) Carte £ 16/23

◆ Attractive late Georgian house on Rothesay promenade with panoramic view of bay and harbour. Furnished in keeping with house's age. Individually styled rooms. Elegant, clean-lined dining room with daily changing menu of Scottish based dishes.

SCOTLAND

CADBOLL – Highland – see Tain

CAIRNBAAN – Argyll and Bute – 501 D 15 – see Lochgilphead

CALLANDER – Stirling – 501 H 15 – pop. 2 754 *Scotland* 28 C2

Edinburgh 52 m – Glasgow 43 m – Oban 71 m – Perth 41 m

Rob Roy and Trossachs Visitor Centre, Ancaster Sq (08707) 200628, robroyandt@eillst.ossian.net

18 Aveland Rd, ✆ (01877) 330090 .

Town★

The Trossachs★★★ (Loch Katrine★★) – Hilltop Viewpoint★★★ (✳ ★★★) W : 10 m. by A 821

Roman Camp

Main St ✉ FK17 8BG – ✆ (01877) 330 003 – mail@romancamphotel.co.uk – Fax (01877) 331 533

10 rm – 🚹£ 85 🚹🚹£ 175 – 4 suites

Rest *The Restaurant* – see restaurant listing

◆ Part 17C hunting lodge set in extensive gardens. Traditionally and charmingly decorated rooms with open fires, floral prints and antiques. Individually decorated bedrooms.

Lubnaig without rest

Leny Feus ✉ FK17 8AS – ✆ (01877) 330 376 – info@lubnaighouse.co.uk – Fax (01877) 330 376 – May-October

8 rm – 🚹£ 47/55 🚹🚹£ 72/80

◆ Built in 1864, a characterful Victorian house on the outskirts of town. Well-kept mature gardens visible from communal rooms. Homely bedrooms, two in converted stables.

Brook Linn without rest

Leny Feus ✉ FK17 8AU – ✆ (01877) 330 103 – derek@blinn.freeserve.co.uk – Fax (01877) 330 103 – Easter-October

4 rm – 🚹🚹£ 60/70

◆ Victorian house in a fairly secluded rural location. Homely style lounge and wood furnished dining room for breakfast. Traditional, well-kept bedrooms.

XXX **The Restaurant** – at Roman Camp H.

Main St ✉ FK19 8BG – ✆ (01877) 330 003 – mail@romancamphotel.co.uk – Fax (01877) 331 533

Rest – Menu £ 25/44 – Carte approx. £ 55

◆ Spacious, formal restaurant set with crisp, linen-covered tables bedecked with lillies. Modern Scottish cooking proudly made with locally sourced produce.

CAMPBELTOWN – **Argyll and Bute** – **501** D 17 – **see Kintyre (Peninsula)**

CARDROSS – **Argyll and Bute** – **501** G 16 *Scotland* 25 **A-B1**

Edinburgh 63 m – Glasgow 17 m – Helensburgh 5 m

The Clyde Estuary★

Kirkton House without rest

Darleith Rd ✉ G82 5EZ – ✆ (01389) 841 951 – mich@kirktonhouse.co.uk – Fax (01389) 841 868 – Closed December-January

6 rm – †£ 45 ††£ 70

◆ Former farmhouse with origins in 18C; quiet, elevated spot overlooking North Clyde. Ideal stop-off between Glasgow airport and Highlands. Bedrooms all have country views.

CARINISH – **Western Isles** – **501** Y 11 – **see Uist (Isles of)**

CARNOUSTIE – **Angus** – **501** L 14 – **pop. 10 561** 28 **D2**

Edinburgh 68 m – Aberdeen 59 m – Dundee 12 m

1B High St ✆ (01241) 852258 (Easter-September)

Monifieth Golf Links Princes St, Medal Starter's Box, ✆ (01382) 532 767 ;

Burnside Links Par, ✆ (01241) 855 789 ;

Panmure Barry, ✆ (01241) 855 120 ;

Buddon Links Links Par, ✆ (01241) 853 249 .

The Old Manor without rest

Panbride, Northeast : 1 ¼ m. by A 930 on Panbride Rd ✉ DD7 6JP – ✆ (01241) 854 804 – stay@oldmanorcarnoustie.com – Fax (01241) 855 327 – Closed 25 December-4 January

5 rm – †£ 50/60 ††£ 70/80

◆ Substantial 18C house five minutes' drive from championship golf course. Good views of Tay Estuary. Hearty Scottish breakfast guaranteed. Smart rooms, some with brass beds.

XX **11 Park Avenue**

11 Park Ave ✉ DD7 7JA – ✆ (01241) 853 336 – 11parkavenue@fsmail.net – Closed Sunday

Rest – (dinner only) Carte £ 25/33 **s**

◆ A former Masonic hall tucked away off the High Street. Comfortable, traditional surroundings and accomplished modern cooking from classic Scottish ingredients.

CARRADALE – **Argyll and Bute** – **501** D 17 – **see Kintyre Peninsula**

CASTLE DOUGLAS – **Dumfries and Galloway** – **501** I 19 – **pop. 3 671** 25 **B3**

Scotland

Edinburgh 98 m – Ayr 49 m – Dumfries 18 m – Stranraer 57 m

Market Hill ✆ (01556) 502611 (Easter-October)

Abercromby Rd, ✆ (01556) 502 801 .

Threave Garden★★ **AC**, SW : 2 ½ m. by A 75 – Threave Castle★ **AC**, W : 1 m

Douglas House without rest

63 Queen St ✉ DG7 1HS – ✆ (01556) 503 262 – info@douglas-house.com

4 rm – †£ 32/55 ††£ 60/85

◆ Attractive stone built house (1880) with some original features near the high street. Communal breakfast table in guest lounge. Comfortable individually decorated bedrooms.

Smithy House without rest
The Buchan, Southwest : ¾ on A 75 (Stranraer rd) ✉ DG7 1TH – ✆ (01556) 503 841 – enquiries@smithyhouse.co.uk – Closed Christmas-New Year
3 rm – £70 £75
♦ Converted 14C smithy in large garden 10 minutes walk from town. Communal breakfast table. Guests' lounge featuring original forge. Pleasant bedrooms facing garden or loch.

at Kirkpatrick Durham **Northeast : 5 ½ m. by A 75 and B 794 – ✉ Castle Douglas**

Chipperkyle without rest
✉ DG7 3EY – ✆ (01556) 650 223 – Closed 15-27 December
3 rm – £60 £90
♦ Georgian manor house in rural location. Charming country house atmosphere in a family style environment. Comfortable, spacious rooms.

CASTLEBAY – Western Isles – 501 X 12/13 – see Barra (Isle of)

CAWDOR – Highland – 501 I 11 – ✉ Inverness 30 D2

Edinburgh 170 m – Aberdeen 100 m – Inverness 14 m

Cawdor Tavern
The Lane ✉ IV12 5XP – ✆ (01667) 404 777 – cawdortavern@btopenworld.com – Fax (01667) 404 777 – Closed 25-26 December and 1 January
Rest – (booking essential Saturday-Sunday) Carte £ 17/26
♦ Country inn within stone's throw of castle. Well run with an emphasis on the food. Friendly staff serve dishes from large menu offering traditional or more adventurous fare.

CHIRNSIDE – Borders – 501 N 16 – pop. 1 204 – ✉ Duns 26 D1

Edinburgh 52 m – Berwick-upon-Tweed 8 m – Glasgow 95 m – Newcastle upon Tyne 70 m

Chirnside Hall
East : 1 ¼ m. on A 6105 ✉ TD11 3LD – ✆ (01890) 818 219 – reception@chirnsidehallhotel.com – Fax (01890) 818 231 – Closed March
10 rm – £85 £165 – **Rest** – (dinner only) (booking essential for non-residents) Menu £30
♦ Large, imposing, Victorian country house in a rural location. Well appointed interiors with good quality period atmosphere. Individually decorated bedrooms. Smart place settings in a traditionally appointed dining room.

CLACHAN SEIL – Argyll and Bute – 501 D 15 – see Seil (Isle of)

CLYDEBANK – West Dunbartonshire – 501 G 16 – pop. 29 858 25 B1

Edinburgh 52 m – Glasgow 6 m
Clydebank Municipal Dalmuir Overtoun Rd, ✆ (0141) 952 2070 .

The Beardmore
rm,
Beardmore St, off A 814 ✉ G81 4SA – ✆ (0141) 951 6000 – info@beardmore.scot.nhs.uk – Fax (0141) 951 6019
160 rm – £99 £124, £12.95 – 6 suites
Rest *Arcoona* – (dinner only) Carte £ 23/35 **s**
Rest *B bar cafe* – (lunch only) Carte £ 16/23 **s**
♦ Hotel on banks of River Clyde known for its conference facilities and its attachment to an NHS hospital. Well-equipped bedrooms, some with views over the river. Formal Arcoona restaurant offers globally-influenced menu. Bright, open-plan B Bar café serves light snacks.

SCOTLAND

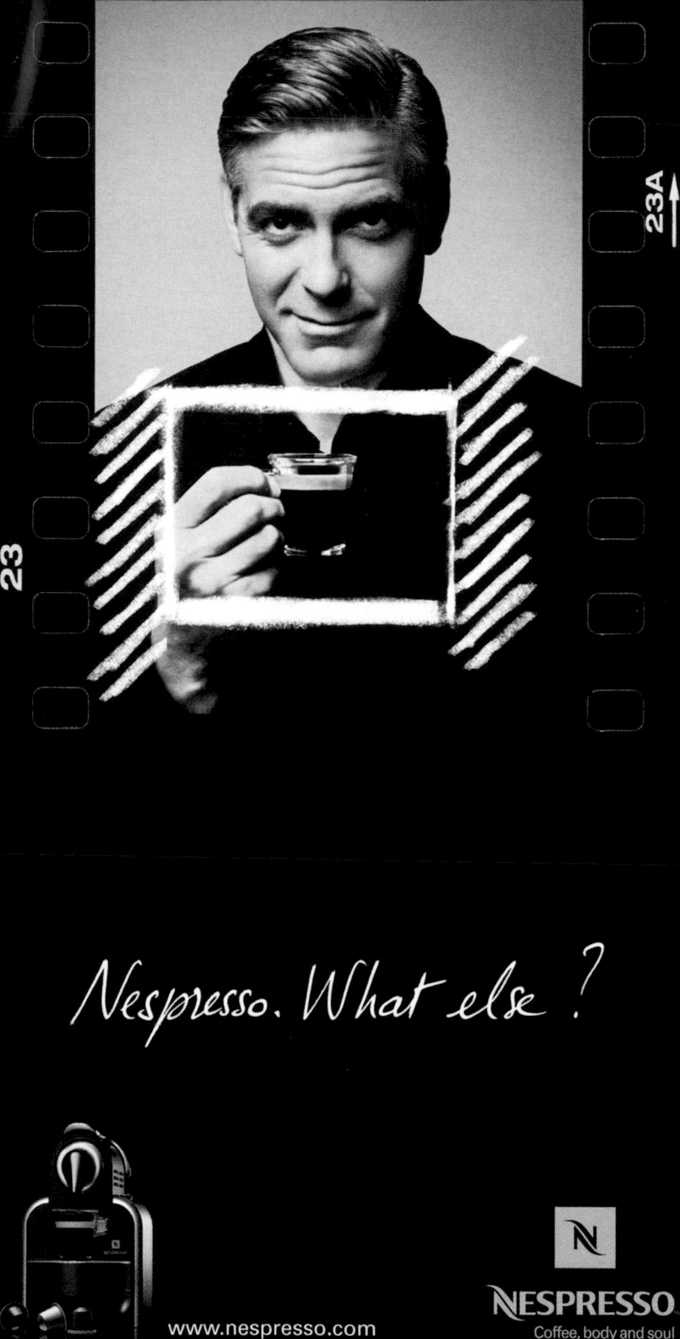

23A

23

Nespresso. What else?

www.nespresso.com

"a range of travel products and services for professionals..."

Michelin Maps & Guides

attracting new customers

driving sales

encouraging customer loyalty

motivating employees

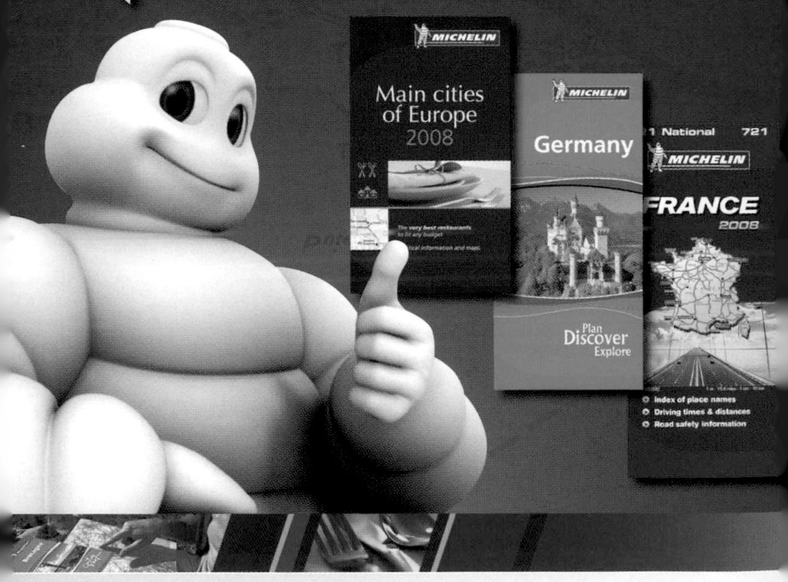

Main cities of Europe 2008

Germany

Plan Discover Explore

National 721

FRANCE 2008

Index of place names

Driving times & distances

Road safety information

CONTACT US: 01923 205253

travelpubsales@uk.michelin.com

COLONSAY (Isle of) – Argyll and Bute – 501 B 15 — 27 A2

from Scalasaig to Oban (Caledonian MacBrayne Ltd) 3 weekly (2 h) – from Scalasaig to Kintyre Peninsula (Kennacraig) via Isle of Islay (Port Askaig) (Caledonian MacBrayne Ltd) weekly

Isle of Colonsay, ✆ (019512) 316.

Scalasaig – Argyll and Bute – ✉ Colonsay — 27 A2

The Colonsay

✉ PA61 7YP – ✆ (01951) 200 316 – reception@thecolonsay.com – Fax (01951) 200 353 – Closed mid January-March

9 rm – †£ 60 ††£ 85/140, £ 6.50 – **Rest** – (bar lunch) Carte £ 17/25

◆ Listed building from mid-18C; a thoroughly rural, remote setting. Public areas include excellent photos of local scenes and the only bar on the island. Bright, modern rooms. Welcoming, informal dining room.

COMRIE – Perth. and Kinross – 501 I 14 – pop. 1 839 — 28 C2

Edinburgh 66 m – Glasgow 56 m – Oban 70 m – Perth 24 m

Comrie Laggan Braes, ✆ (01764) 670055 .

The Royal

Melville Sq ✉ PH6 2DN – ✆ (01764) 679 200 – reception@royalhotel.co.uk – Fax (01764) 679 219 – closed 25-26 December

13 rm – †£ 90 ††£ 140

Rest *Royal* – Carte £ 20/31

◆ 18C coaching inn in centre of town: Queen Victoria once stayed here. Stylish, contemporary feel, especially individually decorated bedrooms, with four posters and antiques. Restaurant with two rooms: conservatory brasserie or intimate dining room.

SCOTLAND

Look out for red symbols, indicating particularly pleasant establishments.

CONON BRIDGE – Highland – 501 G 11 — 30 C2

Edinburgh 168 m – Inverness 12 m

Kinkell House

Easter Kinkell, Southeast : 3 m. by B 9163 and A 835 on B 9169 ✉ IV7 8HY – ✆ (01349) 861 270 – info@kinkellhousehotel.com – Fax (01349) 867 240 – Closed 22 December-8 January

9 rm – †£ 70/100 ††£ 70/100 – **Rest** – (lunch by arrangement Monday-Saturday) Menu £ 25

◆ Peacefully located house in a rural location makes for a welcoming country house atmosphere, keenly overseen by a young team. Homely bedrooms. Traditional dining room overlooks the garden.

CONNEL – Argyll and Bute – 501 D 14 – ✉ Oban — 27 B2

Edinburgh 118 m – Glasgow 88 m – Inverness 113 m – Oban 5 m

Ards House without rest

on A 85 ✉ PA37 1PT – ✆ (01631) 710 255 – ardsconnel@aol.com – Fax (01631) 710 857 – Closed Christmas and New Year

4 rm – †£ 50/65 ††£ 76/90

◆ Victorian house overlooking Loch Etive. Well run with a smart and elegant atmosphere. Traditional décor and appointments throughout communal areas and bedrooms.

Ronebhal without rest

on A 85 ✉ PA37 1PJ – ✆ (01631) 710 310 – ronebhal@btinternet.com – Fax (01631) 710 310 – Easter-October

6 rm – †£ 25/65 ††£ 50/80

◆ Victorian house built in granite, with fine views over Loch Etive. Attractive guests' lounge with plenty of local information. Individually decorated bedrooms.

The Oyster Inn with rm

✉ *PA37 1PJ – ✆ (01631) 710666 – stay@oysterinn.co.uk – Fax (01631) 710042*
11 rm – £52/65 £104 – **Rest** – Carte £15/30 **s**
◆ Three in one: a modern restaurant with loch view; adjacent bar/pub, The Ferryman's; comfy, modish bedrooms. Fresh, home-made dishes throughout: seafood specials prevail. Comfortable, modern bedrooms, with bunk-style budget rooms also available for groups.

at Benderloch North : 2½ m. by A 828 – ✉ Connel

Dun Ma Mara without rest — Ardmucknish Bay and Isle of Mull,
✉ *PA37 1RT – ✆ (01631) 720233 – stay@dunnamara.com*
– February-November
7 rm – £50/55 £80/105
◆ Fully restored Edwardian home with fine views. Minimalistic, intimate interior. Pleasant gardens lead to idyllic private beach. Individual, modish rooms boast clean lines.

CRAIGHOUSE – **Argyll and Bute** – **501** C 16 – **see Jura (Isle of)**

CRAIGNURE – **Argyll and Bute** – **501** C 14 – **see Mull (Isle of)**

CRAILING – **Borders** – **501** M 17 – **see Jedburgh**

CRIEFF – **Perth and Kinross** – **501** I 14 – **pop. 6 579** *Scotland* 28 **C2**

Edinburgh 60 m – Glasgow 50 m – Oban 76 m – Perth 18 m
Town Hall, High St ✆ (01764) 652578, criefftic@perthshire.co.uk
Perth Rd, ✆ (01764) 652909;
Muthill Peat Rd, ✆ (01764) 681523.
Town★
Drummond Castle Gardens★ **AC**, S : 2 m. by A 822. Scone Palace★★ **AC**, E : 16 m. by A 85 and A 93

Merlindale

Perth Rd, on A 85 ✉ PH7 3EQ – ✆ (01764) 655205 – merlin.dale@virgin.net
– Fax (01764) 655205 – Closed mid December-mid January
3 rm – £45/78 £78/85 – **Rest** – (by arrangement, communal dining) Menu £30
◆ Traditional, stone-built house close to the town. Well-equipped bedrooms are individually decorated and very comfortable. Accomplished evening meals at a communal table.

The Bank

32 High St ✉ PH7 3BS – ✆ (01764) 656575 – mail@thebankrestaurant.co.uk
– Fax (01764) 656575 – Closed 3 weeks January, 1 week July, 25-26 December, Sunday and Monday
Rest – (booking essential at lunch) Carte £19/27
◆ Impressive, Gothic, former bank dating from 1901 which dominates the high street. Traditional, good value cooking using fine ingredients and an informal, friendly atmosphere.

CRINAN – **Argyll and Bute** – **501** D 15 – ✉ **Lochgilphead** *Scotland* 27 **B2**

Edinburgh 137 m – Glasgow 91 m – Oban 36 m
Hamlet★
Kilmory Knap (Macmillan's Cross★) SW : 14 m

Crinan — Loch Crinan and Sound of Jura,

✉ *PA31 8SR – ✆ (01546) 830261 – reservations@crinanhotel.com*
– Fax (01546) 830292 – Closed 22 December- 1 February
20 rm (dinner included) – £95/120 £300 – **Rest** – (Bar Lunch) Menu £45
◆ Superbly located in a commanding setting with exceptional views of Loch Crinan and Sound of Jura. Cosy, wood panelled, nautically themed bar. Bright, pleasant bedrooms. Restaurant provides wonderful views and interesting cuisine with seafood predominance.

SCOTLAND

CROCKETFORD - Dumfries and Galloway - 501 I 18 - ✉ Castle Douglas ▮ *Scotland* 25 **B3**

▶ Edinburgh 89 m - Dumfries 9 m - Kirkcudbright 18 m
☐ Sweetheart Abbey★, SE : 10 m. by minor rd - Threave Garden★★ and Threave Castle★, S : 10 m. by A 75

Craigadam

West : 2 m. on A 712 ✉ DG7 3HU - ✆ (01556) 650 233 - inquiry@craigadam.com - Fax (01556) 650 233 - Closed 23 December-3 January

10 rm ☕ - 🚹£ 60 🚹🚹£ 86 - **Rest** - (dinner only) (communal dining) Menu £ 23

◆ 18C country house on working farm. Comfortable, spacious rooms, some with south-facing view. Communal meals. Distinctively themed bedrooms in house or rear courtyard.

CROSSFORD - Fife - 501 J 15 - see Dunfermline

CULLODEN - Highland - 501 H 11 - see Inverness

Do not confuse ✗ with ✿!
✗ defines comfort, while stars are awarded for the best cuisine, across all categories of comfort.

CUPAR - Fife - 501 K 15 - pop. 8 506 28 **C2**

▶ Edinburgh 45 m - Dundee 15 m - Perth 23 m

Ostler's Close

25 Bonnygate ✉ KY15 4BU - ✆ (01334) 655 574 - Fax (01334) 654 036 - closed 1-2 January, 2 weeks Easter, 2 weeks October, 25-26 December, Sunday, Monday and lunch Tuesday-Friday

Rest - Carte £ 23/37

◆ Welcoming restaurant with snug atmosphere and low ceilings. Very personally run, with cottage feel throughout. Particular attention to prime Scottish meat and local fish.

DALRY - North Ayrshire - 501 F 16 25 **A1**

▶ Edinburgh 70 m - Ayr 21 m - Glasgow 25 m

Lochwood Farm Steading without rest

Southwest : 5 m. by A 737 and the Saltcoats rd ✉ KA21 6NG - ✆ (01294) 552 529 - info@lochwoodfarm.co.uk

8 rm ☕ - 🚹£ 39/50 🚹🚹£ 58/70

◆ Excellent hospitality at a good value farmhouse on one hundred acres of dairy farm. Fine views of country and coast from outside hot tub. Pleasant, well-kept little bedrooms.

Langside Farm

North : 2 m. by B 780 (Kilbirnie rd) on B 784 (Largs rd) ✉ KA24 5JZ - ✆ (01294) 834 402 - mail@langsidefarm.co.uk - Fax (0870) 056 93 80 - restricted opening in winter

3 rm ☕ - 🚹£ 37 🚹🚹£ 79 - **Rest** - (by arrangement, communal dining) Menu £ 25 **s**

◆ Converted farmhouse, dating from 1745, set on hillside affording panoramic views. Classic furnishings throughout. Comfortable bedrooms exude a homely, relaxing ambience.

SCOTLAND

Braidwoods

Drumastle Mill Cottage, Southwest : 1½ m. by A 737 on Saltcoats rd
KA24 4LN – (01294) 833 544 – keithbraidwood@btconnect.com
– Fax (01294) 833 553 – closed first 3 weeks January, first 2 weeks September, 25-26 December, Monday, Tuesday lunch and Sunday except lunch September-April
Rest – (booking essential) Menu £ 21/36
Spec. Roast pigeon on beetroot, orange and pine nut salad. Best end of lamb, shepherd's pie, cabbage with lemon and thyme. Caramelised rice pudding with rhubarb compote.
◆ Rurally-set restaurant in whitewashed cottage, keenly run by husband and wife team. Weekly-changing menus feature fresh, seasonal, local produce, simply cooked and presented.

DINGWALL – Highland – 501 G 11 – pop. 5 026 — 30 C2

Edinburgh 172 m – Inverness 14 m

Cafe India Brasserie

Lockhart House, Tulloch St IV15 9JZ – (01349) 862 552
– closed 25 December
Rest – Indian Carte £ 20/29
◆ Bustling, locally regarded Indian restaurant, handily located in town centre. Updated décor is fresh and modern. Authentically prepared, tasty regional Indian food.

DOONFOOT – South Ayrshire – 501 G 17 – see Ayr

DORNOCH – Highland – 501 H 10 – pop. 1 206 *Scotland* — 30 D2

Edinburgh 219 m – Inverness 63 m – Wick 65 m
The Coffee Shop, The Square (01862) 810400
Royal Dornoch Golf Rd, (01862) 810 219 .
Town★

Highfield House without rest

Evelix Rd IV25 3HR – (01862) 810 909 – enquiries@highfieldhouse.co.uk
– Fax (01862) 811 605 – March-October
3 rm – £ 55 £ 75
◆ Purpose-built guesthouse with garden and fine Highland views. Small, spruce lounge; neat and tidy breakfast room. Bedrooms offer ample comforts: one has whirlpool bath.

2 Quail with rm

Castle St IV25 3SN – (01862) 811 811 – bookings@2quail.com
– closed 2 weeks spring, 1 week Christmas
3 rm – £ 90 £ 110 – **Rest** – (closed Sunday-Monday) (dinner only) (set menu only) Menu £ 39
◆ Elegant, book-lined restaurant in town house. Interesting dishes with high levels of skill and sensitivity brought to tasty, well-prepared ingredients. Pleasant guest rooms.

DRUMNADROCHIT – Highland – 501 G 11 – Milton *Scotland* — 30 C2

Edinburgh 172 m – Inverness 16 m – Kyle of Lochalsh 66 m
Loch Ness★★ – Loch Ness Monster Exhibition★ **AC** – The Great Glen★

Drumbuie Farm without rest

Drumbuie, East : ¾ m. by A 82 IV63 6XP – (01456) 450 634
– drumbuie@loch-ness-farm.bandb.co.uk – Fax (01456) 450 595
3 rm – £ 35 £ 56
◆ Immaculate purpose-built guesthouse on working farm with Highland cattle. Conservatory breakfast room has Loch Ness views. Good collection of malt whiskies. Spacious bedrooms.

DUFFUS – Moray – 501 K 11 – see Elgin

SCOTLAND

DULNAIN BRIDGE – Highland – **501** J 12 – see Grantown-on-Spey

DUMFRIES – Dumfries and Galloway – **501** J 18 – pop. 31 146 26 **C3**

Scotland

Edinburgh 80 m – Ayr 59 m – Carlisle 34 m – Glasgow 79 m – Manchester 155 m – Newcastle upon Tyne 91 m

64 Whitesands ✆ (01387) 253862, A

Dumfries & Galloway Maxwelltown 2 Laurieston Ave, ✆ (01387) 253 582 ;

Dumfries & County Edinburgh Rd, Nunfield, ✆ (01387) 253 585 ;

Crichton Bankend Rd, ✆ (01387) 247 894 .

Town★ – Midsteeple★ A **A**

Lincluden College (Tomb★) **AC**, N : 1½ m. by College St A. Drumlanrig Castle★★ (cabinets★) **AC**, NW : 16½ m. by A 76 A – Shambellie House Museum of Costume (Costume Collection★) S : 7¼ m. by A 710 A - Sweetheart Abbey★ **AC**, S : 8 m. by A 710 A – Caerlaverock Castle★ (Renaissance fa½ade★★) **AC**, SE : 9 m. by B 725 B – Glenkiln (Sculptures★) W : 9 m. by A 780 - A - and A 75

DUMFRIES

Aldermanhill Rd	**B**	2
Bank St	**A**	3
Buccleuch St	**A**	4
Cardoness St	**B**	5
Cassalands	**A**	6
Castle Douglas Rd	**A**	8
Castle St	**A**	7
Catherine St	**B**	9
Corberry Ave	**A**	10
Cornwall Mount Rd	**B**	12
Cuckoo Bridge Retail Park	**A**	
Friars Vennel	**A**	13
Galloway St	**A**	14
Glebe St	**B**	15
Great King St	**A**	16
Hermitage Drive	**A**	17
High St	**A**	18
Loreburn Centre	**A**	20
Loreburn St	**A**	21
Nith St	**AB**	22
Queensberry St	**A**	24
Queen St	**B**	23
Rae St	**B**	26
St Mary's St	**B**	27
St Michael St	**B**	28
St Michael's Bridge Rd	**A**	30
Shakespeare St	**B**	31
Union St	**A**	32
Whitesands	**A**	34

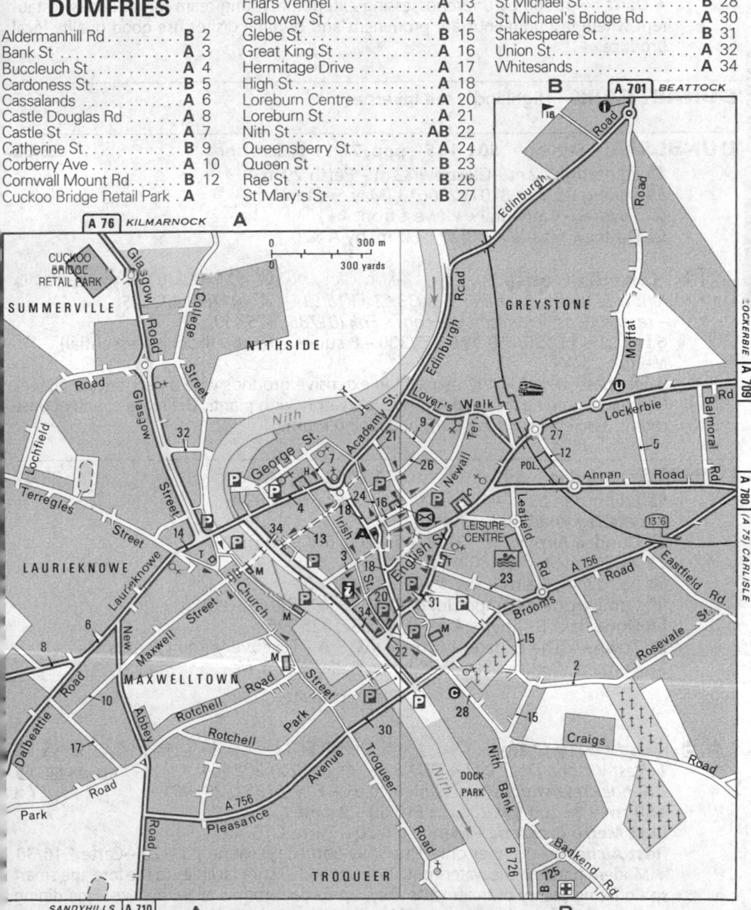

Hazeldean House without rest
4 Moffat Rd ✉ DG1 1NJ – ✆ (01387) 266 178 – Fax (01387) 266 178 B **u**
6 rm – †£ 32/40 ††£ 56/58
◆ Interestingly furnished 19C villa. Entrance door has original stained glass. Characterful antiques and Victoriana in lounge. Conservatory breakfast room. Spacious bedrooms.

Rivendell without rest
105 Edinburgh Rd ✉ DG1 1JX – ✆ (01387) 252 251 – info@rivendellbnb.co.uk – Fax (01387) 263 084 B **i**
5 rm – †£ 25/44 ††£ 50/54
◆ Attractive Rennie Mackintosh style villa with parquet floors, decorative woodwork and brass fittings. Comfortable, pleasant bedrooms with view of large garden.

XX **The Linen Room**
53 St Michael St ✉ DG1 2QB – ✆ (01387) 255 689 – enquiries@linenroom.com – Fax (01387) 253 387 – closed two weeks October, 25 December, 1 January, Monday and lunch Tuesday and Wednesday B **c**
Rest – Menu £ 17 (lunch) – Carte £ 29/35
◆ Don't be put off by unprepossessing exterior: a young team run a serious restaurant where tasting menus are prominent and original dishes use good quality local produce.

SCOTLAND

DUNAIN PARK – Highland – see Inverness

DUNBLANE – Stirling – 501 I 15 – pop. 7 911 *Scotland* 28 **C2**

Edinburgh 42 m – Glasgow 33 m – Perth 29 m
Stirling Rd ✆ (08707) 200613 (May-September)
Town★ – Cathedral★★ (west front★★)
Doune★ (castle★ **AC**) W : 4½ m. by A 820

Cromlix House
Kinbuck, North : 3½ m. on B 8033 ✉ FK15 9JT – ✆ (01786) 822 125 – reservations@cromlixhouse.com – Fax (01786) 825 450
6 rm – †£ 130/250 ††£ 175/300 – 8 suites – **Rest** – (booking essential) Menu £ 25/40
◆ Effortlessly relaxing 19C mansion in extensive grounds with ornate private chapel. Charming morning room; spacious conservatory with plants. Definitive country house rooms. Two elegant, richly furnished dining rooms.

DUNDEE – Dundee – 501 L 14 – pop. 154 674 *Scotland* 28 **C2**

Edinburgh 63 m – Aberdeen 67 m – Glasgow 83 m
Access Tay Road Bridge (toll) Y
Dundee Airport : ✆ (01382) 662200, SW : 1½ m. Z
21 Castle St ✆ (01382) 527527
Caird Park Mains Loan, ✆ (01382) 453 606 ;
Camperdown Camperdown Park, ✆ (01382) 623 398 ;
Downfield Turnberry Ave, ✆ (01382) 825 595 .
Town★ - The Frigate Unicorn★ **AC** Y **A** – Discovery Point★ **AC** Y **B** – Verdant Works★ Z **D** – McManus Galleries★ Y **M**

Plan opposite

Apex City Quay rm, rest,
1 West Victoria Dock Rd ✉ DD1 3JP – ✆ (01382) 202 404 – dundee.reservations@apexhotels.co.uk – Fax (01382) 201 401 Y **a**
150 rm – †£ 200 ††£ 200, £ 12.50 – 2 suites
Rest *Metro Brasserie* – Menu £ 11/20 – Carte £ 16/30
Rest *Alchemy* – (dinner only Thursday-Saturday) Menu £ 11/20 – Carte £ 16/30
◆ Modern hotel on the waterfront. Business and leisure facilities to the fore, the smart spa offering plenty of treatments. Airy, up-to-date rooms all with views. Fine dining in Alchemy. Informal feel suffuses Metro: both restaurants look out over dockside.

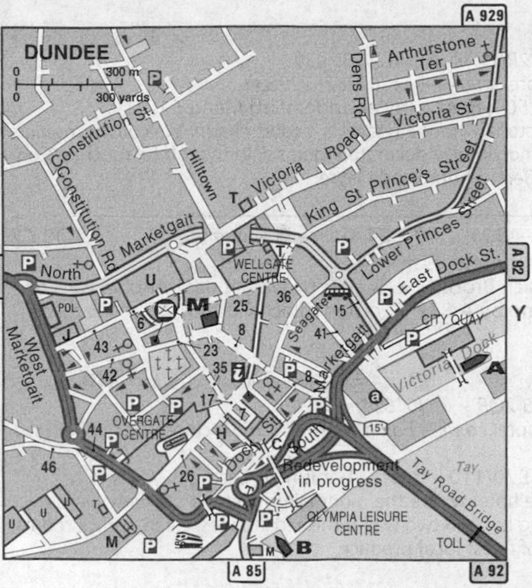

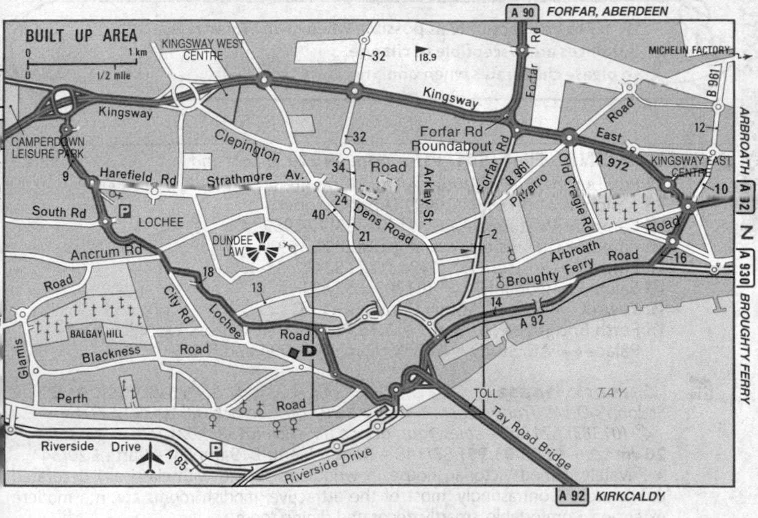

Street	Grid	No.
Albert St	Z	2
Bell St	Y	6
City Quay	Y	
City Square	Y	7
Commercial St	Y	8
Coupar Angus Rd	Z	9
Douglas Rd	Z	10
Drumgeith Rd	Z	12
Dudhope Terrace	Z	13
East Dock St	Z	14
East Marketgait	Y	15
Greendykes Rd	Z	16
High St	Y	17
Kingsway East Shopping Centre	Z	
Kingsway West Shopping Centre	Z	
Logie St	Z	18
Mains Rd	Z	21
Meadowside	Y	23
Moncur Crescent	Z	24
Murraygate	Y	25
Nethergate	Y	26
Old Glamis Rd	Z	32
Overgate Centre	Y	
Provost Rd	Z	34
Reform St	Y	35
St Andrews St	Y	36
Strathmartine Rd	Z	40
Trades Lane	Y	41
Ward Rd	Y	42
Wellgate Centre	Y	
West Bell St	Y	43
West Marketgait	Y	44
West Port	Y	46

at Broughty Ferry East : 4½ m. by A 930 - Z - ✉ Dundee

Broughty Ferry

16 West Queen St ✉ DD5 1AR – ✆ (01382) 480027
– enquiries@hotelbroughtyferry.co.uk – Fax (01382) 739426

16 rm – †£ 75/85 ††£ 95

Rest *Bombay Brasserie* – Indian Carte £ 22/29

◆ Family owned and friendly modern hotel beside the main road. The spacious, individually decorated bedrooms are furnished to a high standard. Brasserie serves elaborate, authentic Indian menus.

Invermark House

23 Monifieth Rd ✉ DD5 2RN – ☏ (01382) 739 430 – enquiries@invermarkhotel.co.uk – Fax (01382) 220 834

6 rm – †£ 25/30 ††£ 50 – **Rest** – (by arrangement) Menu £ 12

◆ Imposing, detached Victorian house retains a period charm. Welcoming owners and relaxed atmosphere. Individually decorated rooms with thoughtful touches. Contemporary dining room offering homemade fayre.

DUNDONNELL – **Highland** – **501** E 10 – ✉ **Garve** *Scotland* 30 **C2**

Edinburgh 215 m – Inverness 59 m

Wester Ross★★★ - Loch Broom★★, N : 4 ½ m. via Allt na h-Airbhe. Falls of Measach★★, SE : 10 m. by A 832 – Corrieshalloch Gorge★, SE : 11 ½ m. by A 832 and A 835

Dundonnell Dundonnell Valley, rm,

Little Loch Broom ✉ IV23 2QR – ☏ (01854) 633 204 – enquiries@dundonnellhotel.co.uk – Fax (01854) 633 366 – closed December and January

32 rm – †£ 35/60 ††£ 70/110 – **Rest** – (bar lunch) Carte £ 17/28 **s**

◆ Up-to-date, comfortable hotel where the mountains meet the sea with views over Dundonnell Valley. Bustling bar and two well-furnished lounges. Clean, spruce rooms. Home baking makes use of finest local produce.

SCOTLAND

We try to be as accurate as possible when giving room rates. But prices are susceptible to change, so please check rates when booking.

DUNFERMLINE – **Fife** – **501** J 15 – **pop. 39 229** *Scotland* 28 **C3**

Edinburgh 16 m – Dundee 48 m – Motherwell 39 m

1 High St ☏ (01383) 720999 (April-October)

Canmore Venturefair Ave, ☏ (01383) 724 969 ;

Pitreavie Queensferry Rd, ☏ (01383) 722 591 ;

Pitfirrane Crossford, ☏ (01383) 723 534 ;

Saline Kinneddar Hill, ☏ (01383) 852 591 .

Town★ - Abbey★ (Abbey Church★★) **AC**

Forth Bridges★★, S : 5 m. by A 823 and B 980. Culross★★ (Village★★★, Palace★★ **AC**, Study★ **AC**), W : 7 m. by A 994 and B 9037

Garvock House

St John's Drive, Transy, East : ¾ m. by A 907 off Garvock Hill ✉ KY12 7TU – ☏ (01383) 621 067 – sales@garvock.co.uk – Fax (01383) 621 168

26 rm – †£ 68/93 ††£ 88/148 – **Rest** – Menu £ 19 (lunch) – Carte £ 20/34

◆ Privately owned Victorian house in woodland setting with classically decorated public areas. Contrastingly, most of the attractive, modish rooms are in a modern extension. Comfortable, smartly decorated dining room.

at Crossford Southwest : **1 ¾ m. on A 994** – ✉ **Dunfermline**

Keavil House rm,

Main St ✉ KY12 8QW – ☏ (01383) 736 258 – sales@keavilhouse.co.uk – Fax (01383) 621 600

73 rm – †£ 90/170 ††£ 110/180

Rest *Cardoon* – Menu £ 13/28 – Carte £ 21/33 **s**

◆ Busy, part 16C country house in woods and gardens on edge of estate. Useful for business traveller. Small bar, extensive leisure facilities. Well-equipped rooms. Elegant, linen-clad conservatory restaurant offering verdant surroundings in which to dine.

DUNFOOT – **South Ayrshire** – **501** G 17 – **see Ayr**

DUNKELD – Perth and Kinross – **501** J 14 – **pop. 1 005** *Scotland* 28 **C2**

Edinburgh 58 m – Aberdeen 88 m – Inverness 98 m – Perth 14 m
The Cross (01350) 727688 (April-October), dunkeldtic@perthshire.co.uk
Dunkeld & Birnam Fungarth, (01350) 727 524 .
Village★ - Cathedral Street★

Kinnaird

Tay valley and hills,

Northwest : 6 ¾ m. by A 9 on B 898 ✉ PH8 0LB – (01796) 482 440 – enquiry@kinnairdestate.com – Fax (01796) 482 289

VISA AE

8 rm (dinner included) – £ 225/425 £ 275/475 – 1 suite –
Rest – Menu £ 55

◆ Imposing Georgian mansion with superb Tay Valley views and sprawling gardens. Antiques, framed oils and country house drapes throughout. Immaculately kept, luxurious rooms. Formal restaurant with hand painted frescoes and ornate ceilings.

Letter Farm without rest

VISA

Loch of the Lowes, Northeast : 3 m. by A 923 on Loch of Lowes rd ✉ PH8 0HH – (01350) 724 254 – letterlowe@aol.com – Fax (01350) 724 254 – mid May-November

3 rm – £ 35 £ 64

◆ Attractive, traditional farm house close to the Loch of Lowes Nature Reserve. Welcoming, homely atmosphere and comfortable bedrooms.

DUNOON – Argyll and Bute – **501** F 16 – **pop. 8 251** *Scotland* 27 **B3**

Edinburgh 73 m – Glasgow 27 m – Oban 77 m
from Dunoon Pier to Gourock Railway Pier (Caledonian MacBrayne Ltd) frequent services daily (20 mn) – from Hunters Quay to McInroy's Point, Gourock (Western Ferries (Clyde) Ltd) frequent services daily (20 mn)
7 Alexandra Parade (08707) 200629, info@dunoon.visitscotland.com
Cowal Ardenslate Rd, (01369) 705 673 ;
Innellan Knockamillie Rd, (01369) 830 242 .
The Clyde Estuary★

Dhailling Lodge

rm, VISA AE

155 Alexandra Parade, North : ¾ m. on A 815 ✉ PA23 8AW – (01369) 701 253 – donald@dhaillinglodge.com – March-October

7 rm – £ 40/60 £ 75 – **Rest** – (dinner only) (booking essential for non-residents) Menu £ 22

◆ Victorian villa with neat and tidy gardens, overlooking Firth of Clyde. Homely lounge boasts books and local guides. Individually decorated rooms with welcoming extra touches. Smart dining room with good views from all tables.

DUNVEGAN – Highland – **501** A 11 – see Skye (Isle of)

DUROR – Argyll and Bute – **501** E 14 29 **B3**

Edinburgh 131 m – Ballachulish 7 m – Oban 26 m

Bealach House

VISA AE

Salachan Glen, Southeast : 4½ m. by A 828 ✉ PA38 4BW – (01631) 740 298 – info@bealach-house.co.uk – closed 20 December-6 January

3 rm – £ 40/55 £ 80 – **Rest** – (by arrangement, communal dining) Menu £ 25 **s**

◆ Down a one-and-a-half mile rural track for total privacy. This former crofter's house, set in eight acres, is immaculate, with snug conservatory and smart, well-kept rooms. Communal dining: daily changing menus have strong local base.

DYKE – Moray – **501** J 11 – see Forres

EAST KILBRIDE – South Lanarkshire – 501 H 16 – pop. 73 796 25 B1

Edinburgh 46 m – Ayr 35 m – Glasgow 10 m
Torrance House Strathaven Rd, ✆ (01355) 248 638 .

Crutherland House

Strathaven Rd, Southeast : 2 m. on A 726
G75 0QZ – ✆ (01355) 577 000 – general.crutherland@macdonald-hotels.co.uk – Fax (01355) 577 047
75 rm – †£ 89/189 ††£ 99/203, £15.95 – **Rest** – (Closed Saturday lunch) Menu £ 20/25 **s** – Carte dinner £ 20/33 **s**

◆ Recently extended country house amidst woodland. Business traveller oriented. Comfortable furnishings and décor throughout. Impressive meeting facilities and well run leisure. Elegant, comfortable dining room: fresh, local produce in tried-and-tested dishes.

EDDLESTON Peebleshire – 501 K 16 – see Peebles

EDINBANE – Highland – 501 A 11 – see Skye (Isle of)

SCOTLAND

Undecided between two equivalent establishments? Within each category, establishments are classified in our order of preference.

M.P. Renier/MICHELIN

EDINBURGH

County: Edinburgh
Michelin REGIONAL map: n° 501 K 16
Glasgow 46 m – Newcastle upon Tyne 105 m

Population: 430 082
Scotland

26 **C1**

PRACTICAL INFORMATION

Tourist Information

Edinburgh & Scotland Information Centre, 3 Princes St (0131) 4733800, info@visitscotland.co.uk

Edinburgh Airport, Tourist Information Desk (0845) 2255121

Airport

Edinburgh Airport: (0870) 040 0007, W: 6 m. by A 8 AV

Golf Courses

Braid Hills Braid Hills Rd, (0131) 447 6666 ;
Carrick Knowe Glendevon Park, (0131) 661 7688 ;
Duddingston Duddingston Road West, (0131) 661 7688 ;
Silverknowes Parkway, (0131) 336 3843 ;
Liberton 297 Gilmerton Rd, (0131) 664 3009 ;
Marriott Dalmahoy Hotel & C.C. Kriknewton, (0131) 225 8010 ;
Portobello Stanley St, (0131) 669 4361.

SCOTLAND

SIGHTS

IN TOWN

City★★★ - Edinburgh International Festival★★★ (August) - Royal Museum of Scotland★★★ EZ **M2** – National Gallery of Scotland★★ DY **M4** - Royal Botanic Garden★★★ AV – The Castle★★ **AC** DYZ : Site★★★ - Palace Block (Honours of Scotland★★★) - St Margaret's Chapel (✻ ★★★) - Great Hall (Hammerbeam Roof★★) – ⩽ ★★ from Argyle and Mill's Mount DZ - Abbey and Palace of Holyroodhouse★★ **AC** (Plasterwork Ceilings★★★, ✻ ★★ from Arthur's Seat) BV – Royal Mile★★ : St Giles' Cathedral★★ (Crown Spire★★★) EYZ - Gladstone's Land★ **AC** EYZ **A** - Canongate Talbooth★ EY **B** – New Town★★ (Charlotte Square★★★ CY **14** - The Georgian House★ **AC** CY **D** – Scottish National Portrait Gallery★ EY **M6** - Dundas House★ EY **E**) – Scottish National Gallery of Modern Art★ AV **M1** - Victoria Street★ EZ **84** – Scott Monument★ (⩽ ★) **AC** EY **F** - Craigmillar Castle★ **AC**, SE: 3 m. by A 7 BX - Calton Hill (✻ ★★★ **AC** from Nelson's Monument) EY – Dean Gallery★ AV opposite **M1** - Royal Yacht Britannia★ BV

ON THE OUTSKIRTS

Edinburgh Zoo★★ **AC** AV – Hill End Ski Centre (✻ ★★) **AC**, S: 5 ½ m. by A 702 BX – The Royal Observatory (West Tower ⩽ ★) **AC** BX – Ingleston, Scottish Agricultural Museum★, W: 6 ½ m. by A 8 AV

IN THE SURROUNDING AREA

Rosslyn Chapel★★ **AC** (Apprentice Pillar★★★) S: 7 ½ m. by A 701 - BX - and B 7006 – Forth Bridges★★, NW: 9 ½ m. by A 90 AV – Hopetoun House★★ **AC**, NW: 11 ½ m. by A 90 - AV - and A 904 – Dalmeny★ - Dalmeny House★ **AC**, St Cuthbert's Church★ (Norman South Doorway★★) NW: 7 m. by A 90 AV – Crichton Castle (Italianate courtyard range★) **AC**, SE: 10 m. by A 7 - X - and B 6372

EDINBURGH

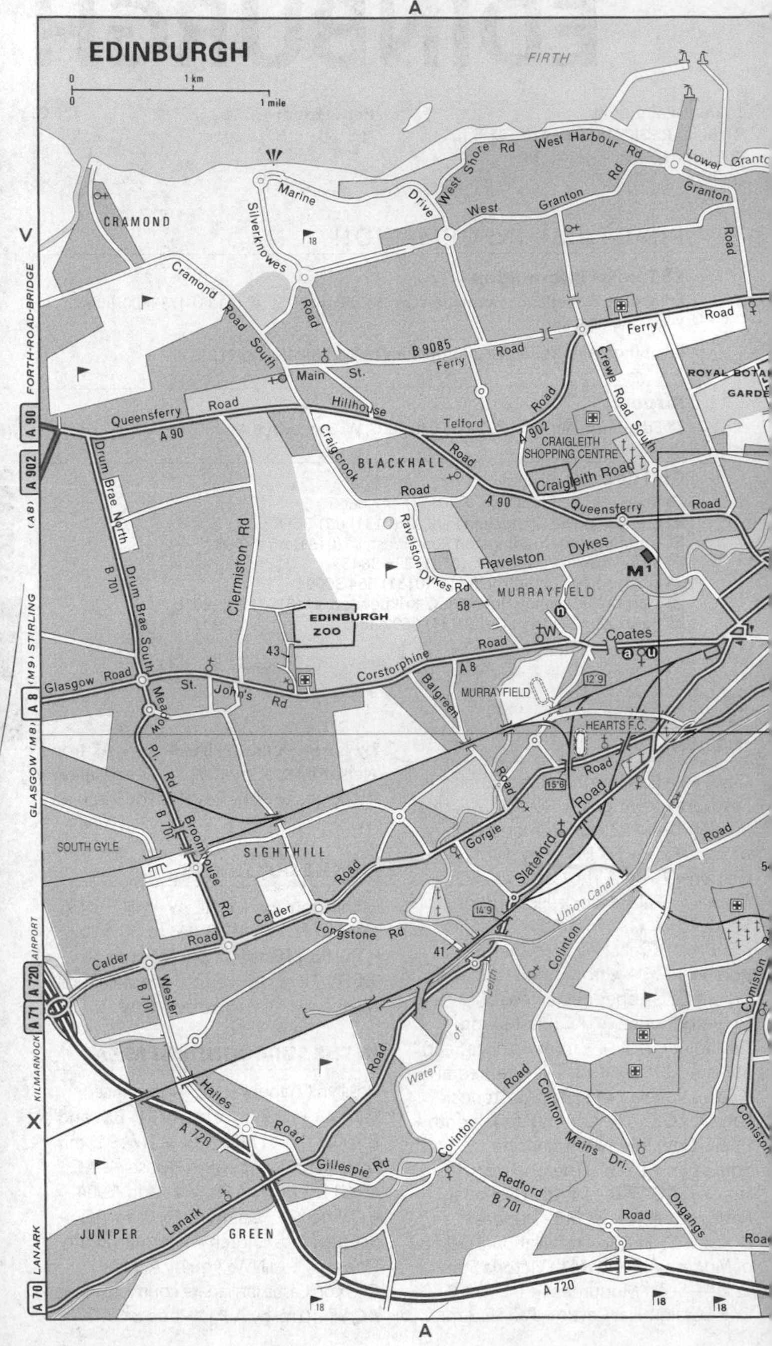
EDINBURGH
0 1 km
0 1 mile
A
V
X
FIRTH
West Harbour Rd
West Shore Rd
Lower Granton
Granton Road
West Granton Rd
Marine Drive
Silverknowes Road
CRAMOND
Cramond Road South
Main St.
B 9085 Ferry Road
Hillhouse
Telford Road
Ferry Road
Crewe Road South
ROYAL BOTANIC GARDEN
CRAIGLEITH SHOPPING CENTRE
Craigleith Road
A 902
Queensferry Road
A 90
Craigcrook Road
BLACKHALL
Ravelston Dykes
Ravelston Dykes Rd
MURRAYFIELD
M1
Coates
Drum Brae North
Drum Brae South
B 701
Clermiston Rd
EDINBURGH ZOO
43
58
Glasgow Road
St. John's Rd
Corstorphine Road
A 8
Balgreen Road
MURRAYFIELD
HEARTS F.C.
12'9
15'6
14'9
Meadow Pl. Rd
Broomhouse Rd
SOUTH GYLE
SIGHTHILL
Gorgie Road
Slateford Road
Union Canal
Calder Road
Longstone Rd
41
Colinton Road
Comiston Road
Wester Hailes Road
Water of Leith
Colinton Mains Dri.
Colinton
Gillespie Rd
Redford Road
B 701
Oxgangs Road
A 720
JUNIPER GREEN
Lanark
18
FORTH-ROAD-BRIDGE
A 90
A 902
(A8)
GLASGOW (M8) (M9) STIRLING
A 8
AIRPORT
A 720
KILMARNOCK
A 71
LANARK
A 70

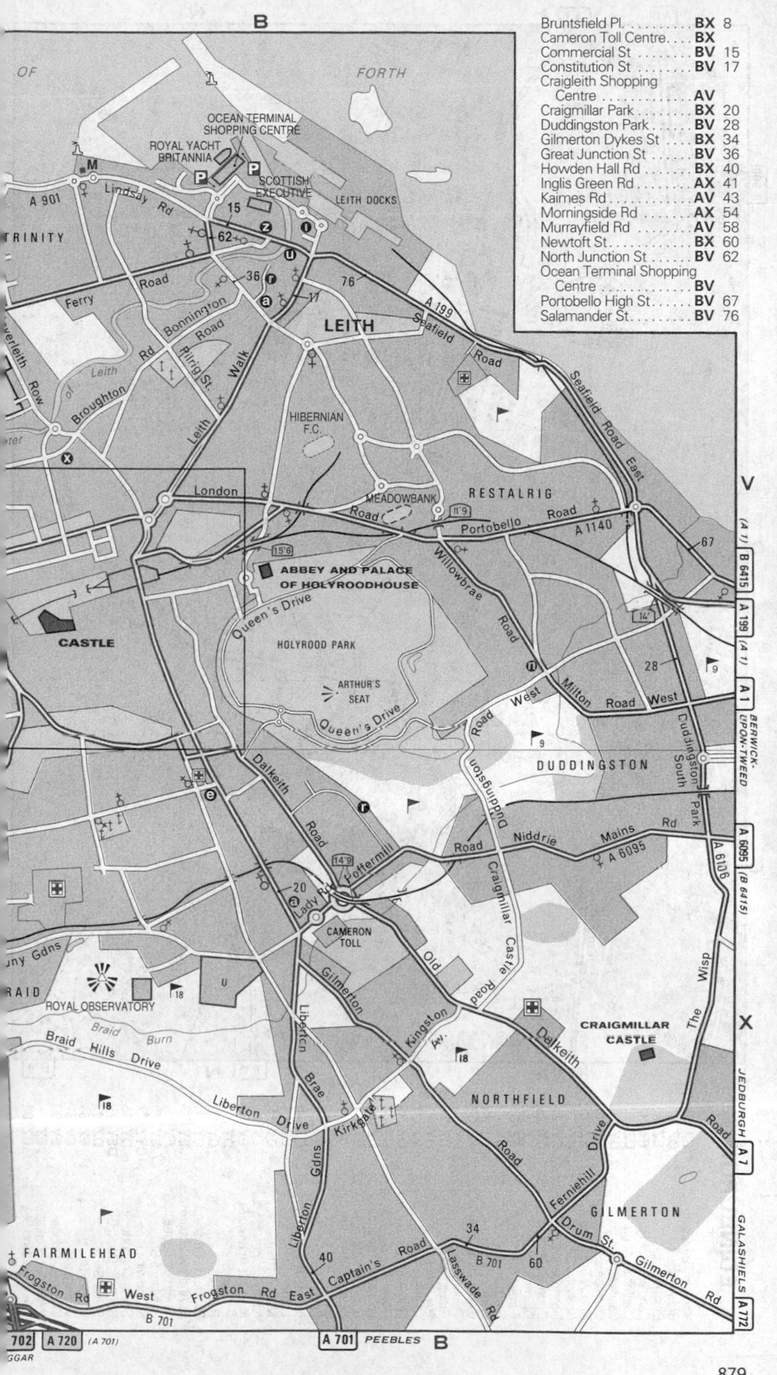

Bruntsfield Pl.	**BX**	8
Cameron Toll Centre	**BX**	
Commercial St	**BV**	15
Constitution St	**BV**	17
Craigleith Shopping Centre	**AV**	
Craigmillar Park	**BX**	20
Duddingston Park	**BV**	28
Gilmerton Dykes St	**BX**	34
Great Junction St	**BV**	36
Howden Hall Rd	**BX**	40
Inglis Green Rd	**AX**	41
Kaimes Rd	**AV**	43
Morningside Rd	**AX**	54
Murrayfield Rd	**AV**	58
Newtoft St	**BX**	60
North Junction St	**BV**	62
Ocean Terminal Shopping Centre	**BV**	
Portobello High St	**BV**	67
Salamander St	**BV**	76

EDINBURGH

Street	Grid	No.
Bernard Terrace	EZ	3
Bread St	DZ	6
Bristo Pl.	EZ	7
Candlemaker Row	EZ	9
Castlehill	DZ	10
Castle St	DY	
Chambers St	EZ	12
Chapel St	EZ	13
Charlotte Square	CY	14
Deanhaugh St	CY	23
Douglas Gardens	CY	25
Drummond St	EZ	27
Forrest Rd	EZ	31
Frederick St	DY	
Gardner's Crescent	CZ	32
George IV Bridge	EZ	33
George St	DY	
Grassmarket	DZ	35
Hanover St	DY	
High St	EYZ	37
Home St	DZ	38
Hope St	CY	39
Johnston Terrace	DZ	42
King's Bridge	DZ	44
King's Stables Rd	DZ	45
Lawnmarket	EYZ	46
Leith St	EY	47
Leven St	DZ	48
Lothian St	EZ	51
Mound (The)	DY	55
North Bridge	EY	61
North St Andrew St	EY	66
Princes St	DY	
Raeburn Pl.	CY	69
Randolph Crescent	CY	71
St Andrew Square	EY	73
St James Centre	EY	
St Mary's St	EY	75
Shandwick Pl.	CYZ	77
South Charlotte St	DY	78
South St David St	DEY	79
Spittal St	DZ	83
Victoria St	EZ	84
Waterloo Pl.	EY	87
Waverley Bridge	EY	89
Waverley Market	EY	
West Maitland St	CZ	92

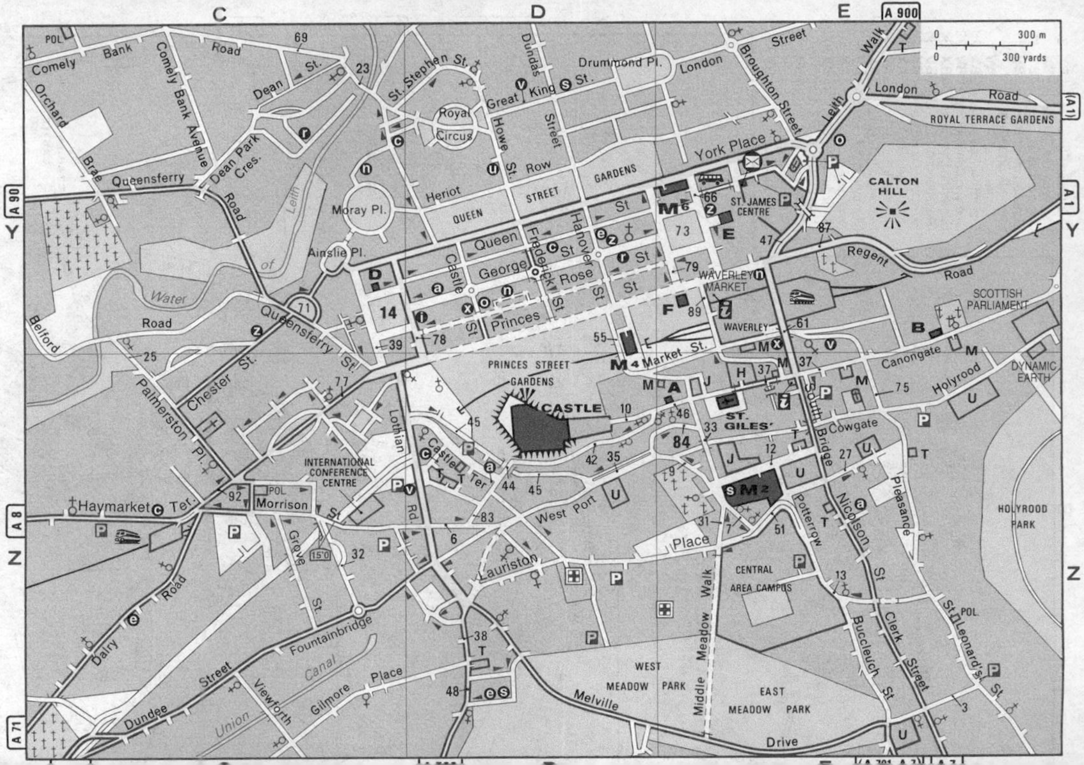

The Balmoral

1 Princes St ✉ EH2 2EQ – ✆ (0131) 556 2414
– reservations.balmoral@roccofortecollection.com
– Fax (0131) 557 8740 EY **n**

167 rm – †£ 305/490 ††£ 360/555, ☕ £ 18.50 – 21 suites

Rest Number One and **Hadrian's** – see restaurant listing

◆ Richly furnished rooms in grand baronial style complemented by contemporary furnishings in the Palm Court exemplify this de luxe Edwardian railway hotel and city landmark.

Sheraton Grand H & Spa

1 Festival Sq ✉ EH3 9SR – ✆ (0131) 229 9131
– grandedinburgh.sheraton@sheraton.com
– Fax (0131) 229 9631 CDZ **v**

244 rm – †£ 209/219 ††£ 229/239, ☕ £ 18 – 16 suites

Rest Grill Room and **Santini** – see restaurant listing

Rest *Terrace* – (buffet) Menu £ 21/22

◆ A modern, centrally located and smartly run hotel. A popular choice for the working traveller, as it boasts Europe's most advanced urban spa. Comfy, well-kept rooms. Glass expanse of Terrace restaurant overlooks Festival Square.

The George

19-21 George St ✉ EH2 2PB – ✆ (0131) 225 1251
– george.reservations@principal-hotels.com
– Fax (0131) 226 5644 DY **z**

196 rm – †£ 129/299 ††£ 129/299, ☕ £ 16.50 – 1 suite

Rest *The Tempus* – Carte £ 24/40

◆ Grade II listed Georgian classic in the heart of the city's most chic street; makes the most of Robert Adam's listed design. Modern decor allied to smartly refurbished rooms. Interesting modern menus at The Tempus.

SCOTLAND

Prestonfield

Priestfield Rd ✉ EH16 5UT – ✆ (0131) 662 2300
– mail@prestonfield.com – Fax (0131) 220 4392 BX **r**

20 rm ☕ – †£ 225/275 ††£ 225/275 – 2 suites

Rest *Rhubarb* – ✆ (0131) 225 7800 – Carte £ 36/52

◆ Superbly preserved interior, tapestries and paintings in the main part of this elegant country house, built in 1687 with modern additions. Set in parkland below Arthur's Seat. Two-roomed, period-furnished 18C dining room with fine views of the grounds.

The Howard

34 Great King St ✉ EH3 6QH – ✆ (0131) 274 7402 – reserve@thehoward.com
– Fax (0131) 274 7405 DY **s**

14 rm – †£ 145 ††£ 275, ☕ £ 16.50 – 4 suites

Rest *The Atholl* – (booking essential for non-residents) Carte £ 27/36

◆ Crystal chandeliers, antiques, richly furnished rooms and the relaxing opulence of the drawing room set off a fine Georgian interior. An inviting "boutique" hotel. Elegant, linen-clad tables for sumptuous dining.

The Scotsman

20 North Bridge ✉ EH1 1YT – ✆ (0131) 556 5565
– reservations@thescotsmanhotelgroup.co.uk – Fax (0131) 652 3652 EY **x**

57 rm – †£ 200/260 ††£ 210/270, ☕ £ 17.50 – 12 suites

Rest *Vermilion* – (closed Monday-Tuesday) (dinner only) Carte £ 32/47

Rest *North Bridge Brasserie* – Carte £ 20/45

◆ Imposing former offices of "The Scotsman" newspaper, with marble reception hall and historic prints. Notably impressive leisure facilities. Well-equipped modern bedrooms. Modern, Scottish food in Vermilion. North Bridge Brasserie boasts original marble pillars.

Channnings

15 South Learmonth Gdns ✉ EH4 1EZ – ☎ (0131) 315 2226 – reserve@channings.co.uk – Fax (0131) 332 9631 CY **e**

38 rm – ♦£ 135/155 ♦♦£ 175/185 – 3 suites – **Rest** – Menu £ 17 (lunch) – Carte £ 22/40 **s**

◆ Sensitively refurbished rooms and fire-lit lounges blend an easy country house elegance with original Edwardian character. Individually appointed bedrooms. A warm, contemporary design doesn't detract from the formal ambience pervading this basement restaurant in which classic Gallic flavours hold sway.

The Bonham

35 Drumsheugh Gdns ✉ EH3 7RN – ☎ (0131) 274 7400 – reserve@thebonham.com – Fax (0131) 274 7405 CY **z**

46 rm – ♦£ 145/165 ♦♦£ 195 – 2 suites – **Rest** – Carte £ 30/36 **s**

◆ A striking synthesis of Victorian architecture, eclectic fittings and bold, rich colours of a contemporary décor. Numerous pictures by "up-and-coming" local artists. Chic dining room with massive mirrors and "catwalk" in spotlights.

The Glasshouse without rest

2 Greenside Pl ✉ EH1 3AA – ☎ (0131) 525 8200 – resglasshouse@theetoncollection.com – Fax (0131) 525 8205 EY **o**

65 rm – ♦£ 180/295 ♦♦£ 180/295

◆ Glass themes dominate the discreet style. Modern bedrooms, with floor to ceiling windows, have views of spacious roof garden or the city below. Breakfast room to the rear.

SCOTLAND

The Roxburghe

38 Charlotte Sq ✉ EH2 4HG – ☎ (0131) 240 5500 – roxburghe@macdonald-hotels.co.uk – Fax (0131) 240 5555 DY **i**

196 rm – ♦£ 95/200 ♦♦£ 95/255 – 1 suite

Rest *The Melrose* – (closed Saturday lunch) (dinner only and Sunday lunch) Menu £ 21.50/26.50 – Carte £ 25/32

◆ Attentive service, understated period-inspired charm and individuality in the British style. Part modern, part Georgian but roomy throughout; welcoming bar. Restaurant reflects the grandeur of architect Robert Adam's exterior.

Tigerlily

125 George St ✉ EH2 4JN – ☎ (0131) 225 5005 – info@tigerlilyedinburgh.co.uk – Fax (0131) 225 7046 – closed Christmas Day DY **a**

33 rm – ♦£ 175 ♦♦£ 175 – **Rest** – Carte £ 20/34

◆ Coverted Georgian townhouse boasting hip interior, including pink furnished bar, buzzy basement nightclub and glamourous, well-appointed bedrooms. Busy dining room offers wide choice of dishes, with Asian tendencies.

Le Monde

16 George St ✉ EH2 2PF – ☎ (0131) 270 3900 – info@lemondehotel.co.uk – Fax (0131) 270 3901 – Closed 24-26 December DY **r**

18 rm – ♦£ 135/205 ♦♦£ 165/395

Rest *Paris* – Carte £ 16/34 **s**

◆ Smartly appointed hotel in city centre, with two trendy bars and a nightclub. Contemporary bedrooms are themed on cities from around the world, even down to the DVDs. First floor restaurant offers simple menu.

Edinburgh Marriott

111 Glasgow Rd, West : 4½ m. on A 8 ✉ EH12 8NF – ☎ (0131) 334 9191 – mhrs.edieb.frontdesk@marriotthotels.com – Fax (0131) 316 4507

241 rm – ♦£ 115/145 ♦♦£ 125/155, £ 14.95 – 4 suites

Rest *Mediterrano* – (dinner only and lunch Saturday-Sunday) Menu £ 23 (dinner) – Carte £ 17/37 **s**

◆ Excellent road connections for the airport and Glasgow and well-equipped rooms make this large, group-operated hotel a practical choice for business travel. Modern restaurant with Mediterranean twist.

Christopher North House without rest
6 Gloucester Place ✉ EH3 6EF – ✆ (0131) 225 2720 – reservations@christophernorth.co.uk – Fax (0131) 220 4706 CY **c**
32 rm – †£ 88/108 ††£ 108/148
◆ Georgian house on cobbled street in quiet residential area; a chintzy feel overlays the contemporary interior. Eclectically styled bedrooms feature homely extra touches.

Ten Hill Place without rest
10 Hill Place ✉ EH8 9DS – ✆ (0131) 662 2080 – reservations@tenhillplace.com – Fax (0131) 662 2082 – Closed Christmas EZ **a**
78 rm – †£ 95/172 ††£ 95/172
◆ Brand new hotel owned by Royal College of Surgeons and next to main college. Contemporary bedrooms boast state-of-the-art facilities; views from Skyline rooms worth extra cost.

The Lodge without rest
6 Hampton Terrace, West Coates ✉ EH12 5JD – ✆ (0131) 337 3682 – info@thelodgehotel.co.uk – Fax (0131) 313 1700 AV **u**
12 rm – †£ 50/70 ††£ 80/135
◆ A converted Georgian manse, family owned and immaculately kept. Individually designed bedrooms and lounge decorated with taste and care; close to Murrayfield rugby stadium.

Kildonan Lodge
27 Craigmillar Park ✉ EH16 5PE – ✆ (0131) 667 2793 – info@kildonanlodgehotel.co.uk – Fax (0131) 667 9777 – closed one week Christmas BX **a**
15 rm – †£ 69/78 ††£ 78/149 – **Rest** – (dinner only, by arrangement) Carte £ 16/22 **s**
◆ Privately managed, with a cosy, firelit drawing room which feels true to the Lodge's origins as a 19C family house. One room has a four-poster bed and a fine bay window. Privately managed, with a cosy, firelit drawing room which feels true to the Lodge's origins as a 19C family house. One room has a four-poster bed and a fine bay window.

Davenport House without rest
58 Great King St ✉ EH3 6QY – ✆ (0131) 558 8495 – davenporthouse@btinternet.com – Fax (0131) 558 8496 – closed Christmas DY **v**
6 rm – †£ 65/110 ††£ 75/110
◆ Three-storey Georgian townhouse on cobbled street. Welcoming period style lounge; chintzy breakfast room. The bedrooms are of varying styles and sizes; all are well equipped.

Kew House without rest
1 Kew Terrace, Murrayfield ✉ EH12 5JE – ✆ (0131) 313 0700 – info@kewhouse.com – Fax (0131) 313 0747 AV **a**
8 rm – †£ 75/120 ††£ 88/155
◆ Secure private parking and good road access for the city or Murrayfield Stadium. Neat, carefully kept rooms which are modern and well-proportioned.

Elmview without rest
15 Glengyle Terrace ✉ EH3 9LN – ✆ (0131) 228 1973 – nici@elmview.co.uk – 24 March-October DZ **e**
5 rm – †£ 75/100 ††£ 95/120
◆ Basement of a Victorian house in pretty terrace overlooking The Meadows. Bedrooms are spotlessly kept and feature a host of extras: videos, fridges, sherry and more.

SCOTLAND

The Glenora without rest
14 Rosebery Crescent – (0131) 337 1186 – enquiries@glenorahotel.co.uk – Fax (0131) 337 1119 CZ **c**
11 rm – £ 45/85 £ 80/130
◆ Capacious Georgian house split over three floors with modern, stylish décor and generously sized bedrooms. Exclusively organic produce served at breakfast.

Seven Danube Street without rest
7 Danube St EH4 1NN – (0131) 332 2755 – seven.danubestreet@virgin.net – Fax (0131) 343 3648 – closed Christmas CY **r**
3 rm – £ 70/120 £ 110/150
◆ Bright, traditionally styled rooms with antique furnishings in a residential street. Breakfasts taken around one large table add to a feeling of engaging hospitality.

The Beverley without rest
40 Murrayfield Ave EH12 6AY – (0131) 337 1128 – enquiries@thebeverley.com – Fax (0131) 313 3275 – closed 21-27 December AV **n**
8 rm – £ 35/80 £ 60/100
◆ Elegant 19C bay windowed house in quiet, tree-lined avenue close to the rugby stadium. Good value, individually appointed rooms with modern facilties and thoughtful extras.

Castle View without rest
30 Castle St EH2 3HT – (0131) 226 5784 – coranne@castleviewgh.co.uk – Fax (0131) 226 1603 – closed 23-29 December DY **x**
7 rm – £ 45/100 £ 70/100
◆ As name implies, set in great position for tourists. Lounge with comfy sofas. Well-kept, individual rooms in a terraced house; those at front have castle views.

Number One – at The Balmoral H.
1 Princes St EH2 2EQ – (0131) 622 8831 – numberone@roccofortecollection.com – Fax (0131) 557 8740 EY **n**
Rest – (dinner only) Menu £ 63
Spec. Seared scallops, caramelized cauliflower risotto, spiced squid. Hazelnut crusted pork loin, belly parmentier, sauce Robert. Millefeuille of raspberries, peach coulis, raspberry sorbet.
◆ Opulently-appointed basement restaurant offering fine dining in grand railway hotel. Luxurious feel. Complex and elaborate cooking showcases Scottish produce.

Oloroso
33 Castle St EH2 3DN – (0131) 226 7614 – info@oloroso.co.uk – Fax (0131) 226 7608 – closed first week January and 25-26 December DY **o**
Rest – Carte £ 34/50
◆ Modish third floor restaurant in heart of city. Busy, atmospheric bar. Lovely terrace with good castle views to the west. Stylish, modern cooking with Asian influence.

Grill Room – at Sheraton Grand H & Spa.
1 Festival Sq EH3 9SR – (0131) 221 6422 – Fax (0131) 229 6254 – closed Saturday lunch, Sunday and Monday CDZ **v**
Rest – Carte £ 29/50
◆ Ornate ceilings, wood panels and modern glass make an ideal setting for imaginative, well presented cooking. Local ingredients with a few European and Pacific Rim elements.

Abstract
33-35 Castle Terrace EH1 2EL – (0131) 229 1222 – reservations@abstractrestaurant.com – Closed Sunday DZ **a**
Rest – French Menu £ 17 (lunch) – Carte £ 30/43
◆ Tucked away behind the castle, all mock snakeskin furniture and vibrant wallpaper. Seasonal French cooking is balanced and thoughtful; formal service by a well-versed team.

SCOTLAND

XX **Santini** – at Sheraton Grand H & Spa.
8 Conference Sq ✉ EH3 8AN – ✆ (0131) 221 7788
– Fax (0131) 221 7789 CDZ **v**
Rest – Italian Menu £ 21/22 – Carte £ 27.50/46.50 **s**
♦ The personal touch is predominant in this stylish restaurant appealingly situated under a superb spa. Charming service heightens the enjoyment of tasty, modern Italian food.

XX **Atrium**
10 Cambridge St ✉ EH1 2ED – ✆ (0131) 228 8882 – eat@atriumrestaurant.co.uk – Fax (0131) 228 8808 – closed 25-26 December, 1 January, Sunday and Saturday lunch except during Edinburgh Festival DZ **c**
Rest – Menu £ 20/27 – Carte £ 37/47
♦ Located inside the Traverse Theatre, an adventurous repertoire enjoyed on tables made of wooden railway sleepers. Twisted copper lamps subtly light the ultra-modern interior.

XX **Hadrian's** – at The Balmoral H.
2 North Bridge ✉ EH1 1TR – ✆ (0131) 557 5000
– hadrians@roccofortecollection.com – Fax (0131) 557 3747 EY **n**
Rest – Carte £ 33/48
♦ Drawing on light, clean-lined styling, reminiscent of Art Deco, and a "British new wave" approach; an extensive range of contemporary brasserie classics and smart service.

XX **Forth Floor - Restaurant (at Harvey Nichols)** ← Castle and city skyline,
30-34 St Andrew Sq ✉ EH2 2AD
– ✆ (0131) 524 8350 – fourthfloorreservations@harveynichols.com
– Fax (0131) 524 8351 – closed 25 December, 1 January and dinner Sunday Monday EY **z**
Rest – Menu £ 18 – Carte £ 20/38
♦ Stylish restaurant with delightful outside terrace affording views over the city. Half the room in informal brasserie-style and the other more formal. Modern, Scottish menus.

XX **The Stockbridge**
54 St Stephens St ✉ EH3 5AL – ✆ (0131) 226 6766 – closed 2 weeks January, 25 December, Monday CY **n**
Rest – (dinner only Wednesday - Friday) Menu £ 15/22 – Carte £ 24/43
♦ Intimate neighbourhood restaurant, its black walls hung with colourful Scottish art. Professional staff serve a mix of classical and more modern dishes, precisely prepared.

XX **Duck's at Le Marche Noir**
14 Eyre Pl ✉ EH3 5EP – ✆ (0131) 558 1608 – enquiries@ducks.co.uk
– Fax (0131) 556 0798 – Closed 25-26 December and lunch Sunday-Monday BV **x**
Rest – Menu £ 16/28
♦ Confident, inventive cuisine with a modern, discreetly French character, served with friendly efficiency in bistro-style surroundings - intimate and very personally run.

XX **The Tower**
Museum of Scotland (5th floor), Chambers St ✉ EH1 1JF – ✆ (0131) 225 3003
– mail@tower-restaurant.com – Fax (0131) 220 4392
– Closed 25-26 December EZ **s**
Rest – Menu £ 19 (lunch) – Carte £ 31/41
♦ Game, grills and seafood feature in a popular, contemporary brasserie style menu. On the fifth floor of the Museum of Scotland - ask for a terrace table and admire the view.

XX **La Garrigue**
31 Jeffrey St ✉ EH1 1DH – ✆ (0131) 557 3032 – pugarrigue@btconnect.com
– Fax (0131) 557 30 32 – closed 25-26 December, 1 January and Sunday EY **v**
Rest – French Menu £ 17/29
♦ Very pleasant restaurant near the Royal Mile: beautiful handmade wood tables add warmth to rustic décor. Authentic French regional cooking with classical touches.

SCOTLAND

XX **Roti** VISA MC AE

73 Morrison St ✉ EH3 8BU – ✆ (0131) 221 9998 – info@roti.uk.com – Fax (0131) 225 5374 – Closed Saturday lunch, Sunday and Monday DZ

Rest – Indian Carte £ 23/27

◆ Modern Indian restaurant in central location; traditional carved wood meets funky new fittings. Accomplished kitchen serves authentic dishes; tasting menus a highlight.

X **First Coast** AC VISA MC AE

97-101 Dalry Rd ✉ EH11 2AB – ✆ (0131) 313 4404 – info@first-coast.co.uk – Fax (0131) 346 7811 – closed Sunday, 25-26 December and 1-2 January CZ **e**

Rest – Carte £ 18/26

◆ Informal restaurant near Haymarket station. The exposed stone walls in one of the rooms lend a rustic aspect. Sizeable menus boast a classic base with modern twists.

X **Nargile** VISA MC AE

73 Hanover St ✉ EH2 1EE – ✆ (0131) 225 5755 – info@nargile.co.uk – closed 25-26 December, 1 January, Monday lunch and Sunday DY **e**

Rest – Turkish Menu £ 20/23 – Carte £ 18/26

◆ Unpretentious and welcoming restaurant with simple décor and enthusiastic service. A la carte, set menus and lunch time mezes of tasty, well-prepared Turkish cuisine.

SCOTLAND

X **Fenwicks** VISA MC AE

15 Salisbury Pl ✉ EH9 1SL – ✆ (0131) 667 4265 – enquiries@fenwicks-restaurant.co.uk – Fax (0131) 667 4285 – closed 25-26 December and 2 January BX **e**

Rest – Menu £ 15/22 – Carte £ 17/25

◆ Cosy and unpretentious with a neighbourhood feel. Colourful French posters on the walls. Good value menus: the cooking is rustic Scottish with dashes of French inspiration.

X **Blue** AC VISA MC AE

10 Cambridge St ✉ EH1 2ED – ✆ (0131) 221 1222 – eat@bluebarcafe.com – Fax (0131) 228 8808 – closed 25-26 December, 1 January and Sunday except during Edinburgh Festival DZ **c**

Rest – Carte £ 23/27

◆ Strikes a modern note with bright, curving walls, glass and simple settings. A café-bar with a light, concise and affordable menu drawing a young clientele. Bustling feel.

X **Le Café Saint-Honoré** VISA MC AE

34 North West Thistle Street Lane ✉ EH2 1EA – ✆ (0131) 226 2211 – Fax (0131) 477 2716 – Closed 3 days Christmas and 3 days New Year DY **c**

Rest – (booking essential) Carte £ 27/35

◆ Tucked away off Frederick St, a bustling, personally run bistro furnished in the classic French style of a century ago. Good-value cuisine with a pronounced Gallic flavour.

Iglu VISA MC AE

2B Jamaica Street ✉ EH3 6HH – ✆ (0131) 476 5333 – mail@theiglu.com – Closed 25 December and Monday-Thursday lunch DY **u**

Rest – (booking essential) Menu £ 13/15 – Carte £ 22/35

◆ Vivid blue façade. Plasma screens, low tub chairs and funky music; fish tanks and potted plants upstairs. Their ethos is ethical eating; their motto 'wild, organic and local.'

Leith – Edinburgh 26 **C1**

Malmaison

1 Tower Pl ✉ EH6 7DB – ✆ (0131) 468 5000 – edinburgh@malmaison.com – Fax (0131) 468 5002 BV **i**

95 rm – †£ 145/235 ††£ 145/235, ☕ £13.95 – 5 suites

Rest *Brasserie* – Menu £ 14/15 – Carte £ 26/41

♦ Imposing quayside sailors' mission converted in strikingly elegant style. Good-sized rooms, thoughtfully appointed, combine more traditional comfort with up-to-date overtones. Sophisticated brasserie with finely wrought iron.

Martin Wishart

54 The Shore ✉ EH6 6RA – ✆ (0131) 553 3557 – info@martin-wishart.co.uk – Fax (0131) 467 7091 – closed 2 weeks January, Sunday and Monday BV **u**

Rest – (booking essential) Menu £ 23/50

Spec. Lobster and smoked haddock soufflé, Poached Anjou pigeon, calamari risotto. Saint Felician and apple cannelloni.

♦ Simply decorated dockside conversion with a fully formed reputation. Modern French-accented menus characterised by clear, intelligently combined flavours.

The Kitchin

78 Commercial Quay ✉ EH6 6LX – ✆ (0131) 555 1755 – info@thekitchin.com – Fax (0131) 553 0608 – closed 1-22 January, 1-16 July, Sunday and Monday BV **z**

Rest – Menu £ 20 (lunch) – Carte £ 40/51

Spec. Roast langoustine, boned and rolled pig's head, crispy ear salad. Saddle of rabbit filled with spinach and foie gras, girolles and roasted beetroot. Cocktail of Valrhona chocolate, raspberry and praline sundae.

♦ Former dockside warehouse, the industrial feel enhanced by original metal supports and battleship grey décor. Well-priced menus offering skilful, accomplished, modern cooking.

Plumed Horse

50-54 Henderson St ✉ EH6 6DE – ✆ (0131) 554 5556 – plumedhorse@aol.com – closed 2 weeks July, 1 week March, 1week July, 25-26 December, 1 January, Sunday and Monday BV **a**

Rest – Menu £ 21 (lunch) – Carte £ 31/38

♦ Homely, personally run restaurant with ornate ceiling, vivid paintings, an intimate feel and formal service. Classic cooking makes good use of seasonal Scottish ingredients.

The Vintners Rooms

The Vaults, 87 Giles St ✉ EH6 6BZ – ✆ (0131) 554 6767 – enquiries@thevintnersrooms.com – Fax (0131) 555 5653 – closed 23 December-7 January, Sunday and Monday BV **r**

Rest – Menu £ 20 (lunch) – Carte £ 33/42

♦ Atmospheric 18C bonded spirits warehouse with high ceilings, stone floor, rug-covered walls and candlelit side-room with ornate plasterwork. French/Mediterranean cooking.

The Kings Wark

36 The Shore ✉ EH6 6QU – ✆ (0131) 554 9260 – Closed 25 December and 1 January BV **u**

Rest – Carte £ 18/28

♦ Distinctive blue façade and cosy, characterful interior with exposed stone and beams. Hearty, unpretentious Scottish cooking. Well known for its all day weekend breakfasts.

SCOTLAND

at Kirknewton Southwest : 7 m. on A 71 - AX – ✉ Edinburgh

Dalmahoy H. & Country Club
✉ *EH27 8EB* rm, rest,
– ✆ *(0131) 333 1845 – mhrs.edigs.frontdesk@marriotthotels.com*
– *Fax (0131) 333 1433*
212 rm – £ 110/140 £ 110/140 – 3 suites
Rest *Pentland* – (dinner only) Menu £ 32 (dinner) – Carte £ 27/42
Rest *The Long Weekend* – Carte £ 18/27 **s**
◆ Extended Georgian mansion in 1000 acres with 2 Championship golf courses. Comprehensive leisure club, smart rooms and a clubby cocktail lounge. Tranquil atmosphere with elegant comfort in Pentland restaurant. Informal modern dining at The Long Weekend.

EDNAM – Borders – **501** – see Kelso

EDZELL – Angus – **501** M 13 – **pop. 783** *Scotland* 28 **D2**
Edinburgh 94 m – Aberdeen 36 m – Dundee 31 m
Castle★ AC (The Pleasance★★★) W : 2 m. Glen Esk★, NW : 7 m

Glenesk
High St ✉ DD9 7TF – ✆ (01356) 648 319 – gleneskhotel@btconnect.com
– Fax (01356) 647 333 – Closed 2-15 January
22 rm – £ 50/80 £ 90/150 – **Rest** – (bar lunch) Menu £ 28 **s**
– Carte £ 17/35 **s**
◆ Well run and family owned, a substantial 19C hotel with the pleasant village on its doorstep. Friendly atmosphere prevails; simple rooms of varying shapes and sizes. Restaurant overlooks golf course and gardens.

SCOTLAND

ELGIN – Moray – **501** K 11 – **pop. 20 829** *Scotland* 28 **C1**
Edinburgh 198 m – Aberdeen 68 m – Fraserburgh 61 m – Inverness 39 m
17 High St ✆ (01343) 542666
Moray Lossiemouth Stotfield Rd, ✆ (01343) 812 018 ;
Hardhillock Birnie Rd, ✆ (01343) 542 338 ;
Hopeman Moray, ✆ (01343) 830 578 .
Town★ - Cathedral★ (Chapter house★★)AC
Glenfiddich Distillery★, SE : 10 m. by A 941

Mansion House
The Haugh, via Haugh Rd ✉ IV30 1AW – ✆ (01343) 548 811
– reception@mhelgin.co.uk – Fax (01343) 547 916 – closed 3-10 January
23 rm – £ 86/100 £ 175/200 – **Rest** – Menu £ 20/32 – Carte £ 19/35
◆ 19C Baronial mansion surrounded by lawned gardens. Country house-style interior. Rooms in main house most characterful, those in purpose-built annex more modern. The formal restaurant is decorated in warm yellows and blues.

The Pines without rest
East Rd, East : ½ m. on A 96 ✉ IV30 1XG – ✆ (01343) 552 495
– enquiries@thepinesguesthouse.com – Fax (01343) 552 495
6 rm – £ 40/45 £ 60/64
◆ Detached Victorian house with a friendly and warm ambience amidst comfy, homely décor. Bedrooms are of a good size and furnished with colourful, modern fabrics.

The Croft without rest
10 Institution Rd, via Duff Ave ✉ IV30 1QX – ✆ (01343) 546 004
– thecroftelgin@hotmail.com – Fax (01343) 546 004 – closed mid December-end January
3 rm – £ 35/50 £ 64/70
◆ Victorian family home with delightful garden. Large, comfortable, library-style lounge and a breakfast room with fine dining suite. Comfy, pine furnished rooms.

The Lodge

20 Duff Ave ✉ IV30 1QS – ✆ (01343) 549 981 – info@thelodge-elgin.com – Fax (01343) 540 527

8 rm – ♦£ 32/50 ♦♦£ 56/66 – **Rest** – (by arrangement) Carte £ 16/24

◆ Victorian house with a distinctive facade. Antique furnished hall and homely lounge with open fires. Comfortable bedrooms with dark wood furniture. Tasty home-cooked meals.

at Urquhart East : 5 m. by A 96 – ✉ Elgin

Parrandier

The Old Church of Urquhart, Meft Rd, Northwest : ¼ m. by Main St and Meft Rd ✉ IV30 8NH – ✆ (01343) 843 063 – info@oldchurch.eu – Fax (01343) 843 063

3 rm – ♦£ 35 ♦♦£ 68 – **Rest** – (by arrangement, communal dining) Menu £ 12

◆ Former 19C church in quiet rural location converted to provide open plan lounge and split level dining area. Comfortable bedrooms with original church features.

at Duffus Northwest : 5 ½ m. by A 941 on B 9012 – ✉ Elgin

Burnside House without rest

Northwest : 1 ¾ m. by B 9012 on B 9040 ✉ IV30 5QS – ✆ (01343) 835 165 – burnsidehouse@hotmail.com – Fax (01343) 835 165

4 rm – ♦£ 34 ♦♦£ 56

◆ 19C house with garden; the residence of the founder of Gordonstoun School nearby. Attractive rooms with view; snooker table. Large bedrooms with tartan themes.

Your opinions are important to us:
please write and let us know about your discoveries and experiences – good and bad!

ELIE – Fife – **501** L 15 28 **D2**

Edinburgh 44 m – Dundee 24 m – St Andrews 13 m

Sangster's

51 High St ✉ KY9 1BZ – ✆ (01333) 331 001 – bruce@sangsters.co.uk – Fax (01333) 331 001 – closed 1 week January, 1 week November, 25-26 December,Monday Tuesday, dinner Sunday and lunch Saturday

Rest – (booking essential) Menu £ 20/33

◆ Husband and wife team run this homely, modern restaurant with local artwork for sale on the walls. The classical style of cooking employs notable use of good, local produce.

ERISKA (Isle of) – **Argyll and Bute** – **501** D 14 – ✉ **Oban** 27 **B2**

Edinburgh 127 m – Glasgow 104 m – Oban 12 m

Isle of Eriska ← Lismore and mountains,

Benderloch ✉ PA37 1SD rm, rest,

– ✆ (01631) 720 371 – office@eriska-hotel.co.uk – Fax (01631) 720 531 – closed January

23 rm – ♦£ 155/230 ♦♦£ 310/360 – 4 suites – **Rest** – (light lunch residents only) (booking essential) Menu £ 40

◆ On a private island, a wonderfully secluded 19C Scottish Baronial mansion with dramatic views of Lismore and mountains. Highest levels of country house comfort and style. Elegant dining.

SCOTLAND

EUROCENTRAL – Glasgow – see Glasgow

FAIRLIE – North Ayrshire – 501 F 16 25 A1

Edinburgh 75 m – Ayr 50 m – Glasgow 36 m

Fins

Fencebay Fisheries, Fencefoot Farm, South : 1½ m. on A 78 ✉ KA29 0EG – ✆ (01475) 568 989 – fencebay@aol.com – Fax (01475) 568 921 – Closed 25-26 December, 1 January, Sunday dinner and Monday

Rest – Seafood (booking essential) Carte £ 24/50

◆ Converted farm buildings house a simple, flag-floored restaurant, craft shops and a traditional beech smokery. Friendly service and fresh seasonal seafood.

FASNACLOICH – Argyll and Bute – ✉ Appin 27 B2

Edinburgh 133 m – Fort William 34 m – Oban 19 m

Lochside Cottage

< Loch Baile Mhic Chailen and mountains,

✉ PA38 4BJ – ✆ (01631) 730 216 – broadbent@lochsidecottage.net – Fax (01631) 730 216 – closed Christmas and New Year

3 rm – £ 32/38 £ 64/76 – **Rest** – (by arrangement, communal dining) Menu £ 28

◆ Captivating views of surrounding mountains and Loch Baile Mhic Chailen, on whose shore it stands in idyllic seclusion. Log fires in the lounge and inviting, cosy bedrooms. Dinners take place with a house party atmosphere as guests dine together at one table.

SCOTLAND

If breakfast is included the symbol appears after the number of rooms.

FIONNPHORT – Argyll and Bute – 501 A 15

- Shipping Services : see Mull (Isle of)

FLODIGARRY – Highland – 501 B 11 – see Skye (Isle of)

FORGANDENNY – Perth. and Kinross – 501 J 14 – see Perth

FORRES – Moray – 501 J 11 – pop. 8 967 *Scotland* 28 C1

Edinburgh 165 m – Aberdeen 80 m – Inverness 27 m

116 High St ✆ (01309) 672938 (Easter-October)

Muiryshade, ✆ (01309) 672949.

Sueno's Stone★★, N : ½ m. by A 940 on A 96 – Brodie Castle★ **AC**, W : 3 m. by A 96. Elgin★ (Cathedral★, chapter house★★ **AC**), E : 10 ¼ m. by A 96

Knockomie

rm,

Grantown Rd, South : 1½ m. on A 940 ✉ IV36 2SG – ✆ (01309) 673 146 – stay@knockomie.co.uk – Fax (01309) 673 290 – Closed 24-26 December

15 rm – £ 110/140 £ 170/210

Rest *The Grill Room* – Menu £ 38 (dinner) – Carte £ 28/38

◆ Extended Arts and Crafts house in comfortable seclusion off a country road. Country house atmosphere. Bedrooms in main house older and more characterful. The Grill baronial style restaurant specializes in Scottish beef.

Ramnee

Victoria Rd ✉ IV36 3BN – ✆ (01309) 672 410 – info@ramneehotel.com – Fax (01309) 673 392 – Closed 25 December and 1-3 January

18 rm – £ 65/88 £ 90/120 – 1 suite

Rest *Hamlyns* – Menu £ 26 (dinner) – Carte £ 17/28

◆ Family owned Edwardian building in town centre with extensive lawned grounds. Welcoming public areas include panelled reception and pubby bar. Warmly traditional bedrooms. Formal dining room in traditional style.

Cluny Bank
St Leonard's Rd, South : ½ m. by Tolbooth St ✉ IV36 1DW – ☎ (01309) 674 304 – mtb@clunybankhotel.co.uk – Fax (01309) 671 400 – Closed 2 weeks January
8 rm ☐ – †£ 75/85 ††£ 140 – **Rest** – (dinner only) Carte £ 22/33 **s**
◆ Personally run 19C listed house, nestling beneath Cluny Hill. Extended in 1910, it boasts antiques, oak staircase, original floor tiling and simple, pleasant, airy bedrooms. Dining room features much work by local artist.

at Dyke West : 3 ¾ m. by A 96 – ✉ **Forres**

The Old Kirk without rest
Northeast : ½ m. ✉ IV36 2TL – ☎ (01309) 641 414 – oldkirk@gmx.net
3 rm ☐ – †£ 40/45 ††£ 60/66
◆ Former 19C church in country location. Stained glass window in first floor lounge; wood furnished breakfast room. Pleasantly furnished bedrooms with original stonework.

FORT WILLIAM – Highland – 501 E 13 – pop. 9 908 *Scotland* 30 C3

Edinburgh 133 m – Glasgow 104 m – Inverness 68 m – Oban 50 m
Cameron Sq ☎ (01397) 703781
North Rd, ☎ (01397) 704 464 .
Town★
The Road to the Isles★★ (Neptune's Staircase (≤ ★★), Glenfinnan★ ≤ ★, Arisaig★, Silver Sands of Morar★, Mallaig★), NW : 46 m. by A 830 – Ardnamurchan Peninsula★★ - Ardnamurchan Point (≤ ★★), NW : 65 m. by A 830, A 861 and B 8007 - SE : Ben Nevis★★ (≤ ★★) - Glen Nevis★

Inverlochy Castle ≤ loch and mountains,
Torlundy, Northeast : 3 m. on A 82 ✉ PH33 6SN – ☎ (01397) 702 177 – info@inverlochy.co.uk – Fax (01397) 702 953
17 rm ☐ – †£ 250/490 ††£ 450/550 – 1 suite – **Rest** – (booking essential for non-residents) Menu £ 35/65
Spec. Lobster and cauliflower salad, yoghurt beignets, bisque mousseline. Herb poached veal, boudin blanc and voilet artichoke. Apple trifle, apple filled doughnuts.
◆ Victorian castle in extensive parkland with beautiful gardens, panoramic views and luxurious, antique-filled interior. Great Hall sets the tone. Sumptuous bedrooms. Cooking has classical roots with original, modern touches and uses top quality, Scottish produce.

Distillery House without rest
Nevis Bridge, North Rd ✉ PH33 6LR – ☎ (01397) 700 103 – disthouse@aol.com – Fax (01397) 702 980
10 rm ☐ – †£ 30/45 ††£ 56/92
◆ Conveniently located a short walk from the centre of town, formerly part of Glenlochy distillery. Cosy guests' lounge and comfortable rooms, some with views of Ben Nevis.

The Grange without rest
Grange Rd, South : ¾ m. by A 82 and Ashburn Lane ✉ PH33 6JF – ☎ (01397) 705 516 – info@grangefortwilliam.com – March-October
4 rm ☐ – †£ 90/100 ††£ 98/110
◆ Large Victorian house with attractive garden, in an elevated position in a quiet residential part of town. Very comfortable and tastefully furnished with many antiques.

Crolinnhe without rest
Grange Rd, South : ¾ m. by A 82 and Ashburn Lane ✉ PH33 6JF – ☎ (01397) 702 709 – crolinnhe@yahoo.com – Easter-October
3 rm ☐ – ††£ 130
◆ Very comfortably and attractively furnished Victorian house, run with a real personal touch. Relaxing guests' sitting room and well furnished bedrooms.

SCOTLAND

Lochan Cottage without rest

Lochyside, North : 2½ m. by A 82, A 830 on B 8006 ✉ PH33 7NX – ✆ (01397) 702 695 – lochanco@btopenworld.com – February-October

6 rm – ††£ 52/60

◆ Spotlessly kept, whitewashed cottage with homely public areas. Breakfast taken in conservatory overlooking delightfully landscaped gardens. Neat, well-kept rooms.

Ashburn House without rest

18 Achintore Rd, South : ½ m. on A 82 ✉ PH33 6RQ – ✆ (01397) 706 000 – christine@no-1.fsworld.co.uk – Fax (01397) 702 024 – Closed Christmas

7 rm – †£ 45/55 ††£ 90/110

◆ Attractive Victorian house overlooking Loch Linnhe, on the main road into town which is a short walk away. Well furnished bedrooms and a comfortable conservatory lounge.

Lawriestone without rest

Achintore Rd, South : ½ m. on A 82 ✉ PH33 6RQ – ✆ (01397) 700 777 – susan@lawriestone.co.uk – Fax (01397) 700 777 – closed 25-26 December and 1-2 January

5 rm – †£ 60/90 ††£ 60/90

◆ Victorian house overlooking Loch Linnhe; not far from town centre, ideal for touring Western Highlands. Especially proud of Scottish breakfasts. Airy rooms; some with views.

SCOTLAND

Lime Tree An Ealdhain with rm

Achintore Rd ✉ PH33 6RQ – ✆ (01397) 701 806 – info@limetreefortwilliam.co.uk – Fax (01397) 701 806

9 rm – †£ 66/99 ††£ 88/110 – **Rest** – Carte £ 24/30

◆ Restaurant, art gallery and hotel in one, with comfy, contemporary lounges, popular decked terrace and rustic dining area. Daily-changing menu; Scottish/Mediterranean dishes. Stylish bedrooms; some with Loch views.

Crannog Loch Linnhe,

Town Pier ✉ PH33 6DB – ✆ (01397) 705 589 – olivia@crannog.net – Fax (01397) 708 666 – Closed dinner 24 December, 25 December and 1 January

Rest – Seafood (booking essential) Carte £ 23/34

◆ Lochside dining on Fort William town pier; choose a window table for the view. Interior of bright reds and yellows with some Celtic artwork. Locally sourced seafood dishes.

at Banavie North : 3 m. by A 82 and A 830 on B 8004 – ✉ Fort William

Moorings

✉ PH33 7LY – ✆ (01397) 772 797 – reservations@moorings-fortwilliam.co.uk – Fax (01397) 772 441 – closed 26 December

27 rm – †£ 84/106 ††£ 114/142 – **Rest** – (bar lunch) Carte £ 14/34 **s**

◆ Modern accommodation in traditional style. Adjacent to Caledonian Canal and at start of "Road to the Isles". Most rooms boast views of mountains and Neptune's Staircase. Meals served in panelled lounge bar with views of Ben Nevis.

FORT AUGUSTUS

30 **C3**

Lovat Arms rm,

✉ PH32 4DU – ✆ (01456) 459 250 – info@lovatarms-hotel.com – Fax (01320) 366 677

29 rm – †£ 60/105 ††£ 180/250 – **Rest** – (dinner only) Carte £ 18/37

◆ Professionally run, refurbished 19C hotel at southern end of Loch Ness. Superb bedrooms; the largest have traditional furnishings; those on 2nd floor more contemporary in style. Simple dishes, created using quality ingredients.

FORTINGALL Perth. and Kinross – **501** H 14 – see ABERFELDY

FORTROSE Highland – Highland – **501** H 11 – **pop. 1 174** 30 **C2**

London 574 m – Edinburgh 168 m – Inverness 14 m – Nairn 27 m

Water's Edge without rest Moray Firth,
Canonbury Terrace, on A 832 ✉ IV10 8TT – ✆ (01381) 621 202 – gill@watersedge.uk.com – Fax (08704) 296 806 – March-November
3 rm – £ 70 £ 110/115
◆ Charming guest house in fishing village boasts excellent comforts. Bedrooms have French windows onto terrace. Lounge with brick fire, large oak table and stunning views.

GALSON – **Western Isles Outer Hebrides – 501** A 8 – **see Lewis and Harris (Isle of)**

GATEHOUSE OF FLEET – **Dumfries and Galloway – 501** H 19 – **pop. 919** 25 **B3**

Edinburgh 113 m – Dumfries 33 m – Stranraer 42 m
Car Park ✆ (01557) 814212 (Easter-October)
Gatehouse InnisfreeCastle Douglas, ✆ (01557) 814766 .

Cally Palace
East : ½ m. on B 727 ✉ DG7 2DL – ✆ (01557) 814341 – info@callypalace.co.uk – Fax (01557) 814522 – Closed February except weekends and January
50 rm (dinner included) – £ 97/125 £ 184/196 – 5 suites –
Rest – Menu £ 30 (dinner) – Carte lunch £ 15/22
◆ Highly impressive 18C mansion with golf course. Sitting room with fantastically ornate ceiling of original gilding. Small leisure centre. Large rooms with delightful views. Elegant dining room serving Galloway produce. Pianist in attendance.

Red = Pleasant. Look for the red and symbols.

GATTONSIDE – **Borders – see Melrose**

GIGHA (Isle of) – **Argyll and Bute – 501** C 16 27 **A3**

Edinburgh 168 m
to Tayinloan (Caledonian MacBrayne Ltd) 8-10 daily (20 mn)

Gigha Sound of Gigha and Kintyre Peninsula,
✉ PA41 7AA – ✆ (01583) 505 254 – hotel@gigha.org.uk – Fax (01583) 505 244 – Closed 25 December
13 rm – £ 35/55 £ 60/91 – **Rest** – (bar lunch) (booking essential for non-residents) Carte £ 14/28
◆ 18C whitewashed house on island owned by residents; views over Ardminish Bay to Kintyre. Cosy pine-panelled bar. Elegant lounge. Simple, clean and tidy rooms. Inviting restaurant with exposed stone walls and pine tables.

GLAMIS – **Angus – 501** K/L 14 – ✉ **Forfar** 28 **C2**

Edinburgh 69 m – Dundee 13 m – Forfar 7 m
Town★ – Castle★★
Meigle Museum★ **AC** W : 7 m. by A 94

Castleton House
West : 3 ¼ m. on A 94 ✉ DD8 1SJ – ✆ (01307) 840 340 – hotel@castletonglamis.co.uk – Fax (01307) 840 506
6 rm – £ 130/150 £ 200/240
Rest *The Conservatory* – Menu £ 40 (dinner) **s** – Carte lunch £ 15/28 **s**
◆ Moat still visible in gardens of this 20C country house built on site of medieval fortress. Appealing lounges, cosy bar. Individually designed, attractively appointed rooms. Stylish conservatory restaurant looks out to garden.

O. Forir/MICHELIN

GLASGOW

County: Glasgow
Michelin REGIONAL map: n° **501** H 16
▶ Edinburgh 46 m – Manchester 221 m

Population: 624 501
Scotland

25 **B1**

PRACTICAL INFORMATION

Tourist Information

11 George Sq ✆ (0141) 204 4400, enquiries@seeglasgow.com

Glasgow Airport, Tourist Information Desk ✆ (0141) 848 4440

Airports

Glasgow Airport: ✆ (0870) 0400008, W: 8 m. by M 8, AV

Access to Oban by helicopter

Golf courses

18 Littlehill Auchinairn Rd, ✆ (0141) 772 1916 ;

18 Rouken Glen Thornlibank Stewarton Rd, ✆ (0141) 638 7044 ;

18 Linn Park Simshill Rd, ✆ (0141) 633 0377 ; Lethamhill Cumbernauld Rd, ✆ (0141) 770 6220 ;

9 Alexandra Park Dennistoun, ✆ (0141) 556 1294 ;

9 King's Park Croftfoot 150a Croftpark Ave, ✆ (0141) 630 1597 ;

9 Knightswood Lincoln Ave, ✆ (0141) 959 6358 ;

9 Ruchill Park Brassey St, ✆ (0141) 946 7676.

SCOTLAND

SIGHTS

IN TOWN

City★★★ – Cathedral★★★ (⩽ ★) DZ - The Burrell Collection★★★ AX M1 – Hunterian Art Gallery★★ (Whistler Collection★★★ - Mackintosh Wing★★★) AC CY M4 – Museum of Transport★★ (Scottish Built Cars★★★, The Clyde Room of Ship Models★★★) AV M6 – Art Gallery and Museum Kelvingrove★★ CY – Pollok House★ (The Paintings★★) AX D – Tolbooth Steeple★ DZ - Hunterian Museum (Coin and Medal Collection★) CY M5 – City Chambers★ DZ C – Glasgow School of Art★ AC CY M3 – Necropolis (⩽ ★ of Cathedral) DYZ – Gallery of Modern Art★ – Glasgow (National) Science Centre★, Pacific Quay AV

ON THE OUTSKIRTS

Paisley Museum and Art Gallery (Paisley Shawl Section★), W: 4 m. by M 8 AV

IN THE SURROUNDING AREA

The Trossachs★★★, N: 31 m. by A 879 - BV -, A 81 and A 821 – Loch Lomond★★, NW: 19 m. by A 82 AV – New Lanark★★, SE: 20 m. by M 74 and A 72 BX

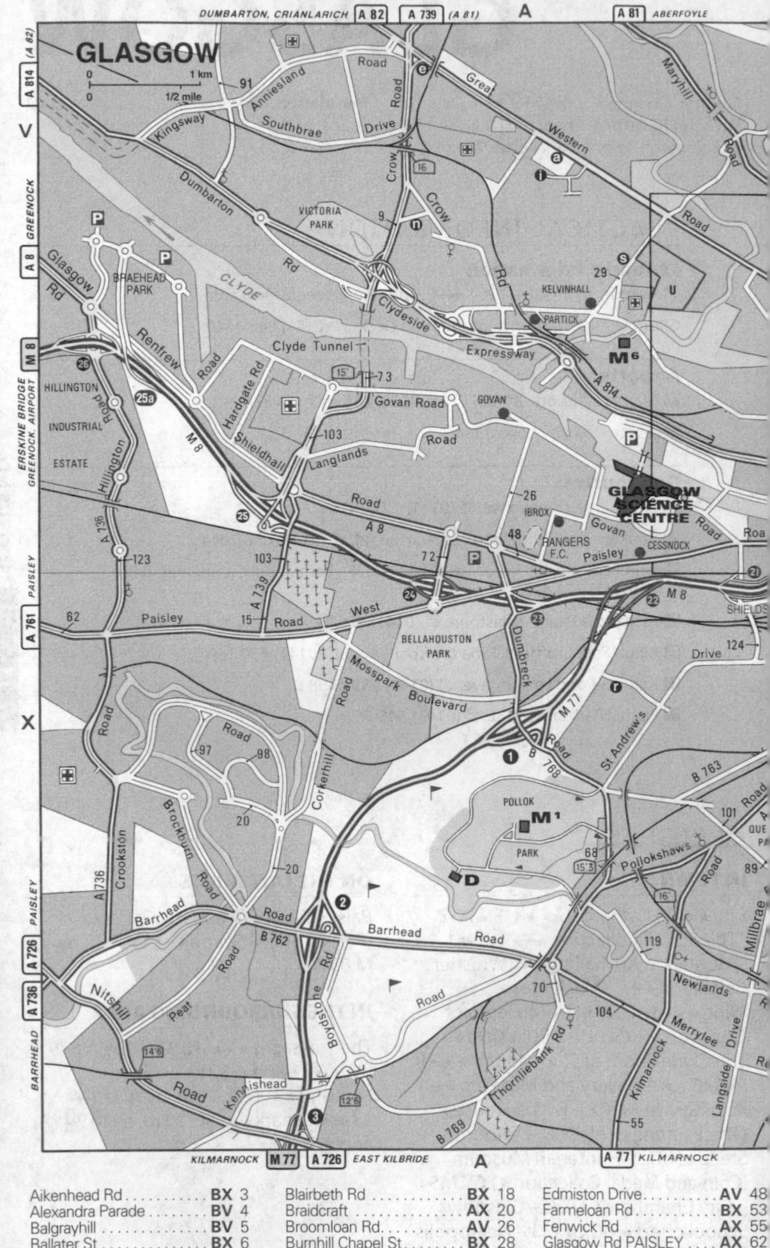

Aikenhead Rd . . . . **BX** 3
Alexandra Parade . . . . **BV** 4
Balgrayhill . . . . **BV** 5
Ballater St . . . . **BX** 6
Balornock Rd . . . . **BV** 8
Balshagray Ave. . . . . **AV** 9
Battlefield Rd . . . . **BX** 12
Berryknowes Rd . . . . **AX** 15
Bilsland Drive . . . . **BV** 16
Blairbeth Rd . . . . **BX** 18
Braidcraft . . . . **AX** 20
Broomloan Rd. . . . . **AV** 26
Burnhill Chapel St. . . . . **BX** 28
Byres Rd . . . . **AV** 29
Caledonia Rd . . . . **BX** 30
Carmunnock Rd . . . . **BX** 33
Cook St . . . . **BV** 38
Cumbernauld Rd . . . . **BV** 40
Edmiston Drive. . . . . **AV** 48
Farmeloan Rd . . . . **BX** 53
Fenwick Rd . . . . **AX** 55
Glasgow Rd PAISLEY . . . . . **AX** 62
Gorbals St . . . . **BX** 63
Grange Rd. . . . . **BX** 67
Haggs Rd . . . . **AX** 68
Harriet St. . . . . **AX** 70
Helen St . . . . **AV** 72

A 803 KIRKINTILLOCH
B
BISHOPBRIGGS
A 879
Balmore
Road
16
SPRINGBURN PARK
Road
8
88
Wallacewell
Rd
B 765
Saughs
Rd
M 80
STIRLING
A 80
Broomfield Rd
118
Keppochhill
Rd
Petershill
Road
Royston
Road
Pinkston
Springburn
Ring
Road
Rd
Royston
See following pages
M 8
14
13
12
40
114
9
ALEXANDRA PARK
A 8
4
Edinburgh Road
Road
EDINBURGH
B 765
18
V
Inner
Duke
Street
40
131
Carntyne
Carntynehall
Cardowan
Rd
Road
(M 74, M 8)
THE FORGE SHOPPING CENTRE
A 89
Gallowgate
London
Rd
Shettleston
Road
A 89
138
Tollcross
GLASGOW
GREEN
A 74 Rd
B 763
CELTIC F.C.
POL.
Road
38
63
WEST ST.
6
75
A 74
83
79
Main St.
Dalmarnock
Springfield
TOLLCROSS PARK
London
Rd
30
Eglinton St.
A 749
Rutherglen
RICHMOND PARK
A 749
Road
CARLISLE
A 74
M 74
Victoria Rd
Road
3
Calder St.
Allison St.
Road
Glasgow
A 730
Road
CLYDE
Cambuslang
QUEEN'S PARK
90
A 728
Cathcart
112
136
53
67
B 768
28
112
Main
Street
Rd
12
HAMPDEN PARK (M)
84
RUTHERGLEN
Mill
Stonelaw
X
74
King's
3
Park
Avenue
B 762
Street
Road
Road
B 762
Glasgow
Rd
A 724
Duke's
Brownside
Road
HAMILTON
Clarkston Rd
33
3
KING'S PARK
9
A 730
18
East Kilbride Road
Croftfoot
Road
33
B 766
18
B
EAST-KILBRIDE
A 749

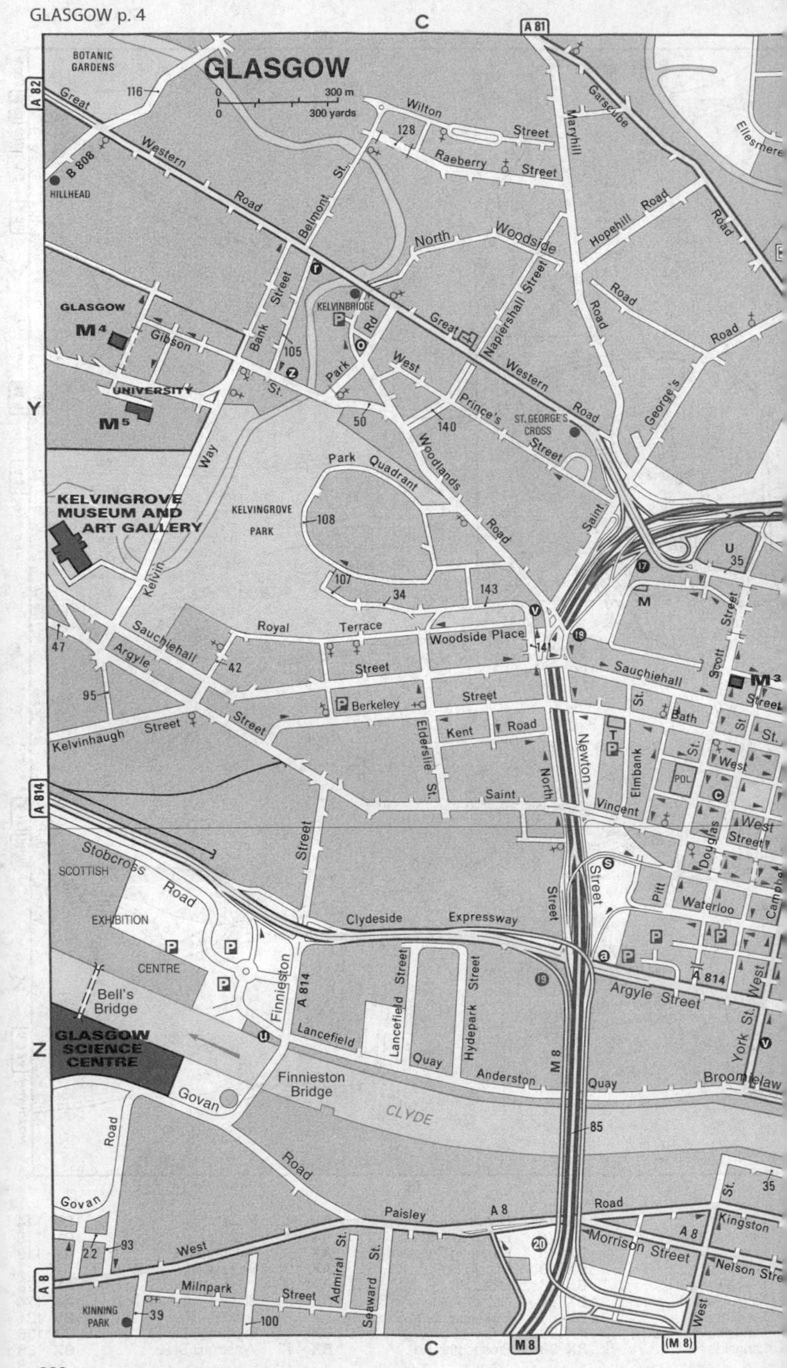
C
A 81
GLASGOW
300 m
300 yards
BOTANIC GARDENS
A 82
Great Western Road
B 808
HILLHEAD
Wilton Street
Raeberry Street
Belmont St.
North Woodside
Maryhill Road
Garscube Road
Hopehill Road
Ellesmere
Napiershall Street
GLASGOW M4
Gibson St.
Bank Street
KELVINBRIDGE
Park Rd
West Prince's Street
UNIVERSITY M5
ST. GEORGE'S CROSS
St. George's Road
Y
Park Quadrant
Woodlands Road
KELVINGROVE MUSEUM AND ART GALLERY
KELVINGROVE PARK
Kelvin Way
Saint
Royal Terrace
Woodside Place
Sauchiehall Street
Argyle Street
Berkeley Street
Kent Road
Kelvinhaugh Street
Elderslie St.
North Street
Newton Street
Scott Street
Bath St.
West St.
Elmbank St.
POL.
Vincent St.
West Street
Douglas St.
Pitt St.
Waterloo
Campbell
A 814
Stobcross Road
SCOTTISH EXHIBITION CENTRE
Clydeside Expressway
Finnieston Street
Lancefield Street
Hydepark Street
Lancefield Quay
Anderston Quay
Bell's Bridge
GLASGOW SCIENCE CENTRE
Z
Finnieston Bridge
Govan Road
CLYDE
M 8
Quay
Broomielaw
York St.
West St.
Paisley Road West
A 8
Morrison Street
Kingston St.
Nelson Street
Milnpark Street
Admiral St.
Seaward St.
KINNING PARK
(M 8)
116 128 105 50 140 108 107 34 143 141 47 42 95 35 85 93 22 39 100

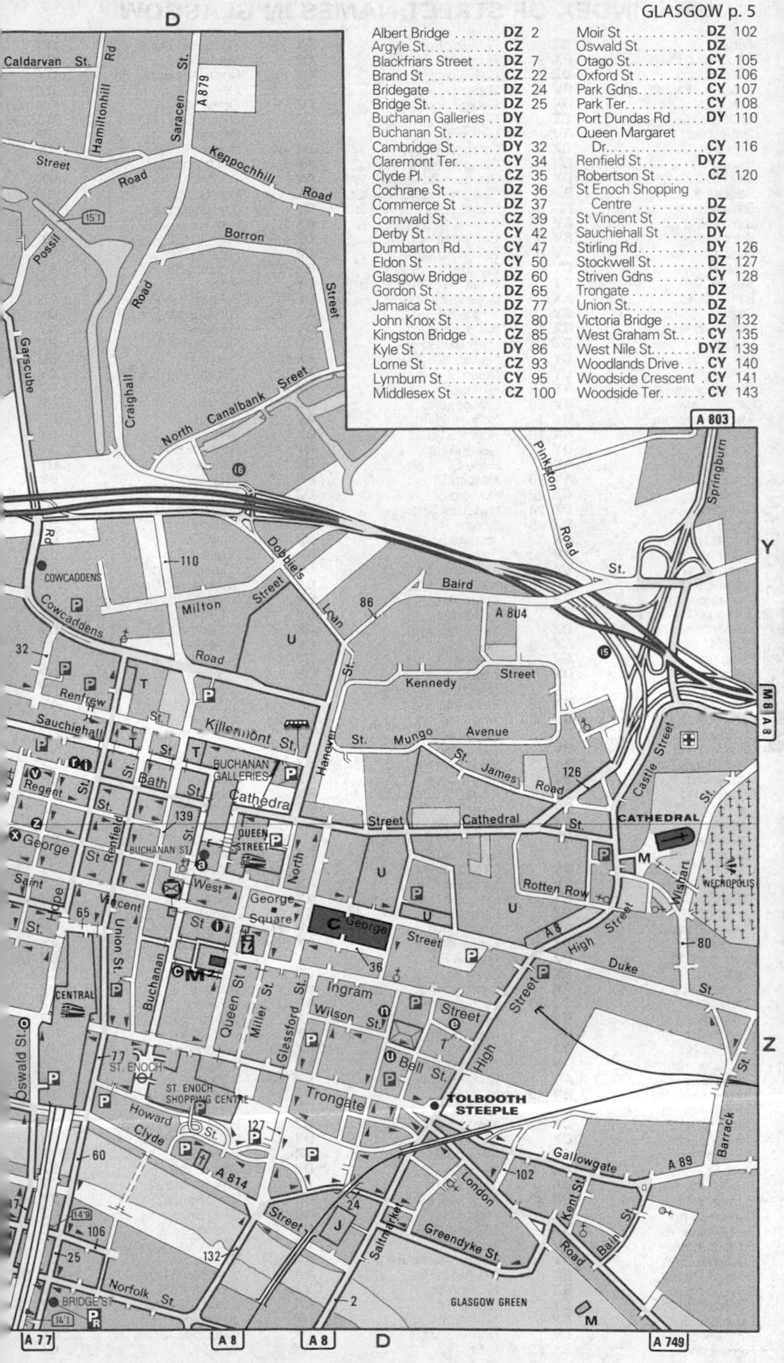

Street	Grid	No.
Albert Bridge	**DZ**	2
Argyle St	**CZ**	
Blackfriars Street	**DZ**	7
Brand St	**CZ**	22
Bridegate	**DZ**	24
Bridge St	**DZ**	25
Buchanan Galleries	**DY**	
Buchanan St	**DZ**	
Cambridge St	**DY**	32
Claremont Ter	**CY**	34
Clyde Pl.	**CZ**	35
Cochrane St	**DZ**	36
Commerce St	**DZ**	37
Cornwald St	**CZ**	39
Derby St	**CY**	42
Dumbarton Rd	**CY**	47
Eldon St	**CY**	50
Glasgow Bridge	**DZ**	60
Gordon St	**DZ**	65
Jamaica St	**DZ**	77
John Knox St	**DZ**	80
Kingston Bridge	**CZ**	85
Kyle St	**DY**	86
Lorne St	**CZ**	93
Lymburn St	**CY**	95
Middlesex St	**CZ**	100
Moir St	**DZ**	102
Oswald St	**DZ**	
Otago St	**CY**	105
Oxford St	**DZ**	106
Park Gdns	**CY**	107
Park Ter	**CY**	108
Port Dundas Rd	**DY**	110
Queen Margaret Dr.	**CY**	116
Renfield St	**DYZ**	
Robertson St	**CZ**	120
St Enoch Shopping Centre	**DZ**	
St Vincent St	**DZ**	
Sauchiehall St	**DY**	
Stirling Rd	**DY**	126
Stockwell St	**DZ**	127
Striven Gdns	**CY**	128
Trongate	**DZ**	
Union St	**DZ**	
Victoria Bridge	**DZ**	132
West Graham St	**CY**	135
West Nile St	**DYZ**	139
Woodlands Drive	**CY**	140
Woodside Crescent	**CY**	141
Woodside Ter	**CY**	143

INDEX OF STREET NAMES IN GLASGOW

SCOTLAND

Hotel du Vin at One Devonshire Gardens

1 Devonshire Gardens ✉ G12 0UX
– ☎ (0141) 339 2001 – Fax (0141) 337 1663 AV **a**
45 rm – ♦£ 140/305 ♦♦£ 140/305, ☕ £17 – 4 suites
Rest *Bistro* – (Closed Saturday lunch) Menu £ 18 (lunch) – Carte £ 36/53
◆ Collection of adjoining 19C houses in terrace, refurbished with attention to detail. Warm, intimate and comfortable bedrooms are named after wines. High levels of service. Smart Bistro offers classic grill menu as well as more innovative carte.

Radisson SAS

301 Argyle St ✉ G2 8DL – ☎ (0141) 204 3333
– reservations.glasgow@radissonsas.com – Fax (0141) 204 3344 DZ **o**
246 rm – ♦£ 149/200 ♦♦£ 149/200, ☕ £16 – 1 suite
Rest *Collage* – Mediterranean (Closed Sunday lunch) Menu £ 15 – Carte £ 23/34
Rest *TaPaell'Ya* – Tapas (Closed Sunday) Carte £ 21/31
◆ A stunning, angular, modish exterior greets visitors to this consummate, modern commercial hotel. Large, stylish, eclectically furnished bedrooms. Collage is a bright modern restaurant. Ta Paell'Ya serves tapas.

Hilton Glasgow

1 William St ✉ G3 8HT – ☎ (0141) 204 5555
– reservations.glasgow@hilton.com – Fax (0141) 204 5004 CZ **s**
317 rm – ♦£ 97/210 ♦♦£ 97/210, ☕ £17.95 – 2 suites
Rest *Camerons* – (Closed Saturday lunch and Sunday) Carte £ 29/40
Rest *Minsky's* – Buffet Menu £ 15/25
◆ A city centre tower with impressive views on every side. Comfortable, comprehensively fitted rooms. Extensive leisure and conference facilities. Spacious, modern Minsky's has the style of a New York deli. Contemporary cuisine served in formal Camerons.

SCOTLAND

Malmaison

278 West George St ✉ G2 4LL – ☎ (0141) 572 1000 – glasgow@malmaison.com
– Fax (0141) 572 1002 CY **c**
68 rm – ♦£ 180 ♦♦£ 240, ☕ £13.95 – 4 suites
Rest *The Brasserie* – Menu £ 15 – Carte £ 32/41
◆ Visually arresting former Masonic chapel. Comfortable, well-proportioned rooms seem effortlessly stylish with bold patterns and colours and thoughtful extra attentions. Informal Brasserie with French themed menu and Champagne bar.

Abode Glasgow

129 Bath St ✉ G2 2SZ – ☎ (0141) 221 6789
– reservationsglasgow@abodehotels.co.uk – Fax (0141) 221 6777 – Closed 1-2 January DY **v**
60 rm – ♦£ 125 ♦♦£ 225, ☕ £13
Rest *Michael Caines* – see restaurant listing
Rest *Cafe Bar* – Carte £ 16/31
◆ Near Mackintosh's School of Art, an early 20C building decorated with a daring modern palette: striking colour schemes and lighting in the spacious, elegantly fitted rooms. All-day dining in stylish Café Bar.

Glasgow Marriott

500 Argyle St, Anderston ✉ G3 8RR – ☎ (0141) 226 5577
– frontdesk.glasgow@marriotthotels.co.uk – Fax (0141) 221 9202 CZ **a**
302 rm – ♦£ 119/175 ♦♦£ 119/245, ☕ £14.95 – **Rest** – Mediterranean (dinner only) Carte £ 25/36 **s**
◆ Internationally owned city centre hotel with every necessary convenience for working travellers and an extensive lounge and café-bar. Upper floors have views of the city. Strong Mediterranean feel infuses restaurant.

Carlton George

44 West George St ✉ G2 1DH – ✆ (0141) 353 6373 – resgeorge@carltonhotels.co.uk – Fax (0141) 353 6263 – Closed 24-26 December and 1-2 January DZ **a**

64 rm – †£ 175 ††£ 175, ☕ £14

Rest *Windows* – Menu £ 18/24 – Carte diner £ 24/30

◆ A quiet oasis away from the city bustle. Attractive tartan decorated bedrooms bestow warm tidings. Comfortable 7th floor business lounge. An overall traditional ambience. Ask for restaurant table with excellent view across city's rooftops.

Sherbrooke Castle

11 Sherbrooke Ave, Pollokshields ✉ G41 4PG – ✆ (0141) 427 4227 – mail@sherbrooke.co.uk – Fax (0141) 427 5685 AX **r**

16 rm ☕ – †£ 95 ††£ 125 – 2 suites

Rest *Morrisons* – Carte £ 22/32

◆ Late 19C baronial Romanticism given free rein inside and out. The hall is richly furnished and imposing; rooms in the old castle have a comfortable country house refinement. Panelled Victorian dining room with open fire.

City Inn

Finnieston Quay ✉ G3 8HN – ✆ (0141) 240 1002 – glasgow.reservations@cityinn.com – Fax (0141) 248 2754 – closed 24-25 December CZ **u**

164 rm – †£ 69/169 ††£ 69/169, ☕ £ 12.50 – **Rest** – Menu £ 15/17 – Carte £ 26/36

◆ Quayside location and views of the Clyde. Well priced hotel with a "business-friendly" ethos; neatly maintained modern rooms with sofas and en suite power showers. Restaurant fronts waterside terrace.

Marks

110 Bath St ✉ G2 2EN – ✆ (0141) 353 0800 – reservations@markshotels.com – Fax (0141) 353 0900 – Closed 23-26 December DY **r**

102 rm – †£ 89/109 ††£ 89/109, ☕ £ 10 – 1 suite

Rest *One Ten Bar & Grill* – Carte £ 24/28 **s**

◆ In the middle of Glasgow's shopping streets, with fashionable front bar. Modern bedrooms have bold fushia print wallpaper; mezzanine suites are worth the upgrade. Contemporary dining room with booth seating.

Park House without rest

13 Victoria Park Gardens South ✉ G11 7BX – ✆ (0141) 339 1559 – mail@parkhouseglasgow.co.uk – closed 2 weeks spring, Christmas and New Year AV **n**

3 rm ☕ – †£ 45/55 ††£ 70/80

◆ An extensive, smartly kept suburban house retaining much of its Victorian character. Comfortable, classically stylish bedrooms combine period furniture with CD systems.

The Town House without rest

4 Hughenden Terrace ✉ G12 9XR – ✆ (0141) 357 0862 – hospitality@thetownhouseglasgow.com – Fax (0141) 339 9605 AV **i**

10 rm ☕ – †£ 60 ††£ 72

◆ Elegant, personally run town house with fine Victorian plasterwork: spacious, pleasantly decorated rooms and an inviting firelit lounge. Hearty breakfasts.

Rococo

202 West George St ✉ G2 2NR – ✆ (0141) 221 5004 – info@rococoglasgow.co.uk – Fax (0141) 221 5006 DYZ **z**

Rest – Menu £ 20/42 – Carte lunch £ 21/31

◆ In style, more like studied avant-garde: stark, white-walled cellar with vibrant modern art and high-backed leather chairs. Accomplished, fully flavoured contemporary menu.

SCOTLAND

XXX **Lux**

1051 Great Western Rd ✉ G12 0XP – ✆ (0141) 576 7576 – enquiries@luxstazione.co.uk – Fax (0141) 576 0162 – Closed 25-26 December, 1-2 January and Sunday AV **e**

Rest – (dinner only) Menu £ 34

◆ 19C railway station converted with clean-lined elegance: dark wood, subtle lighting and vivid blue banquettes. Fine service and flavourful, well-prepared modern menus.

XXX **Brian Maule at Chardon d'Or**

176 West Regent St ✉ G2 4RL – ✆ (0141) 248 3801 – info@brianmaule.com – Fax (0141) 248 3901 – Closed 2 weeks January, 2 weeks July-August, 25 December, Saturday lunch, Sunday and Bank Holidays CY **i**

Rest – Menu £ 19 (lunch) – Carte £ 34/46

◆ Large pillared Georgian building. Airy refurbished interior with ornate carved ceiling. Classical French cooking made with fine Scottish produce. Function rooms in basement.

XXX **Rogano**

11 Exchange Place ✉ G1 3AN – ✆ (0141) 248 4055 – rogano@btconnect.com – Closed 25 December and 1 January DZ **C**

Rest – Seafood specialities Menu £ 23/45 – Carte £ 33/67

◆ Long-standing Glasgow institution; art deco, with original panelling, stained glass windows and etched mirrors. Classic menus lean towards local seafood. Table 16 most popular.

XX **Michael Caines** – at Abode Glasgow H.

129 Bath St ✉ G2 2SZ – ✆ (0141) 572 6011 – Closed Sunday DY **v**

Rest – Menu £ 18 (lunch) **s** – Carte £ 35/47 **s**

◆ Smart, stylish restaurant in boutique hotel, a mirrored wall creating impression of size. Quality décor matched by clean, unfussy cooking prepared with finesse and skill.

XX **Urban**

23-25 St Vincent Place ✉ G1 2DT – ✆ (0141) 248 5636 – info@urbanbrasserie.co.uk – Closed 1-2 January and 25 26 December dz **l**

Rest – Menu £ 15 – Carte £ 19/36

◆ Imposing 19C building in heart of city centre. Stylish, modern interior with individual booths and illuminated glass ceiling. Modern English cooking. Live piano at weekends.

XX **Manna**

104 Bath St ✉ G2 2EN – ✆ (0141) 332 6678 – info@mannarestaurant.co.uk – Fax (0141) 332 6549 – Closed 25-26 December, 1-2 January and Sunday lunch DY **i**

Rest – Menu £ 13 (lunch) – Carte £ 21/35

◆ Parrot motifs recur everywhere, even on the door handles! Well-spaced tables and mirrored walls add a sense of space to the basement. A free-ranging fusion style prevails.

XX **Gamba**

225a West George St ✉ G2 2ND – ✆ (0141) 572 0899 – info@gamba.co.uk – Fax (0141) 572 0896 – Closed 25-26 December, 1-2 January and Sunday lunch DZ **x**

Rest – Seafood Menu £ 16 (lunch) – Carte £ 26/44

◆ Seafood specialists: an enterprising diversity of influences and well-priced lunches. Compact, brightly decorated basement in hot terracotta with a pleasant cosy bar.

XX **La Parmigiana**

447 Great Western Rd, Kelvinbridge ✉ G12 8HH – ✆ (0141) 334 0686 – s.giovanazzi@btclick.com – Fax (0141) 357 5595 – closed 25-26 December, 1-2 January and Sunday CY **r**

Rest – Italian (booking essential) Menu £ 12 (lunch) – Carte £ 24/38 **s**

◆ Compact, pleasantly decorated traditional eatery with a lively atmosphere and good local reputation. Obliging, professional service and a sound, authentic Italian repertoire.

SCOTLAND

XX **Ho Wong**

82 York St ✉ G2 8LE – ☎ (0141) 221 3550 – ho.wong@amserve.com – Fax (0141) 248 5330 – Closed Chinese New Year CZ **v**

Rest – Chinese Menu £ 10/29 – Carte approx. £ 23

◆ In an up-and-coming part of town, a long-established restaurant with a modern style. Authentic Chinese cuisine with the emphasis on Peking dishes.

XX **Shish Mahal**

60-68 Park Rd ✉ G4 9JF – ☎ (0141) 339 82 56 – reservations@shishmahal.co.uk – Fax (0141) 572 0800 – Closed 25 December and Sunday lunch CY **o**

Rest – Indian Carte £ 12/21

◆ Tandoori specialities in a varied pan-Indian menu, attentive service and an evocative modern interior of etched glass, oak and Moorish tiles have won city-wide recognition.

X **The Dhabba**

44 Candleriggs ✉ G1 1LE – ☎ (0141) 553 1249 – info@thedhabba.com – Fax (0141) 553 1730 – Closed 25 December and 1 January DZ **u**

Rest – Indian Menu £ 10 (lunch) – Carte £ 23/33

◆ In the heart of the Merchant City, this large, modern restaurant boasts bold colours and huge wall photos. Concentrates on authentic, accomplished North Indian cooking.

SCOTLAND

X **Stravaigin**

28 Gibson St, (basement) ✉ G12 8NX – ☎ (0141) 334 2665 – stravaigin@btinternet.com – Fax (0141) 334 4099 – Closed 25 December, 1 January and lunch Monday-Wednesday CY **z**

Rest – Menu £ 14 (lunch) – Carte £ 25/38

◆ Basement restaurant with bright murals. A refined instinct for genuinely global cuisine produces surprising but well-prepared combinations - ask about pre-theatre menus.

X **Stravaigin 2**

8 Ruthven Lane, off Byres Rd ✉ G12 9BG – ☎ (0141) 334 7165 – stravaigin2@btinternet.com – Fax (0141) 357 4785 – Closed 25 December and 1 January AV **s**

Rest – Carte £ 16/32

◆ Lilac painted cottage tucked away in an alley off Byres Road. Simple, unfussy, modern bistro-style interior. Contemporary menu offering eclectic range of original dishes.

X **Dakhin**

First Floor, 89 Candleriggs ✉ G1 1NP – ☎ (0141) 553 2585 – info@dakhin.com – Fax (0141) 553 2492 – Closed 25 December and 1 January DZ **n**

Rest – South Indian Menu £ 10 – Carte £ 23/33

◆ Large open plan first floor restaurant in redeveloped area of city serving authentic, flavoursome South Indian cooking. Friendly, informal atmosphere; knowledgable service.

Babbity Bowster

16-18 Blackfriars St ✉ G1 1PE – ☎ (0141) 552 5055 – Fax (0141) 552 7774 – Closed 25 December DZ **e**

Rest – Carte £ 13/26

◆ Well regarded pub of Georgian origins with columned façade. Paradoxically simple ambience: gingham-clothed tables, hearty Scottish dishes, slightly more formal in evenings.

at Eurocentral East : 12 m. by M 8 off A 8 – ✉ Glasgow

Dakota rm,

✉ ML1 4WJ – ☎ (0870) 220 82 81 – info@dakotaeurocentral.co.uk – Fax (01698) 835 445

92 rm – †£ 89 ††£ 89

Rest ***Grill*** – Carte £ 20/34

◆ Stylish, modern hotel with sleek, masculine feel. Well-thought out bedrooms have king-sized beds and plasma TVs. Comfortable lounge popular for afternoon tea. Open plan bar and grill offers good selection of modern cooking.

GLENDALE – Highland – see Skye (Isle of)

GLENDEVON – Perth and Kinross – 501 I/J 15 28 C2

Edinburgh 37 m – Perth 26 m – Stirling 19 m

Tormaukin Country Inn with rm

FK14 7JY – (01259) 781 252 – enquiries@tormaukin.co.uk – Fax (01259) 781 526 – Closed 23-26 December

14 rm – £85 £120 – **Rest** – Menu £14/20 – Carte £18/50

◆ Extended 18C drovers' inn tucked away in this picturesque glen. Traditional Scottish fare is served in the atmospheric bar or in the cosy restaurant. Comfortable bedrooms.

GLENROTHES – Fife – 501 K 15 – pop. 38 679 *Scotland* 28 C2

Edinburgh 33 m – Dundee 25 m – Stirling 36 m

18 Thornton Station Rd, (01592) 771 173 ;

18 Golf Course Rd, (01592) 758686 ;

18 Balbirnie Park Markinch, (01592) 612095 ;

9 Auchterderran Cardenden Woodend Rd, (01592) 721579 ;

9 Leslie Balsillie Laws, (01592) 620040 .

Falkland★ (Palace of Falkland★ AC, Gardens★ AC) N : 5½ m. by A 92 and A 912

Balbirnie House

Markinch, Northeast : 1 ¾ m. by A 911 and A 92 on B 9130 KY7 6NE – *(01592) 610066 – info@balbirnie.co.uk – Fax (01592) 610529*

28 rm – £135 £195 – 2 suites

Rest *Orangery* – Menu £18/37

Rest *Bistro* – Carte £15/24

◆ Highly imposing part Georgian mansion in Capability Brown-styled grounds. Several lounges and library bar with period style and individually furnished country house rooms. Glass-roofed restaurant; friendly service from kilted staff. Informal dining in the Bistro.

GRANTOWN-ON-SPEY – Highland – 501 J 12 – pop. 2 166 30 D2

Edinburgh 143 m – Inverness 34 m – Perth 99 m

54 High St (01479) 872773 (April-October)

18 Golf Course Rd, (01479) 872079 ;

9 Abernethy Nethy Bridge, (01479) 821 305.

Culdearn House

Woodlands Terrace PH26 3JU – *(01479) 872106 – enquiries@culdearn.com – Fax (01479) 873641 – Closed March*

7 rm – £88/92 £176/204 – **Rest** – (dinner only) (booking essential for non-residents) Menu £32 **s**

◆ Personally run Victorian granite stone hotel offering a high degree of luxury, including beautifully furnished drawing room and very tastefully furnished bedrooms. Formally attired dining room; good Scottish home cooking.

The Pines

Woodside Ave PH26 3JR – *(01479) 872092 – info@thepinesgrantown.co.uk – March-October*

7 rm (dinner included) – £95 £190 – **Rest** – (dinner only) (residents only, set menu only) Menu £33

◆ Top level hospitality in an attractive 19C house with lovely rear garden leading onto woods and Spey. Elegant lounges display fine pieces of art. Individually appointed rooms. Candlelit dinners, full of Scottish flavours, are a special event!

Ravenscourt House

Seafield Ave PH26 3JG – *(01479) 872286 – info@ravenscourthouse.co.uk*

8 rm – £50/60 £80/85 – **Rest** – (dinner only) (booking essential for non-residents) Menu £13 (lunch) – Carte dinner £13/27

◆ 19C former manse. Solid stone exterior. Interiors designed to enhance original house. Two comfortable drawing rooms; very welcoming, spacious bedrooms. Huge conservatory dining room with menu of locally sourced produce.

XX **The Glass House**

Grant Rd ✉ PH26 3LD – ☎ (01479) 872 980 – Fax (01479) 872 980 – Closed 25-26 December, 1-2 January, 2 weeks November, Sunday dinner, Monday and Tuesday lunch

Rest – Menu £ 14 (lunch) – Carte dinner £ 26/34

◆ Conservatory style dining in a house extension near the high street. Light-filled interior overlooks the garden. Amiable owner serves tasty, seasonal modern British dishes.

at Dulnain Bridge **Southwest : 3 m. by A 95 on A 938 – ✉ Grantown-on-Spey**

Muckrach Lodge

West : ½ m. on A 938 ✉ PH26 3LY – ☎ (01479) 851 257 – info@muckrach.co.uk – Fax (01479) 851 325

10 rm – †£ 60/110 ††£ 100/160 – 2 suites

Rest *Conservatory* – (dinner only) Carte £ 19/35

◆ 19C country house whose name translates as "haunt of the wild boar". Log fires and soft sofas in lounges. Bedrooms with fresh flowers and old books. Modern, original dining in Conservatory.

GRETNA GREEN – Dumfries and Galloway 26 **C3**

Edinburgh 88 m – Annan 10 m – Carlisle 11 m

Smiths

✉ DG16 5EA – ☎ (01461) 337 007 – info@gretnagreen.com

49 rm – †£ 115 ††£ 135 – 1 suite – **Rest** – Menu £ 21 (lunch) – Carte £ 26/35

◆ Family owned hotel near famous Blacksmiths Shop. Airy, open-plan lounge/bar. Rooms and suites are the strength - all are modern and well equipped: revolving bed in penthouse. Brasserie dishes in bright, spacious restaurant.

SCOTLAND

GRULINE – Argyll and Bute – see Mull (Isle of)

GULLANE – East Lothian – 501 L 15 – pop. 2 172 *Scotland* 26 **D1**

Edinburgh 19 m – North Berwick 5 m

Dirleton★ (Castle★) NE : 2 m. by A 198

Greywalls Gardens and Muirfield golf course,

Duncur Rd, Muirfield ✉ EH31 2EG – ☎ (01620) 842 144 – hotel@greywalls.co.uk – Fax (01620) 842 241 – Closed January-February

23 rm – †£ 140/285 ††£ 240/300 – **Rest** – (Closed lunch Monday-Thursday) (booking essential for non-residents) Menu £ 25/45

◆ Crescent shaped Edwardian country house by Lutyens; formal gardens by Jekyll. Superb views of Muirfield golf course. Beautifully kept sitting room. Charming, stylish rooms. Inviting dining room with warm, pretty country house style, view of golf course.

at Aberlady **Southwest : 1 1/2 m. on A 198 – pop. 873**

X **Duck's at Kilspindie House** with rm

Main St ✉ EH32 0RE – ☎ (01875) 870 682 – kilspindie@ducks.co.uk – Fax (01875) 870 504 – Accommodation closed 24-25 December

26 rm – †£ 50 ††£ 100 – **Rest** – Menu £ 18/28 – Carte £ 25/35

◆ Late 17C house in golfing capital of Scotland. Steaks, salmon and the like available in casual bar; more ambitious, seasonal menu in formal main dining room. Comfortable bedrooms, currently being refurbished.

HARRIS (Isle of) – Western Isles Outer Hebrides – 501 Z 10 – see Lewis and Harris (Isle of)

HAWICK – Borders – 501 – pop. 14 573 *Scotland* 26 **C2**

Edinburgh 51 m – Galashiels 18 m – Jedburgh 12 m

Jedburgh★ - Abbey★★, Mary Queen of Scots Visitor Centre★, NE : 11 m. by A 698 and B 6358 – Bowhill★★, N : 15 m. by A 7, B 7009 and B 7039

Glenteviot Park

Hassendeanburn, Northeast : 3 ¾ m. by A 698 TD9 8RU – (01450) 870 660 – enquiries@glenteviotpark.com – Fax (01450) 870 154

5 rm – £85 £140 – **Rest** – (dinner only) (residents only) Menu £30 **s**

◆ Purpose-built hotel idyllically sited overlooking River Teviot and surrounding hills. Rustic bar/lounge, sauna and snooker room. Individually furnished, well-equipped rooms. Cosy dining room offering homecooked menus.

INVERGARRY – Highland – 501 F 12 – Inverness *Scotland* 30 **C3**

Edinburgh 159 m – Fort William 25 m – Inverness 43 m – Kyle of Lochalsh 50 m

The Great Glen★

Glengarry Castle

on A 82 PH35 4HW – (01809) 501 254 – castle@glengarry.net – Fax (01809) 501 207 – 14 March-10 November

26 rm – £73/93 £146/160 – **Rest** – (light lunch Monday-Saturday) Menu £28

◆ On shores of Loch Oich, and named after eponymous Victorian castle whose ruin stands in grounds. Warm country house feel throughout; many bedrooms retain original fittings. Dining room shares the warm, country house style of the hotel.

Look out for red symbols, indicating particularly pleasant establishments.

SCOTLAND

INVERGORDON – Ross-shire – 501 H 10 30 **C2**

Kincraig House rm,

on A 9 IV18 0LF – (01349) 852 587 – info@kincraig-house-hotel.co.uk – Fax (01349) 852 193

15 rm – £70/120 £150/190 – **Rest** – (Bar lunch) Menu £34

◆ In an enviably elevated position, this Georgian house has been restored with style, retaining wood panelling and Adams fireplaces. Some of the comfy rooms are four-postered. Smart restaurant serves locally sourced, traditional dishes.

INVERKEILOR – Angus – 501 M 14 – Arbroath 28 **D2**

Edinburgh 85 m – Aberdeen 32 m – Dundee 22 m

Gordon's with rm

32 Main St DD11 5RN – (01241) 830 364 – gordonsrest@aol.com – Closed 2 weeks January and 1 week November

4 rm – £65 £100/150 – **Rest** – (Closed Monday, lunch Tuesday and Sunday dinner to non-residents) (booking essential) Menu £27/45

◆ Family owned restaurant in small village. Welcoming atmosphere, beams, open fires and rugs on the wood floors. Classic cooking with modern twists. Pleasant, pine fitted rooms.

INVERMORISTON – Inverness – 501 G 12 30 **C2**

Tigh na Bruach without rest

Southwest : ½ m. on A 82 IV63 7YE – (01320) 351 349 – tighnabruach@btconnect.com

3 rm – £63/100 £96/110

◆ Don't be put off by rather unprepossessing exterior: located by Loch Ness, it has beautiful gardens, and very comfy rooms with pleasant little terraces overlooking a lake.

INVERNESS – Highland – 501 H 11 – pop. 40 949 ▮ *Scotland* 30 **C2**

Edinburgh 156 m – Aberdeen 107 m – Dundee 134 m
Inverness Airport, Dalcross : ✆ (01667) 464000, NE : 8 m. by A 96 Y
Castle Wynd ✆ (01463) 234353 Y, invernesstic@host.co.uk
Culcabock Rd, ✆ (01463) 239 882 ;
Torvean Glenurquhart Rd, ✆ (01463) 711 434 .
Town★ – Museum and Art Gallery★ Y **M**
Loch Ness★★, SW : by A 82 Z – Clava Cairns★, E : 9 m. by Culcabock Rd, B 9006 and B 851 Z – Cawdor Castle★ **AC**, NE : 14 m. by A 96 and B 9090 Y

Plan opposite

Rocpool Reserve
Culduthel Rd ✉ IV2 4AG – ✆ (01463) 240 089 – info@rocpool.com – Fax (01463) 248 431 Z **r**
11 rm – †£ 115/165 ††£ 175/280, ☕ £ 10
Rest *Reserve* – Carte £ 27/46 **s**
◆ 19C house reborn as a boutique hotel - the talk of the city! Look cool in sexy, stylish bar and sleep in rooms the ultimate in chic design, with breathtaking bathrooms. Italian twists enhance accomplished modern dishes in sleek restaurant.

Glenmoriston Town House
20 Ness Bank ✉ IV2 4SF – ✆ (01463) 223 777 – reception@glenmoristontownhouse.com – Fax (01463) 712 378 Z **x**
30 rm ☕ – †£ 95/105 ††£ 130/170
Rest *Abstract* – see restaurant listing
Rest *Contrast* – Carte £ 11/41 **s**
◆ Chic, stylish town house. Modern cocktail bar a trendy meeting point. Bedrooms are individualistic, those on the front enjoying river views; those at the rear are quieter. Locally sourced cooking at Contrast.

Ballifeary House without rest
10 Ballifeary Rd ✉ IV3 5PJ – ✆ (01463) 235 572 – info@ballifearyguesthouse.co.uk – Fax (01463) 717 583 – Closed 2 weeks November and 24-26 December Z **n**
7 rm ☕ – †£ 35/70 ††£ 70/76
◆ Immaculately kept Victorian house with a pretty rear garden. Peaceful and relaxing feel as no children under 15 years are taken. A wholly non-smoking establishment.

Moyness House without rest
6 Bruce Gdns ✉ IV3 5EN – ✆ (01463) 233 836 – stay@moyness.co.uk – Fax (01463) 233 836 – Closed 25-26 December Z **c**
6 rm ☕ – †£ 50/80 ††£ 72/100
◆ Immaculately clipped hedges frame this attractive Victorian villa. Bedrooms vary in shape and size but all are comfortable, individually decorated and fully en suite.

Eden House without rest
8 Ballifeary Rd ✉ IV3 5PJ – ✆ (01463) 230 278 – edenhouse@btinternet.com – Fax (01463) 230 278 Z **o**
4 rm ☕ – †£ 40/60 ††£ 60/74
◆ Pleasant ten minute walk into the city centre. Friendly proprietors run a neat and spotless house. Pretty little conservatory and good sized bedrooms.

XXX Abstract – at Glenmoriston Town House
20 Ness Bank ✉ IV2 4SF – ✆ (01463) 223 777 – Fax (01463) 712 378 – Closed Sunday Z **x**
Rest – (dinner only) Carte £ 30/43 **s**
◆ Restaurant, bar and conservatory with considerable style. Vast wall mirror offsets abstract ink pictures. Accomplished cooking with Gallic accent is impressively original.

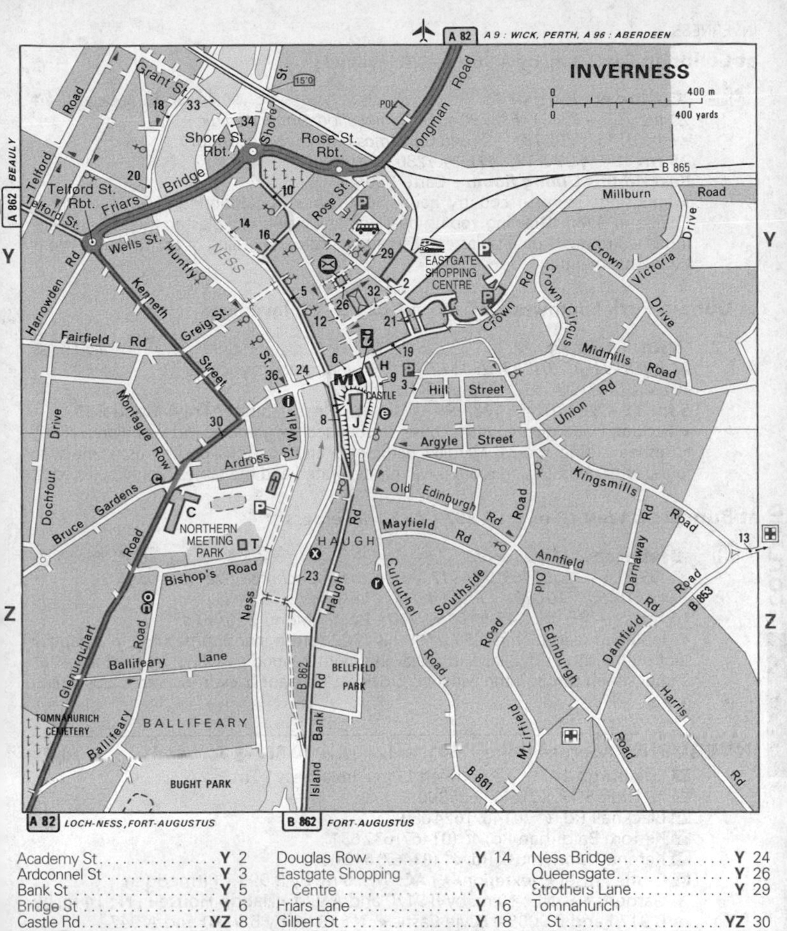

Academy St . . . . . Y 2	Douglas Row . . . . . Y 14	Ness Bridge . . . . . Y 24
Ardconnel St . . . . . Y 3	Eastgate Shopping Centre . . . . . Y	Queensgate . . . . . Y 26
Bank St . . . . . Y 5	Friars Lane . . . . . Y 16	Strothers Lane . . . . . Y 29
Bridge St . . . . . Y 6	Gilbert St . . . . . Y 18	Tomnahurich St . . . . . YZ 30
Castle Rd . . . . . YZ 8	High St . . . . . Y 19	Union St . . . . . Y 32
Castle St . . . . . Y 9	Huntly Pl. . . . . . Y 20	Waterloo Bridge . . . . . Y 33
Chapel St . . . . . Y 10	Inglis St . . . . . Y 21	Waterloo Pl. . . . . . Y 34
Church St . . . . . Y 12	Ness Bank . . . . . Z 23	Young St . . . . . Y 36
Culcabock Rd . . . . . Z 13		

XX **Rocpool Rendezvous** AC VISA MC

1 Ness Walk ✉ IV3 5NE – ✆ (01463) 717 274 – info@rocpool.com – Closed 25 December, 1 January and Sunday lunch Y **i**

Rest – Carte £ 20/34

◆ On the banks of the river Ness, this modern, cosmopolitan restaurant has a stylish ambience, popular with business diners. Modern cooking with a British/Mediterranean axis.

X **Café 1** VISA MC AE

Castle St ✉ IV2 3EA – ✆ (01463) 226 200 – info@cafe1.net – Fax (01463) 716 363 – Closed 25 December, 1 January and Sunday Y **e**

Rest – Carte £ 20/31 **s**

◆ Personally run bistro opposite the castle with an informal touch, enhanced by tiled flooring and modish chairs. Local ingredients feature in regularly changing modern menus.

at Culloden East : 3 m. by A 96 - Y – ✉ Inverness

Culloden House

✉ *IV2 7BZ – ☎ (01463) 790461 – info@cullodenhouse.co.uk – Fax (01463) 792181 – Closed Christmas and 2 weeks January*
25 rm – †£ 90/175 ††£ 140/280 – 3 suites
Rest *Adams Dining Room* – Carte £ 30/45
◆ Imposing Georgian country house in 40 acres, requisitioned by Bonnie Prince Charlie in 1746. Drawing rooms boast ornate wall-hung plaster friezes. Antique-furnished rooms. Adam's plaster reliefs adorn walls and ceiling of grand dining room; traditional menu.

at Dunain Park Southwest : 2½ m. on A 82 - Z – ✉ Inverness

Dunain Park

✉ *IV3 8JN – ☎ (01463) 230512 – info@dunainparkhotel.co.uk – Fax (01463) 224532 – Closed 3-31 January*
5 rm – †£ 125 ††£ 178/198 – 8 suites – **Rest** – (dinner only) Menu £ 35
◆ Secluded Georgian country house, surrounded by gardens and woodland. Nicely furnished sitting rooms. Marbled bathrooms and spacious bedrooms, some with four-poster beds. Dining room is warmly decorated and the tables highly polished.

at Bunchrew West : 3 m. on A 862 - Y – ✉ Inverness

SCOTLAND

Bunchrew House

rm,

✉ *IV3 8TA – ☎ (01463) 234917 – welcome@bunchrew-inverness.co.uk – Fax (01463) 710620 – Closed 4 days Christmas*
16 rm – †£ 105/145 ††£ 150/260 – **Rest** – Menu £ 26/40 **s**
◆ Unhurried relaxation is assured at this 17C Scottish mansion nestling in a tranquil spot on the shores of Bealy Firth. Drawing room is wood panelled; bedrooms restful. Gardens seen through the windows provide a pleasant backdrop to spacious dining room.

INVERURIE – Aberdeenshire – 501 M 12 – pop. 10 882 *Scotland* 28 D1

Edinburgh 147 m – Aberdeen 17 m – Inverness 90 m
18 High St ☎ (01467) 625800
Blackhall Rd, ☎ (01467) 624080 ;
Kintore Balbithan Rd, ☎ (01467) 632631 ;
Kemnay Monymusk Rd, ☎ (01467) 642060 .
Castle Fraser★ (exterior★★) **AC**, SW : 6 m. by B 993 – Pitmedden Gardens★★, NE : 10 m. by B 9170 and A 920 – Haddo House★, N : 14 m. by B 9170 and B 9005 – Fyvie Castle★, N : 13 m. by B 9170 and A 947

Strathburn

rest,

Burghmuir Drive, Northwest : 1¼ m. by Inverness rd (A 96) ✉ AB51 4GY – ☎ (01467) 624422 – strathburn@btconnect.com – Fax (01467) 625133 – Closed 25-26 December and 1-2 January
25 rm – †£ 80 ††£ 110 – **Rest** – (Closed lunch Saturday and Sunday) Carte £ 15/32 **s**
◆ Uncluttered purpose-built hotel in a residential area of town and conveniently located for A96. Well-planned modern interiors. Rooms in uniform fitted style. Dining available in the comfortable lounge-bar area or the adjacent dining room.

ISLAY (Isle of) – Argyll and Bute – 501 B 16 27 A3

Port Ellen Airport : ☎ (01496) 302022
from Port Askaig to Isle of Jura (Feolin) (Caledonian MacBrayne Ltd) frequent services daily (approx. 4 mn) – from Port Ellen or Port Askaig to Kintyre Peninsula (Kennacraig) (Caledonian MacBrayne Ltd) 1-2 daily – from Port Askaig to Oban via Isle of Colonsay (Scalasaig) (Caledonian MacBrayne Ltd) weekly – from Port Askaig to Isle of Colonsay (Scalasaig) and Kintyre Peninsula (Kennacraig) (Caledonian MacBrayne Ltd) weekly
The Square, Main St, Bowmore ☎ (01496) 810254
Port Ellen 25 Charlotte St, ☎ (01496) 300094 .

Ballygrant – Argyll and Bute 27 A3

Kilmeny
Southwest : ½ m. on A 846 ✉ PA45 7QW – ✆ (01496) 840 668 – info@kilmeny.co.uk – Fax (01496) 840 668 – Closed Christmas and New Year
5 rm – £ 90 £ 106/130 – **Rest** – (by arrangement, communal dining) Menu £ 32
◆ 19C converted farmhouse on a working farm. Its elevated position affords far reaching countryside views. Best of Scottish hospitality, home-cooking and comfort.

Bowmore – Argyll and Bute 27 A3

Harbour Inn with rm
The Square ✉ PA43 7JR – ✆ (01496) 810 330 – info@harbour-inn.com – Fax (01496) 810 990 – Closed 25-26 December
7 rm – £ 65 £ 110 – **Rest** – Carte £ 25/40
◆ Attractive whitewashed inn in busy little town, short walk from distillery. Panelled bar and a dining room with bay views. Menus centre on Islay produce. Bright bedrooms.

Port Charlotte – Argyll and Bute 27 A3

Port Charlotte
Main St ✉ PA48 7TU – ✆ (01496) 850 360 – info@portcharlottehotel.co.uk – Fax (01496) 850 361 – Closed 24-26 December
10 rm – £ 85 £ 130 – **Rest** – (bar lunch) Carte £ 18/35
◆ Simple, well-modernised, Victorian building in attractive conservation village. Pine panelled bar and relaxing lounge with open fires. Rooms furnished with fine old pieces. Attractive wood furnished restaurant with stone walls and views over the bay.

Port Ellen – Argyll and Bute 27 A3

Glenegedale House
Northwest : 4 ¾ m. on A 846 ✉ PA42 7AR – ✆ (01496) 300 400 – info@glenegedalehouse.com
9 rm (dinner included) – £ 95 £ 150 – **Rest** – (by arrangement) Menu £ 40
◆ Refurbished in elegantly sympathetic style, this stalwart house proffers neutral tones with quality soft furnishings. Antiques abound. Well-equipped rooms. Handy for airport. Spacious dining room with homely cooked fare.

Glenmachrie Farmhouse without rest
Northwest : 4 ½ m. on A 846 ✉ PA42 7AQ – ✆ (01496) 302 560 – glenmachrie@lineone.net – Fax (01496) 302 560
5 rm – £ 65 £ 80
◆ Modern farmhouse on a working farm a short drive from a number of Islay's distilleries and Duich Nature Reserve. Run on "green" low-impact policies. Warm welcoming rooms.

JEDBURGH – Borders – 501 M 17 – pop. 4 090 *Scotland* 26 D2

Edinburgh 48 m – Carlisle 54 m – Newcastle upon Tyne 57 m
Murray's Green ✆ (01835) 863435
Jedburgh Dunion Rd, ✆ (01835) 863 587 .
Town★ - Abbey★★ **AC** – Mary Queen of Scots House Visitor Centre★ **AC** – The Canongate Bridge★
Waterloo Monument (✻ ★★) N : 4 m. by A 68 and B 6400

Jedforest
Camptown, South : 4 m. on A 68 ✉ TD8 6PJ – ✆ (01835) 840 222 – info@jedforesthotel.com – Fax (01835) 840 226
12 rm – £ 75 £ 100/140 – **Rest** – (dinner only) Carte £ 25/30
◆ Extended country house with outbuildings and attractive views. Public areas include spacious and comfortable drawing room. Bedrooms in varying co-ordinated styles and sizes. Formal dining room decorated to have an intimate feel with alcoves and low lighting.

SCOTLAND

The Spinney without rest
Langlee, South : 2 m. on A 68 ✉ TD8 6PB – ✆ (01835) 863 525 – thespinney@btinternet.com – March-November
3 rm – ££55/60
◆ Good value accommodation with homely atmosphere and ambience. Traditional feel from the gardens to the lounge. Bedrooms of a good size overlooking the attractive gardens.

Hundalee House without rest
South : 1½ m. by A 68 ✉ TD8 6PA – ✆ (01835) 863 011 – sheila.whittaker@btinternet.com – Fax (01835) 863 011 – March-October
5 rm – £30/45 £55/58
◆ 18C country lodge in a rural location, with good gardens featuring mature topiary. County house feel and a warm welcome. Distinctive period décor and some antiques.

at Crailing **Northeast : 4 m. by A 68 on A 698 – ✉ Jedburgh**

Crailing Old School
on B 6400 ✉ TD8 6TL – ✆ (01835) 850 382 – info@crailingoldschool.co.uk – closed 25,26,31 December and 1 January
3 rm – £35/50 £60/65 – **Rest** – (by arrangement, communal dining) Menu £25
◆ Former village school well sited for touring and golfing. Attractive guests' lounge also used for communal breakfast. Comfortable bedrooms in the house and the garden lodge. Home-cooked dinners.

The ✿ award is the crème de la crème.
This is awarded to restaurants
which are really worth travelling miles for!

SCOTLAND

JOHN O'GROATS – Highland – 501 K 8

– Shipping Services : see Orkney Islands

JURA (Isle of) – Argyll and Bute – 501 C 15 27 A3

from Feolin to Isle of Islay (Port Askaig) (Caledonian MacBrayne Ltd) frequent services daily (approx. 4 mn)

Craighouse – Argyll and Bute – ✉ Jura 27 A3

Jura ← Small Isles Bay,
✉ PA60 7XU – ✆ (01496) 820 243 – jurahotel@aol.com – Fax (01496) 820 249 – Closed 20 December-5 January
16 rm – £50 £100 – 1 suite – **Rest** – (bar lunch) Carte £17/24 s
◆ The only hotel on one of the wildest and quietest of the Scottish islands. Next door to the distillery. Relaxed, traditional and simple in style. Many rooms with fine views. Dining room shares the feel of the establishment with wooden chairs and fine views.

KELSO – Borders – 501 M 17 – pop. 5 116 *Scotland* 26 D2

Edinburgh 44 m – Hawick 21 m – Newcastle upon Tyne 68 m
Town House, The Square ✆ (01573) 223464 (mornings only in winter)
Berrymoss Racecourse Rd, ✆ (01573) 23 009 .
Town★ - The Square★★ – ← ★ from Kelso Bridge
Tweed Valley★★ - Floors Castle★ **AC**, NW : 1½ m. by A 6089. Mellerstain★★ (Ceilings★★★, Library★★★) **AC**, NW : 6 m. by A 6089 – Waterloo Monument (✻ ★★), SW : 7 m. by A 698 and B 6400 – Jedburgh Abbey★★ **AC**, SW : 8½ m. by A 698 - Dryburgh Abbey★★ **AC** (setting★★★), SW : 10½ m. by A 6089, B 6397 and B 6404 – Scott's View★★, W : 11 m. by A 6089, B 6397, B 6404 and B 6356 – Smailholm Tower★ (✻ ★★), NW : 6 m. by A 6089 and B 6397 - Lady Kirk (Kirk o'Steil★), NE : 16 m. by A 698, A 697, A 6112 and B 6437

The Roxburghe

Heiton, Southwest : 3½ m. by A 698 ✉ TD5 8JZ – ✆ (01573) 450 331 – hotel@roxburghe.net – Fax (01573) 450 611

20 rm – ♦£ 128/140 ♦♦£ 160/264 – 2 suites – **Rest** – Menu £ 37 – Carte lunch £ 12/20 **s**

◆ Wonderfully characterful Jacobean style mansion built in 1853. Sitting rooms with log fires and fresh flowers. Lovely conservatory, attractive library bar. Luxurious rooms. Warmly hued, formal restaurant with collection of horse racing pictures.

Ednam House

Bridge St ✉ TD5 7HT – ✆ (01573) 224 168 – contact@ednamhouse.com – Fax (01573) 226 319 – closed Christmas and New Year

32 rm – ♦£ 84 ♦♦£ 156 – **Rest** – (bar lunch Monday-Saturday) Menu £ 25

◆ Dominant Georgian mansion on Tweed. Distinctive décor exudes period appeal. Three impressively ornate lounges. Bar with fishing theme. Traditional rooms. Spacious dining room with relaxed atmosphere, overlooking gardens and river.

Bellevue House without rest

Bowmont St, North : ½ m. on A 6089 ✉ TD5 7DZ – ✆ (01573) 224 588 – bellevuekelso@aol.com – closed 2 weeks November and 24 December-2 January

6 rm – ♦£ 40 ♦♦£ 60/65

◆ Victorian house 5 minutes from the Market Square. Individually decorated bedrooms. Good hospitality and range of breakfast dishes.

at Ednam North : 2 ¼ m. on B 6461 – ✉ Kelso

Edenwater House

off Stichill rd ✉ TD5 7QL – ✆ (01573) 224 070 – relax@edenwaterhouse.co.uk – Fax (01573) 226 615 – Closed first 2 weeks January

4 rm – ♦£ 65 ♦♦£ 100 – **Rest** – (Closed Sunday-Wednesday for non-residents) (dinner only) (booking essential) Menu £ 38 **s**

◆ Charming house in rural location next to 17C kirk. Beautiful gardens with stream and meadows beyond. Antique filled lounges. Rooms boast fine quality furnishings. Elegant dining room serving traditionally based meals using local produce.

KENMORE – Perth and Kinross – 501 I 14 *Scotland* 28 C2

Edinburgh 82 m – Dundee 60 m – Oban 71 m – Perth 38 m

Taymouth Castle Aberfeldy, ✆ (01887) 830 228 ;

Mains of Taymouth, ✆ (01887) 830 226 .

Village★

Loch Tay★★. Ben Lawers★★, SW : 8 m. by A 827

Kenmore

The Square ✉ PH15 2NU – ✆ (01887) 830 205 – reception@kenmorehotel.co.uk – Fax (01887) 830 262

40 rm – ♦£ 65/75 ♦♦£ 99/119

Rest *Taymouth* – Carte £ 14/30

◆ Scotland's oldest inn. Standing on the Tay, it is now a smart, white-fronted hotel with Poet's Parlour featuring original pencilled verse by Burns. Cosy, well-kept rooms. Restaurant with panoramic river views.

KILBERRY – Argyll and Bute – 501 D 16 – see Kintyre (Peninsula)

The red symbol?
This denotes the very essence of peace – only the sound of birdsong first thing in the morning …

KILCHRENAN – Argyll and Bute – 501 E 14 – ✉ Taynuilt ▮ *Scotland* 27 **B2**

Edinburgh 117 m – Glasgow 87 m – Oban 18 m

Loch Awe★★, E : 1 ¼ m

Ardanaiseig ⋖ gardens and Loch Awe,

Northeast : 4 m. ✉ PA35 1HE – ✆ (01866) 833 333 – ardanaiseig@clara.net – Fax (01866) 833 222 – closed 2 January- 1 February

17 rm – †£ 88/154 ††£ 240/386 – 1 suite – **Rest** – (light lunch) (booking essential for non-residents) Menu £ 45

◆ Substantial country house in extensive informal gardens beside Loch Awe. Undisturbed peace. Impressively elegant interior; antiques to the fore. Tasteful bedrooms. Dining room boasts views to loch; classic country house cooking.

Roineabhal rm,

✉ PA35 1HD – ✆ (01866) 833 207 – maria@roineabhal.com – Fax (01866) 833 477 – closed Christmas

3 rm – †£ 55 ††£ 90 – **Rest** – (by arrangement) Menu £ 35

◆ Large stone house, built by the owners, enviably located by rushing stream and close to Loch Awe. Rusticity prevails in welcoming interior; spacious rooms with homely extras. By arrangement five-course communal dinner, home-cooked using local produce.

KILDRUMMY – Aberdeenshire – 501 L 12 – ✉ Alford ▮ *Scotland* 28 **D1**

Edinburgh 137 m – Aberdeen 35 m

Castle★ AC

Huntly Castle (Heraldic carvings★★★) N : 15 m. by A 97 – Craigievar Castle★, SE : 13 m. by A 97, A 944 and A 980

Kildrummy Castle ⋖ gardens and Kildrummy Castle,

South : 1 ¼ m. on A 97 ✉ AB33 8RA – ✆ (019755) 71 288 – bookings@kildrummycastlehotel.co.uk – Fax (019755) 71 345 – Closed January

16 rm – †£ 87/97 ††£ 197

Rest *The Dining Room* – Menu £ 23/34 **s**

◆ Imposing, stone built 19C mansion in superb grounds with fine view of original 13C castle. Baronial, country house style abounds: lounges flaunt antiques. Variable rooms. Delightfully wood-panelled dining room; homely Scottish cooking.

KILLEARN – Stirling – 501 G 15 – ✉ Glasgow 27 **B3**

Edinburgh 60 m – Glasgow 19 m – Perth 55 m – Stirling 22 m

The Black Bull

2 The Square ✉ G63 9NG – ✆ (01360) 550 215 – sales@blackbullhotel.com – Fax (01360) 550 143

14 rm – †£ 70/75 ††£ 95 – 1 suite

Rest *The Black Bull* – Menu £ 15/30 – Carte £ 15/30

◆ Pleasant little inn in centre of small village close to Campsie Fells. Local artwork is on display in all areas. Contemporary bar and rooms that offer neat and tidy comforts. Trendy, modern brasserie.

KILLIECRANKIE – Perth and Kinross – 501 I 13 – see Pitlochry

KILLIN – Stirling – 501 H 14 – pop. 666 ▮ *Scotland* 27 **B2**

Edinburgh 72 m – Dundee 65 m – Oban 54 m – Perth 43 m

Breadalbane Folklore Centre, Falls of Dochart ✆ (0870) 200627

Killin, ✆ (01567) 820 312 .

Loch Tay★★, Ben Lawers★★, NE : 8 m. by A 827

Dall Lodge Country House without rest

Main St, on A 827 ✉ FK21 8TN – ✆ (01567) 820 217 – connor@dalllodge.co.uk – Fax (01567) 820 726 – Easter-September

9 rm – †£ 30/45 ††£ 76

◆ Victorian hotel of stone, proudly overlooking river Lochay. Walls adorned by foreign artefacts and local oils. Conservatory with exotic plants. Stylish, halogen lit rooms.

Breadalbane House

Main St ✉ FK21 8UT – ✆ (01567) 820 134 – info@breadalbanehouse.com
5 rm – £ 35/45 £ 50/60 – **Rest** – (by arrangement) Menu £ 15
◆ Surrounded by Ben Lawers, Loch Tay, Glen Lochay and the Falls of Dochart, this cosy guesthouse offers simple, homely comforts. Clean, well-kept rooms with good views. Evening meals available by prior arrangement in the simple, pine furnished dining room.

at Ardeonaig Northeast : 6 ¾ m. – ✉ Killin (Stirling) 28 **C2**

Ardeonaig

South Loch Tay, By Killin ✉ FK21 8SU – ✆ (01567) 820 400 – info@ardeonaighotel.co.uk – Fax (01567) 820 282
20 rm – £ 125 £ 300
Rest ***The Restaurant*** – see restaurant listing
◆ 17C inn and super, modern, airy lochside suite, in wooded meadows on shore of Loch Tay. Cheery, well-stocked bar. Cosy sitting room. Library with fine views. Smart rooms.

The Restaurant – at Ardeonaig H.

South Loch Tay ✉ FK21 8SU – ✆ (01567) 820 400 – info@ardeonaighotel.co.uk – Fax (01567) 820 282
Rest – Menu £ 27 – Carte £ 33/50
◆ Located in Ardeonaig hotel extension. Rennie Mackintosh style chairs, white linen-clad tables. Good value dishes: South African influences merge well with local ingredients.

Good food and accommodation at moderate prices?
Look for the Bib symbols:
red Bib Gourmand for food, blue Bib Hotel for hotels

SCOTLAND

KILMARNOCK – East Ayrshire – **501** *Scotland* 25 **B2**

Edinburgh 64 m – Ayr 13 m – Glasgow 25 m
Dean Castle (arms and armour★, musical instruments★)

The Park

rm,

Kilmarnock Football Club, Rugby Park, off Dundonald Rd ✉ KA1 2DP – ✆ (01563) 545 999 – enquiries@theparkhotel.uk.com – Fax (01563) 545 322
50 rm – £ 150 £ 160
Rest ***Blues*** – Menu £ 12 (lunch) – Carte £ 17/34
◆ Adjacent to Kilmarnock Football Club, who are its owners, this stylish, glass structured hotel offers up-to-date facilities. Spacious, well-equipped and comfortable bedrooms. Mezzanine-level restaurant boasts tables with views of the pitch.

KILMORY – North Ayrshire – **501** E 17 – **see Arran (Isle of)**

KINCLAVEN – Perth and Kinross – **501** J 14 – **pop. 394** – ✉ **Stanley** 28 **C2**

Edinburgh 56 m – Perth 12 m

Ballathie House

rm,

Stanley ✉ PH1 4QN – ✆ (01250) 883 268 – email@ballathiehousehotel.com – Fax (01250) 883 396
38 rm – £ 119/160 £ 280/300 – 3 suites – **Rest** – Menu £ 22/42
◆ Imposing mid 19C former shooting lodge on banks of Tay, imbued with tranquil, charming atmosphere. Elegant, individually furnished bedrooms with a floral theme. Richly alluring restaurant overlooking river.

KINGUSSIE – Highland – 501 H 12 – pop. 1 410 Scotland 30 C3

Edinburgh 117 m – Inverness 41 m – Perth 73 m

Gynack Rd, ✆ (01540) 661 600 .

Highland Wildlife Park★ AC, NE : 4 m. by A 9. Aviemore★, NE : 11 m. by A 9 – The Cairngorms★★ (≤ ★★★) - ★★★ from Cairn Gorm, NE : 18 m. by B 970

Hermitage

Spey St ✉ PH21 1HN – ✆ (01540) 662 137 – thehermitage@clara.net – Fax (01540) 662 177 – closed 25-26 December

5 rm – †£ 35/50 ††£ 56/80 – **Rest** – (by arrangement) Menu £ 18

◆ Pleasant Victorian detached house with views of Cairngorms. Attractive lawned garden. Homely, welcoming lounge with log fire. Colourful, floral rooms. Garden views from conservatory style dining room.

Homewood Lodge without rest

Newtonmore Rd ✉ PH21 1HD – ✆ (01540) 661 507 – jenniferander5@hotmail.com – April - October

4 rm – ††£ 55/60

◆ An immaculate whitewashed exterior and a prominent hilltop position attract the visitor's eye to this Victorian villa guesthouse with its uncluttered feel and simple rooms.

SCOTLAND

The Cross at Kingussie with rm

Tweed Mill Brae, Ardbroilach Rd ✉ PH21 1LB – ✆ (01540) 661 166 – relax@thecross.co.uk – Fax (01540) 661 080 – Closed Christmas, mid January-mid February, Sunday and Monday

8 rm (dinner included) – †£ 135/155 ††£ 190/260 – **Rest** – (dinner only) (booking essential) Menu £ 43 **s**

◆ Personally run converted tweed mill restaurant in four acres of waterside grounds with beamed ceilings and modern artwork. Modish Scottish cuisine. Comfortable rooms.

Do not confuse X with ✿!
X defines comfort, while stars are awarded for the best cuisine, across all categories of comfort.

KINROSS – Perth and Kinross – 501 J 15 – pop. 4 681 28 C2

Edinburgh 28 m – Dunfermline 13 m – Perth 18 m – Stirling 25 m

Heart of Scotland Visitor Centre, junction 6, M 90 ✆ (01577) 863680 (closed weekends October-April)

Green Hotel 2 The Muirs, ✆ (01577) 863 407 ;

Milnathort South St, ✆ (01577) 864 069 ;

Bishopshire Kinnesswood, ✆ (01592) 783 003 .

The Green

2 Muirs ✉ KY13 8AS – ✆ (01577) 863 467 – reservations@green-hotel.com – Fax (01577) 863 180 – Closed 24-27 December

46 rm – †£ 65/95 ††£ 90/150

Rest *Basil's* – (dinner only) Menu £ 30 **s**

◆ 18C former coaching inn in neat grounds off village high street. Spacious, welcoming lounge. Leisure complex includes curling rink. Comfortable, modern rooms. Bright, airy modern restaurant with modish menus to match.

Burnbank without rest

79 Muirs, North : ¾ m. on A 922 ✉ KY13 8AZ – ✆ (01577) 861 931 – bandb@burnbank-kinross.co.uk

3 rm – †£ 38/40 ††£ 60/70

◆ Well-kept, proudly run guesthouse: cosy reception room full of maps and local info. Owners make their own breakfast bread and preserves. Lomond Hills vistas from smart rooms.

KINTYRE (Peninsula) – Argyll and Bute – 501 D 16 Scotland 27 B3

Campbeltown Airport : ✆ (01586) 553797

from Claonaig to Isle of Arran (Lochranza) (Caledonian MacBrayne Ltd) frequent services daily (30 mn) – from Kennacraig to Isle of Islay (Port Ellen or Port Askaig) (Caledonian MacBrayne Ltd) 1-3 daily – from Kennacraig to Oban via Isle of Colonsay (Scalasaig) and Isle of Islay (Port Askaig) 3 weekly

27 Machrihanish Campbeltown, ✆ (01586) 810 213 ;

18 Dunaverty Campbeltown Southend, ✆ (01586) 830 677 ;

9 Gigha Isle of Gigha, ✆ (01583) 505 242 .

Carradale★ – Saddell (Collection of grave slabs★)

Campbeltown – Argyll and Bute 27 A3

Edinburgh 176 m

Mackinnon House, The Pier ✆ (08707) 200609, info@campbeltown.visitscotland.com

Craigard House

Low Askomil, East : ¾ m. by B 842 on no through rd ✉ PA28 6EP – ✆ (01586) 554 242 – info@craigard-house.co.uk – Fax (01586) 551 137

14 rm – £ 55/90 £ 75/120 – **Rest** – (dinner only) (booking essential for non-residents) Carte £ 19/25

◆ Built 1882 by distillery owner on shores of Campbeltown Loch. Fine hallway with stained-glass window. Individually decorated rooms named after local geographical features. Tables at bow window looking out to loch are popular in period styled dining room.

Carradale – Argyll and Bute 27 B3

Dunvalanree

Port Righ Bay ✉ PA28 6SE – ✆ (01583) 431 226 – eat@dunvalanree.com – Fax (01583) 431 339 – closed January and February

7 rm – £ 80 £ 140 – **Rest** – (dinner only) Menu £ 25

◆ 1930s house on the bay facing Arran and Kilbrannan Sound. Comfortable firelit lounge, "Arts and Crafts" stained glass entrance and well-fitted rooms, one in Mackintosh style. Intimate dining room takes up the period style.

Kilberry – Argyll and Bute 27 A3

Edinburgh 165 m – Glasgow 121 m – Oban 75 m

The Kilberry Inn with rm

✉ PA29 6YD – ✆ (01880) 770 223 – relax@kilberryinn.com – Closed January to mid-March and Monday-Thursday November-December

4 rm – £ 45 £ 90 – **Rest** – Carte £ 20/30

◆ Characterful, cosy, red tin-roofed cottage incorporating open fires, beams, exposed stone. Walls hung with local artists' work. Well-priced dishes. Stylish, modern bedrooms.

KIPPEN – Stirling – 501 H 15 – pop. 934 Scotland 28 C2

Edinburgh 75 m – Glasgow 62 m – Stirling 16 m

Doune★ - Castle★, NE : 8 m. by A 811, B 8075 and A 84 – Dunblane★ - Cathedral★★, NE : 13 m. by A 811 and M 9 – Stirling★★ - Castle★★, Argyll and Sutherland Highlanders Regimental Museum★, Argyll's Lodging★, Church of the Holy Rude★, E : 9 m. by A 811

The Inn at Kippen with rm

Fore Rd ✉ FK8 3DT – ✆ (01786) 871 010 – info@theinnatkippen.co.uk – Fax (01786) 871 011 – Closed 25 December and 1-2 January

4 rm – £ 40 £ 85 – **Rest** – Menu £ 10 – Carte £ 20/40

◆ Village inn with modern interior and photos of former village life. Large lunch and dinner menu of popular pub and restaurant style dishes. Simple wood-furnished bedrooms.

SCOTLAND

KIRK YETHOLM - Borders 26 D2

Mill House without rest

Main St ✉ TD5 8PE – ✆ (01573) 420604 – millhousebb@tiscali.co.uk

3 rm – 🛉£45 🛉🛉£80

◆ Converted grain mill with a spacious and immaculately presented interior, full of homely, warm touches. Well appointed bedrooms add the final touch to a most appealing house.

KIRKBEAN - Dumfries and Galloway - 501 *Scotland* 26 C3

Edinburgh 92 m – Dumfries 13 m – Kirkcudbright 29 m

Sweetheart Abbey★, N : 5 m. by A 710. Threave Garden★★ and Threave Castle★, W : 20 m. by A 710 and A 745

Cavens

✉ DG2 8AA – ✆ (01387) 880234 – enquiries@cavens.com – Fax (01387) 880467 – closed January-March

6 rm – 🛉£80/120 🛉🛉£80/160 – **Rest** – (dinner only) Menu £30

◆ 18C house with extensions set in mature gardens. Very comfortable lounges opening onto terrace. Spacious well furnished bedrooms. Simple refreshing meals using local produce.

KIRKCOLM - Dumfries and Galloway - 501 E 19 - see Stranraer

KIRKCUDBRIGHT - Dumfries and Galloway - 501 H 19 - pop. 3 447 25 B3

Scotland

Edinburgh 108 m – Dumfries 28 m – Stranraer 50 m

Harbour Sq ✆ (01557) 330494 (Easter-October)

Stirling Crescent, ✆ (01557) 330314 .

Town★

Dundrennan Abbey★ AC, SE : 5 m. by A 711

Selkirk Arms

High St ✉ DG6 4JG – ✆ (01557) 330402 – reception@selkirkarmshotel.co.uk – Fax (01557) 331639

17 rm – 🛉£60/80 🛉🛉£98/108 – **Rest** – (bar lunch) Menu £25 – Carte £18/32

◆ Traditional coaching inn in centre of quaint town; Burns reputedly wrote "The Selkirk Grace" here. Rustic interior. Large bar serving simple food. Good sized rooms. Comfortable dining room with seasonal, classically based menu.

Gladstone House

48 High St ✉ DG6 4JX – ✆ (01557) 331734 – hilarygladstone@aol.com – Fax (01557) 331734

3 rm – 🛉£45 🛉🛉£69 – **Rest** – (by arrangement) Menu £20

◆ Attractive Georgian house. Spacious, comfortably furnished sitting room and breakfast room. Evening meals offered. Traditional rooms with stripped wooden furnishings.

KIRKMICHAEL - Perth and Kinross - 501 J 13 28 C2

Edinburgh 73 m – Aberdeen 85 m – Inverness 102 m – Perth 29 m

Cruachan Country Cottage without rest

on A 924 ✉ PH10 7NZ – ✆ (01250) 881226 – cruachan@strathardle.co.uk

3 rm – 🛉£37/39 🛉🛉£59/63

◆ Extended stone cottage with neat garden, overlooking River Ardle. Homely lounge with open fire and interesting, local prints. Individually decorated bedrooms.

KIRKNEWTON - Edinburgh - 501 J 16 - see Edinburgh

KIRKPATRICK DURHAM - Dumfries and Galloway - 501 I 18 - see Castle Douglas

SCOTLAND

KIRKTON OF GLENISLA – Perth. and Kinross – 501 K 13 – 28 C2

✉ Blairgowrie

Edinburgh 73 m – Forfar 19 m – Pitlochry 24 m

Glenmarkie Health Spa and Riding Centre

East : 3 ¾ m. by B 951 ✉ PH11 8QB – ✆ (01575) 582 295
– holidays@glenmarkie.freeserve.co.uk – Fax (01575) 582 295

3 rm – £ 40 £ 56 – **Rest** – (by arrangement) Menu £ 20

◆ Stunningly located, cosy little farmhouse in beautiful glen. Horse riding and massages available, not necessarily in that order. Simple, individually decorated bedrooms.

KIRKWALL – Orkney Islands – 501 L 7 – see Orkney Islands (Mainland)

KIRRIEMUIR – Angus – 501 K 13 – pop. 5 963 28 C2

Edinburgh 65 m – Aberdeen 50 m – Dundee 16 m – Perth 30 m

1 Cumberland Close ✆ (01575) 574097 (Easter-September)

Purgavie Farm

Lintrathen, West : 5½ m. on B 951 ✉ DD8 5HZ – ✆ (01575) 560 213
– purgavie@aol.com – Fax (01575) 560 213

3 rm – £ 30 £ 54 – **Rest** – (by arrangement, communal dining) Menu £ 14

◆ Farmhouse on working farm at foot of Glen Isla, part of lovely Glens of Angus. Homely lounge with open fire. Large, comfortable rooms with panoramic views. Meals are taken communally in the comfortable dining room.

We try to be as accurate as possible when giving room rates. But prices are susceptible to change, so please check rates when booking.

SCOTLAND

KYLESKU – Highland – 501 E 9 *Scotland* 30 C1

Edinburgh 256 m – Inverness 100 m – Ullapool 34 m

Loch Assynt★★, S : 6 m. by A 894

Kylesku with rm — Loch Glencoul and mountains,

✉ IV27 4HW – ✆ (01971) 502 231 – info@kyleskuhotel.co.uk
– Fax (01971) 502 313 – March-mid October

8 rm – £ 60 £ 88 – **Rest** – (in bar Monday dinner and lunch) Menu £ 29 – Carte £ 15/25

◆ Stunningly located inn, at the end of the pier overlooking loch, mountain and countryside. Spacious establishment with interesting, intriguing, individual rooms. Restaurant in superb spot with great views: local, seasonal ingredients with strong seafood slant.

LADYBANK – Fife – 501 K 15 – pop. 1 487 *Scotland* 28 C2

Edinburgh 38 m – Dundee 20 m – Stirling 40 m

Ladybank Annsmuir, ✆ (01337) 830 814 .

Falkland★ – Palace of Falkland★ – Gardens★ – Village★, S : ½ m. by A 914 on A 912

Redlands Country Lodge without rest

Pitlessie Rd, East : ¾ m. by Kingskettle rd taking first left after railway bridge
✉ KY15 7SH – ✆ (01337) 831 091 – info@redlandslodge.com

4 rm – £ 35/40 £ 60/70

◆ Detached cottage on a quiet country lane in a rural location. Bedrooms, which have a simple snug air, are located in an adjacent pine lodge.

LAIRG – Highland – **501** G9 – **pop. 857** 30 **C2**

Edinburgh 218 m – Inverness 61 m – Wick 72 m

Ferrycroft Countryside Centre, Sutherland ✆ (01549) 402160 (April-October)

Park House

✉ IV27 4AU – ✆ (01549) 402 208 – david-walker@park-house.freeserve.co.uk – Fax (01549) 402 693 – closed Christmas and New Year

3 rm – £ 30/48 ££ 60/72 – **Rest** – (by arrangement) Menu £ 20

◆ Victorian house on the banks of Loch Shin, comfortable and well furnished with high ceilings and views of the loch. Good spacious bedrooms. Country pursuits organised. Hunting and fishing activities of the establishment reflected in the home-cooked menus.

LAMLASH – North Ayrshire – **501** E 17 – see Arran (Isle of)

LANGASS – Western Isles – see Uist (Isles of)

LARGOWARD – Fife – **501** L 15 – ✉ St Andrews 28 **D2**

Edinburgh 44 m – Glenrothes 14 m – St Andrews 7 m

The Inn at Lathones with rm

Northeast : ¾ m. on A 915 ✉ KY9 1JE – ✆ (01334) 840 494 – lathones@theinn.co.uk – Fax (01334) 840 694 – closed 2 weeks January

21 rm – £ 120/180 ££ 180/245 – **Rest** – Menu £ 18/45 – Carte £ 33/44

◆ Early 17C inn; now a restaurant where modern styles and adventurous combinations are the order of the day: bold diners can try the innovative 'Trilogy' menu. Stylish rooms.

LAUDER – Berwickshire – **501** L 16 – **pop. 1 108** 26 **D2**

Edinburgh 27 m – Berwick-upon-Tweed 34 m – Carlisle 74 m – Newcastle upon Tyne 77 m

Galashiels Rd, ✆ (01578) 722 526 .

The Lodge

Carfraemill, Northwest : 4 m. by A 68 on A 697 ✉ TD2 6RA – ✆ (01578) 750 750 – enquiries@carfraemill.co.uk – Fax (01578) 750 751

10 rm – £ 60 ££ 90

Rest *Jo's Kitchen* – Carte £ 20/28

◆ Family run hotel, once a coaching inn, just off the Newcastle-Edinburgh road. Warmly traditional style of décor and a welcoming ambience. Well-equipped bedrooms. A choice of informal eating areas with a traditional farmhouse feel.

Black Bull with rm

13-15 Market Place ✉ TD2 6SR – ✆ (01578) 722 208 – enquiries@blackbull-lauder.com – Fax (01578) 722 419 – Closed February and 26 December

8 rm – £ 60 ££ 90 – **Rest** – Carte £ 16/28 **s**

◆ Hanging baskets catch the eye outside this former coaching inn. Various snugs provide a cosy welcome. Extensive menus of popular, home-cooked dishes. Clean, well-kept rooms.

LEITH – Edinburgh – **501** K 16 – see Edinburgh

LERWICK – Shetland Islands – **501** Q 3 – see Shetland Islands (Mainland)

LEVERBURGH – Western Isles Outer Hebrides – **501** Y 10 – see Lewis and Harris (Isle of)

LEWIS and HARRIS (Isle of) – 501 A 9 Scotland 29 A1

from Stornoway to Ullapool (Mainland) (Caledonian MacBrayne Ltd) 2/3 daily (2 h 40 mn) – from Kyles Scalpay to the Isle of Scalpay (Caledonian MacBrayne Ltd) (10 mn) – from Tarbert to Isle of Skye (Uig) (Caledonian MacBrayne Ltd) 1-2 daily (1 h 45 mn) – from Tarbert to Portavadie (Caledonian MacBrayne Ltd) (summer only) frequent services daily (25 mn) – from Leverburgh to North Uist (Otternish) (Caledonian MacBrayne Ltd) (3-4 daily) (1 h 10 mn)

Callanish Standing Stones★★ – Carloway Broch★ – St Clement's Church, Rodel (tomb★)

LEWIS – Western Isles

Aird Uig – Western Isles 29 A1

Bonaventure with rm

HS2 9JA – (01851) 672 474 – jo@bonaventurelewis.co.uk

5 rm – £33 £60 – **Rest** – (dinner only) (booking essential) Menu £31

◆ Former 1950s RAF radar station in a stunning setting converted to spacious bistro style dining room with Scottish/French menu serving local produce. Basic bedrooms.

Breasclete – Western Isles 29 B1

Eshcol

21 Breasclete HS2 9ED – (01851) 621 357 – neil@eshcol.com – Fax (01851) 621 357 – March-October

3 rm – £49 £78 – **Rest** – (by arrangement) Menu £25

◆ Friendly, family run house in rural location, set against a backdrop of delightful scenery. Immaculately kept throughout with a homely atmosphere and views from most rooms. Dinners served at Loch Roag next door.

Loch Roag

22A Breasclete HS2 9EF – (01851) 621 357 – donald@lochroag.com – Fax (01851) 621 357 – March-October

4 rm – £37/49 £78 – **Rest** – (by arrangement) Menu £25

◆ Charming rural location with super views. Run by same family as Eshcol! Bedrooms are decorated in traditional style and the house as a whole has a snug welcoming atmosphere. Simple uncluttered dining room with lovely loch view.

Galson – Western Isles 29 B1

Galson Farm

South Galson HS2 0SH – (01851) 850 492 – galsonfarm@yahoo.com – Fax (01851) 850 492

4 rm – £44/72 £86 – **Rest** – (by arrangement, communal dining) Menu £22 **s**

◆ Characterful working farm in a very remote location. Close to the ocean and ideally placed for exploring the north of the island. Cosy, comfortable, well-kept bedrooms. Traditionally styled dining room where meals are taken communally at a large central table.

Stornoway – Western Isles 29 B1

26 Cromwell St (01851) 703088, witb@visitthehebrides.co.uk

Lady Lever Park, (01851) 702 240 .

Cabarfeidh rest,

Manor Park, North : ½ m. on A 859 HS1 2EU – (01851) 702 604 – cabarfeidh@calahotels.com – Fax (01851) 705 572

46 rm – £85/92 £105/125 – **Rest** – Carte £25/35 **s**

◆ Modern purpose-built hotel surrounded by gardens and close to golf course. Up-to-date, well-equipped bedrooms. Range of banqueting and conference facilities. Restaurant is divided into four areas including conservatory, bistro and garden rooms.

SCOTLAND

Braighe House without rest
20 Braighe Rd, Southeast : 3 m. on A 866 ✉ HS2 0BQ – ✆ (01851) 705 287 – alison@braighehouse.co.uk
5 rm – ♦£55 ♦♦£70
◆ Spacious proportions allied to enviable coastal outlook. Style and taste predominate in the large, comfy lounge and airy bedrooms. Hearty breakfasts set you up for the day.

HARRIS – Western Isles

Ardhasaig – Western Isles 29 A1

Ardhasaig House with rm
← Ardhasaig bay and North Harris mountains,
✉ HS3 3AJ – ✆ (01859) 502 500 – accommodation@ardhasaig.co.uk – Fax (01859) 502 077 – April-October
6 rm – ♦£55 ♦♦£150 – **Rest** – (dinner only) (booking essential for non-residents) (set menu only) Menu £48
◆ Purpose built house with wild, dramatic views. Smart dining room with daily changing menu; accomplished dishes feature seasonal island produce. Well-kept bedrooms.

Leverburgh – Western Isles 29 A2

Carminish
← Carminish Islands and Sound of Harris,
1a Strond, South : 1 m. on Srandda rd ✉ HS5 3UD – ✆ (01859) 520 400 – info@carminish.com – restricted opening in Winter
3 rm – ♦£25/50 ♦♦£50/62 – **Rest** – (by arrangement, communal dining) Menu £21 **s**
◆ Idyllically located guesthouse with spectacular views of the Carminish Islands and Sound of Harris. Comfortable lounge. Well-kept rooms. Hearty meals in communal setting.

Scalpay – Western Isles 29 B2

Hirta House without rest
✉ HS4 3XZ – ✆ (01859) 540 394 – m.mackenzie@tiscali.co.uk – Fax (01859) 540 394
3 rm – ♦£40/50 ♦♦£60/70
◆ Enter Scalpay by impressive modern bridge and admire the hills of Harris from this stylish guesthouse with its bold wall colours, vivid artwork and nautically inspired rooms.

Scarista – Western Isles 29 A2

9, ✆ (01859) 550 226 .

Scarista House
← Scarista Bay,
✉ HS3 3HX – ✆ (01859) 550 238 – timandpatricia@scaristahouse.com – Fax (01859) 550 277 – Closed Christmas, January, February and last 2 weeks October
5 rm – ♦£110/145 ♦♦£189/199 – **Rest** – (dinner only) (booking essential for non-residents) (set menu only) Menu £40
◆ Sympathetically restored part 18C former manse, commanding position affords delightful views of Scarista Bay. Elegant library and inviting antique furnished bedrooms. Strong local flavour to the daily changing menu.

Tarbert – Western Isles – pop. 795 – ✉ Harris 29 A2

Ceol na Mara
7 Direcleit ✉ HS3 3DP – ✆ (01859) 502 464 – midgie@madasafish.com
4 rm – ♦£50 ♦♦£80 – **Rest** – (by arrangement, communal dining) Menu £25 **s**
◆ Wonderful views and a loch's edge setting enhance the allure of this idyllically set house with smart decking area, peaceful garden, lovely lounge and simple, spacious rooms. Share home-cooked meals with your fellow guests.

Hillcrest without rest
Northwest : 1 ¾ m. on A 859 ✉ HS3 3AH – ✆ (01859) 502 119
– angusahillcrest@tiscali.co.uk – Fax (01859) 502 119
3 rm – †£ 40 ††£ 50
◆ A private house, family run, in a commanding position overlooking Loch Tarbert. Small cosy sitting room and spacious bedrooms, most enjoying sea views.

LEWISTON – Highland – 501 G 12 *Scotland* 30 C2

Edinburgh 173 m – Inverness 17 m
Loch Ness★★ – The Great Glen★

Woodlands without rest
East Lewiston ✉ IV63 6UJ – ✆ (01456) 450 356
– stay@woodlands-lochness.co.uk – Fax (01456) 459 343 – closed November-March
4 rm – †£ 30/38 ††£ 52/64
◆ Spacious, purpose-built guesthouse with large garden and decked terrace situated just away from the town. Airy, immaculately kept and comfortable bedrooms.

Glen Rowan without rest
West Lewiston ✉ IV63 6UW – ✆ (01456) 450 235 – info@glenrowan.co.uk
– Fax (01456) 450 817
3 rm – †£ 23/30 ††£ 46/60
◆ Purpose-built house in a quiet spot with pleasant garden bordering a mountain stream. Tea served to arriving guests. Compact but charming and well-kept bedrooms.

If breakfast is included the symbol appears after the number of rooms.

SCOTLAND

LINLITHGOW – West Lothian – 501 J 16 – pop. 13 370 *Scotland* 26 C1

Edinburgh 19 m – Falkirk 9 m – Glasgow 35 m
Burgh Hall, The Cross ✆ (08452) 255121 (April-October)
Braehead, ✆ (01506) 842 585 ;
West Lothian Airngath Hill, ✆ (01506) 826 030 .
Town★★ – Palace★★ **AC** : Courtyard (fountain★★), Great Hall (Hooded Fireplace★★), Gateway★ – Old Town★ – St Michaels★
Cairnpapple Hill★ **AC**, SW : 5 m. by A 706 – House of the Binns (plasterwork ceilings★) **AC**, NE : 4½ m. by A 803 and A 904. Hopetoun House★★ **AC**, E : 7 m. by A 706 and A 904 – Abercorn Parish Church (Hopetoun Loft★★) NE : 7 m. by A 803 and A 904

Arden House without rest
Belsyde, Southwest : 2 ¼ m. on A 706 ✉ EH49 6QE – ✆ (01506) 670 172
– info@ardencountryhouse.com – Fax (01506) 670 172 – closed 25 December
3 rm – †£ 48/80 ††£ 72/96
◆ Charmingly run guesthouse set in peaceful location with lovely rural views. Thoughtful extras include scones and shortbread on arrival. Rooms boast a luxurious style.

Champany Inn with rm
Champany, Northeast : 2 m. on A 803 at junction with A 904 ✉ EH49 7LU
– ✆ (01506) 834 532 – reception@champany.com – Fax (01506) 834 302 – closed 25-26 December, 1-2 January, Saturday lunch and Sunday
16 rm – †£ 105 ††£ 135 – **Rest** – Beef specialities Menu £ 20 (lunch) – Carte £ 45/74
Spec. Prawns with white wine butter sauce. Rib eye of Aberdeen Angus beef with bearnaise sauce. Raspberry soufflé, chantilly cream.
◆ Personally run restaurant offers precise cooking, specialising in succulently-flavoured prime Scotch beef, with a superb South African wine list. Formal service from 'wenches.' Handsomely equipped bedrooms are themed around tartan colour schemes.

XX **Livingston's**

52 High St ✉ EH49 7AE – ✆ (01506) 846565 – contact@livingstons-restaurant.co.uk – closed first two weeks January, end two weeks June, third week October, Sunday and Monday

Rest – Menu £ 19/34

♦ Friendly restaurant tucked away off high street. Menus offer good value meals using fresh regional produce; comfortable dining room, conservatory and summer terrace.

The Chop and Ale House – at Champany Inn

Champany, Northeast : 2 m. on A 803 at junction with A 904 ✉ EH49 7LU – ✆ (01506) 834532 – reception@champany.com – Fax (01506) 834302 – Closed 25-26 December and 1 January

Rest – Carte £ 18/30

♦ Former bar of Champany Inn: a more relaxed alternative to its restaurant. Stone walls filled with shotguns and animal heads. Meat is all-important; try the homemade burgers.

LOANS – South Ayrshire – **501** G 17 – see Troon

LOCH HARRAY – Orkney Islands – **501** K 6 – see Orkney Islands (Mainland)

LOCHALINE – Argyll and Bute – **501** C 14 29 **B3**

Edinburgh 162 m – Craignure 6 m – Oban 7 m

X **Whitehouse**

✉ PA34 5XT – ✆ (01967) 421777 – info@whitehouserestaurant.co.uk – Fax (01967) 421220 – Easter-October and restricted opening in winter

Rest – (Closed Sunday dinner and Monday) Carte £ 23/30

♦ Remote setting adds to welcoming feel endorsed by hands-on owners. Two lovely, cosy, wood-lined dining rooms where the ethos of seasonal and local cooking shines through.

LOCHBOISDALE – Western Isles Outer Hebrides – **501** Y 12 – see Uist (Isles of)

LOCHEARNHEAD – Stirling – **501** H 14 *Scotland* 28 **C2**

Edinburgh 65 m – Glasgow 56 m – Oban 57 m – Perth 36 m

Mansewood Country House

South : ½ m. on A 84 ✉ FK19 8NS – ✆ (01567) 830213 – stay@mansewoodcountryhouse.co.uk – restricted opening in Winter

5 rm – †£ 40 ††£ 60 – **Rest** – (dinner only) (residents only) Menu £ 20 **s**

♦ An attractive stone building, once a toll house and later a manse. Comfortable lounge and a bar area, well stocked with whiskies. Bedrooms have a cosy snug feel.

LOCHGILPHEAD – Argyll and Bute – **501** D 15 – **pop. 2 326** 27 **B2**

Scotland

Edinburgh 130 m – Glasgow 84 m – Oban 38 m

Lochnell St ✆ (08707) 200618 (April-October), info@lochgilphead.visitscotland.org

Blarbuie Rd, ✆ (01546) 602340 .

Loch Fyne★★, E : 3½ m. by A 83

Empire Travel Lodge without rest

Union St ✉ PA31 8JS – ✆ (01546) 602381 – enquiries@empirelodge.co.uk – Fax (01546) 606606 – closed Christmas-New Year

9 rm – †£ 30 ††£ 55

♦ Former cinema whose interior walls are decorated with classic posters of screen stars. Provides simple, spacious, good value accommodation.

at Cairnbaan **Northwest : 2 ¼ m. by A 816 on B 841 – ✉ Lochgilphead**

Cairnbaan
✉ PA31 8SJ – ✆ (01546) 603 668 – info@cairnbaan.com – Fax (01546) 606 045
12 rm – £ 80/85 £ 125/155 – **Rest** – (bar lunch) Carte £ 18/33
◆ 18C former coaching inn overlooking the Crinan Canal. Comfortable lounges and panelled bar. Well-equipped, individually decorated rooms, some in attractive contemporary style. Light, airy restaurant with modern art decorating the walls.

LOCHINVER – **Highland** – **501** E 9 – ✉ **Lairg** *Scotland* 30 **C1**
Edinburgh 251 m – Inverness 95 m – Wick 105 m
Assynt Visitor Centre, Main St ✆ (01571) 844330 (April-October)
Village ★
Loch Assynt ★★, E : 6 m. by A 837

Inver Lodge ← Loch Inver Bay, Suilven and Canisp mountains,
Iolaire Rd ✉ IV27 4LU – ✆ (01571) 844 496
– stay@inverlodge.com – Fax (01571) 844 395 – April-October
20 rm – £ 150 £ 200 – **Rest** – (bar lunch) Menu £ 35 **s**
◆ Comfy, modern hotel set in hillside above the village, surrounded by unspoilt wilderness. Choice of spacious lounges. Superior bedrooms with ocean views are particularly good. Restaurant boasts wonderful outlook.

Veyatie without rest ← Loch Inver Bay, Suilven and Canisp mountains
66 Baddidarroch,
West : 1 ¼ m. by Baddidarroch rd ✉ IV27 4LP – ✆ (01571) 844 424
– veyatie-lochinver@tiscali.co.uk – Fax (01571) 844 424 – closed mid December-February
3 rm – £ 38/46 £ 54/60
◆ An idyllic secluded haven with stunning views of Loch Inver Bay and mountains. Lovely conservatory. Friendly welcome, relaxing gardens and simple, snug bedrooms.

Davar without rest ← Loch Inver Bay and Suilven,
Baddidarroch, West : ½ m. on Baddidarroch rd ✉ IV27 4LJ
– ✆ (01571) 844 501 – jean@davar36.fsnet.co.uk – March-November
3 rm – £ 30/35 £ 50/54
◆ Modern guesthouse in an excellent position which affords wonderful views of Loch Inver Bay and Suilven. Homely and simple with well-kept bedrooms and communal breakfast.

The Albannach with rm ← Loch Inver Bay, Suilven and Canisp mountains,
Baddidarroch, West : 1 m. by Baddidarroch rd ✉ IV27 4LP – ✆ (01571) 844 407
– info@thealbannach.co.uk – Fax (01571) 844 285
– closed January February
5 rm – £ 170/190 £ 215/250 – **Rest** – (closed Monday) (dinner only) (booking essential for non-residents) (set menu) Menu £ 48
◆ Pleasant restaurant and conservatory with predominantly Scottish feel and exceptional views. Daily changing menu makes fine use of Highland produce. Warm inviting bedrooms.

LOCHMADDY – **Western Isles Outer Hebrides** – **501** Y 11 – see Uist (Isles of)

Undecided between two equivalent establishments?
Within each category, establishments are classified
in our order of preference.

LOCHRANZA – North Ayrshire – **501** E 16 – see Arran (Isle of)

see Arran (Isle of)

LOCKERBIE – Dumfries and Galloway – **501** – pop. 4 009 26 **C3**

Edinburgh 74 m – Carlisle 27 m – Dumfries 13 m – Glasgow 73 m
Corrie Rd, (01576) 203 363;
Lochmaben Castlehill Gate, (01387) 810 552.

Dryfesdale Country House

Northwest : 1 m. by Glasgow rd off B 7076 ✉ DG11 2SF – (01576) 202 427 – reception@dryfesdalehotel.co.uk – Fax (01576) 204 187
28 rm – £ 75/85 £ 110 – **Rest** – Menu £ 17/30 – Carte £ 23/33
◆ Extended, commercially oriented 17C house in a rural setting with pleasant countryside views. Lounge bar with fine selection of malts. Refurbished rooms are modish and smart. Enjoy the vistas from renovated dining room.

LUSS – Argyll and Bute – **501** G 15 – **pop. 402** *Scotland* 27 **B2**

Edinburgh 89 m – Glasgow 26 m – Oban 65 m
Village★
E : Loch Lomond★★

Lodge on Loch Lomond

Loch Lomond, rm,

✉ G83 8PA – (01436) 860 201 – res@loch-lomond.co.uk – Fax (01436) 860 203
46 rm – £ 120/169 £ 139/169 – 1 suite – **Rest** – (light lunch Monday-Saturday) Menu £ 16/30 **s** – Carte £ 20/32 **s**
◆ Busy family run establishment in a superb spot on the shores of Loch Lomond. Most of the cosy pine panelled rooms have balconies; all of them can boast a sauna. Restaurant and bar lounge carefully designed on two levels, opening the view to every table.

Red = Pleasant. Look for the red and symbols.

MAIDENS – South Ayrshire – **501** F 18 25 **A2**

Edinburgh 99 m – Glasgow 53 m – Maybole 7 m

Wildings

rest,

21 Harbour Rd ✉ KA26 9NR – (01655) 331 401 – bookings@wildingsrestaurant.co.uk – Fax (01655) 331 330 – Closed 25-26 December
12 rm – £ 45 £ 80/130 – **Rest** – Seafood Menu £ 15/23
◆ Don't be put off by dated exterior. Popular, bustling hotel adjacent to harbour in coastal hamlet. Refurbished bedrooms; those at front overlook sea. Ground floor restaurant; window tables popular. Seafood orientated menus with plenty of daily specials.

MAYBOLE – South Ayrshire – **501** 402 – **pop. 4 552** *Scotland* 25 **A2**

Edinburgh 93 m – Ayr 10 m – New Galloway 35 m – Stranraer 42 m
Memorial Park, (01655) 889 770 .
Culzean Castle★ **AC** (setting★★★, Oval Staircase★★) W : 5 m. by B 7023 and A 719

Ladyburn

South : 5½ m. by B 7023 and B 741 (Girvan rd) on Walled Garden rd ✉ KA19 7SG – (01655) 740 585 – jh@ladyburn.co.uk – Closed Christmas-New Year
5 rm – £ 60/80 £ 110/130 – **Rest** – (by arrangement) (residents only set menu only) Menu £ 27
◆ Friendly and relaxed family run dower house in beautiful rose gardens. Elegant, bay windowed drawing room, firelit library, charming rooms with antique furniture and prints. Richly flavoured Scottish or Gallic dishes served at candlelit tables.

MELROSE – Borders – 501 L 17 – pop. 11 656 Scotland 26 D2

Edinburgh 38 m – Hawick 19 m – Newcastle upon Tyne 70 m
Abbey House, Abbey St ✆ (01896) 822555
Melrose Dingleton, ✆ (01896) 822 855 .
Town★ - Abbey★★ (decorative sculpture★★★) AC
Eildon Hills (✳ ★★★) – Scott's View★★ – Abbotsford★★ AC, W : 4 ½ m. by A 6091 and B 6360 – Dryburgh Abbey★★ AC (setting★★★), SE : 4 m. by A 6091 – Tweed Valley★★. Bowhill★★ AC, SW : 11 ½ m. by A 6091, A 7 and A 708 – Thirlestane Castle (plasterwork ceilings★★) AC, NE : 21 m. by A 6091 and A 68

Burts

Market Square ✉ TD6 9PL – ✆ (01896) 822 285 – burtshotel@aol.com – Fax (01896) 822 870 – Closed 26 December and 2-3 January
20 rm – †£ 60/85 ††£ 120 – **Rest** – Carte £ 22/30
◆ One-time coaching inn on main square - traditionally appointed and family run. Unpretentious rooms behind a neat black and white façade, brightened by pretty window boxes. Cosy, clubby restaurant.

The Townhouse

Market Sq ✉ TD6 9PQ – ✆ (01896) 822 645 – enquiries@thetownhousemelrose.co.uk – Fax (01896) 823 474 – Closed 26 December and 2-3 January
11 rm – †£ 70/120 ††£ 100/120
Rest – Menu £ 23/29
Rest *Brasserie* – Carte £ 19/31
◆ Refreshed and refurbished, this 17C townhouse has a spruce, clean-lined appeal throughout. The bedrooms continue the theme of simple, well-kept attention to detail. Warm and intimate restaurant or informal brasserie options.

at Gattonside North : 2 m. by B 6374 on B 6360 – ✉ Melrose

Fauhope House without rest

East : ¼ m. by B 6360 taking unmarked lane to the right of Monkswood Rd at edge of village ✉ TD6 9LU – ✆ (01896) 823 184 – fauhope@bordernet.co.uk Fax (01896) 823 184
3 rm – †£ 55 ††£ 90
◆ Melrose Abbey just visible through the trees of this charming 19C country house with its antiques and fine furniture. Valley views at breakfast. Flower strewn, stylish rooms.

METHVEN – Perth and Kinross – 501 J 14 – see Perth

MOFFAT – Dumfries and Galloway – 501 J 17 – pop. 2 135 Scotland 26 C2

Edinburgh 61 m – Carlisle 43 m – Dumfries 22 m – Glasgow 60 m
Churchgate ✆ (01683) 220620 (Easter-October)
Coatshill, ✆ (01683) 220 020 .
Grey Mare's Tail★★, NE : 9 m. by A 708

Bridge House

Well Rd, East : ¾ m. by Selkirk rd (A 708) taking left hand turn before bridge ✉ DG10 9JT – ✆ (01683) 220 558 – info@bridgehousemoffat.co.uk – Closed Christmas-mid Feburary
7 rm – †£ 40/50 ††£ 65/75 – **Rest** – (by arrangement) Menu £ 25
◆ Personally run early Victorian guesthouse. Lots of room to stretch out in comfy, modish lounge overlooking garden. Front two bedrooms have best views, one boasts four poster. Local, seasonal menus in linen-laid dining room.

Well View

Ballplay Rd, East : ¾ m. by Selkirk rd (A 708) ✉ DG10 9JU – ✆ (01683) 220 184 – info@wellview.co.uk – Fax (01683) 220 088
3 rm – †£ 60/80 ††£ 100/120 – **Rest** – (by arrangement, communal dining) Menu £ 35
◆ Well established, family run 19C house. The bedrooms are the strong point: traditionally furnished, they're of a good size and most comfortable.

MONTROSE – Angus – 501 M 13 – pop. 10 845 Scotland 28 D2

Edinburgh 92 m – Aberdeen 39 m – Dundee 29 m
Bridge St ✆ (01674) 672000 (Easter-September)
Traill Drive, ✆ (01674) 672 932.
Edzell Castle★ (The Pleasance★★★) AC, NW : 17 m. by A 935 and B 966 – Cairn O'Mount Road★ (≤ ★★) N : 17 m. by B 966 and B 974 – Brechin (Round Tower★) W : 7 m. by A 935 – Aberlemno (Aberlemno Stones★, Pictish sculptured stones★) W : 13 m. by A 935 and B 9134

36 The Mall without rest

36 The Mall, North : ½ m. by A 92 at junction with North Esk Road ✉ DD10 8SS – ✆ (01674) 673 646 – enquiries@36themall.co.uk – Fax (01674) 673 646

3 rm – ♦£ 35/50 ♦♦£ 50/70

♦ Bay windowed 19C former manse with pleasant conservatory lounge to rear. Impressive plate collection the talking point of communal breakfast room. Sizable, well-kept rooms.

MOTHERWELL – North Lanarkshire – 501 I 16 25 B1

Edinburgh 38 m – Glasgow 12 m

Hilton Strathclyde

rm, rest, VISA AE

Phoenix Crescent, Bellshill, Northwest : 4 m. by A 721 on A 725 ✉ ML4 3JQ – ✆ (01698) 395 500 – reservations.strathclyde@hilton.com – Fax (01698) 395 511

111 rm – ♦£ 154 ♦♦£ 164, £ 15.95 – **Rest** – (closed lunch Saturday) Menu £ 12/22 – Carte dinner £ 25/40

♦ Group owned and smoothly run; a regular choice for business travellers, drawn by smartly laid-out modern rooms, open-plan lounge and coffee shop and superb leisure complex. Restaurant sets out to put a subtle new spin on classic dishes.

Alona

rm, rest, VISA AE

Strathclyde Country Park, Northwest : 4½ m. by A 721 and B 7070 off A 725 ✉ ML1 3RT – ✆ (01698) 333 888 – reservations@alonahotel.co.uk – Fax (01698) 338 720

51 rm – ♦£ 120 ♦♦£ 120 – **Rest** – Carte £ 15/40

♦ Attractively set modern hotel in 1500 acres of Strathclyde Country Park. Conservatory atrium with open-plan lounge and bar. Good-sized bedrooms exuding contemporary taste. Restaurant affords pleasant lakeside views.

MUIR OF ORD – Highland – 501 G 11 – pop. 1 812 30 C2

Edinburgh 173 m – Inverness 10 m – Wick 121 m
Great North Rd, ✆ (01463) 870 825.

Dower House

VISA

Highfield, North : 1 m. on A 862 ✉ IV6 7XN – ✆ (01463) 870 090 – enquiries@thedowerhouse.co.uk – Fax (01463) 870 090 – Closed 2 weeks November and Christmas

3 rm (dinner included) – ♦£ 70/90 ♦♦£ 120/160 – 1 suite – **Rest** – (booking essential for non-residents) (set menu only, lunch by arrangement) Menu 38

♦ Personally run, part 17C house in mature garden. Stacked bookshelves, soft fireside armchairs, cosy bedrooms and fresh flowers: a relaxed but well-ordered country home. Dining room offers careful cooking of fine fresh ingredients.

Your opinions are important to us: please write and let us know about your discoveries and experiences – good and bad!

SCOTLAND

MULL (Isle of) – Argyll and Bute – 501 B/C – pop. 2 838 Scotland 27 A2

from Craignure to Oban (Caledonian MacBrayne Ltd) frequent services daily (45 mn) – from Fishnish to Lochaline (Mainland) (Caledonian MacBrayne Ltd) frequent services daily (15 mn) – from Tobermory to Isle of Tiree (Scarinish) via Isle of Coll (Arinagour) (Caledonian MacBrayne Ltd) 3 weekly (2 h 30 mn) – from Tobermory to Kilchoan (Caledonian MacBrayne Ltd) 4 daily (summer only) (35 mn)

from Fionnphort to Isle of Iona (Caledonian MacBrayne Ltd) frequent services daily (10 mn) – from Pierowall to Papa Westray (Orkney Ferries Ltd) (summer only) (25 mn)

The Pier, Craignure ☎ (08707) 200610Main Street, Tobermory ☎ (01688) 302182 (April-October)

Craignure Scallastle, ☎ (01688) 302517 .

Island★ - Calgary Bay★★ – Torosay Castle **AC** (Gardens★ ← ★)

Isle of Iona★ (Maclean's Cross★, St Oran's Chapel★, St Martin's High Cross★, Infirmary Museum★ **AC** (Cross of St John★))

Bunessan – Argyll and Bute 27 A2

Reef

Main St ✉ PA67 6DG – ☎ (01681) 700291 – Fax (01681) 700534 – Closed October-March, Saturday lunch and Sunday

Rest – Seafood Carte £ 15/27

◆ Don't be put off by simple tea-room façade and standard menu. Come here to enjoy the supremely fresh, excellent value daily blackboard seafood specials - owner is a fisherman.

Craignure – Argyll and Bute 27 B2

Birchgrove without rest

Lochdon, Southeast : 3 m. on A 849 ✉ PA64 6AP – ☎ (01680) 812364 – birchgrove.mull@btinternet.com – 20 March-12 October

3 rm – †£ 46/54 ††£ 64/72

◆ Modern guesthouse with landscaped gardens in peaceful setting with good views. Close to ferry pier. Clean, well-kept rooms, all boasting pleasant island outlook.

Gruline – Argyll and Bute 27 A2

Gruline Home Farm

✉ PA71 6HR – ☎ (01680) 300581 – boo@gruline.com – Fax (01680) 300573

3 rm (dinner included) – †£ 145 ††£ 180 – **Rest** – (by arrangement, communal dining) Menu £ 35

◆ Spot deer, eagles and buzzards in utter tranquillity at this delightful farm, located off the beaten track with fine views over nearby mountains. Beautifully appointed rooms. Creative cooking brings out true flavour of island produce.

Tiroran – Argyll and Bute 27 A2

Tiroran House ← Loch Scridain,

✉ PA69 6ES – ☎ (01681) 705232 – info@tiroran.com – Fax (01681) 705240

7 rm – †£ 135 ††£ 165 – **Rest** – (dinner only) (booking essential) (residents only) Menu £ 43

◆ Attractive whitewashed hotel sited in remote location with superb views across Loch Scridain. Well-decorated lounges with country house style. Individually appointed rooms. Home-cooked dinners in vine-covered dining room or conservatory.

Tobermory – Argyll and Bute – pop. 2 708 27 A2

Erray Rd, ☎ (01688) 302387 .

Tobermory ← rm,

53 Main St ✉ PA75 6NT – ☎ (01688) 302091 – tobhotel@tinyworld.co.uk – Fax (01688) 302254 – Closed 13 January-9 February and 1 week Christmas

16 rm – †£ 38/94 ††£ 90/118

Rest *Waters Edge* – (dinner only) (booking essential for non-residents) Menu £ 31

◆ Pink-painted, converted fishing cottages - cosy, well-run and informal - on the pretty quayside. Soft toned bedrooms in cottage style, most overlooking the bay. Intimate setting: linen-clad tables and subtly nautical décor.

SCOTLAND

Ptarmigan House without rest

The Fairways, North : ½ m. by Back Brae and Erray Rd ✉ PA75 6PS – ✆ (01688) 302 863 – ptarmiganhouse@hotmail.co.uk – Fax (01688) 302 913

3 rm – †£ 110 ††£ 145

◆ Immaculately nuanced, with super Sound of Mull views from smart decked terrace. Enjoy a swim in the pool, then take in vista from your room: one has terrace, one a balcony.

Brockville without rest

Raeric Rd, by Back Brae ✉ PA75 6RS – ✆ (01688) 302 741 – helen@brockville-tobermory.co.uk – Fax (01688) 302 741

3 rm – †£ 35/65 ††£ 35/65

◆ Modern guesthouse in the residential part of town. The communal breakfast room has good views over the sea. Cottagey rooms have extra touches including videos and CDs.

Highland Cottage with rm

Breadalbane St, via B 8073 ✉ PA75 6PD – ✆ (01688) 302 030 – davidandjo@highlandcottage.co.uk – March-October

6 rm – †£ 130 ††£ 185 – **Rest** – (dinner only) (booking essential for non-residents) Menu £ 43

◆ Modern cottage near the harbour. Prettily set dining room shows the same care and attention as the locally sourced menu. Individually styled rooms with good views.

SCOTLAND

NAIRN – Highland – 501 I 11 – pop. 8 418 *Scotland* 30 D2

Edinburgh 172 m – Aberdeen 91 m – Inverness 16 m

Seabank Rd, ✆ (01667) 453 208 ;

Nairn Dunbar Lochloy Rd, ✆ (01667) 452 741 .

Forres (Sueno's Stone★★) E : 11 m. by A 96 and B 9011 - Cawdor Castle★ **AC**, S : 5½ m. by B 9090 – Brodie Castle★ **AC**, E : 6 m. by A 96. Fort George★, W : 8 m. by A 96, B 9092 and B 9006

Golf View

rest,

The Seafront ✉ IV12 4HD – ✆ (01667) 458 807 – sales.golf view@crevarmgmt.com – Fax (01667) 455 267

41 rm – †£ 97/120 ††£ 146/210 – 1 suite

Rest *Restaurant* – Carte £ 19/22

Rest *Conservatory* – Carte £ 19/27 **s**

◆ Non-golfers may prefer the vista of the Moray Firth from one of the sea-view rooms or a poolside lounger. Smart, traditional accommodation, up-to-date gym and beauty salon. Half-panelled dining room. Stylish, spacious conservatory restaurant.

Claymore House

rm,

45 Seabank Rd ✉ IV12 4EY – ✆ (01667) 453 731 – claymorehouse@btconnect.com – Fax (01667) 455 290

15 rm – †£ 48/55 ††£ 95/115 – 1 suite – **Rest** – (bar lunch) Carte £ 17/22 **s**

◆ A privately-run, extended 19C house in a residential area. Comfortable lounge and conservatory. Modern rooms in warm colours are quieter at the rear. Neatly laid-out dining room: choose from a range of traditional Scottish favourites.

Boath House

rm,

Auldearn, East : 2 m. on A 96 ✉ IV12 5TE – ✆ (01667) 454 896 – wendy@boath-house.com – Fax (01667) 455 469 – closed 2 weeks over Christmas

8 rm – †£ 140/190 ††£ 220 – **Rest** – (closed for non-residents Monday-Wednesday lunch) (booking essential) Menu £ 27/55

◆ 1820s neo-classical mansion, owned by a charming couple, hosts modern Highland art collections. Intimate, elegant rooms may have half-tester beds or views of the trout lake. Dining room with 18C garden views: precise, accomplished cooking in a modern style.

Sunny Brae
Marine Rd ✉ IV12 4EA – ✆ (01667) 452 309 – reservations@sunnybraehotel.com – Fax (01667) 454 860 – Closed 21 December-January
8 rm – £ 69/138 £ 78/138 – **Rest** – (lunch only for residents)
Carte approx. £ 28
◆ Behind an unassuming façade, this family-owned hotel offers sizeable, neatly kept bedrooms in cheerful patterns - many, like the terrace, have views of the shore. Light, summery dining room; traditional Scottish menus.

Bracadale House without rest
Albert St ✉ IV12 4HF – ✆ (01667) 452 547 – hannah@bracadalehouse.com
3 rm – £ 30/35 £ 55/60
◆ This elegant Victorian house, near the beach, is enthusiastically run by a friendly owner. There's an attractive first floor lounge and rooms finished with a tasteful palette.

The Classroom
1 Cawdor St ✉ IV12 4QD – ✆ (01667) 455 999 – enquiries@cawdortavern.info – Fax (01667) 455 999 – closed 25-26 December and 1-2 January
Rest – Carte £ 14/25
◆ Extended former school house in town centre. Split level modern brasserie style with L-shaped bar and pictures of pupils on the walls. Extensive menu with daily specials.

Look out for red symbols, indicating particularly pleasant establishments.

SCOTLAND

NETHERLEY – Aberdeenshire – 501 N 13 – see Stonehaven

NEW LANARK – Lanarkshire – 501 I 17 *Scotland* 25 B2

Edinburgh 44 m – Dumfries 55 m – Glasgow 31 m
Town★★

New Lanark Mill
Mill One, New Lanark Mills ✉ ML11 9DB – ✆ (01555) 667 200 – hotel@newlanark.org – Fax (01555) 667 222
38 rm – £ 75 £ 109
Rest *Mill One* – (carvery lunch Sunday, bar lunch Monday-Saturday)
Menu £ 26 **s**
◆ Converted Clydeside cotton mill on the riverside in this superbly restored Georgian village, a World Heritage site. Usefully equipped, modern accommodation. Formal restaurant overlooking the river.

NEWTON STEWART – Dumfries and Galloway – 501 G 19 – pop. 3 573 *Scotland* 25 B3

Edinburgh 131 m – Dumfries 51 m – Glasgow 87 m – Stranraer 24 m
Stewart Dashwood Sq ✆ (01671) 402431 (Easter-October)
Minnigaff Kirroughtree Ave, ✆ (01671) 402 172 ;
Wigtownshire County Glenluce Mains of Park, ✆ (01581) 300 420 .
Galloway Forest Park★, Queen's Way★ (Newton Stewart to New Galloway) N : 19 m. by A 712

Kirroughtree House < woodland and Wigtown Bay,
Northeast : 1½ m. by A 75 on A 712 ✉ DG8 6AN – ✆ (01671) 402 141 – info@kirroughtreehouse.co.uk – Fax (01671) 402425 – closed 2 January-mid February
15 rm – £ 95/105 £ 190/210 – 2 suites – **Rest** – (booking essential for non-residents) Menu £ 33 (dinner) **s** – Carte lunch £ 19/25 **s**
◆ Grand 1719 mansion dominates acres of sculpted garden. Well-proportioned bedrooms; firelit lounge with antiques, period oils and French windows leading to the croquet lawn. Elegant fine dining, in keeping with formal grandeur of the house.

Rowallan

Corsbie Rd, via Jubilee Rd off Dashwood Sq ✉ DG8 6JB – ✆ (01671) 402 520 – enquiries@rowallan.co.uk – Fax (01671) 402 520

6 rm – †£ 39 ††£ 68 – **Rest** – (by arrangement) Menu £ 14

◆ Victorian house in attractive large garden not far from town centre. Large lounge with bar; meals served in conservatory. Brightly decorated bedrooms.

NORTH BAY – Western Isles – see Barra (Isle of)

NORTH BERWICK – East Lothian – 501 L 15 – pop. 5 871 *Scotland* 26 D1

Edinburgh 24 m – Newcastle upon Tyne 102 m

Quality St ✆ (01620) 892197

North Berwick Beach Rd, West Links, ✆ (01620) 890 312 ;

The Glen East Links, ✆ (01620) 892 726 .

North Berwick Law (✳ ★★★) S : 1 m. - Tantallon Castle★★ (clifftop site★★★) **AC**, E : 3½ m. by A 198 – Dirleton★ (Castle★ **AC**) SW : 2½ m. by A 198. Museum of Flight★, S : 6 m. by B 1347 – Preston Mill★, S : 8½ m. by A 198 and B 1047 – Tyninghame★, S : 7 m. by A 198 – Coastal road from North Berwick to Portseton★, SW : 13 m. by A 198 and B 1348

Glebe House without rest

Law Rd ✉ EH39 4PL – ✆ (01620) 892 608 – gwenscott@glebehouse-nb.co.uk – Fax (01620) 893 588 – closed 25-26 December

3 rm – †£ 50/60 ††£ 80/90

◆ Owned by a likeable couple, a classically charming 1780s manse in secluded gardens. En suite rooms are pleasantly unfussy and well-kept. Breakfasts at a long communal table.

Beach Lodge without rest

5 Beach Rd ✉ EH39 4AB – ✆ (01620) 892 257 – william@beachlodge.co.uk

3 rm – †£ 50/60 ††£ 80/90

◆ Friendly and well-run: breakfast room and compact, modern bedrooms share an appealing, clean-lined style. All rooms have fridges and videos, one overlooks the sea.

**The ✿ award is the crème de la crème.
This is awarded to restaurants
which are really worth travelling miles for!**

NORTH QUEENSFERRY – Fife – 501 J 15 – pop. 1 102 28 C3

Edinburgh 13 m – Dunfermline 6 m – Glasgow 45 m

The Wee Restaurant

17 Main St ✉ KY11 1JG – ✆ (01383) 616 263 – closed 25 and 26 December Sunday-Monday

Rest – Menu £ 15 (lunch) **s** – Carte £ 26/30 **s**

◆ Small, intimate restaurant, as suggested by its name. Simple wooden tables. Delightful local photos. Tasty, carefully prepared food with a French flavour. Chatty service.

NORTH UIST – Western Isles Outer Hebrides – 501 X/Y – see Uist (Isles of)

SCOTLAND

Edinburgh 123 m – Dundee 116 m – Glasgow 93 m – Inverness 118 m

Access Access to Glasgow by helicopter

to Isle of Mull (Craignure) (Caledonian MacBrayne Ltd) (45 mn) – to Isle of Tiree (Scarinish) via Isle of Mull (Tobermory) and Isle of Coll (Arinagour) (Caledonian MacBrayne Ltd) – to Isle of Islay (Port Askaig) and Kintyre Peninsula (Kennacraig) via Isle of Colonsay (Scalasaig) (Caledonian MacBrayne Ltd) (summer only) – to Isle of Lismore (Achnacroish) (Caledonian MacBrayne Ltd) 2-3 daily (except Sunday) (55 mn) – to Isle of Colonsay (Scalasaig) (Caledonian MacBrayne Ltd) 3 weekly (2 h)

Church Building, Argyll Sq (08707) 200630, info@oban.org.uk

Glencruitten Glencruitten Rd, (01631) 562 868 .

Loch Awe★★, SE : 17 m. by A 85 – Bonawe Furnace★, E : 12 m. by A 85 – Cruachan Power Station★ **AC**, E : 16 m. by A 85 – Seal and Marine Centre★ **AC**, N : 14 m. by A 828

Manor House
< Oban harbour and bay, P VISA AE

Gallanach Rd PA34 4LS – (01631) 562 087 – info@manorhouseoban.com – Fax (01631) 563 053 – closed 25-26 December

11 rm (dinner included) – £ 114/172 £ 186/239 – **Rest** – (lunch by arrangement) Menu £ 34

◆ Period furniture and colour schemes bring out the character of this 18C dower house, once part of the Argyll ducal estate. Individual rooms, most with fine views of the bay. Green and tartan restaurant warmed by an ancient range.

Knipoch House
< P VISA AE

Southwest : 6 m. on A 816 PA34 4QT – (01852) 316 251 – reception@knipochhotel.co.uk – Fax (01852) 316 249

20 rm – £ 81/87 £ 162/174 – 1 suite – **Rest** – (bar lunch) Carte £ 23/35 **s**

◆ Between wooded hills and Loch Feochan, a relaxing, traditional environment of wood panelling and roaring fires. Comfortable, well-equipped rooms; most look on to the water. Unpretentious Scottish cooking and lake views in three separate rooms.

Lerags House
< P VISA

Lerags, Southwest : 4½ m. by A 816 on Lerags rd PA34 4SE – (01631) 563 381 – stay@leragshouse.com – restricted opening in winter

6 rm (dinner included) – £ 105 £ 190 – **Rest** – (dinner only) (booking essential)

◆ Peacefully located, characterful Georgian house with extensions in mature gardens near Loch Feochan. Comfortable, welcoming lounge. Sizeable rooms boasting homely extras. Simple dining room with garden aspect.

The Barriemore without rest
< Oban bay, Kerrera and Isle of Mull, P VISA

Corran Esplanade PA34 5AQ – (01631) 566 356 – reception@barriemore-hotel.co.uk – Fax (01631) 571 084 – closed January, 2 weeks November and Christmas

11 rm – £ 45/65 £ 80/90

◆ Gabled 1890s house overlooking town and islands. A comfortable blend of modern and period styling - front bedrooms are larger and look towards Oban Bay, Kerrera and Mull.

Glenburnie House without rest
< Oban bay, Kerrera and Isle of Mull, P VISA

Corran Esplanade PA34 5AQ – (01631) 562 089 – graeme.strachan@btinternet.com – Fax (01631) 562 089 – March-November

12 rm – £ 45/50 £ 80/95 – 1 suite

◆ Bay-windowed Victorian house has enviable views over the bay. Pleasant lounge with a hint of homely informality and usefully equipped rooms, one with a four-poster bed.

Alltavona without rest
< Oban bay, Kerrera and Isle of Mull, P VISA

Corran Esplanade PA34 5AQ – (01631) 565 067 – carol@alltavona.co.uk – Fax (01631) 565 067

10 rm – £ 25/80 £ 70/90

◆ 19C villa on smart esplanade with fine views of Oban Bay. Attractively furnished interiors in keeping with the house's age. Fine oak staircase and individually styled rooms.

SCOTLAND

XX **Coast**

104 George St ✉ PA34 5NT – ✆ (01631) 569 900 – coastoban@yahoo.co.uk – Fax (01631) 569 901 – closed 25 December

Rest – Menu £ 12 (lunch) – Carte dinner £ 21/34

◆ Former bank building in town centre. Contemporary interior of stripped wood floors and khaki coloured walls. Appealing modern menus including plenty of fish and shellfish.

X **Ee-usk at The North Pier** ← Oban harbour and bay,

The North Pier ✉ PA34 5DQ – ✆ (01631) 565 666 – eeusk.fishcafe@virgin.net – Fax (01631) 570 282 – closed 6-16 January

Rest – Seafood Carte £ 21/31

◆ A smart addition to the pier with its harbour proximity; excellent views of the bay add a relaxing charm. Fresh seafood menus with daily specials.

X **The Waterfront** ← Oban harbour and bay,

No 1, The Pier ✉ PA34 4LW – ✆ (01631) 563 110 – Fax (01631) 562 853 – closed 4 weeks Christmas

Rest – Seafood Carte £ 18/32 **s**

◆ Converted quayside mission with fine views of harbour and bay; airy, open-plan interior. Flavourful but simple seafood: blackboard specials feature the day's fresh catch.

SCOTLAND

The red symbol?
This denotes the very essence of peace
– only the sound of birdsong first thing in the morning …

OLDMELDRUM – Aberdeenshire – 501 N 11 *Scotland* 28 D1

Edinburgh 140 m – Aberdeen 17 m – Inverness 87 m

Oldmeldrum Kirkbrae, ✆ (01651) 872 648 .

Haddo House★, NE : 9 m. by B 9170 on B 9005

Cromlet Hill without rest

South Rd ✉ AB51 0AB – ✆ (01651) 872 315 – johnpage@cromlethill.co.uk – Fax (01651) 872 164 – closed Christmas

3 rm – †£ 45 ††£ 70

◆ Half Georgian, half Victorian house with attractive front garden. Characterful sitting room; smart, airy, well-equipped rooms. Communal breakfast at antique dining table.

ONICH – Highland – 501 E 13 – ✉ Fort William 29 B3

Edinburgh 123 m – Glasgow 93 m – Inverness 79 m – Oban 39 m

Lodge on the Loch ← Loch Linnhe and mountains,

on A 82 ✉ PH33 6RY – ✆ (01855) 821 238 – info@lodgeontheloch.com – Fax (01855) 821 190

14 rm – †£ 105/125 ††£ 130/230 – 1 suite – **Rest** – (dinner only) Carte approx. £ 30 **s**

◆ Steam shower or sleigh bed, Shaker or Art Nouveau styling: carefully composed bijou rooms in a Victorian hotel above Loch Linnhe - classically cosy lounges have fine views. Formally set tables in the dining room and a great view south across the water.

ORKNEY ISLANDS – 501 K/L 6/ – pop. 19 612 Scotland 31 A3

- see Kirkwall
- service between Isle of Hoy (Longhope), Isle of Hoy (Lyness), Isle of Flotta and Houton (Orkney Ferries Ltd) – from Stromness to Scrabster (P & O Scottish Ferries) (1-3 daily) (2 h) – from Stromness to Shetland Islands (Lerwick) and Aberdeen (Northlink Ferries) 1-2 daily – from Kirkwall to Westray, Stronsay via Eday and Sanday (Orkney Ferries Ltd) – from Tingwall to Wyre via Egilsay and Rousay (Orkney Ferries Ltd) – from Kirkwall to Shapinsay (Orkney Ferries Ltd) (25 mn) – from Stromness to Isle of Hoy (Moness) and Graemsay (Orkney Ferries Ltd) – from Kirkwall to North Ronaldsay (Orkney Ferries Ltd) weekly (2 h 40 mn) - from Kirkwall to Invergordon (Orcargo Ltd) daily (8 h 30 mn) – from Houton to Isle of Hoy (Lyness), Flotta and Longhope (Orkney Ferries Ltd)
- from Burwick (South Ronaldsay) to John O'Groats (John O'Groats Ferries) 2-4 daily (40 mn) (summer only)
- Old Man of Hoy★★★ – Islands★★ – Maes Howe★★ **AC** – Skara Brae★★ **AC** – Kirkbuster Museum and Corrigal Farm Museum★ **AC** – Brough of Birsay★ **AC** – Birsay (< ★) – Ring of Brodgar★ – Unstan Cairn★

MAINLAND – Orkney Islands

Burray – Orkney Islands 31 A3

Sands

KW17 2SS – (01856) 731 298 – info@thesandshotel.co.uk – Fax (01856) 731 303

6 rm – †£ 70/80 ††£ 85/140 – **Rest** – (bar lunch) Carte £ 17/28 **s**

◆ Former fish store, just 20 yards' walk from main pier. Totally modern interior with plenty of space and lots of seafaring knick-knacks. Popular bar. Sizeable, modish bedrooms. Spacious dining room with views of bay: light or formal choice of menus.

Kirkwall – Orkney Islands – pop. 5 952 Scotland 31 A3

- Kirkwall Airport : (01856) 886210, S : 3½ m
- 6 Broad St (01856) 872856
- Grainbank, (01856) 872457 .
- Kirkwall★★ - St Magnus Cathedral★★ – Western Mainland★★, Eastern Mainland (Italian Chapel★) - Earl's Palace★ **AC** – Tankerness House Museum★ **AC** – Orkney Farm and Folk Museum★

Ayre

Ayre Rd KW15 1QX – (01856) 873 001 – enquiries@ayrehotel.co.uk – Fax (01856) 876 289 – Closed 25 December and 1 January

33 rm – †£ 75 ††£ 110 – **Rest** – Carte £ 15/30

◆ Smoothly run by an experienced family team, this hotel by the harbour offers modern, practically fitted bedrooms and one of the island's most spacious conference rooms. Dining room decorated in simple, modern style.

St Ola without rest 

Harbour St KW15 1LE – (01856) 875 090 – enquiries@stolahotel.co.uk – Fax (01856) 875 090 – Closed Christmas and New Year

6 rm – †£ 42 ††£ 58

◆ Practically furnished, converted town house facing the harbour and convenient for the ferry terminal. Neat bedrooms in co-ordinating fabrics. Simple public bar.

Lav'rockha

Inganess Rd, Southeast : 1¼ m. by A 960 KW15 1SP – (01856) 876 103 – lavrockha@orkney.com – Fax (01856) 876 103 – closed February

5 rm – †£ 35/40 ††£ 50/56 – **Rest** – (by arrangement) Menu £ 14.95

◆ Personally run in an enthusiastic spirit. Spotless en suite rooms in floral fabrics or dark tartans. Homely, uncluttered lounge with useful tourist information. Popular, traditional menu, served in the simplest of settings.

Polrudden without rest

Peerie Sea Loan, West : 1 m. by Pickaquoy Rd ✉ KW15 1UH – ✆ (01856) 874761 – linda@polrudden.com – closed Christmas and New Year

7 rm ☐ – 🚹£35/45 🚹🚹£50/60

◆ Well-kept en suite accommodation - over two floors - with matching fabrics and varnished pine in a sizeable converted house just outside the town centre. Friendly owner.

Brekk-Ness without rest

Muddisdale Rd, West : ¾ m. by Pickaquoy Rd ✉ KW15 1RS – ✆ (01856) 874317 – sandrabews@aol.com – Fax (01856) 874317 – closed Christmas

11 rm ☐ – 🚹£40/45 🚹🚹£60/70

◆ In the fields on the edge of the town, an unassuming guesthouse, neatly maintained by a likeable couple. Bedrooms are practically fitted and en suite.

Foveran with rm

St Ola, Southwest : 3 m. on A 964 ✉ KW15 1SF – ✆ (01856) 872389 – foveranhotel@aol.com – Fax (01856) 876430 – restricted opening in winter

8 rm ☐ – 🚹£62/80 🚹🚹£104 – **Rest** – (dinner only) Carte £19/31

◆ Modern restaurant enjoys beautiful view of Scapa Flow. Simple, soft-toned bedrooms, furnished in warm wood and a firelit lounge, in same style, where apéritifs are served. Orkney fudge cheesecake a dining room regular.

Loch Harray – Orkney Islands 31 A3

Merkister ← Loch Harray,

off A 986 ✉ KW17 2LF – ✆ (01856) 771366 – merkister-hotel@ecosse.net – Fax (01856) 771515 – closed 23 December-5 January

16 rm ☐ – 🚹£30/70 🚹🚹£60/140 – **Rest** – (bar lunch Monday-Saturday) (booking essential) Menu £25 – Carte £22/35

◆ In a peaceful spot above Loch Harray, a popular angling base, family run with friendly efficiency. Trim bedrooms; public bar with a quiet buzz of far-fetched fishing tales. Restaurant offers an extensive menu on a distinctly Scottish base.

St Margaret's Hope – Orkney Islands 31 A3

Creel with rm

Front Rd ✉ KW17 2SL – ✆ (01856) 831311 – alan@thecreel.freeserve.co.uk – April-mid October

3 rm ☐ – 🚹£70/80 🚹🚹£95/115 – **Rest** – Seafood (dinner only) Menu £33

◆ Smart, family run restaurant; flavourful local dishes without culinary curlicues: menu devised daily based upon the best seasonal produce. Friendly staff. Neat, homely rooms.

ISLAND OF WESTRAY – Orkney Islands 31 A2

Cleaton House ← Papa Westray, rm,

✉ *KW17 2DB – ✆ (01857) 677508 – cleaton@orkney.com – Fax (01857) 677442*

6 rm ☐ – 🚹£50/60 🚹🚹£80/125 – **Rest** – (bar lunch) (booking essential for non-residents) Menu £32 (dinner)

◆ Originally built as mansion for Laird of Cleat in 1850, this charming guesthouse is idyllically situated halfway up the island. Charming lounge. Individually appointed rooms. Country house dining room overlooks garden.

PEAT INN – Fife 28 D2

Peat Inn with rm

✉ *KY15 5LH – ✆ (01334) 840206 – stay@thepeatinn.co.uk – Fax (01334) 840530 – closed 1-3January, 25-26 December and Sunday-Monday*

8 rm – 🚹£95/135 🚹🚹£145/165 – **Rest** – (booking essential) Menu £16/32 – Carte £25/45

◆ Former coaching inn with a homely country house style.Three dining rooms serve tasty, traditional dishes. Annex bedrooms are very strong and full of charming extra touches.

SCOTLAND

TIERCE MAJEURE

RESERVE DE LA COMTESSE
SECOND VIN DU CHATEAU
PICHON LONGUEVILLE COMTESSE DE LALANDE

CHATEAU PICHON LONGUEVILLE
COMTESSE DE LALANDE
GRAND CRU CLASSE EN 1855 - PAUILLAC

CHATEAU BERNADOTTE
HAUT-MEDOC

33250 Pauillac - France - Tel. 33 (0)5 56 59 19 40 - Fax. 33 (0)5 56 59 29 78

WWW.PICHON-LALANDE.COM

The MICHELIN Guide

A collection to savor!

Belgique & Luxembourg
Deutschland
España & Portugal
France
Great Britain & Ireland
Italia
Nederland
Österreich
Portugal
Suisse-Schweiz-Svizzera
Main Cities of Europe

Also:

Las Vegas
London
Los Angeles
New York City
Paris
San Francisco
Tokyo

PEEBLES – Borders – 501 K 17 – pop. 8 065 *Scotland* 26 C2

Edinburgh 24 m – Glasgow 53 m – Hawick 31 m
High St ✆ (01721) 720138
Kirkland St, ✆ (01721) 720 197.
Tweed Valley★★. Traquair House★★ **AC**, SE : 7 m. by B 7062 – Rosslyn Chapel★★ **AC**, N : 16½ m. by A 703, A 6094, B 7026 and B 7003

Cringletie House

Edinburgh Rd, North : 3 m. on A 703 ✉ EH45 8PL – ✆ (01721) 725 750 – enquiries@cringletie.com – Fax (01721) 725 751
13 rm – †£ 140/175 ††£ 260/310 – **Rest** – Carte approx. £ 43
♦ Smoothly run and handsomely furnished Victorian hotel in country house style with contemporary edge. Rooms are modern, well-equipped and peaceful. Spacious, formal restaurant with a trompe l'oeil ceiling.

Peebles Hydro

Innerleithen Rd ✉ EH45 8LX – ✆ (01721) 720 602 – info@peebleshydro.com – Fax (01721) 722 999
126 rm – †£ 132/138 ††£ 135/147 – 3 suites – **Rest** – Menu £ 21/30
♦ Grand Edwardian spa hotel, now offering everything from aromatherapy to reflexology plus a crèche and supervised activities to keep children busy. Modern, soft-toned bedrooms. High ceilinged, classically styled restaurant.

Castle Venlaw

Edinburgh Road, North : 1¼ m. by A 703 ✉ EH45 8QG – ✆ (01721) 720 384 – stay@venlaw.co.uk – Fax (01721) 724 066
12 rm – †£ 75/95 ††£ 130/230 – **Rest** – (booking essential for non-residents) Menu £ 33 **s**
♦ Renovated 18C Scottish baronial style house in wooded gardens: friendly and privately run. Well-appointed rooms; family suite in tower. Afternoon tea in firelit Library bar. Parquet-floored dining room with pleasant views through the trees.

SCOTLAND

Park

Innerleithen Rd ✉ EH45 8BA – ✆ (01721) 720 451 – reserve@parkhotelpeebles.co.uk – Fax (01721) 723 510
24 rm – †£ 85/99 ††£ 156/208 – **Rest** – Menu £ 18/27 **s**
♦ Extended town-centre hotel - tidy and unpretentious - overlooks a well-tended lawn. Simple bar with tartan sofas, neatly kept rooms: a good address for the mature traveller. Wood-panelled restaurant continues the traditional décor and atmosphere of the hotel.

Rowanbrae without rest

103 Northgate ✉ EH45 8BU – ✆ (01721) 721 630 – john@rowanbrae.freeserve.co.uk – Fax (01721) 723 324 – closed Christmas-New Year
3 rm – †£ 35 ††£ 50
♦ Built for the manager of a 19C woollen mill. Pleasant, affordable rooms, well kept by a cheerful couple. Fortifying breakfasts with posies of garden flowers on each table.

Halcyon

39 Eastgate ✉ EH45 8AD – ✆ (01721) 725 100 – mail@halcyonrestaurant.com – closed Christmas, New Year and Sunday-Monday
Rest – Menu £ 15 – Carte £ 21/38
♦ Chef/owner prepares and cooks alone in kitchen; regulars at this cosy restaurant appreciate his constantly evolving menus featuring skilfully prepared, excellent value dishes.

at Eddleston North : 4 1/2 m. on A 703

The Horseshoe Inn with rm

✉ EH45 8QP – ✆ (01721) 730 225 – reservations@horseshoe.inn.co.uk – Fax (01721) 730 268 – Closed 1 week January, 1 week October, 25 December and dinner Sunday-Monday
8 rm – †£ 70/80 ††£ 100/120
Rest – Menu £ 17 (lunch) – Carte dinner £ 28/43
Rest ***Bistro*** – Carte £ 22/28
♦ It's easy to drive past this roadside former pub but stop off for serious cooking from experienced French chef or lighter dishes in adjacent bistro. Simple, comfy bedrooms.

PERTH – Perth and Kinross – **501** J 14 – pop. 43 450 *Scotland* 28 **C2**

Edinburgh 44 m – Aberdeen 86 m – Dundee 22 m – Dunfermline 29 m – Glasgow 64 m – Inverness 112 m – Oban 94 m

Lower City Mills, West Mill St ✆ (01738) 450600, perthtic@perthshire.co.uk

Craigie Hill Cherrybank, ✆ (01738) 620 829 ;

King James VI Moncreiffe Island, ✆ (01738) 625 170 ;

Murrayshall New Scone, ✆ (01738) 554 804 ;

North Inch, c/o Perth & Kinross Council 5 High St, ✆ (01738) 636 481 .

City★ – Black Watch Regimental Museum★ Y **M1** – Georgian Terraces★ Y – Museum and Art Gallery★ Y **M2**

Scone Palace★★ **AC**, N : 2 m. by A 93 Y – Branklyn Garden★ **AC**, SE : 1 m. by A 85 Z – Kinnoull Hill (≤ ★) SE : 1 ¼ m. by A 85 Z – Huntingtower Castle★ **AC**, NW : 3 m. by A 85 Y – Elcho Castle★ **AC**, SE : 4 m. by A 912 - Z - and Rhynd rd. Abernethy (11C Round Tower★), SE : 8 m. by A 912 - Z - and A 913

Plan opposite

Huntingtower
rm, VISA AE

Crieff Rd, West : 3½ m. by A 85 ✉ PH1 3JT – ✆ (01738) 583 771 – reservations@huntingtowerhotel.co.uk – Fax (01738) 583 777

34 rm – †£ 65/139 ††£ 85/159

Rest *Oak Room* – (bar lunch) Menu £ 13/28 – Carte £ 17/50

◆ Late Victorian half-timbered country house named after nearby castle. Choose bedrooms in the more traditional old house or modern, executive rooms. Restaurant with views towards lawn and stream.

Parklands
VISA

2 St Leonard's Bank ✉ PH2 8EB – ✆ (01738) 622 451 – info@theparklandshotel.com – Fax (01738) 622 046 Z **n**

15 rm – †£ 89/129 ††£ 119/169

Rest *Acanthus* – (dinner only) Menu 30 – Carte £ 21/32

Rest *No.1 The Bank* – Carte £ 21/32

◆ Privately run, these two well-kept houses are handily positioned opposite railway station. Rooms, in co-ordinated patterns, are named after local places: most face garden. New-British dishes in contemporary Acanthus. Conservatory bistro fare at No 1 The Bank.

Beechgrove without rest
VISA

Dundee Rd ✉ PH2 7AQ – ✆ (01738) 636 147 – beechgrove.h@sol.co.uk – Fax (01738) 636 147 Z **s**

8 rm – †£ 60/75 ††£ 60/80

◆ Virginia creeper clad Georgian manse, immaculately kept. Bedrooms with mahogany furniture and a few added extras; comfy firelit lounge in traditional décor. Friendly hosts.

Taythorpe without rest

Isla Rd, North : 1 m. on A 93 ✉ PH2 7HQ – ✆ (01738) 447 994 – stay@taythorpe.co.uk – Fax (01738) 447 994 Y **a**

3 rm – †£ 35/42 ††£ 60/70

◆ Immaculately kept, modern guesthouse close to Scone Palace. Good value accommodation. Welcoming, homely lounge. Cosy, communal breakfasts. Warmly inviting, well-kept bedrooms.

Kinnaird without rest
VISA AE

5 Marshall Pl ✉ PH2 8AH – ✆ (01738) 628 021 – info@kinnaird-guesthouse.co.uk Z **c**

7 rm – †£ 40/60 ††£ 60/75

◆ Neatly kept Georgian town house behind a tidy front lawn edged with flowers. Traditional sitting room with a touch of period style. Individual rooms, thoughtfully appointed.

SCOTLAND

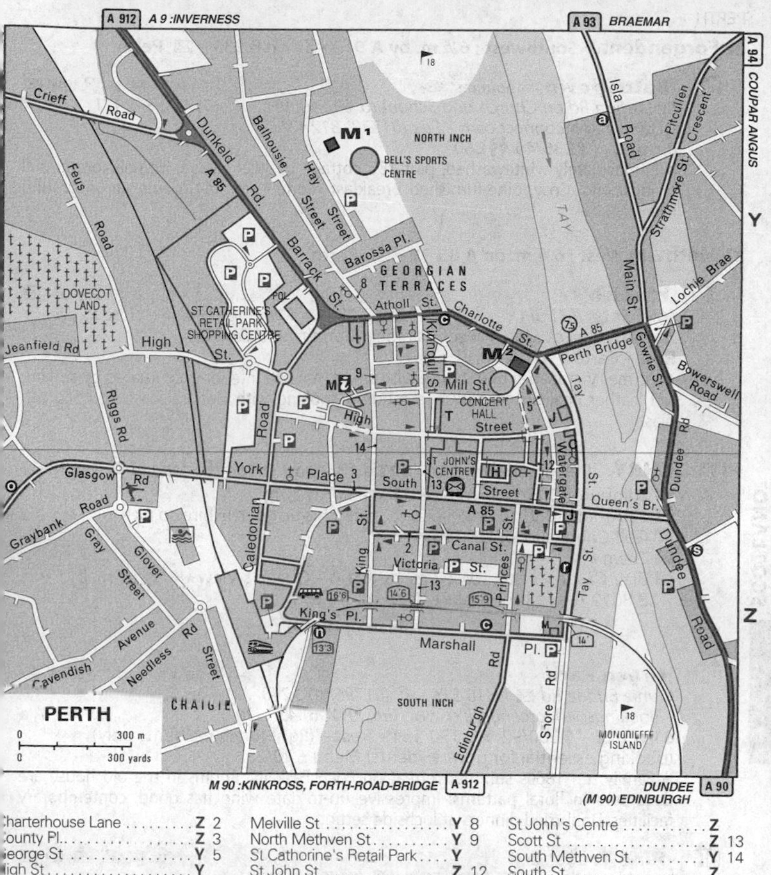

harterhouse Lane	Z 2	Melville St	Y 8	St John's Centre	Z		
ounty Pl.	Z 3	North Methven St	Y 9	Scott St	Z 13		
eorge St	Y 5	St Catherine's Retail Park	Y	South Methven St	Y 14		
igh St	Y	St John St	Z 12	South St	Z		

XX 63 Tay Street

VISA MC AE

63 Tay St ✉ PH2 8NN – ✆ (01738) 441 451
– Fax (01738) 441 461
– closed 2 weeks late December, 1week July, Sunday and Monday Z **r**

Rest – Menu £ 18/28

◆ Contemporary style restaurant close to the riverside. Subtle décor with bright sea-blue chairs. Well-priced modern cuisine with penchant for seasonal ingredients.

XX Deans @ Let's Eat

VISA MC

77-79 Kinnoull St ✉ PH1 5EZ – ✆ (01738) 643 377
– deans@letseatperth.co.uk – Fax (01738) 621 464
– closed Sunday and Monday Y **c**

Rest – Carte £ 21/34

◆ Polite, unflustered service and relaxed, warm-toned setting combine in a strong neighbourhood favourite. Robust, varied modern dishes at a good price.

at Forgandenny Southwest : 6½ m. by A 912 - Z - on B 935 – ✉ Perth

Battledown without rest
by Station Rd on Church and School rd ✉ PH2 9EL – ☎ (01738) 812471 – i.dunsire@btconnect.com – Fax (01738) 812471
3 rm – £35/40 £60
◆ Immaculately whitewashed, part 18C cottage in quiet village. Homely lounge full of local info. Cosy, pine-furnished breakfast room. Neat, tidy rooms, all on ground level.

at Methven West : 6½ m. on A 85 - Y – ✉ Perth

Hamish's
Main St ✉ PH1 3PU – ☎ (01738) 840505 – info@hamishs.co.uk – closed 2 weeks January, 1 week May, 1 week October, Monday and Tuesday
Rest – Carte £16/28 **s**
◆ Former Victorian school-house with smart, modish interior accentuated by striking red leather chairs. Accomplished modern cooking with classical base and Scottish bias.

PITLOCHRY – Perth and Kinross – 501 I 13 – pop. 2 564 *Scotland* 28 C2

Edinburgh 71 m – Inverness 85 m – Perth 27 m
22 Atholl Rd ☎ (01796) 472215, pitlochrytic@perthshire.co.uk
Golf Course Rd, ☎ (01796) 472792 .
Town★
Blair Castle★★ AC, NW : 7 m. by A 9 A – Queen's View★★, W : 7 m. by B 8019 A – Falls of Bruar★, NW : 11 m. by A 9 A

Plan opposite

Green Park
Clunie Bridge Rd ✉ PH16 5JY – ☎ (01796) 473248 – bookings@thegreenpark.co.uk – Fax (01796) 473520 A **a**
51 rm – £60/92 £130/184 – **Rest** – (light lunch residents only) (booking essential for non-residents) Menu £20/28
◆ Family run 1860s summer retreat on Loch Faskally. Rooms in the old house are decorated in floral patterns; impressive up-to-date wing has good, contemporary facilities. Unhurried dinners at lochside setting.

Pine Trees
Strathview Terrace ✉ PH16 5QR – ☎ (01796) 472121 – info@pinetreeshotel.co.uk – Fax (01796) 472460 A **b**
20 rm – £57/75 £134/170 – **Rest** – Menu £26 – Carte £14/26 **s**
◆ Extended 1892 mansion: superb wood-panelled hall with open fire, period prints and antiques. Modern rooms in warm décor; those at front have best views of 8-acre gardens. Two eating alternatives: dining room or bistro area.

Craigatin House and Courtyard without rest
165 Atholl Rd ✉ PH16 5QL – ☎ (01796) 472478 – enquiries@craigatinhouse.co.uk – Fax (01796) 470167 – closed December and January A **e**
12 rm – £35/75 £60/85 – 1 suite
◆ 19C detached house with converted stables. Smart, stylish décor, including comfy conservatory lounge and breakfast room. Eye-catchingly inviting rooms, some in the annexe.

Knockendarroch House
2 Higher Oakfield ✉ PH16 5HT – ☎ (01796) 473473 – bookings@knockendarroch.co.uk – Fax (01796) 474068 – March-October B **m**
12 rm – £75/100 £116/160 – **Rest** – (dinner only) Menu £27
◆ A handsome late Victorian house in a neat garden. Most of the large, light bedrooms have good views; comfortably furnished, bright, airy, two-room lounge. Cosy, homely dining room.

SCOTLAND

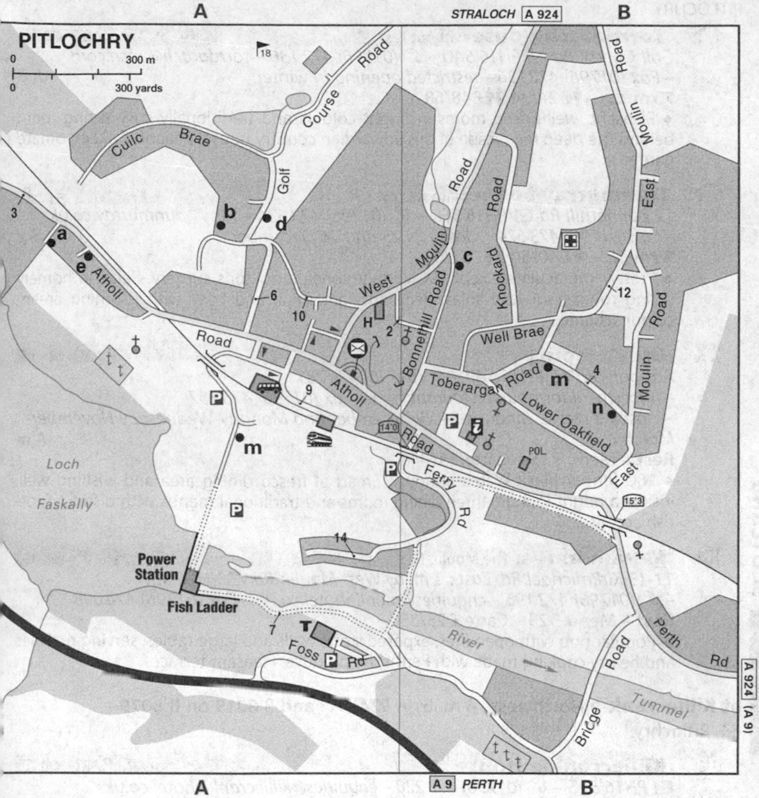

PITLOCHRY

hurch Rd.	AB 2	Larchwood Rd.	A 6	Strathview Terrace	A 10
unie Bridge Rd	A 3	Port Na Craig Rd	A 7	Tom Na Moan Rd	B 12
gher Oakfield	B 4	Station Rd	A 9	Tummel Crescent	A 14

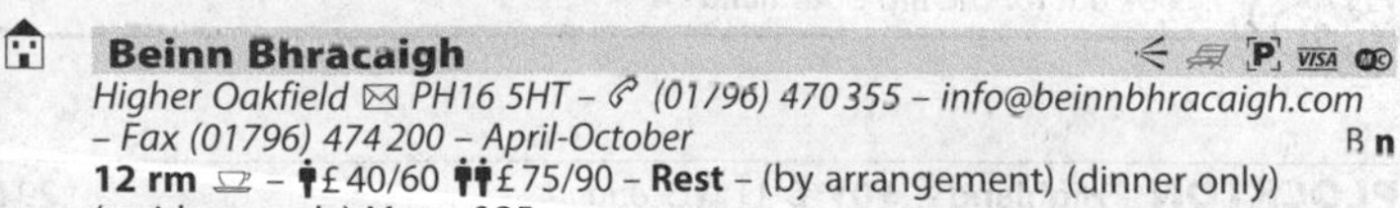

Beinn Bhracaigh

Higher Oakfield ✉ *PH16 5HT – ✆ (01796) 470 355 – info@beinnbhracaigh.com – Fax (01796) 474 200 – April-October* B **n**

12 rm – 🚹£ 40/60 🚹🚹£ 75/90 – **Rest** – (by arrangement) (dinner only) (residents only) Menu £ 25

◆ Affordable, spacious, refurbished bedrooms - with good town views from front - in a local stone house of late 19C origin. Impressive range of whiskies in residents' bar. Simple homecooked fare served in wood-floored dining rooms.

The Moulin Inn

Kirkmichael Road, East : 1 m. by West Moulin Rd ✉ *PH16 5EH – ✆ (01796) 472 196 – enquiries@moulinhotel.co.uk – Fax (01796) 474 098*

18 rm – 🚹£ 45 🚹🚹£ 85

Rest *Moulin Inn* – see restaurant listing

◆ Whitewashed 300 year old inn in pleasant conservation village, away from centre of town. Traditional Scottish feel. Cosy residential bar. Comfortable bedrooms.

Torrdarach House without rest

Golf Course Rd ✉ PH16 5AU – ✆ (01796) 472 136 – torrdarach@msn.com – Fax (01796) 472 136 – restricted opening in winter A **d**

7 rm – 🯅£ 24/34 🯅🯅£ 48/68

◆ Pleasant, well-priced rooms in bright colours and traditionally cosy sitting room behind the deep red façade of this Edwardian country house. Beautifully kept, ornate gardens.

Dunmurray Lodge without rest

72 Bonnethill Rd ✉ PH16 5ED – ✆ (01796) 473 624 – tony@dunmurray.co.uk – Fax (01796) 473 624 – closed 24,25 and 26 December B **c**

4 rm – 🯅£ 40/50 🯅🯅£ 52/68

◆ Pretty, immaculately kept 19C cottage, once a doctor's surgery. Relax in homely sitting room's squashy sofas. Bedrooms are small and cosy with soothing cream colour scheme.

Old Armoury

Armoury Rd ✉ PH16 5AP – ✆ (01796) 474 281 – info@theoldarmouryrestaurant.com – Fax (01796) 473 157 – closed 3 weeks January, 24-29 December and Monday-Wednesday November-March A **m**

Rest – Menu £ 19 – Carte £ 16/40

◆ 18C former Black Watch armoury. Smart al fresco dining area and wishing well. Inside: a bright lounge, three dining rooms and traditional menus with distinct Scottish accent.

Moulin Inn – at The Moulin H.

11-13 Kirkmichael Rd, East : 1 m. by West Moulin Rd ✉ PH16 5EW – ✆ (01796) 472 196 – enquiries@moulinhotel.co.uk – Fax (01796) 474 098

Rest – Menu £ 23 – Carte £ 25/35

◆ Popular pub with open fires, exposed stone walls and large tables, serving real ales and hearty cooking made with Perthshire produce. Pleasant terrace.

at Killiecrankie Northwest : 4 m. by A 924 - A - and B 8019 on B 8079 – ✉ Pitlochry

Killiecrankie House

✉ PH16 5LG – ✆ (01796) 473 220 – enquiries@killiecrankiehotel.co.uk – Fax (01796) 472 451 – 3 January-1 March

9 rm – 🯅£ 95/105 🯅🯅£ 210/230 – 1 suite – **Rest** – (bar lunch) Menu £ 34

◆ Quiet and privately run, a converted 1840 vicarage with a distinct rural feel. Mahogany panelled bar; sizeable rooms in co-ordinated patterns overlook pleasant countryside. Warm, red dining room; garden produce prominent on menus.

Good food without spending a fortune?
Look out for the Bib Gourmand

PLOCKTON – Highland – 501 D 11 *Scotland* 29 **B2**

Edinburgh 210 m – Inverness 88 m
Village ★
Wester Ross ★★★

Plockton Loch Carron and mountains, rm,

41 Harbour St ✉ IV52 8TN – ✆ (01599) 544 274 – info@plocktonhotel.co.uk – Fax (01599) 544 475 – Closed 25 December and 1 January

15 rm – 🯅£ 45 🯅🯅£ 100

Rest *Plockton* – Carte £ 15/45

◆ Enlarged traditional inn commands fine views of the mountains and Loch Carron. Convivial, half-panelled bar; local ale. New rooms in particular have a simple, stylish feel. Popular menu served in the spacious modern restaurant.

Plockton Inn with rm
Innes Street ✉ IV52 8TW – ☎ (01599) 544 222 – info@plocktoninn.co.uk – Fax (01599) 544 487 – closed 25-26 December
14 rm – †£ 35 ††£ 88 – **Rest** – Seafood Carte £ 15/26
◆ Family run converted manse, with a cosy locals bar refreshingly short on airs and graces. Welcoming lounges for dining on local fish and shellfish. Trim, cheerful bedrooms.

PORT APPIN – Argyll and Bute – 501 D 14 – ✉ Appin 27 B2

Edinburgh 136 m – Ballachulish 20 m – Oban 24 m

Airds ← Loch Linnhe and mountains of Kingairloch,
✉ PA38 4DF – ☎ (01631) 730 236 – airds@airds-hotel.com – Fax (01631) 730 535 – closed 6-23 January
11 rm (dinner included) – †£ 180/230 ††£ 270/340 – **Rest** – (booking essential for non-residents) Menu £ 50 **s** – Carte lunch only £ 26/33
◆ Former ferry inn with superb views of Loch Linnhe and mountains. Charming rooms - antiques and floral fabrics. Firelit, old-world sitting rooms hung with landscapes. Smartly set tables, picture windows looking across the water in the restaurant.

PORT CHARLOTTE – Argyll and Bute – 501 A 16 – see Islay (Isle of)

PORT ELLEN – Argyll and Bute – 501 B 17 – see Islay (Isle of)

PORTMAHOMACK – Highland – 501 I 10 30 D2

Edinburgh 194 m – Dornoch 21 m – Tain 12 m

The Oystercatcher with rm
Main St ✉ IV20 1YB – ☎ (01862) 871 560 – gordon@burtonrobertson.fsnet.co.uk – Fax (01862) 871 777 – restricted opening in winter
3 rm – †£ 43 ††£ 98 – **Rest** – Seafood (closed Monday-Tuesday) (booking essential) Carte £ 28/74 **s**
◆ Personally run bistro and piscatorially themed main dining room in a lovely setting, ideal for sunsets. Enjoyable local fish dishes, with lobster a speciality. Homely rooms.

PORTPATRICK – Dumfries and Galloway – 501 E 19 – pop. 585 – ✉ Stranraer 25 A3

Edinburgh 141 m – Ayr 60 m – Dumfries 80 m – Stranraer 9 m
Golf Course Rd, ☎ (01776) 810 273 .

Knockinaam Lodge
Southeast : 5 m. by A 77 off B 7042 ✉ DG9 9AD – ☎ (01776) 810 471 – reservations@knockinaamlodge.com – Fax (01776) 810 435
9 rm (dinner included) – †£ 165 ††£ 210/400 – **Rest** – (booking essential for non-residents) (set menu only) Menu £ 38/50
Spec. Lobster salad with a citrus emulsion. Lamb with basil mousse, shallot purée, garlic beignet, juniper and thyme jus. Raspberry crème brûlee, raspberry sorbet, vodka and elderflower jelly.
◆ Idyllically-situated in its own private cove, this family-run Victorian house exudes a warm, friendly feel. Country house style bedrooms; most with sea view. Fine selection of malt whiskies. Daily-changing set 4 course menu uses fine local produce: carefully-prepared and accomplished modern dishes.

Fernhill ← Portpatrick and the North Channel, rm,
Heugh Rd ✉ DG9 8TD – ☎ (01776) 810 220 – info@fernhillhotel.co.uk – Fax (01776) 810 596 – closed 3 January-8 February
36 rm – †£ 66/81 ††£ 66/108 – **Rest** – Menu £ 17/33 **s**
◆ Family owned hotel in an elevated position; comfortable lounge and bar with fine view of the harbour and sea. Rooms vary in size; the more luxurious have balconies. Unpretentious restaurant and conservatory with menu which changes with the seasons.

SCOTLAND

The Waterfront ← AC rest, VISA AE
North Crescent ✉ DG9 8SX – ☎ (01776) 810 800 – info@waterfronthotel.co.uk – Fax (01776) 810 850 – Closed 1 week Christmas
8 rm – †£ 65/70 ††£ 90/100 – **Rest** – (bar lunch) Menu £ 22.50
◆ 18C harbourside hotel with good views and pleasant terraced seating. Modern, stylish décor with a light, arty feel. Compact, contemporary styled rooms overlooking the harbour. Pleasant, pine-panelled dining room with extensive menu.

XX **Campbells** ← Portpatrick harbour, VISA
1 South Crescent ✉ DG9 8JR – ☎ (01776) 810 314 – dianecampbell@campbellsrestaurant.wanadoo.co.uk – Fax (01776) 810 361 – closed 2 weeks February, 25 December, 1 January, and Monday
Rest – Seafood Carte £ 18/30
◆ Personally run attractive harbourside restaurant with modern rustic feel throughout. Tasty, appealing menus, full of seafood specialities and Scottish ingredients.

PORTREE – Highland – 501 B 11 – see Skye (Isle of)

QUOTHQUAN – South Lanarkshire – 501 J 27 – ✉ Biggar *Scotland* 26 C2

Edinburgh 32 m – Dumfries 50 m – Glasgow 36 m
Biggar★ (Gladstone Court Museum★ **AC** – Greenhill Covenanting Museum★ **AC**) SE : 4½ m. by B 7016

Shieldhill Castle ← P VISA AE
Northeast : ¾ m. ✉ ML12 6NA – ☎ (01899) 220 035 – enquiries@shieldhill.co.uk – Fax (01899) 221 092
26 rm – †£ 90 ††£ 230
Rest *Chancellors* – Menu £ 20 – Carte £ 33/41
◆ Part 12C fortified manor with 16C additions and invitingly comfortable panelled lounge. Large rooms, individually furnished, some with vast sunken baths. Popular for weddings. Accomplished cooking in 16C dining room with high carved ceilings.

RANNOCH STATION – Perth and Kinross – 501 G 13 27 B2

Edinburgh 108 m – Kinloch Rannoch 17 m – Pitlochry 36 m

Moor of Rannoch ← Rannoch Moor, P VISA
✉ PH17 2QA – ☎ (01882) 633 238 – bookings@moorofrannoch.co.uk – 14 February-4 November
5 rm – †£ 48 ††£ 80 – **Rest** – (closed Saturday and Sunday lunch) (booking essential for non-residents) Carte £ 19/25 **s**
◆ Immaculately whitewashed 19C property "in the middle of nowhere", next to railway station with link to London! Comfy, sofa-strewn lounges. Rustic rooms with antiques. Home-cooked menus in characterful dining room with conservatory.

RHICONICH – Highland – 501 F 8 – ✉ Lairg *Scotland* 30 C1

Edinburgh 249 m – Thurso 87 m – Ullapool 57 m
Cape Wrath★★★ (← ★★) **AC**, N : 21 m. (including ferry crossing) by A 838 and minor rd

Rhiconich ← Loch Inchard, P VISA
✉ IV27 4RN – ☎ (01971) 521 224 – rhiconichhotel@aol.com – Fax (01971) 521 732 – Closed Christmas and New Year
11 rm – †£ 45 ††£ 86 – **Rest** – (bar lunch) Menu £ 22 – Carte £ 14/22
◆ White-fronted hotel sitting majestically at the head of Loch Inchard. Stylish rooms offer loch views; larger, well located superior rooms feature pastel co-ordinated décor. Dining room, with stunning views and serving local produce.

ROTHESAY – Argyll and Bute – 501 – see Bute (Isle of)

SCALASAIG – Argyll and Bute – **501** B 15 – see Colonsay (Isle of)

SCALPAY – Western Isles – **501** A 10 – see Lewis and Harris (Isle of)

SCARISTA – Western Isles Outer Hebrides – **501** Y 10 – see Lewis and Harris (Isle of)

SCOURIE – Highland – **501** E 8 – ✉ **Lairg** *Scotland* 30 **C1**

Edinburgh 263 m – Inverness 107 m

Cape Wrath★★★ (≤ ★★) **AC**, N : 31 m. (including ferry crossing) by A 894 and A 838 – Loch Assynt★★, S : 17 m. by A 894

Eddrachilles ≤ Badcall Bay and islands,

Badcall Bay, South : 2½ m. on A 894 ✉ IV27 4TH – ℘ (01971) 502 080 – enq@eddrachilles.com – Fax (01971) 502 477 – mid March-mid October

11 rm – †£ 67 ††£ 94 – **Rest** – (bar lunch) Menu £ 25

◆ Isolated hotel, converted from small part 19C building, magnificently set at the head of Badcall Bay and its islands. Conservatory lounge. Traditional, well-kept rooms. Dining room with stone walls and flagstone floors.

SEIL (Isle of) – Argyll and Bute – **501** D 15 – ✉ **Oban** 27 **B2**

SCOTLAND

Clachan Seil – Argyll and Bute – ✉ **Oban** 27 **B2**

Willowburn

✉ PA34 4TJ – ℘ (01852) 300 276 – willowburn.hotel@virgin.net – mid March-mid November

7 rm – †£ 84/130 ††£ 168 – **Rest** – (dinner only) (booking essential for non-residents) Menu £ 37

◆ Simple, white-painted hotel overlooking Clachan Sound. Comfortable lounge with birdwatching telescope. Cosy bedrooms show an individual, personal touch. Airy dining room overlooks the water.

SELKIRK – Borders – **501** L 17 – **pop. 5 772** *Scotland* 26 **C2**

Edinburgh 48 m – Hawick 11 m – Newcastle upon Tyne 77 m

Halliwell's House ℘ (01750) 20054 (Easter-October), selkirk@scot-borders.co.uk

The Hill, ℘ (01750) 20 621 .

Bowhill★★ **AC**, W : 3½ m. by A 708 – Abbotsford★★ **AC**, NE : 5½ m. by A 7 and B 6360 – Tweed Valley★★. Melrose Abbey★★ (decorative sculpture★★★) **AC**, NE : 8½ m. by A 7 and A 6091 – Eildon Hills (✳ ★★★) NE : 7½ m. by A 699 and B 6359

Philipburn Country House (heated)

West : 1 m. by A 707 at junction with A 708 ✉ TD7 5LS – ℘ (01750) 20 747 – info@philipburnhousehotel.co.uk – Fax (01750) 721 690

14 rm – †£ 85/105 ††£ 99/130

Rest *1745* – Menu £ 29 (dinner) – Carte £ 18/29

Rest *Charleys Bistro* – (dinner only) Carte £ 15/28

◆ Extended 18C house along private driveway with smart gardens. Eclectic variety of rooms, most having pleasant rural outlook, two overlooking outdoor pool. Linen-laid 1745 has fine dining menu. Informal Charleys for bistro favourites.

Good food and accommodation at moderate prices?
Look for the Bib symbols:
red Bib Gourmand for food, blue Bib Hotel for hotels

SHETLAND ISLANDS – 501 P/Q 3 – pop. 22 522 Scotland 31 B2

Tingwall Airport : (01595) 840306, NW : 6½ m. of Lerwick by A 971

from Lerwick (Mainland) to Aberdeen and via Orkney Islands (Stromness) (P and O Scottish Ferries) – from Vidlin to Skerries (Shetland Islands Council) booking essential 3-4 weekly (1 h 30 mn) – from Lerwick (Mainland) to Skerries (Shetland Islands Council) 2 weekly (booking essential) (2 h 30 mn) – from Lerwick (Mainland) to Bressay (Shetland Islands Council) frequent services daily (7 mn) – from Laxo (Mainland) to Isle of Whalsay (Symbister) (Shetland Islands Council) frequent services daily (30 mn) – from Toft (Mainland) to Isle of Yell (Ulsta) (Shetland Islands Council) frequent services daily (20 mn) – from Isle of Yell (Gutcher) to Isle of Fetlar (Oddsta) and via Isle of Unst (Belmont) (Shetland Islands Council) – from Fair Isle to Sumburgh (Mainland) (Shetland Islands Council) 3 weekly (2 h 40 mn)

from Foula to Walls (Shetland Islands Council) 1-2 weekly (2 h 30 mn) – from Fair Isle to Sumburgh (Shetland Islands Council) 1-2 weekly (2 h 40 mn)

Islands★ - Up Helly Aa (last Tuesday in January) – Mousa Broch★★★ **AC** (Mousa Island) – Jarlshof★★ - Lerwick to Jarlshof★ (< ★) – Shetland Croft House Museum★ **AC**

MAINLAND – Shetland Islands 31 B2

SCOTLAND

Brae – Shetland Islands 31 B1

Busta House

Southwest : 1½ m. by A 970 ✉ ZE2 9QN – (01806) 522 506 – reservations@bustahouse.com – Fax (01806) 522 588 – Closed 23 December-6 January

22 rm – ♦£ 75 ♦♦£ 110 – **Rest** – (bar lunch Monday-Saturday) Menu £ 35

◆ Part 16C and 18C house on Busta Voe. Good-sized traditional rooms, some have canopy beds. Elegant "long room" with ancestral portraits. House of Commons gargoyles in garden. Garden views add balance to sober dining room.

Lerwick – Shetland Islands – pop. 7 590 Scotland 31 B2

The Market Cross, Lerwick (08701) 999440

Shetland Gott Dale, (01595) 840 369 .

Clickhimin Broch★

Gulber Wick (< ★), S : 2 m. by A 970

Kveldsro House

Greenfield Pl ✉ ZE1 0AQ – (01595) 692 195 – reception@kveldsrohotel.co.uk – Fax (01595) 696 595 – Closed 1-2 January, 24-26 and 31 December

17 rm – ♦£ 90/100 ♦♦£ 115 – **Rest** – (bar lunch Monday-Saturday, carvery lunch Sunday) Carte £ 18/34 **s**

◆ Neat, modern style in evidence throughout this smoothly run hotel - its name comes from the Norse for "evening peace". Tidy rooms, well-equipped and furnished in pale wood. Classically smart and formally set restaurant.

Grand

149 Commercial St ✉ ZE1 0EX – (01595) 692 826 – info@kgqhotels.co.uk – Fax (01595) 694 048 – Closed 24 December-4 January

24 rm – ♦£ 75/89 ♦♦£ 99 – **Rest** – (bar lunch) Carte £ 14/29

◆ Handsome period hotel with turret and stepped gables. Above the row of ground-floor shops are neatly kept rooms with modern fittings, a simple lounge bar and a night-club. Comfortably furnished dining room with a formal atmosphere.

Shetland

Holmsgarth Rd ✉ ZE1 0PW – (01595) 695 515 – reception@shetlandhotel.co.uk – Fax (01595) 695 828

63 rm – ♦£ 80/98 ♦♦£ 98 – 1 suite – **Rest** – (bar lunch) Carte £ 15/29 **s**

◆ Purpose-built hotel near the harbourside. Mahogany furnished bar, a choice of modern conference rooms and usefully fitted rooms in co-ordinated fabrics. Simply but formally arranged dining room.

Glen Orchy House rm, VISA
20 Knab Rd ✉ ZE1 0AX – ✆ (01595) 692 031 – glenorchy.house@virgin.net – Fax (01595) 692 031
24 rm – £ 50 £ 80 – **Rest** – Thai (dinner only) (booking essential) (residents only) Carte £ 12/16 **s**
◆ Built as a convent in the 1900s and sympathetically extended. Colourful public areas. Bright honesty bar. Spotless bedrooms with neat modern fabrics and fittings. Restaurant offers authentic Thai menus.

Veensgarth – Shetland Islands 31 B2

Herrislea House VISA
✉ ZE2 9SB – ✆ (01595) 840 208 – hotel@herrisleahouse.co.uk – Fax (01595) 840 630 – Closed Christmas, New Year and 3 weeks January
13 rm – £ 50/70 £ 80/110 – **Rest** – (bar lunch) (booking essential for non-residents) Carte £ 15/29 **s**
◆ Purpose-built hotel run by native islanders; a homely hall, with mounted antlers, leads to tidy bedrooms, pleasantly furnished in solid pine, and an angling themed bar. Neatly laid out but fairly informal restaurant.

ISLAND OF UNST – Shetland Islands 31 B1

Baltasound – Shetland Islands

Buness House Balta Sound, VISA
East : ½ m. by A 968 and Springpark Rd ✉ ZE2 9DS – ✆ (01957) 711 315 – buness-house@zetnet.co.uk – Fax (01957) 711 815 – Restricted opening December-February
3 rm (dinner included) – £ 105 £ 180 – **Rest** – (by arrangement, communal dining) Menu £ 30 **s**
◆ Whitewashed house of 16C origin. Cosy, well-stocked library. Comfortable rooms facing Balta Sound, one decorated with Victorian prints and découpages. Nearby nature reserve. Willow-pattern china and sea views from the conservatory dining room.

SHIELDAIG – Highland – 501 D 11 – ✉ Strathcarron *Scotland* 29 B2

Edinburgh 226 m – Inverness 70 m – Kyle of Lochalsh 36 m
Wester Ross★★★

Tigh An Eilean Shieldaig Islands and Loch, VISA AE
✉ IV54 8XN – ✆ (01520) 755 251 – tighaneileanhotel@keme.co.uk – Fax (01520) 755 321 – mid March-October
11 rm – £ 75 £ 160 – **Rest** – (bar lunch) (booking essential for non-residents) Menu £ 44
◆ In a sleepy lochside village, an attractive, personally run 19C inn with fine views of the Shieldaig Islands. Cosy, well-kept bedrooms and a comfy lounge with a homely feel. Linen-clad dining room showing eclectic variety of art; Scottish produce to the fore.

SKIRLING – Peebleshire – 501 – ✉ Biggar *Scotland* 26 C2

Edinburgh 29 m – Glasgow 45 m – Peebles 16 m
Biggar★ - Gladstone Court Museum★, Greenhill Covenanting Museum★, S : 3 m. by A 72 and A 702. New Lanark★★, NW : 16 m. by A 72 and A 73

Skirling House VISA
✉ ML12 6HD – ✆ (01899) 860 274 – enquiry@skirlinghouse.com – Fax (01899) 860 255 – Closed January-February and 1 week Autumn
5 rm – £ 60 £ 100 – **Rest** – (by arrangement) Menu £ 30
◆ Attractive Arts and Crafts house (1908). 16C Florentine carved ceiling in drawing room. Comfortable bedrooms with modern conveniences. Daily dinner menu using fresh produce.

SCOTLAND

SKYE (Isle of) – Highland – 501 B 11 – pop. 8 868 Scotland 29 B2

from Mallaig to Armadale (Caledonian MacBrayne Ltd) 1-5 daily (30 mn) – from Uig to North Uist (Lochmaddy) or Isle of Harris (Tarbert) (Caledonian MacBrayne Ltd) 1-3 daily (1 h 50 mn) – from Sconser to Isle of Raasay (Caledonian MacBrayne Ltd) 9-10 daily (except Sunday) (15 mn)

from Mallaig to Isles of Eigg, Muck, Rhum and Canna (Caledonian MacBrayne Ltd) (summer only) – from Mallaig to Armadale (Caledonian MacBrayne Ltd) (summer only) 1-2 weekly (30 mn)

Island★★ - The Cuillins★★★ – Skye Museum of Island Life★ **AC**

N : Trotternish Peninsula★★ – W : Duirinish Peninsula★ – Portree★

Broadford – Highland 29 B2

Broadford Hotel

Torrin Rd ✉ *IV49 9AB – ☎ (01471) 822 204 – broadford@macleodhotels.co.uk – Fax (01471) 822 414*

8 rm – £ 70/110 £ 82/250 – **Rest** – Carte £ 14/23

◆ Contemporary, well-run hotel, dating from 1611 and spiritual home of Drambuie. Refurbished, lively bar and lounge; comfortable bedrooms, some with views of water and hills. Bar/bistro has views of garden and across to mainland.

Tigh an Dochais without rest

Broadford Bay and Applecross peninsular,

13 Harrapool, on A 87 ✉ *IV49 9AQ – ☎ (01471) 820 022 – hopeskye@btinternet.com – Closed Christmas-New Year*

3 rm – £ 45/50 £ 65/75

◆ Stylish, award-winning architecture; this is a striking house, full of glass, in a fabulous setting. Superb views at breakfast and stark, clean-lined surroundings at night.

SCOTLAND

Dunvegan – Highland 29 B2

Roskhill House

Roskhill, Southeast : 2½ m. by A 863 ✉ *IV55 8ZD – ☎ (01470) 521 317 – stay@roskhillhouse.co.uk – Closed Christmas and January-mid February*

5 rm – £ 30/51 £ 60/74 – **Rest** – (by arrangement) Menu £ 20

◆ In friendly personal ownership, an extended, traditional 19C croft house which preserves its exposed brick walls and peat fires. Bedrooms are homely and unpretentious. Once a post office, the dining room offers homely cooking at simple wooden tables.

The Three Chimneys & The House Over-By with rm

Colbost, Northwest : 5 ¾ m. by A 863 on B 884 (Glendale) ✉ *IV55 8ZT – ☎ (01470) 511 258 – eatandstay@threechimneys.co.uk – Fax (01470) 511 358 – Closed 6-25 January*

6 rm – £ 140/255 £ 140/255 – **Rest** – Seafood (Closed Sunday lunch) (dinner only in winter) (booking essential) Menu £ 30/50

◆ Internationally renowned crofter's cottage restaurant on Loch Dunvegan shores. Accomplished Skye seafood dishes, plus Highland lamb, beef and game. Sumptuous bedrooms.

Edinbane – Highland 29 B2

Greshornish House

North : 3 ¾ m. by A 850 in direction of Dunvegan ✉ *IV51 9PN – ☎ (01470) 582 266 – info@greshornishhouse.com – Fax (01470) 582 345 – restricted opening in winter*

9 rm – £ 58/150 £ 120/165 – **Rest** – (booking essential at lunch) Menu £ 23/34

◆ Utter tranquillity: a beautifully sited hotel in 10 acres of grounds, with cluttered sitting rooms, snooker room, smart bedrooms with a view - and Skye's only tennis court! Conservatory breakfasts; Western Isle ingredients to fore in the dining room.

Flodigarry – Highland – ✉ Staffin 29 **B2**

Flodigarry Country House ← Staffin Island and coastline,
✉ *IV51 9HZ – ☎ (01470) 552 203* rm, P VISA AE
– info@flodigarry.co.uk – Fax (01470) 552 301 – Closed last 3 weeks January
18 rm – †£ 50/100 ††£ 60/190 – **Rest** – (bar lunch Monday-Saturday)
Carte £ 20/36 **s**
◆ With views of Staffin and the coast, a curio-filled country house once home to Flora Macdonald. Traditional down to its old-world rooms, peat fire and 19C conservatory. Semi-panelled candlelit restaurant.

Glendale – Highland 29 **A2**

Clach Ghlas without rest ← Loch Pooltieh and Dunvegan Head,
Lower Milovaig ✉ IV55 8WR – ☎ (01470) 511 205 P
– info@clachghlas.co.uk – Fax (01470) 511 205
3 rm – †£ 140 ††£ 140
◆ Modern house commanding superb hillside spot and vistas to lochs and headlands. Attractive breakfast conservatory; relaxing sitting room. Quiet bedrooms and super Jacuzzis.

Portree – Highland – pop. 2 126 29 **B2**

i Bayfield House, Bayfield Rd ☎ (08452) 255121

Cuillin Hills ← Portree bay and the Cuillins, rm,
Northeast : ¾ m. by A 855 ✉ IV51 9QU P VISA AE
– ☎ (01478) 612 003 – info@cuillinhills-hotel-skye.co.uk – Fax (01478) 613 092
27 rm – †£ 70/150 ††£ 150/240 – **Rest** – (bar lunch Monday-Saturday, buffet lunch Sunday) Menu £ 33 – Carte £ 16/33
◆ Enlarged 19C hunting lodge in 15-acre grounds above lochside with fine views. Well-proportioned drawing room with broad Chesterfields; usefully equipped rooms vary in size. Smart and spacious dining room with views of Portree Bay.

Bosville ← VISA AE
Bosville Terrace ✉ IV51 9DG – ☎ (01478) 612 846
– bosville@macleodhotels.co.uk – Fax (01478) 613 434
19 rm – †£ 69/220 ††£ 86/250
Rest *Chandlery* – see restaurant listing
Rest *Bistro* – Carte £ 15/29
◆ Well-established, busy hotel overlooking harbour and hills. First-floor sitting room and tidy, modern accommodation in co-ordinated décor. Buzzy ground floor bistro.

Rosedale ← harbour, P VISA
Beaumont Crescent ✉ IV51 9DB – ☎ (01478) 613 131
– rosedalehotelsky@aol.com – Fax (01478) 612 531 – 20 March-October
18 rm – †£ 30/60 ††£ 60/130 – **Rest** – (dinner only) Menu £ 26
◆ Converted quayside terrace of fishermen's houses with fine views over the water. Neat and cosy lounge and compact but immaculately kept bedrooms in floral prints. First-floor, linen-clad restaurant with a traditionally based, seasonal menu.

Almondbank without rest ← Portree Bay, P VISA
Viewfield Rd, Southwest : ¾ m. on A 87 ✉ IV51 9EU – ☎ (01478) 612 696
– j.n.almondbank@btconnect.com – Fax (01478) 613 114
– Closed 15-24 December
4 rm – †£ 50/58 ††£ 68/75
◆ Situated away from the town centre, a converted modern house, well maintained by the friendly owner. Spotless bedrooms; superb views across Portree Bay.

XX **The Chandlery** – at Bosville H. AE
Bosville Terrace ✉ IV51 9DG – ☎ (01478) 612 846 – Fax (01478) 613 434
Rest – Seafood (dinner only) (booking essential) Menu £ 40
◆ Purple colour scheme distinguishes this formal but relaxed restaurant from adjacent bistro. Skilfully executed seafood dishes display a proven touch of orginality and flair.

SCOTLAND

Struan – Highland 29 B2

Ullinish Country Lodge Loch Harport and Cuillin Hills,
West : 1½ m. by A 863 ✉ IV56 8FD – ✆ (01470) 572 214
– ullinish@theisleofskye.co.uk – Fax (01470) 572 341 – Closed January
6 rm – £ 90 £ 160 – **Rest** – (booking essential for non-residents)
Menu £ 15/40
◆ Country lodge comforts in superb windswept spot with fine views. Chilled sitting room; each bedroom has a distinct style with luxury fabrics and character beds built of wood. Skye ingredients put to compelling, highly original use on creative modern dishes.

Teangue – ✉ Skeabost Bridge

Toravaig House
Knock Bay, on A 851 ✉ IV44 8RE – ✆ (01471) 820 200 – info@skyehotel.co.uk
– Fax (01471) 833 231
9 rm – £ 75/140 £ 120/170 – **Rest** – (closed for lunch in winter)
(booking essential for non-residents) Menu £ 33/43 **s**
◆ Quality range of fabrics and furniture in a whitewashed house on road to Mallaig ferry. Small but perfectly formed lounge. Rooms designed to a high standard. Hearty sea views. Dine on best Skye produce in attractive surroundings.

SCOTLAND

Waternish – Highland 29 A2

Stein Inn Loch bay,
MacLeod Terr, Stein, Isle of Skye ✉ IV55 8GA – ✆ (01470) 592 362
– angus.teresa@steininn.co.uk – closed 25 December and 1 January and lunch Monday-Friday from November -March
5 rm – £ 27 £ 54 – **Rest** – Seafood (residents only Monday dinner except Bank Holidays) Carte £ 13/20
◆ The oldest inn on Skye with dramatic waterfront views. Charming friendly place serving locally brewed ale and over 90 malt whiskies. Comfy well-kept rooms with seaview. Solid traditional fare in the dining room.

Loch Bay Seafood
1 MacLeod Terrace, Stein ✉ IV55 8GA – ✆ (01470) 592 235
– david@lochbay-seafood-restaurant.co.uk – Fax (01470) 592 235
– Easter-October
Rest – Seafood (closed Sunday and Monday) (booking essential) Carte £ 19/31
◆ Cottage restaurant with simple wooden tables and benches. Tiny, atmospheric room where the freshest local seafood, including halibut, sole and turbot, is prepared faultlessly.

SORN – East Ayrshire – 501 H 17 25 B2

Edinburgh 67 m – Ayr 15 m – Glasgow 35 m

The Sorn Inn with rm
35 Main St ✉ KA5 6HU – ✆ (01290) 551 305 – craig@sorninn.com
– Fax (01290) 553 470 – Closed 2 weeks in January and Monday
4 rm – £ 40 £ 90 – **Rest** – Carte £ 15/25
◆ Family run, traditional pub in small village. Its hub is the dining room, where good value, locally sourced modern dishes are cooked in an accomplished way. Comfy rooms.

Do not confuse X with ✿!
X defines comfort, while stars are awarded for the best cuisine, across all categories of comfort.

SOUTH QUEENSFERRY – Midlothian – 501 J 15 – pop. 9 370 26 C1

Edinburgh 9 m – Dunfermline 8 m – Glasgow 41 m

Dakota

Ferrymuir Retail Park ✉ EH30 9QZ – ☎ (0870) 423 42 93 – info@dakotahotels.co.uk – Fax (0131) 319 3699

132 rm – †£ 89 ††£ 89, ☕ £ 10

Rest ***Bar & Grill*** – Carte £ 21/40

◆ Vast, vibrant black block on retail park; has modern, minimalistic décor and eponymous aeroplane memorabilia. Comfortable, spacious bedrooms with contemporary, quality feel. Spacious Bar and Grill serves something to suit all tastes.

SOUTH UIST – Western Isles Outer Hebrides – 501 X/Y – see Uist (Isles of)

SPEAN BRIDGE – Highland – 501 F 13 30 C3

Edinburgh 143 m – Fort William 10 m – Glasgow 94 m – Inverness 58 m – Oban 60 m

☎ (08452) 255121 (April-October)

☎ (01397) 703 907.

Corriegour Lodge

Loch Lochy, North : 8 ¾ m. on A 82 ✉ PH34 4EA – ☎ (01397) 712 685 – info@corriegour-lodge-hotel.com – Fax (01397) 712 696 – Closed December-February except New Year

12 rm (dinner included) – †£ 95/115 ††£ 190/230 – **Rest** – (dinner only) (booking essential for non-residents) Menu £ 49

◆ Enthusiastically run 19C hunting lodge in woods and gardens above Loch Lochy. Bright, individually decorated rooms and a cosy bar and lounge share a warm, traditional feel. Formally set dining room with wide picture windows.

Spean Lodge without rest

✉ PH34 4EP – ☎ (01397) 712 004 – welcome@speanlodge.co.uk – Closed 24-26 December

3 rm ☕ – †£ 50/60 ††£ 60/70

◆ 19C former shooting lodge whose gardens are filled with mature trees. Antiques and period furnishings abound. Utterly restful sitting room. Pleasantly individual rooms.

Corriechoille Lodge

Grey Corries and Aonach Mor, rm,

East : 2 ¾ m. on Corriechoille rd ✉ PH34 4EY – ☎ (01397) 712 002 – Closed November-March

4 rm ☕ – †£ 46 ††£ 73 – **Rest** – (Closed Monday and Tuesday) (by arrangement) Menu £ 25

◆ Off the beaten track in quiet estate land, a part 18C lodge: stylishly modern lounge, spacious en suite rooms: those facing south have fine views of the Grey Corries.

Russel's at Smiddy House with rm

Roybridge Road ✉ PH34 4EU – ☎ (01397) 712 335 – enquiry@smiddyhouse.co.uk – Fax (01397) 712 043 – Closed 2 weeks January and 2 weeks November

4 rm ☕ – †£ 70/80 ††£ 70/80 – **Rest** – (dinner only) (booking essential) Menu £ 30 **s**

◆ Spacious Victorian house in small Highland village with intimate, candlelit dining rooms and attentive service. Weekly-changing menu with strong, locally sourced seafood base. Immaculately-kept, individually decorated bedrooms.

Old Pines with rm

rm,

Northwest : 1 ½ m. by A 82 on B 8004 ✉ PH34 4EG – ☎ (01397) 712 324 – enquiries@oldpines.co.uk – Closed November-February except Christmas and New Year

7 rm ☕ – †£ 45/70 ††£ 90/110 – **Rest** – (booking essential for non-residents) Menu £ 35 (dinner) – Carte lunch £ 19/39

◆ You're encouraged to share tables in this restaurant which favours a dinner party atmosphere. Emphasis on the seasonal and the organic. Friendly staff. Well-kept rooms.

SPITTAL OF GLENSHEE – Perth and Kinross – 501 J 13 – ✉ Blairgowrie Scotland 28 C2

Edinburgh 69 m – Aberdeen 74 m – Dundee 35 m
Glenshee (✳ ★★) (chairlift AC)

Dalmunzie House

✉ *PH10 7QG – ✆ (01250) 885 224 – reservations@dalmunzie.com – Fax (01250) 885 225 – Closed 1-30 December*
17 rm – ♦£ 65/110 ♦♦£ 100/150 – **Rest** – (bar lunch) Menu £ 38
◆ Edwardian hunting lodge in a magnificent spot, encircled by mountains. Traditional rooms mix antique and pine furniture. Bar with cosy panelled alcove and leather chairs. Modern dining room with views down the valley.

Look out for red symbols, indicating particularly pleasant establishments.

ST ANDREWS – Fife – 501 L 14 – pop. 14 209 Scotland 28 D2

Edinburgh 51 m – Dundee 14 m – Stirling 51 m
70 Market St ✆ (01334) 472021
Duke's Craigtoun Park, ✆ (01334) 474 371 .
City★★ - Cathedral★ (✳ ★★) AC B – West Port★ A
Leuchars (parish church★), NW : 6 m. by A 91 and A 919. The East Neuk★★, SE : 9 m. by A 917 and B 9131 B – Crail★★ (Old Centre★★, Upper Crail★) SE : 9 m. by A 917 B – Kellie Castle★ AC, S : 9 m. by B 9131 and B 9171 B – Ceres★, SW : 9 m. by B 939 - E : Inland Fife★ A

Plan opposite

Old Course H. Golf Resort and Spa

Championship golf course and St Andrews Bay, rm,
Old Station Rd ✉ KY16 9SP – ✆ (01334) 474 371 – reservations@oldcoursehotel.co.uk – Fax (01334) 477 668 A b
116 rm – ♦£ 162/325 ♦♦£ 235/490 – 28 suites – ♦♦£ 410/1175
Rest *Road Hole Grill* – (dinner only) Carte £ 35.50/52
Rest *Sands* – Carte £ 18.75/31.50
◆ Relax into richly composed formal interiors and comprehensive luxury with a fine malt or a spa mudpack. Bright, stylish rooms. Unrivalled views of the bay and Old Course. Road Hole Grill has a fine view of the 17th hole. Worldwide flavours at Sands brasserie.

Fairmont St Andrews

rm, A/C
Southeast : 3 m. on A 917 ✉ KY16 8PN – ✆ (01334) 837 000 – standrews.scotland@fairmont.com – Fax (01334) 471 115
192 rm – ♦£ 169/310 ♦♦£ 169/310 – 17 suites
Rest *The Squire* – Menu £ 32/44 **s** – Carte £ 32/44
Rest *Esperante* – (closed Monday-Tuesday) (dinner only) Menu £ 43.50/85 **s**
◆ Golf oriented modern, purpose-built hotel on clifftop site with wonderful Tayside views and pristine fairways. Extensive conference facilities. Stylish, modern rooms. Golf chat to the "fore" in informal Squire. Mediterranean influenced Esperante.

Rufflets Country House

rm,
Strathkinness Low Rd, West : 1½ m. on B 939 ✉ KY16 9TX – ✆ (01334) 472 594 – reservations@rufflets.co.uk – Fax (01334) 478 703
22 rm – ♦£ 115/145 ♦♦£ 185/230 – 2 suites
Rest *Garden* – (dinner only and Sunday lunch) Menu £ 40
Rest *Music Room* – (lunch only Monday-Saturday) Menu £ 13
◆ Handsome 1920s house set in ornamental gardens. Traditional drawing room with cosy fireside sofas, thoughtfully appointed rooms are pristine and characterful. Garden restaurant offers fine vantage point to view the lawns. Informal Music Room for lunch.

ST ANDREWS

SCOTLAND

St Andrews Golf

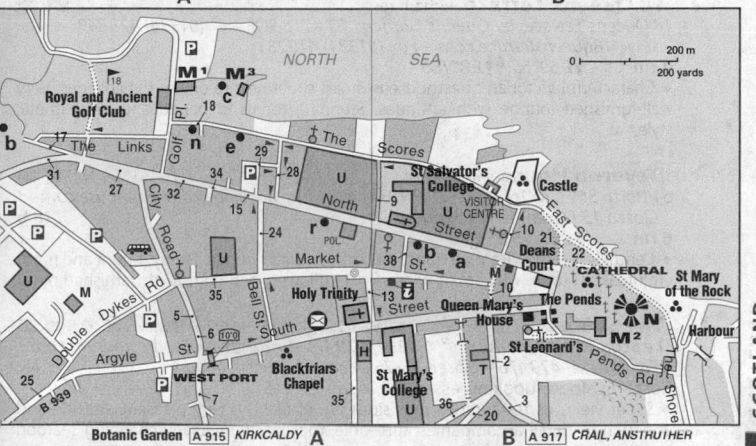

40 The Scores ✉ KY16 9AS – ✆ (01334) 472 611
– reception@standrews-golf.co.uk – Fax (01334) 472 188
– Closed 24-27 December **A e**
22 rm – £ 135/200 £ 180/250
Rest *Number 40* – Carte £ 25/40

◆ Two converted 19C town houses: well-established and family run with a relaxing feel. Bar with delightful rear terrace. Wide range of impressive, refurbished bedrooms. Contemporary dining room; appealing menu offers unfussy dishes cooked with Scottish ingredients.

The Scores

76 The Scores ✉ KY16 9BB – ✆ (01334) 472 451 – reception@scoreshotel.co.uk
– Fax (01334) 473 947 **A n**
29 rm – £ 86/126 £ 122/182 – 1 suite
Rest *Alexanders* – (dinner only) Menu £ 25 (dinner) – Carte £ 14/27

◆ Practically equipped rooms in a handsome 1880s terrace by the Old Course and facing the bay. Bar celebrates Scots heroes and the filming of "Chariots of Fire" on the beach. Formal, classic restaurant; views out to sea.

Albany

56-58 North St ✉ KY16 9AH – ✆ (01334) 477 737 – enq@standrewsalbany.co.uk
– Fax (01334) 477 742 – Closed 2 weeks Christmas and New Year **B a**
22 rm – £ 55/100 £ 80/130
Rest *Garden* – (Closed Sunday diner and Monday) Menu £ 28 (dinner) – Carte lunch approx. £ 15

◆ Well-kept, pleasingly unfussy rooms - quieter at the rear - in a family run 1790s house. Homely, firelit lounge with stacked bookshelves, antique sideboards and deep sofas. Basement dining room serves dishes with Italian roots.

Aslar House without rest
120 North St ✉ KY16 9AF – ✆ (01334) 473 460 – enquiries@aslar.com – Fax (01334) 477 540 – Closed 1-15 November, Christmas and New Year A **r**
6 rm – £ 42/70 ££ 84/90
◆ Victorian house, privately run in a welcoming spirit. Homely, pine furnished rooms, all en suite, are larger on the top floor; most overlook a quiet rear garden. Good value.

18 Queens Terrace without rest
18 Queens Terrace, by Queens Gardens ✉ KY16 9QF – ✆ (01334) 478 849 – stay@18queensterrace.com – Fax (01334) 470 283
4 rm – £ 60/65 £ 80/85
◆ Characterful Victorian guesthouse in smart street next to one of the colleges. Very well-furnished lounge with antiques. Stunning rooms in period and sympathetic style.

Deveron House without rest
64 North St ✉ KY16 9AH – ✆ (01334) 473 513 – bookings@deveronhouse.com – Closed 15 December-19 January B **b**
6 rm – £ 55/75 £ 90
◆ Centrally located Victorian guesthouse. Cosy, clean lounge. Sunny, bright and modern breakfast room with smart wicker chairs. Flowery bedrooms with varnished pine.

SCOTLAND

The Seafood < West Sands and St Andrews Bay,
The Scores ✉ KY16 9AB – ✆ (01334) 479 475 – info@theseafoodrestaurant.com – Fax (01334) 479 476 – closed 25-26 December and 1 January A **c**
Rest – Seafood (booking essential) Menu £ 26/45
◆ Super views as restaurant's four sides are of glass. A very pleasant attitude and attention to detail accompanies agreeable, top quality, regularly changing seafood menus.

ST BOSWELLS – Borders – 501 L 17 – pop. 2 092 – ✉ Melrose 26 D2

Scotland

Edinburgh 39 m – Glasgow 79 m – Hawick 17 m – Newcastle upon Tyne 66 m
St Boswells, ✆ (01835) 823 527 .
Dryburgh Abbey★★ AC (setting★★★), NW : 4 m. by B 6404 and B 6356 – Tweed Valley★★. Bowhill★★ AC, SW : 11 ½ m. by A 699 and A 708

Dryburgh Abbey rm,
North : 3 ½ m. by B 6404 on B 6356 ✉ TD6 0RQ – ✆ (01835) 822 261 – enquiries@dryburgh.co.uk – Fax (01835) 823 945
36 rm – £ 63/73 £ 126/166 – 2 suites
Rest *Tweed* – (bar lunch Monday-Saturday) Menu £ 33
◆ With the dramatic ruins of the abbey in its grounds, a restored country house near the river Tweed. Comfortable, well-equipped bedrooms, named after salmon-fishing flies. Spacious, soft-toned setting for armchair dining.

Whitehouse
Northeast : 3 m. on B 6404 ✉ TD6 0ED – ✆ (01573) 460 343 – whitehouse.tyrer@tiscali.co.uk
3 rm – £ 65 £ 98 – **Rest** – (by arrangement) Menu £ 27
◆ Appreciate the good rural views from enticingly comfortable country house style lounge in this 19C former dower house. Nourishing breakfast specials. Airy, welcoming rooms. Home-cooked meals in dining room overlooking the fields.

Clint Lodge < River Tweed and Cheviot Hills,
North : 2 ¼ m. by B 6404 on B 6356 ✉ TD6 0DZ – ✆ (01835) 822 027 – clintlodge@aol.com – Fax (01835) 822 656
5 rm – £ 50/70 £ 100 – **Rest** – (dinner only) Menu £ 28
◆ Personally run Victorian shooting lodge with sweeping prospects of the Tweed Valley and Cheviots. Antiques, open fires, fishing memorabilia and comfortable, classic rooms. A choice of tables allows for private or communal dining.

ST CYRUS – Aberdeenshire – **501** M 13 – **pop. 1 365** *Scotland* 28 **D2**

Edinburgh 93 m – Aberdeen 32 m – Montrose 5 m

Dunnottar Castle★★, N : 15 m. by A 92

Woodston Fishing Station ← St Cyrus Bay,

Northeast : 1 m. by A 92 ✉ DD10 0DG – ✆ (01674) 850 226
– info@woodstonfishingstation.co.uk – Fax (01674) 850 343
5 rm – †£80 ††£80 – **Rest** – Menu £24

◆ Superbly sited on an isolated wind-swept cliff top. High degree of comfort. Simple Victorian style rooms with fine views of bay and nature reserve. Communal breakfast room. Superbly sited on an isolated wind-swept cliff top. High degree of comfort. Simple Victorian style rooms with fine views of bay and nature reserve. Communal breakfast room.

ST FILLANS – Perth. and Kinross – **501** H 14 28 **C2**

Edinburgh 65 m – Lochearnhead 8 m – Perth 29 m

Achray House ← Loch Earn,

✉ PH6 2NF – ✆ (01764) 685 231 – info@achray-house.co.uk
– Fax (01764) 685 320 – closed 3-28 January
8 rm – †£40/70 ††£100/120 – **Rest** – Carte £18/33

◆ Well run, former Edwardian villa with a stunning Loch Earn view. A homely warmth pervades all areas. Bedrooms are clean and simple; some are suitable for families. Freshly prepared seafood a feature of dining room menus.

ST MARGARET'S HOPE – **Orkney Islands** – **501** K 6 – **see Orkney Islands**

ST MONANS – **Fife** – **501** L 15 – **pop. 3 965** 28 **D2**

Edinburgh 47 m – Dundee 26 m – Perth 40 m – Stirling 56 m

The Seafood ←

16 West End ✉ KY10 2BX – ✆ (01333) 730 327 – info@theseafoodrestaurant.com
– Fax (01333) 730 508 – closed 25-26 December and 1-2 January
Rest – Seafood (booking essential) Menu £20/36

◆ Informal former pub in a quiet fishing village; nautical memorabilia abounds. Smart lounge bar leads into a neatly set restaurant with sea views. Tasty, locally caught dishes.

STEVENSTON – N Ayrshire – **501** F 17 – **pop. 9 129** 25 **A2**

Edinburgh 82 m – Ayr 19 m – Glasgow 36 m

Ardeer Farm Steading without rest

Ardeer Mains Farm, East : ¾ m. by A 738 and B 752, on no through rd
✉ KA20 3DD – ✆ (01294) 465 438 – info@ardeersteading.co.uk
6 rm – †£32/35 ††£45/48

◆ Comfortable family-owned guest house has contemporary furnishings, with bright cushions and bed throws. Pleasant breakfast room and modern lounge with cream leather sofas.

STIRLING – Stirling – **501** I 15 – **pop. 32 673** *Scotland* 28 **C2**

Edinburgh 37 m – Dunfermline 23 m – Falkirk 14 m – Glasgow 28 m – Greenock 52 m – Motherwell 30 m – Oban 87 m – Perth 35 m

Dumbarton Rd ✆ (08707) 200621, stirlingtic@aillst.ossian.netRoyal Burgh Stirling Visitor Centre ✆ (01786) 479901 - Pirnhall, Motorway Service Area, junction 9, M 9 ✆ (01786) 814111 (April-October)

Town★★ – Castle★★ **AC** (Site★★★, external elevations★★★, Stirling Heads★★, Argyll and Sutherland Highlanders Regimental Museum★) B – Argyll's Lodging★ (Renaissance decoration★) B **A** – Church of the Holy Rude★ B **B**

Wallace Monument (✳ ★★) NE : 2½ m. by A 9 - A - and B 998. Dunblane★ (Cathedral★★, West Front★★), N : 6½ m. by A 9 A

Plan on next page

SCOTLAND

STIRLING

Street	Grid	No.
Barnton St.	B	2
Borestone Crescent	A	3
Causewayhead Rd	A, B	4
Cornton Rd	A	7
Corn Exchange Rd	B	5
Coxithill Rd	A	8
Drummond Pl.	B	9
Dumbarton Rd	B	10
Goosecroft Rd	B	12
King St	B	13
Leisure Centre	B	
Murray Pl.	B	15
Newhouse	A	16
Park Pl.	A	18
Port St.	B	
Queen St	B	20
Randolph Terrace	A	22
St John St.	B	23
St Mary's Wynd	B	24
Seaforth Pl.	B	25
Shirra's Brae Rd	A	26
Spittal St	B	27
Thistle Centre	B	
Union St	B	28
Upper Craigs	B	29
Weaver Row	A	31

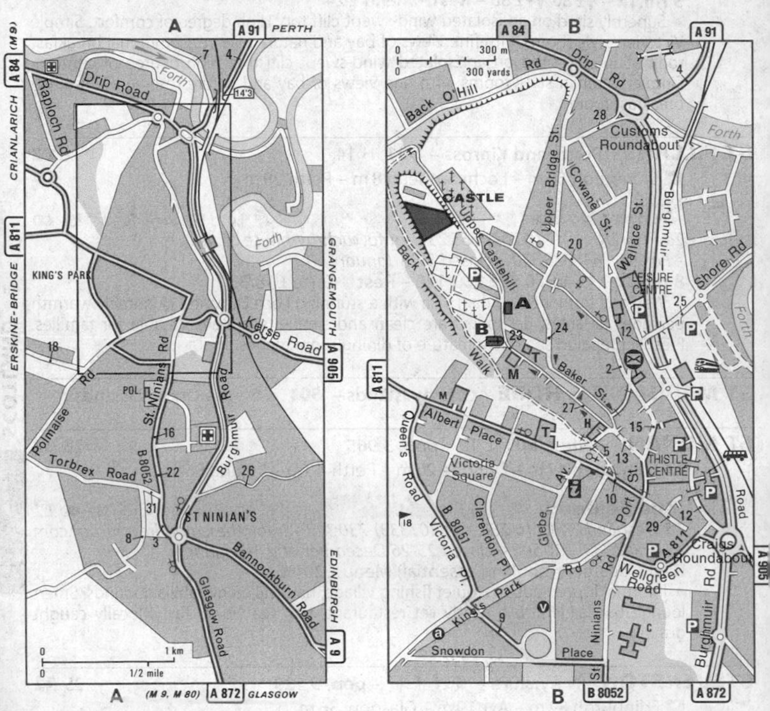

Park Lodge

32 Park Terrace ✉ FK8 2JS – ✆ (01786) 474 862 – info@parklodge.net – Fax (01786) 449 748 – Closed Christmas and New Year **B a**

9 rm – †£ 65/85 ††£ 95/135 – **Rest** – (Closed Sunday) Menu £ 15/25 – Carte £ 18/28

◆ Creeper-clad Georgian and Victorian house, still in private hands and furnished with an enviable collection of antiques. Compact but well-equipped rooms with a stylish feel. Intimate dining room overlooking a pretty garden.

Number 10 without rest

Gladstone Pl ✉ FK8 2NN – ✆ (01786) 472 681 – cameron-10@tinyonline.co.uk – Fax (01786) 472 681 **B v**

3 rm – †£ 40/60 ††£ 55/60

◆ Surprisingly spacious 19C terrace house in a pleasant suburb. Pine furnished en suite bedrooms are characteristically well kept and comfortable. Friendly owner.

West Plean House without rest

South : 3½ m. on A 872 (Denny rd) ✉ FK7 8HA – ✆ (01786) 812208 – moira@westpleanhouse.com – Fax (01786) 480550 – Closed mid December-mid January

3 rm – ♀£ 38/42 ♀♀£ 64/70

◆ Dating back to the 1800s, a homely and traditional house under pleasant personal ownership. Simple en suite accommodation. Neat gardens, duckpond and working farm close by.

STONEHAVEN – Aberdeenshire – 501 N 13 Scotland 28 D2

Edinburgh 109 m – Aberdeen 16 m – Montrose 22 m

Dunnottar Castle★★, S : 1½ m. by A 92

Tolbooth

Old Pier, Harbour ✉ AB39 2JU – ✆ (01569) 762287 – enquiries@tolbooth-restaurant.co.uk – Fax (01569) 762287 – Closed 25 December-10 January, Sunday and Monday

Rest – Seafood Menu £ 16 – Carte £ 27/37

◆ Stonehaven's oldest building, delightfully located by the harbour. Rustic interior with lovely picture window table. Varied menus with seafood base accompanied by great views.

Carron

20 Cameron St ✉ AB39 2HS – ✆ (01569) 760460 – Fax (01569) 760460 – Closed 25 December-12 January, Sunday and Monday

Rest – Carte £ 19/28

◆ 1930s Art Deco elegance fully restored to its original splendour. Panelled walls with old mono photos. Sunny front terrace. Popular menus highlighted by daily lobster dishes.

at Netherley North : 6 m. by B 979 – ✉ Aberdeenshire

The Crynoch – at Lairhillock Inn

Northeast : 1½ m. by B 979 on Portlethen rd ✉ AB39 3QS – ✆ (01569) 730220 – info@lairhillock.co.uk – Fax (01569) 731175 – Closed 25-26 December, 1-2 January and Monday

Rest – (dinner only and Sunday lunch) Carte £ 19/44

◆ Converted cattle shed with beamed ceiling, wood panelling and open fire. Traditional dishes using locally sourced ingredients.

STORNOWAY – Western Isles Outer Hebrides – 501 A 9 – see Lewis and Harris (Isle of)

STRACHUR – Argyll and Bute – 501 E 15 – pop. 628 27 B2

Edinburgh 112 m – Glasgow 66 m – Inverness 162 m – Perth 101 m

The Creggans Inn ← Loch Fyne,

✉ PA27 8BX – ✆ (01369) 860279 – info@creggans-inn.co.uk – closed 25-26 December

14 rm – ♀£ 65/85 ♀♀£ 170 – 1 suite – **Rest** – Menu 32 – Carte £ 22/30

◆ Locally renowned inn, with splendid views over Loch Fyne. Cosy bar with busy pub dining trade and two lounges, one with fine outlook. Individually styled, comfy rooms. Large dining room with wood floor and warm colour scheme.

Inver Cottage ← Loch Fyne and mountains,

Strathlaclan, Southwest : 6½ m. by A 886 on B 8000 ✉ PA27 8BU – ✆ (01369) 860537 – April-September, weekends October-Christmas, lunch only except Thursday-Saturday July, August and October

Rest – (closed Monday except July-August and Bank Holidays) Carte £ 17/33

◆ Wonderfully located former crofters' cottage with fine views over lake and mountains. The simple little restaurant, with its own craft shop, serves tasty Scottish based menus.

STRANRAER – Dumfries and Galloway – 501 E 19 – pop. 10 851 25 A3

Scotland

Edinburgh 132 m – Ayr 51 m – Dumfries 75 m

to Northern Ireland (Belfast) (Stena Line) (1 h 45 mn) – to Northern Ireland (Belfast) (Stena Line) 4-5 daily (1 h 45 mn/3 h 15 mn)

Harbour Sq (01776) 702595

Creachmore Leswalt, (01776) 870 245 .

Logan Botanic Garden ★ **AC**, S : 11 m. by A 77, A 716 and B 7065

Glenotter without rest

Leswalt Rd, Northwest : 1 m. on A 718 ✉ DG9 0EP – (01776) 703 199 – enquiries@glenotter.co.uk – closed 25-26 December and 1 January

3 rm – £ 38/49 £ 52/58

◆ Homely guesthouse run by a husband and wife team, on main road just out of town, convenient for ferry. Well-kept rooms in co-ordinated colours are simple and sensibly priced.

at Kirkcolm Northwest : 6 m. by A 718 – ✉ Stranraer

Corsewall Lighthouse

Corsewall Point, Northwest : 4 ¼ m. by B 738 ✉ DG9 0QG – (01776) 853 220 – info@lighthousehotel.co.uk – Fax (01776) 854 231

6 rm (dinner included) – £ 130/150 £ 200/250 – 3 suites –

Rest – Carte £ 28/32

◆ Sensitively converted and family run, a 19C working lighthouse at the mouth of Loch Ryan. Snug bedrooms in traditional fabrics - views of the sea or the windswept promontory. Simple, characterful restaurant with seascapes and old black beams.

STRATHPEFFER – Highland – 501 G 11 – pop. 918 30 C2

Edinburgh 174 m – Inverness 18 m

The Square (01997) 421415 (April-October)

Strathpeffer Spa, (01997) 421 219 .

Craigvar without rest

The Square ✉ IV14 9DL – (01997) 421 622 – craigvar@talk21.com – Fax (01997) 421 622 – Closed 24 December-7 January and 2 weeks October

3 rm – £ 35/38 £ 64/68

◆ Georgian house overlooking main square of pleasant former spa town. Charming owner guarantees an agreeable stay. Bedrooms are crammed with antiques and original fittings.

STRATHYRE – Stirling – 501 H 15 – ✉ Callander Scotland 27 B2

Edinburgh 62 m – Glasgow 53 m – Perth 42 m

The Trossachs ★★★ (Loch Katrine ★★) SW : 14 m. by A 84 and A 821 – Hilltop viewpoint ★★★ (✲ ★★★) SW : 16 ½ m. by A 84 and A 821

Ardoch Lodge

West : ¼ m. ✉ FK18 8NF – (01877) 384 666 – ardoch@btinternet.com – Fax (01877) 384 666 – Easter-mid November

3 rm – £ 58 £ 112 – **Rest** – (by arrangement) Menu £ 30

◆ Victorian in origin, a family-owned country house set in wooded hills above Strathyre's river. Simple accommodation and traditionally decorated sitting room. Home cooking prepared with pride.

Creagan House with rm

on A 84 ✉ FK18 8ND – (01877) 384 638 – eatandstay@creaganhouse.co.uk – Fax (01877) 384 319 – Closed February, 2-21 November and 24-26 December

5 rm – £ 70 £ 120 – **Rest** – (Closed Wednesday and Thursday) (dinner only) (booking essential) Menu £ 28

◆ Surrounded by hills which inspired Sir Walter Scott; a feast for the eye to be enjoyed in baronial style dining room. French classics with Scottish overtones. Cosy rooms.

STRONTIAN – Highland – 501 D 13 — 29 B3

Edinburgh 139 m – Fort William 23 m – Oban 66 m
Acharacle ✆ (01967) 402131 (April-October)

Kilcamb Lodge

PH36 4HY – ✆ (01967) 402 257 – enquiries@kilcamblodge.co.uk – Fax (01967) 402 041 – Closed January

10 rm – £ 115/140 £ 250/330 – **Rest** – (booking essential for non-residents at dinner) Menu £ 48 (dinner) – Carte lunch £ 18/35

◆ A spectacular location in 19 acres of lawn and woodland, leading down to a private shore on Loch Sunart. The idyll continues indoors: immaculate bedrooms; thoughtful extras. Savour views from large windows and tuck into roast grouse.

STRUAN – Highland – see Skye (Isle of)

STRUY – Highland – 501 F 11 — 30 C2

Edinburgh 180 m – Inverness 19 m – Kyle of Lochalsh 82 m

The Glass at the Struy Inn

IV4 7JS – ✆ (01463) 761 219

Rest – (dinner only and Sunday lunch) (booking essential) Carte £ 18/24

◆ Converted inn retains a traditional, almost homely feel. Wide-ranging menu of wholesome, satisfying dishes, plus a blackboard listing daily specials and fresh seafood.

SWINTON – Borders – 501 N 16 – pop. 472 – ✉ Duns — 26 D2

Edinburgh 49 m – Berwick-upon-Tweed 13 m – Glasgow 93 m – Newcastle upon Tyne 66 m

The Wheatsheaf with rm

Main Street ✉ TD11 3JJ – ✆ (01890) 860 257 – reception@wheatsheaf-swinton.co.uk – Fax (01890) 860 688 – Closed 25-26 December

10 rm – £ 69 £ 102 – **Rest** – (closed Sunday dinner December-February) Carte £ 22/36

◆ A village inn with firelit real ale bar and comfortable, well-furnished rooms. Classic, unfussy seasonal dishes bring out the distinctive flavour of local produce.

TAIN – Highland – 501 H 10 — 30 D2

Edinburgh 191 m – Inverness 35 m – Wick 91 m
18 Tain Chapel Rd, ✆ (01862) 892 314 ;
9 Tarbat Portmahomack, ✆ (01862) 871 278 .

Golf View House without rest

13 Knockbreck Rd ✉ IV19 1BN – ✆ (01862) 892 856 – golfview@hotmail.co.uk – Fax (01862) 892 856 – March-November

5 rm – £ 35/50 £ 54/65

◆ Built as a vicarage, a local sandstone house overlooking the Firth and the fairways. Simple rooms are well kept and tidy. Lawn and flowers shaded by beech trees.

at Cadboll Southeast : 8½ m. by A 9 and B 9165 (Portmahomack rd) off Hilton rd – ✉ Tain

Glenmorangie House

Fearn ✉ IV20 1XP – ✆ (01862) 871 671 – relax@glenmorangieplc.co.uk – Fax (01862) 871 625 – closed January

9 rm – £ 190 £ 380 – **Rest** – (dinner only) (booking essential for non-residents) (communal dining, set menu only) Menu £ 50

◆ Restored part 17C house owned by the famous distillery. Tasteful, old-world morning room and more informal firelit lounge; house party ambience prevails. Smart, comfy rooms. Imposing communal dining room: gilt-framed portraits, eastern rugs and a long table.

TALMINE – Highland – **501** G 8 – ✉ **Lairg** 30 **C1**

Edinburgh 245 m – Inverness 86 m – Thurso 48 m

Cloisters without rest ← Rabbit Islands and Tongue Bay,

Church Holme ✉ IV27 4YP – ✆ (01847) 601 286 – reception@cloistertal.demon.co.uk – Fax (01847) 601 286 – closed Christmas and New Year

3 rm – £ 30/33 £ 50/56

◆ Purpose-built guesthouse, by a converted church, offers simple but trim and spotless rooms in bright fabrics and superb view of Rabbit Islands and Tongue Bay. Friendly host.

TARBERT – **Western Isles Outer Hebrides** – **501** Z 10 – **see Lewis and Harris (Isle of)**

TARBET – Argyll and Bute – **501** F 15 – ✉ **Arrochar** 27 **B2**

Edinburgh 88 m – Glasgow 42 m – Inverness 138 m – Perth 78 m

Lomond View without rest ← Loch Lomond,

on A 82 ✉ G83 7DG – ✆ (01301) 702 477 – lomondviewhouse@aol.com – Fax (01301) 702 477

3 rm – £ 55/65 £ 75

◆ Purpose-built guesthouse which lives up to its name: there are stunning loch views. Spacious sitting room. Light and airy breakfast room. Sizeable, modern bedrooms.

TAYVALLICH – Argyll and Bute – **501** D 15 – ✉ **Lochgilphead** 27 **B2**

Edinburgh 148 m – Glasgow 103 m – Inverness 157 m

Tayvallich Inn

✉ PA31 8PL – ✆ (01546) 870 282 – rfhanderson@aol.com – closed Monday-Wednesday November-February and 25 December

Rest – Carte £ 18/40

◆ Well-regarded pub in little coastal hamlet close to the shores of Loch Sween. Interior of pine panelling and log fires. Simple or creative seafood dishes are the speciality.

TEANGUE – **Highland** – **see Skye (Isle of)**

THORNHILL – **Dumfries and Galloway** – **501** I 18 – **pop. 1 512** 25 **B2**

Scotland

Edinburgh 64 m – Ayr 44 m – Dumfries 15 m – Glasgow 63 m

Drumlanrig Castle★★ (cabinets★) **AC**, NW : 4 m. by A 76

Trigony House

Closeburn, South : 1½ m. on A 76 ✉ DG3 5EZ – ✆ (01848) 331 211 – info@trigonyhotel.co.uk – Closed 25-26 December

10 rm (dinner included) – £ 65 £ 140/180 –

Rest – (dinner only) Carte £ 21/27 **s**

◆ Ivy-clad Victorian shooting lodge, family owned, mixes period décor and modern art. Cosy bar with an open fire. Traditional rooms overlook four acres of woodland and garden. Tasty, locally inspired dishes.

Gillbank House without rest

8 East Morton St ✉ DG3 5LZ – ✆ (01848) 330 597 – hanne@gillbank.co.uk – Fax (01848) 331 713

6 rm – £ 45 £ 65

◆ Victorian stone built personally run house just off town square. Guests' sitting room and airy breakfast room. Spacious, well-furnished bedrooms with bright décor.

THURSO – Highland – 501 J 8 – pop. 7 737 *Scotland* 30 **D1**

Edinburgh 289 m – Inverness 133 m – Wick 21 m

from Scrabster to Stromness (Orkney Islands) (P and O Scottish Ferries) (2 h)

Riverside ☎ (01847) 892371 (April-October)

Newlands of Geise, ☎ (01847) 893 807 .

Strathy Point★ (≤ ★★★) W : 22 m. by A 836

Forss House

Forss, West : 5½ m. on A 836 ✉ KW14 7XY – ☎ (01847) 861 201 – anne@forsshousehotel.co.uk – Fax (01847) 861 301 – closed 23 December-6 January

12 rm – †£ 76 ††£ 145 – 1 suite – **Rest** – (dinner only) Carte £ 29/35

◆ Traditional décor sets off the interior of this 19C house, smoothly run in a friendly style. Good-sized, comfy rooms. Angling themed bar, drying room and warm atmosphere. Vast choice of malts in restaurant bar.

Station

54 Princes St ✉ KW14 7DH – ☎ (01847) 892 003 – stationhotel@northhotels.co.uk – Fax (01847) 891 820

30 rm – †£ 50/60 ††£ 70/120 – **Rest** – (dinner only) Carte £ 16/25

◆ Personally run with care and immaculate housekeeping. Co-ordinated bedrooms are bright, attractive and well-appointed. Some rooms in Coach House annex are slightly larger. Simple, neat restaurant with traditional menus.

Murray House

1 Campbell St ✉ KW14 7HD – ☎ (01847) 895 759 – enquiries@murrayhousebb.com – closed Christmas and New Year

5 rm – †£ 25/30 ††£ 30/56 – **Rest** – Menu £ 15 **s**

◆ A centrally located and family owned Victorian town house. Pine furnished bedrooms, half en suite, are simple but carefully maintained. Modern dining room where home-cooked evening meals may be taken.

TIGHNABRUAICH – Argyll and Bute – 501 E 16 27 **B3**

Edinburgh 113 m – Glasgow 63 m – Oban 66 m

An Lochan

✉ PA21 2BE – ☎ (01700) 811 239 – info@anlochan.co.uk – Fax (01700) 811 300 – closed Christmas

12 rm – †£ 100 ††£ 250 – **Rest** – (Dinner Monday -Tuesday set menu only) Carte £ 31/40

◆ Privately owned 19C hotel with firelit shinty bar, in an unspoilt village overlooking the Kyles of Bute. Deep burgundy walls, vivid landscapes and modernised bedrooms. Formal restaurant with fine loch views. Innovative cooking from a dynamic young team.

TILLICOULTRY – Clackmannanshire – 501 I 15 – pop. 5 400 28 **C2**

Edinburgh 35 m – Dundee 43 m – Glasgow 38 m

Alva Rd, ☎ (01259) 750 124 .

Harviestoun Country Inn

Dollar Rd, East : ¼ m. by A 91 ✉ FK13 6PQ – ☎ (01259) 752 522 – harviestounhotel@aol.com – Fax (01259) 752 523

11 rm – †£ 60 ††£ 80 – **Rest** – Carte £ 17/27

◆ Converted Georgian stable block, now a smoothly run modern hotel. Neat, unfussy, pine furnished bedrooms, half facing the Ochil hills; coffees and home baking in the lounge. Beams and flagstones hint at the restaurant's rustic past.

TIRORAN – Argyll and Bute – see Mull (Isle of)

TOBERMORY – Argyll and Bute – 501 B 14 – see Mull (Isle of)

TONGUE – Highland – 501 G 8 – ✉ Lairg Scotland 30 C1

Edinburgh 257 m – Inverness 101 m – Thurso 43 m

Cape Wrath★★★ (≤ ★★) W : 44 m. (including ferry crossing) by A 838 – Ben Loyal★★, S : 8 m. by A 836 – Ben Hope★ (≤ ★★★) SW : 15 m. by A 838 – Strathy Point★ (≤ ★★★) E : 22 m. by A 836 – Torrisdale Bay★ (≤ ★★) NE : 8 m. by A 836

Tongue

Main St ✉ IV27 4XD – ✆ (01847) 611 206 – info@tonguehotel.co.uk – Fax (01847) 611 345

19 rm – †£ 45/65 ††£ 100/130 – **Rest** – (bar lunch) Carte £ 16/34

◆ Former hunting lodge of the Duke of Sutherland overlooking Kyle of Tongue. Smart interiors include intimate bar and beamed lounge. Individually styled rooms with antiques. Restaurant with fireplace and antique dressers.

Ben Loyal

≤ Ben Loyal and Kyle of Tongue,

Main St ✉ IV27 4XE – ✆ (01847) 611 216 – stay@btinternet.com – Fax (01847) 611 212 – March-November

11 rm – †£ 40/60 ††£ 80 – **Rest** – Carte £ 23/35 **s**

◆ Unassuming hotel in the village centre enjoys excellent views of Ben Loyal and the Kyle of Tongue - a useful hiking or fishing base. Rooms are unfussy, modern and well kept. Pine furnished restaurant overlooks the hills and sea.

TORRIDON – Highland – 501 D 11 – ✉ Achnasheen Scotland 29 B2

Edinburgh 234 m – Inverness 62 m – Kyle of Lochalsh 44 m

Wester Ross★★★

The Torridon

≤ Upper Loch Torridon and mountains, rm,

South : 1½ m. on A 896 ✉ IV22 2EY – ✆ (01445) 791 242 – info@thetorridon.com – Fax (01445) 712 253 – closed January, Monday and Tuesday from November-March

18 rm – †£ 120/255 ††£ 325/455 – 1 suite – **Rest** – (bar lunch) (booking essential) Menu £ 42

◆ 19C hunting lodge; idyllic view of Loch Torridon and mountains. Ornate ceilings, peat fires and Highland curios add to a calm period feel shared by the more luxurious rooms. Formal, pine-panelled restaurant uses fine local produce, some from the grounds.

Torridon Inn

rm,

South : 1½ m. on A 896 ✉ IV22 2EY – ✆ (01445) 791 242 – inn@thetorridon.com – Fax (01445) 712 253 – March-October

12 rm – †£ 60/85 ††£ 85 – **Rest** – Carte £ 20/25

◆ Simple, modern, affordable rooms - some sleeping up to six - in a converted stable block, set in a quiet rural spot and named after the mountain nearby. Spacious pubby bar. Traditionally styled and informal restaurant.

TROON – South Ayrshire – 501 G 17 – pop. 14 766 25 A2

Edinburgh 77 m – Ayr 7 m – Glasgow 31 m

to Northern Ireland (Larne) (P and O Irish Sea) 2 daily

Troon Municipal Harling Drive, ✆ (01292) 312 464 .

Lochgreen House

Monktonhill Rd, Southwood, Southeast : 2 m. on B 749 ✉ KA10 7EN – ✆ (01292) 313 343 – lochgreen@costley-hotels.co.uk – Fax (01292) 318 661

43 rm – †£ 125 ††£ 180 – 1 suite

Rest *Tapestry* – see restaurant listing

◆ Attractive, coastal Edwardian house in mature grounds. Lounges exude luxurious country house feel. Large rooms, modern or traditional, have a good eye for welcoming detail.

Tapestry – at Lochgreen House H.

Monktonhill Rd, Southwood, Southeast : 2 m. on B 749 ✉ KA10 7EN – ✆ (01292) 313 343 – Fax (01292) 318 661

Rest – Carte £ 25/40

◆ Spacious dining room with baronial feel. Elegant chandeliers; large pottery cockerels. Classical, modern cooking, with a strong Scottish base.

at Loans East : 2 m. on A 759 – ✉ Troon

Highgrove House
Old Loans Rd, East : ¼ m. on Dundonald rd ✉ KA10 7HL – ☎ (01292) 312511 – highgrove@costleyhotels.co.uk – Fax (01292) 318228
9 rm – †£69 ††£110 – **Rest** – Carte £20/35
◆ Immaculate whitewashed hotel in elevated position, offering superb coastal panorama. Comfy floral bedrooms; 1 and 2 have the best views. Tartan carpets remind you where you are. Large restaurant with floor to ceiling windows and granite coloumns. Popular, long-established menus.

TURNBERRY – South Ayrshire – 501 F 18 – ✉ Girvan *Scotland* 25 A2
Edinburgh 97 m – Ayr 15 m – Glasgow 51 m – Stranraer 36 m
Culzean Castle★ AC (setting★★★, Oval Staircase★★) NE : 5 m. by A 719

The Westin Turnberry Resort
golf courses, bay, Ailsa Craig and Mull of Kintyre, rm, rest,
on A 719 ✉ KA26 9LT – ☎ (01655) 331000 – turnberry@westin.com – Fax (01655) 331706 – Closed Christmas
211 rm – †£230/375 ††£250/395 – 8 suites
Rest *Turnberry* – (Closed Sunday- Monday) (dinner only) Menu £49 – Carte £49/67 **s**
Rest *Stagioni* – (Closed Tuesday-Wednesday) Menu £26 **s** – Carte £28/43 **s**
Rest *Tappie Toorie* – Menu £20 (dinner) **s** – Carte £23/44 **s**
◆ Impeccably run part Edwardian hotel with panoramic views of coast and world famous golf courses. Much original charm intact. Superbly equipped with every conceivable facility. Fine dining in Turnberry. Italian cuisine in smart Stagioni. Informal Tappie Toorie Grill.

UDDINGSTON – South Lanarkshire – 501 H 16 – pop. 5 576 – ✉ Glasgow 25 B1
Edinburgh 41 m – Glasgow 10 m
Coatbridge Townhead Rd, ☎ (01236) 28975.

Redstones
rest,
8-10 Glasgow Rd ✉ G71 7AS – ☎ (01698) 813774 – info@redstoneshotel.com – Fax (01698) 815319 – Closed 1 and 2 January
12 rm – †£89 ††£99 – **Rest** – Menu £15 (lunch) – Carte £20/28
◆ Renovated Victorian houses in distinctive red sandstone - the conservatory lounge is a later addition; usefully-equipped bedrooms feel stylish and modern. Formal dining room.

UIST (Isles of) – 501 X/Y 10 – pop. 3 510 29 A2
see Liniclate
from Lochmaddy to Isle of Skye (Uig) (Caledonian MacBrayne Ltd) 1-3 daily (1 h 50 mn) – from Otternish to Isle of Harris (Leverburgh) (Caledonian MacBrayne Ltd) (1 h 10 mn)

NORTH UIST – Western Isles 29 A2

Carinish – Western Isles 29 A2

Temple View
✉ HS6 5EJ – ☎ (01876) 580676 – templeviewhotel@aol.com – Fax (01876) 580682
10 rm – †£55/75 ††£105/115 – **Rest** – (bar lunch) Carte £14/24 **s**
◆ Extended Victorian house on main route from north to south. Pleasantly refurbished, it offers a smart sitting room, cosy bar with conservatory, and up-to-date bedrooms. Extensive local specialities the highlight of small dining room.

Langass – Western Isles 29 A2

Langass Lodge ⟨ Ben Eaval and Langass Loch, rm,
HS6 5HA – (01876) 580 285
– *langasslodge@btconnect.com – Fax (01876) 580 385*
12 rm – £ 65 £ 120 – **Rest** – (dinner only and Sunday lunch) Menu £ 30
♦ Former Victorian shooting lodge boasting superb views, classical comforts, a modish conservatory extension, and bedrooms styled from traditional to clean-lined modernity. Superior cooking of fine Hebridean produce from land and sea.

Lochmaddy – Western Isles 29 A2

Tigh Dearg rm,
HS6 5AE – (01876) 500 700 – info@tighdearghotel.co.uk
– Fax (01876) 500 701
8 rm – £ 79/90 £ 89/139 – **Rest** – Carte £ 15/28 **s**
♦ 'The Red House', visible from a long distance, is an outpost of utterly stylish chic. Modish bar matched by well-equipped gym, sauna and steam room, and sleek 21C bedrooms. Hebridean produce well sourced in designer-style restaurant.

SOUTH UIST – Western Isles 29 A2

Lochboisdale – Western Isles 29 A2

Brae Lea
Lasgair, Northwest : 1 m. by A 865 HS8 5TH – (01878) 700 497
– braelea@supanet.com – Fax (01878) 700 497
6 rm – £ 30/35 £ 60/70 – **Rest** – (by arrangement) Menu £ 15
♦ In a quiet spot yet convenient for the ferry, a purpose-built guesthouse, well-established and family run. Neat, pine-fitted rooms, homely lounge with wide picture windows. Unpretentious home-cooked dinners in a suitably simple setting.

ULLAPOOL – Highland – 501 E 10 – pop. 1 308 *Scotland* 30 C2

Edinburgh 215 m – Inverness 59 m
to Isle of Lewis (Stornoway) (Caledonian MacBrayne Ltd) (2 h 40 mn)
Argyle St (01854) 612135
Town★
Wester Ross★★★ - Loch Broom★★. Falls of Measach★★, S : 11 m. by A 835 and A 832 - Corrieshalloch Gorge★, SE : 10 m. by A 835 – Northwards to Lochinver★★, Morefield (⟨ ★★ of Ullapool), ⟨ ★ Loch Broom

Ardvreck without rest ⟨ Loch Broom and mountains,
Morefield Brae, Northwest : 2 m. by A 835 IV26 2TH
– (01854) 612 028 – ardvreck.guesthouse@btinternet.com
– Fax (01854) 613 000 – February-October
10 rm – £ 32/70 £ 60/75
♦ Peacefully located hotel boasting fine views of loch and mountains. Well appointed breakfast room with splendid vistas. Spacious rooms: some with particularly fine outlooks.

Tanglewood House ⟨ Loch Broom,
on A 835 IV26 2TB – (01854) 612 059 – tanglewoodhouse@ecosse.net
– closed Christmas, New Year
3 rm – £ 66/73 £ 84 – **Rest** – (by arrangement, communal dining) Menu £ 33
♦ Blissfully located guesthouse on heather covered headland. Drawing room has a 20 foot window overlooking loch. Homely, pastel shaded rooms, all with vistas. Meals taken at communal table.

The Sheiling without rest ⟨ Loch Broom,
Garve Rd IV26 2SX – (01854) 612 947 – mail@thesheilingullapool.co.uk
– Fax (0870) 123 61 65
6 rm – £ 50/76 £ 66/76
♦ Welcoming guesthouse by the shores of Loch Broom. Renowned breakfasts include a platter of locally smoked fish. Homely lounge and comfortable bedrooms.

Point Cottage without rest — Loch Broom

West Shore St ✉ IV26 2UR – ☎ (01854) 612494 – macrae@pointcottage.co.uk – March-October

3 rm – £30/55 £44/64

◆ Converted fisherman's cottage of 18C origin. Rooms in bright modern fabrics enjoy beautiful views across Loch Broom to the hills. Substantial breakfasts.

Dromnan without rest

Garve Rd ✉ IV26 2SX – ☎ (01854) 612333 – info@dromnan.com

7 rm – £32/65 £65/75

◆ Family run, modern house overlooking Loch Broom. Television lounge with deep leather chairs. Practically equipped rooms vary in décor from patterned pastels to dark tartan.

UNST (Island of) – Shetland Islands – 501 R 1 – see Shetland Islands

---

URQUHART – Moray – see Elgin

VEENSGARTH – Shetland Islands – see Shetland Islands (Mainland)

WALKERBURN – Borders 26 C2

Edinburgh 30 m – Galashiels 23 m – Peebles 8 m

Windlestraw Lodge

Tweed Valley, on A 72 ✉ EH43 6AA – ☎ (01896) 870636 – reception@windlestraw.co.uk – Fax (01896) 870639 – closed 3 weeks February,1 week Autumn, 23 December-4 January

6 rm – £80/90 £130/180 – **Rest** – (dinner only and Sunday lunch) (booking essential for non-residents) Menu £24 (lunch) – Carte approx. £40

◆ Edwardian country house in picturesque Tweed Valley: lovely views guaranteed. Period style lounges serviced by well-stocked bar. Half the good-sized rooms enjoy the vista. Linen-clad dining room.

WATERNISH – Highland – see Skye (Isle of)

WESTRAY (Island of) – Orkney Islands – 501 K/L 6/ – see Orkney Islands

---

WHITING BAY – North Ayrshire – 501 E 17 – see Arran (Isle of)

WICK – Highland – 501 K 8 – pop. 7 333 *Scotland* 30 D1

Edinburgh 282 m – Inverness 126 m

Wick Airport : ☎ (01955) 602215, N : 1 m

Whitechapel Rd ☎ (01955) 602596

Reiss, ☎ (01955) 602726 .

Duncansby Head★ (Stacks of Duncansby★★) N : 14 m. by A 9 – Grey Cairns of Camster★ (Long Cairn★★) S : 17 m. by A 9 – The Hill O'Many Stanes★, S : 10 m. by A 9

The Clachan without rest

South Rd, South : ¾ m. on A 99 ✉ KW1 5NJ – ☎ (01955) 605384 – enquiry@theclachan.co.uk – closed Christmas and New Year

3 rm – £35/40 £46/50

◆ This detached 1930s house on the town's southern outskirts provides homely en suite accommodation in pastels and floral patterns. Charming owner.

Bord De L'Eau

2 Market St (Riverside) ✉ KW1 4AR – ☎ (01955) 604400 – closed first 3 weeks January, 25-26 December, Sunday lunch and Monday

Rest – French Carte £21/32

◆ Totally relaxed little riverside eatery with French owner. Friendly, attentive service of an often-changing, distinctly Gallic repertoire. Keenly priced dishes.

Y. Duhamel/MICHELIN

Towns
from A to Z

Villes
de A à Z

Città
de A a Z

Städte
von A bis Z

Wales

ABERAERON – Ceredigion – 503 H 27 33 B3

Cardiff 90 m – Aberystwyth 16 m – Fishguard 41 m

Ty Mawr Mansion Country House

Cilcennin, East : 4½ m. by A 482 ✉ SA48 8DB – ✆ (01570) 470033 – info@tymawrmansion.co.uk – Closed 27 December-10 January

8 rm – †£ 80/120 ††£ 160/240 – 1 suite

– **Rest** – (Closed Sunday-Monday) (dinner only) Carte £ 32/45

◆ Grade II listed Georgian stone mansion in 12 acres of grounds. Three sumptuous reception rooms matched by luxurious bedrooms, which are oversized and full of top facilities. Chefs rear pigs for locally renowned restaurant boasting bold edge to cooking.

Llys Aeron without rest

Lampeter Rd, on A 482 ✉ SA46 0ED – ✆ (01545) 570276 – enquiries@llysaeron.co.uk

3 rm – †£ 40/70 ††£ 60/70

◆ Imposing Georgian house on main road. Hearty Aga cooked breakfasts overlooking well established rear walled garden. Comfy lounge; light, airy rooms in clean pastel shades.

Harbourmaster with rm

Quay Parade ✉ SA46 0BA – ✆ (01545) 570755 – info@harbour-master.com – Closed 25 December and Monday

9 rm – †£ 55 ††£ 150 – **Rest** – Menu £ 17 – Carte £ 20/30

◆ Good value, former harbour master's house, located on attractive quayside. Stylish décor throughout and run in a relaxing style. Snug bar; individually styled bedrooms. Contemporary dining room with a seafood grounding.

WALES

ABERDOVEY (Aberdyfi) – Gwynedd – 503 H 26 32 B2

London 230 m – Dolgellau 25 m – Shrewsbury 66 m

Snowdonia National Park★★★

Llety Bodfor without rest

Bodfor Terrace ✉ LL35 0EA – ✆ (01654) 767475 – info@lletybodfor.co.uk – Fax (01654) 767836 – Closed 23-29 December

8 rm – †£ 45/90 ††£ 145

◆ Two 19C seafront terraces painted pale mauve with modish interior featuring sitting/breakfast room with piano and hi-fi; luxurious bedrooms have blue/white seaside theme.

Penhelig Arms with rm

< Dyfi Estuary, A/C rest,

✉ LL35 0LT – ✆ (01654) 767215 – info@penheligarms.com – Fax (01654) 767690 – Closed 25-26 December

16 rm – †£ 55 ††£ 130 – 1 suite – **Rest** – Menu £ 18/28 – Carte £ 18/26

◆ Standing by the harbour, looking across Dyfi Estuary, this part 18C inn boasts superior bedrooms, with views from most, and strongly seafood based menus, mostly local.

at Pennal Northeast : 6½ m. on A 493 – ✉ Aberdovey

Penmaendyfi without rest

(heated)

Cwrt, Southwest : 1¼ m. by A 493 ✉ SY20 9LD – ✆ (01654) 791246 – shana@penmaendyfi.co.uk – Fax (01654) 791616 – Closed December-January

6 rm – †£ 50/60 ††£ 90/100

◆ Impressive late 16C mansion with elegant sweeping grounds and ancient trees: a peaceful location. Sumptuous lounge. Spacious, smartly appointed rooms with fine country views.

ABERGAVENNY (Y-Fenni) – **Monmouthshire** – **503** L 28 – **pop. 14 055** 33 **C4**

London 163 m – Cardiff 31 m – Gloucester 43 m – Newport 19 m – Swansea 49 m
Swan Meadow, Monmouth Rd ✆ (01873) 857588
Monmouthshire Llanfoist, ✆ (01873) 852 606.
Town★ - St Mary's Church★ (Monuments★★)
Brecon Beacons National Park★★ – Blaenavon Ironworks★, SW : 5 m. by A 465 and B 4246. Raglan Castle★ **AC**, SE : 9 m. by A 40

Llansantffraed Court

Llanvihangel Gobion, Southeast : 6½ m. by A 40 and B 4598 off old Raglan rd ✉ NP7 9BA – ✆ (01873) 840 678 – reception@llch.co.uk – Fax (01873) 840 674
21 rm – 🛉£ 86/110 🛉🛉£ 110/135 – **Rest** – Menu £ 20/30 – Carte £ 24/40
◆ 12C hotel, set in 19 acres of land with ornamental trout lake; built in country house style of William and Mary; popular for weddings. Magnolia rooms with mahogany furniture. Welsh seasonal fare in chintz dining room.

The Angel

15 Cross St ✉ NP7 5EN – ✆ (01873) 857 121 – mail@angelhotelabergavenny.com – Fax (01873) 858 059 – Closed 25 December
30 rm – 🛉£ 60/70 🛉🛉£ 85 – **Rest** – Carte £ 24/30
◆ Updated Georgian building with a warm and cosy bar lit by real fire. Impressive public areas; locally renowned afternoon tea. Cocktails taken before dinner. Functional rooms. Stylish restaurant offers classic French and British blend.

The Hardwick

Old Raglan Rd, Southeast : 2 m. by A 40 on B 4598 ✉ NP7 9AA – ✆ (01873) 854 220 – stephen@thehardwick.co.uk – Fax (01873) 854 623 – Closed 25 December, Sunday dinner and Monday
Rest – Carte £ 20/37
◆ Unassuming façade belies 'feelgood' interior with beams and wood burner. Talented kitchen: former Walnut Tree owner/chef offers great choice of neat, wholesome, modern dishes.

at Nant Derry **Southeast : 6½ m. by A 40 off A 4042 – ✉ Abergavenny**

The Foxhunter

✉ NP7 9DD – ✆ (01873) 881 101 – info@thefoxhunter.com – Closed 2 weeks February, 25-26 December, Monday and Bank Holidays
Rest – Menu £ 22 – Carte £ 22/35
◆ Bright, contemporary feel within flint-stone former 19C station master's house. Light and airy in summer and cosy in winter. Modern menus using fine local ingredients.

at Llanwenarth **Northwest : 3 m. on A 40 – ✉ Abergavenny**

Llanwenarth

Brecon Rd ✉ NP8 1EP – ✆ (01873) 810 550 – info@llanwenarthhotel.com – Fax (01873) 811 880
17 rm – 🛉£ 63 🛉🛉£ 85 – **Rest** – (Closed 26 December and 1 January) Menu £ 14/16 – Carte £ 21/32
◆ Part 16C inn; perches on banks of river Usk, famed for salmon, trout fishing. Most bedrooms have balconies from which to enjoy panoramas of Blorenge Mountain and Usk Valley. Tall-windowed dining room with fine valley views and varied menus.

Your opinions are important to us: please write and let us know about your discoveries and experiences – good and bad!

ABERSOCH – Gwynedd – 502 G 25 – ✉ Pwllheli 32 B2

London 265 m – Caernarfon 28 m – Shrewsbury 101 m
Golf Rd, ✆ (01758) 712636 .
Lleyn Peninsula★★ – Plas-yn-Rhiw★ AC, W : 6 m. by minor roads. Bardsey Island★, SW : 15 m. by A 499 and B 4413 – Mynydd Mawr★, SW : 17 m. by A 499, B 4413 and minor roads

Neigwl

Cardigan Bay, VISA

Lon Sarn Bach ✉ LL53 7DY – ✆ (01758) 712363 – relax@neigwl.com – Fax (01758) 712544 – closed January

9 rm – £70/95 £130/165
– **Rest** – (dinner only) (booking essential) Menu £29 **s**

◆ A comfortable, family owned hotel close to town yet with fine sea vistas. Rooms are perfectly neat and individually decorated whilst the lounge is the ideal place to relax. The restaurant overlooks sea and mountains.

at Bwlchtocyn South : 2 m. – ✉ Pwllheli

Porth Tocyn

Cardigan Bay and mountains, (heated) VISA

✉ LL53 7BU – ✆ (01758) 713303 – bookings@porthtocyn.fsnet.co.uk – Fax (01758) 713538 – Easter-October

17 rm – £67/167 £90/167, £6
– **Rest** – (bar lunch Monday-Saturday, buffet lunch Sunday) Menu £40 **s**

◆ Originally a row of miners' cottages; family run for three generations and family orientated. A pleasant headland location: panoramas of bay and mountains. Pretty bedrooms. Sunday buffet lunch, described as a family event. Interesting, varied menus.

WALES

ABERYSTWYTH – Ceredigion – 503 H 26 – pop. 15 935 32 B2

London 238 m – Chester 98 m – Fishguard 58 m – Shrewsbury 74 m
Terrace Rd ✆ (01970) 612125, aberystwythtic@ceredigion.gov.uk
Bryn-y-Mor, ✆ (01970) 615104.
Town★★ - The Seafront★ – National Library of Wales (Permanent Exhibition★)
Vale of Rheidol★★ (Railway★★ AC) - St Padarn's Church★, SE : 1 m. by A 44. Devil's Bridge (Pontarfynach)★, E : 12 m. by A 4120 – Strata Florida Abbey★ AC (West Door★), SE : 15 m. by B 4340 and minor rd

Bodalwyn without rest

Queen's Ave ✉ SY23 2EG – ✆ (01970) 612578 – enquiries@bodalwyn.co.uk – Fax (01970) 639261 – Closed 24 December-2 January

8 rm – £35/48 £55/65

◆ Victorian house, run enthusiastically and to a very good standard by a young owner. Rooms blend modern and traditional, numbers 3 and 5 being particularly enticing.

at Chancery (Rhydgaled) South : 4 m. on A 487 – ✉ Aberystwyth

Conrah Country House

VISA

✉ SY23 4DF – ✆ (01970) 617941 – enquiries@conrah.co.uk – Fax (01970) 624546

17 rm – £85/110 £160 – **Rest** – Menu £30 (dinner) – Carte lunch £19/27

◆ Part 18C mansion, elegant inside and out. Lovely grounds, kitchen garden, pleasant views. Airy country house rooms include three very smart new ones in converted outbuildings. Scenic vistas greet restaurant diners.

BARMOUTH (Abermaw) – Gwynedd – 502 H 25 – pop. 2 251 32 B2

London 231 m – Chester 74 m – Dolgellau 10 m – Shrewsbury 67 m
The Station, Station Rd ✆ (01341) 280787, (summer only) barmouth.tic@gwynedd.gov.uk
Town★ - Bridge★ AC
Snowdonia National Park★★★

Bae Abermaw Mawddach estuary and Cardigan Bay,
Panorama Rd ✉ LL42 1DQ – ✆ (01341) 280 550
– enquiries@baeabermaw.com – Fax (01341) 280 346
– Closed last week January and first week February
14 rm – ♦£ 83/107 ♦♦£ 132/158
– **Rest** – (Closed lunch Monday-Wednesday) Carte £ 30/35
◆ Victorian house with inspiring views over Cardigan Bay. Classic façade allied to minimalist interior, typified by an uncluttered, airy lounge. Brilliant white bedrooms. Pleasant, comfy restaurant with appealing modern menus.

at Llanaber **NW : 1 ½ m. on A 496 – ✉ Barmouth**

Llwynd¡ Farmhouse
Northwest : 2 ¼ m. on A 496 ✉ LL42 1RR – ✆ (01341) 280 144
– intouch@llwyndu-farmhouse.co.uk
– Closed 25-26 December
7 rm – ♦£ 88/92 ♦♦£ 88/94 – **Rest** – (by arrangement) Menu £ 26
◆ Characterful part 16C farmhouse and 18C barn conversion on a hillside overlooking Cardigan Bay. Bunk beds and four-posters amidst stone walls and wood beams. An eclectic style of home-cooking using traditional regional ingredients.

BARRY (Barri) – Vale of Glamorgan – 503 K 29 – pop. 50 661 — 33 C4

London 167 m – Cardiff 10 m – Swansea 39 m
The Promenade, The Triangle, Barry Island ✆ (01446) 747171, tourism@valeofglamorgan.gov.uk
RAF St Athan, ✆ (01446) 751 043 .

Egerton Grey Country House
Southwest : 4 ½ m. by B 4226 and A 4226 and Porthkerry rd via Cardiff Airport
✉ CF62 3BZ – ✆ (01446) 711 666 – info@egertongrey.co.uk
– Fax (01446) 711 690
10 rm – ♦£ 90/110 ♦♦£ 170 – **Rest** – Menu £ 17/30 **s**
◆ A secluded country house with a restful library and drawing room. Part Victorian rectory. Bedrooms overlook gardens with views down to Porthkerry Park and the sea. Intimate dining room with paintings and antiques.

BEAUMARIS – Anglesey – 502 H 24 – pop. 1 513 — 32 B1

London 253 m – Birkenhead 74 m – Holyhead 25 m
Baron Hill, ✆ (01248) 810 231 .
Town★★ - Castle★ **AC**
Anglesey★★ – Penmon Priory★, NE : 4 m. by B 5109 and minor roads. Plas Newydd★ **AC**, SW : 7 m. by A 545 and A 4080

Ye Olde Bull's Head Inn
Castle St ✉ LL58 8AP – ✆ (01248) 810 329 – info@bullsheadinn.co.uk
– Fax (01248) 811 294
– Closed 25-26 December, 1 January Sunday dinner and Monday
13 rm – ♦£ 77 ♦♦£ 105
Rest *The Loft* – see restaurant listing
Rest *Ye Olde Bull's Head Inn* – (bookings not accepted) Carte £ 14/22
◆ Part 17C inn on the high street. Cosy pubby bar area sets the tone with period charm, brasses and bric-a-brac. Well decorated bedrooms, most named after Dickens characters. Less formal dining facility decorated in an attractive modern style.

Bishopsgate House
54 Castle St ✉ LL58 8BB – ✆ (01248) 810 302 – hazel@bishopgatehotel.co.uk
– Fax (01248) 810 166
9 rm – ♦£ 55/62 ♦♦£ 85 – **Rest** – (dinner only and Sunday lunch) (booking essential for non-residents) Menu £ 18 **s** – Carte £ 24/28 **s**
◆ Georgian townhouse on the high street. Chesterfields in the lounge, a rare Chinese Chippendale staircase and a small bar area. Individually decorated bedrooms. Neatly decorated dining room in keeping with the character of the establishment.

Cleifiog without rest — Menai Strait and Snowdonia, VISA
Townsend ✉ LL58 8BH – ✆ (01248) 811 507 – liz@cleifiogbandb.com
– Closed Christmas-New Year
3 rm – †£45/65 ††£75/95
◆ Lovely views from this seafront part Georgian house with 16C origins. Comfy, relaxing period style lounge. Bedrooms mix Arts and Crafts with up-to-date style and facilities.

The Loft – at Ye Olde Bull's Head Inn H. — VISA AE
Castle St ✉ LL58 8AP – ✆ (01248) 810 329 – info@bullsheadinn.co.uk
– Fax (01248) 811 294
– Closed Sunday
Rest – (dinner only) Menu £38
◆ In contrast to the inn, The Loft has a contemporary feel and style engendered by bold décor and modern lighting. Modish menus: a fresh approach to traditional ingredients.

BEDDGELERT – Gwynedd – 502 H 24 – pop. 535 — 32 B1

London 249 m – Caernarfon 13 m – Chester 73 m
Snowdonia National Park★★★ - Aberglaslyn Pass★, S : 1½ m. on A 498

Sygun Fawr Country House — Snowdon and Gwynant valley, P VISA
Northeast : ¾ m. by A 498 ✉ LL55 4NE
– ✆ (01766) 890 258 – sygunfawr@aol.com
– Restricted opening in winter
11 rm – †£57 ††£75/105
– **Rest** – (dinner only) (booking essential for non-residents) Menu £23 **s**
◆ Part 16C stone built house in Gwynant Valley. Superbly located, an elevated spot which affords exceptional views of Snowdon, particularly from double deluxe rooms. Dine in new conservatory extension or traditional room in house.

BENLLECH – Anglesey – 502 H 24 — 32 B1

London 277 m – Caernarfon 17 m – Chester 76 m – Holyhead 29 m

Hafod without rest — P
Amlwch Rd ✉ LL74 8SR – ✆ (01248) 853 092
– Closed 25 December
3 rm – †£40/45 ††£60/65
◆ Sensitively renovated 19C house with lawned garden and views of sea and bays. Comfortably finished bedrooms, well maintained by the charming owner.

BETWS GARMON – Gwynedd — 32 B1

Cardiff 194 m – Betws-y-Coed 25 m – Caernarfon 5 m

Betws Inn — P VISA
Northwest : 1 m. on A 4085 ✉ LL54 7YY – ✆ (01286) 650 324
– stay@betws-inn.co.uk
3 rm – †£60/70 ††£70/80 – **Rest** – (by arrangement) Menu £18/25
◆ Former village coaching inn with characterful beamed lounge. After a day's trekking, sleep in well-priced, good sized rooms with quality wood furniture and smart fabrics. Home-cooked local produce proudly served in rustic dining room.

BETWS-Y-COED – Conwy – 502 I 24 – pop. 848 — 32 B1

London 226 m – Holyhead 44 m – Shrewsbury 62 m
Royal Oak Stables ✆ (01690) 710426
Clubhouse, ✆ (01690) 710 556 .
Town★
Snowdonia National Park★★★. Blaenau Ffestiniog★ (Llechwedd Slate Caverns★ AC), SW : 10½ m. by A 470 – The Glyders and Nant Ffrancon (Cwm Idwal★), W : 14 m. by A 5

WALES

Tan-y-Foel Country House Vale of Conwy and Snowdonia,
East : 2 1/2 m. by A 5, A 470 and Capel Garmon rd on Llanwrst rd ✉ LL26 0RE – ✆ (01690) 710507 – enquiries@tyfhotel.co.uk – Fax (01690) 710681 – Closed December-January
6 rm – †£ 110/155 ††£ 140/180
Rest – (dinner only) (booking essential) Menu £ 42
◆ Part 16C country house, stylishly decorated in modern vein. Stunning views of Vale of Conwy and Snowdonia. Lovely rooms revel in the quality and elegance of the establishment. Contemporary rear room makes up the restaurant.

Henllys The Old Courthouse without rest
Old Church Rd ✉ LL24 0AL – ✆ (01690) 710534 – welcome@guesthouse-snowdonia.co.uk – Fax (01690) 710884 – Closed January
9 rm – †£ 35/70 ††£ 70/84
◆ Former Victorian magistrates' court and police station overlooking the River Conwy. Comfortable rooms with homely feel. Police memorabilia all around.

Bryn Bella without rest Vale of Conwy,
Lôn Muriau, Llanrwst Rd, Northeast : 1 m. by A 5 on A 470 ✉ LL24 0HD – ✆ (01690) 710627 – welcome@bryn-bella.co.uk
5 rm – †£ 60/65 ††£ 60/70
◆ Smart guesthouse in an elevated position with splendid views of the Vale of Conwy. Affordable accommodation; modern colours. Convenient base for touring the Snowdonia region.

Pengwern without rest
Allt Dinas, Southeast : 1½ m. on A 5 ✉ LL24 0HF – ✆ (01690) 710480 – gwawr.pengwern@btopenworld.co.uk – Closed 24 December-3 January
3 rm – †£ 55/70 ††£ 68/80
◆ Former Victorian artist 'colony' with a comfy, homely and stylish lounge, warmly decorated breakfast room and individually appointed bedrooms, two with superb valley vistas.

Llannerch Goch without rest
Capel Garmon, East : 2 m. by A 5 and A 470 on Capel Gorman rd ✉ LL26 0RL – ✆ (01690) 710261 – eirian@betwsycoed.co.uk – February-October
3 rm – †£ 45/62 ††£ 62/70
◆ Very peaceful 17C country house with original features. Pleasant sun lounge overlooking the garden. Set in four idyllic acres. Cosy sitting room, smart bedrooms.

Glyntwrog House without rest
Southeast : ¾ m. on A 5 ✉ LL24 0SG – ✆ (01690) 710930 – glyntwrog@betws-y-coed.org
4 rm – †£ 38/44 ††£ 56/68
◆ Victorian stone house set just off the road and surrounded by woodland. Pleasantly renovated to a homely and attractive standard. Comfortable bedrooms in varying sizes.

at Penmachno Southwest : 4 ¾ m. by A 5 on B 4406 – ✉ Betws-y-Coed 32 **B1**

Penmachno Hall
on Ty Mawr rd ✉ LL24 0PU – ✆ (01690) 760410 – stay@penmachnohall.co.uk – Fax (01690) 760410 – Closed Christmas-New Year
3 rm – †£ 90 ††£ 90 – **Rest** – (by arrangement, communal dining) Menu £ 30
◆ Former rectory built in 1862 with neat garden; super country setting. Sunny morning room where breakfast is served. Modern, bright bedrooms personally styled by the owners. Tasty home-cooking in deep burgundy communal dining room.

WALES

BODUAN – Gwynedd – **502** – see Pwllheli

BONVILSTON (Tresimwn) – **Vale of Glamorgan** – **503** J 29 33 **C4**

London 164 m – Cardiff 9 m – Swansea 25 m

The Great Barn without rest

Lillypot, Northwest : 1 m. by A 48 off Tre-Dodridge rd ✉ CF5 6TR – ☎ (01446) 781 010 – nina@greatbarn.com – Fax (01446) 781 185 – closed 25 December

6 rm – £40 £65/70

◆ Converted corn barn, personally run in simple country home style. Pleasant antiques, pine and white furniture in rooms. Great traditional breakfasts; relax in conservatory.

Good food and accommodation at moderate prices?
Look for the Bib symbols:
red Bib Gourmand for food, blue Bib Hotel for hotels

BRECON – Powys – **503** J 28 – **pop. 7 901** 33 **C3**

London 171 m – Cardiff 40 m – Carmarthen 31 m – Gloucester 65 m

Cattle Market Car Park ☎ (01874) 622485, brectic@powys.gov.uk

CradocPenoyre Park, ☎ (01874) 623 658 ;

Newton Park Llanfaes, ☎ (01874) 622 004 .

Town★ - Cathedral★ **AC** – Penyclawdd Court★

Brecon Beacons National Park★★. Llanthony Priory★★, S : 8 m. of Hay-on-Wye by B 4423 - Dan-yr-Ogof Showcaves★ **AC**, SW : 20 m. by A 40 and A 4067 – Pen-y-Fan★★, SW : by A 470

Canal Bank without rest

off B 4601 over bridge on unmarked rd ✉ LD3 7HG – ☎ (01874) 623 464 – enquiries@accommodation-breconbeacons.co.uk – Closed Christmas

3 rm – £65/80 £65/80

◆ Delightfully stylish and peaceful 18C canalside cottage. Charming garden with pergola and access to Usk. Organic breakfasts. Immaculate rooms with extra attention to detail.

Cantre Selyf without rest

5 Lion St ✉ LD3 7AU – ☎ (01874) 622 904 – enquiries@cantreselyf.co.uk – Fax (01874) 622 315 – closed December-January

3 rm – £48 £75

◆ An engaging 18C townhouse in town centre. Georgian fireplaces and beamed ceilings. Lovely quiet rooms with period feel. Attractive rear walled garden with sun house.

Felin Glais

Aberyscir, West : 4 m. by Upper Chapel rd off Cradoc Golf Course rd turning right immediately after bridge ✉ LD3 9NP – ☎ (01874) 623 107 – felinglais@keme.co.uk – Fax (01874) 623 107

4 rm – £75 £75

Rest – (by arrangement, communal dining) Menu £30

◆ Mid-17C house in a tranquil hamlet with a wonderfully relaxing sitting room and comfy rooms which boast many thoughtful extras, such as cosy seating areas with magazines. Seriously considered menus: fresh, country cooking on large-choice menus.

Coach House
Orchard St ✉ LD3 8AN – ✆ (07050) 691 216 – info@coachhousebrecon.co.uk – Fax (07050) 691 217
8 rm – £45/60 £60/80
Rest – (by arrangement) Menu £25 – Carte £18/33
◆ 17C building just over Usk Bridge a short walk from town. Rear garden and terrace. The bedrooms are modern, co-ordinated and well-equipped, with stylish fabrics and Wi-Fi. Dining room offers best local produce on a classic Welsh base.

The Felin Fach Griffin with rm
Felin Fach, Northeast : 4 ¾ m. by B 4602 off A 470 ✉ LD3 0UB – ✆ (01874) 620 111 – enquiries@eatdrinksleep.ltd.uk – Fax (01874) 620 120 – Closed early January, 4-25 December, Monday and Sunday lunch
7 rm – £68 £125 – **Rest** – (Closed Monday lunch except Bank Holidays) Menu 28 – Carte £30/35
◆ Terracotta hued traditional pub, once a farmhouse. Characterful interior boasts log fire with sofas, antiques and reclaimed furniture. Modern menus and smart bedrooms.

BRIDGEND (Pen-y-Bont) – Bridgend – 503 J 29 – pop. 39 427 — 33 B4

London 177 m – Cardiff 20 m – Swansea 23 m
McArthur Glen Design Outlet Village, The Derwen, junction 36, M 4 ✆ (01656) 654906, bridgendtic@bridgend.gov.uk

at Coychurch (Llangrallo) East : 2 ¼ m. by A 473 – ✉ Bridgend

Coed-y-Mwstwr (heated)
North : 1 m. by Bryn Rd ✉ CF35 6AF – ✆ (01656) 860 621 – enquiries@coed-y-mwstwr.com – Fax (01656) 863 122
28 rm – £105 £195 – 2 suites
Rest *Eliots* – Menu £13/29
◆ Meaning "whispering trees", this Victorian mansion overlooks Vale of Glamorgan and woodland. Local golf courses, comfortable lounge bar. Sizeable country house rooms. Well-kept restaurant with a formal, traditional ambience.

at Laleston West : 2 m. on A 473 – ✉ Bridgend

Great House
High St, on A 473 ✉ CF32 0HP – ✆ (01656) 657 644 – enquiries@great-house-laleston.co.uk – Fax (01656) 668 892 – Closed Christmas
16 rm – £75/100 £120/150
Rest *Leicester's* – see restaurant listing
◆ 15C Grade II listed building, believed to have been a gift from Elizabeth I to the Earl of Leicester. Personally run - attention to detail particularly evident in the rooms.

Leicester's – at Great House H. 
High St, on A 473 ✉ CF32 0HP – ✆ (01656) 657 644 – enquiries@great-house-laleston.co.uk – Fax (01656) 668 892 – closed Christmas and Sunday dinner
Rest – Menu £13 (lunch) – Carte £20/35
◆ Comfortable dining courtesy of exposed beams, original windows and owner's personal touches and nuances. Imaginative, seasonal menus using finest local and Welsh produce.

If breakfast is included the symbol appears after the number of rooms.

WALES

BUILTH WELLS (Llanfair-ym-Muallt) – Powys – 503 J 27 33 C3

London 191 m – Cardiff 63 m – Brecon 20 m

XX **The Drawing Room** with rm

Twixt Cwmbach, Newbridge-on-Wye, North : 3½ m. on A 470 ✉ LD2 3RT – ✆ (01982) 552 493 – post@the-drawing-room.co.uk – Closed Sunday-Monday

3 rm (dinner included) – £ 125 £ 210/240

Rest – (dinner only) (booking essential) Menu £ 40

◆ Delightful Georgian house with 19C additions: sumptuous country style at every turn. Carefully sourced seasonal menu with distinct French classic emphasis. Very stylish rooms.

BWLCHTOCYN – Gwynedd – 502 G 25 – see Abersoch

CAERNARFON – Gwynedd – 502 H 24 – pop. 9 695 32 B1

London 249 m – Birkenhead 76 m – Chester 68 m – Holyhead 30 m – Shrewsbury 85 m

Oriel Pendeitsh, Castle St. ✆ (01286) 672232, caernarfon.tic@gwynedd.gov.uk

Aberforeshore Llanfaglan, ✆ (01286) 673 783 .

Town★★ - Castle★★★ AC

Snowdonia National Park★★★

Celtic Royal rm, VISA AE

Bangor St ✉ LL55 1AY – ✆ (01286) 674 477 – admin@celtic-royal.co.uk – Fax (01286) 674 139

110 rm – £ 81 £ 115/145

Rest – (bar lunch) – Carte £ 17/24 **s**

◆ Updated Victorian hotel which now caters primarily for the corporate market. Good access to Holyhead and Bangor. Strong leisure and conference facilities. Modern rooms. Comfortable, split-level restaurant with classic style.

WALES

at Llanrug East : 3 m. on A 4086 – ✉ Caernarfon

Plas Tirion Farm without rest

South : 1 m. by Ffordd Glanmoelyn Rd on Waenfawr rd ✉ LL55 4PY – ✆ (01286) 673 190 – cerid@plastirion.plus.com – Fax (01286) 671 883 – April-October

3 rm – £ 30/40 £ 60

◆ Stone built farmhouse on dairy farm surrounded by 300 acres. Relaxing, homely sitting room. Generous portions served in airy breakfast room with log burner. Cottagey rooms.

at Saron Southwest : 3 ¼ m. by A 487 on Saron rd – ✉ Caernarfon

Pengwern

Southwest : ¼ m. ✉ LL54 5UH – ✆ (01286) 831 500 – janepengwern@aol.com – Fax (01286) 830 741 – May-September

3 rm – £ 45 £ 60/80 – **Rest** – (by arrangement) Menu £ 25

◆ Charming farmhouse on working farm, picturesquely situated between mountains and sea. Snowdonia views. Neat and tidy guest areas. Bedrooms of traditional quality. Owner serves fresh, robust farmhouse cuisine including home-reared beef and lamb.

**The ✿ award is the crème de la crème.
This is awarded to restaurants
which are really worth travelling miles for!**

CAERSWS – Powys – 502 J 26 32 C2

London 194 m – Aberystwyth 39 m – Chester 63 m – Shrewsbury 42 m

at Pontdolgoch Northwest : 1 ½ m. on A 470 – ✉ Newtown

The Talkhouse with rm

✉ *SY17 5JE – ☎ (01686) 688 919 – info@talkhouse.co.uk*
– closed first 2 weeks January, 25-26 December and Monday
3 rm – †£ 70 ††£ 95
Rest – (dinner only and Sunday lunch) (booking essential) Carte £ 21/30
◆ Owner-run 17C coaching inn on Aberystwyth-Shrewsbury road. Ornate rustic bar. Dining room opening onto terrace and gardens. Locally-based blackboard menu. Stylish bedrooms.

Y. Duhamel/MICHELIN

CARDIFF (*Caerdydd*)

County: Cardiff
Michelin REGIONAL map: n° 503 K 29

London 155 m – Birmingham 110 m 33 **C4**
– Bristol 46 m – Coventry 124 m
Population: 292 150

PRACTICAL INFORMATION

Tourist Information

16 Wood St, ☎ (029) 2022 7281

Airport

Cardiff (Wales) Airport: ☎ (01446) 711111, SW: 8 m. by A 48 AX

Golf Courses

Dinas Powis Old Highwalls, ☎ (029) 5105 2727.

WALES

SIGHTS

IN TOWN

City★★★ - National Museum and Gallery★★★ **AC** (Evolution of Wales★★, Picture galleries★★) BY – Castle★ **AC** BZ – Llandaff Cathedral★ AV **B** – Cardiff Bay★ (Techniquest★ **AC**) AX

ON THE OUTSKIRTS

Museum of Welsh Life★★ **AC**, St Fagan's, W: 5 m. by A 4161 AV – Castell Coch★★ **AC**, NW: 5 m. by A 470 AV

IN THE SURROUNDING AREA

Caerphilly Castle★★ **AC**, N: 7 m. by A 469 AV – Dyffryn Gardens★ **AC**, W: 8 m. by A 48 AX

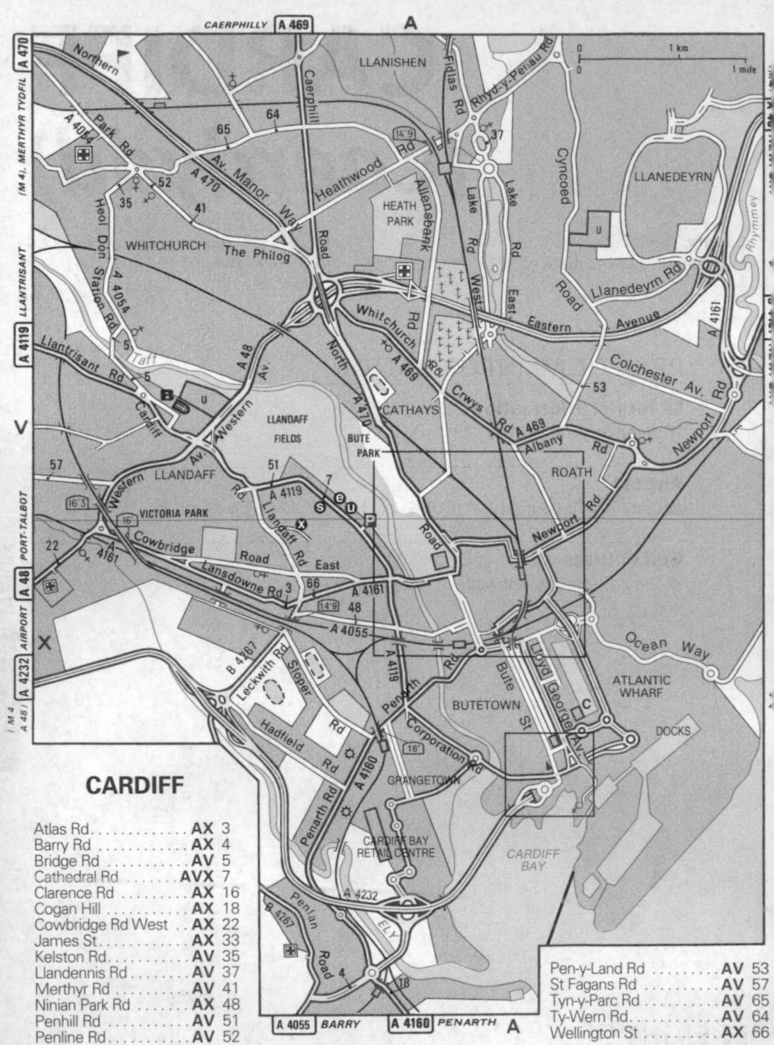

CARDIFF

Atlas Rd	AX	3
Barry Rd	AX	4
Bridge Rd	AV	5
Cathedral Rd	AVX	7
Clarence Rd	AX	16
Cogan Hill	AX	18
Cowbridge Rd West	AX	22
James St	AX	33
Kelston Rd	AV	35
Llandennis Rd	AV	37
Merthyr Rd	AV	41
Ninian Park Rd	AX	48
Penhill Rd	AV	51
Penline Rd	AV	52
Pen-y-Land Rd	AV	53
St Fagans Rd	AV	57
Tyn-y-Parc Rd	AV	65
Ty-Wern Rd	AV	64
Wellington St	AX	66

The St David's H. & Spa

Havannah St, Cardiff Bay, South : 1 ¾ m. by Bute St
✉ CF10 5SD – ✆ (029) 2045 4045 – *reservations.stdavids@principalhotels.com*
– Fax (029) 2031 3075 CU **a**

120 rm – £ 120 £ 320 – 12 suites
Rest *Tides Grill* – Menu £ 23/35 – Carte £ 36/59
Rest *Waves* – (buffet lunch) (booking essential) Menu £ 35 – Carte £ 36/59

◆ Striking modern hotel with panoramic views across waterfront. High-tech meeting rooms and fitness club. Well-proportioned rooms, all with balconies, in minimalist style. Informal Tides Grill. Welsh sourced menus at Waves.

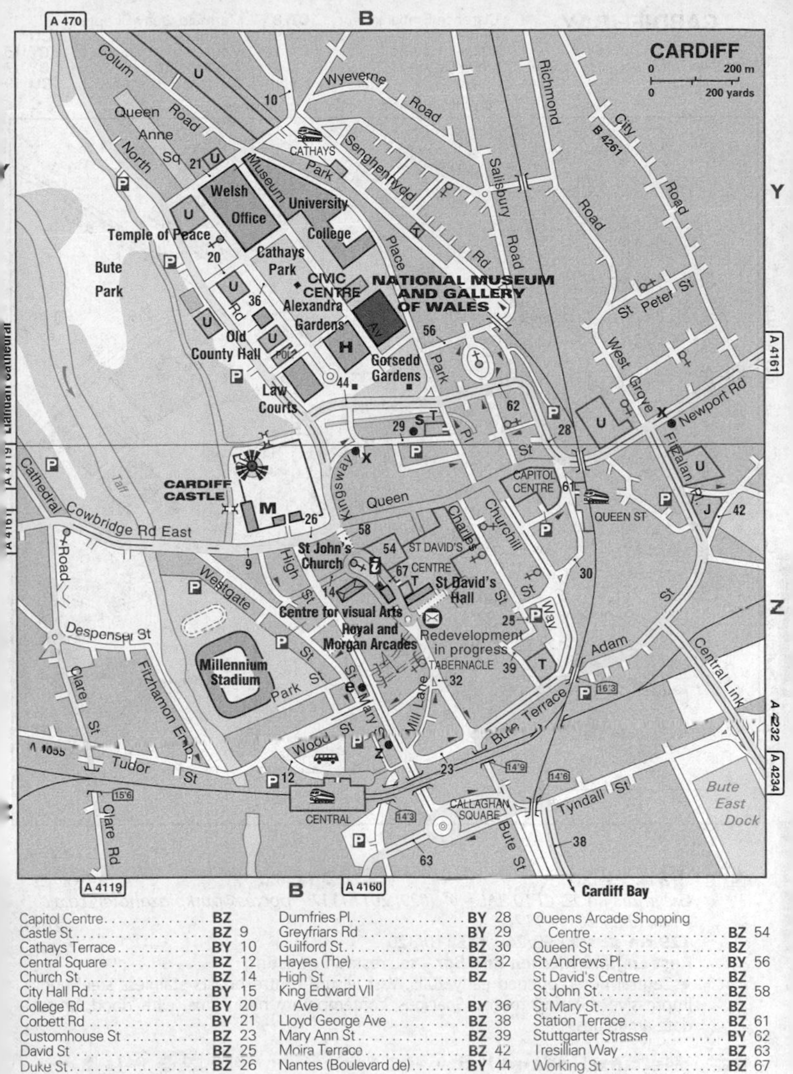

Capitol Centre	BZ		Dumfries Pl.	BY	28	Queens Arcade Shopping Centre	BZ	54
Castle St	BZ	9	Greyfriars Rd	BY	29	Queen St	BZ	
Cathays Terrace	BY	10	Guilford St	BZ	30	St Andrews Pl.	BY	56
Central Square	BZ	12	Hayes (The)	BZ	32	St David's Centre	BZ	
Church St	BZ	14	High St	BZ		St John St	BZ	58
City Hall Rd	BY	15	King Edward VII Ave	BY	36	St Mary St	BZ	
College Rd	BY	20	Lloyd George Ave	BZ	38	Station Terrace	BZ	61
Corbett Rd	BY	21	Mary Ann St	BZ	39	Stuttgarter Strasse	BY	62
Customhouse St	BZ	23	Moira Terrace	BZ	42	Tresillian Way	BZ	63
David St	BZ	25	Nantes (Boulevard de)	BY	44	Working St	BZ	67
Duke St	BZ	26						

Hilton Cardiff

rm,

Kingsway ✉ CF10 3HH
– ✆ (0800) 856 80 00
– Fax (029) 2064 6333 BZ **x**

193 rm – £ 99/350 £ 99/350, ☕ £ 17.95 – 4 suites

Rest – Menu £ 19/27 **s**

♦ State-of-the-art meeting rooms and leisure facilities feature in this imposingly modern corporate hotel. Spacious, comfy bedrooms boast fine views of castle or City Hall. Popular menu in conservatory-style restaurant.

CARDIFF BAY

Britannia Quay . . . . CU 2
Bute Crescent . . . . CT 4
Clarence Embankment . . . CT 8
Dudley St . . . . CU 9
Hemingway Rd . . . . CT 12
Lloyd George Ave . . . . CT 14
Mermaid Quay Shopping Centre . . . . CU
Mount Stuart Square . . . . CT 15
Pomeroy St. . . . . CT 17
Windsor Esplanade . . . . . CU 19

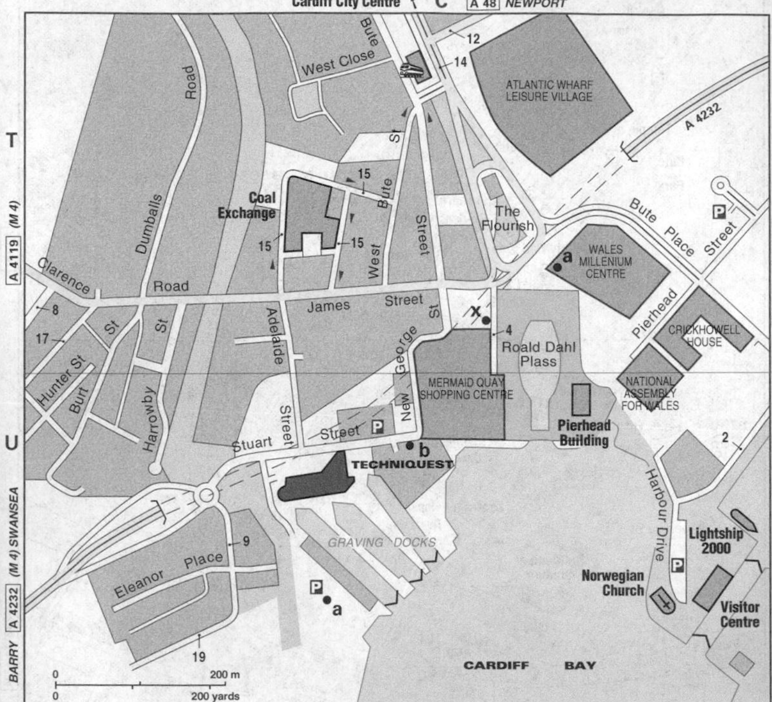

Park Plaza

Greyfriars Rd ✉ CF10 3AL – ✆ (029) 2011 1111 – ppcres@parkplazahotels.co.uk – Fax (029) 2011 1112 BY **s**

129 rm – 👤£ 90/260 👤👤£ 110/320

Rest *Laguna Kitchen and Bar* – see restaurant listing

◆ Central hotel, opened early 2005. Vast leisure centre boasts stainless steel pool. Impressive meeting rooms. Spacious, contemporary bedrooms, with good, up-to-date amenities.

Mercure Holland House H & Spa

rm,

24-26 Newport Rd ✉ CF24 0DD – ✆ (029) 2043 5000 – h6622@accor.com – Fax (029) 2048 8894 BY **x**

160 rm – 👤£ 70/215 👤👤£ 80/225 – 5 suites

Rest – Menu £ 22 **s** – Carte dinner £ 28/36 **s**

◆ 14-storey converted office block that opened as an hotel in 2004. Large marbled lobby; spacious busy bar. State-of-the-art gym and therapy rooms. Airy, well-equipped rooms. Modern menus with local produce to fore in informal restaurant.

Royal without rest

10 St Mary St ✉ CF10 5DW – ✆ (029) 2055 0750 – enquiries@theroyalhotelcardiff.com – Fax (029) 2055 0760 BZ **e**

64 rm – 👤£ 85 👤👤£ 134, £3.50

◆ Don't be put off by stark entrance. This central hotel has an extensive continental breakfast buffet and sleek rooms with bold fabrics, crisp Egyptian bedding and DVD library.

Jolyon's without rest
5 Bute Crescent, Cardiff Bay ✉ CF10 5AN – ✆ (029) 2048 8775
– info@jolyons.co.uk – Fax (029) 2048 8775 CT **x**
6 rm – £89/140 £89/140
◆ Georgian townhouse within Cardiff Bay's oldest terrace. Boutique style prevails. Rustic, slate-floored bar with log stove, red leather sofas. Light, modern, stylish bedrooms.

Lincoln House without rest
118-120 Cathedral Rd ✉ CF11 9LQ – ✆ (029) 2039 5558
– reservations@lincolnhotel.co.uk – Fax (029) 2023 0537 AV **e**
23 rm – £60/80 £85/100
◆ Sympathetically restored Victorian house close to the attractive Bute Gardens. Friendly service by eager-to-please owners. Four-poster room in period style most comfortable.

The Town House without rest
70 Cathedral Rd ✉ CF11 9LL – ✆ (029) 2023 9399 – thetownhouse@msn.com
– Fax (029) 2022 3214 AV **u**
8 rm – £50/63 £70/73
◆ Carefully restored Victorian house, hospitably run by owners. Light and airy bedrooms have some thoughtful touches and are well appointed: ones at front are the most spacious.

Annedd Lon without rest
157 Cathedral Rd ✉ CF11 9PL – ✆ (029) 2022 3349
– Closed 23-29 December AV **s**
6 rm – £45/50 £65
◆ Victorian house with Gothic influences located within a conservation area. Genuine hospitality in a friendly house. Portmeirion China at breakfast. Comfortable bedrooms.

Le Gallois
6-10 Romilly Cres ✉ CF11 9NR – ✆ (029) 2034 1264 – info@legallois-ycymro.com
– Fax (029) 2023 7911
– Closed Christmas-New Year, Sunday dinner and Monday AX **x**
Rest – Menu £14 (lunch) – Carte £25/36
◆ Bright and relaxed restaurant where keen owners provide both the friendly service and the assured modern European cooking. Gallic and Welsh combinations with inventive edge.

Laguna Kitchen and Bar – at Park Plaza H.
Greyfriars Rd ✉ CF10 3AL – ✆ (029) 2011 1103
– ppc-lkb@parkplazahotels.co.uk BY **s**
Rest – Menu £15 (lunch) – Carte £18/31
◆ On ground floor of hotel, this smart, modern restaurant serves an intriguing mix of local or international dishes.There's a bar, too, with an area of booths for casual dining.

Woods Brasserie
The Pilotage Building, Stuart St, Cardiff Bay, South : 1½ m. by Bute St
✉ CF10 5BW – ✆ (029) 2049 2400 – serge@woodsbrasserie.com
– Fax (029) 2048 1998
– Closed 24-26 December CU **b**
Rest – (closed Sunday evening in winter) (booking essential at dinner)
Menu £17/35 – Carte £21/36 **s**
◆ Modern brasserie dishes and European influences from an open kitchen. Bay view from the first-floor terrace. Popular for business lunches and bay visitors in the evening.

Brazz
Wales Millennium Centre, Bute Place, Cardiff Bay ✉ CF10 5AL
– ✆ (029) 2045 9000 – cardiff@brazz.co.uk – Fax (029) 2044 0270
– Closed 25 December and 1 January CT **a**
Rest – Menu £16 – Carte £20/25
◆ Based in the stunning Wales Millennium Centre. In two sections: the intimate Club or more spacious Brasserie. Eclectic, daily changing menus offer a modern and classic blend.

at Thornhill North : 5 ¼ m. by A 470 - AV - on A 469 – ✉ **Cardiff**

Manor Parc
Thornhill Rd, on A 469 ✉ CF14 9UA – ✆ (029) 2069 3723
– enquiry@manorparc.com – Fax (029) 2061 4624
– Closed 26 December-2 January
21 rm – †£ 65/72 ††£ 95/130
Rest – (Closed Sunday dinner)
Menu £ 19/24
◆ Personally run country house set in attractive terraced gardens. Some of the well-appointed rooms have south facing balconies and views over the Bristol Channel. Bright, airy orangery restaurant with Continental menu.

at Penarth South : 3 m. by A 4160 - AX – ✉ **Cardiff**

The Olive Tree
21 Glebe St ✉ CF64 1EE – ✆ (029) 2070 7077
– Closed Sunday dinner-Monday
Rest – (dinner only and Sunday lunch) Menu £ 25 (weekdays) – Carte Saturday £ 25/37
◆ Rewarding discovery tucked away in the centre of town. Relaxing feel augmented by vivid artwork. Warm, friendly service of good value, seasonal, frequently changing dishes.

WALES

at Pentyrch Northwest : 7 m. by A 4119 - AV – ✉ **Cardiff**

De Courcey's
Tyla Morris Ave (off Church Rd), South : 1 m. ✉ CF15 9QN – ✆ (029) 2089 2232
– dinedecourceys@aol.com – Fax (029) 2089 1949
– Closed January and 25-31 December, Monday and Tuesday
Rest – (dinner only and Sunday lunch) Menu £ 20/30 – Carte £ 31/38
◆ Long-standing restaurant in an ornately decorated neo-Georgian house. Formal yet homely atmosphere. Accomplished traditional cuisine, served by smartly attired staff.

The red symbol?
This denotes the very essence of peace
– only the sound of birdsong first thing in the morning ...

CARDIGAN – Ceredigion – 503 G 27 – pop. 4 082 — 33 A3

London 250 m – Carmarthen 30 m – Fishguard 19 m
Theatr Mwldan, Bath House Rd ✆ (01239) 613230, cardigan.tic@ceredigion.gov.uk
Gwbert-on-Sea, ✆ (01239) 612 035 .
Pembrokeshire Coast National Park★★

at Gwbert on Sea Northwest : 3 m. on B 4548 – ✉ **Cardigan**

Gwbert ← Cardigan Bay, rest,
on B 4548 ✉ SA43 1PP – ✆ (01239) 612 638 – gwbert@enterprise.net
– Fax (01239) 621 474
17 rm – †£ 40/49 ††£ 97/137 – **Rest** – Carte £ 17/28
◆ Traditional seaside hotel on banks of Teifi with inspiring views of Cardigan Bay. Contemporary public areas and smart bar. Well-kept rooms with co-ordinated neutral scheme. Bistro/brasserie with panoramic views of Pembroke National Park coastline.

CARMARTHEN – Carmarthenshire – 503 H 28 – pop. 14 648 33 B3

London 219 m – Fishguard 47 m – Haverfordwest 32 m – Swansea 27 m
113 Lammas St (01267) 231557, tourism@carmarthenshire.gov.uk
Kidwelly Castle★ – National Botanic Garden★

at Felingwm Uchaf Northeast : 8 m. by A 40 on B 4310 – Carmarthen

Allt y Golau Uchaf without rest
North : ½ m. on B 4310 SA32 7BB – (01267) 290455 – alltygolau@btinternet.com – Fax (01267) 290743 – Closed Christmas
3 rm – £40 £60
◆ Georgian farmhouse in uplifting elevated position, perfect for walkers. Tranquil garden bursts to life in spring. Home-baked breakfasts of repute. Neat, pretty, compact rooms.

at Nantgaredig East : 5 m. on A 40 – Carmarthen

Y Polyn VISA AE
South : 1 m. by B 4310 on B 4300 SA32 7LH – (01267) 290000 – ypolyn@hotmail.com – Closed 2 weeks October
Rest – (closed Monday, Saturday lunch and Sunday dinner) Menu £ 28 – Carte £ 19/25
◆ Roadside hostelry enhanced by pleasant summer terrace and stream. Bright, fresh interior with rich, rose-painted walls. Classic, rustic menus with Gallic/Welsh starting point.

Good food and accommodation at moderate prices?
Look for the Bib symbols:
red Bib Gourmand for food, blue Bib Hotel for hotels

CEMAES (Cemais) – Anglesey – 502 G 23 32 B1

London 272 m – Bangor 25 m – Caernarfon 32 m – Holyhead 16 m
Anglesey★★

Hafod Country House without rest VISA
South : ½ m. on Llanfechell rd LL67 ODS – (01407) 711645 – hbr1946@aol.com – April-September
3 rm – £40 £65
◆ Pleasant Edwardian guesthouse with very welcoming owner on outskirts of picturesque fishing village. Comfortable sitting room. The bedrooms are in immaculately kept order.

CHANCERY = Rhydgaled – Ceredigion – 503 H 26 – see Aberystwyth

CHEPSTOW (Cas-gwent) – Monmouthshire – 503 M 29 – pop. 10 821 33 C4

London 131 m – Bristol 17 m – Cardiff 28 m – Gloucester 34 m
Castle Car Park, Bridge St (01291) 623772
Town★ - Castle★★ AC
Wynd Cliff★, N : 2½ m. by A 466 – Caerwent★ (Roman Walls★), SW : 4 m. by A 48

at Shirenewton East : 5 m. by B 4293 off B 4235 – Chepstow

Coalpits Farm without rest VISA AE
South : 1 m. on Crick rd NP16 6LS – (01291) 641820 – Fax (01291) 641820
3 rm – £35/45 £60
◆ Extended stone farmhouse, extraordinarily welcoming owner, horses at the window, woodland walks, charming garden, fine breakfasts, immaculate rooms...what more can we add?

WALES

CLYNNOG-FAWR – Gwynedd – 503 G 24 32 B1

Bryn Eisteddfod
✉ *LL54 5DA – ✆ (01286) 660 431 – info@bryneisteddfod.com*
8 rm – †£ 60 ††£ 80 – **Rest** – (dinner only) (residents only) Menu £ 23
◆ Owner of this 19C former rectory is local guide, full of useful info. Enjoy breakfast in the conservatory, and relax in homely lounge. Front rooms look to bay and mountains. Dining room has views through conservatory and offers tasty home-cooked dishes.

COLWYN BAY (Bae Colwyn) – Conwy – 502 I 24 – pop. 30 269 32 B1

London 237 m – Birkenhead 50 m – Chester 42 m – Holyhead 41 m
Imperial Buildings, Station Sq, Princes Drive ✆ (01492) 530478 - The Promenade, Rhos-on-Sea ✆ (01492) 548778 (summer only)
Abergele Tan-y-Goppa Rd, ✆ (01745) 824 034 ;
Old Colwyn Woodland Ave, ✆ (01492) 515 581 .
Welsh Mountain Zoo★ **AC** (★)
Bodnant Garden★★ **AC**, SW : 6 m. by A 55 and A 470

Rathlin Country House without rest (heated)
48 Kings Rd, Southwest : 1/4 m. on B 5113 ✉ LL29 7YH
– ✆ (01492) 532 173 – enquiries@rathlincountryhouse.co.uk
– Fax (0871) 661 9887
– Closed Christmas
3 rm – †£ 59/85 ††£ 85
◆ Surrounded by almost an acre of mature gardens, this personally run guesthouse has a large summer pool, inglenook fireplace, oak panelling and slightly modish rooms of style.

Pen-y-Bryn
Pen-y-Bryn Rd, Upper Colwyn Bay, Southwest : 1 m. by B 5113 ✉ LL29 6DD
– ✆ (01492) 533 718 – Fax (01492) 536 127
– Closed dinner 25-26 December and 1 January
Rest – Carte £ 17/32
◆ Built in the 1970s, with lawned garden and bay view. Spacious interior with large, polished wood tables. Extensive menus feature Welsh dishes with eclectic influences.

at Rhos-on-Sea Northwest : 1 m. – ✉ Colwyn Bay

Plas Rhos without rest
Cayley Promenade ✉ LL28 4EP – ✆ (01492) 543 698 – info@plasrhos.co.uk
– Fax (01492) 540 088
– Closed 20 December-February
8 rm – †£ 40/60 ††£ 80/90
◆ 19C house on first promenade from Colwyn Bay. Homely front lounge with bay view. Breakfasts feature local butcher's produce. Immaculately kept rooms: superior ones to front.

CONWY – Conwy – 502 I 24 – pop. 3 847 32 B1

London 241 m – Caernarfon 22 m – Chester 46 m – Holyhead 37 m
Conwy Castle Visitor Centre ✆ (01492) 592248
Penmaenmawr Conway Old Rd, ✆ (01492) 623 330 .
Town★★ - Castle★★ **AC** – Town Walls★★ - Plas Mawr★★
Snowdonia National Park★★★ – Bodnant Garden★★ **AC**, S : 8 m. by A 55 and A 470 – Conwy Crossing (suspension bridge★)

Sychnant Pass House
Sychnant Pass Rd, Southwest : 2 m. by A 547 and Sychnant rd, turning right at T junction ✉ LL32 8BJ – ✆ (01492) 596 868 – bre@sychnant-pass-house.co.uk
– Fax (01492) 585 486
– Closed 24-26 December
12 rm – †£ 75/85 ††£ 130/180 – 1 suite – **Rest** – (dinner only) (booking essential for non-residents) Menu £ 30
◆ Country house with Snowdonia National Park providing utterly peaceful backdrop. Charming sitting room with attractive décor. Comfy rooms, named after cats from T.S. Elliott. Informal dining room with rustic style and seasonal menus.

Castle

High St ⊠ LL32 8DB – ✆ (01492) 582800 – mail@castlewales.co.uk – Fax (01492) 582300 – Closed 26 December

27 rm – †£ 88/90 ††£ 165/170 – 1 suite

Rest *Shakespeare's* – Menu £ 17 (lunch) – Carte dinner £ 32/35

◆ Two eye-catching ex-coaching inns on site of former Cistercian abbey. Characterful interior with original features in situ. Refurbished rooms have a stylish period feel. Dining room features paintings of Shakespearean characters by John Dawson-Watson.

at Llansanffraid Glan Conwy **Southeast : 2½ m. A 547 on A 470 – ⊠ Conwy**

Old Rectory Country House without rest — Conwy estuary,

Llanrwst Rd, on A 470 ⊠ LL28 5LF – ✆ (01492) 580611 – info@oldrectorycountryhouse.co.uk – Closed 17 December-12 January

6 rm – †£ 79/99 ††£ 139/159

◆ Enjoys fine position on estuary; once home to parish rectors, renovated in Georgian style. House motto: "beautiful haven of peace"; antiques throughout, watercolours abound.

at Tyn-y-Groes **South : 4 m. on B 5106 – ⊠ Conwy**

The Groes Inn

North : 1½ m. on B 5106 ⊠ LL32 8TN – ✆ (01492) 650545 – reception@groesinn.com – Fax (01492) 650855 – Closed 25 December

14 rm – †£ 79/95 ††£ 175

Rest – Menu £ 18 – Carte £ 22/28

◆ Part 16C inn, Wales' first licensed house. Beamed ceilings, log fires and historic bric-a-brac. Immaculately sumptuous bedrooms, some with super rural views. Georgian-style dining room.

COWBRIDGE (Y Bont Faen) – Vale of Glamorgan – 503 J 29 – pop. 3 616 33 B4

London 170 m – Cardiff 15 m – Swansea 30 m

Huddarts

69 High St ⊠ CF71 7AF – ✆ (01446) 774645 – Fax (01446) 772215 – closed 1 week spring, 1 week autumn, 26 December-8 January, Sunday dinner and Monday

Rest – Carte £ 24/31

◆ Intimate, family run restaurant located on high street of this ancient market town. Welsh tapestries on wall. Skilfully executed traditional dishes with modern influences.

COYCHURCH = Llangrallo – Bridgend – 503 J 29 – see Bridgend

CRICCIETH – Gwynedd – 502 H 25 – pop. 1 826 32 B2

London 249 m – Caernarfon 17 m – Shrewsbury 85 m

Ednyfed Hill, ✆ (01766) 522154 .

Lleyn Peninsula★★ – Ffestiniog Railway★★

Mynydd Ednyfed Country House

Caernarfon Rd, Northwest : ¾ m. on B 4411 ⊠ LL52 0PH – ✆ (01766) 523269 – myndd-ednyfed@criccieth.net – Fax (01766) 522929 – Closed 22 December-4 January

9 rm – †£ 60/68 ††£ 100/115

Rest – (closed Sunday) (dinner only) Carte £ 18/25

◆ Idyllically located 17C country house in eight acres of gardens and woods overlooking Tremadog Bay. Refurbished lounge bar. Airy conservatory for breakfasts. Homely rooms. Small, cosy, comfortable dining room.

WALES

London 169 m – Abergavenny 6 m – Brecon 14 m – Cardiff 40 m – Newport 25 m

Beaufort Chambers, Beaufort St (01873) 812105

Brecon Beacons National Park★★. Llanthony Priory★★, NE : 10 m. by minor roads

Gliffaes Country House

West : 3 ¾ m. by A 40 NP8 1RH – (01874) 730371 – calls@gliffaeshotel.com – Fax (01874) 730463 – closed 2-31 January

23 rm – £ 82/100 £ 215 –

Rest – (light lunch Monday-Saturday) Menu £ 34 **s**

◆ 19C country house and gardens on banks of Usk, offering great tranquillity. Welcoming bar, lounge and conservatory. Popular for outdoor pursuits. Luxuriously individual rooms. Bold, country house dining room has pleasant garden views.

The Bear

High St NP8 1BW – (01873) 810408 – bearhotel@aol.com – Fax (01873) 811696 – Closed 25 December

34 rm – £ 84/115 £ 150 – 2 suites

Rest ***The Restaurant*** – see restaurant listing

Rest – Carte £ 18/25

◆ Imposing, part 15C former coaching inn with maze of public areas. Bustling bar and lounges. Good conference facilities. Plush, spacious bedrooms with individual furnishings. Tried-and-tested, hearty bar menus.

Ty Croeso

The Dardy, West : 1 ½ m. by A 4077 off Llangynidr rd NP8 1PU – (01873) 810573 – tycroeso@gmail.com – Fax (01873) 810573

8 rm – £ 45/60 £ 85/95 –

Rest – (dinner only) Menu £ 18 – Carte £ 20/30

◆ Small hotel of Welsh stone, originally part of a Victorian workhouse. Personally run by pleasant owners. Large bar with log fire. Neatly designed rooms have rewarding views. Interesting menus feature well-sourced ingredients.

Glangrwyney Court

South : 2 m. on A 40 NP8 1ES – (01873) 811288 – info@glancourt.co.uk – Fax (01873) 810317

5 rm – £ 50/80 £ 70/95 –

Rest – (by arrangement) Menu £ 30

◆ Spacious Georgian house with sizeable garden and warm welcome. Large front lounge in chintz with antiques and trinkets. Pleasantly cluttered, well-kept rooms.

The Restaurant – at Bear H.

High St NP8 1BW – (01873) 810408 – bearhotel@aol.com – Fax (01873) 811696 – Closed Sunday-Monday

Rest – (dinner only) Carte £ 22/30

◆ Charming dining rooms - with polite service, wide-ranging menus employing classical base underpinned by Welsh ingredients - are a sedate option to the ever busy bar.

Nantyffin Cider Mill Inn

Brecon Rd, West : 1 ½ m. on A 40 NP8 1SG – (01873) 810775 – info@cidermill.co.uk – Fax (01873) 810986 – Closed 25-26 December and Monday

Rest – Menu £ 17 – Carte £ 20/40

◆ Converted 16C cider mill, its working parts still in situ. Choose between bars or Mill Room. Local farm meat, fish and - yes - cider on offer on Drovers menu or blackboard.

CROSSGATES – **Powys** – **503** J 27 – **see Llandrindod Wells**

CWMBRAN (Cwmbrân) – **Torfaen** – **503** K 29 – **pop. 47 254** 33 **C4**

London 149 m – Bristol 35 m – Cardiff 17 m – Newport 5 m

Parkway rm, rest,

Cwmbran Drive, South : 1 m. by A 4051 ✉ NP44 3UW – ✆ (01633) 871 199 – enquiries@parkwayhotel.co.uk – Fax (01633) 869 160

69 rm – †£ 115 ††£ 130 – 1 suite

Rest *Ravello's* – (dinner only and Sunday lunch) Menu £ 20 – Carte £ 21/31 **s**

◆ Purpose-built hotel aimed at the business traveller with extensive conference facilities. Spacious lounge. Smart, well-kept bedrooms benefit from refurbishment. Small, comfortable restaurant with formal chairs and water fountain in centre.

DEGANWY – **Conwy** – **502** I 24 – **see Llandudno**

DOLFOR Powys – **Powys** – **503** K 26 32 **C2**

London 199 – Cardiff 93 – Oswestry 34 – Ludlow 39

Old Vicarage

North : 1/2 m. off A 483 – ✆ (01686) 629 051 – tim@theoldvicaragedolfor.co.uk

3 rm – †£ 60/80 ††£ 90/110 – **Rest** – (booking essential at lunch) Menu £ 23 **s**

◆ 19C former vicarage with pleasant garden and homely lounge with fireplace. Comfy bedrooms; the green room is the largest, with an equally big bathroom. Polished antique tables and candles in attractive dining room. Most of the produce is local or from the garden.

DOLGELLAU – **Gwynedd** – **502** I 25 – **pop. 2 407** 32 **B2**

London 221 m – Birkenhead 72 m – Chester 64 m – Shrewsbury 57 m

Ty Meirion, Eldon Sq ✆ (01341) 422888

Hengwrt Estate Pencefn Rd, ✆ (01341) 422 603 .

Town★

Snowdonia National Park★★★ - Cadair Idris★★★ - Precipice Walk★, NE : 3 m. on minor roads

Penmaenuchaf Hall ← Rhinog mountains and Mawddach estuary,

Penmaenpool, West : 1 ¾ m. on A 493 (Tywyn Rd) ✉ LL40 1YB – ✆ (01341) 422 129 – relax@penhall.co.uk – Fax (01341) 422 787 – Closed 2-15 January and 10-20 December

14 rm – †£ 90/135 ††£ 140/210 – **Rest** – Menu £ 18/35 – Carte £ 35/43

◆ From a handsome drawing room, enjoy the enviable position of this Victorian mansion with its Rhinog Mountain and Mawddach Estuary vistas. Bedrooms are tastefully furnished. Dine in smart garden room with outside terrace.

Tyddyn Mawr without rest ← Cader Idris,

Islawdref, Cader Rd, Southwest : 2½ m. by Tywyn rd on Cader Idris rd ✉ LL40 1TL – ✆ (01341) 422 331 – Closed December-mid February

3 rm – †£ 55 ††£ 66

◆ Part 18C farmhouse with sympathetic extension: boasts spectacular views from breathtaking position. Timbered breakfast room. Superb rooms: one with patio, one with balcony.

EAST ABERTHAW (Aberddawan) – **Vale of Glamorgan** – **503** J 29 33 **B-C4**
– ✉ Barry

London 180 m – Cardiff 20 m – Swansea 33 m

The Blue Anchor Inn

✉ CF62 3DD – ✆ (01446) 750 329

Rest – Menu £ 19 – Carte £ 15/26

◆ Characterful thatched and creeper covered inn, dating back to 1380. Nooks, crannies and warrens invoke charming atmosphere. Wide-ranging menus with traditional dishes.

WALES

ERWOOD Powys – Powys – **503** K 27 – **pop. 1 815** 33 **C3**

London 183 m – Cardiff 56 m – Merthyr Tydfil 35 m – Hereford 34 m

Trericket Mill
rm,

South : 3/4 m. off A 470 ✉ LD2 3TQ – ☎ (01982) 560312 – mail@trericket.co.uk – Closed 15 January-8 February

3 rm – ♀£ 42 ♀♀£ 64 – **Rest** – Vegetarian Menu £ 18 **s**

◆ Red brick, grade II listed water corn mill with a comfy, rustic feel, log fires and riverside garden. Simple bedrooms; the Mill Room has its own little balcony. Vegetarian menu served in dining room, which also houses the mill machinery.

FELINGWM UCHAF – Carmarthenshire – see Carmarthen

FISHGUARD – Pembrokeshire – **503** F 28 – **pop. 3 193** 33 **A3**

London 265 m – Cardiff 114 m – Gloucester 176 m – Holyhead 169 m – Shrewsbury 136 m – Swansea 76 m

to Republic of Ireland (Rosslare) (Stena Line) 2-4 daily (1 h 50 mn/ 3 h 30 mn)

Town Hall, The Square ☎ (01348) 873484 - Ocean Lab, The Parrog, Goodwick ☎ (01348) 872037

Pembrokeshire Coast National Park★★

Manor Town House
VISA

11 Main St ✉ SA65 9HG – ☎ (01348) 873 260 – enquiries@manortownhouse.com – Fax (01348) 873 260

6 rm – ♀£ 40/60 ♀♀£ 80/90

Rest – (by arrangement) Menu £ 20

◆ Georgian Grade II listed house. Bedrooms are individually styled and furnished with antiques, choose from Victorian and Art Deco; some with harbour and sea views. Welsh ingredients intrinsic to proudly served home-cooked dishes.

at Welsh Hook Southwest : 7 ½ m. by A 40 – ✉ Haverfordwest

Stone Hall with rm
VISA AE

✉ SA62 5NS – ☎ (01348) 840 212 – Fax (01348) 840 815 – Closed 25 December-15 January

5 rm – ♀£ 70/80 ♀♀£ 100 – **Rest** – (dinner only) (booking essential) Menu £ 29 – Carte £ 29/33

◆ Charming part-14C manor house with 17C additions. Tranquil setting and personal hospitality. Home-cooked, French-style dishes using prime seasonal produce. Comfy rooms.

GELLILYDAN – Gwynedd – see Llan Ffestiniog

GRESFORD = Groes-ffordd – Wrexham – **502** – see Wrexham

GWBERT ON SEA – Ceredigion – **503** F 27 – see Cardigan

HARLECH – Gwynedd – **502** H 25 – **pop. 1 233** 32 **B2**

London 241 m – Chester 72 m – Dolgellau 21 m

Gwyddfor House, High St ☎ (01766) 780658

Royal St David's, ☎ (01766) 780 203 .

Castle★★ **AC**

Snowdonia National Park★★★

Hafod Wen
Tremadoc Bay and Snowdonia, VISA

South : ¾ m. on A 496 ✉ LL46 2RA – ☎ (01766) 780 356 – enquiries@harlechguesthouse.co.uk – Fax (01766) 780 356 – March-October

3 rm – ♀£ 70 ♀♀£ 100 – **Rest** – (Closed Sunday) (by arrangement) Menu £ 30

◆ Unusual house with Dutch colonial architectural references. Superb views of Tremadoc Bay and Snowdonia from most of the antique and curio filled bedrooms. Footpath to beach. The dining room shares in the establishment's delightful views.

WALES

Gwrach Ynys without rest
North : 2¼ m. on A 496 ✉ LL47 6TS – ✆ (01766) 780 742
– info@gwrachynys.co.uk – Fax (01766) 781 199
7 rm – †£ 28/50 ††£ 60/70
◆ Edwardian house in good location for exploring Snowdonia and Cardigan Bay. Welcoming owners. Traditional bedrooms, two of which are ideal for families.

Castle Cottage with rm
Pen Llech, off B 4573 ✉ LL46 2YL – ✆ (01766) 780 479
– glyn@castlecottageharlech.co.uk
– Closed 3 weeks November
7 rm – †£ 75 ††£ 150 – **Rest** – (dinner only) (booking essential) Menu £ 33
◆ A little cottage just a short distance from the imposing Harlech Castle. Stylish, modern restaurant where Welsh food with a modern twist is served. Smart contemporary rooms.

HAVERFORDWEST (Hwlffordd) – Pembrokeshire – 503 F 28 – pop. 13 367

33 **A3**

London 250 m – Fishguard 15 m – Swansea 57 m
Old Bridge ✆ (01437) 763110
Arnolds Down, ✆ (01437) 763 565 .
Scolton Museum and Country Park★
Pembrokeshire Coast National Park★★. Skomer Island and Skokholm Island★, SW : 14 m. by B 4327 and minor roads

Lower Haythog Farm
Spittal, Northeast : 5 m. on B 4329 ✉ SA62 5QL – ✆ (01437) 731 279
– nesta@lowerhaythogfarm.co.uk – Fax (01437) 731 279
5 rm – †£ 35/45 ††£ 75 – **Rest** – (by arrangement) Menu £ 23
◆ Friendly atmosphere, traditional comforts and a warm welcome at this 250 acre working dairy farm with accessible woodland walks. Well kept and comfortable throughout. Dining room in homely, country style reflected in hearty, home-cooked food.

HAWARDEN (Penarlâg) – Flintshire – 502 K 24

32 **C1**

London 205 m – Chester 9 m – Liverpool 17 m – Shrewsbury 45 m

The Hawarden Brasserie
68 The Highway ✉ CH5 3DH – ✆ (01244) 536 353 – Fax (01244) 520 888
– Closed 1 January
Rest – (booking essential) Carte £ 21/31
◆ Neutral walls, wood floors and spot lighting contribute to the busy, modern ambience in this good value, small restaurant; well reputed locally. Cuisine with a Welsh tone.

HAY-ON-WYE (Y Gelli) – Powys – 503 K 27 – pop. 1 846

33 **C3**

London 154 m – Brecon 16 m – Cardiff 59 m – Hereford 21 m – Newport 62 m
Craft Centre, Oxford Rd ✆ (01497) 820144
Rhosgoch Builth Wells, ✆ (01497) 851 251 .
Town★
Brecon Beacons National Park★★. Llanthony Priory★★, SE : 12 m. by minor roads

The Swan at Hay
Church St ✉ HR3 5DQ – ✆ (01497) 821 188 – info@swanathay.co.uk
– Fax (01497) 821 424
– Closed 2 weeks January
18 rm – †£ 75/89 ††£ 120 – **Rest** – (bar lunch) Carte £ 23/34
◆ Constantly evolving 18C former coaching inn bordered by neat book-lovers' garden. Restyled front bar is light, airy and inviting. Guest lounge with 21C makeover. Spruce rooms. French influenced modern menus in the restaurant.

WALES

Hardwicke Green without rest
East : 3 m. by B 4348 on B 4352 ✉ HR3 5HA – ✆ (01497) 831051 – info@hardwickegreen.co.uk – closed January, Christmas and New Year
3 rm – †£ 22/46 ††£ 56
◆ Ex-farmhouse built in 1740 with later addition. Charming garden in six acres. Comfy conservatory lounge. Stay in Farmhouse or Victorian rooms: immaculately smart rustic chic.

Old Black Lion with rm
26 Lion St ✉ HR3 5AD – ✆ (01497) 820841 – info@oldblacklion.co.uk – Fax (01497) 822960 – Closed 24-26 December
10 rm – †£ 43 ††£ 115 – **Rest** – Carte £ 20/30
◆ Inn with parts dating back to 13C and 17C when it reputedly hosted Oliver Cromwell. A friendly place with a traditional atmosphere, popular menu and comfortable bedrooms.

at Llanigon Southwest : 2½ m. by B 4350 – ✉ Hay-on-Wye

Old Post Office without rest
✉ HR3 5QA – ✆ (01497) 820008 – March-November
3 rm – †£ 45/70 ††£ 70/90
◆ Dating from 17C, a converted inn. Near the "book town" of Hay-on-Wye. Smart modern ambience blends with characterful charm. Pine furnished rooms with polished floors.

WALES

HENSOL – Rhondda Cynon Taff 33 C4

London 161 m – Bridgend 10 m – Cardiff 8 m – Cowbridge 7 m
Museum of Welsh Life★★, E : 8 m. by minor rd north to Miskin, A 4119 and minor rd south

Llanerch Vineyard without rest
✉ CF72 8GG – ✆ (01443) 225877 – enquiries@llanerch-vineyard.co.uk – Fax (01443) 225546
12 rm – †£ 50/55 ††£ 70/75
◆ Rurally set, fully functioning vineyard in woodland with 20 acres of vines. The modern breakfast area is furnished with Welsh art. Immaculate, state of the art bedrooms.

HOLYHEAD (Caergybi) – Anglesey – 502 G 24 – pop. 11 237 32 B1

London 269 m – Birkenhead 94 m – Cardiff 215 m – Chester 88 m – Shrewsbury 105 m – Swansea 190 m
to Republic of Ireland (Dun Laoghaire) (Stena Line) 4-5 daily (1 h 40 mn) – to Republic of Ireland (Dublin) (Irish Ferries) 2 daily (3 h 15 mn) – to Republic of Ireland (Dublin) (Stena Line) 1-2 daily (3 h 45 mn)
Terminal 1, Stena Line ✆ (01407) 762622
South Stack Cliffs★, W : 3 m. by minor roads

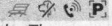

Yr Hendre without rest
Porth-y-Felin Rd, Northwest : ½ m. turning left at war memorial and by Thomas St ✉ LL65 1AH – ✆ (01407) 762929 – rita@yr-hendre.freeserve.co.uk – Fax (01407) 765936 – closed 25-26 December
3 rm – †£ 45 ††£ 65
◆ Detached house dating from the 1920s in a pleasant, residential area of town and ideally located for the ferry terminus. Comfortable and well-furnished bedrooms.

HOWEY – Powys – see Llandrindod Wells

Look out for red symbols, indicating particularly pleasant establishments.

KNIGHTON (Trefyclawdd) – Powys – **503** K 26 – pop. 2 743 33 **C3**

London 162 m – Birmingham 59 m – Hereford 31 m – Shrewsbury 35 m
Offa's Dyke Centre, West St ✆ (01547) 529424
Little Ffrydd Wood, ✆ (01547) 528 646 .
Town★
Offa's Dyke★, NW : 9½ m

Milebrook House

Ludlow Rd, Milebrook, East : 2 m. on A 4113 ✉ LD7 1LT – ✆ (01547) 528 632 – hotel@milebrook.kc3ltd.co.uk – Fax (01547) 520 509

10 rm – ♦£ 71 ♦♦£ 109 – **Rest** – (closed Monday lunch) Menu £ 17/33

◆ Located in the Teme Valley; good for exploring the Welsh Marches. Possesses a fine, formal garden well stocked with exotic plants. Rooms are large and pleasingly decorated. The kitchen garden provides most of the vegetables which appear in the restaurant.

LAKE VYRNWY – Powys – **502** J 25 – ✉ **Llanwddyn** 32 **C2**

London 204 m – Chester 52 m – Llanfyllin 10 m – Shrewsbury 40 m
Unit 2, Vyrnwy Craft Workshops ✆ (01691) 870346, laktic@powys.gov.uk
Lake★

Lake Vyrnwy

< Lake Vyrnwy, rm,

✉ SY10 0LY – ✆ (01691) 870 692 – info@lakevyrnwyhotel.co.uk – Fax (01691) 870 259

51 rm – ♦£ 95/100 ♦♦£ 145/150 – 1 suite – **Rest** – Menu £ 18/34 **s** – Carte Lunch £ 16/20

◆ Victorian country house built from locally quarried stone overlooking the lake; an RSPB sanctuary and sporting estate, ideal for game enthusiasts. Rooms have timeless chic. Spectacular lakeside views from the restaurant are matched by accomplished cooking.

WALES

Do not confuse X with ✿!
X defines comfort, while stars are awarded for the best cuisine, across all categories of comfort.

LALESTON – Bridgend – **503** J 29 – see Bridgend

LAMPHEY = Llandyfai – Pembrokeshire – **503** F 28 – see Pembroke

LLAN FFESTINIOG – Gwynedd 32 **B2**

London 234 m – Bangor 35 m – Wrexham 52 m
Llechwedd Slate Caverns★ AC N : 4 m. by A 470

Cae'r Blaidd Country House

< Vale of Ffestiniog and Moelwyn mountains,

North : ¾ m. by A 470 on Blaenau Rd ✉ LL41 4PH – ✆ (01766) 762 765 – info@caerblaidd.fsnet.co.uk – Fax (01766) 762 765 – closed January

3 rm – ♦£ 45 ♦♦£ 75 – **Rest** – (communal dining) Menu £ 18

◆ Spacious Victorian country house in wooded gardens; spectacular views of Ffestiniog and Moelwyn Mountains. Smart, uncluttered rooms. Guided tours and courses are organised. A huge dining room; large refectory table where communal dinners are served.

at Gellilydan Southwest : 2 ¾ m. by A 470 off A 487 – ✉ **Ffestiniog**

Tyddyn du Farm

East : ½ m. by A 487 on A 470 ✉ LL41 4RB – ✆ (01766) 590 281 – paula@snowdoniafarm.com

5 rm – ♦£ 45/70 ♦♦£ 78/95 – **Rest** – (by arrangement) Menu £ 18

◆ 400-year old farmhouse set against Moelwyn Mountains. Guests can participate in farming activities or visit Roman site. Some rooms have large jacuzzis; all are very spacious. Cooking takes in free-range farm eggs; soups and rolls are home-made.

LLANARMON DYFFRYN CEIRIOG - Wrexham - 502 K 25 - 32 C2

✉ Llangollen (Denbighshire)

London 196 m - Chester 33 m - Shrewsbury 32 m

West Arms

✉ LL20 7LD - ✆ (01691) 600665 - gowestarms@aol.com - Fax (01691) 600622

13 rm - †£ 70 ††£ 179 - 2 suites - **Rest** - (bar lunch Monday-Saturday) Menu £ 33 (dinner) - Carte £ 21/30

♦ Set in Ceiriog Valley; enjoys many original fixtures associated with a part 16C country inn - slate-flagged floors, inglenooks, timberwork. Bedrooms with matching ambience. A concise but well-balanced menu offered in atmospheric dining room.

LLANBEDR - Gwynedd - 502 H 25 - pop. 1 101 32 B2

Cardiff 150 m - Dolgellau 18 m - Harlech 3 m

Harlech Castle★★, N : 3 m. by A 496

Pensarn Hall without rest

North : ¾ m. on A 496 ✉ LL45 2HS - ✆ (01341) 241 236
- welcome@pensarn-hall.co.uk
- February-October

7 rm - †£ 50 ††£ 75/80

♦ Late 19C house on an estuary. Impressive entrance with original tiled floor. Pleasant front conservatory. Breakfast room has good view. Simple, well-kept rooms.

LLANDEILO - Carmarthenshire - 503 I 28 - pop. 1 731 33 B3

London 218 m - Brecon 34 m - Carmarthen 15 m - Swansea 25 m

Town★ - Dinefwr Park★ AC

Brecon Beacons National Park★★ - Black Mountain★, SE : by minor roads - Carreg Cennen Castle★ AC, SE : 4 m. by A 483 and minor roads

Cawdor

rm,

Rhosmaen St ✉ SA19 6EN - ✆ (01558) 823 500 - cawdor@morganshotel.co.uk
- Fax (01558) 822 399

25 rm - †£ 65 ††£ 200 - **Rest** - Menu £ 15/25 - Carte £ 23/32

♦ Vividly hued coaching inn on main street. Public areas are leather furnished, 'loungey', relaxed and modern. Main strength lies in bedrooms: contemporary, sleek and sassy. Menus add Mediterranean edge to prominent Welsh base.

Plough Inn

rm,

Rhosmaen, North : 1 m. on A 40 ✉ SA19 6NP - ✆ (01558) 823 431
- enquiries@ploughrhosmaen.co.uk - Fax (01558) 823 969

14 rm - †£ 65 ††£ 90/120 - **Rest** - Carte £ 25/29

♦ Once a farmhouse, the perfect base for country pursuits. Rooms, named after characters from Mabinogion, are well-kept and co-ordinated; large windows for views. Wholesome favourites to fore in light, airy and relaxed modern dining room.

at Salem North : 3 m. by A 40 off Pen y banc rd - ✉ Llandeilo

The Angel Inn

✉ SA19 7LY - ✆ (01558) 823 394 - eat@angelsalem.co.uk
- Closed 2 weeks January, Sunday dinner, Monday and Tuesday lunch

Rest - Carte £ 25/35

♦ Cream coloured pub next to chapel in small village. Inviting bar lounge with chair and sofa assortment. Edwardian style dining room: elaborate cooking utilising local fare.

LLANDENNY - Monmouthshire - 503 L 28 - see Usk

**We try to be as accurate as possible when giving room rates.
But prices are susceptible to change,
so please check rates when booking.**

WALES

LLANDOVERY Carmarthenshire – Carmarthenshire – **503** I 28 – pop. 2 870 33 **B3**

London 207 m – Cardiff 61 m – Swansea 37 m – Merthyr Tydfil 34 m

New White Lion
rm, P VISA MO

43 Stone St ✉ SA20 0BZ – ✆ (01550) 720 685 – info@newwhitelion.co.uk

6 rm – ✝£ 60 ✝✝£ 95 – **Rest** – (dinner only) Menu £ 17 **s**

◆ Stylish grade II listed hotel with individually designed bedrooms named after characters from local folklore, and cool sitting room with honesty bar. Cosy dining room; homemade dishes make good use made of local, seasonal produce.

LLANDRILLO – Denbighshire – **502** J 25 – ✉ Corwen 32 **C2**

London 210 m – Chester 40 m – Dolgellau 26 m – Shrewsbury 46 m

Tyddyn Llan with rm
P VISA MO

✉ LL21 0ST – ✆ (01490) 440 264 – tyddynllan@compuserve.com
– Fax (01490) 440 414
– closed 3 weeks January

13 rm – ✝£ 85/130 ✝✝£ 120/240 – **Rest** – (dinner only and lunch Friday-Sunday) (booking essential) Menu £ 28/45

◆ Charming sitting areas for pre-dinner drinks. Two dining rooms with blue painted wood panels. Classic menus employing local produce. Fine selection of country house rooms.

Undecided between two equivalent establishments? Within each category, establishments are classified in our order of preference.

LLANDRINDOD WELLS – Powys – **503** J 27 – pop. 5 024 33 **C3**

London 204 m – Brecon 29 m – Carmarthen 60 m – Shrewsbury 58 m

Old Town Hall, Memorial Gardens ✆ (01597) 822600, llandtic@powys.gov.uk

Llandrindod Wells, ✆ (01597) 823 873 .

Elan Valley★★ (Dol-y-Mynach and Claerwen Dam and Reservoir★★, Caban Coch Dam and Reservoir★, Garreg-ddu Viaduct★, Pen-y-Garreg Reservoir and Dam★, Craig Goch Dam and Reservoir★), NW : 12 m. by A 4081, A 470 and B 4518

Metropole
rm, P VISA MO AE

Temple St ✉ LD1 5DY – ✆ (01597) 823 700 – info@metropole.co.uk
– Fax (01597) 824 828

120 rm – ✝£ 85/110 ✝✝£ 110 – 2 suites – **Rest** – (bar lunch) Menu £ 26 (dinner) – Carte £ 19/28

◆ Run by Baird-Murray family for 100 years and popular for hosting vintage car rallies. Leisure complex is in 19C style conservatory. Eight "Tower" rooms with adjoining lounge. Expect to find cuisine committed to using local ingredients.

at Crossgates Northeast : 3 ½ m. on A 483 – ✉ Llandrindod Wells

Guidfa House
P VISA MO

✉ LD1 6RF – ✆ (01597) 851 241 – guidfa@globalnet.co.uk
– Fax (01597) 851 875

6 rm – ✝£ 55 ✝✝£ 68/79 – **Rest** – (by arrangement) Menu £ 27

◆ Georgian house with white painted façade and pleasant garden to relax in. Indoors, find spacious, bright bedrooms. A friendly welcome is given with tips on local activities. Seasonally changing menu of zesty home cooking in traditionally decorated dining room.

at Howey South : 1 ½ m. by A 483 – ✉ **Llandrindod Wells**

Acorn Court Country House without rest
Chapel Rd, Northeast : ½ m. ✉ LD1 5PB – ✆ (01597) 823 543
– info@acorncourt.co.uk – Fax (01597) 823 543
– closed 5 December-1 February
4 rm – £ 40/45 £ 65/70
◆ Chalet-style house in lovely countryside; guests can fish in the lake. Bedrooms are large with many extra touches: hairdryers, stationery, soft toys - homely and welcoming.

LLANDUDNO – Conwy – **502** I 24 – **pop. 14 872** 32 **B1**

London 243 m – Birkenhead 55 m – Chester 47 m – Holyhead 43 m
1-2 Chapel St ✆ (01492) 876413
Rhos-on-Sea Penrhyn Bay, ✆ (01492) 549 641 ;
72 Bryniau Rd West Shore, ✆ (01492) 875 325 ;
Hospital Rd, ✆ (01492) 876 450 .
Town★ - Pier★ B – The Great Orme★ (panorama★★, Tramway★, Ancient Copper Mines★ **AC**) AB
Bodnant Garden★★ **AC**, S : 7 m. by A 470 B

Plan opposite

Bodysgallen Hall ← gardens and mountains, rm,
Southeast : 2 m. on A 470
✉ LL30 1RS – ✆ (01492) 584 466 – info@bodysgallen.com
– Fax (01492) 582 519
18 rm – £ 140/145 £ 175, £6.95 – 16 suites –
Rest – (booking essential) Menu £ 22/42
◆ Majestic and rare sums up this part 17C-18C hall with tower, once a soldier's lookout, now a place to take in views of mountains and terraced gardens. Antique filled rooms. Formal dining room with tall windows; serves fine and distinctive dishes.

The Empire (heated) rm,
73 Church Walks ✉ LL30 2HE – ✆ (01492) 860 555
– reservations@empirehotel.co.uk – Fax (01492) 860 791
– closed 21-30 December A **e**
46 rm – £ 60/90 £ 105/130 – 7 suites
Rest *Watkins and Co.* – (dinner only and Sunday lunch) Menu £ 15/21
◆ A porticoed façade sets the Victorian tone found in bedrooms with original cast iron beds, antiques and Russell Flint prints on walls. 21C mod cons bring them bang up-to-date. Fine menus with a mix and match of the Celtic and the Continental.

Osborne House
17 North Parade ✉ LL30 2LP – ✆ (01492) 860 330 – sales@osbornehouse.com
– Fax (01492) 860 791
– closed 21-30 December A **c**
6 rm – £ 145/210 £ 145/210
Rest *Osborne's Cafe Grill* – see restaurant listing
◆ Sumptuous interior: huge rooms extend length of house; bedrooms epitomise Victorian luxury - original wood flooring, elaborate silk drapes, fine antiques. Richly hued lounge.

St Tudno
North Parade ✉ LL30 2LP – ✆ (01492) 874 411 – sttudnohotel@btinternet.com
– Fax (01492) 860 407 A **c**
17 rm – £ 75/95 £ 95/115 – 1 suite
Rest *Terrace* – see restaurant listing
◆ Prime position on the promenade opposite a Victorian pier; boasts sitting room, lounge in charming period style with seafront vistas. Comfortable rooms with fine fabrics.

WALES

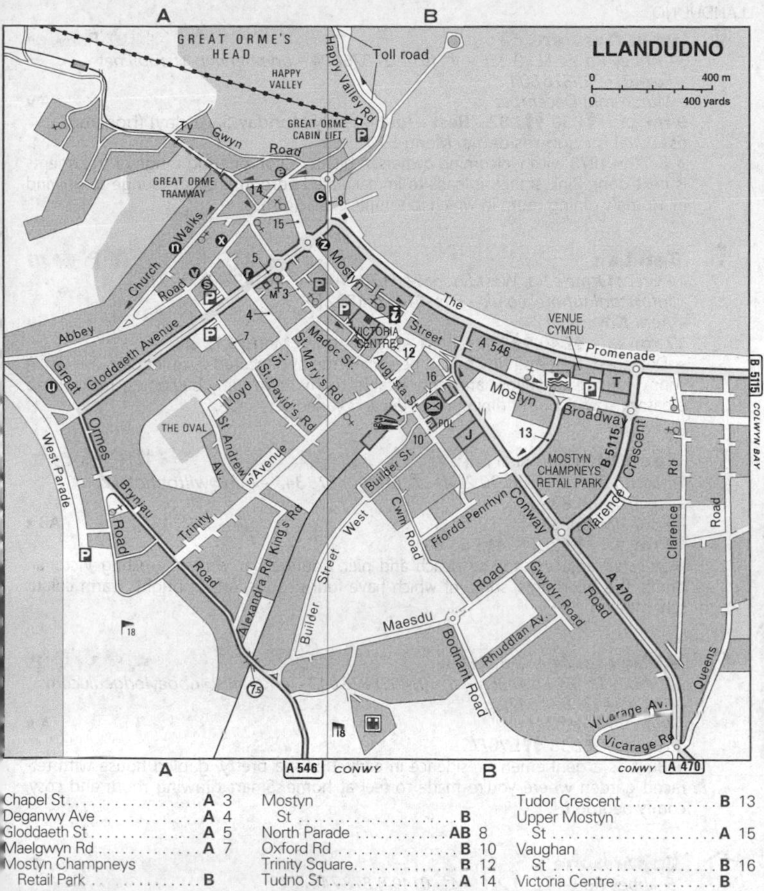

Dunoon

Gloddaeth St ✉ LL30 2DW – ✆ (01492) 860 787 – reservations@dunoonhotel.co.uk – Fax (01492) 860 031 – 1 March-16 December

A **r**

49 rm ☕ – 🛉£ 67/98 🛉🛉£ 133 – **Rest** – (bar lunch Monday-Saturday) Menu £ 22

◆ A hospitable hotel; a panelled hallway leads to the "Welsh Dresser Bar" furnished with an antique cooking range. Bygone era ambience. Rooms are individually styled. Restaurant, modernised in a traditional style, with menu to match.

Escape Boutique B & B without rest

48 Church Walks ✉ LL30 2HL – ✆ (01492) 877 776 – info@escapebandb.co.uk – Fax (01492) 878 777 – Closed 23-27 December

A **n**

9 rm ☕ – 🛉£ 60/105 🛉🛉£ 120

◆ Ornate, elevated Victorian villa with ultra contemporary furnishings. Modish breakfast room with fine choice. Cool beige/brown or 'French boudoir' rooms. B and B with style.

Bryn Derwen
34 Abbey Rd ✉ LL30 2EE – ✆ (01492) 876 804 – brynderwen@fsmail.net
– Fax (01492) 876 804
– March-mid December A **v**
9 rm – £ 50 £ 82 – **Rest** – (dinner only Monday-Saturday) (booking essential for non-residents) Menu £ 20
◆ Built in 1878 with welcoming owners. A beauty salon offering range of treatments is next door. Pine staircase leads to immaculate bedrooms. Quiet lounge to unwind in. Homely dining room in which to sample classic dishes.

Tan Lan
14 Great Orme's Rd, West Shore ✉ LL30 2AR – ✆ (01492) 860 221
– info@tanlanhotel.co.uk – Fax (01492) 870 219
– April-November A **u**
17 rm – £ 40 £ 70 – **Rest** – (dinner only) Menu £ 15 **s**
◆ Detached, neat and tidy house, personally run and located in quiet part of town. A sunny lounge in yellow and comfortable rooms, two with balconies, make for a pleasant stay. A bright dining room delivers varied set meals.

The Wilton without rest
14 South Parade ✉ LL30 2LN – ✆ (01492) 878 343 – info@wiltonhotel.com
– Fax (01492) 878 343
– April-November AB **z**
14 rm – £ 30/42 £ 60/64
◆ Situated adjacent to the beach and pier. Lounge bar with interesting Victorian prints; the bedrooms, some of which have four-posters, are in bright, warm colour schemes.

Abbey Lodge without rest
14 Abbey Rd ✉ LL30 2EA – ✆ (01492) 878 042 – enquiries@abbeylodgeuk.com
– Fax (01492) 878 042
– March-November A **x**
4 rm – £ 38 £ 70/75
◆ Built as a gentlemen's residence in early 1850s; a pretty, gabled house with terraced garden where you're made to feel at home. Smart drawing room and cosy, comfy bedrooms.

Epperstone
15 Abbey Rd ✉ LL30 2EE – ✆ (01492) 878 746
– epperstonehotel@btconnect.com – Fax (01492) 871 223 A **s**
8 rm – £ 27/35 £ 54/70 – **Rest** – (by arrangement) Menu £ 16
◆ A period house, evident in the fixtures: stained glass, ornate fireplace, mahogany staircase. Other attractions include a marine aquarium in conservatory and neat bedrooms. Intimate dining room serving varied dishes using fresh, local ingredients.

Sefton Court without rest
49 Church Walks ✉ LL30 2HL – ✆ (01492) 875 235 – seftoncourt@aol.com
– Fax (01492) 879 560
– March-November A **n**
11 rm – £ 33/50 £ 62/66
◆ Imposing Victorian house, fully refurbished in 2006, perched on quiet hillside. Large, comfy lounge; spacious breakfast room. Smart, homely rooms. Near Great Orme Tramway.

Terrace – at St Tudno H.
North Parade ✉ LL30 2LP – ✆ (01492) 874 411 – Fax (01492) 860 407 A **c**
Rest – Menu £ 18 (lunch) – Carte approx. £ 38 **s**
◆ Smart and formal dining room incorporating blown-up photograph of Lake Como and, on a smaller scale, a neat little water feature. Accomplished and precise modern cooking.

WALES

Osborne's Cafe Grill – at Osborne House H.
17 North Parade ✉ LL30 2LP – ✆ (01492) 860 330
– sales@osbornehouse.com – Fax (01492) 860 791
– Closed 21-30 December A c
Rest – Carte £ 20/33
◆ Impressive, ornate main dining room with velvet drapes and ornate gold lighting. Eclectic, modern menus, and the bustling informal style of a bistro; enthusiastic service.

at Deganwy South : 2 ¾ m. on A 546 - A – ✉ Llandudno

Nikki Ip's
57 Station Rd ✉ LL31 9DF – ✆ (01492) 596 611
– Fax (01492) 596 600
Rest – Chinese (dinner only) (booking essential) Menu £ 25 – Carte £ 21/30
◆ Good value, stylish and unconventional, but beware: no signage outside. Particularly welcoming owners. Coral interior; Cantonese, Peking and Szechuan specialities are served.

LLANDYRNOG – Denbighshire – 503 J/K 24 32 C1

Cardiff 158 m – Denbigh 7 m – Ruthin 6 m

Pentre Mawr (heated)
North : 1 ¼ m. by B 5429 taking left hand fork after ¾ m. ✉ LL16 4LA
– ✆ (01824) 790 732 – bre@sychnant-pass-house.co.uk
– March-October
5 rm – £ 70/100 £ 120 – **Rest** – (by arrangement, communal dining) Menu £ 20
◆ Spacious, rebuilt 17C former farmhouse in nearly 200 acres. Very comfortable, with period style lounges, morning room, pool, terrace and tastefully individualistic rooms. Communal dining room offers classic décor and homely touches.

LLANELLI – Carmarthenshire – 503 H 28 33 B4

London 202 m – Cardiff 54 m – Swansea 12 m

Llwyn Hall
Llwynhendy, East : 3 ½ m. by A 484 ✉ SA14 9LJ – ✆ (01554) 777 754
– infor@llwynhall.co.uk – Fax (01554) 777 754
6 rm – £ 50/70 £ 70/85 – **Rest** – (by arrangement) Carte approx. £ 24
◆ Pretty yellow-and-white 19C gabled house with extension. Country style soft furnishings. Chintzy rooms of pleasant individuality: those at front face garden and North Gower.

Fairyhill Bar and Brasserie golf course, Loughor estuary and Gower Peninsula,
Machynys Golf Club,
Nicklaus Ave, Machynys, South : 3 m. by A 484 off Machynys rd ✉ SA15 2DG
– ✆ (01554) 744 944 – machynys@fairyhill.net
– closed 25 December
Rest – Carte approx. £ 20
◆ On first floor of golf clubhouse with pleasant views of course and estuary. Choose between lounge bar with leather sofas or bustling brasserie for well prepared modern dishes.

LLANERCHYMEDD – Anglesey – 502 G 24 32 B1

London 262 m – Bangor 18 m – Caernarfon 23 m – Holyhead 15 m
Anglesey★★

Llwydiarth Fawr without rest
North : 1 m. on B 5111 ✉ LL71 8DF – ✆ (01248) 470 321
– llwydiarth@hotmail.com
– closed 25 December
4 rm – £ 38/60 £ 80/85
◆ Part of an 800-acre cattle and sheep farm, Georgian in style with picturesque vistas. Guests can enjoy nature walks, fishing on lake; welcoming owner. Airy, well-kept rooms.

WALES

Drws-Y-Coed without rest
East : 1½ m. by B 5111 on Benllech rd ✉ *LL71 8AD* – *(01248) 470 473*
– drwsycoed2@hotmail.com
– Closed Christmas
3 rm – £ 45 £ 70
◆ Meaning "Door of the Wood"; 1960s house, run by Welsh speaking family in 550-acre farm of cattle and cereal crops. Countryside views add to enjoyment of neat and tidy rooms.

LLANFIHANGEL – Powys – 502 J 25 – see Llanfyllin

LLANFYLLIN – Powys – 502 K 25 32 C2

London 188 m – Chester 42 m – Shrewsbury 24 m – Welshpool 11 m
Pistyll Rhaeadr★, NW : 8 m. by A 490, B 4391, B 4580 and minor roads

Seeds
5 Penybryn Cottages, High St ✉ *SY22 5AP* – *(01691) 648 604*
– closed 1 week March, 1 week October, 25 December, Monday, Tuesday, Wednesday and Sunday dinner
Rest – (restricted opening in winter) Menu £ 23 (dinner) – Carte £ 19/28
◆ Converted 16C rustic cottages with eclectic décor: souvenirs from owner's travels. Blackboard menu offers modern or traditional dishes. Local seasonal ingredients to the fore.

WALES

at Llanfihangel Southwest : 5 m. by A 490 and B 4393 on B 4382 – ✉ Llanfyllin

Cyfie Farm Meifod valley,
South : 1½ m. by B 4382 ✉ *SY22 5JE* – *(01691) 648 451*
– info@cyfiefarm.co.uk – Fax (01691) 648 363
– restricted opening in winter
4 rm – £ 85 £ 90/110 – **Rest** – (by arrangement, communal dining) Menu £ 25
◆ 17C longhouse, now a sheep farm, with super views of Meifod Valley. One room has distinctly quaint feel. Luxurious new cottages: outdoor hot tub affords great vistas. Cordon Bleu trained owners serve at communal table.

If breakfast is included the symbol appears after the number of rooms.

LLANGAMMARCH WELLS – Powys – 503 J 27 33 B3

London 200 m – Brecon 17 m – Builth Wells 8 m – Cardiff 58 m

Lake Country House and Spa
East : ¾ m. ✉ *LD4 4BS* rm,
– (01591) 620 202 – info@lakecountryhouse.co.uk – Fax (01591) 620 457
17 rm – £ 115/180 £ 270 – 11 suites – **Rest** – (booking essential) Menu £ 22/43
◆ 19C country house in mature grounds. Welsh teas a speciality. Rooms in house or Lodge full of antiques, flowers and extravagant fabrics. Tranquil spa adds to the experience. Candlelit dining; super wine list.

LLANGOLLEN – Denbighshire – 502 K 25 – pop. 2 930 32 C2

London 194 m – Chester 23 m – Holyhead 76 m – Shrewsbury 30 m
Town Hall, Castle St (01978) 860828
Vale of Llangollen Holyhead Rd, (01978) 860 906.
Town★ - Railway★ **AC** - Plas Newydd★ **AC**
Pontcysyllte Aqueduct★★, E : 4 m. by A 539 - Castell Dinas Bran★, N : by footpath – Valle Crucis Abbey★ **AC**, N : 2 m. by A 542. Chirk Castle★★ **AC** (wrought iron gates★), SE : 7½ m. by A 5 – Rug Chapel★ **AC**, W : 11 m. by A 5 and A 494

Bryn Howel
East : 2 ¾ m. by A 539 ✉ LL20 7UW – ✆ (01978) 860 331
– hotel@brynhowel.com – Fax (01978) 860 119
35 rm – ♦£ 70/80 ♦♦£ 100/110 – 1 suite
Rest *Cedar Tree* – Menu £ 10/20 – Carte £ 22/32 **s**
◆ Built 1896 for owner of Ruabon brick company, mock Jacobean in style with Vale of Llangollen views. Bar has unique "Anthem Fireplace". Rooms in main house and modern wing. Admire panoramas and dine on classic Welsh cuisine.

Gales
18 Bridge St ✉ LL20 8PF – ✆ (01978) 860 089 – richard@galesoflangollen.co.uk
– Fax (01978) 861 313
– closed 24 December-1 January
13 rm – ♦£ 60 ♦♦£ 80, £ 5 – 2 suites – **Rest** – (closed Sunday) Carte £ 17/26
◆ Part 17C and 18C town house; rooms are divided between two buildings and display many historic features: wattle and daub walls, brass and walnut beds, beams and inglenooks. A wooden floored dining room and bar with inn-like ambience.

Oakmere without rest
Regent St, on A 5 ✉ LL20 8HS – ✆ (01978) 861 126 – oakmeregh@aol.com
6 rm – ♦£ 45/55 ♦♦£ 60/68
◆ A restored Victorian house with an immaculate garden. Indoors are polished pitch pine furnishings, a breakfast room with conservatory area and tidy bedrooms.

Hillcrest without rest
Hill St, on Plas Newydd rd ✉ LL20 8EU – ✆ (01978) 860 208
– drayment@btconnect.com – Fax (01978) 860 208
7 rm – ♦£ 35/38 ♦♦£ 55
◆ A semi-detached house with large garden, close to the town centre. Homely and tidy inside with nicely decorated bedrooms and some original features: a slate fireplace.

The Corn Mill
Dee Lane ✉ LL20 8PN – ✆ (01978) 869 555
– Closed 25-26 December
Rest – Carte £ 20/28
◆ Imposing corn mill on banks of the Dee with large decked seating area extending into the river. Inside are two restored water wheels, slate and brick rooms. Rustic cuisine.

LLANGRANNOG – Ceredigion – 503 G 27 — 33 B3

The Grange
Pentregat, Southeast : 3 m. by B 4321 on A 487 ✉ SA44 6HW
– ✆ (01239) 654 121 – theresesexton@madasafish.com – Fax (01239) 654 121
4 rm – ♦£ 55 ♦♦£ 75 – **Rest** – (by arrangement) Menu £ 20
◆ Pink washed Georgian house with most welcoming owner. Afternoon tea trolley in real silver. Immaculate room décor in keeping with house age. Very handy for coast and country. Breakfast and country dinner proudly served: honest, fresh home cooking.

LLANIGON – Powys – 503 K 27 – see Hay-on-Wye

LLANRHIDIAN – Swansea – 503 H 29 – see Swansea

LLANRUG – Gwynedd – 502 H 24 – see Caernarfon

LLANSANFFRAID GLAN CONWY – Conwy – 502 I 24 – see Conwy

LLANTWIT MAJOR (Llanilltud Fawr) – Vale of Glamorgan – 503 J 29 – pop. 13 366

33 **B4**

London 175 m – Cardiff 18 m – Swansea 33 m

West House Country

West St ✉ CF61 1SP – ✆ (01446) 792 406 – enq@westhouse-hotel.co.uk – Fax (01446) 796 147

20 rm – †£ 60/65 ††£ 68/75 – **Rest** – Menu £ 20 (dinner) – Carte £ 18/35

◆ 16C hotel in Vale of Glamorgan. After a bracing cliff top walk, relax in the welcoming bar. Rooms vary in style; traditional dominates. Conservatory used for small weddings. Light, clean Heritage restaurant with seasonal, local produce to fore.

LLANUWCHLLYN – Gwynedd – 503 I/J 25

32 **B2**

Cardiff 147 m – Dolgellau 13 m – Llangollen 27 m

Eifionydd without rest

✉ LL23 7UB – ✆ (01678) 540 622 – stay@eifionydd.com – April-October

3 rm – †£ 40 ††£ 65/70

◆ Good value guesthouse with lovely gardens and inspiring mountain views. Comfy lounge; linen-clad breakfast room; relaxing conservatory. Individual rooms with homely touches.

LLANWENARTH – Monmouthshire – see Abergavenny

WALES

LLANWRTYD WELLS – Powys – 503 J 27 – pop. 649

33 **B3**

London 214 m – Brecon 32 m – Cardiff 68 m – Carmarthen 39 m

Ty Barcud, The Square ✆ (01591) 610666, tic@celt.rural.wales.org

Abergwesyn-Tregaron Mountain Road★, NW : 19 m. on minor roads

Lasswade Country House

Station Rd ✉ LD5 4RW – ✆ (01591) 610515 – info@lasswadehotel.co.uk – Fax (01591) 610611

8 rm – †£ 50/70 ††£ 85/105 – **Rest** – (dinner only) Menu £ 28

◆ Personally run Edwardian country house, with fine views of mid-Wales countryside from the breakfast conservatory; cosy lounge. Bedrooms in traditional style. Proudly pro-organic meals on the daily menu.

Carlton Riverside with rm

Irfon Crescent ✉ LD5 4ST – ✆ (01591) 610 248 – info@carltonrestaurant.co.uk – closed December

4 rm – †£ 40/80 ††£ 80/90 – **Rest** – (dinner only and Sunday lunch) (booking essential) Menu £ 23 – Carte £ 27/42

◆ 400 yards from the old premises, overlooking the River Irfon. Skilled cooking based on traditional combinations uses quality ingredients. Two comfy lounges and courteous host. Simple, well-priced bedrooms.

LLYSWEN – Powys – 503 K 27 – ✉ Brecon

33 **C3**

London 188 m – Brecon 8 m – Cardiff 48 m – Worcester 53 m

Brecon Beacons National Park★★

Llangoed Hall

Northwest : 1 ¼ m. on A 470 ✉ LD3 0YP – ✆ (01874) 754 525 – enquiries@llangoedhall.com – Fax (01874) 754 545

20 rm – †£ 180/360 ††£ 225/430 – 3 suites – **Rest** – (booking essential for non-residents) Menu £ 25/45

◆ Set up by Sir Bernard Ashley of Laura Ashley group: rooms furnished accordingly. River Wye to rear. Tennis court, gardens, carved staircase; guests can arrive by helicopter. Dining room menu has classic Welsh roots; Rex Whistler etchings in adjoining room.

MACHYNLLETH – Powys – 502 – pop. 2 147 32 B2

London 220 m – Shrewsbury 56 m – Welshpool 37 m
Canolfan Owain Glyndwr ✆ (01654) 702401, machtic@powys.gov.uk
Ffordd Drenewydd, ✆ (01654) 702 000 .
Town★ - Celtica★ AC
Snowdonia National Park★★★ - Centre for Alternative Technology★★ AC, N : 3 m. by A 487

Ynyshir Hall
Eglwysfach, Southwest : 6 m. on A 487 ✉ SY20 8TA – ✆ (01654) 781 209 – info@ynyshir-hall.co.uk – Fax (01654) 781 366 – closed first two weeks January
6 rm – †£ 110/250 ††£ 285 – 3 suites – **Rest** – (booking essential) Menu £ 32/65 **s**
◆ Part Georgian house set within 1000 acre RSPB reserve; bright, individually appointed bedrooms, classically cosy drawing room with art, antiques and Welsh pottery. Modern cooking with a refined style.

MENAI BRIDGE (Porthaethwy) – Anglesey – 502 H 24 32 B1

London 270 m – Caernarfon 10 m – Chester 69 m – Holyhead 22 m

Neuadd Lwyd
Penmynydd, Northwest : 4 ¾ m. by B 5420 on Eglwys St Gredifael Church rd ✉ LL61 5BX – ✆ (01248) 715 005 – post@neuaddlwyd.co.uk
4 rm – †£ 125 ††£ 155 – **Rest** – (by arrangement) Menu £ 38
◆ This fine 19C rectory, set in a beautiful rural location, has had a sleek and stylish refit, lending it a luxurious air. Elegant interiors are matched by stunning bedrooms. Freshest Welsh ingredients incorporated into tasty evening meals.

Wern Farm without rest
Pentraeth Rd, North : 2 ¼ m. by B 5420 off A 5025 ✉ LL59 5RR – ✆ (01248) 712 421 – wernfarmanglesey@onetel.com – Fax (01248) 712 421 – March-October
3 rm – †£ 45/75 ††£ 65/75
◆ Attractive Georgian farmhouse run by a friendly couple. Bedrooms are spacious and comfortable. Enjoy countryside views in conservatory where vast breakfast is offered.

XX **Ruby**
Dale St ✉ LL59 5AW – ✆ (01248) 714 999 – www.rubymenai.com – Fax (01248) 717 888 – closed 26 December and 1 January
Rest – Menu £ 17 (lunch) – Carte £ 25/31
◆ Former firestation and council offices; now a lively, bustling eatery on two floors with good local reputation. Eclectic, global menus employing flavoursome, vibrant cooking.

MOLD (Yr Wyddgrug) – Flintshire – 502 K 24 – pop. 9 586 32 C1

London 211 m – Chester 12 m – Liverpool 22 m – Shrewsbury 45 m
Library, Museum and Art Gallery, Earl Rd ✆ (01352) 759331
18 Pantmywyn Clicain Rd, ✆ (01352) 740 318 ;
27 Clicain Rd Station Rd, Old Padeswood, ✆ (01244) 547 701 ;
18 Padeswood & Buckley Station Lane, The Caia, ✆ (01244) 550 537 ;
9 Caerwys, ✆ (01352) 721 222 .
St Mary's Church★

Tower without rest
Nercwys, South : 1 m. by B 5444, Nercwys rd on Treuddyn rd ✉ CH7 4EW – ✆ (01352) 700 220
3 rm – †£ 50 ††£ 80
◆ Last of the Welsh fortified border houses, owned by the same family for 500 years. Combined lounge/breakfast room. Spacious, simply furnished rooms overlook private parkland.

The Stables – at Soughton Hall H.

North : 2½ m. by A 5119 and Alltami Rd ✉ CH7 6AB – ✆ (01352) 840 577 – info@soughtonhall.co.uk – Fax (01352) 840 872

Rest – (booking essential) Carte £ 24/31

◆ 17C stable block in grounds of wedding venue hotel; bar and first-floor brasserie in bare brick and scrubbed pine. Tasty classics from open kitchen. Terrace for summer lunch.

Glas Fryn

Raikes Lane, Sychdyn, North : 1 m. by A 5119 on Civic Centre rd (Theatr Clwyd) ✉ CH7 6LR – ✆ (01352) 750 500 – glasfryn@brunningandprice.co.uk – Fax (01352) 751 923 – Closed 25-26 December

Rest – Carte £ 22/28

◆ Informal and open-plan; sepia prints, crammed bookshelves and rows of old bottles surround wooden tables. Varied brasserie menu draws a lively young set.

Look out for red symbols, indicating particularly pleasant establishments.

MONMOUTH (Trefynwy) – Monmouthshire – 503 L 28 – pop. 8 547 33 C4

London 135 m – Abergavenny 19 m – Cardiff 40 m

Town★

at Whitebrook South : 8 ¼ m. by A 466 – ✉ Monmouth

The Crown at Whitebrook with rm

✉ NP25 4TX – ✆ (01600) 860 254 – info@crownatwhitebrook.co.uk – Fax (01600) 860 607 – closed 26 December-8 January, Sunday evening, Monday and Tuesday

8 rm – †£ 75/90 ††£ 130 – **Rest** – (booking essential) Menu £ 28/43 **s**

Spec. Roast and confit quail with foie gras and beetroot and orange. Slow roast pigeon, lemon barley, glazed beets and camomile emulsion. Coconut parfait, mango espuma, chilled cucumber soup.

◆ Attentively run, with modern feel; lounge bar with deep leather sofas and immaculately laid dining room. Well-presented dishes are elaborate, original and flavoursome. Smart bedrooms in contemporary colours.

at Rockfield Northwest : 2 ½ m. on B 4233 – ✉ Monmouth

Stonemill

West : 1 m. on B 4233 ✉ NP25 5SW – ✆ (01600) 716 273 – Fax (01600) 715 257 – Closed 2 weeks January, Sunday dinner and Monday

Rest – Carte £ 25/30

◆ Converted 16C stone cider mill with exposed timbers; leather sofa in sitting area/bar. Attentive service. Well sourced modern seasonal dishes using small local suppliers.

MONTGOMERY (Trefaldwyn) – Powys – 503 K 26 32 C2

London 194 m – Birmingham 71 m – Chester 53 m – Shrewsbury 30 m

Town★

Little Brompton Farm without rest

Southeast : 2 m. on B 4385 ✉ SY15 6HY – ✆ (01686) 668 371 – gaynor.brompton@virgin.net – Fax (01686) 668 371 – closed 25-26 December, 1 January

3 rm – †£ 30 ††£ 52

◆ Part 17C cottage on working farm, run by friendly couple: husband's lived here all his life! Cosy beamed lounge and inglenook. Hearty breakfast. Traditionally appointed rooms.

MUMBLES (The) – Swansea – 503 I 29 – see Swansea

NANNERCH – Flintshire – 502 K 24 – ✉ Mold 32 C1

London 218 m – Chester 19 m – Liverpool 29 m – Shrewsbury 52 m

Old Mill without rest

Melin-y-Wern, Denbigh Rd, Northwest : ¾ m. on A 541 ✉ CH7 5RH – ☎ (01352) 741 542 – mail@old-mill.co.uk

6 rm – £ 46/51 ££ 62/72

♦ Renovated stone-built Victorian stables set in well-kept gardens on a busy road. The beamed bedrooms are comfortable, modern and pine-fitted.

NANT DERRY – Monmouthshire – see Abergavenny

NANTGAREDIG – Carmarthenshire – 503 H 28 – see Carmarthen

NEWPORT – Newport – 503 L 29 – pop. 116 143 33 C4

London 145 m – Bristol 31 m – Cardiff 12 m – Gloucester 48 m

Museum and Art Gallery, John Frost Sq ☎ (01633) 842962

Caerleon Broadway, ☎ (01633) 420 342 ;

Parc Coedkernew Church Lane, ☎ (01633) 680 933 .

Museum and Art Gallery★ AX **M** - Transporter Bridge★ **AC** AY - Civic Centre (murals★) AX

Caerleon Roman Fortress★★ **AC** (Fortress Baths★ - Legionary Museum★ - Amphitheatre★), NE : 2½ m. by B 4596 AX – Tredegar House★★ (Grounds★ - Stables★), SW : 2½ m. by A 48 AY. Penhow Castle★, E : 8 m. by A 48 AX

Plan on next page

Celtic Manor Resort rm,

Coldra Woods, East : 3 m. on A 48 ✉ NP18 1HQ – ☎ (01633) 413 000 – bookings@celtic-manor.com – Fax (01633) 412 910

298 rm – £ 165 ££ 198, £16.95 – 32 suites – ££ 410/1500

Rest *Owens* – (closed Sunday and Monday) (dinner only) Menu £ 48

Rest *The Olive Tree* – Carte approx. £ 28

♦ Classical, Celtic and country house motifs on a grand modern scale. Smart contemporary rooms boast hi-tech mod cons. State-of-the-art gym, golf academy and spa. Elaborate Welsh-derived fusion food at Owens. Buffets sometimes served in the Olive Tree bistro.

The Chandlery

77-78 Lower Dock St ✉ NP20 1EH – ☎ (01633) 256 622 – food@thechandleryrestaurant.com – Fax (01633) 256 633 – Closed 1 week Christmas, Saturday lunch, Sunday and Monday AY **a**

Rest – Menu £ 13 (lunch) – Carte £ 19/30 **s**

♦ Converted 18C chandler's store by the Usk. Spacious split-level restaurant. Polite service. Wide-ranging menu of freshly prepared dishes: confident, good-value modern cooking.

at Tredunnock Northeast : 8 ¾ m. by A 4042 AX, B 4596 and B 4236, off Usk rd, turning right at Cwrt Bleddyn Hotel – ✉ Newport 33 C4

The Newbridge with rm

East : ¼ m. ✉ NP15 1LY – ☎ (01633) 451 000 – eatandsleep@thenewbridge.co.uk – Fax (01633) 451 001 – Closed 26-31 December

6 rm – £ 95 ££ 120 – **Rest** – Carte £ 15/25

♦ Bright, comfy pub idyllically set by bridge overlooking Usk. Modern and classical techniques applied to locally based dishes. Superb contemporary bedrooms exude immense style.

WALES

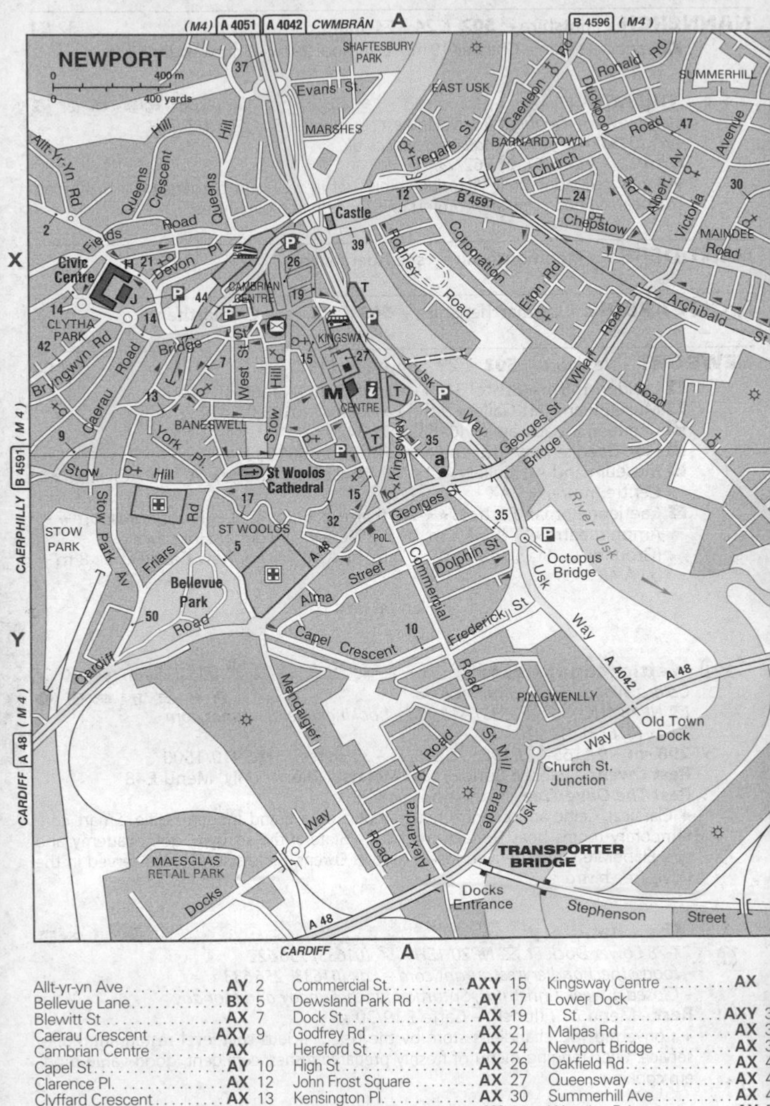

Allt-yr-yn Ave . . . . AY 2
Bellevue Lane . . . . BX 5
Blewitt St . . . . AX 7
Caerau Crescent . . . . AXY 9
Cambrian Centre . . . . AX
Capel St . . . . AY 10
Clarence Pl. . . . . AX 12
Clyffard Crescent . . . . AX 13
Clytha Park Rd . . . . AX 14
Commercial St . . . . AXY 15
Dewsland Park Rd . . . . AY 17
Dock St . . . . AX 19
Godfrey Rd . . . . AX 21
Hereford St . . . . AX 24
High St . . . . AX 26
John Frost Square . . . . AX 27
Kensington Pl. . . . . AX 30
Keynsham Ave . . . . AY 32
Kingsway Centre . . . . AX
Lower Dock St . . . . AXY 3
Malpas Rd . . . . AX 3
Newport Bridge . . . . AX 3
Oakfield Rd . . . . AX 4
Queensway . . . . AX 4
Summerhill Ave . . . . AX 4
Waterloo Rd . . . . AY 5

at Redwick Southeast : 9½ m. by M 4 - AY - off B 4245 – ✉ Magor

Brick House Country without rest

North Row ✉ NP26 3DX – ✆ (01633) 880 230 – brickhouse@compuserve.com – Fax (01633) 882 441

7 rm ☕ – 🚹£40/50 🚹🚹£60

◆ Ivy-covered Georgian house on edge of peaceful village boasts faultlessly neat bedrooms with traditional floral décor and a spacious front lounge and bar.

at St Brides Wentlooge Southwest : 4 ½ m. by A 48 - AY - on B 4239 – ✉ Newport

The Inn at The Elm Tree

✉ *NP10 8SQ – ☎ (01633) 680 225 – inn@the-elm-tree.co.uk – Fax (01633) 681 035*
10 rm – £ 80 £ 90/130 – **Rest** – Menu £ 10 (lunch) – Carte £ 22/38
◆ Converted 19C barn. Pristine, pine-furnished rooms in bright fabrics thoughtfully supplied with 21C mod cons; all individually styled. Lounge bar serves Champagne on ice. Immaculately set dining room; wide-ranging, Welsh-based dishes.

NEWPORT (Trefdraeth) – **Pembrokeshire** – **503** F 27 – **pop. 1 162** 33 **A3**
London 258 m – Fishguard 7 m
2 Bank Cottages, Long St ☎ (01239) 820912 (summer only)
Newport, ☎ (01239) 820 244 .
Pembrokeshire Coast National Park★★

Cnapan

East St, on A 487 ✉ SA42 0SY – ☎ (01239) 820 575 – cnapan@ukonline.co.uk – Fax (01239) 820 878 – Closed January-February and Christmas
5 rm – £ 42/50 £ 84 – **Rest** – (closed Tuesday and lunch Sunday) (light lunch) (booking essential) Menu £ 29
◆ Pine-fitted bedrooms with floral fabrics and individual character in a genuinely friendly guest house, family run for over 15 years. Homely lounge has a wood-burning stove. Clothed tables and family photographs set the tone in the traditional dining room.

Llysmeddyg with rm
East St ✉ SA42 0SY – ☎ (01239) 820 008 – louise@llysmeddyg.com – Closed 25-26 December
6 rm – £ 70/90 £ 90/130 – **Rest** – (Closed Sunday dinner and Monday) (light lunch May-October) (booking essential at lunch) Carte £ 26/34
◆ Earnestly laid-back style; lunch offered in Mediterranean herb kitchen garden. Dinner, with fine art surroundings, has modern Welsh/Italian edge. Superbly stylish bedrooms.

Red = Pleasant. Look for the red and symbols.

WALES

PEMBROKE (Penfro) – **Pembrokeshire** – **503** F 28 – **pop. 7 214** 33 **A4**
London 252 m – Carmarthen 32 m – Fishguard 26 m
Access Cleddau Bridge (toll)
to Republic of Ireland (Rosslare) (Irish Ferries) 2 daily (4 h) – to Republic of Ireland (Cork) (Swansea Cork Ferries) daily (8 h 30 mn)
Pembroke Visitor Centre, Commons Rd ☎ (01646) 622388 (summer only)
Pembroke Dock Military Rd, ☎ (01646) 621 453 .
Town★★ - Castle★★ **AC**
Pembrokeshire Coast National Park★★ - Carew Castle★ **AC**, NE : 4 m. by A 4075. Bosherston (St Govan's Chapel★), S : 7 m. by B 4319 and minor roads – Stack Rocks★, SW : 9 m. by B 4319 and minor roads

at Lamphey East : 1 ¾ m. on A 4139 – ✉ **Pembroke**

Lamphey Court
✉ *SA71 5NT – ☎ (01646) 672 273 – info@lampheycourt.co.uk – Fax (01646) 672 480*
38 rm – £ 88/95 £ 105/165 – **Rest** – Menu £ 27 (dinner) – Carte £ 28/35 **s**
◆ Large Georgian mansion surrounded by parkland, built by Charles Mathias in an idyllic location. Well furnished throughout with fine mahogany in the co-ordinated bedrooms. Formal restaurant with a good country house-style menu.

Lamphey Hall

✉ *SA71 5NR – ✆ (01646) 672394 – Fax (01646) 672369*
11 rm ☕ – 🚹£50/65 🚹🚹£85 – **Rest** – Carte £19/31
◆ Small country house with a neat garden and a rich style of décor throughout. Bedrooms are a mix of shapes and sizes and all are individually styled. The restaurant or bar offers spacious, comfortable surroundings in which to enjoy Welsh produce.

PENALLY = Penalun – **Pembrokeshire** – **503** F 29 – **see Tenby**

PENARTH – **Cardiff** – **503** K 29 – **see Cardiff**

PENMACHNO – **Conwy** – **502** I 24 – **see Betws-y-Coed**

PENNAL – **Gwnyedd** – **503** I 26 – **see Aberdovey**

The ✿ award is the crème de la crème.
This is awarded to restaurants
which are really worth travelling miles for!

WALES

PENTYRCH – **Cardiff** – **503** K 29 – **see Cardiff**

PONTDOLGOCH – **Powys** – **see Caersws**

PONTYPRIDD – **Rhondda Cynon Taff** – **503** K 29 – **pop. 29 781** 33 **C4**

London 164 m – Cardiff 9 m – Swansea 40 m
Pontypridd Museum, Bridge St ✆ (01443) 490748
Rhondda Heritage Park★ **AC**, NW : 4 m. by A 4058. Caerphilly Castle★★ **AC**, SE : 7 m. by A 470 and A 468 – Llancaiach Fawr Manor★ **AC**, NE : 6½ m. by A 4054, A 472, B 4255 and B 4254

Llechwen Hall

Llanfabon, Northeast : 4¼ m. by A 4223 off A 4054 ✉ CF37 4HP – ✆ (01443) 742050 – llechwen@aol.com – Fax (01443) 742189 – Closed 24-29 December
20 rm – 🚹£60 🚹🚹£105, ☕ £8.95 – **Rest** – Carte £23/32
◆ 17C house with Victorian frontage, overlooks the Aberdare and Merthyr Valleys. Smart country house style and comforts. Spotless bedrooms in either the main or coach house. Two dining options, both decorated in similar traditional style.

PORTH – **Rhondda Cynon Taff** – **503** J 29 – **pop. 6 225** – ✉ **Pontypridd** 33 **C4**

London 168 m – Cardiff 13 m – Swansea 45 m
Trehafod (Rhondda Heritage Park★), E : 1½ m. by A 4058

Heritage Park

rm, rest,

Coed Cae Rd, Trehafod, on A 4058 ✉ CF37 2NP – ✆ (01443) 687057 – reservations@heritageparkhotel.co.uk – Fax (01443) 687060 – Closed 24-26 December
44 rm ☕ – 🚹£86/96 🚹🚹£109
Rest ***The Loft*** – Menu £18 – Carte £15/20
◆ Brick-built hotel in Rhondda Valley, adjacent to Heritage Park Centre; Museum of Mining close by. Countryside location, yet not far from Cardiff. Co-ordinated, classic rooms. Loft dining with verandah or conservatory options.

PORTHCAWL – Bridgend – 503 I 29 – pop. 15 640 33 B4

London 183 m – Cardiff 28 m – Swansea 18 m

The Old Police Station, John St ✆ (01656) 786639, porthcawltic@bridgend.gov.uk

Glamorgan Heritage Coast★

Fairways

West Drive ✉ CF36 3LS – ✆ (01656) 782 085 – info@thefairwayshotel.co.uk – Fax (01656) 785 351

19 rm – †£ 77/88 ††£ 99/110 – **Rest** – Menu £ 10 (lunch) **s** – Carte dinner £ 17/22 **s**

◆ Traditionally attired 18C seafront hotel. Relaxed, easy-going public areas. Half the rooms have sea views: check out Room 1, which is particularly airy and boasts Jacuzzi. 'Safe' classics in cloth-clad dining room.

Foam Edge without rest

9 West Drive ✉ CF36 3LS – ✆ (01656) 782 866 – hywelandhelen@aol.com – Closed Christmas

3 rm – †£ 35/55 ††£ 65/80

◆ Enjoy original breakfast dishes and Bristol Channel views. Impressive front bedrooms: one's a four poster with sun lounge, other's nicely co-ordinated in neutral shades.

Coast

2-4 Dock St ✉ CF36 3BL – ✆ (01656) 782 025 – james@coastrestaurants.co.uk – closed 1-8 January, 26-31 December, Sunday dinner and Monday except July and December

Rest – Carte £ 19/37

◆ Locally renowned, this airy, up-to-date restaurant has a front lounge and rear dining room, where you can choose between the tried-and-tested or dishes with an original edge.

PORTHGAIN – Pembrokeshire – see St Davids

PORTHMADOG – Gwynedd – 503 H 25 32 B2

Cardiff 162 m – Blanau Ffestiniog 12 m – Caernarfon 19 m

Plas Tan-yr-Allt

< Tremadog Bay and countryside,

Tremadog, North : 1½ m. by A 487 on A 498 ✉ LL49 9RG – ✆ (01766) 514 545 – info@tanyrallt.co.uk – Closed Christmas, 3 weeks February and Monday-Tuesday in winter

6 rm – †£ 90/120 ††£ 175 – **Rest** – (dinner only) (booking essential) (communal dining) Menu £ 35 **s**

◆ Fully refurbished, this former home of Shelley, built into wooded cliffside, has an airy, stylish and comfy feel bordering on the luxurious. Charming, individualistic rooms. Dine en-famille style: a Welsh Country House menu prevails.

PORTMEIRION – Gwynedd – 502 H 25 32 B2

London 245 m – Caernarfon 23 m – Colwyn Bay 40 m – Dolgellau 24 m

Village★★★ AC

Snowdonia National Park★★★ - Lleyn Peninsula★★ – Ffestiniog Railway★★ AC

Portmeirion

< village and estuary, (heated)

✉ LL48 6ET – ✆ (01766) 770 000 – hotel@portmeirion-village.com – Fax (01766) 771 331

35 rm (dinner included) – †£ 137/186 ††£ 190/284 – 16 suites – **Rest** – (booking essential for non-residents) Menu £ 18/38 **s** – Carte dinner £ 27/50 **s**

◆ Set in private Italianate village in extensive gardens and woodland designed by Sir Clough Williams-Ellis. Delightful views of village and estuary. Antique furnished rooms. Restaurant offers lovely views of the estuary and an open and light style of décor.

Castell Deudraeth 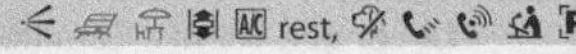 rest,

LL48 6EN – (01766) 772 400 – hotel@portmeirion-village.com – Fax (01766) 771 771 – Closed third week January

9 rm – £ 142 £ 277 – 2 suites

Rest ***Grill*** – Menu £ 17 – Carte £ 17/25

◆ Crenellated 19C manor, its modern decor in harmony with the original Welsh oak, slate and stone. Superbly stylish rooms in blues, greys and pale wood. Restored walled garden. Victorian solarium, converted into a modish minimalist restaurant.

PWLLHELI – Gwynedd – 502 G 25 – pop. 3 861 — 32 B2

London 261 m – Aberystwyth 73 m – Caernarfon 21 m

MinyDon, Station Sq (01758) 613000, pwllheli.tic@gwynedd.gov.uk

Golf Rd, (01758) 701 644.

Lleyn Peninsula★★

Plas Bodegroes (Chris Chown) with rm 

Northwest : 1 ¾ m. on A 497 LL53 5TH – (01758) 612 363 – gunna@bodegroes.co.uk – Fax (01758) 701 247 – March-16 November

11 rm – £ 50/90 £ 170 –

Rest – (closed Sunday-Monday, except Bank Holidays) (dinner only and Sunday lunch) (booking essential) Menu £ 40

Spec. Foie gras with fig jelly. Tronçon of turbot with lime hollandaise and star anise. Lemon verbena crème brûlée, summer berry compote.

◆ Delightful Grade II listed Georgian house in secluded gardens. Local art decorates the pale green dining room. Food is classically based and utilises top quality local ingredients. Contemporary, Scandinavian style bedrooms.

WALES

at Boduan Northwest : 3 ¾ m. on A 497 – Pwllheli — 32 B2

The Old Rectory without rest

LL53 6DT – (01758) 721 519 – thepollards@theoldrectory.net – Fax (01758) 721 519 – Closed 1 week Christmas, restricted opening in Winter and Spring

3 rm – £ 65/85 £ 90

◆ Part Georgian house with garden and paddock, adjacent to church. Well restored providing comfortable, individually decorated bedrooms and attractive sitting room.

RAGLAN – Monmouthshire – 503 L 28 – Abergavenny — 33 C4

London 154 m – Cardiff 32 m – Gloucester 34 m – Newport 18 m – Swansea 58 m

Castle★ AC

The Clytha Arms with rm

West : 3 m. on Clytha rd (old Abergavenny Rd) NP7 9BW – (01873) 840 206 – clythaarms@tiscali.co.uk – Fax (01873) 840 209 – Closed 2 weeks January, 25 December, Sunday dinner and Monday lunch

4 rm – £ 60 £ 100 – **Rest** – Menu £ 20 – Carte £ 25/33

◆ Personally run converted dower house. Welcoming, open fires; traditional games sprinkled around tapas-serving bar. Generous, eclectic menus utilise the best of Welsh produce. Individually styled bedrooms include one four poster.

REDWICK – Newport – 503 L 29 – see Newport (Newport)

The red symbol?
This denotes the very essence of peace
– only the sound of birdsong first thing in the morning …

RHAYADER – Powys – 503 J 27 – pop. 1 783 33 B3

London 195 m – Aberystwyth 39 m – Carmarthen 67 m – Shrewsbury 60 m

The Leisure Centre, North Street (01597) 810591

Beili Neuadd without rest

Northeast : 2 m. by A 44 off Abbey-cwm-hir rd LD6 5NS – (01597) 810 211 – rhayaderbreaks@yahoo.co.uk

3 rm – ††£60

◆ Part 16C stone-built farmhouse in a secluded rural setting with countryside views. Personally run with comfortable bedrooms. Close to Rhayader and the "Lakeland of Wales".

RHOS-ON-SEA = Llandrillo-yn-Rhos – Conwy – 502 I 24 – see Colwyn Bay

RHYL – Denbighshire – 502 J 24 – pop. 25 390 32 C1

Cardiff 182 m – Chester 34 m – Llandudno 18 m

Rhuddlan Castle★★, S : 3 m. by A 525 – Bodelwyddan★★, S : 5 m. by A 525 and minor rd – St Asaph Cathedral★, S : 5 m. by A 525. Llandudno★, W : 16 m. by A 548, A 55 and B 5115

Barratt's at Ty'n Rhyl with rm

167 Vale Rd, South : ½ m. on A 525 LL18 2PH – (01745) 344 138 – ebarratt5@aol.com – Fax (01745) 344 138 – Closed Monday and Tuesday

3 rm – †£60 ††£80

– **Rest** – (residents only Sunday dinner) (dinner only and Sunday lunch) (booking essential) Menu £18 (lunch) – Carte dinner approx. £30

◆ Rhyl's oldest house boasts comfortable lounges with rich oak panelling. Dine in either new conservatory or original house. Ambitious cooking on classic base. Individual rooms.

ROCKFIELD – Monmouthshire – 503 L 28 – see Monmouth

RUTHIN (Rhuthun) – Denbighshire – 502 K 24 – pop. 5 218 32 C1

London 210 m – Birkenhead 31 m – Chester 23 m – Liverpool 34 m – Shrewsbury 46 m

Ruthin Craft Centre, Park Rd (01824) 703992

Ruthin-Pwllglas, (01824) 702 296 .

Llandyrnog (St Dyfnog's Church★), Llanrhaeder-yng-Nghinmeirch (Jesse Window★★), N : 5½ m. by A 494 and B 5429. Denbigh★, NW : 7 m. on A 525

Firgrove

Llanfwrog, West : 1¼ m. by A 494 on B 5105 LL15 2LL – (01824) 702 677 – meadway@firgrovecountryhouse.co.uk – Fax (01824) 702 677 – March-November

3 rm – †£55 ††£80 – **Rest** – (by arrangement, communal dining) Menu £25

◆ Well-furnished house with tasteful interiors set within attractive gardens. Bedrooms are comfortable; one is a self-contained cottage with a small kitchen. Close to the town. Traditionally furnished dining room with meals taken at a communal table.

Eyarth Station (heated)

Llanfair Dyffryn Clwyd, South : 1 ¾ m. by A 525 LL15 2EE – (01824) 703 643 – stay@eyarthstation.com – Fax (01824) 707 464

6 rm – †£50 ††£70 – **Rest** – (by arrangement) Menu £16

◆ Former railway station with a fine collection of photographs of its previous life. Pleasant country location. Traditional décor in bedrooms, sitting room and a small bar. Views over the countryside and hearty home-cooked food in the dining room.

SALEM – Carmarthenshire – see Llandeilo

SARON – Gwynedd – see Caernarfon

SAUNDERSFOOT – Pembrokeshire – 503 F 28 33 **A4**

London 241 m – Cardiff 90 m – Pembroke 12 m

St Brides Spa H. ← Harbour and Carmarthen Bay, rm,

St Brides Hill SA69 9NH – (01834) 812 304
– reservations@stbridesspahotel.com – Fax (01834) 811 766
35 rm – £ 105/165 £ 150/270
Rest *Cliff* – Carte £ 23/33 **s**

◆ Occupying a great position over Carmarthen Bay, with breathtaking spa equipped to the highest spec. Fabulous terraces and outdoor infinity pool. Superbly designed bedrooms. Modern European cooking in fine dining restaurant with informal style.

Gower

Milford Terrace SA69 9EL – (01834) 813 452 – tim.rowe@rotels.com
– Fax (01834) 813 452
20 rm – £ 62 £ 94 – **Rest** – (dinner only and Sunday lunch) Menu £ 24
– Carte £ 23/32

◆ Four-storey yellow hued hotel, refurbished in 2004, close to the beach. Leather chesterfields enhance wood-floored bar. Immaculate bedrooms in a uniform style. Bright, spacious dining room with conservatory extension; good choice of fish.

SHIRENEWTON – Monmouthshire – 503 L 29 – see Chepstow

SKENFRITH – Monmouthshire 33 **C4**

London 135 m – Hereford 16 m – Ross-on-Wye 11 m

The Bell at Skenfrith with rm

NP7 8UH – (01600) 750 235 – enquiries@skenfrith.co.uk
– Fax (01600) 750 525
– Closed 2 weeks late January to early February
8 rm – £ 75 £ 180 – **Rest** – (booking essential) Carte £ 25/32

◆ Michelin's 2007 Pub of the Year is a charming 17C coaching inn with antiques, curios, open fires and tasty modern menus. Very comfy rooms have state-of-the-art appointments.

ST BRIDES WENTLOOGE – Newport – 503 K 29 – see Newport

ST CLEARS – Carmarthenshire – 503 G 28 33 **B3**

Coedllys Country House without rest

Llangynin, Northwest : 3½ m. by A 40
on Glyn-car Paradise Valley track in village SA33 4JY – (01994) 231 455
– coedlly@btinternet.com – Fax (01944) 231 441
– closed 23-28 December
3 rm – £ 53/68 £ 90/100

◆ Idyllic country house and animal sanctuary with picture-perfect façade. Delightful owner keeps everything immaculate. Superb breakfasts. Rooms with unerring eye for detail.

ST DAVIDS (Tyddewi) – Pembrokeshire – 503 E 28 – pop. 1 959 – Haverfordwest 33 **A3**

London 266 m – Carmarthen 46 m – Fishguard 16 m
National Park Visitor Centre, The Grove (01437) 720392, enquiries@stdavids.pembrokeshirecoast.org.uk
St Davids City Whitesands Bay, (01437) 721 751.
Town★ – Cathedral★★ - Bishop's Palace★ **AC**
Pembrokeshire Coast National Park★★

WALES

Warpool Court

Southwest : ½ m. by Porth Clais rd ✉ SA62 6BN – ✆ (01437) 720 300 – info@warpoolcourthotel.com – Fax (01437) 720 676 – closed January

25 rm – £ 110/180 £ 170/260 – **Rest** – Menu £ 29/35

◆ Over 3000 hand-painted tiles of Celtic or heraldic design decorate the interior of this 19C house. Modern bedrooms, some with views over neat lawned gardens to the sea. Daily changing classic menus accompanied by fine views.

Old Cross

Cross Sq ✉ SA62 6SP – ✆ (01437) 720 387 – enquiries@oldcrosshotel.co.uk – Fax (01437) 720 394 – closed January

16 rm – £ 40/85 £ 72/110 – **Rest** – (dinner only) Carte £ 20/27

◆ Overlooking the old market square, a long-established, ivy-clad hotel: rooms are modern and simply decorated. Beamed lounge - club chairs grouped around a brick fireplace. Wheelback chairs and yellow linen-clad tables in an unassuming, traditional restaurant.

Crug-Glas

Abereiddy, Northeast : 5½ m. on A 487 ✉ SA62 6XX – ✆ (01348) 831 302 – janet@crugglas.wanadoo.co.uk – Fax (01348) 831 302 – closed Christmas and New Year

5 rm – £ 60 £ 100/130 – **Rest** – (by arrangement) Menu £ 25

◆ Imposing family run Georgian house on a farm believed to have been worked since 12/13C. Partake of honesty bar then retire to one of the luxurious bedrooms: ask for no. 5. Good local choice on tried-and-tested evening menu.

WALES

Ramsey House

Lower Moor ✉ SA62 6RP – ✆ (01437) 720 321 – info@ramseyhouse.co.uk – March-October

5 rm – £ 40/70 £ 70/75 – **Rest** – (by arrangement) Menu £ 25

◆ Detached house just outside town centre. Spotlessly kept, homely interior with small bar overlooking gardens. Compact, neat and tidy rooms. Dinners cooked using fresh Pembrokeshire produce. Fine breakfasts employ tasty home baking.

The Waterings without rest

Anchor Drive, High St, East : ¼ m. on A 487 ✉ SA62 6QH – ✆ (01437) 720 876 – enquiries@waterings.co.uk – Fax (01437) 720 876

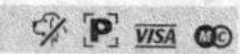

5 rm – £ 50/70 £ 75/80

◆ Set in peaceful landscaped gardens and named after a sheltered cove on Ramsey Island. Spacious rooms, furnished in solid pine, around a central courtyard. Likeable hosts.

Y-Gorlan without rest

77 Nun St ✉ SA62 6NU – ✆ (01437) 720 837 – mikebohlen@aol.com – closed 2 weeks February and Christmas

5 rm – £ 34/50 £ 65/72

◆ Run by a friendly couple, Y-Gorlan - "the fold" - offers comfortable, spotless modern rooms, all en suite. Homely lounge looks towards Whitesands Bay. Good breakfasts.

at Porthgain Northeast : 7 ¾ m. by A 487 – ✉ St Davids

The Shed

The Quay ✉ SA62 5BN – ✆ (01348) 831 518 – caroline@theshedporthgain.co.uk – Fax (01348) 831 803 – restricted opening in winter

Rest – Seafood (booking essential) Carte £ 29/43

◆ At the tip of the harbour in a charming spot, this locally renowned rustic eatery started life as a lobster pot store and now serves simply prepared, tasty seafood dishes.

SWANSEA – Swansea – **503** I 29 – pop. 169 880 33 **B4**

- London 191 m – Birmingham 136 m – Bristol 82 m – Cardiff 40 m – Liverpool 187 m – Stoke-on-Trent 175 m
- Plymouth St ✆ (01792) 468321, tourism@swansea.gov.uk
- Morriston 160 Clasemont Rd, ✆ (01792) 771 079 ; Clyne Mayals 120 Owls Lodge Lane, ✆ (01792) 401 989 ; Langland Bay, ✆ (01792) 366 023;
- Fairwood Park Upper Killay Blackhills Lane, ✆ (01792) 297 849 ;
- Inco Clydach, ✆ (01792) 841 257 ;
- Allt-y-Graban Pontllin Allt-y-Graban Rd, ✆ (01792) 885 757 ;
- Palleg Swansea Valley Lower Cwmtwrch, ✆ (01639) 842 193 .
- Town★ - Maritime Quarter★ B – Maritime and Industrial Museum★ B – Glynn Vivian Art Gallery★ B – Guildhall (British Empire Panels★ A **H**)
- Gower Peninsula★★ (Rhossili★★), W : by A 4067 A. The Wildfowl and Wetlands Trust★. Llanelli. NW : 6½ m. bv A 483 and A 484 A

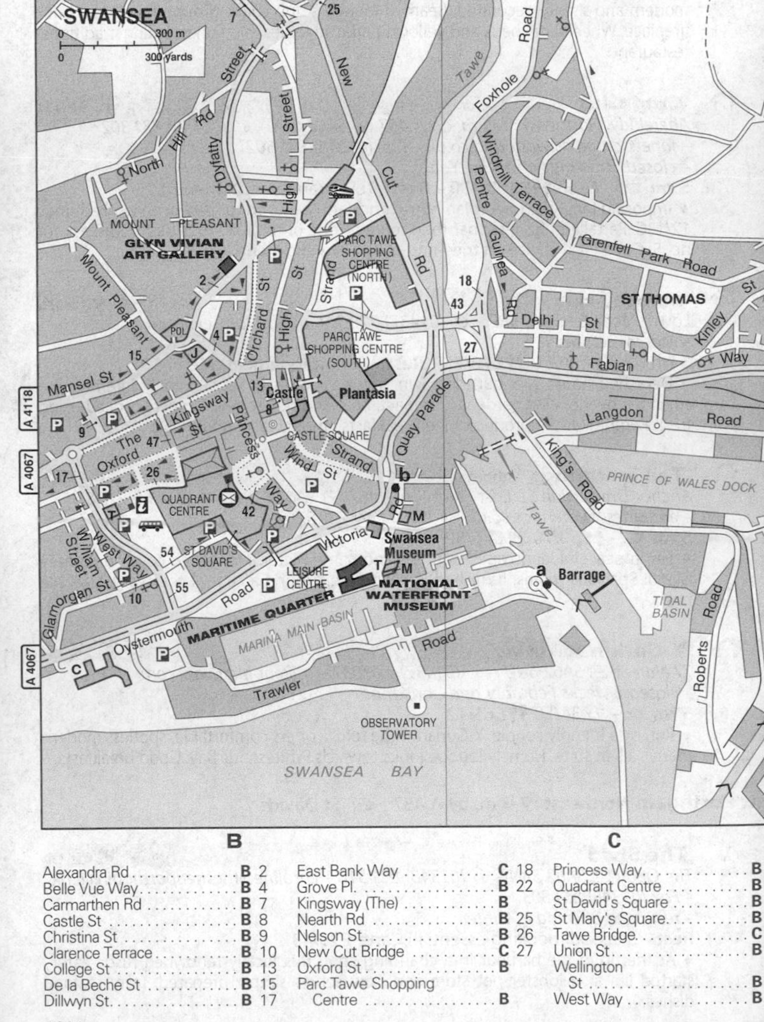

B **C**

Alexandra Rd . . . . **B** 2
Belle Vue Way . . . . **B** 4
Carmarthen Rd . . . . **B** 7
Castle St . . . . **B** 8
Christina St . . . . **B** 9
Clarence Terrace . . . . **B** 10
College St . . . . **B** 13
De la Beche St . . . . **B** 15
Dillwyn St. . . . . **B** 17
East Bank Way . . . . **C** 18
Grove Pl. . . . . **B** 22
Kingsway (The) . . . . **B**
Nearth Rd . . . . **B** 25
Nelson St. . . . . **B** 26
New Cut Bridge . . . . **C** 27
Oxford St . . . . **B**
Parc Tawe Shopping Centre . . . . **B**
Princess Way. . . . . **B**
Quadrant Centre . . . . **B**
St David's Square . . . . **B**
St Mary's Square. . . . . **B**
Tawe Bridge. . . . . **C**
Union St. . . . . **B**
Wellington St . . . . **B**
West Way . . . . **B**

SWANSEA

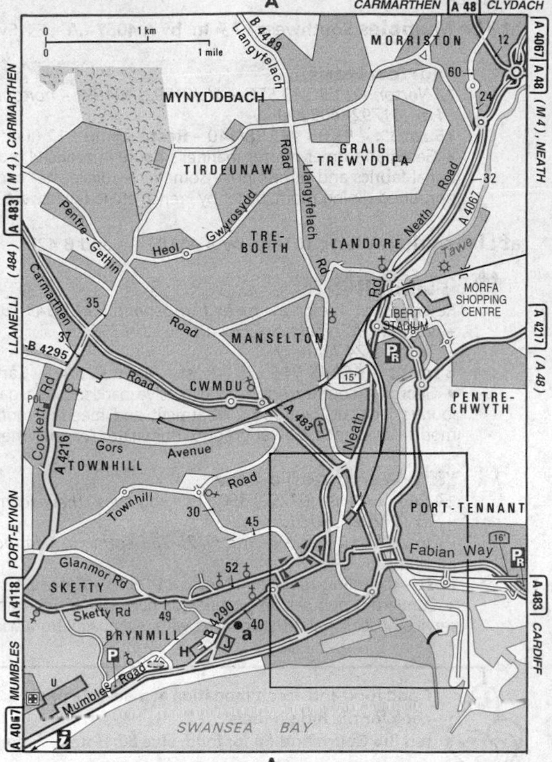

Morgans

rm,

Somerset Place ✉ SA1 1RR – ✆ (01792) 484 848
– reception@morganshotel.co.uk – Fax (01792) 484 849 B **b**

41 rm – £ 80/250 £ 80/250 – **Rest** – Menu £ 15 (lunch) – Carte £ 25/34 **s**

◆ Converted hotel near docks. Contemporary feel: neutral colours, leather sofas. Splendid original features include soaring cupola. Very stylish rooms. Modish cooking in sleek surroundings.

Didier & Stephanie's

56 St Helens Rd ✉ SA1 4BE – ✆ (01792) 655 603 – Fax (01792) 470 563
– closed Christmas and New Year, Sunday and Monday A **a**

Rest – French (booking essential) Menu £ 15 (lunch) – Carte £ 15/30

◆ Cosy, neighbourhood-styled restaurant with a strong Gallic influence. Welcoming owners provide tasty, good value, seasonally changing menus with lots of French ingredients.

The Restaurant

Pilot House Wharf, Trawler Rd, Swansea Marina ✉ SA1 1UN
– ✆ (01792) 466 200 – therestaurant@aol.com – Fax (01792) 281 528
– closed 24-26 December, Sunday and Monday C **a**

Rest – Seafood (booking essential) Menu £ 15 (lunch) – Carte £ 21/39

◆ Friendly, easygoing restaurant above a tackle shop and in sight of the harbour. Blackboard fish specials are the pick of a carefully sourced repertoire. Good value lunch.

at The Mumbles **Southwest : 7 ¾ m. by A 4067 - A - ✉ Swansea**

Norton House

17 Norton Rd ✉ SA3 5TQ – ✆ (01792) 404 891 – nortonhouse@btconnect.com – Fax (01792) 403 210

15 rm – 🛉£ 86 🛉🛉£ 98/140 – **Rest** – Menu £ 12 (lunch) – Carte £ 22/32

◆ Georgian former master mariner's house in peaceful grounds. Tidy rooms in traditional fabrics and furnishings - some have four-poster beds. Elegant, classically proportioned dining room, offset by French etched glassware.

at Llanrhidian **West : 10 ½ m. by A 4118 - A - and B 4271 – ✉ Reynoldston**

Fairyhill

Reynoldston, West : 2 ½ m. by Llangennith Rd ✉ SA3 1BS – ✆ (01792) 390 139 – postbox@fairyhill.net – Fax (01792) 391 358 – Closed 1-24 January

8 rm – 🛉£ 145 🛉🛉£ 275 – **Rest** – Menu £ 20/40 – Carte lunch £ 21/43

◆ Georgian country house in extensive parkland and gardens. Mix includes sleek lounge, eclectic bedrooms, treatment and meeting rooms, all set within general modish ambience. Gower produce dominates seasonal menus.

The Welcome To Town

✉ SA3 1EH – ✆ (01792) 390 015 – enquiries@thewelcometotown.co.uk – Fax (01792) 390 015 – Closed last 2 weeks February, 25-26 December, 1 January, Sunday evening and Monday.

Rest – (booking essential) Menu £ 14/33 **s** – Carte £ 16/41

◆ Converted pub set on picturesque peninsula. Cosy, traditional interior with good service of seasonal dishes cooked with real quality from wide choice menu.

Good food and accommodation at moderate prices?
Look for the Bib symbols:
red Bib Gourmand for food, blue Bib Hotel for hotels

TALSARNAU – **Gwynedd** – **502** H 25 – **pop. 647** – ✉ **Harlech** 32 **B2**

London 236 m – Caernafon 33 m – Chester 67 m – Dolgellau 25 m

Snowdonia National Park★★★

Maes-y-Neuadd

South : 1 ½ m. by A 496 off B 4573 ✉ LL47 6YA – ✆ (01766) 780 200 – maes@neuadd.com – Fax (01766) 780 211

14 rm – 🛉£ 74/120 🛉🛉£ 180/190 – 1 suite – **Rest** – Menu £ 17/35

◆ Part 14C country house with pleasant gardens in delightful rural seclusion. Furnished throughout with antiques and curios. Charming service. Individually styled bedrooms. Traditional dining room with linen-clad tables.

TAL-Y-LLYN – **Gwynedd** – **502** I 25 – ✉ **Tywyn** 32 **B1**

London 224 m – Dolgellau 9 m – Shrewsbury 60 m

Snowdonia National Park★★★ - Cadair Idris★★★

Tynycornel ≤ Tal-y-Llyn Lake and Cadair Idris,

on B 4405 ✉ LL36 9AJ – ✆ (01654) 782 282 – reception@tynycornel.co.uk – Fax (01654) 782 679

21 rm – 🛉£ 60/75 🛉🛉£ 120/150 – 1 suite –

Rest – (bar lunch Monday-Saturday) Menu £ 25 – Carte approx. £ 20

◆ Extended former inn with fine views of Tal-y-Llyn Lake, renowned for its fishing, and Cadair Idris. Comfortable rooms with good facilities, some in converted outbuildings. Purpose-built extension houses modern restaurant.

TENBY – Pembrokeshire – 503 F 28 – pop. 4 934 33 A4

London 247 m – Carmarthen 27 m – Fishguard 36 m
The Croft ☎ (01834) 842404
The Burrows, ☎ (01834) 842978 .
Town★★ – Harbour and seafront★★
Pembrokeshire Coast National Park★★ - Caldey Island★, S : by boat

Broadmead

Heywood Lane, Northwest : 3/4 m. ✉ SA70 8DA – ☎ (01834) 842641 – Fax (01834) 845757 – closed 23 December-28 February

20 rm – ♦£ 32/48 ♦♦£ 78/90 – **Rest** – (dinner only) Menu £ 21 **s**

◆ Privately owned country house hotel. Traditionally styled public rooms include conservatory overlooking gardens. Individually decorated rooms with modern amenities. Dining room in the traditional style common to the other parts of the house.

Fourcroft

(heated)

North Beach ✉ SA70 8AP – ☎ (01834) 842886 – staying@fourcroft-hotel.co.uk – Fax (01834) 842888

40 rm – ♦£ 55/130 ♦♦£ 110/140 – **Rest** – (bar lunch) Menu £ 25 – Carte £ 24/38 **s**

◆ Well-established, family owned hotel forming part of a Georgian terrace. Sea facing rooms benefit from large original windows. Attractions and water activities nearby. The dining room overlooks the sea and is decorated in traditional style.

at Penally (Penalun) Southwest : 2 m. by A 4139 – ✉ Tenby

Penally Abbey

✉ SA70 7PY – ☎ (01834) 843033 – penally.abbey@btinternet.com – Fax (01834) 844714

17 rm (dinner included) – ♦£ 135 ♦♦£ 170/185 – **Rest** – (booking essential at lunch) Menu £ 36 – Carte £ 26/36 **s**

◆ Gothic style, stone built house with good views of Carmarthen Bay and surrounded by woodland. Calm, country house décor and atmosphere. Lodge rooms are particularly pleasant. Candlelit dining room, decorated in the country style of the establishment.

Wychwood House

✉ SA70 7PE – ☎ (01834) 844387 – wychwoodbb@aol.com

3 rm – ♦£ 50 ♦♦£ 80 – **Rest** – (by arrangement) Menu £ 26 **s**

◆ Large 1940s house with a comfy, friendly ambience. Well-appointed guest drawing room. Individually styled bedrooms exude a winningly retro 'Noel Coward' feel. Serious dining: far eastern and modern European dominate owner's repertoire.

Do not confuse X with ✿!
X defines comfort, while stars are awarded for the best cuisine, across all categories of comfort.

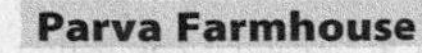

THORNHILL – Cardiff – 503 K 29 – see Cardiff

TINTERN (Tyndyrn) – Monmouthshire – 503 L 28 – ✉ Chepstow 33 C4

London 137 m – Bristol 23 m – Gloucester 40 m – Newport 22 m
Abbey★★ AC

Parva Farmhouse

on A 466 ✉ NP16 6SQ – ☎ (01291) 689411 – parvahoteltintern@fsmail.net – Fax (01291) 689941

8 rm – ♦£ 50/60 ♦♦£ 68/85 – **Rest** – (dinner only) Carte £ 19/24 **s**

◆ Mid 17C stone farmhouse adjacent to River Wye; refurbished to country standard. Traditional cooking, warm hospitality and a pleasant ambience. Comfortable rooms.

TREARDDUR BAY – **Anglesey** – **502** G 24 – ✉ **Holyhead** 32 **B1**

London 269 m – Bangor 25 m – Caernarfon 29 m – Holyhead 3 m

Anglesey★★. Barclodiad y Gawres Burial Chamber★, SE : 10 m. by B 4545, A 5 and A 4080

Trearddur Bay

✉ LL65 2UN – ✆ (01407) 860 301 – enquiries@trearddurbayhotel.co.uk – Fax (01407) 861 181

40 rm – †£ 99 ††£ 153/175 – **Rest** – (dinner only and Sunday lunch) Carte £ 17/28

♦ Situated next to "Blue Flag" beach. Well run with good facilities, including pool and spacious, comfortable rooms: go for balcony rooms with bay window seating. Modern dining room; drinks in cocktail lounge before dining.

TREDUNNOCK – **Newport** – **503** L 29 – **see Newport**

TREMEIRCHION – **Denbighshire** – **502** J 24 – ✉ **St Asaph** 32 **C1**

London 225 m – Chester 29 m – Shrewsbury 59 m

Bach-Y-Graig without rest

Southwest : 2 m. by B 5429 off Denbigh rd ✉ LL17 0UH – ✆ (01745) 730 627 – anwen@bachygraig.co.uk

3 rm – †£ 38/52 ††£ 68/78

♦ Attractive brick-built farmhouse dating from 16C, on working farm. In quiet spot with woodland trails nearby. Large open fires and wood furnished rooms with cast iron beds.

We try to be as accurate as possible when giving room rates. But prices are susceptible to change, so please check rates when booking.

TYN-Y-GROES – **Gwynedd** – **see Conwy (Aberconwy and Colwyn)**

USK – **Monmouthshire** – **503** L 28 – **pop. 2 318** 33 **C4**

London 144 m – Bristol 30 m – Cardiff 26 m – Gloucester 39 m – Newport 10 m

Alice Springs Bettws Newydd, ✆ (01873) 880 708 .

Raglan Castle★ **AC**, NE : 7 m. by A 472, A 449 and A 40

Glen-yr-Afon House rm, rest,

Pontypool Rd ✉ NP15 1SY – ✆ (01291) 672 302 – enquiries@glen-yr-afon.co.uk – Fax (01291) 672 597

27 rm – †£ 88 ††£ 130 – **Rest** – Menu £ 15 (lunch) – Carte £ 24/30

♦ Across bridge from town is this warmly run 19C villa with relaxing country house ambience. Several welcoming lounges and comfy, warm, well-kept bedrooms. Friendly welcome. Stylish restaurant.

at Llandenny **Northeast : 4 ¼ m. by A 472 off B 4235** – ✉ **Usk**

Raglan Arms

✉ NP15 1DL – ✆ (01291) 690 800 – raglanarms@aol.com – Fax (01291) 690 155 – Closed 25-27 December, Sunday dinner and Monday

Rest – Menu £ 21 – Carte £ 29/32

♦ Stone-faced pub in the middle of small village. Busy central bar: eating area includes big leather sofas in front of the fire, and good value dishes enhanced by sharp cooking.

WELSH HOOK – **Pembrokeshire** – **503** F 28 – **see Fishguard**

WHITEBROOK – Monmouthshire – see Monmouth

WOLF'S CASTLE (Cas-Blaidd) – Pembrokeshire – 503 F 28 – ✉ Haverfordwest 33 A3

London 258 m – Fishguard 7 m – Haverfordwest 8 m
Pembrokeshire Coast National Park★★

Wolfscastle Country H.

✉ *SA62 5LZ – ☎ (01437) 741 225 – enquiries@wolfscastle.com*
– Fax (01437) 741 383
– Closed 24-26 December

20 rm – †£ 65/85 ††£ 95/125 – **Rest** – (lunch by arrangement Monday-Saturday) Carte £ 17/34

◆ Spacious, family run country house; tidy rooms in traditional soft chintz, modern conference room and simply styled bar with a mix of cushioned settles and old wooden chairs. Dining room with neatly laid tables in pink linens.

WREXHAM (Wrecsam) – Wrexham – 502 L 24 – pop. 42 576 32 C1

London 192 m – Chester 12 m – Liverpool 35 m – Shrewsbury 28 m
Lambpit St ☎ (01978) 292015, tic@wrexham.gov.uk
Chirk, ☎ (01691) 774 407 ;
Clays Bryn Estyn Rd, ☎ (01978) 661 406 ;
Moss Valley Moss Rd, ☎ (01978) 720 518 ;
Pen-y-Cae Ruabon Rd, ☎ (01978) 810 108 ;
The Plassey Eyton, ☎ (01978) 780 020 .
St Giles Church★
Erddig★★ **AC** (Gardens★★), SW : 2 m – Gresford (All Saints Church★), N : 4 m. by A 5152 and B 5445

at Gresford Northeast : 3 m. by A 483 on B 5445

Pant-yr-Ochain

Old Wrexham Rd, South : 1 m. ✉ LL12 8TY – ☎ (01978) 853 525
– pant.yr.ochain@brunningandprice.co.uk – Fax (01978) 853 505
– Closed 25-26 December

Rest – (booking essential) Carte £ 18/27

◆ Bustling part 16C inn overlooking a lake with pleasant gardens and terrace. Open-plan dining rooms, bar and library. Blackboard menu and real ales.

O. Forir/MICHELIN

Ireland

O. Forir/MICHELIN

Towns
from A to Z

Villes
de A à Z

Città
de A a Z

Städte
von A bis Z

Northern Ireland

ANNAHILT – Down – 712 N/O 4 – see Hillsborough

ARMAGH – Armagh – 712 M 4 35 C3

Belfast 39 m – Dungannon 13 m – Portadown 11 m

St Patrick's Cathedral★ (Anglican) - St Patrick's Cathedral★ (Roman Catholic) - The Mall★ : Armagh County Museum★ **AC**, Royal Irish Fusiliers Museum★ **AC**

Navan Fort★ **AC** W : 2 m. by A 28. The Argory★ **AC** N : 10 m. by A 29 and minor road right

Armagh City H.

2 Friary Rd BT60 4FR – (028) 3751 8888 – info@armaghcityhotel.com – Fax (028) 3751 2777 – Closed 25 December

82 rm – £ 84 £ 97 – **Rest** – (dinner only and Sunday lunch) Carte £ 19/25

◆ Modern purpose-built hotel well geared-up to the business traveller. Stylish, wood furnished bedrooms, the city's two cathedrals visible from those to the front. Large, split-level restaurant serving traditional dishes.

BALLYCLARE – Antrim – 712 N/O 3 35 D2

Oregano

29 Ballyrobert Rd, South : 3¼ m. by A 57 on B 56 BT39 9RY – (028) 9084 0099 – info@oreganorestaurant.co.uk – Fax (028) 9084 0033 – Closed 7-14 July, 25-29 December, Monday and Saturday lunch

Rest – Menu £ 18 (lunch) – Carte £ 22/32

◆ Traditional facade contrasts with modish interior. Light, bright dining room is spacious and contemporary, in keeping with the flavoursome, modern European dishes on offer.

BALLYMENA (An Baile Meánach) – Antrim – 712 N 3 – pop. 58 610 35 C2

Ireland

Belfast 27 m – Dundalk 78 m – Larne 21 m – Londonderry 51 m – Omagh 53 m

76 Church St (028) 2563 8494, ballymenatic@hotmail.com

128 Raceview Rd, (028) 2586 1207 .

Antrim Glens★★★ - Murlough Bay★★★ (Fair Head ≤ ★★★), NE : 32 m. by A 26, A 44, A 2 and minor road - Glengariff Forest Park★★ **AC** (Waterfall★★), NW : 13 m. by A 43 – Glengariff★, NE : 18 m. by A 43 - Glendun★, NE : 19 m. by A 43, B 14 and A2 – Antrim (Round Tower★) S : 9½ m. by A 26

Rosspark

rm, rest,

20 Doagh Rd, Southeast : 6 m. by A 36 on B 59 BT42 3LZ – (028) 2589 1663 – info@rosspark.com – Fax (028) 2589 1477 – Closed 25 December

39 rm – £ 60/75 £ 80/130 – 1 suite – **Rest** – Menu £ 24 (dinner) – Carte £ 16/24

◆ Off the beaten track, yet fully equipped with all mod cons. Rooms are smart and contemporarily styled, some with sofas. Executive rooms have large working areas. Restaurant in the heart of the hotel decorated in terracotta colours.

Marlagh Lodge

71 Moorfields Rd, Southeast : 2¼ m. on A 36 BT42 3BU – (028) 2563 1505 – info@marlaghlodge.com – Fax (028) 2564 1590

3 rm – £ 45 £ 90 – **Rest** – (by arrangement) Menu £ 33

◆ Substantial 19C house with immediate, if busy, road connection. Many original features restored; stained glass in front door and hall. Tasteful, individually furnished rooms. Guests treated to seasonally changing five course dinner, upon arrangement.

NORTHERN IRELAND

at Galgorm West : 4 m. by A 42 on Fenaby rd – ✉

Galgorm rm, rest,
136 Fenaghy Rd ✉ BT42 1EA – ✆ (028) 2588 1001
– sales@galgorm.com – Fax (028) 2588 0080
75 rm – †£ 145/165 ††£ 145/165
Rest *Gillies* – Carte £ 20/32
◆ Former manor house with extensions; a delightful mix of the modern and the more traditional. Bedrooms are furnished in a contempoary style; the best are in the new buildings. The all day restaurant opens out onto gardens, an outdoor bar and games area.

BANGOR (Beannchar) – **Down** – **712** O/P 4 *Ireland* 35 **D2**

Belfast 15 m – Newtownards 5 m
34 Quay St ✆ (028) 9127 0069, bangor@nitic.net
North Down Heritage Centre★
Ulster Folk and Transport Museum★★ **AC**, W : 8 m. by A 2. Newtownards : Movilla Priory (Cross Slabs★) S : 4 m. by A 21 - Mount Stewart★★★ **AC**, SE : 90 m. by A 21 and A 20 – Scrabo Tower (≤ ★★) S : 6½ m. by A 21 – Ballycopeland Windmill★, SE : 10 m. by B 21 and A 2, turning right at Millisle – Strangford Lough★ (Castle Espie Centre★ **AC** - Nendrum Monastery★) - Grey Abbey★ **AC**, SE : 20 m. by A 2, A 21 and A 20

Clandeboye Lodge rm,
10 Estate Rd, Clandeboye, Southwest : 3 m. by A 2 and Dundonald rd following signs for Blackwood Golf Centre ✉ BT19 1UR – ✆ (028) 9185 2500
– info@clandeboyelodge.co.uk – Fax (028) 9185 2772
– Closed 25-26 December
43 rm – †£ 85/120 ††£ 105/130
Rest *Lodge* – (bar lunch Monday-Saturday) Carte £ 20/34
◆ On site of former estate school house, surrounded by 4 acres of woodland. Well placed for country and coast. Meetings and weddings in separate extension. Contemporary rooms. Restaurant boasts minimal, stylish décor. Modish menus.

Cairn Bay Lodge
278 Seacliffe Rd, East : 1¼ m. by Quay St ✉ BT20 5HS – ✆ (028) 9146 7636
– info@cairnbaylodge.com – Fax (028) 9145 7728
3 rm – †£ 60/65 ††£ 70/80 – **Rest** – (by arrangement) Menu £ 15
◆ Built in 1913; retains lots of period charm: Dutch fireplaces, stained glass, panelling. Beach views; individually styled rooms. Attractive garden. Health/beauty treatments.

Hebron House without rest
68 Princetown Rd ✉ BT20 3TD – ✆ (028) 9146 3126
– reception@hebron-house.com – Fax (028) 9146 3126
– Closed 23 December-2 January
3 rm – †£ 50/75 ††£ 70/75
◆ Redbrick double fronted 19C property in elevated location. Immaculate styling, yet in keeping with age of house. Ultra stylish rooms offer every conceivable facility.

Shelleven House
59-61 Princetown Rd ✉ BT20 3TA – ✆ (028) 9127 1777
– shellevenhouse@aol.com – Fax (028) 9127 1777
– Restricted opening in winter
11 rm – †£ 35/65 ††£ 70/80 – **Rest** – (by arrangement) Menu £ 35
◆ Personally run, end of terrace, double front Victorian house; short stroll to marina. Large, uniformly appointed rooms: ask for a large one at the front. Homely, good value.

Coyle's
44 High St ✉ BT20 5AZ – ✆ (028) 9127 0362 – Fax (028 9127 0362
– Closed 25 December
Rest – Carte £ 14/25
◆ Black exterior advertising real music and hard liquor! Also serves super dishes in an Art Deco upstairs restaurant: safe steaks meet ambitious, well executed surprises.

NORTHERN IRELAND

O. Forir/MICHELIN

BELFAST (Béal Feirste)

County: Antrim
Michelin REGIONAL map: n°712 O 4
Dublin 103 m – Londonderry 70 m

Population: 277 391
Ireland

35 **D2**

PRACTICAL INFORMATION

Tourist Information

47 Donegal Pl ✆ (028) 9024 6609, info@nitic.com

Belfast International Airport, Information desk ✆ (028) 9442 2888

Belfast City Airport, Sydenham Bypass ✆ (028) 9093 9093

Airports

Belfast International Airport, Aldergrove: ✆ (028) 9448 4848, W: 15 ½ m. by A 52 AY

George Best Belfast City Airport: ✆ (028) 9093 9093

Ferries and Shipping Lines

to Isle of Man (Douglas) (Isle of Man Steam Packet Co. Ltd) (summer only) (2 h 45 mn) – to Stranraer (Stena Line) 4-5 daily (1 h 30 mn/3 h 15 mn), (Seacat Scotland) March-January (90 mn) – to Liverpool (Norfolkline Irish Sea) daily (8 h 30 mn)

Golf Courses

18 Balmoral 518 Lisburn Rd, ✆ (029) 9038 1514 ;
18 Belvoir Park Newtonbreda Church Rd, ✆ (028) 9049 1693 ;
18 Fortwilliam Downview Ave, ✆ (028) 9037 0770 ;
18 The Nock Club Dundonald Summerfield, ✆ (028) 9048 2249 ;
18 Shandon Park 73 Shandon Park, ✆ (028) 9080 5030 ;
9 Cliftonville Westland Rd, ✆ (028) 9074 4158 ;
9 Ormeau 50 Park Road, ✆ (028) 9064 1069.

SIGHTS

IN TOWN

City★ - Ulster Museum★★ (Spanish Armada Treasure★★ , Shrine of St Patrick's Hand★) AZ **M1** – City Hall★ BY – Donegall Square★ BY **20** – Botanic Gardens (Palm House★) AZ – St Anne's Cathedral★ BX – Crown Liquor Saloon★ BY – Sinclair Seamen's Church★ BX – St Malachy's Church★ BY

ON THE OUTSKIRTS

Belfast Zoological Gardens★★ **AC**, N: 5 m. by A 6 AY

IN THE SUROUNDING AREA

Carrickfergus (Castle★★ **AC**, St Nicholas' Church★) NE: 9 ½ m. by A 2 – Talnotry Cottage Bird Garden, Crumlin★ **AC**, W: 13 ½ m. by A 52

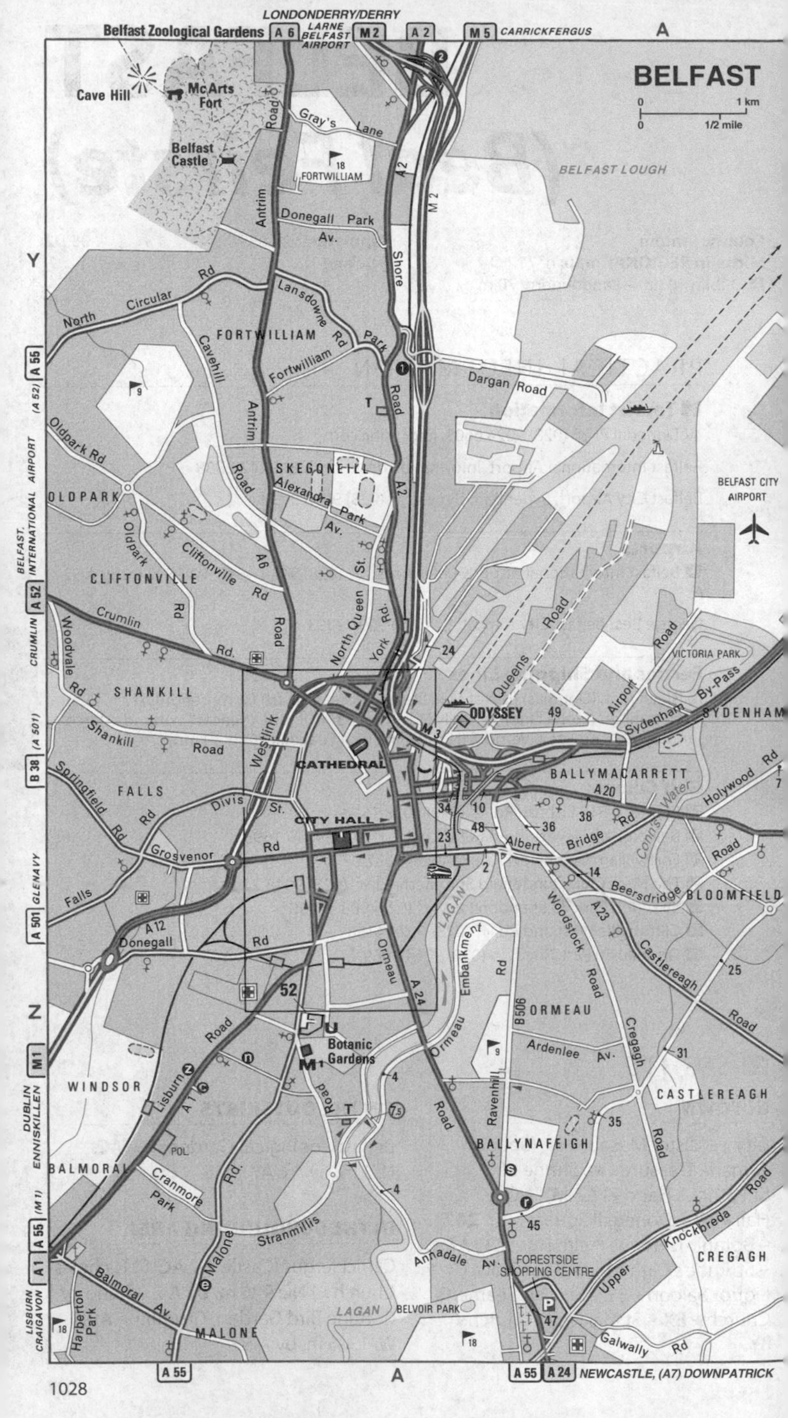
BELFAST
0 1 km
0 1/2 mile
LONDONDERRY/DERRY
Belfast Zoological Gardens
A 6
LARNE BELFAST AIRPORT
M 2
A 2
M 5
CARRICKFERGUS
Cave Hill
McArts Fort
Belfast Castle
FORTWILLIAM
BELFAST LOUGH
Gray's Lane
Antrim Road
Donegall Park Av.
Shore Road
North Circular Rd
Lansdowne Rd
Park
FORTWILLIAM
Fortwilliam
Cavehill Road
Dargan Road
Oldpark Rd
OLDPARK
SKEGONEILL
Alexandra Park Av.
BELFAST CITY AIRPORT
Oldpark Rd
Cliftonville Rd
CLIFTONVILLE
North Queen St.
York Rd.
Crumlin Rd.
Woodvale Rd
SHANKILL
Queens Road
Airport Road
VICTORIA PARK
By-Pass
SYDENHAM
Sydenham
ODYSSEY
M 3
Westlink
Shankill Road
CATHEDRAL
FALLS
Springfield Rd
Divis St.
CITY HALL
BALLYMACARRETT
A 20
Holywood Rd
Conn's Water
Grosvenor Rd
Albert Bridge Rd
Road
Falls
Beersbridge
BLOOMFIELD
A 12
Donegall Rd
Ormeau
LAGAN
Embankment
Woodstock Road
A 23
Castlereagh Road
A 24
Rd
B506
ORMEAU
52
Botanic Gardens
Ardenlee Av.
Cregagh
Road
Lisburn
A1
WINDSOR
Road
Ormeau Road
Ravenhill
CASTLEREAGH
POL
BALLYNAFEIGH
BALMORAL
Cranmore Park
Rd.
Road
Knockbreda Road
Stranmillis
Malone
Annadale Av.
FORESTSIDE SHOPPING CENTRE
Upper
CREGAGH
Balmoral Av.
Harberton Park
LAGAN
BELVOIR PARK
MALONE
Galwally Rd
A 55
A
A 55
A 24
NEWCASTLE, (A7) DOWNPATRICK
A 55
(A 52)
BELFAST INTERNATIONAL AIRPORT
A 52
CRUMLIN
(A 501)
B 38
GLENAVY
A 501
M1
DUBLIN ENNISKILLEN
(M1)
A 55
A1
LISBURN CRAIGAVON
Y
Z
A

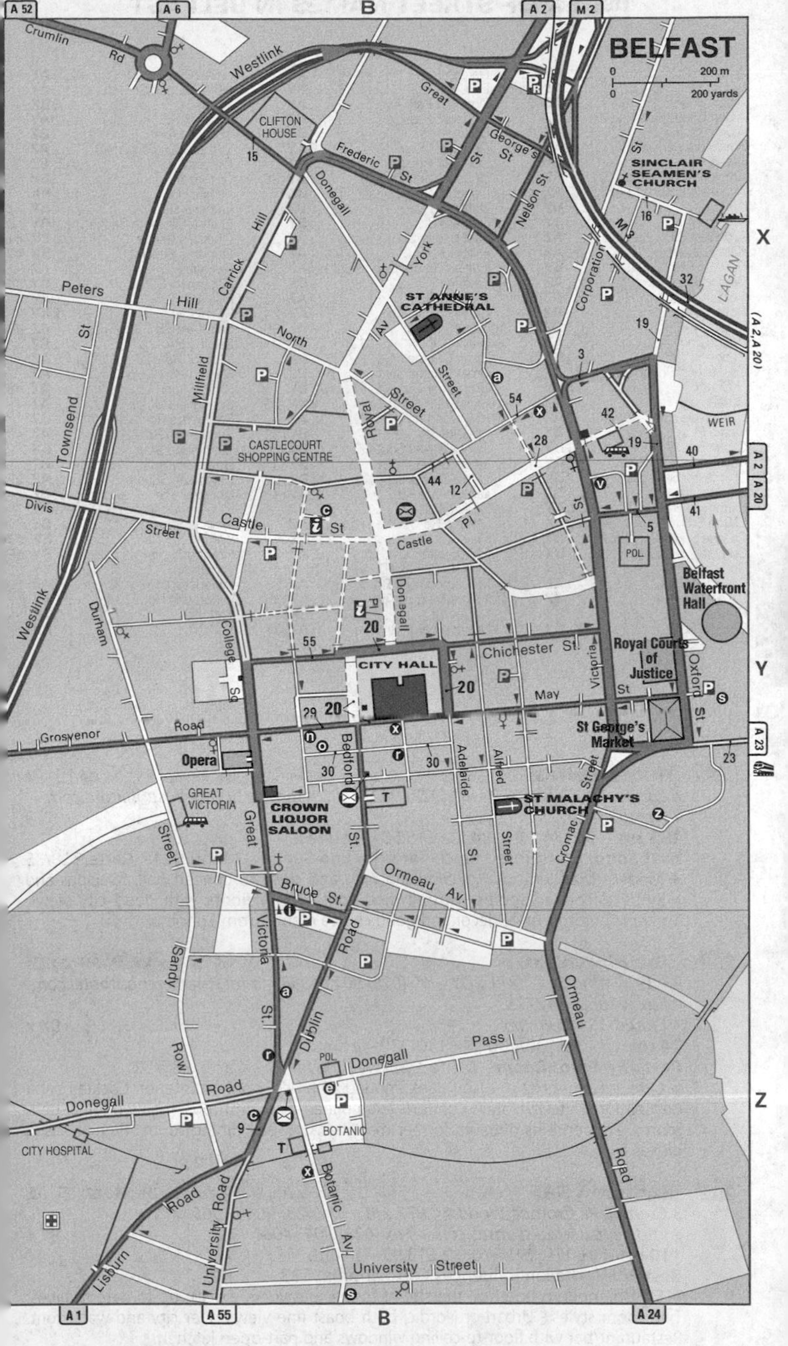
BELFAST
200 m
200 yards
A 52
A 6
B
A 2
M 2
X
Y
Z
A 1
A 55
A 24
A 23
(A 2,A 20)
Crumlin Rd
Westlink
Great George's St
Frederic St
CLIFTON HOUSE
SINCLAIR SEAMEN'S CHURCH
Nelson St
Corporation St
Donegall St
York St
Carrick Hill
Peters Hill
North Street
Royal Av
ST ANNE'S CATHEDRAL
LAGAN
WEIR
Millfield
Townsend St
CASTLECOURT SHOPPING CENTRE
Divis Street
Castle St
Castle Pl
Donegall Pl
POL.
Belfast Waterfront Hall
Westlink
Durham
College Sq
Chichester St.
Victoria St
Royal Courts of Justice
Oxford St
CITY HALL
May St
Grosvenor Road
St George's Market
Opera
Bedford St.
Adelaide St
Alfred Street
Cromac Street
ST MALACHY'S CHURCH
GREAT VICTORIA Street
Great Victoria St.
CROWN LIQUOR SALOON
Ormeau Av.
Bruce St.
Sandy Row
Dublin Road
Ormeau Road
Donegall Pass
Donegall Road
CITY HOSPITAL
BOTANIC
Botanic Av.
Lisburn Road
University Road
University Street

INDEX OF STREET NAMES IN BELFAST

Adelaïde St **BY**
Airport Rd **AY**
Albert Bridge **AZ** 2
Albert Bridge Rd **AZ**
Albert Square **BX** 3
Alexandre Park Ave **AY**
Alfred St **BY**
Annadale Ave **AZ**
Annadale Embankment **AZ** 4
Ann St **BY** 5
Antrim Rd **AY**
Ardenlee Rd **AZ**
Balmoral Ave **AZ**
Bedford St **BY**
Beersdridge Rd **AZ**
Belmont Rd **BZ** 7
Botanic Ave **BZ**
Bradbury Pl **BZ** 9
Bridge End **AZ** 10
Bridge St **BY** 12
Castlecourt Shopping Centre **BXY**
Castlereagh Rd **AZ**
Castlereagh St **AZ** 14
Castle Pl **BY**
Castle St **BY**
Cavehill Rd **AY**
Chichester St **BX**
City Hospital St **BZ**
Cliftonville Rd **AY**
Clifton St **BX** 15
College Square **BY**
Corporation Square **BX** 16
Corporation St **BX**
Cranmore Park **AZ**
Cregagh Rd **AZ**
Cromac St **BY**
Crumlin Rd **AY, BX**
Dargan Rd **AY**
Divis St **BY**
Donegall Park Ave **AY**
Donegall Pass **BZ**
Donegall Pl **BY**
Donegall Quay **BXY** 19
Donegall Rd **AZ, BZ**
Donegall Square **BY** 20
Donegall St **BX**
Dublin Rd **BZ**
Durham St **BY**
East Bridge St **AZ** 23
Falls Rd **AZ**
Forestside Shopping Centre **AZ**
Frederic St **BX**
Galwally Rd **AZ**
Garmoyle St **AY** 24
Grand Parade **AZ** 25
Gray's Lane **AY**
Great George's St **BX**
Great Victoria St **BY, BZ**
Grosvenor Rd **AZ, BY**
High St **BXY** 28
Holywood Rd **AZ**
Howard St **BY** 29
James Street South **BY** 30
Ladas Drive **BY** 31
Lagan Bridge **BX** 32
Lansdowne Rd **AY**
Lisburn Rd **AZ, BZ**
Malone Rd **AZ**
May St **BX**
Middlepath St **AZ** 34
Millfield Carrick Hill **BXY**
Mountpottinger Rd **AZ** 36
Mount Merrion Ave **AZ** 35
Nelson St **BX**
Newtownards Rd **AZ** 38
North Circular Rd **AY**
North Queen St **AY**
North St **BX**
Oldpark Rd **AY**
Ormeau Ave **BZ**
Ormeau Embankment **AZ**
Ormeau Rd **AZ, BZ**
Oxford St **BY**
Peters Hill **BX**
Queens Rd **AY**
Queen Elizabeth Bridge **BY** 40
Queen's Bridge **BY** 41
Queen's Square **BX** 42
Ravenhill **AZ**
Rosemary St **BY** 44
Rosetta Park **AZ** 45
Royal Ave **BXY**
Saintfield Rd **AZ** 47
Sandy Row **BZ**
Shankill Rd **AZ**
Shore Rd **AY**
Short Strand **AZ** 48
Springfiel Rd **AZ**
Stranmillis Rd **AZ**
Sydenham Rd **AZ** 49
Townsend St **BX**
University Rd **BZ**
University Square **AZ** 52
University St **BZ**
Upper Knockbreda Rd **AZ**
Victoria St **BY**
Waring St **BX** 54
Wellington Pl **BY** 55
Westlink **BY**
Woodstock Rd **AZ**
Woodvalle Rd **AY**
York Rd **AY**
York St **BX**

Hilton Belfast rm, VISA
4 Lanyon Pl ✉ BT1 3LP – ✆ (028) 9027 7000 – reservation.belfast@hiltom.com – Fax (028) 9027 7277 BY **s**
193 rm – †£ 174 ††£ 184, ☕ £15.50 – 4 suites
Rest *Sonoma* – (Closed lunch Saturday and Sunday) Menu £ 21 – Carte £ 28/35
♦ Modern branded hotel overlooking river and close to concert hall. Spacious and brightly decorated rooms with all mod cons. Upper floors with good city views. Striking California-style décor and good choice menus from Sonoma.

The Merchant rm, VISA
35-39 Waring St ✉ BT1 2DY – ✆ (028) 9023 4888 – info@themerchanthotel.com – Fax (028) 9024 7775 – Closed 25 December BX **x**
24 rm ☕ – †£ 130/230 ††£ 130/230 – 2 suites
Rest *The Great Room* – Menu £ 22 (weekdays)/27 – Carte £ 35/52
♦ Ornate former HQ of Ulster Bank imbued with rich, opulent interior. Cocktail bar a destination in itself. Hotel's comforts exemplified by sumptuous, highly original bedrooms. Tremendous detail in former main banking hall dining room.; French based dishes.

Radisson SAS rm, VISA
3 Cromac Pl, Cromac Wood ✉ BT7 2JB – ✆ (028) 9043 4065 – info.belfast@radissonsas.com – Fax (028) 9043 4066 BY **z**
119 rm – †£ 170 ††£ 170, ☕ £13.95 – 1 suite
Rest *Filini* – Italian influences Carte approx. £ 33
♦ Stylish, modern hotel on the site of former gasworks. Smart, up-to-date facilities. Two room styles - Urban or Nordic; both boast fine views over city and waterfront. Restaurant/bar with floor-to-ceiling windows and part-open kitchen.

Malmaison
rm, rest, VISA

34-38 Victoria St ✉ BT1 3GH – ✆ (028) 9022 0200 – belfast@malmaison.com – Fax (028) 9022 0220 BY **v**

62 rm – 🚹£ 135 🚹🚹£ 145, ☕ £ 12.95 – 2 suites

Rest *Brasserie* – (Closed lunch 11-14 July and Christmas-New Year) Carte £ 19/32

◆ An unstuffy, centrally located hotel hides behind its intricate Victorian façade. Originally two warehouses, many original features remain. Modern, comfortable rooms. Stylish, comfortable, modern dining in Brasserie.

Ten Square
rm, VISA

10 Donegall Square South ✉ BT1 5JD – ✆ (028) 9024 1001 – reservations@tensquare.co.uk – Fax (028) 9024 3210 – closed 25 December BY **x**

23 rm ☕ – 🚹£ 170 🚹🚹£ 170

Rest *Grill Room* – Carte £ 19/29 **s**

◆ Victorian mill building in heart of city renovated to a thoroughly contemporary standard. Notably spacious deluxe bedrooms. Access to private bar for guests. Smart, stylish Grill Room.

Malone Lodge
rm, rest, P VISA

60 Eglantine Ave ✉ BT9 6DY – ✆ (028) 9038 8000 – info@malonelodgehotel.com – Fax (028) 9038 8088 AZ **n**

51 rm ☕ – 🚹£ 75/160 🚹🚹£ 95/160

Rest *The Green Door* – (Closed Sunday dinner) Menu £ 15/23 **s** – Carte dinner £ 17/26 **s**

◆ Imposing hotel in 19C terrace in quiet residential area. Elegant lobby lounge and smart bar. Conference facilities. Basement gym. Stylish, modern rooms with good comforts. Restaurant provides a comfortable, contemporary environment.

The Crescent Townhouse
rm, rest, VISA

13 Lower Crescent ✉ BT7 1NR – ✆ (028) 9032 3349 – info@crescenttownhouse.com – Fax (028) 9032 0646 – Closed 11-13 July, 24-26 December and 1 January BZ **x**

17 rm ☕ – 🚹£ 90 🚹🚹£ 110/150

Rest *Metro Brasserie* – (Closed lunch Sunday to Tuesday) Menu £ 19 – Carte £ 19/28

◆ Intimate Regency house that blends original features with modern amenities. Relaxed, discreet atmosphere. Spacious and luxurious rooms with interior designed period feel. Modern classic brasserie with a lively and relaxed ambience.

Benedicts
rm, rest, VISA

7-21 Bradbury Pl, Shaftsbury Sq ✉ BT7 1RQ – ✆ (028) 9059 1999 – info@benedictshotel.co.uk – Fax (028) 9059 1990 – Closed 24-25 December and 11-12 July BZ **c**

32 rm ☕ – 🚹£ 65 🚹🚹£ 75/85

Rest *Benedicts Restaurant* – Menu £ 20 (dinner) – Carte £ 24/30

◆ A lively, strikingly designed bar with nightly entertainment can be found at the heart of this busy commercial hotel. Well-appointed bedrooms above offer modern facilities. Relaxed, popular restaurant.

Ravenhill House without rest
P VISA

690 Ravenhill Rd ✉ BT6 0BZ – ✆ (028) 9020 7444 – info@ravenhillhouse.com – Fax (028) 9028 2590 – Closed 1 week Christmas, 1-4 January and 1 week spring AZ **s**

5 rm ☕ – 🚹£ 45/55 🚹🚹£ 70

◆ Personally run detached 19C house, attractively furnished in keeping with its age. The largely organic breakfast is a highlight. Good sized rooms with bold shades predominant.

NORTHERN IRELAND

Ash Rowan Town House without rest
12 Windsor Ave ✉ BT9 6EE – ☎ (028) 9066 1758 – Fax (028) 9066 3227
– closed 22 December-7 January AZ **c**
5 rm ☕ – †£ 59/66 ††£ 96
◆ Late 19C house in quiet tree-lined avenue. Personally run; interestingly "cluttered" interior. Comfy conservatory sitting room. Well-judged bedrooms with thoughtful touches.

The Old Rectory without rest
148 Malone Rd ✉ BT9 5LH – ☎ (028) 9066 7882 – info@anoldrectory.co.uk
– Fax (028) 9068 3759
– Closed Christmas-New Year AZ **e**
5 rm ☕ – †£ 39/49 ††£ 74
◆ Former 19C rectory in residential area; period charm retained. Attractive drawing room. Traditionally furnished rooms. Super breakfasts: speciality sausages, organic produce.

Roseleigh House without rest
19 Rosetta Park, South : 1½ m. by A 24 (Ormeau Rd) ✉ BT6 0DL
– ☎ (028) 9064 4414 – info@roseleighhouse.co.uk
– Closed Christmas and New Year AZ **r**
9 rm ☕ – †£ 42/50 ††£ 62
◆ Imposing Victorian house close to the Belvoir Park golf course and in a fairly quiet residential suburb. Brightly decorated and well-kept bedrooms with modern amenities.

Deanes
34-40 Howard St ✉ BT1 6PF – ☎ (028) 9033 1134 – info@michaeldeane.co.uk
– Fax (028) 9056 0001
– Closed 25-26 December, 12-13 July and Sunday BY **n**
Rest – Menu £ 21 (lunch) – Carte £ 28/44
Spec. Pork belly, roast langoustine, cabbage, black pudding and apple caramel. Dover sole, cured cucumber, shrimps, capers, lemon and parsley butter. Coffee millefeuille, cappuccino ice cream.
◆ Refurbished ground floor restaurant with bar and lounge. Polished service by approachable team. Menu of refined, classically based modern Irish dishes; lunch is a simpler affair.

Roscoff Brasserie
7-11 Linenhall St ✉ BT2 8AA – ☎ (028) 9031 1150 – Fax (028) 9031 1151
– Closed lunch Saturday and Sunday BY **r**
Rest – Menu £ 20 (weekdays) – Carte dinner £ 31/41
◆ Not your typical brasserie - more formal and a little quieter than most, but stylish and modern. Confidently prepared modish cooking with classic base. Good value lunches.

James Street South
21 James Street South ✉ BT2 7GA – ☎ (028) 9043 4310
– info@jamesstreetsouth.co.uk – Fax (028) 9043 4310
– Closed 1 January, 12 July, 25-26 December and Sunday lunch BY **o**
Rest – Menu £ 16 **s** – Carte £ 28/43 **s**
◆ Tucked away down back alley in heart of the city. 19C façade hides distinctly modish interior. Good value menus; modern cooking based upon well-sourced, fine quality produce.

Cayenne
7 Ascot House, Shaftesbury Sq ✉ BT2 7DB – ☎ (028) 9033 1532
– reservations@cayennerestaurant.com – Fax (028) 9026 1575
– Closed 25-26 December, 1 January, 12-13 July and lunch Saturday and Sunday BZ **r**
Rest – (booking essential) Menu £ 16 (lunch) – Carte £ 29/38
◆ Striking modern artwork and a lively atmosphere feature in this busy, relaxed and stylish restaurant. Carefully prepared selection of creative Asian influenced dishes.

XX **Shu**

253 Lisburn Rd ✉ BT9 7EN – ☎ (028) 9038 1655 – eat@shu-restaurant.com – Fax (028) 9068 1632 – Closed 1 January, 12-13 July, 24-26 December and Sunday AZ **z**

Rest – Menu £ 13/25 – Carte £ 21/34

◆ Trendy, modern restaurant on the Lisburn Road. Converted from terraced houses, it is spacious and uncluttered with neutral and black décor. Eclectic, contemporary dishes.

XX **Aldens**

229 Upper Newtownards Rd, East : 2 m. on A 20 ✉ BT4 3JF – ☎ (028) 9065 0079 – info@aldensrestaurant.com – Fax (028) 9065 0032 – Closed Sunday and Bank Holidays

Rest – (booking essential) Menu £ 13 (lunch) – Carte £ 24/35

◆ Well established, spacious and contemporary restaurant in "up-and-coming" area. Extensive menus of classic and modern dishes. Moderately priced midweek menu, friendly service.

XX **The Wok**

126 Great Victoria St ✉ BT2 7BG – ☎ (028) 9023 3828 – Closed 25-26 December and lunch Saturday-Sunday BZ **a**

Rest – Chinese Menu £ 19/23 – Carte £ 13/26

◆ Smart, modern Chinese restaurant with pleasant ambience. Menus feature classic interpretations and less well-known authentic dishes: most regions of China are represented.

X **Nick's Warehouse**

35-39 Hill St ✉ BT1 2LB – ☎ (028) 9043 9690 – info@nickswarehouse.co.uk – Fax (028) 9023 0514 – Closed 25-26 December, Easter, 12 July, Saturday lunch, Monday dinner and Sunday BX **a**

Rest – Carte £ 17/37

◆ Built in 1832 as a bonded whiskey store. On two floors, the ground floor Anix is relaxed and buzzy. Upstairs more formal. Well informed service of an eclectic menu.

X **The Ginger Tree**

23 Donegall Pass ✉ BT7 1DQ – ☎ (028) 9032 7151 – Closed 25 December, 11-12 July and Sunday lunch BZ **e**

Rest – Japanese Menu £ 9/19 – Carte £ 15/28

◆ Cosy Japanese eatery boasting distinctive black tables and chairs with red cushions. One wall highlighted by striking Japanese dress. Endearing service of authentic dishes.

X **Ginger**

7-8 Hope St ✉ BT12 5EE – ☎ (028) 9024 4421 – Closed 2 weeks January, 2 weeks July, Sunday and Monday BYZ **i**

Rest – Carte £ 21/32

◆ Simple, intimate neighbourhood diner with chocolate ceiling and aluminium duct pipes; modern art for sale. Local produce to fore on eclectic menus with distinct global twists.

X **Molly's Yard**

1 College Green Mews, Botanic Ave ✉ BT7 1LW – ☎ (028) 9032 2600 – Closed 1 January, 25-26 December and Sunday BZ **s**

Rest – (booking essential) Menu 26 – Carte £ 19/28

◆ Converted stables and coach house with popular summer courtyard. Downstairs a cosy bistro; upstairs a casual restaurant. Both serve fresh, earthy and robust seasonal dishes.

X **Mourne Seafood Bar**

34 Bank St ✉ BT1 1HJ – ☎ (028) 9024 8544 – Closed 24-26 December, 10-13 July and dinner Sunday and Monday

Rest – Seafood (booking essential at dinner) Carte £ 22/26

◆ Classic seafood menu supplemented by daily specials; mussels are a speciality, served in black enamel pots. Gets very busy, so arrive early, or be prepared to wait.

at Belfast International Airport West : 15 ½ m. by A 52 - AY - ✉ Belfast

Park Plaza Belfast

✉ BT29 4ZY - ✆ (028) 9445 7000 - reception@parkplazabelfast.com
- Fax (028) 9442 3500

106 rm - †£ 145 ††£ 145/200, ☕ £12 - 2 suites

Rest ***Circles*** - (dinner only) (booking essential) Carte approx. £ 26 **s**

♦ Imposingly up-to-date hotel with sun-filled lobby, 50 metres from terminal entrance. Terrace, secluded garden, cocktail bar; conference facilities. Distinctively modern rooms. Formal restaurant with smart, cosmopolitan ambience.

BELFAST INTERNATIONAL AIRPORT = Aerphort Béal Feirste - Antrim - 712 N 4 - see Belfast 35 C2

BELLEEK (Béal Leice) - Fermanagh - 712 H 4 *Ireland* 34 A2

Belfast 117 m - Londonderry 56 m

Belleek Pottery **AC**

Carlton

Main St ✉ BT93 3FX - ✆ (028) 6865 8282 - reception@hotelcarlton.co.uk
- Fax (028) 6865 9005

34 rm ☕ - †£ 53/60 ††£ 75/90 - **Rest** - (carvery lunch Monday-Saturday) Carte £ 15/30

♦ Located in the heart of Ireland's Lake District, bordering the river Erne and ideal for fishing enthusiasts. Bedrooms are in soft pastel colours and most have river views. Classic styled daily menu in contemporary restaurant.

BUSHMILLS (Muileann na Buaise) - Antrim - 712 M 2 - ✉ Bushmills 35 C1

Ireland

Belfast 57 m - Ballycastle 12 m - Coleraine 10 m

Bushfoot Portballintrae 50 Bushfoot Rd, ✆ (028) 2073 1317 .

Giant's Causeway★★★ (Hamilton's Seat ≤ ★★) N : 2 m. by A 2 and minor road - Dunluce Castle★★ **AC** W : 3 m. by A 2 - Carrick-a-rede Rope Bridge★★★ **AC**, E : 8 m. by A 2 - Magilligan Strand★★, W : 18 m. by A 2, A 29 and A 2 - Gortmore Viewpoint★★, SW : 23 m. by A 2, A 29, A 23 and minor road from Downhill - Downhill★ (Mussenden Temple★), W : 15 m. by A 2, A 29 and A 2

Bushmills Inn

9 Dunluce Rd ✉ BT57 8QG - ✆ (028) 2073 3000 - mail@bushmillsinn.com
- Fax (028) 2073 2048
- Closed 24-25 December

32 rm ☕ - †£ 68/158 ††£ 138/168

Rest ***The Restaurant*** - (carvery lunch Sunday) Carte £ 24/34

♦ Very characterful part 18C inn near famous whiskey distillery. Period features include turf fires, oil lamps, grand staircase and circular library. Rooms in house and mill. Try Irish coffee with Bushmills in restaurant overlooking courtyard.

Craig Park without rest

24 Carnbore Rd, Southeast : 2½ m. by B 66 and Ballycastle rd (B 17), off Billy rd
✉ BT57 8YF - ✆ (028) 2073 2496 - jan@craigpark.co.uk

3 rm ☕ - †£ 40 ††£ 65

♦ Pleasant country house with views of Donegal mountains, Antrim Hills, dramatic coastal scenery. Communal breakfast room to start the day; bright, airy bedrooms await at night.

The Distillers Arms

140 Main St ✉ BT57 8QE - ✆ (028) 2073 1044 - simon@distillersarms.com
- Fax (028) 2073 2843

Rest - (Closed lunch Monday-Friday and Monday dinner in winter) Carte £ 17/25

♦ Modern rusticity in village centre. Sit in squashy sofas in peat fired sitting area. Eat tasty dishes from frequently changing menus with a seasonal Irish base.

CARRICKFERGUS (Carraig Fhearghais) – Antrim – 712 O 3 Ireland 35 D2

Belfast 11 m – Ballymena 25 m
Heritage Plaza, Antrim Street (028) 9335 8049 (April-September), touristinfo@carrickfergus.org
35 North Rd, (028) 9336 3713 .
Castle★ AC - St Nicholas' Church★ AC

Clarion

75 Belfast Rd, on A 2 BT38 8PH – (028) 9336 4556 – reservations1@clarioncarrick.com – Fax (028) 9335 1620 – Closed 24-25 December

68 rm – £ 68/95 £ 75/125

Rest *Red Pepper* – (dinner only) Carte £ 15/26

◆ A large, purpose-built hotel with trim, neatly furnished bedrooms; some suites have jacuzzis and views of Belfast Lough; the Scottish coastline can be seen on a clear day. Expect modern French 'prestige' and à la carte menu.

CASTLEDAWSON – Londonderry – 712 M 3 35 C2

Belfast 34 m – Antrim 17 m – Ballymena 23 m

The Inn at Castledawson with rm

47 Main St BT45 8AA – (028) 7946 9777 – info@theinnatcastledawson.co.uk – Fax (028) 7946 9888

12 rm – £ 59 £ 79 – **Rest** – Carte £ 15/30

◆ Stylishly updated restaurant, with pine rafters, in 200 year-old inn. Accomplished cooking blends classic and modern styles with finesse. Sleek rooms; fine views from rear.

CASTLEWELLAN – Down – 712 O 5 – pop. 2 496 Ireland 35 D3

Belfast 32 m – Downpatrick 12 m – Newcastle 4 m
Castlewellan Forest Park★★ AC
Mourne Mountains★★ (Silent Valley Reservoir★), SW : 15 m. by A 50, B 180 and B 27 – Dundrum Castle★ AC E : 6 m. by A 50 and A 180

Slieve Croob Inn

119 Clanvaraghan Rd, North : 5½ m. by A 25 off B 175 BT31 9LA – (028) 4377 1412 – info@slievecroobinn.com – Fax (028) 4377 1162 – Restricted opening in winter

7 rm – £ 40 £ 75 – **Rest** – (bar lunch Monday-Saturday) Carte £ 16/23 **s**

◆ Pleasant inn in stunningly attractive mountainous area with panoramic sea views. Modern, rustic style. Bedooms with simple comforts. Peace and quiet aplenty. Roof timbers and fine views in open, buzzy dining room: same menu also in bar.

COLERAINE (Cúil Raithin) – Londonderry – 712 L 2 – pop. 56 315 35 C1

Ireland

Belfast 53 m – Ballymena 25 m – Londonderry 31 m – Omagh 65 m
Railway Rd (028) 7034 4723, colerainetic@btconnect.com
Castlerock Circular Rd, (028) 7084 8314 ;
Brown Trout 209 Agivey Rd, (028) 7086 8209 .
Giant's Causeway★★★ (Hamilton's Seat ★★), NE : 14 m. by A 29 and A2 - Dunluce Castle★★ AC, NE : 8 m. by A 29 and A 2 – Carrick-a-rede-Rope Bridge★★★ AC, NE : 18 m. by A 29 and A2 – Benvarden★ AC E : 5 m. by B 67 – Magilligan Strand★★, NW : 8 m. by A 2 - Gortmore Viewpoint★★, NW : 12 m. by A 2 and minor road from Downhill - Downhill★ AC (Mussenden Temple★), NE : 7 m. by A 2

Bushtown House

283 Drumcroone Rd, South : 2½ m. on A 29 BT51 3QT – (028) 7035 8367 – reception@bushtownhotel.com – Fax (028) 7032 0909 – Closed 25 December

39 rm – £ 70/75 £ 100/105 – **Rest** – (Carvery lunch) Carte £ 16/22 **s**

◆ Set in mature gardens on outskirts of university town. Indoors, comfortable and homely with various rooms to relax in. Traditional, co-ordinated bedrooms in muted colours. Intimately lit, cosy restaurant with wide variety of simple menus.

Brown Trout Golf and Country Inn
209 Agivey Rd, Aghadowey, Southeast : 9 m. on A 54
✉ BT51 4AD – ✆ (028) 7086 8209 – bill@browntroutinn.com
– Fax (028) 7086 8878
15 rm – †£60/70 ††£80/110 – **Rest** – Carte £16/20
◆ A farm and blacksmith's forge was here in 1600s; now an inn well set up for those with an active disposition - fishing, golf, shooting are on hand. Simple rooms in annexe. Traditionally styled restaurant offers fresh home-cooked meals.

Greenhill House without rest
24 Greenhill Rd, Aghadowey, South : 9 m. by A 29 on B 66 ✉ BT51 4EU
– ✆ (028) 7086 8241 – greenhill.house@btinternet.com
– Fax (028) 7086 8365
– March-October
6 rm – †£40 ††£60
◆ An agreeably clean-lined Georgian house with large windows overlooking fields. Game and course fishing available locally. Neat bedrooms replete with extra touches.

Look out for red symbols, indicating particularly pleasant establishments.

NORTHERN IRELAND

COMBER – Down – 712 O 4 35 D2

Anna's House without rest
Tullynagee, 35 Lisbarnett Rd, Southeast : 3½ m. by A 22 ✉ BT23 6AW
– ✆ (028) 9754 1566 – anna@annashouse.com
– closed Christmas-New Year
3 rm – †£50/60 ††£80/90
◆ Farmhouse with cosy lounge and comfy bedrooms with lovely vistas. Glass-walled extension has geo-thermal heating and lake views. Organic breakfasts utilise produce from garden.

CRUMLIN (Cromghlinn) – Antrim – 712 N 4 – pop. 2 697 35 C2

Belfast 14 m – Ballymena 20 m

Caldhame Lodge without rest
102 Moira Rd, Nutts Corner, Southeast : 1¼ m. on A 26 ✉ BT29 4HG
– ✆ (028) 9442 3099 – info@caldhamelodge.co.uk
– Fax (028) 9442 3313
8 rm – †£38/45 ††£58/75
◆ Spic and span, with thoroughly polished, wood furnished hall, complete with grandfather clock. Immaculate, co-ordinated, individualistic rooms; bridal suite with whirlpool.

DONAGHADEE (Domhnach Daoi) – Down – 712 P 4 *Ireland* 35 D2

Belfast 18 m – Ballymena 44 m
Warren Rd, ✆ (028) 9188 3624 .
Ballycopeland Windmill★ **AC** S : 4 m. by A 2 and B 172. Mount Stewart★★★ **AC**, SW : 10 m. by A 2 and minor road SW – Movilla (cross slabs★), Newtownards, SW : 7 m. by B 172

Grace Neill's
33 High St ✉ BT21 0AH – ✆ (028) 9188 4595 – info@graceneills.com
– Fax (028) 9188 9631
– Closed 25 December
Rest – Carte £14/28
◆ Reputedly Ireland's oldest pub; dates from 1611. Thoroughly traditional bar; contemporary restaurant. Modern dishes full of freshness. Good value early evening meals for two.

Pier 36 with rm

36 The Parade ✉ BT21 0HE – ✆ (028) 9188 4466 – info@pier36.co.uk – Fax (028) 9188 4636 – Closed 25 December

4 rm – ♦£ 50/90 ♦♦£ 85 – **Rest** – Seafood Carte £ 17/35

◆ Personally run spacious pub by the harbour. Appealing rustic feel with stone flooring, curios and wood panelling. Extensive menus with an global range. Modern, comfy bedrooms.

DOWNPATRICK (Dún Pádraig) – Down – 712 O 4/5 *Ireland* 35 D3

Belfast 23 m – Newry 31 m – Newtownards 22 m

Cathedral★ AC - Down County Museum★ AC

Struell Wells★ AC, SE : 2 m. by B 1 - Ardglass★ (Jordan's CastleAC), SE : 7 m. by B 1 – Inch Abbey★ AC, NW : 2 m. by A 7 – Quoile Countryside Centre★ AC, E : 2 m. by A 25 – Castle Ward★★ AC (Audley's Castle★), E : 8 m. by A 25

Pheasants' Hill Farm without rest

37 Killyleagh Rd, North : 3 m. on A 22 ✉ BT30 9BL – ✆ (028) 4461 7246 – info@pheasantshill.com – Fax (028) 4461 7246 – Restricted opening in winter

5 rm – ♦£ 45 ♦♦£ 59/68

◆ Purpose-built house surrounded by an organic smallholding with livestock which provides many ingredients for hearty breakfasts. Homely, pine furnished bedrooms.

DUNDRUM – Down – 712 O 5 *Ireland* 35 D3

Belfast 29 m – Downpatrick 9 m – Newcastle 4 m

Castle★ AC

Castlewellan Forest Park★★ AC, W : 4 m. by B 180 and A 50 - Tollymore Forest Park★ AC, W : 3 m. by B 180 - Drumena Cashel and Souterrain★, W : 4 m. by B 180

The Carriage House without rest

71 Main St ✉ BT33 0LU – ✆ (028) 4375 1635 – inbox@carriagehousedundrum.com

3 rm – ♦£ 40/45 ♦♦£ 60/70

◆ Charming owner runs super, comfy guesthouse: lilac exterior, very well-appointed guest areas. Breakfast sources local organic ingredients. Warm bedrooms with personal touches.

Buck's Head Inn

77-79 Main St ✉ BT33 0LU – ✆ (028) 4375 1868 – buckshead1@aol.com – Fax (028) 4481 1033 – Closed 25 December and Monday October-April

Rest – Seafood Menu 27 – Carte £ 17/25

◆ Traditional high street bar. Interesting, well-cooked dishes with strong seafood base served in conservatory or cosy front room. Early evening high tea popular with walkers.

Mourne Seafood Bar

10 Main St ✉ BT33 0LU – ✆ (028) 4375 1377 – bob@mourneseafood.com – Fax (028) 4375 1161 – Closed 25 December, Monday and Tuesday in winter

Rest – Seafood (booking essential in summer) Carte £ 16/28

◆ Simple, casual seafood pub featuring the day's local catch. Tasty, out-of-ordinary menus based on fish with healthy stocks, rather than threatened species. Reasonably priced.

Your opinions are important to us: please write and let us know about your discoveries and experiences – good and bad!

NORTHERN IRELAND

DUNGANNON (Dún Geanainn) – Tyrone – 712 L 4 Ireland 35 C2

Belfast 42 m – Ballymena 37 m – Dundalk 47 m – Londonderry 60 m

The Argory★, S : 5 m. by A 29 and east by minor rd. Ardboe Cross★, NW : 17 m. by A 45, B 161 and B 73 – Springhill★ **AC**, NE : 24 m. by A 29 – Sperrin Mountains★ : Wellbrook Beetling Mill★ **AC**, NW : 22 m. by A 29 and A 505 - Beaghmore Stone Circles★, NW : 24 m. by A 29 and A 505

Grange Lodge

7 Grange Rd, Moy, Southeast : 3½ m. by A 29 ✉ BT71 7EJ – ✆ (028) 8778 4212 – stay@grangelodgecountryhouse.com – Fax (028) 8778 4313 – Closed 20 December-1 February

5 rm – ♦£ 59/65 ♦♦£ 85 – **Rest** – (by arrangement) Menu £ 32/38

♦ Attractive Georgian country house surrounded by well-kept mature gardens with a peaceful ambience. Fine hospitality and period furnishings. Tastefully decorated bedrooms. Large dining room furnished with elegant antiques and fine tableware.

ENNISKILLEN (Inis Ceithleann) – Fermanagh – 712 J 4 – pop. 11 436 34 A2

Ireland

Belfast 87 m – Londonderry 59 m

Wellington Rd ✆ (028) 6632 3110, tourism@fermanagh.gov.uk

Castlecoole, ✆ (028) 6632 5250 .

Castle Coole★★★ **AC**, SE : 1 m – Florence Court★★ **AC**, SW : 8 m. by A 4 and A 32 – Marble Arch Caves and Forest Nature Reserve★ **AC**, SW : 10 m. by A 4 and A 32. NW by A 26 : Lough Erne★★ : Cliffs of Magho Viewpoint★★★ **AC**- Tully Castle★ **AC** – N by A 32, B 72, A 35 and A 47 : Devenish Island★ **AC** - Castle Archdale Forest Park★ **AC** - White Island★ - Janus Figure★

Manor House

Killadeas, North : 7½ m. by A 32 on B 82 ✉ BT94 1NY – ✆ (028) 6862 2200 – info@manor-house-hotel.com – Fax (028) 6862 1545

81 rm – ♦£ 105 ♦♦£ 130 – **Rest** – Menu £ 16/25

♦ In a commanding position overlooking Lough Erne. Noted for fine Italian plasterwork evident in guest areas. Relaxing conservatory lounge. Spacious, comfortable bedrooms. Classically appointed dining room featuring chandeliers and ornate plasterwork.

Cedars

North : 10 m. by A 32 on B 82 ✉ BT94 1PG – ✆ (028) 6862 1493 – info@cedarsguesthouse.com – Fax (028) 6862 8335 – closed Christmas

10 rm – ♦£ 40 ♦♦£ 180

Rest *Rectory Bistro* – (closed Monday-Tuesday in winter) (dinner only and Sunday lunch) Carte £ 18.90/31.90

♦ Good value, converted 19C former rectory with pleasant gardens. Exudes impression of spaciousness; country style décor. Individually styled bedrooms: ask for numbers 2 or 5. Country style bistro serves hearty cuisine.

GALGORM Antrim – 712 N 3 – see BALLYMENA

HILLSBOROUGH (Cromghlinn) – Down – 712 N 4 Ireland 35 C2

Belfast 12 m

The Square ✆ (028) 9268 9717, hillsborough@nitic.net

Town★ – Fort★

Rowallane Gardens★ **AC**, Saintfield, E : 10 m. by B 178 and B 6. The Argory★, W : 25 m. by A 1 and M 1

The Plough Inn

3 The Square ✉ BT26 6AG – ✆ (028) 9268 2985 – Fax (028) 9268 2472 – Closed 25 December

Rest – Carte £ 15/25

Rest *Bar Retro* – (closed Monday) Carte £ 20/30

♦ Well-established, family run inn. The traditional bar is popular with older diners; youngsters tend to head upstairs to the trendy bistro, while families tend towards the café. A mix of traditional and more modern dishes come in generous portions.

at Annahilt Southeast : 4 m. on B 177 – ✉ **Hillsborough**

Fortwilliam without rest
210 Ballynahinch Rd, Northwest : ¼ m. on B 177 ✉ BT26 6BH
– ☎ (028) 9268 2255 – info@fortwilliamcountryhouse.com – Fax (028) 9268 9608
4 rm – †£45 ††£65
◆ Large house on a working farm with attractive gardens. Charming hospitality amidst traditional farmhouse surroundings. Characterful bedrooms with a range of extras.

The Pheasant
410 Upper Ballynahinch Rd, North : 1 m. on Lisburn rd ✉ BT26 6NR
– ☎ (028) 9263 8056 – pheasantinn@aol.com – Fax (028) 9263 8026
– Closed 25-26 December and 12-13 July
Rest – Menu £15/24 – Carte £15/25
◆ Modern rustic feel with peat fires and wood floors. Extensive menu offers hearty portions of classic country dishes. Live music on Fridays. A local favourite.

If breakfast is included the symbol appears after the number of rooms.

NORTHERN IRELAND

HOLYWOOD (Ard Mhic Nasca) – Down – 712 O 4 – pop. 9 252 — 35 D2

Ireland

Belfast 7 m – Bangor 6 m
Holywood Demesne Rd, Nuns Walk, ☎ (028) 9042 2138 .
Cultra : Ulster Folk and Transport Museum★★ AC, NE : 1 m. by A 2

Culloden rest,
142 Bangor Rd, East : 1½ m. on A 2 ✉ BT18 0EX
– ☎ (028) 9042 1066 – res@cull.hastingshotel.com – Fax (028) 9042 6777
76 rm – †£230 ††£230 3 suites
Rest *Mitre* – (dinner only and Sunday lunch) Menu £40 **s**
Rest *Cultra Inn* – Carte £24/29 **s**
◆ Part Victorian Gothic manor, originally built as an official residence for the Bishops of Down. Top class comfort amid characterful interiors. Smart, comfortable bedrooms. The Mitre has a smart and well-kept air. Timbered, flagged Cultra Inn.

Rayanne House
60 Demesne Rd, by My Lady's Mile Rd ✉ BT18 9EX – ☎ (028) 9042 5859
– rayannehouse@hotmail.com – Fax (028) 9042 5859
11 rm – †£70/95 ††£98/130 – **Rest** – (booking essential) Menu £35/42
◆ Redbrick house with attractive views of town. Very personally run with smart, alluring interiors. Individually styled rooms feature hand-painted murals and personal trinkets. Warm, attentive service and fine choice menu.

Beech Hill without rest
23 Ballymoney Rd, Craigantlet, Southeast : 4½ m. by A 2 on Craigantlet rd
✉ BT23 4TG – ☎ (028) 9042 5892 – info@beech-hill.net – Fax (028) 9042 5892
3 rm – †£50 ††£85
◆ Country house in rural location. Pleasant clutter of trinkets and antiques in guest areas which include a conservatory. Neat, traditionally styled bedrooms: a very fine home.

Fontana
61A High St ✉ BT18 9AE – ☎ (028) 9080 9908
– fontanarestaurant@btinternet.com – Fax (028) 9080 9912
– Closed 1-2 January, 11-13 July, Monday, Sunday dinner and Saturday lunch
Rest – (Sunday brunch) (booking essential) Menu £13/18 – Carte £22/30
◆ Modish dining room. Friendly staff. Tasty, unfussy, modern Irish food with refreshing Californian and Mediterranean influences. Choose between main or 'mini' good value menus.

KIRCUBBIN (Cill Ghobáin) – Down – 712 P 4 35 D2

Belfast 20 m – Donaghadee 12 m – Newtownards 10 m

XX Paul Arthurs with rm

66 Main St ✉ BT22 2SP – ✆ (028) 4273 8192 – info@paularthurs.com – Closed January, 25-26 December, Monday and Sunday dinner

7 rm – †£ 50 ††£ 70 – **Rest** – (dinner only and Sunday lunch) Carte £ 23/35

◆ Distinctive salmon/coral façade. Cosy ground floor lounge. Upstairs dining room flaunts modern Belfast art. Confident, unfussy menus exude bold, classic flavours. Comfy rooms.

LARNE (Latharna) – Antrim – 712 O 3 – pop. 30 832 *Ireland* 35 D2

Belfast 23 m – Ballymena 20 m

to Fleetwood (Stena Line) daily (8 h) – to Cairnryan (P & O Irish Sea) 3-5 daily (1 h/2 h 15 mn)

Narrow Gauge Rd ✆ (028) 2826 0088

Cairndhu Ballygally 192 Coast Rd, ✆ (028) 2858 3954 .

SE : Island Magee (Ballylumford Dolmen★), by ferry and 2 m. by B 90 or 18 m. by A 2 and B 90. NW : Antrim Glens★★★ - Murlough Bay★★★ (Fair Head ≤ ★★★), N : 46 m by A 2 and minor road – Glenariff Forest Park★★ **AC** (Waterfall★★), N : 30 m. by A 2 and A 43 - Glenariff★, N : 25 m. by A 2 - Glendun★, N : 30 m. by A 2 – Carrickfergus (Castle★★ - St Nicholas' Church★), SW : 15 m. by A 2

Manor House without rest

23 Olderfleet Rd, Harbour Highway ✉ BT40 1AS – ✆ (028) 2827 3305 – welcome@themanorguesthouse.com – Fax (028) 2826 0505 – Closed 25-26 December

8 rm – †£ 25/30 ††£ 50/55

◆ Spacious Victorian terraced house two minutes from ferry terminal. Well-furnished lounge with beautifully varnished wood floors. Small breakfast room. Cosy, homely bedrooms.

LIMAVADY (Léim an Mhadaidh) – Londonderry – 712 L 2 *Ireland* 34 B1

Belfast 62 m – Ballymena 39 m – Coleraine 13 m – Londonderry 17 m – Omagh 50 m

Council Offices, 7 Connell St ✆ (028) 7776 0307, tourism@limavady.gov.uk

Benone Par Three Benone 53 Benone Ave, ✆ (028) 7775 0555 .

Sperrin Mountains★ : Roe Valley Country Park★ **AC**, S : 2 m. by B 68 - Glenshane Pass★, S : 15 m. by B 68 and A 6

Radisson SAS Roe Park H. & Golf Resort

Roe Park, West : ½ m. on A 2 ✉ BT49 9LB – ✆ (028) 7772 2222 – reservations@radissonroepark.com – Fax (028) 7772 2313

rm, rest,

117 rm – †£ 100 ††£ 146 – 1 suite

Rest *Greens* – (Closed Sunday dinner and Monday) (dinner only and Sunday lunch) Carte £ 22/28 **s**

Rest *The Coach House* – Carte £ 18/33 **s**

◆ A golfer's idyll with academy and driving range in the grounds of Roe Park. Good leisure centre. Spacious modern bedrooms. Complimentary broadband. Greens is formal in character with menu to match. Brasserie Coach House with open fire and all day service.

X Lime Tree

60 Catherine St ✉ BT49 9DB – ✆ (028) 7776 4300 – info@limetreerest.com – Closed 25 February-10 March, 1 week July, 25-26 December, Sunday and Monday

Rest – (dinner only) Menu £ 24 – Carte £ 23/32

◆ Well regarded, contemporary neighbourhood restaurant, personally run by friendly husband and wife team. Seasonal produce often includes seafood and a Mediterranean influence.

LONDONDERRY/DERRY (Doire) – Londonderry – 712 K 2/3 – 34 B1

pop. 72 334 *Ireland*

Belfast 70 m – Dublin 146 m

City of Derry Airport : ✆ (028) 7181 0784, E : 6 m. by A 2

44 Foyle St ✆ (028) 7126 7284, info@derry.visitor.com

City of Derry 49 Victoria Rd, ✆ (028) 7134 6369 .

Town★ - City Walls and Gates★★ – Guildhall★ **AC** – Long Tower Church★ – St Columb's Cathedral★ **AC** – Tower Museum★ **AC**

Grianan of Aileach★★ (≤ ★★) (Republic of Ireland) NW : 5 m. by A 2 and N 13. Ulster-American Folk Park★★, S : 33 m. by A 5 - Ulster History Park★ **AC**, S : 32 m. by A 5 and minor road – Sperrin Mountains★ : Glenshane Pass★ (≤ ★★), SE : 24 m. by A 6 - Sawel Mountain Drive★ (≤ ★★), S : 22 m. by A 5 and minor roads via Park – Roe Valley Country Park★ **AC**, E : 15 m. by A 2 and B 68 – Beaghmore Stone Circles★, S : 52 m. by A 5, A 505 and minor road

City

rm, rest, P VISA AE

Queens Quay ✉ BT48 7AS – ✆ (028) 7136 5800
– reservations@cityhotelderry.com – Fax (028) 7136 5801
– Closed 24-26 December

144 rm – †£ 130 ††£ 130, ☕ £ 10 – 1 suite

Rest *Thompson's on the River* – (bar lunch Monday-Saturday) Menu £ 20 **s** – Carte £ 20/27 **s**

◆ Hotel in purpose-built modern style. Well located, close to the city centre and the quay. Smart rooms ordered for the business traveller. Useful conference facilities. Modern restaurant overlooks water.

Beech Hill Country House

rm, P VISA AE

32 Ardmore Rd, Southeast : 3½ m. by A 6 ✉ BT47 3QP
– ✆ (028) 7134 9279 – info@beech-hill.com – Fax (028) 7134 5366
– closed 24-25 December

25 rm ☕ – †£ 80 ††£ 100 – 2 suites

Rest *The Ardmore* – Menu £ 18/30 – Carte £ 28/43

◆ 18C country house, now personally run but once a US marine camp; one lounge is filled with memorabilia. Accommodation varies from vast rooms to more traditional, rural ones. Restaurant housed within conservatory and old billiard room. Fine garden.

Ramada H. Da Vinci's

rm, rest, P VISA AE

15 Culmore Rd, North : 1 m. following signs for Foyle Bridge ✉ BT48 8JB – ✆ (028) 7127 9111 – info@davincishotel.com
– Fax (028) 7127 9222
– closed 24-25 December

65 rm ☕ – †£ 70/99 ††£ 70/99

Rest *The Grill Room* – (dinner only and Sunday lunch) Carte £ 19/26 **s**

◆ Modern purpose-built hotel at northern end of city's quayside close to major through routes. Stylish lobby area. Large, atmospheric bar. Good sized, well-equipped bedrooms. Spacious restaurant has an elegant ambience.

Mandarin Palace

VISA AE

Lower Clarendon St ✉ BT48 7AW – ✆ (028) 7137 3656
– info@mandarinpalace.net – Fax (028) 7137 3636
– closed 25-26 December and Saturday lunch

Rest – Chinese Carte £ 17/24

◆ Oriental restaurant, with good views of Foyle river and bridge. Smart staff oversee the service of unfussy, well-executed Chinese cuisine, featuring good value set menus.

MAGHERA (Machaire Rátha) – Londonderry – 712 L 3 35 C2

Belfast 40 m – Ballymena 19 m – Coleraine 21 m – Londonderry 32 m

Ardtara Country House

rm, P VISA

8 Gorteade Rd, Upperlands, North : 3 ¼ m. by A 29 off B 75 ✉ BT46 5SA
– ✆ (028) 7964 4490 – Fax (028) 7964 5080

9 rm ☕ – †£ 80/100 ††£ 120/150 – **Rest** – (booking essential for non-residents) (lunch by arrangement) Carte £ 18/30

◆ 19C house with a charming atmosphere. The interior features "objets trouvés" collected from owner's travels; original fireplaces set off the individually styled bedrooms. Restaurant set in former billiard room with hunting mural and panelled walls.

NEWCASTLE (An Caisleán Nua) – Kildare – 712 O 5 – pop. 7 214 35 D3

Ireland

Belfast 32 m – Londonderry 101 m

10-14 Central Promenade ☎ (028) 4372 2222, newcastletic@downdc.gov.uk

Castlewellan Forest Park★★ AC, NW : 4 m. by A 50 – Tolymore Forest Park★ AC, W : 3 m. by B 180 – Dundrum Castle★ AC, NE : 4 m. by A 2. Silent Valley Reservoir★ (≤ ★) - Spelga Pass and Dam★ - Kilbroney ForestPark (viewpoint★) – Annalong Marine Park and Cornmill★ AC, S : 8 m. by A 2 – Downpatrick : Cathedral★ AC, Down Country Museum★ AC, NE : 20 m. by A 2 and A 25

Slieve Donard

Downs Rd ✉ BT33 0AH – ☎ (028) 4372 1066 – gm@sdh.hastingshotels.com – Fax (028) 4372 1166

178 rm – †£ 155/215 ††£ 180/240

Rest *Oak* – Menu £ 28/32

Rest *Percy French* – Carte £ 19/26

◆ Victorian grand old lady with sea views. Domed lobby with open fire. Highly impressive spa and leisure. Chaplins bar named after Charlie, who stayed here. Modern rooms. Grand style dining in semi-panelled Oak. Percy French bar-restaurant has easy-going menu.

Burrendale H. & Country Club

51 Castlewellan Rd, North : 1 m. on A 50

✉ BT33 0JY – ☎ (028) 4372 2599 – reservations@burrendale.com – Fax (028) 4372 2328

69 rm – †£ 80 ††£ 120 – 1 suite

Rest *Vine* – (dinner only and Sunday lunch) Menu £ 28 **s** – Carte £ 17/26 **s**

Rest *Cottage Kitchen* – Menu £ 15/20 – Carte £ 16/23 **s**

◆ Set between the Mourne Mountains and Irish Sea, with the Royal Country Down Golf Course nearby. Leisure oriented. Range of rooms from small to very spacious. Linen-clad Vine for traditional dining. Homely cooking to the fore at Cottage Kitchen.

NEWTOWNARDS (Baile Nua na hArda) – Down – 712 O 4 35 D2

Belfast 10 m – Bangor 144 m – Downpatrick 22 m

Edenvale House without rest

130 Portaferry Rd, Southeast : 2 ¾ m. on A 20 ✉ BT22 2AH – ☎ (028) 9181 4881 – edenvalehouse@hotmail.com – closed 20 December-7 January

3 rm – †£ 50 ††£ 80

◆ Attractive Georgian house with fine views of the Mourne Mountains. Elegant sitting room. Communal breakfasts featuring home-made bread and jams. Individually styled rooms.

PORTAFERRY (Port an Pheire) – Down – 712 P 4 *Ireland* 35 D3

Belfast 29 m – Bangor 24 m

The Stables, Castle St ☎ (028) 4272 9882 (Easter-September)

Exploris★ AC

Castle Ward★★ AC (Audley's Castle★), W : 4 m. by ferry and A 25

Portaferry

10 The Strand ✉ BT22 1PE – ☎ (028) 4272 8231 – info@portaferryhotel.com – Fax (028) 4272 8999 – Closed 24-25 December

14 rm – †£ 40/55 ††£ 79/110 – **Rest** – (bar lunch Monday-Saturday) Carte £ 18/31

◆ Formerly private dwellings, this hotel dates from 18C. Located on Strangford Lough, most rooms have waterside views. Lounge features Irish paintings. Crisp and fresh dining room with strong emphasis on local produce.

NORTHERN IRELAND

PORTRUSH (Port Rois) – **Antrim** – **712** L 2 – **pop. 5 703** *Ireland* 35 **C1**

Belfast 58 m – Coleraine 4 m – Londonderry 35 m
Dunluce Centre, Sandhill Drive ✆ (028) 7082 3333 (March-October), portrush@nitic.net
Royal Portrush Dunluce Rd, ✆ (028) 7082 2311 .
Giant's Causeway★★★ (Hamilton's Seat ≤ ★★, E: 9 m by A 2) - Carrick-a-rede Rope Bridge★★★, E: 14 m. by A 2 and B 15 - Dunluce Castle★★ **AC**, E: 3 m. by A 2 – Gortmore Viewpoint★★, E: 14 m. by A 29, A 2 and minor road - Magilligan Strand★★, E: 13 m. by A 29 and A 2 – Downhill★ (Mussenden Temple★), E: 12 m. by A 29 and A 2

Beulah without rest

16 Causeway St ✉ BT56 8AB – ✆ (028) 7082 2413
– stay@beulahguesthouse.com
– closed Christmas
9 rm – ♦£ 38/40 ♦♦£ 60/66
◆ Terraced Victorian house in perfect central location. Sound Irish breakfasts. Homely guest lounge. Colourful, co-ordinated and immaculately kept modern bedrooms.

The Harbour Bistro

6 Harbour Rd ✉ BT56 8DF – ✆ (028) 7082 2430 – Fax (028) 7082 3194
– Closed 24-26 December
Rest – (dinner only) (bookings not accepted) Carte £ 17/24
◆ Buzzy bistro in the old part of town near to popular beach. Modern décor. Wide ranging menus providing generous servings. Expect to order and carry your own drinks from bar.

Red = Pleasant. Look for the red X and symbols.

TEMPLEPATRICK (Teampall Phádraig) – **Antrim** – **712** N 3 – ✉ **Ballyclare** 35 **D2**

Belfast 13 m – Ballymena 16 m – Dundalk 65 m – Larne 16 m

Templeton

882 Antrim Rd ✉ BT39 0AH – ✆ (028) 9443 2984
– reception@templetonhotel.com – Fax (028) 9443 3406
– closed 25-26 December
24 rm – ♦£ 75/97 ♦♦£ 95/125
Rest *Raffles* – (closed Monday-Tuesday) (dinner only and Sunday lunch) Carte £ 19/29
Rest *Upton Grill* – Carte £ 12/25
◆ Large and distinctive pine "chalet" appearance. Inside, a swish atrium leads you to a pillared lounge; bedrooms are warm and light. Very popular for weddings. Peaceful library themed Raffles for fine dining. Buzzy Upton Grill with popular menu.

WARRENPOINT – **Down** – **712** N 5 35 **C3**

Copper

4 Duke St ✉ BT34 3JY – ✆ (028) 4175 3047 – info@copperrestaurant.co.uk
– closed 24-26 December, Saturday lunch and Monday
Rest – Menu £ 16 – Carte £ 18/32
◆ Modish restaurant with an eye-catching blood red interior and high ceiling. Chatty, attentive service. Interestingly balanced menus: classic repertoire with ambitious touches.

Restaurant 23

23 Church St ✉ BT34 3HN – ✆ (028) 4175 3222 – restaurant23@btconnect.com
– Fax (028) 4177 4323
– closed 24-25 December, third week January, Monday and Tuesday
Rest – Carte £ 25/30 **s**
◆ A very stylish interior makes most of intimate space. Easy-going, good value brasserie style lunches; evening dishes - adopting a more original slant - are more serious.

NORTHERN IRELAND

PORTRUSH (Port Rois) – Antrim – 712 L2 – pop. 5 703 [illegible]

Belfast 58 mi – Coleraine 4 mi – Londonderry 35 mi.

Dunluce Centre, Sandhill Drive (028) 7082 3333 (March-October) [illegible]

Royal Portrush Dunluce Rd (028) 7082 2311

Giant's Causeway ★★ [illegible] Dunluce Castle ★★ AC [illegible]

[illegible]

[illegible]
closed [illegible]

[illegible] Victorian house in central location [illegible] breakfast [illegible]

[illegible]

O. Forir/MICHELIN

[illegible] distinctive [illegible] a [illegible] popular for weddings [illegible]

WARRENPOINT – Down – 712 N5

[illegible]
closed 24-26 December [illegible]

[illegible]

[illegible]
closed 25 December [illegible] January, Monday [illegible]

[illegible] good value [illegible]

Towns
from A to Z

Villes
de A à Z

Città
de A a Z

Städte
von A bis Z

Republic of Ireland

ABBEYLEIX (Mainistir Laoise) – **Laois** – **712** J 9 *Ireland* 39 **C2**

Dublin 96 km – Kilkenny 35 km – Limerick 108 km

Abbeyleix Rathmoyle, (0502) 31 450.

Emo Court★★ **AC**, N : 17 km by R 425 and R 419 – Rock of Dunamase★, NE : 10 km by R 425 and N 80 – Stradbally Steam Museum★ **AC**, NE : 19 km by R 425 and R 427 – Timahoe Round Tower★, NE : 15 km by R 430 and a minor road

Abbeyleix Manor

rm, AC, P, VISA, MC, AE

Cork Rd, Southwest : ¾ km on N 8 – (05787) 30 111
– info@abbeyleixmanorhotel.com – Fax (15787) 30 220
– closed 25 December

46 rm – €65/75 €110/130 – **Rest** – (closed Sunday-Tuesday dinner) (carvery lunch Monday-Friday, bar lunch Saturday) Carte €20/42 **s**

◆ Modern purpose-built hotel painted a distinctive yellow. Mural decorated public areas. Well-kept bar and a games room. Uniform bedrooms with simple, comfortable style. Restaurant has a bright modern feel.

ACHILL ISLAND (Acaill) – **Mayo** – **712** B 5/6 *Ireland* 36 **A2**

Achill (098) 45384 (July-August)

Achill Island Keel, (098) 43 456 .

Island★

Doogort (Dumha Goirt) – ✉ Achill Island

Gray's

P

– (098) 43 244
– closed Christmas

14 rm – €50/60 €100/110 – **Rest** – (by arrangement) Menu €32

◆ A row of tranquil whitewashed cottages with a homely atmosphere; popular with artists. Cosy sitting rooms with fireplaces and simple but spotless bedrooms. Local scene paintings adorn dining room walls.

Keel (An Caol) – ✉ Achill Island

Achill Cliff House

Keel Bay and Minaun Cliffs, P, VISA, MC, AE

– (098) 43 400 – info@achillcliff.com – Fax (098) 43 007
– closed 21-28 December

10 rm – €50/140 €90/160 – **Rest** – (dinner only) Menu €18/27 – Carte €29/37

◆ Whitewashed modern building against a backdrop of countryside and ocean. Within walking distance of Keel beach. Well-kept, spacious bedrooms with modern furnishings. Spacious restaurant with sea views.

ADARE (Áth Dara) – **Limerick** – **712** F 10 *Ireland* 38 **B2**

Dublin 210 km – Killarney 95 km – Limerick 16 km

Heritage Centre, Mains St (061) 396255

Town★ – Adare Friary★ - Adare Parish Church★

Rathkeale (Castle Matrix★ **AC** - Irish Palatine Heritage Centre★) W : 12 km by N 21 – Newcastle West★, W : 26 km by N 21 – Glin Castle★ **AC**, W : 46½ km by N 21, R 518 and N 69

Adare Manor H. and Golf Resort

18, P, VISA, MC, AE

– (061) 396 566
– reservations@adaremanor.com – Fax (061) 396 124

62 rm – €270/695 €270/695, €25

Rest *The Oakroom* – (dinner only) Carte €50/78

Rest *The Carraigehouse* – Carte €22/40

◆ Part 19C Gothic mansion on banks of River Maigue in extensive parkland. Impressively elaborate interiors and capacious lounges. Most distinctive rooms in the oldest parts. Oak-panelled dining room overlooks river. Informal Carraigehouse.

Dunraven Arms
Main St – ☎ (061) 605 900 – reservations@dunravenhotel.com – Fax (061) 396 541
86 rm – ††€ 135/200, ☕ €25
Rest *Maigue Restaurant* – ☎ (061) 396 633 (dinner only and Sunday lunch) Carte € 33/41
Rest *The Inn Between* – ☎ (061) 396 633 (closed Sunday and Monday) (bar lunch) Carte € 24/34
◆ Considerably extended 18C building opposite town's charming thatched cottages. Understated country house style. Comfortable bedrooms in bright magnolia. Well-equipped gym. Burgundy décor, antique chairs and historical paintings create a classic traditional air. Menus offer some eclectic choice on an Irish backbone. Formal yet friendly service. Welcoming bistro in charming thatched cottage.

Carrabawn Guesthouse without rest
Killarney Rd, Southwest : ¾ km on N 21 – ☎ (061) 396 067 – carrabawnhouse@eircom.net – Fax (061) 396 067 – March-October
8 rm ☕ – †€ 55/65 ††€ 80/90
◆ Well-established guesthouse with genuine homely style and large mature garden. Sitting room with games and books and comfortable sun lounge. Well-kept co-ordinated bedrooms.

Berkeley Lodge without rest
Station Rd – ☎ (061) 396 857 – berlodge@iol.ie – Fax (061) 396 857
6 rm ☕ – †€ 55/60 ††€ 75/80
◆ Good value accommodation with a friendly and well-run ambience. Hearty breakfast choices include pancakes and smoked salmon. Simply furnished traditional bedrooms.

The Wild Geese
Rose Cottage – ☎ (061) 396 451 – wildgeese@indigo.ie – closed 24 December-3 January, Sunday in winter and Monday
Rest – (dinner only) (booking essential) Menu € 42 – Carte approx. € 51
◆ Traditional 18C cottage on main street. Friendly service and cosy welcoming atmosphere. Varied menu with classic and international influences uses much fresh local produce.

ARAN ISLANDS (Oileáin Árann) – **Galway** – **712** CD 8 *Ireland* 38 **B1**

Access Access by boat or aeroplane from Galway city or by boat from Kilkieran, Rossaveel or Fisherstreet (Clare) and by aeroplane from Inverin
Cill Ronain, Inis Mor ☎ (099) 61263
Islands★ – Inishmore (Dún Aonghasa★★★)

Inishmore – Galway – ✉ Aran Islands 38 **A1**

Óstán Árann
Kilronan – ☎ (099) 61 104 – info@aranislandshotel.com – Fax (099) 61 225 – Closed 20-28 December
22 rm ☕ – †€ 75/140 ††€ 110/240 – **Rest** – Menu € 38 (dinner) – Carte € 30/40
◆ Comfortable, family-owned hotel with great view of harbour. Bustling bar with live music every night in the season. Spacious, up-to-date bedrooms decorated in bright colours. Traditional dishes served in wood-floored restaurant.

Pier House
Kilronan – ☎ (099) 61 417 – pierh@iol.ie – Fax (099) 61 122 – 16 March-October
10 rm ☕ – †€ 50/120 ††€ 90/120
Rest *The Restaurant* – see restaurant listing
◆ Purpose-built at the end of the pier with an attractive outlook. Spacious, planned interiors and spotlessly kept bedrooms furnished in a comfortable modern style.

REPUBLIC OF IRELAND

Ard Einne Guesthouse Killeany Bay,

Killeany – (099) 61 126 – ardeinne@eircom.net – Fax (099) 61 388
– Closed December and January

14 rm – €60/90 €80/120 – **Rest** – (by arrangement) Menu €25

♦ Purpose-built chalet-style establishment in isolated spot with superb views of Killeany Bay. Homely atmosphere amidst traditional appointments. Simple, comfortable bedrooms. Spacious dining room provides home-cooked meals.

Kilmurvey House

Kilmurvey – (099) 61 218 – kilmurveyhouse@eircom.net – Fax (099) 61 397
– April-October

12 rm – €50/75 €90/120 – **Rest** – (by arrangement) Menu €30 **s**

♦ Extended stone-built house in tranquil, secluded location with the remains of an ancient fort in grounds. Well-kept traditional style throughout. Simply decorated bedrooms. Traditional dining room. Good use of fresh island produce.

The Restaurant – at Pier House H.

Kilronan – (099) 61 417 – pierh@iol.ie – Fax (099) 61 122
– 16 March-October

Rest – (light lunch) Menu €30 (dinner)

♦ Cosy, snug, cottagey restaurant, typified by its rustic, wooden tables. Light lunches are replaced by more serious dinner menus with strong selection of local fish dishes.

REPUBLIC OF IRELAND

ARDFINNAN (Ard Fhíonáin) – Tipperary – 712 I 11 — 39 C2

Dublin 185 km – Caher 9 km – Waterford 63 km

Kilmaneen Farmhouse

East : 4 ¼ km by Goatenbridge rd – (052) 36 231 – kilmaneen@eircom.net
– Fax (052) 36 231
– mid March-mid November and Sunday

5 rm – €50 €85 – **Rest** – (by arrangement) Menu €28

♦ Traditional farmhouse on dairy farm hidden away in the countryside. Cosy and neat, with a welcoming lounge. Comfortable bedrooms are well kept and individually furnished. Tasty menus with a rural heart.

ARTHURSTOWN (Colmán) – Wexford – 712 L 11 — 39 D2

Dublin 166 km – Cork 159 km – Limerick 162 km – Waterford 42 km

Dunbrody Country House rm,

– (051) 389 600 – dunbrody@indigo.ie
– Fax (051) 389 601
– closed 21-25 December

17 rm – €140/360 €275/360 – 5 suites – **Rest** – (bar lunch Monday-Saturday) (booking essential for non-residents) (residents only Sunday dinner) Carte €38/60

♦ A fine country house hotel with a pristine elegant style set within a part Georgian former hunting lodge, affording much peace. Smart comfortable bedrooms. Elegant dining room in green damask and burgundy.

ASHBOURNE (Cill Dhéagláin) – Meath – 712 M 7 — 37 D3

Dublin 21 km – Drogheda 26 km – Navan 27 km

Ashbourne Marriott rm,

The Rath, North : 2 km by R 135 at junction with N 2 motorway – (01) 835 0800 – info@marriottashbourne.com
– Fax (01) 801 0301
– Closed 25 December

144 rm – €95/105 €130/140 – 4 suites – **Rest** – (bar lunch Monday-Saturday) Carte €21/49

♦ Modern hotel with striking glass front. Trendy bar furnished in red with karaoke room. Well equipped leisure club. Bedrooms are stylish, with bright decor and smart bathrooms. Restaurant specialises in steak and seafood.

Broadmeadow Country House without rest

Bullstown, Southeast : 4 km by R 135 on R 125 (Swords rd) – (01) 835 2823 – info@irishcountryhouse.com – Fax (01) 835 2819 – closed 23 December-2 January

8 rm – €60/80 €100/150

◆ Substantial ivy-clad guesthouse and equestrian centre in rural area yet close to airport. Light and airy breakfast room overlooks garden. Spacious rooms have country views.

ASHFORD – **Wicklow** – **712** N 8 – **pop. 1 215** 39 **D2**

Dublin 43 km – Rathdrum 17 km – Wicklow 6 km

Ballyknocken House

Glenealy, South : 4 ¾ km on L 1096 – (0404) 44 627 – cfulvio@ballyknocken.com – Fax (0404) 44 696 – closed Christmas, January, Sunday and Monday

7 rm – €75/100 €119/134 – **Rest** – (by arrangement) Menu €45

◆ Part Victorian guesthouse on a working farm: the comfy bedrooms are furnished with antiques, and some have claw foot baths: most are in the new wing. Charming owner proud of home cooking.

ATHLONE (Baile Átha Luain) – **Westmeath** – **712** I 7 – **pop. 15 544** 37 **C3**

Ireland

Dublin 120 km – Galway 92 km – Limerick 120 km – Roscommon 32 km – Tullamore 38 km

Athlone Castle (090) 649 4630 (April-October)

Hodson Bay, (0902) 92 073 .

Clonmacnois★★★ (Grave Slabs★, Cross of the Scriptures★) S : 21 km by N 6 and N 62 – N : Lough Ree (Ballykeeran Viewpoint★)

Radisson SAS rm, rest,

Northgate St – (090) 644 26 00 – info.athlone@radissonsas.com – Fax (090) 644 26 55

127 rm – €130/205 €165/345 –

Rest – (buffet lunch Monday-Saturday) Menu € 38 – Carte €30/49

◆ Overlooks River Shannon, cathedral and marina. Quayside bar with super terrace. Impressive leisure and meeting facilities. Very modern rooms with hi-tech mod cons. Modish restaurant serving buffet or à la carte.

Shelmalier House without rest

Retreat Rd, Cartrontroy, East : 2½ km by Dublin rd (N 6) – (090) 647 22 45 – shelmalier@eircom.net – Fax (090) 647 31 90 – 15 March - November

7 rm – €48/50 €72

◆ Modern house with large garden in a quiet residential area of town. Homely décor throughout, including comfortable bedrooms which are well kept.

Cooson Cottage without rest

Cooson Point Rd, North : 3 ¾ km by Northgate St and following signs to Cooson Point – (090) 647 34 68 – info@ecoguesthouse.com

10 rm – €50 €100

◆ First eco-guest house in Ireland; keenly run with friendly, welcoming owners. Comfy lounge, good-sized bedrooms and bright breakfast room with decked area overlooking garden.

Riverview House without rest

Summerhill, Galway Rd, West : 4 km on N 6 – (090) 649 45 32 – riverviewhouse@hotmail.com – Fax (090) 649 45 32 – 1st March-18 December

4 rm – €45/50 €70/75

◆ Modern house with well-kept garden. Homely, comfortable lounge and wood furnished dining room. Uniformly styled fitted bedrooms. Good welcome.

REPUBLIC OF IRELAND

Left Bank Bistro

Fry Pl – ✆ (090) 649 44 46 – info@leftbankbistro.com – Fax (090) 649 45 09 – closed 25 December-8 January, Sunday and Monday

Rest – (light lunch) Carte € 33/49

♦ Glass-fronted with open-plan wine store and bright, modern bistro buzzing with regulars. Salads and foccacias, plus modern Irish dishes and fish specials in the evening.

at Glassan Northeast : 8 km on N 55 – ✉ Athlone

Wineport Lodge

Lough Ree, rm, VISA AE

Southwest : 1 ½ km – ✆ (090) 643 90 10 – lodge@wineport.ie – Fax (090) 648 54 71 – closed 24-26 December

28 rm – †€ 145 ††€ 220/250 – 1 suite –

Rest – (dinner only) Menu € 69 – Carte € 55/70

♦ Beautifully located by Lough Ree. Come in from the delightful terrace and sip champagne in stylish bar. Superb rooms of limed oak and ash boast balconies and lough views. Smart restaurant with separate galleried area for private parties.

Glasson Golf H. & Country Club

Golf course and Lough Ree, rm, rm, VISA AE

West : 2 ¾ km – ✆ (090) 648 51 20 – info@glassongolf.ie – Fax (090) 648 54 44 – Closed 24-25 December

63 rm – †€ 85/145 ††€ 130/260 – 2 suites –

Rest – (bar lunch) Menu € 38 **s**

♦ Family owned hotel commands fine views of Lough Ree and its attractive golf course. Modern bedrooms are spacious with superior rooms making most of view. Original Georgian house restaurant with wonderful outlook.

Glasson Stone Lodge without rest

VISA

– ✆ (090) 648 50 04 – glassonstonelodge@eircom.net – April-November

5 rm – †€ 45/65 ††€ 70/80

♦ A warm welcome and notable breakfasts with home-baked breads and locally sourced organic bacon. Bedrooms and communal areas are airy and tastefully furnished.

Harbour House without rest

VISA

Southwest : 2 km – ✆ (090) 648 50 63 – ameade@indigo.ie – May-October

6 rm – †€ 45 ††€ 70

♦ Sited in quiet rural spot a stone's throw from Lough Ree. Traditionally styled lounge with stone chimney breast; adjoining breakfast room. Comfy bedrooms overlook garden.

Your opinions are important to us:
please write and let us know about your discoveries and experiences – good and bad!

REPUBLIC OF IRELAND

ATHY (Baile Átha Í) – Kildare – 712 L 9 – pop. 5 306 *Ireland* 39 D2

Dublin 64 km – Kilkenny 46 km – Wexford 95 km

Athy Geraldine, ✆ (059) 863 1729 .

Emo Court★★, N : 32 km by R 417 (L 18), west by N 7 (T 5) and north by R 422 – Stradbally Steam Museum★ **AC**, W : 13 km by R 428 - Castledermot High Crosses★, SE : 15 ¼ km by R 418 – Moone High Cross★, E : 19 ¼ km by Ballitore minor rd and south by N9 - Rock of Dunamase★ (≤ ★), NW : 19 ¼ km by R 428 (L109) and N80 (T16) – Timahoe Round Tower★, W : 16 km by R 428 (L 109) and N 80 (T 16)

Clanard Court
Dublin Rd, Northeast : 2 km on N 78 – ✆ (059) 864 06 66 – sales@clanardcourt.ie – Fax (059) 864 08 88 – closed 25 December
38 rm – €79/129 €138/198
Rest *Courtyard Bistro* – (closed Sunday-Wednesday dinner) (carvery lunch) Carte €20/36
◆ Commercially oriented modern hotel in bright yellow which opened in 2005. Well-equipped meeting rooms. Large bar to snack, sup and unwind. Comfy, smart bedrooms. Restaurant offers Mediterranean/North African style and menus.

AUGHRIM (Eachroim) – **Wicklow** – **712** N 9 39 **D2**
Dublin 74 km – Waterford 124 km – Wexford 96 km
The Battle of Aughrim Visitors Centre, Ballinasloe ✆ (0909) 742604 (summer only)

Brooklodge H & Wells Spa
Macreddin Village, North : 3 ¼ km – ✆ (0402) 36 444 – brooklodge@macreddin.ie – Fax (0402) 36 580
77 rm – €135/155 €200/240 – 13 suites
Rest *Orchard Cafe* – Carte €18/20
Rest *Strawberry Tree* – (dinner only and Sunday lunch) Menu €65
◆ Very individual hotel in idyllic parkland setting. Self-contained microbrewery, smokehouse and bakery. Well-appointed bedrooms and a friendly comfortable style throughout. Orchard Cafe is relaxed, informal eatery. Organic ingredients in Strawberry Tree.

AVOCA (Abhóca) – **Wicklow** – **712** N 9 *Ireland* 39 **D2**
Dublin 75 km – Waterford 116 km – Wexford 88 km
Avondale★, N : by R 752 – Meeting of the Waters★, N : by R 752

Keppel's Farmhouse without rest
Ballanagh, South : 3 ¼ km by unmarked rd – ✆ (0402) 35 168 – keppelsfarmhouse@eircom.net – Fax (0402) 30 950 – 14 May-15 October
5 rm – €55/60 €75/90
◆ Farmhouse set in seclusion at end of long drive on working dairy farm. Attractively simple modern and traditional bedrooms; those in front have far-reaching rural views.

BAGENALSTOWN (Muine Bheag) – **Carlow** – **712** L 9 39 **D2**
Dublin 101 km – Carlow 16 km – Kilkenny 21 km – Wexford 59 km

Kilgraney Country House
South : 6 ½ km by R 705 (Borris Rd) – ✆ (059) 977 52 83 – info@kilgraneyhouse.com – Fax (059) 977 55 95 – March-November
8 rm – €100/155 €130/240 – **Rest** – (closed Monday-Tuesday March-November) (dinner only) (booking essential) Menu €48 **s**
◆ 18C house with individual interiors featuring Far Eastern artefacts from owners' travels. Sitting room in dramatic colours, paintings resting against wall. Stylish rooms. Communal dining in smart surroundings.

BALLINA (Béal an Átha) – **Mayo** – **712** E 5 – **pop. 10 056** *Ireland* 36 **B2**
Dublin 241 km – Galway 117 km – Roscommon 103 km – Sligo 59 km
Cathedral Rd ✆ (096) 70848 (April-October)
Mossgrove Shanaghy, ✆ (096) 21 050 .
Rosserk Abbey★, N : 6 ½ km by R 314. Moyne Abbey★, N : 11 ¼ km by R 314 - Pontoon Bridge View (≤ ★), S : 19 ¼ km by N 26 and R 310 – Downpatrick Head★, N : 32 km by R 314

REPUBLIC OF IRELAND

Mount Falcon

Faxford Rd, South : 6 1/4 km on N 26 – ✆ (096) 74 472 – info@mountfalcon.com – Fax (096) 74 473 – Closed 6-29 January and 25 December

31 rm – †€ 165/185 ††€ 200/220 – 1 suite

Rest *The Kitchen* – (bar lunch) Menu € 57 **s** – Carte € 53/62 **s**

◆ Classic Victorian style country house in 100 acres of mature grounds. Most bedrooms are in the new extension; comfortable and furnished in keeping with character of the house. High-ceilinged, formal restaurant, in what was the original kitchen and pantry.

Ramada

Dublin Rd, South : 3 km by N 26 – ✆ (096) 23 600 – stay@ramadaballina.ie – Fax (096) 23 623 – Closed 24-26 December

87 rm – †€ 85/110 ††€ 150/220 –

Rest – (bar lunch and dinner weekdays) Menu € 45 – Carte € 33/47

◆ Very spacious and modern purpose built hotel, with huge bar, well-equipped leisure facilities and comfortable, contemporary bedrooms of generous proportions. Formal dining in restaurant.

Crockets on the Quay with rm

The Quay Village, Northeast : 2 1/2 km by N 59 – ✆ (096) 75 930 – info@crocketsonthequay.ie – Fax (096) 70 069 – Closed 25 December and Good Friday

8 rm – †€ 45/60 ††€ 80/90 – **Rest** – Carte € 28/47

◆ Friendly, atmospheric Irish pub on the river, with plasma screens, terrace and dining area in beamed former boat house. Hearty, fresh cooking uses quality ingredients. Modest bedrooms; 6, 7 and 8 are the quietest.

REPUBLIC OF IRELAND

BALLINADEE = Baile na Daidhche – **Cork** – **712** G 12 – **see Kinsale**

BALLINASLOE (Béal Átha na Sluaighe) – **Galway** – **712** H 8 – 36 **B3**

pop. 5 723 *Ireland*

Dublin 146 km – Galway 66 km – Limerick 106 km – Roscommon 58 km – Tullamore 55 km

✆ (0909) 742604 (July-August)

Rossgloss, ✆ (0905) 42 126 ;

Mountbellew, ✆ (0905) 79 259.

Clonfert Cathedral★ (west doorway★★), SW : by R 355 and minor roads. Turoe Stone, Bullaun★, SW : 29 km by R 348 and R 350 – Loughrea (St Brendan's Cathedral★), SW : 29 km by N 6 – Clonmacnoise★★★ (grave slabs★, Cross of the Scriptures★) E : 21 km by R 357 and R 444

Carlton Shearwater

Marina Point – ✆ (090) 963 0400 – info.shearwater@carlton.ie – Fax (090) 963 0401

84 rm – †€ 70/150 ††€ 130/280 – 20 suites –

Rest – Menu € 24/39 – Carte approx. € 41

◆ Striking building on edge of town centre, with huge lobby and lounge and two stylish bars. State-of-the-art leisure failities; large, modern bedrooms. Irish and European menu served in spacious restaurant.

Moycarn Lodge

Shannonbridge Rd, Southeast : 2 1/2 km by N 6 off R 357 – ✆ (090) 964 5050 – info@moycarnlodge.ie – Fax (090) 964 4760

15 rm – †€ 59 ††€ 99 – **Rest** – Menu € 13 (lunch) – Carte € 19/49

◆ Pleasant rural spot next to River Suck, with berthing available for boats and family cruisers for hire. Light, simply furnished bedrooms; some with river view. Hospitable owners. Rustically-styled restaurant.

BALLINCLASHET = Baile na Claise – **Cork** – **712** G 12 – **see Kinsale**

BALLINCOLLIG Cork – **712** D 12 38 **B3**

Oriel House & rm,

West : 1 km on A 608 – ✆ (021) 420 84 00 – info@orielhousehotel.ie – Fax (021) 487 58 80

76 rm – †€ 130 ††€ 160 – 2 suites –
Rest – Menu € 40 (dinner) – Carte approx. € 55

◆ Former manor house with modern extensions boasts smart spa, conference suite and contemporary bar. Most bedrooms are in the new wings; those at the rear are quieter. Simple menu served in smart, airy restaurant.

BALLINGARRY (Baile an Gharraí) – **Limerick** – **712** F 10 *Ireland* 38 **B2**

Dublin 227 km – Killarney 90 km – Limerick 29 km

Kilmallock★ (Kilmallock Abbey★, Collegiate Church★), SE : 24 km by R 518 – Lough Gur Interpretive Centre★ **AC**, NE : 29 km by R 519, minor road to Croom, R 516 and R 512 – Monasteranenagh Abbey★, NE : 24 km by R 519 and minor road to Croom

Mustard Seed at Echo Lodge & rm,

– ✆ (069) 68 508 – mustard@indigo.ie – Fax (069) 68 511 – closed 13 January-8 February, 24-27 December

13 rm – †€ 125 ††€ 160 – 2 suites – **Rest** – (closed Monday in winter) (dinner only) (booking essential for non-residents) Menu € 60

◆ Converted convent with very neat gardens and peaceful appeal. Cosy lounge with fireplace and beautiful fresh flowers. Individually furnished rooms with mix of antiques. Meals enlivened by home-grown herbs and organic farm produce.

BALLINROBE Mayo – **Mayo** – **712** E 7 – **pop. 2 098** 36 **B3**

Dublin 163 km – Castlebar 18 km – Galway 31 km – Westport 20 km

JJ Gannons with rm & rm,

Main St – ✆ (094) 954 1008 – info@jjgannons.com – Fax (094) 952 0018 – closed 25 December

10 rm – †€ 75/100 ††€ 150/200 – **Rest** – Carte € 24/43

◆ Stylish modern pub in very centre of town boasts seductive lighting, bucket chairs and banquettes, as well as dimly lit 'chill out' area and modern restaurant with terrace. Bedrooms in bold, bright colours; sleek bathrooms.

BALLINTOGHER Sligo – **Co Sligo** – **712** G 5 – **pop. 182** 36 **B2**

Dublin 135 km – Sligo 11 km – Carrick-on-Shannon 32 km – Castlerea 42 km

Kingsfort Country House without rest

– ✆ (071) 911 5111 – info@kingsfortcountryhouse.com – Fax (071) 911 5979 – Closed 23-26 December

8 rm – †€ 70/170 ††€ 120/180

◆ Relaxed French bohemian feel to converted 18C courthouse in centre of rural village; bedrooms in main house are larger; those in outbuilding are cosy and characterful.

BALLSBRIDGE = Droichead na Dothra – **Dublin** – **712** N 8 – **see Dublin**

BALLYBOFEY (Bealach Féich) – **Donegal** – **712** I 3 – **pop. 3 047** 37 **C1**

Dublin 238 km – Londonderry 48 km – Sligo 93 km

Ballybofey & Stranorlar The Glebe, ✆ (074) 31 093 .

Kee's

Main St, Stranorlar, Northeast : ¾ km on N 15 – ✆ (074) 913 10 18 – info@keeshotel.ie – Fax (074) 913 19 17

53 rm – †€ 78/105 ††€ 156/176 – **Rest** – Carte € 25/40

◆ Very comfortable hotel established over 150 years ago. Smart lobby with plush sofas. Atmospheric bar and raised lounge area. Comfortable rooms. Popular favourites served in the restaurant.

Villa Rose rm, rest, VISA AE

Main St – (074) 913 22 66 – info@villarose.net – Fax (074) 913 06 66 – Closed 25-26 December

58 rm – €65/99 €138/250 – **Rest** – Menu €19/35 – Carte €16/31

◆ Under private ownership, a modern hotel in the centre of the town. Neat, well-appointed accommodation, furnished in co-ordinated colours and fabrics. Bright, airy dining room with contemporary style and wide international choice.

BALLYBUNION (Baile an Bhuinneánaigh) – **Kerry** – **712** D 10 *Ireland* 38 **A2**

Dublin 283 km – Limerick 90 km – Tralee 42 km

Ballybunnion Sandhill Rd, (068) 27 146 .

Rattoo Round Tower★, S : 10 km by R 551. Ardfert★, S : 29 km by R 551, R 556 and minor road W – Banna Strand★, S : 28 km by R 551 – Carrigafoyle Castle★, NE : 21 km by R 551 – Glin Castle★ **AC**, E : 30½ km by R 551 and N 69

Harty Costello Townhouse VISA AE

Main St – (068) 27 129 – hartycostello@eircom.net – Fax (068) 27 489 – April-October

8 rm – €60/85 €120/185 – **Rest** – (closed Sunday) (dinner only) Menu €23/26 – Carte **s**

◆ This personally run hotel, set around and above the pub downstairs, is smart, stylish and contemporary. A popular choice for visitors to this golfing town. Local fish in spruce, welcoming restaurant.

Teach de Broc Country House rm, P VISA AE

Link Rd, South : 2½ km on Golf Club rd – (068) 27 581 – info@ballybunniongolf.com – Fax (068) 27 919 – April-October

14 rm – €90/150 €135/180 – **Rest** – (closed Monday) (dinner only) Carte €28/46

◆ Clean, tidy guesthouse with coastal proximity and great appeal to golfers as it's adjacent to the famous Ballybunion golf course. Home cooked meals. Neat, spacious rooms.

The 19th Lodge without rest P VISA

Golf Links Rd, South : 2¾ km by Golf Club rd – (068) 27 592 – the19thlodge@eircom.net – Fax (068) 27 830 – March-November

14 rm – €80/150 €130/200

◆ Orange washed house aimed at golfers playing at adjacent course. First floor lounge with honesty bar and comfy sofas. Linen-clad breakfast room. Luxurious rooms.

Cashen Course House without rest P VISA AE

Golf Links Rd, South : 2¾ km by Golf Club rd – (068) 27 351 – golfstay@eircom.net – Fax (068) 28 934 – closed 1 January-15 March

10 rm – €80/120 €130/150

◆ Overlooks first hole at the Cashen Course: clubhouse just one minute away. Bright, breezy breakfast room; quality furnishings in comfy lounge. Spacious, colourful rooms.

BALLYCASTLE (Baile an Chaisil) – **Mayo** – **712** D 5 *Ireland* 36 **B2**

Dublin 267 km – Galway 140 km – Sligo 88 km

Céide Fields★, AC, NE : 8 km by R 314

Stella Maris Bunatrahir Bay, rm, P VISA

Northwest : 3 km by R 314 – (096) 43 322 – info@stellamarisireland.com – Fax (096) 43 965 – April-September

11 rm – €155 €250 – **Rest** – (dinner only) Carte €37/47

◆ Former coastguard station and fort in a great spot overlooking the bay. Public areas include a long conservatory. Attractive rooms with antique and contemporary furnishings. Modern menus in stylish dining room.

BALLYCONNELL (Báal Atha Conaill) – **Cavan** – **712** J 5 37 **C2**

Dublin 143 km – Drogheda 122 km – Enniskillen 37 km
Slieve Russell, ✆ (049) 952 6458 .

Slieve Russell

Southeast : 2 ¾ km on N 87 – ✆ (049) 952 6444
– slieve-russell@quinn-hotels.com – Fax (049) 952 6474
218 rm (dinner included) – €115/210 €170/390 – 4 suites
Rest *Conall Cearnach* – (dinner only and Sunday lunch) Menu €28/47 **s**
Rest *Setanta* – Menu €18 (lunch) **s** – Carte €28/44 **s**

◆ Purpose-built hotel set in extensive gardens and golf course. Marbled entrance, large lounges, leisure and conference facilities. Spacious, modern rooms. Conall Cearnach has sophisticated appeal. Modern, informal, Mediterranean menu in Setanta.

Carnagh House without rest

Clinty, West : 3 km on N 87 – ✆ (049) 952 3300 – caraghhouse@eircom.net
– Fax (049) 952 3300
10 rm – €40/50 €65/70

◆ Modern guesthouse with pleasant rural aspect. Warmly run by owners: tea and sandwiches await guests on arrival. Comfortable lounge with views. Good-sized bedrooms.

The ✿ award is the crème de la crème.
This is awarded to restaurants
which are really worth travelling miles for!

REPUBLIC OF IRELAND

BALLYCOTTON (Baile Choitín) – **Cork** – **712** H 12 *Ireland* 39 **C3**

Dublin 265 km – Cork 43 km – Waterford 106 km
Cloyne Cathedral★, NW : by R 629

Bayview

< Ballycotton Bay and harbour,
– ✆ (021) 464 67 46 – res@thebayviewhotel.com – Fax (021) 464 60 75
– April-October
33 rm – €117/142 €170/220 – 2 suites – **Rest** – (bar lunch Monday-Saturday) Menu €35/55 – Carte €48/65

◆ A series of cottages in an elevated position with fine views of bay, harbour and island. Bar and lounge in library style with sofas. Spacious, comfy rooms with ocean views. Warm, inviting dining room.

BALLYDAVID (Baile na nGall) – **Kerry** – **712** A 11 – ✉ **Dingle** 38 **A2**

Dublin 362 km – Dingle 11 km – Tralee 58 km

Gorman's Clifftop House

< Smerwick Harbour, Ballydavid Head and the Three Sisters,
Glaise Bheag, North : 2 km on Feomanagh rd. – ✆ (066) 915 51 62
– info@gormans-clifftophouse.com – Fax (066) 915 50 03
– restricted opening in winter
9 rm – €95/135 €150/190 – **Rest** – (closed Sunday) (dinner only) Menu €40 – Carte €30/50

◆ Fine views of Ballydavid Head and the Three Sisters from this peaceful modern house. Cosy sitting room with log fire; stylish, spacious rooms in vibrant colours and old pine. Bright restaurant invites diners to look out over the water.

Old Pier

< Smerwick Harbour, Ballydavid Head and the Three Sisters,
An Fheothanach, North : 3 km on Feomanagh rd
– ✆ (066) 915 52 42 – info@oldpier.com
– March-November, restricted opening in Winter
5 rm – €45/55 €80/90 – **Rest** – (by arrangement) Menu €33 – Carte €26/58

◆ Run by the charming owner, a pretty clifftop house surveying the harbour and the Three Sisters. Immaculate rooms with bright bedspreads and cherrywood floors.

BALLYFERRITER - Kerry - **712** A 11 - ✉ **Dingle** Ireland 38 **A2**

Dublin 363 km – Killarney 85 km – Limerick 167 km
Ceann Sibeal, ✆ (066) 915 62 55.
Corca Dhuibhne Regional Museum★ **AC**
Gallarus Oratory★★, E : 4 km by F 559 – Kilmalkedar★, E : 8 km by R 559 – Slea Head★★ (beehive huts★), S : 14 km by R 559. Blasket Islands★, S : 8 km by R 559 and by boat from Dunquin – Connor Pass★★, NE : 24 km by R 559 and minor road

Smerwick Harbour

East : 4½ km on R 559 – ✆ (066) 915 64 70 – info@smerwickhotel.com – Fax (066) 915 64 73 – April-October

33 rm – †€ 50/85 ††€ 100/160 – **Rest** – Carte € 32/39 **s**

◆ Purpose-built hotel in dramatic Dingle Peninsula, Ireland's most westerly point. Large, atmospheric oak tavern with local artefacts. Sizeable rooms have spectacular views. Inviting dining room has fire with large brick surround.

BALLYGAWLEY Sligo - Sligo - **712** G 5 - **pop. 186** 36 **B2**

Dublin 131 km – Sligo 10 km – Ballina 38 km – Carrick-on-Shannon 29 km

Castle Dargan

rm, rest,

East : 1/2 km on R 290 – ✆ (071) 911 8080 – sales@castledargan.com – Fax (071) 911 8090

24 rm – †€ 99/165 ††€ 160/240 – 24 suites – **Rest** – Menu € 45 – Carte € 27/50

◆ Modern, annexed hotel with castle ruins in its extensive grounds. Contemporary bar and outside terrace with views over golf course. Well-equipped bedrooms. Dining room serves popular menus.

BALLYLICKEY (Béal Átha Leice) - Cork - **712** D 12 - ✉ **Bantry** Ireland 38 **A3**

Dublin 347 km – Cork 88 km – Killarney 72 km
Bantry Bay Donemark, ✆ (027) 50 579.
Bantry Bay★ - Bantry House★ **AC**, S : 5 km by R 584. Glengarriff★ (Ilnacullin★★, access by boat) NW : 13 km by N 71 - Healy Pass★★ (< ★★) W : 37 km by N 71, R 572 and R 574 – Slieve Miskish Mountains (< ★★) W : 46 ¾ km by N 71 and R 572 – Lauragh (Derreen Gardens★ **AC**) NW : 44 km by N 71, R 572 and R 574 – Allihies (copper mines★) W : 66 ¾ km by N 71, R 572 and R 575 – Garnish Island (< ★) W : 70 ¾ km by N 71 and R 572

Seaview House

rm,

– ✆ (027) 50 462 – info@seaviewhousehotel.com – Fax (027) 51 555 – mid March-mid November

25 rm – †€ 95/105 ††€ 165/220 – **Rest** – (dinner only and Sunday lunch) Menu € 45 **s**

◆ Tall, well-run, whitewashed Victorian house set amidst lush gardens which tumble down to Bantry Bay. Traditional lounges with bar and spacious, individually designed rooms. Warmly decorated dining room.

Ballylickey House without rest

(heated)

– ✆ (027) 50 071 – ballymh@eircom.net – Mid April-October

6 rm – †€ 80/95 ††€ 110/175

◆ Impressive hotel with attractive gardens set amongst Bantry Bay's ragged inlets. Spacious, cosy bedrooms, named after flowers and birds. Breakfast room with fireside armchairs.

Look out for red symbols, indicating particularly pleasant establishments.

BALLYLIFFIN – Donegal – 712 J 2 37 C1

Ballyliffin Lodge
Shore Rd – (074) 937 82 00 – info@ballyliffinlodge.com
– Fax (074) 937 89 85
40 rm – €105/120 €160/200 – **Rest** – (bar lunch Monday-Saturday) Menu €40 (dinner) – Carte €35/74
◆ Nick Faldo part-designed golf course set close to this new hotel with rural/beach views. Well-appointed lounge and good quality spa. Well-equipped rooms, some with sea vistas. Fine dining restaurant inspired by classical cuisine.

BALLYMACARBRY (Baile Mhac Cairbre) – Waterford – 712 I 11 – 39 C2
Clonmel *Ireland*

Dublin 190 km – Cork 79 km – Waterford 63 km
Clonmel★ (St Mary's Church★, County Museum★ AC), N : 16 km by R 671 – Lismore★ (Castle Gardens★ AC, St Carthage's Cathedral★), SW : 26 km by R 671and N 72 – W : Nier Valley Scenic Route★★

Hanora's Cottage
Nire Valley, East : 6½ km by Nire Drive rd and Nire Valley Lakes rd
– (052) 36 134 – hanorascottage@eircom.net – Fax (052) 36 540
– closed 1 week Christmas, 1 week after Easter, 1 week after October Bank Holiday
10 rm – €95 €190/250 – **Rest** – (closed Sunday) (dinner only) (booking essential for non-residents) Carte approx. €50
◆ Pleasant 19C farmhouse with purpose-built extensions in quiet location at foot of mountains. Very extensive and impressive breakfast buffet. Stylish rooms, all with jacuzzis. Locally renowned menus, brimming with fresh produce.

Glasha Farmhouse

Northwest : 4 km by R 671 – (052) 36 108 glasha@eircom.net
– Fax (052) 36 108
– closed 1-28 December
6 rm – €60/65 €100/120 – **Rest** – (by arrangement) Carte €25/40
◆ Immaculate farmhouse rurally set on working farm. Garden water feature is focal point. Spacious conservatory. Wonderful breakfasts with huge choice. Neat, tidy rooms.

Cnoc-na-Ri without rest
Nire Valley, East : 6 km on Nire Drive rd – (052) 36 239
– richardharte@eircom.net
– February-October
5 rm – €45 €70/80
◆ Purpose-built guesthouse situated in the heart of the unspoilt Nire Valley, a perfect location for walking holidays. Immaculately kept, clean and spacious bedrooms.

BALLYMOTE – Sligo – 712 G 5 – Sligo 36 B2

Dublin 199 km – Longford 77 km – Sligo 24 km
Ballymote Ballinascarrow, (071) 83 504 .

Mill House without rest

Keenaghan – (071) 918 34 49 – millhousebb@eircom.net
– March-October
6 rm – €35/51 €66/70
◆ Simple guesthouse situated on edge of busy market town. Very friendly welcome. Small, comfortable sitting room. Light, airy breakfast room. Spacious, immaculate bedrooms.

REPUBLIC OF IRELAND

BALLYNAHINCH (Baile na hInse) – Galway – 712 C 7 – ✉ Recess 36 A3

Ireland

Dublin 225 km – Galway 66 km – Westport 79 km

Connemara★★★ – Roundstone★, S : by R 341 – Cashel★, SE : by R 341 and R 340

Ballynahinch Castle ← Owenmore River and woods,

– ✆ (095) 31 006 – bhinch@iol.ie

– Fax (095) 31 085

– *Closed February and 2 weeks Christmas*

37 rm – ♦€ 140/160 ♦♦€ 210/410 – 3 suites –

Rest – (bar lunch) (booking essential for non-residents) Menu € 55

♦ Grey stone, part 17C castle in magnificent grounds with fine river views. Two large sitting rooms, characterful bar frequented by fishermen. Spacious rooms with antiques. Inviting dining room with stunning river views.

REPUBLIC OF IRELAND

BALLYNAMULT (Béal na Molt) – Waterford 39 C2

Dublin 194 km – Clonmel 21 km – Waterford 63 km

Sliabh gCua Farmhouse without rest

Tooraneena, Southeast : 2 km – ✆ (058) 47 120

– *breedacullinan@sliabhgcua.com*

– *April-October*

4 rm – ♦€ 50 ♦♦€ 90

♦ Creeper clad early 19C house in quiet hamlet with rural views. Tea and scones on arrival. Comfy lounge with real fire. Individually decorated rooms boast period furniture.

BALLYSHANNON (Béal Atha Seanaidh) – Donegal – 712 H 4 – pop. 2 775 39 D2

Dublin 53 km – Donegal 272 km – Letterkenny 283 km – Sligo 215 km

Heron's Cove

Creevy, Northwest : 3 km on R 231 – ✆ (071) 982 20 70 – *info@heronscove.ie*

– *Fax (071) 982 20 75*

– *closed last three weeks January, 24-28 December*

10 rm – ♦€ 83/99 ♦♦€ 120/150 –

Rest – (closed Sunday-Tuesday in winter) (dinner only and Sunday lunch) Menu € 25/48 – Carte approx. € 48

♦ A well priced, friendly and informal destination on the road to Rossnowlagh. Identical bedrooms are clean and light with contemporary soft furnishings. An informal dining room offers a good choice menu with local seafood specialities.

BALLYVAUGHAN (Baile Uí Bheacháin) – Clare – 712 E 8 – pop. 257 38 B1

Ireland

Dublin 240 km – Ennis 55 km – Galway 46 km

The Burren★★ (Scenic Route★★, Aillwee Cave★ **AC** (Waterfall★★), Corcomroe Abbey★, Poulnabrone Portal Tomb★) – Kilfenora (Crosses★, Burren Centre★ **AC**), S : 25 km N 67 and R 476. Cliffs of Moher★★★, S : 32 km by N 67 and R 478

Gregans Castle ← countryside and Galway Bay,

Southwest : 6 km on N 67 – ✆ (065) 707 7005

– *stay@gregans.ie* – *Fax (065) 707 7111*

– *14 February-1 December*

17 rm – ♦€ 153/193 ♦♦€ 195/235 – 4 suites –

Rest – (bar lunch) Carte € 46/56 **s**

♦ Idyllically positioned, family owned hotel with fine views to The Burren and Galway Bay. Relaxing sitting room, cosy bar lounge, country house-style bedrooms. Sizeable conservatory dining room specialising in seasonal, regional dishes.

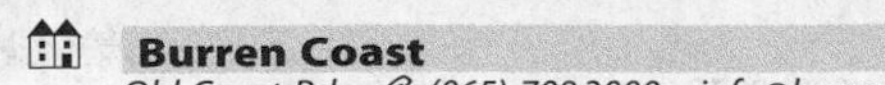

Burren Coast rm,
Old Coast Rd – (065) 708 3000 – info@burrencoast.ie – Fax (065) 708 3001
20 rm – †€ 100/140 ††€ 150/250 – **Rest** – (weekends only in winter) Carte € 30/43
◆ Tucked away on western side of village, this modern hotel boasts comfortable, stylish bedrooms, a traditional beamed bar and garden terrace which looks onto pretty quay. Restaurant with mezzanine floor offers traditional menu.

Drumcreehy House without rest
Northeast : 2 km on N 67 – (065) 707 73 77 – info@drumcreehyhouse.com – Fax (065) 707 73 79 – booking essential in winter
10 rm – †€ 56/100 ††€ 100/120
◆ Pristine house overlooking Galway Bay. Bedrooms are excellent value: spacious, comfortable and furnished in German stripped oak.

Rusheen Lodge without rest
Southwest : 1 km on N 67 – (065) 707 70 92 – rusheen@iol.ie – Fax (065) 707 71 52 – mid February-mid November
8 rm – †€ 65/70 ††€ 90/100 – 1 suite
◆ Cheery yellow façade decked with flowers, lounge with fine sofas and rooms in pale woods and floral patterns. Pretty gardens complete the picture. Charming, welcoming owner.

Ballyvaughan Lodge without rest
– (065) 707 72 92 – ballyvau@iol.ie – Fax (065) 707 72 87 – closed 24-28 December
11 rm – †€ 45/65 ††€ 80/90
◆ Red hued guesthouse, attractively furnished throughout. Light and airy sitting room with large windows. Home-made bread and jams for breakfast. Clean, tidy bedrooms.

Cappabhaile House without rest
Southwest : 1½ km on N 67 – (065) 707 72 60 – cappabhaile@oceanfree.net – March-October
8 rm – †€ 60/80 ††€ 84/100
◆ Stone clad bungalow with pleasant gardens and good views across the Burren. Spacious open-plan lounge-cum-breakfast room with central fireplace. Very large, spotless rooms.

BALTIMORE (Dún na Séad) – Cork – 712 D 13 *Ireland* 38 **A3**

Dublin 344 km – Cork 95 km – Killarney 124 km
Sherkin Island★ (by ferry) – Castletownshend★, E : 20 km by R 595 and R 596 – Glandore★, E : 26 km by R 595, N 71 and R 597

Casey's of Baltimore rest,
East : ¾ km on R 595 – (028) 20 197 – info@caseysofbaltimore.com – Fax (028) 20 509 – closed 20-27 December
14 rm – †€ 100/115 ††€ 154/182 – **Rest** – Carte € 31/49
◆ Popular hotel near sea-shore. Cosy bar with open fires and traditional music at weekends, with beer garden overlooking bay. Large, well-decorated rooms with pine furniture. Great sea views from dining room.

Baltimore Townhouse without rest
– (028) 20 197 – info@baltimoretownhouse.com – Fax (028) 20 509
6 rm – †€ 120/150 ††€ 120/150
◆ Six open plan suites comprising bedroom, living area, small kitchen and bathroom: check in at Casey's on your way into village. Freshly baked bread delivered in morning.

Slipway without rest — Baltimore Harbour,

The Cove, East : ¾ km – (028) 20 134 – theslipway@hotmail.com – Fax (028) 20 134 – April-October

4 rm – €65/75 €72/80

◆ Relaxed, informal guesthouse with yellow façade and lovely views of local harbour, particularly from veranda outside breakfast room. Simple, individualistic, well-kept rooms.

Customs House

Main St – (028) 20 200 – gillian@thecustomshouse.com – April-September

Rest – (weekends only April, May and September, closed Monday and Tuesday in June, Monday in July and August) (dinner only) (booking essential) Menu €38/48

◆ Converted customs house, consisting of three small rooms with a painted wood floor, decorated with modern art. Good value menu: all dishes are tasty and carefully prepared.

Good food and accommodation at moderate prices?
Look for the Bib symbols:
red Bib Gourmand for food, blue Bib Hotel for hotels

REPUBLIC OF IRELAND

BANDON Cork – Cork – 712 F 12 – pop. 4 101 — 38 B3

Dublin 181 km – Cork 20 km – Carrigaline 28 km – Cobh 33 km

Poacher's Inn

Clanakilty Rd, Southwest : 1 1/2 km on N 71 – (023) 41 159

Rest – Carte €28/41

◆ Busy refurbished pub with downstairs bar, sofas and wood burning stove; simple menu served all day. Small restaurant upstairs offers larger selection, including lots of fish.

BANGOR (Baingear) – Mayo – 712 C 5 *Ireland* — 36 A2

Dublin 281 km – Ballina 42 km – Westport 63 km

Cáide Fields★ AC, NE : 30 km by minor road and R 314

Teach Iorrais — rm, rest,

Geesala, Southwest : 12 km on Geesala rd – (097) 86 888 – teachlor@iol.ie – Fax (097) 86 855

31 rm – €61/75 €72/120 – **Rest** – (bar lunch Monday-Saturday) Menu €20 (lunch) – Carte €33/41

◆ Purpose-built hotel with views of Neifin mountains. Public bar with live music at weekends and quieter residents lounge. Bright bedrooms, those to the front with best views. Charming views from window tables of Gothic styled restaurant.

BANTRY Cork – 712 D 12 – pop. 2 936 — 38 A3

The Maritime — Bantry Bay, rm,

The Quay – (027) 54 700 – info@themaritime.ie – Fax (027) 54 701

114 rm – €120/180 €150/280

Rest – Carte approx. €50

Rest *Ocean* – Carte approx. €50

◆ Situated on the quayside, with a modern style and spacious feel. Smart, comfortable bedrooms; the best at the front have a bay view, and 4th floor suites have a roof terrace. Bar offers carvery in informal atmosphere. Ocean restaurant offers traditional fare.

BARNA (Bearna) – **Galway** – **712** E 8 36 **B3**

Dublin 227 km – Galway 9 km

The Twelve

rm, AC, VISA, MC, AE, DC

Barna Crossroads – (091) 597 000 – enquire@thetwelvehotel.ie – Fax (091) 597 003

38 rm – €112/150 €120/160 – 10 suites

Rest *West* – (Closed Sunday dinner and Monday) (dinner only and Sunday lunch) Menu €26/39 – Carte €37/46

Rest *The Pins* – Menu €25 – Carte €26/32 **s**

◆ Boutique hotel whose bedrooms are stylish and modern with quality furniture, up-to-date technology and designer toiletries. Original menu offered in elegant West restaurant. The Pins offers an interesting menu of European dishes in an informal atmosphere.

O'Grady's on the Pier

Barna Harbour and Galway Bay, AC, VISA, MC, AE

– (091) 592 223 – ogradysonthepier@hotmail.com – Fax (091) 590 677 – Closed 1 week Christmas and lunch Monday-Saturday November-April

Rest – Seafood (booking essential) Carte €20/50

◆ Converted quayside pub on two floors with great views of Galway Bay. Cheerful, attentive staff and daily menus of simple, flavourful seafood have earned good local reputation.

BARRELLS CROSS – **Cork** – **see Kinsale**

BEAUFORT = Lios an Phúca – **Kerry** – **712** D 11 – **see Killarney**

BELMULLET **Mayo** – **Mayo** 36 **A2**

Dublin 200 km – Castlebar 47 km – Crossmolina 32 km

Broadhaven Bay

rm, VISA, MC

– (097) 20 600 – info@broadhavenbay.com – Fax (097) 20 610

88 rm – €80/140 €120/190 –

Rest – Menu €30 (dinner) – Carte €30/45

◆ Smart hotel on the eastern side of town with good view over sea, towards mountains. Spacious lobby, quality bedrooms and modern bar/lounge popular with locals. Linen-clad restaurant with coastal aspect.

BETTYSTOWN (Baile an Bhiataigh) – **Co Meath** – **712** N 6 – **pop. 5 597** 37 **D3**

Dublin 46 km – Drogheda 10 km – Dundalk 59 km

Bettystown Court

rm, AC rest, VISA, MC, AE, DC

– (041) 981 2900 – info@bettystowncourthotel.com – Fax (041) 981 2989

116 rm – €110/140 €190/220 – 4 suites –

Rest – (bar lunch Monday-Saturday) Menu €30 (dinner) – Carte €20/42

◆ Unimposing façade belies light, airy interior featuring stylish conference and leisure facilities. Spacious bedrooms continue contemporary theme; those at back have sea view. Restaurant serves traditional Irish dishes with a modern twist. Carvery at Sunday lunch.

Do not confuse with !
defines comfort, while stars are awarded for the best cuisine, across all categories of comfort.

BIRR – Offaly – **712** I 8 – **pop. 4 193** *Ireland* 39 **C1**

Dublin 140 km – Athlone 45 km – Kilkenny 79 km – Limerick 79 km
Brendan St ✆ (0509) 20110
The Glenns, ✆ (0509) 20 082.
Town★ – Birr Castle Demesne★★ **AC** (Telescope★★)
Clonfert Cathedral★ (West doorway★★), NW : 24 km by R 439, R 356 and minor roads – Portumna★ (Castle★ **AC**), W : 24 km by R 489 – Roscrea★ (Damer House★ **AC**) S : 19 ¼ km by N 62 – Slieve Bloom Mountinas★, E : 21 km by R 440

The Maltings

Castle St – ✆ (057) 91 21 345 – themaltingsbirr@eircom.net – Fax (057) 91 22 073 – Closed 24-27 December

13 rm – €55 €80 – **Rest** – (Closed dinner in winter) Menu €30 – Carte €18/30

◆ Characterful 19C hotel on riverside near Birr Castle, originally built to store malt for Guinness. Cosy bar and lounge. Bedrooms enriched by flowery fabrics and drapes. Sizeable, bustling restaurant with chintz fabrics and spot lighting.

BLACKLION (An Blaic) – **Cavan** – **712** I 5 37 **C2**

Dublin 194 km – Drogheda 170 km – Enniskillen 19 km
Blacklion Toam, ✆ (072) 53 024 .

Mac Nean House with rm

Main St – ✆ (071) 985 30 22 – info@macneanhouse.com – Fax (071) 985 34 04 – Closed January-12 February

10 rm – €80 €160 –
Rest – (Closed Monday-Wednesday) (dinner only and Sunday lunch) (booking essential) Menu €65

◆ Family run, contemporary restaurant with stylish lounge in the heart of border town. Local produce to the fore in high quality, original menus. Refurbished bedrooms.

We try to be as accurate as possible when giving room rates. But prices are susceptible to change, so please check rates when booking.

BLARNEY (An Bhlarna) – **Cork** – **712** G 12 – **pop. 1 963** – ✉ **Cork** 38 **B3**
Ireland

Dublin 268 km – Cork 9 km
✆ (021) 4381624
Blarney Castle★★ **AC** – Blarney Castle House★ **AC**

Killarney House without rest

Station Rd, Northeast : 1 ½ km – ✆ (021) 438 18 41 – info@killarneyhouseblarney.com – Fax (021) 438 18 41

6 rm – €47/55 €66/76

◆ Spacious, modern guesthouse set above attractive village. Very comfortable lounge. Breakfast room equipped to high standard. Sizeable, immaculately kept rooms.

at Tower West : 3 ¼ km on R 617 – ✉ Cork

Ramada rm,

– ✆ (021) 438 4477 – info.blarney@ramada.com – Fax (021) 451 6453

60 rm – €85/110 €95/120 – 4 suites –
Rest – Menu €40 (dinner) – Carte €36/46

◆ Two storey, purpose built hotel set around John Daly designed 18 hole golf course. Traditional bedrooms all have views; the more popular executive-style rooms have balconies. Traditional Irish fare served in restaurant.

Ashlee Lodge

– ✆ (021) 438 53 46 – info@ashleelodge.com – Fax (021) 438 57 26
– closed 20 December-20 January
10 rm – €75/95 €100/140 – **Rest** – (closed Sunday-Monday) (dinner only) Carte €31/50 **s**

◆ Relaxing modern house, ideally located for Blarney Castle. Breakfast room with extensive menu. Outdoor Canadian hot tub. Very well-equipped rooms, some with whirlpool baths.

Maranatha Country House without rest

East : 3/4 km on R 617 – ✆ (021) 438 51 02
– info@maranathacountryhouse.com – Fax (021) 438 29 78
– 19 February - November
6 rm – €50/90 €70/120

◆ Charming Victorian house in acres of peaceful grounds. Antique furnished drawing room. Relaxing, individual bedrooms, one lined with books, another with a large circular bath.

BOYLE (Mainistir na Búille) – Roscommon – 712 H 6 – pop. 1 690 36 B2

Ireland

Dublin 175 km – Longford 53 km – Sligo 45 km
King House★ AC
Boyle Abbey★ AC, E : 2 km by N 4 – Lough Key Forest Park★ AC, E : 3 1/4 km by N 4. Arigna Scenic Drive★ (< ★), NE : 20 km by N 4, R 280 and R 207 – Curlew Mountains (< ★), NW : 3 1/2 km by N 4

Rosdarrig House without rest

Dublin Rd – ✆ (071) 966 20 40 – rosdarrig@yahoo.co.uk
5 rm – €50 €70/75

◆ Comfortable, well-kept guesthouse with friendly owners. Attractive lounge and appealing wood-floored breakfast room. Good sized, smartly decorated rooms overlooking garden.

BRAY (Bré) – Wicklow – 712 N 8 – pop. 27 923 *Ireland* 39 D1

Dublin 21 km – Wicklow 32 km
Woodbrook Dublin Rd, ✆ (01) 282 4799 ;
Old Conna Ferndale Rd, ✆ (01) 282 6055 ;
Greystones Rd, ✆ (01) 276 3200 .
Powerscourt★★ (Waterfall★★ AC) W : 6 1/2 km - Killruddery House and Gardens★ AC, S : 3 1/4 km by R 761. Wicklow Mountains★★

Ramada Woodland Court

Southern Cross, South : 4 km by R 761 on Greystones rd
– ✆ (01) 276 0258 – info@ramadawoodlandcourt.com – Fax (01) 276 0298
– closed 24-26 December
86 rm – €75/85 €85, €10 – **Rest** – (bar lunch) Menu €25 – Carte €26/35 **s**

◆ Bright, yellow painted hotel and smart garden. Warm lounge and bar boasts burgundy and dark green sofas and chairs. Comfortable rooms with thick carpeting and rich décor. Afternoon tea a staple of airy restaurant.

Cape Greko

51 Main St Bray / Bré – ✆ (01) 286 0006 – info@capegreko.ie
– Closed 25-26 December, Good Friday and lunch Monday-Wednesday
Rest – Greek Menu €20 – Carte €27/37

◆ Spacious and homely restaurant with simple wood tables and sasso floor. Fresh, authentic and appealing Greek dishes include all the holiday favourites. Efficient service.

BUNBEG – Donegal – 712 H 2 *Ireland* 37 C1

Dublin 314 km – Donegal 106 km – Londonderry 88 km

The Rosses★, S : by R 257

Ostan Gweedore

< Gweedore Bay,

– ✆ (074) 953 11 77 – reservations@ostangweedore.com
– Fax (074) 953 17 26
– weekends only November-March

31 rm – †€ 95/105 ††€ 169/185 – 3 suites

Rest *Restaurant* – (dinner only) Carte € 21/48 **s**

Rest *Sundowner* – Tapas (dinner only) Carte € 20/28 **s**

◆ Traditional hotel in a prominent position commanding spectacular views over Gweedore Bay. Large bar and pleasant sitting room. Treatment room. Classic, spacious bedrooms. Fresh, local produce to fore in Restaurant. Tapas menus in informal Sundowner.

BUNCLODY – Co. Wexford – 712 M 10 39 D2

The Carlton Millrace

rm,

Carrigduff – ✆ (053) 937 51 00 – reservationsmillrace@carlton.ie
– Fax (053) 937 51 24

56 rm – †€ 120/150 ††€ 190/250 – 16 suites

Rest *Lady Lucys* – (dinner only) Carte € 30/50 **s**

Rest *Bistro* – Carte € 23/44 **s**

◆ A family friendly hotel of vivid hues which also incorporates meeting facilties and sizable leisure centre. Spacious family apartments and suites are in adjacent block. Panoramic views from fourth floor Lady Lucys; formal menus. All-day, popular Bistro.

Undecided between two equivalent establishments?
Within each category, establishments are classified
in our order of preference.

BUNDORAN – Donegal – 712 H 4 – pop. 1 796 *Ireland* 37 C2

Dublin 259 km – Donegal 27 km – Sligo 37 km

The Bridge, Main St ✆ (071) 9842539 (April-October)

Creevykeel Court Cairn★, S : 5 km by N 15 – Rossnowlagh Strand★★, N : 8½ km by N 15 and R 231

Fitzgerald's

– ✆ (071) 984 13 36 – info@fitzgeraldshotel.com – Fax (071) 984 21 21
– restricted opening in winter

16 rm – †€ 68/84 ††€ 105/145

Rest *The Bistro* – (closed Monday-Tuesday except residents July-August) (dinner only) Menu € 32 – Carte € 27/38 **s**

◆ Family owned hotel in centre of popular seaside town overlooking Donegal Bay. Reception rooms warmed by wood-burning stove. Sumptuous sofas abound. Sea-facing front bedrooms. Linen-clad, informal Bistro with carefully compiled menu.

BUNRATTY (Bun Raite) – Clare – 712 F 9 *Ireland* 38 B2

Dublin 207 km – Ennis 24 km – Limerick 13 km

Town★★ – Bunratty Castle★★

Bunratty Manor

rm,

– ✆ (061) 707 984 – bunrattymanor@eircom.net – Fax (061) 360 588
– Closed 22 December-6 January

23 rm – †€ 95/115 ††€ 135/165 – **Rest** – (Closed Sunday) (dinner only) Menu € 45 – Carte € 39/49

◆ Purpose-built, tourist-oriented hotel in village centre. Comfy lounge with chintz suites; Neat, modern rooms in colourful fabrics and drapes. Smart terrace fringed by pleasant garden. Popular menus.

Bunratty Grove without rest
Castle Rd, North : 2½ km – ✆ (061) 369 579 – bunrattygrove@eircom.net – Fax (061) 369 561 – closed 20 December-2 January
6 rm – €50/70 €65/75
◆ Pink painted guesthouse on country road with peaceful ambience. Large lounge-cum-library and pleasant, cottagey breakfast room. Immaculate rooms with polished wood floors.

Bunratty Woods without rest
Low Rd, North : 1½ km – ✆ (061) 369 689 – bunratty@iol.ie – Fax (061) 369 454 – April-November
14 rm – €60/70 €110/120
◆ Characterful guesthouse with large front garden. Owner collects and restores assorted items to decorate rooms, such as farmyard tools and old food tins. Sizeable bedrooms.

BUTLERSTOWN = Baile an Bhuitléaraigh – **Waterford** – **see Waterford**

CAHERDANIEL (Cathair Dónall) – **Kerry** – **712** B 12 – ✉ **Killarney** 38 **A3**
Ireland

Dublin 383 km – Killarney 77 km
Ring of Kerry★★ – Derrynane National Historic Park★★ – Skellig Islands★★ **AC**, by boat – Sneem★, E : 19 km by N 70 – Staigue Fort★, E : 8 km by N 70 and minor road

Iskeroon without rest
West : 8 m. by N 70, Bunavalla Pier rd taking left turn at junction then turning left onto track immediately before pier – ✆ (066) 947 51 19 – info@iskeroon.com – Fax (066) 947 54 88 – May-September, minimum stay 2 nights
3 rm – €100 €150
◆ A "design icon", this low-lying house looking out to Derrynane Harbour was built in 1930s by the Earl of Dunraven. Lush gardens; boldly designed, vividly coloured bedrooms.

Derrynane Bay House without rest
West : ¾ km on N 70 – ✆ (066) 947 54 04 – derrynanebayhouse@eircom.net – Fax (066) 947 54 36 – 15 March-October
6 rm – €50/60 €76/80
◆ Purpose-built house on the Ring of Kerry with vast views over namesake bay. Stone Age monuments in the surrounding hills. Family-friendly; spacious bedrooms.

CAHERLISTRANE (Cathair Loistreáin) – **Galway** – **712** E 7 36 **B3**

Dublin 256 km – Ballina 74 km – Galway 42 km

Lisdonagh House
Northwest : 2½ km by Shrule rd – ✆ (093) 31 163 – cooke@lisdonagh.com – Fax (093) 31 528 – May-October
10 rm – €120/170 €240/280 – 4 suites – **Rest** – Carte €39/49 **s**
◆ Georgian house overlooking Lough Hacket; row across to island in the middle. A grand entrance hall with fine murals leads to antique filled rooms named after Irish artists. Locally caught fish predominant in dining room.

Your opinions are important to us: please write and let us know about your discoveries and experiences – good and bad!

REPUBLIC OF IRELAND

CAHERSIVEEN (Cathair Saidhbhín) – Kerry – 712 B 12 Ireland 38 A2

Dublin 355 km – Killarney 64 km

Ring of Kerry★★

O'Neill's (The Point) Seafood Bar

≤ Valencia Harbour and Island, P

Renard Point, Southwest : 2 ¾ km by N 70 – ☎ (066) 947 2165 – oneillsthepoint@eircom.net – Fax (087) 259 2165

– Closed November to mid December; January-April, Monday-Thursday lunch Friday-Sunday lunch April to mid-May

Rest – Seafood (bookings not accepted) Carte approx. € 30

◆ At the end of a road leading to Valencia Island ferry, this simply furnished pub offers concise menus of dishes, all seafood based, freshly prepared, unpretentiously served.

CAMPILE (Ceann Poill) – Wexford – 712 L 11 Ireland 39 D2

Dublin 154 km – Waterford 35 km – Wexford 37 km

Dunbrody Abbey★, S : 3 ¼ km by R 733 – J F Kennedy Arboretum★, N : 3 ¼ km by R 733. Tintern Abbey★, SE : 12 ¾ km by R 733 – Duncannon Fort★, S : 12 ¾ km by R 733

Kilmokea Country Manor

≤ rm, P VISA AE

West : 8 km by R 733 and Great Island rd – ☎ (051) 388 109

– kilmokea@eircom.net – Fax (051) 388 776

– Restricted opening in winter

6 rm – †€ 75/155 ††€ 180/300 – **Rest** – (booking essential for non-residents) Menu € 50 (dinner) **s** – Carte € 25/35 **s**

◆ Former Georgian rectory in large public gardens. Elegantly furnished. Games room, tennis and fishing. Comfortable bedrooms in house and converted stable block. Formal dining room with polished tables and period style; breakfast in conservatory.

The ✿ award is the crème de la crème. This is awarded to restaurants which are really worth travelling miles for!

CAPPOQUIN (Ceapach Choinn) – Waterford – 712 I 11 Ireland 39 C2

Dublin 219 km – Cork 56 km – Waterford 64 km

Lismore★ (Lismore Castle Gardens★ **AC**, St Carthage's Cathedral★), W : 6½ km by N 72. The Gap★ (≤ ★) NW : 14½ km by R 669

Richmond House with rm

P VISA AE

Southeast : ¾ km on N 72 – ☎ (058) 54 278 – info@richmondhouse.net

– Fax (058) 54 988

– Closed 23 December-20 January and Monday

9 rm – †€ 70/140 ††€ 150/200 – **Rest** – (dinner only) Menu € 55

◆ Built for Earl of Cork and Burlington in 1704; retains Georgian style with stately, cove-ceilinged dining room: local produce to the fore. Individually decorated period rooms.

at Millstreet East : 11 ¼ km by N 72 on R 671 – ✉ Cappoquin

Castle Country House

P VISA AE

– ☎ (058) 68 049 – castlefm@iol.ie – Fax (058) 68 099

– April-October

5 rm (dinner included) – ††€ 90/110 – **Rest** – (by arrangement) Menu € 35

◆ Extended farmhouse on working dairy and beef farm with 15C origins. Rural location and lovely gardens. Individual bedrooms with cottage style decor.

CARAGH LAKE (Loch Cárthaí) – Kerry – 712 C 11 Ireland 38 A2

Dublin 341 km – Killarney 35 km – Tralee 40 km
Dooks Glenbeigh, ✆ (066) 976 82 05 .
Lough Caragh★
Iveragh Peninsula★★ (Ring of Kerry★★)

Ard-Na-Sidhe
– ✆ (066) 976 91 05 – hotelsales@liebherr.com – Fax (066) 976 92 82
– May-16 October
18 rm – €150/270 €170/300 – **Rest** – (Closed Monday) (dinner only) (booking essential for non-residents) Carte €41/53
◆ Built 1880 by an English Lady who called it "House of Fairies". Elizabethan in style; gardens lead down to lake. Possesses atmosphere of private home. Antique filled rooms. Tasteful dining room with intimate feel.

Carrig Country House Lough Caragh,
– ✆ (066) 976 91 00 – info@carrighouse.com
– Fax (066) 976 91 66
– March-November
17 rm – €125/140 €150/180 – **Rest** – (dinner only) (booking essential for non-residents) Carte €29/49
◆ Down a wooded drive, the yellow ochre façade of the house immediately strikes you. Its loughside setting assures good views. Ground floor rooms have their own private patio. Caragh Lough outlook from dining room windows.

Red = Pleasant. Look for the red and symbols.

REPUBLIC OF IRELAND

CARLINGFORD (Cairlinn) – Louth – 712 N 5 Ireland 37 D2

Dublin 106 km – Dundalk 21 km
Town★
Windy Gap★, NW : 12 ¾ km by R 173 – Proleek Dolmen★, SW : 14½ km by R 173

Four Seasons rm, rest,
– ✆ (042) 937 35 30 – info@fshc.ie – Fax (042) 937 35 31
59 rm – €95/129 €130/198 – **Rest** – (bar lunch Monday-Saturday) Menu €42 **s** – Carte €33/38 **s**
◆ Impressive purpose-built hotel on outskirts of scenic market town. Extensive conference facilities; smart leisure centre. Spacious and well-equipped bedrooms. Popular bar leading to intimate dining room with Irish menus.

Beaufort House without rest
– ✆ (042) 937 38 79 – michaelcaine@beauforthouse.net – Fax (042) 937 38 78
5 rm – €100 €100
◆ Modern house attractively sited on shores of Carlingford Lough. Very comfortable, spacious rooms with sea or mountain views. Substantial breakfasts served overlooking lough.

CARLOW (Ceatharlach) – Carlow – 712 L 9 – pop. 14 979 39 D2

Dublin 80 km – Kilkenny 37 km – Wexford 75 km
Tullow St ✆ (059) 9131554
Carlow Dublin Rd, Deer Park, ✆ (0503) 31 695 .

Seven Oaks
Athy Rd – ✆ (059) 913 13 08 – info@sevenoakshotel.com – Fax (059) 913 21 55
– Closed 25-26 December
89 rm – €75/160 €140/180 – **Rest** – (carvery lunch Saturday) Menu €25/38 **s** – Carte dinner €22/35 **s**
◆ Close to the sights of the River Barrow walk, this neat hotel in a residential area makes a good resting place. Well-kept rooms: ask for those on first or second floor. Intimate booths in tranquil dining room.

Barrowville Town House without rest
Kilkenny Rd, South : 3/4 km on N 9 – ✆ (059) 914 33 24 – barrowvilletownhouse@eircom.net – Fax (059) 914 19 53 – Closed 24-27 December
7 rm – †€ 50/70 ††€ 100/120
◆ Regency townhouse professionally managed. Its conservatory breakfast room looks out over the garden containing ancient grape producing vine. Orthopaedic beds in all rooms.

CARNAROSS – **Meath** – **712** L 6 – ✉ **Kells** 37 **D3**
Dublin 69 km – Cavan 43 km – Drogheda 48 km

The Forge
Pottlereagh, Northwest : 5½ km by N 3 on Oldcastle rd – ✆ (046) 924 50 03 – theforgerest@eircom.net – Fax (046) 924 59 17 – Closed 24-26, 31 December-2 January, Sunday dinner and Monday
Rest – (dinner only and Sunday lunch) Menu € 40 – Carte € 41/50
◆ Former forge tucked away in rural isolation. Family run, traditionally styled restaurant serving tried-and-tested dishes with modern twist: ample, good value choice.

CARNE – **Wexford** – **712** M 11 39 **D3**
Dublin 169 km – Waterford 82 km – Wexford 21 km

The Lobster Pot
– ✆ (053) 913 1110 – Fax (053) 913 1401 – Closed January, 1 week February, 25-26 December Monday lunch, Good Friday and Tuesday after Bank Holiday Monday
Rest – Seafood Carte € 35/55
◆ Idiosyncratic pub crammed with engaging clutter: ornaments, pictures and metal signs. Friendly staff serve fish orientated dishes against the background of Irish music.

CARRICKMACROSS – **Monaghan** – **712** L 6 – **pop. 3 832** *Ireland* 37 **D2**
Dublin 92 km – Dundalk 22 km
Nuremore, ✆ (042) 967 1368 .
Dún a' Rí Forest Park★, SW : 8 km by R 179 – St Mochta's House★, E : 7 km by R 178 and minor road S

Nuremore
South : 1½ km on N 2 – ✆ (042) 966 14 38 – info@nuremore.com – Fax (042) 966 18 53
72 rm – †€ 150 ††€ 230/285
Rest ***The Restaurant*** – see restaurant listing
◆ Much extended Victorian house in attractive grounds; a rural retreat in which to swim, ride or practice golf. Comfortable rooms, most with views over countryside.

The Restaurant – at Nuremore H.
South : 1½ km on N 2 – ✆ (042) 966 14 38 – Fax (042) 966 18 53 – Closed Saturday lunch
Rest – Menu € 28/52 **s**
◆ Split-level dining room; tables laid with white linen, bone china and stylish glassware. Menu of seasonal dishes influenced by French fine dining. Attentive service.

CARRICK-ON-SHANNON – **Leitrim** – **712** H 6 – **pop. 2 237** *Ireland* 37 **C2**
Dublin 156 km – Ballina 80 km – Galway 119 km – Roscommon 42 km – Sligo 55 km
Old Barrel Store ✆ (0719) 620170 (April-October)
Carrick-on-Shannon Woodbrook, ✆ (079) 67 015 .
Town★
Lough Rynn Demesne★

REPUBLIC OF IRELAND

The Landmark

on N 4 – ✆ (071) 962 22 22 – reservations@thelandmarkhotel.com – Fax (071) 962 22 33 – Closed 24-25 December

60 rm – †€ 129/150 ††€ 220/240

Rest *CJ's* – (dinner only) Carte € 28/42

◆ Overlooks the Shannon; some areas reminiscent of a luxury liner: wooden floors, panelled ceiling. Marble fountain in lobby. Richly furnished rooms; water scenes on walls. CJ's boasts pleasant river views.

Hollywell without rest

Liberty Hill, off N 4, taking first left over bridge – ✆ (071) 962 11 24 – hollywell@esatbiz.com – Fax (071) 962 11 24 – March-October

4 rm – †€ 70/90 ††€ 140

◆ A charming part 18C house in a peaceful spot by the river. Read up on area in a well-appointed lounge, take breakfast in dining room run by hospitable owner. Neat rooms.

The Oarsman

Bridge St – ✆ (071) 962 1733 – info@theoarsman.com – Fax (071) 962 1734 – Closed 25 December, Sunday, Monday and Good Friday

Rest – Carte € 25/45

◆ Recently modernised bar, retaining its traditional charm and atmosphere. Flagged floors, exposed stone and beams, pubby bric-a-brac plus mezzanine. Menus with modern flavours.

The red symbol?
This denotes the very essence of peace
– only the sound of birdsong first thing in the morning …

REPUBLIC OF IRELAND

CARRIGALINE (Carraig Uí Leighin) – Cork – 712 G 12 – pop. 11 191 — 38 B3

Dublin 262 km – Cork 14 km

Fernhill, ✆ (021) 437 2226 .

Carrigaline Court

Cork Rd – ✆ (021) 485 21 00 – reception@carrigcourt.com – Fax (021) 437 11 03 – Closed 25-26 December

89 rm – †€ 120 ††€ 186 – 2 suites

Rest *The Bistro* – (carvery lunch) Carte € 30/45 **s**

◆ Modern hotel with airy interiors; rooms are spacious, with all mod cons, whilst leisure centre boasts a 20m pool, steam room, sauna. Corporate friendly with large ballroom. Local products to the fore in stylish restaurant

Raffeen Lodge without rest

Ringaskiddy Rd, Monkstown, Northeast : 4 km by R 611 and N 28 off R 610 – ✆ (021) 437 16 32 – info@raffeenlodge.com – Fax (021) 437 16 32 – Closed 20 December-3 January

6 rm – †€ 45 ††€ 70/76

◆ A short drive from the fishing village of Ringaskiddy and Cork airport. A neat and tidy, good value house; rooms are uniformly decorated in pastel shades, simple in style.

Shannonpark House without rest

Cork Rd, North : 1½ km on R 611 – ✆ (021) 437 2091

6 rm – †€ 40/50 ††€ 70/80

◆ Breakfasts at the lace-topped communal table in this simple, homely guesthouse. Cosy little sitting room; bedrooms, always immaculate, furnished in dark wood.

CARRIGANS (An Carraigain) – **Donegal** – **712** J 3 37 **C1**

Dublin 225 km – Donegal 66 km – Letterkenny 230 km – Sligo 124 km

Mount Royd without rest

– *(074) 914 01 63 – jmartin@mountroyd.com – Fax (074) 914 04 00*
– March-November

4 rm – €40/48 €65/70

◆ Genuinely hospitable owners keep this creeper-clad period house in excellent order. En suite rooms are cosy and individually styled. Traditional, pleasantly cluttered lounge.

CASHEL – **Galway** – **712** C 7 *Ireland* 36 **A3**

Dublin 278 km – Galway 66 km

Town★

Connemara★★★

Cashel House

– *(095) 31 001 – res@cashel-house-hotel.com – Fax (095) 31 077*
– Closed 5 January-5 February

32 rm – €95/240 €230/350 – **Rest** – (bar lunch Monday-Saturday) (booking essential for non-residents) Menu €55 – Carte €30/55

◆ Built 1840; a very comfortable and restful country house, warmly decorated with delightful gardens. General de Gaulle stayed in one of the luxurious country house rooms. Dining room, with Queen Anne style chairs, opens into elegant conservatory.

Zetland Country House Cashel Bay,

– *(095) 31 111 – zetland@iol.ie – Fax (095) 31 117*

22 rm – €159/175 €228/250 – **Rest** – (bar lunch) Menu €60 **s**

◆ Lord Zetland's sporting lodge in 1800s; a splendid position in gardens sweeping down to Cashel Bay. Snooker, scuba diving, hunting organised. Pastel rooms. Dining room with silver cutlery, peerless views.

Look out for red symbols, indicating particularly pleasant establishments.

CASHEL – **Tipperary** – **712** I 10 – **pop. 2 770** *Ireland* 39 **C2**

Dublin 162 km – Cork 96 km – Kilkenny 55 km – Limerick 58 km – Waterford 71 km

Heritage Centre, Town Hall, Main St (062) 62511

Town★★★ – Rock of Cashel★★★ **AC** – Cormac's Chapel★★ – Round Tower★ – Museum★ – Cashel Palace Gardens★ – GPA Bolton Library★ **AC**

Holy Cross Abbey★★, N : 14½ km by R 660 – Athassel Priory★, W : 8 km by N 74. Caher (Castle★★, Swiss Cottage★), S : 18 km by N 8 – Glen of Aherlow★, W : 21 km by N 74 and R 664

Cashel Palace

Main St – (062) 62 707 – reception@cashel-palace.ie – Fax (062) 61 521
– Closed 24-27 December

23 rm – €175/205 €260/430 – **Rest** – (carvery lunch Monday-Saturday) Menu €48 – Carte €35/55

◆ A stately Queen Anne house, once home to an Archbishop, in walled gardens with path leading up to Cashel Rock. Inside, an extensive, pillared lounge and capacious rooms. Harmonious dining room: vaulted ceilings, open fire and light, bright colours.

Baileys of Cashel rm,

Main St – (062) 61 937 – info@baileys-ireland.com – Fax (062) 63 957
– Closed 23-28 December

20 rm – €95 €150/290 – **Rest** – (dinner only and Sunday lunch) Carte €25/45

◆ Extended Georgian townhouse, used as grain store during Irish famine. Contemporary bedrooms are furnished to a high standard. Small lounge with library; bar area in basement. Restaurant with open plan kitchen serves modern European cooking.

Aulber House without rest

Deerpark, Golden Rd, West : ¾ km on N 74 – ☎ (062) 63 713 – info@aulberhouse.com – Fax (062) 63 715 – Closed December-5 January

12 rm – †€ 60/80 ††€ 80/110

◆ Modern house in Georgian style with lawned gardens; five minutes from town centre. Comfy, leather furnished lounge. Smart, individually styled rooms.

Hill House without rest — Rock of Cashel,

Palmershill – ☎ (062) 61 277 – hillhouse1@eircom.net – April-October

5 rm – †€ 70/90 ††€ 120

◆ Historic, family run 18C guest house with charming garden and well appointed lounge. Bedrooms 3, 4 and 5 have views of famous Rock of Cashel; 4 and 5 also have four posters.

Chez Hans

Rockside, Moor Lane St – ☎ (062) 61 177 – Fax (062) 61 177 – Closed 2 weeks January, 1 week September, 25 December, Sunday and Monday

Rest – (dinner only) (booking essential) Carte € 33/62

◆ A converted synod hall with stained glass windows, near Cashel Rock: an unusual setting for a restaurant. Carefully prepared and cooked meals, using local ingredients.

Cafe Hans

Rockside, Moore Lane St – ☎ (062) 63 660 – closed 2 weeks January, 1 week September, Sunday and Monday

Rest – (lunch only) (bookings not accepted) Carte approx. € 20

◆ Next door to Chez Hans; white emulsioned walls, open kitchen and glass roof. Simple, tasty dishes are prepared with good, local ingredients. Come early as you can't book.

CASTLEBALDWIN (Béal Átha na gCarraigíní) – Sligo – 712 G 5 – 36 B2

✉ Boyle (Roscommon) *Ireland*

Dublin 190 km – Longford 67 km – Sligo 24 km

Carrowkeel Megalithic Cemetery (< ★★), S : 4 ¾ km. Arigna Scenic Drive★, N : 3 ¼ km by N 4 - Lough Key Forest Park★ **AC**, SE : 16 km by N 4 – View of Lough Allen★, N : 14 ½ km by N 4 on R 280 – Mountain Drive★, N : 9 ½ km on N 4 – Boyle Abbey★ **AC**, SE : 12 ¾ km by N 4 - King House★, SE : 12 ¾ km by N 4

Cromleach Lodge — Lough Arrow and Carrowkeel Cairns,

Ballindoon, Southeast : 5 ½ km – ☎ (071) 916 51 55 – info@cromleach.com – Fax (071) 916 54 55 – Closed 3 days Christmas

24 rm – †€ 125/149 ††€ 150/398 – **Rest** – Carte € 40/60

◆ Contrasting with ancient Carrowkeel Cairns, overlooking Lough Arrow, this is a smart, modern chalet with abundant local artwork indoors. Capacious rooms with large windows. Modern dishes and attentive service in refurbished restaurant.

CASTLEGREGORY (Caisleán Ghriaire) – Kerry – 712 B 11 – 38 A2

Dublin 330 km – Dingle 24 km – Killarney 54 km

The Shores Country House

Conor Pass Rd, Kilcummin, Southwest : 6 km on Brandon rd – ☎ (066) 713 91 95 – theshores@eircom.net – Fax (066) 713 91 96 – March-15 November

6 rm – †€ 60/90 ††€ 70/90 – **Rest** – (by arrangement) Menu € 35

◆ Between Stradbally Mountain and a long sandy beach, a modern guest house run by the friendly longstanding owner. Immaculate, comfortable rooms, some with antique beds. Dining room faces the Atlantic.

REPUBLIC OF IRELAND

CASTLEKNOCK = Caisleán Cnucha – Dublin – see Dublin

CASTLELYONS (Caisleán Ó Liatháin) – Cork – 712 H 11 – pop. 164 38 B2

Dublin 219 km – Cork 30 km – Killarney 104 km – Limerick 64 km

Ballyvolane House

Southeast : 5½ km by Midleton rd on Britway rd – (025) 36 349 – info@ballyvolanehouse.ie – Fax (025) 36 781 – Closed Christmas-New Year

6 rm – €130/140 €210/230 – **Rest** – (by arrangement, communal dining) Menu €60

◆ Stately 18C Italianate mansion mentioned in local legend, with lakes in parkland. Name means "place of springing heifers". Antique-filled rooms, some with Victorian baths. Dining room with silver candlesticks and balanced dishes.

CASTLEMARTYR Cork – 712 H 12 39 C3

Capella

– (021) 464 4050 – info.castlemartyr@capellahotels.com – Fax (021) 464 4051

83 rm – €360/425 €360/425, €30 – 26 suites

Rest *Bell Tower* – Menu €40 (lunch) **s** – Carte dinner €63/90 **s**

Rest *Garden Room* – Menu €40 **s**

◆ Grand 17C manor house in 220 acres, with river, castle ruins, golf course and spa. Maximum luxury; from the meeting room and lounge to the contemporary bedrooms and suites. Traditional fine dining in the Bell Tower. Breakfast or lunch in the Garden Room, overlooking the formal gardens and fountain.

Good food and accommodation at moderate prices?
Look for the Bib symbols:
red Bib Gourmand for food, blue Bib Hotel for hotels

CASTLEPOLLARD – Westmeath – 712 K 6 37 C3

Dublin 63 km – Mullingar 13 km – Tullamore 37 km – Édenderry 36 km

Lough Bishop House

Derrynagarra, Collinstown, Southeast : 6 km by R 394 taking left turn on unmarked rd opposite church and school after 4 km – (044) 966 13 13 – chkelly@eircom.net – Fax (044) 966 13 13 – Closed Christmas-New Year

3 rm – €60/100 €150 – **Rest** – (by arrangement, communal dining) Menu €30

◆ Renovated 19C farmhouse on south-facing hillside. Well-kept, with homely lounge and simple, antique-furnished bedrooms; the two larger with countryside views. Home cooked dishes made with local produce, including meat and eggs from the farm and fruit from the orchard.

CASTLEREA – Co Roscommon – 712 G 6 36 B2

Dublin 115 km – Roscommon 19 km – Newbridge 33 km – Carrick-on-Shannon 24 km

Fallons without rest

Knock Rd, West : 2 km on N 60 – (094) 962 11 83

5 rm – €40/60 €60/75

◆ Modern guest house on main road on outskirts of town - popular with those travelling to Knock - with simple, neat bedrooms and homely, wood-furnished breakfast room.

REPUBLIC OF IRELAND

CASTLETOWNBERE (Baile Chaisleáin Bhéarra) – Cork – 712 C 13 38 A3

– pop. 926 *Ireland*

Dublin 360 km – Cork 130 km – Killarney 93 km

Berehaven Millcove, (027) 70 700 .

Ring of Beara★, W : by R 572 (Allihies, mines★ - Garnish Bay ≤ ★) – Slieve Miskish Mountains (≤ ★)

Rodeen without rest

East : 3 ¼ km by R 572 – (027) 70 158 – rodeen@iolfree.ie
– 17 March-17 October

6 rm – †€ 40/60 ††€ 90

◆ Owner used to run a horticulture business and this is evident in the variety of shrubs in the garden. Rooms are compact but nicely decorated; some look out to Bantry Bay.

CASTLETOWNSHEND (Baile an Chaisleáin) – Cork – 712 E 13 38 B3

Ireland

Dublin 346 km – Cork 95 km – Killarney 116 km

Glandore★, NE : 10 km R 596 – Sherkin Island★ AC, W : 15 km by R 596 and R 595 and ferry

Mary Ann's

– (028) 36 146 – maryanns@eircom.net – Fax (028) 36 920
– Closed 24-26 December, 8-31 January and Monday November-March

Rest – (bookings not accepted) Carte € 20/45

◆ A pleasant 19C pub in pretty village. Tempting dishes are distinguished by the fact that almost everything is homemade. Sunny terrace is popular for lunch.

CAVAN – Cavan – 712 J 6 – pop. 6 098 *Ireland* 37 C2

Dublin 114 km – Drogheda 93 km – Enniskillen 64 km

Farnham St (049) 4331942 (April-September), irelandnorthwest@eircom.net

Killykeen Forest Park★, W : 9 ½ km by R 198

Radisson SAS Farnham Estate (heated) rm, rest,

Farnham Estate, Northwest : 3 ¾ km on R 198 – (049) 437 77 00
– info@farnhamestate.com – Fax (049) 437 77 01

152 rm – †€ 105/125 ††€ 130/150 – 6 suites

Rest *Botanica* – Carte € 35/54 s

◆ Period charm and acres of mature parkland in this renovated 400-year old mansion, offset by 21C hotel with meeting facilities, Wellness Centre and snazzy, well-equipped rooms. Universal menus at Botanica.

Cavan Crystal rm, rest,

Dublin Rd, East : 1 ½ km on N 3 – (049) 436 0600
– info@cavancrystalhotel.com – Fax (049) 436 0699
– closed 24-26 December

85 rm – †€ 90/120 ††€ 160/190

Rest *Opus One* – Carte € 30/42

◆ Modern hotel next to Cavan Crystal factory. Vast atrium is distinctive and stylish. Extensive meeting and leisure facilities. Comfy, well-equipped, modish bedrooms. Dining room serves menus true to Irish roots with stylish twists.

at Cloverhill North : 12 km by N 3 on N 54 – Belturbet

Rockwood House without rest

– (047) 55 351 – jbmac@eircom.net – Fax (047) 55 373
– closed 10 December-1 February

4 rm – †€ 40 ††€ 64

◆ Stone-faced house with a charming garden located in a woodland clearing. Comfortable guests' lounge and a conservatory for breakfast. Simply appointed, comfortable bedrooms.

REPUBLIC OF IRELAND

XX **The Olde Post Inn** with rm

– ✆ *(047) 55 555 – gearoidlynch@eircom.net – Fax (047) 55 111*
– Closed 24-28 December and Monday
6 rm – €60 €100 – **Rest** – (dinner only and Sunday lunch)
Menu €29/53 – Carte €38/49
◆ Former village post office; now a restaurant with much character: exposed stone and brick, large rafters. A feel of genuine hospitality prevails. Fine dining with Gallic edge.

CLAREMORRIS Mayo – Mayo – 712 E/F 6 – pop. 2 595 36 B2

Dublin 149 km – Castlebar 18 km – Galway 39 km – Newbridge 41 km

McWilliam Park rm, rest,

Knock Rd, East : 2 km on N 60 – ✆ (094) 937 3333
– info@mcwilliamparkhotel.ie – Fax (094) 937 3631
101 rm – €110/130 €85/105 – 2 suites – **Rest** – Carte €30/45 **s**
◆ Named after a local 18C landowner, this busy, purpose built hotel is located on the outskirts of town, convenient for the N17, Knock and the airport. Modern bedrooms. Stylish restaurant offers dishes made using local produce.

CLARINBRIDGE (Droichead an Chláirín) – Galway – 712 F 8 *Ireland* 36 B3

Dublin 233 km – Galway 17 km
Dunguaire Castle★ **AC**, S: 12 km by N 18 and N 67. Thoor Ballylee★ **AC**, S : 16 km by N 18 and minor road

XX **The Old Schoolhouse**

– ✆ *(091) 796 898 – kenc@iol.ie – Fax (091) 796 117*
– Closed 24-27 and 31 December-3 January and Monday
Rest – (dinner only and Sunday lunch) (booking essential) Menu €25 – Carte €29/40
◆ A converted school room is now the dining room and has been transformed by warm hued walls and elegant tableware. The speciality is the catch of the day and rock oysters.

CLIFDEN – Galway – 712 B 7 *Ireland* 36 A3

Dublin 291 km – Ballina 124 km – Galway 79 km
Galway Rd ✆ (095) 21163 (March-October)
Connemara★★★, NE : by N 59 – Sky Road★★ (< ★★), NE : by N 59 – Connemara National Park★, NE : 1½ km by N 59 – Killary Harbour★, NE : 35 km by N 59 – Kylemore Abbey★ **AC**, N : 18 km by N 59

Clifden Station House rm,

– ✆ *(095) 21 699 – reservations@clifdenstationhouse.com*
– Fax (095) 21 667
– Closed 24-25 December
78 rm – €79/149 €100/250 – **Rest** – (bar lunch) Menu €36 – Carte €30/45
◆ A modern hotel on site of the Galway-Clifden railway line closed in 1935. Now forms part of a complex which includes a museum. Good sized rooms in cheerful colours. Traditional fare offered in restaurant.

Ardagh < Ardbear Bay,

Ballyconneely rd, South : 2¾ km on R 341 – ✆ (095) 21 384
– ardaghhotel@eircom.net – Fax (095) 21 314
– Easter-October
16 rm – €125/135 €179/219 – 3 suites – **Rest** – (dinner only)
Menu €53 – Carte €52/62
◆ Family run hotel on edge of Ardbear Bay. A welcoming, domestically furnished interior with turf fires, piano, pictures and plants. Bedrooms are large, especially superiors. Fresh, pine dining room with views.

Dolphin Beach Country House
Clifden Bay,

Lower Sky Rd, West : 5½ km by Sky Rd – (095) 21 204 – stay@dolphinbeachhouse.com – Fax (095) 22 935 – 14 February-5 November

9 rm – †€ 80/120 ††€ 140/180 – **Rest** – (residents only, by arrangement) Menu € 40 **s**

◆ Terracotta coloured former farmhouse, perched on side of hill with stunning views of bay. Delightful sitting room with huge windows to accommodate vista. Attractive rooms. Tasty, home-cooked meals.

The Quay House

Beach Rd – (095) 21 369 – thequay@iol.ie – Fax (095) 21 608 – mid March-early November

14 rm – †€ 85/125 ††€ 140/180 – **Rest** – (lunch only) Carte € 18/26

◆ Once a harbour master's residence, then a Franciscan monastery. Rooms are divided between the main house: bohemian in style, and new annex: spacious with kitchenettes. Homecooking served in flower-filled conservatory.

Byrne Mal Dua House without rest

Galway Rd, East : 1¼ km on N 59 – (095) 21 171 – info@maldua.com – Fax (095) 21 739

14 rm – †€ 39/105 ††€ 79/150

◆ A white, detached house in well-tended gardens. Deep colours and subdued lighting indoors. Bedrooms are immaculately kept with fitted furniture.

Sea Mist House without rest

– (095) 21 441 – sgriffin@eircom.net – Closed 22-28 December and weekends only in winter

6 rm – †€ 55/85 ††€ 90/140

◆ 20C terraced stone house with sloping garden in town centre. Good choice at breakfast in cheerful room. Lounge at front and in conservatory. Spacious, modern bedrooms.

Buttermilk Lodge without rest

Westport Rd – (095) 21 951 – buttermilklodge@eircom.net – Fax (095) 21 953 – Closed January-February

11 rm – †€ 45/75 ††€ 80/110

◆ Yellow painted, name refers to nearby lough, a theme which is continued indoors as each room bears the name of a lough. Daily breakfast specials; maps provided for exploring.

Connemara Country Lodge without rest

Westport Rd – (095) 21 122 – connemara@unison.ie – Fax (095) 21 122 – Closed 22-28 December

10 rm – †€ 50/75 ††€ 70/100

◆ Affordable accommodation in a personally run guest house. Breakfasts include home-baked raisin bread and scones: owner has tendency to break into song at this point!

Benbaun House without rest

Westport Rd – (095) 21 462 – benbaunhouse@eircom.net – Fax (095) 21 462 – April-October

10 rm – †€ 45/60 ††€ 70/80

◆ Family owned house to the north of the town: modern bedrooms - simple, spacious and decorated in cheerful patterned fabrics - represent very good value for money.

Joyce's Waterloo House

Galway Rd, East : 1½ km off N 59 – (095) 21 688 – pkp@joyces-waterloo.com – Fax (095) 22 044 – Closed 22-27 December

8 rm – †€ 55/114 ††€ 76/114 – **Rest** – (by arrangement) Menu € 30

◆ Guesthouse announced by bright yellow exterior. Cosy, welcoming lounge. Smart bedrooms: owner puts national flag of guest outside each! All have VCRs and local art on walls.

CLOGHEEN – Co Tipperary – 712 I 11 39 C2

Dublin 122 km – Tipperary 23 km – Clonmel 21 km – Dungarvan 28 km

Old Convent with rm

Mount Anglesby, Southeast : 1/2 km on R 668 (Lismore rd) – ✆ (052) 65 565 – info@theoldconvent.ie – Closed 3 weeks late January-early February and Monday-Wednesday

7 rm – €110/120 €150/190 – **Rest** – (dinner only) (booking essential) (set menu only) Menu €58

◆ Home to the Sisters of Mercy for over 100 years, this converted convent retains a serene feel. Dine in the candlelit former chapel on seasonal 8 course tasting menu. Comfortable bedrooms, decorated in calming colours.

CLONAKILTY – Cork – 712 F 13 – pop. 3 698 Ireland 38 B3

Dublin 310 km – Cork 51 km

25 Ashe St ✆ (023) 33226

Dunmore Muckross Dunmore House, ✆ (023) 34644 .

West Cork Regional Museum★ AC

Courtmacsherry★, E : 12 km by R 600 and R 601 – Timoleague Friary★, E : 8 km by R 600. Carbery Coast★ (Drombeg Stone Circle★, Glandore★, Castletownshend★) by N 71 and R 597

Inchydoney Island Lodge & Spa rm, rest,

South : 5 1/4 km by N 71 following signs for Inchydoney Beach – ✆ (023) 33 143 – reservations@inchydoneyisland.com – Fax (023) 35 229 – Closed 24-26 December

63 rm – €225/240 €330/360 – 4 suites

Rest *The Gulfstream* – (dinner only) Menu €60

Rest *Dunes Bistro* – Carte €25/44

◆ Set on a headland looking out to sea. Range of leisure facilities; treatments - aquamarine spa, underwater massages - are especially good. Big, bright bedrooms with extras. The Gulfstream has fine sea views. The Dunes Bistro has a hearty, nautical theme.

Quality rm, rest,

Clogheen, West : 3/4 km by N 71 (Skibbereen rd) – ✆ (023) 36 400 – info.clonakilty@qualityhotels.ie – Fax (023) 35 404 – Closed 23-26 December

77 rm – €63/104 €98/168 – 20 suites –

Rest – (carvery lunch Monday-Saturday) Menu €26 **s** – Carte €22/34 **s**

◆ Modern hotel; rooms are uniformly decorated with matching fabrics. What distinguishes it is the three screen multiplex cinema, the "KidKamp" in summer, and leisure complex. Menus feature popular favourites.

An Garrán Coir

Castlefreke, Rathbarry, West : 6 1/2 km by N 71 – ✆ (023) 48 236 – angarrancoir@eircom.net – Fax (023) 48 236

5 rm – €55/65 €80/100 – **Rest** – (by arrangement) Menu €28

◆ Working farm overlooking rolling countryside: organic garden supplies ingredients for dinner. Homely lounge, well-kept rooms in bright, cheery colours. Good base for walking.

Gleesons

3-4 Connolly St – ✆ (023) 21 834 – reservations@gleeson.ie – Fax (023) 21 944 – Closed 24-26 December, 2 weeks spring, Monday and Sunday except at Bank Holidays

Rest – (dinner only) Menu €35 – Carte €33/59

◆ Town centre restaurant with wood blinds. Low beamed interior with wood burning stove. Classically based menus; dishes have individual twist and local produce is to the fore.

An Súgán VISA MC

41 Wolfe Tone St – ☎ (023) 33 498 – ansugan4@eircom.net – Fax (023) 33 825 – Closed 25-26 December and Good Friday

Rest – Carte € 25/40

◆ Situated in the old quays area of town. Homely wooden bar leads upstairs to restaurant hung with old photographs. Known for lobster, baked crab and black pudding terrine.

CLONBUR – Galway – 712 D 7 36 A3

Dublin 260 km – Ballina 79 km – Galway 46 km

John J Burke with rm VISA MC

Mount Gable House – ☎ (094) 954 6175 – tibhurca@eircom.net – Closed 25 December and Good Friday; October to March bar meals only

4 rm – †€ 40 ††€ 80 – **Rest** – Carte € 23/40

◆ Family run for several generations; hearty food includes home-baked soda bread. Irish music at weekends. Simple exterior belies the vast interior.

Do not confuse X with ✿!
X defines comfort, while stars are awarded for the best cuisine, across all categories of comfort.

CLONDALKIN – Dublin – 712 M 8 – see Dublin

CLONEGALL Carlow – 712 M 9 39 D2

Sha Roe Bistro VISA MC

Main St – ☎ (053) 937 56 36 – sha-roebistro@hotmail.com – Closed January, 1 week April, 1 week September, Christmas and Sunday-Tuesday

Rest – (booking essential dinner only and Sunday lunch) Menu € 32 (lunch) – Carte dinner € 31/42

◆ Spacious sitting room, comfy sofas, rustic artwork and candles help create relaxing feel. Simple dining room with inglenook fireplace; seasonal cooking uses local ingredients.

CLONMEL (Cluain Meala) – Tipperary – 712 I 10 – pop. 16 910 *Ireland* 39 C2

Dublin 174 km – Cork 95 km – Kilkenny 50 km – Limerick 77 km – Waterford 46 km

Community Office, Town Centre ☎ (052) 22960

Lyreanearla Mountain Rd, ☎ (052) 24 050 .

Town★ - County Museum★, St Mary's Church★

Fethard★, N : 13 km by R 689. Nier Valley Scenic Route★★ - Ahenny High Crosses★, E : 30½ km by N 24 and R 697 - Ormond Castle★, E : 33 ¾ km by N 24

Minella rm, rest, VISA MC AE

Coleville Rd, Southeast : ½ km – ☎ (052) 22 388 – frontdesk@hotelminella.ie – Fax (052) 24 381 – Closed 23-28 December

90 rm – †€ 110/200 ††€ 200 – **Rest** – Menu € 28/40 **s**

◆ Heavily extended Georgian house on banks of River Suir. Excellent leisure facility. Bedrooms decorated in soft pinks and blues; garden rooms have pleasant views. Basement restaurant has river vistas.

CLONTARF = Cluain Tarbh – Dublin – 712 N 7 – see Dublin

CLOVERHILL – Cavan – **712** J 5 – see Cavan

COBH – Cork – **712** H 12 – **pop. 9 811** Ireland 38 **B3**

Dublin 264 km – Cork 24 km – Waterford 104 km

Ballywilliam, ☎ (021) 812 399.

Town★ – St Colman's Cathedral★ – Lusitania Memorial★

Fota Island★ (Fota House★★ **AC**, Fota Wildlife Park★ **AC**), N : 6½ km by R 624 – Cloyne Cathedral★, SE : 24 km by R 624/5, N 25, R 630 and R 629

WatersEdge ← Cork harbour, rm, rest, VISA AE

(next to Cobh Heritage Centre) – ☎ *(021) 481 5566* – *info@watersedgehotel.ie* – *Fax (021) 481 2011* – *closed 24-26 December*

18 rm – €85/120 €120/180 – 1 suite

Rest *Jacob's Ladder* – (light lunch) Carte €28/37 **s**

◆ Next to the Heritage Centre, a converted salvage yard office overlooking Cork harbour. Some of the spacious, soft-toned rooms have French windows opening on to the veranda. Stylish restaurant with waterside setting.

Knockeven House without rest VISA

Rushbrooke, West : 2 km off R 624 – ☎ *(021) 481 1778* – *info@knockevenhouse.com* – *Fax (021) 481 1719* – *Closed 16-27 December*

4 rm – €75/85 €120/130

◆ Characterful house with friendly owners and tea and scones on arrival. Comfy lounge with fireplace and flowers, antique-furnished bedrooms; two largest overlook front garden.

CONG (Conga) – **Mayo** – **712** E 7 *Ireland* 36 **A3**

Dublin 257 km – Ballina 79 km – Galway 45 km

☎ (094) 9546542 (March-October)

Town★

Lough Corrib★★. Ross Errilly Abbey★ (Tower ← ★) – Joyce Country★★ (Lough Nafooey★) W : by R 345

Ashford Castle

– ☎ *(094) 954 6003* – *ashford@ashford.ie* – *Fax (094) 954 6260* VISA AE

78 rm – €244/452 €244/452, €28.75 – 5 suites

Rest *Connaught Room* – ☎ (094) 954 4321 – (Closed January-mid March, Sundays from October to March and Monday-Tuesday) (dinner only) Menu €60/95

Rest *George V Room* – (dinner only and Sunday lunch October-May) (residents only) Menu €70

Rest *Cullens* – Carte €26/40

◆ Hugely imposing restored castle in formal grounds on Lough Corrib. Suits of armour and period antiques in a clubby lounge. Handsomely furnished country house rooms. Smart fine dining in Connaught Room. George V imbued with air of genteel formality. Hugely imposing restored castle in formal grounds on Lough Corrib. Suits of armour and period antiques in a clubby lounge. Handsomely furnished country house rooms.

Lisloughrey Lodge rm,

The Quay, Southeast : 2 km by R 346 – ☎ *(094) 954 5400* – *lodge@lisloughrey.ie* – *Fax (094) 954 5424* – *Closed 25 and 26 December* VISA AE

41 rm – €200/250 €220/270 – 9 suites

Rest *Salt* – Menu €65 (dinner) – Carte €28/65

◆ Traditional exterior belies modernity of this stylish boutique hotel, with its sexy black and red lounge. Bedrooms set around courtyard; 'Duplex', the most comfortable. First floor restaurant boasts Lough view; modern menus use local produce and offer some unusual combinations.

REPUBLIC OF IRELAND

Michaeleen's Manor without rest
Quay Rd, Southeast : 1 1/2 km by R 346 – ✆ (094) 954 60 89
– info@quietman-cong.com – Fax (094) 954 64 48
11 rm – 🕴€ 60/75 🕴🕴€ 100
◆ Named after the lead charater in the film 'The Quiet Man,' filmed in the village; comfortable, brightly decorated bedrooms follow suit. Homely lounges; airy breakfast room.

Ballywarren House
East : 3½ km on R 346 – ✆ (094) 954 69 89 – ballywarrenhouse@gmail.com
– Fax (094) 954 69 89
– Closed 2 weeks spring and 2 weeks autumn
3 rm – 🕴€ 98/136 🕴🕴€ 148 – **Rest** – (by arrangement) Menu € 42 **s**
◆ Modern but 18C in style - open fires, galleried landing, oak staircase. Fresh colours: mint green, pink contrast pleasingly with woodwork. Carved pine beds; one four poster. Meals include own vegetables and daughter's farm eggs.

CORK – Cork – **712** G 12 – **pop. 186 239** *Ireland* 38 **B3**

- Dublin 248 km
- Cork Airport : ✆ (021) 4313131, S : 6½ km by L 42 X
- to France (Roscoff) (Brittany Ferries) weekly (14 h/16 h) – to Pembroke (Swansea Cork Ferries) 2-6 weekly (8 h 30 mn)
- Cork City, Grand Parade ✆ (021) 4255100Cork Airport, Freephone facility at Arrivals Terminal
- Douglas, ✆ (021) 489 10 86 ;
- Mahon Blackrock Cloverhill, ✆ (021) 429 25 43 ;
- Monkstown Parkgarriffe, ✆ (021) 484 13 76 ;
- Harbour Point Little Island Clash, ✆ (021) 435 34 51.
- City★★ – Shandon Bells★★ Y, St Fin Barre's Cathedral★★ **AC** Z, Cork Public Museum★ X **M** – Grand Parade★ Z , South Mall★ Z , St Patrick Street★ Z , Crawford Art Gallery★ Y – Elizabethan Fort★ Z
- Dunkathel House★ **AC**, E : 9 ¼ km by N 8 and N 25 X. Fota Island★ (Fota House★★ **AC**, Fota Wildlife Park★ **AC**), E : 13 km by N 8 and N 25 X – Cobh★ (St Colman's Cathedral★, Lusitania Memorial★) SE : 24 km by N 8, N 25 and R 624 X

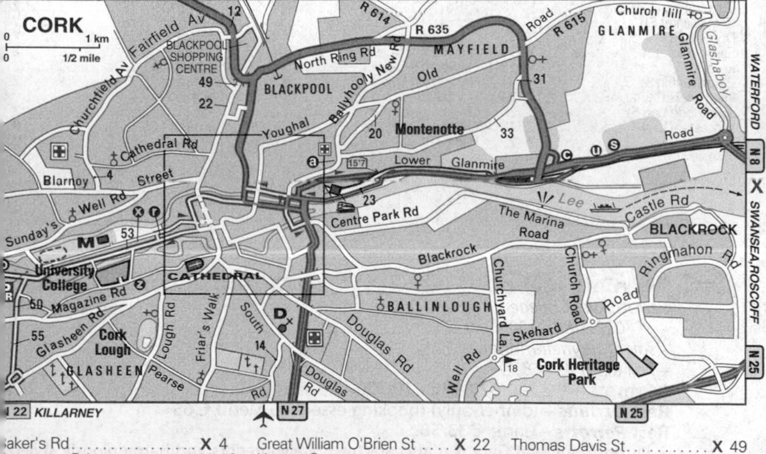

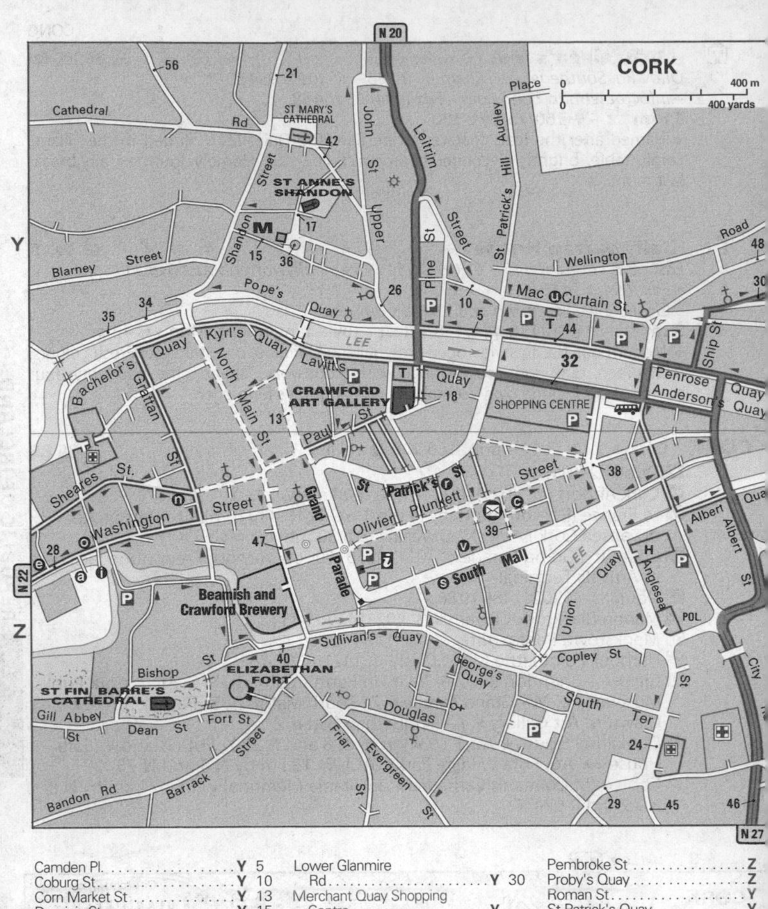

Camden Pl. .... Y 5	Lower Glanmire Rd .... Y 30	Pembroke St .... Z
Coburg St................... Y 10	Merchant Quay Shopping Centre .... Y	Proby's Quay .... Z
Corn Market St .... Y 13	Merchant's Quay.............. Y 32	Roman St.................... Y
Dominic St.................. Y 15	Newsom's Quay............... Y 34	St Patrick's Quay........... Y
Eason Hill.................. Y 17	North Main Street .... YZ	St Patrick's St.............. Z
Emmet Pl. .... Y 18	North Mall .... Y 35	Southern Rd................ Z
Gerald Griffin St........... Y 21	Olivier Plunkett St .... Z	South Link .... Z
Infirmary Rd .... Z 24	O'Connell's Square .... Y 36	South Main St .... Z
John Redmond St........... Y 26	Parnell Pl. .... Z 38	Summer Hill................. Y
Lancaster Quay .... Z 28		Wolfe Tone St............... Y
Langford Row .... Z 29		

Hayfield Manor

Perrott Ave, College Rd
– ✆ (021) 484 59 00
– sales@hayfieldmanor.ie
– Fax (021) 431 68 39 X z
84 rm ☕ – 🚹€ 200/320 🚹🚹€ 220/320 – 4 suites
Rest *Orchids* – (dinner only) (booking essential) Menu € 65
Rest *Perrotts* – Carte € 33/50

◆ Purpose-built yet Georgian in character. Stately interiors and harmoniously styled bedrooms with marble bathrooms and quality furniture - armchairs, coffee tables and desks. Twin dining options to suit all tastes.

Maryborough House H. and Spa
Maryborough Hill,
Douglas, Southeast : 4 ¾ km by R 609 and R 610 – ✆ (021) 436 55 55
– info@maryborough.ie – Fax (021) 436 56 62
– Closed 25-26 December
88 rm – €195 €350 – 5 suites
Rest *Zing's* – Menu €30/49 – Carte €46/54 **s**
◆ Built as a home for a wealthy merchant, an extended Georgian house. Five very characterful bedrooms in original house; others are sleek, stylish and contemporary. Restaurant boasts walk-in wine cellar.

The Kingsley
Victoria Cross – ✆ (021) 480 05 55
– resv@kingsleyhotel.com – Fax (021) 480 05 26 X **o**
129 rm – €280 €280 – 2 suites
Rest *Otters* – Carte €37/50 **s**
◆ An inviting spot by river Lee, once site of Lee baths: outdoor hot tub and indoor pool takes their place. Relax in smart rooms or take tea in the lounge overlooking the weir. Airy restaurant has private booths and banquettes.

Silversprings Moran H.
Tivoli, East : 4 km by N 8 – ✆ (021) 450 75 33
– silverspringsres@moranhotels.com – Fax (021) 450 76 41
– Closed 24-26 December X **c**
109 rm – €115/205 €150/300 –
Rest – Menu €22/35 – Carte €31/40 **s**
◆ Conference oriented hotel surrounded by gardens and grounds. Smartly furnished public areas includes business and leisure centres. Comfortably appointed bedrooms. After dining, relax in smart, contemporary lounge.

Jurys
Western Rd – ✆ (021) 425 27 00 – cork@jurysdoyle.com – Fax (021) 427 44 77
– Closed 24-26 December Z **a**
182 rm – €229/289 €249/289, €15.95 –
Rest – (Closed lunch Saturday and Sunday) Menu €25/32 **s** – Carte €38/58 **s**
◆ Contemporary city hotel by River Lee with light, spacious feel and complementary health club. Good-sized, modern bedrooms; the higher you go, the better the view. Weir bar and restaurant has terrace overlooking river.

The Ambassador
Military Hill – ✆ (021) 453 90 00 – info@ambassadorhotel.ie – Fax (021) 455 19 97
– Closed 25-26 December X **a**
69 rm – €85/120 €110/180 – 1 suite –
Rest – Menu €25/40 **s** – Carte €21/41 **s**
◆ Built as a military hospital; its high position affords city views from which most rooms benefit. All are furnished to a comfortable standard and most have a balcony. Home-made treats adorn dining room menus.

Isaacs
48 MacCurtain St – ✆ (021) 450 0011 – cork@isaacs.ie
– Fax (021) 450 6355 Y **u**
50 rm – €90/100 €110/130
Rest *Greenes* – Menu €45 (dinner) – Carte €40/50
◆ Refurbished hotel across from the theatre in city centre. Bedrooms are modern and comfortable; most of them situated around a small courtyard. Two-roomed restaurant overlooks waterfall; one room is traditional in style, the other modern and bright. French chef cooks dishes with global influences. Friendly staff.

Lancaster Lodge without rest
Lancaster Quay, Western Rd – ✆ (021) 425 11 25 – info@lancasterlodge.com
– Fax (021) 425 11 26
– Closed 23-28 December Z **i**
48 rm – €92/105 €125/140
◆ Purpose-built hotel with crisp, modern interior. Bedrooms are chintz-free, pleasingly and sparingly decorated. Largest rooms on the fourth floor; rear rooms are quieter.

Lotamore House without rest
Tivoli, East : 4 ¾ km on N 8 – ✆ (021) 482 23 44 – lotamore@iol.ie – Fax (021) 482 22 19 – closed 17 December-5 January X s
18 rm – €75/85 €130/150
◆ Georgian house perched on hill with fine view over river and harbour. Country house style lounge with antiques. Individually styled rooms; relish vista from one at the front.

Crawford House without rest
Western Rd – ✆ (021) 427 90 00 – info@crawfordguesthouse.com – Fax (021) 427 99 27 – closed 22 December-20 January X x
12 rm – €70/90 €110/130
◆ Victorian-style building offering bright, airy and comfortable guesthouse accommodation. Modern interiors with a choice of wood floors or carpeting in guest rooms.

Garnish House without rest
Western Rd – ✆ (021) 427 51 11 – garnish@iol.ie – Fax (021) 427 38 72 X r
21 rm – €70/100 €180
◆ Justifiably proud of gourmet breakfast: 30 options include pancakes and porridge. Guests are welcomed with home-made scones in cosy rooms; those at the rear have quiet aspect.

Achill House without rest
Western Rd – ✆ (021) 427 94 47 – info@achillhouse.com – Fax (021) 427 94 47 Z e
9 rm – €65/95 €95/140
◆ Immaculate accommodation in a well run terrace house, five minutes from the centre; the two attic rooms, decorated in warm pastel tones, are the most cosy and characterful.

Flemings with rm
Silver Grange House, Tivoli, East : 4½ km on N 8 – ✆ (021) 482 16 21 – info@flemingsrestaurant.ie – Fax (021) 482 18 00 – Closed 24-27 December and Sunday dinner-Monday lunch June-September X u
3 rm – €80/90 €95/110 –
Rest – Menu €30 – Carte €43/50
◆ Classical cuisine, French bias; uses local produce, organically home-grown vegetables, herbs. Two dining rooms in keeping with Georgian character of house. Period furnished bedrooms.

Jacobs on the Mall
30A South Mall – ✆ (021) 425 15 30 – info@jacobsonthemall.com – Fax (021) 425 15 31 – Closed 25-26 December, Sunday and lunch on Bank Holidays Z s
Rest – (booking essential) Carte €30/45
◆ 19C former Turkish bath has retained its old steam windows and added contemporary Irish art. Modern dishes reveal a taste for bold, original combinations.

Ambassador
3 Cook St – ✆ (021) 427 32 61 – Fax (021) 427 23 57 – Closed 25-26 December and Good Friday Z r
Rest – Chinese (dinner only and lunch in December) Menu €26 – Carte €33/43
◆ Richly hued oak panelling and smoothly professional service add to the enjoyment of dishes prepared with care and fine ingredients in a long-established Chinese favourite.

Jacques
Phoenix St – ✆ (021) 427 73 87 – jacquesrestaurant@eircom.net – Fax (021) 427 06 34 – Closed 24 December-2 January and Sunday Z **c**

Rest – (dinner only) Carte € 36/47

◆ A long, warmly decorated room with modern tables on which old Irish classics are delivered. Farm ducks, wild game, fresh fish and organic vegetables are used in the cooking.

Les Gourmandises
17 Cook St – ✆ (021) 425 19 59 – info@lesgourmandises.ie – Fax (021) 489 90 05 – Closed 2 weeks March, 2 weeks August and Sunday Z **v**

Rest – French (dinner only and Friday lunch) (booking essential) Menu € 42 **s** – Carte € 41/53 **s**

◆ Relaxed city centre restaurant boasting stained glass door, skylight and comfy lounge bar with red banquettes and modern art. Irish produce employed on classic French menus.

Isaacs Restaurant
48 MacCurtain St – ✆ (021) 450 38 05 – isaacs@iol.ie – Fax (021) 455 13 48 – closed 1 week Christmas, lunch Sunday and Bank Holidays Y **u**

Rest – (booking essential) Carte € 25/43

◆ Tall brick arches and modern art in converted warehouse: buzzy, friendly and informal. Modern and traditional brasserie dishes plus home-made desserts and blackboard specials.

Cafe Paradiso with rm
16 Lancaster Quay, Western Rd – ✆ (021) 427 79 39 – info@cafeparadiso.ie – Fax (021) 427 49 73 – Closed Sunday and Monday Z **o**

3 rm – †€ 160 ††€ 160 – **Rest** – Vegetarian (booking essential) Carte € 30/50

◆ A growing following means booking is essential at this relaxed vegetarian restaurant. Colourful and inventive international combinations; blackboard list of organic wines. Spacious bedrooms in bright colours; the back one is the quietest.

Fenn's Quay
5 Sheares St – ✆ (021) 427 95 27 – polary@eircom.net – Fax (021) 427 95 26 – Closed 25 December, Sunday and Bank Holidays Z **n**

Rest – Menu € 20 (lunch) **s** – Carte € 29/41 **s**

◆ In a renovated 18C terrace in historic part of the city, this informal café-restaurant boasts modern art on display. Popular for mid-morning coffees and, light lunches.

at Little Island East : 8½ km by N 25 - X - and R 623 – ✉ Cork

Radisson SAS
rm, rest,

Ditchley House – ✆ (021) 429 70 00 – info.cork@radissonsas.com – Fax (021) 429 71 01

120 rm – †€ 110/180 ††€ 120/240 – 9 suites

Rest ***The Island Grill Room*** – (buffet lunch Monday-Saturday) Menu € 40 – Carte € 26/49

◆ Opened in 2005 around the core of an 18C house: stylish and open-plan. Superbly equipped spa. Modish rooms in two themes: choose from Urban or highly individual Ocean! Island Grill Room serves an eclectic range of dishes.

at Cork Airport South : 6½ km by N 27 - X – ✉ Cork

International Airport
rm,

– ✆ (021) 454 9800 – info@corkairporthotel.com – Fax (021) 454 9999

150 rm – †€ 100/120 ††€ 110/130 –

Rest – Menu € 20 (lunch) – Carte approx. € 35

◆ Quirky hotel with aviation theme and various eateries. Decently-sized bedrooms come in Economy, Business and First Class. The superb Pullman lounge resembles cabin of a plane. Modern restaurant with interesting smoking terrace.

CORK AIRPORT Cork – 712 G 12 – see Cork

CORROFIN – Clare – 712 E 9 38 B1

Dublin 228 km – Gort 24 km – Limerick 51 km

Fergus View without rest

Kilnaboy, North : 3 ¼ km on R 476 – ☎ (065) 683 76 06 – deckell@indigo.ie – Fax (065) 683 71 92 – March-October

6 rm – †€ 53 ††€ 76

◆ Originally built for the owner's grandfather as a schoolhouse, with good countryside views. Conservatory entrance into cosy lounge with piles of books. Pristine bedrooms.

CRAUGHWELL (Creachmhaoil) – Galway – 712 F 8 *Ireland* 36 B3

Dublin 194 km – Galway 24 km – Limerick 88 km

Loughrea (St Brendan's Cathedral★), SE : 13 km by N 6 – Turoe Stone★, E : 16 km by N 6 and R 350

St Clerans

Southeast : 5 3/4 km by N 6 taking second turning left after 1 ½ km then veering left after a further 3 ¼ km – ☎ (091) 846 555 – stclerans@iol.ie – Fax (091) 846 752

12 rm – †€ 200/325 ††€ 250/495 – **Rest** – (dinner only) (booking essential for non-residents) Menu € 65 **s**

◆ Grand, secluded 18C country house stands in rolling meadowland with fishing and hunting nearby. Former home of film director John Huston. Finely furnished and themed rooms. Great finesse in evidence in the elegant dining room.

CROOKHAVEN (An Cruachán) – Cork – 712 C 13 38 A3

Dublin 373 km – Bantry 40 km – Cork 120 km

Galley Cove House without rest

West : ¾ km on R 591 – ☎ (028) 35 137 – info@galleycovehouse.com – Fax (028) 35 137 – 10 March-15 November

4 rm – †€ 50/70 ††€ 78/90

◆ Perched overlooking eponymous bay and its pleasant harbour. Conservatory breakfast room has bamboo seating. Rooms are neat and tidy, and enhanced by colourful fabrics.

CROSSMOLINA (Crois Mhaoilíona) – Mayo – 712 E 5 – pop. 1 103 36 B2

Ireland

Dublin 252 km – Ballina 10 km

Errew Abbey★, SE : 9 ½ km by R 315. Cáide Fields★ **AC**, N : 24 km by R 315 and R 314 W – Killala★, NE : 16 km by R 315 and minor road – Moyne Abbey★, NE : 18 km by R 115, minor road to Killala, R 314 and minor road – Rosserk Abbey★, NE : 18 km by R 115, minor road to Killala, R 314 and minor road

Enniscoe House

Castlehill, South : 3 ¼ km on R 315 – ☎ (096) 31 112 – mail@enniscoe.com – Fax (096) 31 773 – April-October and New Year

6 rm – †€ 120/140 ††€ 200/232 – **Rest** – (dinner only) (booking essential for non-residents) Menu € 31 **s**

◆ Georgian manor, overlooking Lough Conn, on Enniscoe estate with walled garden and heritage centre. Hallway boasts original family tree; antique beds in flower-filled rooms. Home cooked country dishes served in the dining room.

DALKEY (Deilginis) – Dublin – 712 N 8 Ireland — 39 D1

Dublin 13 km – Bray 9 km
Killiney Bay (≤ ★★), S : by coast road

✕✕ Jaipur

21 Castle St – ☎ (01) 285 0552 – dalkey@jaipur.ie – Fax (01) 284 0900 – Closed 25 December

Rest – Indian (dinner only) Carte € 34/52

◆ Central location and smart, lively, brightly coloured, modern décor. Well-spaced, linen-clad tables. Warm, friendly ambience. Contemporary Indian dishes.

DINGLE – Kerry – 712 B 11 – pop. 1 828 Ireland — 38 A2

Dublin 347 km – Killarney 82 km – Limerick 153 km
The Quay ☎ (066) 9151188
Town★ – St Mary's Church★ – Diseart (stained glass★ **AC**)
Gallarus Oratory★★, NW : 8 km by R 559 – NE : Connor Pass★★ – Kilmalkedar★, NW : 9 km by R 559. Dingle Peninsula★★ – Connor Pass★★, NE : 8 km by minor road – Stradbally Strand★★, NE : 17 km via Connor Pass – Corca Dhuibhne Regional Museum★ **AC**, NW : 13 km by R 559 – Blasket Islands★, W : 21 km by R 559 and ferry from Dunquin

Plan on next page

Dingle Skellig

– ☎ (066) 915 02 00 – reservations@dingleskellig.com – Fax (066) 915 15 01 – weekends only November-mid February — Y **e**

111 rm – ♦€ 90/155 ♦♦€ 130/250 – 2 suites –
Rest – (bar lunch) Menu € 45

◆ Large purpose-built hotel with views of Dingle Bay. Interior decorated in a modern style with good levels of comfort: the smartest executive rooms are on the third floor. Restaurant makes most of sea and harbour view.

Benners without rest

Main St – ☎ (066) 915 16 38 – info@dinglebenners.com – Fax (066) 915 14 12 – Closed 21-27 December — Z **b**

52 rm – ♦€ 90/130 ♦♦€ 130/210

◆ Traditional-style property located on town's main street. Comfortable public areas include lounge bar and guest's sitting room. Rooms in extension have a more modern feel.

Emlagh Country House without rest

– ☎ (066) 915 23 45 – info@emlaghhouse.com – Fax (066) 915 23 69 – 15 March-October — Y **d**

10 rm – ♦€ 125/185 ♦♦€ 240/300

◆ Modern hotel in Georgian style. Inviting lounge with a log fire and well-fitted, antique furnished bedrooms: the colours and artwork of each are inspired by a local flower.

Heatons without rest

The Wood, West : ¾ km on R 559 – ☎ (066) 915 22 88 – heatons@iol.ie – Fax (066) 915 23 24 – Closed 1-27 December — Y **c**

16 rm – ♦€ 57/102 ♦♦€ 94/156

◆ Carefully planned and recently built house with a spacious, modern look: comfortably furnished lounge area and bedrooms take up the contemporary style.

Castlewood House without rest

The Wood – ☎ (066) 915 2788 – castlewoodhouse@eircom.net – Fax (066) 915 2110 — Y **w**

12 rm – ♦€ 80/130 ♦♦€ 90/195

◆ Well run, spacious and comfortable house. Individually decorated bedrooms; some with antique brass beds, others more contemporary. All have jacuzzi bath; most have view.

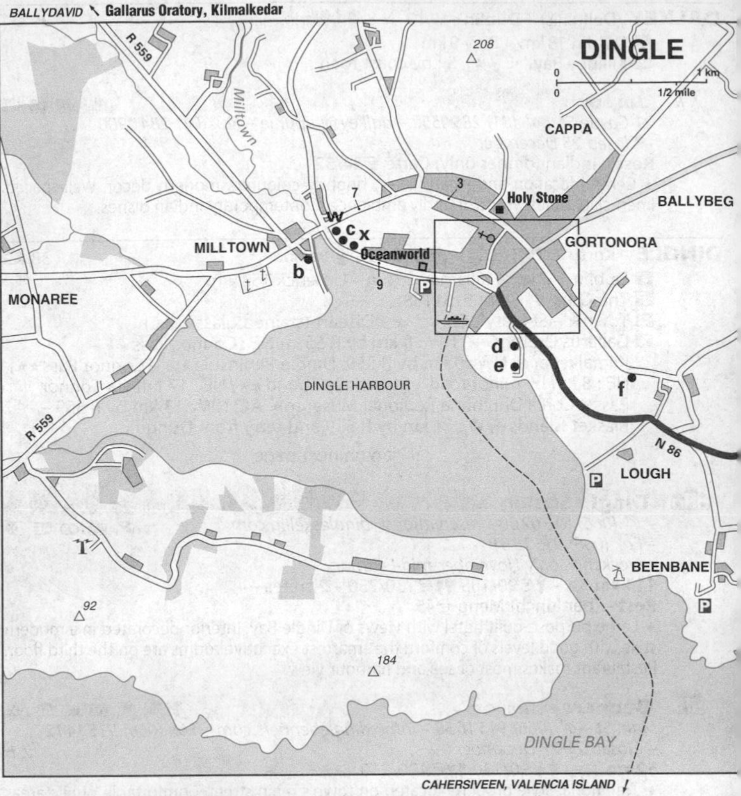

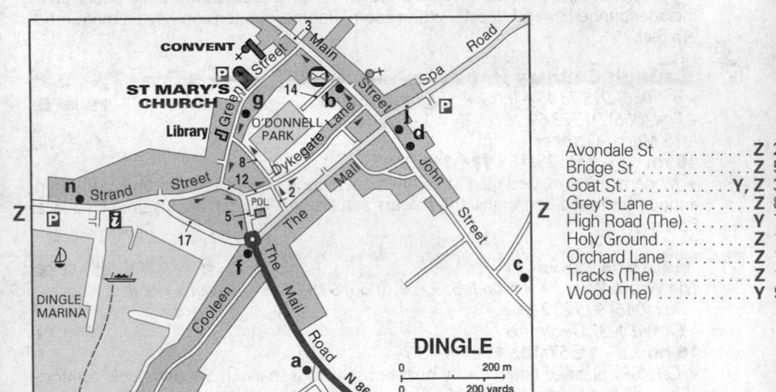

Milltown House without rest

– (066) 915 13 72 – info@milltownhousedingle.com – Fax (066) 915 10 95
– 28 April-28 October Y **b**

10 rm – €100/135 €130/160

◆ Warm, welcoming establishment in a good location outside Dingle. Conservatory breakfast room and personally furnished and comfortable bedrooms, all with seating area.

Doyle's Townhouse

5 John St – ☏ (066) 915 11 74 – cdoyles@iol.ie – Fax (066) 915 18 16 – Closed first 3 weeks December, 7 January-early February Z **d**

8 rm – €100/156 €100/166

Rest *Doyle's Seafood Bar* – see restaurant listing

◆ Attractive house in the town centre. Tasteful guests' lounge with some antique furniture. Well-run accommodation including bedrooms decorated in homely, traditional style.

Greenmount House without rest

Gortonora – ☏ (066) 915 14 14 – info@greenmount-house.com – Fax (066) 915 19 74 – Closed 12-27 December Z **c**

14 rm – €50/130 €100/180

◆ Large, yellow painted, extended house located above the town. Two comfortable lounges and a conservatory-style breakfast room. Newest bedrooms most comfortably appointed.

Pax House without rest

Upper John St – ☏ (066) 915 15 18 – paxhouse@iol.ie – Fax (066) 915 08 65 – March-November Y **f**

12 rm – €50/70 €110/160

◆ Family run guesthouse sited away from the town in an elevated position. Lounges are comfortable and traditionally appointed; bedrooms are colourful and personally designed.

Coastline without rest

The Wood – ☏ (066) 915 24 94 – coastlinedingle@eircom.net – Fax (066) 915 24 93 – March-November Y **x**

7 rm – €48/78 €80/110

◆ Hard to miss modern guesthouse with bright pink façade. Comfy, homely interior with lots of local info. All rooms have pleasant view; those at the front face Dingle harbour.

Bambury's without rest

Mail Rd – ☏ (066) 915 12 44 – info@bamburysguesthouse.com – Fax (066) 915 17 86 Z **a**

12 rm – €40/80 €80/130

◆ Modern house located just on the edge of the town with garden and views over the sea. Large lounge and wood-floored breakfast room. Well-kept, comfortable bedrooms.

The Chart House

The Mall – ☏ (066) 915 22 55 – charthse@iol.ie – Fax (066) 915 22 55 – closed Tuesday except June-September and restricted opening in winter Z **f**

Rest – (dinner only) Menu €35 – Carte €37/43

◆ Attractive cottage close to a main route into town. Snug interior with exposed flint walls and wooden ceiling. Modern flourish applied to local ingredients.

Doyle's Seafood Bar

4 John St – ☏ (066) 915 11 74 – cdoyles@iol.ie – Fax (066) 915 18 16 – Closed first 3 weeks December, 7 January-early February Z **d**

Rest – (Closed Sunday) (dinner only) Carte €30/45

◆ Formerly a bar and retaining the traditional pubby interior with bric-a-brac and simple wooden tables. Offers a classic style menu with seafood as the backbone.

The Half Door

3 John St – ☏ (066) 915 16 00 – halfdoor@iol.ie – Fax (066) 915 18 83 – Closed 20 December-14 February Z **j**

Rest – Seafood Menu €32/40 – Carte €32/55

◆ A cosy atmosphere amid beams, wood and stone flooring. Menus offer a mix of dishes though the emphasis is on seafood in the classic French style. Lobsters from the tank.

Out of the Blue

Waterside – ☎ (066) 915 08 11 – info@outoftheblue.ie
– Closed mid November-mid March and Wednesday Z **n**
Rest – Seafood (booking essential at dinner) (lunch bookings not accepted)
Carte € 31/49
◆ Pleasingly unpretentious, this brightly painted shack with corrugated iron roof has fish on display at the front, and tasty seafood menus in the rustic restaurant to the rear.

DONABATE Dublin – Co Dublin – 712 N 7 – pop. 5 499 39 D1

Dublin 14 km – Swords 5 km – Dún Laoghaire 22 km – Bray 34 km

The Waterside House

East : 2 km – ☎ (01) 843 6155 – info@watersidehousehotel.ie – Fax (01) 843 6111
35 rm – € 60 € 120
Rest *Signal* – Menu € 20/30 – Carte € 20/60
◆ Hidden away, yet close to city; set on a pretty beach and surrounded by golf courses, with large open bar and lovely decked area. Worth paying more for a front facing bedroom. Small formal ground floor dining room has good views.

Red = Pleasant. Look for the red and symbols.

DONEGAL (Dún na nGall) – Donegal – 712 H 4 – pop. 2 453 *Ireland* 37 C1

Dublin 264 km – Londonderry 77 km – Sligo 64 km
Donegal Airport ☎ (074) 954824
The Quay ☎ (074) 9721148, irelandnorthwest@eircom.net
Donegal Castle★ **AC**
Donegal Coast★★ - Cliffs of Bunglass★★, W : 48 ¼ km by N 56 and R 263 – Glencolmcille Folk Village★★ **AC**, W : 53 km by N 56 and R 263 - Rossnowlagh Strand★★, S : 35 ½ km by N 15 and R 231 – Trabane Strand★, W : 58 km by N 56 and R 263

Harvey's Point Louch Eske,

Lough Eske, Northeast : 7 ¼ km by T 27 (Killybegs rd)
– ☎ (074) 972 22 08 – info@harveyspoint.com – Fax (074) 972 23 52
– Closed Sunday dinner-Wednesday November-12 March
55 rm – € 149 € 198 – 4 suites
Rest *The Restaurant* – see restaurant listing
◆ Large hotel in tranquil setting on shores of Lough Eske and at foot of Blue Stack Mountains. Large, luxury bedrooms, some with Lough views.

Mill Park rm,

The Mullins, Northwest : ¾ km by N 56 on Letterbarrow rd – ☎ (074) 972 28 80
– info@millparkhotel.com – Fax (074) 972 26 40
– Closed 24-26 December
110 rm – € 95/145 € 160/290 –
Rest – Menu € 28/40 – Carte dinner € 20/43
◆ Open-plan lounge in timber and stone leads to a well-equipped gym and large, comfortable bedrooms generously provided with mod cons - a useful family option. Spacious mezzanine restaurant; its tall pine trusses lend a rustic feel.

St Ernan's House Donegal Bay,

St Ernan's Island, Southwest : 3 ½ km by N 267 – ☎ (074) 972 10 65
– res@sainternans.com – Fax (074) 972 20 98
– May-September
4 rm – € 240/290 – 2 suites –
Rest – (dinner only Tuesday, Friday and Saturday) (residents only) Menu € 52
◆ Very attractive Georgian house, enchantingly secluded on a wooded tidal island with delightful views of Donegal Bay. Country house-style interiors and individual bedrooms. Dining room offers concise choice of simply prepared, well sourced produce.

REPUBLIC OF IRELAND

Ardeevin without rest ⚘ — < Lough Eske, ⚘ ⚘ P

Lough Eske, Barnesmore, Northeast : 9 km by N 15 following signs for Lough Eske Drive – ✆ (074) 972 17 90 – seanmcginty@eircom.net – Fax (074) 972 17 90 – 18 March-30 November

5 rm ☕ – †€ 45/50 ††€ 65/70

◆ Inviting, individual rooms, almost all with superb views of Lough Eske and the quiet countryside. Hearty Irish breakfasts with fresh bread baked by the long-standing owners.

Island View House without rest — < ⚘ ⚘ P

Ballyshannon Rd, Southwest : 1 ¼ km on R 267 – ✆ (074) 972 24 11 – dowds@indigo.ie – Closed Christmas

4 rm ☕ – †€ 45/50 ††€ 70

◆ Simple, homely establishment overlooking Donegal Bay. Though a modern building, it has a traditional appearance and style. Neatly kept bedrooms.

The Restaurant – at Harvey's Point — < Lough Eske, ⚘ AC P

Lough Eske, Northeast : 7 ¼ km by T 27 (Killybegs rd) – ✆ (074) 972 22 08 – Fax (074) 972 23 52 – Closed Sunday dinner-Wednesday November-12 March — VISA MC AE

Rest – Menu € 30 (lunch) **s** – Carte € 45/55 **s**

◆ Wonderful views in a loughside setting. Very comfy, spacious cocktail lounge and bar. Huge restaurant: appealing menu uses regional ingredients and international elements.

at Laghy South : 5 ½ km on N 15 – ✉ Donegal

Coxtown Manor ⚘

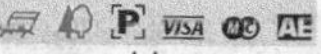

South : 3 km. on Ballintra rd – ✆ (074) 973 4575 – coxtownmanor@oddpost.com – Fax (074) 973 4576 – 3 February-November and 6 December-6 January

9 rm ☕ – †€ 105/115 ††€ 150/190 – **Rest** – (closed Monday) (dinner only) (booking essential) Carte € 37/52 **s**

◆ Serenely located, this attractive, creeper-clad Georgian house boasts a comfy, country-house style sitting room and bedrooms which have a warm aura of luxury about them. Affable Belgian owner guarantees top-notch desserts using chocolate from his homeland!

Good food without spending a fortune?
Look out for the Bib Gourmand ☺

DONNYBROOK = Domhnach Broc – **Dublin** – **712** N 8 – **see Dublin**

DOOGORT = Dumha Goirt – **Mayo** – **712** B 5/6 – **see Achill Island**

DOOLIN (Dúlainm) – **Clare** – **712** D 8 *Ireland* — 38 **B1**

Dublin 275 km – Galway 69 km – Limerick 80 km

The Burren★★ (Cliffs of Moher★★★, Scenic Route★★, Aillwee Cave★ **AC** (Waterfall★★), Poulnabrone Portal Tomb★, Corcomroe Abbey★, Kilfenora Crosses★, Burren Centre★ **AC**)

Tír Gan Éan — ♿ rm, AC ⚘ P VISA MC

– ✆ (065) 707 57 26 – info@tirganean.ie – Fax (065) 707 57 34 – closed 25 December

12 rm – †€ 80/95 ††€ 120/180 – **Rest** – (closed Wednesday and Thursday) (dinner only and Sunday lunch) Menu € 25 (lunch) – Carte approx. € 37

◆ Stylish boutique hotel on main through road, with contemporary open plan bar. Bedrooms come in creams and browns, with flat screens, fridges and modern art. Accessible menu; local produce.

H. Doolin
Fitz's Cross – ✆ (065) 707 41 11 – info@hoteldoolin.ie – Fax (065) 707 57 72 – Closed 25 December
17 rm – €70/105 €140/170
Rest *South Sound* – Menu €22/38 – Carte €29/44
◆ Boutique hotel, integrating a parade of shops and a tourist information centre. Contemporary, cream coloured bedrooms come with flat screen TVs and vivid artwork. Spacious South Sound restaurant offers modern menu.

Aran View House
Coast Rd, Northeast : ¾ km – ✆ (065) 707 44 20 – aranview@eircom.net – Fax (065) 707 45 40 – 18 April-October
19 rm – €70/80 €100/140 – **Rest** – (dinner only) Menu €35 – Carte €30/44
◆ Georgian house set in 100 acres of working farmland, located on the main coastal road. Well-kept public areas and bedrooms, some in adjacent converted barn. Simply styled restaurant with a snug feel and traditional furnishings.

Ballyvara House without rest
Southeast : 1 km – ✆ (065) 707 44 67 – info@ballyvarahouse.ie – Fax (065) 707 48 68 – April-September
11 rm – €70/120 €120/180 – 2 suites
◆ Pleasant rural views from this 19C former farm cottage, close to tourist village. Comfy lounge with squashy sofas; outside a smart decked courtyard. Bright, impressive rooms.

Cullinan's with rm
– ✆ (065) 707 41 83 – cullinans@eircom.net – Fax (065) 707 42 39 – Accommodation closed mid December-mid February,
8 rm – €50/80 €80/100 – **Rest** – (Closed November-April, Sunday and Wednesday) (dinner only) (booking essential) Carte €36/49
◆ Simple wood-floored restaurant serving contemporary dishes which make good use of local produce. Friendly service and charming setting with garden views and fresh flowers. Immaculate, pine-furnished bedrooms; some overlooking a little river.

DROGHEDA (Droichead Átha) – Louth – 712 M 6 – pop. 31 020 — 37 D3
Ireland

- Dublin 46 km – Dundalk 35 km
- Bus Eireann Station, Donore Rd ✆ (041) 9837070 (May-September)
- Seapoint Termonfeckin, ✆ (041) 982 23 33 ;
- Towneley Hall Tullyallen, ✆ (041) 984 42 229 .
- Town★ – Drogheda Museum★ – St Laurence Gate★
- Monasterboice★★, N : 10½ km by N 1 – Boyne Valley★★, on N 51 – Termonfeckin★, NE : 8 km by R 166. Newgrange★★★, W : 5 km by N 51 on N 2 – Mellifont Old Abbey★ AC - Knowth★

The D
Scotch Hall – ✆ (041) 987 77 00 – thed@monogramhotels.ie – Fax (041) 987 77 02 – Closed 24-29 December
104 rm – €180/285 €180/350 – **Rest** – Menu €30/40 **s** – Carte €34/56 **s**
◆ Stylish hotel adjacent to shopping centre on banks of the Boyne. Modish, minimalistic interiors include two comfy bars and spacious bedrooms with a cool, clinical appeal. Popular menus in the airy dining room.

Boyne Valley H. and Country Club
Southeast : 2 km on N 1 – ✆ (041) 983 77 37 – reservations@boyne-valley-hotel.ie – Fax (041) 983 91 88
71 rm – €90 €160/180 – **Rest** – Menu €26/34 – Carte €33/40
◆ Extended, ivy-clad house dating from the 1840s, with some character and set in pretty grounds. Well run and kept with well-proportioned bedrooms, the best have garden views. Basement bistro with original cast-iron range; intimate booths.

REPUBLIC OF IRELAND

Scholars Townhouse

King St, by West St, Lawrence St turning left at Lawrence's Gate – (041) 983 54 10 – info@scholarshotel.com – Fax (041) 987 77 52 – Closed Christmas and Good Friday

19 rm – €80/90 €130/160 – **Rest** – Carte €25/50

◆ Wood panelling and ornate coving reflect Victorian style of this tastefully refurbished 19C townhouse. Some bedrooms have original stained glass windows; good level of facilities. Formal restaurant serves classically-based menus. Dine under ceiling murals commemorating the Battle of the Boyne.

DRUMSHANBO (Droim Seanbhó) – Leitrim – 712 H 5 *Ireland* 37 C2

Dublin 166 km – Carrick-on-Shannon 14 km – Sligo 48 km

Arigna Scenic Drive★ (≤ ★), N : 8 km by R 280

Ramada H. and Suites at Lough Allen

rm, rest,

on Keadew rd – (071) 964 01 00 – info@loughallenhotel.com – Fax (071) 964 01 01 – Closed 25-26 December

72 rm – €95/105 €155/390

Rest *Rushes* – (dinner only and Sunday lunch) Menu €35 **s** – Carte €35/43 **s**

◆ Purpose-built hotel, beside Lough Allen, with part-stone exterior. Airy, up-to-the-minute bar. Pleasant terrace includes hot tub. Well-equipped spa. Minimalist, modern rooms. Dining room boasts stylish blond wood and seasonal menus.

O. Forir/MICHELIN

DUBLIN (*Dublin*)

County: Dublin
Michelin REGIONAL map: n° 712 N 7
▶ Belfast 166 km – Cork 248 km – Londonderry 235 km

Population: 1 004 614
Ireland

39 **D1**

PRACTICAL INFORMATION

Tourist Information

Bord Failte Offices, Baggot Street Bridge ✆ (01) 602 4000, information@dublintourism.ie

Airport

✈ Dublin Airport: ✆ (01) 814 1111, N: 9 km by N 1 BS

Ferries

to Holyhead (Irish Ferries) 4 daily (3 h 15 mn) – to Holyhead (Stena Line) 1-2 daily (3 h 45 mn) – to the Isle of Man (Douglas) (Isle of Man Steam Packet Co. Ltd) (2 h 45 mn/4 h 45 mn) – to Liverpool (P & O Irish Sea) (8 h)

Golf Courses

18 Elm Park DonnybrookNutley House, ✆ (01) 269 3438 ;
18 Milltown Lower Churchtown Rd, ✆ (01) 497 6090 ;
18 Royal Dublin Dollymount North Bull Island, ✆ (01) 833 6346 ;
18 Forrest Little Cloghran, ✆ (01) 628 2106 ;
18 Lucan Celbridge Rd, ✆ (01) 628 2106 ;
18 Edmondstown, ✆ (01) 493 24 61 ;
18 Coldwinters St Margaret'sNewtown house, ✆ (01) 864 0324.

SIGHTS

IN TOWN

Suffolk St - Arrivals Hall, Dublin Airport - The Square Shopping Centre, Tallaght City★★★ - Trinity College★★ JY - Old Library★★★ (Treasury★★★, Long Room★★) – Dublin Castle★★ (Chester Beatty Library★★★) HY - Christ Church Cathedral★★ HY - St Patrick's Cathedral★★ HZ - Marsh's Library★★ HZ – National Museum★★ (The Treasury★★) KZ - National Gallery★★ KZ - Newman House★★ JZ - Bank of Ireland★★ JY – Custom House★★ KX - Kilmainham Gaol Museum★★ AT **M6** - Kilmainham Hospital★★ AT – Phoenix Park★★ AS - National Botanic Gardens★★ BS - Marino Casino★★ CS – Tailors' Hall★ HY - City Hall★ HY - Temple Bar★ HJY - Liffey Bridge★ JY – Merrion Square★ KZ - Number Twenty-Nine★ KZ **D** - Grafton Street★ JYZ - Powerscourt Centre★ JY – Rotunda Hospital Chapel★ JX - O'Connell Street★ (GPO Building★) JX - Hugh Lane Municipal Gallery of Modern Art★ JX **M4** – Pro-Cathedral★ JX - Bluecoat School★ BS **F** - Guinness Museum★ BT **M7** - Rathfarnham Castle★ AT – Zoological Gardens★ AS – Ceol★ BS **n**

ON THE OUTSKIRTS

The Ben of Howth★ (⩽ ★), NE: 9 ½ km by R 105 CS

IN THE SURROUNDING AREA

Powerscourt★★ (Waterfall★★ **AC**), S: 22 ½ km by N 11 and R 117 EV – Russborough House★★★, SW: 35 ½ km by N 81 BT

DUBLIN

Street	Grid	No.
Adelaïde Rd	BT	3
Alfie Byrne Rd	CS	5
Bath Ave	CT	9
Benburb St	BS	15
Berkeley Rd	BS	16
Botanic Rd	BS	19
Canal Rd	BT	30
Clanbrassil St	BT	40
Conyngham Rd	AS	48
Denmark St	BS	52
Donnybrook Rd	CT	54
Dorset St	BS	55
Drimnagh Rd	AT	57
Eglinton Rd	CT	63
Grand Parade	BT	72
Inchicore Rd	AT	79
Infirmary Rd	AS	81
James St	BT	84
Leeson St Upper	BT	94
Macken St	BST	99
Morehampton Rd	BT	108
Mount St Upper	BT	112
Palmerston Park	BT	123
Phibsborough Rd	BS	132
Rathmines Rd Upper	BT	135
Ringsend Rd	CT	139
St Agnes Rd	AT	141
St Alphonsus Rd	BS	144
St John's Rd West	AS	147
Sandford Rd	BT	151
Shelbourne Rd	CT	157
Shrewsbury Rd	CT	159
South Circular Rd	AS	162
Suir Rd	AT	168
Terenure Rd East	BT	172
Thomas St West	BT	174
Victoria Quay	BS	178
Western Way	BS	184
Wolfe Tone Quay	BS	195

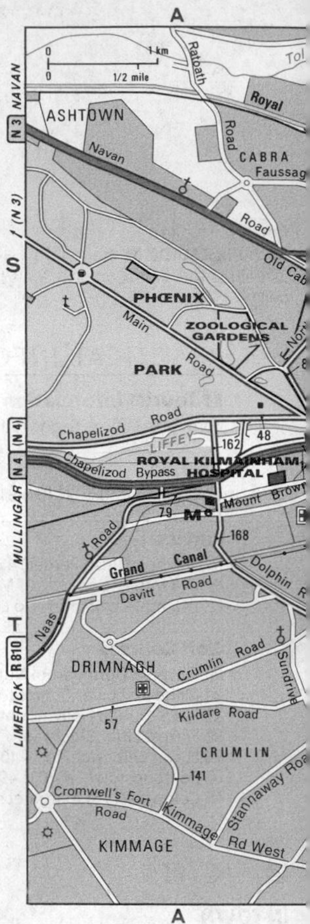

The Shelbourne

27 St Stephen's Green – ✆ (01) 663 4500 – info@renaissancehotels.com – Fax (01) 661 6006 JZ **c**

246 rm – †€ 260/340 ††€ 260/340, ☕ €31 – 19 suites

Rest *The Saddle Room* – see restaurant listing

◆ A delightful refit of a grand old hotel, with elegant meeting rooms and sumptuous bedrooms offering a host of extras. The historic Horseshoe Bar and Lord Mayor's Room remain.

The Merrion

Upper Merrion St – ✆ (01) 603 0600 – info@merrionhotel.com – Fax (01) 603 0700 KZ **e**

133 rm – †€ 475 ††€ 595, ☕ €29 – 10 suites

Rest The Cellar and **The Cellar Bar** – see restaurant listing

◆ Classic hotel in series of elegantly restored Georgian town houses; many of the individually designed grand rooms overlook pleasant gardens. Irish art in opulent lounges.

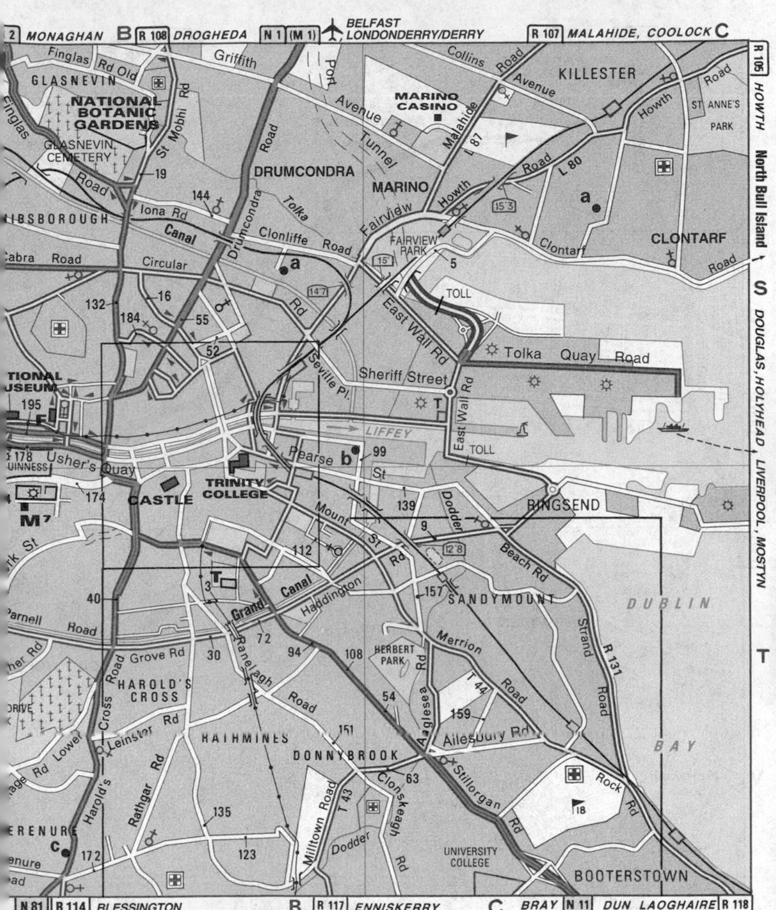

The Westin

College Green, Westmoreland St – ✆ (01) 645 1000
– reservations.dublin@westin.com – Fax (01) 645 1234 — JY **n**

150 rm – 🚹€ 189/489 🚹🚹€ 189/489, ☕ €27 – 13 suites

Rest *The Exchange* – (Closed Saturday lunch and Monday) Menu € 26 (lunch) **s** – Carte dinner € 41/59 **s**

Rest *The Mint* – Carte approx. € 27

◆ Immaculately kept and consummately run hotel in a useful central location. Smart, uniform interiors and an ornate period banking hall. Excellent bedrooms with marvellous beds. Elegant, Art Deco 1920s-style dining in Exchange. More informal fare at The Mint.

The Westbury

Grafton St – ✆ (01) 679 1122 – westbury@jurysdoyle.com
– Fax (01) 679 7078 — JY **b**

197 rm – 🚹€ 435 🚹🚹€ 435, ☕ €28 – 8 suites

Rest *Russell Room* – Menu € 32/62 – Carte € 53/68

Rest *The Sandbank* – ✆ (01) 646 3353 (Closed Sunday and Bank Holidays) Menu € 30/50 – Carte € 40/53 **s**

◆ Imposing marble foyer and stairs lead to lounge famous for afternoon teas. Stylish Mandarin bar. Luxurious bedrooms offer every conceivable facility. Russell Room has distinctive, formal feel. Informal, bistro-style Sandbank.

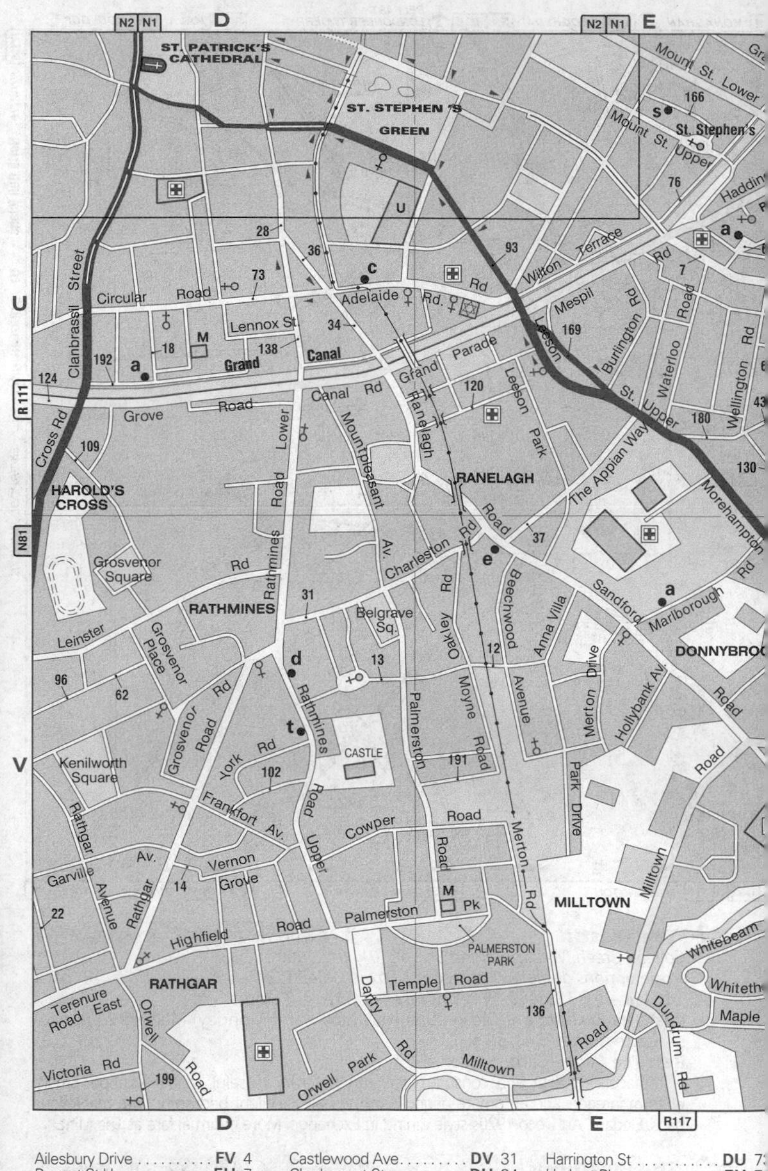
N2 N1
D
N2 N1
E
ST. PATRICK'S CATHEDRAL
ST. STEPHEN'S GREEN
Mount St. Lower
Mount St. Upper
St. Stephen's
166
76
Haddington
U
28
36
93
73
Circular Road
Clanbrassil Street
Adelaide Rd.
Rd
Wilton Terrace
Mespil Rd
Burlington Rd
Waterloo Road
Wellington Rd
Lennox St.
34
M
18
138
Grand Canal
192
124
R 111
Canal Rd
Grand Parade
Leeson St. Upper
169
7
120
Leeson Park
Grove Road
Lower
Cross Rd
109
HAROLD'S CROSS
Mountpleasant Av.
Ranelagh
RANELAGH
The Appian Way
180
130
43
Morehampton Rd
Road
37
N81
Grosvenor Square
Rd
Rathmines Road
Charleston Rd
e
Oakley Rd
Beechwood Avenue
Anna Villa
Sandford
Marlborough
a
31
RATHMINES
Belgrave Sq.
12
Leinster
Grosvenor Place
Road
d
13
DONNYBROOK
96
62
Rd
Grosvenor Road
Rathmines
Palmerston
Moyne Road
Merton Drive
Hollybank Av.
Road
t
Rd
CASTLE
V
Kenilworth Square
York Rd
102
191
Park Drive
Road
Frankfort Av.
Road
Cowper Road
Merton Rd
Rathgar Av.
Garville Avenue
Vernon Grove
Upper
Road
Milltown
14
Rathgar
M
Pk
MILLTOWN
22
Highfield Road
Palmerston
PALMERSTON PARK
Whitebeam
RATHGAR
Temple Road
Whitethorn
Terenure Road East
Orwell
Dartry Rd
136
Maple
Road
Dundrum Rd
Victoria Rd
199
Road
Orwell Park
Milltown
D
E
R117

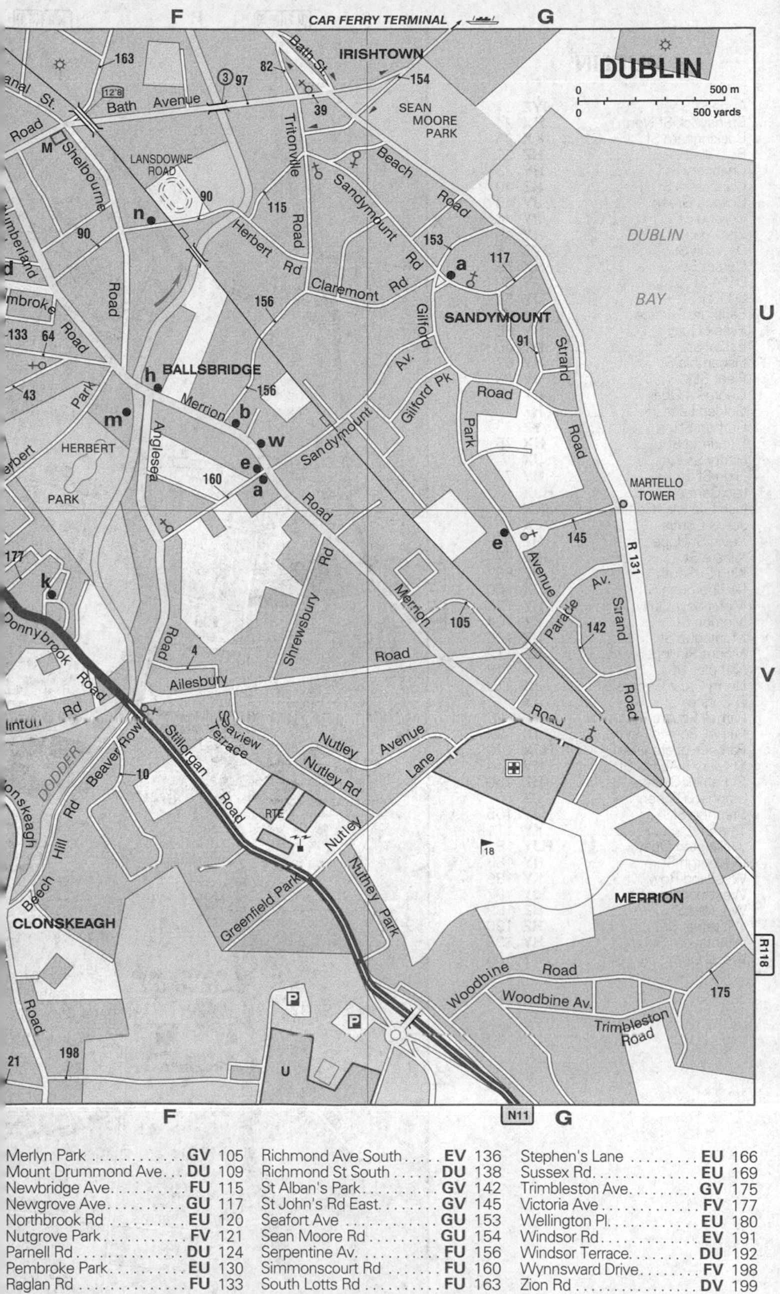

F
CAR FERRY TERMINAL
G
IRISHTOWN
DUBLIN
0
500 m
0
500 yards
Bath St.
82
154
163
97
3
Bath
Avenue
12'8
39
Canal St.
Road
SEAN
MOORE
PARK
M
Shelbourne
Tritonville
Beach
Road
LANSDOWNE
ROAD
90
115
Road
Sandymount
Rd
Herbert
Rd
n
90
153
a
117
DUBLIN
BAY
Claremont
Rd
Road
Pembroke
Road
156
Gilford
Av.
SANDYMOUNT
91
Strand
U
133
64
h
BALLSBRIDGE
156
Gilford Pk
Road
Park
Road
43
Park
m
Merrion
b
w
Sandymount
HERBERT
PARK
Anglesea
e
a
160
Road
MARTELLO
TOWER
e
145
Avenue
R 131
177
k
Shrewsbury
Rd
Merrion
105
Parade
Av.
142
Strand
Donnybrook
Road
Road
4
Aylesbury
Road
Road
V
Road
Rd
Clinton
Seaview
Terrace
Nutley
Avenue
Nutley Rd
Lane
DODDER
Beaver Row
10
Stillorgan
Road
RTE
Nutley
18
Clonskeagh
Rd
Hill
Nutley
Park
Beech
Greenfield Park
MERRION
CLONSKEAGH
R118
Woodbine
Road
175
Woodbine Av.
Trimbleston
Road
Road
P
P
U
21
198
F
N11
G

DUBLIN

Street	Grid	No.
Anne St South	**JYZ**	6
Brunswick St North	**HX**	24
Buckingham St	**KX**	25
Bull Alley	**HZ**	27
Chancery St	**HY**	33
Clanbrassil St	**HZ**	40
College Green	**JY**	45
College St	**JY**	46
Cornmarket	**HY**	49
Dawson St	**JYZ**	
Dorset St	**HX**	55
Duke St	**JY**	58
D'Olier St	**JY**	51
Earlsford Terrace	**JZ**	60
Essex Quay	**HY**	65
Essex St	**HY**	66
Fishamble St	**HY**	67
Fleet St	**JY**	68
George's Quay	**KY**	69
Golden Lane	**HZ**	70
Grafton St	**JYZ**	
Henrietta St	**HX**	75
Henry St	**JX**	
High St	**HY**	78
Ilac Centre	**HJX**	
Irish Life Mall Centre	**JKX**	
Jervis Centre	**HJX**	
Kevin St Upper	**HZ**	85
Kildare St	**JKZ**	87
King St South	**JZ**	88
Marlborough St	**JX**	100
Merchants Quay	**HY**	103
Merrion St	**KZ**	104
Montague St	**JZ**	106
Mount St Upper	**KZ**	112
Nicholas St	**HY**	118
North Great George's St	**JX**	119
O'Connell St	**JX**	
Parnell Square East	**JX**	126
Parnell Square North	**JX**	127
Parnell Square West	**HJX**	129
St Mary's Abbey St	**HY**	148
St Patrick Close	**HZ**	150
Stephens Green	**JZ**	
Stephen St	**HJY**	165
Tara St	**KY**	171
Wellington Quay	**HJY**	181
Werburgh St	**HY**	183
Westland Row	**KY**	186
Westmoreland St	**JY**	187
Wexford St	**HZ**	189
Whitefriar St	**HZ**	190
Winetavern St	**HY**	193
Wood Quay	**HY**	196

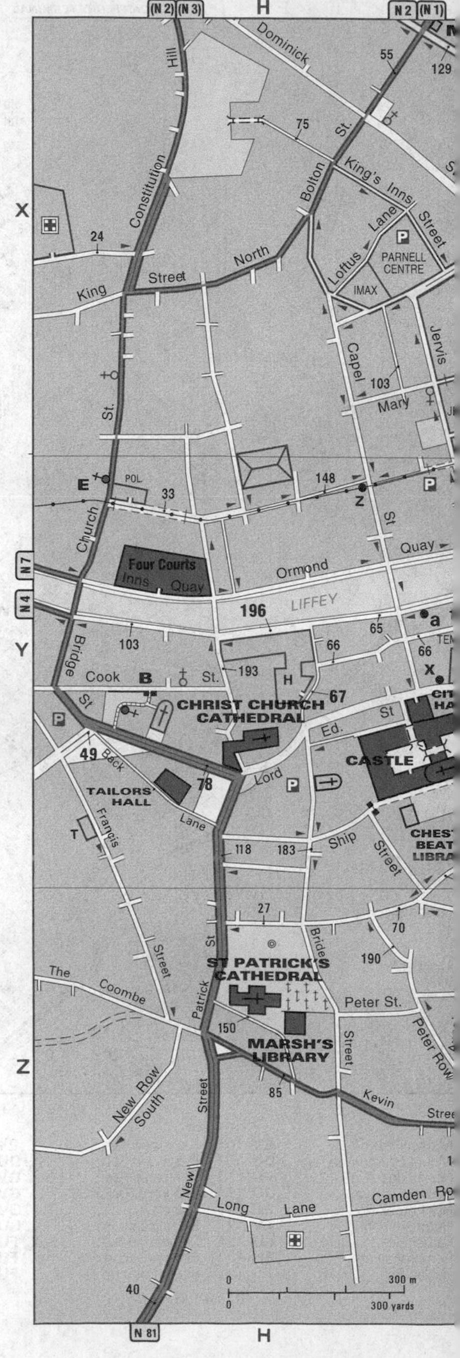

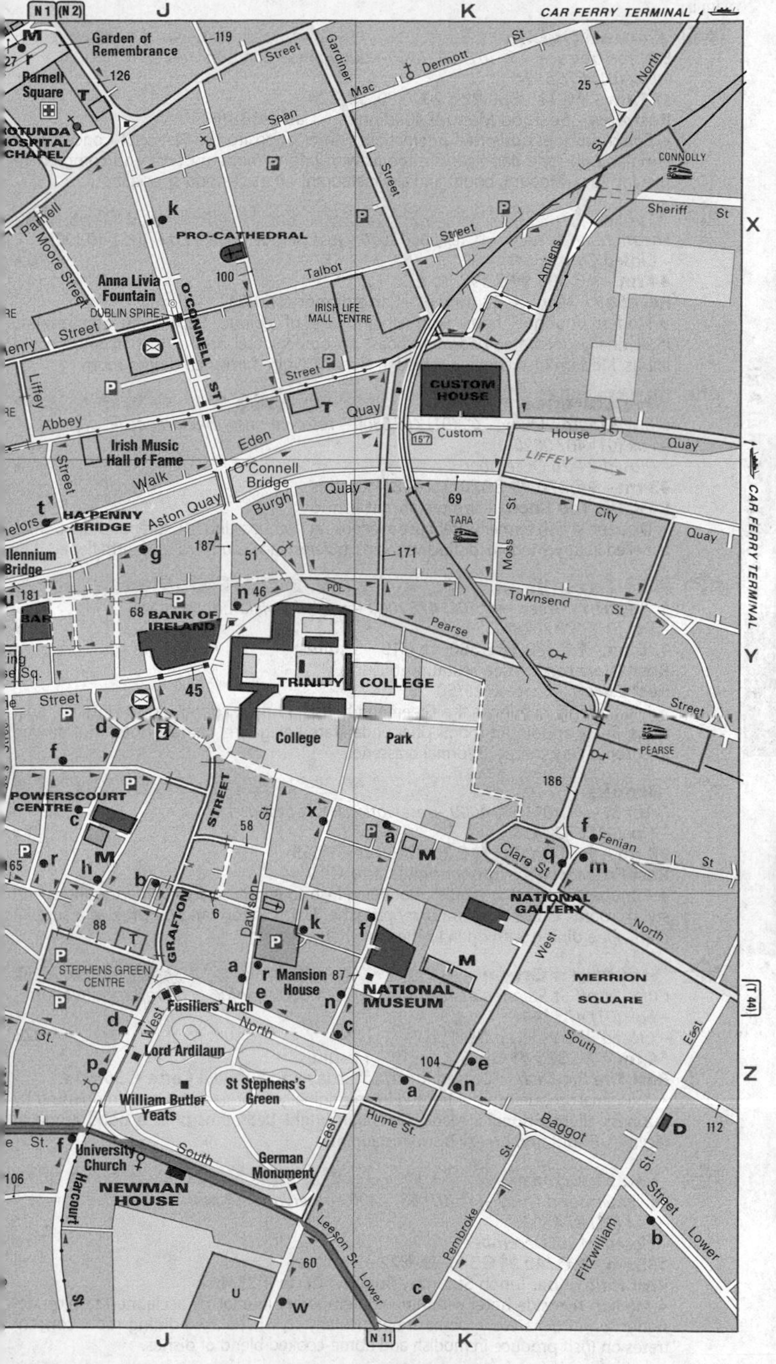

J
K
CAR FERRY TERMINAL
Garden of Remembrance
Parnell Square
ROTUNDA HOSPITAL CHAPEL
CONNOLLY
PRO-CATHEDRAL
Anna Livia Fountain
DUBLIN SPIRE
IRISH LIFE MALL CENTRE
O'CONNELL ST
CUSTOM HOUSE
Irish Music Hall of Fame
O'Connell Bridge
LIFFEY
HA'PENNY BRIDGE
Millennium Bridge
TARA
BANK OF IRELAND
TRINITY COLLEGE
College Park
PEARSE
POWERSCOURT CENTRE
GRAFTON STREET
Mansion House
NATIONAL MUSEUM
NATIONAL GALLERY
MERRION SQUARE
STEPHENS GREEN CENTRE
Fusiliers' Arch
Lord Ardilaun
St Stephens's Green
William Butler Yeats
University Church
NEWMAN HOUSE
German Monument
X
Y
Z

Conrad Dublin

Earlsfort Terrace – ✆ (01) 602 8900 – dublininfo@conradhotels.com – Fax (01) 676 5424 JZ **w**

191 rm – †€ 185/380 ††€ 200/380, ☕ €24

Rest *Alex* – Seafood Menu € 40 (dinner) – Carte € 38/68

◆ Smart, business oriented international hotel opposite the National Concert Hall. Popular, pub-style bar. Spacious rooms with bright, modern décor and comprehensive facilities. Modern, bright and airy restaurant offers seafood specialities.

Dylan

Eastmoreland Place – ✆ (01) 660 3000 – justask@dylan.ie – Fax (01) 660 3005 – Closed Christmas EU **a**

44 rm – †€ 395 ††€ 395, ☕ €30

Rest *Still* – Menu € 38 (lunch) – Carte dinner € 60/84

◆ Modern boutique hotel with vibrant use of colour. Supremely comfortable, individually decorated bedrooms boast an opulent feel and a host of unexpected extras. Modern Irish cooking served in elegant, white-furnished dining room.

The Clarence

6-8 Wellington Quay – ✆ (01) 407 0800 – reservations@theclarence.ie – Fax (01) 407 0820 – Closed 24-26 December HY **a**

43 rm – †€ 370 ††€ 370, ☕ €28 – 5 suites

Rest *The Tea Room* – see restaurant listing

◆ Discreet, stylish former warehouse overlooking river boasting 21C interior design. Small panelled library. Modern, distinctive rooms: quietest face courtyard on fourth floor.

The Fitzwilliam

St Stephen's Green – ✆ (01) 478 7000 – enq@fitzwilliamhotel.com – Fax (01) 478 7878 JZ **d**

136 rm – †€ 380 ††€ 380, ☕ €19 – 3 suites

Rest *Thornton's* – see restaurant listing

Rest *Citron* – Carte € 25/50

◆ Rewardingly overlooks the Green and boasts a bright contemporary interior. Spacious, finely appointed rooms offer understated elegance. Largest hotel roof garden in Europe. Very trendy, informal brasserie.

Brooks

Drury St – ✆ (01) 670 4000 – reservations@brookshotel.ie – Fax (01) 670 4455 JY **r**

98 rm – †€ 170/185 ††€ 200/215, ☕ €17.95

Rest *Francesca's* – (dinner only) Carte € 19/44

◆ Commercial hotel in modish, boutique, Irish town house style. Smart lounges and stylish rooms exude contemporary panache. Extras in top range rooms, at a supplement. Fine dining with open kitchen for chef-watching.

Stephen's Green

Cuffe St, off St Stephen's Green – ✆ (01) 607 3600 – info@ocallaghanhotels.com – Fax (01) 478 1444 – Closed 23-28 December JZ **f**

64 rm – †€ 325 ††€ 325, ☕ €16 – 11 suites

Rest *The Pie Dish* – (Closed lunch Saturday and Sunday) Carte € 35/60 **s**

◆ This smart modern hotel housed in an originally Georgian property frequented by business clients; popular Magic Glass bar. Bright bedrooms offer a good range of facilities. Bright and breezy bistro restaurant.

The Morrison

Lower Ormond Quay – ✆ (01) 887 2400 – reservations@morrisonhotel.ie – Fax (01) 874 4039 – closed 24-27 December HY **r**

135 rm – †€ 340 ††€ 340, ☕ €22 – 3 suites

Rest *Halo* – (bar lunch Saturday-Sunday) Carte € 33/46 **s**

◆ Modern riverside hotel with ultra-contemporary interior by acclaimed fashion designer John Rocha. New rooms are particularly stylish. Relaxed dining room concentrates on Irish produce in modish and home-cooked blend of dishes.

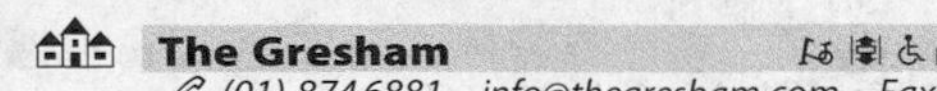

The Gresham
– ✆ *(01) 874 6881 – info@thegresham.com – Fax (01) 878 7175* JX **k**
283 rm – †€ 600 ††€ 600, ☕ €23 – 6 suites
Rest *23* – 23 Upper O'Connell St (dinner only) Carte € 34/40
Rest *The Gallery* – 23 Upper O'Connell St (closed Saturday and Sunday lunch) Menu € 26 (lunch) – Carte € 34/40
◆ Long-established restored 19C property in a famous street offers elegance tinged with luxury. Some penthouse suites. Well-equipped business centre, lounge and Toddy's bar. 23 is named after available wines by glass. The Gallery boasts formal ambience.

Jurys Croke Park
Jones's Rd – ✆ (01) 871 4444 – info@crokepark.ie – Fax (01) 871 4400 – Closed Christmas BS **a**
230 rm – †€ 149/189 ††€ 149/189, ☕ €19.50 – 2 suites –
Rest – (bar lunch) Carte € 24/32 **s**
◆ Corporate styled hotel opposite Croke Park Stadium. Stylish 'Side Line' bar with terrace. Rooms are a strong point: spacious with good business amenities. Bistro boasts the Canal terrace and modern/Mediterranean influenced menus.

O'Callaghan Alexander
Fienian St, Merrion Sq – ✆ (01) 607 3700 – info@ocallaghanhotels.com – Fax (01) 661 5663 – Closed 23-28 December KY **f**
98 rm – †€ 450 ††€ 450, ☕ €16 – 4 suites
Rest *Caravaggio's* – (bar lunch Saturday and Sunday) Carte € 38/45
◆ This bright corporate hotel, well placed for museums and Trinity College, has a stylish contemporary interior. Spacious comfortable rooms and suites with good facilities. Stylish contemporary restaurant with wide-ranging menus.

O'Callaghan Davenport
Lower Merrion St, off Merrion Sq – ✆ (01) 607 3500 – info@ocallaghanhotels.com – Fax (01) 661 5663 KY **m**
113 rm – †€ 450 ††€ 450, ☕ €16 – 2 suites
Rest *Lanyon* – Carte € 40/47
◆ Sumptuous Victorian gospel hall façade heralds elegant hotel popular with business clientele. Tastefully furnished, well-fitted rooms. Presidents bar honours past leaders. Dining room with fine choice menu.

La Stampa
35-36 Dawson St – ✆ (01) 677 4444 – hotel@lastampa.ie – Fax (01) 677 4411
27 rm – †€ 170/220 ††€ 170/220, ☕ €15 – 1 suite
Rest Balzac – see restaurant listing
Rest *Tiger Becs* – Thai (dinner only) Carte approx. € 40
◆ Silks and oriental furnishings give an Eastern feel to this substantial Georgian house. Elegant bar, beautiful spa and individually appointed, well-equipped bedrooms. Basement restaurant Tiger Becs serves an authentic Thai menu.

O'Callaghan Mont Clare without rest
Lower Merrion St, off Merrion Sq – ✆ (01) 607 3800 – info@ocallaghanhotels.com – Fax (01) 661 5663 – Closed 23-28 December KY **q**
74 rm – †€ 330 ††€ 330, ☕ €14
◆ Classic property with elegant panelled reception and tasteful comfortable rooms at heart of Georgian Dublin. Corporate suites available. Traditional pub style Gallery bar.

Buswells
23-25 Molesworth St – ✆ (01) 614 6500 – buswells@quinn-hotels.com – Fax (01) 676 2090 – Closed Christmas KZ **f**
65 rm ☕ – †€ 245 ††€ 288 – 2 suites
Rest *Trumans* – (carvery lunch) Carte approx. € 20 **s**
◆ Elegant little hotel in quiet central location offering modern amenities while retaining its Georgian charm. Relax in cushioned lounge or cosy, pleasingly furnished rooms. Smart Trumans for formal dining.

REPUBLIC OF IRELAND

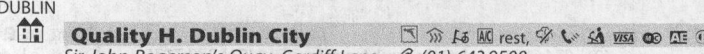

Quality H. Dublin City rest,
Sir John Rogerson's Quay, Cardiff Lane – (01) 643 9500 – info.dublin@qualityhotels.ie – Fax (01) 643 9510 BS **b**
213 rm – €259 €259, €13.50 – **Rest** – (bar lunch) Menu €35 **s** – Carte €30/46 **s**
◆ Based in 'new generation' quayside area. Sleek Vertigo bar named after U2 song. Impressive health club with large pool. Spacious, modern rooms, 48 boasting balconies. Irish and European mix of dishes in open plan restaurant.

Trinity Lodge
12 South Frederick St – (01) 617 0900 – trinitylodge@eircom.net – Fax (01) 617 0999 – Closed Christmas JY **x**
16 rm – €110/140 €140/180
Rest ***George's wine bar*** – (closed Sunday) Carte €25/46 **s**
◆ Elegant, centrally located Georgian town houses near local landmarks. Airy, well-furnished bedrooms with good level of comfort: the modern deluxe rooms are worth asking for. Warm, welcoming wine bar.

Eliza Lodge without rest
23-24 Wellington Quay – (01) 671 8044 – info@dublinlodge.com – Fax (01) 671 8362 – Closed Christmas JY **u**
18 rm – €85/95 €180/200
◆ Ideally placed for Temple Bar nightlife. Small and friendly hotel with comfortable, practical rooms: the balconied penthouse floor has fine river views.

Kilronan House without rest
70 Adelaide Rd – (01) 475 5266 – info@kilronanhouse.com – Fax (01) 478 2841 – Closed Christmas DU **c**
12 rm – €55/120 €160
◆ In the heart of Georgian Dublin, a good value, well-kept town house run by knowledgeable, friendly couple. Individually styled rooms; sustaining breakfasts.

Patrick Guilbaud (Guillaume Lebrun)
21 Upper Merrion St – (01) 676 4192 – restaurantpatrickguilbaud@eircom.net – Fax (01) 661 0052 – Closed 25-26 December, 17 March, Good Friday, Sunday and Monday KZ **e**
Rest – Menu €47 (lunch) – Carte €88/131
Spec. Lobster ravioli in coconut scented cream. Veal sweetbread in liquorice with parsnip sauce. Assiette of chocolate.
◆ Run by consummate professional offering accomplished and acclaimed Irish-influenced dishes in redesigned Georgian town house. Glass-roofed terrace planned for 2008.

Thornton's – at The Fitzwilliam H.
128 St Stephen's Green – (01) 478 7008 – thorntonsrestaurant@eircom.net – Fax (01) 478 7009 – Closed 2 weeks Christmas, Sunday, Monday and lunch Tuesday and Wednesday
Rest – Menu €45/95 – Carte €92/102 JZ **d**
Spec. Sautéed prawns and bisque, truffle sabayon. Magret of Mallard duck with girolles and Madeira sauce. Blood orange soufflé with sorbet.
◆ Sample canapés in spacious lounge; dine at linen-clad tables in restaurant, hung with the chef's striking photos. Luxury ingredients are prepared with balance and knowledge.

Shanahan's on the Green
119 St Stephen's Green – (01) 407 0939 – sales@shanahans.ie – Fax (01) 407 0940 – Closed 2 weeks Christmas and Good Friday JZ **p**
Rest – (dinner only and Friday lunch) (booking essential) Carte €76/122
◆ Sumptuous Georgian town house; upper floor window tables survey the Green. Supreme comfort enhances your enjoyment of strong seafood dishes and choice cuts of Irish beef.

REPUBLIC OF IRELAND

XXX ✿

L'Ecrivain (Derry Clarke)

109A Lower Baggot St – ✆ (01) 661 1919 – enquiries@lecrivain.com – Fax (01) 661 0617 – Closed 10 days Christmas, Easter, Saturday lunch, Sunday and Bank Holidays KZ **b**

Rest – (booking essential) Menu € 45/80 – Carte dinner € 80/100

Spec. Seared tuna, pear sauce and fritter, Oscietra caviar. Suckling pig, pithivier, celeriac, apple fondant, sage and bacon foam. Chocolate fondant, mint ice cream, triple chocolate mousse.

◆ Well-established restaurant serving well prepared, modern Irish menus with emphasis on fish and game. Attentive service from well-versed team. Delightful private dining room.

XXX ✿

Chapter One (Ross Lewis)

The Dublin Writers Museum, 18-19 Parnell Sq – ✆ (01) 873 2266 – info@chapteronerestaurant.com – Fax (01) 873 2330 – Closed first 2 weeks August, 24 December-8 January, Sunday, Monday and Saturday Lunch JX **r**

Rest – Menu € 35 (lunch) – Carte dinner € 55/75 **s**

Spec. Boudin of pig's trotter, lentil, apple and horseradish compote. Veal, macaroni, girolles, spinach, red wine, basil and caper sauce. Orange and Campari jelly, chocolate mousse, vanilla ice cream.

◆ Stylish restaurant in basement of historic building; rustic walls filled with contemporary art. Seasonal, classically-based cooking demonstrates skill and understanding.

XXX

The Saddle Room – at The Shelbourne H.

27 St Stephen's Green – ✆ (01) 663 4500 – info@renaissancehotels.com – Fax (01) 651 6066 JZ **c**

Rest – Menu € 50 – Carte € 50/68

◆ Smart restaurant in heart of hotel with delightful seafood bar. Grill/seafood menu offers quality Irish produce including superior 21 day hung steaks. Two private dining rooms.

XX

Balzac – at La Stampa H.

35-36 Dawson St – ✆ 677 4444 – hotel@lastampa.ie – Fax 677 4411 – closed Saturday and Sunday lunch JZ **A**

Rest – French Menu € 22 – Carte € 40/50

◆ Elegant yet spacious restaurant with high ceiling, blond wood bar, mirrors, banquette seating and a real bistro feel. Tasty, classical French cooking from an appealing menu.

XX

Locks

Number 1, Windsor Terrace – ✆ (01) 454 3391 – closed 1 week Easter, 1 week Christmas-New Year, Saturday lunch, Sunday and Bank Holidays DU **a**

Rest – Menu € 29/49 – Carte € 59/75

◆ Quirky modern restaurant by the canal boasting stylish inner with wooden floor, comfy leather seating and dining split over 2 floors. French menu includes some regional dishes.

XX

The Tea Room – at The Clarence H.

6-8 Wellington Quay – ✆ (01) 407 0813 – tearoom@theclarence.ie – Fax (01) 407 0826 – Closed 24-26 December and Saturday lunch HY **a**

Rest – (booking essential) Menu € 31 – Carte € 49/81

◆ Spacious elegant ground floor room with soaring coved ceiling and stylish contemporary décor offers interesting modern Irish dishes with hint of continental influence.

REPUBLIC OF IRELAND

XX **Dax** VISA AE

23 Pembroke Street Upper – ✆ (01) 676 1494 – olivier@dax.ie
– Closed Christmas and New Year, Sunday and Monday KZ **c**

Rest – (booking essential) Menu € 27 **s** – Carte € 46/56 **s**

◆ Hidden away in basement of Georgian terrace, with rustic inner, immaculately laid tables, wine cellar and bar serving tapas. Knowledgable staff serve French influenced menus.

XX **Fallon & Byrne** VISA AE

First Floor, 11-17 Exchequer St – ✆ (01) 472 1000 – Fax (01) 472 1016
– Closed 25-26 December and Good Friday JY **f**

Rest – Bistro Carte € 27/55

◆ Food emporium boasting vast basement wine cellar, ground floor full of fresh quality produce, and first floor French style bistro with banquettes, mirrors and tasty bistro food.

XX **The Cellar** – at The Merrion H. A/C VISA AE

Upper Merrion St – ✆ (01) 603 0630 – Fax (01) 603 0700
– Closed Saturday lunch KZ **e**

Rest – Menu € 25 (lunch) – Carte dinner € 31/58

◆ Smart open-plan basement restaurant with informal ambience offering well-prepared formal style fare crossing Irish with Mediterranean influences. Good value lunch menu.

XX **One Pico** A/C VISA AE

5-6 Molesworth Pl – ✆ (01) 676 0300 – eamonnoreilly@ireland.com
– Fax (01) 676 0411
– Closed 25 December-3 January, Sunday and Bank Holidays JZ **k**

Rest – Menu € 30/45 – Carte dinner € 53/102 **s**

◆ Wide-ranging cuisine, classic and traditional by turns, always with an original, eclectic edge. Décor and service share a pleasant formality, crisp, modern and stylish.

XX **Rhodes D7** A/C VISA AE

The Capel Buildings, Mary's Abbey – ✆ (01) 804 4444 – info@rhodesd7.com
– Fax (01) 804 4445
– Closed 25-26 December, dinner Sunday and Monday HY **z**

Rest – Carte € 35/48

◆ Cavernous restaurant: take your pick from four dining areas. Bright, warm décor incorporating bold, colourful paintings accompanies classic Rhodes menus given an Irish twist.

XX **Les Frères Jacques** A/C VISA AE

74 Dame St – ✆ (01) 679 4555 – info@lesfreresjacques.com – Fax (01) 679 4725
– Closed 24 December-3 January, Saturday lunch, Sunday and Bank Holidays HY **x**

Rest – French Menu € 23/36 – Carte € 50/90

◆ Smart and well established, offering well prepared, classic French cuisine with fresh fish and seafood a speciality, served by efficient French staff. Warm, modern décor.

XX **Peploe's** A/C VISA AE

16 St Stephen's Green – ✆ (01) 676 3144 – reception@peploes.com
– Fax (01) 676 3154
– Closed 24-29 December and Good Friday JZ **e**

Rest – Carte € 43/56

◆ Fashionable restaurant - a former bank vault - by the Green. Irish wall mural, Italian leather chairs, suede banquettes. Original dishes with pronounced Mediterranean accents.

REPUBLIC OF IRELAND

XX **Town Bar and Grill**

21 Kildare St – ✆ (01) 662 4724 – reservations@townbarandgrill.com – Fax (01) 662 3857 – Closed 25-26 December, 1 January and Good Friday JZ **n**

Rest – Menu € 28 (lunch) – Carte dinner € 39/60

◆ Located in wine merchant's old cellars: brick pillars divide a large space; fresh flowers and candles add a personal touch. Italian flair in bold cooking with innovative edge.

XX **Dobbin's**

15 Stephen's Lane, (off Stephen's Place) off Lower Mount St – ✆ (01) 661 9536 – dobbinsbistro@g.mail.com – Fax (01) 661 3331 – Closed 1 week Christmas-New Year, Good Friday, Saturday lunch, Sunday dinner and Bank Holidays EU **s**

Rest – (booking essential) Menu € 21/35 – Carte € 47/61

◆ In the unlikely setting of a former Nissen hut, and now with contemporary styling, this popular restaurant, something of a local landmark, offers good food to suit all tastes.

XX **Jacobs Ladder**

4-5 Nassau St – ✆ (01) 670 3865 – dining@jacobsladder.ie – Fax (01) 670 3868 – closed 2 weeks Christmas, 1 week August, Good Friday, 17 March, Sunday and Monday KY **a**

Rest – (booking essential) Menu € 44 (dinner) **s** – Carte € 31/62 **s**

◆ Up a narrow staircase, this popular small first floor restaurant with unfussy modern décor and a good view offers modern Irish fare and very personable service.

XX **Siam Thai**

14-15 Andrew St – ✆ (01) 677 3363 – siam@eircom.net – Fax (01) 670 7644 – Closed 25-26 December and lunch Saturday and Sunday JY **d**

Rest – Thai Menu € 15/35 – Carte € 29/44

◆ Invariably popular, centrally located restaurant with a warm, homely feel, embodied by woven Thai prints. Daily specials enhance Thai menus full of choice and originality.

XX **Jaipur**

41 South Great George's St – ✆ (01) 677 0999 – dublin@jaipur.ie – Fax (01) 677 0979 JY **a**

Rest – Indian (dinner only and lunch in December) Menu € 50 – Carte € 35/45

◆ Vivid modernity in the city centre; run by knowledgeable team. Immaculately laid, linen-clad tables. Interesting, freshly prepared Indian dishes using unique variations.

XX **Bang Café**

11 Merrion Row – ✆ (01) 676 0898 – bangcafe@eircom.net – Fax (01) 676 0899 – Closed 2 weeks late December-early January and Sunday KZ **a**

Rest – (booking essential) Menu € 40/50 – Carte € 31/48

◆ Stylish feel, closely set tables and an open kitchen lend a lively, contemporary air to this established three-tier favourite. Menus balance the classical and the creative.

X **The Winding Stair**

40 Lower Ormond Quay – ✆ (01) 872 7320 – Closed 25-26 December and 1 January JY **t**

Rest – (booking essential) Carte € 30/48

◆ Delightfully rustic restaurant on banks of River Liffey, unusually set above a bookshop. Open dining room with wooden tables; frequently-changing menu has strong organic base.

X **Pearl Brasserie**

20 Merrion St Upper – ✆ (01) 661 3572 – info@pearl-brasserie.com – Fax (01) 661 3629 – Closed 25 December, Saturday lunch and Sunday KZ **n**

Rest – French Carte € 29/49

◆ A metal staircase leads down to this intimate, newly refurbished, vaulted brasserie where Franco-Irish dishes are served at smart, linen-laid tables. Amiable, helpful service.

Eden

Meeting House Sq, Temple Bar – ☎ (01) 670 5372 – eden@edenrestaurant.ie – Fax (01) 670 3330 – Closed 25 December-2 January and Bank Holidays HY **e**

Rest – Menu € 26/44 – Carte € 36/48

◆ Modern minimalist restaurant with open plan kitchen serves good robust food. Terrace overlooks theatre square, at the heart of a busy arty district. The place for pre-theatre.

Mermaid Café

69-70 Dame St – ☎ (01) 670 8236 – info@mermaid.ie – Fax (01) 670 8205 HY **d**

Rest – (Sunday brunch) (booking essential) Menu € 27 (lunch) – Carte € 40/51

◆ This informal restaurant with unfussy décor and bustling atmosphere offers an interesting and well cooked selection of robust modern dishes. Efficient service.

L'Gueleton

1 Fade St – ☎ (01) 675 3708 – closed 25 December-1 January, Sunday and Bank Holidays JY **c**

Rest – French (bookings not accepted) Carte € 27/42

◆ Busy, highly renowned recent arrival. Rustic style: mish-mash of roughed-up chairs and tables with candles or Parisian lamps. Authentic French country dishes full of flavour.

Bleu

Joshua House, Dawson St – ☎ (01) 676 7015 – Fax (01) 676 7027 – Closed 25-26 December JZ **r**

Rest – Menu € 22/30 – Carte dinner € 25/42

◆ Distinctive modern interior serves as chic background to this friendly all-day restaurant. Appealing and varied menu, well executed and very tasty. Good wine selection.

La Maison des Gourmets

15 Castlemarket – ☎ (01) 672 7258 – Fax (01) 672 7238 – Closed 25 December-2 January and Bank Holidays JY **c**

Rest – French (lunch only) (bookings not accepted) Carte € 18/24

◆ Neat, refurbished eatery on first floor above an excellent French bakery. Extremely good value Gallic meals with simplicity the key. Get there early or be prepared to wait!

The Cellar Bar – at The Merrion H.

Upper Merrion St – ☎ (01) 603 0600 – info@merrionhotel.com – Fax (01) 603 0700 – Closed 25 December and Sunday KZ **e**

Rest – (carvery lunch) Carte € 35/50

◆ Characterful stone and brick bar-restaurant in the original vaulted cellars with large wood bar. Popular with Dublin's social set. Offers wholesome Irish pub lunch fare.

Clarendon Café Bar

32 Clarendon Street – ☎ (01) 679 2909 – Fax (01) 670 6900 – Closed 25-26 December, 1 January, dinner Friday-Sunday and Good Friday JY **h**

Rest – (Sunday brunch) (bookings not accepted) Carte € 15/42

◆ Sleek, contemporary metal and glass dining pub on three levels. Chocolate leather box seats and scatter cushions. Modern menus all the way from casual to serious in style.

at Sandymount – Dublin

Itsa 4

6A Sandymount Green – ☎ (01) 219 4676 – itsa4@itsabagel.com – Fax (01) 219 4654 – Closed 1 week Christmas, Good Friday and Monday except Bank Holidays GU **a**

Rest – (booking essential) Carte € 32/51

◆ Dark wood and bright lime green chairs seduce the eye in this smart contemporary restaurant in smart suburb. Traceability of ingredients key to tasty, easy-going menu.

at Ballsbridge

Four Seasons

Simmonscourt Rd – ✆ (01) 665 4000
– sales.dublin@fourseasons.com – Fax (01) 665 4099 FU **e**
157 rm – ††€ 445/490, ☕ €29 – 40 suites
Rest *Seasons* – Menu € 35 (lunch) – Carte dinner € 62/84
Rest *The Cafe* – Carte € 38/75 **s**

◆ Every inch the epitome of international style - supremely comfortable rooms with every facility; richly furnished lounge; a warm mix of antiques, oils and soft piano études. Dining in Seasons guarantees luxury ingredients. Good choice menu in The Café.

Herbert Park

– ✆ (01) 667 2200 – reservations@herbertparkhotel.ie
– Fax (01) 667 2595 FU **m**
151 rm – †€ 250 ††€ 385, ☕ €21.50 – 2 suites
Rest *The Pavilion* – Menu € 26 – Carte € 36/72

◆ Stylish contemporary hotel. Open, modern lobby and lounges. Excellent, well-designed rooms with tasteful décor: fifth floor Executive rooms boast several upgraded extras. French-windowed restaurant with alfresco potential; oyster/lobster specialities.

Merrion Hall without rest

54-56 Merrion Rd – ✆ (01) 283 7916 – merrionhall@aol.ie
– Fax (01) 283 7877 FU **b**
34 rm ☕ – †€ 99/119 ††€ 139/169 – 2 suites

◆ Manor house hotel has comfy sitting rooms with Georgian feel and some original features plus rear breakfast room with conservatory. Minimalist bedrooms boast quality feel.

The Schoolhouse

2-8 Northumberland Rd – ✆ (01) 667 5014 – reservations@schoolhousehotel.com
– Fax (01) 667 5015
– Closed 24-26 December EU **a**
31 rm ☕ – †€ 169/500 ††€ 199/500
Rest *Canteen* – (brunch Saturday and Sunday) Menu € 24 (lunch) – Carte € 29/49

◆ Spacious converted 19C schoolhouse, close to canal, boasts modernity and charm. Inkwell bar exudes a convivial atmosphere. Rooms contain locally crafted furniture. Old classroom now a large restaurant with beamed ceilings.

Ariel House without rest

50-54 Lansdowne Rd – ✆ (01) 668 5512 – reservations@ariel-house.net
– Fax (01) 668 5845
– Closed 21-28 December FU **n**
37 rm ☕ – †€ 72/110 ††€ 130/250

◆ Restored, listed Victorian mansion in smart suburb houses personally run, traditional small hotel. Rooms feature period décor and some antiques; comfy four poster rooms.

Bewley's

Merrion Rd – ✆ (01) 668 1111 – ballsbridge@bewleyshotels.com
– Fax (01) 668 1999
– closed 24-26 December FU **a**
304 rm – †€ 109/119 ††€ 109/119, ☕ €11
Rest *O'Connells* – (carvery lunch) Menu € 28 **s** – Carte € 27/37 **s**

◆ Huge hotel offers stylish modern accommodation behind sumptuous Victorian façade of former Masonic school. Location, facilities and value for money make this a good choice. Informal modern O'Connells restaurant, cleverly constructed with terrace in stairwell.

REPUBLIC OF IRELAND

Aberdeen Lodge
53-55 Park Ave – ✆ (01) 283 8155 – aberdeen@iol.ie
– Fax (01) 283 7877 GV **e**
17 rm – €99/119 €139/300 – **Rest** – (residents only, light meals)
Carte €25/34 **s**
◆ Neat red brick house in smart residential suburb. Comfortable rooms with Edwardian style décor in neutral tones, wood furniture and modern facilities. Some garden views. Comfortable, traditionally decorated dining room.

Pembroke Townhouse without rest
90 Pembroke Rd – ✆ (01) 660 0277 – info@pembroketownhouse.ie
– Fax (01) 660 0291
– closed 22 December-3 January FU **d**
48 rm – €90/165 €130/230
◆ Period-inspired décor adds to the appeal of a sensitively modernised Georgian terrace town house in the smart suburbs. Neat, simple accommodation.

Glenogra House without rest
64 Merrion Rd – ✆ (01) 668 3661 – info@glenogra.com – Fax (01) 668 3698
– Closed 22 December-10 January FU **w**
13 rm – €85/105 €119/159
◆ Neat and tidy bay-windowed house in smart suburb. Personally-run to good standard with bedrooms attractively decorated in keeping with a period property. Modern facilities.

Siam Thai
Sweepstake Centre – ✆ (01) 660 1722 – siam@eircom.net
– Fax (01) 660 1537
– Closed 25-26 December, lunch Saturday and Sunday and Good Friday FU **h**
Rest – Thai Menu €15/35 – Carte €29/44
◆ Unerringly busy restaurant that combines comfort with liveliness. Efficient staff serve authentic Thai cuisine, prepared with skill and understanding. Good value lunches.

Roly's Bistro
7 Ballsbridge Terrace – ✆ (01) 668 2611 – ireland@rolysbistro.ie
– Fax (01) 660 3342 FU **r**
Rest – (booking essential) Menu €21/42 – Carte €39/51
◆ A Dublin institution: this roadside bistro is very busy and well run with a buzzy, fun atmosphere. Its two floors offer traditional Irish dishes and a very good value lunch.

at Donnybrook

Marble Hall without rest
81 Marlborough Rd – ✆ (01) 497 7350 – marblehall@eircom.net
– Closed Christmas EV **a**
3 rm – €60/65 €90/100
◆ Georgian townhouse with effusive welcome guaranteed. Individually styled throughout, with plenty of antiques and quality soft furnishings. Stylish, warmly decorated bedrooms.

Poulot's
Mulberry Gardens, off Morehampton Rd – ✆ (01) 269 3300 – Fax (01) 269 3260
– Closed 25 December-5 January, Sunday and Monday FV **k**
Rest – Menu €35 (lunch) – Carte dinner €50/72
◆ A light, airy ambience is enhanced by garden views from all tables. Vivid oils and prints liven up white walls. Modern, complex dishes with distinctive French starting point.

at Ranelagh

XX ✿ **Mint** (Dylan Mac Grath)
47 Ranelagh – ✆ (01) 497 8655 – info@mintrestaurant.ie – Fax (01) 497 9035 – Closed 23 December-6 January, 6-17 April, Sunday, Monday and Saturday lunch EV **e**
Rest – Menu € 30/75 – Carte € 37/75
Spec. Roast lobster, minced veal, truffle macaroni, hen's egg. Roast turbot, broccoli purée, braised snails, Spanish ham and red wine. Ginger ice cream, ginger savarin and lime parfait.
◆ Intimate, pastel-hued restaurant in up and coming area of the city. Ambitious, confident kitchen serving uncompromisingly rich and elaborate dishes with French influences.

at Rathmines

Uppercross House
26-30 Upper Rathmines Rd – ✆ (01) 497 54 86 – reservations@uppercrosshousehotel.com – Fax (01) 497 53 61 – Closed 24-28 December DV **d**
49 rm – †€ 75/109 ††€ 124/158 – **Rest** – (dinner only and lunch Saturday and Sunday) Menu € 20/35 – Carte € 23/45
◆ Privately run suburban hotel in three adjacent town houses with modern extension wing. Good size rooms and standard facilities. Live music midweek in traditional Irish bar. Restaurant offers a mellow and friendly setting with welcoming wood décor.

XX **Zen**
89 Upper Rathmines Rd – ✆ (01) 497 94 28 – Fax (01) 491 17 28 DV **t**
Rest – Chinese (dinner only and lunch Friday) Menu € 18 **s** – Carte € 27/31 **s**
◆ Renowned family run Chinese restaurant in the unusual setting of an old church hall. Imaginative, authentic oriental cuisine with particular emphasis on spicy Szechuan dishes.

at Terenure South : 9 1/2 km by N 81

XX **Vermilion**
1st Floor above Terenure Inn, 94-96 Terenure Road North – ✆ (01) 499 1400 – mail@vermilion.ie – Fax (01) 499 1300 – Closed 25-26 December and Good Friday BT **c**
Rest – Indian (dinner only and Sunday lunch) Carte € 29/46
◆ Smart restaurant above a busy pub in a residential part of town. Vividly coloured dining room and efficient service. Well-balanced, modern Indian food with a Keralan base.

at Dublin Airport North : 10½ km by N 1 - BS - and M 1 – ✉ Dublin

Hilton Dublin Airport
Northern Cross, Malahide Rd, East : 3 km by A 32 – ✆ (01) 866 18 00 reservations.dublinairport@hilton.com – Fax (01) 866 18 66
162 rm – †€ 86/240 ††€ 86/270, ☕ € 19.50 – 4 suites
Rest *Solas* – (dinner only and Sunday lunch) Menu € 38 **s** – Carte € 36/48 **s**
◆ Opened in 2005, just five minutes from the airport, adjacent to busy shopping centre. Modish feel throughout. State-of-the-art meeting facilities. Airy, well-equipped rooms. Spacious Solas serves modern dishes with Irish and international flavours.

Carlton H. Dublin Airport
Old Airport Rd, Cloughran, on R 132 Santry rd – ✆ (01) 866 7500 – info@carltondublinairport.com – Fax (01) 862 3114 – Closed 3 days Christmas
99 rm – †€ 330 ††€ 330, ☕ € 16 – 1 suite
Rest *Clouds* – (dinner only and Sunday lunch) Carte € 35/53 **s**
◆ Purpose-built hotel on edge of airport. State-of-the-art conference rooms. Impressive bedrooms, though many a touch compact, in warm colours with high level of facilities. Fine dining restaurant: worldwide cooking accompanied by excellent views.

REPUBLIC OF IRELAND

Bewleys

Baskin Lane, East : 1 1/2 km on A 32 – ✆ (01) 871 1000 – dublinairport@bewleyshotels.com – Fax (01) 871 1001 – Closed 24-25 December

466 rm – €89/99 €89/99, €11

Rest *The Brasserie* – Menu € 15/27 **s** – Carte € 27/34 **s**

◆ Immense eight floor hotel, ten minutes from the airport, with selection of small meeting rooms. Immaculately kept bedrooms; good value for money. Wide-ranging menu served in The Brasserie.

at Clontarf Northeast : 5 ½ km by R 105 – ✉ Dublin

Clontarf Castle

Castle Ave – ✆ (01) 833 2321 – info@clontarfcastle.ie – Fax (01) 833 0418 – Closed 25 December CS **a**

108 rm – €130/160 €400, €23 – 3 suites

Rest *Templars Bistro* – (carvery lunch Monday-Friday) Menu € 45 – Carte € 45/65

◆ Set in an historic castle, partly dating back to 1172. Striking medieval style entrance lobby. Modern rooms and characterful luxury suites, all with cutting edge facilities. Restaurant with grand medieval style décor reminiscent of a knights' banqueting hall.

at Dundrum Southeast : 8 km by N 11 - CT – ✉ Dublin

First Floor – at Harvey Nichols

Town Square, Sandyford Rd – ✆ (01) 291 0488 – michael.andrews@harveynichols.ie – Fax (01) 291 0489 – Closed 25-26 December, dinner Sunday and Monday

Rest – Menu € 25/30 – Carte dinner € 43/56

◆ Up the lift to ultra-stylish bar and plush, designer-led restaurant. Attentive, professional service. Dishes are modern, seasonal and confident with a fine dining feel.

Cafe Mao

Town Square, Sandyford Rd – ✆ (01) 296 2802 – dundrum@cafemao.com – Fax (01) 296 2813

Rest – South East Asian (bookings not accepted) Carte € 25/34

◆ Situated in an upmarket 21C shopping centre, this café has a smart terrace and balconies from which you can watch the elegant dancing fountains. Wide-ranging, Asian menus.

at Stillorgan Southeast : 8 km on N 11 - CT – ✉ Dublin

Radisson SAS St Helen's

Stillorgan Rd – ✆ (01) 218 6000 – info.dublin@radissonsas.com – Fax (01) 218 6010

130 rm – €145/170 €200/350, €22 – 21 suites

Rest *Talavera* – Italian (dinner only) Carte € 32/56

◆ Imposing part 18C mansion with substantial extensions and well laid out gardens. Well run with good level of services. Smart modern rooms with warm feel and all facilities. Delicious antipasti table at basement Talavera.

Stillorgan Park

Stillorgan Rd – ✆ (01) 200 1800 – sales@stillorganpark.com – Fax (01) 283 1610 – Closed 25 December

158 rm – €109/196 €109/196, €13.50

Rest *Purple Sage* – (carvery lunch) Menu € 26/36 – Carte € 25/40

◆ Modern commercial hotel in southside city suburb. Spacious rooms with modern facilities. Interesting horse theme décor in large stone floored bar with buffet. Mosaics, frescoes and hidden alcoves add spice to popular Irish dishes in Purple Sage.

REPUBLIC OF IRELAND

at Sandyford **Southeast : 9 km by N 11 - CT - off Leopardstown Rd – ✉ Dublin**

The Beacon

rest, VISA AE

Beacon Court, Sandyford Business Region – ✆ (01) 291 5000 – sales@thebeacon.com – Fax (01) 291 5005 – Closed 25-26 December

88 rm – €120 €300, €20

Rest *My Thai* – Thai Carte €20/30

◆ Ultra-stylish hotel with uniquely quirky entrance lobby featuring a chandelier on the floor and bed with central seating! Modish bar, low-key meeting rooms, sleek bedrooms. Funky, relaxed restaurant serving authentic Asian dishes.

at Foxrock **Southeast : 13 km by N 11 - CT – ✉ Dublin**

Bistro One

VISA

3 Brighton Rd – ✆ (01) 289 7711 – bistroone@eircom.net – Fax (01) 207 0742 – Closed 25 December-3 January, Sunday and Monday

Rest – (booking essential) Menu €20 (lunch) – Carte €34/48

◆ Pleasantly set and homely, with beams and walls of wine racks. Simple menu offers well-prepared, distinctively seasonal Irish, Asian or Italian classics. Passionate owner.

at Leopardstown **Southeast : 12 km by N 11 - CT – ✉ Dublin**

Bewleys

rm, rest, VISA AE

Central Park – ✆ (01) 293 5000 – leopardstown@bewleyshotels.com – Fax (01) 293 5099 – Closed 24-25 December

352 rm – €89 €89, €11

Rest *Brasserie* – (carvery lunch) Menu €25/30 – Carte €19/25 **s**

◆ Handily placed next to racecourse, this modern hotel boasts smart bar with leather armchairs, decked terrace, and comfy, uniform bedrooms with good facilities. Informal brasserie with neutral, stylish tones.

at Clondalkin **Southwest : 12 km by N 7 on R 113 - AT – ✉ Dublin**

Red Cow Moran

rm, P VISA AE

Naas Rd, Southeast : 3 ¼ km on N 7 at junction with M 50 – ✆ (01) 459 3650 – redcowres@moranhotels.com – Fax (01) 459 1588 – Closed 24-26 December

120 rm – €250 €380 – 3 suites

Rest *The Winter Garden* – Menu €23/35 **s** – Carte €33/62 **s**

◆ Sweeping lobby staircase gives a foretaste of this smart commercial hotel's mix of traditional elegance and modern design. Landmark Red Cow inn and Diva nightclub. Large characterful Winter Garden restaurant with bare brick walls and warm wood floor.

Bewley's H. Newlands Cross

rm, rest, P VISA AE

Newlands Cross, Naas Rd (N 7) – ✆ (01) 464 0140 – res@bewleyshotels.com – Fax (01) 464 0900 – Closed 24-26 December

299 rm – €99 €99, €11 – **Rest** – (carvery lunch) Menu €25 – Carte €28/38

◆ Well run, busy, commercial hotel popular with business people. Spacious rooms with modern facilities can also accommodate families. Represents good value for money. Large, busy café-restaurant with traditional dark wood fittings and colourful décor.

at Lucan West : 12 km by N 4 - AT – ✉ Dublin

Clarion H. Dublin Liffey Valley rm, rest,

Liffey Valley, off N 4 at M 50 junction
– ✆ (01) 625 80 00 – info@clarionhotelliffeyvalley.com
– Fax (01) 625 80 01
– closed 24-28 December
254 rm – †€ 99/260 ††€ 260, ☕ €18 – 31 suites
Rest *Sinergie* – (dinner only and Sunday lunch) Menu € 30/45 – Carte € 30/41
Rest *Kudos* – Carte € 19/25
◆ U-shaped hotel opened in 2005; bright, open public areas. Well equipped conference facilities; smart leisure club. Sizable, up-to-date rooms with high quality furnishings. Irish dishes with a twist at Sinergie. Asian themed Kudos with on-view wok kitchen.

at Castleknock Northwest : 13 km by N 3 (Caven Rd) - AS - and Auburn Ave – ✉ Dublin

Castleknock H. & Country Club rm, rest,

Porterstown Rd, Southwest : 1½ km
by Castleknock Rd and Porterstown Rd – ✆ (01) 640 63 00 – info@chcc.ie
– Fax (01) 640 63 03
– Closed 24-26 December
140 rm ☕ – †€ 290 ††€ 330 – 4 suites
Rest *The Park* – (dinner only) Carte € 39/62
◆ Impressive corporate hotel incorporating golf course and 160 acres of grounds. Stylish, contemporary design; extensive business and leisure facilities; well equipped rooms. Formal Park restaurant with golf course views.

DUBLIN AIRPORT – Dublin – **712** N 7 – see Dublin

DUN LAOGHAIRE (Dún Laoghaire) – Dublin – **712** N 8 *Ireland* 39 **D1**

Dublin 14 km
to Holyhead (Stena Line) 4-5 daily (1 h 40 mn)
Ferry Terminal ✆ (01) 602 4000
Dun Laoghaire Eglinton Park, ✆ (01) 280 3916.
≤ ★★ of Killiney Bay from coast road south of Sorrento Point

Plan opposite

Rasam

1st Floor (above Eagle House pub), 18-19 Glasthule Rd – ✆ (01) 230 0600
– info@rasam.ie – Fax (01) 230 1000
– Closed 25-26 December and Good Friday **e**
Rest – Indian (dinner only) Carte € 38/49
◆ Located above Eagle House pub, this airy, modern, stylish restaurant shimmers with silky green wallpaper. Interesting, authentic dishes covering all regions of India.

Cavistons

58-59 Glasthule Rd – ✆ (01) 280 9245 – info@cavistons.com – Fax (01) 284 4054
– Closed Sunday and Monday **a**
Rest – (lunch only) (booking essential) Carte € 28/52
◆ Simple, informal restaurant attached to the well-established seafood shop which specialises in finest piscine produce. Mermaid friezes and quality crustacean cuisine.

Tribes

57a Glasthule Rd – ✆ (01) 236 5971 – tribesrestaurant@yahoo.com
– Closed 25 December and Good Friday **x**
Rest – (dinner only and Sunday lunch) Carte € 33/46
◆ Personally run neighbourhood restaurant next to Cavistons. Smart, original interior harmonises seamlessly with creative modern European menus that evolve slowly over time.

Café Mao

A/C VISA

The Pavilion – (01) 214 8090 – dunlaoghaire@cafemao.com
– Fax (01) 214 7064
– Closed 25-26 December **r**

Rest – South East Asian (bookings not accepted) Carte € 25/34

◆ Modern and informal with the background bustle of the Pavillion Centre and open kitchen. Quick, tasty meals find favour with hungry shoppers: try Vietnamese, Chinese or Thai.

DUNBOYNE – Meath – **712** M 7 37 **D3**

Dublin 17 km – Drogheda 45 km – Newbridge 54 km

Dunboyne Castle

rm, A/C

– (01) 801 35 00 – info@dunboynecastlehotel.com
– Fax (01) 436 68 01

VISA AE

141 rm – † € 280 †† € 340 – 4 suites –

Rest – (bar lunch Monday-Friday) Carte € 29/54

◆ Extended Georgian house in 26 acres. Ornate ceilings typify style in original house. Some bedrooms have balconies; most overlook grounds. Popular choice for conferences. Discreet, stylish spa. Large, formal restaurant serves classic Irish dishes.

DUNCANNON (Dún Canann) – Wexford – 712 L 11 – pop. 318 — 39 D2

Ireland

Dublin 167 km – New Ross 26 km – Waterford 48 km
Fort★ AC
Dunbrody Abbey★ AC, N : 9 km by R 733 – Kilmokea Gardens★ AC, N : 11 km by R 733 – Tintern Abbey★ AC, E : 8 km by R 737 and R 733. Kennedy Arboretum★ AC, N : 21 km by R 733

XX Aldridge Lodge with rm

South : 1 km by Hook Head Rd – (051) 389 116 – info@aldridgelodge.com – Fax (051) 389 116
– Closed 5 January-8 February, Tuesday February-June and Monday
3 rm – †€ 50 ††€ 100 – **Rest** – (dinner only and Sunday lunch) (booking essential) Menu € 38
◆ Close to the beach, a smart, cheery restaurant with gardens serving good value, quality local menus: lobster a speciality as owner's dad's a lobster fisherman! Cosy rooms.

X Sqigl

Quay Rd – (051) 389 188 – sqiglrestaurant@eircom.net
– Closed 24-26 December, Good Friday, Sunday, Monday and Tuesday in winter
Rest – (dinner only) (booking essential) Menu € 45 – Carte € 30/51
◆ Stone-built restaurant; a converted barn standing behind a popular bar in this coastal village. Faux leopard skin banquettes. Modern European cuisine with amiable service.

REPUBLIC OF IRELAND

DUNDALK – Louth – 712 M 5/6 – pop. 32 505 *Ireland* — 37 D2

Dublin 82 km – Drogheda 35 km
Killinbeg Bridge a Chrin Killin Park, (042) 933 93 03 .
Dún a' Rí Forest Park★, W : 34 km by R 178 and R 179 – Proleek Dolmen★, N : 8 km by N 1 R 173

Ballymascanlon

Northeast : 5 ¾ km by R 132, N 52 on R 173
– (042) 935 82 00 – info@ballymascanlon.com – Fax (042) 937 15 98
90 rm – †€ 115/120 ††€ 185 – 3 suites – **Rest** – Menu € 35/49
◆ Victorian house with modern extensions, surrounded by gardens and golf course. Good size leisure club. Bedrooms and various lounges are in a modern style. Bright restaurant with stylish terrace bar.

Rosemount without rest

Dublin Rd, South : 2½ km on R 132 – (042) 933 58 78 – maisieb7@eircom.net – Fax (042) 933 58 78
9 rm – †€ 50 ††€ 70
◆ A modern house a short drive from the town with good access to the M1. Well-appointed guests' lounge and attractive breakfast room. Comfortably furnished bedrooms.

XX Rosso

5 Roden Pl – (042) 935 6502 – Fax (042) 935 6503
– Closed Christmas, Saturday lunch and Monday
Rest – Carte € 36/45
◆ Traditional on the outside, contemporary on the inside, with stylish furnishings and banquette seating. Front windows overlook cathedral. Classic cooking with a modern twist.

We try to be as accurate as possible when giving room rates. But prices are susceptible to change, so please check rates when booking.

DUNDRUM – Dublin – **712** N 8 – see Dublin

DUNFANAGHY (Dún Fionnachaidh) – **Donegal** – **712** I 2 – **pop. 290** 37 **C1**
– ✉ **Letterkenny** ▮ *Ireland*

Dublin 277 km – Donegal 87 km – Londonderry 69 km
Dunfanaghy Letterkenny, ☎ (074) 913 6335 .
Horn Head Scenic Route★, N : 4 km. Doe Castle★, SE : 11 ¼ km by N 56 – The Rosses★, SW : 40 ¼ km by N 56 and R 259

Arnolds
Main St – ☎ (074) 913 62 08 – enquiries@arnoldshotel.com – Fax (074) 913 63 52 – April-2 November
30 rm – €75/115 €150/170
Rest ***Sea Scapes*** – (light lunch) Menu €45 – Carte €28/47
◆ Pleasant traditional coaching inn with a variety of extensions. Spacious lounge area and a charming bar with open fires. Family run with traditional bedrooms. Informal Seascapes serves wide-ranging menus.

The Mill with rm New Lake and Mount Muckish,
Southwest : ¾ km on N 56 – ☎ (074) 913 69 85
– themillrestaurant@oceanfree.net – Fax (074) 913 69 85
– April-November and weekends only November-mid December and late March
6 rm – €70 €100 – **Rest** – (Closed Monday) (dinner only) Menu €45
◆ Flax mill on New Lake with Mount Muckish view. Locally renowned and warmly run; enhanced by personally decorated ambience. Well-judged modern Irish menu. Pleasant rooms.

REPUBLIC OF IRELAND

DUNGARVAN – **Waterford** – **712** J 11 – **pop. 7 425** ▮ *Ireland* 39 **C3**

Dublin 190 km – Cork 71 km – Waterford 48 km
The Courthouse ☎ (058) 41741
Knocknagrannagh, ☎ (058) 41 605 ;
Gold Coast Ballinacourty, ☎ (058) 42 249.
East Bank (Augustinian priory, ★)
Ringville (★), S : 13 km by N 25 and R 674 – Helvick Head★ (★), SE : 13 km by N 25 and R 674

An Bohreen
Killineen West, East : 8 km by N 25 – ☎ (051) 291 010
– mulligans@anbohreen.com – Fax (051) 291 010
– April -late October
4 rm – €65/70 €90/100 – **Rest** – (by arrangement) Menu €40
◆ Very personally run bungalow with fine views over countryside and bay. Cosy sofa area within large open plan layout. Individually designed rooms are tastefully furnished. Dinner menu employs best local ingredients and is cooked with some passion.

Powersfield House
Ballinamuck West, Northwest : 2½ km on R 672 – ☎ (058) 45 594
– eunice@powersfield.com – Fax (058) 45 550
5 rm – €65/75 €100/120 – **Rest** – (by arrangement) Menu €30
◆ Set on main road just out of town. Georgian style exterior welcomes guests into a cosy lounge. All bedrooms have individual style with warm feel and some antique furniture.

Gortnadiha Lodge without rest
South : 6½ km by N 25 off R 674 – ☎ (058) 46 142
– gortnadihalodge@eircom.net
– February-November
3 rm – €55 €80/90
◆ Friendly guesthouse set in its own glen with fine bay views, a first floor terrace for afternoon tea, homemade jams and breads for breakfast, and antique furnished bedrooms.

XX **Tannery** with rm — AC rest, VISA MC AE

10 Quay St, via Parnell St – ✆ (058) 45 420 – tannery@cablesurf.com – Fax (058) 45 814 – Closed late January-early February, 1 week September, Monday, Saturday lunch and Sunday dinner except in summer

7 rm – †€ 60/70 ††€ 160 – **Rest** – Carte € 30/49

◆ Characterful 19C former tannery. Informal ambience and contemporary styling with high ceilings and wood floors. Imaginative modern menus. Stylish rooms in adjacent townhouse.

XX **Q82 at Quealy's** — AC VISA MC

first floor, 82 O'Connell St – ✆ (058) 24 555 – info@quealys.com – Fax (058) 24 555 – Closed 27 January-11 February, Christmas, 1 January, Good Friday, Sunday and Monday

Rest – (dinner only) Carte € 39/53

◆ Contemporary upstairs restaurant on main road; candlelit in winter and sunny in summer, thanks to skylights in roof. Modern, seasonal French cooking uses fine ingredients.

DUNKINEELY – Donegal – 712 G 4 — 37 C1

XX **Castle Murray House** with rm — McSwyne's Bay, P VISA MC

– ✆ (074) 973 70 22 – info@castlemurray.com – Fax (074) 973 73 30 – Closed mid January-mid February and 24-26 December

10 rm – †€ 80/95 ††€ 150/160 – **Rest** – Seafood (dinner only and Sunday lunch, light lunch June-September) Menu € 50

◆ In delightful, picturesque position with view of sea and sunsets from the conservatory. Pleasant dining room. Good local seafood. Comfortable, individually themed bedrooms.

DUNLAVIN (Dún Luáin) – Wicklow – 712 L 8 — 39 D2

Dublin 50 km – Kilkenny 71 km – Wexford 98 km

Rathsallagh, ✆ (045) 403 316 .

Rathsallagh House — rm, P VISA MC AE

Southwest : 3 ¼ km on Grangecon Rd – ✆ (045) 403 112 – info@rathsallagh.com – Fax (045) 403 343 – Closed 4 January-March

28 rm – †€ 195 ††€ 320 – 1 suite – **Rest** – (dinner only) Menu € 65

◆ 18C converted stables set in extensive grounds and golf course. Picturesque walled garden. Characterful, country house-style public areas and cosy, individual bedrooms. Kitchen garden provides ingredients for welcoming dining room.

DUNMORE EAST (Dún Mór) – Waterford – 712 L 11 – pop. 1 750 — 39 C2

✉ Waterford *Ireland*

Dublin 174 km – Waterford 19 km

Dunmore East, ✆ (051) 383 151.

Village★

The Beach without rest — P VISA MC AE

1 Lower Village – ✆ (051) 383 316 – beachouse@eircom.net – Fax (051) 383 319 – March-October

7 rm – †€ 50/65 ††€ 80/100

◆ Modern house close to the beach. Wonderful views from conservatory breakfast/lounge area. Very spacious bedrooms with pine furniture and modern facilities; some with balcony.

Look out for red symbols, indicating particularly pleasant establishments.

DUNSANY (Dún Samhnaí) – Co Meath – 712 M 7 37 D3

Dublin 42 km – Dunboyne 23 km – Navan 17 km

Dunsany Lodge

Butterjohn Cross, Dublin Rd, Southwest : 3½ km, at junction with R 154 – (046) 902 63 39 – info@dunsanylodge.ie – Fax (046) 902 63 42

10 rm – **†€ 50/55 ††€ 90/98 – Rest** – Menu € 15/32 **s** – Carte € 26/35 **s**

◆ Modern lounge and bar with red and cream leather seats. Uniformly-sized bedrooms with up-to-date facilities; the rear rooms are the quietest. Lawned garden. Smart formal restaurant with decked terrace serves tried-and-tested dishes.

DURROW (Darú) – Laois – 712 J 9 39 C2

Dublin 108 km – Cork 141 km – Kilkenny 27 km

Castle Durrow

– (057) 87 36 555 – info@castledurrow.com – Fax (057) 87 36 559 – Closed 31 December-18 January

41 rm – **†€ 100/140 ††€ 20/280 – Rest** – (dinner only) Menu € 50

◆ Imposing greystone early 18C country mansion set in carefully manicured gardens and 30 acres of parkland. Eye-catching stained glass. Modern, understated bedrooms. High, ornate ceilings and views across gardens from the dining room.

Undecided between two equivalent establishments? Within each category, establishments are classified in our order of preference.

DURRUS (Dúras) – Cork – 712 D 13 38 A3

Dublin 338 km – Cork 90 km – Killarney 85 km

Blairs Cove House

Southwest : 1½ km on R 591 – (027) 61 127 – blairscove@eircom.net – Fax (027) 61 487 – Restricted opening in winter

4 rm – **†€ 125/145 ††€ 190/230**

Rest Blairs Cove (Restaurant) – see restaurant listing

◆ Fine Georgian house with outbuildings and sea views, set around a courtyard. Spacious, modern suites come with own kitchens and dining areas.

Blairs Cove (Restaurant)

Southwest : 1½ km on R 591 – (027) 62 913 – blairscove@eircom.net – Fax (027) 61 487 – Restricted opening in winter

Rest – (dinner only and Sunday lunch) (booking essential) Menu € 29/56 **s**

◆ Cosy bar with roaring fire leads to converted 17C barn. Imposing chandelier and candelabras; grand piano doubles as sweet trolley. Meats are a speciality, cooked in open grill.

Good Things Cafe

Ahakista Rd, West : ¾ km on Ahakista rd – (027) 61 426 – info@thegoodthingscafe.com – Fax (027) 62 896 – Closed September-20 June except Easter and Bank Holiday weekends

Rest – (Closed Tuesday and Wednesday) Carte € 21/39

◆ Simple and unpretentious. Walls filled with shelves full of books and foods of all kinds for sale. Open-plan kitchen serves accomplished dishes full of quality local produce.

ENNIS (Inis) – Clare – 712 F 9 – pop. 22 051 Ireland 38 B2

Dublin 228 km – Galway 67 km – Limerick 35 km – Roscommon 148 km – Tullamore 149 km
Arthurs Row (065) 6828366
Drumbiggle Rd, (065) 682 40 74 .
Ennis Friary★ AC
Dysert O'Dea★, N : 9 ¾ km by N 85 and R 476, turning left after 6 ½ km and right after 1 ½ km - Quin Franciscan Friary★, SE : 10 ½ km by R 469 – Knappogue Castle★ **AC**, SE : 12 ¾ km by R 469 – Corrofin (Clare Heritage Centre★ **AC**), N : 13 ¾ km by N 85 and R 476 – Craggaunowen Centre★ **AC**, SE : 17 ¾ km by R 469 - Kilmacduagh Churches and Round Tower★, NE : 17 ¾ km by N 18 – Kilrush★ (Scattery Island★ by boat) SW : 43 ½ km by N 68 - Bridge of Ross, Kilkee★, SW : 57 km by N 68 and N 67

Temple Gate

The Square – (065) 682 33 00 – info@templegatehotel.com – Fax (065) 682 33 22 – closed 25-26 December
68 rm – €105/125 €150/180 – 2 suites
Rest *JM's bistro* – (carvery lunch Monday-Saturday) Menu 38 – Carte €32/46
◆ A professional yet friendly mood prevails at this privately run hotel in modern, subtly neo-Gothic style. Panelled library and well-fitted rooms in traditional patterns. JM's Bistro serves popular, carefully presented modern dishes in informal surroundings.

Old Ground

rm,

O'Connell St – (065) 682 81 27 – reservations@oldgroundhotel.ie – Fax (065) 682 81 12 – Closed 25 December
105 rm – €90/150 €120/230
Rest *O'Brien's* – Carte €27/39 **s**
Rest *Town Hall* – Carte €27/39 **s**
◆ Handsome ivy-clad hotel. Firelit lounge and inviting panelled bar with paintings, curios and book-lined snugs. Traditional rooms in cream, burgundy and dark wood. Gilt-framed mirrors and white linen lend a formal aspect to O'Brien's. Informal Town Hall.

ENNISCORTHY (Inis Córthaidh) – Wexford – 712 M 10 – pop. 8 964 39 D2

Ireland

Dublin 122 km – Kilkenny 74 km – Waterford 54 km – Wexford 24 km
Castle Museum (0539) 234699
Knockmarshal, (054) 921 33 191 .
Enniscorthy Castle★ (County Museum★)
Ferns★, NE : 13 km by N 11 – Mount Leinster★, N : 27 ¼ km by N 11

Monart

rest,

The Still, Northwest : 3 km by N 11 (Dublin rd) Enniscorthy / Inis Córthaidh – (053) 923 8999 – info@monart.ie – Closed 24-27 December
68 rm – €230/350 €500/750 – 2 suites
Rest *The Restaurant* – (dinner only and Sunday lunch) Menu €70 **s**
Rest *Garden Lounge* – Carte €50/60 **s**
◆ Spa resort in 100 acres; enter via the elegant Georgian house and experience various therapies in state-of-the-art treatment rooms. Bedrooms all have views; many have balconies. Formal dining in The Restaurant. Enjoy lighter dishes in the Garden Lounge or out on the terrace.

Riverside Park

rm, rest,

The Promenade – (053) 923 7800 – info@riversideparkhotel.com – Fax (053) 923 7900 – closed 24-26 December
59 rm – €115/135 €190/210 – 1 suite
Rest *The Moorings* – (closed Sunday lunch) (carvery lunch Monday-Saturday) Carte €40/47 **s**
◆ Purpose-built hotel just outside the town: a high, airy lobby leads into smart bedrooms in matching patterns, modern meeting rooms and a rustic, "no-frills" wood-fitted bar. Spacious, modern Moorings restaurant with light, soft tones.

Ballinkeele House

Ballymurn, Southeast : 10½ km by unmarked road on Curracloe rd – ✆ (053) 91 38 105 – john@ballinkeele.com – Fax (053) 91 38 468 – February-30 November

5 rm – €90/110 €100/110 – **Rest** – (by arrangement, communal dining) Menu €45

◆ High ceilinged, firelit lounge plus sizeable rooms with period-style furniture and countryside views add to the charm of a quiet 1840 manor, well run by experienced owners. Dining room enriched by candlelight and period oils.

ENNISTIMON (Inis Díomáin) – Clare – 712 E 9 – pop. 920 *Ireland* 38 B1

Dublin 254 km – Galway 83 km – Limerick 63 km

The Burren★★ : Cliffs of Moher★★★, Scenic Route★★, Aillwee Cave★ **AC** (waterfall★★), Corcomroe Abbey★, Kilfenora High Crosses★, Burren Centre★ **AC**

Grovemount House without rest

Lahinch Rd, West : ¾ km on N 67 – ✆ (065) 707 14 31 – grovmnt@eircom.net – Fax (065) 707 18 23 – May-October

7 rm – €45/55 €70/80

◆ Spotless bedrooms in warm oak and a homely lounge in this modern guesthouse, run by the friendly owner. A short drive to the sandy beach at Lahinch and the Cliffs of Moher.

FARRAN (An Fearann) – Cork – 712 F 12 *Ireland* 38 B3

Dublin 436 km – Cork 21 km – Mallow 48 km

Blarney Castle★★, NE : 22½ km by N 22 and R 579 – Cork★★ – St Fin Barre's Cathedral★★, Shandon Bells★★ – Grand Parade★, South Mall★, St Patrick's St★, Crawford Art Gallery★, Cork Public Museum★, E : 17 ¾ km by N 22

Farran House

– ✆ (021) 733 12 15 – info@farranhouse.com – 15 March -15 November

4 rm – €107/118 €164/198 – **Rest** – (by arrangement) Menu €45

◆ Italianate 18C-19C house in mature gardens overlooking Bride Valley. Spacious and elegantly furnished; rooms have fine views.

FETHARD (Fiodh Ard) – Tipperary – 712 I 10 *Ireland* 39 C2

Dublin 161 km – Cashel 16 km – Clonmel 13 km

Cashel★★★ : Rock of Cashel★★★ **AC** (Cormac's Chapel★★, Round Tower★), Museum★ **AC**, Cashel Palace Gardens★, GPA Bolton Library★ **AC**, NW : 15 km by R 692 – Clonmel★ : County Museum★ **AC**, St Mary's Church★, S : 13 km by R 689

Mobarnane House

North : 8 km by Cashel rd on Ballinure rd – ✆ (052) 31 962 – info@mobarnanehouse.com – Fax (052) 31 962 – March-October

4 rm – €105 €150/190 – **Rest** – (by arrangement, communal dining) Menu €45

◆ Very personally run classic Georgian house with mature gardens in quiet rural setting, tastefully restored to reflect its age. Ask for a bedroom with its own sitting room. Beautiful dining room for menus agreed in advance.

An-Teach

Killusty, Southeast : 8 km by R 706 (Kilsheelan rd) – ✆ (052) 32 088 – anteach@anteach.com – Fax (052) 32 178

10 rm – €55/65 €100 – **Rest** – (by arrangement) Menu €35 **s**

◆ Extended family home against the backdrop of the Sliabh na Mban mountains. Airy en suite rooms in solid pine, two facing the hills. Carefully prepared wholesome meals.

REPUBLIC OF IRELAND

FOTA ISLAND – Cork – **712** H 12 — 38 **B3**

Sheraton Fota Island rm,
– ✆ (021) 467 3000 – reservations.fota@sheraton.com
– Fax (021) 488 3713
123 rm – €150 €300 – 8 suites
Rest *The Cove* – (Closed Sunday and Monday) (dinner only) Carte €40/80
Rest *Fota* – (dinner only and Sunday lunch) Carte €25/70
◆ All-encompassing resort location within Ireland's only wildlife park boasting Wellness Centre with 'walking river' and 18 hole golf course. Stylish rooms from the top drawer. The Cove is a very formal place to dine. Fota's appealing menus suit all tastes.

FOXROCK = Carraig an tSionnaigh – **Dublin** – **712** N 7 – **see Dublin**

FURBOGH/FURBO (Na Forbacha) – **Galway** – **712** E 8 — 36 **A3**

Dublin 228 km – Galway 11 km

Connemara Coast ← Galway Bay, rm,
– ✆ (091) 592 108 – info@connemaracoast.ie
– Fax (091) 592 065
– Closed 24-26 December
141 rm – €129/165 €189/250 – 1 suite
Rest *The Gallery* – (bar lunch) Menu €40
◆ Sprawling hotel with super views of Galway Bay, The Burren and Aran from the well-kept bedrooms. Marbled reception area. Characterful Players bar. Good leisure facilities. Two informal dining areas overlooking the bay.

Your opinions are important to us:
please write and let us know about your discoveries and experiences – good and bad!

GALWAY – **Galway** – **712** E 8 – **pop. 66 163** *Ireland* — 36 **B3**

Dublin 217 km – Limerick 103 km – Sligo 145 km
Carnmore Airport : ✆ (091) 755569, NE : 6½ km
Galway City Aeas Failte, Forster St ✆ (091) 537700, info@irelandwest.ieSalthill Promenade ✆ (091) 520500 (May-August)
Galway Salthill Blackrock, ✆ (091) 522 033.
City★★ – St Nicholas' Church★ BY - Roman Catholic Cathedral★ AY – Eyre Square : Bank of Ireland Building (sword and mace★) BY
NW : Lough Corrib★★. W : by boat, Aran Islands (Inishmore - Dun Aenghus★★★) BZ - Thoor Ballylee★, SE : 33¾ km by N 6 and N 18 D – Dunguaire Castle, Kinvarra★ **AC**, S : 25¾ km by N 6, N 18 and N 67 D – Aughnanure Castle★, NW : 25¾ km by N 59 - Oughterard★ (← ★★), NW : 29 km by N 59 - Knockmoy Abbey★, NE : 30½ km by N 17 and N 63 D – Coole Park (Autograph Tree★), SE : 33¾ km by N 6 and N 18 D - St Mary's Cathedral, Tuam★, NE : 33¾ km by N 17 D – Loughrea (St Brendan's Cathedral★), SE : 35½ km by N 6 D - Turoe Stone★, SE : 35½ km by N 6 and north by R 350

Plans on following pages

Glenlo Abbey

Bushypark, Northwest : 5 ¼ km on N 59 – ✆ (091) 526666 – info@glenloabbey.ie – Fax (091) 527800 – Closed 24-27 December

42 rm – †€ 190/295 ††€ 275/400, ☕ € 18 – 4 suites

Rest *River Room* – (dinner only) Carte € 44/56

Rest *Pullman* – (Closed Monday) (dinner only) Carte € 36/51

◆ Imposing 18C greystone country house with adjacent church and bay views. Formal service. Very comfortable lounge, leading into chapel. Spacious, smart rooms. River Room boasts golfcourse views. Pullman, a converted railway carriage offers modern dishes with an Asian base.

Radisson SAS

Lough Atalia Rd – ✆ (091) 538300 – sales.galway@radissonsas.com – Fax (091) 538380 D **a**

259 rm ☕ – †€ 175/195 ††€ 300/550 – 2 suites

Rest *Marinas* – (bar lunch Monday-Saturday) Carte € 37/50 **s**

◆ Striking atrium leads to ultra-modern meeting facilities and very comfortable accommodation: sumptuous 5th floor rooms have private glass balconies. Superb penthouse suite. Split-level dining in dark walnut wood.

The G

Wellpark – ✆ (091) 865200 – reservetheg@monogramhotels.ie – Fax (091) 865203 – Closed 23-26 December D **g**

100 rm ☕ – †€ 230 ††€ 720 – 1 suite

Rest *Riva at the G* – Italian influences Menu € 45/60 **s** – Carte € 33/62 **s**

◆ Uber-hip hotel cutting edge design from renowned milliner Philip Treacy. Vividly assured sitting room styles; décor imbued with fashion shoot portraits. Cool, slinky bedrooms. Sexy purple restaurant. Understated cooking with Mediterranean influences.

Clayton

Ballybrit, East : 4 km on N 6 – ✆ (091) 721900 – info@clayton.ie – Fax (091) 721901

196 rm – †€ 130/180 ††€ 150/190, ☕ € 14 – **Rest** – (bar lunch) Carte € 30/45

◆ Striking angular building on edge of city, with stylish, modern interior and bar with buffet carvery. Smart white bedrooms have a minimalistic feel, with dark wood furniture. Large first floor restaurant offers traditional menu.

The Ardilaun

Taylor's Hill – ✆ (091) 521433 – info@theardilaunhotel.ie – Fax (091) 521546 – closed 23-27 December C **a**

120 rm ☕ – †€ 105/380 ††€ 150/380 – 5 suites

Rest – (bar lunch Saturday) Menu € 18/41 – Carte dinner € 34/49

Rest *Camilaun* – Menu € 18/41 – Carte dinner € 34/49

◆ Georgian style country house hotel in five acres of gardens and ancient trees. Informal bar. Extensive leisure facilities. Spacious rooms in dark woods with quilted fabrics. Seafood, including oysters, feature strongly in restaurant. Stylish, formal Camilaun.

The Westwood

Dangan, Upper Newcastle – ✆ (091) 521442 – info@westwoodhousehotel.com – Fax (091) 521400 – closed 25 December C **c**

58 rm ☕ – †€ 119/159 ††€ 159/209

Rest *The Meridian* – (dinner only and Sunday lunch) Menu € 25 – Carte € 20/43

◆ Striking hotel with pastel orange painted exterior on outskirts of town. Impressive reception area and huge bar on two levels. Small conservatory. Modern, comfy rooms. Appealing carvery restaurant.

REPUBLIC OF IRELAND

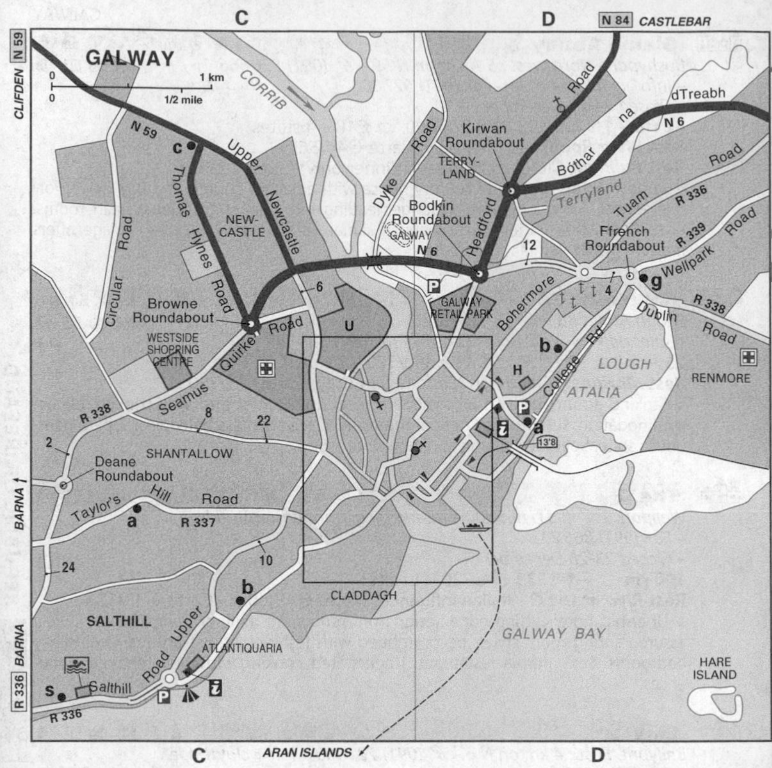

Park House

rm, rest, VISA AE

Forster St, Eyre Sq – (091) 564 924
– parkhousehotel@eircom.net
– Fax (091) 569 219
– closed 24-26 December

BY **c**

84 rm – €250/400 €250/400 – **Rest** – Menu €45 (dinner) **s** – Carte €24/41 **s**

♦ Popular greystone hotel in city centre. Marble reception and comfy seating areas. Boss Doyle's Bar is busy and spacious. Dark wood bedrooms with rich, soft fabrics. Strong international flavours define restaurant menus.

The House

rm, VISA AE

Spanish Parade – (091) 538 900
– info@thehousehotel.ie – Fax (091) 568 262
– closed 24-27 December

BZ **e**

39 rm – €250/325 €300/650 – 1 suite – **Rest** – (bar lunch) Carte €31/45

♦ Luxury boutique hotel, blending contemporary design with a cosy, relaxed style. Bedrooms are divided between cosy, classy and swanky. Modern menus take on a global reach; try to get a seat on the outdoor deck.

GALWAY

Bothar Ui Eithir	BY 2	High St	BY 8	Presentation St	AY 17
Claddagh Bridge	AZ 3	Main Guard St	BY 9	Quay St	BZ 18
Corrib Shopping Centre	BY	Market St	BY 10	St Francis St	BY 20
Courthouse St	BZ 4	Mary St	BY 11	St Vincent's Ave	BY 21
Dominick St	AZ 5	Newton Smith	BY 14	Shantalla Rd	AY 22
Father Griffin Ave	AZ 6	New Dock St	BZ 13	Shop St	BY 24
Forster St	BY 7	O'Brien Bridge	AY 15	William St	BY 25

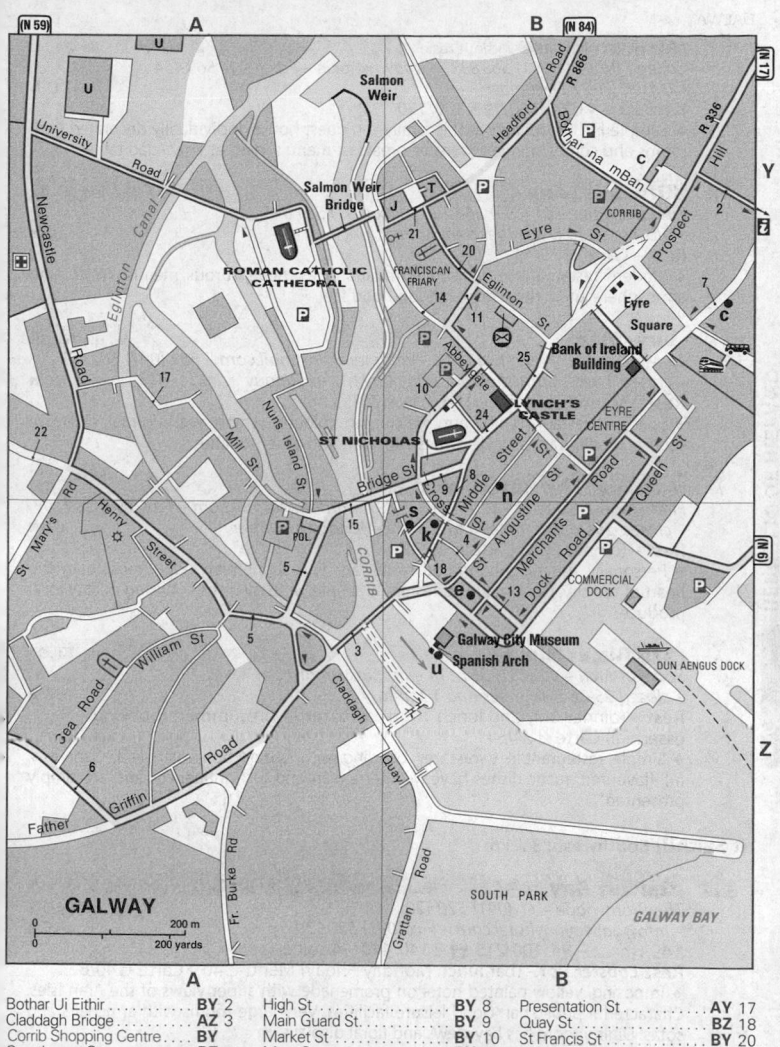

Killeen House without rest

Killeen Bushypark, Northwest : 6½ km on N 59
– ✆ (091) 524 179 – killeenhouse@ireland.com
– Fax (091) 528 065
– 14 February-14 November

6 rm – ♦€ 100/150 ♦♦€ 140/190

◆ Whitewashed mid 19C guesthouse with pleasant gardens. Cosy sitting room with Art Nouveau styled furniture. Very comfortable, individually furnished bedrooms.

Ardawn House without rest

College Rd – (091) 568 833 – ardawn@iol.ie – Fax (091) 563 454
– closed 21-27 December D **b**
8 rm – €60/160 €100/170
◆ Sample Irish hospitality at this family-run guest house. Individually decorated bedrooms and comfy lounge. Extensive breakfast menu served at linen-clad tables.

Kirwan's Lane

Kirwan's Lane – (091) 568 266 – Fax (091) 561 645
– Closed 24-30 December and Sunday lunch BZ **s**
Rest – Carte €29/49
◆ Modern restaurant in warm, autumnal shades. Adventurous menus. Welcoming atmosphere and a genuine neighbourhood feel.

Vina Mara

19 Middle St – (091) 561 610 – vinamara@hotmail.com – Fax (091) 562 607
– closed 1week Christmas, Saturday lunch and Sunday BY **n**
Rest – Menu €28 (dinner) – Carte €36/55
◆ Spacious restaurant in warm welcoming colours - smart yet informal; attentive service. Mediterranean style dishes with Irish and other touches.

Ard Bia (The Restaurant)

First Floor, 2 Quay St – (091) 539 897 – ardbia@gmail.com – Fax (091) 539 897
– closed 25-26 December and Sunday-Monday in winter BZ **k**
Rest – (dinner only) Carte €20/37
◆ Personally run neighbourhood restaurant with bohemian edge, located in the heart of the city. Good value, refreshingly simple, unfussy dishes utilising quality local produce.

Ard Bia at Nimmos

Spanish Arch – (091) 561 114 – ardbia@gmail.com
– closed 25-26 December and 1 January BZ **u**
Rest – (dinner only and lunch Thursday-Saturday in summer) (booking essential) Carte €34/54
◆ Simple restaurant in two-storey building with buzzy, bohemain feel. Generous, full-flavoured, rustic dishes have Mediterranean and Irish influences and are simply presented.

at Salthill Southwest : 3 ¼ km

Galway Bay

Galway Bay, rm, rest,

The Promenade – (091) 520 520
– info@galwaybayhotel.com – Fax (091) 520 530 C **s**
149 rm – €100/215 €140/440 – 4 suites
Rest *Lobster Pot* – (bar lunch Monday-Friday) Menu €40 – Carte €40/62
◆ Imposing, yellow painted hotel on promenade with super views of the Aran Isles. Characterful public bar. Good leisure facilities. Very large rooms with armchairs and sofas. Dining room has bay views and floral displays.

West Winds without rest

5 Ocean Wave, Dr Colohan Rd – (091) 520 223 – westwinds@eircom.net
– Fax (091) 520 223
– May-August C **b**
8 rm – €45/100 €75/120
◆ Detached guesthouse in an ideal spot for holiday makers: right on the seafront. Cosy sitting room; breakfast room has conservatory extension. Simple, spotlessly kept bedrooms.

The red symbol?
This denotes the very essence of peace
– only the sound of birdsong first thing in the morning ...

GARRYKENNEDY – Co Tipperary 39 **C2**

Dublin 176 km – Killaloe 14 km – Youghal 2 km

Larkins

– ✆ (067) 23 232 – info@larkinspub.com – Fax (067) 23 933
– Closed 25 December, Good Friday and lunch October-March
Rest – Carte € 23/40
◆ Thatched whitewashed inn - bigger inside than it looks from the outside - sparks nostalgia with classic adverts and tins of food. Honest hearty cooking comes in generous portions.

GARRYVOE (Garraí Uí Bhuaigh) – Cork – 712 H 12 – ✉ Castlemartyr 39 **C3**

Dublin 259 km – Cork 37 km – Waterford 100 km

Garryvoe

– ✆ (021) 464 67 18 – res@garryvoehotel.com – Fax (021) 464 68 24
– closed 24-25 December
48 rm – †€ 105/120 ††€ 160/190 – 1 suite – **Rest** – (bar lunch Monday-Saturday) Menu € 30/45 – Carte € 41/49
◆ Traditionally styled hotel adjacent to the beach with good sea views, to be enjoyed in characterful locals bar. A purpose-built, up-to-date wing features smart, modern rooms. Bright, colourful, contemporary restaurant.

GLASLOUGH = Glasloch – Monaghan – 712 L 5 – see Monaghan

GLASSAN = Glasán – Westmeath – 712 I 7 – see Athlone

GLIN (An Gleann) – Limerick – 712 E 10 *Ireland* 38 **B2**

Dublin 244 km – Limerick 51 km – Tralee 51 km
Glin Castle★ AC

Glin Castle

– ✆ (068) 34 173 – knight@iol.ie – Fax (068) 34 364
– closed January and February
15 rm – †€ 310 ††€ 495 – **Rest** – (dinner only) (residents only) Menu € 55
◆ Crenellated Georgian country house, overlooking the Shannon estuary, with superb collection of antique furnishings, paintings and porcelain. Beautifully appointed rooms. Home cooked meals full of local produce.

GOREY (Guaire) – Wexford – 712 N 9 – pop. 5 282 *Ireland* 39 **D2**

Dublin 93 km – Waterford 88 km – Wexford 61 km
Main St ✆ (055) 21248
Courtown Kiltennel, ✆ (055) 25 166 .
Ferns★, SW : 17 ¾ km by N 11

Amber Springs

Wexford Rd, East : 1 km on R 741 – ✆ (053) 948 40 00
– info@amberspringshotel.ie – Fax (053) 948 44 94
80 rm – †€ 110/140 ††€ 170/230
Rest ***Kelby's Bistro*** – (carving lunch) Menu € 43
◆ Large modern hotel with open main reception, vast selection of state-of-the-art meeting rooms, lively bar, basement spa and luxurious bedrooms with every conceivable extra. Delightfully elegant first floor bistro offers appealing menu with a rustic, seasonal base.

Seafield

Ballymoney, East : 8 km by R 742 – ✆ (053) 942 4000 – Fax (053) 942 4050
161 rm – †€ 110/140 ††€ 160/250 – 3 suites –
Rest – (dinner only) Carte € 35/64
◆ New build hotel on what was originally a farm, with extensive gardens, fringed by an immaculate golf course. Elegant, contemporary décor; spacious bedrooms with balconies. Traditional Irish menu served in high-ceilinged, formal dining room.

REPUBLIC OF IRELAND

Marlfield House

Courtown Rd, Southeast : 1½ km on R 742 – (053) 942 11 24 – info@marlfieldhouse.ie – Fax (053) 942 15 72 – Closed 16 December-31 January

19 rm – €120/155 €245/285 – 1 suite –

Rest – (dinner only and Sunday lunch) (booking essential for non-residents) Menu €65

◆ Luxuriously comfortable Regency mansion, with extensive gardens and woods. Utterly charming public areas with fine antiques and splendid fabrics. Thoughtfully furnished rooms. Very comfortable conservatory restaurant utilising produce from the garden.

Ashdown Park

rm, rest,

Coach Rd – (053) 948 05 00 – info@ashdownparkhotel.com – Fax (053) 948 07 77 – closed 25 December

79 rm – €115/145 €180/240

Rest *Rowan Tree* – (053) 940 500 (dinner only and Sunday lunch) Menu €44

◆ Imposing hotel for business traveller in heart of market town. Atrium with sumptuous sofas. State-of-art leisure centre. Very comfortable rooms boast rich velvet curtains. Fine dining in the Rowan Tree restaurant.

GRAIGUENAMANAGH (Gráig na Manach) – Kilkenny – 712 L 10 — 39 D2

Ireland

Dublin 125 km – Kilkenny 34 km – Waterford 42 km – Wexford 26 km

Duiske Abbey★★ **AC**

Jerpoint Abbey★★ **AC**, W : 15 km by R 703 and N 9 – Inistioge★, SW : 8 km by minor road – Kilfane Glen and Waterfall★ **AC**, SW : 17 km by R 703 and N 9

Waterside with rm

The Quay – (059) 972 42 46 – info@watersideguesthouse.com – Fax (059) 972 47 33 – closed 25 December and January

10 rm – €67/75 €110 – **Rest** – (restricted opening in winter, dinner only and Sunday lunch) Carte €32/42

◆ Converted 19C cornstore on banks of river Barrow, at foot of Brandon Hill. Base for hillwalkers. Modern cooking with Mediterranean flourishes. Beamed rooms with river views.

GREYSTONES (Na Clocha Liatha) – Wicklow – 712 N 8 – pop. 11 913 — 39 D1

Ireland

Dublin 35 km

Greystones, (01) 287 6624 .

Killruddery House and Gardens★ **AC**, N : 5 km by R 761 – Powerscourt★★ (Waterfall★★) **AC**, NW : 10 km by R 761, minor road, M 11 and minor road via Enniskerry. Wicklow Mountains★★

Chakra by Jaipur

First Floor, Meridan Point Centre, Church Rd – (01) 201 7222 – info@chakra.ie – Fax (01) 201 7220 – Closed 25 December

Rest – Indian (dinner only) Carte €36/48

◆ Red and ochre restaurant overlooked by elephant god, Ganesh, on 1st floor of modern shopping centre. Vibrant Indian cooking represents all regions; a blend of old and new.

Hungry Monk

Church Rd – (01) 287 5759 – info@thehungrymonk.ie – Fax (01) 287 7183 – closed 24-26 December and Monday

Rest – (dinner only and Sunday lunch) Carte €40/57

◆ Busy, long-established, candlelit restaurant above a wine bar. Pictures of monks in all areas. Robust, traditional cooking including blackboard seafood specials.

GWEEDORE (Gaoth Dobhair) – Donegal – 712 H 2 37 C1

Dublin 278 km – Donegal 72 km – Letterkenny 43 km – Sligo 135 km

Gweedore Court

on N 56 – (074) 953 2900 – anchuirt@eircom.net – Fax (074) 953 2929 – closed January and 23-28 December

69 rm – €120/150 €190/240 – **Rest** – (bar lunch Monday-Saturday) Menu €45 – Carte €29/46

◆ Rebuilt 19C house sharing grounds with a Gaelic heritage centre. Spacious accommodation in classic patterns; east-facing rooms enjoy superb views of Glenreagh National Park. Classic menu matched by traditional surroundings and period-inspired décor.

HORSE AND JOCKEY – Tipperary 39 C2

Dublin 146 km – Cashel 14 km – Thurles 9 km

The Horse and Jockey

– (0504) 44 192 – info@horseandjockeyhotel.com – Fax (0504) 44 747 – Closed 25 December

65 rm – €180 €210 – 1 suite – **Rest** – Carte €25/39

◆ Much extended hotel with stylish, state-of-the-art meeting rooms, superb spa and great gift shop. Bar full of horse racing pictures on walls. Spacious, contemporary bedrooms. Easy going dining room with traditional menus.

HOWTH – Dublin – 712 N 7 – Dublin *Ireland* 39 D1

Dublin 16 km

Deer Park Hotel Howth Castle, (01) 832 6039.

The Cliffs★ (< ★)

Inisradharc without rest

Balkill Rd, North : ¾ km – (01) 832 23 06 – harbour-view@msn.com – closed 12 December-10 January

3 rm – €68/78 €80/90

◆ High above the pretty fishing village with views of the harbour and Eye Island. Conservatory breakfast room and spacious en suite bedrooms share a homely style.

Aqua

< Ireland's Eye and coastline,

1 West Pier – (01) 832 0690 – dine@aqua.ie – Fax (01) 832 0687 – closed 25-26 December, Good Friday and lunch Monday

Rest – Seafood Menu €30 (lunch) – Carte €40/63 **s**

◆ Glass sided, first floor restaurant affording super bay views. Intimate bar filled with local photos, whetting the appetite for accomplished dishes of freshly caught seafood.

King Sitric with rm

rest,

East Pier – (01) 832 5235 – info@kingsitric.ie – Fax (01) 839 2442 – closed Christmas

8 rm – €110/145 €205 – **Rest** – Seafood (closed Sunday and Bank Holidays) Menu €30/58 – Carte €44/68

◆ Well established for 50 years; one of Ireland's original seafood restaurants. Enjoy locally caught produce in first floor dining room with bay views. Modern, comfy bedrooms.

Deep

12 West Pier – (01) 806 39 21 – info@deep.ie – Fax (01) 806 39 21 – closed 25-26 December, 1 January and Monday

Rest – Carte €31/52

◆ Personally run, intimate restaurant on busy pier. Deep brown leather banquettes accentuate stylish feel. Wide-ranging, freshly prepared menus underpinned by local seafood.

INISHCRONE (Inis Crabhann) – Sligo – 712 E 5 Ireland 36 B2

Dublin 257 km – Ballina 13 km – Galway 127 km – Sligo 55 km
Rosserk Abbey★, W : 16 km by R 297, N 59 and R 314 – Moyne Abbey★, W : 19 km by R 297, N 59 and R 314. Killala★, W : 21 km by R 297, N 59 and R 314

Ceol na Mara without rest
Main St – (096) 36 351 – ceolnamara@eircom.net – restricted opening in winter
9 rm – €50 €50/86
◆ At the centre of town, a sizeable guest house kept spotless by the friendly long-standing owners. Simply appointed bedrooms are all en suite, with sea views to the rear.

INISHMORE – Galway – 712 C/D 8 – see Aran Islands

INISTIOGE (Inis Tíog) – Co Kilkenny – 712 K 10 39 C2

Dublin 82 km – Kilkenny 16 km – Waterford 19 km – Wexford 33 km

Bassetts at Woodstock
Woodstock Gardens, Northwest : 3 km – (056) 775 8820 – info@bassetts.ie – Closed last 2 weeks January, first week February, Monday, Tuesday, dinner Sunday and Bank Holidays
Rest – (light lunch) Carte €36/54
◆ Personally run restaurant at entrance to Woodstock gardens. Homely inner with delightful terrace. Food is ethical, seasonal and traceable, and the owner rears his own pigs.

Good food and accommodation at moderate prices?
Look for the Bib symbols:
red Bib Gourmand for food, blue Bib Hotel for hotels

KANTURK – Cork – 712 F 11 – pop. 1 651 Ireland 38 B2

Dublin 259 km – Cork 53 km – Killarney 50 km – Limerick 71 km
Fairy Hill, (029) 50534 .
Town★ - Castle★

Glenlohane without rest
East : 4 km by R 576 and Charlville rd on Cecilstown rd – (029) 50014 – glenlohane@iol.ie
3 rm – €100 €200
◆ In the family for over 250 years, a Georgian country house at the centre of wooded parkland and a working farm. Library and cosy, en suite rooms overlooking the fields.

KEEL = An Caol – Mayo – 712 B 5/6 – see Achill Island

KENMARE (Neidín) – Kerry – 712 D 12 – pop. 1 844 Ireland 38 A3

Dublin 338 km – Cork 93 km – Killarney 32 km
Heritage Centre (064) 41233 (April-October) AY
Kenmare, (064) 41 291 .
Town★
Ring of Kerry★★ - Healy Pass★★ (≤ ★★), SW : 30½ km by R 571 and R 574 AY – Mountain Road to Glengarriff (≤ ★★) S : by N 71 AY - Slieve Miskish Mountains (≤ ★★), SW : 48¼ km by R 571 AY – Gougane Barra Forest Park★★, SE : 16 km AY - Lauragh (Derreen Gardens★ **AC**), SW : 23½ km by R 571 AY – Allihies (Copper Mines★), SW : 57 km by R 571 and R 575 AY – Garnish Island (≤ ★), SW : 68½ km by R 571, R 575 and R 572 AY

Plan opposite

KENMARE

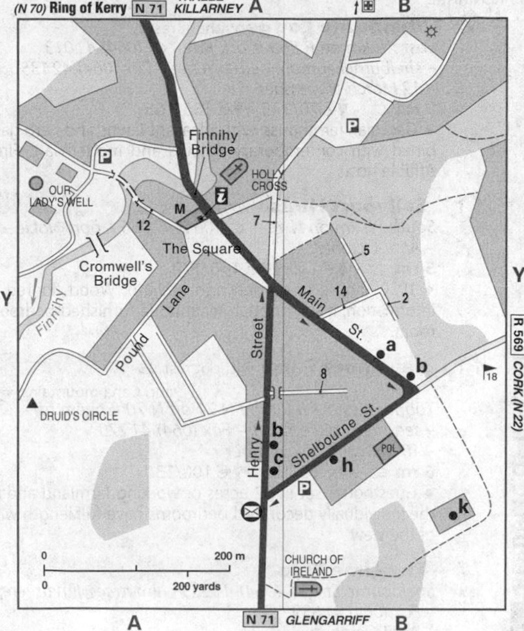

Park

Kenmare Bay and hills, rm,

– (064) 41 200 – info@parkkenmare.com
– Fax (064) 41 402
– *closed 3 January-1 April, 1 November - 23 December. Weekends only March and November* BY **k**

46 rm – €220/320 €450/600 – **Rest** – (dinner only) Menu €75

◆ Privately run country house boasts many paintings and antiques. Superb spa facilities. Inviting, classically tasteful rooms; many offer superb views of Kenmare Bay and hills. Grand, bay-windowed dining room; local produce to fore.

Sheen Falls Lodge

Sheen Falls, rm,

Southeast : 2 km by N 71
– (064) 41 600 – info@sheenfallslodge.ie – Fax (064) 41 386
– *closed 3 January-2 February*

57 rm – €300 €445, €24 – 9 suites – €465/1860

Rest *La Cascade* – (dinner only) Carte €63/84 **s**

Rest *Oscar's* – (dinner only and Sunday lunch in summer) Carte €33/50 **s**

◆ On the banks of the Sheen; modern but classically inspired. Spacious rooms with stunning extras. Extensive spa, gym and stables. Attentive, formal service. Floodlit river views at La Cascade. Oscars, more informal, also overlooks the falls.

Brook Lane

rm,

Gortamullen, North : 1 km by N 71 on N 70 – (064) 42 077
– info@brooklanehotel.com – Fax (064) 40 869
– *Closed Christmas*

20 rm – €85/110 €120/170

Rest *Silver Spoon* – Menu €25/38 – Carte dinner €31/48

Rest *Casey's Bistro* – Menu €25/35 – Carte €28/47

◆ Modern hotel meets country house resulting in homely charms with a designer edge. Main strength here is the airy bedrooms, which are delightfully comfy with a host of extras. Pleasant bar/bistro serving Irish favourites.

Shelburne Lodge without rest
East : ¾ km on R 569 (Cork Rd) – ✆ (064) 41 013
– shelburnekenmare@eircom.net – Fax (064) 42 135
– 12 March-November
9 rm – €70/125 €155/165
◆ Georgian farmhouse with pleasant lawns and herb garden. Antiques stylishly combined with contemporary colours and modern art. Firelit lounge and cosy rooms. Affable hosts.

Sallyport House without rest
South : ½ km on N 71 – ✆ (064) 42 066 – port@iol.ie – Fax (064) 42 067
– April-October
5 rm – €110 €140/170
◆ 1930s house in garden and orchard. Wood floored hall, full of books and local information, leads to pristine, antique furnished bedrooms and a pretty front sitting room.

Sea Shore Farm without rest — Kenmare River and Caha mountains,
Tubrid, West : 1½ km by N 71 off N 70 (Sneem rd) – ✆ (064) 41 270
– seashore@eircom.net – Fax (064) 41 270
– 10 March- 10 November
6 rm – €65/100 €100/130
◆ Guesthouse set in 32 acres of working farmland and park with lovely views. All of the individually decorated bedrooms have full length windows which make the most of the view.

REPUBLIC OF IRELAND

The Lime Tree
Shelbourne St – ✆ (064) 41 225 – limetree@limetreerestaurant.com
– Fax (064) 41 839
– April-October BY **h**
Rest – (dinner only) Carte €34/44
◆ Tasty, unelaborate modern Irish cooking in a 19C former schoolhouse: stone walls, modern art on walls and in first-floor gallery. Busy, affordable and unfailingly friendly.

Mulcahys
36 Henry St – ✆ (064) 42 383 – Fax (064) 42 383
– closed 24-27 December, 10-14 January AY **c**
Rest – (closed Tuesday and Wednesday January- June and October-December) (dinner only) Menu €35 – Carte €25/48
◆ Stylish wine racks, high-backed chairs, polished tables and friendly, attentive service set the tone here. Modern dishes appeal to the eye and palate alike.

D'Arcy's Oyster Bar and Grill
Main St – ✆ (064) 41 589 – keatingrestaurants@ownmail.net
– Restricted opening in winter BY **b**
Rest – (dinner only) (booking essential) Carte €34/50 **s**
◆ Restaurant set in striking, green-painted former bank. Pop in for oysters or fresh Kerry seafood at Oyster Bar or modern Irish menu in restaurant, with open fire and candles.

Leath Phingin Eile
35 Main St – ✆ (064) 41 559
– Closed Christmas, March, Tuesday in winter and Monday BY **a**
Rest – (dinner only) (booking essential) Carte €30/52
◆ Simply styled restaurant set over two floors serving classical dishes which follow the seasons. Excellent breads and tapenade. Popular with locals, its name means 'halfpenny'.

Packies
Henry St – ✆ (064) 41 508
– mid March - December AY **b**
Rest – (restricted opening November and December, closed Sunday) (dinner only) (booking essential) Carte €28/45
◆ Locally popular, personally run little place with understated rustic feel. Handwritten menu of fresh modern Irish dishes prepared with care and simplicity. Personable staff.

KESHCARRIGAN (Ceis Charraigin) – **Leitrim** – **712** I 5 – 37 **C2**
✉ **Carrick-on-Shannon**

Dublin 162 km – Carrick-on-Shannon 14 km – Ballinamore 14 km

Canal View House

East : ½ km – ✆ (071) 964 24 04 – canalviewcountryhouse@eircom.net – Fax (071) 964 22 61

6 rm – ♦€ 35 ♦♦€ 70 – **Rest** – (dinner only and Sunday lunch) Menu € 28 (lunch) – Carte approx. € 40

◆ Agreeably located, overlooking the Shannon/Erne waterway and countryside beyond: sit for hours watching the canal boats. Comfy conservatory lounge with view. Sizeable rooms. Agreeably located, overlooking the Shannon/Erne waterway and countryside beyond: sit for hours watching the canal boats. Comfy conservatory lounge with view. Sizeable rooms.

KILBRITTAIN – **Cork** – **712** F 12 38 **B3**

Dublin 289 km – Cork 38 km – Killarney 96 km

The Glen without rest

Southwest : 6½ km by un-marked rd off R 600 – ✆ (023) 49 862 – info@glencountryhouse.com – Fax (023) 49 862 – 21 March - October

6 rm – ♦€ 75/85 ♦♦€ 130/140

◆ 130 year-old family house, part of working farm close to beach. Delicious organic farmhouse breakfasts. Lovingly restored bedrooms elegantly furnished to a high standard.

Casino House

Coolmain Bay, Southeast : 3½ km by unmarked rd on R 600 – ✆ (023) 49 944 – chouse@eircom.net – Fax (023) 49 945 – closed January-17 March and Wednesday

Rest – (dinner only and Sunday lunch) Carte € 32/51 **s**

◆ Whitewashed walls, Shaker style furniture and art on a culinary theme in this converted farmhouse run by a husband and wife. Locally sourced menu is balanced and flavourful.

KILCOLGAN (Cill Cholgáin) – **Galway** – **712** F 8 – ✉ **Oranmore** 36 **B3**

Dublin 220 km – Galway 17 km

Moran's Oyster Cottage

The Weir, Northwest : 2 km by N 18 – ✆ (091) 796 113 – moranstheweir@eircom.net – Closed 24-26 December and Good Friday

Rest – Seafood Carte € 26/60

◆ Likeable thatched pub in sleepy village. Settle down in one of the beamed snugs and parlours to enjoy prime local seafood - simple and fresh - or soups, salads and sandwiches.

KILKEE – **Clare** – **712** D 9 – **pop. 1 331** *Ireland* 38 **A2**

Dublin 285 km – Galway 124 km – Limerick 93 km

The Square ✆ (065) 9056112 (June-early September), tourisminfo@shannon-dev.ie

Kilkee East End, ✆ (065) 905 60 48 .

Kilrush★ (Scattery Island★ by boat), SE : 16 m. by N 67 – SW : Loop Head Peninsula (Bridge of Ross★)

Stella Maris

– ✆ (065) 905 64 55 – info@stellamarishotel.com – Fax (065) 906 00 06

20 rm – ♦€ 55/75 ♦♦€ 90/150 – **Rest** – Carte € 25/40

◆ Family-run hotel in centre of bustling seaside town, whose refurbished bedrooms offer a surprising amount of space. Terrace, with view of bay, is popular spot from which to people-watch. Enjoy traditional fare in the atmospheric bar or on the veranda.

Halpin's
Erin St – (065) 905 60 32 – halpinshotel@iol.ie – Fax (065) 905 63 17
– 15 March-October
12 rm – €75/85 €90/130 – **Rest** – (bar lunch Monday-Saturday)
Menu € 26 – Carte € 22/37
◆ Attractive terraced house offering good value accommodation and a warm welcome. Pub-style bar in the basement and uniform bedrooms with fitted furniture. Traditionally appointed ground floor restaurant.

Kilkee Thalassotherapy Centre and Guest House
without rest
Grattan St – (065) 905 67 42 – info@kilkeethalasso.com – Fax (065) 905 67 62
– closed 20-30 December
5 rm – €40/80 €80/110
◆ Modern guest house with combined breakfast room and sitting room. Spacious well-equipped bedrooms. Preferential booking for guests in the adjoining thalassotherapy centre.

KILKENNY – Kilkenny – 712 K 10 – pop. 20 735 *Ireland* 39 **C2**

Dublin 114 km – Cork 138 km – Killarney 185 km – Limerick 111 km – Tullamore 83 km – Waterford 46 km
Shee Alms House (056) 7751500
Glendine, (056) 772 5136 ;
Callan Geraldine, (056) 25 136 ;
Castlecomer Drumgoole, (056) 444 1139.
Town★★ – St Canice's Cathedral★★ – Kilkenny Castle and Park★★ **AC** – Black Abbey★ – Rothe House★
Jerpoint Abbey★★ **AC**, S : 19 ¼ km by R 700 and N 9 – Kilfane Glen and Waterfall★ **AC**, S : 21 km by R 700 and N 9 – Kells Priory★, S : 12 ½ km by R 697 – Dunmore Cave★ **AC**, N: 11 ¼ km by N 77 and N 78

Kilkenny rm, rest,
College Rd, Southwest : 1 ¼ km at junction with N 76 – (056) 776 20 00
– experience@hotelkilkenny.ie – Fax (056) 776 59 84
138 rm – €97/185 €142/260
Rest *Taste* – Menu € 40 (dinner) – Carte € 34/47
◆ Well run, refurbished hotel boasts contemporary interior with silver finishes and black wallpaper, spacious meeting rooms, well equipped leisure centre and comfy bedrooms. Italian menu served in split level dining room.

The Hibernian rm, rest,
1 Ormonde St – (056) 777 18 88 – info@kilkennyhibernianhotel.com
– Fax (056) 777 18 77
– Closed 25 December
43 rm – €95/145 €150/230 – 3 suites – **Rest** – (bar lunch Monday-Friday) Menu € 20/32 **s** – Carte € 29/50 **s**
◆ Part Georgian hotel, set in former bank, in sight of Kilkenny Castle: classically proportioned, understated modern bedrooms, spacious bar in dark wood with long tan sofas. Comfortable restaurant with traditional appeal.

Butler House without rest
15-16 Patrick St – (056) 776 57 07 – res@butler.ie – Fax (056) 776 56 26
– Closed 23-29 December
12 rm – €80/155 €150/220 – 1 suite
◆ Substantial part Georgian house. Spacious accommodation with 1970s-style furnishings - superior bow-fronted bedrooms to the rear overlook neat, geometric lawned gardens.

Blanchville House without rest
Dunbell, Maddoxtown, Southeast : 10 ½ km by N 10
turning right ¾ km after the Pike Inn – (056) 772 71 97 – mail@blanchville.ie
– Fax (056) 772 76 36 – March-October
6 rm – €65/80 €120/130
◆ Follow the tree-lined drive to this restored Georgian country house in quiet farmland. Firelit drawing room. Charming bedrooms furnished with antiques and family heirlooms.

REPUBLIC OF IRELAND

Fanad House without rest
Castle Rd, South : ¾ km on R 700 – ✆ (056) 776 41 26
– fanadhouse@hotmail.com – Fax (056) 775 60 01
8 rm – €50/90 €80/110
◆ Modern, purpose-built, green painted house within the castle walls. A warm welcome and bright, well-appointed bedrooms await the visitor.

Zuni with rm
26 Patrick St – ✆ (056) 772 39 99 – info@zuni.ie – Fax (056) 775 64 00
– closed 23-28 December
13 rm – €65/80 €150/170 – **Rest** – Carte €33/45
◆ Chic modern design in leather and dark wood draws the smart set to this former theatre. Friendly service; bold, generous and eclectic cooking. Stylish, good-value rooms.

Ristorante Rinuccini
1 The Parade – ✆ (056) 776 15 75 – info@rinuccini.com – Fax (056) 775 12 88
– closed 25-26 December
Rest – Italian Menu €28 (dinner) – Carte €21/52
◆ Named after the 17C archbishop, "bon viveur" and papal nuncio to Ireland, a family owned restaurant with basement dining room: Italian classics served at closely set tables.

KILLALOE – Clare – 712 G 9 *Ireland* 38 B2

Dublin 175 km – Ennis 51 km – Limerick 21 km – Tullamore 93 km
The Bridge ✆ (061) 376866, tourisminfo@shannon-dev.ie
Town★ – St Flannan's Cathedral★
Graves of the Leinstermen (< ★), N : 7 ¼ km by R 494 – Castleconnell★, S : 16 km by R 494 and R 466 – Clare Glens★, S : 24 km by R 494, R 504 and R 503. Nenagh (Castle★), NE : 19 ¼ km by R 496 and N 7 – Holy Island★ **AC**, N : 25 ¾ km by R 463 and boat from Tuamgraney

Cherry Tree
Lakeside, Ballina, following signs for Lakeside H. – ✆ (061) 375 688
– Fax (061) 375 689
– closed 23-25 December, first two weeks January, Good Friday, Sunday dinner and Monday
Rest – (dinner only and Sunday lunch) Menu €29/48 – Carte €45/61
◆ Contemporary, relaxing interior, polite staff and a wide range of original, well-sourced modern Irish dishes on offer from an open kitchen. Seasonal produce of the essence.

KILLARNEY – Kerry – 712 D 11 – pop. 13 137 *Ireland* 38 A2

Dublin 304 km – Cork 87 km – Limerick 111 km – Waterford 180 km
Kerry (Farranfore) Airport : ✆ (066) 976 4644, N : 15 ¼ km by N 22
Beech Rd ✆ (064) 31633, user@cktourism.ie
Mahoney's Point, ✆ (064) 31 034 .
Town★★ – St Mary's Cathedral★ CX
Killarney National Park★★★ (Muckross Friary★, Muckross House and Farms★) AZ - Gap of Dunloe★★, SW : 9 ½ km by R 562 AZ – Ross Castle★ **AC**, S : 1 ½ km by N 71 and minor rd – Torc Waterfall★, S : 8 km by N 71 BZ. Ring of Kerry★★ – Ladies View★★, SW : 19 ¼ km by N 71 BZ – Moll's Gap★, SW : 25 km by N 71 BZ

Plan on next page

Killarney Park
– ✆ (064) 35 555 – info@killarneyparkhotel.ie
– Fax (064) 35 266
– closed 24-27 December DX **k**
67 rm – €275/400 €275/400 – 3 suites
Rest ***Park*** – (bar lunch) Carte €47/63
◆ Smart modern hotel. Firelit library, panelled billiard room and the bedrooms' décor and fine details balance old-world styling and contemporary convenience. Armchair dining beneath sparkling chandeliers and Corinthian capitals.

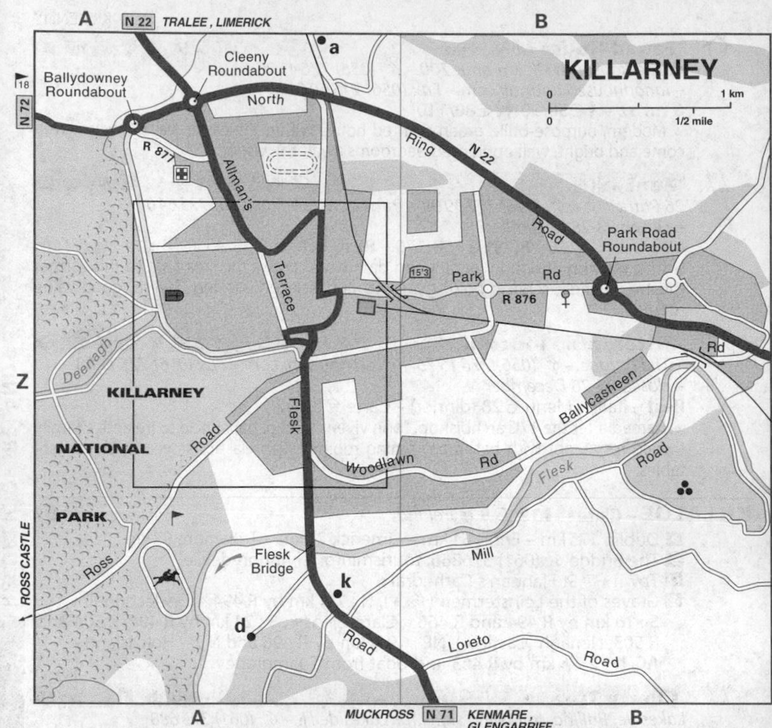

Aghadoe Heights H. and Spa

< Lough Leane, Macgillycuddy's Reeks and countryside, rm,

Northwest : 4½ km by N 22 – ☎ (064) 31 766 – info@aghadoeheights.com – Fax (064) 31 345

72 rm – †€ 315/435 ††€ 250/370, ☕ € 19 – 2 suites

Rest *Lake Room* – (bar lunch Monday-Saturday) Menu € 70

♦ Striking glass-fronted hotel: stylish bar, modern health and fitness centre and contemporary rooms, many with sumptuous sofas. Balconied front rooms offer views of the lough. Picture-windowed restaurant with rural views.

Europe

< Lough Leane and Macgillycuddy's Reeks, rm,

Fossa, West : 4 ¾ km by R 562 on N 72 – ☎ (064) 71 350 – hotelsales@liebherr.com – Fax (064) 37 900 – 16 March-15 December

185 rm ☕ – †€ 170/200 ††€ 290/350 – 5 suites – **Rest** – (light lunch) Carte € 30/59 **s**

♦ Spacious lounges and bedrooms plus excellent prospects of Macgillicuddy's Reeks and Lough Leane. Fully equipped modern comfort, even luxury, on a vast but well managed scale. Restaurant offers Lough views.

The Brehon

rm,

Muckross Rd – ☎ (064) 30 700 – info@thebrehon.com – Fax (064) 30 701 AZ **k**

120 rm ☕ – †€ 121/165 ††€ 179/264 – 5 suites

Rest *The Brehon* – (bar lunch) Carte € 41/58

♦ Spacious hotel near Muckross Park with views to mountains. High standards of comfort. Basement Wellness Centre. Airy bedrooms are well equipped with latest mod cons. Stylish restaurant for formal, original dining.

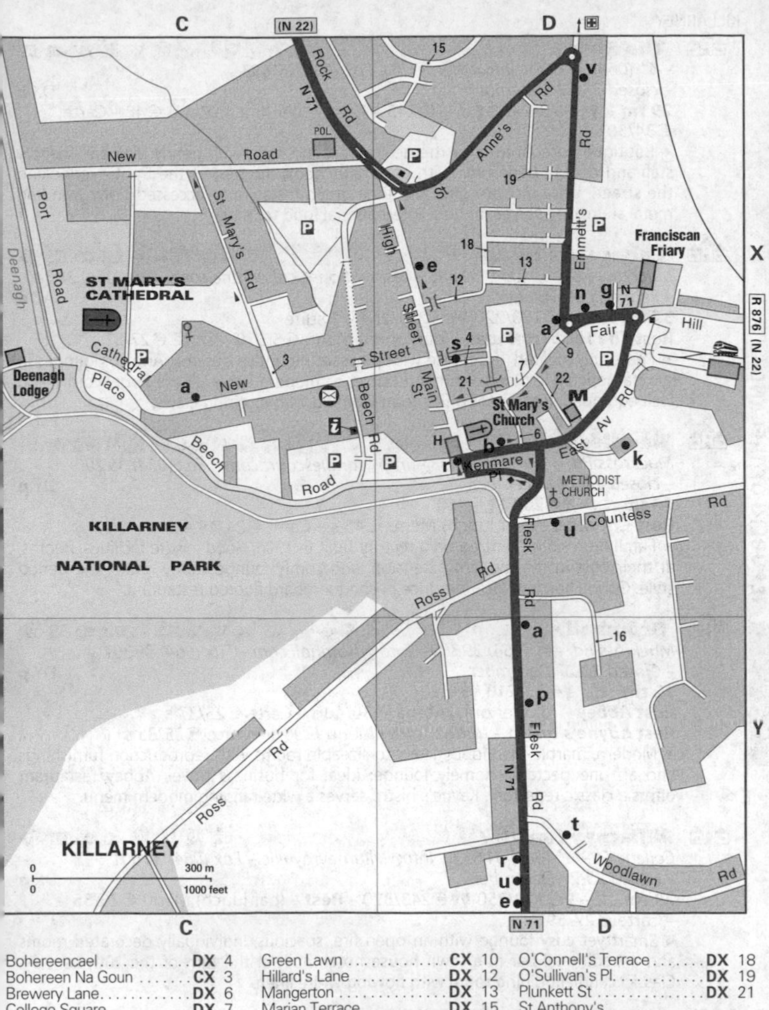

Muckross Park

South : 5 1/2 km on N 71 – ✆ (064) 23 400
– info@muckrosspark.com
– Fax (064) 31 965
– Closed 3 weeks January
62 rm – 🛉€ 180 🛉🛉€ 280 – 6 suites
Rest *Blue Pool* – (dinner only) Menu € 45
Rest *G. B. Shaw* – (Closed Monday and Tuesday) (dinner only) Carte € 50/60
◆ Extended, refurbished 18C hotel boasts high levels of comfort. Includes spa with outdoor hot tub and yoga terrace. Comfortable bedrooms; those in extension more contemporary. Modern main restaurant offers traditional menus. Seafood served in G. B. Shaw.

The Ross

– ✆ (064) 31 855 – info@theross.ie – Fax (064) 27 633
– *closed 24-27 December* DX **b**
29 rm – †€ 170/245 ††€ 170/245 – **Rest** – (bar lunch) Menu € 48 – Carte € 34/50

◆ Boutique hotel boasting extreme comfort and style, with trendy pink bar, friendly staff and quality bedrooms with enormous beds; the best at the front overlooking the street. Ultra modern pink and lime green restaurant - accessed down winding metal staircase - serves modern international food to match.

Cahernane House

Muckross Rd – ✆ (064) 31 895 – reservations@cahernane.com – Fax (064) 34 340
– February-November AZ **d**
37 rm – †€ 180/220 ††€ 224/264 – 1 suite
Rest ***The Herbert Room*** – (bar lunch) Menu € 50/70 – Carte € 27/51

◆ Peacefully located 19C house with pleasant mountain outlook. Array of lounges in sympathetic style. Rooms in main house or modern wing: all are large, comfy and well equipped. Restaurant offers formal dining with inspiring views.

Randles Court

Muckross Rd – ✆ (064) 35 333 – info@randlescourt.com – Fax (064) 35 206
– closed 24-27 December DY **p**
78 rm – †€ 200 ††€ 260
Rest ***Checkers*** – (bar lunch) Menu € 45 **s** – Carte € 31/48 **s**

◆ Family run hotel, centred on a rectory built in 1906. Good leisure facilities. Rooms, at their best in the modern extension, and comfy lounge subtly reflect the period style. Good choice of local produce in chequerboard floored restaurant.

Dromhall

Muckross Rd – ✆ (064) 39 300 – info@dromhall.com – Fax (064) 39 301
– Closed 22-27 December DY **p**
72 rm – †€ 75/210 ††€ 90/240
Rest ***Abbey*** – (dinner only) Menu € 30/40 **s** – Carte € 25/37 **s**
Rest ***Kayne's Bistro*** – (dinner only) Menu € 30 **s** – Carte € 25/35 **s**

◆ Modern, marble-tiled lobby leads to sizeable rooms with reproduction furnishings and an unexpectedly homely lounge: ideal for business travel. Abbey restaurant offers a classic repertory. Kayne's bistro serves a wide-ranging modern menu.

Killarney Royal

College St – ✆ (064) 31 853 – info@killarneyroyal.ie – Fax (064) 34 001
– closed 23-27 December DX **g**
29 rm – †€ 120/250 ††€ 240/320 – **Rest** – (bar lunch) Menu € 25/35 – Carte € 27/59

◆ Smart yet cosy lounge with an open fire, spacious, individually decorated rooms and a traditional bar in a town house hotel, built at the turn of the 20th century. Classic, candlelit dining room with flowing white linen.

Killeen House

Aghadoe, Northwest : 5 ¾ km by N 22 – ✆ (064) 31 711 – charming@indigo.ie
– Fax (064) 31 811
– April-October
23 rm – †€ 75/115 ††€ 150 – **Rest** – (dinner only) Menu € 55

◆ Extended 19C rectory run by a friendly couple. Rooms in bright matching prints. Thousands of golf balls cover the walls of a cosy "bar"; deluxe rooms particularly comfy. Homely dining room with garden views.

Fairview

College St – ✆ (064) 34 164 – info@fairview.killarney.com – Fax (064) 71 777
– closed 24-25 December DX **a**
29 rm – †€ 65/195 ††€ 130/250 – **Rest** – (dinner only) Menu € 35 – Carte € 26/54 **s**

◆ Stylish townhouse with smart, leather furnished lounge. Bright, up-to-date bedrooms exude distinctively individualistic flourishes; penthouse has whirlpool bath and roof terrace. Modern restaurant serves traditional menu of local meat and fish.

McSweeney Arms rm, rest,
College St – (064) 31 211 – mcsweeney@eircom.net – Fax (065) 34 553 – closed January and February DX **n**
26 rm – €85/150 €130/200 – **Rest** – Menu €39 – Carte €35/48
◆ The hotel's unusual corner tower provides extra seating areas in some rooms; the characterful bar has been family run for over 50 years. Well-fitted rooms in modern tones. Long-standing owner lends a hand in the bar and restaurant.

Foley's Townhouse rest,
23 High St – (064) 31 217 – info@foleystownhouse.com – Fax (064) 34 683 – Closed 1-27 December DX **e**
28 rm – €70/120 €110/150 – **Rest** – (bar lunch) Carte €34/50
◆ Formerly a posting inn, now a likeable town-centre hotel, still personally owned and run; spacious modern accommodation is individually styled with a good range of mod cons. Appetising range of seafood in restaurant.

Killarney Lodge without rest
Countess Rd – (064) 36 499 – klylodge@iol.ie – Fax (064) 31 070 – March-October DX **u**
16 rm – €85/100 €120/140
◆ Run by a likeable couple, a purpose-built hotel offering comfortable, thoughtfully furnished rooms. Within easy walking distance of the town centre.

Earls Court House without rest
Woodlawn Junction, Muckross Rd – (064) 34 009 – info@killarney-earlscourt.ie – Fax (064) 34 366 – March-15 November DY **t**
36 rm – €80/120 €100/180
◆ Behind an unassuming façade, reproduction furniture combines well with modern facilities in spotlessly kept rooms. Tasty breakfasts served at antique dining tables.

Old Weir Lodge without rest
Muckross Rd – (064) 35 593 – oldweirlodge@eircom.net – Fax (064) 35 583 – closed 20-30 December DY **r**
30 rm – €65/95 €100/140
◆ Just south of the centre, a sizeable modern hotel owned and run by a welcoming couple. Neat rooms - particularly spacious on the second floor - and hearty breakfasts.

Fuchsia House without rest
Muckross Rd – (064) 33 743 – fuchsiahouse@eircom.net – Fax (064) 36 588 – March-November DY **u**
10 rm – €50/90 €95/140
◆ Inviting bedrooms, firelit lounge and a leafy conservatory in carefully chosen fabrics and patterns; homely without a trace of preciousness or fuss. Personally run.

Kathleens Country House without rest
Madams Height, Tralee Rd, North : 3¼ km on N 22 – (064) 32 810 – info@kathleens.net – Fax (064) 32 340 – 20 March-20 October
17 rm – €60/100 €120/140
◆ Cosy lounge with broad, pine-backed armchairs facing an open fire and neat bedrooms in traditional patterns - an extended house run by the eponymous owner for over 20 years.

Abbey Lodge without rest
Muckross Rd – (064) 34 193 – abbeylodgekly@eircom.net – Fax (064) 35 877 – closed 20-28 December DY **a**
15 rm – €65/120 €100/150
◆ Smart accommodation not far from the centre of town. Cosy lounge in cheerful yellows. Spotless, well-equipped rooms with Queen size beds and CD players.

REPUBLIC OF IRELAND

Gleann Fia Country House without rest
Old Deerpark, North : 2 km by Emmett's Rd – (064) 35 035 – info@gleannfia.com – Fax (064) 35 000 AZ **a**
19 rm – €45/85 €60/140
◆ Meaning "Glen of the Deer", a substantial, purpose-built hotel in country house style, ringed by woods. Smartly kept bedrooms are usefully supplied with modern facilities.

Kingfisher Lodge without rest
Lewis Rd – (064) 37 131 – kingfisherguesthouse@eircom.net – Fax (064) 39 871 – March-October DX **v**
10 rm – €45/90 €70/120
◆ Friendly owners, a mine of local information, keep this modern guesthouse in immaculate order. Affordable accommodation in pastel shades; rear rooms face a quiet garden.

Rivermere without rest
Muckross Rd, South : ¾ km on N 71 – (064) 37 933 – info@killarney-rivermere.com – Fax (064) 37 944 – April-15 October DY **e**
9 rm – €60/70 €110/130
◆ Well-maintained house; large bedrooms simply furnished in dark wood; those at the rear are quieter. Breakfast room overlooks walled garden. Hearty breakfast at clothed tables.

Chapter Forty
40 New St – (064) 71 833 – info@chapter40.ie – closed Sunday CX **a**
Rest – (dinner only) Menu €50 – Carte €45/50
◆ Refurbished restaurant in contemporary browns and creams with small bar area and window looking into kitchen. Large menu includes some eclectic combinations. Great soda bread.

Mentons
Killarney Plaza Hotel – (064) 21 150 – info@mentons.com – Fax (064) 41 839 – closed last three weeks January and 1st week February, 24-26 December DX **r**
Rest – Carte €30/35
◆ Contemporary restaurant; open plan kitchen and long bar counter. Tables for two by window overlook St. Mary's church. Modern, eclectic menu; large portions - lighter at lunch.

Cooperage
Old Market Lane – (064) 37716 – info@cooperagerestaurant.com – Fax (064) 37716 – Closed 24-26 December and lunch Sunday-Wednesday DX **s**
Rest – (light lunch) Menu €23 – Carte €27/34
◆ Stylish, slate-floored town centre bar-restaurant lit by eye-catching modern "chandeliers". Flavourful modern dinners. Good choice of daily specials.

at Beaufort West : 9 ¾ km by R 562 - AZ - off N 72 – Killarney

Dunloe Castle ← Gap of Dunloe and Macgillycuddy's Reeks,
Southeast : 1½ km on Dunloe Golf Course rd – (064) 71 350 – hotelsales@liebherr.com – Fax (064) 44 583 – April-October
100 rm – €170/250 €210/290 – 2 suites – **Rest** – (light lunch) Carte €25/58
◆ Creeper-clad modern hotel offers sizeable, well-equipped rooms and smart conference suites, not forgetting an impressive view of the Gap of Dunloe and Macgillicuddy's Reeks. Restaurant serves Irish classic dishes.

KILLASHANDRA (Cill na Seanrátha) – Cavan – 712 J 5 37 C2

Dublin 133 km – Belturbet 14 km – Cavan 19 km

Eonish Lodge without rest

Eonish, Northeast : 4 ¾ km by Belturbet rd – ☎ (049) 433 44 87 – eonishlodge@eircom.net – closed November, January and February

4 rm – †€ 60 ††€ 100

◆ Just a stone's throw from Lough Oughter, in Killykeen Forest Park. Perfect for fishermen and walkers. Simple, neatly furnished bedrooms; front two have best views over lough.

KILLEAGH (Cill la) – Cork – 712 H 12 – pop. 362 39 C3

Dublin 243 km – Cork 37 km – Waterford 85 km

Ballymakeigh House

North : 1 ½ km – ☎ (024) 95 184 – ballymakeigh@eircom.net – Fax (024) 95 523 – March-October

5 rm – †€ 75 ††€ 130 – **Rest** – (by arrangement) Carte approx. € 45 **s**

◆ Smoothly run modern country house on a working dairy farm. Attractive conservatory lounge and en suite rooms simply but thoughtfully decorated without starchiness or fuss.

Red = Pleasant. Look for the red and symbols.

KILLENARD Laois – Laois 39 D1

Dublin 48 km – Portlaoise 19 km – Naas 25 km – Carlow 36 km

The Heritage

– ☎ (057) 864 55 00 – info@theheritage.com – Fax (057) 864 23 50

94 rm – †€ 160/200 ††€ 180/245 – 25 suites

Rest *The Arlington* – Menu € 65 (dinner) – Carte approx. € 75

Rest *Greens* – Carte approx. € 45

Rest *Sol Oriens* – Carte approx. € 33

◆ Stunning hotel surrounded by extensive gardens and golf course. State-of-the-art meeting facilities and superb spa. Capacious, elegant bedrooms offer supreme comforts. Formal dining in The Arlington. More of a brasserie feel to Greens, in the leisure centre. Pizza, pasta, salad and steaks in informal Sol Oriens.

KILLORGLIN – Kerry – 712 C 11 *Ireland* 38 A2

Dublin 333 km – Killarney 19 km – Tralee 26 km

Killorglin Steelroe, ☎ (066) 976 19 79.

Lough Caragh★, SW : 9 km by N 70 and minor road S. Ring of Kerry★★

Bianconi without rest

Annadale Rd – ☎ (066) 976 11 46 – bianconi@iol.ie – Fax (066) 976 19 50 – closed 23-28 December

15 rm – †€ 70/75 ††€ 110/115

◆ Classic street-corner pub; tiled lounge bar with stools and banquettes and likeable mis-match of paintings, old photos and vintage Guinness posters. Trim, soft-toned bedrooms.

Grove Lodge without rest

Killarney Rd, East : ¾ km on N 72 – ☎ (066) 976 11 57 – info@grovelodge.com – Fax (066) 976 23 30 – closed December and January

10 rm – †€ 50/65 ††€ 45/60

◆ Comfortable, well-fitted rooms - one with four-poster bed and private patio - in a smoothly run riverside house. Try smoked salmon and eggs or a full Irish breakfast.

KILLYBEGS (Na Cealla Beaga) – Donegal – 712 G 4 *Ireland* 36 B1

Dublin 291 km – Donegal 27 km – Londonderry 103 km – Sligo 92 km
Cliffs of Bunglass★★, W : 27 km by N 56, R 263 and minor road – Glencolmcille Folk Village★★ **AC**, W : 25 km by R 263 – Glengesh Pass★★, SW : 24 km by N 56 and R 263 – Donegal Castle★ **AC**, E : 29 km by N 56 – Gweebarra Estuary★, NE : 31 km by R 262 and R 252 - Trabane Strand★, W : 32 km by R263 and minor road

Tara

rm, rest,

– *(074) 974 17 00 – info@tarahotel.ie – Fax (074) 974 17 10*
31 rm – €68/98 €145/165 – **Rest** – (bar lunch) Carte €20/46
◆ Town centre hotel, its bright, commercial style typified by sleek bar with plasma TVs. Light, co-ordinated rooms: ask for one on first floor with balcony overlooking harbour. International menus in contemporary dining room.

KILMALLOCK – Limerick – 712 G 10 *Ireland* 38 B2

Dublin 212 km – Limerick 34 km – Tipperary 32 km
Abbey★ - Collegiate Church★
Lough Gur Interpretive Centre★ **AC**, N : 16 km by R 512 and minor road – Monasteranenagh Abbey★, N : 24 km by R 512 to Holycross and minor road W

Flemingstown House

Southeast : 4 km on R 512 – (063) 98 093 – info@flemingstown.com
– Fax (063) 98 546
– February-November
5 rm – €65 €120 – **Rest** – (by arrangement) Menu €45
◆ Creeper clad, extended 19C house in centre of 200 acre working farm. The attractively decorated bedrooms boast countryside vistas and pieces of antique furniture. Satisfying homemade fare served in comfy dining room.

REPUBLIC OF IRELAND

KILMESSAN – Meath – 712 L/M 7 37 D3

Dublin 38 km – Navan 16 km – Trim 11 km

The Station House

– *(046) 902 52 39 – info@thestationhousehotel.com*
– Fax (046) 902 55 88
20 rm – €76/95 €120/190 –
Rest – Menu €20/45 – Carte €28/46
◆ Former 19C railway station. Bedrooms spread around between station house and converted engine shed! The Signal Suite, the original signal box, now offers four poster comforts. Appealing restaurant using local ingredients.

KILTIMAGH Mayo – Mayo – pop. 1 096 36 B2

Dublin 150 km – Castlebar 17 km – Ballina 22 km – Westport 26 km

Park

rm, rest,

Swinford Rd, Northeast : 1 km on R 320 – (094) 937 49 22
– info@parkhotelmayo.com – Fax (094) 937 49 24
42 rm – €90 €140 – **Rest** – Carte approx. €35
◆ Spacious hotel - near Marian shrine - boasts contemporary design, from its stylish lounge and bar to its up-to-date bedrooms. Well-equipped gym; hot tubs outside on balcony. Bright elegant restaurant.

Do not confuse X with ✿!
X defines comfort, while stars are awarded for the best cuisine, across all categories of comfort.

KINLOUGH (Cionn Locha) – Leitrim – 712 H 4 37 C2

Dublin 220 km – Ballyshannon 11 km – Sligo 34 km

Courthouse with rm

Main St – (071) 984 23 91 – thecourthouserest@eircom.net – Fax (071) 984 28 24 – Closed 1 week spring, 1 week November, Christmas, Tuesday and Monday-Wednesday January, February and November

4 rm – €40/45 €70/80 – **Rest** – Italian influences (dinner only and Sunday lunch) Carte €25/40

◆ Simple, unassuming, pink-painted former courthouse has terracotta palette and wall-mounted gargoyles. Prominent Italian menus include home-made breads, pasta, desserts.

KINNEGAD (Cionn Átha Gad) – Westmeath – 712 K 7 37 C3

Dublin 61 km – Mullingar 20 km – Tullamore 41 km

Hilamar rm, rest,

Main St – (044) 939 17 19 – info@hilamarhotel.com – Fax (044) 939 17 18

45 rm – €89/120 €110/220 – **Rest** – (carvery lunch) Carte €22/39

◆ Trendy hotel with relaxed feel. Stylish bedrooms decorated in bright, modern colours, with quality furniture and up-to-date facilities. Flat screens in bar. Pavement terrace. Modern restaurant.

KINSALE – Cork – 712 G 12 – pop. 3 554 *Ireland* 38 B3

Dublin 286 km – Cork 27 km

Pier Rd (021) 4772234, user@cktourism.ie

Town ★★ – St Multose Church ★ Y – Kinsale Regional Museum ★ AC Y M1

Kinsale Harbour ★ (< ★ from St Catherine's Anglican Church, Charles Fort ★). Carbery Coast ★, W : 61 km by R 600

Plan on next page

Carlton < Oysterhaven Bay, rm,

Rathmore Rd, East : 5 km off R 600 – (021) 470 60 00 – reservations.kinsale@carlton.ie – Fax (021) 470 60 01 – Closed 24-26 December

90 rm – €85/185 €160/290 – **Rest** – Carte €33/56 **s**

◆ Hotel built partially into side of cliff with well run spa complex and Captain's bar. Contemporary bedrooms; some in main hotel, others linked by covered walkway. Traditional menu served in modern restaurant.

Actons < rest,

Pier Rd – (021) 477 99 00 – info@actonshotelkinsale.com – Fax (021) 477 22 31 – Closed 6-31 January, Christmas and mid-week November, December and February Z **p**

73 rm – €109/159 €109/159 – **Rest** – (bar lunch Monday-Saturday) Menu €35 – Carte €32/49 **s**

◆ Group owned and business oriented. Smart modern lounge, panelled in warm wood, and well-appointed bedrooms in a classic palette, at their best in two newer wings. Stylish dining room.

Perryville House without rest

Long Quay – (021) 477 27 31 – sales@perryville.iol.ie – Fax (021) 477 22 98 – 15 April-31 October Y **f**

26 rm – €200 €380, €12

◆ Imposing Georgian house facing the harbour. Antiques and lavish bouquets fill the hall and two period lounges. Rooms are spacious and stylish, the service keen and friendly.

REPUBLIC OF IRELAND

Trident
World's End, South : 3/4 km on R 600 – ✆ (021) 477 9300
– info@tridenthotel.com – Fax (021) 477 4173
74 rm – †€ 90/120 ††€ 130/190 – 1 suite
Rest *Pier One* – Menu € 35 – Carte approx. € 45
Rest *Wharf* – Carte approx. € 15
◆ At end of the harbour, right by the water's edge. Good-sized bedrooms all have sea view; some have balconies. Executive rooms most recently refurbished, with large bathrooms. Upstairs is the formal Pier One restaurant. Lunchtime carvery and traditional evening menu in nautical but nice Wharf bar.

Blue Haven
rest,
3 Pearse St – ✆ (021) 477 22 09 – info@bluehavenkinsale.com
– Fax (021) 477 42 68
– closed 25 December Y **c**
17 rm – †€ 110/140 ††€ 200/250
Rest *Blu* – (dinner only) Menu € 50 – Carte € 27/50 **s**
Rest *Blue Haven* – Carte € 28/52 **s**
◆ Well established hotel in centre of town boasts refurbished public areas and floral bedrooms of varying size, named after wine estates; the largest at the front. Blu serves a traditional British menu. Wood panelled Blue Haven looks like the interior of a yacht, and has small terrace.

Old Bank House without rest
11 Pearse St – ✆ (021) 477 40 75 – info@oldbankhousekinsale.com
– Fax (021) 477 42 96
– closed 22-29 December Y **d**
17 rm – †€ 80/170 ††€ 120/230
◆ Personally and enthusiastically run town house: cosy lounge and comfortable, neatly kept accommodation - bedrooms above the post office are slightly larger.

Harbour Lodge
Kinsale harbour,
Scilly – ✆ (021) 477 23 76 – relax@harbourlodge.com
– Fax (021) 477 26 75
– closed Christmas-New Year Z **r**
9 rm – †€ 130/150 ††€ 165/240 – **Rest** – Carte € 23/38
◆ Modern waterfront house; well kept, with fresh white walls and light carpets. Spacious conservatory and five of the comfortable bedrooms overlook the yachts in Kinsale harbour. Traditional menu offered.

The Old Presbytery without rest
43 Cork St – ✆ (021) 477 20 27 – info@oldpres.com – Fax (021) 477 21 66
– 14 February-November Y **a**
9 rm – †€ 60/85 ††€ 170/180
◆ Tucked away down a side street, a Georgian house run by a husband and wife team. Comfortable, thoughtfully furnished bedrooms in old Irish pine.

Blindgate House without rest
Blindgate – ✆ (021) 477 78 58 – info@blindgatehouse.com – Fax (021) 477 78 68
– mid March-December Z **a**
11 rm – †€ 145/180 ††€ 145/180
◆ Friendly and modern: stylish, clean-lined bedrooms in crisp, light colours, a little front sitting room and smart, wood-floored breakfast room with high backed chairs.

Chart House without rest
6 Denis Quay – ✆ (021) 477 45 68 – charthouse@eircom.net – Fax (021) 477 79 07
– March-October and New Year Z **b**
4 rm – †€ 80/110 ††€ 110/140
◆ Elegant, cream-painted Georgian guesthouse with cosy, quaint ambience. William IV dining suite for breakfast. Bedrooms boast antique beds with crisp white linen.

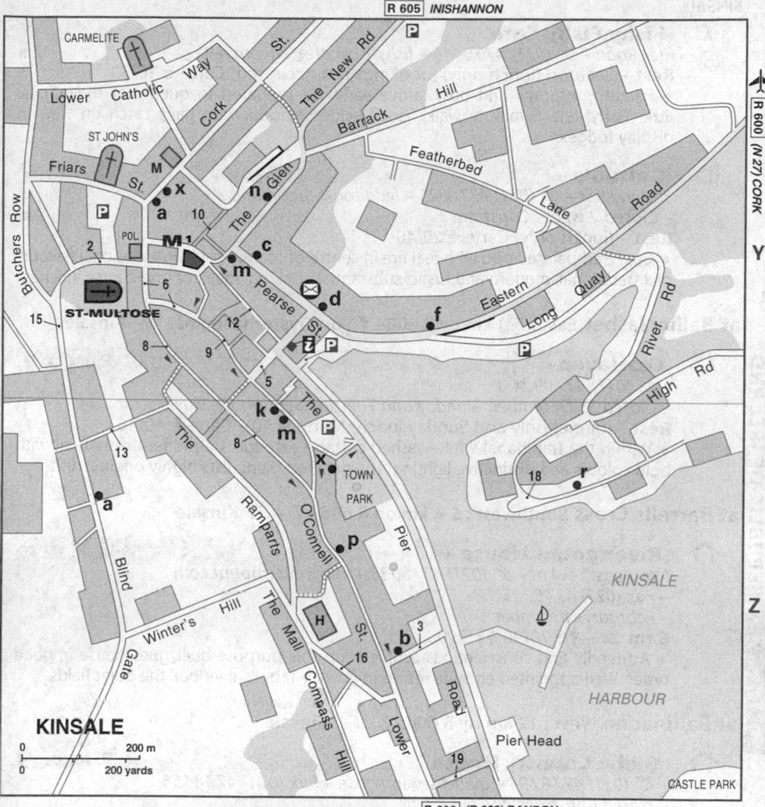

Church St	Y 2	Main St	Y 9	Rose Abbey	Y 15
Denis Quay	Z 3	Market Pl.	Y 10	St John's Hill	Z 16
Emmet St	Y 5	Market Quay	Y 12	Seilly Walk	Z 18
Guardwell	Y 6	Ramparts Lane	Z 13	World's End	Z 19
Higher O'Connel St	YZ 8				

Desmond House without rest
42 Cork St – ✆ (021) 477 35 35 – desmondhouse@gmail.com Y **x**
4 rm – €80/140 €110/140
◆ Small guest house with comfortable lounge and breakfast room. Traditional bedrooms have period furniture and jacuzzi baths and are named after castles. Friendly owners.

Toddies
Kinsale Brew Co., The Glen – ✆ (021) 477 77 69 – toddies@eircom.net
– closed 8 January-14 February, 24-27 December and Sunday Y **n**
Rest – (booking essential) Carte €36/56
◆ Delightful terrace leading to lively restaurant set over two floors, with lots modern artwork. Traditional menus; fish dishes are particularly popular. Charming service.

Max's
Main St – ✆ (021) 477 24 43
– March-mid December and Tuesday Z **m**
Rest – Carte €32/62
◆ Unadorned yet intimate restaurant: try light lunches, early evening menu or full à la carte menu. Keenly devised wine list. Friendly service.

Fishy Fishy Cafe
Pier Road – ✆ (021) 470 04 15 – fishyfishycafe@eircom.net Z **x**
Rest – Seafood (lunch only) (bookings not accepted) Carte € 36/50
◆ Friendly, informal and busy: arrive early, be prepared to queue (or the original little 'Fishy' is a 5 minute walk). Good-value seafood, with daily catch on view in display fridges.

Dalton's
3 Market St – ✆ (021) 477 8025 – fedalton@eircom.net
– Closed 2 weeks Christmas Y **m**
Rest – (lunch only) Carte € 20/40
◆ Cosy, red-painted pub with real fire in centre of town. Simple international flavours mix traditional, modern and rustic: substantial cooking, ideal for one-course lunches.

at Ballinclashet East : 7 ¾ km by R 600 - Y - on Oysterhaven rd – ✉ Kinsale

Oz-Haven
– ✆ (021) 477 09 74
– Closed 25 December, Monday and Tuesday September-May
Rest – (dinner only and Sunday lunch) Menu € 40 – Carte € 40/46
◆ Within the traditional white-washed cottage exterior is a modern restaurant with bold colours and distinctive lighting. The detailed menu lists highly original dishes.

at Barrells Cross Southwest : 5 ¾ km on R 600 - Z – ✉ Kinsale

Rivermount House without rest
Northeast : ¾ km – ✆ (021) 477 80 33 – info@rivermount.com
– Fax (021) 477 82 25
– February-November
6 rm – 🚹€ 70/90 🚹🚹€ 90
◆ A friendly and conscientious couple keep this purpose-built guesthouse in good order. Well-appointed en suite rooms in flowery fabrics overlook the quiet fields.

at Ballinadee West : 12 km by R 600 - Z – ✉ Kinsale

Glebe Country House
– ✆ (021) 477 82 94 – glebehse@indigo.ie – Fax (021) 477 84 56
– closed Christmas and New Year
4 rm – 🚹€ 60/70 🚹🚹€ 90/110 – **Rest** – (closed Sunday and Wednesday) (by arrangement) Menu € 35
◆ Creeper-clad Georgian rectory. Handsomely furnished drawing room; well-chosen fabrics and fine wooden beds in pretty rooms, one with french windows on to the garden. Guests are welcome to bring their own wine.

Look out for red symbols, indicating particularly pleasant establishments.

KINSALEY – **Dublin** – **712** N 7 – **see Malahide**

KINSEALEY – **Dublin** – **712** N 7 – **see Malahide**

KINVARRA (Cinn Mhara) – **Galway** – **712** F 8 36 **B3**
Dublin 228 km – Galway 27 km – Limerick 59 km

Keogh's Bar
Main St – ✆ (091) 637 145 – keoghsbar@eircom.net – Fax (091) 637 028
– Closed 25-26 December
Rest – Carte € 16/30
◆ Centrally located, yellow fronted pub: the eponymous owners have been here for many years. Rear dining room serves appealing, unfussy meals with renowned seafood specials.

REPUBLIC OF IRELAND

KNIGHTS TOWN – Kerry – 712 B 12 – see Valencia Island

KNOCK (An Cnoc) – Mayo – 712 F 6 *Ireland* 36 B2

Dublin 212 – Galway 74 – Westport 51
Knock (Connaught) Airport : (094) 9367222, NE : 14½ km by N 17
Knock Village (094) 9388193 (May-September)Knock Airport (094) 9367247 (June-September)
Basilica of our Lady, Queen of Ireland★
Museum of Country Life★★ AC, NW : 26 km by R 323, R 321 and N 5
Hotels see : Cong SW : 58 km by N 17, R 331 R 334 and R 345

LAGHY = An Lathaigh – Donegal – 712 H 4 – see Donegal

LAHINCH – Clare – 712 D 9 *Ireland* 38 B1

Dublin 260 km – Galway 79 km – Limerick 66 km
Lahinch, (065) 708 10 03 ;
Spanish Point Miltown Malbay, (065) 708 42 19.
Cliffs of Moher★★★ – Kilfenora (Burren Centre★ AC, High Crosses★), NE : 11 km by N 85 and R 481

Vaughan Lodge

rm, VISA AE

Ennistymon Rd – (065) 708 11 11 – info@vaughanlodge.ie – Fax (065) 708 10 11 – April - November

22 rm – €130/175 €180/250 – **Rest** – (closed Monday) (dinner only) Menu €45 – Carte €42/71

◆ Stylish reception area and comfortable lounge and bar offering large array of malts and satellite TV to keep abreast of the golf. Modern bedrooms of a good size; one balcony. Contemporary restaurant decorated with photos of local coastline.

Moy House

< Lahinch Bay, VISA AE

Southwest : 4 km on N 67 (Milltown Malbay rd) – (065) 708 28 00 – moyhouse@eircom.net – Fax (065) 708 25 00 – closed January

8 rm – €145/255 €240/280 – 1 suite – **Rest** – (dinner only) (residents only) Menu €55

◆ Early 19C country house in lovely spot away from town and with delightful views of Lahinch Bay. Genuine country house atmosphere with antiques and curios; charming bedrooms. Stylishly understated dining room.

Greenbrier Inn without rest

VISA

Ennistymon Rd – (065) 708 12 42 – gbrier@indigo.ie – Fax (065) 708 12 47 – 8 March-November

14 rm – €55/115 €120/170

◆ Smartly appointed guesthouse with a modern feel. Conservatory-style breakfast room overlooking Lahinch golf course. Well-kept pine furnished bedrooms.

Dough Mor Lodge without rest

VISA

Station Rd – (065) 708 20 63 – dough@gofree.indigo.ie – Fax (065) 707 13 84 – March-October

6 rm – €50/80 €90/140

◆ Attractive, well-kept guesthouse with large front garden, a minute's walk from the town centre. Cosy lounge; Gingham-clad breakfast room. Spacious bedrooms in white or cream.

**Undecided between two equivalent establishments?
Within each category, establishments are classified in our order of preference.**

REPUBLIC OF IRELAND

LEENANE (An Líonán) – **Galway** – **712** C 7 – ✉ **Clifden** *Ireland* 36 **A3**

Dublin 278 km – Ballina 90 km – Galway 66 km

Killary Harbour★

Joyce Country★★ – Lough Nafooey★, SE : 10½ km by R 336 – Aasleagh Falls★, NE : 4 km. Connemara★★★ – Lough Corrib★★, SE : 16 km by R 336 and R 345 – Doo Lough Pass★, NW : 14½ km by N 59 and R 335

Delphi Lodge

Northwest : 13¼ km by N 59 on Louisburgh rd – (095) 42 222 – stay@delphilodge.ie – Fax (095) 42 296 – closed 18 December-6 January

12 rm – €130 €260 – **Rest** – (dinner only) (residents only, communal dining, set menu only) Menu €55

◆ Georgian sporting lodge in a stunning loughside setting with extensive gardens and grounds. Haven for fishermen. Country house feel and simple bedrooms. Communal dining table: fisherman with the day's best catch sits at its head.

LEIGHLINBRIDGE Carlow – **Carlow** – **712** L 9 – **pop. 674** 39 **D2**

Dublin 63 km – Carlow 8 km – Kilkenny 16 km – Athy 22 km

Lord Bagenal

rm,

Main St – (059) 977 40 00 – info@lordbagenal.com – Fax (059) 972 26 29 – Closed 25-26 December

40 rm – €65/120 €99/199

Rest *Waterfront* – (dinner only and Sunday lunch) Carte €44/64

Rest *Lord Bagenal* – (carving lunch) Menu €38 – Carte €21/48

◆ Impressive hotel on banks of River Barrow; originally a coaching inn, now with vast new extension. Characterful bar with excellent collection of Irish art. Spacious bedrooms. Appealingly formal cooking in the elegant, Roman style Waterside. More informal Lord Bagenal bar and restaurant.

Your opinions are important to us: please write and let us know about your discoveries and experiences – good and bad!

LEIXLIP (Léim an Bhradáin) – **Kildare** – **712** M 7 – **pop. 15 016** 39 **D1**

Dublin 22 km – Drogheda 63 km – Galway 201 km – Kilkenny 117 km

Leixlip House

Captain's Hill – (01) 624 2268 – info@leixliphouse.com – Fax (01) 624 4177 – closed 25-26 December

19 rm – €120 €200

Rest *The Bradaun* – see restaurant listing

◆ Georgian house on town's main street. Well-geared up to banquets. Luxurious soft furnishings and antiques in bedrooms; front-facing rooms with particularly large windows.

The Bradaun – at Leixlip House H.

Captain's Hill – (01) 624 2268 – Fax (01) 624 4177 – Closed 24-26 December and Monday

Rest – (dinner only and Saturday-Sunday lunch) Menu €30 – Carte €43/53

◆ Good size room with high ceilings and large windows commensurate with the age of the property. Simple, fresh décor. Classic dishes with modern and Irish influences.

LEOPARDSTOWN - Dublin - 712 N 7 - see Dublin

LETTERFRACK (Leitir Fraic) - Galway - 712 C 7 Ireland 36 A3

Dublin 304 km – Ballina 111 km – Galway 91 km
Connemara★★★ - Sky Road★★ (≤ ★★) – Connemara National Park★ – Kylemore Abbey★, E : 4 ¾ km by N 59

Rosleague Manor ≤ Ballynakill harbour and mountains,
West : 2½ km on N 59 – ✆ (095) 41 101 – info@rosleague.com – Fax (095) 41 168 – 2 March-mid November
20 rm – †€ 110/140 ††€ 170/230 – **Rest** – (dinner only) Menu € 48 **s** – Carte € 35/45 **s**
◆ Imposing, part 19C manor in a secluded, elevated position affording delightful views of Ballynakill harbour and mountains. Antique furnished, old fashioned comfort. Country house-style dining room: distinctive artwork on walls.

LETTERKENNY - Donegal - 712 I 3 - pop. 15 231 Ireland 37 C1

Dublin 241 km – Londonderry 34 km – Sligo 116 km
Neil T Blaney Rd ✆ (074) 9121160, donegaltourism@eircom.net
Dunfanaghy, ✆ (074) 913 6335.
Glenveagh National Park★★ (Gardens★★), NW : 19 ¼ km by R 250, R 251 and R 254 – Grianan of Aileach★★ (≤ ★★) NE : 28 km by N 13 – Church Hill (Glebe House and Gallery★ **AC**) NW : 16 km by R 250

Radisson SAS rm, rest,
Paddy Hart Rd – ✆ (074) 919 44 44 – info.letterkenny@radissonsas.com – Fax (074) 919 44 55
114 rm – †€ 101/115 ††€ 129/179 – **Rest** – (bar lunch) Menu € 34 – Carte € 24/40
◆ Corporate accommodation in town centre. Bar serves a daily changing menu; rooms are identically appointed: all are clean, modern and spacious. Business class has extras. Dinner in restaurant offers modern international choice.

Castlegrove House
Ramelton Rd, Northeast : 7¼ km by N 13 off R 245 – ✆ (074) 915 11 18 – marytsweeney@hotmail.com – Fax (074) 915 13 84 – Closed 22-30 December
13 rm – †€ 80/120 ††€ 150/190 – 1 suite – **Rest** – (Closed Sunday-Monday November-February) (booking essential at lunch) Menu € 55/65 – Carte € 38/57
◆ Extended country house, dating from the 17C, in very quiet location. Comfortable sitting room with open fires. All rooms of a good size, the newer ones are most comfortable. Capacious dining room with views of gardens and grounds.

Gallaghers
100 Main St – ✆ (074) 912 20 66 – info@gallaghershotel.com – Fax (074) 916 40 96
92 rm – †€ 65/95 ††€ 95/180 – **Rest** – (carvery lunch) Menu € 32 **s** – Carte € 20/29 **s**
◆ Totally refurbished hotel in town centre: its striking glass façade is eye-catching. Two bars: one on upper level is minimal and stylish. Modish rooms have plush white beds. Modern restaurant offers easy-going international menus.

Pennsylvania House without rest
Curraghleas, Mountain Top, North : 3½ km by N 56 – ✆ (074) 912 68 08 – info@accommodationdonegal.com – Fax (074) 912 89 05 – closed 20-26 December
7 rm – †€ 55/75 ††€ 110
◆ Comfortable house run by a welcoming couple: rooms in floral fabrics, comfortable lounge decorated with Eastern artefacts, hilltop views towards the Derryveagh Mountains.

Ballyraine Guesthouse without rest
Ramelton Rd, East : 2 ¾ km by N 14 on R 245 – ✆ (074) 912 44 60
– ballyraineguesthouse@eircom.net – Fax (074) 912 08 51
8 rm – ♦€ 35/50 ♦♦€ 70/85
♦ Purpose-built guest house in the suburbs of this busy market town. Wood floored breakfast room in warm pine. En suite bedrooms are spacious and usefully equipped.

LIMERICK (Luimneach) – Limerick – 712 G 9 – pop. 86 998 *Ireland* 38 B2

Dublin 193 km – Cork 93 km
Shannon Airport : ✆ (061) 712000, W : 25 ¾ km by N 18 Z
Arthur's Quay ✆ (061) 317522 Y, limericktouristoffice@shannondev.ie
City★★ - St Mary's Cathedral★ Y – Hunt Museum★★ **AC** Y - Georgian House★ **AC** Z – King John's Castle★ **AC** Y - Limerick Museum★ Z **M2** – John Square★ Z **20** – St John's Cathedral★ Z
Bunratty Castle★★ **AC**, W : 12 km by N 18 – Cratloe Wood (< ★) NW : 8 km by N 18 Z. Castleconnell★, E : 11 ¼ km by N 7 - Lough Gur Interpretive Centre★ **AC**, S : 17 ¾ km by R 512 and R 514 Z – Clare Glens★, E : 21 km by N 7 and R 503 Y – Monasteranenagh Abbey★, S : 21 km by N 20 Z

Plan opposite

Hilton rm,
Ennis Rd – ✆ (061) 421 800 – reservations.limerick@hilton.com
– Fax (061) 421 866 Y **z**
184 rm – ♦€ 109/229 ♦♦€ 119/239, €10
Rest *River Restaurant* – (dinner only and Sunday lunch) Menu € 45 – Carte approx. € 45
♦ Extensive function and leisure facilities. Modern bedrooms come in dark wood and autumnal browns and oranges; Junior suites have balconies. Terrace bar overlooks River Shannon. River restaurant serves mix of traditional and more modern dishes.

Limerick Marriott rm,
– ✆ (061) 448 700 – reservations@limerickmarriott.ie – Fax (061) 448 701 Z **c**
94 rm – ♦€ 140/170 ♦♦€ 150/195 – **Rest** – Menu € 33 (lunch) – Carte € 38/58
♦ In heart of city centre; bedrooms are modern and stylish, some with balconies. Liszt lounge and Savoy bar reflect the history of the old Savoy Theatre. Contemporary restaurant.

Absolutehotel.com rm,
Sir Harry's Mall – ✆ (061) 463 600 – info@absolutehotel.com
– Fax (061) 463 601 Y **a**
99 rm – ♦€ 95 ♦♦€ 189, € 12.50 – **Rest** – Carte € 33/49 **s**
♦ Stylish, modern hotel and spa on outskirts of city centre; designed like an old mill to reflect the area's industrial heritage. Clever use of space in light-coloured bedrooms. Restaurant serves traditional menu and overlooks river.

Radisson SAS rm, rest,
Ennis Rd, Northwest : 6 ½ km on N 18 – ✆ (061) 456 200
– sales.limerick@radissonsas.com – Fax (061) 327 418
152 rm – ♦€ 115/125 ♦♦€ 135/165 – 2 suites
Rest *Porters* – (dinner only carvery lunch) Menu € 30 **s** – Carte € 31/48 **s**
♦ Modern hotel with tastefully used chrome and wood interiors. Well-equipped conference rooms and a leisure centre which includes tennis court. Smart, state-of-the-art bedrooms. Informal Porters restaurant with traditional menus.

The Clarion < River Shannon and City, rm,
Steamboat Quay – ✆ (061) 444 100
– info@clarionhotellimerick.com – Fax (061) 444 101
– closed 24-26 December Z **n**
155 rm – ♦€ 130/170 ♦♦€ 145/185 – 3 suites
Rest *Sinergie* – Menu € 23/42 **s** – Carte € 33/48 **s**
♦ Impressive newly built hotel by the River Shannon with excellent views of the city. Contemporary décor throughout and great views from the pool. Well-appointed, modern rooms. Formal dining room with modern menu.

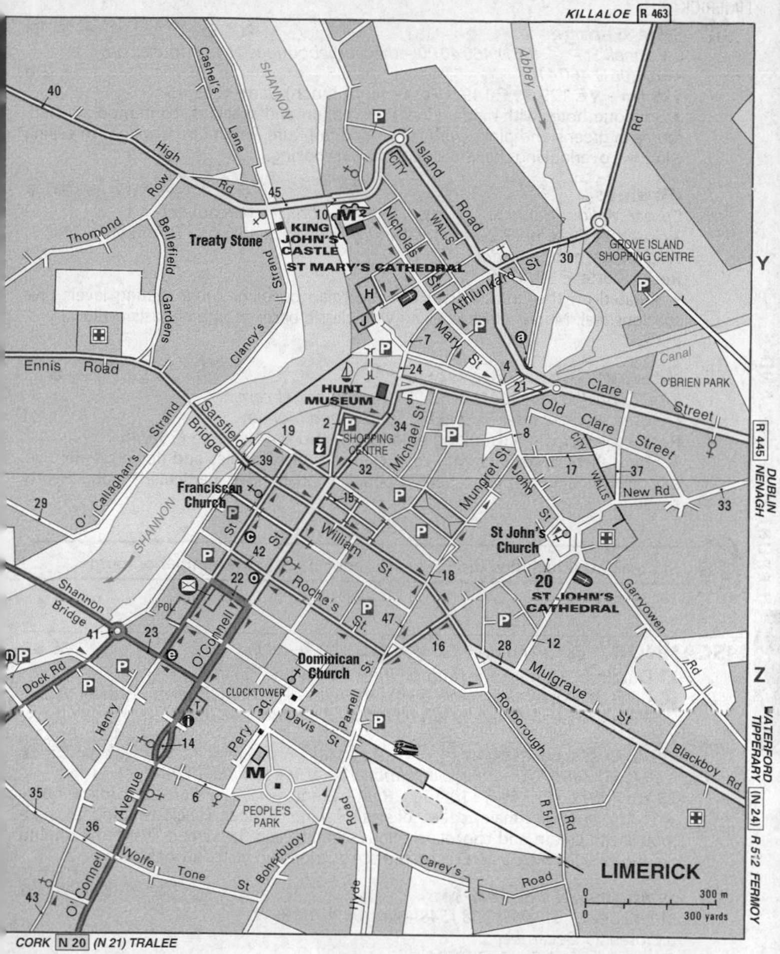

LIMERICK

KILLALOE R 463 — R 445 DUBLIN NENAGH — WATERFORD TIPPERARY (N 24) R 512 FERMOY — CORK N 20 (N 21) TRALEE

Arthur Quay	Y	2
Arthur Quay Shopping Centre	Y	
Baal's Bridge	Y	4
Bank Pl.	Y	5
Barrington St	Z	6
Bridge St	Y	7
Broad St	Y	8
Castle St	Y	10
Cathedral Pl.	Z	12
Charlotte's Quay	Y	13
Cruises St.	Z	15
Gerald Griffen St	Z	16
Grattan St.	Y	17
Grove Island Shopping Centre	Y	
High St	Z	18
Honan's Quay	Y	19
John Square	Z	20
Lock Quay	Y	21
Lower Cecil St	Z	22
Lower Mallow St.	Z	23
Mathew Bridge	Y	24
Newtown Mahon	Z	28
North Circular Rd	Z	29
O'Connell St	Z	
O'Dwyer Bridge	Y	30
Patrick St	YZ	32
Penniwell Rd	Z	33
Roches St	Z	
Rutland St	Y	34
St Alphonsus St.	Z	35
St Gerard St	Z	36
St Lelia St	YZ	37
Sarfield St	Y	39
Sexton St North	Y	40
Shannonside Roundabout	Z	41
Shannon St	Z	42
South Circular Rd.	Z	43
The Crescent	Z	14
Thomond Bridge	Y	45
Wickham St	Z	47
William St.	Z	

Look out for red symbols, indicating particularly pleasant establishments.

The George

O'Connell St – ☎ (061) 460 40 00 – thegeorgeboutique@lynchhotels.com – Fax (061) 460 410 Z **o**

125 rm – †€ 129 ††€ 149 – **Rest** – (light lunch) Carte € 35/45

◆ Boutique hotel with modern low lit reception and spacious, contemporary bedrooms in greens and pinks, with light wood furniture. Restaurant has floor to ceiling windows overlooking the street. Tasty Italian cooking.

Brûlées

Corner Mallow/Henry St – ☎ (061) 319 931 – brulees@eircom.net – closed 24 December-2 January, Sunday, Monday and lunch Tuesday, Wednesday and Saturday Z **e**

Rest – Carte € 30/47 **s**

◆ Situated on the ground floor of a Georgian building. Three seating levels give spacious feel. Modern Irish cooking with classic base: good emphasis on local produce.

Market Square Brasserie

74 O'Connel St – ☎ (061) 316 311 – abranigan@eircom.net – Closed 25 December-3 January, Sunday and Monday Z **i**

Rest – (dinner only) (booking essential) Menu € 44 – Carte € 35/46

◆ Atmospheric restaurant with cosy, clothed tables, candles and flowers. Extensive, seasonally-changing menu; beef is popular and desserts particularly good. Hearty portions.

If breakfast is included the ☕ symbol appears after the number of rooms.

REPUBLIC OF IRELAND

LISCANNOR (Lios Ceannúir) – Clare – 712 D 9 *Ireland* 38 **B1**

Dublin 272 km – Ennistimmon 9 km – Limerick 72 km

Cliffs of Moher★★★, NW : 8 km by R 478 – Kilfenora (Burren Centre★ **AC**, High Crosses★), NE : 18 km by R 478, N 67 and R 481

The Cliffs of Moher

– ☎ (065) 708 67 70 – info@cliffsofmoherhotel.ie – Fax (065) 708 67 71

23 rm – †€ 65/85 ††€ 110/130 – **Rest** – Menu € 15/27 – Carte approx. € 40

◆ Stylish hotel on main street of small fishing village. Spacious, modern bedrooms with cream and chocolate colour schemes and flat screen TVs; some on 2nd floor have balconies. Smart restaurant serves tried-and-tested dishes.

Vaughan's Anchor Inn

Main Street – ☎ (065) 708 1548 – Fax (065) 706 8977 – Closed 25 December

Rest – Seafood Carte € 22/36

◆ Close to Cliffs of Moher, this long-standing, family owned pub is awash with nautical bits and bobs. Appealing menus with emphasis on seafood. A bustling venue.

LISDOONVARNA – Clare – 712 E 8 *Ireland* 38 **B1**

Dublin 268 km – Galway 63 km – Limerick 75 km

The Burren★★ (Cliffs of Moher★★★, Scenic Route★★, Aillwee Cave★ **AC** (Waterfall★★), Corcomroe Abbey★, Kilfenora Crosses★)

Ballinalacken Castle Country House

≤ Aran Islands,

Coast Rd, Northwest : 4 ¾ km by N 67 (Doolin rd) on R 477 – ☎ (065) 707 40 25 – ballinalackencastle@eircom.net – Fax (065) 707 40 25 – 15 April-October

11 rm ☕ – †€ 120/160 ††€ 160/200 – 1 suite – **Rest** – (closed Tuesday) (dinner only) Carte € 41/51

◆ 1840's house with purpose-built extension overlooked by imposing ruin of a 15C castle. Characterful communal areas in traditional style. Large, antique furnished bedrooms. Diners greeted by open fireplace and linen-clad tables.

Sheedy's Country House

Sulphir Hill – ✆ (065) 707 40 26 – info@sheedys.com – Fax (065) 707 45 55 – April-September

11 rm – €90/130 €160/200

Rest *The Restaurant* – see restaurant listing

◆ Classic late 19C mustard painted property in an elevated position. Public areas centre around the bright, wicker furnished sun lounge. Neat, well-equipped bedrooms.

Kincora House

– ✆ (065) 707 43 00 – kincorahotel@eircom.net – Fax (065) 707 44 90 – April-October

14 rm – €50/100 €80/130 – **Rest** – (closed Tuesday dinner) Carte €28/36 **s**

◆ Charming hotel; oldest part dating back to 1860. Attractive walled garden to the rear. Comfy sitting room with plenty of local books. Light, airy bedrooms. Spacious rustic bar with open fires and bar menu.

Woodhaven without rest

Doolin Coast Rd, West : 1½ km by N 67 (Doolin rd) off R 478 – ✆ (065) 707 40 17 – woodhavenbb@eircom.net – closed Christmas

5 rm – €47/51 €64/70

◆ Whitewashed house on a country lane with pretty gardens. Traditionally styled interior decoration to the lounge and breakfast room. Simple bedrooms with a homely feel.

The Restaurant – at Sheedy's Country House H.

Sulphir Hill – ✆ (065) 707 40 26 – info@sheedys.com – Fax (065) 707 45 55 – April-September

Rest – (dinner only) (booking essential for non-residents) Carte €35/51 **s**

◆ Attractive, comfortable restaurant at the front of the building. Linen covered tables and smart place settings. Interesting menus using freshest, local produce.

LISMORE (Lios Mór) – Waterford – 712 I 11 — 39 C2

Dublin 227 km – Cork 56 km – Fermoy 26 km

Lismore House

Main St – ✆ (058) 72 966 – info@lismorehousehotel.com – Fax (058) 53 068 – closed 24-26 December

29 rm – €60/135 €120/270 – **Rest** – (bar lunch) Carte approx. €45

◆ Georgian house with purpose built rear. Bedrooms are all brand new with up-to-date facilities including plasmas and playstations; several overlook the Millennium Gardens. Intimate dining room.

Northgrove without rest

Tourtane, West : 1½ km by N 72 on Ballyduff rd – ✆ (058) 54 325 – johnhoward1@eircom.net – closed Christmas-New Year

3 rm – €45/70 €40/80

◆ Modern guesthouse providing a keenly priced and accessible resting place for visitors to this historic town. Good sized, pine furnished bedrooms with colourful décor.

LISTOWEL – Kerry – 712 D 10 – pop. 3 393 *Ireland* — 38 B2

Dublin 270 km – Killarney 54 km – Limerick 75 km – Tralee 27 km

St John's Church ✆ (068) 22590 (June-September), tourisminfo@shannon-dev.ie

Ardfert★ **AC**, SW : 32 km by N 69 and minor roads via Abbeydorney – Banna Strand★, SW : 35 km by N 69 and minor roads via Abbeydorney – Carrigafoyle Castle★, N : 17 km by R 552 and minor road – Glin Castle★ **AC**, N : 24 km by N 69 – Rattoo Round Tower★, W : 19 km by R 553, R 554 and R 551

Allo's Bar with rm
41 Church St – ✆ (068) 22 880 – allos@eircom.net – Fax (068) 22 803 – Closed 25 December, Sunday and Monday
3 rm – †€ 45/65 ††€ 80/100 – **Rest** – (booking essential) Carte € 18/70
◆ Brightly-painted pub with covered terrace and cosy, citrus snug; once a handy hidey-hole for the local priest to sup a swift drink. Classic menu has international touches. Comfortable, antique-furnished bedrooms - but no breakfast served.

LITTLE ISLAND = An tOileán Beag – Cork – 712 G/H 12 – see Cork

LONGFORD – Longford – 712 I 6 37 C3

Dublin 124 km – Drogheda 120 km – Galway 112 km – Limerick 175 km
45 Dublin St ✆ (043) 46566

Viewmount House without rest
Dublin Rd, Southeast : 1 ½ km by R 393 – ✆ (043) 41 919 – info@viewmounthouse.com – Fax (043) 42 906
13 rm – †€ 60/75 ††€ 110/160
◆ Impressive Georgian house in four acres; breakfast room has attractive vaulted ceiling, lounge reached by fine staircase. Rooms boast antique beds and period furniture.

LUCAN = Leamhcán – Dublin – 712 M 7 – see Dublin

MACROOM (Maigh Chromtha) – Cork – 712 F 12 – pop. 2 985 38 B3

Dublin 299 km – Cork 40 km – Killarney 48 km
Lackaduve, ✆ (026) 41 072 .

Castle
Main St – ✆ (026) 41 074 – castlehotel@eircom.net – Fax (026) 41 505 – Closed 24-28 December
58 rm – †€ 90/115 ††€ 160/190
Rest *B's* – (dinner only) Menu € 25/43
◆ A traditional hotel with gabled windows located in the town centre. Boasts a stylish leisure complex and neat, comfortable bedrooms. Informal B's.

MALAHIDE (Mullach Íde) – Dublin – 712 N 7 – pop. 13 826 *Ireland* 39 D1

Dublin 14 km – Drogheda 38 km
Beechwood The Grange, ✆ (01) 846 1611 .
Castle★★
Newbridge House★ AC, N : 8 km by R 106, M1 and minor road

Bon Appétit (Oliver Dunne)
(First Floor) No.9 St James Terrace – ✆ (01) 845 0314 – info@bonappetit.ie – Fax (01) 845 5363 – Closed 25-26 December, first week January, first 2 weeks August, Sunday and Monday
Rest – French (dinner only) (booking essential) Menu € 65
Spec. Beetroot tart, feta cheese sorbet and pickled girolles. Lobster, duck neck terrine, pea mousse and lobster jelly. Berries with honey, raspberry cream and Sauternes granita.
◆ Set in delightful converted Georgian terrace. Sumptuous bar; formally set dining room with fine china and linen. Cooking uses classic combinations and has a French accent.

Cruzzo
Marina Village – ✆ (01) 845 0599 – info@cruzzo.ie – Fax (01) 845 0602 – Closed 25-26 December, 1 January, Good Friday and Monday lunch except Bank Holidays when open for dinner
Rest – Carte € 34/51
◆ Modern glass and designer furnishings in a striking marina restaurant above the water. Pleasantly distinctive ground-floor bar for lighter dishes. Tasty, modern cuisine.

XX **Siam Thai** A/C VISA MC AE

1 The Green, off Strand St – ✆ (01) 845 4698 – siammalahide@eircom.net – Fax (01) 845 4489 – closed 25-26 December and Good Friday

Rest – Thai (booking essential) Menu € 15/35 – Carte € 29/44

◆ Centrally located restaurant with piano bar providing a light feel. Immaculately set tables and ornate, carved chairs. Richly authentic Thai cuisine, freshly prepared.

XX **Jaipur** A/C VISA MC AE

5 St James Terrace – ✆ (01) 845 5455 – info@jaipur.ie – Fax (01) 845 5456 – Closed 25 December

Rest – Indian (dinner only) Menu € 50 – Carte € 31/47

◆ Friendly basement restaurant in impressive Georgian terraced parade. Well-run by efficient, welcoming staff. Simple but lively modern décor. Contemporary Indian dishes.

XX **Cafe Bon** A/C VISA MC AE

(basement) No.9 St James Terrace – ✆ (01) 845 0314 – info@bonappetit.ie – Fax (01) 835 5365 – Closed 25-26 December, first week January and first 2 weeks August

Rest – Bistro (dinner only and Sunday lunch) (booking essential) Menu € 29 (lunch) **s** – Carte dinner € 35/47 **s**

◆ In basement of Georgian terraced house - a popular alternative to the more formal 'Bon Appetit' upstairs - serving classical bistro dishes such as moules or steak frites.

X **Cape Greko** A/C VISA MC

First Floor, Unit One, New St – ✆ (01) 845 6288 – info@capegreko.ie – Fax (01) 845 6289 – Closed 25-26 December, Good Friday and lunch Monday-Thursday

Rest – Menu € 14 (lunch) – Carte € 27/37

◆ Hidden away in the town centre, this light, airy dining room, located up steep stairs, evokes happy, sunshine days with an authentic menu of combined Greek and Cypriot dishes.

at Kinsaley Southwest : 4 km by R 106 on R 107 – ✉ Malahide

Belcamp Hutchinson without rest P VISA MC

Carrs Lane, Balgriffin, South : 1½ km by R 107 – ✆ (01) 846 0843 – belcamphutchinson@eircom.net – Fax (01) 848 5703 – February-20 December

8 rm ☕ – 🚹€ 75 🚹🚹€ 150

◆ Distinguished, creeper clad Georgian country house full of charm and character; eponymously named original owner. Walled garden with maze; airy rooms in strong, dark colours.

MALLOW – Cork – 712 F 11 – pop. 8 937 *Ireland* 38 B2

▶ Dublin 240 km – Cork 34 km – Killarney 64 km – Limerick 66 km

18 Ballyellis, ✆ (022) 21 145 .

◉ Town★ – St James' Church★

Ⓖ Annes Grove Gardens★, E : 17 ¾ km by N 72 and minor rd – Buttevant Friary★, N : 11 ¼ km by N 20 – Doneraile Wildlife Park★ AC, NE : 9 ½ km by N 20 and R 581 – Kanturk★ (Castle★), W : 16 km by N 72 and R 576

Longueville House P VISA MC AE

West : 5½ km by N 72 – ✆ (022) 47 156 – info@longuevillehouse.ie – Fax (022) 47 459 – Closed 6 January-15 March

20 rm ☕ – 🚹€ 110/200 🚹🚹€ 235/360

Rest *Presidents* – (dinner only) (booking essential) Menu € 60

◆ Part Georgian manor; exudes history from oak trees planted in formation of battle lines at Waterloo and views of Dromineen Castle to richly ornate, antique-filled bedrooms. Restaurant offers gourmet cuisine.

REPUBLIC OF IRELAND

MAYNOOTH – Kildare – 712 M 7 – pop. 10 151 Ireland 39 D1

Dublin 24 km

Castletown House★★ AC, SE : 6 ½ km by R 405

Carton House

East : 3 km on R 148 Lexlip Road – ✆ (01) 505 20 00 – reservations@cartonhouse.com – Fax (01) 651 77 03

150 rm – ♦€ 155/205 ♦♦€ 170/220 – 15 suites

Rest *The Linden Tree* – (bar lunch) Menu € 50 – Carte € 43/57

◆ Beautifully blended 18C home and modern hotel: boasts two golf courses, rose garden, superb spa, meeting rooms and graceful bedrooms: a winning mixture of charm and character. Popular, seasonal menus in modern dining room.

Glenroyal

rm, AC rest,

Straffan Rd – ✆ (01) 629 0909 – info@glenroyal.ie – Fax (01) 629 0919 – Closed 25 December

113 rm – ♦€ 89/115 ♦♦€ 99/160

Rest *Bistro* – (dinner only carvery lunch) Carte € 26/41 **s**

Rest *Lemongrass* – Asian Carte € 27/35 **s**

◆ Adjacent to shopping centre, ideal for conferences and weddings. Rooms are furnished in smart fabrics with good quality furniture. Informal bistro. Authentic Asian menus at Lemongrass.

MILLSTREET – Waterford – 712 I 11 – see Cappoquin

MILLTOWN MALBAY Clare – 712 D 9 38 B2

The Black Oak

< Liscannor Bay,

Rineen, North : 6 km on N 67 – ✆ (065) 708 44 03 – closed Easter, Christmas, Sunday and Monday

Rest – (dinner only) (booking essential) Menu € 40

◆ Long-standing restaurant with stunning views of sea and cliffs - deservedly busy, so book early for a window table. Tasty, traditional cooking served by friendly, efficient team.

MOATE – Westmeath – 712 I 7 37 C3

Dublin 67 km – Mullingar 28 km – Tullamore 14 km – Athlone 12 km

Temple Country Retreat and Spa

Horseleap, East : 8 km by N 6 rm, AC rest,

– ✆ (057) 933 5118 – reservations@templespa.ie – Fax (057) 933 5008 – Closed 21-27 December

22 rm – ♦€ 145/195 ♦♦€ 250/350 – 1 suite – **Rest** – ✆ (057) 933 51 18 (dinner only and Sunday lunch) Menu € 48 – Carte € 39/52

◆ Smart modern spa in what was originally a farmhouse. Bedrooms in new building are furnished in contemporary creams and browns; those in original house more cottagey in style. Healthy, modern menus offered in smart dining room.

MOHILL – Co Leitrim – 712 I 6 39 C2

Dublin 98 km – Carrick-on-Shannon 11 km – Cavan 41 km – Castlerea 44 km

Lough Rynn Castle

rm, AC

East : 4 km by R 201 and Drumlish rd – ✆ (071) 963 27 00 – enquiries@loughrynn.ie – Fax (071) 963 27 10

40 rm – ♦€ 280 ♦♦€ 280 – 2 suites

Rest *The Sandstone* – Carte € 46/64 **s**

◆ Extended 18C house on large estate. Bedrooms in main house and converted stables have warm décor and a high level of facilities. Baronial Hall features huge original fireplace. French influenced menus served in formal, intimate dining room.

MONAGHAN – Monaghan – 712 L 5 – pop. 5 936 37 D2

Dublin 133 km – Belfast 69 km – Drogheda 87 km – Dundalk 35 km – Londonderry 120 km

Clones Rd ✆ (047) 81122 (April-October)

Four Seasons rm, rest, VISA AE

Coolshannagh, North : 1½ km on N 2 – ✆ (047) 81 888 – info@4seasonshotel.ie – Fax (047) 83 131 – Closed 25 December

59 rm – €50/150 €158/198

Rest *Avenue* – (Closed Monday, Tuesday and Sunday dinner) (dinner only and Sunday lunch) Carte €26/41 **s**

Rest *The Range* – Carte €22/43 **s**

♦ A hotel which offers a blend of the traditional and the modern. Bedrooms are in uniform style and there is an atmospheric pub. Avenue offers modern dining. The Range has a farmhouse feel with beams and dressers.

Westenra Arms VISA

The Diamond – ✆ (047) 74 400 – info@westenrahotel.com – Fax (047) 74 440 – Closed 25 December

22 rm – €80/130 €130/195 – **Rest** – (carvery lunch) Carte €25/35

♦ Red brick town centre hotel offers refurbished bedrooms with gold carpets, warm fabrics and a good level of facilities. The two executive rooms are larger with four posters. Large gothic bar with snack menu. Glass-roofed courtyard serves lunchtime carvery while Diamond restaurant offers à la carte.

at Glaslough Northeast : 9½ km by N 12 on R 185 – ✉ Monaghan

The Hunting Lodge at Castle Leslie Spa VISA AE

– ✆ (047) 88 100 – info@castleleslie.com – Fax (047) 88 256

29 rm – €140 €190 – 1 suite

Rest *Snaffles* – Carte €25/42

♦ Estate set in 1000 acres, with 55 horses and a large indoor arena; contemporary bedrooms have balconies which overlook equestrian centre. The Castle now operates a member's club. Snaffles mezzanine brasserie has open kitchen and serves Mediterranean meets Irish cooking.

MONKSTOWN (Baile na Mhanaigh) – Cork – 712 G/H 12 38 B3

Dublin 257 km – Cork 14 km – Waterford 120 km

Parkgarriffe, ✆ (021) 841 376.

The Bosun rest, VISA AE

The Pier – ✆ (021) 484 21 72 – info@thebosun.ie – Fax (021) 484 20 08 – Closed 24-26 December and Good Friday

15 rm – €70 €120 – **Rest** – Menu €32/49 – Carte €26/50

♦ After a walk along the waterway, unwind in the cosy environment of this quayside hotel. There is a private entrance for the bedrooms which are neatly and simply furnished. Seaside location reflected in restaurant menus.

MULLAGHMORE Sligo – Co Sligo – pop. 147 36 B2

Dublin 157 km – Sligo 18 km – Donegal 29 km – Bundoran 10 km

Pier Head rm, rest, VISA AE

– ✆ (071) 916 61 71 – pierheadreception@eircom.net – Fax (071) 916 64 73 – closed 1 week Christmas

40 rm – €50/105 €115/161 – **Rest** – (dinner only) Menu €25 **s** – Carte approx. €37 **s**

♦ Family owned hotel in pleasant harbour village. Simple bedrooms; the best have views over the bay, and some on the top floor have French doors, a paved roof and hot tub. Large restaurant with superb vista.

REPUBLIC OF IRELAND

MULLINGAR - Westmeath - 712 J/K 7 - pop. 15 621 *Ireland* 37 C3

Dublin 79 km - Drogheda 58 km

Dublin Rd ✆ (0449) 348650

Belvedere House and Gardens★ **AC**, S : 5½ km by N 52. Fore Abbey★, NE : 27¼ km by R 394 - Multyfarnhan Franciscan Friary★, N : 12¾ km by N 4 - Tullynally★ **AC**, N : 21 km by N 4 and R 394

Mullingar Park

rm, rest,

Dublin Rd, East : 2½ km on Dublin Rd (N 4)
- ✆ (044) 933 7500 - info@mullingarparkhotel.com - Fax (044) 933 5937
- closed 24-26 December

94 rm - €90/150 €150/240 - 1 suite - **Rest** - (buffet lunch) Menu €30/48 - Carte €42/49 **s**

◆ Spacious modern hotel with a strong appeal to business and leisure travellers: there's a hydrotherapy pool and host of treatment rooms. Airy, light bedrooms with mod cons. Smart, airy restaurant with international menus.

REPUBLIC OF IRELAND

Marlinstown Court without rest

Dublin Rd, East : 2½ km on Dublin Rd (N 4) - ✆ (044) 934 00 53
- marlinstownct@eircom.net - Fax (044) 934 00 57
- Closed Christmas

5 rm - €45/50 €75/80

◆ Clean, tidy guesthouse close to junction with N4. Modern rear extension. Light and airy pine-floored lounge and breakfast room overlooking garden. Brightly furnished bedrooms.

Hilltop Country House without rest

Delvin Rd, Rathconnell, Northeast : 4 km by N 52 - ✆ (044) 9348 958
- hilltopcountryhouse@eircom.net
- March-November

4 rm - €45/50 €70/80

◆ Chalet styled house with attractive gardens. Reception and lounge areas cheered by paintings. Good Irish breakfast served. Snug, homely rooms with pleasant views.

**The ✿ award is the crème de la crème.
This is awarded to restaurants
which are really worth travelling miles for!**

MULRANNY - Mayo - 712 C 6 36 A2

Dublin 270 km - Castlebar 35 km - Westport 29 km

Park Inn

< Clew Bay, rm, rest,

on N 59 - ✆ (098) 36 000 - info@parkinnmulranny.ie
- Fax (098) 36 899
- Closed Christmas

39 rm - €75/145 €150/240 - 21 suites
Rest Neptune - see restaurant listing
Rest *Waterfront Bistro* - (bar lunch Monday-Saturday) Menu €39 - Carte €39/53

◆ Purpose-built business oriented hotel behind 19C façade: lovely Clew Bay views. Impressive leisure and conference facilities. Airy rooms with slightly minimalist interiors. Waterfront Bistro has informal, relaxing ambience.

Nephin - at Park Inn H.

< Clew Bay and Murrisk mountains,

on N 59 - ✆ (098) 36 000 - info@parkinnmulranny.ie - Fax (098) 36 899
- Closed Christmas

Rest - (dinner only) Menu €49 - Carte approx. €40

◆ Large, lively restaurant with fine southerly views. Modern, intricately presented cooking offers interesting combinations based around well sourced, quality ingredients.

NAAS – Kildare – 712 L/M 8 – pop. 18 288 Ireland

39 **D1**

Dublin 30 km – Kilkenny 83 km – Tullamore 85 km
Kerdiffstown Naas, ✆ (045) 874 644 .
Russborough★★★ **AC**, S : 16 km by R 410 and minor road – Castletown House★★ **AC**, NE : 24 km by R 407 and R 403

Killashee House H. & Villa Spa

South : 1½ km on R 448 (Kilcullen Rd) rm, rest, VISA
– ✆ (045) 879 277 – reservations@killasheehouse.com – Fax (045) 879 266
– Closed 24-25 December
129 rm – €144/170 €198/260 – 12 suites
Rest *Turners* – (dinner only and Sunday lunch) Menu €40/60
Rest *Nun's Kitchen* – Carte €29/44 **s**
◆ Imposing part 1860s hunting lodge in acres of parkland. Rooms in the original house are most characterful: French antique furniture, original panelling and fireplaces. Elegant Turners overlooking garden. Informal Nun's Kitchen.

Les Olives

VISA
10 South Main St, (above Kavanagh's pub) – ✆ (045) 894 788
– lesolives@eircom.net
– Closed Sunday, Monday and Tuesday after Bank Holidays
Rest – (dinner only) (booking essential) Carte €44/71
◆ Above a pub looking down on high street; three sunny rooms complemented by colourful artwork, generous sized tables. French inspired cuisine with international flourishes.

The red symbol?
This denotes the very essence of peace
– only the sound of birdsong first thing in the morning …

NAVAN – Meath – 712 L 7 – pop. 19 417 Ireland

37 **D3**

Dublin 48 km – Drogheda 26 km – Dundalk 51 km
Moor Park Mooretown, ✆ (046) 27 661 ;
Royal Tara Bellinter, ✆ (046) 922 5244 .
Brú na Bóinne : Newgrange★★★ **AC**, Knowth★, E : 16 km by minor road to Donore – Bective Abbey★, S : 6½ km by R 161 – Tara★ **AC**, S : 8 km by N 3. Kells★ (Round Tower and High Crosses★★, St Columba's House★), NW : by N 3 – Trim★ (castle★★), SW : 12¾ km by R 161

Bellinter House

VISA
Southeast : 9¼ km by N 3 on Trim rd – ✆ (046) 903 09 00
– info@bellinterhouse.com
– Closed 24-27 December
34 rm – €225/320 €225/320
Rest *Eden* – Menu €35/49 – Carte €29/48
◆ Beautiful 18C manor house with bohemian style; perfect for modern traveller in search of luxury and comfort. Bedrooms furnished to an excellent standard. Relaxing atmosphere. Eden restaurant serves classic dishes.

Newgrange

rm, rest, VISA
Bridge St – ✆ (046) 907 41 00 – info@newgrangehotel.ie – Fax (046) 907 39 77
– closed 25 December
62 rm – €89/130 €140/180 – **Rest** – (carvery lunch) – Carte €20/40
◆ Warm-toned, well-fitted modern rooms and an inviting, traditionally styled bar, plus ample meeting space, make this town centre hotel a popular function venue. Smart, bright brasserie

Ma Dwyers without rest

VISA
Dublin Rd, South : 1¼ km on N 3 – ✆ (046) 907 79 92 – Fax (046) 907 79 95
– Closed 25 December
9 rm – €55 €90
◆ Yellow-painted, mock-Georgian house; comfortable guest lounge, modern breakfast room. Hospitality trays in equally bright, simple bedrooms.

Killyon without rest
Dublin Rd, South : 1½ km on N 3 – ✆ (046) 907 12 24 – info@killyonguesthouse.ie – Fax (046) 907 27 66 – Closed 24-26 December
6 rm – €45/50 €100
◆ Very good value, comfortable guesthouse, overlooking the river Boyne, run by husband and wife team. Bedrooms are individually decorated. Home baking and good breakfast choice.

NENAGH – **Tipperary** – **712** H 9 – **pop. 6 454** *Ireland* 39 **C2**

Dublin 154 km – Galway 101 km – Limerick 42 km
The Governor's House, Connolly St ✆ (067) 31610 (mid May-mid September), tourisminfo@shannon-dev.ie
Nenagh Birchwood, ✆ (067) 31 476 .
Castle★

Abbey Court rm,
Dublin Rd, East : ½ km – ✆ (067) 41 111 – info@abbeycourt.ie – Fax (067) 41 022 – Closed 25-26 December
82 rm – €100/110 €170/200 –
Rest – (carvery lunch) Carte €20/32 **s**
◆ A castellated façade, clock tower and arched windows add a historical theme to a modern hotel. Fitness club offers all amenities including hair salon. Modern bedrooms. Wooden statue of monk distinguishes beamed dining room.

NEW ROSS (Ros Mhic Thriúin) – **Wexford** – **712** L 10 – **pop. 6 537** – 39 **D2**
✉ **Newbawn** *Ireland*

Dublin 141 km – Kilkenny 43 km – Waterford 24 km – Wexford 37 km
Dunbrody Heritage Centre ✆ (051) 421857
St Mary's Church★
Kennedy Arboretum, Campile★ **AC**, S : 12 km by R 733 – Kilmokea Gardens★ **AC**, S : 15 km by R 733 and minor road W – Dunbrody Abbey★, S : 12 ¾ km by R 733 – Inistioge★, NW : 16 km by N 25 and R 700 – Graiguenamanagh★ (Duiske Abbey★★ **AC**), N : 17 ¾ km by N 25 and R705

Riversdale House without rest
Lower William St – ✆ (051) 422 515 – riversdalehouse@eircom.net – March-November
4 rm – €50 €75
◆ Conservatory lounge and home baking are among the attractions of a good-value guesthouse, run by a friendly owner. Well-tended garden, neat bedrooms with electric blankets.

NEWCASTLE Kildare – **712** M 8 39 **D1**

The Mill
The Village at Lyons, Northwest : 3 1/2 km by Athgoe Rd – ✆ (01) 630 3500 – info@villageatlyons.com – Fax (01) 630 3505 – closed 18 March - 3 April, lunch Monday-Wednesday and Sunday dinner
Rest – Menu €42 (lunch) – Carte €80/120
◆ Restored Georgian village on towpath of Grand Canal. Elegant dining room boasts beautiful high ceiling and 17C fireplaces. Cooking is luxurious, with strong French overtones.

Cafe La Serre
The Village at Lyons, Northwest : 3 1/2 km by Athgoe Rd – ✆ (01) 630 3500 – info@villageatlyons.com – Fax (01) 630 35 05 – Closed 18 March to 3 April and Monday
Rest – Carte €39/56
◆ Delightful restaurant in 17C Turner designed conservatory, with rustic courtyard for outdoor dining. Emphasis is on simplicity, with fish pies, steak and chips or oysters.

REPUBLIC OF IRELAND

NEWMARKET-ON-FERGUS (Cora Chaitlín) – Clare – 712 F 7 – 38 B2
pop. 1 542 Ireland

Dublin 219 km – Ennis 13 km – Limerick 24 km

Dromoland Castle, (061) 368 444 .

Bunratty Castle★★ AC, S : 10 km by N 18 – Craggaunowen Centre★ AC, NE : 15 km by minor road towards Moymore – Knappogue Castle★ AC, NE : 12 km N 18 and minor roads via Quin – Quin Friary★ AC, N : 10 km by N 18 and minor road to Quin

Dromoland Castle
Northwest : 2½ km – (061) 368 144
– sales@dromoland.ie – Fax (061) 363 355

93 rm – €238/442 €238/442, €30 – 5 suites

Rest *Earl of Thomond* – (dinner only and Sunday lunch) Menu €65 – Carte €60/85

Rest *Fig Tree* – (bar lunch) Menu €42

◆ Restored 16C castle with 375 acres of woodland and golf course. Sumptuous rooms with plenty of thoughtful extras. Waterford crystal chandeliers and gilded mirrors in the Earl of Thormond restaurant. More informal style in the Fig Tree, popular with golfers.

Good food and accommodation at moderate prices?
Look for the Bib symbols:
red Bib Gourmand for food, blue Bib Hotel for hotels

NEWPORT – Mayo – 712 D 6 Ireland 36 A2

Dublin 264 km – Ballina 59 km – Galway 96 km

James St, Westport (098) 25711

Burrishoole Abbey★, NW : 3¼ km by N 59 – Furnace Lough★, NW : 4¾ km by N 59. Achill Island★, W : 35 km by N 59 and R 319

Newport House
– (098) 41 222 – info@newporthouse.ie – Fax (098) 41 613
– 18 March-mid October

18 rm – €181/190 €310/328 – **Rest** – (dinner only) Menu €65 **s** – Carte approx. €52 **s**

◆ Mellow ivy-clad Georgian mansion; grand staircase up to gallery and drawing room. Bedrooms in main house or courtyard; some in self-contained units ideal for families. Enjoy the fresh Newport estate produce used in the dishes served in the elegant dining room.

NEWTOWNMOUNTKENNEDY (Baile An Chinnéidieh) – Wicklow – 712 N 8 39 D2

Dublin 35 km – Glendalough 22 km – Wicklow 16 km

Marriott Druids Glen H. & Country Club
rm,

East : 2¾ km off Kilcoole rd – (01) 287 0800
– mhrs.dubgs.reservations@marriotthotels.com – Fax (01) 287 0801

134 rm – €125/265 €125/290 – 11 suites

Rest *Druids* – (dinner only) Carte €33/56

Rest *Flynn's Steakhouse* – (dinner only and Sunday lunch) Carte €55/78

◆ Modern hotel in 400 acres, next to golf course. Spacious marble and granite atrium; leisure, conference facilities. Very comfortable rooms, with every conceivable facility. Druids offers a popular buffet. Classic grill dishes at Flynn's Steakhouse.

REPUBLIC OF IRELAND

OUGHTERARD (Uachtar Ard) – Galway – 712 E 7 Ireland

Dublin 240 km – Galway 27 km
Community Office ☎ (091) 552808
Gortreevagh, ☎ (091) 552131.
Town★
Lough Corrib★★ (Shore road - NW - ≤ ★★) – Aughnanure Castle★ AC, SE : 3¼ km by N 59

Ross Lake House

Rosscahill, Southeast : 7¼ km by N 59 – ☎ (091) 550109 – rosslake@iol.ie – Fax (091) 550184 – 15 March-October

12 rm – †€ 105/125 ††€ 150/190 – 1 suite – **Rest** – (dinner only) (booking essential to non-residents) Menu € 50

◆ Georgian country house set in its own estate of woods and attractive gardens. The period theme is carried right through interiors. Bright bedrooms with antiques. Spacious, comfortable dining room with smartly set polished tables.

Currarevagh House

Northwest : 6½ km on Glann rd – ☎ (091) 552312 – rooms@currarevagh.com – Fax (091) 552731 – 15 March-25 October

12 rm – †€ 90/140 ††€ 190/220 – **Rest** – (dinner only) (booking essential to non-residents) (set menu only) Menu € 45 **s**

◆ Victorian manor on Lough Corrib, set in 170 acres. Period décor throughout plus much fishing memorabilia. Two lovely sitting rooms. Comfortable, well-kept rooms. Country house style dining room, popular with fishing parties.

Railway Lodge without rest

West : ¾ km by Costello rd taking first right onto unmarked road – ☎ (091) 552945 – railwaylodge@eircom.net

4 rm – †€ 70/80 ††€ 100/110

◆ Elegantly furnished modern guest house in remote farm location. Communal breakfast with plenty of choice. Open fires, books and magazine but no TV. Beautifully kept bedrooms.

Waterfall Lodge without rest

West : ¾ km on N 59 – ☎ (091) 552168 – kdolly@eircom.net

6 rm – †€ 60 ††€ 90

◆ Two minutes from the centre, a well-priced guesthouse rebuilt with gleaming wood and original Victorian fittings. A good fishing river flows through the charming gardens.

PASSAGE EAST – 712 L 11

39 C2

Parkswood

≤ Waterford Estuary and Cheekpoint,

on R 683 – ☎ (051) 380863 – info@parkswood.com – Closed Christmas-New Year

4 rm – †€ 140 ††€ 140 – **Rest** – (by arrangement) Menu € 28

◆ Delightful hosts give a friendly welcome, with tea and scones, to their 17C house, with super views and charming garden. Immaculate bedrooms are colour themed, with balconies. Tasty homecooking; the choice depends on the latest catch and what's available locally.

Do not confuse ✗ with ✿!
✗ defines comfort, while stars are awarded for the best cuisine, across all categories of comfort.

PORTLAOISE (Port Laoise) – Laois – 712 K 8 39 C2

Dublin 88 km – Carlow 40 km – Waterford 101 km

The Heritage

rm, rest,

Jessop St – (0502) 78 588 – res@theheritagehotel.com
– Fax (0502) 78 577
– closed 23-28 December

109 rm – €170/190 €190/250 – 1 suite

Rest *The Fitzmaurice* – (carvery lunch) (booking essential) Menu €30/40 – Carte €27/43 **s**

Rest *Kellys Foundry* – Beef specialities (dinner only and Sunday lunch) Carte €24/40

Rest *Spago* – Italian (dinner only) Carte €28/45 **s**

◆ Impressive, purpose-built hotel in central location. Extensive leisure facilities include a large pool. Thoroughly spacious throughout. Well equipped bedrooms. Formal Fitzmaurice serving a modern menu. More relaxed Italian-style Spago restaurant.

Ivyleigh House without rest

Bank Pl, Church St – (057) 862 20 81 – info@ivyleigh.com – Fax (057) 866 33 43
– Closed Christmas and New Year

6 rm – €70/80 €125/150

◆ Attractive Georgian listed house with gardens. Breakfast a feature: owner makes it all herself from fresh produce. Charming period drawing room. Airy bedrooms with antiques.

PORTMAGEE (An Caladh) – Kerry – 712 A 12 *Ireland* 38 A2

Dublin 365 km – Killarney 72 km – Tralee 82 km

Ring of Kerry★★

Moorings

rest,

– (066) 947 71 08 – moorings@iol.ie – Fax (066) 947 72 20
– Closed 19 December-9 January

16 rm – €60/70 €90/100 – **Rest** – (closed Monday dinner except Bank Holidays) (bar lunch) Menu €40 – Carte €32/61

◆ Pub-style hotel in the high street of this attractive village. Spacious, nautical themed bar and trim upstairs lounge. Bedrooms with views over harbour and its fishing boats. Stone-walled, candlelit dining room with seafaring curios.

PORTMARNOCK (Port Mearnóg) – Dublin – 712 N 7 – pop. 8 376 39 D1

Ireland

Dublin 8 km – Drogheda 45 km

Malahide Castle★★ AC, N : 4 km by R 124 – Ben of Howth★, S : 8 km by R 124 – Newbridge House★ AC, N : 16 km by R 124, M 1 and minor road east

Portmarnock H. and Golf Links

rest,

Strand Rd – (01) 846 0611
– reservations@portmarnock.com – Fax (01) 846 2442

138 rm – €120 €300

Rest *The Osborne* – see restaurant listing

◆ Large golf-oriented hotel with challenging 18-hole course. Original fittings embellish characterful, semi-panelled Jamesons Bar. Very comfortable, individually styled rooms.

The Osborne – at Portmarnock H. and Golf Links

– (01) 846 0611

Rest – (dinner only) Menu €45 – Carte €40/65

◆ Distinctively formal restaurant named after artist Walter Osborne. Regularly changing menus balance the modern and traditional. Professionally run with good golf course views.

RANELAGH = Raghnallach – Dublin – 712 N 7 – see Dublin

RATHMELTON (Ráth Mealtain) – **Donegal** – **712** J 2 *Ireland* 37 **C1**

Dublin 248 km – Donegal 59 km – Londonderry 43 km – Sligo 122 km

Town★

Ardeen without rest

turning by the Town Hall – (074) 915 12 43 – ardeenbandb@eircom.net
– Fax (074) 915 12 43
– Easter-October

5 rm – €40/50 €80

◆ Simple Victorian house, with very welcoming owner, on edge of village. Homely ambience in lounge and breakfast room. Immaculately kept bedrooms.

RATHMINES = Ráth Maonais – **Dublin** – **712** N 7 – **see Dublin**

RATHMULLAN (Ráth Maoláin) – **Donegal** – **712** J 2 – **pop. 491** – 37 **C1**

Letterkenny *Ireland*

Dublin 265 km – Londonderry 58 km – Sligo 140 km

Otway Saltpans, (074) 915 1665 .

Knockalla Viewpoint★, N : 12 ¾ km by R 247 – Rathmelton★, SW : 11 ¼ km by R 247

Rathmullan House

North : ½ m. on R 247 – (074) 915 81 88 – info@rathmullanhouse.com
– Fax (074) 915 82 00
– Closed 6 January-7 February

34 rm – €105/185 €210/320 – **Rest** – (bar lunch) Menu €53 – Carte €53/63

◆ Part 19C country house with fine gardens in secluded site on Lough Swilly. Choose a lounge as pleasant spot for lunch. Stylish, individualistic rooms: newer ones very comfy. Restaurant boasts serious dinner menus at linen-clad tables.

Fort Royal

North : 1½ km by R 247 – (074) 915 81 00 – fortroyal@eircom.net
– Fax (074) 915 81 03
– April-10 October

15 rm – €85/95 €170/190 – **Rest** – (Closed Sunday) (bar lunch) Menu €49

◆ Early 19C house in a very quiet location with attractive gardens that run down to the beach. Two comfortable lounges and a spacious bar. Characterful, homely bedrooms. Lunchtime sandwiches in the bar; main evening meal in comfy restaurant.

We try to be as accurate as possible when giving room rates. But prices are susceptible to change, so please check rates when booking.

RATHNEW = Ráth Naoi – **Wicklow** – **712** N 8 – **see Wicklow**

RECESS (Sraith Salach) – **Galway** – **712** C 7 *Ireland* 36 **A3**

Dublin 278 km – Ballina 116 km – Galway 58 km

Connemara★★★ – Cashel★, SW : by N 59 and R 340

Lough Inagh Lodge Lough Inagh and The Twelve Bens,

Northwest : 7 ¾ km by N 59 on R 344
– (095) 34 706 – inagh@iol.ie – Fax (095) 34 708
– March-mid December

13 rm – €122/150 €193/283 – **Rest** – (bar lunch) (booking essential for non-residents) Carte €28/43

◆ Part 19C former fishing lodge with enchanting views of Lough Inagh and The Twelve Bens. Warm, welcoming feel and ambience; cosy bedrooms. Attentive service in country house-style restaurant.

REPUBLIC OF IRELAND

REDCASTLE – Donegal – 712 K 2 37 D1

Dublin 266 km – Muff 14 km – Redcastle 33 km

Carlton Redcastle H.+C.Spa

rm, rest,

on R 238 – ✆ (074) 938 55 55
– info@carltonredcastle.ie – Fax (074) 938 54 44
– Closed 25 December

83 rm – €80/119 €110/188 – 10 suites –
Rest – (bar lunch Monday-Saturday) Menu €49

◆ An extensive range of treatments attracts majority to this refurbished hotel with enviable Lough Foyle setting. Boasts Thalasso pool and juice bar. Streamlined, stylish rooms. Restaurant in stunning spot with super outdoor terrace.

RIVERSTOWN (Baile idir Dhá Abhainn) – Sligo – 712 G 5 36 B2

Dublin 198 km – Sligo 21 km

Coopershill

– ✆ (071) 916 51 08 – ohara@coopershill.com – Fax (071) 916 54 66
– April-October

8 rm – €153/171 €236/272 –
Rest – (dinner only) (booking essential for non-residents) Menu €57

◆ Magnificent Georgian country house set within 500 acre estate. Home to six generations of one family. Antique furnished communal areas and rooms exude charm and character. Family portraits, antique silver adorn dining room.

ROSCOMMON – Roscommon – 712 – pop. 4 489 Ireland 36 B3

Dublin 151 km – Galway 92 km – Limerick 151 km
Harrison Hall ✆ (090) 6626342 (June-August)
Moate Park, ✆ (09066) 26 382 .
Castle★
Castlestrange Stone★, SW : 11 ¼ km by N 63 and R 362 – Strokestown★ (Famine Museum★ AC, Strokestown Park House★ AC), N : 19 ¼ km by N 61 and R 368 – Castlerea : Clonalis House★ AC, NW : 30 ½ km by N 60

Abbey

rm,

on N 63 (Galway rd) – ✆ (090) 662 62 40 – info@abbeyhotel.ie
– Fax (090) 662 60 21
– Closed 24-26 December

50 rm – €150/160 €260/280 –
Rest – Menu €50 – Carte €36/44

◆ Part 19C house with modern extensions, convenient central location and surrounded by attractive gardens. Excellent leisure facilities. Comfortable bedrooms. Spacious restaurant overlooks ruins of Abbey.

Gleeson's Townhouse

rest,

Market Sq – ✆ (090) 662 69 54 – info@gleesonstownhouse.com
– Fax (090) 662 74 25
– closed 25-26 December

21 rm – €55/70 €110/120 – 2 suites –
Rest – Carte €17/28 **s**

◆ 19C former manse with courtyard overlooking the market square. This substantial stone-built edifice was once a minister's residence. Comfortable, well-equipped bedrooms. Meals available in the farmhouse-style restaurant.

Westway without rest

Galway Rd, Southwest : 1 ¼ km on N 63 – ✆ (090) 662 69 27
– westwayguests@eircom.net
– March-October

5 rm – €64

◆ Modern guesthouse with friendly welcome near town centre. Comfy, traditional residents' lounge. Breakfast room with conservatory extension. Brightly decorated rooms.

ROSCREA – Tipperary – **712** I 9 *Ireland* 39 **C2**

Dublin 125 km – Birr 19 km – Nenagh 34 km

Town★ – Damer House★ **AC**

Racket Hall

rm, rest,

Dublin Rd, East : 2 ¾ km on N 7 – (0505) 21 748 – info@rackethall.ie – Fax (0505) 23 701

40 rm – €69/99 €119/149 – **Rest** – (carvery lunch) Menu €33 – Carte €24/40

◆ Bright yellow, creeper-clad, extended roadside inn. Huge rustic pubby area with sofas and shelves of books. Bedrooms offer good levels of comfort and modern facilities. Formal dining to the rear.

ROSSLARE – Wexford – **712** M 11 *Ireland* 39 **D2**

Dublin 167 km – Waterford 80 km – Wexford 19 km

Kilrane (053) 33232 (April-September)

Rosslare Strand, (053) 913 2203 .

Irish Agricultural Museum, Johnstowon Castle★★ **AC**, NW : 12 km by R 740, N 25 and minor road. Kilmore Quay★, SW : 24 km by R 736 and R 739 – Saltee Islands★, SW : 24 km by R 736, R 739 and ferry

Kelly's Resort

rm, rest,

– (053) 91 32 114 – info@kellys.ie – Fax (053) 91 32 222 – Closed 10 December-February

121 rm – €120/190 €240/280

Rest *Beaches* – Menu €25/45

Rest *La Marine* – Carte €30/41

◆ Large, purpose-built hotel on the beachfront of this popular holiday town. Good range of leisure facilities; well-appointed rooms. Kelly's dining room offers a classic popular menu. La Marine is a French inspired, bistro-style restaurant.

ROSSLARE HARBOUR (Calafort Ros Láir) – **Wexford** – **712** N 11 39 **D2**

Dublin 169 km – Waterford 82 km – Wexford 21 km

to France (Cherbourg and Roscoff) (Irish Ferries) (17 h/15 h) – to Fishguard (Stena Line) 1-4 daily (1 h 40 mn/3 h 30 mn) – to Pembroke (Irish Ferries) 2 daily (3 h 45 mn)

Kilrane (053) 33232 (April-October)

Ferryport House

on N 25 – (053) 91 33 933 – info@ferryporthouse.com – Fax (053) 91 61 707 – Closed 24-27 December

16 rm – €55/65 €80/100

Rest *Fusion* – Chinese (dinner only) Carte €31/48

◆ Contemporary hotel conveniently located for the ferry terminus. Simple communal areas include a pine furnished breakfast room. Comfortable bedrooms with fitted wood furniture. Seafood and Chinese cuisine in Fusion.

at Tagoat West : 4 km on N 25 – ✉ Rosslare

Churchtown House

rm,

North : ¾ km on Rosslare rd – (053) 913 2555 – info@churchtownhouse.com – Fax (053) 913 2577 – March-October

12 rm – €85/120 €130/155 – **Rest** – (053) 32 555 (dinner only) (booking essential) (residents only) Menu €40 **s**

◆ Part 18C house with extension, set in spacious, well-kept garden. Traditional country house-style lounge and wood furnished dining room. Individually decorated rooms. Fresh country cooking in the Irish tradition.

Undecided between two equivalent establishments? Within each category, establishments are classified in our order of preference.

REPUBLIC OF IRELAND

ROSSNOWLAGH (Ros Neamhlach) – Donegal – 712 H 4 Ireland 37 C2

Dublin 246 km – Donegal 22 km – Sligo 50 km

Rossnowlagh Strand★★

Sand House ← bay, beach and mountains, rm,

– ✆ (071) 985 1777 – info@sandhouse.ie

– Fax (071) 985 2100

– Closed December-January

50 rm – ♦€ 110/150 ♦♦€ 250/310 –

Rest – (dinner only and Sunday lunch) Menu € 55

♦ Victorian sandstone hotel in coastal location with superb views of bay, beach and mountains. Real fire in the hall. Spacious, individual rooms with modern styling. Attractive dining room with a comfortable atmosphere and classic traditional feel.

ROUNDSTONE (Cloch na Rón) – Galway – 712 C 7 Ireland 36 A3

Dublin 310 km – Galway 75 km

Town★

Connemara★★★: Sky Road, Clifden★★, W : 24 km by R 341 and minor road – Cashel★, E : 15 km by R 341 – Connemara National Park★ **AC**, N : 40 km by R 341 and N 59 – Kylemore Abbey★ **AC**, N : 44 km by R 341 and N 59

Eldon's

– ✆ (095) 35 933 – eldonshotel@eircom.net – Fax (095) 35 722

– Closed January-February

19 rm – ♦€ 50/75 ♦♦€ 70/160 –

Rest – (Closed Monday and restricted opening October-December) Carte € 15/25

♦ Near the harbour of this fishing village with views of the bay and the Twelve Pin Mountains. Wood floored bar with open fires. Annex bedrooms are most comfortable. Seafood inspired menus.

Your opinions are important to us:
please write and let us know about your discoveries and experiences – good and bad!

SALTHILL = Bóthar na Trá – Galway – 712 E 8 – see Galway

SANDYFORD – Dublin – 712 N 8 – see Dublin

SANDYMOUNT – Dublin – see Dublin

SCHULL – Cork – 712 D 13 – see Skull

SHANAGARRY (An Seangharraí) – Cork – 712 H 12 – ✉ Midleton 39 C3

Ireland

Dublin 262 km – Cork 40 km – Waterford 103 km

Cloyne Cathedral★, NW : 6½ km by R 629

Ballymaloe House (heated)

Northwest : 2¾ km on L 35 – ✆ (021) 465 25 31

– res@ballymaloe.ie – Fax (021) 465 20 21

– Closed 24-26 December and 8-20 January

33 rm – ♦€ 150/195 ♦♦€ 280/320 –

Rest – (buffet dinner Sunday) (booking essential) Menu € 42/72 **s**

♦ Hugely welcoming part 16C, part Georgian country house surrounded by 400 acres of farmland. Characterful sitting room with cavernous ceiling. Warm, comfortable bedrooms. Characterful dining room divided into assorted areas.

SHANNON (Sionainn) – Clare – 712 F 9 – pop. 8 561 Ireland 38 B2

Dublin 219 km – Ennis 26 km – Limerick 24 km
Shannon Airport : (061) 712000
Shannon Airport, Arrivals Hall (061) 471664, info@shannondev.ie
Shannon Airport, (061) 471 020.
Bunratty Castle★★ AC, E : 11 km by N 19 and N 18 – Cratloe Wood (≤ ★), E : 14 km by N 19 and N 18. Craggaunowen Centre★ AC, NE : 20 km by N 19, N 18 S, R 471 and R 462 – Knappogue Castle★ AC, N : 26 km by N 19, N 18 and minor road via Quin – Quin Friary★ AC, N :22 km by N 19, N18 N and minor road to Quin

Oak Wood Arms
rm, rest, VISA AE

– (061) 361 500 – reservations@oakwoodarms.com – Fax (061) 361 414
– Closed 24-25 December
98 rm – €95/105 €130/150 – 2 suites
Rest *Palm Court* – (carvery lunch Monday-Saturday) Menu € 35 **s** – Carte € 29/41 **s**
◆ Low rise hotel with good access to Shannon International airport. Large bar with carvery. Lots of small lounges. Good conference facilities. Spacious rooms with fresh décor. Dining room decorated with aeronautical memorabilia.

REPUBLIC OF IRELAND

SKERRIES – Dublin – 712 N 7 – pop. 9 149 Ireland 39 D1

Dublin 30 km – Drogheda 24 km
Skerries Mills (01) 849 5208, skerriesmills@indigo.ie
Skerries, (01) 849 1576 .
Malahide Castle★★ AC, S : 23 km by R 127, M 1 and R 106 – Ben of Howth (≤ ★), S : 23 km by R 127, M 1 and R 106 – Newbridge House★ AC, S : 16 km by R 217 and minor road

Redbank House with rm
rm, VISA AE

5-7 Church St – (01) 849 1005 – info@redbank.ie – Fax (01) 849 1598
– Closed 24-26 December
18 rm – €65/85 €120 – **Rest** – Seafood (Closed Sunday dinner) (dinner only and Sunday lunch) Menu €35/55 **s** – Carte €48/63 **s**
◆ One of Ireland's most well-renowned and long-standing restaurants. Fresh seafood from Skerries harbour is served simply or in more elaborate fashion. Smart, comfy bedrooms.

SKULL/SCHULL (An Scoil) – Cork – 712 D 13 Ireland 38 A3

Dublin 363 km – Cork 104 km – Killarney 103 km
Coosheen Schull Coosheen, (077) 28 182 .
Town★
Mount Gabriel (≤ ★), N : 3 km by minor road. Sherkin Island★ (by ferry)

Corthna Lodge without rest
VISA

West : 1 ¼ km by R 592 – (028) 28 517 – info@corthna-lodge.net
– Fax (028) 28 032
– 27 April-September
6 rm – €60/70 €85/95
◆ 100 year old ivy covered guesthouse with many original features remaining. Large garden. Bright breakfast room. Smart bedrooms boast stencilled walls, modern soft furnishings.

SLIGO – Sligo – 712 G 5 – pop. 17 735 Ireland 36 B2

Dublin 214 km – Belfast 203 km – Dundalk 170 km – Londonderry 138 km
Sligo Airport, Strandhill : (071) 68280
Aras Reddan, Temple St (071) 9161201
Rosses Point, (071) 917 7134 .
Town★★ – Abbey★ AC – Model Arts and the Niland Gallery★ AC
SE : Lough Gill★★ – Carrowmore Megalithic Cemetery★ AC, SW : 4 ¾ km – Knocknarea★ (≤ ★★) SW : 9 ½ km by R 292. Drumcliff★, N : by N 15 - Parke's Castle★ AC, E : 14 ½ km by R 286 – Glencar Waterfall★, NE : 14 ½ km by N 16 – Creevykeel Court Cairn★, N : 25 ¾ km by N 15

Clarion

Clarion Rd, Northeast : 3 km by N 16 – ✆ (071) 911 90 00 – info@clarionhotelsligo.com – Fax (071) 911 90 01 – Closed 23-26 December

163 rm – 🛉€ 250 🛉🛉€ 250, ☕ €16 – 149 suites

Rest *Kudos* – Carte € 26/37 **s**

Rest *Sinergie* – (dinner only) Menu € 35 – Carte € 34/49

◆ Extensive Victorian building with granite façade: now the height of modernity with excellent leisure club, and impressive, spacious bedrooms, the majority being plush suites. Informal Asian inspired Kudos. Modern European menus at Sinergie.

Radisson SAS H & Spa

Ballincar, Northwest : 4 km by N4 on R 291 – ✆ (071) 914 00 08 – info.sligo@radissonsas.com – Fax (071) 914 00 05

129 rm ☕ – 🛉€ 99/110 🛉🛉€ 170/190 – 3 suites –

Rest – (bar lunch Monday-Saturday) Menu € 35 – Carte € 32/48

◆ Modern, spacious hotel two miles from centre. Impressive conference and leisure facilities with comprehensive spa treatments. Stylish, airy, modish rooms, some with king beds. Smart yet informal restaurant overlooking Sligo Bay.

Tree Tops without rest

Cleveragh Rd, South : 1 ¼ km by Dublin rd – ✆ (071) 916 01 60 – treetops@iol.ie – Fax (071) 916 23 01 – Closed 23 December-7 January

5 rm ☕ – 🛉€ 48/52 🛉🛉€ 72/76

◆ Pleasant guesthouse in residential area. Stunning collection of Irish art. Cosy public areas include small lounge and simple breakfast room. Neat, comfortable rooms.

Montmartre

Market Yard – ✆ (071) 916 99 01 – Fax (071) 919 22 32 – closed 24-26 December, Sunday and Monday

Rest – (dinner only) Carte € 28/45

◆ Smart, modern restaurant near cathedral with small bar at entrance and plenty of light from windows. Efficient, formal staff serve broadly influenced classic French food.

SNEEM Kerry – Kerry – **712** C 12 – **pop. 279** 38 **A3**

Dublin 228 km – Tralee 56 km – Cill Airne / Killarney 37 km – Bantry 45 km

Sneem Hotel

Goldens Cove, East : 1/2 km on N 70 – ✆ (064) 75 100 – information@sneemhotel.com – Fax (064) 75 199

69 rm – 🛉€ 95/135 🛉🛉€ 110/190 –

Rest – (dinner only and bar lunch) Carte approx. € 40

◆ Modern hotel overlooking tidal cove and mountains. Lounge with fireplace for a drink or afternoon tea; comfy bedrooms - the largest have balconies, and 221 is the best. Traditional Irish fare served in restaurant with terrace.

SPANISH POINT (Rinn na Spáinneach) – Clare – **712** D 9 – ✉ 38 **B2**

Milltown Malbay

Dublin 275 km – Galway 104 km – Limerick 83 km

Admiralty Lodge

– ✆ (065) 708 50 07 – info@admiralty.ie – Fax (065) 708 50 30 – Restricted opening November-March

11 rm ☕ – 🛉€ 145/165 🛉🛉€ 160/230

Rest Piano Room – see restaurant listing

◆ Purpose-built coastal hotel built around a former 19C seamans lodge. Three warm, comfy lounges bring out period character. Individually stylish rooms a notably strong point.

REPUBLIC OF IRELAND

XXX **The Piano Room** – at Admiralty Lodge H.
– *(065) 708 50 07 – info@admiralty.ie – Fax (065) 708 50 30*
– Restricted opening November-March
Rest – (booking essential to non-residents) (lunch residents only, booking essential) Menu € 42
◆ Keen young French chef produces well presented, sophisticated cooking; a mix of classic and more modern dishes. Piano playing at weekends.

STILLORGAN – Dublin – 712 N 8 – see Dublin

STRAFFAN (Teach Srafáin) – Kildare – 712 M 8 – pop. 341 *Ireland* 39 D1

Dublin 24 km – Mullingar 75 km
Naas Kerdiffstown, (045) 874 644 .
Castletown House, Celbridge★ **AC**, NW : 7 km by R 406 and R 403

 **The K Club**
– *(01) 601 7200 – resortsales@kclub.ie*
– Fax (01) 601 7297
– restricted opening in January
79 rm – € 380/565 € 380/565 – 13 suites
Rest *Byerley Turk* – (Closed Sunday-Monday) (booking essential for non-residents) Carte € 63/166
Rest *Legends* – Carte € 39/72
Rest *River Room* – Carte € 28/54
◆ Part early 19C country house overlooking River Liffey, with gardens, arboretum and championship golf course. Huge leisure centre. Exquisitely sumptuous rooms. Opulent food in the formal Byerley Turk. Informal Legends has views of the golf course. Accessible menu offered in The River Room.

 **Barberstown Castle**
North : ¾ km – (01) 628 8157
– info@barberstowncastle.ie – Fax (01) 627 7027
– Closed January and 25-26 December
59 rm – € 150 € 230 –
Rest – (Closed Sunday-Tuesday) (dinner only) (booking essential)
Carte € 56/85 **s**
◆ Whitewashed Elizabethan and Victorian house with 13C castle keep and gardens. Country house style lounges exude style. Individually decorated, very comfortable bedrooms. Dine in characterful, stone-clad keep.

SWORDS – Co Dublin – 712 N 7 – pop. 27 175 *Ireland* 39 D1

Dublin 13 km – Drogheda 35 km
Balheary Ave, (01) 840 9819.
Fingal★ – Newbridge House★, N : by N 1 and east by R 126. Malahide Castle★★, SE : by N 1 and R 106

Kettle's Country House
Lispopple, Northwest : 6 km on R 125 – (01) 813 8511 – Info@kettleshotel.ie
– Fax (01) 813 8510
– closed 25 December
24 rm – € 90/129 € 115/159 – 1 suite –
Rest – Menu € 25 – Carte approx. € 50
◆ Built on the site of a former pub, this stylish hotel has very well kept bedrooms with flat screen TVs. Pristine bar with carvery.

The ✿ award is the crème de la crème. This is awarded to restaurants which are really worth travelling miles for!

TAGOAT = Teach Gót – **Wexford** – **712** M 11 – see Rosslare Harbour

TAHILLA (Tathuile) – **Kerry** – **712** C 12 *Ireland* 38 **A3**

Dublin 357 km – Cork 112 km – Killarney 51 km
Ring of Kerry★★ – Sneem★, NW : 6½ km by N 70

Tahilla Cove ← Coongar harbour and Caha Mountains,
– ✆ (064) 45 204 – *tahillacove@eircom.net*
– *Fax (064) 45 104*
– *Easter-mid October*
9 rm – ♦€ 105 ♦♦€ 150 – **Rest** – (closed Tuesday-Wednesday) (dinner only set menu only) (booking essential) (set menu only) Menu € 35
♦ Two houses surrounded by oak forest, with Caha Mountains as a backdrop and garden sweeping down to Coongar harbour. Some bedrooms have balconies from which to savour views. Locally derived cuisine proudly served by hospitable owner.

TERENURE – **Dublin** – **712** N 8 – see Dublin

The red symbol?
This denotes the very essence of peace
– only the sound of birdsong first thing in the morning …

TERMONBARRY – **Longford** – **712** I 6 *Ireland* 37 **C3**

Dublin 130 km – Galway 137 km – Roscommon 35 km – Sligo 100 km
Strokestown★ (Famine Museum★ **AC**, Strokestown Park House★ **AC**), NW : by N 5

Shannonside House without rest
– ✆ (043) 26 052 – *info@keenans.ie* – *Fax (043) 26 198*
– *closed 23-27 December*
7 rm – ♦€ 50 ♦♦€ 90
♦ Hospitable owner and well-proportioned bedrooms are among the guesthouse's chief attractions. Good value and comfortable. Located close to the Shannon River.

THOMASTOWN – **Kilkenny** – **712** K 10 – **pop. 1 600** – ✉ **Kilkenny** 39 **C2**
Ireland

Dublin 124 km – Kilkenny 17 km – Waterford 48 km – Wexford 61 km
Jerpoint Abbey★★, SW : 3 km by N9 – Graiguenamanagh★ (Duiske Abbey★★ **AC**), E : 16 km by R 703 – Inistioge★, SE : 8 km by R 700 – Kilfane Glen and Waterfall★ **AC**, SE : 5 km by N 9

Abbey House without rest
Jerpoint Abbey, Southwest : 2 km on N 9 – ✆ (056) 772 41 66
– *abbeyhsejerpoint@eircom.net* – *Fax (056) 772 41 92*
– *closed 22-30 December*
7 rm – ♦€ 50/70 ♦♦€ 100/110
♦ Neat inside and out, this whitewashed house in well-kept gardens offers simple but spacious rooms and pretty wood furnished breakfast room. Read up on area in lounge.

Carrickmourne House without rest
New Ross Rd, Southeast : 3¼ km by R 700 – ✆ (056) 772 41 24
– *carrickmournehouse@eircom.net* – *Fax (056) 772 41 24*
– *closed December*
5 rm – ♦€ 45/50 ♦♦€ 70/76
♦ Modern, split-level house looks down on peaceful countryside. Agreeably simple, traditional décor and gleaming wood floors in pristine rooms: homely and well priced.

THURLES – Tipperary – 712 I9 – pop. 7 425 Ireland 39 C2

Dublin 148 km – Cork 114 km – Kilkenny 48 km – Limerick 75 km – Waterford 93 km

Turtulla, ✆ (0504) 21 983 .

Holy Cross Abbey★★ AC, SW : 8 km by R 660

Inch House

rest, VISA

Northwest : 6½ km on R 498 – ✆ (0504) 51 348 – mairin@inchhouse.ie – Fax (0504) 51 754 – closed Christmas and New Year

5 rm – †€ 80 ††€ 140 – **Rest** – (closed Sunday-Monday) (dinner only) (booking essential for non-residents) Menu € 55

◆ 1720s country house on a working farm; lovely rural views. Handsomely restored with a fine eye for decorative period detail. Individually styled en suite bedrooms. Classically proportioned yet intimate dining room.

at Twomileborris East : 6 ¾ km on N 75 – ✉ Thurles

The Castle

VISA

Two Mile Borris – ✆ (0504) 44 324 – info@thecastletmb.com – Fax (0504) 44 352

4 rm – †€ 50/65 ††€ 90/110 – **Rest** – (by arrangement) Menu € 55

◆ Charming 17C house adjacent to partly ruined tower of the local castle which runs close to back door. Furnished with numerous period pieces. Pleasantly decorated rooms. Traditionally furnished dining room.

Good food and accommodation at moderate prices?
Look for the Bib symbols:
red Bib Gourmand for food, blue Bib Hotel for hotels

TIPPERARY (Tiobraid Árann) – Co Tipperary – 712 H 10 39 C2

Dublin 116 km – Limerick 26 km – Clonmel 25 km – Thurles 28 km

Ballykisteen

rm, rest, VISA AE

Limerick Junction, Northwest : 4 km on N 24 – ✆ (062) 33 333 – info@ballykisteenhotel.com – Fax (062) 31 555

40 rm – †€ 95/184 ††€ 109/199 – **Rest** – ✆ (062) 32 117 (dinner only and Sunday lunch) Menu € 25 (lunch) – Carte approx. € 35

◆ Handy for the gee gees as it's situated opposite the racecourse, this small, modern hotel is also surrounded by an 18 hole golf course. Comfortable bedrooms with views. Informal restaurant.

TOORMORE (An Tuar Mór) – Cork – 712 D 13 – ✉ Goleen 38 A3

Dublin 355 km – Cork 109 km – Killarney 104 km

Fortview House without rest

Gurtyowen, Northeast : 2½ km on Durrus rd (R 591) – ✆ (028) 35 324 – fortviewhousegoleen@eircom.net – Fax (028) 35 324 – March-October

5 rm – †€ 65 ††€ 100

◆ Stone built farmhouse; antique country pine furniture in coir carpeted rooms and brass, iron bedsteads. Fresh vegetable juice, home-made museli, potato cake for breakfast.

Rock Cottage

VISA

Barnatonicane, Northeast : 3¼ km on Durrus rd (R 591) – ✆ (028) 35 538 – rockcottage@eircom.net – Fax (028) 35 538

3 rm – †€ 95 ††€ 130 – **Rest** – (by arrangement) Menu € 45

◆ Georgian former hunting lodge idyllically set in 17 acres of parkland. Very well appointed lounge: modern art on walls. Immaculate, light and airy bedrooms.

TOWER – Cork – 712 G 12 – see Blarney

TRALEE – Kerry – 712 C 11 – pop. 21 987 *Ireland* 38 A2

Dublin 297 km – Killarney 32 km – Limerick 103 km
Ashe Memorial Hall ✆ (066) 7121288, tourisminfo@shannon-dev.ie
Kerry - The Kingdom★ AC
Blennerville Windmill★ AC, SW : 3 ¼ km by N 86 – Ardfert★, NW : 8 km by R 551. Banna Strand★, NW : 12 ¾ km by R 551 - Crag Cave★ AC, W : 21 km by N 21 – Rattoo Round Tower★, N : 19 ¼ km by R 556

Fels Point

Fels Point, East: 2Km. on N70 – ✆ (066) 711 9986 – info@felspointhotel.ie – Fax (066) 711 9987 – Closed 24-27 December

166 rm – †€ 79/109 ††€ 130/200

Rest *Morels* – Traditional (Closed Sunday lunch) Menu € 40 (dinner) – Carte € 29/44

◆ Corporate hotel on outskirts of city centre with contemporary style throughout. Bedrooms come in three grades; all are a good size, Executive come with a balcony and view. Traditional dishes served in Morels restaurant.

Manor West

Killarney Rd, Southwest: 2.5m. on N21 – ✆ (066) 719 4500 – info@manorwesthotel.ie – Fax (066) 719 4545 – Closed 25-26 December

77 rm – †€ 100/140 ††€ 160/240

Rest *Mercantile* – Traditional (dinner only) Carte approx. € 40

Rest *Walnut* – Traditional (dinner only) Menu € 40 – Carte approx. € 50

◆ New build hotel next to large retail park of same name. Bedrooms are spacious, with modern furnishings and good level of facilities; marble-floored lobby features piano. Modern, airy Mercantile for informal dining. Walnut for buffet style breakfast and traditional dinner menus.

The Meadowlands

Oakpark, Northeast : 1 ¼ km on N 69 – ✆ (066) 718 04 44 – info@meadowlandshotel.com – Fax (066) 718 09 64 – closed 24-27 December

56 rm – †€ 105/125 ††€ 170/310 – 2 suites –

Rest – (closed Sunday dinner) (bar lunch) Menu € 39 – Carte € 34/49

◆ Smart, terracotta hotel, a good base for exploring area. Inside are warmly decorated, air conditioned rooms and mellow library lounge with open fire and grandfather clock. Proprietor owns fishing boats, so seafood takes centre stage in dining room.

The Grand

rest,

Denny St – ✆ (066) 712 14 99 – info@grandhoteltralee.com – Fax (066) 712 28 77

44 rm – †€ 60/85 ††€ 120/150 –

Rest – Menu € 22/35 **s** – Carte € 22/29 **s**

◆ Established 1928; enjoys a central position in town. Rooms are decorated with mahogany furniture whilst the popular bar, once a post office, bears hallmarks of bygone era. Appetising dinners in restaurant with historic ambience.

Brook Manor Lodge without rest

Fenit Rd, Spa, Northwest : 3 ½ km by R 551 on R 558 – ✆ (066) 712 04 06 – brookmanor@eircom.net – Fax (066) 712 75 52

8 rm – †€ 65/85 ††€ 100/140

◆ Modern purpose-built manor in meadowland looking across to the Slieve Mish mountains: good for walks and angling. Breakfast in conservatory. Immaculate bedrooms.

The Forge without rest

Upper Oakpark, Northeast : 2 ½ km on N 69 – ✆ (066) 712 52 45 – theforgebnb@gmail.com – Fax (066) 712 52 45 – closed 8 December-31 January

6 rm – †€ 45/50 ††€ 70/80

◆ Comfortable, family-run house; sporting activities and scenic spots on doorstep. Hallway with hexagonal light leads upstairs to cosy rooms. Complimentary drinks on arrival.

XX **David Norris** VISA MC AE

Ivy Terrace – ✆ (066) 718 56 54 – restaurantdavidnorris@eircom.net – Fax (066) 712 66 00 – closed 1 week Spring, 1 week Summer, 1 week Autumn, 25-26 December, Sunday and Monday

Rest – (dinner only) Carte € 27/44

◆ Pleasant restaurant on first floor of unprepossessing modern building, featuring Rennie Macintosh style chairs. Good blend of cuisine: exotic hints and popular favourites.

TRAMORE (Trá Mhór) – Waterford – 712 K 11 – pop. 8 305 Ireland 39 C2

Dublin 170 km – Waterford 9 km

✆ (051) 381572 (June-August)

Dunmore East★, E : 18 km by R 675, R 685 and R 684

Glenorney without rest VISA MC AE

Newtown, Southwest : 1½ km by R 675 – ✆ (051) 381 056 – info@glenorney.com – Fax (051) 381 103

6 rm – †€ 60/90 ††€ 80/90

◆ On a hill overlooking Tramore Bay. Inside are personally decorated rooms: family photographs and curios; sun lounge with plenty of books. Rear rooms have lovely bay views.

Do not confuse X with ✿!
X defines comfort, while stars are awarded for the best cuisine, across all categories of comfort.

TRIM – Meath – 712 L 7 – pop. 5 894 Ireland 37 D3

Dublin 43 km – Drogheda 42 km – Tullamore 69 km

Old Town Hall, Castle St ✆ (046) 9437111 (May-September)

County Meath Newtownmoynagh, ✆ (046) 943 1463 .

Trim Castle★★ – Town★

Bective Abbey★, NE : 6½ km by R 161

 **Knightsbrook** rm, VISA MC AE

Dublin Rd, Southeast : 4 km by R 154, turning right at roundabout after 2¼ km – ✆ (046) 948 2100 – info@knightsbrook.com

127 rm – †€ 160 ††€ 210 – 4 suites –

Rest – (bar lunch Saturday) Menu € 25/48 – Carte € 37/61

◆ Luxurious hotel set in 186 acres, palatial furnishings typified by marble floored entrance hall with glass chandelier. Spacious bedrooms; some suites have balconies and two-seater jacuzzi baths. Terrace bar and lounge has views of 18 hole golf course. Restaurant serves classic Irish cooking.

Trim Castle rm, rest, VISA MC AE

Castle St – ✆ (046) 948 3000 – info@trimcastlehotel.com – Fax (046) 948 3077 – closed 25 December

68 rm – †€ 130/145 ††€ 145/160 – **Rest** – Menu € 17/31 **s** – Carte € 32/48 **s**

◆ Newly-built hotel. Decently-sized, contemporary bedrooms; those at the front overlook Trim Castle, as does the third floor roof terrace. Ideal venue for wedding receptions. All-day café serves light dishes. More formal dining in first floor restaurant.

Highfield House without rest VISA MC

Maudlins Rd – ✆ (046) 943 63 86 – highfieldhouseaccom@eircom.net – Fax (046) 943 81 82

8 rm – †€ 40/55 ††€ 80/84

◆ 19C former maternity home in lawned gardens overlooking Trim Castle and River Boyne. Sizeable bedrooms in cheerful colours offer a welcome respite after sightseeing.

Crannmór without rest
Dunderry Rd, North : 2 km – ✆ (046) 943 16 35 – cranmor@eircom.net
– Fax (046) 943 80 87
– March-November
5 rm – €50/55 €76/80
♦ Particularly friendly owners run this creeper-clad Georgian farmhouse in a rural location, offering bright and comfortable bedrooms and a cosy atmosphere.

TUBERCURRY Sligo 36 B2

Murphy's rm, rest,
Teeling St – ✆ (071) 918 55 98 – info@murphyshotel.ie – Fax (071) 918 50 34
– Closed 23 December-2 January
17 rm – €55/60 €85/90 – **Rest** – (dinner only carvery lunch) Menu €20 (lunch) – Carte dinner €24/37
♦ Family owned hotel on main road of rural market town. Decently-sized rooms are simply decorated with a good level of facilities; those to the rear are quieter. Tried and tested menu offered in smart cream dining room.

TULLAMORE (Tulach Mhór) – Offaly – 712 J 8 – pop. 11 098 39 C1

Dublin 104 km – Kilkenny 83 km – Limerick 129 km
Bury Quay Tullamore ✆ (0506) 52617
Tullamore Brookfield, ✆ (0506) 21 439 .

Tullamore Court rm, rest,
on N 80 (Portlaoise rd) – ✆ (057) 934 6666
– info@tullamorecourthotel.ie – Fax (057) 934 6677
– Closed 24-26 December
99 rm – €175 €310/350 – 5 suites – **Rest** – Carte €30/46
♦ Contemporarily styled hotel with curved walls, plenty of marble, glass, rich coloured interiors. Has state-of-the-art leisure centre; children's holiday activities arranged. Stylish, spacious dining room.

Bridge House rm, rest,
off Main St – ✆ (057) 93 22 000 – info@bridgehouse.com
– Fax (057) 93 25 690
– closed 25 December
70 rm – €85/115 €150/190 – **Rest** – (bar lunch) Menu €40 – Carte €24/41
♦ The grand, pillared entrance with steps leading to an ornate reception with crystal chandelier sums up rarified ambience. Polished library bar and impressive bedrooms. Dining options with restaurant or bar carvery.

TULLY CROSS – Galway – 712 C 7 36 A3

Dublin 301 km – Galway 85 km – Letterfrack 3 km

Maol Reidh rm,
– ✆ (095) 43 844 – maolreidhhotel@eircom.net – Fax (095) 43 784
– February-October
12 rm – €95/115 €150/190 – **Rest** – (bar lunch) Carte €26/38
♦ This good value, personally run hotel was built with local stone and a noteworthy attention to detail. Cosy rear bar and sitting room. Good sized bedrooms. Stylish restaurant with modern menus.

We try to be as accurate as possible when giving room rates.
But prices are susceptible to change,
so please check rates when booking.

REPUBLIC OF IRELAND

TWOMILEBORRIS = Buiríos Léith – **Tipperary** – **712** I 9 – **see Thurles**

VALENCIA ISLAND (Dairbhre) – **Kerry** – **712** A/B 12 38 **A2**

Dublin 381 km – Killarney 88 km – Tralee 92 km

Knights Town – **Kerry** 38 **A2**

Glanleam House

Glanleam, West : 2 km taking right fork at top of Market St – (066) 947 61 76 – info@glanleam.com – Fax (066) 947 61 08 – mid March-October

5 rm – €70/105 €140/220 – 1 suite – **Rest** – (dinner only) (booking essential for non-residents) (communal dining) Menu €40/50 **s**

◆ Part 17C and 18C country house in extensive sub-tropical gardens, superbly located off West Kerry coast. Art Deco interiors. Spacious drawing room. Individually styled rooms. Communal dining; produce grown in hotel's 19C walled gardens.

WATERFORD – **Waterford** – **712** K 11 – **pop. 46 736** *Ireland* 39 **C2**

Dublin 154 km – Cork 117 km – Limerick 124 km

Waterford Airport, Killowen : (051) 846600

41 The Quay (051) 875823 Y, info@southeasttourism.ie Waterford Crystal Visitor Centre (051) 358397 (Jan-Oct)

Newrath, (051) 876 784 .

Town★ - City Walls★ – Waterford Treasures★ **AC** Y

Waterford Crystal★, SW : 2½ km by N 25 Y. Duncannon★, E : 19¼ km by R 683, ferry from Passage East and R 374 (south) Z – Dunmore East★, SE : 19¼ km by R 684 Z – Tintern Abbey★, E : 21 km by R 683, ferry from Passage East, R 733 and R 734 (south) Z

Plan opposite

Waterford Castle H. and Golf Club

The Island, Ballinakill, East : 4 km by R 683, Ballinakill Rd and private ferry – (051) 878 203 – info@waterfordcastle.com – Fax (051) 879 316 – closed January and 24-27 December

14 rm – €160/335 €195/335, €20 – 5 suites

Rest ***The Munster Dining Room*** – (bar lunch Monday-Saturday) Menu €63 – Carte €41/55

◆ Part 15C and 19C castle in charmingly secluded, historic river island setting. Classic country house ambience amid antiques and period features. Comfortable, elegant rooms. Oak panelled dining room with ornate ceilings and evening pianist.

Granville rm, rest,

Meagher Quay – (051) 305 555 – stay@granville-hotel.ie – Fax (051) 305 566 – closed 25-26 December Y **a**

98 rm – €78/95 €99/200

Rest ***Bianconi Room*** – (dinner only and Sunday lunch) Menu €26 – Carte €25/39

◆ Early 19C hotel that reputedly once hosted Charles Stewart Parnell. Individually styled bedrooms with a consistent traditional standard of décor. Some views of river Suir. Etched glass, drapes and panelling enhance gravitas of classic dining room.

Athenaeum House rest,

Christendom, Ferrybank, Northeast : 1½ km by N 25 – (051) 833 999 – info@athenaeumhotel.com – Fax (051) 833 977 – closed 25-27 December Z **n**

29 rm – €150/170 €200/250, €12.50

Rest ***Zak's*** – (light lunch) Carte €35/53 **s**

◆ In a quiet residential area, this extended Georgian house has retained some original features; elsewhere distinctly modern and stylish. Well equipped rooms exude modish charm. Eclectic mix of dishes in restaurant overlooking garden.

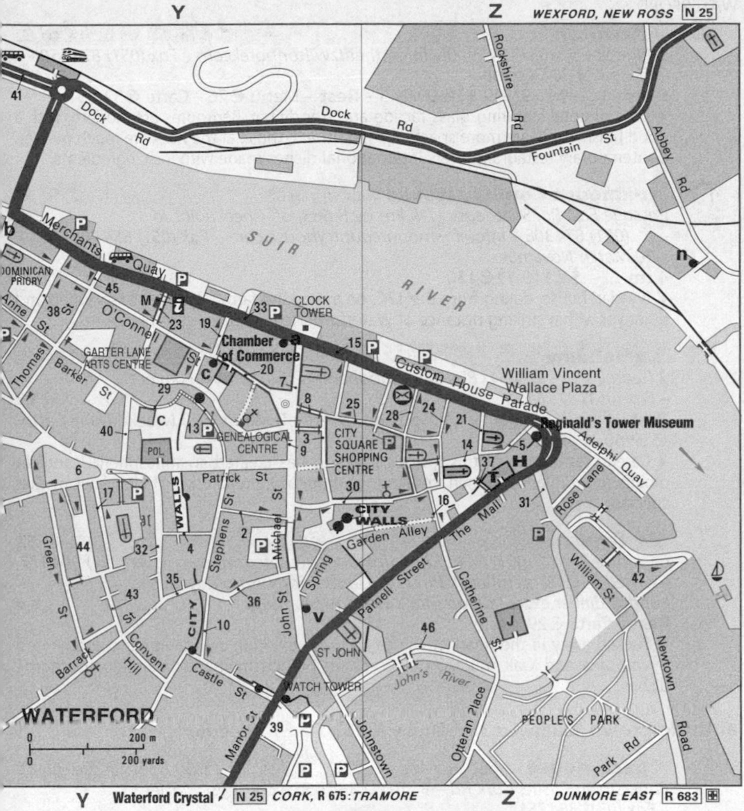

Y Z WEXFORD, NEW ROSS N 25

WATERFORD

Y Waterford Crystal N 25 CORK, R 675 : TRAMORE Z DUNMORE EAST R 683

Street	Grid	No.
Alexander St	Y	2
Arundel Square	Y	3
Bachelors Walk	Y	4
Bailey's New St	Z	5
Ballybricken Green	Y	6
Barronstrand St	Y	7
Blackfriars St	Y	8
Broad St	Y	9
Brown's Lane	Y	10
Carrigeen Park	Y	13
Cathedral Square	Z	14
City Square Shopping Centre	YZ	
Coal Quay	Y	15
Colbeck St	Z	16
Five Alley Lane	Y	17
George St	Y	20
Gladstone St	Y	19
Greyfriar's St	Z	21
Hanover St	Y	23
Henrietta St	Z	24
High St	YZ	25
Jenkin's Lane	Y	27
Keiser St	Z	28
King's Terrace	Y	29
Lady Lane	YZ	30
Lombard St	Z	31
Mayors Walk	Y	32
Meagher's Quay	Y	33
Newgate St	Y	35
New St	Y	36
Palace Lane	Z	37
Penrose Lane	Y	38
Railway Square	Y	39
St Patrick Terrace	Y	40
Sally Park	Y	41
Scotch Quay	Z	42
Shortcourse	Y	43
Trinity Square	Y	44
Vulcan St	Y	45
Water Side	Z	46

Arlington Lodge

Johns Hill, South : 1 ¼ km by N 25, John St and Johnstown Rd
– ✆ (051) 878 584
– info@arlingtonlodge.com
– Fax (051) 878 127
– closed 24-31 December

20 rm ☕ – 🚹€ 130/150 🚹🚹€ 230/250

Rest *Robert Paul* – (closed Sunday) (dinner only) Menu € 35 – Carte € 36/51

◆ Stylish, personally run Georgian former bishop's residence: period style precision. Antiques, gas fires in most of the very comfy and spacious individually styled rooms. Local produce richly employed in tasty menus.

Fitzwilton rm, VISA AE

Bridge St – (051) 846 900 – info@thefitzwiltonhotel.com – Fax (051) 878 650 – Closed 24-26 December Y **b**

91 rm – €79/109 €99/245 – **Rest** – Menu €26 – Carte €32/39

◆ Central hotel featuring glass façade and trendy bar. Bedrooms are modern, with a good finish: some are more spacious than others; those at the back are much quieter. Contemporary restaurant offers international dishes made with Irish ingredients.

Foxmount Country House without rest

Passage East Rd, Southeast : 7¼ km by R 683, off Cheekpoint rd – (051) 874 308 – info@foxmountcountryhouse.com – Fax (051) 854 906 – 10 March-November

4 rm – €110 €130

◆ Ivy-clad house, dating from the 17C, on a working farm. Wonderfully secluded and quiet yet within striking distance of Waterford. Neat, cottage-style bedrooms.

La Bohème VISA AE

2 George's St – (051) 875 645 – labohemerestaurant@eircom.net – Fax (051) 875 645 Y **c**

Rest – French (dinner only) (booking essential) Menu €29 (weekdays) – Carte €39/60

◆ Careful restoration of this historic building has created an atmospheric, candlelit dining room. Classic French cooking, traditionally prepared, includes daily market specials.

Bodéga AC VISA AE

54 John's St – (051) 844 177 – info@bodegawaterford.com – Fax (051) 844 177 – closed 25-26 December, 1 January, Good Friday, Saturday lunch, Sunday dinner except before Bank Holiday Mondays Y **v**

Rest – Carte €29/44

◆ Tucked away in the heart of the city. Purple exterior; orange interior, augmented by mosaics and wall murals. Classic rustic French menus or warming lunchtime dishes.

at Butlerstown Southwest : 8½ km by N 25 - Y – ✉ Waterford

Coach House without rest P VISA AE

Butlerstown Castle, Cork Rd – (051) 384 656 – coachhse@iol.ie – Fax (051) 384 751 – Easter-October

7 rm – €70 €110

◆ Victorian house in grounds of Butlerstown Castle. Smart traditional communal areas with warmly decorated breakfast room. Tasteful bedrooms offering good comforts.

Red = Pleasant. Look for the red and symbols.

WATERVILLE – Kerry – 712 B 12 *Ireland* 38 **A3**

Dublin 383 km – Killarney 77 km

(066) 9474646 (June-September)

Ring of Kerry, (066) 947 41 02 .

Ring of Kerry★★ – Skellig Islands★★, W: 12¾ km by N 70, R 567 and ferry from Ballinskelligs – Derrynane National Historic Park★★ AC, S: 14½ km by N70 – Leacanabuaile Fort (≤ ★★), N: 21 km by N 70

Butler Arms P VISA AE

– (066) 947 41 44 – reservations@butlerarms.com – Fax (066) 947 45 20 – mid March-mid December

36 rm – €90/110 €160/350 – **Rest** – (bar lunch) Carte €31/56

◆ Built 1862; Charlie Chaplin's holiday retreat. Family owned for three generations. Sea views from most bedrooms: spacious junior suites particularly comfortable and luxurious. Unstinting devotion to locally sourced cuisine.

Brookhaven House without rest
New Line Rd, North : 1 ¼ km on N 70 – ✆ (066) 947 44 31
– brookhaven@esatclear.ie – Fax (066) 947 47 24
– March-15 December
6 rm – €70/120 €100/130
◆ Spacious modern guesthouse overlooking Waterville golf course; large and neat, with restful lounge and cottage style bedrooms. Proud of its home-baked breakfasts.

WESTPORT – Mayo – **712** D 6 – **pop. 5 634** *Ireland* 36 **A2**

Dublin 262 km – Galway 80 km – Sligo 104 km
James St ✆ (098) 25711
Town★★ (Centre★) – Westport House★★ **AC**
Ballintubber Abbey★, SE : 21 km by R 330. SW : Murrisk Peninsula★★ – Croagh Patrick★, W : 9 ½ km by R 335 – Bunlahinch Clapper Bridge★, W : 25 ¾ km by R 335 - Doo Lough Pass★, W : 38 ½ km by R 335 – Aasleagh Falls★, S : 35 ½ km by N 59

Westport Plaza rm,
Castlebar St – ✆ (098) 51 166
– info@westportplazahotel.ie – Fax (098) 51 133
85 rm – €100/210 €130/320 – 3 suites
Rest *Merlot* – (dinner only) Menu €40 – Carte €27/43 **s**
◆ Contemporary lobby sets tone for this hotel, with deep leather sofas and marble floors. Trendy bar and terrace; well-equipped, spacious bedrooms boast flat screens and jacuzzis. Formal dining in stylish Merlot.

Carlton Atlantic Coast rm,
The Quay, West : 1 ½ km by R 335 – ✆ (098) 29 000
– reservations@atlanticcoasthotel.com – Fax (098) 29 111
84 rm – €60/135 €100/270 – 1 suite
Rest *Blue Wave* – (bar lunch Monday-Saturday) Menu €36 – Carte €25/38
◆ Striking 18C mill conversion on shores of Clew Bay. Enjoy a seaweed treatment in the hydrotherapy jet bath or a drink in the lively Harbourmaster bar. Well-kept bedrooms. Top floor restaurant with harbour and bay views.

Hotel Westport rm,
Newport Rd, off Newport Rd – ✆ (098) 25 122
– reservations@hotelwestport.ie – Fax (098) 26 739
129 rm – €70/150 €110/260 – **Rest** – (dinner only and Sunday lunch) Menu €39 **s** – Carte €26/46 **s**
◆ In attractive grounds running down to Carrowbeg river, a modern hotel appealing to families and conferences alike."Panda Club" and leisure centre will keep the kids busy. Sample traditional Irish fare on the daily changing menu in "Islands".

Ardmore Country House
The Quay, West : 2 ½ km on R 335 – ✆ (098) 25 994 – ardmorehotel@eircom.net
– Fax (098) 27 795
– closed January-February and 22-28 December
13 rm – €120/150 €150/240 – **Rest** – (closed Sunday and Monday in winter to non-residents) (dinner only) Carte €38/53
◆ Attractive family-run hotel in commanding setting with views across gardens and Clew Bay. Bedrooms are stylishly appointed with a country house feel. Chef owner proudly promotes organic produce.

The Wyatt rm,
The Octagon – ✆ (098) 25 027 – info@wyatthotel.com – Fax (098) 26 316
– closed 25-26 December
52 rm – €90/190 €150/240 – **Rest** – (dinner only and Sunday lunch) Menu €37 **s** – Carte €32/42
◆ Refurbished hotel with some style located in the very centre of town. Comfortable furniture and décor from the spacious bar to the deeply carpeted bedrooms. Contemporary menus served in warmly painted dining room.

REPUBLIC OF IRELAND

Augusta Lodge without rest
Golf Links Rd, North : ¾ km off N 59 – ✆ (098) 28 900 – info@augustalodge.ie
– Fax (098) 28 995
– closed 1 week Christmas
10 rm – €60/70 €90/100
♦ Family run, purpose-built guesthouse, convenient for Westport Golf Club; the owner has a collection of golfing memorabilia. Spacious, brightly decorated rooms.

Ashville House without rest
Castlebar Rd, East : 3 ¼ km on N 5 – ✆ (098) 27 060
– ashvilleguesthouse@eircom.net – Fax (098) 27 060
– March-2 November
9 rm – €80 €100
♦ Set back from the main road two miles outside town with sun-trap patio to the side of the house. Comfortable appointments throughout and countryside views from the lounge.

Quay West without rest
Quay Rd, West : ¾ km – ✆ (098) 27 863 – quaywest@eircom.net
– Fax (098) 28 379
6 rm – €40/55 €68/76
♦ Purpose-built guesthouse located within walking distance of the town centre. Simply appointed throughout providing sensibly priced, well kept rooms.

REPUBLIC OF IRELAND

Sheebeen
Rosbeg, West : 3 km on R 335 – ✆ (098) 26 528 – info@croninssheebeen.com
– Fax (098) 24 396
– 17 March - mid October
Rest – Carte €25/40
♦ Thatched roadside pub to west of town. Cosy front bar has some tables but main dining is upstairs. Fresh, accurate cooking; go for the fresh local fish and seafood specials.

WEXFORD – Wexford – **712** M 10 – **pop. 17 235** *Ireland* 39 **D2**

Dublin 141 km – Kilkenny 79 km – Waterford 61 km
Crescent Quay ✆ (053) 23111
Mulgannon, ✆ (053) 42 238 .
Town★ - Main Street★ YZ - Franciscan Friary★ Z – St Iberius' Church★ Y D - Twin Churches★ Z
Irish Agricultural Museum, Johnstown Castle★★ **AC**, SW : 7 ¼ km X – Irish National Heritage Park, Ferrycarrig★ **AC**, NW : 4 km by N 11 V – Curracloe★, NE : 8 km by R 741 and R 743 V. Kilmore Quay★, SW : 24 km by N 25 and R 739 (Saltee Islands★ - access by boat) X – Enniscorthy Castle★ (County Museum★ **AC**) N : 24 km by N 11 V

Plan opposite

Whites rm,
Abbey St – ✆ (053) 912 2311 – info@whitesofwexford.ie – Fax (053) 914 5000
– Closed 24-26 December Y **a**
152 rm – €100/120 €150/190 – 5 suites – **Rest** – Menu €20/45 – Carte €28/45
♦ Smart new hotel built around a paved central courtyard. Spacious and modern, with a busy bar, popular meeting rooms, superb leisure facilities and very comfortable bedrooms. Traditional menu served in formal dining room.

Ferrycarrig < River Slaney and estuary, rm, rest,
Ferrycarrig, Northwest : 4 ½ km on N 11
– ✆ (053) 91 20 999 – reservations@ferrycarrighotel.com
– Fax (053) 91 20 982 V **a**
98 rm – €120/200 €190/450 – 4 suites
Rest ***Reeds*** – (dinner only and Sunday lunch) Carte €28/47 **s**
♦ Imposing hotel idyllically set on River Slaney and estuary. Public areas on enchanting waterfront curve. Good leisure facilities. Modern rooms with super views and balconies. Lively, informal Reeds.

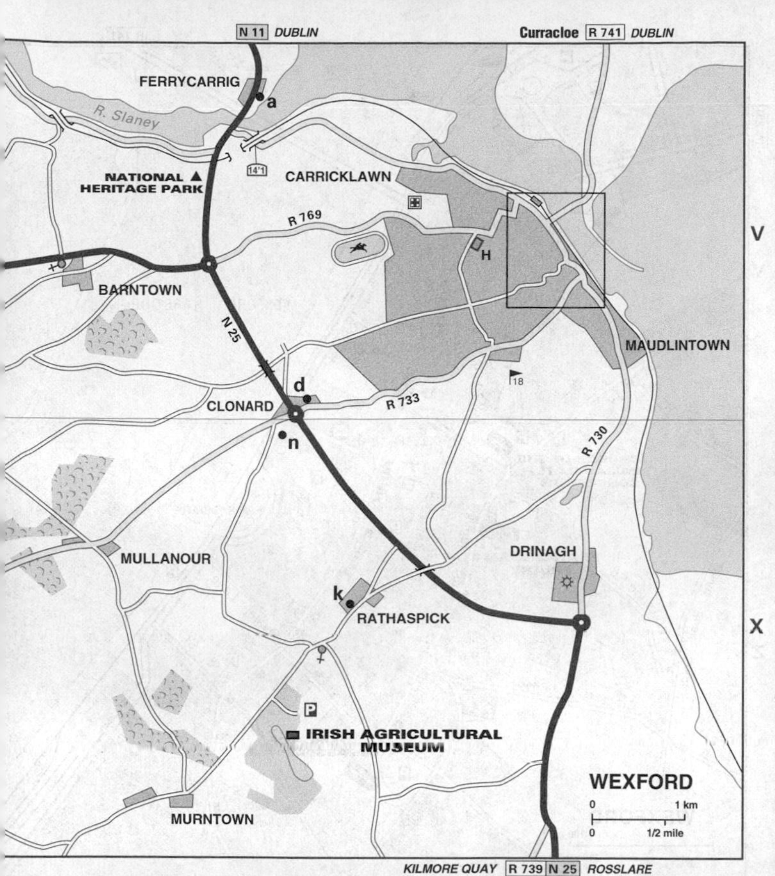

Whitford House

New Line Rd, West : 3½ km on R 733 – ✆ (053) 91 43 444 – info@whitford.ie – Fax (053) 91 46 399 – closed 24-26 December V **d**

36 rm – €68/186 €118/218 – **Rest** – (carvery lunch Monday-Saturday) Menu €25 **s** – Carte €27/44 **s**

◆ Late 20C hotel with bright yellow exterior. Lounge bar has traditional food and nightly entertainment. Conference facilities. Spacious, well-kept rooms, some with patios. Dining room has eye-catching lemon interior.

Rathaspeck Manor without rest

Rathaspeck, Southwest : 6½ km by Rosslare Rd off Bridgetown rd – ✆ (053) 914 16 72 – May-October X **k**

4 rm – €70 €140

◆ Georgian country house with 18-hole golf course half a mile from Johnstone Castle. Period furnishings adorn the public rooms. Comfortable, spacious bedrooms.

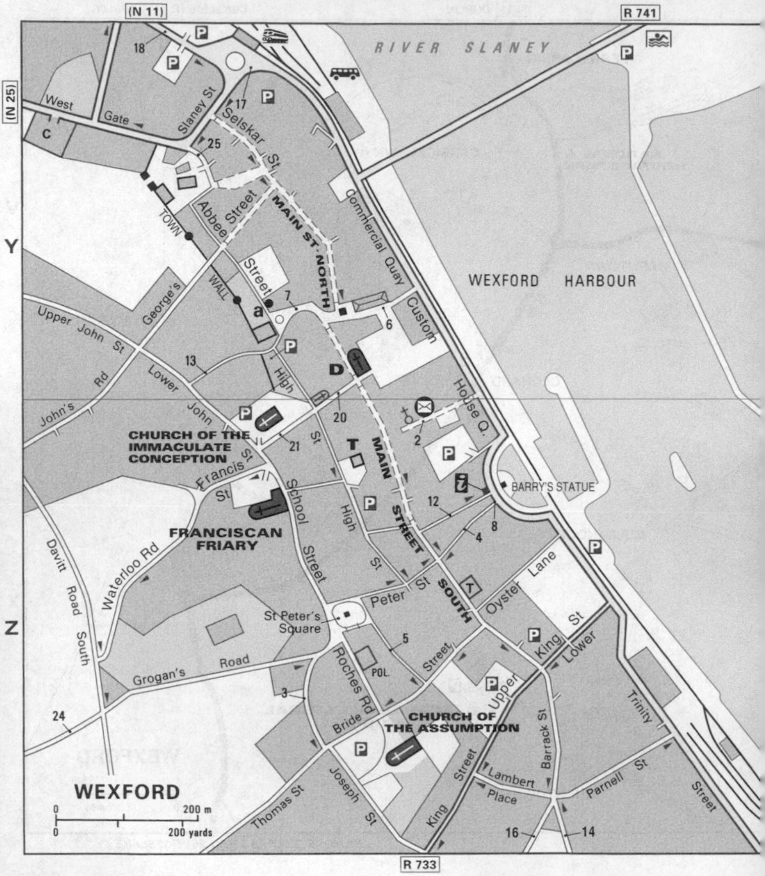

Anne St.	Z	2	Henrietta St	Z	12	Redmond Rd	Y	1
Carrigeen St	Z	3	John's Gate St	Y	13	Rowe St Lower	YZ	2
Cinema Lane	Z	4	Kevin Barry St	Z	14	Rowe St Upper	Z	2
Clifford St	Z	5	Main St North	Y		Selskar St	Y	
Common Quay St	Y	6	Main St South	Z		Summerhill Rd	Z	2
Cornmarket	Y	7	Michael St	Z	16	Temperance Row	Y	2
Crescent Quay	Z	8	Redmond Pl.	Y	17			

Look out for red symbols, indicating particularly pleasant establishments.

WICKLOW – Wicklow – 712 N 9 – pop. 9 355 ▮ *Ireland* 39 D2

▶ Dublin 53 km – Waterford 135 km – Wexford 108 km

ℹ Fitzwilliam Sq ✆ (0404) 69117, wicklowtouristoffice@eircom.net

Ⓖ Mount Usher Gardens, Ashford★ **AC**, NW : 6½ km by R 750 and N 11 – Devil's Glen★, NW : 12 ¾ km by R 750 and N 11. Glendalough★★★ (Lower Lake★★★, Upper Lake★★, Cathedral★★, Round Tower★★, St Kevin's Church★★, St Saviour's Priory★) – W : 22½ km by R 750, N 11, R 763, R 755 and R 756 Wicklow Mountains★★ (Wicklow Gap★★, Sally Gap★★, Avondale★, Meeting of the Waters★, Glenmacnass Waterfall★, Glenmalur★, – Loughs Tay and Dan★)

at Rathnew Northwest : 3 ¼ km on R 750 – ✉ Wicklow

Tinakilly House

on R 750 – ☎ (0404) 69274 – reservations@tinakilly.ie – Fax (0404) 67806 – Closed 24-27 December

50 rm – €175/202 €228/282 – 1 suite

Rest *The Brunel Room* – (bar lunch) Carte €45/52

◆ Part Victorian country house with views of sea and mountains. Grand entrance hall hung with paintings. Mix of comfortable room styles, those in main house most characterful. Large dining room with rich drapes, formal service.

Hunter's

Newrath Bridge, North : 1 ¼ km by N 11 on R 761 – ☎ (0404) 40106 – reception@hunters.ie – Fax (0404) 40338 – closed 24-26 December

16 rm – €95/100 €190/210 – **Rest** – Menu €27/45

◆ Converted 18C coaching inn set in 2 acres of attractive gardens. Characterful, antique furnished accommodation. Elegant, traditionally appointed communal areas. Dining room in hotel's welcoming country style.

WOODENBRIDGE – Wicklow – 712 N 9 39 D2

Dublin 74 km – Waterford 109 km – Wexford 66 km

Woodenbridge Arklow, ☎ (0402) 35202 .

Woodenbridge

Vale of Avoca – ☎ (0402) 35146 – reservations@woodenbridgehotel.com – Fax (0402) 35573

22 rm – €60/70 €100/110 – **Rest** – Menu €26/39 **s** – Carte €22/41 **s**

◆ Reputedly the oldest hotel in Ireland, dating from about 1608. Situated in the picturesque Vale of Avoca. Period furnishings abound. Well-appointed rooms, some with balconies. Dining room has warm, friendly ambience.

Woodenbridge Lodge

Vale of Avoca – ☎ (0402) 35146 – reservations@woodenbridgehotel.com – Fax (0402) 35573

40 rm – €60/70 €100/110 – **Rest** – (dinner only Friday-Sunday) Carte €22/42 **s**

◆ Sister hotel to Woodenbridge, sympathetically built to blend into local hills. Bedrooms in yellow or pink: ask for one overlooking the lyrical Avoca River. Bright dining room with large windows and high ceilings.

YOUGHAL – Cork – 712 I 12 – pop. 6 597 *Ireland* 39 C3

Dublin 235 km – Cork 48 km – Waterford 75 km

Market Sq ☎ (024) 20170 (May-September)

Knockaverry, ☎ (024) 92787.

Town★ – St Mary's Collegiate Church★★ – Town Walls★ - Clock Gate★

Helvick Head★ (≤ ★), NE : 35 ½ km by N 25 and R 674 – Ringville (≤ ★), NE : 32 ¼ km by N 25 and R 674 – Ardmore★ - Round Tower★ - Cathedral★ (arcade★), N : 16 km by N 25 and R 674 – Whiting Bay★, SE : 19 ¼ km by N 25, R 673 and the coast road

Aherne's with rm

163 North Main St – ☎ (024) 92424 – ahernes@eircom.net – Fax (024) 93633 – Closed 23-28 December

12 rm – €125/130 €170/240 – **Rest** – Seafood (bar lunch) Menu €50 – Carte €37/62

◆ Comfy sofas, books and sitting room fire announce this pleasant restaurant, which has modern art on walls and elegant linen-clad tables. Renowned seafood menus. Smart rooms.

REPUBLIC OF IRELAND

- → *Discover the best restaurant?*
- → *Find the nearest hotel?*
- → *Find your bearings using our maps and guides?*
- → *Understand the symbols used in the guide...*

Follow the red Bibs!

Advice on restaurants from **Chef Bib**.

Tips and advice from **Clever Bib** on finding your way around the guide and on the road.

Advice on hotels from **Bellboy Bib**.

The MICHELIN Guide

A collection to savor!

Belgique & Luxembourg
Deutschland
España & Portugal
France
Great Britain & Ireland
Italia
Nederland
Österreich
Portugal
Suisse-Schweiz-Svizzera
Main Cities of Europe

Also:

Las Vegas
London
Los Angeles
New York City
Paris
San Francisco
Tokyo

Distances in miles

(except for the Republic of Ireland: km). The distance is given from each town to other nearby towns and to the capital of each region as grouped in the guide. To avoid excessive repetition some distances have only been quoted once – you may therefore have to look under both town headings.
The distances quoted are not necessarily the shortest but have been based on the roads which afford the best driving conditions and are therefore the most practical.

Distances en miles

Pour chaque région traitée, vous trouverez au texte de chacune des localités sa distance par rapport à la capitale et aux villes environnantes.
La distance d'une localité à une autre n'est pas toujours répétée aux deux villes intéressées : voyez au texte de l'une ou de l'autre.
Ces distances ne sont pas nécessairement comptées par la route la plus courte mais par la plus pratique, c'est-à-dire celle offrant les meilleures conditions de roulage.

	Belfast	Cork	Dublin	Dundalk	Galway	Killarney	Limerick	Londonderry	Omagh	Sligo	Tullamore
Cork	261										
Dublin	105	155									
Dundalk	53	209	52								
Galway	196	122	135	156							
Killarney	299	56	193	246	136						
Limerick	230	57	123	177	66	71					
Londonderry	72	295	147	103	173	276	207				
Omagh	67	262	114	69	157	243	173	34			
Sligo	123	204	133	105	91	218	148	83	67		
Tullamore	137	125	64	85	83	141	72	152	118	98	
Waterford	207	73	101	154	144	128	79	241	207	182	84

133 Miles
Dublin - Sligo

Distanze in miglia

Per ciascuna delle regioni trattate, troverete nel testo di ogni località la sua distanza dalla capitale e dalle città circostanti.
Le distanza da una località all'altra non è sempre ripetuta nelle due città interessate : vedere nel testo dell'una o dell'altra.
Le distanze non sono necessariamente calcolate seguendo il percorso più breve, ma vengono stabilite secondo l'itinerario più pratico, che offre cioè le migliori condizioni di viaggio.

Entfernungsangaben in Meilen

Die Entfernungen der einzelnen Orte zur Landeshauptstadt und zu den nächstgrößeren Städten in der Umgebung sind im allgemeinen Orstext angegeben.
Die Entfernung zweier Städte voneinander können Sie aus den Angaben im Ortstext der einen oder der anderen Stadt ersehen.
Die Entfernungsangaben gelten nicht immer für der kürzesten, sondern für den günstigsten Weg.

Distances between major towns
Distances entre principales villes
Distanze tra le principali città
Entfernungen zwischen den größeren Stäten

Edinburgh - Southampton: 435 Miles

	Aberdeen	Ayr	Birmingham	Blackpool	Brighton	Bristol	Cambridge	Cardiff	Carlisle	Coventry	Dover	Dumfries	Dundee	Edinburgh	Glasgow	Inverness	Ipswich	Kingston-upon-Hull	Leeds	Leicester	Liverpool	London	Manchester	Middlesbrough	Newcastle	Norwich	Nottingham	Oban	Oxford	Plymouth	Portsmouth	Sheffield	Southampton	Stoke-on-Trent	Swansea
Ayr	184																																		
Birmingham	424	328																																	
Blackpool	330	234	127																																
Brighton	597	501	178	300																															
Bristol	505	410	92	208	166																														
Cambridge	484	393	100	222	121	187																													
Cardiff	526	430	113	229	199	45	206																												
Carlisle	230	134	196	101	369	278	261	298																											
Coventry	442	346	23	145	159	95	87	124	214																										
Dover	621	525	202	323	105	203	122	236	392	180																									
Dumfries	210	59	229	134	402	311	294	331	35	248	426																								
Dundee	68	124	363	268	535	445	414	465	168	382	530	146																							
Edinburgh	128	89	294	199	467	376	354	396	100	313	471	82	57																						
Glasgow	147	38	291	197	464	373	357	393	97	310	488	79	88	53																					
Inverness	105	208	449	354	622	531	514	551	255	468	646	237	139	158	171																				
Ipswich	535	444	151	273	127	209	55	241	311	137	129	344	464	405	406	565																			
Kingston-upon-Hull	395	303	138	139	277	228	164	248	171	142	281	203	324	264	266	424	215																		
Leeds	350	259	121	86	260	210	152	230	126	124	269	159	279	220	222	380	203	62																	
Leicester	444	348	45	147	166	120	72	151	216	31	187	249	368	309	311	470	123	119	102																
Liverpool	355	259	98	58	271	180	194	200	127	117	295	159	289	225	222	380	245	127	74	120															
London	538	442	119	241	54	120	63	152	310	98	77	342	473	405	405	563	84	215	198	104	213														
Manchester	350	254	90	53	262	172	171	192	122	109	287	154	285	220	217	375	222	98	45	109	34	204													
Middlesbrough	290	227	175	132	314	265	201	285	95	179	318	127	219	159	190	320	252	112	67	156	142	253	114												
Newcastle	252	192	208	151	347	297	234	317	60	211	350	93	181	122	155	283	285	144	99	188	174	285	146	44											
Norwich	532	441	163	284	178	243	66	276	308	149	179	341	461	402	404	562	45	212	200	133	256	119	219	249	281										
Nottingham	412	321	52	135	191	142	91	162	189	55	207	221	342	282	284	442	142	92	75	29	110	130	82	129	161	138									
Oban	182	126	388	293	561	470	453	490	194	407	585	175	121	130	98	110	504	363	318	410	319	503	315	287	252	501	380								
Oxford	501	405	82	204	107	86	107	119	273	62	144	305	435	371	368	526	139	193	176	82	176	60	173	230	262	174	108	465							
Plymouth	620	524	206	323	219	132	286	153	391	208	287	424	554	490	487	645	307	342	325	233	295	217	291	378	411	342	257	584	206						
Portsmouth	580	484	161	283	53	123	152	156	352	142	140	384	515	450	447	605	161	272	255	161	255	84	252	309	342	209	187	544	84	172					
Sheffield	386	295	91	103	230	180	133	200	162	94	250	195	315	256	258	416	184	66	43	71	90	168	50	103	135	181	44	355	145	293	224				
Southampton	565	469	146	267	66	108	151	140	336	126	152	369	499	435	432	590	172	257	240	145	239	83	236	293	326	207	172	529	69	154	19	209			
Stoke-on-Trent	382	286	45	85	218	127	141	147	154	64	242	186	317	252	249	407	192	128	93	63	57	160	54	161	193	203	54	346	122	240	201	80	189		
Swansea	530	434	148	232	235	80	241	42	301	156	271	334	464	400	397	555	277	283	266	186	184	187	201	320	353	303	198	494	154	187	190	236	179	183	
Wick	206	309	550	455	722	632	615	652	355	569	747	337	243	259	272	105	666	525	480	572	481	665	477	422	384	663	542	214	627	745	706	516	694	508	655

Birmingham	Cardiff	Dublin	Glasgow	London	
251	464	407	344	305	**Amsterdam**
1018	1051	1174	1304	892	**Barcelona**
619	652	775	906	493	**Basel**
776	809	931	724	650	**Berlin**
680	714	836	967	555	**Bern**
536	531	692	823	598	**Bordeaux**
1051	1085	1207	1338	926	**Bratislava**
1451	1484	1607	1737	1325	**Brindisi**
319	352	475	605	193	**Bruxelles-Brussel**
161	156	317	448	86	**Cherbourg**
637	671	793	924	512	**Clermont-Ferrand**
445	479	601	732	320	**Düsseldorf**
567	600	723	853	441	**Frankfurt am Main**
664	697	820	950	538	**Genève**
510	700	666	603	541	**Hamburg**
699	889	855	792	730	**København**
265	298	421	552	139	**Lille**
1258	1253	1414	1545	1320	**Lisboa**
452	486	608	739	327	**Luxembourg**
668	701	824	954	542	**Lyon**
966	961	1122	1253	1028	**Madrid**
1298	1293	1453	1585	1360	**Málaga**
861	894	1017	1148	736	**Marseille**
831	864	987	1117	705	**Milano**
783	816	939	1069	657	**München**
350	345	506	637	274	**Nantes**
1744	1778	1900	2031	1619	**Palermo**
369	402	525	656	244	**Paris**
1184	1179	1340	1471	1246	**Porto**
888	921	1044	1175	762	**Praha**
1197	1230	1353	1483	1071	**Roma**
680	674	835	967	742	**San Sebastián**
580	614	736	867	455	**Strasbourg**
795	828	951	1082	669	**Toulouse**
1232	1265	1387	1518	1106	**Valencia**
1111	1144	1267	1060	986	**Warszawa**
1009	1042	1164	1295	883	**Wien**
1120	1153	1276	1406	994	**Zagreb**

For distances refer to the colour key in the table

Les distances sont indiquées dans la couleur du point de passage

Le distanze sono indicate con il colore del punto di passaggio

Die Entfernungen sind angegeben in der Farbe des betroffenen Passagepinktes

● FOLKESTONE (CHANNEL TUNNEL)
● SOUTHAMPTON
● TYNEMOUTH

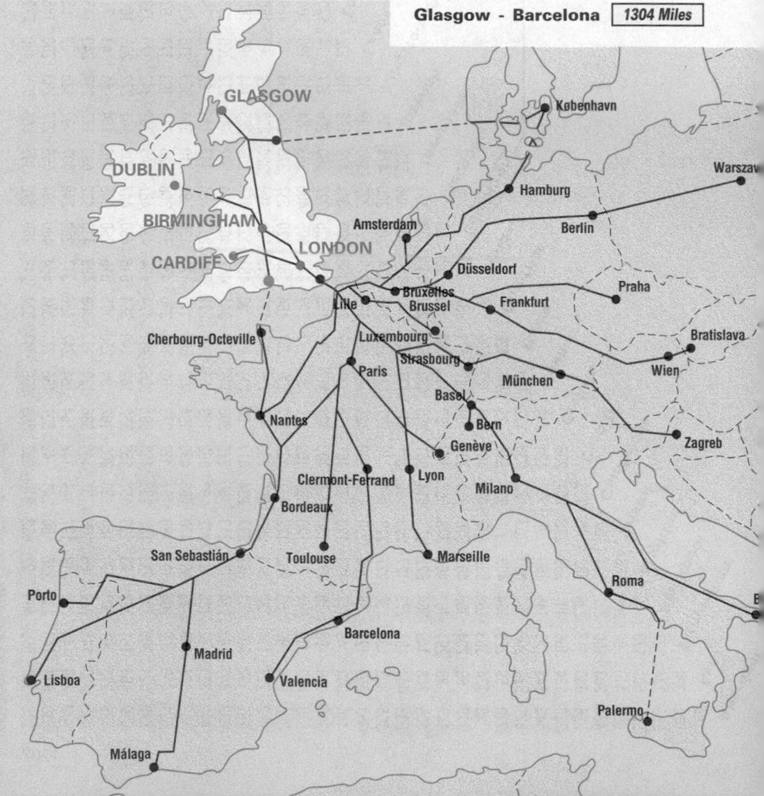

Index of towns

Index des localités

Indice delle località

Ortsverzeichnis

C

D Page

E Page

F Page

G Page

H Page

I Page

M

N Page

S

Page

T

Page

Y — Page

Z — Page

Major hotel groups

Central reservation telephone numbers

Principales chaînes hôtelières

Centraux téléphoniques de réservation

Principali catene alberghiere

Centrali telefoniche di prenotazione

Die wichtigsten Hotelketten

Zentrale für telefonische Reservierung

ACCOR HOTELS (MERCURE & NOVOTEL)	0208 2834500
CHOICE HOTELS	0800 444444 *(Freephone)*
DE VERE HOTELS PLC	0870 6063606
FOLIO HOTELS	08457 334400
HILTON HOTELS	08705 515151
HOLIDAY INN WORLDWIDE	0800 897121 *(Freephone)*
HYATT HOTELS WORLDWIDE	0845 8881234
INTERCONTINENTAL HOTELS LTD	0800 0289387 *(Freephone)*
JURYS/DOYLE HOTELS	0870 9072222
MACDONALD HOTELS PLC	08457 585593
MARRIOTT WORLDWIDE	0800 221222 *(Freephone)*
MILLENNIUM & COPTHORNE HOTELS PLC	0845 3020001
RADISSON HOTELS WORLDWIDE	0800 374411 *(Freephone)*
SHERATON HOTELS & RESORTS WORLDWIDE	0800 353535 *(Freephone)*
THISTLE HOTELS	0800 181716 *(Freephone)*

International Dialling Codes

Note: When making an international call, do not dial the first (0) of the city codes (except for calls to Italy).

Indicatifs téléphoniques internationaux

Important : pour les communications internationales, le zéro (0) initial de l'indicatif interurbainn'est pas à composer (excepté pour les appels vers l'Italie).

from \ to	A	B	CH	CZ	D	DK	E	FIN	F	GB	GR
A Austria		0032	0041	00420	0049	0045	0034	00358	0033	0044	0030
B Belgium	0043		0041	00420	0049	0045	0034	00358	0033	0044	0030
CH Switzerland	0043	0032		00420	0049	0045	0034	00358	0033	0044	0030
CZ Czech Republic	0043	0032	0041		0049	0045	0034	00358	0033	0044	0030
D Germany	0043	0032	0041	00420		0045	0034	00358	0033	0044	0030
DK Denmark	0043	0032	0041	00420	0049		0034	00358	0033	0044	0030
E Spain	0043	0032	0041	00420	0049	0045		00358	0033	0044	0030
FIN Finland	0043	0032	0041	00420	0049	0045	0034		0033	0044	0030
F France	0043	0032	0041	00420	0049	0045	0034	00358		0044	0030
GB United Kingdom	0043	0032	0041	00420	0049	0045	0034	00358	0033		003
GR Greece	0043	0032	0041	00420	0049	0045	0034	00358	0033	0044	
H Hungary	0043	0032	0041	00420	0049	0045	0034	00358	0033	0044	003
I Italy	0043	0032	0041	00420	0049	0045	0034	00358	0033	0044	0030
IRL Ireland	0043	0032	0041	00420	0049	0045	0034	00358	0033	0044	003
J Japan	00143	00132	00141	001420	00149	00145	00134	001358	00133	00144	0013
L Luxembourg	0043	0032	0041	00420	0049	0045	0034	00358	0033	0044	003
N Norway	0043	0032	0041	00420	0049	0045	0034	00358	0033	0044	0030
NL Netherlands	0043	0032	0041	00420	0049	0045	0034	00358	0033	0044	003
PL Poland	0043	0032	0041	00420	0049	0045	0034	00358	0033	0044	0030
P Portugal	0043	0032	0041	00420	0049	0045	0034	00358	0033	0044	003
RUS Russia	81043	81032	81041	6420	81049	81045	*	810358	81033	81044	*
S Sweden	0043	0032	0041	00420	0049	0045	0034	00358	0033	0044	003
USA	01143	01132	01141	001420	01149	01145	01134	01358	01133	01144	0113

** Direct dialling not possible*

** Pas de sélection automatiqu*

Indicativi Telefonici Internazionali

Importante: per le comunicazioni internazionali, non bisogna comporre lo zero (0) iniziale del prefisso interurbano (escluse le chiamate per l'Italia).

Telefon-Vorwahlnummern International

Wichtig: bei Auslandsgesprächen darf die Null (0) der Ortsnetzkennzahl nicht gewählt werden (außer bei Gesprächen nach Italien).

H	I	IRL	J	L	N	NL	PL	P	RUS	S	USA	
0036	0039	00353	0081	00352	0047	0031	0048	00351	007	0046	001	**A Austria**
0036	0039	00353	0081	00352	0047	0031	0048	00351	007	0046	001	**B Belgium**
0036	0039	00353	0081	00352	0047	0031	0048	00351	007	0046	001	**CH Switzerland**
0036	0039	00353	0081	00352	0047	0031	0048	00351	007	0046	001	**CZ Czech Republic**
0036	0039	00353	0081	00352	0047	0031	0048	00351	007	0046	001	**D Germany**
0036	0039	00353	0081	00352	0047	0031	0048	00351	007	0046	001	**DK Denmark**
0036	0039	00353	0081	00352	0047	0031	0048	00351	007	0046	001	**E Spain**
0036	0039	00353	0081	00352	0047	0031	0048	00351	007	0046	001	**FIN Finland**
0036	0039	00353	0081	00352	0047	0031	0048	00351	007	0046	001	**F France**
0036	0039	00353	0081	00352	0047	0031	0048	00351	007	0046	001	**GB United Kingdom**
0036	0039	00353	0081	00352	0047	0031	0048	00351	007	0046	001	**GR Greece**
	0039	00353	0081	00352	0047	0031	0048	00351	007	0046	001	**H Hungary**
0036		00353	0081	00352	0047	0031	0048	00351	*	0046	001	**I Italy**
0036	0039		0081	00352	0047	0031	0048	00351	007	0046	001	**IRL Ireland**
0136	00139	001353		001352	00147	00131	00148	001351	*	001146	0011	**J Japan**
0036	0039	00353	0081		0047	0031	0048	00351	007	0046	001	**L Luxembourg**
0036	0039	00353	0081	00352		0031	0048	00351	007	0046	001	**N Norway**
0036	0039	00353	0081	00352	0047		0048	00351	007	0046	001	**NL Netherlands**
0036	0039	00353	0081	00352	0047	0031		00351	007	0046	001	**PL Poland**
0036	0039	00353	0081	00352	0047	0031	048		007	0046	001	**P Portugal**
1036	*	*	*	*	*	81031	1048	*		*	*	**RUS Russia**
0036	0039	00353	0081	00352	0047	0031	0048	00351	007		001	**S Sweden**
1136	01139	011353	01181	011352	01147	01131	01148	011351	*	011146		**USA**

Selezione automatica impossibile ** Automatische Vorwahl nicht möglich*

Great Britain & Ireland in 39 maps

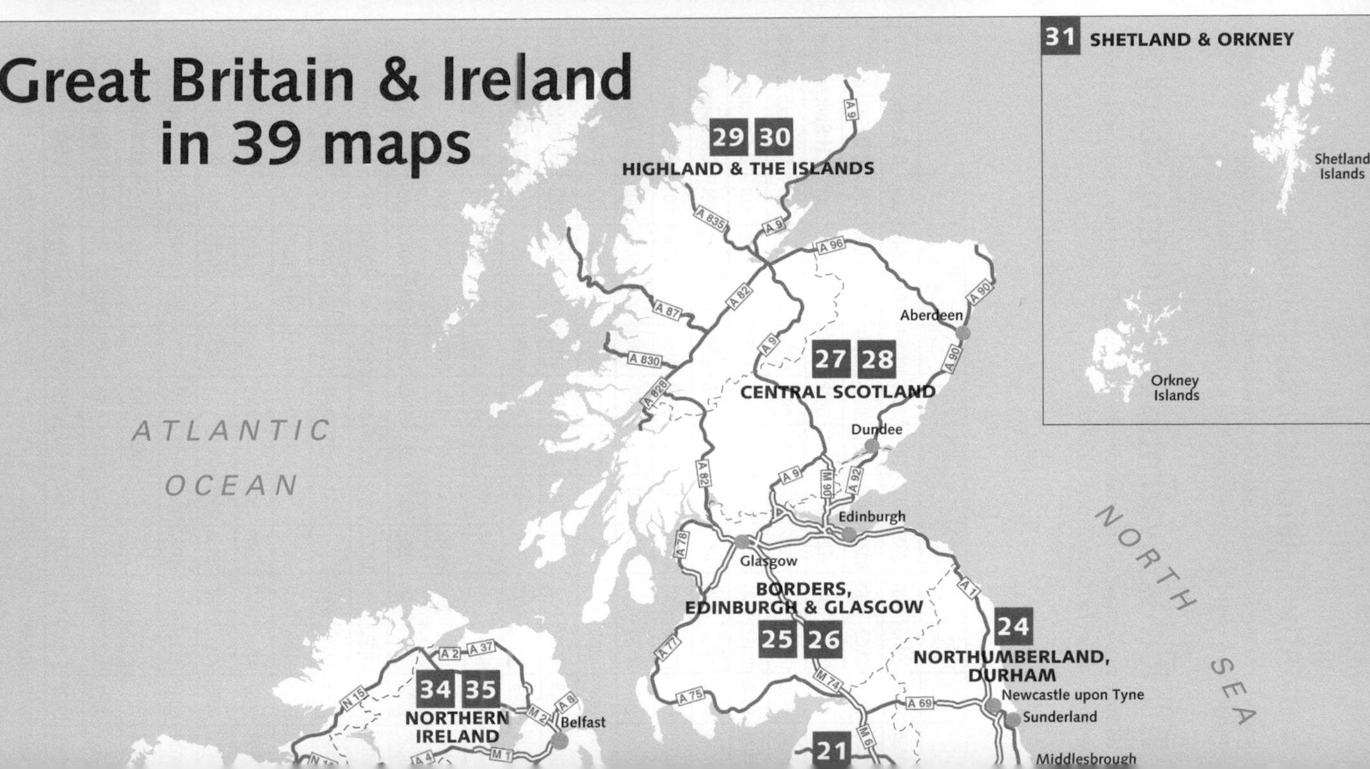

36 37
REPUBLIC OF IRELAND
IRISH SEA
22 23
NORTH YORKSHIRE
20
CHESHIRE, LANCASHIRE, ISLE OF MAN
Blackpool
Leeds
Bradford
Kingston upon Hull
Dublin
Manchester
Liverpool
Birkenhead
Sheffield
16 17
DERBYSHIRE, LEICESTERSHIRE, NORTHAMPTONSHIRE, RUTLAND, LINCOLNSHIRE, NOTTINGHAMSHIRE
Stoke-on-Trent
38 39
REPUBLIC OF IRELAND
32 33
WALES
Nottingham
Wolverhampton
Leicester
Norwich
18 19
HEREFORDSHIRE, WORCESTERSHIRE, SHROPSHIRE, STAFFORDSHIRE, WARWICKSHIRE
Birmingham
14 15
NORFOLK, SUFFOLK, CAMBRIDGESHIRE
Coventry
Northampton
Cork
Ipswich
10 11
OXFORDSHIRE, BUCKINGHAMSHIRE
BEDFORDSHIRE, HERTFORDSHIRE, ESSEX
12 13
CELTIC SEA
Cardiff
Bristol
Reading
LONDON
Southend-on-Sea
SOMERSET, DORSET, GLOUCESTERSHIRE, WILTSHIRE
3 4
CORNWALL, DEVON, ISLES OF SCILLY
1 2
Southampton
Portsmouth
Brighton
Bournemouth
8 9
EAST SUSSEX, KENT
HAMPSHIRE, ISLE OF WIGHT, SURREY, WEST SUSSEX
6 7
Plymouth
FRANCE
ENGLISH CHANNEL
LA MANCHE
Isles of Scilly
5
Alderney
Guernsey
Jersey
CHANNEL ISLANDS

1 Cornwall, Devon, Isles of Scilly

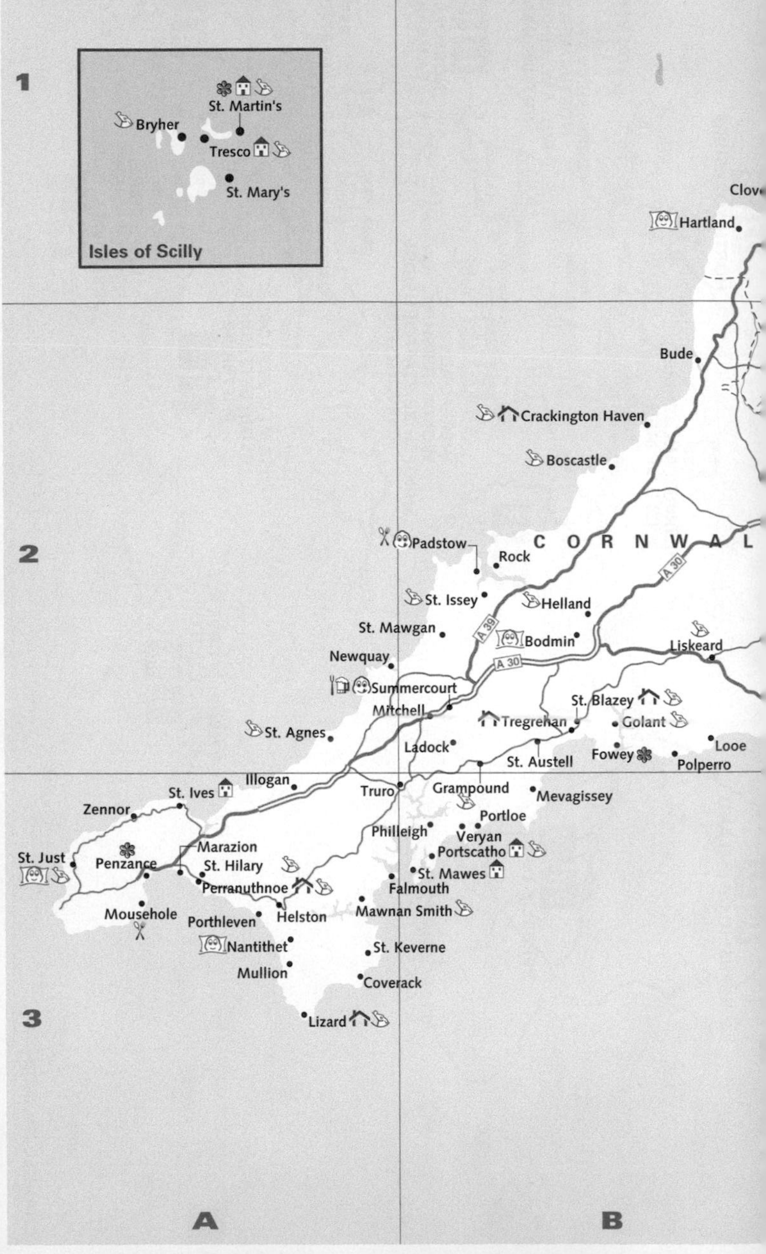

A B

BRI

1

Isles of Scilly

St. Martin's
Bryher
Tresco
St. Mary's

Clov
Hartland
Bude
Crackington Haven
Boscastle

2

Padstow
Rock
CORNWAL
A 30
St. Issey
Helland
St. Mawgan
A 39
Bodmin
Liskeard
Newquay
A 30
Summercourt
Mitchell
St. Blazey
Tregrehan
Golant
St. Agnes
Ladock
Looe
Fowey
Polperro
St. Austell
Illogan
Truro
Grampound
Mevagissey
St. Ives
Zennor
Portloe
Philleigh
Veryan
Marazion
Portscatho
St. Just
Penzance
St. Hilary
St. Mawes
Perranuthnoe
Falmouth
Mousehole
Porthleven
Helston
Mawnan Smith
Nantithet
St. Keverne
Mullion
Coverack

3

Lizard

A B

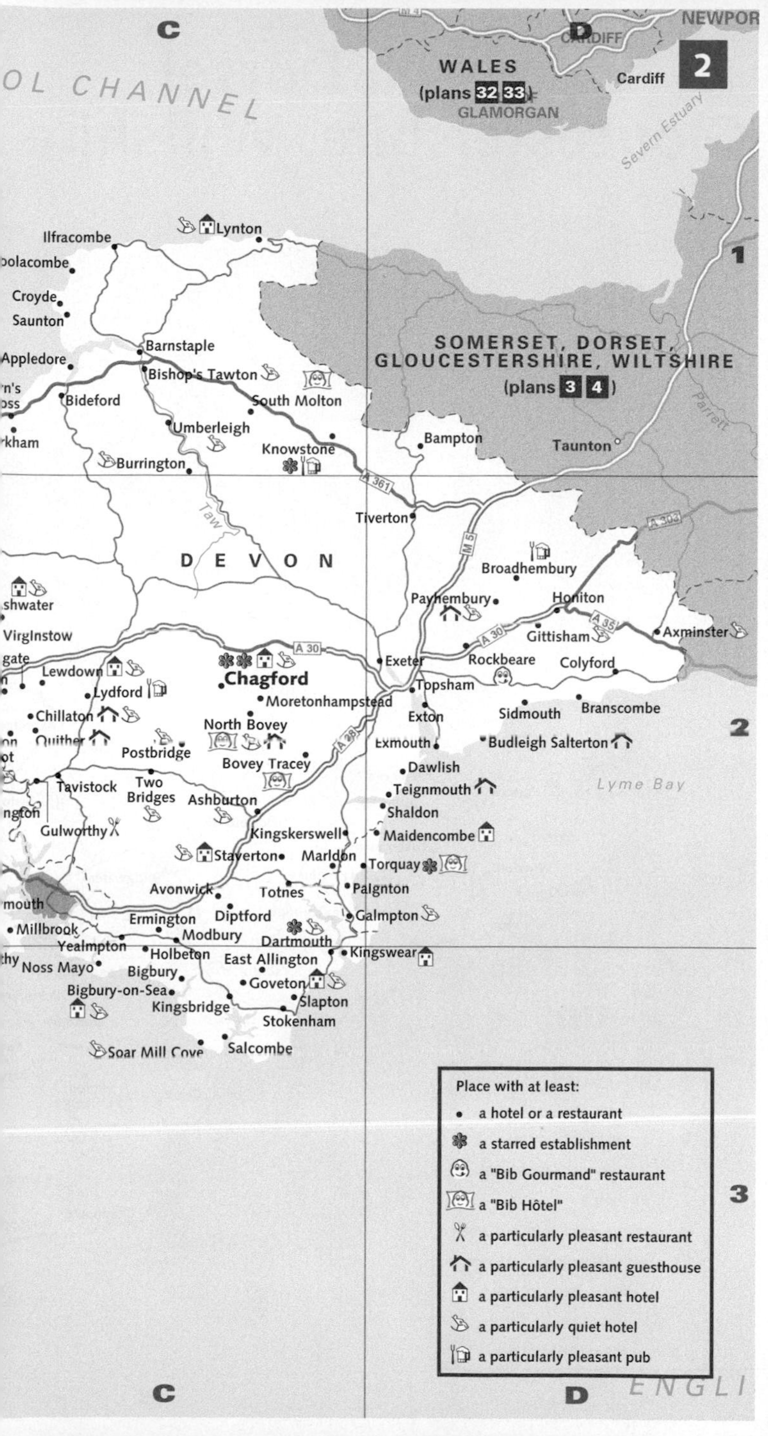

C
D
NEWPOR
OL CHANNEL
CARDIFF
WALES
(plans 32 33)
GLAMORGAN
Cardiff
2
Severn Estuary
1
Lynton
Ilfracombe
Woolacombe
Croyde
Saunton
Barnstaple
Appledore
Bishop's Tawton
Bideford
South Molton
Umberleigh
Knowstone
Burrington
SOMERSET, DORSET,
GLOUCESTERSHIRE, WILTSHIRE
(plans 3 4)
Parrett
Bampton
Taunton
A 361
Tiverton
Taw
M 5
A 303
DEVON
Broadhembury
Payhembury
Honiton
A 35
Gittisham
Axminster
A 30
Virginstow
Lewdown
Chagford
Exeter
Rockbeare
Colyford
Topsham
Lydford
Moretonhampstead
Chillaton
North Bovey
Exton
Sidmouth
Branscombe
Quither
Postbridge
Exmouth
Budleigh Salterton
A 38
Bovey Tracey
Dawlish
Tavistock
Two Bridges
Teignmouth
Lyme Bay
Ashburton
Shaldon
Gulworthy
Kingskerswell
Maidencombe
Staverton
Marldon
Torquay
Avonwick
Totnes
Paignton
Ermington
Diptford
Galmpton
Millbrook
Modbury
Dartmouth
Yealmpton
Holbeton
Kingswear
Noss Mayo
East Allington
Bigbury
Goveton
Bigbury-on-Sea
Slapton
Kingsbridge
Stokenham
Soar Mill Cove
Salcombe
Place with at least:
a hotel or a restaurant
a starred establishment
a "Bib Gourmand" restaurant
a "Bib Hôtel"
a particularly pleasant restaurant
a particularly pleasant guesthouse
a particularly pleasant hotel
a particularly quiet hotel
a particularly pleasant pub
3
ENGLI

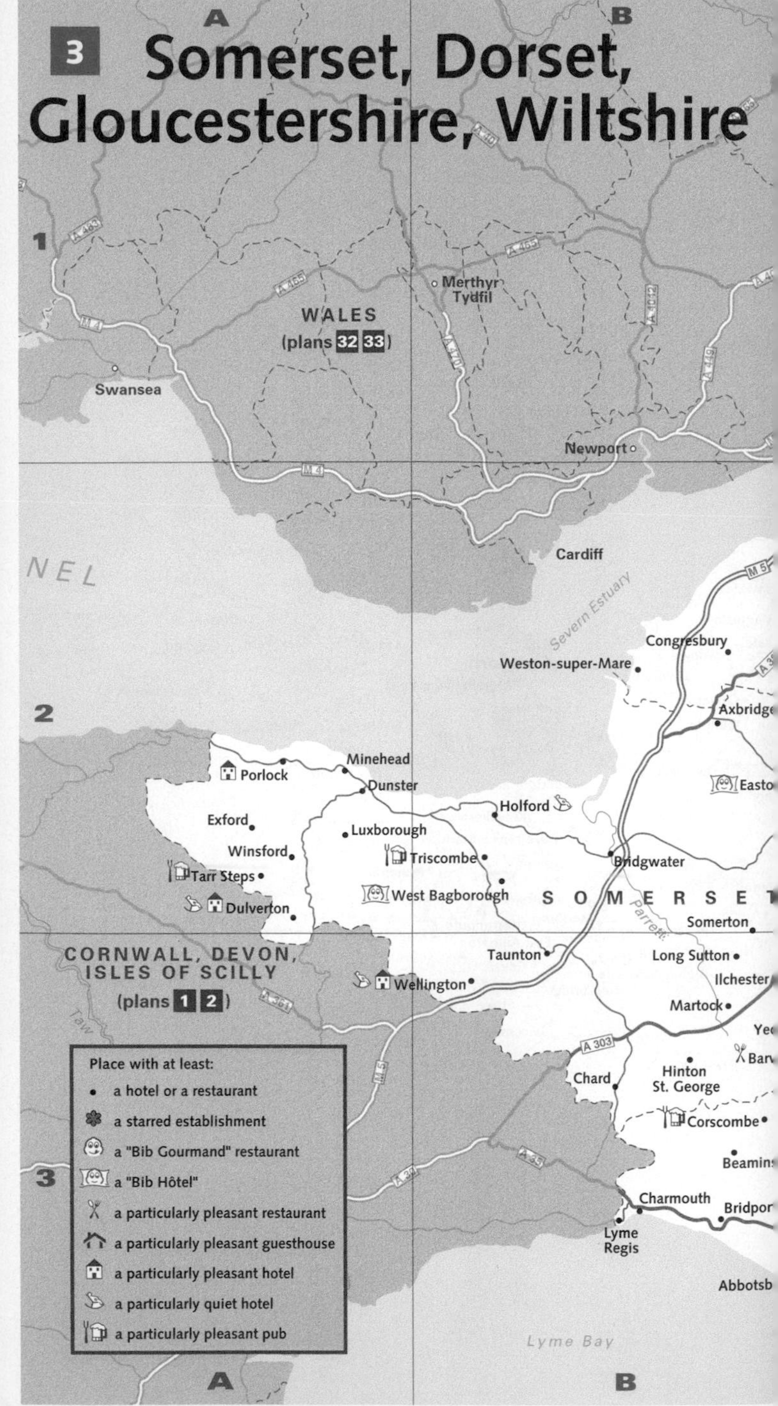

3 Somerset, Dorset, Gloucestershire, Wiltshire
A
B
1
2
3
WALES
(plans 32 33)
Merthyr Tydfil
Swansea
Newport
Cardiff
NEL
Severn Estuary
Congresbury
Weston-super-Mare
Axbridge
Minehead
Porlock
Dunster
Holford
Exford
Luxborough
Winsford
Triscombe
Bridgwater
Tarr Steps
West Bagborough
SOMERSET
Dulverton
Parrett
Somerton
Taunton
Long Sutton
CORNWALL, DEVON, ISLES OF SCILLY
(plans 1 2)
Wellington
Ilchester
Martock
Taw
Chard
Hinton St. George
Corscombe
Beamins
Charmouth
Bridpor
Lyme Regis
Abbotsb
Lyme Bay
Place with at least:
a hotel or a restaurant
a starred establishment
a "Bib Gourmand" restaurant
a "Bib Hôtel"
a particularly pleasant restaurant
a particularly pleasant guesthouse
a particularly pleasant hotel
a particularly quiet hotel
a particularly pleasant pub

4
C
D
HEREFORDSHIRE, WORCESTERSHIRE, SHROPSHIRE, STAFFORDSHIRE, WARWICKSHIRE
(plans 18 19)
GLOUCESTERSHIRE
Chipping Campden
Broad Campden
Paxford
Buckland
Blockley
Moreton-in-Marsh
Tewkesbury
Winchcombe
Lower Swell
Lower Oddington
Cheltenham
Guiting Power
Stow-on-the-Wold
A 40
Lower Slaughter
Bourton-on-the-Water
1
Coleford
Arlingham
Cockleford
M 5
Painswick
Blakeney
A 417
Stroud
Barnsley
Bibury
Coln St. Aldwyns
A 48
Frampton Mansell
Sapperton
Fairford
Nailsworth
Cirencester
Poulton
Thames
Lechlade
Tortworth
Thornbury
Tetbury
Oaksey
Highworth
Malmesbury
OXFORDSHIRE, BUCKINGHAMSHIRE
(plans 10 11)
Purton
Swindon
Patchway
M 4
Castle Combe
Bristol
Chippenham
Colerne
Calne
Corsham
Box
Marlborough
Axford
Bath
Whitley
Lacock
Hunstrete
Bradford-on-Avon
Avon
Melksham
Little Bedwyn
Newbury
Combe Hay
Devizes
Trowbridge
Potterne
2
Midsomer Norton
Norton St. Philip
WILTSHIRE
Bratton
Lower Vobster
Mells
Westbury
Frome
A 34
Warminster
Shepton Mallet
Batcombe
A 36
Codford St. Mary
Amesbury
Bruton
Stourton
A 303
Castle Cary
Teffont Magna
HAMPSHIRE, ISLE OF WIGHT, SURREY, WEST SUSSEX
(plans 6 7)
Wincanton
Hindon
Salisbury
Gillingham
South
Buckhorn Weston
Shaftesbury
Sherborne
Nomansland
Alweston
Sturminster Newton
A 27
A 31
Blandford Forum
Southampton
Plush
DORSET
Wimborne Minster
3
A 31
A 35
Bournemouth
Dorchester
Poole
Highcliffe
Christchurch
Wareham
Studland
West Lulworth
Corfe Castle
Swanage
Isle of Wight

Place with at least

- ● a hotel or a restaurant
- a starred establishment
- a « Bib Gourmand » restaurant
- a « Bib Hotel »
- a particularly pleasant restaurant
- a traditional pub serving good food
- a particularly pleasant hotel
- a particularly pleasant guesthouse
- a particularly quiet hotel

Localité possédant au moins

- ● un hôtel ou un restaurant
- une table étoilée
- un restaurant « Bib Gourmand »
- un hôtel « Bib Hôtel »
- un restaurant agréable
- un pub traditionnel servant des repas
- un hôtel agréable
- une maison d'hôte agréable
- un hôtel très tranquille

La località possiede come minimo

- ● un albergo o un ristorante
- una delle migliori tavole dell'anno
- un ristorante « Bib Gourmand »
- un albergo « Bib Hotel »
- un ristorante molto piacevole
- un pub tradizionali con cucina
- un albergo molto piacevole
- locande e affittacamere ameni
- un esercizio molto tranquillo

Ort mit mindestens

- ● einem Hotel oder Restaurant
- einem der besten Restaurants des Jahres
- einem Restaurant « Bib Gourmand »
- einem Hotel « Bib Hotel »
- einem sehr angenehmen Restaurant
- einem traditionelle Pubs, die Speisen anbieten
- einem sehr angenehmen Hotel
- einem Privatzimmer
- einem sehr ruhigen Haus

Channel Islands 5

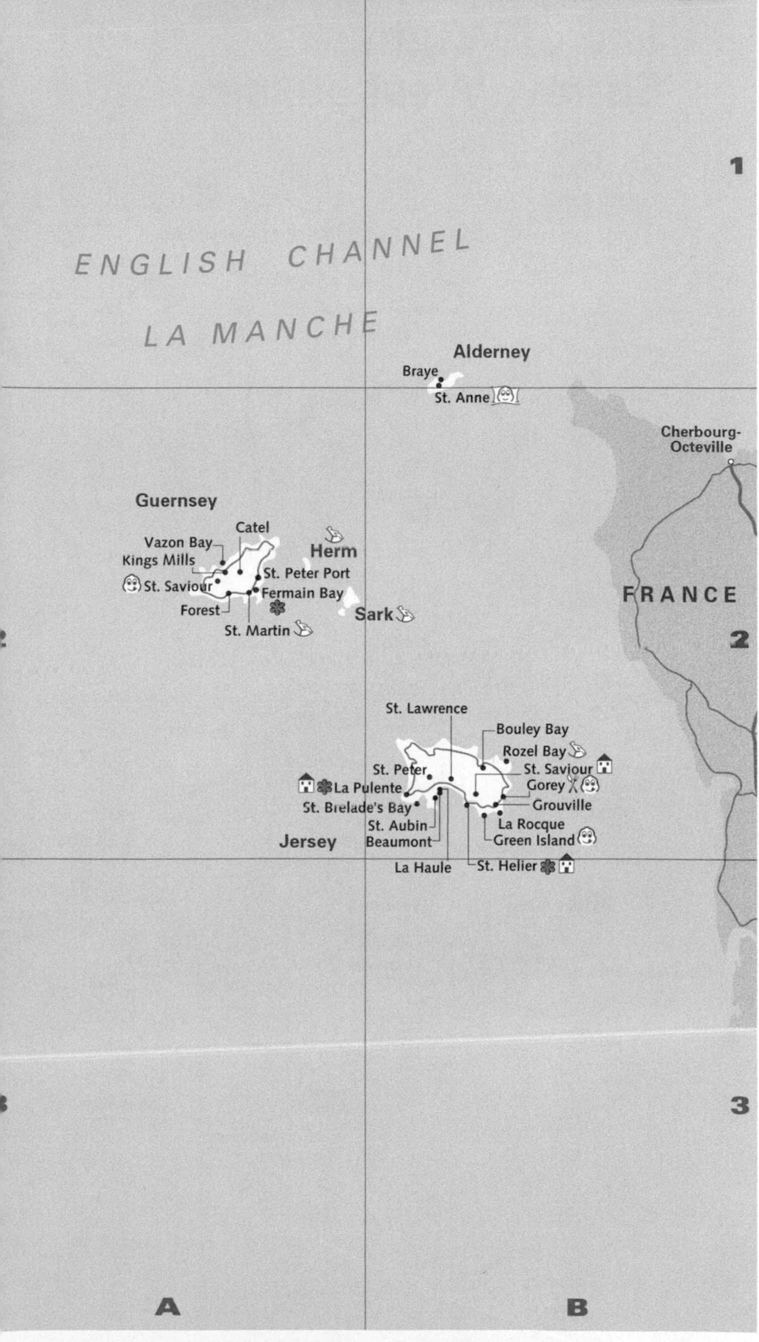

A B

1

ENGLISH CHANNEL

LA MANCHE

Alderney
Braye
St. Anne

Cherbourg-Octeville

Guernsey
Catel
Vazon Bay
Kings Mills
St. Saviour
Forest
St. Martin
Herm
St. Peter Port
Fermain Bay
Sark

FRANCE

2

St. Lawrence
Bouley Bay
Rozel Bay
St. Saviour
Gorey
Grouville
La Rocque
Green Island
St. Helier
La Haule
Beaumont
St. Aubin
St. Brelade's Bay
La Pulente
St. Peter
Jersey

3

A B

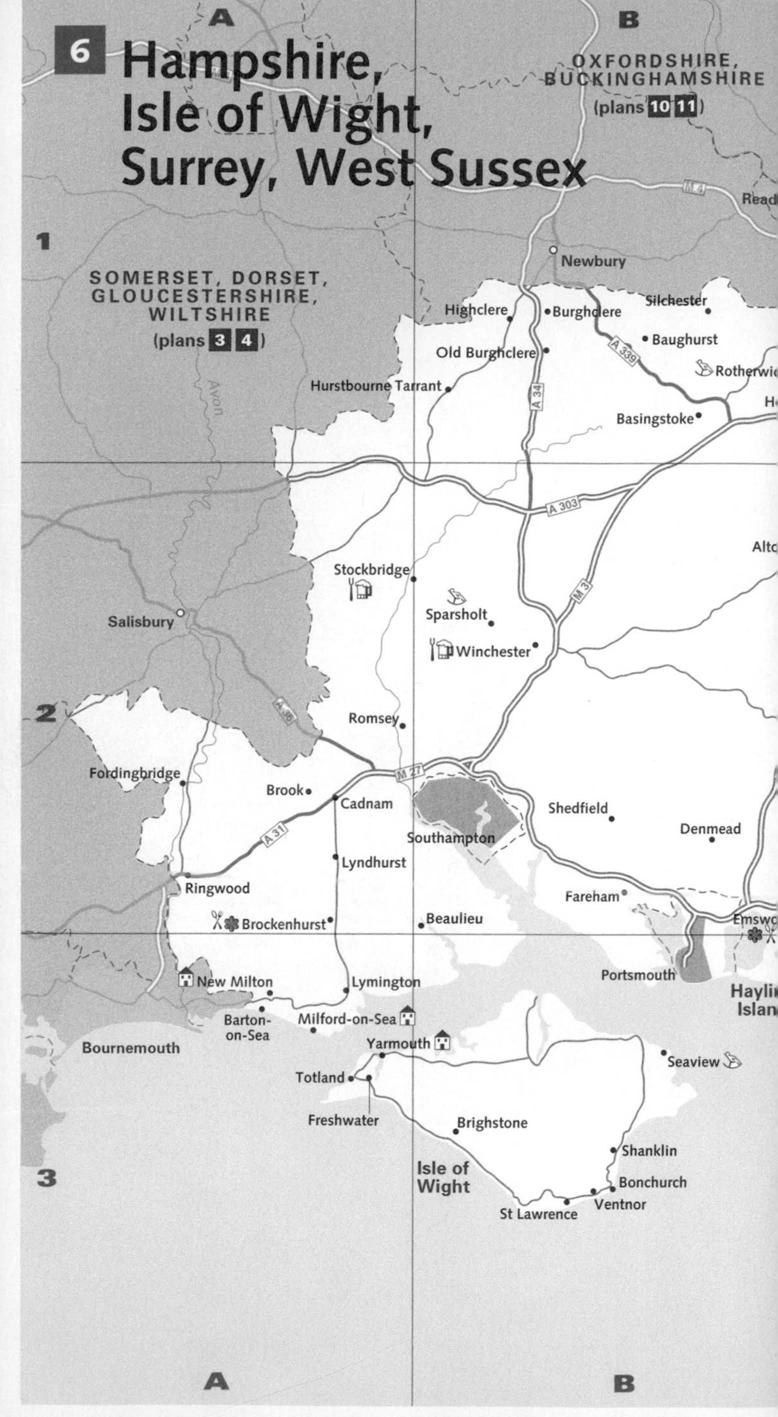

6
Hampshire, Isle of Wight, Surrey, West Sussex
A
B
OXFORDSHIRE, BUCKINGHAMSHIRE
(plans 10 11)
SOMERSET, DORSET, GLOUCESTERSHIRE, WILTSHIRE
(plans 3 4)
1
2
3
Newbury
Highclere
Burghclere
Silchester
Baughurst
Old Burghclere
Hurstbourne Tarrant
Basingstoke
Avon
A 34
A 339
A 303
M 3
M 4
M 27
A 31
A 36
Stockbridge
Sparsholt
Winchester
Salisbury
Romsey
Fordingbridge
Brook
Cadnam
Southampton
Shedfield
Denmead
Lyndhurst
Ringwood
Fareham
Brockenhurst
Beaulieu
New Milton
Lymington
Portsmouth
Barton-on-Sea
Milford-on-Sea
Yarmouth
Bournemouth
Seaview
Totland
Freshwater
Brighstone
Shanklin
Isle of Wight
Bonchurch
Ventnor
St Lawrence

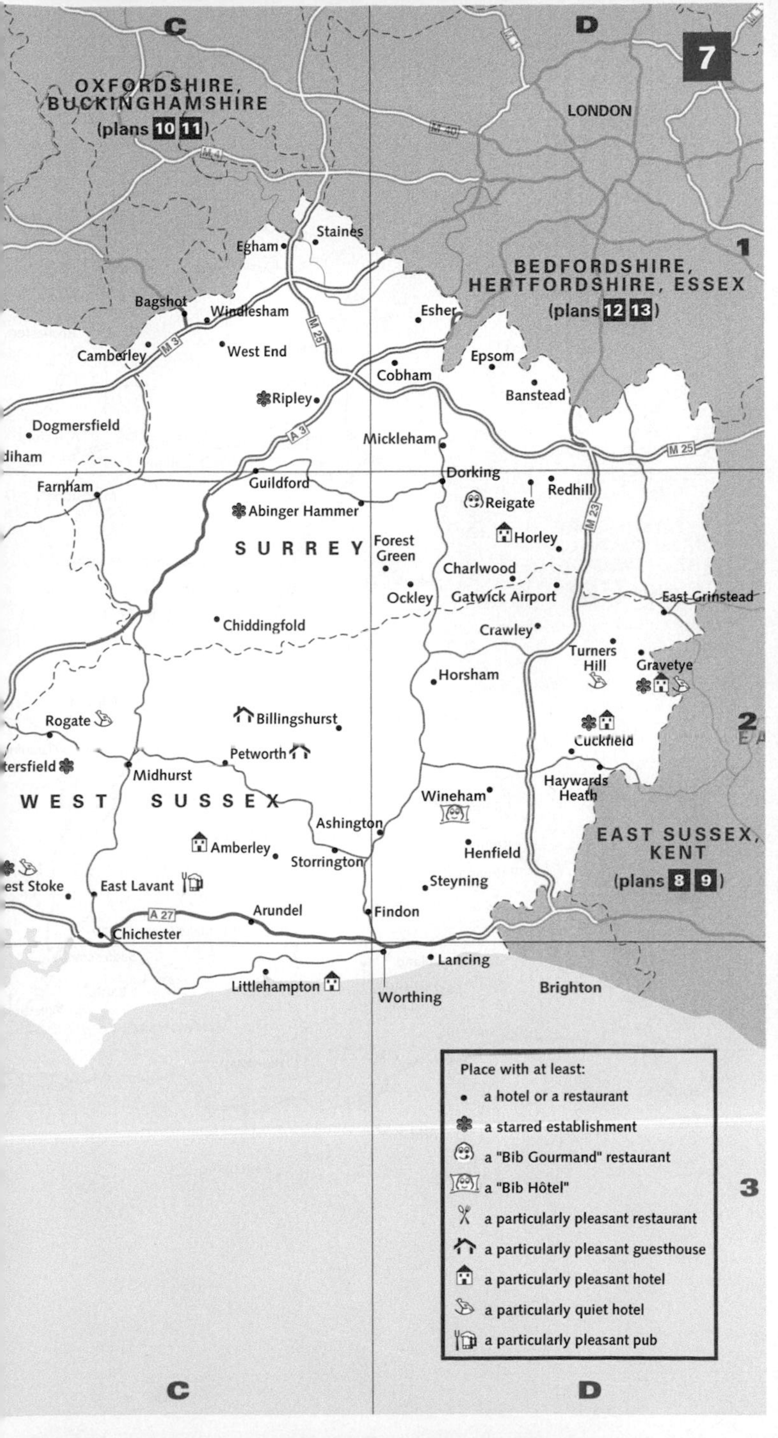
7
C
D
OXFORDSHIRE, BUCKINGHAMSHIRE
(plans 10 11)
LONDON
BEDFORDSHIRE, HERTFORDSHIRE, ESSEX
(plans 12 13)
EAST SUSSEX, KENT
(plans 8 9)
SURREY
WEST SUSSEX
M 40
M 4
M 3
M 25
A 3
M 23
A 27
Staines
Egham
Bagshot
Windlesham
Camberley
West End
Esher
Epsom
Cobham
Banstead
Ripley
Dogmersfield
Odiham
Mickleham
Dorking
Guildford
Farnham
Redhill
Reigate
Abinger Hammer
Horley
Forest Green
Charlwood
Ockley
Gatwick Airport
East Grinstead
Chiddingfold
Crawley
Turners Hill
Gravetye
Horsham
Rogate
Billingshurst
Cuckfield
Petersfield
Petworth
Midhurst
Haywards Heath
Wineham
Ashington
Amberley
Henfield
Storrington
West Stoke
East Lavant
Steyning
Arundel
Findon
Chichester
Lancing
Littlehampton
Worthing
Brighton
1
2
3
Place with at least:
a hotel or a restaurant
a starred establishment
a "Bib Gourmand" restaurant
a "Bib Hôtel"
a particularly pleasant restaurant
a particularly pleasant guesthouse
a particularly pleasant hotel
a particularly quiet hotel
a particularly pleasant pub

8 East Sussex, Kent

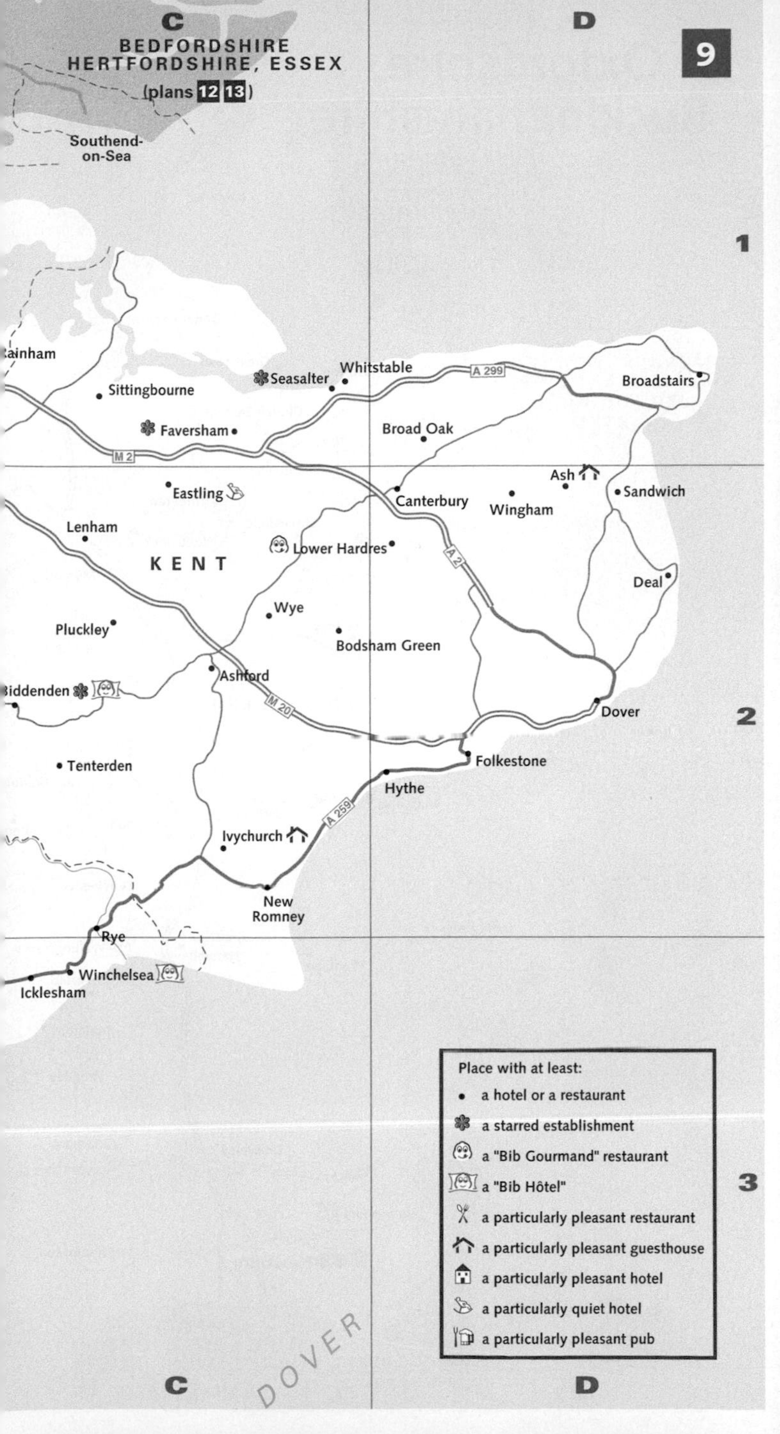
C
D
9
BEDFORDSHIRE
HERTFORDSHIRE, ESSEX
(plans 12 13)
Southend-on-Sea
1
Whitstable
A 299
Broadstairs
Seasalter
Sittingbourne
Faversham
Broad Oak
M 2
Ash
Eastling
Canterbury
Wingham
Sandwich
Lenham
Lower Hardres
KENT
A 2
Deal
Wye
Pluckley
Bodsham Green
Ashford
M 20
Dover
2
Tenterden
Folkestone
Hythe
A 259
Ivychurch
New Romney
Rye
Winchelsea
Icklesham
Place with at least:
a hotel or a restaurant
a starred establishment
a "Bib Gourmand" restaurant
a "Bib Hôtel"
a particularly pleasant restaurant
a particularly pleasant guesthouse
a particularly pleasant hotel
a particularly quiet hotel
a particularly pleasant pub
3
DOVER
C
D

10 Oxfordshire, Buckinghamshire
A
B
1
2
3
HEREFORDSHIRE, WORCESTERSHIRE, SHROPSHIRE, STAFFORDSHIRE, WARWICKSHIRE
(plans 18 19)
SOMERSET, DORSET, GLOUCESTERSHIRE, WILTSHIRE
(plans 3 4)
Banbury
Deddington
Great Tew
Chipping Norton
Church Enstone
Kingham
Churchill
Enstone
Kirtlington
Stonesfield
Woodstock
Leafield
Murcott
Burford
Witney
A 34
Stanton-St. John
A 40
Oxford
OXFORDSHIRE
Clanfield
Thames
Toot Baldon
Buckland Marsh
Buckland
Fyfield
Abingdon
Stadhamp
Dorchester
Uffington
Wallingford
Harwell
Wantage
Aston Tirrold
Swindon
M 4
Moulsford
Streatley
Gor
Chieveley
Yattendon
Hungerford
Newbury
Woolhampton
HAMPSHIRE, ISLE OF WIGHT, SURREY, WEST SUSSEX
(plans 6 7)
A 46
A 339
Place with at least:
a hotel or a restaurant
a starred establishment
a "Bib Gourmand" restaurant
a "Bib Hôtel"
a particularly pleasant restaurant
a particularly pleasant guesthouse
a particularly pleasant hotel
a particularly quiet hotel
a particularly pleasant pub

11
C
D
DERBYSHIRE,
LEICESTERSHIRE,
NORTHAMPTONSHIRE,
UTLAND, LINCOLNSHIRE
NOTTINGHAMSHIRE
(plans 16 17)
Newport Pagnell
Milton Keynes
M 1
BEDFORDSHIRE
HERTFORDSHIRE, ESSEX
(plans 12 13)
1
Buckingham
Gt. Ouse
Newton Longville
A 6
A 5
BUCKINGHAMSHIRE
Luton
Waddesdon
Aylesbury
Easington
Cuddington
Aston Clinton
BEDFORDSHIRE
HERTFORDSHIRE, ESSEX
(plans 12 13)
Ford
ng Crendon
Haddenham
2
A 41
reat Milton
Tetsworth
Bledlow
Chinnor
Great Missenden
Speen
Radnage
Amersham
Chenies
Little Chalfont
Britwell
Salome
Christmas
Common
Stokenchurch
Watford
High
Wycombe
Penn
Turville
Maidensgrove
Beaconsfield
Nettlebed
Cookham Dean
Marlow
Denham
oke Row
Cookham
Satwell
Stoke
Poges
Rotherfield
Peppard
Henley-
on-Thames
Hurley
Taplow
Farnham Royal
M 40
Maidenhead
Slough
M 4
Wargrave
BRAY-ON-
THAMES
Bray Marina
Sonning
Windsor
3
Reading
Ascot
Shinfield
Sunningdale
HAMPSHIRE,
ISLE OF WIGHT,
SURREY, WEST SUSSEX
(plans 6 7)
M 3
C
D

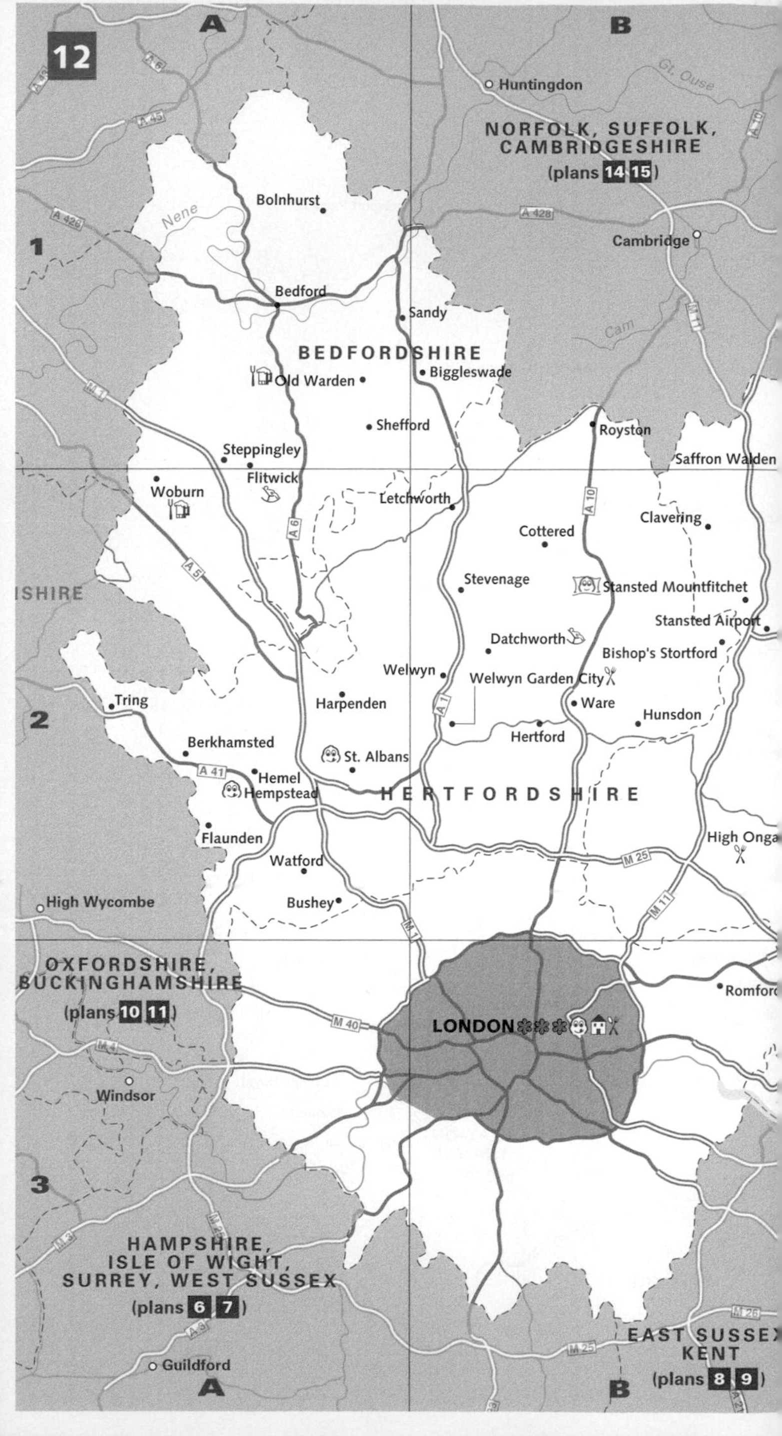
12
A
B
Huntingdon
Gt. Ouse
NORFOLK, SUFFOLK, CAMBRIDGESHIRE
(plans 14 15)
A 428
Cambridge
Cam
M 11
A 10
A 45
A 6
Nene
Bolnhurst
1
Bedford
Sandy
BEDFORDSHIRE
Old Warden
Biggleswade
M 1
Shefford
Royston
Saffron Walden
Steppingley
Flitwick
Woburn
Letchworth
A 6
A 10
Clavering
Cottered
A 5
Stevenage
Stansted Mountfitchet
ISHIRE
Stansted Airport
Datchworth
Bishop's Stortford
Welwyn
Welwyn Garden City
2
Tring
Harpenden
A 1
Ware
Hunsdon
Hertford
Berkhamsted
St. Albans
A 41
Hemel Hempstead
HERTFORDSHIRE
Flaunden
High Onga
Watford
M 25
High Wycombe
Bushey
M 1
M 11
OXFORDSHIRE, BUCKINGHAMSHIRE
(plans 10 11)
Romford
M 40
LONDON
M 4
Windsor
3
M 3
HAMPSHIRE, ISLE OF WIGHT, SURREY, WEST SUSSEX
(plans 6 7)
M 26
EAST SUSSEX, KENT
M 25
A 3
Guildford
(plans 8 9)

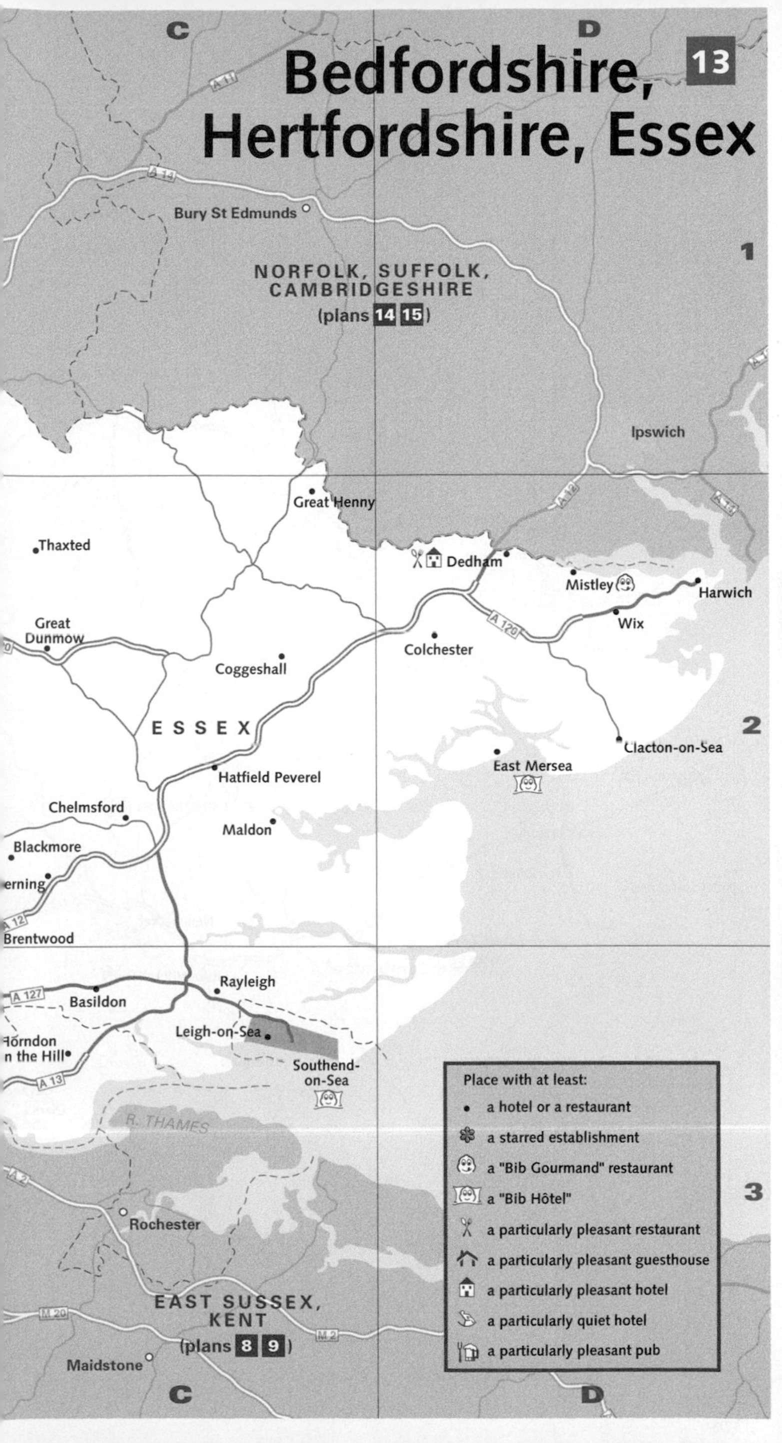

C
D
Bedfordshire, Hertfordshire, Essex
13
A 11
A 14
Bury St Edmunds
1
NORFOLK, SUFFOLK, CAMBRIDGESHIRE
(plans 14 15)
Ipswich
A 12
A 14
Great Henny
Thaxted
Dedham
Mistley
Harwich
Great Dunmow
A 120
Wix
Colchester
Coggeshall
ESSEX
2
Clacton-on-Sea
East Mersea
Hatfield Peverel
Chelmsford
Maldon
Blackmore
A 12
Brentwood
Rayleigh
A 127
Basildon
Leigh-on-Sea
Horndon on the Hill
A 13
Southend-on-Sea
R. THAMES
A 2
3
Rochester
EAST SUSSEX, KENT
(plans 8 9)
M 20
M 2
Maidstone
C
D
Place with at least:
a hotel or a restaurant
a starred establishment
a "Bib Gourmand" restaurant
a "Bib Hôtel"
a particularly pleasant restaurant
a particularly pleasant guesthouse
a particularly pleasant hotel
a particularly quiet hotel
a particularly pleasant pub

14
Norfolk, Suffolk, Cambridgeshire
A
B
The Wash
Ringstead
Hunstanton
Heacham
Snettisham
1
DERBYSHIRE, LEICESTERSHIRE, NORTHAMPTONSHIRE, RUTLAND, LINCOLNSHIRE, NOTTINGHAMSHIRE
(plans 16 17)
Spalding
A 17
King's Lynn
Grimsto
A 47
Welland
A 1
Stamford
Nene
Great Ouse
A 10
A 47
Peterborough
Elton
Stilton
CAMBRIDGESHIRE
A 1(M)
A 605
2
Keyston
Ely
Little Thetford
A 11
Gt. Ouse
Huntingdon
Buckden
A 14
A 10
Great Staughton
A 14
Newmarket
A 428
Cambridge
Little Wilbraham
SHIRE
Cam
M 11
Whittlesford
Duxford
Cavend
Clare
Place with at least:
a hotel or a restaurant
a starred establishment
a "Bib Gourmand" restaurant
a "Bib Hôtel"
a particularly pleasant restaurant
a particularly pleasant guesthouse
a particularly pleasant hotel
a particularly quiet hotel
a particularly pleasant pub
3
A 10
BEDFORDSHIRE, HERTFORDSHIRE, ESSEX
(plans 12 13)
A 120
Bishop's Stortford
A
B

C D

ncaster
taithe
Holkham
Wells-next-the-Sea
Blakeney
Sheringham
urnham
Market
Morston
Cromer
Hindringham
Holt
1
Thorpe Market
Thursford Green
eat
cham
Erpingham
Walcott
Itteringham
North Walsham
Wellingham
NORFOLK
Coltishall
Wroxham
East Dereham
Norwich
A 47
Bure
Brundall
Great
Yarmouth
Watton
Wymondham
Stoke Holy Cross
Yare
A 11
Fritton
A 12
Somerleyton
Lowestoft
Bungay
2
Pulham Market
Waveney
Diss
Fressingfield
Stanton
Southwold
Bramfield
Thornham Magna
Bury
St Edmunds
Westleton
Kelsale
Beyton
Framlingham
Saxmundham
Stowmarket
Snape
SUFFOLK
Aldeburgh
A 12
Lavenham
Bildeston
Orford
Monks Eleigh
Woodbridge
Long Melford
Hintlesham
Ipswich
Sudbury
Hadleigh
3
A 12
A 14
Stoke-by-Nayland
Levington
Nayland
Harwich
A 120
Colchester

C D

16
A
B
Manchester
Barnsley
Doncaster
NORTH YORKSHIRE
(plans 22 23)
Glossop
Rotherham
Sheffield
Hope
Hathersage
Blyth
Retford
CHESHIRE, LANCASHIRE, ISLE OF MAN
(plan 20)
Chapel-en-le-Frith
Buxton
Froggatt
Baslow
Holbeck
Bakewell
Beeley
Rowsley
DERBYSHIRE
Hartington
Birchover
Matlock
Winster
Mansfield
South Normanton
NOTTINGHAMSHIRE
Halam
Stoke-on-Trent
Ashbourne
Belper
R. Trent
Darley Abbey
Nottingham
Derby
Bingham
Colston Bassett
HEREFORDSHIRE, WORCESTERSHIRE, SHROPSHIRE, STAFFORDSHIRE, WARWICKSHIRE
(plans 18 19)
Castle Donington
Kegworth
Stathern
Nottingham East Midlands Airport
Loughborough
Shepshed
Melton Mowbray
LEICESTERSHIRE
Leicester
Wolverhampton
Hinckley
Kibworth Harcourt
Kibworth Beauchamp
Birmingham
Bruntingthorpe
North Kilworth
Market Harborough
Coventry
NORTHAMPTONSHIRE
Daventry
Northampton
Towcester
Roade
Gr. Ouse
1
2
3
Place with at least:
a hotel or a restaurant
a starred establishment
a "Bib Gourmand" restaurant
a "Bib Hôtel"
a particularly pleasant restaurant
a particularly pleasant guesthouse
a particularly pleasant hotel
a particularly quiet hotel
a particularly pleasant pub

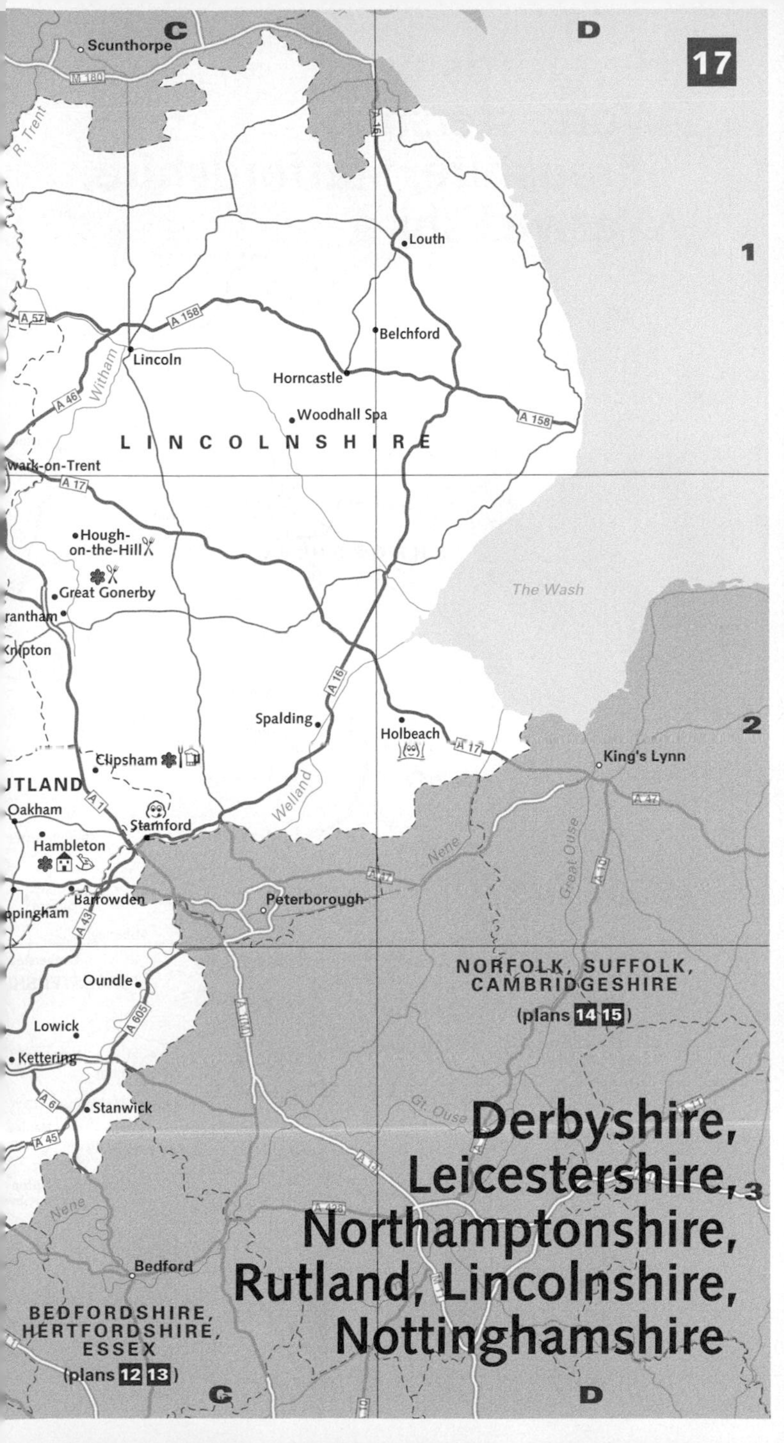

Derbyshire, Leicestershire, Northamptonshire, Rutland, Lincolnshire, Nottinghamshire

18 Herefordshire, Worcestershire, Shropshire, Staffordshire, Warwickshire

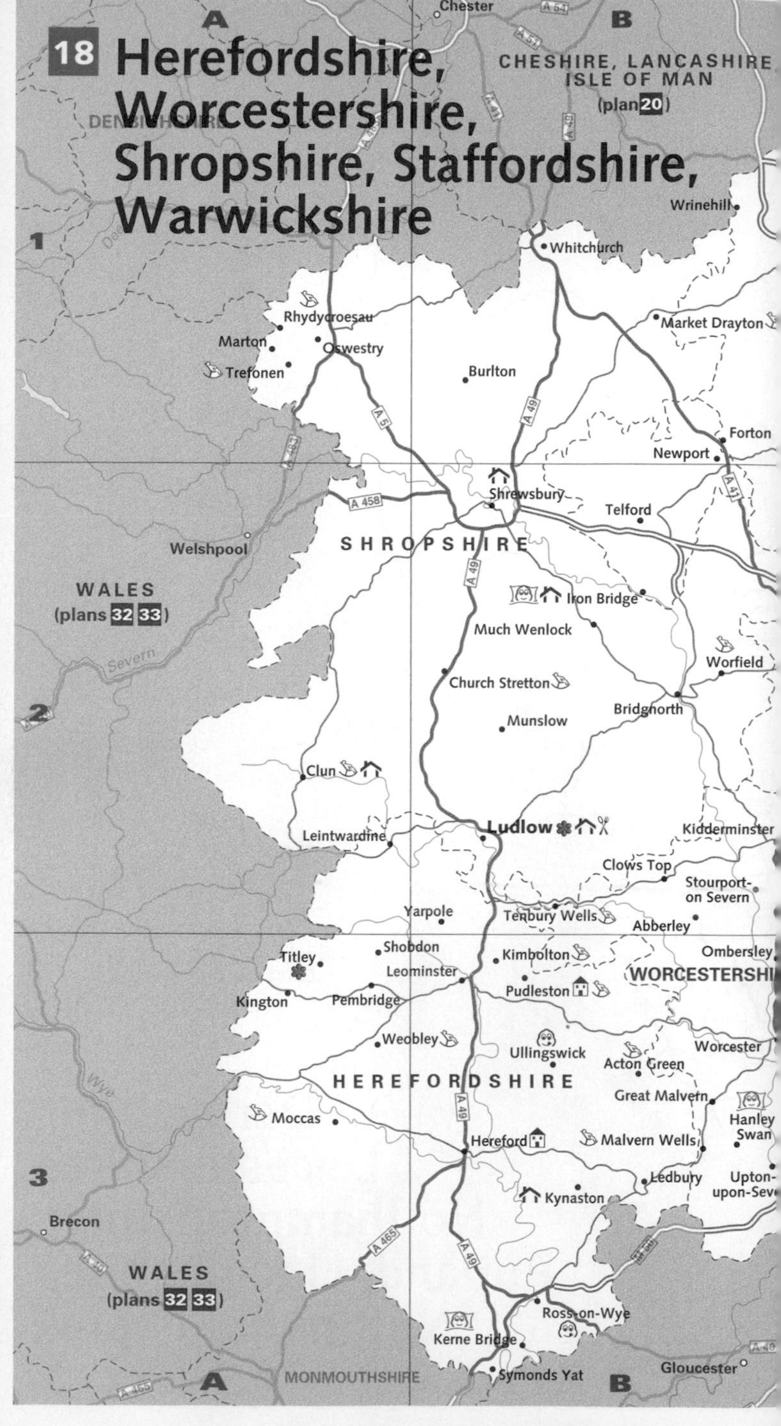

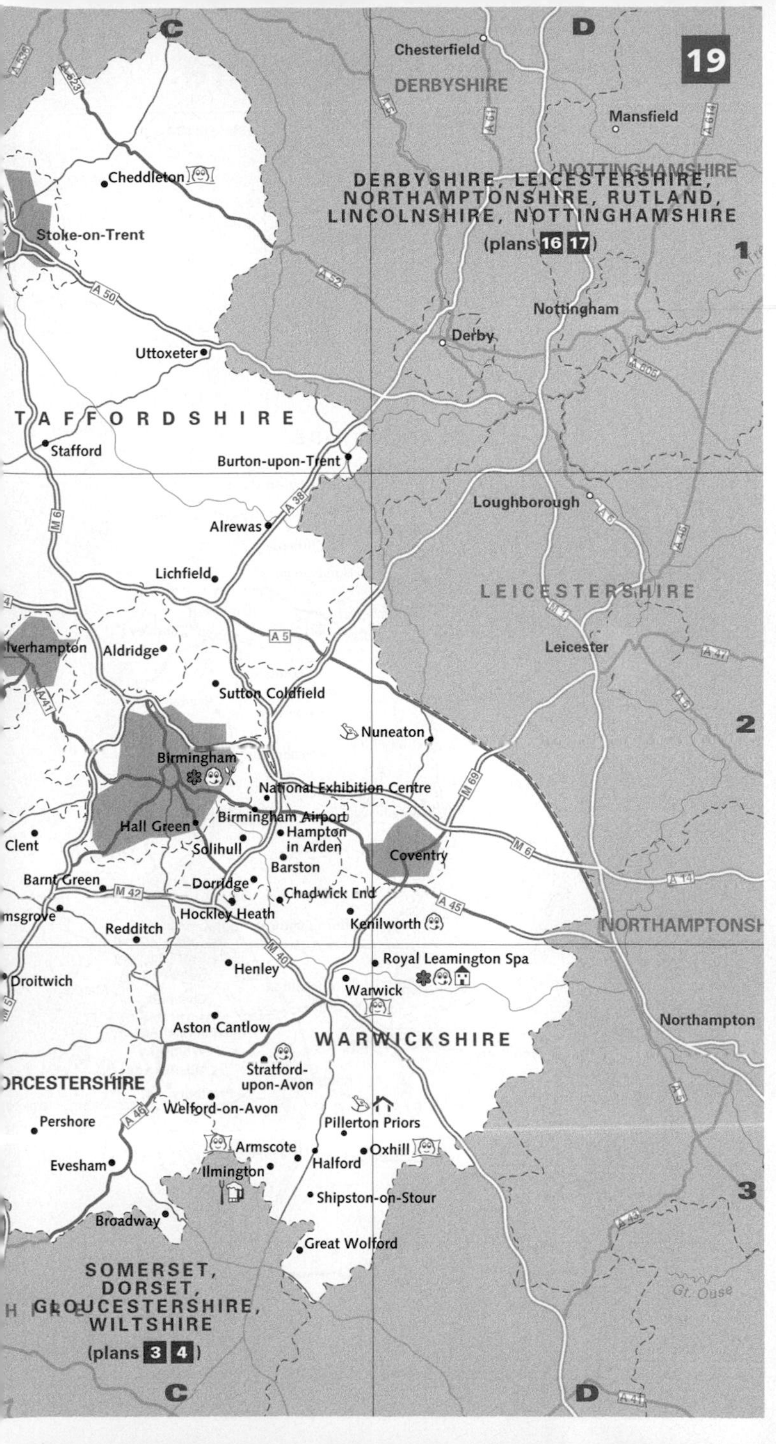

C
D
Chesterfield
DERBYSHIRE
Mansfield
NOTTINGHAMSHIRE
DERBYSHIRE, LEICESTERSHIRE, NORTHAMPTONSHIRE, RUTLAND, LINCOLNSHIRE, NOTTINGHAMSHIRE
(plans 16 17)
1
Cheddleton
Stoke-on-Trent
Nottingham
Derby
Uttoxeter
STAFFORDSHIRE
Stafford
Burton-upon-Trent
Loughborough
Alrewas
Lichfield
LEICESTERSHIRE
Leicester
Aldridge
Sutton Coldfield
Nuneaton
2
Birmingham
National Exhibition Centre
Birmingham Airport
Hall Green
Hampton in Arden
Clent
Solihull
Coventry
Barston
Barnt Green
Dorridge
Chadwick End
Hockley Heath
Redditch
Kenilworth
NORTHAMPTONSH
Royal Leamington Spa
Henley
Droitwich
Warwick
Northampton
Aston Cantlow
WARWICKSHIRE
Stratford-upon-Avon
WORCESTERSHIRE
Welford-on-Avon
Pershore
Pillerton Priors
Armscote
Oxhill
Evesham
Halford
Ilmington
Shipston-on-Stour
3
Broadway
Great Wolford
SOMERSET, DORSET, GLOUCESTERSHIRE, WILTSHIRE
(plans 3 4)
Gt. Ouse
C
D

20 Cheshire, Lancashire, Isle of Man
A
B
1
2
3
CUMBRIA
(plans 21)
ISLE OF MAN
Ramsey
Douglas
Port Erin
Port St Mary
Barrow-in-Furness
Morecambe Bay
Cowan Bridge
Lancaster
NORTH YORKSHIRE
(plans 22 23)
LANCASHIRE
Bolton-by-Bowland
Garstang
Whitewell
Sawley
Gisburn
Skipton
Chipping
Clitheroe
Thornton
Blackpool
Longridge
Hurst Green
Whalley
Ribble
Ribchester
Padiham
Kirkham
Preston
Langho
Burnley
Lytham St Anne's
Blackburn
Clayton-le-Woods
Darwen
Rawtenstall
Halifa
Southport
Eccleston
Chorley
Ramsbottom
Rochdale
Horwich
Bury
Standish
Oldham
Blundellsands
Manchester
Worsley
Knowsley Industrial Park
Salford Quays
Bay
Wallasey
Trafford Centre
Trafford Park
Liverpool
Urmston
Chorlton-cum-Hardy
West Didsbury
Birkenhead
Didsbury
West Kirby
Sale
Grassendale
Warrington
Altrincham
Marple
Speke
Cheadle
Heswall
Thornton Hough
Manchester International Airport
Lower Whitley
Frodsham
Wilmslow
Alderley Edge
Ellesmere Port
Knutsford
Prestbury
CHESHIRE
Buxto
Sandiway
Macclesfield
Chester
Holmes Chapel
Middlewich
Tarporley
Aldford
Congleton
Tattenhall
WALES
(plans 32 33)
Broxton
Crewe
HEREFORDSHIRE
WORCESTERSHIRE
SHROPSHIRE,
STAFFORDSHIRE
WARWICKSHIRE
(plans 18 19)
Tilston
Wrexham
Nantwich
Malpas
Stoke-on-Trent
M 6
M 55
M 58
M 57
M 61
M 66
M 62
M 60
M 56
A 59
A 565
A 590
A 595
A 65
A 677
A 6
A 49
A 54
A 51
A 41
A 536
A 523
A 55
A 483
A 50

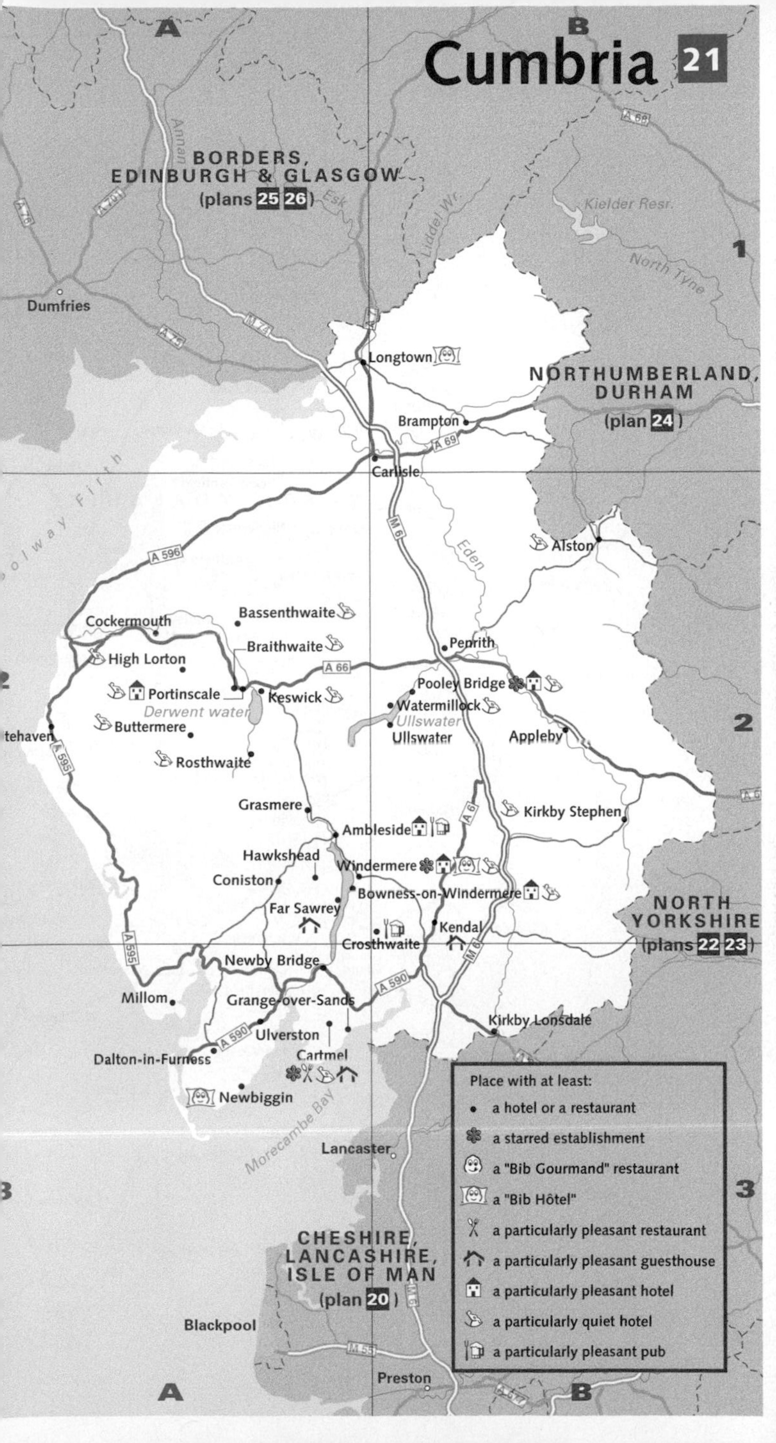

Cumbria 21
A
B
BORDERS, EDINBURGH & GLASGOW (plans 25 26)
Kielder Resr.
North Tyne
Dumfries
Longtown
NORTHUMBERLAND, DURHAM (plan 24)
Brampton
A 69
Carlisle
Solway Firth
A 596
M 6
Eden
Alston
Bassenthwaite
Cockermouth
Braithwaite
Penrith
High Lorton
A 66
Portinscale
Keswick
Pooley Bridge
Derwent water
Watermillock
Ullswater
Buttermere
Ullswater
Appleby
Whitehaven
A 595
Rosthwaite
Grasmere
Kirkby Stephen
A 6
Ambleside
Hawkshead
Windermere
Coniston
Bowness-on-Windermere
Far Sawrey
Kendal
Crosthwaite
NORTH YORKSHIRE (plans 22 23)
Newby Bridge
A 590
Millom
Grange-over-Sands
Kirkby Lonsdale
Ulverston
Dalton-in-Furness
Cartmel
Newbiggin
Morecambe Bay
Lancaster
CHESHIRE, LANCASHIRE, ISLE OF MAN (plan 20)
Blackpool
Preston
M 55
1
2
3
Place with at least:
a hotel or a restaurant
a starred establishment
a "Bib Gourmand" restaurant
a "Bib Hôtel"
a particularly pleasant restaurant
a particularly pleasant guesthouse
a particularly pleasant hotel
a particularly quiet hotel
a particularly pleasant pub

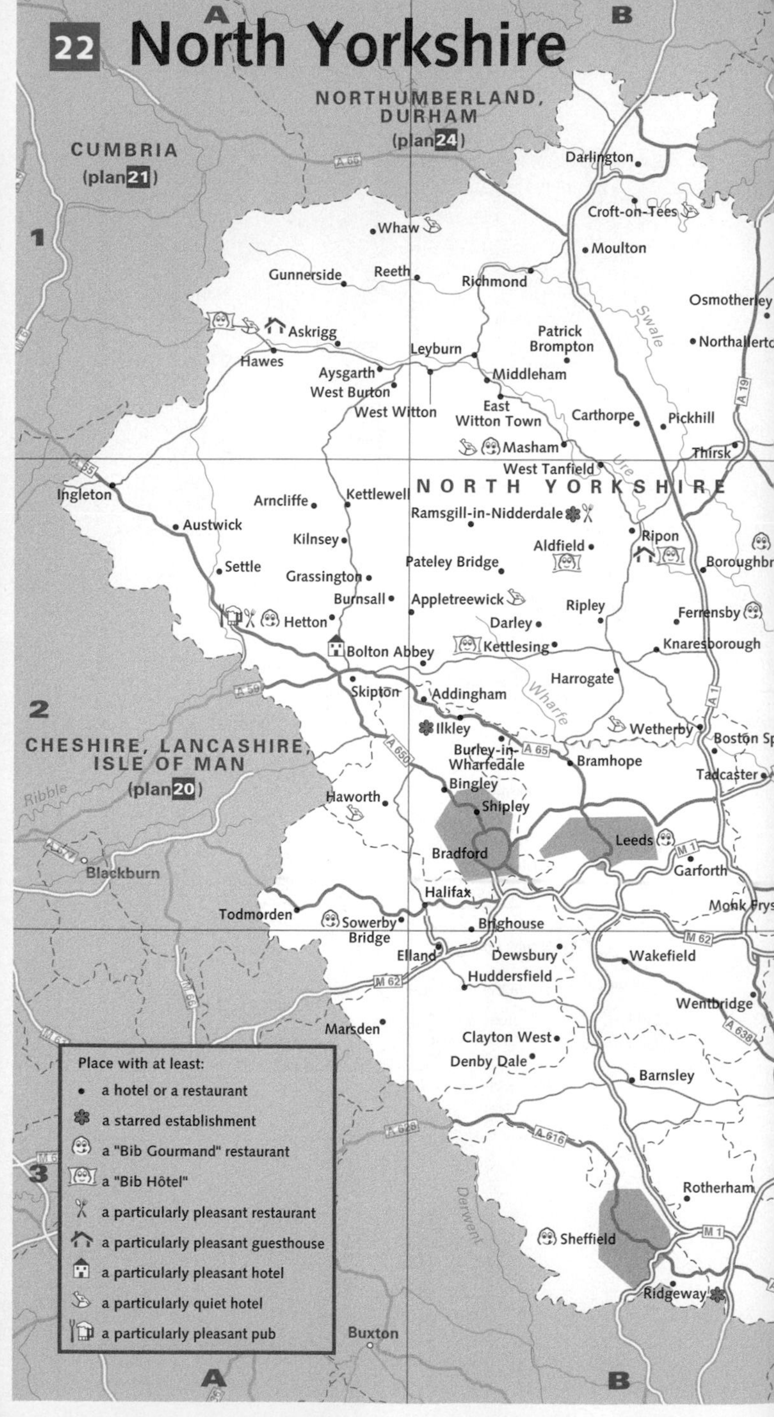
22 North Yorkshire
NORTHUMBERLAND, DURHAM (plan 24)
CUMBRIA (plan 21)
CHESHIRE, LANCASHIRE, ISLE OF MAN (plan 20)
NORTH YORKSHIRE
Darlington
Croft-on-Tees
Moulton
Whaw
Gunnerside
Reeth
Richmond
Osmotherley
Askrigg
Hawes
Leyburn
Patrick Brompton
Northallerton
Aysgarth
West Burton
West Witton
Middleham
East Witton Town
Carthorpe
Pickhill
Masham
Thirsk
West Tanfield
Ingleton
Arncliffe
Kettlewell
Ramsgill-in-Nidderdale
Austwick
Kilnsey
Aldfield
Ripon
Settle
Grassington
Pateley Bridge
Boroughbridge
Burnsall
Appletreewick
Ripley
Ferrensby
Hetton
Darley
Bolton Abbey
Kettlesing
Knaresborough
Harrogate
Skipton
Addingham
Ilkley
Wetherby
Burley-in-Wharfedale
Bramhope
Boston Spa
Tadcaster
Bingley
Haworth
Shipley
Leeds
Bradford
Garforth
Blackburn
Halifax
Todmorden
Sowerby Bridge
Brighouse
Monk Fryston
Elland
Dewsbury
Wakefield
Huddersfield
Wentbridge
Marsden
Clayton West
Denby Dale
Barnsley
Rotherham
Sheffield
Ridgeway
Buxton
Swale
Ure
Wharfe
Ribble
Derwent
A 66
A 65
A 59
A 650
A 19
A 1
M 1
M 62
M 66
A 628
A 616
A 638
Place with at least:
a hotel or a restaurant
a starred establishment
a "Bib Gourmand" restaurant
a "Bib Hôtel"
a particularly pleasant restaurant
a particularly pleasant guesthouse
a particularly pleasant hotel
a particularly quiet hotel
a particularly pleasant pub
A
B
1
2
3

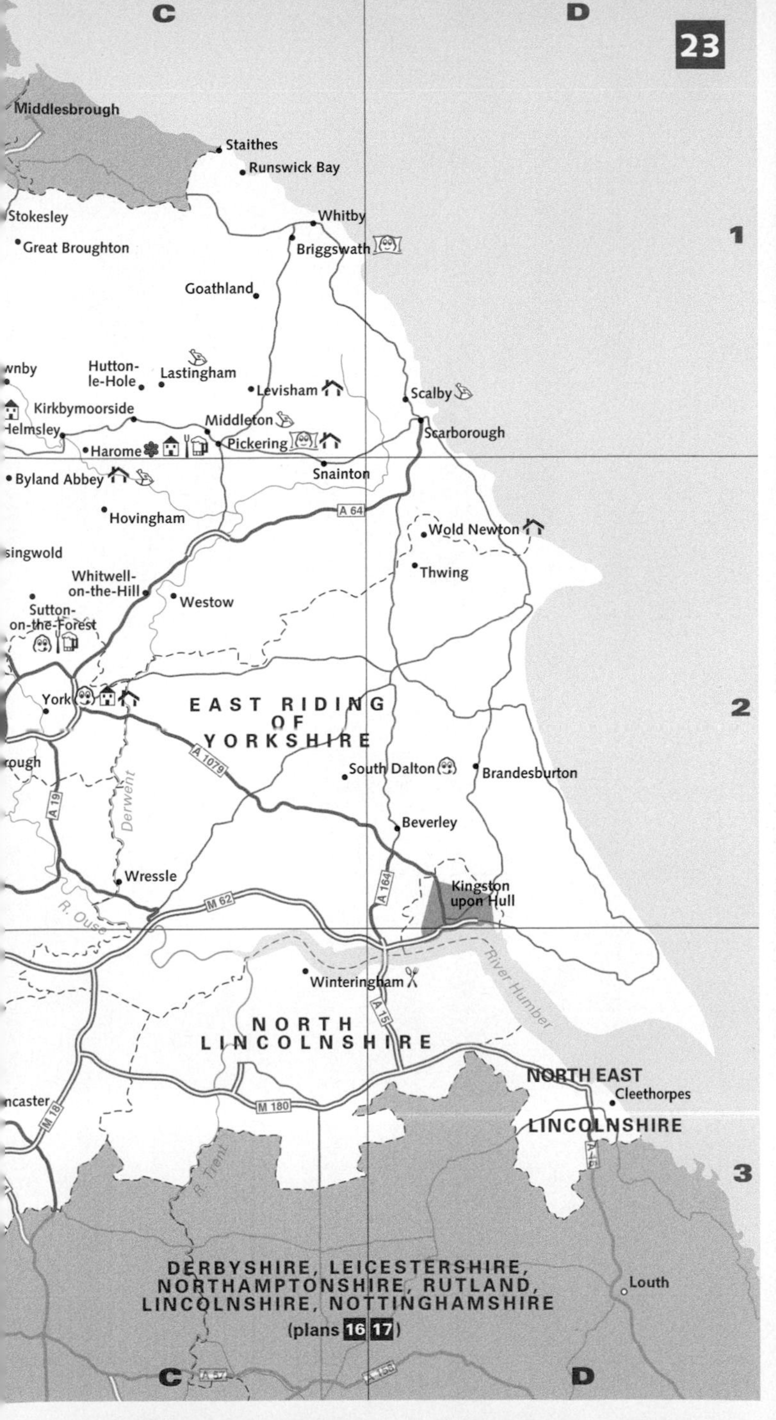
C
D
Middlesbrough
Staithes
Runswick Bay
Stokesley
Whitby
1
Great Broughton
Briggswath
Goathland
wnby
Hutton-
le-Hole
Lastingham
Levisham
Scalby
Kirkbymoorside
Middleton
Helmsley
Scarborough
Harome
Pickering
Snainton
Byland Abbey
Hovingham
A 64
Wold Newton
singwold
Thwing
Whitwell-
on-the-Hill
Westow
Sutton-
on-the-Forest
York
EAST RIDING
OF
YORKSHIRE
2
rough
A 1079
South Dalton
Brandesburton
A 19
Derwent
Beverley
Wressle
A 164
Kingston
upon Hull
M 62
R. Ouse
River Humber
Winteringham
A 15
NORTH
LINCOLNSHIRE
NORTH EAST
Cleethorpes
ncaster
M 180
LINCOLNSHIRE
M 18
R. Trent
3
DERBYSHIRE, LEICESTERSHIRE,
NORTHAMPTONSHIRE, RUTLAND,
LINCOLNSHIRE, NOTTINGHAMSHIRE
(plans 16 17)
Louth
C
A 57
A 158
D

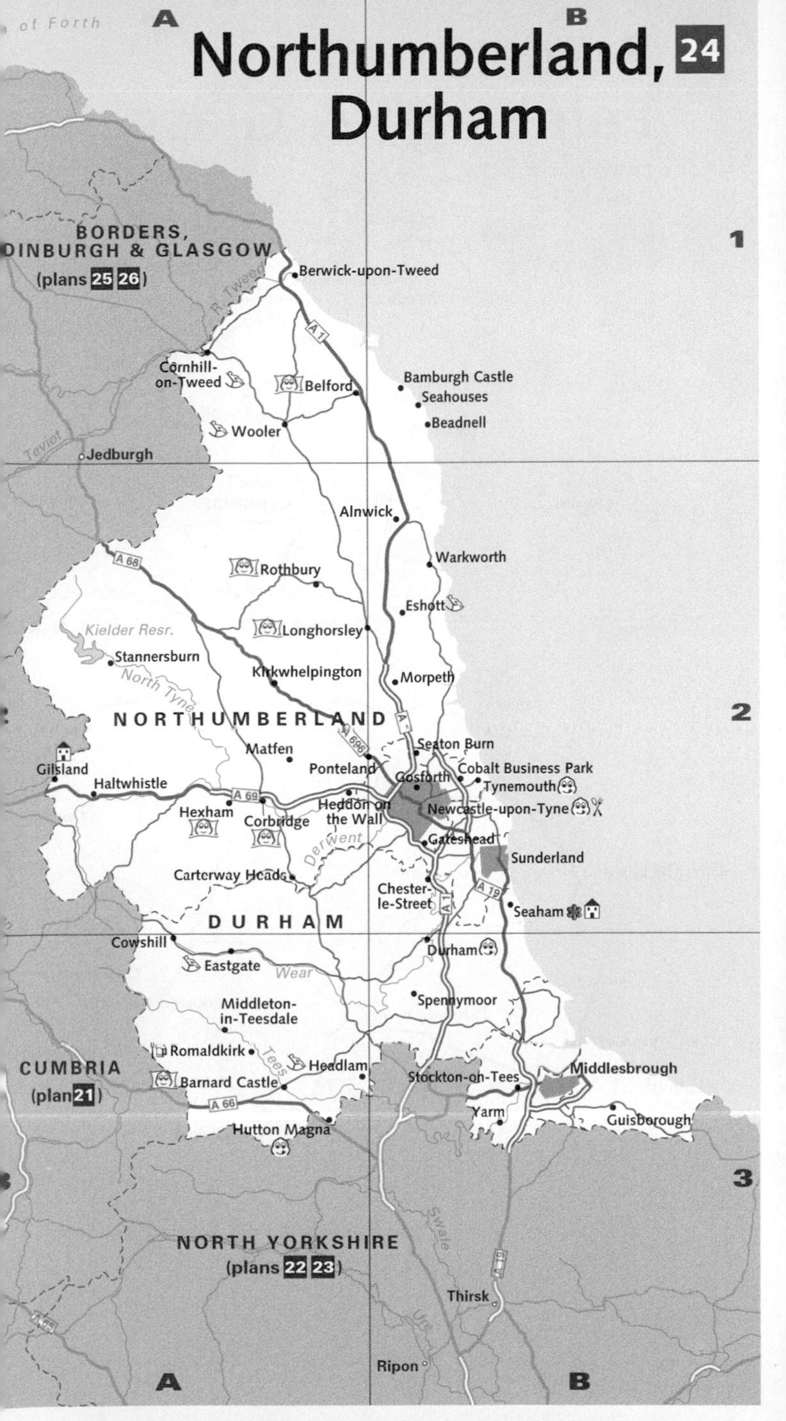

Northumberland, Durham
24
A
B
1
2
3
of Forth
BORDERS, EDINBURGH & GLASGOW
(plans 25 26)
R. Tweed
Teviot
Berwick-upon-Tweed
A 1
Cornhill-on-Tweed
Belford
Bamburgh Castle
Seahouses
Beadnell
Wooler
Jedburgh
Alnwick
A 68
Warkworth
Rothbury
Eshott
Longhorsley
Kielder Resr.
Stannersburn
North Tyne
Kirkwhelpington
Morpeth
NORTHUMBERLAND
A 696
Seaton Burn
Matfen
Ponteland
Gosforth
Cobalt Business Park
Tynemouth
Gilsland
Haltwhistle
A 69
Heddon on the Wall
Newcastle-upon-Tyne
Hexham
Corbridge
Derwent
Gateshead
Sunderland
Carterway Heads
Chester-le-Street
A 19
Seaham
DURHAM
Cowshill
Durham
Eastgate
Wear
Spennymoor
Middleton-in-Teesdale
Romaldkirk
Tees
Headlam
CUMBRIA
(plan 21)
Barnard Castle
Stockton-on-Tees
Middlesbrough
A 66
Yarm
Guisborough
Hutton Magna
Swale
NORTH YORKSHIRE
(plans 22 23)
A 65
Thirsk
Ure
Ripon

25
Borders, Edinburgh & Glasgow
CENTRAL SCOTLAND
(plans 27 28)
A
B
1
2
3
Dunoon
Rothesay
Balloch
Cardross
WEST DUNBARTONSHIRE
EAST DUNBARTONSHIRE
Milngavie
FALK
Bishopton
INVERCLYDE
Clydebank
NORTH LANARKSHIR
Glasgow
RENFREWSHIRE
Fairlie
NORTH AYRSHIRE
EAST RENFREWSHIRE
Uddingston
Motherwell
East Kilbride
Dalry
Stevenston
EAST AYRSHIRE
Kilmarnock
Brodick
New Lanark
Kilbrannan Sound
Troon
SOUT
LANAR
Sorn
Ayr
Annbank
Isle of Arran
Firth of Clyde
Maidens
Maybole
Turnberry
SOUTH AYRSHIRE
Thornhill
Ballantrae
DUMFRIE
Crocketford
Kirkcolm
Newton Stewart
Kirkpatrick Durham
Stranraer
Castle Douglas
Portpatrick
Gatehouse of Fleet
Kirkcudbright
Auchencairn
Luce Bay
Wigtown Bay
A 82
A 78
A 8
M 8
A 80
M 77
M 74
A 76
A 77
A 75

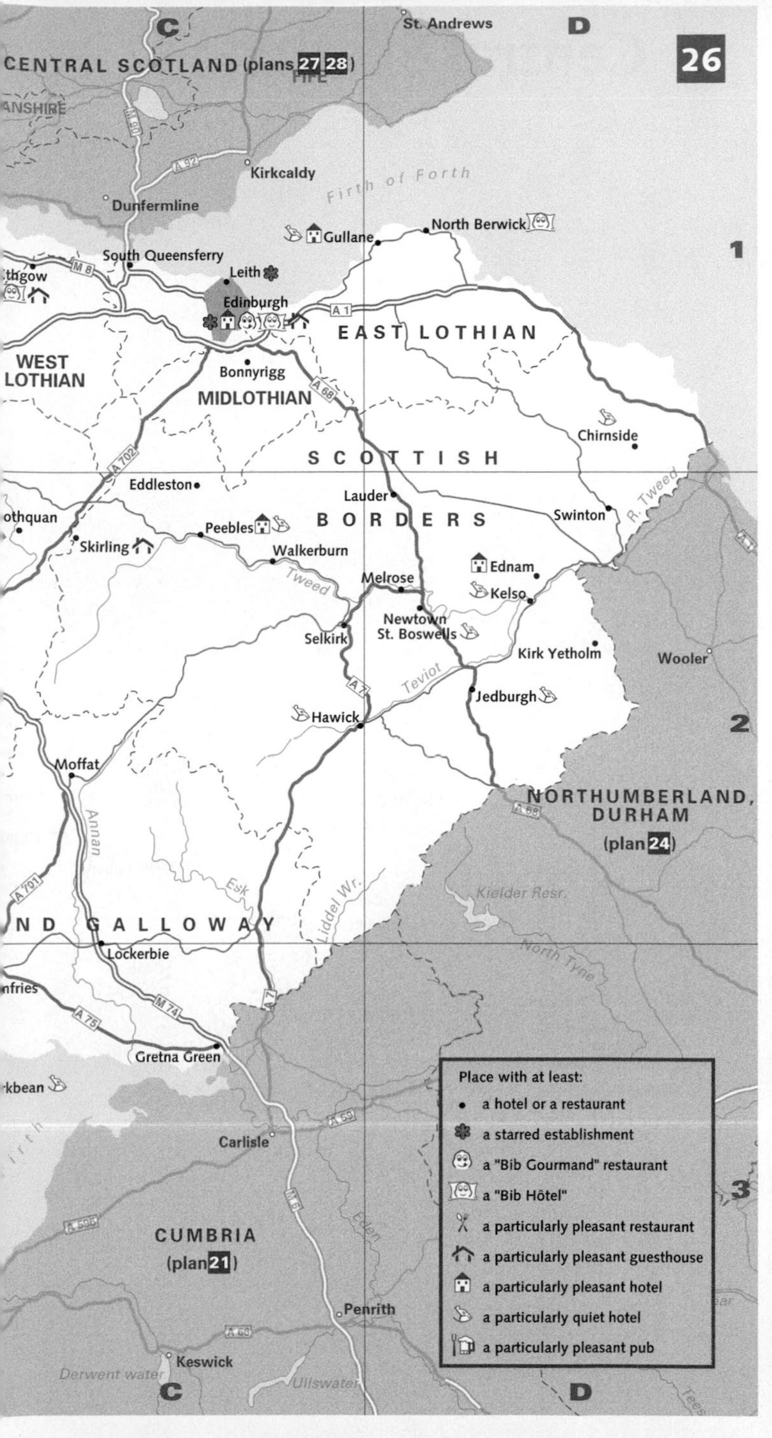
C
D
St. Andrews
CENTRAL SCOTLAND (plans 27 28)
FIFE
Kirkcaldy
Firth of Forth
Dunfermline
North Berwick
Gullane
South Queensferry
Leith
Edinburgh
EAST LOTHIAN
WEST LOTHIAN
Bonnyrigg
MIDLOTHIAN
Chirnside
SCOTTISH
BORDERS
Eddleston
Lauder
Swinton
R. Tweed
Peebles
Skirling
Walkerburn
Ednam
Melrose
Kelso
Tweed
Newtown St. Boswells
Selkirk
Kirk Yetholm
Wooler
Teviot
Jedburgh
Hawick
Moffat
NORTHUMBERLAND, DURHAM
(plan 24)
Annan
Esk
Liddel Wr.
Kielder Resr.
North Tyne
GALLOWAY
Lockerbie
Gretna Green
Carlisle
Eden
CUMBRIA
(plan 21)
Penrith
Keswick
Derwent water
Ullswater
Tees
1
2
3
Place with at least:
a hotel or a restaurant
a starred establishment
a "Bib Gourmand" restaurant
a "Bib Hôtel"
a particularly pleasant restaurant
a particularly pleasant guesthouse
a particularly pleasant hotel
a particularly quiet hotel
a particularly pleasant pub

27 Central Scotland

C
D
Moray Firth
Elgin
Urquhart
Banff
Dyke
Forres
Archiestown
Aberlour
Deveron
1
HIGHLAND
& THE ISLANDS
(plans 29 30)
MORAY
Kildrummy
Oldmeldrum
Inverurie
Balmedie
Don
ABERDEENSHIRE
Aberdeen
Aboyne
Ballater
Dee
Braemar
Banchory
Stonehaven
N. Esk
PERTH AND KINROSS
Spittal of Glenshee
ANGUS
Blair Atholl
Edzell
Kirkmichael
Kirkton of Glenisla
St. Cyrus
Pitlochry
Bridgend of Lintrathen
S. Esk
Montrose
Aberfeldy
Kirriemuir
Kenmore
Alyth
Blairgowrie
Inverkeilor
Dunkeld
Glamis
Loch Tay
Tay
2
Ardeonaig
Kinclaven
Arbroath
Dundee
Carnoustie
St. Fillans
Comrie
Earn
Crieff
Perth
Auchterarder
St. Andrews
Cupar
Peat Inn
Ladybank
Glendevon
FIFE
Largoward
Dunblane
Kinross
Anstruther
Glenrothes
St. Monans
Elie
Stirling
Tillicoultry
Firth of Forth
Dunfermline
North Berwick
North Queensferry
Edinburgh
Peebles
3
BORDERS,
EDINBURGH
& GLASGOW
(plans 25 26)
Tweed
Teviot
Clyde
Annan
Esk
Kielder Resr.
Place with at least:
a hotel or a restaurant
a starred establishment
a "Bib Gourmand" restaurant
a "Bib Hôtel"
a particularly pleasant restaurant
a particularly pleasant guesthouse
a particularly pleasant hotel
a particularly quiet hotel
a particularly pleasant pub

29 Highland & The Islands

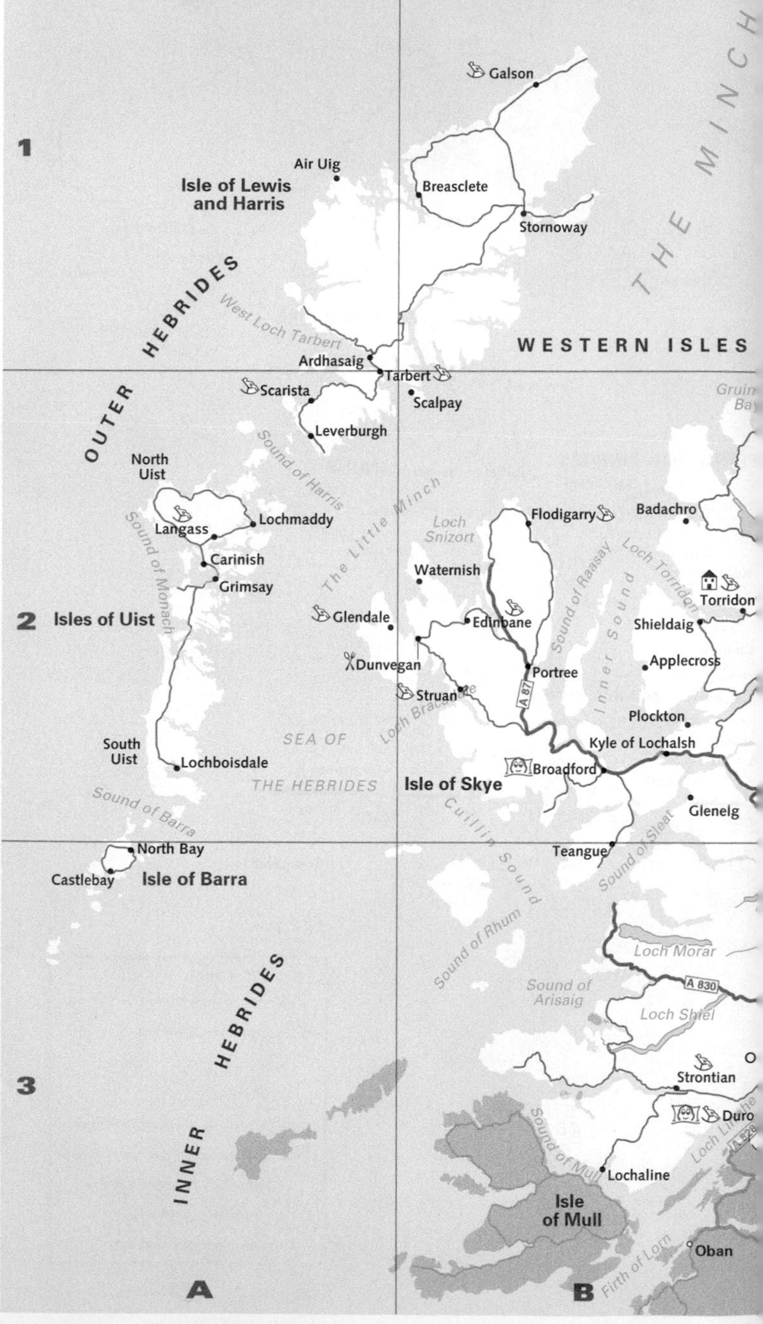

A
B

1

Galson
Air Uig
Isle of Lewis and Harris
Breasclete
Stornoway
THE MINCH
OUTER HEBRIDES
West Loch Tarbert
WESTERN ISLES
Ardhasaig
Tarbert
Scarista
Scalpay
Gruin Bay
Leverburgh
Sound of Harris
North Uist
The Little Minch
Flodigarry
Badachro
Langass
Lochmaddy
Loch Snizort
Sound of Monach
Carinish
Waternish
Sound of Raasay
Loch Torridon
Grimsay
Torridon
Inner Sound

2

Isles of Uist
Glendale
Edinbane
Shieldaig
Dunvegan
Portree
A 87
Applecross
Struan
Loch Bracadale
Plockton
South Uist
SEA OF THE HEBRIDES
Kyle of Lochalsh
Lochboisdale
Broadford
Isle of Skye
Sound of Barra
Cuillin Sound
Glenelg
North Bay
Teangue
Sound of Sleat
Castlebay
Isle of Barra
Sound of Rhum
Loch Morar
Sound of Arisaig
A 830
Loch Shiel
INNER HEBRIDES

3

Strontian
Duro
Sound of Mull
Loch Linnhe
A 828
Lochaline
Isle of Mull
Oban
Firth of Lorn

A
B

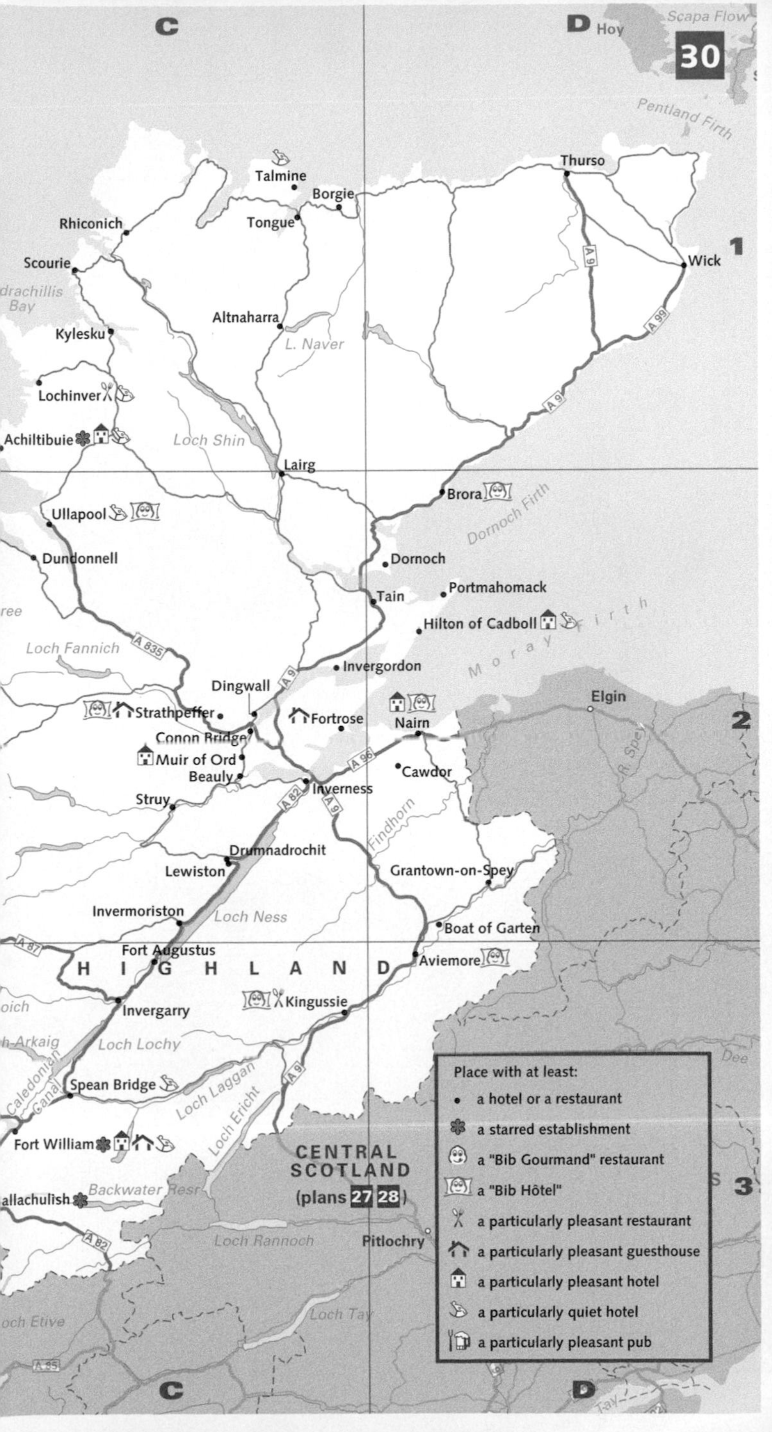

C
D
Hoy
Scapa Flow
30
Pentland Firth
Thurso
Talmine
Borgie
Tongue
Rhiconich
Scourie
drachillis Bay
Wick
1
A 9
A 99
Altnaharra
L. Naver
Kylesku
Lochinver
Achiltibuie
Loch Shin
Lairg
Brora
Dornoch Firth
Ullapool
Dundonnell
Dornoch
Tain
Portmahomack
Hilton of Cadboll
Moray Firth
ree
Loch Fannich
A 835
Invergordon
Dingwall
A 9
Strathpeffer
Fortrose
Nairn
Elgin
2
Conon Bridge
Muir of Ord
Beauly
A 96
Cawdor
R. Spey
Inverness
A 82
A 9
Struy
Findhorn
Drumnadrochit
Lewiston
Grantown-on-Spey
Invermoriston
Loch Ness
Boat of Garten
A 87
Fort Augustus
HIGHLAND
Aviemore
Kingussie
Invergarry
oich
h-Arkaig
Loch Lochy
Caledonian Canal
Spean Bridge
Loch Laggan
Loch Ericht
A 9
Dee
Fort William
CENTRAL SCOTLAND
(plans 27 28)
allachulish
Backwater Resr
3
Loch Rannoch
Pitlochry
A 82
Loch Tay
och Etive
A 85
Tay
Place with at least:
a hotel or a restaurant
a starred establishment
a "Bib Gourmand" restaurant
a "Bib Hôtel"
a particularly pleasant restaurant
a particularly pleasant guesthouse
a particularly pleasant hotel
a particularly quiet hotel
a particularly pleasant pub

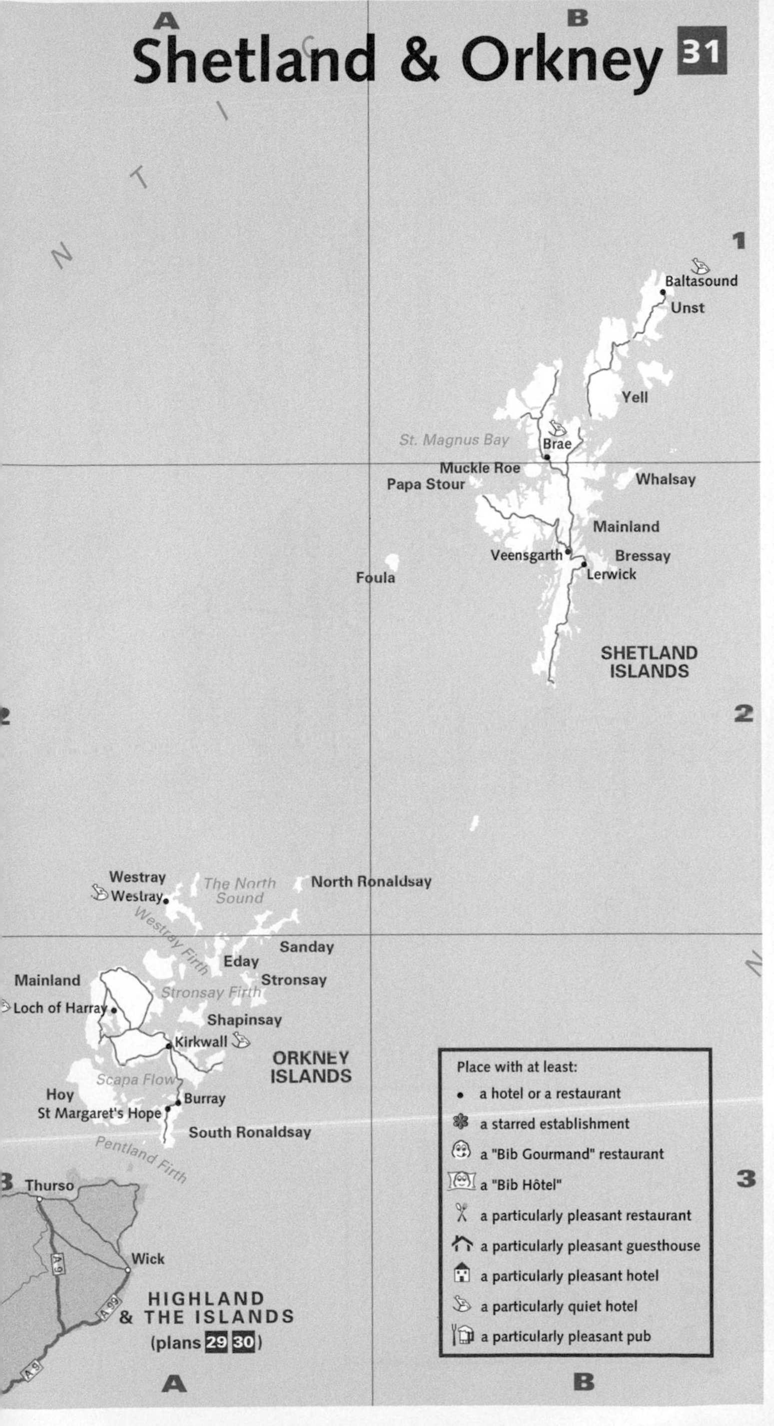
A
B
Shetland & Orkney
31
1
Baltasound
Unst
Yell
St. Magnus Bay
Brae
Muckle Roe
Papa Stour
Whalsay
Mainland
Veensgarth
Bressay
Lerwick
Foula
SHETLAND ISLANDS
2
Westray
Westray
The North Sound
North Ronaldsay
Westray Firth
Sanday
Eday
Mainland
Stronsay
Stronsay Firth
Loch of Harray
Shapinsay
Kirkwall
ORKNEY ISLANDS
Scapa Flow
Hoy
Burray
St Margaret's Hope
South Ronaldsay
Pentland Firth
3
Thurso
Wick
A 9
A 99
HIGHLAND & THE ISLANDS
(plans 29 30)
Place with at least:
a hotel or a restaurant
a starred establishment
a "Bib Gourmand" restaurant
a "Bib Hôtel"
a particularly pleasant restaurant
a particularly pleasant guesthouse
a particularly pleasant hotel
a particularly quiet hotel
a particularly pleasant pub
A
B

Wales

Place with at least:

- • a hotel or a restaurant
- a starred establishment
- a "Bib Gourmand" restaurant
- a "Bib Hôtel"
- a particularly pleasant restaurant
- a particularly pleasant guesthouse
- a particularly pleasant hotel
- a particularly quiet hotel
- a particularly pleasant pub

A
B
C
1
2

Cemaes
Holyhead
Trearddur Bay
Llanerchymedd
Benllech
ANGLESEY
Beaumaris
Menai Bridge
Llandudno
Colwyn Bay
Rhyl
Conwy
Llansanffraid Glan Conwy
Tal y Llyn
CONWY
Tremeirchion
FLINTSHIRE
Nannerch
Mold
Llandyrnog
Hawarden
Chester
Liverpool
Birkenhead
Liverpool Bay
CHESHIRE, LANCASHIRE, ISLE OF MAN
(plan 20)
Caernarfon
Caernarfon Bay
Betws Garmon
Clynnog-Fawr
A 487
A 5
A 55
Betws-y-Coed
Ruthin
DENBIGHSHIRE
Penmachno
Beddgelert
A 483
Wrexham
Boduan
Criccieth
Porthmadog
Llan Ffestiniog
Llangollen
Pwllheli
Portmeirion
Dee
Talsarnau
GWYNEDD
Llandrillo
Abersoch
Harlech
Llanuwchllyn
Llanarmon Dyffryn Ceiriog
Bwlchtocyn
Llanbedr
Lake Vyrnwy
Llanfyllin
Llanaber
Abermaw
Dolgellau
Llanfihangel-yng-Ngwynfa
Shrewsbury
A 458
A 5
A 49
A 41
A 51
M 56
M 57
M 58
CHANNEL
Bay
Machynlleth
POWYS
HEREFORDSHIRE, WORCESTERSHIRE, SHROPSHIRE, STAFFORDSHIRE, WARWICKSHIRE
Aberdovey
Pontdolgoch
Montgomery
Caersws
Severn
Dolfor
(plans 18 19)